YOUR KEY TO CARE..

4 LIGHT

B **Bright light or full sun. Preference for growth:** 4000-8000 foot candles, for average day length. **Tolerance, for maintenance:** 500-2000 foot candles, based on 16 hr. illumination. Intense light is important to most blooming plants, shrubs and trees, also flowering bulbs. Many plants which require sunlight for normal growth can be kept in good condition in the home at much lower light intensity, with artificial light, when **maintenance** only is desired.

F **Filtered or diffused sunlight. Preference:** 1000-3000 foot candles for average day length. **Tolerance:** 100-1000 foot candles, based on 16 hr. illumination. A simple indicator of diffused sunlight is to pass your hand over your plants and barely see its shadow. A place near a clear east window during summer is best, but a southern exposure must be lightly shaded from direct sun by slatted Venetian blinds, a bamboo screen, or curtain. For mere **maintenance** of most plants in this group in good condition in the home, light intensity may go as low as 25 foot candles, though 100 would be better.

N **No** (direct) **sun, shady,** or **away from sun. Preference:** 50-500 foot candles for normal day length. There are very few plants which do not want some sunlight by preference; shade lovers are limited mostly to delicate plants from the forest floor, and ferns. However, a great number of subjects tolerate a minimum amount of energy-giving sunlight, and most of them are classified under the numeral 1 or starred (★). Under artificial illumination, light intensity may be as low as 10 foot candles, but the higher intensity light would be preferable to these plants provided they are shielded from the sun. High humidity is important to the well-being of plants in this group.

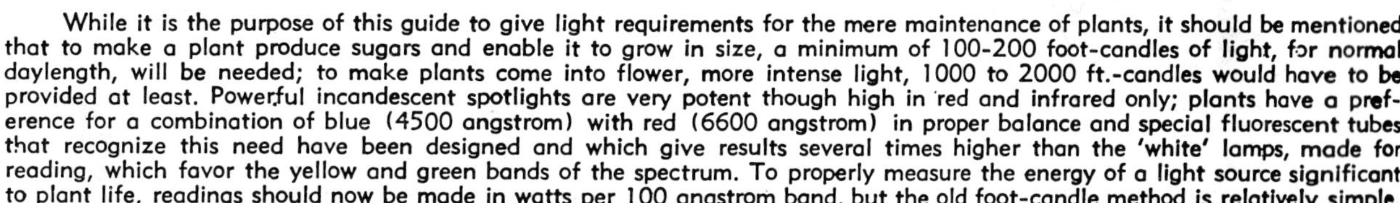

While it is the purpose of this guide to give light requirements for the mere maintenance of plants, it should be mentioned that to make a plant produce sugars and enable it to grow in size, a minimum of 100-200 foot-candles of light, for normal daylength, will be needed; to make plants come into flower, more intense light, 1000 to 2000 ft.-candles would have to be provided at least. Powerful incandescent spotlights are very potent though high in red and infrared only; plants have a preference for a combination of blue (4500 angstrom) with red (6600 angstrom) in proper balance and special fluorescent tubes that recognize this need have been designed and which give results several times higher than the 'white' lamps, made for reading, which favor the yellow and green bands of the spectrum. To properly measure the energy of a light source significant to plant life, readings should now be made in watts per 100 angstrom band, but the old foot-candle method is relatively simple.

During tests made in our office and the living room, to determine various actual light conditions, measured in foot-candles, I recorded the following:

Daylight, 30 cm distant from north window: 220 to 500 ft.-cdle.
Daylight, 1 m distant from north window: 100 to 180 ft.-cdle.
Incandescent bulb, 75 watt, 30 cm distant: 150 ft.-cdle.
Incandescent flood light, 75 watt, 1 m distant: 40 ft.-cdle.
Incandescent bulb, 100 watt, 1 m distant: 40 ft.-cdle.
Incandescent bulb, 150 watt, 1 m distant: 60 ft.-cdle.
Incandescent flood, 150 watt, 1 m distant: 90 ft.-cdle.
Incandescent spot, 300 watt, 1 m distant: 180 ft.-cdle.
Fluorescent tube, 40 watt, 30 cm distant: 120 ft.-cdle.
Fluorescent tube, 40 watt, 60 cm distant: 75 ft.-cdle.
Four fluorescent tubes, 160 watt, 2 m distant: 40 ft.-cdle.
Two 40 w. tubes 1 m 60-80, 1½ m 40-50, 2 m 30 fc.

LIGHT INTENSITY MEASUREMENTS: One footcandle is the amount of light cast by a candle, received on a white surface 1 foot (30 cm) distant, in a dark room. In metric terms 1 ft-cdle, equals 10.76 lux.

5 WATERING

D **Drench thoroughly then allow to become moderately dry between waterings.** This admits air into the soil structure which, in turn, promotes development of a healthy white root system; wiry thick roots being characteristic in this group. Watering means soaking the root-ball penetratingly, holding the pot if necessary in a bucket, sink or tub of tepid water until air bubbles cease to rise. During the cold season, with steam heat in the living room, more frequent watering every day or two is required for most plants than from spring to fall. 'Feel' the soil to determine its need for water. Desert type cacti and similar succulents will stand dryness for longer periods.

M **Evenly moist but not constantly wet.** Plants so classified generally have delicate, hair-like, fibrous roots, subject to rot if kept too wet, and equally easily burning and shrivelling if too dry, especially in hot weather. Standing in a saucer, such plants may be supplied water from the base to a degree where capillary action distributes and maintains uniform moisture throughout the root-ball, without letting the soil become water-soaked and 'sour'. During resting periods and dropping temperatures the soil-ball can be kept more on the dry side.

W **Thoroughly wet, or quite moist:** never allow such plants to dry out. It is good practice to keep them in a saucer of gravel saturated with water, or in a jardiniere, though drainage water should be emptied every few days to keep from becoming stagnant. Such subjects may revel in moisture but resent having 'wet feet', that is having their roots left standing continuously in water. Exceptions, of course, are bog plants, and aquatics when not resting.

d **normally requires dormancy** or rest period, during which little or no water is given, with temperatures reduced correspondingly.

h **winter-hardy** north, sometimes with special protection from the sun, in the vicinity of New York City, where the temperatures in winter may drop to around 0°F (—18°C).

wi-winter; **sp**-spring; **su**-summer; **au**-autumn.

The Designations Tropical, Subtropic, or Warm-Temperate at end of plant descriptions in the text, are intended to serve as general guide to specific climatic area backgrounds, or temperature preference, for plants or trees usually found to grow outdoors in warmer climates:

TROPICAL: Warm surroundings; days 21-28°C (70-85°F), and balmy nights usually not below 15°C (60°F).

SUBTROPIC: Mild climate with warm, sunny days, nights frequently down to 10°C (50°F).

WARM-TEMPERATE: Warm or sometimes cool, and often rainy, in daytime; nights may drop to 5°C (40°F), with occasional frost.

International Metric System

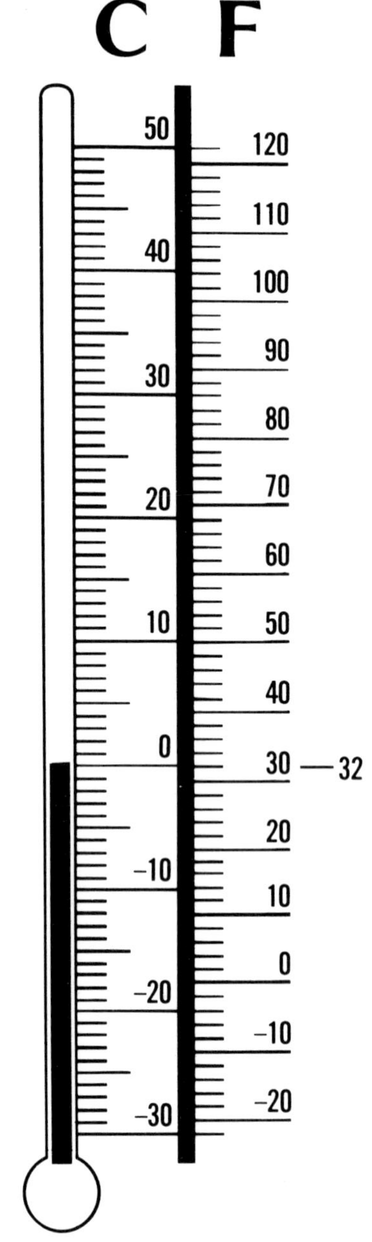

Terms of Measurement
are generally given according to the International Metric System.

1 centimeter (cm) = 0.4 inch;
2½ cm = 1 inch;
10 cm = 4 inches
1 meter (m) = 40 inches (or 3.28 feet)
1 cm = 10 mm;
1 m = 100 cm
1 foot = 30 cm or 300 millimeters
1 gram (g) = 0.035 oz;
1 kilogram (kg) = 2.2 lbs.;
1 liter (l) = 1.06 quarts;
4 liters = 1.06 gal.

Temperature Conversion:
Degrees Fahrenheit vs. Centigrade.
Freezing point
Zero (0) deg. Centigrade = 32 deg. Fahrenheit (F.)
Boiling point
100 deg. Celsius (C) = 212 deg. Fahrenheit (F.)

EXOTICA SERIES 4

INTERNATIONAL

Pictorial Cyclopedia of Exotic Plants from Tropical and Near-tropic Regions

A Treasury of Indoor Ornamentals
for Home, the Office, or Greenhouse —
In Warm Climates the Patio
and the Garden Outdoors

16,300 Photographs
405 plants in color
300 drawings

by Dr. ALFRED BYRD GRAF

Library Edition Volume 2

Guide to Care of Plants
Decorating with Ornamentals
Gardening in the Tropics
Plant Geography and Ecology
Methods of Propagation
Common Names Index
Horticultural Color Chart

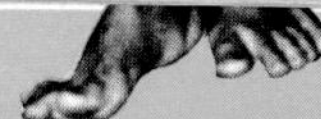

ROEHRS COMPANY *PUBLISHERS*

P. O. Box 125, East Rutherford, New Jersey 07073, U.S.A.

Library of Congress
Card Number 81-52361

International
Standard Book Numbers
ISBN 0-911-266-20-8 (set)
ISBN 0-911-266-21-6 (vol. 1)
ISBN 0-911-266-22-4 (vol. 2)

Lithography:
De Vries Bros.,
Saddle Brook, New Jersey

Sweeney, Krist & Dimm,
Portland, Oregon

C.S. Hammond & Co.,
New York City

Manufactured by:
A. Horowitz & Sons,
Fairfield, New Jersey

Printed 1985 in the United States of America

Chronology:
EXOTICA

Series 1: 1st Ed. Dec. 1957
Series 2: 2nd Ed. Sept. 1959
Series 3: 3rd Ed. Jan. 1963
Series 3: 4th Ed. Jan. 1968
Series 3: 5th Ed. Jan. 1970
Series 3: 6th Ed. Jan. 1973
Series 3: 7th Ed. March 1974
Series 3: 8th Ed. Jan. 1976
Series 3: 9th Ed. July 1976
Series 3: 9th Revised Ed. 1978
Series 3: 10th Ed. Jan. 1980
Series 4: 11th Ed. June 1982
Series 4: 12th Ed. June 1985

CONTENTS

VOLUME 1

VOLUME 2

On Pronunciation of Botanical Names

Botanical nomenclature is basically Latin, or words adopted from other languages, with Latin endings, and conceived to be understandable internationally. Correctly pronounced and clearly enunciated, the recital of botanical names has a stately and noble sound. However, in the words of L. H. Bailey, there is no standard agreement on rules for the pronunciation of botanical binomials. Many English-speaking people pronounce generic and descriptive specific names simply as if the words were English, in what is known as the Traditional English system.

Alternately there is the Restored Academic, or phonetic pronunciation of classical scholars, which comes close to the manner of speech of the ancient Romans. Their idiom has been conserved through the centuries. The Florentine vernacular Latin of Dante in the 14th Century is the touchstone of modern Italian. Castilian Spanish also is an enhanced but faithful perpetuation of spoken Latin practically unchanged since the 5th Century. Anyone conversant with these languages will have no difficulty to articulate Botanical Latin in the classical tradition.

In spoken Latin, much the same as in Italian and Spanish, also in German or even Japanese, the vowels are pronounced precisely and uniformly: a as in apart; e as in pet; i as in pin; o as in note; u as in full; y in phyllus as in the French rue, the German or Chinese ü. Typical of the clear sound of spoken Latin is the Spanish expression "Te amo!".

Combinations of two vowels, or imperfect diphthongs found in Latin or Greek are enunciated separately as two syllables: aë (ah-eh = Gr. aer, Aërides); ai (ah-ee = eye); au (house); ei (eight); eo (areole); eu (eh-oo = aureus); ie (ee-eh = variegata; oi (oh-ee = deltoides); iu (ee-uu = folius); ue (uu-eh = cruentus); ui (ruin).

Exceptions are the perfect diphthongs or inseparable ligatures æ or ae (in caeruleus, Linnaeus, Caesarea), sounded as one vowel halfway between ah and eh, as in hat or fair, in French père, or the German "Umlaut" ä; œ or oe (in Coelogyne, coelestis) as in the French heureux, also the German or Swedish "Umlaut" ö.

Consonants: In the classical Latin used by Cicero in the first century B.C., the Romans never pronounced C like an English s, or G as j, but always like k and g (in get). By 180 A.D. however, the classical standard was gradually lost, and while C was still being pronounced as k before a, o, u – it changed to sound as z or s before ae, e, i, oe, y. G remained hard before a, o, u – as in Gardenia, but became a soft j as in joy before e and i (Geranium).

Many botanical names or epithets are derived from foreign-root personal or geographical names with Latin endings. To be recognizable, these are best pronounced in the idioms of their source, with accent on the preferred syllable.

The accent for nomenclatural Latin names with two syllables is on the first syllable; in words with several syllables the stress is usually on the next-to-the-last. If in doubt, pronounce all syllables with equal emphasis.

With a background of European schooling, I find it appropriate to use the pleasing phonetics of Continental Latin; those employing the English inflections may have difficulty being understood in non-English speaking areas. However, since English is increasingly a universally understood world language, it may well be employed, wherever found to be more convenient, in the pronunciation of Botanical names. I feel that a language should be our servant, not our master.

Alfred B. Graf

FAMILIES featured in VOLUME 2

GESNERIACEAE An Introduction to Gesneriads

Linnaeus (1707-1778) knew about the gesneriads and described 4 genera. Today, more than 120 different genera and 1800 species of **Gesneriaceae** are known. Countless hybrids, chance seedlings and mutations exist. As a giant family, these can be described as handsome, often velvety-leaved plants with wheel-shaped, tubular or bell-shaped flowers. The gesneriads are so variable in foliage texture, growth and flowering habits that an entire greenhouse could be stocked with gesneriads and only a taxonomist would realize that all were members of the same plant family.

Most gesneriads come from the tropics. Combine ample humidity with the heat of today's homes and one has a suitable place to grow these exotic plants. By careful selection and good cultural practices in the window garden, under fluorescent lights, or in a greenhouse, it is possible to grow a showy gesneriad display all year. Where outdoor temperatures permit, certain species are useful out-of-doors.

Gesneriads with Tubers

Rechsteineria, Sinningia and Chrysothemis are gesneriads with tuberous roots. **Sinningia** is the correct name for plants usually called gloxinias. This fleshy tuberous root, an enlarged underground portion of stem, serves in the wild to preserve plants through dry seasons. There are about 75 species of **Rechsteineria** which grow from Brazil north to Mexico. Those available to commerce are among the most easily cultivated gesneriads. The multitude of hybrid sinningias we enjoy today originated from about 15 species, all native to Brazil.

Successful intergeneric crosses have been made between **Rechsteineria** and **Sinningia.** The resultant plants are called **X Gloxinera.** Attractive and easily grown, gloxineras have slipper-shaped flowers, usually of a peachy-pink color.

Gesneriads with Scaly Rhizomes

Some gesneriads form underground scaly rhizomes at the base of the stems. Each scale is a highly modified leaf. Grouped together, they form a catkin-or pine cone- like structure called a scaly rhizome. Most of these do not exceed the size of a fat fuzzy worm, but the length may vary from less than 1cm to more than 8cm. When these appear above ground in leaf-axils or inflorescence, they are called propagules. Of this group, **Achimenes, Kohleria** and **Smithiantha** are most often grown. Others include **Campanea, Diastema, Koellikeria, Titanotrichum** and the true **Gloxinia. Gloxinia perennis** is attractive, even while small, because of its glossy, silvery-green leaves which are usually flushed on the undersides with red. This **Gloxinia** has lavender flowers, reminiscent of Canterbury bells, which open on a stem which often grows more than 60cm tall.

Gesneriads with Fibrous Roots

Two groups of gesneriads, those with two stamens and those with glands are characterized by fibrous root systems.

Because most gesneriads have four, rarely five anther-bearing stamens, those with two stamens form a separate group. Of this group of gesneriads which have two stamens, the **Saintpaulia** is best known. Other gesneriads with two stamens are **Cyrtandra, Didymocarpus, Opithandra, Petrocosmea, Rehmannia, Streptocarpus, Chirita, Rhabdothamnus, Pentarhaphia, Lysionotus, Klugia, Charodrophila, and Boea.**

The other group of fibrous-rooted gesneriads are those with glands. They are characterized by a gland borne at the back and base of a superior ovary. Glands are common on the stems, leaves, petals or flower stalks of many plants. Sometimes they are minute and cannot be seen, but their presence is known by the sticky secretions which they exude. Gesneriads with glands are further set apart because they have a fleshy fruit, and they all belong in the tribe **Columneae.** Temperatures below 12 deg. C are harmful to plants of this group. Almost all of the gesneriads with glands are easily obtainable. They include some of the showiest of all plants to be grown: **Alloplectus, Codananthe, Columnea, Drymonia, Episcia, Hypocyrta, Nautilocalyx and Nematanthus.**

Gesneriads to Grow Outdoors

Haberlea, Jankaea and **Ramonda,** from Europe, and **Conandron, Corallodiscus,** and **Opithandra** from Asia are sometimes grown outdoors in the north and northwest parts of the United States in hardiness zones 2 and 3. With the exception of **Opithandra,** a gesneriad with two stamens, these are classified as plants without visible stems. Gardeners of England and Europe have long known these choice rock-garden plants which should be better known in America.

More Gesneriads

The variance of some gesneriads renders them impossible to classify into a large group. Most important of these is the **Aeschynanthus,** a popular hanging-basket plant. Drawings and descriptions of **Klugia** indicate that this plant will be worthy of a place in indoor gardening when stock is available. **Rehmannia** was once thought to be a foxglove relative. It is useful as a biennial for warm-climate outdoor gardens. A species of the true **Gesneria, G. cuneifolia** is noteworthy because of its compact growth and firecracker-red slipper flowers which appear in the crown. **Rhytidophyllum** is a small shrub which may grow to 1½ m. **Agalmyla, Asteranthera, Briggsia, Loxostigma, Mitraria** and **Monophyllaea** are worthy of at least a trial growing period.

Culture in the home

For plants of wide variation, it is natural that cultural requirements would vary. Basically, gesneriads respond to tropical growing conditions with some deviations as indicated in this article and in the Code to Care included in the varietal descriptions, following the pictorial pages. General culture is outlined here:

Light. A filtered or diffused sunlight is most desirable. If you live in a sunny part of the country that is unshaded by the smoke of industry, more shading will be necessary. In general, if the foliage has good color and the plants grow stockily, they are receiving enough light. If the stems grow long and weak, and the leaves appear at distant intervals, not enough light is being received. When leaves blister and turn to crisp brown, they probably have too much sun. It is known that the amount of light directly influences the amount of bloom of Saintpaulias; 600 to not exceeding 1300 foot-candles, up to 18 hours, best initiate budset. In the window garden, gesneriads will take just about all the light that can be given them during the fall and winter months. As the days lengthen into spring and summer, provide more shade.

Soil. Most gesneriads prefer a soil that is loose and well-drained. The addition of leaf mold, peat moss or compost promotes luxurious growth. A good basic mixture can be composed of equal parts peat moss, well-rotted leaf mold, rich garden loam and clean sand. Pasteurized soil is recommended. If this is impossible, buy a prepared planter mix; one composed basically of peat moss, leaf mold and Perlite mineral is best. Feed actively growing gesneriads regularly with any water-soluble house plant fertilizer.

Moisture. When gesneriads are in active growth, the soil must be kept moist. If the soil is not well-drained, conditions will be set for root rot. Room temperature water can be used to keep the foliage clean. If the temperature of the water varies ten degrees either way from that of the room, harmful results such as spotting will occur. Gesneriads, especially those with hairy leaves, are best given a bath in a warm, shaded place, and returned to the sunlight when the foliage is dry.

Humidity. Gesneriads appreciate a constant rise of moisture about their leaves. This humidity is an important key to success. If a humidity range of 40 to 60 per cent can be obtained in the home, at least in the window gardening area, one should be able to grow gesneriads. To raise humidity in a dry house, group plants together on a tray of moist sand, peat moss, vermiculite or pebbles. If you have radiators keep water in the container provided. The more plants one grows, the more humidity will be available. If all else fails, make a terrarium and grow just the gesneriads small enough to fit into limited space.

Temperature. Gesneriads, excepting the hardy or half-hardy genera, like a nighttime temperature range of 18 to 21°C with a rise of 3 to 5 degrees C. during the day.

Propagation. Excepting the most difficult, gesneriads flower in less than a year from seeds. Chiritas, some streptocarpus and even hybrid sinningias are sometimes grown as annuals, the plants maturing the same year seeds are sown. After flowering, the plants are destroyed and new seeds started. Plant gesneriad seeds according to standard procedure for dust-like seeds.

Most gesneriads may be propagated by leaf and stem cuttings. Some can be divided like any herbaceous plant. Tubers can be divided like a potato. Scaly rhizomes can be broken apart, even to the extent of individual scales, though larger portions of the rhizome are usually planted. Some gesneriads produce runners or stolons which root easily.

Dormancy. Most gesneriads go into dormancy after their heavy flowering season. This dormancy is more pronounced for those with tubers and scaly rhizomes. Storage temperatures ranging from 8 to 20° degrees are said to be appropriate for dormant gesneriad tubers. Albert Buell, successful commercial grower, recommends 15 deg. C. To prevent shriveling, keep the resting tubers barely moist. Watch for new sprouts. When they appear, repot to new soil, being careful not to bruise the tubers, and place in a suitable growing area.

Fibrous-rooted gesneriads have varied means of signaling a rest. In general, those known to be in good health want to rest when they take on a "ratty" appearance. For example, Saintpaulias stop flowering and the center stem will protrude like a long neck out of the pot. Episcias lose their lower leaves and refuse to grow. Hypocyrta loses all its leaves. When a plant rests, withhold all fertilizer. Use this hibernation period for pruning roots and stems. Repot to new soil. If crown leaves grow atop a bare stem, clip off and root for a stocky new plant. Resume normal watering and feeding when the plants begin to grow again.

Pests. Cyclamen mite is the most crippling gesneriad enemy. Mite damage causes plants to grow distorted, sometimes oddly twisted. Repeated application of rotenone or malathion are recommended controls.

gloxinia 'Crispa Waterloo' (grandiflora type)

gloxinia 'Crispa Meteor' (grandiflora type)

gloxinia 'Kegeliana' (grandiflora type)

gloxinia 'Wyoming' (grandiflora type)

gloxinia 'Blanche de Meru' (crassifolia type)

gloxinia 'Etoile de Feu' (crassifolia type)

gloxinia 'Arizona' (crassifolia type)

gloxinia 'Idaho' (crassifolia type)

gloxinia 'Kiss of Fire' (multiflora)

Double gloxinia 'Royal Red Giant'

Double gloxinia 'Thompson Hybrid'

gloxinia 'Antonelli Ruby'

gloxinia 'Buell's Queen Bee'

Double gloxinia 'Monte Cristo'

Sinningia spec. fyfiana (glox. grandiflora) 'Tigrina'

Sinningia (Rechsteineria) leucotricha, the "Brazilian edelweiss" or "Rainha do Abismo" in Brazil

Sinningia (Rechsteineria) cardinalis

Sinningia (Rechsteineria) macropoda

S. cardinalis splendens ("bulbosa")

Sinningia (Rechsteineria) cardinalis (inflor.)

Sinningia (Rechsteineria) cyclophylla (inflor.)

Sinningia (Rechsteineria) cyclophylla

Sinningia macropoda

Sinningia lineata

Sinningia warscewiczii

Sinningia calcaria

Sinningia verticillata 'Purpurea'

Sinningia verticillata as "doeringii", in Brazil

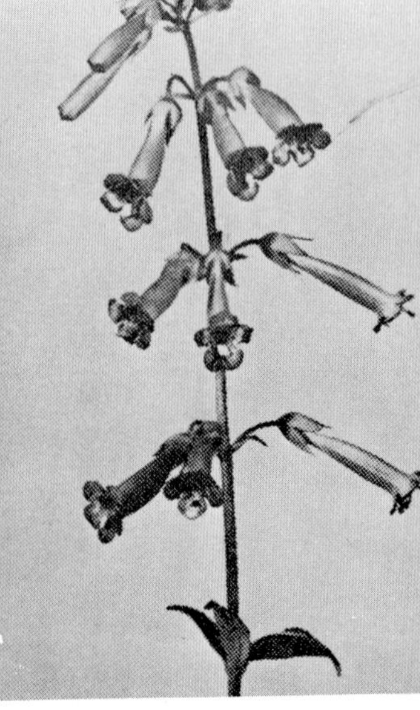
Sinningia sellovii

Sinningia cardinalis

Sinningia leucotricha, showing tuber

Sinningia warscewiczii

Sinningia (Rechsteineria) leucotricha

Sinningia (Rechsteineria) sellovii

Sinningia "splendens" in hort.

Sinningia verticillata (maculata douglasii hort.)

Sinningia (Rechsteineria) magnifica

Sinningia (Rechst.) cardinalis 'Innocence'

Sinningia (Rechsteineria) aggregata

Sinningia (Rechst.) tuberosa (Conn. Exper. Sta.)

Sinningia richii (Carl Clayberg-Connecticut)

Sinningia (Rechsteineria) macrorrhiza

Sinningia (Rechsteineria) cooperi

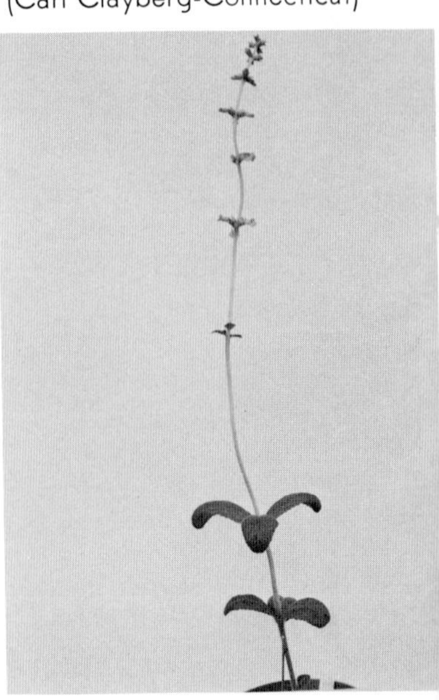
Sinningia (Rechst.) allagophylla

Sinningia speciosa 'Emperor Frederick' 'Tom Thumb', "Miniature gloxinia"

Sinningia pusilla, in glass bowl

Sinningia 'Doll Baby' Sinningia (Gloxinera) 'Connecticut hybrid'

Sinningia speciosa

Sinningia pusilla 'White Sprite' (Munich)

Sinningia rimicola

Sinningia schiffneri

Sinningia hirsuta

Sinningia 'Bright Eyes'

Sinningia discolor

Sinningia schiffneri

Sinningia tubiflora (Conn.Exper.Sta.)

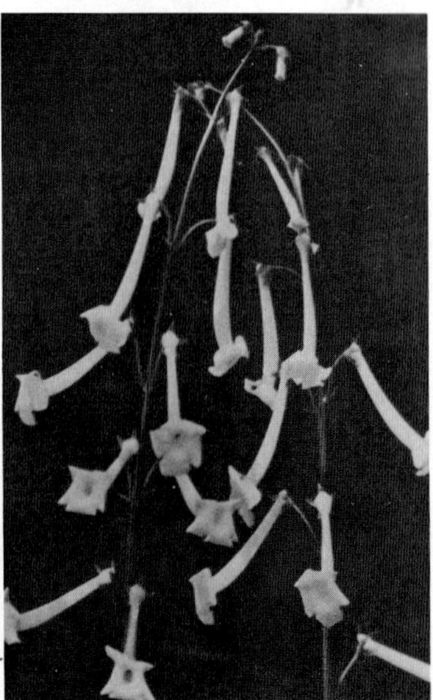
Sinningia tubiflora, inflor.

Sinningia speciosa florepleno 'Chicago', double- flowered gloxinia

Sinningia pusilla, a miniature in 12 cm brandy jar

Smithiantha (Naegelia) hybrida 'Karin Franklin'

Sinningia (x Gloxinera) 'Coral Gem'

Smithiantha 'Canary Bird'

Smithiantha 'Sunburst'

Smithiantha 'Exoniensis' (Snyder)

Sinningia (Rechsteineria) cardinalis 'Unschuld' (E. Hahn)

Sinningia (Rechsteineria) cardinalis 'Feuerschein'

Sinningia speciosa fl. pl. 'Miss America'

Columnea (Trichantha) purpureovittata

Smithiantha 'Rose Queen'

Smithiantha multiflora

Smithiantha cinnabarina

Smithiantha zebrina

Smithiantha 'Zebrina discolor'

Smithiantha 'Orange King'

Smithiantha x hybrida 'Sulphurea'

Smithiantha 'Exoniensis'

Smithiantha x hybrida 'Compacta'

Smithiantha 'Golden King'

Smithiantha (Naegelia) x hybrida 'Typ Lienig'

x Stroxinia hybrida (x Streptogloxinia)

Streptocarpus caulescens

Streptocarpus hyb. 'Farbenwunder'

Streptocarpus hyb. 'Red Orchid'

Streptocarpus hyb. 'Amethyst' (E. Hahn)

Columnea illepida (Trichantha)

Streptocarpus hildebrandtii (Madagascar)

Columnea teuscheri (Trichantha minor in hort.)

Streptocarpus polyanthus

Streptocarpus dunnii

Streptocarpus saundersii

Streptocarpus glandulosissimus

Streptocarpus insignis

Streptocarpus cyanandrus

Streptocarpus vandeleurii

Streptocarpus dunnii, in Transvaal habitat

Streptocarpus phyllanthus, (Longwood Gardens, Penna.)

Streptocarpus grandis, photographed at Sydney Botanic Gardens

Streptocarpus cooksonii (Natal)

Streptocarpus cooperi, at Royal Botanic Garden, Edinburgh

Streptocarpus 'Sutton's Blush Pink'

Streptocarpus saundersii (?), in New Zealand

Streptocarpus polyanthus

Streptocarpus baudertii

Streptocarpus pusillus

Streptocarpus parviflorus

Streptocarpus holstii

Streptocarpus kentaniensis

Streptocarpus dunnii

Streptocarpus wendlandii (close-up)

x Streptogloxinia 'Lorna'

Streptocarpus rexii

Streptocarpus caulescens

Streptocarpus grandis

Streptocarpus saxorum

Streptocarpus rexii

Streptocarpus x hybridus 'Wiesmoor'

Streptocarpus x hybridus 'Achimeniflorus'

Streptocarpus wendlandii

Titanotrichum oldhamii

Streptocarpus x hybridus

Columnea teuscheri (Trichantha minor in hort.)

Phyllostachys sulphurea, at Jardin Botanique "Les Cedres", France

Bambusa beecheyana, container-grown at Chicago Art Institute

Guadua angustifolia, a "Giant bamboo", Montego Bay, Jamaica

Phyllostachys bambusoides, in West Los Angeles

Bambusa glaucescens 'Stripestem' (Fernleaf bamboo)

Bambusa glaucescens (multiplex in hort.)

Bambusa glaucescens riviereorum, the "Chinese Goddess" bamboo

Bambusa glaucescens 'Nana', "Small-leaf bamboo"

Bambusa tuldoides (Punting Pole bamboo)

Pseudosasa japonica 'Metake' (Arrow bamboo)

Phyllostachys aurea, the Fishpole bamboo

Bambusa ventricosa (Buddha's Belly bamboo)

Sasa (Arundinaria) palmata, in New Zealand

Arundinaria funghomii

Arundinaria vagans (N. Z.)

Arundinaria chrysantha, on Long Island, N. Y.

Arundinaria auricoma (N. Z.)

Arundinaria (Phyllostachys) hindsii

Arundinaria viridi-striata (Pleioblastus viridi-striatus)

Dendrocalamus giganteus, the Giant bamboo, on tropical Ceylon

Pseudosasa japonica, in winter's snow, in New Jersey

Bambusa glaucescens var. 'Alphonse Karr'

Bambusa gracillima hort., in N. Z.

Phyllostachys nigra

Bambusa glaucescens var. 'Alphonse Karr'

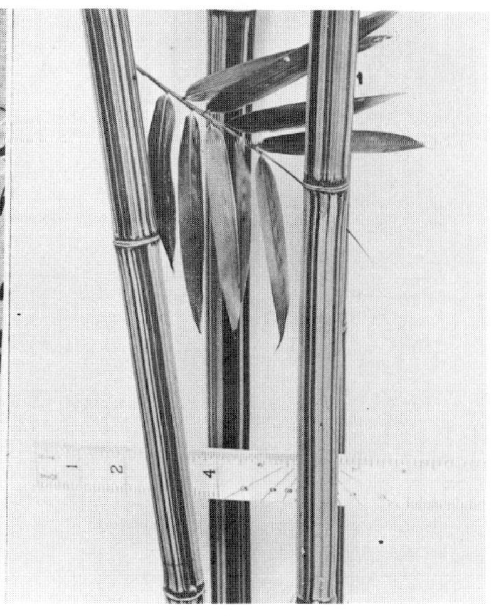

Bambusa eutuldoides, as grown in New Zealand

Bambusa gracilis hort. (J. Isaachsen, Oratia, N. Z.)

Bambusa falcata, branches (N. Z.)

Bambusa gracilis hort., near Auckland, N. Z.

Bambusa falcata, culms, in New Zealand

Bambusa oldhamii (grown in the trade as "falcata"; Los Angeles)

Bambusa glaucescens riviereorum,
the Golden Goddess bamboo, in California

Bambusa eutuldoides,
at Isaachsen Nursery, Oratia, New Zealand

Arundinaria alpina, near Kigezi at 2,700m
on the Kivu border of the Congo

Bambusa textilis, clumps in habitat,
Kwangtung Prov., China

Phyllostachys aureosulcata,
the Yellow-groove bamboo, from Chekiang

Sasa pygmaea

Sasa tessellata, at Glenn Dale, Maryland

Phyllostachys viridis (mitis), in New Zealand

Phyllostachys bambusoides, specimen 20m tall, in Georgia

Bambusa vulgaris, growing along Lake Victoria, Entebbe, Uganda

Bambusa glaucescens (multiplex of hort.) in northern Florida

Phyllostachys aureosulcata, the Yellow-groove bamboo, growing along the west front of U.S. Capitol, Washington, D.C.

Semiarundinaria fastuosa, the Narihira bamboo, near Savannah, Georgia

Phyllostachys nigra, the Black Bamboo, at U.S. Plant Introd. Sta., Savannah

GRAMINEAE: Cortaderia, Festuca, Olyra, Oplismenus, Sasa, Setaria, Stenotaphrum, Uniola

Stenotaphrum secundatum variegatum

Sasa fortunei

Oplismenus hirtellus 'Variegatus'

Uniola paniculata

Festuca ovina glauca (Blue Fescue)

Setaria palmifolia

Cortaderia selloana pumila

Olyra latifolia, a bamboo-like African grass, Mrima Hill, Southern Kenya

Arundo donax versicolor, the 'Variegated-leaved Giant Reed'

Cortaderia selloana, the 'Pampas grass', at Nelson, New Zealand

Saccharum officinarum, the Sugar-cane, which produces sugar and other confections, also rum (see Rumandia, Exotica I)

Arundinaria amabilis, the "Tonkin cane" in Kwangtung Province, South China

Bambusa beecheyanus

Bambusa polymorpha, at Los Angeles Arboretum

Bambusa (Sinocalamus) oldhamii, in San Diego Zoo

Pleioblastus simonii 'Variegata'

Phyllostachys aurea, a "Running bamboo"

Bambusa vulgaris vittata

Chimonobambusa marmorea (Japan)

Phyllostachys aurea (Golden bamboo)

Chimonobambusa quadrangularis

Dendrocalamus giganteus, at Peradeniya, Sri Lanka

Bambusa vulgaris, in Takarazuka, Japan

Bambusa vulgaris 'Aureo-variegata', cut culms in water

Phyllostachys nigra, the "Black bamboo", in California

Zea mays, "Indian corn" (Bonn, Germany)

Saccharum officinarum, "Sugar cane "

Miscanthus sinensis 'Variegatus', "Eulalia"

Coix lacryma jobi, "Job's tears"

Shibataea kumasaca (Japan)

Stenotaphrum secundatum 'Variegatum', "St. Augustine grass"

Zoysia japonica 'Meyeri', "Korean grass", in Honolulu, Hawaii

Zoysia tenuifolia, the "Temple grass"

Ginkgo biloba, grown as Bonsai tree

Welwitschia mirabilis, with male flowers

Clusia rosea

Welwitschia mirabilis, female plant at Stellenbosch

Welwitschia mirabilis (bainesii), plant with male catkins or cones

Clusia rosea

Clusia rosea 'Aurero-variegata'

Clusia "lanceolata"

HALORAGIDACEAE: Gunnera, Myriophyllum; HAMAMELIDACEAE: Hamamelis, Parrotia, Rhodoleia, Trichocladus; HERNANDIACEAE: Hernandia

Gunnera chilensis (Strybing Arboretum, Golden Gate Park, San Francisco) Gunnera manicata

Trichocladus crinitus

Parrotia persica

Rhodoleia championii

Hamamelis japonica

Myriophyllum proserpinacoides

Hernandia ovigera

Gunnera hamiltonii

Wachendorfia paniculata

Gunnera chilensis, inflor.

Wigandia cicosum (Lisbon Bot. Garden)

Aesculus californica (California buckeye)

Aesculus x carnea (Red horse-chestnut)

Clusia rosea, the "Autograph tree"

Clusia grandiflora, flower

Acidanthera laxiflora

Acidanthera tubergenii 'Zwanenburg'

Anaclanthe plicata

Babiana stricta rubrocyanea

Belamcanda chinensis

Aristea lugens

Curtonus paniculatus

Freesia x hybrida 'Fantasy' (double-flowered)

Ferraria undulata

Iris graeberiana

Iris graminea

Iris tenax

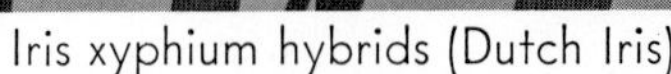
Iris xyphium hybrids (Dutch Iris)

Iris innominata hybrids

Acidanthera bicolor 'Murieliae'

Moraea polystachya

Iris germanica var. florentina variegata

Moraea (Dietes) pavonia var. villosa

Moraea ramosa

Dietes vegeta (Moraea)

Dietes 'Oakhurst hybrid'

Moraea edulis

Dietes vegeta catenulata

Moraea spathacea

Moraea glaucopsis

Dietes grandiflora, in Mozambique

Moraea spathacea

Dietes prolongata hort. (Moraea iridioides prolongata)

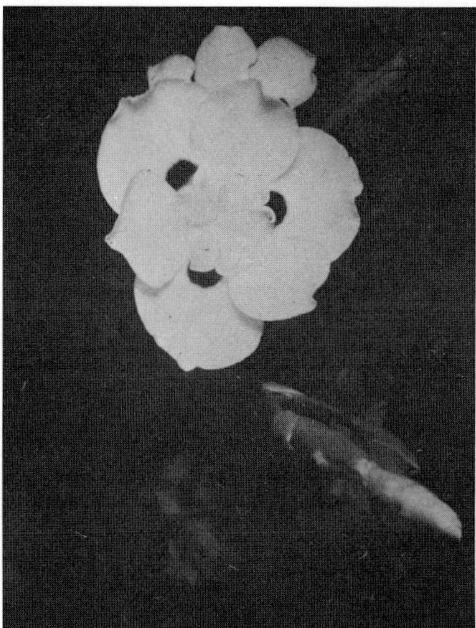

Dietes bicolor

Moraea glaucopsis

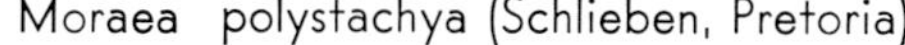

Moraea polystachya (Schlieben, Pretoria)

Dietes vegeta (Moraea iridioides in hort.), "Wild iris"

Tritonia x crocosmaeflora, "Montbretia" of gardens

Crocosmia masonorum, in New Zealand

Hesperantha stanfordiae

Ixia maculata, the "Corn-lily"

Tritonia pottsii, in Malta

Tritonia hyalina

Crocosmia masonorum (Transvaal)

Crocosmia masonorum, at Edinburgh Botanic Garden

Tritonia x crocosmaeflora, known in hort. as "Montbretia"

Neomarica bicolor, "Apostle plant", from Brazil

Tigridia pavonia 'Canariensis', a "Tiger-flower"

Lapeirousia grandiflora

Tigridia pavonia

Aristea ecklonii

Lapeirousia laxa (cruenta)

Watsonia pyramidata in habitat, Hottentot Mts., South Africa

Geissorhiza rochensis (Wine cups)

Romulea (Geissorhiza) sabulosa

Hesperantha stanfordiae

Tigridia pavonia

Hesperantha bauri

Tritonia deusta

Ixia 'Rosy Queen'

Ixia 'Bridesmaid'

Ixiolirion tataricum (Amaryll.)

Ixia scariosa (incarnata)

Ixia viridiflora

Sparaxis tricolor alba

Sparaxis grandiflora

Sparaxis tricolor 'Honneur de Haarlem'

Watsonia humilis maculata

Pterocarya fraxinifolia dumosa

Romulea chloroleuca

Juglans cinerea, the "Butter-nut"

Carya pecan, "Pecan-nut" (Vista, Calif.)

Juglans nigra, "Black walnut" (inflor.)

Coleus lanuginosus

Coleus comosus hort. (T. Everett)

Coleus spicatus (Aethiopia)

Coleus blumei 'Rainbow Amber Beauty' (Sakata)

Coleus blumei 'Red Croton'

Coleus blumei 'Rainbow Salmon Flame' (Sakata)

Glechoma (Nepeta) tuberosa

Pogostemon plectranthoides

Coleus blumei 'Firebird'

Coleus blumei 'Max Levering'

Coleus blumei 'Pride of Autumn'

Coleus blumei 'Lord Alverson'

Coleus blumei 'Rainbow Red'

Coleus blumei 'Firebrand'

Coleus blumei 'Victoria'

Coleus blumei 'Two-tone Red'

Lamium purpureum

Lamium galeobdolon 'Variegatum'

Lamium maculatum

Ocimum basilicum

Pycnostachys dawei

Perilla frutescens crispa

Moluccella laevis

Phlomis italica

Origanum dictamnus (Crete Dittany)

Majorana hortensis (Sweet Pot Majoram)

Lavandula stoechas (French Lavender)

Mentha spicata (Spearmint)

Mentha citrata (Orange Mint)

Mentha piperita (Peppermint)

Mentha requienii

Mentha rotundifolia 'Variegata' (Pineapple min

Mentha spicata (Spearmint)

Majorana hortensis (Sweet Marjoram)

Marrubium candidissimum (Horehound)

Salvia sclarea (Clary)

Melissa officinalis (Lemon Balm)

Glechoma (Nepeta) hederacea (Ground ivy)

Teucrium fruticans (Germander)

Lavandula officinalis (English Lavender)

Pycnostachys dawei

Pycnostachys urticifolia

Lavandula stoechas

Plectranthus coleoides 'Marginatus'

Plectranthus 'Variegated Mintleaf'

Plectranthus ciliatus near Pretoria, Transvaal

Plectranthus myrianthus

Plectranthus madagascariensis, at Kirstenbosch

Plectranthus tomentosus, "Succulent coleus"

Dysophylla verticillata, in Nepal

Plectranthus oertendahlii 'Variegatus'

Plectranthus saccatus, in Natal (Schlieben)

Plectranthus strigosus

Plectranthus nummularius (Pretoria)

Plectranthus 'Variegated Mintleaf'

Plectranthus verticillatus (Pretoria)

Plectranthus nummularius (australis in hort.) Plectranthus oertendahlii Plectranthus purpuratus

Plectranthus nummularius (australis in hort.)

Rosmarinus officinalis prostratus

Moluccella laevis (Bells of Ireland)

Plectranthus oertendahlii

Iboza riparia

Leonotis leonorus

Salvia splendens

Salvia officinalis tricolor (Tricolor Sage)

Glechoma (Nepeta) hederacea variegata

Salvia leucantha (Mexican Bush Sage)

Salvia dorisiana

Salvia coccinea

Salvia nutans

Salvia dorisiana

Salvia glutinosa

Salvia flava

Salvia involucrata

Salvia officinalis (Garden Sage)

Lavandula canariensis

Scutellaria javanica

Scutellaria mociniana, the Scarlet Skullcap

Salvia splendens, the Scarlet Sage

Salvia splendens 'Dwarf'

Salvia patens

Salvia greggii

Salvia argentea

Physostegia virginiana

Pycnostachys caerulea

Pycnostachys dawei

Scutellaria villosa

Scutellaria costaricensis, "Skull-cap"

Scutellaria javanica

Salvia splendens 'Lavender Love'

Salvia microphylla, "Cherry-sage"

Salvia leucantha, "Mexican Bush-sage"

Rosmarinus officinalis, the Rosemary bush

Stachys officinalis

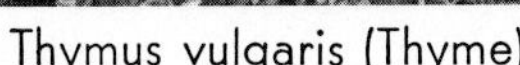
Thymus vulgaris (Thyme)

Thymus vulgaris aureus (Golden Thyme)

Thymus hirsutus

Teucrium fruticans (Germander)

Teucrium flavum

Mentha rotundifolia, infl.

Westringia rosmariniformis

Prostanthera nivea

Thymus serpyllum

Thymus serpyllum var. vulgaris argenteus

Thymus serpyllum lanuginosus

Rosmarinus lavendulaceus, "Prostrate Rosemary"

Origanum pulchellum, a "Marjoram"

Cinnamomum cassia, "Cassia-bark tree"

Persea americana, the "Avocado"

Laurus nobilis, "Bay-leaf"

Umbellularia californica, "California laurel"

Persea americana 'Fuerte'

Lindera benzoin, "Spica bush"

Sassafras albidum, "Sassafras"

Umbellularia californica, "Myrtle-wood" or "California laurel"

Laurus nobilis, the "Roman laurel" or "Bay-tree"

Laurus nobilis, "Bay-tree" standard at Longwood Gardens, Penna.

Laurus nobilis, trained with spiralled trunks, in Germany

Couroupita guianensis, "Cannonball-tree", in Panama

Couroupita guianensis, in flower

Lardizabala biternata

Akebia quinata, the "Chocolate vine"

Akebia quinata, female flower (Lard.)

Lecythis zabucajo, "Sapucaya nut"

Decaisnea fargesii (Lard.)

Barringtonia asiatica, "Fishpoison-tree"

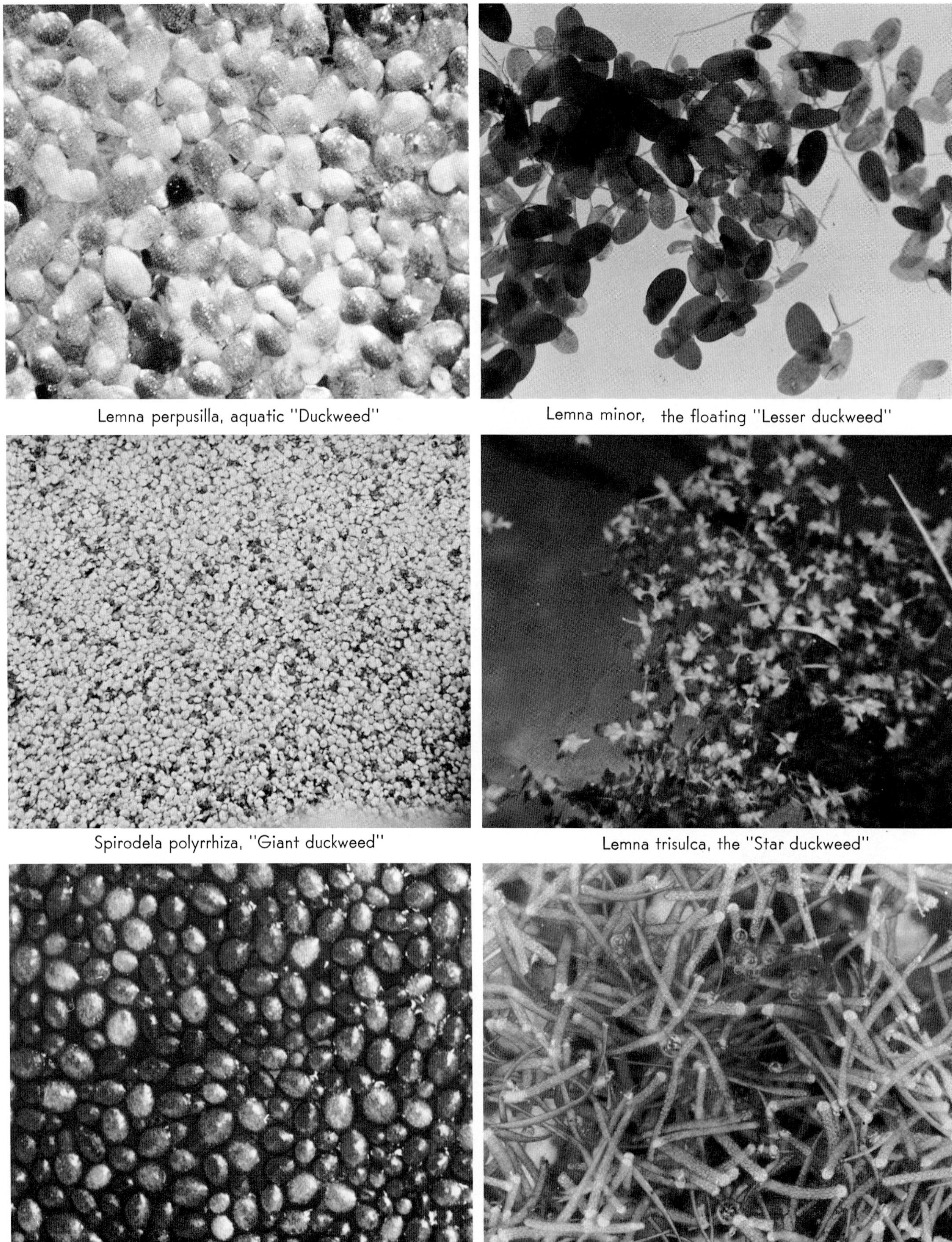

Lemna perpusilla, aquatic "Duckweed"

Lemna minor, the floating "Lesser duckweed"

Spirodela polyrrhiza, "Giant duckweed"

Lemna trisulca, the "Star duckweed"

Wolffia arrhiza, aquatic "Water-meal"

Wolffiella denticulata, submerged aquatic from So. Africa

Erythrina lysistemon, in brilliant flower, at Pretoria, Transvaal

Erythrina indica picta at Brisbane Bot. Gardens, Queensland

Amherstia nobilis, with Sinhalese gardener, Peradeniya, Ceylon

Bolusanthus speciosus, the Tree Wisteria, in Kruger National Park, South Africa

Acacia sieberiana woodii, the "Paperbark-thorn", in the Transvaal

Acacia nigrescens, the "Knob-thorn"

Acacia giraffae, "Camel-thorn"

Acacia sphaerocephala, from Mexico

Acacia neriifolia (Australia)

Acacia robusta, "Enkeldoring"

Acacia karroo, the "Sweet-thorn"

Acacia venulosa, from Queensland

Acacia latifolia, from Northern Australia

Acacia retinodes in horticulture as "floribunda", the "Everblooming acacia"

Acacia cavenia, in Chile habitat

Acacia sphaerocephala, a "Bull-horn acacia" from Mexico

Acacia sieberiana var. woodii

Acacia fimbriata

Acacia cardiophylla

Acacia cornigera, "Bull-horn acacia"

Acacia cyanophylla, "Blue-leaved wattle"

Acacia sowdenii

Acacia decurrens, "Green wattle"

Acacia alata

Acacia baileyana

Acacia longifolia floribunda

Acacia podalyriifolia

Acacia farnesiana

Acacia cultriformis

Acacia decurrens dealbata

Acacia drummondii

Acacia podalyriifolia

Acacia decurrens dealbata, in Australia

Acacia drepanolobium, in the Rift Valley, Kenya

Acacia saligna, at Cape of Good Hope

Acacia nigrescens, on the Transvaal Veld

Acacia mearnsii, in Uganda

Albizia julibrissin

Albizia evansii, in North Transvaal

Acacia armata pendula

Acacia armata (paradoxa)

Acacia latifolia

Acacia retinodes ("floribunda" in hort.)

Acacia longifolia mucronata

Acacia longifolia

Acacia baileyana

Acacia pubescens

Acacia pubescens erecta

Clianthus formosus (dampieri), the Glory-pea

Amherstia nobilis

Brownea coccinea

Adenanthera pavonina, Sandal-wood

Arachis hypogaea, the Peanut vine

Apios americana (tuberosa)

Clianthus formosus (dampieri)

Sesbania grandiflora (Cape Verde Isl.)

Butea frondosa, "Flame of the Forest"

Amherstia nobilis, "Pride of Burma"

Amicia zygomeris, from Mexico

Amorpha fruticosa, "False indigo"

Albizia lebbeck

Abrus precatorius, "Crab's-eye vine"

Brownea coccinea x latifolia

Bauhinia galpinii, in North Transvaal habitat

Bauhinia blakeana, Brisbane Bot. Gardens, Queensland

Bauhinia tomentosa

Bauhinia acuminata

Bauhinia picta

Chorizema cordatum

Bauhinia blakeana

Bauhinia purpurea

Bauhinia monandra, "Pink orchid"

Bauhinia kirkii (Transvaal)

Bauhinia macrantha, "Zambezi coffee"

Bauhinia tomentosa, "Bell bauhinia"

Bauhinia variegata, "Indian ebony"

Bauhinia bowkeri (Schlieben-Pretoria)

Bauhinia blakeana, "Hongkong orchid"

Calliandra emarginata

Calliandra tweedii

Calliandra haematocephala ('tweedii')

Calliandra inaequilatera

Calliandra surinamensis

Cytisus scoparius (Scotch Broom)

Cytisus canariensis

Cytisus x racemosus (florists' genista)

Calliandra harrisii 'Minima' in hort.

Caesalpinia coriaria, the wind-blown "Divi-Divi" on Aruba

Calliandra eriophylla

Calliandra portoricensis (caracasana)

Poinciana (Caesalpinia) gilliesii

Carmichaelia enysii

Camoensia maxima, from Angola

Canavallia ensiformis, "Jack-bean"

Cassia alata, in Miami

Cassia bicapsularis (Escondido, Calif.)

Cassia leptophylla, Vista, California

Cassia multijuga, in Sydney

Cassia excelsa floribunda

Cassia closiana (Chile)

Cassia fistula, "Golden shower"

Cassia surattensis, Nuku Hiva, Marquesas

Cassia marilandica

Cassia marginata, "Red Cassia" at Fairchild's Gardens, Miami

Cassia hybrida, the "Rainbow Shower" of Honolulu

Cassia didymobotrya (nairobensis), in Encinitas, California

Cassia fistula, the "Golden shower" in Rio de Janeiro

Colvillea racemosa, in Brisbane, Australia

G ycyrrhiza glabra

Cassia spectabilis, in Uganda

Caesalpinia sepiaria

Poinciana (Caesalpinia) pulcherrima

Cassia marilandica

Cassia artemisioides

Cassia splendida

Cassia corymbosa ("marilandica")

Ceratonia siliqua, "St. John's-bread"

Ceratonia siliqua, "Carob", in flower

Castanospermum australe, "Moreton Bay chestnut"

Crotalaria agatiflora, "Canary-bird bush"

Chorizema cordatum, "Flame-pea"

Cercis siliquastrum, "Judas tree"

Cytisus battandierii, in Algiers

Cytisus maderensis, at Strybing Arboretum, San Francisco

Dolichos lablab, "Hyacinth-bean"

Elephantorrhiza burkei (Transvaal)

Ebenopsis flexicaulis, "Texas ebony"

Coronilla emerus, "Scorpion senna"

Christia (Lourea) vespertilionis

Coronilla glauca variegata

Flemingia strobilifera

Derris indica (Fairchild Gardens)

Dalbergia tonkinensis, at Leningrad Bot. Garden

Delonix regia (Poinciana), the regal "Flamboyant" in Singapore

Delonix regia, the "Gul Mohur" in India, or "Peacock tree"

Clianthus puniceus, "Parrot's-bill"

Clianthus formosus, "Glory-pea"

Clianthus dampieri (in hort.)

Clitorea ternatea, "Butterfly-pea"

Enterolobium cyclocarpum, "Ear tree"

Eperua jenmanii, in Trinidad

Erythrina x bidwillii

Erythrina humeana, in Vista, California

Erythrina coralloides

Erythrina caffra, the "Coral tree" (Dr. L. E. Codd, South Africa)

Erythrina indica, from Ryukyu Islands

Erythrina crista-galli

Erythrina zeyheri, "Prickly Cardinal"

Erythrina caffra 'Flavescens'

Erythrina humeana

Erythrina falcata, in Brazil

Erythrina caffra

Galega officinalis

Erythrina acanthocarpa

Erythrina abyssinica, at Entebbe, Uganda

Erythrina crista-galli (Coral tree)

Geoffroea inermis, in Balboa, Panama

Mandulea sericea, Transvaal

Lonchocarpus violaceus, "Lance-pod"

Gliricidia sepium, "Madre de Cacao"

Lonchocarpus sericeus, in Senegal

Laburnum x watereri, "Golden chain"

Hardenbergia violacea

Inga edulis, on Moorea

Liparia spherica, in Cape Town

Parkinsonia aculeata, "Jerusalem-thorn"

Mucuna novo-guineensis, in Papua

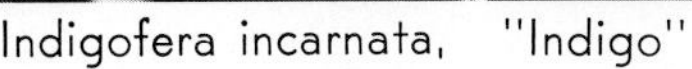

Indigofera incarnata, "Indigo"

Mimosa spegazzinii, a "Sensitive shrub"

Leucaena glauca in the Marquesas

Neptunia oleracea, "Water-mimosa" (Munich Botanic Garden)

Neptunia plena, in tropical pool, Leningrad Botanic Garden

Hovea trisperma

Laburnum x watereri (vossii), the Golden chain-tree

Lathyrus odoratus (Sweet Pea)

Lathyrus odoratus 'Late Spencer'

Lupinus 'Russell's hybrids'

Lotus corniculatus (Tree-foil)

Lotus berthelotii, in flower

Indigofera incarnata (Indigo)

Kennedia rubicunda

Kennedia rubicunda

Vigna sesquipedalis (Asparagus-bean)

Hardenbergia monophylla

Neptunia plena (flava)

Mimosa pudica, the Sensitive Plant folds its leaflets when touched

Phaseolus caracalla (Snail-flower)

Petteria ramentacea

Phaseolus coccineus 'Dwarf Scarlet Runner' bean

Phanera kockiana, climber in Sarawak, North Borneo

Mucuna bennettii, in New Guinea

Pithecellobium unguis-catii

Strongylodon macrobotrys (Jade vine)

Schizolobium parahybum, the fern-like "Bacurubu", from Panama

Saraca indica, the "Asoka tree", in Mysore, India

Phanera williamsii, "Chain liane", jungles of New Guinea

Poinciana (Caesalpinia) pulchella flava, yellow-flowered "Pride of Barbados"

Sophora secundiflora, "Mescal-bean"

Tamarindus indica, "Tamarind"

Phaseolus caracalla, "Corkscrew-flower"

Pterocarpus rotundifolius, "Roundleaf Kiaat"

Samanea saman, "Rain tree"

Ulex europaeus, in Wellington, N.Z.

Schótia brachypetala, "Hottentots-bean"

Piptanthus laburnifolius (Himalayas)

Podalyria calyptrata (So. Africa)

Samanea saman, the Rain-tree, in Trinidad

Robinia pseudoacacia tortuosa, a Yellow Locust

Sophora **tetraptera**

Sophora microphylla, in New Zealand

Tipuana tipu (Rosewood)

Tamarindus indica (Tamarind-tree)

Schotia brachypetala, the Tree fuchsia of the African Veld, Transvaal

Trifolium dubium (Irish Shamrock) Trifolium repens minus, "Shamrock" (5cm pot) Trifolium repens (White Clover)

Trifolium dubium, from Irish seed

Trifolium dubium, the Irish Shamrock, in Dublin, Ireland

Oxytropis lambertii Trifolium arvense Vicia cracca (Vetch)

Wisteria floribunda, the "Japanese wisteria"

Strongylodon macrobotrys, the "Jade vine" from the Philippines

Saraca thaipingensis, in Peradeniya, Ceylon

Sutherlandia frutescens, "Balloon-pea", Pretoria, So. Africa

Swainsona galegifolia var. coronillifolia

Swainsona galegifolia

Thermopsis fabacea

Sutherlandia frutescens, in South Africa

Spartium junceum (Weavers Broom)

Wisteria floribunda violaceo-plena

Wisteria floribunda macrobotrys (multijuga), in Japan

Wisteria floribunda, blooming at Union Buildings, Pretoria, South Africa

Aloe mitriformis, in the landscape of South Africa

Aloe ferox variegata, at Kirstenbosch Botanical Gardens

Aloe aculeata, on the High Veld, Transvaal

Aloe chabaudii with Victoria Falls, Zambia

Aloe variegata ausana

Aloe variegata

x Gastrolea beguinii

Aloe ferox (juv.)

Aloe brevifolia (humilis of the trade)

Aloe brevifolia (young pl.)

Aloe brevifolia var. depressa (suckering plant)

Aloe humilis 'Globosa'

Aloe brevifolia variegata

Aloe barbadensis (vera), in habitat on the island of St. Helena

Aloe ballyi, in Tsavo National Park, Kenya

Aloe salm-dyckiana, blooming at Villa 'Les Cèdres', France

Aloe nobilis, in flower at Exotic Gardens, Monaco

Aloe x spinosissima

Aloe africana

Aloe arborescens

Aloe bainesii

Aloe arborescens

Aloe ciliaris

Aloe vera, young plant

Aloe vera, suckering plant

Aloe 'Ciliaris hybrid' (tidmarshii)

Aloe striata

Aloe marlothii

Aloe acutissima

Aloe 'Soledad hybrid'

Aloe pillansii

Aloe marlothii (juv.)

Aloe melanacantha

Aloe microstigma (juv.)

Aloe sladeniana (specimen)

Aloe aculeata

Aloe aristata

Aloe ciliaris

Aloe macracantha

Aloe confusa

Aloe transvaalensis (juv.)

Aloe nobilis

Aloe virens

Aloe x humvir

Aloe vera chinensis

Aloe distans

Aloe plicatilis

Aloe striata

Aloe latifolia

Aloe zebrina

Aloe melanostigma

Aloe saponaria (10cm pot)

Aloe millotii

Aloe eru 'Maculata' (young plant)

Aloe mitriformis, young plant

Aloe vanbalenii (15cm pot)

Aloe microstigma

Aloe haemanthifolia

Aloe suprafoliata, at Stellenbosch, Cape

Aloe saponaria (inflor.)

Aloe jucunda

Aloe tenuior

Aloe mitriformis

Aloe variegata, flowers

Aloe succotrina

Aloe x spinosissima

Aloe ferox

Aloe claviflora ("cleistiflora" hort.)

Chamaealoe africana x Aloe parvula

Aloe thraskii (9cm pot)

Aloe saponaria x striata

Aloe 'Walmsley's Bronze' (6cm pot)

Aloe 'Walmsley's Blue'

Aloe 'Crosby's Prolific'

Aloe arborescens

Aloe commixta

Aloe microstigma

Aloe ciliaris

Aloe comosa

Aloe ferox (hanburyi)

Aloe brevifolia

Aloe bakeri

Aloe pearsonii

Aloe davyana sobulifera, at Diep River, Cape

Aloe parvibracteata

Aloe succotrina

Aloe eru 'Green form'

Aloe saponaria in habitat, North Transvaal

Aloe arborescens 'Spineless' (speciosa)

Aloe vanbalenii, at Succulenta Nursery, Hout Bay, Cape

Aloe castanea, near Lydensburg, Transvaal

Aloe plicatilis, ancient specimen at Kirstenbosch, So. Africa

Aloe humilis echinata

Aloe "lineata"

Aloe longistyla

Aloe petrophila

Aloe dawei

Aloe plicatilis

Aloe aristata

Apicra egregia (Astroloba)

Aloe dichotoma, at Hout Bay, Cape Prov.

Aloe comosa, on rocky slope, Great Karroo, So. Africa

Aloe bainesii, old tree, with Table Mountain, Cape Town

Aloe marlothii, in Transvaal habitat

Aloe ramosissima (Stellenbosch)

Aloe wickensii (The Wilds, Johannesburg)

Aloe peglerae (pietersii), Transvaal

Aloe brevifolia depressa

Aloe brevifolia, at Stellenbosch, South Africa

Aloe humilis

Aloe microstigma, in Karroo habitat

Aloe mitriformis, snaking downward, Karrooport, Transvaal

Gloriosa rothschildiana

Dracaena goldieana

Aloe arborescens (inflor.)

Aloe variegata

Veltheimia viridifolia (capensis)

Sansevieria trifasciata laurentii

Convallaria majalis rosea

Dracaena fragrans 'Victoriae'

Lilium pumilum (tenuifolium)

Haworthia papillosa

Scilla peruviana

Cordyline terminalis 'Tricolor'

Aloe lineata, on slopes of Table Mountain, Kirstenbosch

Aloe glauca, at Carp's Nursery, Hout Bay, Cape

Aloe arborescens, group at Stellenbosch Botanic Garden, Cape

Aloe plicatilis in habitat, Hottentot-Holland Mountains, So. Africa

Aloe excelsa

Aloe striata x saponaria (seedling mutation 'Picta')

Aloe ecklonis

Aloe ferox, on slopes of Table Mountain, Cape Prov.

Aloe melanacantha, at Stellenbosch

Aloe jex-blakeae, in Kenya

Aloe speciosa, at Kirstenbosch

Aloe mutabilis, Kruger Park, Transvaal

Aloe pearsonii

Aloe arborescens

Aloe barbadensis (vera) on St. Helena

Aloe dinteri, in South West Africa

Aloe candelabrum, in Natal (Schlieben)

Aloe x bortiana

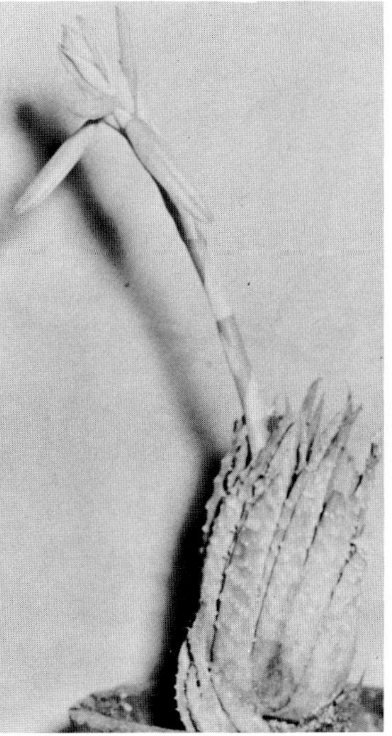

Aloe humilis, in Cape Town

Aloe broomii, Lesotho habitat

Aloe x principis

Aloe littoralis, at Les Cedres, France

Aloe bulbillifera

Aloe conifera (Madagascar)

Aloe gariepensis (Marnier-Lapostolle)

Aloe laxissima (Schlieben)

Aloe peglerae (Transvaal)

Aloe tenuior rubriflora

Aloe vaombe (Marnier-Lapostolle)

Aloe haworthioides (E. Hummel)

Aloe polyphylla, Carlsbad, California

Aloe pachygaster (Schlieben)

Aloe cooperi (Ed.Hummel)

Aloe parvula (H.Johnson)

Aloe aristata 'Variegata'

Aloe concinna (zanzibarica)

Aloe juveana (H.Johnson)

Aloe squarrosa (T.Everett)

Chamaealoe africana

Aloe mubendiensis

Aloe tororoana

Aloe dolomitica (N.Transvaal)

Aloe schweinfurthii

Aloe branddraaiensis

Aloe x delaetii (ciliaris x succotrina)

Aloe affinis

Aloe viguieri

Aloe percrassa

Aloe perfoliata in hort. (vera)

Aloe peckii

Aloe madecassa

Aloe tweediae

Aloe somaliensis

Aloe distans

Aloe descoingsii

Aloe pluridens

Aloe microdonta

Aloe versicolor

Aloe claviflora

Apicra dodsoniana

Apicra deltoidea

Apicra pentagona

Apicra spiralis

Agapanthus africanus

Agapanthus orientalis 'Albidus'

Arthropodium cirrhatum

Aspidistra elatior 'Variegata'

Aspidistra elatior (lurida)

Aspidistra elatior 'Minor'

Asphodelus albus, in Spain

Asphodelus microcarpus, at Mycaene, Greece

Asphodeline lutea, on Mt. Olympus

Albuca nelsonii (crinifolia)

Agapanthus longispathus albus

Arthropodium cirrhatum, "Rock-lily"

Agapanthus africanus minor

Agapanthus africanus, "African lily"

Agapanthus campanulatus

Allium ostrowskianum Allium triquetrum Allium neapolitanum

Allium fistulosum (Spanish Onion)

Allium schoenoprasum (Chives)

Allium porrum (Leeks)

Allium moly

Allium angulosum

Allium neapolitanum

Allium moly, "Golden garlic"

Allium zebdanense, from Lebanon

Allium sphaerocephalum

Allium triquetrum, "Triangle onion"

Allium schoenoprasum, "Chives"

Allium giganteum, "Giant allium"

Allium cepa, the Persian onion

Allium albopilosum (christophii)

Allium karataviense

Allium neapolitanum

Asparagus setaceus (syn. plumosus)

Asparagus falcatus

Asparagus densiflorus 'Sprengeri'

Asparagus asparagoides myrtifolius (Smilax)

Asparagus crispus

Asparagus africanus (cooperi)

Asparagus densiflorus cv.'Myers'

Asparagus densiflorus fa.sarmentosus

Asparagus madagascariensis

Asparagus drepanophyllus

Asparagus densiflorus 'Myriocladus'

Asparagus densiflorus 'Pyramidalis'

Asparagus densiflorus 'Sprengeri'

Asparagus scandens deflexus

Asparagus cooperi

Asparagus retrofractus

Asparagus densiflorus 'Sprengeri'

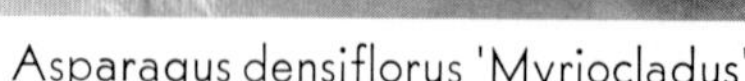

Asparagus densiflorus 'Myriocladus'

Asparagus macrowannii var. zuluensis

Asparagus densiflorus cv. 'Myers'

Asparagus asparagoides myrtifolius, florists "Smilax"

Asparagus retrofractus

Bowiea volubilis, the Sea Onion

Beaucarnea recurvata, from Mexico

Beaucarnea recurvata, in Los Angeles

Dasylirion acrotriche

Beaucarnea recurvata, seedling

Arthropodium cirrhatum (inflor.)

Agapanthus inapertus

Albuca major

Bulbinella robusta

Bulbinella setosa (hookeri)

Bulbinella floribunda

Bulbine latifolia

Bulbine natalensis

Camassia esculenta

Bessera elegans

Androcymbium melanthioides

Bloomeria crocea

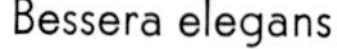

Bulbocodium vernum

Astroloba skinneri

Astelia nervosa

Astelia solandri, epiphytic on Kauri tree (Agathis australis) in N.Z.

Astelia solandri

Bulbine natalensis, at Durban, So. Africa

Bulbine caulescens

Chlorophytum capense (elatum)
(Div. of Botany, Pretoria)

Chlorophytum comosum 'Vittatum'
(Spider plant)

Chlorophytum comosum 'Variegatum'
"Ribbon plant" or "Green-lily"

Chlorophytum comosum 'Picturatum'

Chlorophytum comosum 'Variegatum'

Chlorophytum comosum 'Mandaianum'

Cordyline australis cuprea

Cordyline australis 'Doucetii'

Chlorophytum **bichetii**

Chlorophytum triflorum

Chlorophytum comosum 'Milky Way'

Anthericum liliago

Chlorophytum ignoratum, Missouri Botanic Garden, St. Louis

Calochortus uniflorus, a "Star-tulip" of California

Chlorophytum macrophyllum

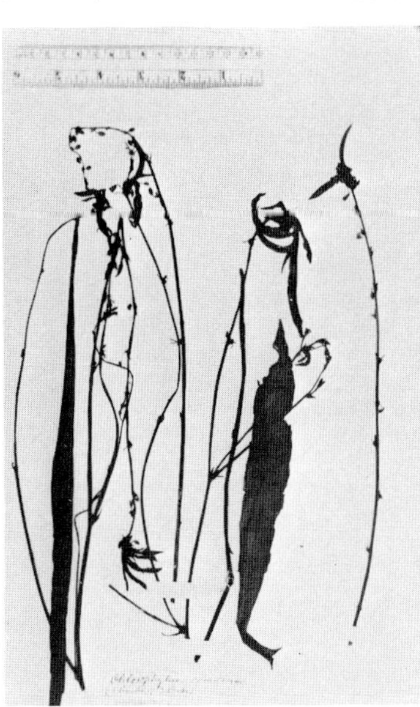
Anthericum comosum, (Botanical Museum Uppsala)

Chlorophytum bichetii

Chionodoxa sardensis

Calochortus amabilis

Chionodoxa luciliae

Convallaria majalis (Lily of the Valley)
in 12cm pot, forced for Easter

Convallaria majalis 'Rosea'

Colchicum autumnale flore pleno 'Water lily'

Colchicum autumnale

Camassia leichtlinii

Cordyline australis, old tree at Christchurch, N. Z.

Cordyline indivisa, near Homer Pass, South Westland, New Zealand

Cordyline australis 'Aureo-striata', in Sydney, Australia

Cordyline banksii, Maitai Valley, New Zealand

Cordyline australis　Cordyline indivisa　Cordyline terminalis 'Ti' (cane section)

Cordyline term. 'Margaret Storey' inflor.　Cordyline terminalis 'Margaret Storey'　Cordyline terminalis 'Bicolor'

Cordyline terminalis 'Baptistii'　Cordyline rubra 'Bruantii'　Cordyline terminalis 'Stricta grandis'

Cordyline terminalis 'Amabilis'

Cordyline terminalis 'Tricolor'

Cordyline terminalis 'Mme. E. Andre'

Cordyline terminalis 'Firebrand'

Cordyline terminalis 'Mad. Eugene Andre'

Cordyline terminalis

Cordyline terminalis 'Ti' (Taetsia fruticosa)

Cordyline terminalis minima 'Baby Ti'

Cordyline terminalis 'Angusta'

Cordyline stricta 'Rubra'

Cordyline indivisa 'Rubra'

Cordyline australis 'Atrosanguinea'

Cordyline 'Volckaertii'

Cordyline terminalis 'Kilimanjari'

Cordyline terminalis 'Negri'

Cordyline terminalis 'General Pershing'

Cordyline 'Hawaiian Bonsai'

Cordyline 'Calypso Queen'

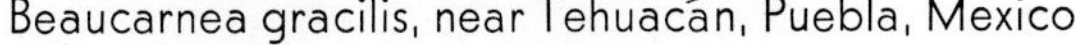

Beaucarnea gracilis, near Tehuacán, Puebla, Mexico

Cordyline terminalis 'Ti', "Good-luck plant", in Hawaii habitat

ordyline australis 'Marginata', air-layer propagation, in Bruges, Belgium

Cordyline indivisa, in oak half-barrel, Germany

Drimiopsis saundersiae, near Pretoria, South Africa

Dasylirion glaucophyllum in Usambara Mts., Tanzania

Erythronium americanum (Trout lily)

Dipcadi serotinum

Dipidax triquetrum

Dianella tasmanica (Flax lily)

Dracaena fragrans in flower

Dracaena deremensis 'Warneckei'

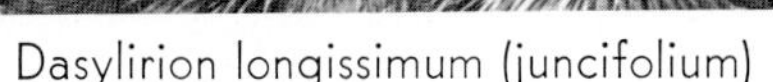
Dasylirion longissimum (juncifolium)

Dasylirion serratifolium, in Oslo, Norway

Dasylirion acrotriche

Dasylirion longissimum

Dracaena "Deeringii" hort, Mexico

Dasylirion wheeleri, in Chicago

Aspidistra minutiflora, from Japan

Dianella longifolia (revoluta)

Beaucarnea gracilis

Cordyline stricta (congesta)

Dracaena hookeriana 'Rothiana'

Cordyline terminalis, in No.Queensland habit.

Dracaena steudneri (Tropical East Africa)

Dracaena reflexa, also known as Pleomele

Dracaena (Pleomele) thalioides

Dracaena pubescens (Trop.West Africa)

Dracaena deremensis 'Compacta'

Dracaena arborea, from Guinea

Drac. frag. 'Massangeana' (sprouting canes)

Beaucarnea recurvata, in San Diego

Dracaena umbraculifera, in flower (Java)

Dracaena deremensis 'Souvenir de Aug. Schryver'

Pleomele reflexa 'Song of India'

Dracaena godseffiana 'Friedman'

Dracaena marginata 'Tricolor', "Rainbow-tree"

Cordyline indivisa 'Purpurea' in Los Angeles

Dracaena arborea, Trop.West Africa

Dracaena deremensis 'Janet Craig', as decorator plant

Dracaena marginata, the "Madagascar Dragontree"

Dracaena fragrans in rainforest habitat, near Ibadan, Nigeria

Dracaena draco, 6m high (Redondo Beach, California)

Dracaena hookeriana in habitat, Southeastern coast of Natal, So. Africa

Dianella caerulea, New South Wales

Dracaena godseffiana

Dracaena godseffiana 'Kelleri'

Dracaena surculosa punctulata

Dracaena sanderiana 'Celes'

Dracaena godseffiana 'Florida Beauty'

Dracaena rothiana (Ill. Hort.)

Dracaena glomerata

Dracaena x masseffiana

Cordyline (Dracaena) dracaenoides

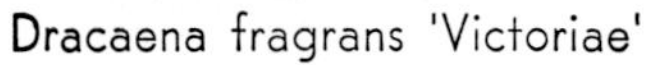

Dracaena fragrans 'Victoriae'

Dracaena goldieana

Dracaena fragrans

Dracaena fragrans 'Massangeana'

Dracaena fragrans 'Lindenii'

Dracaena sanderiana

Dracaena sanderiana 'Borinquensis'

Dracaena sanderiana virescens

Dracaena deremensis 'Roehrs Gold' Cordyline stricta (Dracaena congesta) Dracaena arborea, in Brazil

Dracaena deremensis 'J. A. Truffaut'

Dracaena deremensis 'Bausei' Dracaena deremensis **'Longii'**

Dracaena phrynioides

Dracaena cantleyi

Dracaena kindtiana

Dracaena marginata (gracilis)

Dracaena fragrans 'Massangeana' cane (with Philo. scandens)

Dracaena deremensis 'Warneckei'

Dracaena sanderiana (combination)

Dracaena draco tree, Canary Islands

Dracaena draco, 4 liter can

Dracaena umbraculifera, in Brazil

Dracaena "ensifolia"

Dracaena marginata

Dracaena americana

Dracaena aurea

Pleomele thalioides

Pleomele reflexa 'Song of India'

Pleomele reflexa in India

Dracaena hookeriana — Dracaena 'Gertrude Manda' (hookeriana hyb.) — Dracaena 'Margaret Berkery'

Dracaena deremensis 'Janet Craig' — Dracaena hookeriana 'Rothiana' — Dracaena hookeriana 'Latifolia'

Dracaena goldieana, with inflorescence

Pleomele reflexa angustifolia — Pleomele reflexa gracilis

Eucomis comosa (punctata) (inflor.) | Eucomis comosa (punctata) | Eucomis undulata

Eremurus stenophyllus (bungei) | Eremurus elwesii | Galtonia candicans

Fritillaria pallidiflora | Fritillaria imperialis | Fritillaria meleagris

Eucomis undulata,"Pineapple-flower"

Eucomis humilis, from the Drakensberg

Galtonia candicans, in San Francisco

Drimiopsis maculata

Eucomis bicolor (Natal)

Fritillaria dasyphylla

Eucomis zambeziaca

Fritillaria acmopetala

Chionodoxa lucillae, "Glory-of-the-snow"

Gasteria batesiana | Gasteria batesiana, flowers | Gasteria **trigona**

x Gastrolea smaragdina | **Gasteria transvaalensis**

Gasteria laetipunctata | Gasteria acinacifolia (echinata hort.)

Gasteria maculata

Gasteria verrucosa

Gasteria 'Hybrida'

Gasteria stayneri

Gasteria "armstrongii" of the trade

x Gastrolea 'Spotted Beauty'

Gasteria obtusifolia

Gasteria liliputana

Gasteria caespitosa

Gloriosa rothschildiana

Gloriosa superba lutea

Gasteria lingua

Gasteria croucheri

Gloriosa 'Greeneae' hort. Gloriosa rothschildiana Gloriosa superba

Gloriosa superba

Gloriosa rothschildiana, in habitat near Mariakani, Kenya Coast

Gloriosa verschurii **Gloriosa carsonii** Gloriosa simplex (plantii)

Gloriosa rothschildiana

Gloriosa virescens hort. (Surinam)

Gloriosa simplex, "Glory-lily"

Hesperaloe parviflora

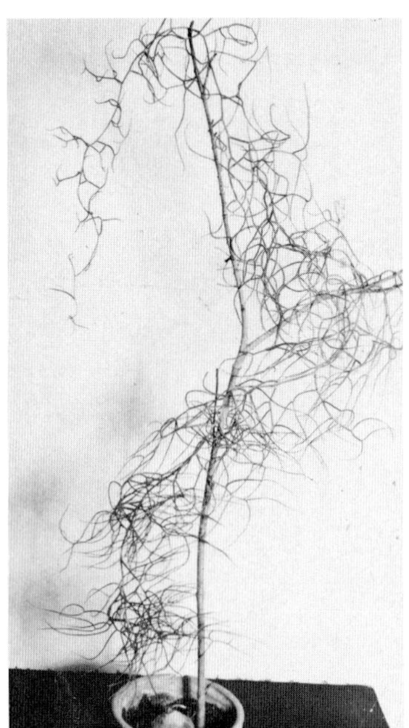
Bowiea volubilis, the "Climbing onion"

Galtonia candicans, Lund Bot.G., Sweden

Gasteria glabra major

Comatophyllum prostratum (Madagascar)

x Gastrolea rebutii

Haworthia fasciata Haworthia "Margaretifera" of the trade Haworthia attenuata clariperla

Haworthia cymbiformis Haworthia turgida Haworthia cuspidata

xGasterhaworthia 'Royal Highness' Haworthia coarctata Haworthia triebneriana

Haworthia tessellata

Haworthia radula

Haworthia dielsiana

Haworthia pygmaea

Haworthia paradoxa

Haworthia atro-fusca

Haworthia planifolia

Haworthia obtusa pilifera

Haworthia rugosa

Haworthia retusa

Haworthia limifolia keithii

Haworthia reinwardtii var. chalwinii

Haworthia reinwardtii

Haworthia reinwardtii kaffirdriftensis

Haworthia ryderiana

Haworthia incurvula

Haworthia emelyae

Haworthia glauca

Haworthia gracilis

Haworthia browniana

Haworthia lateganae

Haworthia limifolia

Haworthia blackbeardiana

Haworthia batesiana

Haworthia schuldtiana

Haworthia chloracantha

Haworthia turgida

Haworthia retusa 'Zebra'

Haworthia viscosa

Haworthia margaritifera maxima

Haworthia papillosa

Haworthia subfasciata

Haworthia mirabilis

Haworthia truncata

Haworthia cooperi

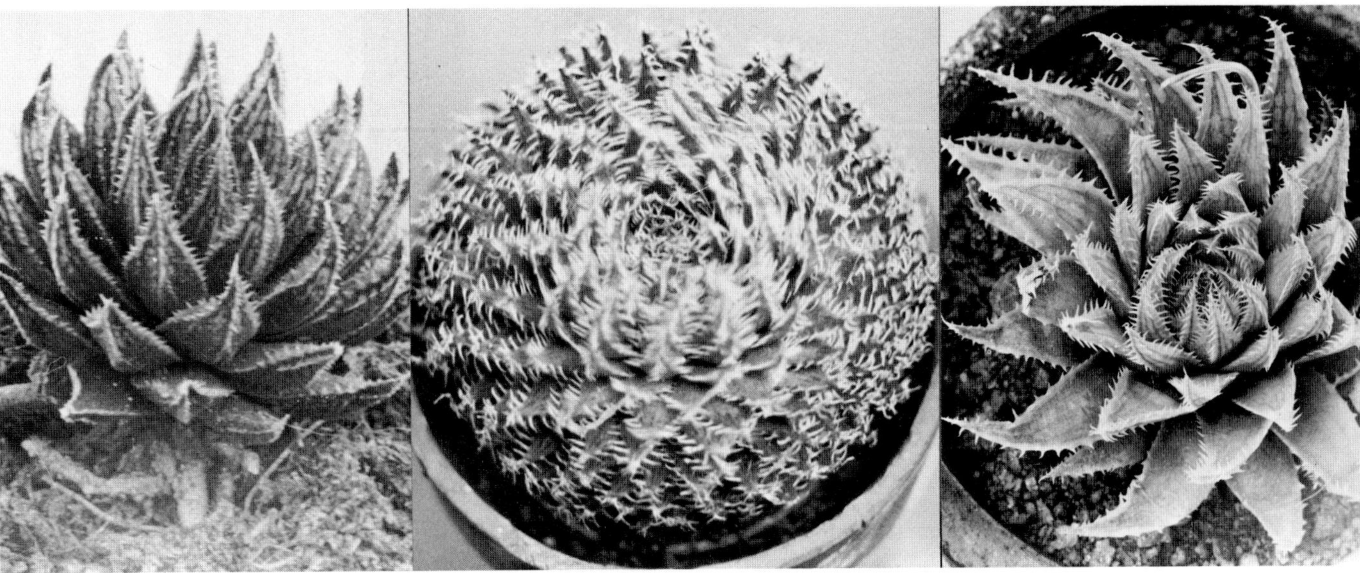

Haworthia herbacea (atrovirens)

Haworthia arachnoidea

Haworthia tenera (minima)

Haworthia armstrongii

Haworthia greenii

Haworthia margaritifera

Haworthia reticulata

Haworthia setata

Haworthia nigra var. schmidtiana

Haworthia herrei depauperata

Haworthia viscosa torquata

Poellnitzia rubriflora

aworthia margaritifera, Gates Nurs., Corona

Haworthia fasciata, true species

Haworthia subfasciata, Corona, California

Guillauminia albiflora (Aloe)

Haworthia bilineata

Haworthia limifolia

Haworthia skinneri

Haworthia turgida

Haworthia cordifolia (trigona hort.)

Eremurus elwesii (Desert Candle)

Hemerocallis fulva 'Mikado'

Hemerocallis lilio-asphodelus, Yellow Day Lily

Drimiopsis kirkii

Kniphofia (Tritoma) uvaria

Kniphofia rufa

Anemarrhena asphodeloides

Kniphofia (Tritoma) uvaria hyb.

Kniphofia zuluandiae

Hosta (Funkia) fortunei

Hosta fortunei 'Marginato-alba'

Hosta fortunei 'Gigantea'

Hosta plantaginea

Hosta undulata 'Medio-picta'

Hosta glauca

Hosta subcordata

Hosta sieboldiana 'Variegata'

Hosta sieboldiana

Hosta decorata 'Minor' ('Thos. Hogg')

Hosta decorata 'Marginata'

Hosta decorata

Hosta lancifolia 'Albo-marginata'

Hosta **lancifolia**

Hosta minor **'Alba'**

Hosta crispula

Hosta ventricosa

Hosta tardiflora

Hyacinthus 'Blue Jacket'

Hyacinthus 'Carnegie'

Hyacinthus 'Blue Giant'

Hyacinthus 'Anne Marie'

Hyacinthus 'Edelweiss'

Hyacinthus 'Ostara'

Hyacinthus tabriziana

Kniphofia multiflora

Hypoxis nitida (Transvaal)

Muscari armeniacum

Hyacinth 'Delft Blue'

Hyacinth 'Pink Pearl'

Hyacinth 'City of Harlem' (yellow)

Hyacinth 'L'Innocence'

Hyacinth 'Lady Derby'

Lachenalia glaucina

Lachenalia aloides (tricolor)

Lachenalia orchioides (mutabilis)

Lachenalia mutabilis

Lachenalia violacea

Lachenalia aloides, a "Cape cowslip"

Lachenalia glaucina pallida

Lachenalia rosea

Lachenalia aloides var. luteola

Lachenalia aloides var. nelsonii

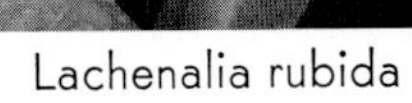

Lachenalia rubida

Lachenalia orchioides

Lachenalia purpurea caerulea

Lachenalia aloides 'Quadricolor'

Lachenalia pendula

Lachenalia lilacina

Lachenalia liliflora

Lachenalia 'Pearsonii'

Lachenalia bachmannii

Lachenalia aloides (tricolor) 'Aurea'

Lachenalia contaminata

Lapageria rosea, the Chile Bells

Lapageria rosea 'Albiflora', at Napier, N. Z.

Leucocoryne ixioides (fam. Amaryll.)

Littonia modesta

Littonia modesta

Merendera bulbocodium

Nothoscordum bivalve

Lilium dauricum   Lilium speciosum   Lilium testaceum

Lilium elegans   Lilium auratum   Lilium x parkmannii 'Jillian Wallace'

Lilium longiflorum eximium 'Georgia Belle'   Lilium longiflorum 'Erabu', 'Creole', 'Jesuit', 'Giganteum green stem'   Lilium longiflorum 'Ace'

Lilium longiflorum formosum 'Erabu'

Lilium longiflorum 'Croft'

Lilium longiflorum giganteum, from Japan

Lilium regale, the Royal lily

Lilium longiflorum eximium (harrisii), the Bermuda lily

Lilium longiflorum 'Croft', fasciation with 23 fl. and buds

Lilium 'Valencia' (Mid-century hybrid)

Lilium tigrinum splendens

Lilium regale

Lilium tigrinum (hollandicum)

Lilium speciosum rubrum

Lilium 'Valencia'

Lilium candidum

Lilium x umbellatum

Lilium x parkmannii Lilium nobilissimum

Lilium 'Imperial Crimson', with originator Jan de Graaff

Lilium 'Empress of India' in Gresham, Oregon

Lilium 'Harlequin' (cernuum x davidii)

Lilium auratum var. pictum

Lilium monadelphum, from Soviet Union

Lilium auratum var. rubrum

Lilium (Mid-Century)'Enchantment'

Lilium (Mid-Century)'Prosperity'

Lilium (Mid-Century)'Harmony'

Lilium canadense

Lilium longiflorum 'Estate' (Oregon)

Lilium superbum, American Turk's-cap

Liriope muscari

Ophiopogon jaburan 'Variegatus'

Liriope muscari 'Variegata'

Ophiopogon planiscapus nigrescens (arabicus in hort.), "Black dragon"

Ophiopogon intermedius 'Argenteo-marginatus'

Ophiopogon japonicus

Ophiopogon jaburan

Liriope muscari 'Variegata' (exiliflora?)

Liriope exiliflora, "Lily-turf"

Ophiopogon japonicus 'Minor'

Liriope platyphylla

Peliosanthes graminea

Ophiopogon japonicus 'Kyoto Dwarf', at Imperial Palace, Kyoto

Liriope gigantea

Peliosanthes speciosa

Liriope graminifolia

Muscari comosum monstrosum

Muscari botryoides album

Muscari racemosum, a "Grape-hyacinth"

Notholirion thomsonianum

Nothoscordum inodorum, "False garlic"

Ornithogalum nutans

Ornithogalum splendens

Ornithogalum stapfii

Ornithogalum thyrsoides, in Lund, Sweden

Ornithogalum thyrsoides (Chincherinchee)

Ornithogalum arabicum

Ornithogalum saundersiae

Urginea maritima (flowers)

Ornithogalum caudatum, the False Sea-Onion or German-flower

Urginea maritima, the Sea-Onion

Rhodocodon urginioides

Phormium tenax, the New Zealand Flax

Nolina bigelovii, in the California desert

Ornithogalum umbellatum (Star of Bethlehem)

arrangement of cut Ornithogalum thyrsoides, the Chincherinchee, at Wonfor's Nursery, Diep River, So. Africa

Phormium colensoi, in New Zealand

Phormium tenax 'Variegatum'

Phormium colensoi 'Tricolor'

Ruscus aculeatus

Ruscus hypoglossum

Phormium tenax 'Atropurpureum'

Polygonatum multiflorum, with fruit

Polygonatum verticillatum (roseum)

Geitonoplesium cymosum

Rohdea japonica 'Aurea-striata'

Rohdea japonica 'Striata', "Sacred Manchu-lily"

Rhadamanthus secundus

Ruscus aculeatus, "Butcher's broom"

Rohdea japonica 'Marginata' in flower

Ruscus aculeatus angustifolius

Ruscus hypoglossum, from Southern Europe

Pleomele angustifolia honoriae (Torres Straits)

Pleomele reflexa 'Song of India'

Pleomele reflexa angustifolia

Pleomele (Dracaena) aurea, on Oahu

Pleomele thalioides (in flower)

Reineckia carnea 'Variegata'

Rohdea japonica 'Marginata'

Rohdea japonica

Sansevieria ehrenbergii in dry steppe habitat, Tanzania

Sansevieria stuckyi, in Zimbabwe, Central Africa

Sansevieria cylindrica, in the Teita Hills, Southern Kenya

Sansevieria desertii, on the Veld of northern Transvaal

Colony of Sansevieria powellii, near Voi, East Africa

Sansevieria trifasciata, in Natal habitat, South Africa

Sansevieria guineensis, along the Guinea Coast, Nigeria, West Africa

Sansevieria guineensis, in Cameroun

Sansevieria 'Hahnii'

Sansevieria 'Golden Hahnii'

Sansevieria 'Silver Hahnii'

Sansevieria guineensis

Sansevieria arborescens

Sansevieria guineensis 'Variegata'

Sansevieria metallica

Sansevieria subspicata

Sansevieria cylindrica

Sansevieria senegambica (cornui)

Sansevieria grandis

Sansevieria stuckyi

Sansevieria parva

Sans. "kirkii" in hort.

Sansevieria ehrenbergii

Sansevieria aubrytiana

Sansevieria trifasciata 'Laurentii', in jardiniere

Sansevieria trifasciata

Sansevieria zanzibarica

Sansevieria trifasc. 'Laurentii compacta'

Sansevieria pearsonii (ehrenbergii in hort.)

Sansevieria senegambica in flower

Sansevieria thyrsiflora, inflor.

Sansevieria trifasc. 'Laurentii' in flower

Sansevieria zeylanica S. trifasciata 'Laurentii' S. trifasciata S. trif. 'Laur. compacta'

Sansevieria nelsonii Sansevieria canaliculata Sansevieria intermedia Sansevieria aubrytiana Sansevieria suffruticosa

Sansevieria trifasciata 'Bantel's Sensation' Sansevieria liberica **Sansevieria trifasc. 'Craigii'**

Sansevieria subspicata ("subscripta")

Sansevieria 'Kirkii' hort.

Sansevieria kirkii

Sansevieria trifasciata 'Goldiana' (Seidel, Brazil)

Sansevieria trifasciata, with fruit

Sansevieria guineensis 'Variegata'

Sansevieria thyrsiflora, at Stellenbosch Botanic Garden, South Africa

Sansevieria metallica, in flower

Sansevieria parva, with runner; in Arcadia, Calif.

Sansevieria suffruticosa, "Spiral snake plant" (Oakhurst G.)

Sansevieria longiflora, from Botswana

Sansevieria grandis, in Natal habitat

Sansevieria aethiopica (Huntington Bot. Garden, California)

Sansevieria scabrifolia, Kew Gardens, London

Sansevieria aethiopica, in Namibia

Sansevieria aubrytiana(Oakhurst.G.)

Sansevieria aethiopica, Munich B. G.

Sansevieria splendens, Royal Botanic Gardens, Kew

Sansevieria senegambica, Kew Gardens, London

Sansevieria singularis, Kew Gardens, London

Sansevieria caespitosa, Munich Botanic Garden

Sansevieria cylindrica (Munich Bot.G.)

Sansevieria singularis (Heidelberg Bot.G.)

Sansevieria desertii (Munich B.G.)

Sansevieria nelsonii (Arcadia, Calif.)

Sansevieria fasciata (Kew Gardens)

Sansevieria gracilis (Munich Bot.G.)

Sansevieria latifolia hort. (E.Hahn,Germany)

Sansevieria kirkii pulchra

Sansevieria dawei

Sansevieria ehrenbergii (Munich Bot. G.)

Sansevieria kirkii pulchra (Munich)

Sansevieria dooneri, from East Africa

Sansevieria patens, from Trop.East Africa

Reineckia carnea, the "Fan-grass" from China

Sansevieria grandicuspis, at Leningrad Botanic Garden, U.S.S.R.

Sansevieria roxburghiana, from India

Sansevieria trifasciata 'Silbersee'

Reineckia carnea, in flower

Sansevieria 'Silver Hahnii marginata'

Sansevieria trifasc. 'Hahnii variegata'

Sansevieria trifasciata cv. 'Hoop's Pride'

Veratrum viride (American Hellebore)

Sandersonia aurantiaca

Trillium grandiflorum

Smilax ornata, in bloom

Smilacina stellata

Smilacina racemosa

Smilax rotundifolia

Smilax ornata

Semele androgyna

Scilla latifolia lusitanica

Scilla violacea

Scilla peruviana

Scilla violacea, clustering plant

Scilla hispanica

Trillium sessile 'Snow Queen'

Trillium recurvatum

Trillium erectum

Scilla sibirica atrocaerulea, "Siberian hyacinth"

Scilla tubergeniana, "Persian bluebell'

Scilla sardensis (T.Everett)

Theropogon pallidus from the Himalayas

Triteleia (Brodiaea) laxa, "Ithuriel's spear"

Smilacina stellata, "False Solomon's-seal"

Pasithea caerulea, from Chile

Tulbaghia violacea variegata, "Society garlic"

Parrot tulip 'Karel Doorman'

Triumph tulip 'Red Giant'

Single early tulip 'Ursa Minor'

Triumph tulip 'Paris'

Darwin hybrid tulip 'Dardanelles'

Parrot tulip 'Fantasy'

Triumph tulip 'Edith Eddy'

Rembrandt tulip 'Cordell Hull'

Lily-flowered tulip 'Golden Duchess'

Cottage tulip 'Jeanne Desor'

Triumph tulip 'Rose Beauty'

Tulipa fosteriana princeps

Triumph tulip 'Alberio'

Tulipa 'Blenda' (Triumph tulip)

Tulipa 'Blizzard' (Triumph)

Tulipa 'Robinea' (Triumph)

Tulipa 'Princess Irene' (Single early)

Tulipa 'Makassar'(Triumph)

Tulipa 'Kees Nelis'(Triumph)

Tulipa 'New Look' (Cottage tulip)

Tulipa greigii 'Red Riding Hood'

Tulipa 'Paradise' (Darwin tulip)

Breeder tulip 'Dillenburg'

Single early tulip 'Yellow Prince'

Cottage tulip 'Inglescombe. Yellow'

Triumph tulip 'Aviator'

Double early tulip 'Orange Nassau'

Double late tulip 'Livingstone'

Darwin tulip 'Bartigon'

Parrot tulip 'Violet Queen'

Mendel tulip 'Weber'

Tulipa pulchella pallida (Southwest Asia)

Tulipa 'Vermilion Brilliant' (single early)

Tulipa 'Duc van Tol Scarlet'

Tulipa clusiana 'Cynthia'

Tulipa acuminata, "Turkish tulip"

Tulipa batalinii (Bokhara)

Tulipa tarda (dasystemon) from Turkestan

Tulipa 'Golden Fleece', a "Cottage tulip"

Broken (bicolor) tulip 'Union Jack' (Div. 6)

Div. 1: tulip Duc van Tol 'Scarlet'

Div. 4: Triumph tulip 'Overdale'

Division 2: Double Early tulip 'Anders Zorn'

Division 1: Single Early tulip 'Mainau'

Division 3: Mendel tulip 'Orange Early Queen'

Division 6: Darwin tulip 'Royal Gold'

Division 5: Darwin hybrid tulip 'Apeldoorn'

Division 9: Rembrandt tulip 'Beauty of Volendam'

Division 8: Breeder tulip 'Orange Beauty'

Division 8: Cottage tulip (Single Late) 'Ossi Oswalda'

Division 7: Lily-flowered tulip 'Celestine'

Division 9: Bizarre tulip 'Madame Dubarry'

Division 10: Parrot tulip 'Lilac Queen'

Division 11: Peony-flowered (Double late) tulip 'Gertraud Kieft'

Division 13: Fosteriana hybrid tulip 'Flaming Youth'

Division 15: Eichleri tulip 'Excelsa'

Division 15: Batalinii hybrid tulip

Division 12: Kaufmanniana hybrid 'Solanus'

Division 15: Marjoletti tulip T. marjolettii

Division 14: Greigii tulip 'Royal Orange'

Division 15: Tubergeniana tulip 'Candida'

Division 15: Tulipa linifolia

Div. 15: Tulipa chrysantha

Tulipa turkestanica

Tulipa clusiana

Div. 15: Tulipa hoogiana

Tulipa primulina

Tulipa urumiensis

Div. 15: Tulipa saxatilis

Tulipa biflora

Tulipa orphanidea

Div. 15: Tulipa kolpakowskiana

Tulipa kaufmanniana

Tulipa tarda (dasystemon)

Veltheimia capensis (viridifolia)

Veltheimia deasii, "Forest lily"

Veltheimia glauca 'Rosalba'

milax ornata, "Mexican greenbrier"

Semele androgyna, "Climbing Butcher's broom"

Urginea maritima, in Cyprus habitat

Nolina parryi, Mohave Desert

Tupistra macrostigma (tupistroides) from India

Samuela carnerosana (Brooklyn Bot.Garden)

Tricyrtis macropoda (Toad-lily)

Xeronema callistemon (moorei)

Tulbaghia fragrans

Uvularia grandiflora

Tulbaghia violacea

Rohdea japonica

Yucca filamentosa 'Variegata'

Yucca elephantipes, in Los Angeles nurse

Veltheimia viridifolia (capensis)

Veltheimia glauca 'Rosalba'

Xanthorrhoea arborea, a Grass-tree
in northern New South Wales, Australia

Yucca australis (filifera) tree in Coahuila, Mexico

Yucca elephantipes 'Variegata'

Yucca filamentosa flaccida 'Variegata'

Yucca aloifolia 'Tricolor'

Yucca rupicola

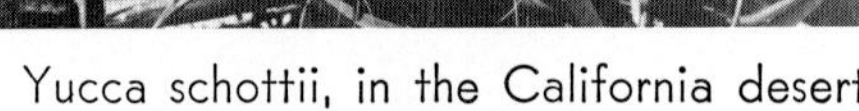

Yucca schottii, in the California desert

Yucca filamentosa in New York

Yucca elephantipes

Yucca aloifolia marginata

Yucca gloriosa

Yucca mohavensis, in bloom on the Mojave Desert, California

Yucca filamentosa variegata, in Christchurch, New Zealand

nthorrhoea preissii, a xerophytic "Black-boy" in Western Australia

Xanthorrhoea undulata (Zurich Botanic Garden)

Yucca aloifolia 'Quadricolor' (Royal Botanic Garden, Edinburgh)

Yucca elephantipes (gigantea) 'Variegata', in Californ

Yucca gloriosa 'Variegata', a "Spanish dagger", California

Yucca filamentosa, the "Adam's needle" under snow, New York C

Yucca glauca, a "Soapweed" in New Mexico

Yucca brevifolia, Joshua trees on the Mojave Desert

Xanthorrhoea arborea, "Grass-trees" in New South Wales

Yucca elephantipes, "Giant yucca" (Los Angeles Arboretum)

ucca baccata, "Datil yucca" (Mesa Verde, Colorado)

Yucca mohavensis, "Mohave yucca" on the desert, with Betty Gay

Yucca australis, in Huntington B.G.,California

Yucca brevifolia, "Joshua tree" of the Mojave, California

Yucca recurvifolia (pendula), at home in Georgia

Yucca elata, the "Soaptree yucca" in Arizona

Lobelia tupa

Lobelia gibberoa, the Giant lobelia, at 2,600m in the Mountains of Kigezi, Central Africa

Lobelia erinus 'Crystal Palace'

Lobelia erinus 'Emperor William'

Lobelia tenella (Dobrowskya)

Isotoma longiflora

Lobelia laxiflora

Isotoma petraea

Centropogon cornutus

Isotoma axillaris

Hippobroma longiflora, in Bali

Pratia guatemalensis

Pratia angulata

Lobelia erinus 'Waverly Blue'

Lobelia gibberoa, Kew Gardens, London

Lobelia vedraiensis hort.

Reinwardtia indica (Lin.)

Linum perenne (Lin.)

Schisandra propinqua (Magnol.)

Spigelia splendens (Log.)

Limnanthes douglasii (Limnanth.)

Buddleja davidii alba (Log.)

Buddleja davidii (Log.)

Buddleja asiatica (Log.)

Buddleja alternifolia

Anthocleista pulcherrima, in Uganda

Anthocleista macrophylla, in Nigeria

Buddleja globosa

Buddleja farquhari

Buddleja crispa

Buddleja madagascariense

Buddleja davidii 'Empire Blue'

Buddleja pikei

Spigelia splendens (Munich Bot.G.)

Gelsemium sempervirens, "False jasmine"

Desfontainea spinosa

Buddleja salvifolia

Buddleja auriculata

Buddleja tubiflora

Linum grandiflorum, "Flowering flax"

Linum hypericifolium, from the Caucasus

Malpighia coccigera (Malp.)

Malpighia coccigera (flower)

Nicodemia diversifolia (Log.)

Stigmaphyllon lingulatum (Malp.)

Stigmaphyllon ciliatum (Malp.)

Galphimia (Thryallis) glauca

Malpighia glabra, flowers

Malpighia glabra, in fruit

Lophanthera lactescens

horadendron flavescens, parasitic in Florida

Viscum album, "Mistletoe", Germany

Phoradendron juniperinum, Grand Canyon

hrygilanthus aphyllus, parasitic on Cereus

Phoradendron flavescens, "American mistletoe"

Viscum album, mistletoe in Britain

Viscum rotundifolium, parastic, in New Zealand

Psittacanthus calyculatus

Lycopodium cernuum, tropical "Ground-pine"

Lycopodium obscurum, "Mystery plant"

Lycopodium gnidioides, a Clubmoss

Lycopodium tetrastichum (New Guinea)

Mayaca fluviatilis, aquatic (Brazil)

Lycopodium remoganense, in Osaka

Frullania tamariscii, an arctic "Liverwort"

Mayaca sellowiana, bogplant from Brazil

Lycopodium phlegmaria, the Queensland Tassel-fern

Lycopodium taxifolium, in Florida

Lycopodium squarrosum, the Rock Tassel, in Queensland

Lycopodium nummularifolius

Galphimia (Thryallis) glauca

Galphimia glauca

Loranthus sansibariensis, in Kenya

Caiophora lateritia

Eucnide bartonioides

Lagerstroemia indica (Lyth.)

Cuphea platycentra (Lyth.)

Cuphea hyssopifolia (Lyth.)

Lagerstroemia indica 'Petite Snow'

Norantea brasiliensis, "Red-hot-poker", in Brazil

Cuphea lanceolata

Lagerstroemia speciosa, "Rose of India"

Cuphea micropetala (Mexico)

Glossocalyx longicuspis (Gabon)

Loasa (Caiophora) hibiscifolia

Rotala macrandra

Michelia figo, "Banana shrub", in South China

Galpinia transvaalica (Schlieben-Pretoria)

Magnolia x soulangeana (Magn.)

Magnolia grandiflora (Magn.)

Liriodendron tulipifera (Magn.)

Magnolia stellata

Magnolia campbellii

Magnolia virginiana

Marcgravia sintenisii (sterile branch)

Marcgravia sintenisii (flowering branch)

Marcgravia rectiflora

Malpighia glabra, "Barbados cherry"

Tristellateia australasiae, in Sydney

Lophanthera lactescens

Acridocarpus natalitius

Peixotoa glabra

Heteropterys chrysophylla

Drimys winteri, "Winter's bark"

Magnolia grandiflora, in Virginia

Illicium anisatum, "Star anise"

Hibiscus syriacus amplissimus

Pavonia multiflora (wiotii)

Hibiscus syriacus coelestis

Hibiscus rosa-sinensis 'Cooperi'

Abutilon x hybridum 'Savitzii'

Hibiscus syriacus albus (Malv.)

Hibiscus huegelii

Abutilon x hybridum 'Golden Fleece'

Hibiscus schizopetalus

Hibiscus rosa-sinensis 'Regius Maximus'

Hibiscus rosa-sinensis plenus

Abutilon x hybridum 'Apricot'

Abutilon megapotamicum 'Variegata'

Malvaviscus penduliflorus

Abutilon pictum 'Thompsonii'

Abutilon x hybridum 'Souvenir de Bonn'

Hibiscus rosa-sinensis 'Cooperi'

Lavatera trimestris

Lagunaria patersonii

Pavonia intermedia rosea hort.

Gossypium herbaceum, the Levant cotton, with fleecy bolls, and in flower

Hoheria populnea 'Argentea', in New Zealand

Gossypium hirsutum, the Upland cotton

Hibiscus rosa-sinensis 'Lateritia Variegata'

Abutilon x hybridum, the Flowering Maple'

Hibiscus rosa-sinensis 'Scarlet', standard in 20cm tub

Abutilon striatum 'Aureo-maculatum'

Abutilon megapotamicum 'Variegata'

Hibiscus rosa-sinensis 'White Wings'

Hibiscus rosa-sinensis 'Agnes Goult'

Hibiscus rosa-sinensis 'California Gold'

Thespesia populnea, "Portia tree", in Hawaii

Hibiscus schizopetalus x rosa-sinensis

Hibiscus rosa-sinensis 'Silver Streak'

Hibiscus rosa-sinensis 'Matensis'

Hibiscus rosa-sinensis 'Snow Queen'

Hibiscus moscheutos 'New Blood-red'

Hibiscus mutabilis, "Confederate Rose"

Hibiscus eedtveldtianus

Hibiscus arnottianus, on Kauai

Hibiscus trionum, in New Zealand

Hibiscus moscheutos 'Southern Belle'

Hibiscus tiliaceus, in Tahiti

Hibiscus malacospermus (Transvaal)

Hibiscus ros.-sin. 'Lateritia' (Germany)

Goethea cauliflora (Heidelberg Bot.Garden)

Hoheria populnea, New Zealand

Goethea strictiflora (Brazil)

Abutilon striatum 'Goldprince'

Abutilon x milleri

Alcea (Althaea) rosea, "Hollyhocks"

Lavatera bicolor, "Tree-mallow"

Malvastrum hypomadarum

Lavatera (Malvastrum) maritima

Pavonia intermedia 'Kermesina'

Pavonia intermedia (Hanover)

Montezuma speciosissima, in Hawaii

Sida fallax, "Ilima" of Oahu

Sphaeralcea umbellata, "Globe-mallow"

Malvaviscus arboreus mexicanus

Hibiscus rosa-sinensis 'Lady Hamilton'

Malvaviscus arboreus, "Turk's-cap"

Hibiscus rosa-sinensis 'Cherie'

Calathea insignis, Calathea ornata 'Roseo-lineata' Calathea p. vandenheckei
Calathea makoyana, Ctenanthe oppenheimiana, Calathea lietzei Calathea "acuminata"
Calathea princeps, C. louisae, C. medio picta, C. zebrina binotii, C. picturata 'Argentea'

Calathea **undulata**

Ctenanthe lubbersiana

Calathea veitchiana   Calathea magnifica   Calathea makoyana

Calathea warscewiczii   Calathea zebrina   Calathea zebrina humilior (tigrina)

Calathea medio-picta

Calathea ornata 'Sanderiana'   Calathea ornata 'Roseo-lineata'

Ctenanthe oppenheimiana

Ctenanthe oppenheimiama 'Tricolor'

Calathea princeps

Calathea lutea

Calathea vittata

Calathea musaica

Calathea wiotii

Calathea insignis

Calathea bachemiana (trifasciata)

Calathea kegeliana

Calathea concinna

Calathea musaica

Calathea veitchiana

Ctenanthe oppenheimiana tricolor

Calathea roseo-picta

Calathea picturata 'Argentea'

Calathea ornata 'Roseo-lineata'

Calathea zebrina

Maranta leuconeura massangeana

Calathea rotundifolia fasciata

Calathea makoyana

Calathea "splendida" hort. Calathea lietzei Calathea louisae

Calathea picturata 'Argentea'

Calathea picturata 'Vandenheckei'

Calathea micans

Calathea orbiculata Calathea lindeniana

Calathea roseo-picta

Ctenanthe glabra Calathea 'Tuxtla' Stromanthe sanguinea (juv.)

Saranthe leptostachya Calathea albicans Calathea rufibarba

Ctenanthe kummeriana (older plant) **Bamburanta arnoldiana** Calathea grandiflora

Calathea rotundifolia 'Fasciata'

Calathea makoyana, the Peacock plant

Calathea bachemiana in Brazil

Calathea kegeliana

Calathea "argyraea" hort.

Calathea clossonii

Calathea concinna

Calathea leopardina

Calathea leoniae

Ctenanthe kummeriana (juv.)

Calathea vittata

Maranta kerchoveana 'Manda's Emerald'

Calathea undulata

Calathea "acuminata"

Calathea metallica

Ctenanthe setosa

Stromanthe amabilis

Ctenanthe compressa ("Bamburanta" hort.) Ctenanthe humilis Ctenanthe compressa luschnathiana

Calathea ornata Calathea grandiflora Calathea crotalifera Pleiostachya pruinosa

Maranta arundinacea Maranta arundinacea 'Variegata' Ctenanthe lubbersiana

Calathea metallica 'Undulata' Stromanthe porteana Calathea carlina Calathea aemula

Calathea zebrina 'Binotii'

Calathea zebrina humilior

Calathea rotundifolia 'Fasciata'

Calathea eximia

Calathea argyraea

Calathea rufibarba

Maranta bicolor

Maranta leuconeura 'Massangeana'

Maranta leuconeura kerchoveana

Calathea crotalifera (inflor.)

Maranta leuconeura kerchoveana, in flower

Stromanthe sanguinea (inflor.)

Calathea louisae, inflorescence

Calathea warscewiczii, infl.

Calathea cylindrica, inflorescence

Maranta "repens" (Rochford-England)

Maranta leuconeura kerchoveana, the Prayer plant, asleep at night

Calathea lucianii   Phrynium dracaenoides

Calathea varians   Stromanthe sanguinea

Calathea carlina, in Brazil

Thalia dealbata, in Lisbon

Calathea pavonii

Calathea albicans (Seidel)

Maranta leuconeura erythroneura

Calathea stromata

Calathea sp. 'Burle Marx' (Fantastic)

Calathea magnifica

Calathea leucostachys

Calathea aurantiaca

Calathea aurantiaca (Sydney Bot.G.)

Maranta leuconeura erythroneura

Calathea grandiflora (inflor.)

Thalia dealbata

Calathea sp. 'Putumayo' (Fantastic)

Stromanthe lutea, inflor.

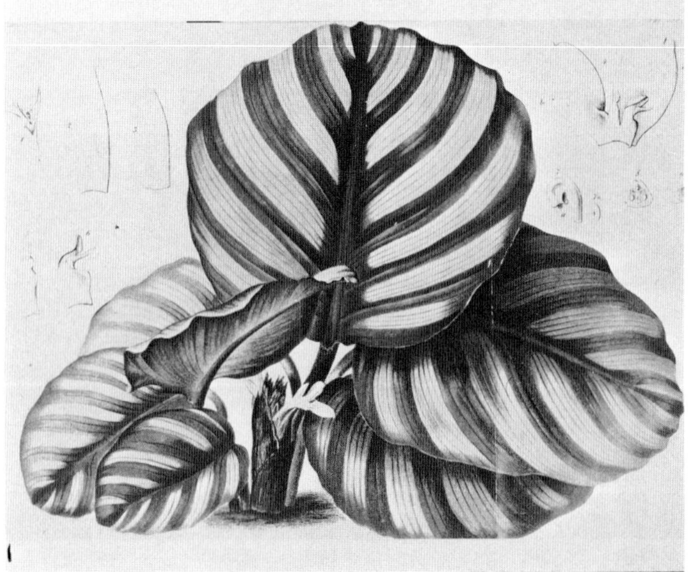

Calathea fasciata (Berlin 1859)

Calathea eximia (Berlin 1871)

Marcgravia paradoxa, fruiting stage

Norantea tepuiensis

Norantea guianensis, "Red popcorn" (Hawaii)

Marcgravia picta, in flower

Marcgravia umbellata

Marcgravia paradoxa, in Puerto Rico

Martynia annua, in Timor

Martynia lutea hort. (Ibicella)

Ibicella lutea

Marchantia calcarea

Marchantia stenolepida

Marchantia geminata

Plagiochasma appendiculata (March.)

Hypopterigium filiculaeforme, the Umbrella-moss, in New Zealand

Marchantia polymorpha, a female Liverwort

Cocculus laurifolius (Men.)

Myrica pensylvanica

Greyia radlkoferi (Encinitas)

Melianthus comosus

Greyia sutherlandii, "Mountain bottlebrush"

Melianthus major, in Hollywood

Tinospora fragosum, "Wonder plant"

Melianthus major, "Honey-bush"

Stephania rotunda (glabra)

Stephania rotunda, tuberous root

Stephania glandulifera (Burma)

Greyia sutherlandii, in the Transvaal

Greyia sutherlandii, inflorescence

Greyia sutherlandii

Proboscidea jussienii, the Unicorn plant, ripe fruit stand

Proboscidea jussienii, forming seed pods

Proboscidea jussienii (Martynia louisianica)

Turraea obtusifolia

Trichilia dregei (roka), "Cape mahogany"

Melia azedarach, "Pride of India"

Ekebergia capensis, "Dog plum"

Cedrela toona (Australia), "Australian red-cedar"

Turraea floribunda, "Tree honeysuckle"(Natal)

Melia azedarach floribunda

Cocculus laurifolius (Univ.of Miami)

Bertolonia lowiana

Phyllagathis rotundifolia

Centradenia floribunda

Centradenia grandifolia (Mexico)

Medinilla scortechinii, from Java

Centradenia inaequilateralis

Dissotis grandiflora

Dissotis princeps

Amphiblemma cymosum

Medinilla magnifica

Miconia calvescens (magnifica in hort.)

Miconia (Cyanophyllum) hookeriana

Bertolonia x houtteana

Amphiblemma cymosum, in flower

Bredia hirsuta

Bredia tuberculata

Dichaetanthera crassinodes

Tibouchina urvilleana (semidecandra hort.)

Schizocentron elegans

Bertolonia marmorata

Bertolonia x houtteana

Bertolonia mosaica

Triolena pustulata (Bertolonia pubescens hort.)

Bertolonia maculata

Bertolonia maculata 'Wentii'

Bertolonia sanguinea

Bertolonia marmorata aenea

Bertolonia hirsuta

Phyllagathis rotundifolia

Monolena primulaeflora, from Colombia

Hypenanthe (Medinilla) venosa

Medinilla magnifica, "Rose-grape"

Medinilla scortechinii

Osbeckia crinita

Tibouchina granulosa

Miconia pulverulenta

Medinilla ledifolia

Medinilla ericarum

Medinilla sedifolia

Melastoma decemfidum (Sydney Bot.G.)

Melastoma malabathricum

Lasiandra macrantha hort. (Tibouchina)

Heterocentrum roseum, "Pearl flower"

Schizocentron elegans, "Spanish shawl"

Swietenia mahoganii, "Mahogany"

Sphaerogyne latifolia

Miconia calvescens (magnifica)

Miconia ovata **in Brazil**

Sonerila margaritacea 'Hendersonii'

Sonerila margaritacea

Sonerila margaritacea 'Argentea'

Sonerila margaritacea 'Mme. Baextele'

Sonerila margaritacea

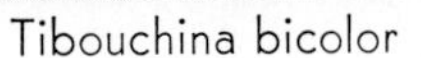

Tibouchina bicolor

Tibouchina granulosa, in Brazil

Tibouchina grandifolia

Tibouchina heteromalla (Brazil)

Blakea trinervia (tuberculata)

Tibouchina paratropica (Pleroma)

Tibouchina granulosa rosea, in Durban

Dorstenia argentata

Dorstenia urceolata variegata

Dorstenia multiradiata

Dorstenia nervosa

Dorstenia yambuyaensis, at Montreal

Dorstenia zanzibarica

Dorstenia barteri

Dorstenia mannii

Dorstenia turneraefolia

Dorstenia ceratosanthes (arifolia)

Dorstenia gigas (Socotra)

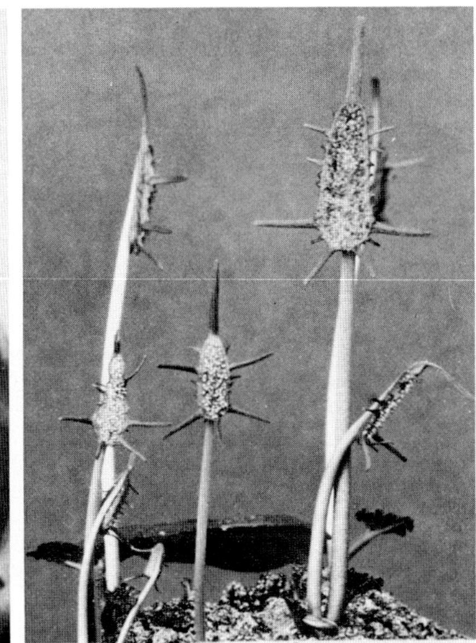
Dorstenia bornimiana (Ethiopia)

Dorstenia elata, from Brazil

Dorstenia hildebrandtii (Kenya)

Dorstenia foetida (So.Arabia)

Dorstenia contrajerva, from Mexico

Dorstenia indica (India)

Dorstenia crispa, from Somalia

Antiaris toxicaria, "Upas tree"

Brosimum galactodendron, "Cow-tree"

Cannabis sativa, "Hemp" or "Marijuana"

Dorstenia drakeana (J.Bogner, Munich Bot.G.)

Ficus pretoriae (Transvaal)

Morus nigra, "Black mulberry"

Humulus lupulus, "European hops"

Ficus aspera (parcellii), the Clown fig

Ficus rubiginosa variegata

Ficus benjamina 'Variegata', in So. California

Ficus elastica 'Doescheri'

Ficus elastica 'Variegata'

Ficus elastica 'Decora'

Ficus elastica

Ficus nekbudu (utilis)

Ficus lyrata (pandurata)

Ficus altissima

Ficus benghalensis

Ficus krishnae

Ficus religiosa

Ficus benjamina, 1½m high

Ficus benjamina 'Exotica', in 25cm tub, 1½m high

Ficus elastica 'Decora' 25cm tub, 1m high

Ficus lyrata (pandurata), 2m high

Cecropia peltata, in Puerto Rico

Ficus pseudopalma, at Miami

Artocarpus altilis (communis), the Breadfruit tree

Ficus carica, the Fig tree

Ficus benjamina 'Exotica' tree, in Florida

Ficus retusa, standards in 45cm tubs, 3m high

Ficus elastica 'Decora' tree, in Florida

Ficus glomerata (racemosa), bearing fruit on trunk

Ficus (Artocarpus) cannonii

Ficus religiosa, at Missouri Bot. Gardens

Ficus parietalis

Ficus cyathistipula

Ficus stipulata, in fruit

Ficus lyrata, fruit

Ficus gillettii, with fruit

Ficus cannonii, in Chicag

Ficus microphylla hort. (rubiginosa)

Ficus macrophylla, in New Zealand

Ficus saussureana

Ficus elastica 'Decora Schrijvereana'

Ficus lyrata 'Phyllis Craig'

Ficus elastica 'Belgica'

Ficus pseudopalma

Ficus sycomorus

Dammaropsis kingiana (juv.)

Ficus stricta ("Philippinense" hort.)

Ficus philippinensis (U. S. D. A.)

Ficus benjamina nuda ("Philippinense" hort

Ficus microphylla hort.

Ficus schlechteri

Ficus benjamina nuda

Ficus ulmaefolia

Ficus dryepondtiana

Ficus benjamina 'Exotica' Ficus nitida **Ficus benjamina**

Ficus stricta ("Philippinense" hort.) Ficus retusa Ficus neriifolia

Ficus rubiginosa Ficus triangularis 'Variegata' Ficus rubiginosa fa. australis

Ficus oblongata

Ficus buxifolia

Ficus barteri

Ficus edulis

Ficus cotinifolia

Ficus jacquinifolia

Ficus eriobotryoides

Ficus hookeri

Ficus dumosa (fulva) Ficus umbellata (platyphylla in Florida) Ficus aspera, with tricolored fruit

Ficus eburnea Ficus petiolaris

Ficus aurea

Ficus macrophylla in N. Z.

Ficus wildemanniana (panduriformis)

Ficus lapathifolia

Ficus quercifolia

Ficus radicans 'Variegata'

Ficus radicans

Ficus pumila minima

Ficus pumila (repens)

Ficus sycomorus

Ficus afzelii (eriobotryoides)

Ficus benjamina 'Exotica' with fruit

Ficus callosa, in Germany

Ficus sarmentosa, juv. form

Ficus quercifolia, with fruit

Ficus quercitolia

Ficus villosa (barbata)

Ficus pumila, grown as a globe

Ficus pumila 'Quercifolia'

Ficus pumila 'Variegata'

Ficus radicans 'Variegata'

Ficus auriculata (roxburghii)

Ficus diversifolia

Ficus elastica 'Rubra'

Morus rubra, the American Red mulberry

Ficus mysorensis

Ficus carica, with edible fruit

Artocarpus altilis (incisa), juv.

Ficus dryepondtiana

Treculia africana

large tree of Ficus retusa, on the mountainous 'Dragon's Back' coast of Kwangtung, South China

Ficus retusa, at Tiger Balm Gardens, Hongkong

Ficus nitida, in the Lung Shan temple, Taipei, Taiwan

old Ficus rubiginosa fa. australis tree, hollowed out for electric lines, near Newcastle, New South Wales, Australia

the ubiquitous African Ficus sycomorus, near Duivelskloof, North Transvaal

old Ficus macrophylla, at Coimbra, Portugal known in Mediterranean area as F. magnolioides

Dammaropsis kingiana, mature branches, in the mountains above Bulolo, New Guinea

gnarled Ficus retusa tree, in South China

Ficus gibbosa (parasitica) in the ruins of Angkor, Cambodia

Ficus macrophylla trees, planted 1863, at Algiers, North Africa

Ficus diversifolia, in Hydro-culture

Ficus pumila covering walls in the Rothschild conservatories, **Vienna, Austria**

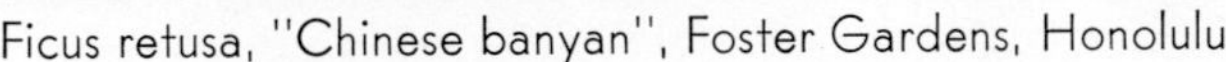

Ficus retusa, "Chinese banyan", Foster Gardens, Honolulu

Ficus religiosa, on the ruins of Angkor, Cambodia

cus elastica, the "India rubber" with aerial roots, in Malaya

Ficus lyrata, at Fantastic Gardens, Miami

Ficus "mexicana", in Florida hort.

Ficus microphylla cv.'Florida' (Wilcox)

Ficus wildemanniana (panduriforme hort

Ficus jacquiniaefolia, "West Indian laurel"

Ficus gilletii obovata (Zaire)

Ficus triangularis

Ficus rubiginosa (Monrovia Nurs.,Calif.)

Ficus pretoriae

Ficus gibbosa (Nymphenburg Bot.Garden)

Ficus nitida (semi-standard), Disneyland

Ficus nitida (multistem), Keeline-Wilcox Nurseries, California

Ficus mysorensis, Keeline-Wilcox Nurseries, Irvine, California

Ficus stricta ("Phillippinense" hort.)

Ficus brandegeei, from Mexico

Ficus palmeri (Tegelberg, Calif.)

Ficus petiolaris (Mexico)

Ficus soldanella, "Rock wild fig"

Ficus elastica 'Decora tricolor'(England)

Ficus vogelii (Senegal to Zaire)

Ficus cyathistipula

Ficus capensis (Fairchild Gard. Miami)

Ficus triangularis (Trop. Africa)

Dammaropsis kingiana, with fruit; Kikiepa, New Guinea

Artocarpus heterophyllus (integra hort.), the "Jackfruit"

Ficus aurea, a "Strangler fig", in Florida

Ficus benjamina, in Balboa Park, San Diego, California

Ficus pumila, maturity stage (Santa Barbara)

Ficus tikoua "Waupahu fig" (Tibet)

Ficus pumila 'Gigas' (Hahn, German

Ficus ramentacea, Munich Bot. Garden

Ficus henneanana, Los Angeles Bot. Garden

Ficus edworthii (Malaya)

Ficus cocculifolia (Madagascar)

Ficus baileyana (Missouri Bot. Garden)

Heliconia caribaea, at Montego Bay, Jamaica

Heliconia platystachys, in Hawaii

Heliconia humilis (wagneriana)

Strelitzia reginae, the Bird-of-Paradise

Ravenala madagascariensis, the Traveler's tree

Heliconia latispatha, Parrot Jungle, Florida

Heliconia psittacorum

Heliconia caribaea var. purpurea

Orchidantha maxillarioides

Heliconia bihai (inflor.)

Heliconia bihai (leaf)

Heliconia choconiana

Ravenala guianensis (flowering)

Ravenala madagascariensis, "Traveler's tree", in Honolulu

Heliconia acuminata 'Espiritu Santo'

Heliconia rostrata, "Hanging lobster-claws" (Perú)

Heliconia metallica

Heliconia hirsuta (Longwood Gardens)

Heliconia latispatha

Heliconia caribaea

Heliconia humilis

Heliconia jacquinii, in Fiji

Heliconia angustifolia (braziliensis)

Heliconia aurantiaca, at Foster Gardens, Hawaii

Heliconia metallica

Heliconia illustris spectabilis

Heliconia velutina

Heliconia illustris rubricaulis

Heliconia illustris 'Aureo-striata'

Heliconia illustris 'Edwardus Rex'

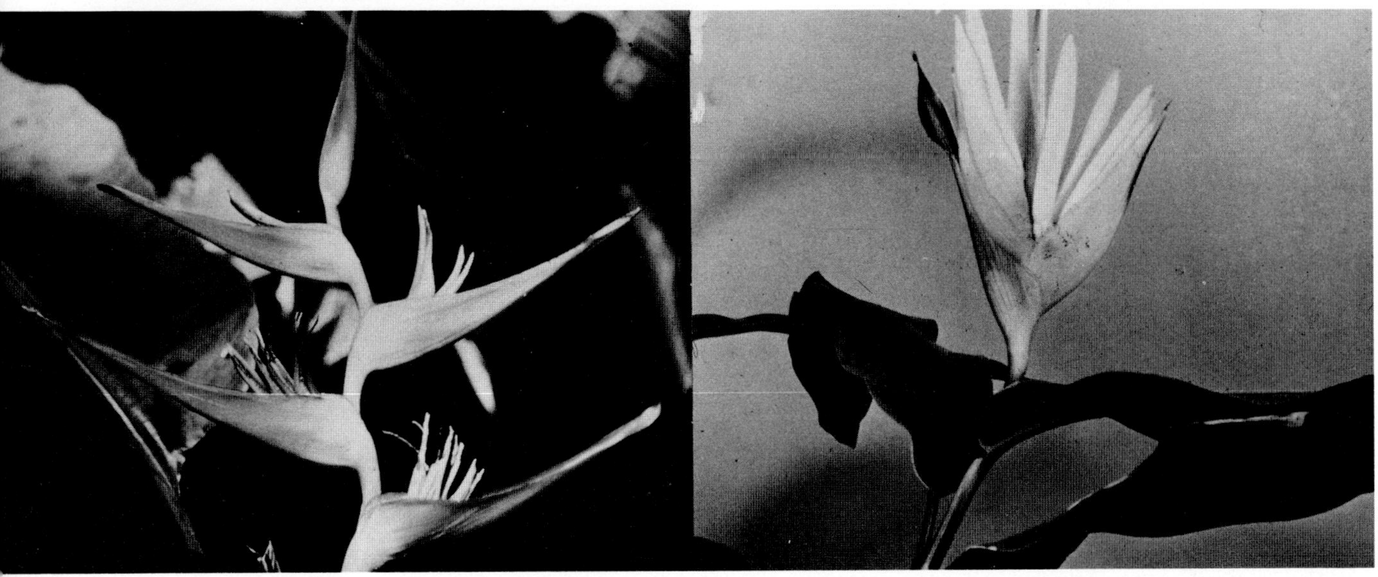

Heliconia latispatha

Heliconia aurantiaca

Heliconia collinsiana, Foster G., Honolulu

Heliconia aurantiaca (with fruit)

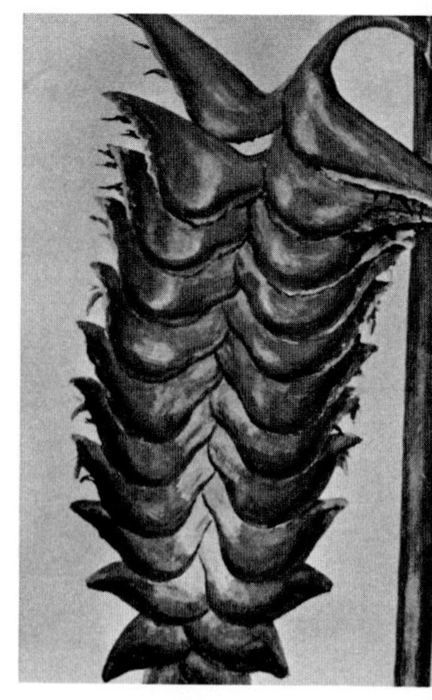
Heliconia mariae hort., in San Francis

Heliconia illustris rubricaulis (Ruzinsky)

Heliconia illustris 'Rubra' (Hummel)

Heliconia illustris 'Aureo-striata', in Chicag

Heliconia caribaea, in Martinique

Heliconia elongata, Central America

Heliconia distans (J. Bogner, Munich)

Musa Fehi (troglodytarum), "Cooking banana" (New Guinea)

Musa nana 'Costa Rican', an "Eating banana"

Musa coccinea, the "Scarlet banana", from China

Ensete maurellii, "Black banana" from Ethiopia

Ensete ventricosum (Musa ensete)

Ensete (Musa) maurelii

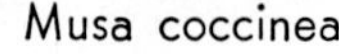

Musa coccinea

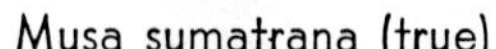

Musa sumatrana (true)

Musa zebrina

Musa rosacea

Musa nepalensis

Musa textilis

Musa velutina

Musa x paradisiaca, the Common banana

Musa nana (cavendishii), Chinese Dwarf banana

Ravenala guyanensis, in Surinam

Ravenala madagascariensis, the Travelers-Tree

Musa x paradisiaca vittata

Musa zebrina (Blood banana)

Musa nana (cavendishii), the Dwarf banana

Musa x paradisiaca (x sapientum)

Ensete ventricosum (Musa ensete), in Central Africa

Musa Fehi, with erect fruit, in Hawaii

Strelitzia parvifolia juncea, in Cape Prov., South Africa

Strelitzia alba (augusta), Valley of 1000 Hills, Natal

Orchidantha maxillarioides, the "Orchid flower"

Orchidantha meleagris (Lowia)

Musa basjoo (male flowers)

Orchidantha meleagris (Lowia)

Musa velutina (inflor.)

Ravenala guianensis (fruiting)

Strelitzia alba (augusta)

Strelitzia reginae farinosa

relitzia alba (augusta), Mormon Temple, Los Angeles

Ravenala madagascariensis, Jardin Botanique Cayenne, French Guyana

Musa basjoo, "Japanese fiber-banana"

Ensete ventricosum (Musa ensete)

Strelitzia nicolai

Strelitzia reginae, with an occasional dual inflorescence

Strelitzia caudata, at Kirstenbosch, South Africa

Strelitzia parvifolia, in South Africa

Myristica fragrans, the Nutmeg

Myoporum 'Carsonii' (laetum cv)

Musa x paradisiaca 'Koae'

Jacquinia pungens, "Cudjoewood" (Mexico)

Jacquinia ruscifolia (Fairchild Garden)

Jacquinia armillaris arborea

Jacquinia armillaris arborea (Fairchild G.)

Myoporum laetum

Myrica pensylvanica, "Bayberry"

Myoporum laetum, "Mouse-hole tree"

Myoporum 'Carsoni' the "Ngaio tree"

Myoporum sandwicense, "Bastard sandalwood"

Suttonia salicina

Myrsine africana

Ardisia wallichii

Ardisia polycephala

Ardisia malouiana

Ardisia humilis

Deherainia smaragdina

Ardisia japonica

Ardisia esculenta, "Hen's eyes"

Ardisia solanacea (Sri Lanka)

Ardisia wallichii

Myristica fragrans, "Nutmeg" in Trinidad

Ardisia polycephala

Theophrasta jussieui, in Santo Domingo

Maesa argentea, from the Himalayas

Psidium guajava

Ardisia crispa (crenulata)

Myrsine africana

Ardisia japonica 'Hinotsukasa'

Ardisia crispa, with berries

Ardisia mamillata (C. China)

Ardisia japonica marginata

Ardisia japonica maculata

Ardisia japonica 'Matsu-Shima'

Melaleuca quinquenervia, "Cajeput tree" (Australia)

Myrtus communis 'Compacta', grown as topiary, in California

Chamaelaucium uncinatum, "Geraldton waxplant"

Leptospermum scoparium 'Ruby Glow', "Double Manuka"

Acmena (Eugenia) smithii, in California

Syzygium paniculatum 'Globulus'

Syzygium malaccense, Rio Bot. Garde

Syzygium paniculatum (Eugenia)

Acmena (Eugenia) smithii

Syzygium aromaticum, "Cloves"

Syzygium paniculatum australis

Eugenia myriophylla (Myrciaria)

Rhodomyrtus tomentosa (India, Ma

Syzygium paniculatum (Eugenia myrtifolia), in California

Clavija tarapotana (Peru, Bolivia)

Syzygium malaccense, "Malay apple" in Rio de Janeiro

Acmena (Eugenia) smithii, "Lilly-Pilly tree"

Feijoa sellowiana, "Pineapple guava", in California

Theophrasta americana (fusca), Edinburgh Bot. Garden

Leptospermum scoparium 'Ruby Glow', "Double Manuka"

Agonis flexuosa, "Willow-myrtle"

Najas madagascariensis, "Pondwe

Psidium guajava, "Guava", in Honolulu

Pimenta dioica, "All-spice" (Jamaica)

Psidium cattleianum lucidum, (Brazil)

Eucalyptus ficifolia

Callistemon lanceolatus

Callistemon coccineus

Eucalyptus erythrocorys, "Red-cap"

Eugenia uniflora

Eucalyptus globulus

Myrtus communis

Myrtus communis 'Variegata'

Myrtus communis 'Microphylla'

Melaleuca hypericifolia

Melaleuca filifolia

Metrosideros excelsus, "Pohutukawa" in N.Z

Melaleuca leucadendron, "Paperbark tree"

Melaleuca radula

Metrosideros robustus, the "Rata"

Regelia megacephala (Western Australia)

Metrosideros scandens (perforatus)

Xanthostemon rubrum (New Caledonia

Callistemon montanus

Callistemon paludosus

Callistemon phoeniceus

Beaufortia sparsa, in Wellington, N.Z.

Calothamnus gilesii

Verticordia nitens, "Feather flower"

Calothamnus homalophyllus, "Claw-flower"

Calothamnus villosus

Calothamnus chrysantheros

Melaleuca huegelii

Metrosideros excelsus (tomentosus) "New Zealand Christmas tree"

Melaleuca genistifolia

Feijoa sellowiana

Callistemon brachyandrus, at Kew

Callistemon rugulosus (probably C. coccineus)

Callistemon acuminata

Callistemon macropunctatus

Callistemon salignus viridiflorus

Eucalyptus polyanthemos (Silver Dollar)

Eucalyptus torquata

Eucalyptus cinerea (Silver Dollar tree)

Acmena smithii

Eucalyptus globulus 'Compacta'

Eucalyptus globulus (flowers)

Chamaelaucium uncinatum

Leptospermum scoparium (Manuka)

Hypocalymma robustum

Eucalyptus polyanthemos (Silver Dollar tree)

Eucalyptus globulus

Syzygium paniculatum (Eugenia myrtifolia)

Tristania conferta 'Aureo-variegata'

Myrtus communis boetica

Myrtus communis

Psidium cattleianum

Leptospermum scoparium

Feijoa sellowiana

Myrtus communis boetica

Myrtus communis romana

Myrtus obcordata purpurea

Myrtus communis, the "True myrtle" of Greece

Bougainvillea 'Harrisii' (Merry Gardens, Maine)

Eucalyptus ficifolia, "Flowering gum"

Melaleuca leucadendron, "Swamp tea-tree"

Heimerliodendron (Pisonia) brunonianum

Bougainvillea x buttiana 'Temple Fire'

Bougainvillea x buttiana 'Praetoria'

Boug. x buttiana 'Mrs. Butt' ('Crimson Lake')

Mirabilis jalapa

Bougainvillea 'Harrisii'

Bougainvillea glabra 'Sanderiana'

Bougainvillea x buttiana 'Praetoria'

Bougainvillea x buttiana 'Barbara Karst'

Bougainvillea glabra

Bougainvillea 'Milflores', in Visayas, Philippines

Bougainvillea 'Manila Red' in Honolulu

Bougainvillea spectabilis 'Miggi Ruser' (Germany)

Bougainvillea 'Tahitian Maid' (Monrovia Nursery)

ugainvillea 'Mary Palmer', Bangalore, India

Bougainvillea x buttiana 'Barbara Karst'

Bougainvillea x buttiana 'San Diego Red'

Eucalyptus caesia, the "Gungurru" in Perth, Western Australia

Eucalyptus ficifolia, "Red-flowering gum"

Eucalyptus macrocarpa, "Mottlecah"

Eucalyptus rhodantha, "Rose mallee"

Eucalyptus globulus, "Blue gum"

Eucalyptus cinerea, "Silver dollar tree"

Eucalyptus sideroxylon, "Red Ironbark"

Eucalyptus polyanthemos, "Red box"

Eucalyptus citriodora, "Lemon-gum" in Vista, California

Eucalyptus falcata, "Silver mallet", Western Australia

Eucalyptus globulus, "Tasmanian Blue gum"

Eucalyptus globulus 'Compacta' (maturity stage)

"Pisonia grandis tricolor" at Chelsea Flower Show 1960

Heimerliodendron (Pisonia) brunonianum 'Variegatum'

Bougainvillea 'Harrisii', in flower

Bougainvillea glabra 'Sanderiana variegata'

Nymphaea x helvola, a "Pygmy water-lily"

Nymphaea flava (mexicana)

merliodendron brunonianum, the "Bird-catcher tree", Queensland

Eucalyptus salubris, the "Gimlet", in Perth, Western Australia

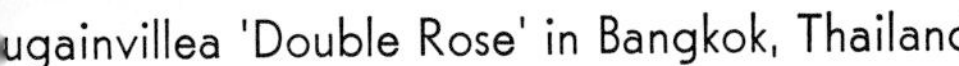

ugainvillea 'Double Rose' in Bangkok, Thailand

Heimerliodendron brunonianum 'Variegatum', variegated "Para-Para" tree

Nelumbo nucifera 'Rosea' pot-grown Lotus in Japan

Nelumbo nucifera

Nuphar luteum, "European pond-lily"

Nymphaea 'Margaret Mary', day-bl. pygmy

Nymphaea Lotus (Bot. Mag. 1804)

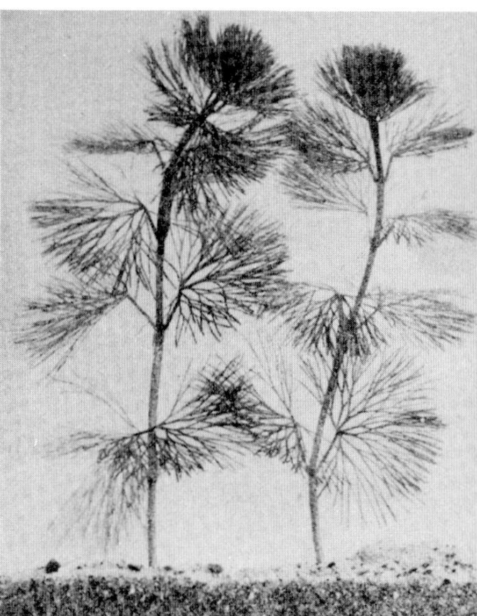
Cabomba aquatica (Aquarium plant)

Nymphaea leucantha, "White lotus of Egypt"

Nymphaea micrantha, (day-bl.), West Africa

Victoria cruziana, Villa 'Les Cèdres', St. Jean-Cap Farrat, France

Euryale ferox, in tropic pool, Munich Botanic Garden

Nymphaea 'St. Louis' (trop. night-bloomer)

Nymphaea capensis var. zanzibariensis, "Cape Blue water-lily"

Nymphaea x daubeniana, "Pygmy water-lily" (trop. day-bl.)

Nymphaea colorata (trop. day-bl.) Longwood Gardens

Nymphaea 'Missouri' (Trop. night-fl.)

Nymphaea x daubeniana

Nymphaea 'Golden West' (Trop. day-bl.)

Nymphaea 'Gloriosa' (hardy)

Nymphaea 'H. A. Haarstick' (Trop. night-fl.)

Nymphaea 'Somptuosa' (hardy)

Nelumbo nucifera, in Java

Nelumbo nucifera 'Alba plena', the Sacred Lotus

Victoria cruziana

Victoria regia on the Rio Negro, Amazonas, Brazil

Nymphaea x daubeniana, a tropical 'Pygmy' Water-lily

Nymphaea 'Col. Lindbergh' (Trop. day-bl.)

Nymphaea x odorata 'Sulphurea' (hardy)

Nymphaea x marliacea 'Chromatella' (hardy)

Nymphaea caerulea (tender)

Nymphaea tuberosa 'Postlingsberg'

Nymphaea 'Pink Pearl' (trop. day-bl.)

Nymphaea gigantea (New Guinea)

Nymphaea 'Gladstoniana' (hardy)

Nymphaea x marliacea rosea

Nymphaea 'Sunrise' (hardy)

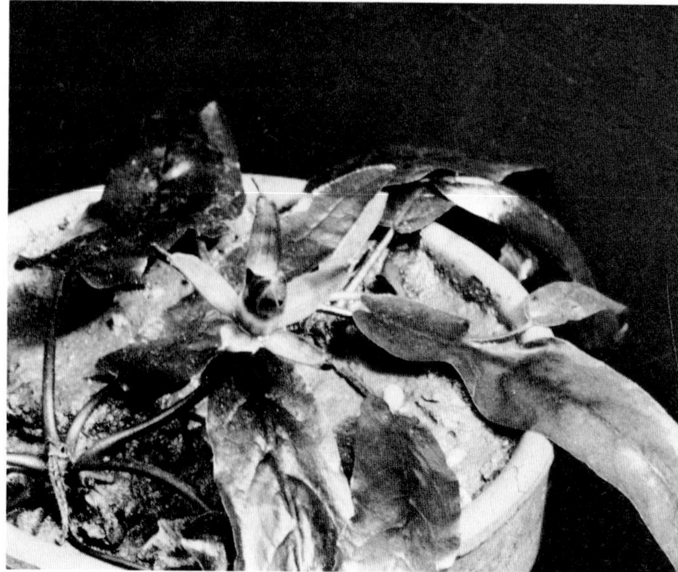

Barclaya longifolia, from Burma

Cabomba aquatica, aquatic "Fanwort"

Osmanthus delavayi

Osmanthus heterophyllus (ilicifolius) 'Variegatus'

Osmanthus fragrans ('Sweet Olive')

Ochna serrulata ('multiflora')

Olea europaea (Olive tree)

Forsythia x intermedia 'Spring Glory'

Syringa 'Mme. Lemoine'

Syringa vulgaris plena

Syringa 'Marie Legraye'

Ochna atropurpurea, a "Mickey Mouse plant"

Ochna pulchra (Angola to Transvaal)

Ochna kirkii, in Australia

Epilobium angustifolium, "Fire-weed"

Clarkia (Godetia) amoena, "Farewell-to-sprir

Ouratea olivaeformis, "Button flower (Brazil)

Eucharidium grandiflorum (California)

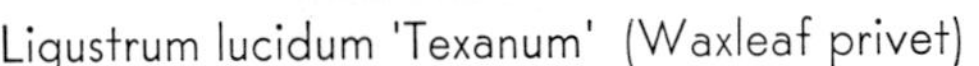
Ligustrum lucidum 'Texanum' (Waxleaf privet)

Ligustrum japonicum

Ligustrum lucidum 'Texanum' (pyramid)

.igustrum lucidum 'Texanum variegatum'

Ligustrum ovalifolium (California privet)

Ligustrum lucidum 'Erectum'

Ligustrum lucidum 'Texanum'

Ligustrum lucidum, the Glossy privet

Jasminum volubile (simplicifolium hort.)

Jasminum simplicifolium (Fiji, Polynesia)

Jasminum angulare, (South Africa)

Jasminum multiflorum in Hawaii

Jasminum parkeri, (Indian Himalaya)

Jasminum polyanthum, "Pink jasmine"

Jasminum nitidum (ilicifolium, gracile magnificum)

Jasminum odoratissimum (M

Jasminum sambac

Jasminum sambac 'Grand Duke of Tuscany'

sminum officinale (floribundum in hort.)

Jasminum rex

Jasminum humile revolutum

Jasminum nudiflorum

Jasminum mesnyi (primulinum)

Jasminum grandiflorum

Olea europaea 'Manzanillo', ornamental Olive-tree standard

Ligustrum japonicum, shaped trees at Union Buildings, Pretoria, South Africa

Chionanthus virginicus

Chionanthus retusus

Jasminum nitidum (gracile magnificum)

Jasminum polyanthum

Chionanthus retusa, "Chinese Fringe-tree"

Olea europaea, ancient "Olive-tree", in Gethsemane, Jerusalem

minum grandiflorum, "Poet's jasmine", in Damascus, Syria

Jasminum sambac 'Maid of Orleans', fragrant "Arabian jasmine"

Ligustrum japonicum 'Compactum'

Ligustrum sinense 'Variegatum'

Ligustrum jap. variegatum (Ravenna, Italy

Noronhia emarginata (Madagascar)

Phillyrea angustifolia (So. Europe)

Ligustrum vulgare•buxifolium, "Privet"

Osmanthus armatus, from China

Osmanthus heterophyllus 'Gulf Tide'

Ligustrum japonicum, in Madrid

Jasminum volubile variegatum

Ligustrum japonicum, in flower

Syringa wolfii

Fuchsia 'Buttons & Bows'

Fuchsia 'Curtain Call'

Fuchsia 'Fort Bragg' (Merry Gardens)

Fuchsia 'South Seas'

Fuchsia 'Texas Longhorn'

Fuchsia 'Dark Eyes'

Fuchsia excorticata, waxy flowers

Fuchsia excorticata, the Tree-fuchsia, foliage

Fuchsia excorticata, forms papery trunks 45cm thick in New Zealand

Fuchsia excorticata tree, on Takaka Hill, N. Z.

Fuchsia triphylla

Fuchsia arborescens

Fuchsia denticulata

Fuchsia 'Winston Churchill'

Fuchsia 'Pride of Orion'

Fuchsia 'Mrs. Marshall'

Fuchsia 'Carmel Blue'

Fuchsia 'Little Beauty'

Fuchsia magellanica variegata

Fuchsia 'Autumnal'

Fuchsia 'Old Smoky'

Fuchsia 'Cascade'

Fuchsia 'Countess of Aberdeen'

Fuchsia triphylla 'Gartenmeister Bohnstedt'

Fuchsia 'Winston Churchill'

Fuchsia 'Black Prince'

Fuchsia magellanica gracilis

Fuchsia magellanica gracilis variegata

Fuchsia fulgens

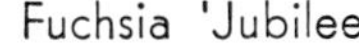

Fuchsia 'Jubilee'

Fuchsia 'Mrs. Rundle'

Fuchsia 'Lord Byron'

Fuchsia 'Harvest Moon'

Fuchsia 'Erecta Novelty'

Fuchsia 'Strawberry Sundae'

Fuchsia triphylla 'Traud chen Bohnstedt'

Fuchsia 'Georgana'

Fuchsia 'Caledonia'

Fuchsia 'Springtime'

Fuchsia 'Flying Cloud'

Fuchsia 'Mrs. Victor Reiter'

Fuchsia 'Lace Petticoats'

Fuchsia 'Whitemost'

Fuchsia triphylla 'Gartenmeister Bohnstedt' (Honey-suckle f.)

Fuchsia 'Sunray', with variegated leaves

Fuchsia 'Lucky Strike'   Fuchsia 'Sleigh Bells'   Fuchsia 'Rollo'

Fuchsia 'Dollar Princess'

Fuchsia 'Thunderbird'

Fuchsia 'Streamliner'

Fuchsia 'Pepita'

Fuchsia 'Voodoo'

Fuchsia 'Rufus'

Fuchsia 'Cascade'

Fuchsia **'Pink Jade'**

Fuchsia 'Golden Glow'

Fuchsia 'Ting-a-Ling'

Fuchsia triphylla 'Gartenmeister Bohnstedt'

Fuchsia 'Golden Marinka'

Fuchsia 'Papoose' Fuchsia 'Pink Jade' Fuchsia 'Swanley Yellow'

Fuchsia 'Madame Dashu' Fuchsia 'Pink Galore'

Fuchsia 'Little Sister' Fuchsia 'Brigadoon' Fuchsia 'Mad. Corneliesen'

Fuchsia 'Golden Glow'

Fuchsia 'Jubilee'

Fuchsia 'Pink Fairy'

Fuchsia 'Blue Waves'

Fuchsia 'Peter Pan'

Fuchsia 'Swingtime'

Fuchsia 'Lilac'n'Rose'

Fuchsia 'Mama Bleuss'

Fuchsia 'Midge'

Fuchsia 'Nightingale'

Fuchsia 'Shady Lane'

Fuchsia 'Candlelight'

Fuchsia 'Waltztime'

Fuchsia 'Sierra Blue'

Fuchsia 'Whirlaway'

Fuchsia 'Frenchi'

Fuchsia 'Pin Wheel'

Fuchsia 'White Bouquet'

Fuchsia 'Chickadee' Fuchsia 'Pink Cloud' Fuchsia 'Fluorescent'

Fuchsia 'My Dear' Fuchsia 'Blue Butterfly' Fuchsia 'Dusky Rose'

Fuchsia 'Guinevere' Fuchsia 'Marietta' Fuchsia 'Midnight Sun'

Fuchsia serratifolia

Fuchsia magellanica

Oenothera tetragona fraseri

Clarkia elegans

Clarkia grandiflora (Godetia)

Clarkia amoena plena

Lopezia coronata

Lopezia lineata (coccinea)

Ouratea ilicifolia

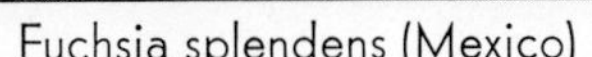

Fuchsia splendens (Mexico)

Fuchsia procumbens (New Zealand)

Fuchsia corymbiflora (Peru).

Jussiaea longifolia

Lopezia lineata, "Mosquito-flower"

Hauya elegans (Mexico)

Ludwigia mulertii, "Swamp-spoon"

Ludwigia helminthorrhiza (Bogner- Munich)

Oenothera caespitosa, "Evening primrose"

x Laeliocattleya 'Golden Girl', a Tribute to Beauty

Arachnis lowii, a "Spider orchid", epiphytic in Borneo

Arachnis massoei, growing in broken brick, Singapore

Cattleya, carved of ivory, in Japan

ORCHIDACEAE An Introduction to the Orchid family

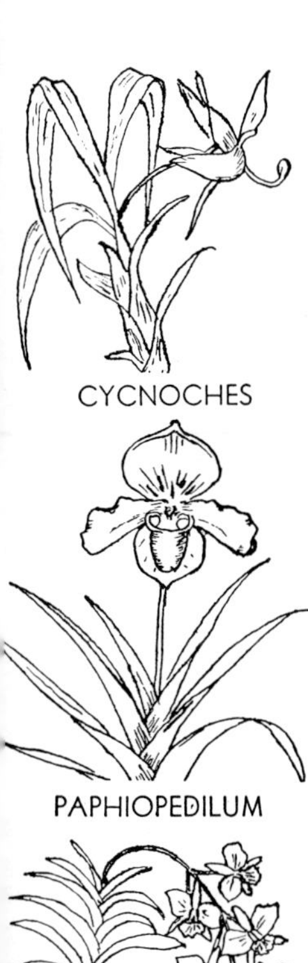

CYCNOCHES

PAPHIOPEDILUM

DENDROBIUM

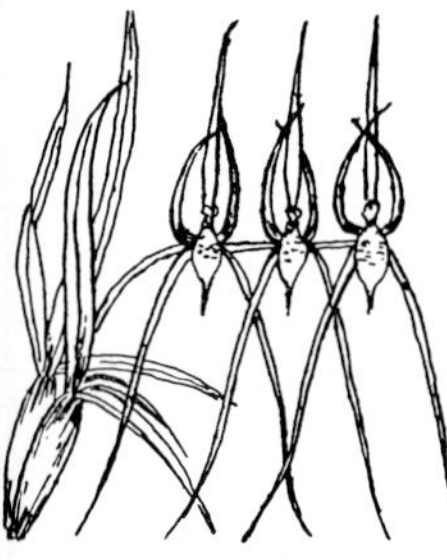

BRASSIA

VANDA

PHALAENOPSIS

The orchid family still reigns as queen of all exotics, and will ever thrill the human heart in its exquisite beauty. While the women of America have particularly adopted the showy Cattleya as their favorite, over 600 other genera in more than 15,000 species have been identified. In fact, descriptions of 800 genera and 35,000 species have been recorded, and an estimated 30,000 hybrids. This large and curious family is as great in the number of genera it includes as it is widely distributed, reaching far north even into the Arctic. Some 85% of the varieties, however, dwell in the tropics and subtropics, and primarily between the Tropic Circles of the Cancer and the Capricorn. However, certain genera are concentrated in fairly well-defined geographical areas within these zones:

Tropical Asia, including Malaysia and the Philippines, probably has the richest representation of orchids in the world. Some of them are the popular Bulbophyllum, Calanthe, Coelogyne, Cymbidium, Dendrobium, Paphiopedilum, Phaius, Phalaenopsis, and Vanda.

Tropical America is distinguished by an almost entirely isolated orchid flora with over 150 endemic genera. Most important are Brassavola, Brassia, Catasetum, Cattleya, Cycnoches, Epidendrum, Laelia, Lycaste, Masdevallia, Maxillaria, Miltonia, Mormodes, Oncidium, Odontoglossum, Peristeria, Pleurothallis, Stanhopea, and Zygopetalum.

Africa has many endemic genera largely of botanical interest and includes Lissochilus, Polystachya, Ansellia, and the mountain-dwelling Disa.

Australia, as a continent, has the least number of orchids in the world, but we find Bulbophyllum, Calanthe, Cymbidium, Dendrobium, Eria, Phaius, Pholidota, Sarchochilus, and Spathoglottis. The adjacent New Guinea is extremely rich in species, estimated at over 2500; the variety of forms is especially numerous in Dendrobium and Bulbophyllum.

The **temperate zones** of **Europe, North America** and **Northeast Asia** are the home of such as the true Cypripedium, Orchis, and Spiranthes.

In the cooler or temperate zones all orchids grow terrestrial. The tropics have a great majority of epiphytes or "air plants", growing attached to other plants, generally trees. Tropical and subtropical orchids usually have the largest flowers and are of richest coloring. But altitude directly determines a climatic zone, and high mountain species even near the equator grow under cool, frequently moist conditions. In the Cordilleras of Colombia, Oncidiums are found at an elevation of 4,500 metres; Odontoglossums and Masdevallias occur at from 2,000 to 2,500 metres.

Orchids belong to the **Monocotyledons,** like palms, lilies, bromeliads and grasses. Their flowers have sepals which are almost always colored, as in iris and tulips, whereas in most other flowers they are green. These petaloid sepals are usually irregular — in Cattleyas the upper sepal is, as a rule, the largest; in Paphiopedilums the lateral lower sepals are grown together, or connate. The corolla consists of three petals, with the two laterals being identical, while the third petal always differs in shape. It may be modified into a trumpet-shaped tube broadening into a conspicuous 'lip' or labellum like in Cattleyas, resemble a pouch or slipper, as in Paphiopedilum, or this lower petal can assume various other shapes. Together, petals and sepals can take on some very characteristic expressions so that we know some orchids variously as 'Dancing Doll', 'Ghost', 'Madonna' and 'Nun orchid', or they may mimic an 'Egret', 'Moth', 'Butterfly', 'Green Swan', 'Bee', 'Frog', 'Spider', 'Rattlesnake' or even a 'Dragon's Mouth'.

An important characteristic in orchids is that their reproductive organs, the style and stamens, are fused together to form a prominent column. The **Diandrae** division which includes the Cypripediums, has two fertile, lateral stamens. In all other orchids, grouped under **Monandrae,** only one stamen is fertile. At the tip of this stamen are the concealed pollinia which, in the form of disks, consist of cells aggregated into pollen masses instead of the separate pollen grains common to other plants. The receptive stigmatic surface is usually sunk into a sticky cavity on the underside of the column just back of the anther.

While the orchid family is divided by botanical authorities into numerous subtribes based on flower construction and other differentiating factors, Lindley, in 1826, distinguished five main tribes, simply determined by the number of fertile stamens, their relative position on the column, and the structure of their pollen masses:

The **EPIDENDREAE,** with one fertile central stamen; the pollinia waxy and free. Includes Brassavola, Bulbophyllum, Calanthe, Cattleya, Chysis, Coelogyne, Dendrochilum, Epidendrum, Eria, Laelia, Phaius, Restrepia, Schomburgkia, Sophronitis, Thunia.

The **VANDEAE,** having one fertile central stamen; the pollinia waxy, but attached by a stemlet, include: Aerides, Angraecum, Anguloa, Bifrenaria, Brassia, Catasetum, Cochlioda, Cycnoches, Cymbidium, Lycaste, Maxillaria, Miltonia, Odontoglossum, Oncidium, Phalaenopsis, Renanthera, Saccolabium, Stanhopea, Trichopilia, Vanda, Zygopetalum.

The **NEOTTIEAE,** also with one fertile central stamen, but their pollinia are powdery or granulated, and free, include: Anoectochilus, Haemaria, Macodes, Sobralia, Vanilla.

The **OPHRYDEAE,** with one fertile central stamen and powdery pollinia, but attached by a little stem or caudicle — these include temperate or cold zone terrestrials only, such as Habenaria, Ophrys and Orchis.

The **CYPRIPEDIEAE** are characterized by having two fertile lateral stamens located on either side of the smooth stigma, while here the pollinia are sticky. Best-known types are Paphiopedilum, Phragmipedium, and Cypripedium.

Orchids are either **monopodial** — having stems, or **sympodial** — without conspicuous stems. A monopodial plant has foliage along its single stems as well as adventitious roots which secure and feed it. The growth of the main stem is continued indefinitely by the terminal bud. Angraecum, Phalaenopsis, Vanda, and apparently Vanilla, are of this type. Most other orchids are sympodial, having a creeping axis or rhizome terminated after one season by a swollen growth known as pseudobulb, and topped by one or more leaves. At its base are two eyes from which further growth takes place. Pseudobulbs store food and moisture which enable the plant to withstand seasonal periods of drought.

Orchids in the Home.

All orchids prefer the controlled growing conditions of the greenhouse but, contrary to general belief, many of them can be grown with success and pleasure in the home.

A sunny, well ventilated room and a place, if possible, next to the window-glass where the temperature is normally lowest, plus a relatively high humidity preferably near 70%, is ideal. As the habitats of various orchids are found in different climatic zones, specialists' greenhouses also aim to provide several ranges of temperature for their cultivation under glass: **Stove or Warm** (16°-26°C), **Intermediate** (12°-21°C), and **Cool** (7°-14°C). Orchids in general however, are rather tolerant and even tough, which allows them to adapt themselves to many conditions encountered in the average home. But, of course, the more nearly their temperature preferences can be satisfied the more these plants will reward by normal growth and flowering. The flowering season of an orchid is not usually the same as in its habitat and may be variable; if taken across the equator it is usually reserevd, more so for those furthest from the equator.

Location

Generally, Dendrobium, Phalaenopsis, and Vandas like it warm but need a humid atmosphere; Vandas must also have bright light to flower. The intermediate types, including the important Cattleya, the mottled-leaf Paphiopedilum, Oncidium and Cycnoches feel perfectly at home in a comfortable apartment, with night temperatures in the low 15°C and days around 21°-24°C. with sun. The cool orchids are represented by Cymbidiums, green-leaf Paphiopedilum, and Odontoglossum, and would do nicely in the cooler rooms of the house, next to an east window, or a glassed-in sunporch. There are always locations about the house a few degrees warmer or cooler than others to fit various temperature requirements. Odontoglossum have given excellent results under air-conditioning, coupled with high humidity.

Close to the window glass there is usually a natural coolness, caused by condensation of moisture, of which plants should be able to take advantage. To best concentrate humidity around orchid plants in a heated living room, it is also good practice to cover them overnight with plastic cloth or bags especially if the temperature cannot be lowered for the night.

Out in the suburbs or in the country, and wherever conditions will permit, remarkably good results with all kinds of orchids have been experienced when the **plants are taken outdoors** during the warmer season into a small lathhouse, or hung under a tree or arbor. Here natural conditions of circulating fresh air, cool nights, morning dew, and occasional rain tend to rebuild jaded tissues, and favor the development of new growth and bud initiation. Brought indoors in autumn, such plants, their vigor renewed, will give excellent flowering response even under the trying conditions of an indoor window sill during winter.

Real delicate items of smaller dimensions, such as Jewel orchids, Haemaria and Anoectochilus, as well as Macodes, Stenoglottis, and the lately so popular miniature orchids, will do fine in a **glass terrarium**, on moist coarse sand or sphagnum moss, together perhaps with ferns and mosses. Where extremely dry conditions are encountered, a glass cover will generate and hold a high percentage of atmospheric moisture for a long time, which means a minimum of additional misting and care.

Light

Most orchids want considerable sunlight for good flowering, particularly the species with hard pseudobulbs. But if the leaves feel hot, this indicates that the sun is too strong and they may be scorched. The pseudobulbless or softer-growthed kinds will prefer a location protected from direct rays of the sun, and an east window would be best during the summer season. In winter and in spring the south or west windows are more desirable because at that time most orchids want all the light they can get. 1000-2000 foot candles, direct reading, or even higher if the light is all from one side, as at a window, should be a good average light for assorted orchids, under normal daylength, depending on season and variety. Cattleyas prefer 2000-3000 foot candles, but the intensity tolerated is influenced by temperature, relative humidity and air circulation. If grown entirely under artificial light, 650 foot candles have proven sufficient, provided an extended light-day of 16 hours can compensate for the lower light-strength. It can happen, however, that certain short-day bloomers, if standing near a reading lamp, may actually be prevented from initiating buds if such light inadvertently extends the daylength to 16 hours — the Cattleya labiata varieties have been found to be sensitive to such a photo period. 1 foot-candle = 10.76 lux.

Watering and Moisture

A shallow tray with pebbles, charcoal, perlite, or slats, on which to set the plants, and partly filled with water, will help to maintain moisture in the pots, as well as increase humidity — rather lacking in a heated living room. Plants growing in coarse materials, like firbark, may be set right into the bottom of the tray or glazed jardiniere, with gravel around the base of the pot.

When they are in full growth and with active roots, orchids should be watered copiously. Broadly speaking, this should be done only when the pot is becoming dry, usually once or twice a week. In any case, watering means soaking thoroughly, even dunking the plant into a bucket, or the kitchen sink with tepid water, until air bubbles stop coming up.

Various orchids have different moisture requirements. Most genera with pseudobulbs, such as the Cattleya group, Epidendrum, Oncidium, and Odontoglossum are epiphytes, with air-roots which like to get on the dry side between watering to keep them from stagnating, but with moisture in the air to coddle them. Depending on the time of year and whether porous clay pots, or impervious plastic pots are used, **a thorough watering** may be needed every three days in mid-summer, while during winter this may be stretched out to 10 days or 2 weeks, provided the plants are kept in temperate-cool surroundings. Bark culture requires more water than osmunda, especially in the home. One may even permit large plants to stand temporarily in water which has drained into the container underneath, to allow pot and bark to absorb back the surplus water which frequently runs right through such coarse material — but then don't water again until at least three days after all standing water has disappeared out of the saucer or tray. **Frequent misting** of the foliage with a hand sprayer is beneficial as it not only provides moisture to compensate for evaporation from their surface as well as cool them, but also cleans the breathing pores of leaves for freer respiration which is needed in the production of healthy tissues. Such misting also helps to keep pseudobulbs plump and turgid, while increased watering may actually do more harm than good, especially if the root system has been weakened.

Vandaceous orchids and Phalaenopsis do not have water-storing pseudobulbs, and will require more moisture than Cattleyas, consequently, potting material should be maintained a little on the damp side. Paphiopedilums, as terrestrials, need an even moisture at their roots. Cymbidiums want an abundance of water but coupled with good aeration and drainage. Place them outside, with some initial shading, into full sun during the frost-free season and keep them wet for best production of flower spikes.

Potting Materials

While the fibrous roots of the osmunda fern have long been used as standard potting medium for most epiphytic orchids, especially Cattleyas, good results have been obtained with other materials such as coconut fiber, tree fern slabs, and shredded firbark, for example our western Abies concolor. Firbark is easy to use: a coarse grade is desirable for Vandas for best drainage; medium-coarse, 6-8mm particles, perhaps with the addition of a little peat-humus or perlite for better retention of moisture and food, are recommended for Cattleyas, Oncidium, Dendrobium, Epidendrum; a finely screened grade, or the addition of 20% peatmoss to hold moisture, for Paphiopedilum. A mixture of 75% medium-grade firbark with 25% peatmoss is best for Phalaenopsis, Miltonia, Odontoglossum, Lycaste. Cymbidium, Peristeria and Phaius like a compost, such as ⅔ coarse humus and ⅓ soil; or ⅓ firbark, ⅓ redwood fiber, ⅓ peatmoss, plus 15% coarse sand; Anoectochilus does well in sphagnum moss.

Feeding

While orchids in osmunda need to be given little thought of feeding, firbark is especially deficient in nitrogen, and plants for maximum growth should be fed regularly, especially during active growth. Water-soluble Ammonium nitrate is a dependable and clean source of nitrogen, given at the rate of one teaspoon per 4 litres of water every 2nd or 3rd watering, but Ammonium nitrate breaks down firbark rapidly. A complete fertilizer formula 30-10-10 diluted 1 teaspoon to 4 litres water has been found satisfactory if given every third watering, during periods of active growth and high light intensity. During winter reduce to half or quarter strength. Ordinary organic fertilizers with their beneficial amounts of ammonium are not too practical in the home, but water-soluble fish-fertilizer emulsion can be used, 1 teaspoon per 4 litres of water every 2 or 3 weeks.

Propagation

While quantity production is largely by seed, this is a slow process requiring laboratory facilities. In such cases the minute seed is sown on sterile cultures of jellied agar-nutrients in flasks, in a warm location at 21°C minimum. From seed, Cattleyas will reach the flowering stage in 5 to 7 years. But in the home, plants may be propagated simply by division of the rhizome, as in Cattleyas and other genera with pseudobulbs. Paphiopedilum and other orchids that form more than one basal growth can also be divided, while Dendrobiums form young plants toward the apex of their slender pseudobulbs, and Phalaenopsis may form plantlets from adventitious buds at the end of their flower stems.

Orchids in flower

When an orchid comes into flower, these may be cut — without leaves — but wait until the blossoms have fully developed on the plant, as they will last much longer than if cut prematurely. Or the whole plant in bloom may be moved to some distinct location in the home, there to reward with matchless beauty that meticulous and affectionate care which brought it to this high point of its being.

Aerides fieldingii

Aerangis stylosa

Aerangis clavigera

Aerangis decaryana

Aerangis biloba

Aerides longicornu

Ancistrorhynchus capitatus

Aerides multiflorum

Acineta densa

Acineta superba

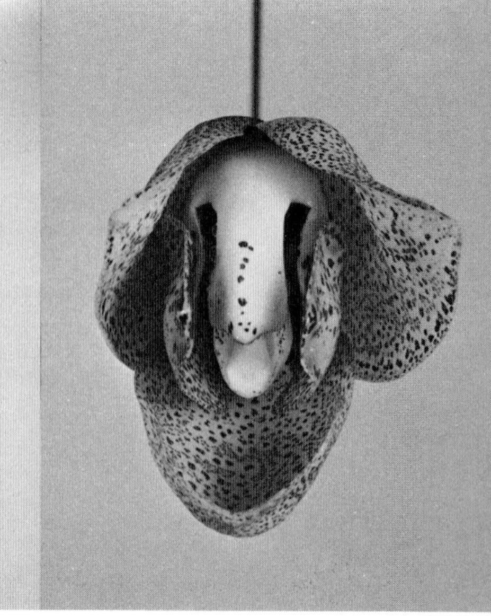
Acineta superba

Aerangis ugandense

Aerangis coriacea, in Kenya

Ada aurantiaca

Aerangis thomsonii

Aerangis rhodosticta

Aerangis kotschyana

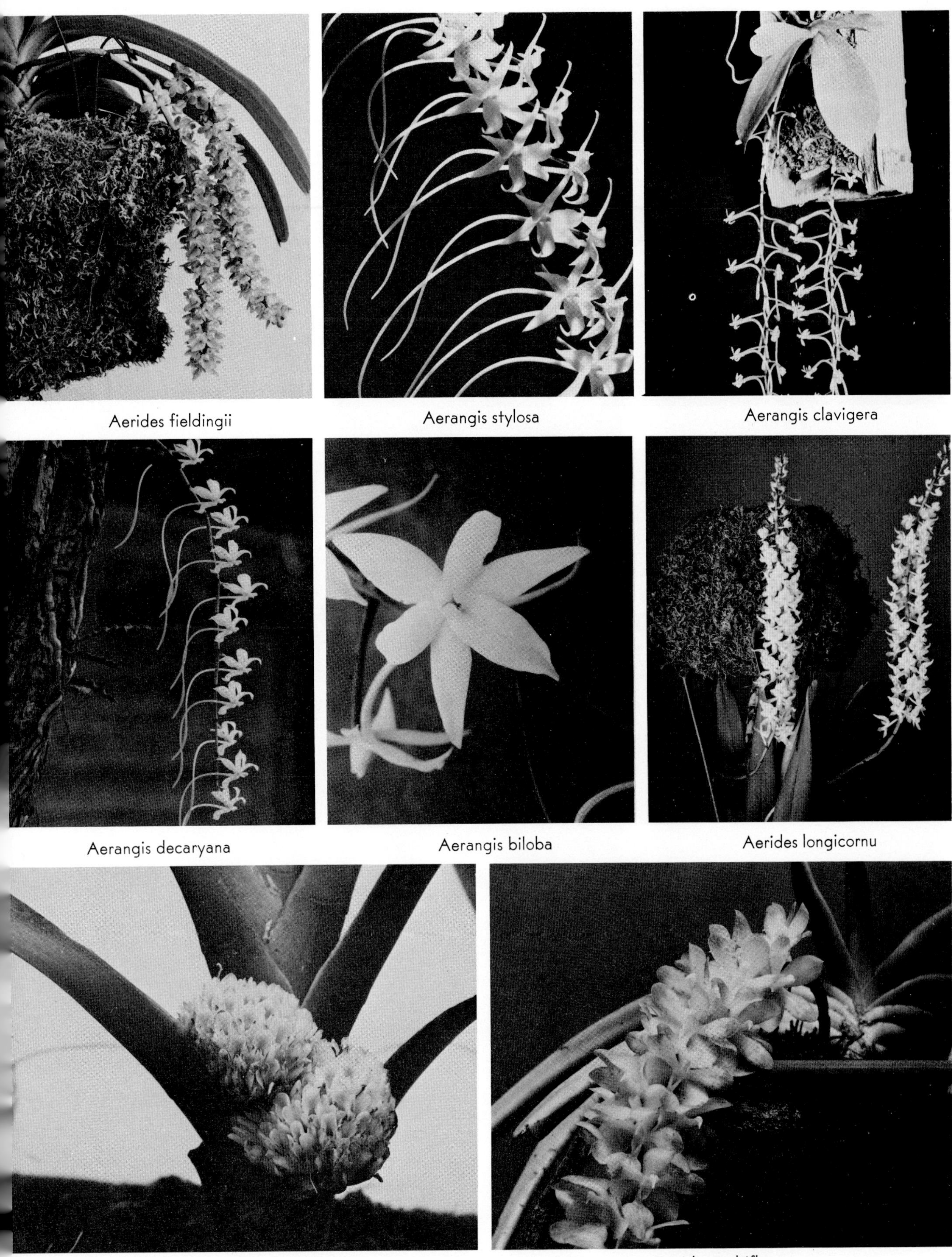

Aerides fieldingii

Aerangis stylosa

Aerangis clavigera

Aerangis decaryana

Aerangis biloba

Aerides longicornu

Ancistrorhynchus capitatus

Aerides multiflorum

Acineta densa

Acineta superba

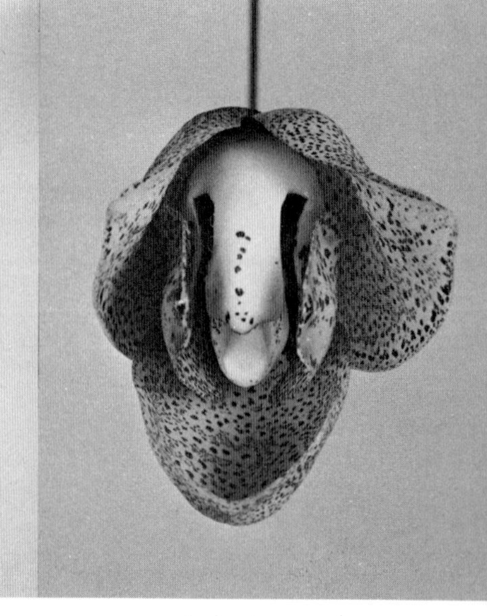
Acineta superba

Aerangis ugandense

Aerangis coriacea, in Kenya

Ada aurantiaca

Aerangis thomsonii

Aerangis rhodosticta

Aerangis kotschyana

Aerides quinquevulnerum

Aerides crispum

Aerides **falcatum**

Aerides vandarum

Aerides virens

Aerides quinquevulnerum

Anguloa virginalis (uniflora)

Anguloa clowesii

Anguloa **ruckeri**

Aerides japonicum (miniature)

Aerides falcatum

Aerides falcatum houlletianum

Aerides fieldingii

Aerides crassifolium

Aerides lawrenceae

Aerides odoratum

Aerides multiflorum

Angraecum bilobum

Angraecum veitchii

Angraecum sesquipedale

Angraecum ramosum

Angraecum smithii (Microcoelia)

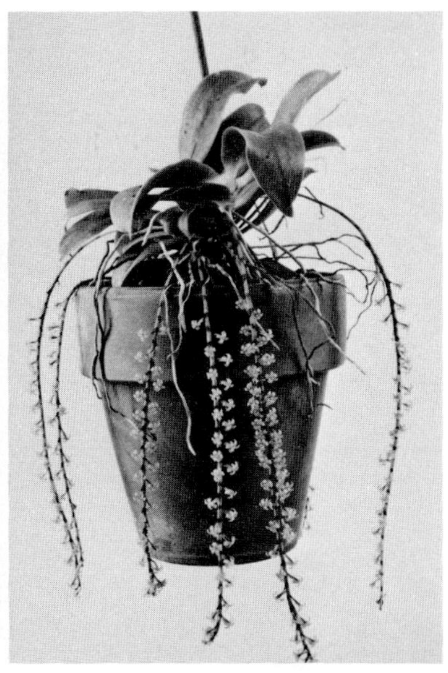

Angraecum hillebrandii

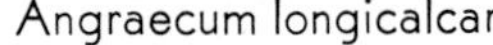

Angraecum longicalcar

Eurychone rothschildiana

Angraecum infundibulare

Angraecum bidens

Angraecum (Mystacidium) capense, **in South** Africa

Neofinetia falcata 'Variegata'

Neofinetia (Angraecum) falcata

Angraecum eichlerianum

Angraecum eburneum

Angraecum sesquipedale

Angraecum giryamae

Angraecum comorense

Ansellia africana

Ansellia africana, in Kenya

Aganisia cyanea

Ansellia gigantea, in Rhodesia

Ansellia africana, near Nairobi

Ansellia nilotica

Angraecum magdalenae (Madagascar)

Ascocentrum (Saccolabium) ampullaceum

Arpophyllum spicatum

Ascoglossum calopterum

Amblostoma cernuum (tridactylum)

Aspasia variegata

Acacallis cyanea

Acampe papillosa

Arundina graminifolia

Arpophyllum giganteum

Anoectochilus regalis

Anoectochilus roxburghii

Anoectochilus hispida

Anoectochilus sikkimensis

x Ascocenda 'Media Arnold'

x Aspasium 'Regal'

x Brapasia 'Panama'

Arachnis lowii (upper flower)

Arachnis flos-aeris (moschifera)

Arachnis lowii (basal flower)

Aspasia epidendroides

Aspasia lunata

Aspasia epidendroides principissa

Bletia patula

Ascotainia viridifusca

Ascocentrum ampullaceum

Bletilla striata

Ascocentrum miniatum

Barbosella anaristella

Bifrenaria tetragona

Bifrenaria harrisoniae

Bifrenaria fuerstenbergiana

Cyclopogon variegatum

Camarotis purpurea

x Cattleytonia 'Rosy Jewel'

Bolusiella mandae, in Zululand habitat

x Aranda maes, in Fiji

Barkeria elegans

x Aspoglossum 'Success'

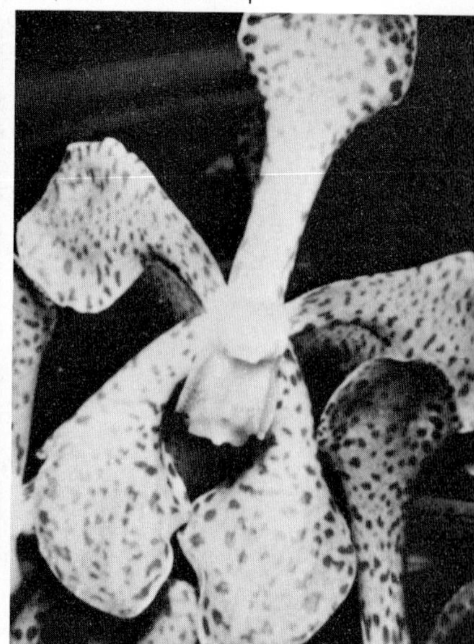

x Aranda 'Daniel Sato'

Alamania punicea (Mexico)

x Ascofinetia 'Peaches'

Barlia longibracteata

Cymbidium 'Doris'

Sophronitis coccinea

Cycnoches ventricosum

Vanda tricolor

Coelogyne pandurata

Stanhopea tigrina

X Laeliocattleya canhamiana alba

Paphiopedilum fairrieanum

Odontoglossum crispum

Oncidium kramerianum

Phalaenopsis amabilis

Epidendrum prismatocarpum

x Brassolaeliocattleya 'New Moon' (R. W. Jones, N.Y.)

x Brassocattleya 'Heatonensis'

Bromheadia aporides (Thailand)

Bifrenaria aurantiaca (Rudolfiella)

Broughtonia sanguinea

Batemania colleyi (Guianas)

Brominiana citrina (Bot. Garden Mayence, Germany)

Brassavola martiana (Brazil)

Brassavola subulifolia hort. (bot. cordata)

Brassavola acaulis

Brassia bidens

Brassavola flagellaris (flabelliformis hort.)

Brassia antherotes (Ecuador)

Brassia mexicana (Don Richardson)

Brassavola cucullata

Brassavola perrinii

Brachycorythis kalbreyeri

Brassavola cordata

Brassavola nodosa

Brassavola glauca

Brassavola digbyana

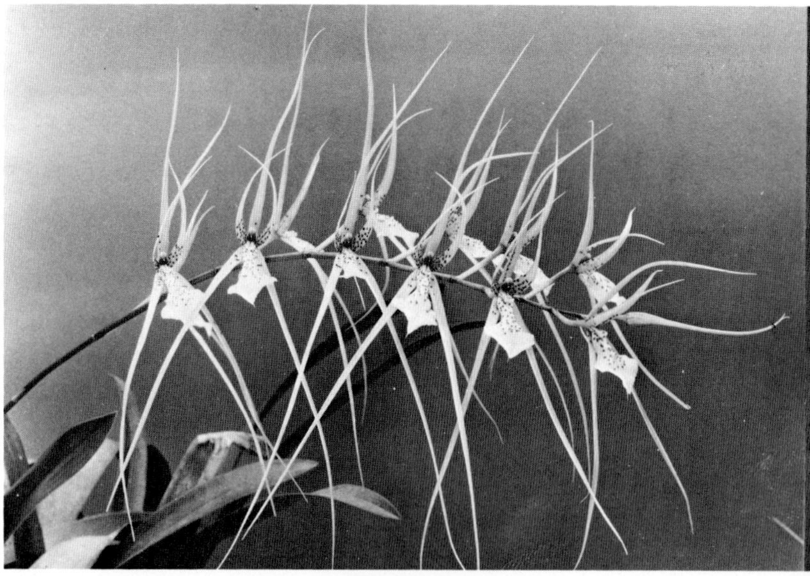

Brassia verrucosa

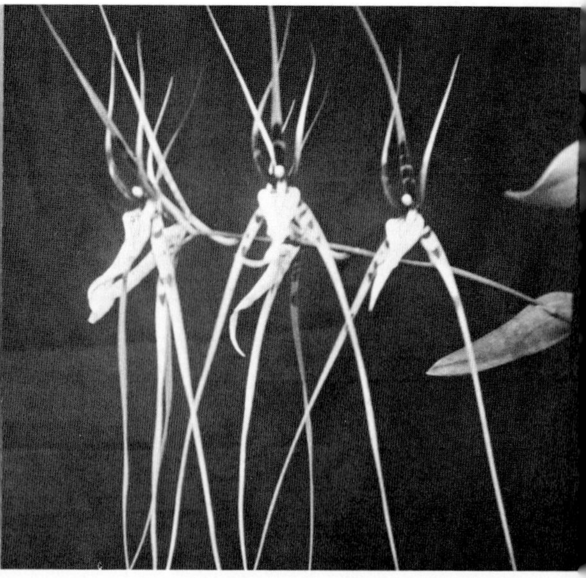

Brassia lawrenceana longissima

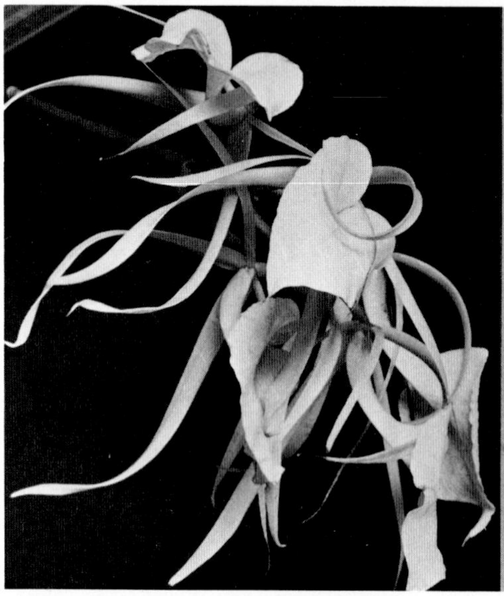

Brassavola nodosa

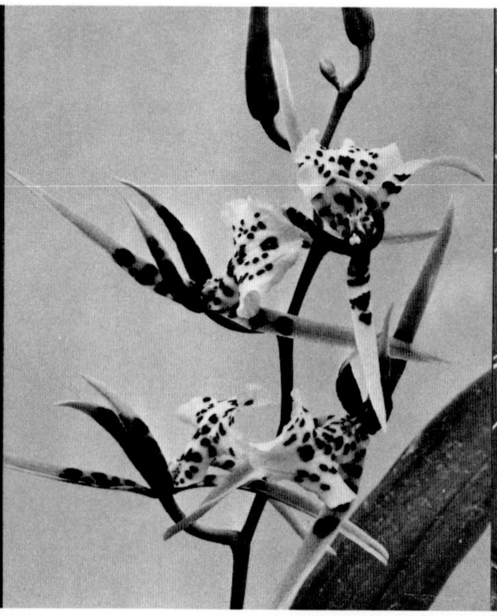

Brassia maculata

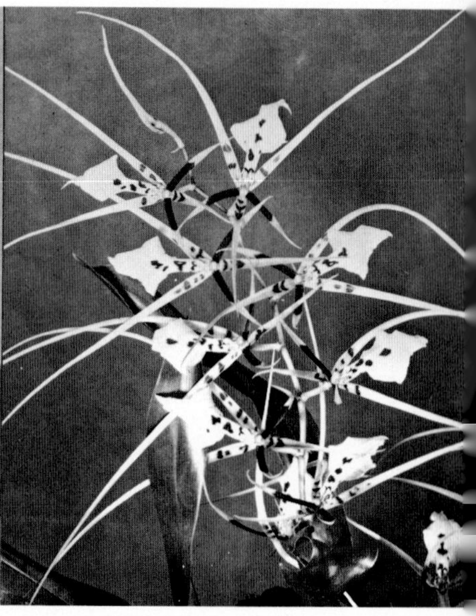

Brassia **gireoudiana**

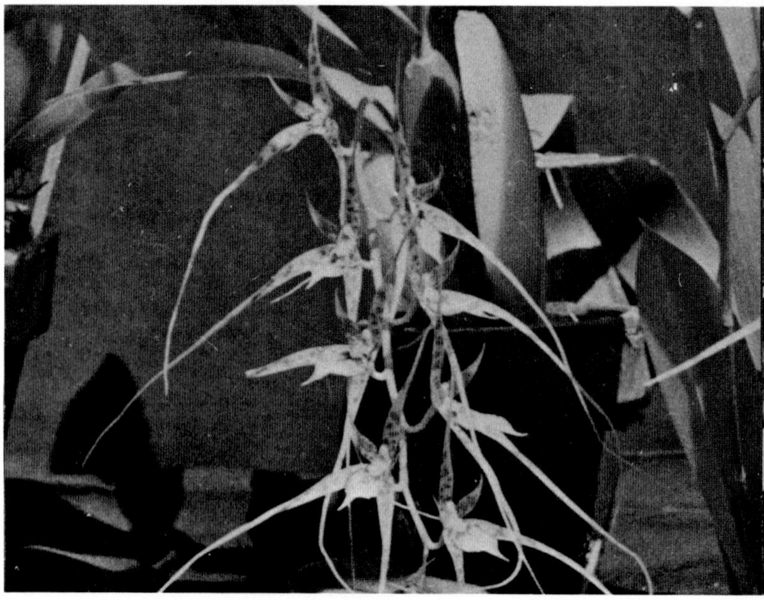

Brassia caudata

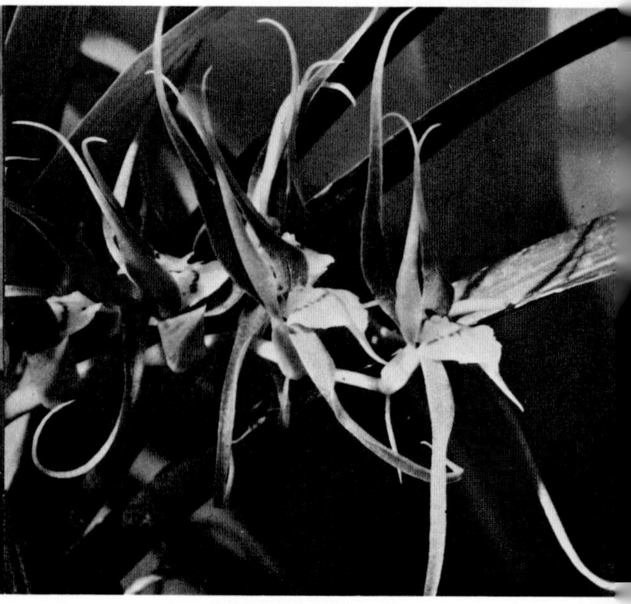

Brassia allenii

Brassia brachiata

Brassia chloroleuca

Brassia lanceana

Brassia chlorops

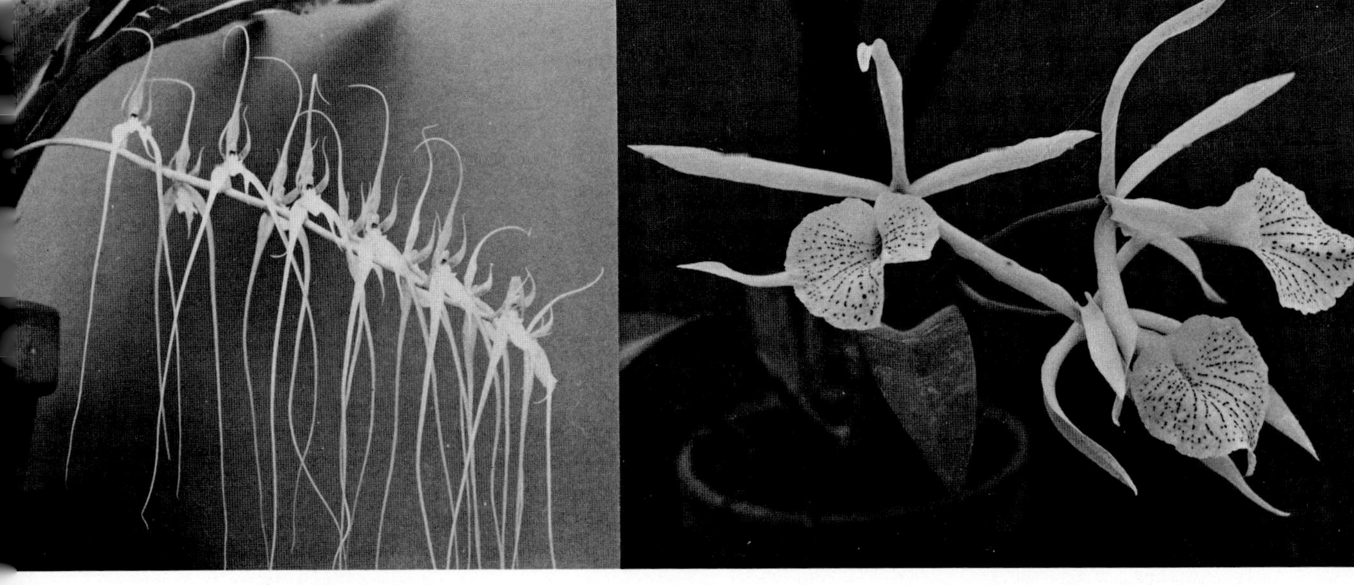

Brassia lawrenceana

x Brassolaelia 'Charles J. Fay'

Bulbophyllum (Cirrhopetalum) gamosepalum

Bulbophyllum lepidum (griffithii) (Malaya)

Bulbophyllum affinis fletcheranum (New Guinea)

Bulbophyllum (Cirrhopetalum) purpurascens

x Brassidium 'Suprem

x Brassoepidendrum 'Alex Hawkes'

Bulbophyllum (Cirrhopetalum) 'Fascination'

Bulbophyllum (Cirrhopetalum) pulchellum

Bulbophyllum (Cirr.) picturatum

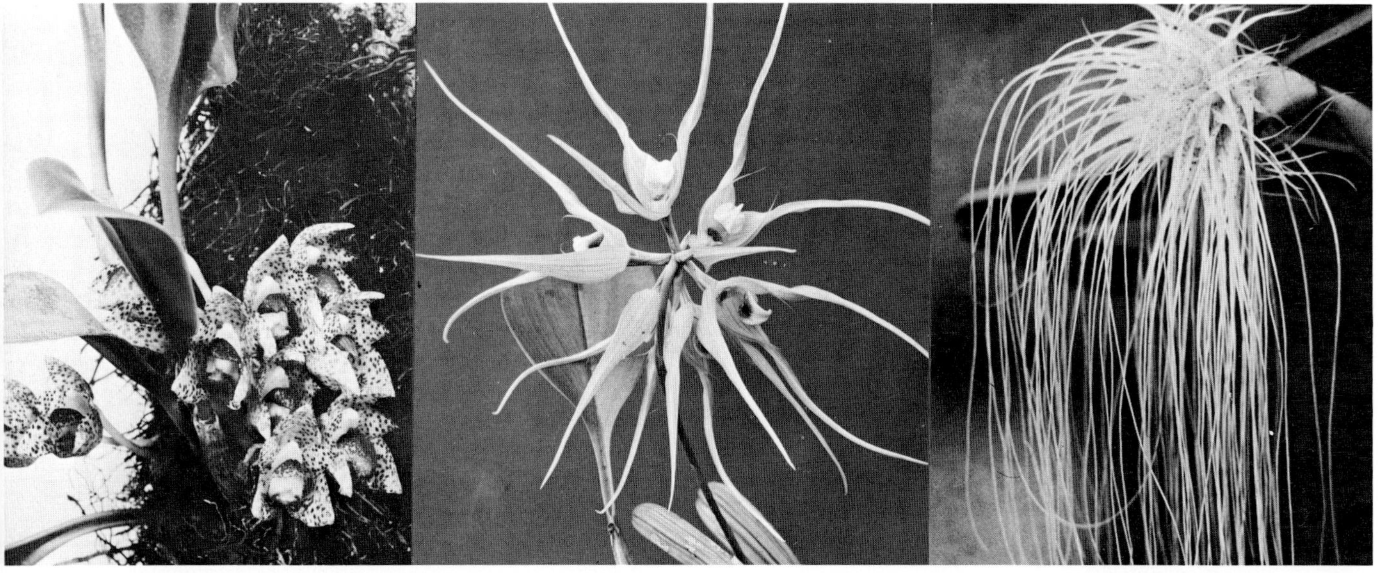

Bulbophyllum leopardinum

Bulbophyllum virescens

Bulbophyllum medusae

Bulbophyllum grandiflorum (Hyalosema)

Bulbophyllum lobbii

Broughtonia sanguinea

Bulbophyllum (Cirrhopetalum) makoyanum

Bulbophyllum ambrosia

Bulboyhyllum barbigerum

Bulbophyllum roxburghii

Bulbophyllum longisepalum

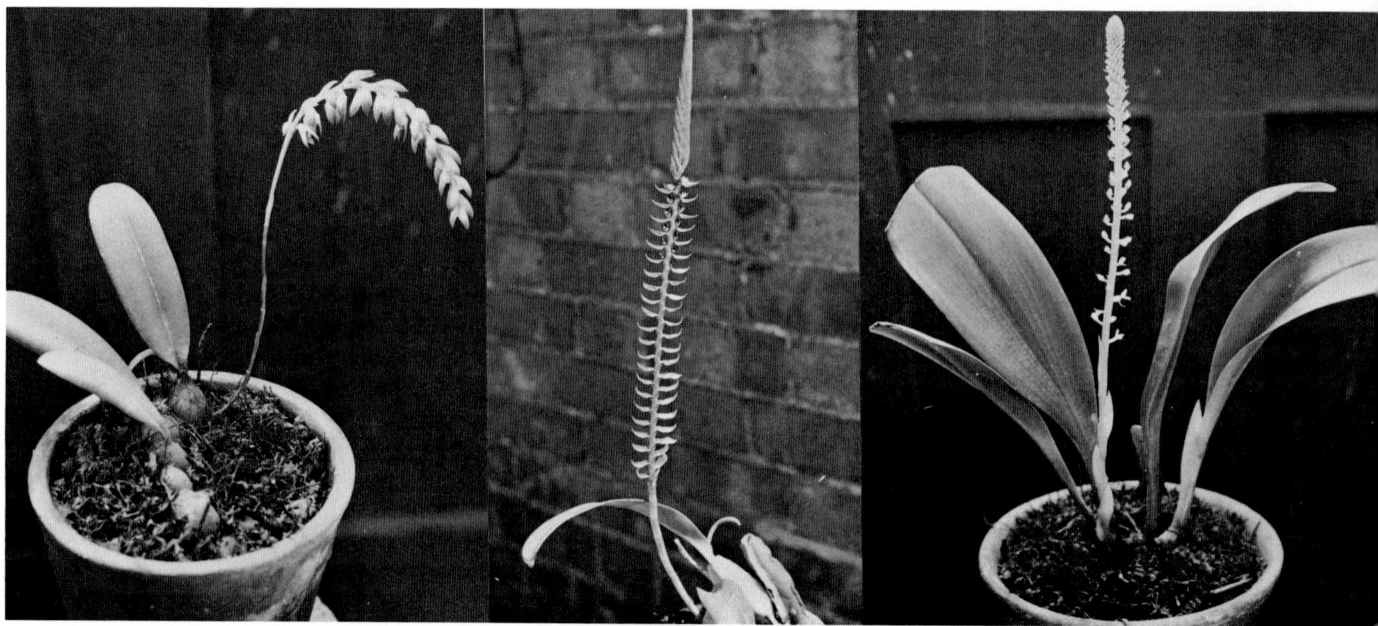

Bulbophyllum porphyroglossum

Bulbophyllum wrightii

Bulbophyllum elatius

Bulbophyllum (Cirrhopetalum) vaginatum

Bulbophyllum pulchrum

Bulbophyllum ornatissimum

Bulbophyllum (Cirrhopetalum) mastersianum

Bulbophyllum grandiflorum

Bulbophyllum (Cirrhopetalum) rothschildianum

Calanthe reflexa

Calanthe x bella

Calanthe striata (sieboldii)

Calanthe x veitchii

Calanthe 'Florence'

Calanthe vestita

Calanthe furcata

Calanthe 'William Murray'

Calanthe elmeri

Bulbophyllum (Cirrhopetalum) guttulatum (India)

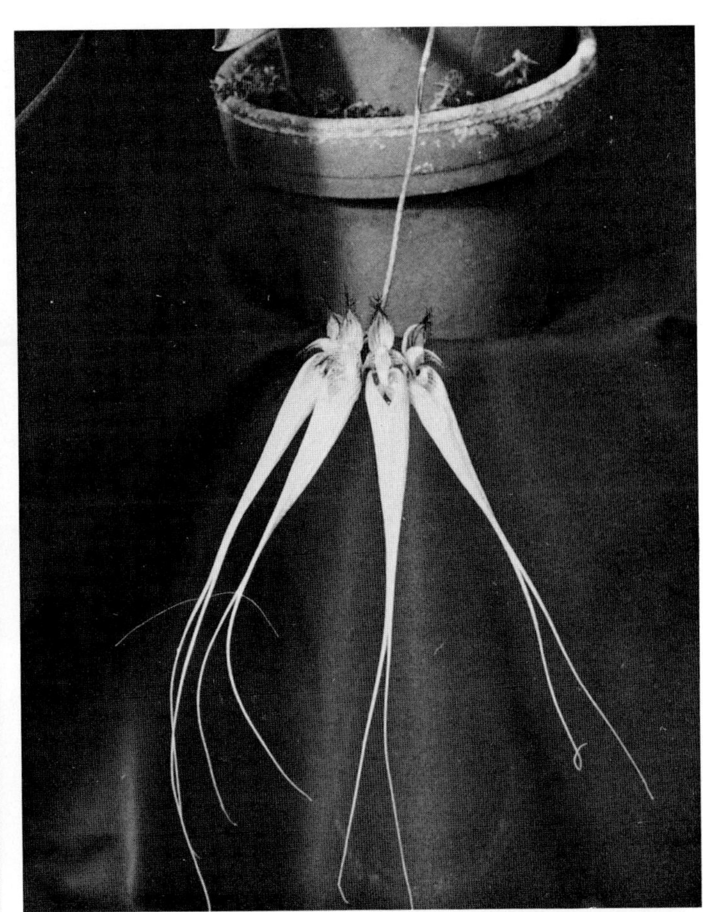

Bulbophyllum (Cirrhopetalum) fascinator (Vietnam)

Catasetum callosum, female inflorescence

Catasetum callosum, pollen-spraying male flowers

Catasetum warscewiczii (scurra)

Catasetum integerrimum

Catasetum fimbriatum

Catasetum sodiroi (Ecuador)

Catasetum discolor rosea-album (T. Everett, N.Y. Bot. G.)

Catasetum appendiculatum (Amazon)

Catasetum macrocarpum (bungerothii hort.)

Catasetum cernuum (Brazil)

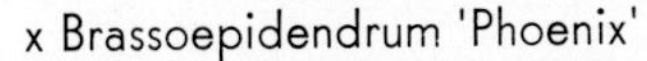

x Brassoepidendrum 'Phoenix'

Bulbophyllum purpureorchachis (Zaire)

Catasetum cristatum

Cadetia ceratostyloides (T. E. Everett)

Cadetia karoense (Bougainville Is.)

Catasetum mooreanum (Peru)

Calanthe triplicata

Calanthe masuca

Campylocentrum micranthum

Catasetum platyglossum

Catasetum "macrocarpum" (bot. oerstedii)

Catasetum viridiflavum

Catasetum roseum

Catasetum x splendens

Catasetum barbatum (bicallosum)

Catasetum russellianum

Catasetum fimbriatum

Catasetum bicolor, female flowers left, pollen-shooting male flowers on right

Bulbophyllum (Cirrhopetalum) longissimum

Cycnoches aureum, male flowers left; female flowers right

Catasetum saccatum christyanum

Catasetum discolor

Catasetum hookeri labiatum

Catasetum discolor

Catasetum pileatum (male fl.)

Catasetum suave

Catasetum barbatum

x Catamodes hybrida

Catasetum trulla (or spitzii)

Cattleya guttata (Brazil)

Cattleya dowiana aurea

Cattleya nobilior hort. (walkeriana)

Cattleya 'Thayeriana'

Cattleyopsis ortgiesiana (Cuba)

Ceratostylis rubra (Philippines)

Brassia lanceana, "Spider orchid"

Cheiradenia imthunii (Venezuela)

Chelonistele sulphurea (S.E. Asia)

Cattleya chocoensis

x Brassocattleya cliftonii magnifica

x Brassocattleya veitchii

Cattleya violacea (loddigesii violacea)

Cattleya warneri (gigas?)

Cattleya amethystoglossa

Cattleya rex (labiata var.), from Peru

Cattleya percivaliana

Cattleya trianaei

Cattleya schroederae

Cattleya mossiae

Cattleya gaskelliana

Cattleya 'Enid'

Cattleya labiata

Cattleya x hardyana alba

x Laeliocattleya bella

Cattleya warscewiczii alba (gigas alba)

Cattleya aurantiaca

Cattleya forbesii

Cattleya x mantinii

Cattleya x guatemalensis

Cattleya citrina

Cattleya luteola

Cattleya forbesii

Cattleya bowringiana

Cattleya skinneri

Cattleya lueddemanniana

Cattleya dowiana

Cattleya intermedia

Cattleya loddigesii (loddig. harrisoniae)

Cattleya schilleriana

Cattleya maxima

Cattleya walkeriana

Cattleya eldorado var. virginalis

Cattleya walkeriana

Cattleya elongata

Cattleya warscewiczii (gigas) alba 'Firmin Lambeau'

Cattleya lawrenceana

Cattleya leopoldii (guttata leopoldii)

Cattleya maxima

Cattleya granulosa

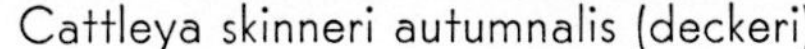

Cattleya skinneri autumnalis (deckeri)

Cattleya bicolor

Cattleya intermedia aquinii

Cattleya intermedia alba

Cattleya skinneri

Chysis x chelsonii

Chysis aurea

Chysis bractescens

Chysis laevis

Coelogyne sulphurea

Coelogyne sulphurea

Coelogyne cristata

Coelogyne massangeana

Coelogyne pandurata

Coelogyne flaccida

Coelogyne parishii

Coelogyne ovalis

Coelogyne huettneriana lactea

Coelogyne graminifolia

Coelogyne lawrenceana

Cochlioda **rosea**

Coelogyne carinata

Coelogyne cristata

Coelogyne massangeana

Coelogyne speciosa

Coelogyne dayana

Coelogyne sparsa

Coelogyne fimbriata (Vietnam)

Coelogyne dayana grandis

Cyrtorchis hamata (West Africa)

Coelogyne mooreana (Vietnam)

Coelogyne nitida (Thailand)

Coelogyne glandulosa (Nilghiris, So. India)

Coelogyne ochracea (High Himalaya)

Cyrtorchis arcuata variabilis

Coelogyne cristata, in hanging basket

Spiranthes "longibracteata"

Gomesa crispa ("Comparettia speciosa" in hort.)

Coelogyne meyeriana

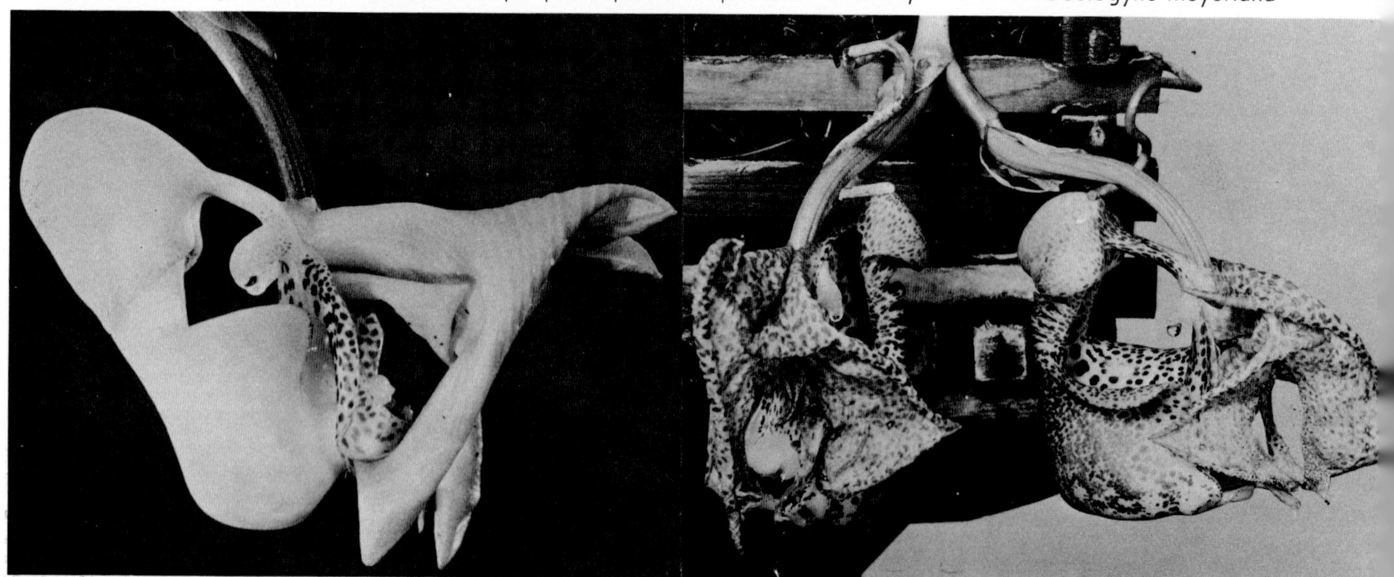

Coryanthes maculata

Coryanthes macrantha

Cochleanthes (Warscewiczella) discolor

Chloraea membranacea (Argentina)

Chysis bractescens (auréa var.)

Chiloschista lunifera

Cynorchis angustipetala

Cynorchis uncinata (Madagascar)

Comparettia falcata

Colax jugosus

Comparettia speciosa (Ecuador)

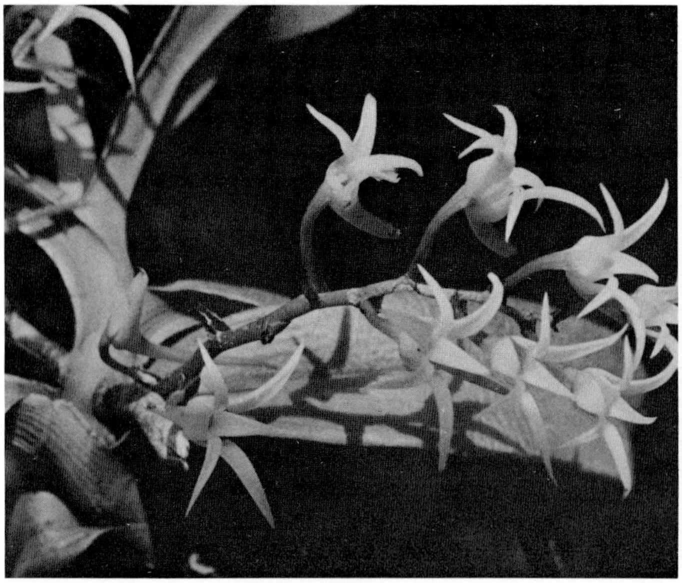

Cyrtorchis arcuata (South Africa)

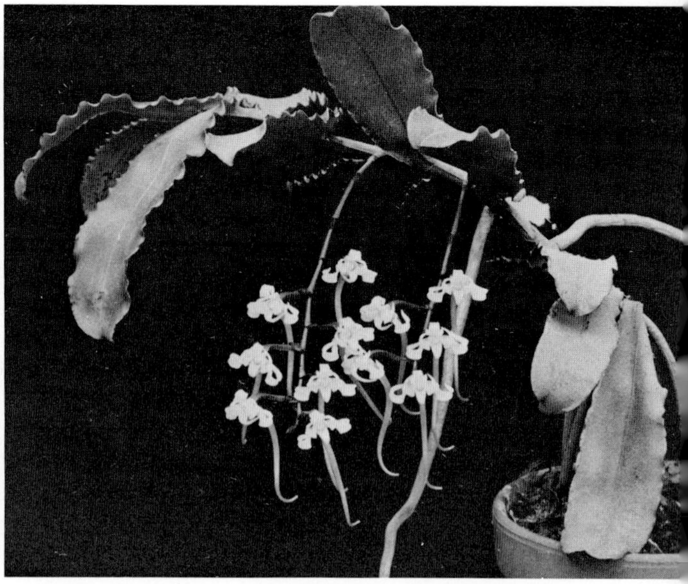

Cyrtorchis monteirae (Nigeria to Angola)

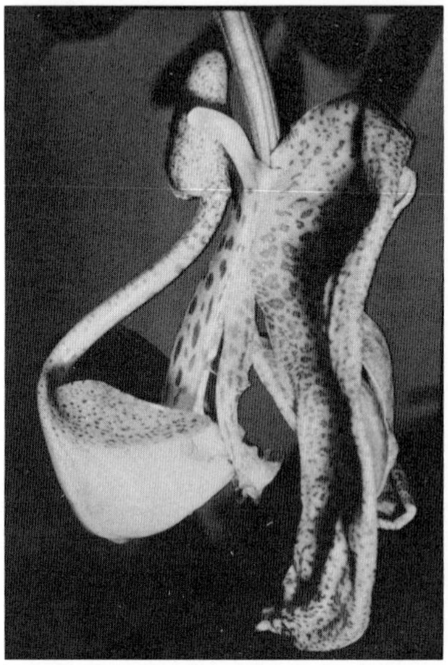

Coryanthes bicalcerata (Peru)

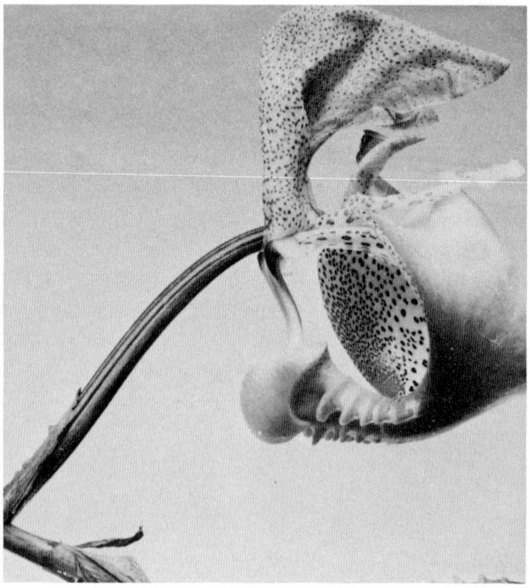

Coryanthes bungerothii

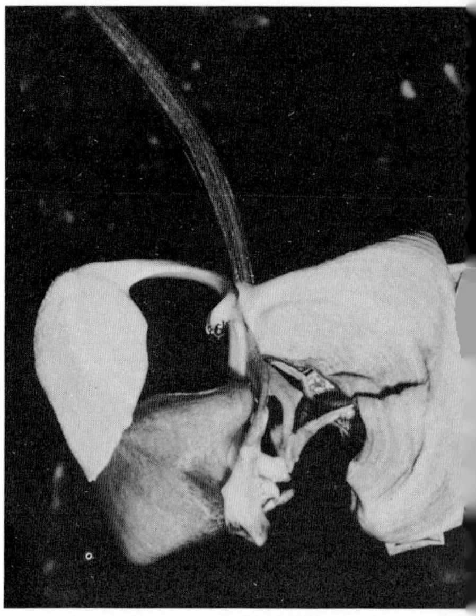

Coryanthes macrocorys (Amazon)

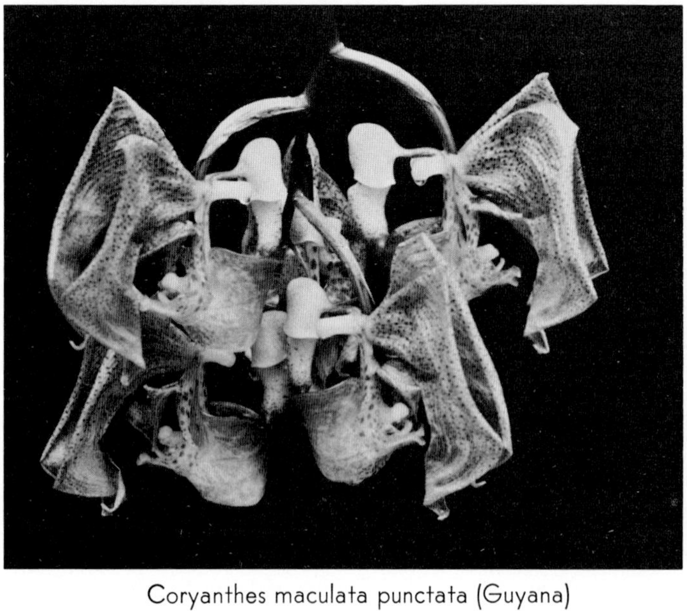

Coryanthes maculata punctata (Guyana)

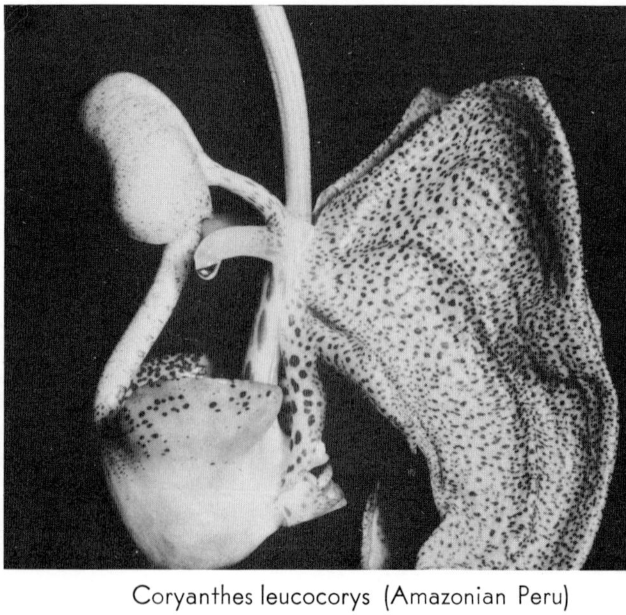

Coryanthes leucocorys (Amazonian Peru)

Cymbidiella humblotti

Cymbidiella rhodochila, growing on Platycerium

Cymbidiella rhodochila

Cryptophoranthus nigriflorus (Trop. America)

Cymbidiella humblotii (Madagascar)

Corymborchis flava (Panama)

Cryptanthemis slateri, "Underground orchid"

Cyrtopodium punctatum

Cycnoches ventricosum

Cycnoches chlorochilum

Cycnoches loddigesii

Cycnoches egertonianum, male flowers

Cycnoches egertonianum, female flowers

Cycnoches pentadactylum

Cycnoches loddigesii

Cycnoches ventricosum

Cycnoches chlorochilum

Cymbidium erythrostylum (Vietnam)

Cyperocymbidium x gammieanum (Sikkim)

Cymbidium ensifolium estriatum (Bot. Reg.)

Cymbidium ensifolium (Bot. Mag.)

Cymbidium ensifolium (Japan)

Cymbidium 'Bo-Peep' (Miniature)

Cymbidium lancifolium (India)

Cymbidium 'Gyokuchin Unge-Kwannon'

Cymbidium x alexanderi

Cymbidium canaliculatum

Cymbidium insigne

Cymbidium 'Moira'

Cymbidium aloifolium (simulans?)

Cymbidium 'Priscilla'

Cymbidium 'Flirtation' (miniature)

Cymbidium 'Candeur' var. Dos Pueblos (large white)

Cymbidium 'Madonna'

Cymbidium 'Peter Pan' (miniature)

Cymbidium 'Flirtation' (miniature)

Cymbidium 'Brentwood', with large green flowers, at New York Flower Show

Cymbidium 'Virginia Knight' Cymbidium 'Doris' Cymbidium 'Nikki'

Cymbidium eburneum

Cymbidium 'Pixie'

Cochleanthes discolor

Cymbidium mastersii — Cymbidium virescens angustifolium — Cymbidium **tigrinum**

Cymbidium pumilum albo-marginatum — Cymbidium virescens var. 'Teikwan' — Cymbidium virescens, in Japan

Cymbidium virescens angustifolium

Cymbidium pumilum 'Shuo-Lan' on Taiwan

ORCHIDACEAE: Coelogyne, Dendrobium, Epidendrum, Physurus, Pleione, Spiranthes, Xylobium

Coelogyne corymbosa

Physurus pictus

Dendrobium kingianum

Epidendrum coronatum (moyobambae)

Epidendrum endresii

Epidendrum cristatum

Xylobium powellii

Spiranthes cerina

Pleione formosana alba

Cypripedium japonicum

Cypripedium macranthum

Cypripedium calceolus pubescens

Cypripedium acaule

Cypripedium reginae

Cypripedium reginae

Cypripedium montanum

Cypripedium arietinum

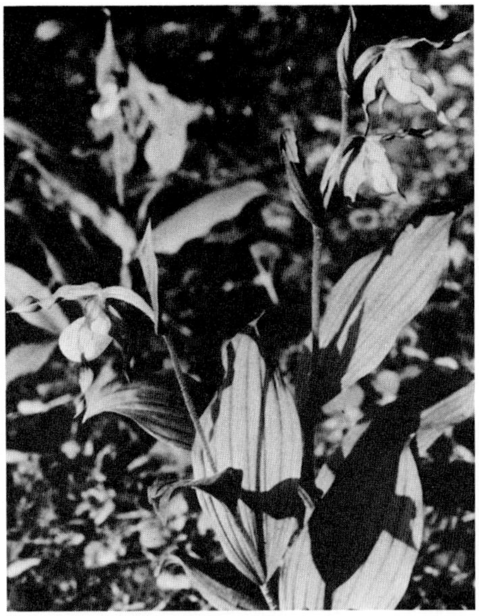

Cypripedium calceolus

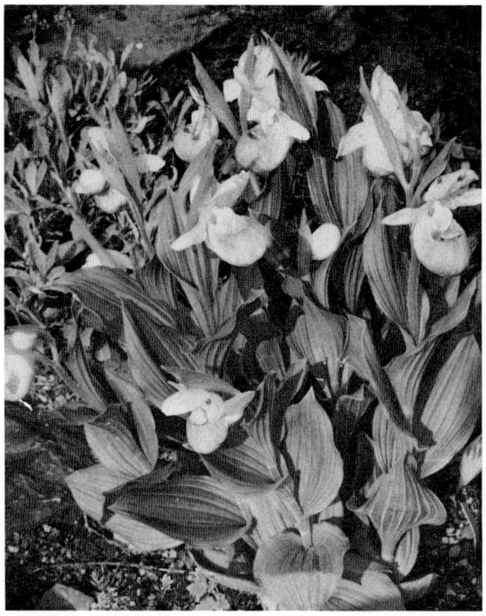

Cypripedium reginae (mandschuricum)

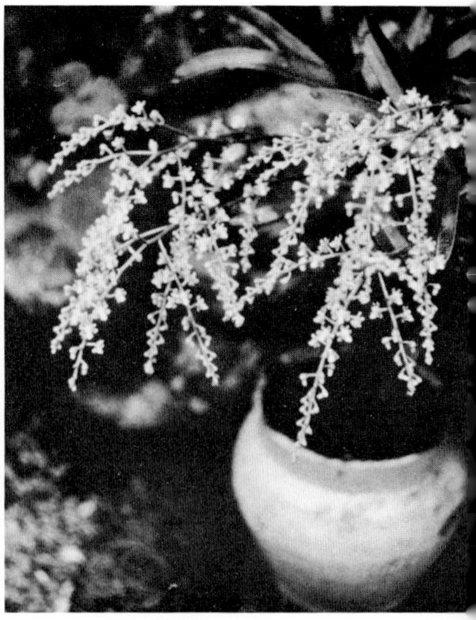

Cleisostoma paniculatum

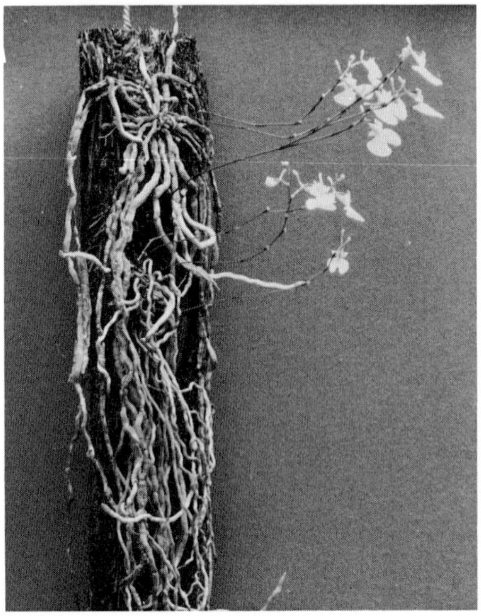

Dendrophylax varius (Cuba)

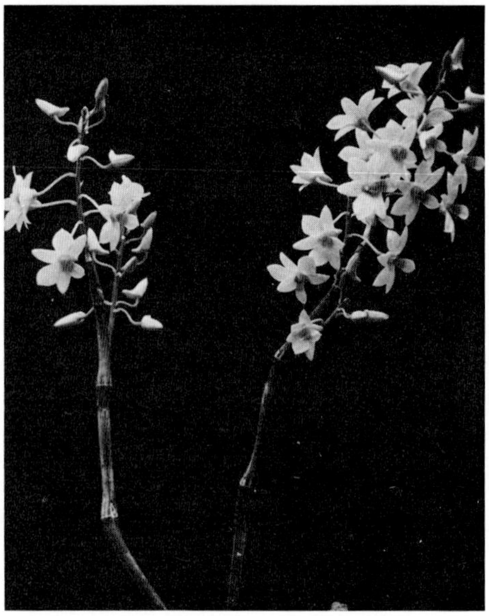

Dendrobium ovatum (India)

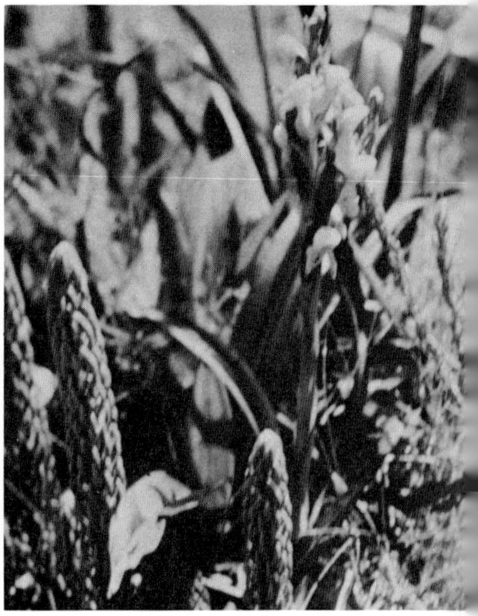

Disa stairsii (Kenya)

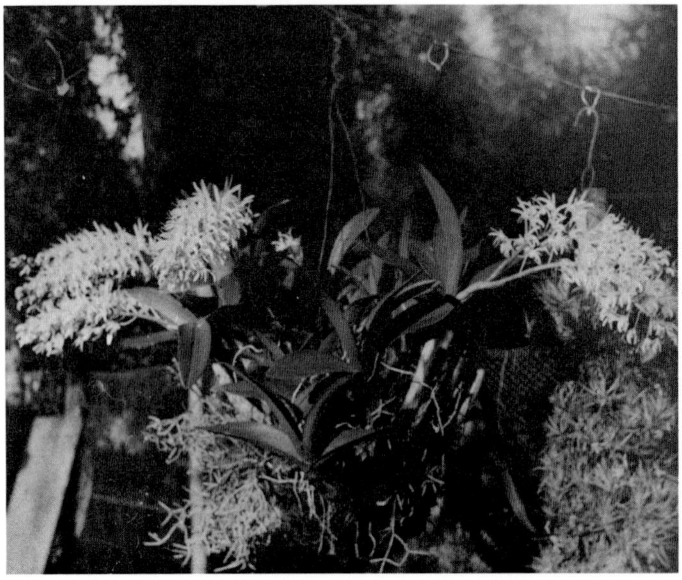

Dendrobium speciosum var. hillii (Australia)

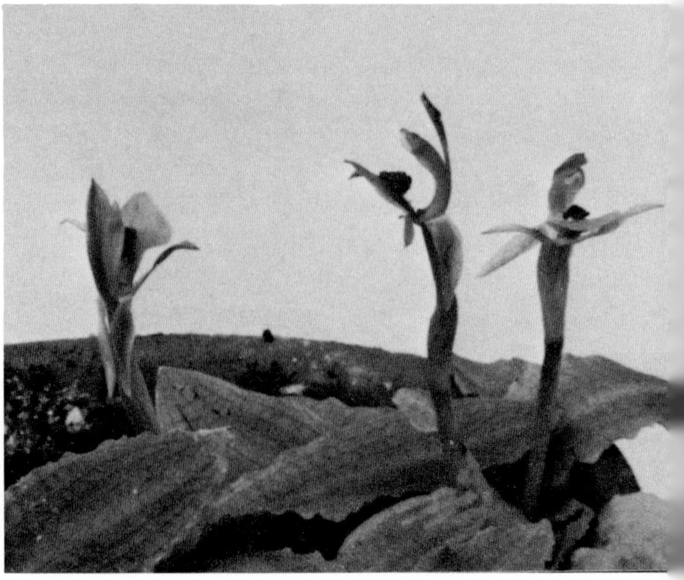

Chiloglottis trapeziformis, from Australia (J. Bogner, Munich)

Dendrobium nobile virginale, from India

Dendrobium macrophyllum, in Wantoat at 2000m, New Guinea

Dendrobium griffithianum, from Burma

Dendrobium densiflorum, at home in the Himalayas

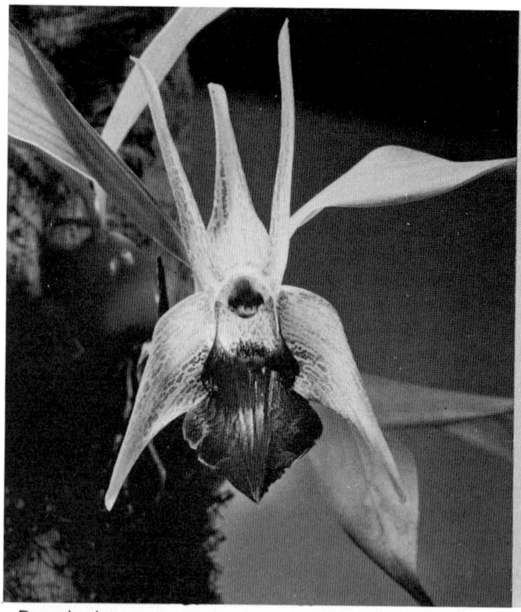

Dendrobium coelogyne, front view

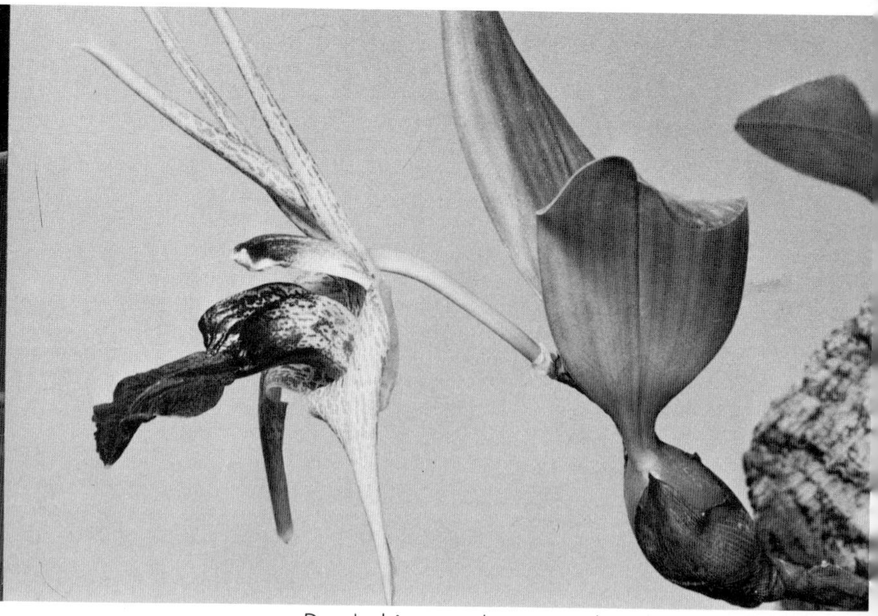

Dendrobium coelogyne, side view

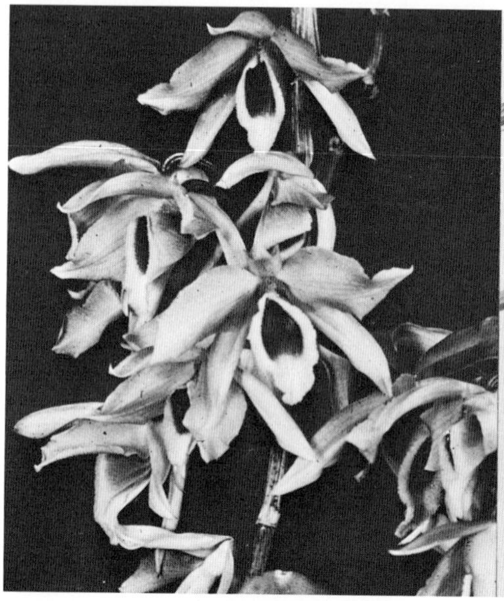

Dendrobium superbum

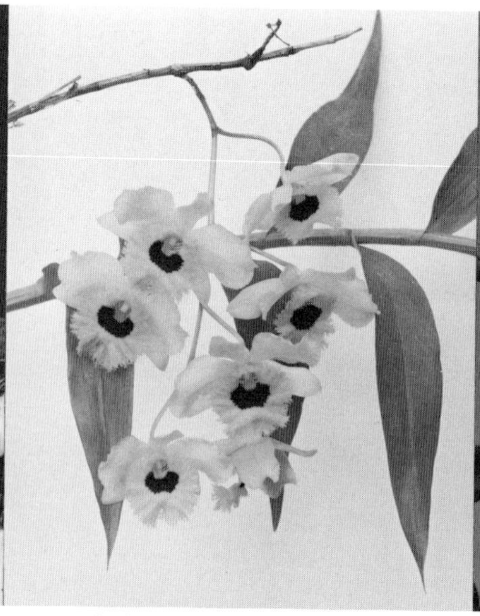

Dendrobium fimbriatum oculatum

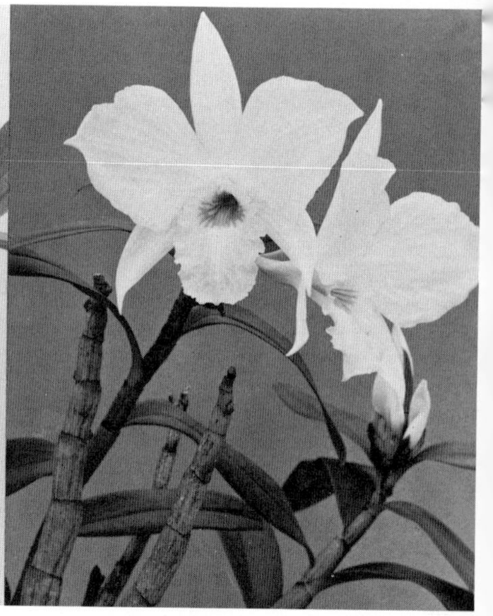

Dendrobium infundibulum

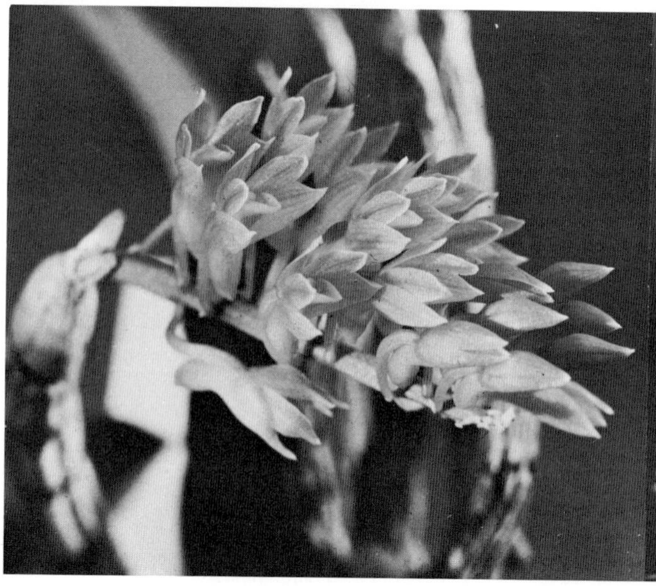

Dendrobium secundum

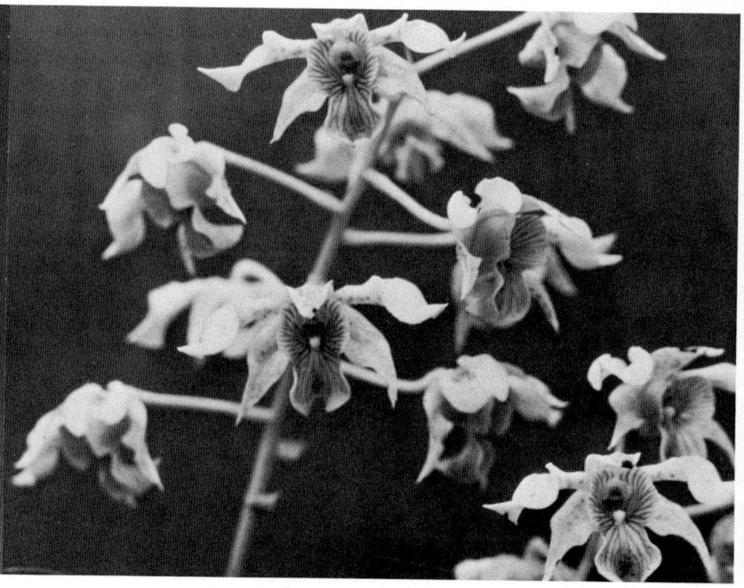

Dendrobium 'New Guinea'

Dendrobium densiflorum

Dendrobium thyrsiflorum

Diacrium bicornutum

Dendrobium chrysotoxum

Dendrobium phal. schroederianum

Dendrobium formosum

Dendrobium phalaenopsis

Dendrobium loddigesii

Dendrobium denudans

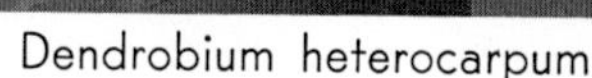

Dendrobium heterocarpum

Dendrobium pulchellum

Dendrobium farmeri

Dendrobium devonianum

Dendrobium atroviolaceum

Dendrobium dearei

Dendrobium moschatum

Dendrobium nobile

Dendrobium aggregatum (lindleyii)

Dendrobium pierardii

Dendrobium primulinum

Dendrobium sanderae

Disa uniflora

Hexisea bidentata

Dendrobium distichum

Dendrobium tetragonum biganteum

Dendrobium d'albertisii, in Papua

Dendrobium johnsoniae (macfarlanei), at Wantoat, New Guinea

Dendrobium x thwaitesiae

Dendrobium veratrifolium, in New Guinea

Dendrobium linguaeforme, in Australia

Dendrobium bullenianum (topaziacum), in the Philippines

Dendrobium capituliflorum, from New Guinea

Dendrobium phalaenopsis 'Pompadour', in Bangkok, Thailand

Dendrobium falconeri (Himalayan Region)

Dendrobium victoriae-reginae

Dendrobium 'Montrose'

Dendrobium uncinatum

Dendrobium bellatulum

Dendrobium sanderae parviflorum

Dendrobium lituiflorum

Dendrobium infundibulum var. jamesianum

Dendrobium macrophyllum, from Java

Dendrobium hercoglossum, miniature from Malaya

Dendrobium sophronitis, a miniature from New Guinea

Dendrobium formosum giganteum

Dendrobium delicatum

Dendrobium dearei (superbum)

Dendrobium finisterrae, from New Guinea

Dendrobium 'Shokei' (T.Everett, N.Y.Bot.Garden)

Dendrobium falcorostrum (Australia)

Dendrobium linguiforme, dwarf epiphyte from Queensland

Dendrobium transparens

Dendrobium speciosum

Dendrobium canaliculatum

Dendrobium senile (Thailand)

Dendrobium undulatum

Dendrobium ionoglossum

Dendrobium chrysanthum

Dendrobium delacouri

Dendrobium johnsoniae

Dendrobium teretifolium

Dendrobium teretifolium fairfaxii

Dendrobium gracilicaule

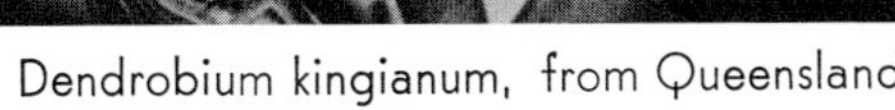

Dendrobium kingianum, from Queensland

Dendrobium victoriae-reginae (Philippines)

x Diacattleya 'Chastity'

x Diacattleya 'Fantasy'

Dendrochilum abbreviatum

Doritis pulcherrima

Cyrtopodium andersonii

Cyrtopodium punctatum

Dendrophylax (Polyrrhiza) lindenii

Diaphananthe fragrantissima

Dendrochilum cobbianum  | Dendrochilum (Platyclinis) glumaceum  | Dendrochilum filiforme

Elleanthus trilobatus  | Dendrochilum latifolium  | Eria ferruginea

x Epicattleya orpetii | **x Epiphronitis veitchii** | **Dendrochilum uncatum**

Epidendrum mathewsii (Perú)

Epidendrum serpens,(Venezuela)

Epidendrum candollei

Epidendrum spondiadum

Epidendrum gracile

Epidendrum lemorea (Perú)

Epidendrum costatum (Mexico)

Epidendrum falcatum

Epidendrum prismatocarpum

Epidendrum phoeniceum

Epidendrum vitellinum

Epidendrum ciliare

Epidendrum alatum

Epidendrum "rhynchophorum" hort.

Epidendrum pentotis

Epidendrum radiatum

Epidendrum ibaguense schomburgkia

Epidendrum **schumannianum**

Epidendrum auritum (boothii)

Epidendrum dichromum

Epidendrum mariae

Epidendrum falcatum

Epidendrum oncidioides

Epidendrum paniculatum

Epidendrum lanipes

Epidendrum fragrans

Epidendrum cochleatum

Epidendrum atropurpureum

Epidendrum erubescens

Epidendrum vespa (variegatum, crassilabium)

Epidendrum medusae

Epidendrum criniferum

Epidendrum conopseum

Epidendrum difforme

Epidendrum stamfordianum

Epidendrum floribundum

Epidendrum brassavolae

Epidendrum **aromaticum**

Epidendrum x o'brienianum

Epidendrum ibaguense (radicans)

Epidendrum tampense

Epidendrum campylostalix

Epidendrum ghiesbreghtianum

Epidendrum boothianum

Epidendrum lockhartioides

Epidendrum latilabrum

Epidendrum polybulbon (6cm pot)

Epidendrum peperomia (porpax)

Epidendrum nemorale

Epidendrum lindleyanum

Epidendrum boothii (Mexico, Cuba, Surinam)

Epidendrum cinnabarinum, in Brazil

Epidendrum circinatum

Epidendrum pseudepidendrum

Epidendrum bahamensis

Epidendrum pentotis (beyrodtianum)

Epidendrum dichromum (Bahia, Brazil)

Epidendrum (Encyclia) bracteatum (Brazil)

Epidendrum fragrans (West Indies)

Epidendrum x fragracarpum

Epidendrum leucochilum

Epidendrum lancifolium

Epidendrum polybulbon

Epidendrum faustum

Epidendrum nutans

Epidendrum pseudowallisii (Costa Rica)

Epidendrum (Nanodes) medusae (Ecuador)

Epidendrum pfavii

Epidendrum diffusum

Epidendrum condylochilum

Epidendrum skinneri

Epidendrum nocturnum

Epidendrum schlechterianum

Epidendrum alatum (Guatemala)

Epidendrum diguetii (Mexico)

Epidendrum eximium

Epidendrum coriifolium

Epidendrum allemanii

Epidendrum bicameratum (Mexico)

Epidendrum altissimum (Bahamas)

Epidendrum brassavolae (Guatemala)

Epidendrum sceptrum

Epidendrum campylostalix

Epidendrum wallisii (Panama)

Epidendrum pygmaeum

Epidendrum stamfordianum (Honduras)

Epidendrum rhynchophorum (Mexico)

x Epigoa 'Olivine'

x Epicattleya 'Ecstasy'

Eulophidium mackenii

Eulophidium ledienii

Elleanthus capitatus

x Epicattleya 'Gaiety'

Eulophia paiveana, in Kenya

Eulophia paiveana borealis

Earina mucronata, in New Zealand

Erythrodes nobilis 'Argyraea'

Erythrodes nobilis argyrocentrus

Epidendrum odoratissimum

Eulophia porphyroglossa

Epipactis palustris

Eurychone rothschildiana

Epipactis latifolia (helleborine) in Europe

Epigeneium (Dendrobium) cymbidioides (Java)

Eriopsis biloba

Eulophidium roseovariegatum

Epipactis gigantea

Eulophiella x rolfei

Eulophidium trinioides

Erycina echinata

Eulophia ovalis bainesii

Eulophia lurida

Eulophia hereroensis

Eulophia (Lissochilus) krebsii

Eulophia angolensis

Eulophia cucullata

Eulophia streptopetala

Eulophia speciosa

Eulophia schimperiana (Arabia)

Eria striolata hort.(javanica)

Eria cymbiformis

Eria javanica

Eria merrillii

Eria flava

Eurychone rothschildiana

Eria spicata (Himalayan Region)

Eria stricta (Burma to Vietnam)

Galeandra baueri

Gastrochilus calceolaris

Galeandra pubicentrum

Graphorkis lurida

Gongora atropurpurea

Goodyera procera

Gomesa sessilis

Gongora truncata

Gomesa crispa (Comparettia speciosa in hort

ophiella roempleriana (Madagascar) with Marcel Lecoufle, France

Gussonaea physophora (Microcoelia), epiphyte of Madagascar

Gongora (Acropera) armeniaca, from Nicaragua

Epigeneium lyonii, in Kew Gardens, London

Galeandra devoniana

Galeandra devoniana

Gongora quinquenervis (bufonia)

Gomesa crispa

Gastrochilus dasypogon

Grammatophyllum papuanum, in New Guinea

Goodyera hispida

Goodyera pubescens, the Rattlesnake orchid

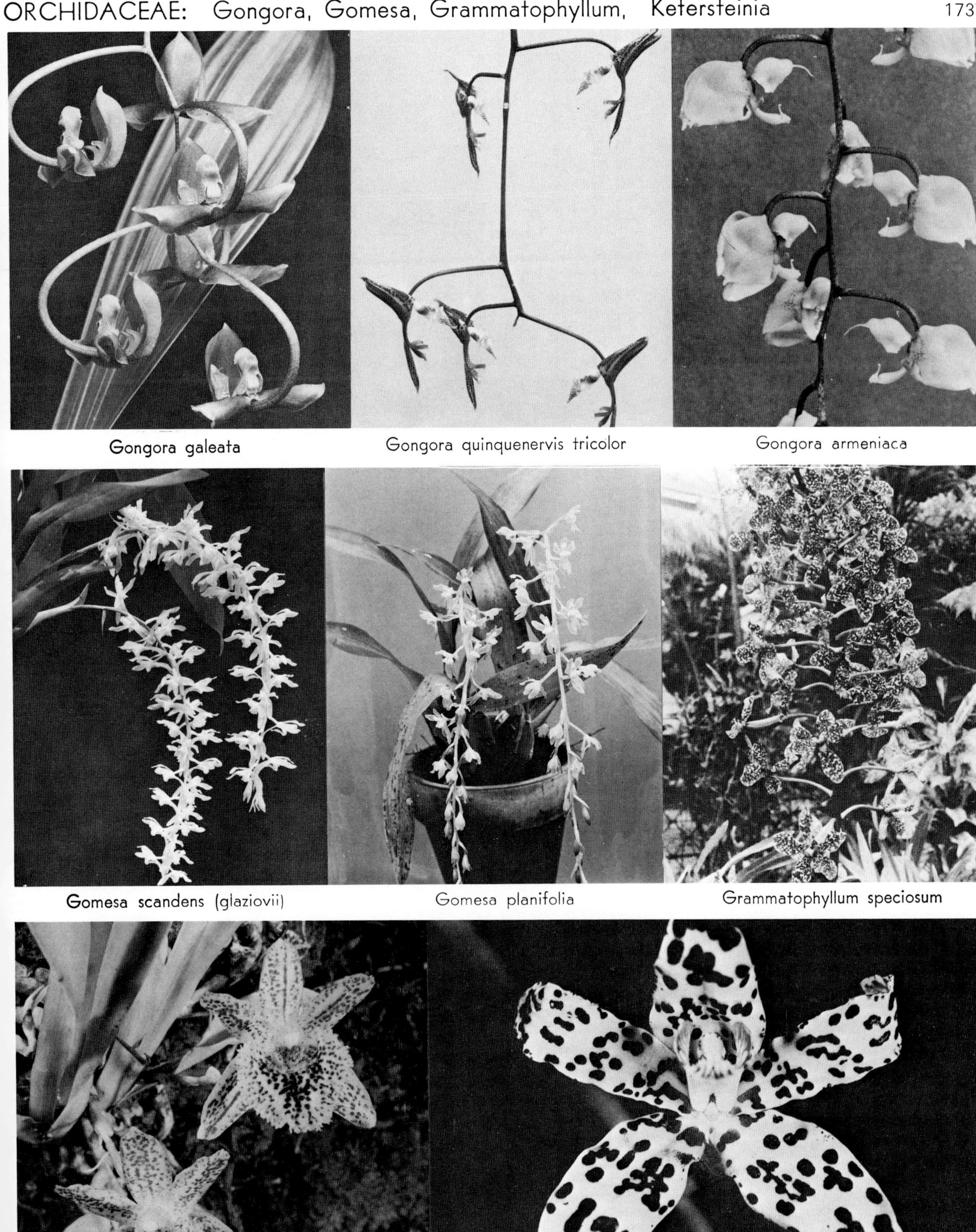

Gongora galeata

Gongora quinquenervis tricolor

Gongora armeniaca

Gomesa scandens (glaziovii)

Gomesa planifolia

Grammatophyllum speciosum

Kefersteinia tolimensis

Grammatophyllum scriptum grandiflorum

Gussonaea exilis* (Microcoelia) a leafless epiphyte

Grobya amherstiae, from Brazil

Comparettia speciosa (Ecuador)

Grammatophyllum measuresianum

Govenia utriculata

Flickingeria comata (Desmotrichum), (Sumatra to Samoa)

Grammatophyllum speciosum, the giant "Queen orchid"

Huntleya meleagris

Haemaria discolor dawsoniana

Helcia sanguinolenta

Ionopsis utricularioides

Habenaria keiskei

Gymnadenia conoptera (conopsea) in Arctic Lapland

Habenaria radiata, the Egret flower

Habenaria psycodes grandiflora

Habenaria psycodes

Habenaria hookeri

Habenaria blephariglottis

Habenaria bracteata

Habenaria rhodocheila

Habenaria (Platanthera) bifolia

Habenaria lacera

Epidendrum pseudowallisii (Costa Rica)

Habenaria antennifera

Haemaria discolor dawsoniana nigricans

Houlletia lansbergii (Costa Rica)

Houlletia wallisii, from Colombia

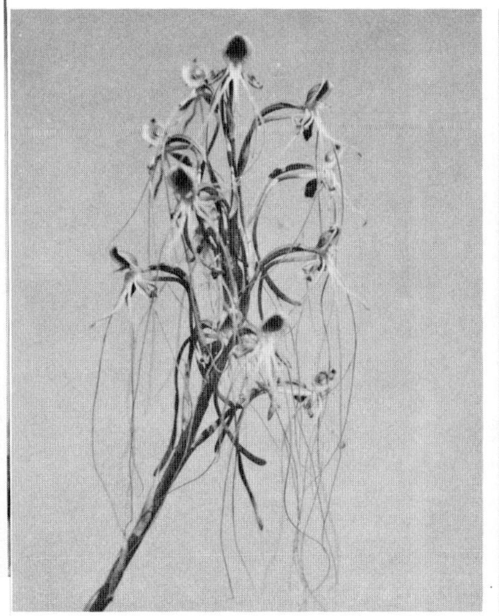
Habenaria kraenzliniana (Transvaal)

Habenaria nivea (Platanthera)

Habenaria tridactylites (Tenerife)

Lepanthes pulchella (Jamaica)

Lepanthopsis astrophora (Venezuela)

Lepanthes wagneri (Venezuela)

Liparis atropurpurea

Liparis elata

Leptotes unicolor (Brazil)

Leptotes bicolor alba (Paraguay)

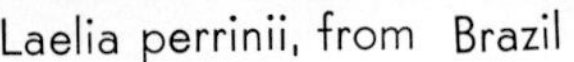

Laelia perrinii, from Brazil

Laelia speciosa (majalis), in Queretaro, Mexico

sochilus hebdingianus (Madagascar)

x Laeliocattleya bella

Laelia x finckeniana

Laelia autumnalis (Mexico)

Laelia tenebrosa (Bahia)

Grammangis ellisii, epiphytic in Madagascar

Laelia x harpophylla

Laelia (Cattleya) dormaniana

Laelia rubescens

Laelia (Brassocattleya) lindleyana

Laelia flava

Laelia autumnalis

Laelia pumila

x Laeliocattleya canhamiana alba

Laelia purpurata

x Laeliocattleya hassallii alba 'Majestica'

x Laeliocattleya 'Queen Mary'

Laelia gouldiana

Laelia superbiens

Laelia crispa

Laelia x finckeniana

Laelia purpurata alba

Laelia jongheana

Laelia grandis

x Laeliocattleya elegans

Laelia albida

Laelia lundii

Laelia cinnabarina

Laelia anceps

Leptotes bicolor

Haemaria discolor dawsoniana

Liparis loeselii

Liparis longipes

Liparis neglecta

Lycaste crinita (Mexico)

Lycaste schilleriana (Colombia)

Lycaste candida

Lycaste dowiana

Lycaste micheliana

Lockhartia pallida (Trinidad) (T.Everett)

Lepanthes wagneri, from Venezuela (Don Richardson)

Lycaste deppei

Lycaste aromatica

Lycaste virginalis alba (skinneri alba)

Lycaste gigantea

Lycaste cruenta

Lycaste macrophylla

Lycaste virginalis (skinneri)

Lycaste xytriophora

Lycaste macrophylla

Lockhartia lunifera

Lockhartia robusta

Lockhartia acuta

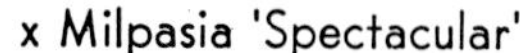

x Milpasia 'Spectacular'

x Milpasia 'Gold Star'

Mesospinidium warscewiczii

Masdevallia veitchiana 'Grandiflora'

Masdevallia infracta purpurea

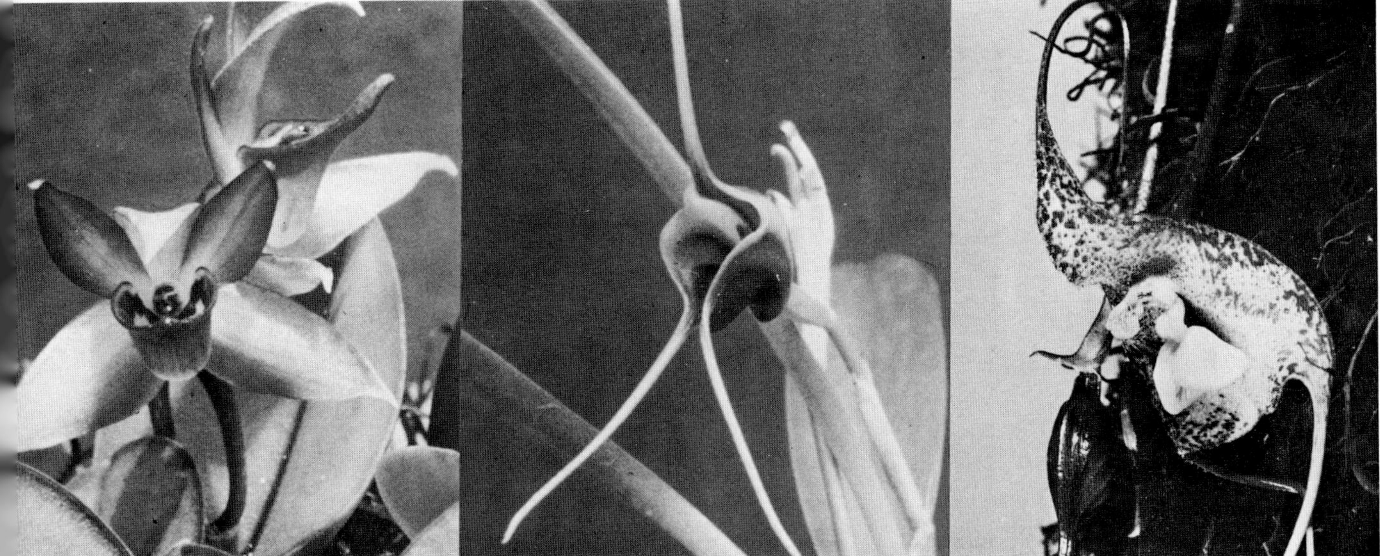

Meiracyllium trinasutum

Masdevallia infracta

Masdevallia bella

Masdevallia x measuresiana

Masdevallia tovarensis

Macodes petola

Macodes petola (inflor.)

Macodes sanderianus

Malaxis lowii

Malaxis calophylla

Masdevallia tovarensis

Masdevallia horrida

Masdevallia grandiflora (Ecuador)

Masdevallia floribunda (Mexico) (Don Richardson)

Masdevallia platycentra

Masdevallia schroederiana

Masdevallia ephippium

Masdevallia ecordata (Chiriqui Highlands)

Masdevallia paranense (Ecuador) (Don Richardson)

Masdevallia leontoglossa (Venezuela)

Masdevallia liliputana, a miniature from Brazil

Masdevallia carderi

Masdevallia x 'Doris'

Masdevallia erythrochaete

Masdevallia simula (Central America)

Masdevallia houtteana (Colombia) (Don Richardson)

Masdevallia deorsa, from Colombia (Don Richardson)

Masdevallia erythrochaete (Andes of Colombia)

Megaclinium purpureorhachis, "Cobra orchid" from Zaire

x Miltassia 'Flower Drum' (T.Everett, N.Y.Bot.Garden)

Masdevallia stroebelii (Andean region)

Masdevallia attenuata, a miniature from Costa Rica

Masdevallia wagenerana

Masdevallia davisii

Masdevallia weberbaueri (Don Richards

Masdevallia laucheana (attenuata) (Peru)

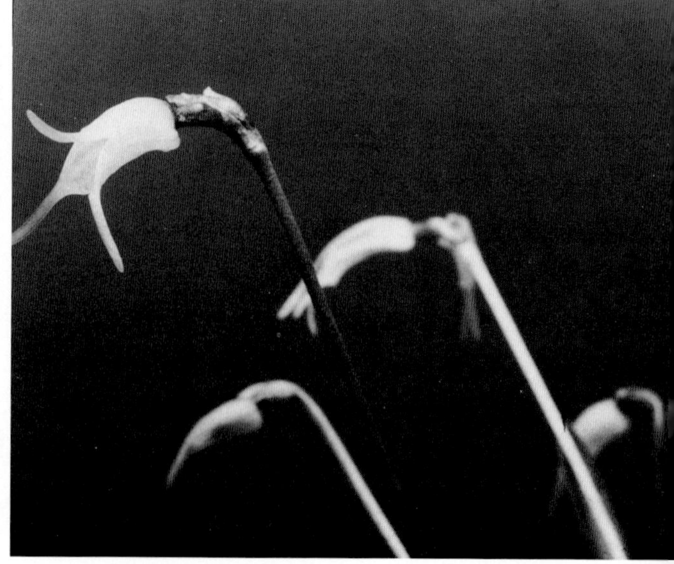

Masdevallia chontalensis, from Chiriqui, Costa Rica

Masdevallia militaris (ignea)

Masdevallia civilis

Masdevallia reichenbachii

Masdevallia chimaera

Masdevallia veitchiana

Masdevallia bella

Maxillaria porphyrostele

Masdevallia pandurilabia

Maxillaria juergensii (Rio Grande do Sul)

Maxillaria triloris in hort.(luteo-alba)

Maxillaria grandiflora

Maxillaria lepidota

Maxillaria rufescens

Nervilea renschiana, in Madagascar

Maxillaria brunnea

Maxillaria seidelii (Brazil)

Macradenia multiflora

Maxillaria sanguinea

Maxillaria picta

Maxillaria tenuifolia

Maxillaria sanderiana

Maxillaria ochroleuca

Mystacidium (Angraecum) distichum

Maxillaria luteo-alba

Maxillaria reichenheimii

Maxillaria variabilis

Maxillaria densa (Ornithidium)

Maxillaria elatior

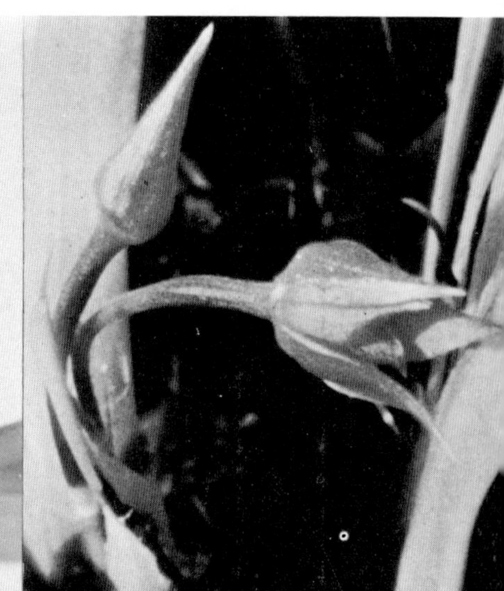

Maxillaria coccinea (Ornithidium)

Miltonia candida 'Grandiflora'

x Miltonidium 'Lustre'

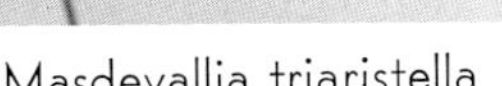

Masdevallia triaristella

Masdevallia militaris

Masdevallia elephanticeps

Malaxis spicata

Malaxis soulei Malaxis ocreata (Mexico)

Microstylis discolor (Malaxis)

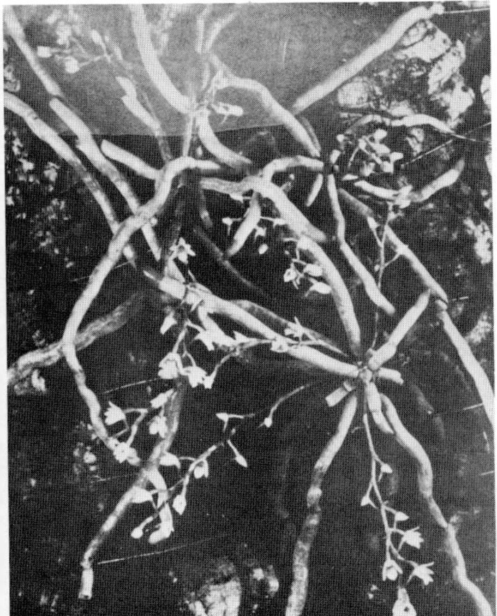

Gussonaea (Microcoelia) guyoniana

Mediocalcar 'New Guinea species'

Gussonaea (Microcoelia) physophora

Miltonia spectabilis

Miltonia laevis

x Miltassia 'Cartagena' (Moir)

Miltonia x bluntii

Miltonia schroederiana

Meiracyllium gemma

Menadenium labiosum (Venezuela)

Mendoncella grandiflora (Mountains of Central America)

Miltonia 'Ketha'

Miltonia roezlii, a 'Pansy orchid'

Miltonia 'Liberte'

x Miltonidium 'Aristocrat'

Miltonia 'Storm'

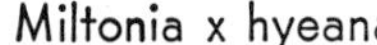

Miltonia x hyeana

Miltonia x gattonensis

Miltonia 'Marietta Armacost'

Miltonia warscewiczii

Miltonia candida

Miltonia spectabilis moreliana

Miltonia flavescens

Miltonia spectabilis

Miltonia regnellii

Miltonia phalaenopsis

Miltonia vexillaria

Miltonia vexillaria 'Volunteer'

Megaclinium (Bulbophyllum) falcatum

Mormodes igneum (cartonii?)

Mormodes colossus

x Odontonia 'Vesta'

Mormodes variabilis

Octomeria tunicola

Notylia xyphophorus

Neottia nidus avis

Neobenthamia gracilis

x Odontioda 'Dolcoath'

x Odontioda 'Lola'

Notylia lyrata (Brazil)

Notylia bungerothii

Notylia sagittifera (Brazil)

Octomeria alboviolacea

Ophrys lutea minor, on Delos

Orchis papilionacea, on Rhodes

Ophrys fusca (South Europe)

Orchis sambucina

Ophrys speculum, on Rhodes

Odontoglossum triumphans

Odontoglossum cervantesii roseum

Odontoglossum laeve reichenheimii

Odontoglossum uroskinneri

Odontoglossum insleayi

Odontoglossum maculatum

Odontoglossum cristatum

Odontoglossum schlieperianum

Odontoglossum convallarioides

Odontoglossum chiriquense (coronarium)

Odontoglossum pulchellum (Guatemala)

Odontoglossum pendulum

x Odontioda 'Wey'

x Odontioda 'Charlette'

Odontoglossum warscewiczii weltonii (T.Everett)

x Odontocidium 'Surprise' (Don Richardson)

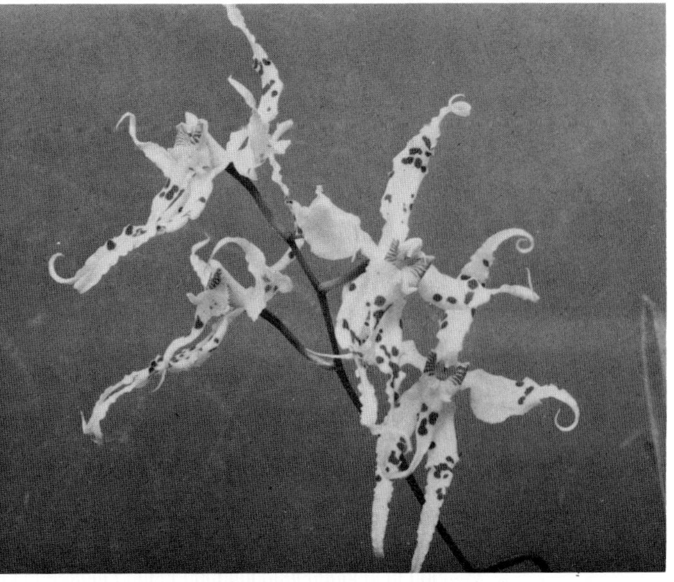
Odontoglossum cirrhosum (Ecuador)

Odontoglossum bictoniense

Odontoglossum rossii

Odontoglossum laeve

Odontoglossum citrosmum album (pendulum)

Odontoglossum cordatum

Odontoglossum luteo-purpureum

Odontoglossum krameri

Odontoglossum pulchellum

Odontoglossum oerstedii

Odontoglossum crispum

Odontoglossum grande

Odontoglossum 'Elise'

Odontoglossum x alispum (crispum hyb.)

Ornithocephalus inflexus (tonduzii) (Honduras)

Oncidium 'Doctor Schragen' (Moir-Honolulu)

x Odontioda 'Gloriosa'

Ornithophora radicans

x Opisanda 'May Kawanashi' (Hawaii hybrid)

Ornithocephalus grandiflorus (Brazil)

Ornithidium (Maxillaria) sophronitis (Venezuela)

Odontoglossum constrictum

Odontoglossum citrosmum

Odontoglossum cariniferum

Oncidium microchilum

Oncidium phalaenopsis

Oncidium sphacelatum

Oncidium pulchellum

Oncidium sphegiferum

Oncidium onustum

Oncidium ornithorhynchum majus (Central America)

Oncidium meirax (Brazil, Venezuela)

Oncidium limminghei

Oncidium maculatum

Oncidium ghiesbrechtianum

Oncidium sarcodes

Oncidium cucullatum macrochilum

Oncidium lankesteri

Oncidium planipes hort.(T.Everett, New York Bot.Garden)

Oncidium 'Helen Brown' (Moir-Honolulu)

Oncidium "alatum" in hort. (Roehrs)

Oncidium pubes (Brazil)

Oncidium cebolleta

Oncidium globuliferum (Costa Rica, Perú)

Oncidium pumilum (Paraguay)

Oncidium carthaginense

Oncidium uniflorum longipes

Oncidium cheirophorum

Oncidium wentworthianum

Oncidium sarcodes

Oncidium tetrapetalum

Oncidium concolor

Oncidium cebolleta

Oncidium triquetrum (6cm pot)

Oncidium haematochilum

Oncidium variegatum

Oncidium varicosum rogersii

Oncidium flexuosum

Oncidium leucochilum

Oncidium lanceanum

Oncidium forbesii

Oncidium pusillum

Oncidium picturatum, flowering at the Montreal Botanic Garden

Oncidium hastatum

Oncidium suscephalum

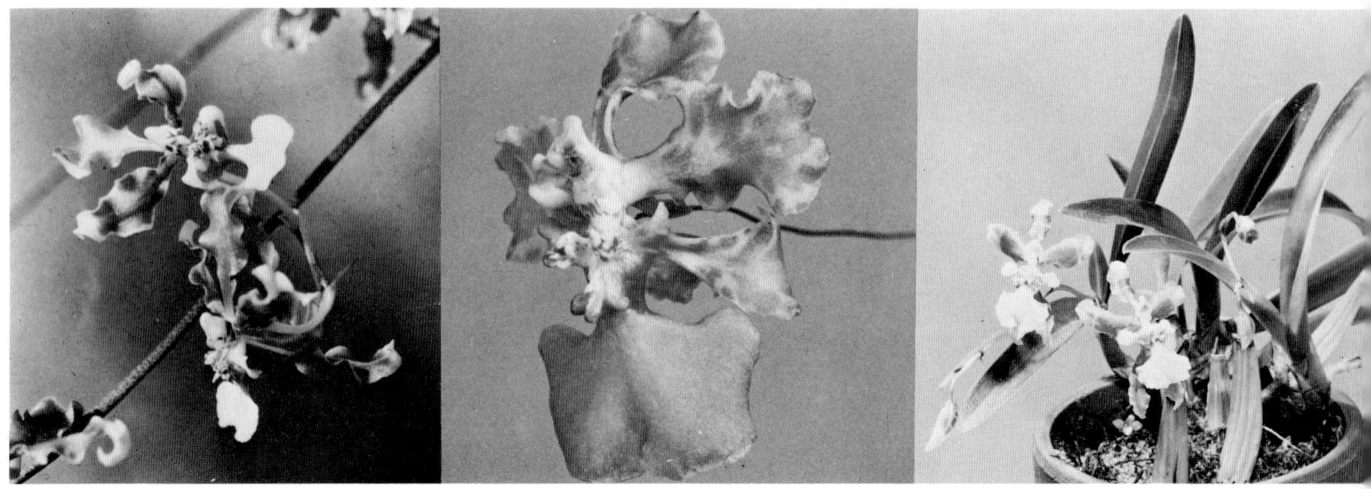

Oncidium pardinum

Oncidium luridum

Oncidium uniflorum

Oncidium crispum
Oncidium kramerianum
Oncidium papilio
Oncidium ornithorhynchum
Oncidium stipitatum
Oncidium 'Java'
Oncidium pulvinatum
Oncidium altissimum
Oncidium powellii

Oncidium splendidum

Oncidum macranthum

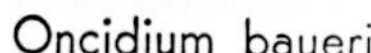

Oncidium baueri

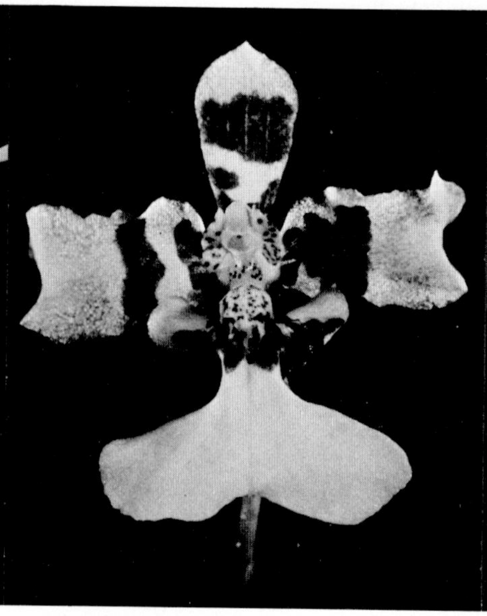

Oncidium excavatum

Oncidium gardneri

Oncidium sphacelatum

Oncidium ampliatum majus

Oncidium lamelligerum

Oncidium powellii

Oncidium carthaginense

Oncidium isthmi

Oncidium falcipetalum

Oncidium jonesianum

Oncidium gardneri

Oncidium phymatochilum

Oncidium cavendishianum

Oncidium panamense

Oncidium tigrinum

Oncidium pulvinatum

Oncidium ansiferum

Oncidium aurisasinorum

Oncidium jonesianum

Oncidium ampliatum

Orchis militaris

Ophrys muscifera

x Luisanda 'Uniwai'

Otochilus fusca

Ornithocephalus dolabratus

Otochilus fusca

Orchis elata

Orchis spectabilis, the Woodland orchid

Ornithochilus fuscus

Peristeria guttata

Ornithocephalus bicornis

Ornithophora (Sigmatostalix) radicans

Ornithocephalus cochleariformis

Pelexia (Spiranthes) maculata

Pelexia maculata

Paphiopedilum x maudiae

Paphiopedilum rothschildianum

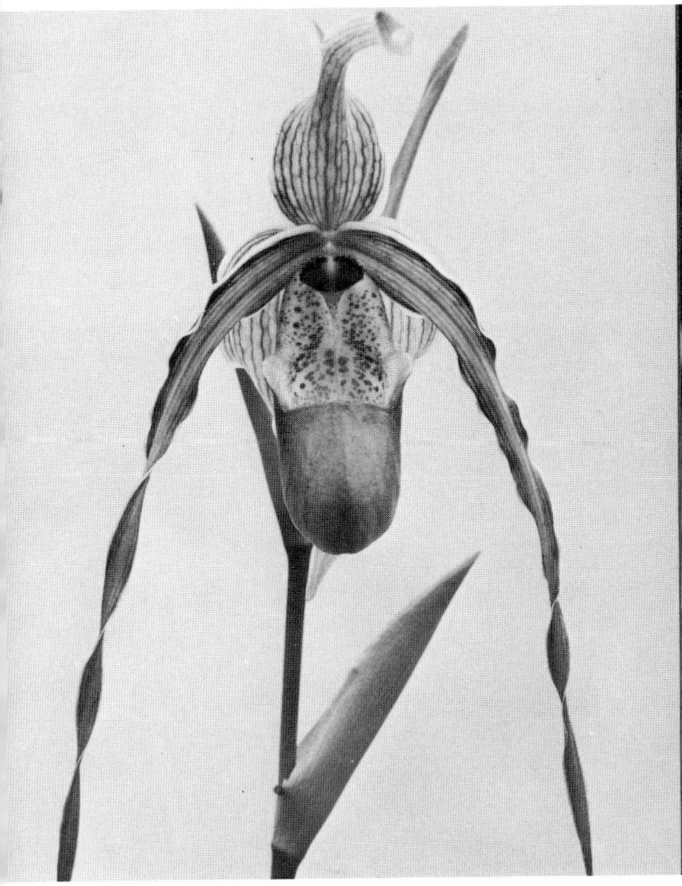

Phragmipedium x grande

Phragmipedium (Selenipedium) caudatum

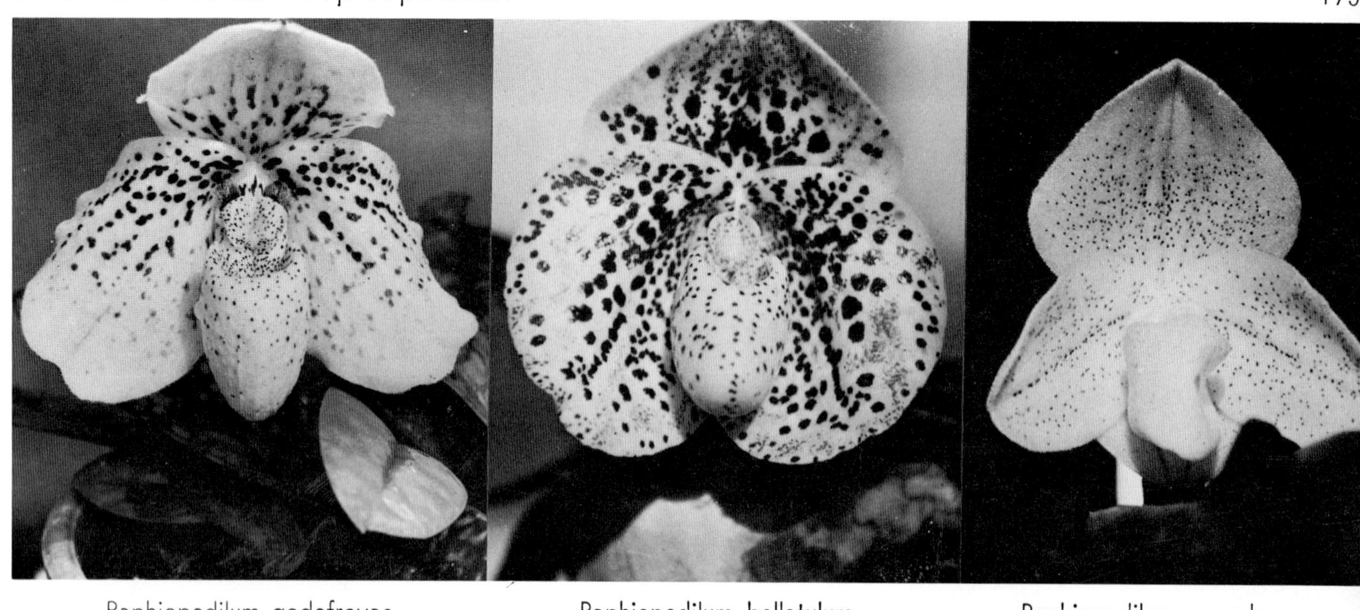

Paphiopedilum godefroyae

Paphiopedilum bellatulum

Paphiopedilum concolor

Paphiopedilum lawrenceanum

Paphiopedilum fairrieanum

Paphiopedilum x maudiae

Paphiopedilum villosum

Paphiopedilum niveum

Paphiopedilum exul, in Thailand

Paphiopedilum insigne 'Harefield Hall'

Paphiopedilum insigne

Paphiopedilum insigne 'Sanderae'

Paphiopedilum venustum

Paphiopedilum x leeanum

Paphiopedilum x nitens

Paphiopedilum x leyburnense **magnificum**

Paphiopedilum x harrisianum superbum

Paphiopedilum callosum splendens

Paphiopedilum x aureum 'Surprise'

Paphiopedilum x leeanum clinkaberryanum

Paphiopedilum x harrisianum 'C. S. Ball'

Paphiopedilum 'Albion'

Paphiopedilum 'Olivia'

Paphiopedilum bellatulum

Paphiopedilum insigne 'Striatifolium'

Phragmipedium parishii

Phragmipedium x grande

Phragmipedium caudatum

Paphiopedilum delenatii

Paphiopedilum lowii

Paphiopedilum curtisii

Paphiopedilum (Cypripedium) insigne

Paphiopedilum chamberlainianum

Paphiopedilum x gaudianum

Phragmipedium x dominianum

Paphiopedilum lowii

Paphiopedilum spicerianum

Paphiopedilum callosum

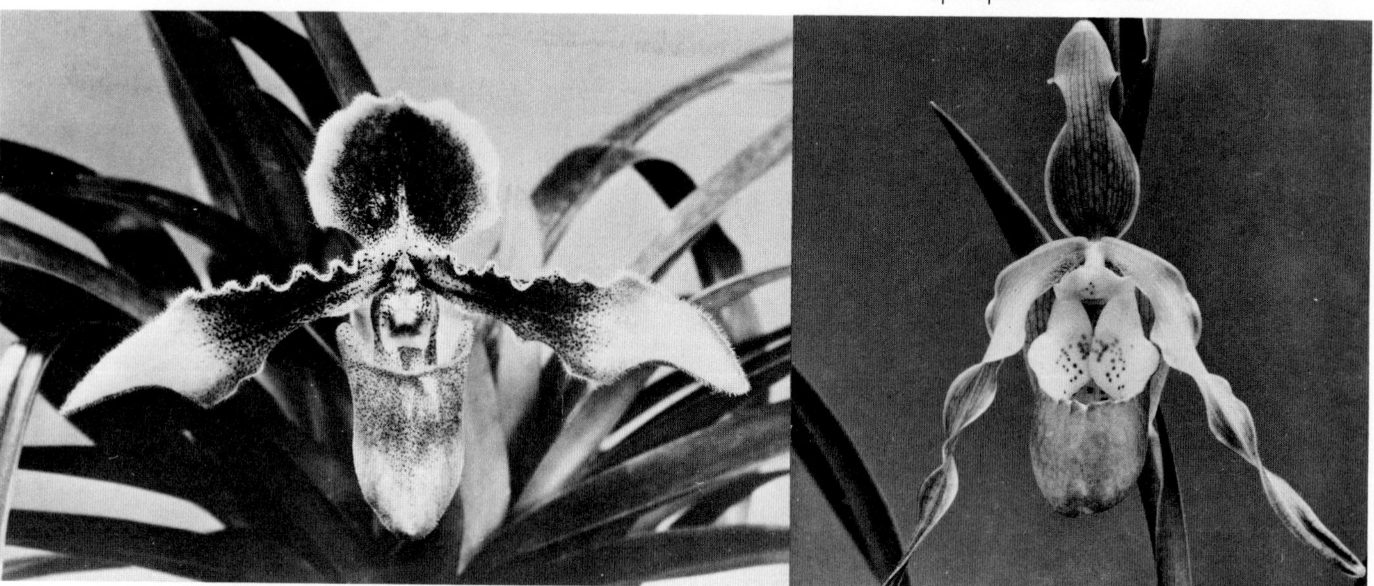
Paphiopedilum hirsutissimum

Phragmipedium x sedenii

Paphiopedilum bullenianum, from Borneo

Phragmipedium (Selenipedium) schroederae (T.Everett, N.Y.Bot.G.)

Phragmipedium klotzscheanum, in Guayana habitat

Paphiopedilum insigne punctatissimum, from the Himalayas

Paphiopedilum philippinense (Mindanao)

Paphiopedilum (Cypripedium) dayanum (Borneo)

Paphiopedilum sukhakulii (Thailand)

Paphiopedilum praestans (New Guinea)

Paphiopedilum hookerae

Phragmipedium longifolium (Costa Rica, Colombia)

Paphiopedilum godefroyae var. leucochilum

Phaius tankervilleae (grandifolius)

Phaius maculatus

Phaius wallichii

Peristeria elata

x Phaiocalanthe 'Stanny'

Phragmipedium 'Brysa'

Phragmipedium longifolium roezlii

Phragmipedium x calurum

Phalaenopsis schilleriana, from the Philippines (Roehrs 1907)

Phalaenopsis lueddemanniana alba (T.Everett, N.Y. Bot.G.)

Phalaenopsis stuartiana (Sumatra)

Phalaenopsis sumatrana purpurata

Phalaenopsis 'Doris'

Phalaenopsis violacea

Phalaenopsis 'Golden Chief'

Phalaenopsis amabilis formosana, at Sun-Moon Lake, Taiwan

Phalaenopsis gigantea, from Borneo (Bogner)

Phalaenopsis Esmeralda (Doritis pulcherrima)

Phalaenopsis 'Rosy Pam' (Vaughn), at St. Petersburg, Florida

Phalaenopsis cornu-cervi

Phalaenopsis kunstleri

Phalaenopsis amabilis formosana, in Taiwa

Phalaenopsis sanderiana 'Burgeffii'

Phalaenopsis sanderiana 'Wuerzburg Self'

Phalaenopsis 'Star of Rio'

Phalaenopsis x intermedia

Phalaenopsis x rothschildiana

Phalaenopsis 'Helle'

Phalaenopsis parishii lobbii (bot. Grafia)

Phalaenopsis schilleriana

Phalaenopsis mannii

Phalaenopsis lueddemanniana

Phalaenopsis buyssoniana

Phalaenopsis schilleriana

Phalaenopsis amabilis 'Summit Snow'

Phalaenopsis amabilis

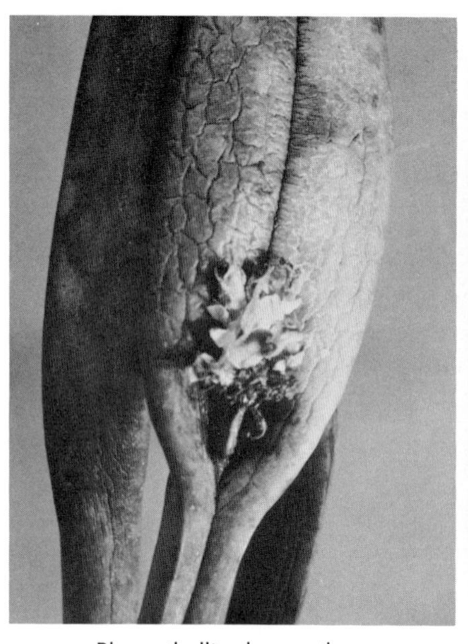

Pleurothallis chrysantha

Pleurothallis wendlandiana

Pleurothallis ophiocephala

Pleurothallis schiedei (Chiapas, So. Mexico)

Pleurothallis calyptrosepala

Pleurothallis immersa

Pleurothallis flexuosa

Pleurothallis sertularioides

Pholidota imbricata, "Rattlesnake orchid"

Phaius tankervilleae, the "Nun's orchid"

Pleurothallis carnosifolia (T. Everett, N.Y. Bot. G.)

Pleurothallis strupifolia (Brazil)

Pleurothallis cogniauxiana

Pleurothallis ghiesbreghtiana

Pleurothallis grandis

Pleurothallis tuerckheimii

Pleurothallis powellii

Pleurothallis leucantha

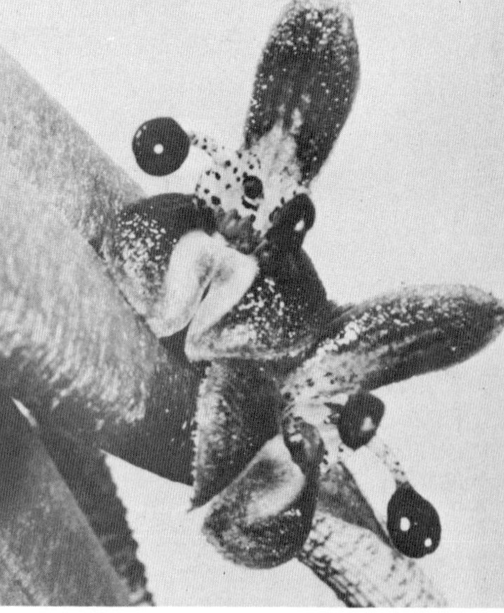

Pleurothallis hystrix

Pleurothallis loranthophylla

Pleurothallis saurocephala Pleurothallis cardiothallis Pleurothallis tribuloides

Pleurothallis longissima Pleurothallis homalantha

Pterostylis banksii, in New Zealand **Pterostylis curta** Ponthieva maculata

Polystachya foliosa (E.Hahn)

Polystachya pubescens

Polystachya cultriformis

Polystachya vulcanica

Polystachya tesselata

Polystachya laxiflora

Polystachya ornata (Colombia)

Pholidota articulata

Rodrigueziopsis microphyta (Brazil

Pescatorea cerina (Chiriqui, Costa Rica)

Peristeria pendula (Panama to Guyana)

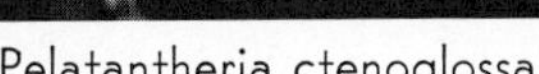

Pelatantheria ctenoglossa

Ponera striata

Peristeria guttata

Porphyrostachys pilifera (Andes of Ecuador)

Paphinia cristata (Colombia to Guianas)

Pleione praecox (wallichiana)

Pleione delaveyi

Pleione pogonioides

Pterygodium catholicum, in South Africa

Plectrophora cultrifolia

Pholidota pallida

Podangis dactyloceras

Pterostylis nutans

Promenaea citrina

x Renanstylis 'Queen Emma'

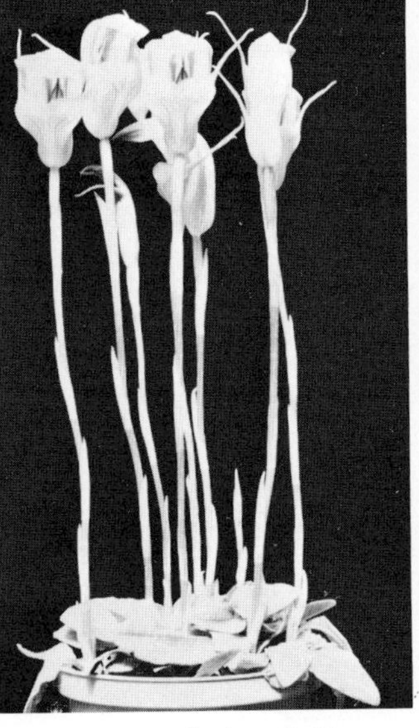
Pterostylis baptistii

Phymatidium tillandsioides

Physosiphon lindleyi (tubatus) (Guatemala)

Platystele ornata, a Pygmy orchid

Polystachya virginea, in Uganda

Polystachya stricta, in the Congo

Polystachya bracteosa

Polystachya cucullata

Polystachya golungensis, in Kenya

Polystachya transvaalensis

Polystachya adansoniae

Polystachya puberula

Polystachya leonensis

Pescatorea cerina

Polystachya stuhlmannii

Pholidota imbricata

Polystachya latilabris

Polystachya luteola

Polystachya bicarinata

Physosiphon tubatus

Polycycnis barbata

Trichoglottis brachiata

Renanthera storiei

Renanthera imschootiana

Restrepia xanthophthalma

Rodriguezia venusta

Rodriguezia secunda

Renanthera monachica

Rodriguezia secunda

Rodriguezia teuscheri (Ecuador)

Rhynchostylis coelestis (Thailand)

Rodriguezia speciosa

Rodriguezia batemanii

Rodriguezia compacta

x Renantanda 'Seminole'

Restrepia lankesteri (Don Richardson)

x Renanthopsis 'Jan Goo'

Renanthera 'Tom Thumb'

Renanthera storiei

Renanthera storiei

Rhynchostylis retusa

Rangaeris amaniensis, in Kenya

Rhynorrchilum standleyi

Rhynchostylis retusa (Saccolabium)

Rhynchostylis gigantea (Saccolabium)

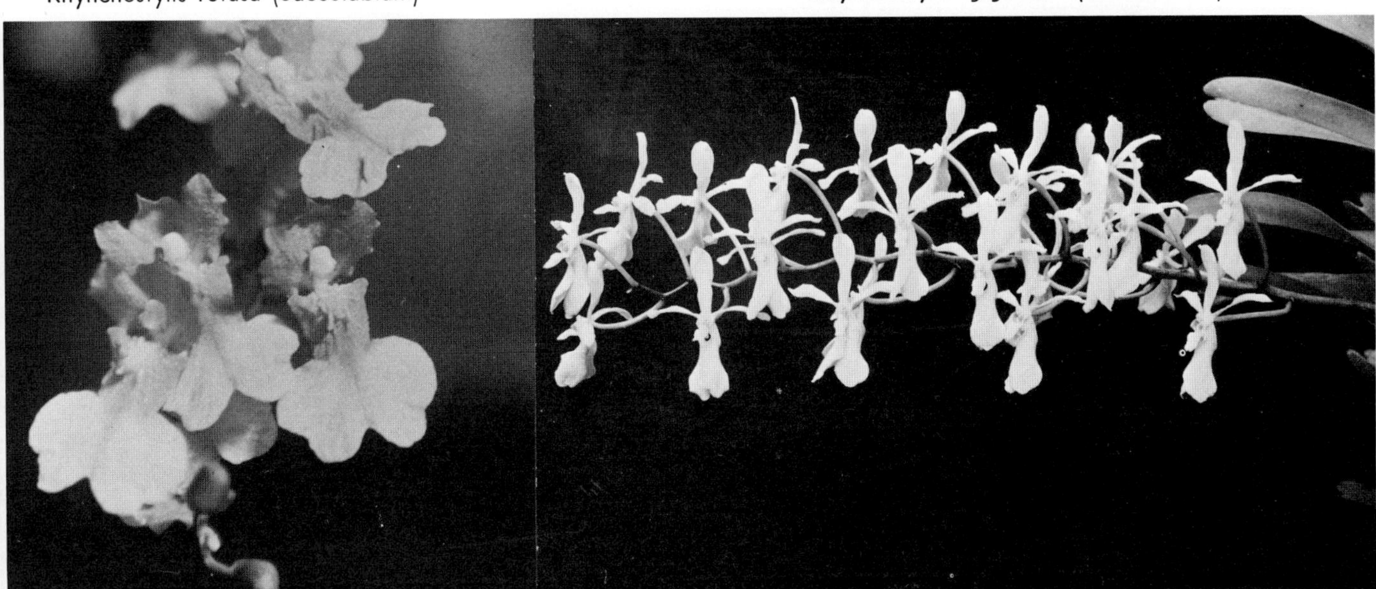

x Rodrocidium 'Tahiti'

x Renantanda sladdenii

Saccolabium bellinum (Calceolaria Hooker)

Symphyglossum sanguineum

Saccolabium calceolare

Saccolabium rhopalorrachis

Sarcochilus luniferus (Chiloschista)

Serapias lingua (So.Europe)

Serapias parviflora

Satyrium erectum (So.Africa)

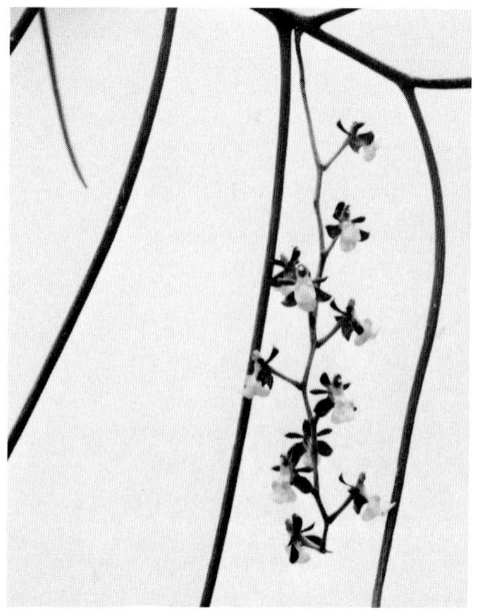
Sarcanthus filiformis

Scaphyglottis lindeniana

Seraphyta diffusa (Jamaica)

Epigeneium lyonii

Spiranthes orchioides (lanceolata)

Scuticaria hadwenii ("steelei" in hort.)

Sobralia decora

Stenoglottis longifolia

Acampe longifolia (Stauropsis gigantea)

Spiranthes romanzoffiana

Sobralia leucoxantha

Sobralia macrantha

Sobralia leucoxantha (Costa Rica)

Sobralia wilsoniana (Central America)

x Schombolaelia 'Kahili' (Hawaii)

Scaphyglottis reedii (Hexadesmia)

Solenangis aphylla (East Africa)

Schomburgkia tibicinis (Laelia) (Costa Rica)

Schomburgkia crispa (Laelia superba)

Schomburgkia (Laelia) undulata

Spathoglottis plicata

Schomburgkia rosea

Schomburgkia lueddemannii

Spathoglottis pacifica, on Samoa

Spiranthes orchioides (lanceolata)

Spathoglottis plicata

Stanhopea hasseloviana (Amazonian Perú)

Stanhopea randii, from Brazil

Stanhopea tricornis (Perú)

Stanhopea martiana

Stanhopea tricornis

Stenorrhynchos bracteatus

Spiranthes acaulis

Stenorrhynchos navarrensis

Stanhopea saccata

Sophronitis coccinea (grandiflora)

Stanhopea bucephalus (graveolens?)

Stanhopea wardii

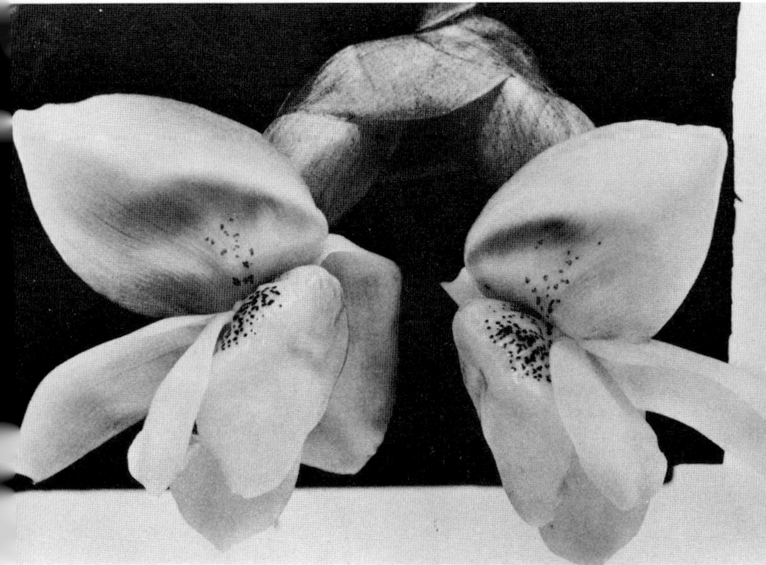
Stanhopea ecornuta

Stanhopea grandiflora (eburnea)

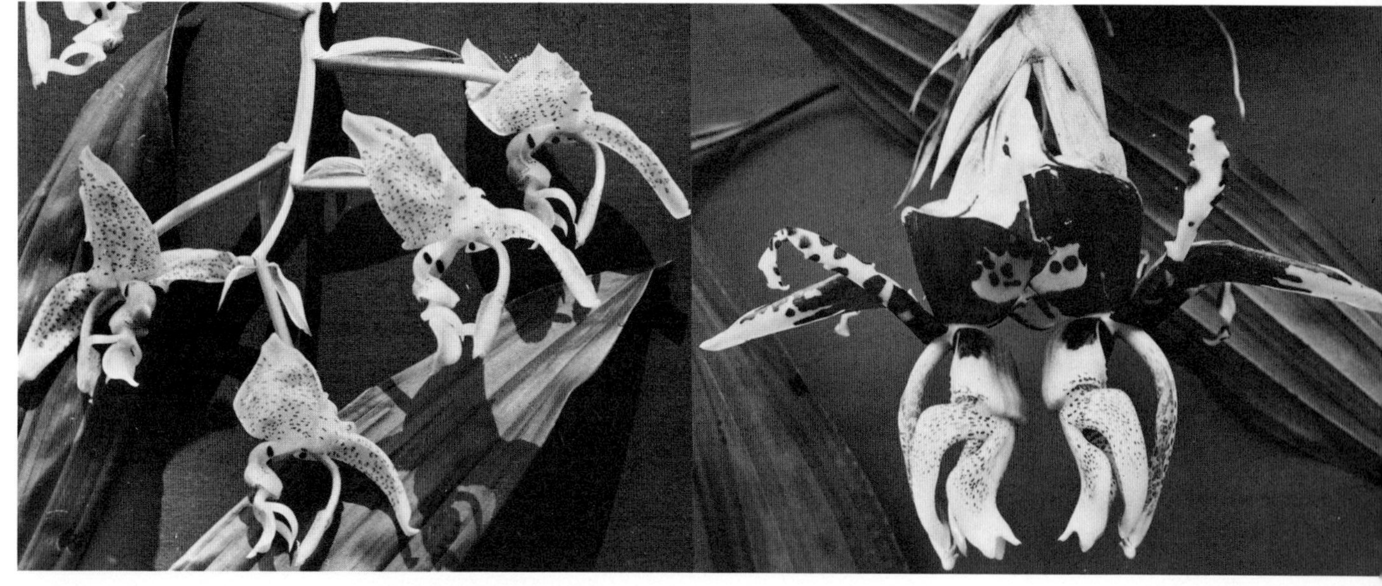

Stanhopea shuttleworthii (guttulata?)

Stanhopea **tigrina**

Stanhopea guttulata

Stanhopea oculata

Stanhopea devoniensis

Stelis ciliaris

Stelis powellii

Spiranthes speciosa  Spiranthes speciosa  Stenorrhynchus standleyi

Spiranthes lindleyana Sarcoglottis metallica 'Variegata' Spiranthes elata

Sophronitis coccinea (grandiflora)

x Sophrolaelia 'Psyche'

x Sophrolaelia 'Psyche' (Laelia x Sophronitis)

Sophronitis coccinea, at Blossfeld Nursery, Sao Paulo

Sophronitis cernua

Sigmatostalix hymenantha

Spathoglottis papuana

x Sophrolaelia marriotiana (Don Richardson)

Spathoglottis aurea, from Java

Ixora javanica

Jasminum rex

Helleborus niger

Strobilanthes dyerianus

Mandevilla (Dipladenia) x amoena

Cissus discolor

Camellia japonica 'Debutante'

Clivia miniata

Hibiscus rosa-sinensis 'Toreador'

Selaginella martensii 'Variegata'

Platycerium "diversifolium" hort.

Pteris ensiformis 'Victoriae'

Symphyglossum (Cochlioda) coccineum (Ecuador)

Scuticaria steelei (Guyana, Venezuela)

Stelis tonduziana (Costa Rica)

Stelis microchila

Sigmatogyne tricallosa

Stelis tricuspis (Costa Rica)

Stelis aemula (Costa Rica)

Trichoglottis brachiata

Taeniophyllum fasciola, tiniest orchid, in Fiji

Sarcanthus lorifolium

Serapias longipetala

Satyrium odorum

Trichoglottis philippinensis

Trichocentrum albo-purpureum

Teuscheria cornucopia

Trichocentrum orthoplectron

elenipedium grande in hort. (bot.Phragmipedium), "Mandarin orchid"

Spiranthes elata, "Ladies tresses", from Costa Rica

Stanhopea eburnea, a "Horned orchid" from Trinidad

Staurochilum (Trichoglottis) ionosma (Philippines)

Trichocentrum candidum

x Renanopsis 'Lena Rowold'

Thelymitra antennifera (Tasmania)

Tetramicra bulbosa (West Indies)

Thelymitra ixioides (Australia, New Zealand)

Trichocentrum candidum (Guatemala)

Trichocentrum albo-coccineum (Perú)

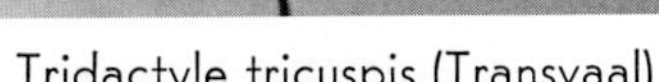
Tridactyle tricuspis (Transvaal)

Trichopilia dasyandra (Aspasia pusilla)

Trichocentrum capitatum (Panama)

Trichopilia powellii (Ecuador)

Trichopilia rostrata

Stenoglottis longifolia

Trichoceros antennifera, "Fly orchid"

Thunia pulchra ("dodgsonii") Thunia alba

Trichocentrum tigrinum Trichocentrum tigrinum Stenoglottis fimbriata

Thrixspermum arachnites

Trichoceros parviflorus

Trichopilia tortilis (Honduras)

Trichopilia coccinea (marginata) (Guatemala)

Trichoglottis brachiata, the "Black orchid"

Tainia cordifolia (J.Bogner, Munich Bot.Garden)

Vanda x amoena

Cochleanthes (Warscewiczella) aromatica

Zygostates grandiflora

Warrea costaricensis

Warrea warreana

Rhyncholaelia (Brassavola) glauca

Vanilla fragrans 'Marginata'

Vanilla ramosa (M.Lecoufle)

Zygopetalum mackayi

x Vandaenopsis 'Frank C. Atherton'

Vanda 'Tatzeri x Ohuohu' (W.Kirch, Honolulu)

x Vandacostylis 'Dawn'

x Vandaenopsis parishii marriottiana

Vanda batemannii hort.

Vandopsis gigantea, from Burma,

x Vandachnis 'Premier' (Arachnis x Vandopsis)

Trichopilia suavis

Trichopilia marginata

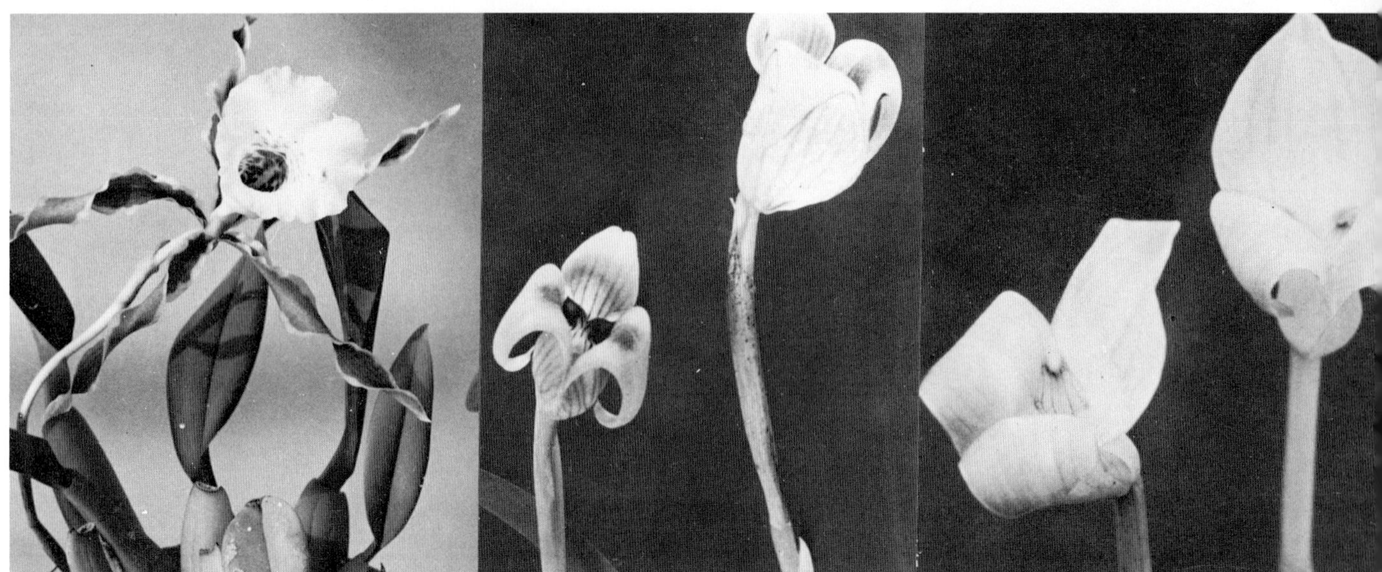

Trichopilia tortilis

Trigonidium obtusum

Trigonidium egertonianum

Vanda parishii marriottiana

Vanda stangeana

Vanda sanderiana

Vanda tricolor planilabris

Vanda coerulea

Harvesting the blooms of Vanda 'Miss Agnes Joaquim', at 'Orchids of Hawaii' nursery in Hilo. Flowering the year round, they are widely used for corsages and leis.

Vanda 'Princess Elizabeth'   Vanda x rothschildiana   Vanda tricolor planilabris (insignis)

Vanda lamellata boxallii   Vanda coerulea   Vanda 'Miss Agnes Joaquim'

Vanda teres   Vanda teres andersonii

Vanda luzonica

Vanda 'Chimey Walker'

Vanda 'Miss Agnes Joaquim'

Vanda bicolor

Vanda cristata

Vanda denisoniana

Vanda deari

Vanda 'Nellie Morley'

Vandopsis lissochiloides

Vanda sanderiana var. 'Terry'

Vanda merrillii

Vanda coerulea

Vanda roeblingiana

Vanda tricolor suavis

Vanda **tricolor**

Vanilla fragrans (planifolia)  | Vanilla pompona (lutescens)  | Vanilla zanzibarensis

Vanilla zanzibarensis  | Vanilla phaeantha  | Vanilla fragrans  | Vanilla pompona (grandiflora)

Vanilla fragrans, producing beans | Vanilla fragans 'Variegata' | Vanilla fragrans 'Marginata'

Vanda cristata | Vanda x rothschildiana | Vanda stangeana

Xylobium elongatum | Vanilla fragrans | Vanilla imperialis

Vandopsis lissochiloides | Zygopetalum wendlandii | Vanilla pompona, at Roehrs

Xylobium elongatum

Xylobium squalens

Zygopetalum mackayii

Zygopetalum blackii ("maxillare" in hort.)

Zygopetalum wendlandii

Zygopetalum grandiflorum (Galeottia)

Zygopetalum mackayi

Zygopetalum crinitum

Oxalis vulcanicola (siliquosa in hort.)

Oxalis gigantea (E.Hummel, Calif.)

Oxalis gigantea (So.America)

Oxalis paucartambensis (E.Hahn)

Oxalis fruticosa

Oxalis enneaphylla (Patagonia)

Oxalis succulentum, in Sydney

Aeginetia indica (India)

Orobanche uniflora

Oxalis carnosa

Oxalis purpurea (variabilis) 'Grand Duchess'

Oxalis rubra (crassipes or 'rosea')

Oxalis pes-caprae (cernua), the Bermuda Buttercup

Oxalis incarnata with leaves resembling Shamrock

Oxalis flava (Trifolium minus at right)

Oxalis hedysaroides rubra, the Fire fern

Oxalis peduncularis

Oxalis pes-caprae florepleno, the "Double Bermuda buttercup"

Oxalis herrerae

Oxalis acetosella

Oxalis hirta

Oxalis bowiei

Biophytum sensitivum

Oxalis ortgiesii

Oxalis deppei ('Lucky Clover')

Oxalis melanosticta

Oxalis bowiei

Oxalis regnellii ("rubra alba" in hort.)

Oxalis lasiandra

Oxalis deppei

Ionoxalis nelsonii

Oxalis hedysaroides rubra

Oxalis carnosa

Oxalis herrerae

Oxalis rubra alba

Oxalis adenophylla

Oxalis flava

Oxalis melanosticta

Oxalis braziliensis

Oxalis deppei

Oxalis oregana, a Woodsorrel sometimes sold as Shamrock

Oxalis martiana 'Aureo-reticulata'

Averrhoa carambola

Biophytum zenkeri (Congo)

Biophytum sensitivum

Oxalis vulcanicola (siliquosa hort.)

Oxalis fruticosa (rusciformis hort.)

Oxalis dispar

Oxalis melanosticta

Oxalis adenophylla

recastrum romanzoffianum (Cocos plumosa), the "Queen palm", Brazil

Archontophoenix alexandrae, "King palm", Australia

Borassus flabellifer, "Palmyra palm", in Sénégal

Attalea cohune, "Cohune palm", in Honduras

Aiphanes acanthophylla

Acrocomia aculeata

Aiphanes erosa

Arenga engleri

Arenga pinnata (Sugar palm)

Arenga engleri

Acrocomia armentalis

Acrocomia sclerocarpa

Acrocomia totai

Archontophoenix alexandrae, the "King palm"

Archontophoenix cunninghamiana, "Piccabeen palm"

ntinckia nicobarica (foreground), (Dr.Darian, Vista, California)

Cocos nucifera; a coconut in germinatión on Moorea, Polynesia

PALMAE: Areca, Arikuryroba, Bactris, Bentinckia, Bismarckia, Borassus, Dictyocaryum

Dictyocaryum globiferum

Borassus flabellifer, on Ceylon

Bactris gasipaes

Bentinckia nicobarica, in Panama

Arikuryroba schizophylla

Areca triandra

Bismarckia nobilis, female tree

Bismarckia nobilis

Bismarckia nobilis, male tree

Arecastrum romanzoffianum (Cocos plumosa), the Queen palm, at Orlando, Florida

Areca catechu, the Betel-nut palm, in New Guinea habitat

Arenga pinnata (saccharifera), the Common Sugar palm

Acrocomia armentalis (crispa), with spindle-shaped trunk

Cocos nucifera 'Dwarf Golden Malay'

Cocos nucifera (Coconut palm)

Cocos nucifera 'Dwarf Samoan'

Caryota rumphiana, a Fishtail palm, showing peculiar leaf pattern

Caryota mitis, with inflorescence

Calamus siphonospathus (Rattan palm)

Deckenia nobilis, in the Seychelles

Bactris major

Butia yatay, from Argentina

Butia capitata, "Jelly palm", Botanic Garden, Madrid

Attalea crassispatha, in Haiti

Butia bonnetii, a "Yatay palm" from Brazil

Aiphanes caryotaefolia, "Spine palm"

Ceroxylon andicola (Colombia)

Arikuryroba schizophylla

Caryota maxima (Java)

Areca langloisiana (Celebes)

Arenga engleri, "Dwarf sugar palm"

Caryota ochlandra, "Chinese Fishtail" from China

Caryota rumphiana, in Algiers, No.Africa

Caryota obtusa (ochlandra)

Caryota mitis, the Clustered Fishtail palm

Caryota urens, the Fishtail palm

Caryota "plumosa"

Catoblastus praemorsus, from Colombia

Chamaedorea elatior

Chamaedorea stolonifera

Chamaedorea radicalis

Chamaedorea glaucifolia

Archontophoenix cunninghamiana

Calamus ciliaris, "Lawyer canes"

Chamaedorea nana (D.Barry)

Bismarckia nobilis

Chamaedorea elegans 'Bella' (Neanthe bella)

Chamaedorea elegans (Collinia)

Chamaedorea erumpens (Bamboo palm)

Chamaedorea brachypoda (stolonifera hort.)

Chamaedorea cataractarum

Chamaedorea seifrizii

Chrysalidocarpus lucubensis

Chrysalidocarpus (Areca) lutescens

Chrysalidocarpus madagascariensis

Chamaedorea radicalis

Chamaedorea metallica (tenella hort.)

Chamaedorea "pacaya" hort.

Chamaedorea klotzschiana

Chamaedorea concolor

Chamaedorea martiana

Chamaedorea costaricana

Chamaedorea elegans (Neanthe bella), the Parlor palm

Livistona chinensis, Chinese Fan palm

Chrysalidocarpus (Areca) lutescens, the Butterfly palm

Coccothrinax miraguama, native of Cuba

Thatch palms at Fairchild Tropical Garden, Miami; two tall and slender Coccothrinax dussiana, and the two shorter Thrinax parviflora

Coccothrinax martii

Coccothrinax fragrans

Coccothrinax argentea

Coccothrinax argentata

Copernicia pauciflora

Copernicia rigida

Copernicia baileyana

amaedorea erumpens, the "Bamboo palm" from Honduras

Chamaerops humilis, arborescent "European fan palm", California

Calamus dealbatus, a "Rattan palm", in Brazil

Chamaedorea concolor, at Leningrad Bot.Garden, U.S.S.R.

Coccothrinax miraguama (Bot.G., St. Louis)

Coccothrinax argentata, "Silver palm"

Coccothrinax fragrans "Butterfly pa

Chrysalidocarpus decipiens

Copernicia australis (Garfield Park, Chicago)

Chambeyronia macrocarpa (Dr.Darian, Cal

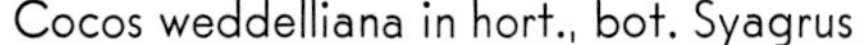

Cocos weddelliana in hort., bot. Syagrus

Cocos nucifera; seed sprouting on the silver beach of Tahit

rypha elata, from Bengal, at Fairchild Gardens, Miami

Corypha umbraculifera, giant "Talipot palm", Botanic Garden Trinidad

Copernicia rigida, a "Wax palm" from Cuba

Copernicia sueroana (Cuba), at Fairchild's Tropical Garden

Chamaerops humilis, bushform, in Andalucia, Spain

Euterpe globosa, "Palma de Sierra" with bromeliads, Puerto Rico

Chrysalidocarpus cabadae (Dr.Darian, Vista)

Chamaerops humilis (N.Y.Bot.Garden)

Chamaerops humilis 'Nana'

Desmoncus horridus, "Fish-hook rattan" on Guyana coast

Brahea (Erythea) arcuata, "Blue Hesperpalm", Baja California

Cyrtostachys lakka, "Sealing wax palm"

Copernicia curbeloi, a "Wax palm" from Cuba

cos nucifera 'Dwarf green', "Green Malay", on Key Largo

Cocos nucifera 'Nino', in Dr.Darian's Palmarium, Vista, California

Cryosophila warscewiczii

Cyrtostachys renda, the Sealing-wax palm in Panama

Chamaedorea ernesti-augusti

Daemonorops didymophyllus

Daemonorops kunstleri

Daemonorops pseudosepal

Daemonorops hystrix

Colpothrinax wrightii, in Cuba

Corozo oleifera, the American Oil palm

Borassus aethiopium, on the Sudan border, northern Uganda

Borassus flabellifer, the Palmyra palm, in South India

Ceroxylon quindiuense, "Andean waxpalm", in Colombia

Corypha umbraculifera, the Talipot palm

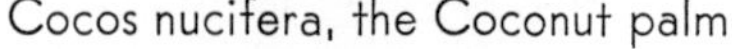

Cocos nucifera, the Coconut palm

Howeia (Kentia) forsteriana, seed harvest on Lord Howe Island

Jubaea chilensis, near Valparaiso

Allagoptera arenaria (Diplothemium maritimum)

Pyrenoglyphis concinna

Phoenix reclinata

Phoenix roebelenii, bearing fruit for seed

graceful coconut palms, Cocos nucifera, swaying in the monsoon, on the Indian Ocean near Mombasa, East Africa

Copernicia macroglossa (torreana,) the Cuban petticoat palm

Euterpe edulis, the slender Assai palm of Brazil

Drymophloeus beguinii

Brahea (Erythea) armata

Hydriastele wendlandiana

Elaeis guineensis

Brahea (Erythea) edulis

Drymophloeus olivaeformis

Desmoncus "polyacanthus" hort.

Desmoncus isthmius, a climbing palm

Desmoncus horridus ("Major")

Dictiosperma aureum, "Yellow Princess palm", in Mauritius

Brahea brandegeei, "Daughter of the West", Los Angeles Arboretum

Brahea edulis, female "Guadalupe Palm" (Mexico)

Brahea armata, "Mexican Blue palm", Huntington Bot. Garden, California

Washingtonia robusta, at Manhattan Beach, California

Aiphanes (Martinezia) caryotaefolia, the Spine palm

Butia capitata (Cocos australis), in North Florida

Chrysalidocarpus (Areca) lutescens, in South Florida

Howeia (Kentia) belmoreana, the Sentry palm at Roehrs Exotic Nurseries, Rutherford, New Jersey, 1900

Phoenix roebelenii (Roehrs 1950)

Licuala grandis

Syagrus (Cocos) weddelliana, in Brazil

Licuala spinosa

Coccothrinax argentata

Licuala peltata, in Penang

Calamus ciliaris

Rhapis excelsa (flabelliformis)

Rhapis humilis

Chamaerops humilis

Chamaerops humilis, in Japan

Trachycarpus nana

Howeia (Kentia) forsteriana, the Paradise palm (20cm tub)

Howeia (Kentia) belmoreana (25cm tub)

Howeia (Kentia) belmoreana (12cm pot. comb.)

Howeia (Kentia) forsteriana (15cm pot. comb.)

PALMAE: Dictyosperma, Elaeis, Euterpe, Gaussia, Heterospathe, Howeia, Hyphaene, Jubaea

Elaeis guineensis, in Nigeria

Hyphaene crinita, on the Limpopo

Jubaea chilensis

Euterpe globosa

Gaussia princeps

Dictyosperma album, the Princess palm

Heterospathe elata

Howeia (Kentia) forsteriana, with seed developing in stages over 6 years

Hyphaene thebaica, the Doum palm, with characteristic forked trunks, in the savannah landscape near Mombasa, East Africa

Hyphaene ventricosa, above the Victoria Falls, Zimbabwe

luxuriously branched specimen of Hyphaene thebaica in rainforest, Tanzania border

Licuala paludosa (amplifrons)

Licuala spinosa

Licuala grandis

Linospadix monostachya in habitat, New South Wales

Linospadix monostachya the Walking-stick palm

Linospadix monostachya (young pl.)

Livistona chinensis

Livistona rotundifolia

Livistona australis

Livistona saribus (cochinchinensis), at the 11th century Khmer temple of Angkor Wat, dedicated to Vishnu the Preserver; Cambodia

Livistona muelleri in the Melaleuca forest, York Peninsula North Queensland

Hyphaene thebaica, the branching Doum palm, Upper Egypt

Latania loddigesii — Latania lontaroides (borbonica) — Latania verschaffeltii

Iguanura geonomaeformis — Korthalsia laciniosa, in the Bahamas

Lodoicea maldivica, the Double Coconut — **Neodypsis decaryi** — Latania lontaroides (borbonica or rubra

Iriartea (Socratea) exorrhiza, in Amazonas, Brazil

Jubaea chilensis (spectabilis), the "Syrup palm"

Latania lontaroides (commersonii), the "Red Latan palm"

Licuala muelleri, at Fairchild Trop.Garden, Miami

Chrysalidocarpus cabadae

Jubaea chilensis, cement-smooth trunk

Jubaea chilensis (spectabilis)

Livistonia mariae

Livistonia australis

Latania loddigesii

Kentiopsis olivaeformis

Kentiopsis macrocarpa, in Rio

Hyphaene coriacea, in Kenya

Hyphaene shatan, with fruit, in Madagascar

Livistona chinensis, crestate form, at Icod, Tenerife

Livistona australis, "Fountain palm", from Australia

Salacca edulis, the "Salac" in Perak, Malaya

Polyandrococos caudescens

Chamaedorea elegans 'Bella'

Mauritia flexuosa

Hedyscepe (Kentia) canterburyana

Copernicia curbeloi (Cuba)

Brahea (Erythea) elegans, "Franceschi palm

Mascarena verschaffeltii, "Spindle palm"

Linospadix (Bacularia) minor

Mascarena revaughanii

Licuala grandis, at Munich Botanic Garden, Germany

Licuala spinosa, on Expedition in Papua 1960

Livistona saribus (cochinchinensis) at Angkor, Cambodia

Livistona rotundifolia, Kebun Raya, Bogor, in Java

Lodoicea maldivica, young tree at Foster Gardens, Honolulu

Lodoicea maldivica, female tree, Mahé Botanic Garden, Seychell

Livistona decipiens, in Huntington Bot.Gardens, California

Lodoicea maldivica, curious fruit of the "Double coconut"

Mascarena revaughanii, from Mauritius (Fairchild Gardens, Miami)

Mascarena lagenicaulis, "Bottle palm", in Rio de Janeiro

Paurotis wrightii, the "Everglades palm" in St. Petersburg, Florida

Neodypsis decaryi, from Madagascar, in Miami

PALMAE: Mascarena, Myrialepis, Normanbya, Nypa, Orbignya, Phoenicophorium

Mascarena verschaffeltii

Mascarena lagenicaulis

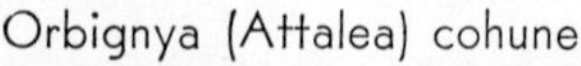

Orbignya (Attalea) cohune

Normanbya normanbyi, the Black palm

Phoenicophorium borsigianum (Stevensonia)

Nypa fruticans, inflorescence

Nypa fruticans, the Nipa palm

Myrialepis scortechinii

Metroxylon sagus, a "Sago palm" on Irian, W.New Guinea

Metroxylon vitiense, from Fiji, at Foster Gardens, Honolulu

Phoenix sylvestris, the "East Indian wine-palm"

Phoenix reclinata, the "Senegal date", Balboa Park, San Diego

Phoenix dactylifera, female tree with fruit, Palm Springs, Calif.

Phoenix humilis, from China (Huntington Bot.G., California)

Phoenix canariensis, container-grown, in California

Phoenix tomentosa hort., Los Angeles County Arboretum, Arcadia

hoenix paludosa, "Siamese date palm", with curious looping trunks

Oncosperma tigillarum, the "Nibong palm", in Ceylon

ashingtonia robusta, with winter cover of rice-straw, in Tokyo

Phoenix canariensis, Huntington B.G., California

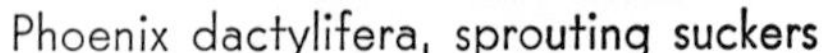

Phoenix dactylifera, sprouting suckers

Lytocaryum hoehnei

Paurotis wrightii (Everglades palm)

Phoenix "taiwaniana," in Taipei

Pseudophoenix vinifera

Phoenix sylvestris, near Bombay

Phoenix rupicola, the Cliff-date

Phoenix reclinata, at Victoria Falls, Zimbabwe

Phoenix reclinata, on the Zambezi River, Central Africa

Phoenix dactylifera 'Deglet Noor'; fruiting Date palms, Coachella Valley, California

Ptychosperma macarthurii, from New Guinea

Pritchardia pacifica, in habitat, Viti Levu, Fiji

Pritchardia macrocarpa, "Loulou palm", in Honolulu

Pritchardia beccariana, from Hawaii

Phytelephas macrocarpa, "Ivory-nut palm" (Ecuador)

Microcoelum insigne, in Royal Botanic Garden, Sydney

Neodypsis lastelliana, from Madagascar (Dr. Darian, Calif.)

Pigafetta filaris, from Celebes, in Dr. Darian's Jungle room

lagodoxa henryana, "Vahana palm", in the Marquesas, French Polynesia

Nypa fruticans, along the Klongs of Bangkok, Thailand

Pinanga kuhlii

Pinanga (Seaforthia) coronata

Pinanga maculata

Ptychosperma elegans (Solitaire palm)

Pinanga malaiana

Ptychosperma angustifolium

Ptychoraphis singaporensis

Pritchardia hillebrandii, in Hawaii

Pritchardia arecina

Nypa fruticans, the aquatic "Nipa palm", in Monsoon Malaysia

Podococcus barteri, in Equatorial Africa (J. Bogner, Munich)

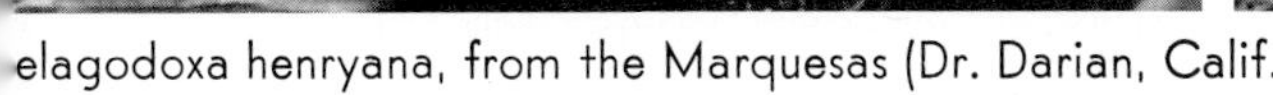

elagodoxa henryana, from the Marquesas (Dr. Darian, Calif.)

Polyandrococos caudescens, from Brazil (Fairchild Gardens)

Ptychosperma macarthurii, the "Hurricane palm", in Miami Shopping Center

Ptychosperma elegans, "Princess palm" (Palm Socie

Kentia forsteriana in hort., bot. Howeia, as decorator plant

Ptychosperma elegans (with Ravenala) in Cherry Hill, New Jersey

Reinhardtia gracilis gracilior

Rhapis excelsa (flabelliformis), the Lady palm

Veitchia (Adonidia) merrillii, the Manila palm

Ptychosperma (Actinophloeus) macarthurii

Syagrus (Cocos) weddelliana, 8cm pot — Phoenix roebelenii, 10cm pot — Sabal texana (seedl.)

Phoenix rupicola — Phoenix roebelenii (Miniature Date palm) — Phoenix canariensis

Rhapis 'Dwarf Japanese' — Rhapis excelsa 'Variegata' — Phoenix dactylifera (Date palm)

Raphia ruffia in hort., bot. farinifera, in the Usambaras, Tanzania

Raphia vinifera, "African Wine palm", in Nigeria

Rhopalostylis baueri, in Brentwood, California

Raphia pedunculata (Heidelberg Bot. Garden, Germany)

Rhopaloblaste ceramica

Rhopalostylis sapida, in New Zealand

Raphia gaertneri

Raphia taedigera (arrow, right)

Raphia farinifera (ruffia), Tanzania

Raphia vinifera, in Cuba

Rhapidophyllum hystrix, at Orlando, Florida

Rhapis excelsa (flabelliformis), above beautiful Sun-Moon Lake, Taiwan

Roystonea regia, an avenue of Royal palms

Sabal causiarum, the Puerto Rican hat palm

Sabal palmetto, at Montgomery Palmetum, Florida

Roystonea oleracea, Jardim Botanico, Rio de Janeiro, Brazil

Verschaffeltia splendida

Licuala spinosa, in Thailand

Reinhardtia simplex

Sabal neglecta (Huntington Bot. Garden)

Sabal deeringiana (Los Angeles Arboretum)

Rhopalostylis baueri

Sabal umbraculifera

Rhapidophyllum hystrix

Roystonea elata, in Everglades National Park, Florida

Roystonea regia, "Cuban Royal palm", in the Climatron, St. Louis

Scheelia liebmanii, from Mexico, at Fairchild Gardens, Miami

Scheelia regia, at Foster Gardens, Honolulu

Sabal palmetto, the "Cabbage palm" in Ft. Pierce, Florida

Sabal exul, "Victoria palm", in Mexico

Sabal minor (louisiana), the "Dwarf palmetto" in Texas

Sabal viatoris, at Huntington Botanical Gardens, San Marino, Calif

Wallichia densiflora, from the Assam Himalayas

Raphia farinifera, a "Raffia palm" on Lake Victoria, Uganda

Trachycarpus fortunei (leaf)

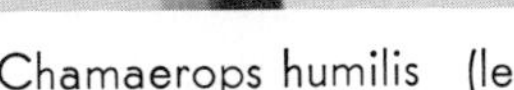

Chamaerops humilis (leaf)

Trithrinax acanthocoma, from Brazil

Washingtonia filifera, the "Petticoat palm" (juvenile)

Sabal havanensis, from Cuba

Serenoa repens, the "Saw palmetto"

Sabal mexicana

Sabal texana

Trachycarpus fortunei, in horticulture as Chamaerops excelsa

Sabal minor, the Dwarf Palmetto

Thrinax microcarpa

Thrinax parviflora

Trithrinax acanthocoma

Rhopalostylis sapida, the Nikau palm, in Westland habitat, New Zealand

Trachycarpus fortunei, the "Chusan" or "Windmill palm"

Thrinax parviflora at Fairchild Tropical Garden, Florida

Syagrus coronata, Montgomery Palmetum, Florida

Rhapis humilis, the "Slender Lady palm", from Thailand

Thrinax argentea (Bot. Garden Leningrad)

Thrinax ekmanii, from Navassa Island, W.Indies

Thrinax microcarpa, "Thatchpalm", in the Florida Keys

achycarpus fortunei, the "Windmill palm"

Washingtonia filifera (2 trees left), W. robusta (trees right), in Palm Springs, California

rachycarpus fortunei 'Nana', at Ono Nursery, Honolulu

Trachycarpus wagnerianus (takil in hort.), from Himalayas

Washingtonia filifera, at Huntington Bot. Garden, San Marino, California

Washingtonia filifera in habitat, Palm Springs Canyon, California

Washingtonia robusta, at Fairchild Tropical Garden, Miami, Florida

Veitchia (Adonidia) merrillii, the Christmas palm

Veitchia joannis, from Fiji (Fairchild Gardens, Miami)

Veitchia merrillii, the "Christmas palm", Philippines

Wallichia disticha, at Dr. Darian's Palmarium, Vista, California

Veitchia arecina, on New Caledonia, in the Coral Sea

Veitchia montgomeryana

Veitchia winin

Roystonea regia

Washingtonia filifera

Wallichia disticha

Wallichia densiflora, leaves and inflorescence

Syagrus (Glaziova) treubiana

Syagrus (Cocos) weddelliana

Scheelia zonensis, in Panama

Pandanus odoratissimus, in the New Hebrides

Pandanus leram, "Nicobar bread fruit", (Sri Lanka)

Pandanus sanderi, in Tahiti, French Polynesia

Pandanus utilis, at New York Botanical Garden

Pandanus veitchii 'Compactus' Pandanus veitchii Pandanus sanderi 'Roehrsianus'

Pandanus utilis Pandanus baptistii Pandanus pacificus Pandanus pygmaeus

Pandanus utilis **Pandanus utilis as tree** **Pandanus heterocarpus**

Pandanus pristis, from Madagascar

Pandanus kirkii, near Dar-es-Salaam, Tanzania

Freycinetia walkeri (J. Bogner)

Freycinetia rigidifolia, in Thailand

Freycinetia elegantula (New Guinea)

Pandanus stellatus (male plant) in Madagascar

Freycinetia funicularis, from Java

Pandanus utilis, showing stilt roots

Freycinetia multiflora, the Climbing pandanus

Pandanus tectorius, in New Guinea

Freycinetia javanica

Freycinetia arborea

Eschscholtzia californica (California poppy)

Papaver orientale (Oriental poppy)

Bocconia frutescens, the "Plume poppy", in Mexico

Phytolacca dioica, La Orotava, Tenerife

Sesamum orientale (indicum), the "Sesame-oil bush"

Uncarina grandidieri, from Madagascar

Sesamum triphyllum (Namibia)

Chelidonium majus fl. pl., "Celandine"

Harpagophytum peglerae (Africa)

Platystemon californicus, "Cream-cups"

Sesamothamnus rivae (Trop. Africa)

Philydrum lanuginosum (Malaysia)

Rivina humilis, the "Rouge plant"

Petiveria alliacea, "Guinea-hen weed"

Romneya coulteri

Papaver alpinum

Hunnemannia fumariaefolia

Orthothylax glaberrimus

Trichostigma peruvianum

Phytolacca americana (decandra)

Rivina humilis, the Rouge plant

Trichostigma peruvianum (Ledenbergia)

Passiflora x caeruleo-racemosa

Passiflora subpeltata

Passiflora capsularis

Passiflora tetraden, in Brazil

Passiflora incarnata

Passiflora coriacea

Passiflora violacea

Passiflora vitifolia

Passiflora x alato-caerulea, the Pink Passion flower

Passiflora caerulea, the Blue Passion flower

Passiflora incarnata

Passiflora quadrangularis

Adenia subglobosa (globosa hort.) in Nairobi, Kenya

the thorny Adenia globosa in habitat, near Moshi, Tanzania

Passiflora trifasciata

Passiflora cinnabarina

Passiflora violacea

Passiflora bryonioides

Passiflora edulis, the "Purple Granadilla" with edible fruit

Passiflora edulis, "Granadilla"

Passiflora molissima, in New Guinea

Passiflora rubra (West Indies)

Passiflora coccinea

Passiflora racemosa

Passiflora quadrangularis

Malesherbia linearifolia (Chile)

Adenia glauca (So. Africa)

Adenia fruticosa (Transvaal)

Passiflora x colvillei

Passiflora 'Imperatrice Eugenie'

Passiflora 'Exoniensis'

Passiflora manicata

Passiflora maliformis, in Tonga

Passiflora incarnata

Passiflora antioquiensis, in Colombia

Passiflora capsularis (W. Tropical America)

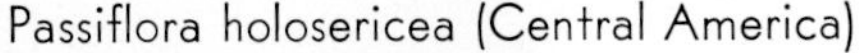

Passiflora holosericea (Central America)

Passiflora mollissima, on Chimbu Pass, New Guinea

Passiflora amethystina (Brazil)

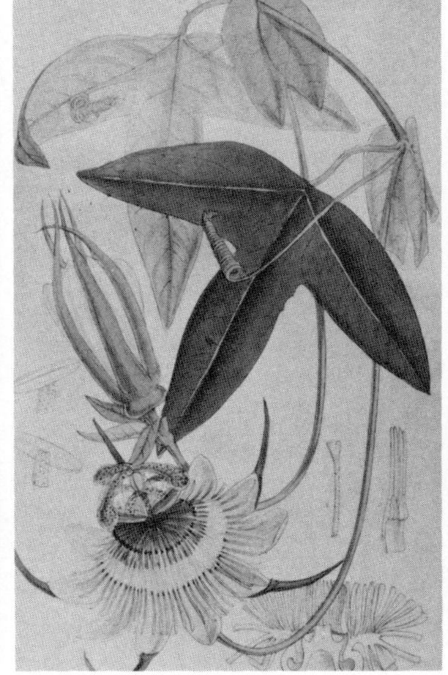

Passiflora violacea (Bot. Mag.)

Passiflora caerulea, "Passion flower"

Passiflora platyfolia, with fruit, in San Salvador

Passiflora aurantia, in the New Hebrides

Passiflora coccinea, a Red Passion flower, in Louisiana

Passiflora maculifolia

Passiflora maculifolia

Passiflora trifasciata

Passiflora racemosa (princeps), a red passion-vine

Passiflora quadrangularis (Granadilla) with edible frui

Peperomia velutina

Peperomia verschaffeltii

Peperomia bicolor

Peperomia polybotrya

Peperomia sandersii (argyreia)

Peperomia peltifolia

Peperomia arifolia litoralis

Peperomia arifolia grandis

Peperomia marmorata 'Silver Heart'

Peperomia fosteri

Peperomia angulata

Peperomia quadrangularis

Peperomia prostrata

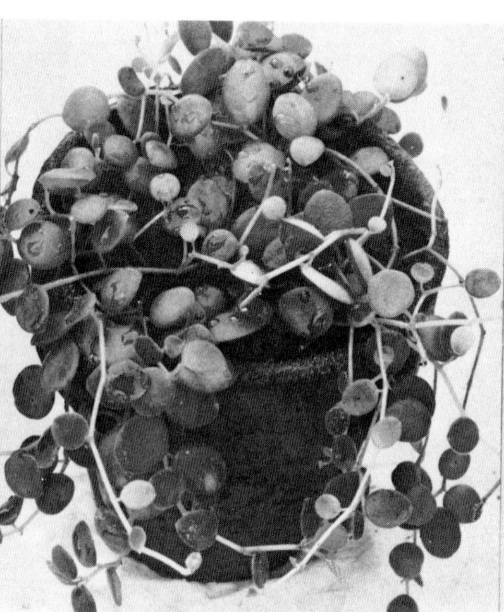

Peperomia rotundifolia (nummularifolia)

Peperomia rubella

Peperomia camptotricha

Peperomia urocarpa

Peperomia trinervis

Peperomia scandens 'Variegata'

Peperomia obtusifolia 'Variegata'

Peperomia glabella 'Variegata'

Peperomia caperata 'Emerald Ripple'

Peperomia caperata 'Tricolor'

Peperomia caperata 'Little Fantasy'

Peperomia ornata

Peperomia puteolata

Peperomia metallica

Peperomia subpeltata

Peperomia sp. 'Crassifolia'

Peperomia clusiifolia

Peperomia gardneriana

Peperomia pulchella (verticillata in hort.)

Peperomia griseo-argentea 'Nigra'

Peperomia obtusifolia 'Alba'

Peperomia blanda

Peperomia obtusifolia 'Lougenii'

Peperomia clusiifolia 'Variegata'

Peperomia dolabriformis

Peperomia orba ("Princess Astrid" in hort.)

Peperomia griseo-argentea 'Blackie'

Peperomia griseo-argentea (hederaefolia)

Peperomia resedaeflora (fraseri)

Peperomia caperata 'Crespa'

Peperomia incana

Peperomia hirta

Peperomia cubensis (rotundifolia of Puerto Rico)

Peperomia cubensis 'Variegata'

Peperomia trinervis

Peperomia acuminata

Peperomia scandens

Peperomia glabella

Peperomia moninii

Peperomia pereskiaefolia

Peperomia calvicaulis

Peperomia prostrata

Peperomia verschaffeltii

Peperomia urocarpa

Peperomia obtusifolia 'Minima'

Peperomia obtusifolia 'Albo-marginata'

Peperomia galioides

Peperomia orba 'Pixie' ("Teardrops")

Peperomia sp "cordata", in Sao Paulo

Peperomia obtusifolia 'Gold Tip'

Peperomia cerea ('Dr. Goodspeed' hort.)

Peperomia resedaeflora (fraseri)

Peperomia sp. 'Horace Anderson'

Peperomia 'Queremal'

Peperomia caperata 'Variegata'

Peperomia "nummularifolia" (Oakhurst G.)

Peperomia "elongata"

Peperomia trinervula

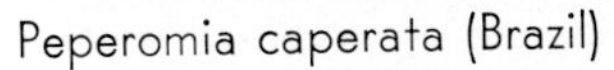

Peperomia caperata (Brazil)

Peperomia campylotropa (Munich Bot.G.)

Peperomia marmorata 'Silver Heart'

Peperomia persicifolia (Botanic Garden, Copenhagen)

Peperomia pereskiaefolia, the "Leaf-cactus peperomia"

Peperomia polybotrya

Peperomia perrottetiana (Mauritius)

Peperomia meridensis (Mexico)

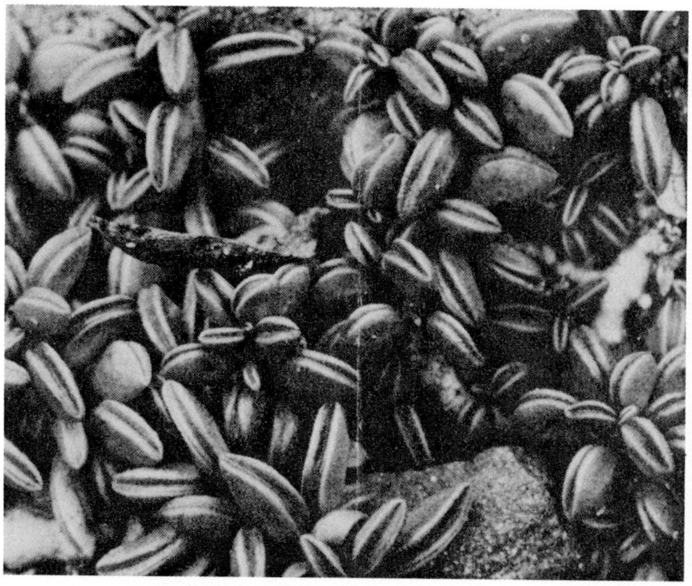

Peperomia pruinosifolia (Perú)

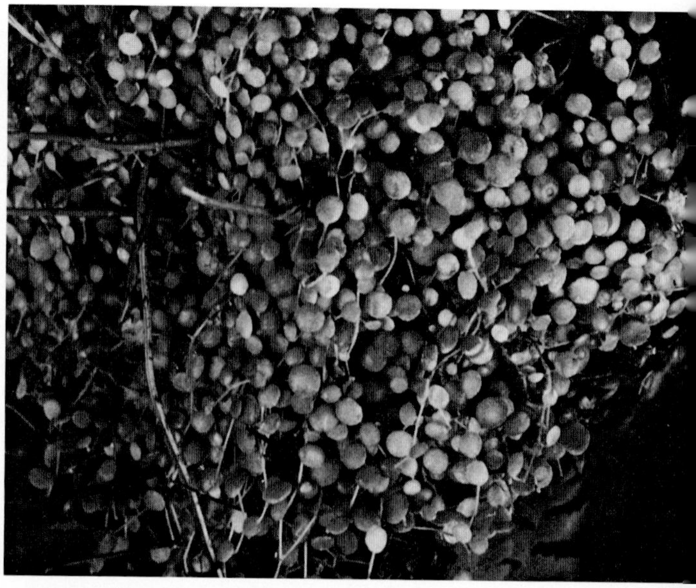

Peperomia rotundifolia (J. Marnier-Lapostolle, France)

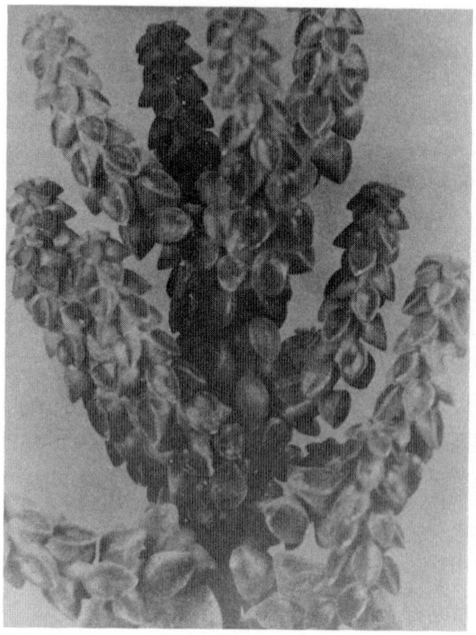

Peperomia columella (Amazonas)

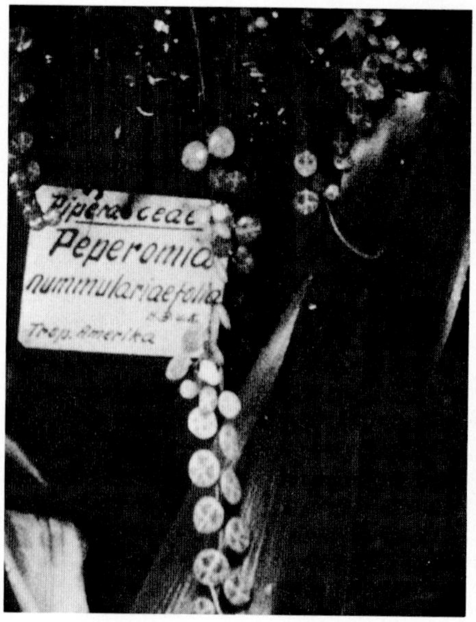

Peperomia nummulariaefolia (Cologne Bot. Garden)

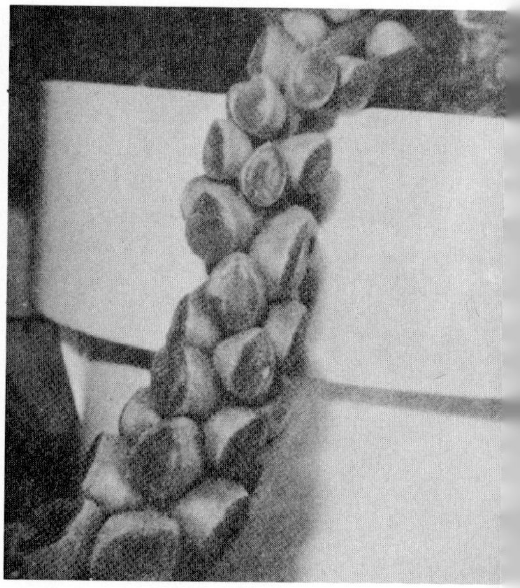

Peperomia columnaris (P. Hutchinson)

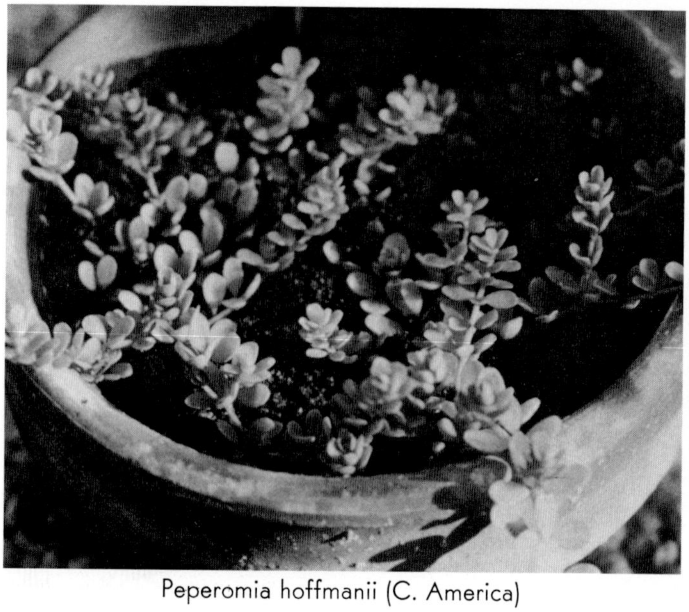

Peperomia hoffmanii (C. America)

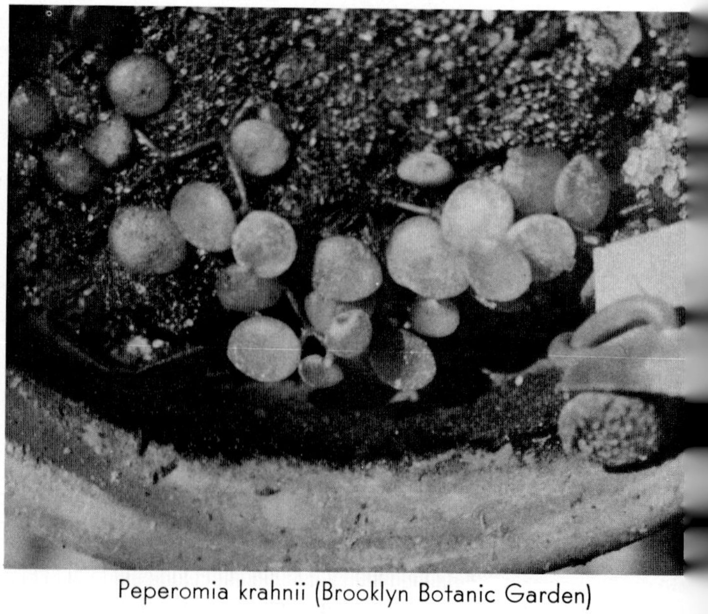

Peperomia krahnii (Brooklyn Botanic Garden)

Peperomia angulata (Venezuela)

Peperomia puteolata, from Perú

Peperomia clusiifolia

Peperomia margaretifera (Brooklyn Bot.G.)

Peperomia cuspidilimba (Heidelberg Bot.G.)

Peperomia longispicata (Central America)

Peperomia obtusifolia 'Variegata'

Peperomia rauhii

Peperomia "masonii" (Perú)

Peperomia "Madisonii" hort. (Humme

Peperomia rosifolia, "Pinkie" (Brazil)

Peperomia serpens

Peperomia spathulifolia (Florida)

Peperomia alata

Peperomia campylotropa (Munich B.G.)

Peperomia verticillata

Peperomia magnoliaefolia

Peperomia obtusifolia

Peperomia viridis

Peperomia nivalis

Peperomia tithymaloides

Peperomia japonica

Peperomia sarcophylla

Peperomia maculosa

Peperomia grandifolia

Piper auritum (Mexico)

Macropiper excelsum

Piper betle, "Betel-pepper"

Peperomia humilis (Florida Keys)

Peperomia tithymaloides

Podomorphe sidaefolia

Peperomia aspercula, in Hawaii

Peperomia deppeana, from Mexico

Piper sylvaticum

the beautiful Piper crocatum, sometimes confused with P. ornatum, at Cairns, in tropical North Queensland

Piper futokadsura, the Japanese Pepper

Piper nigrum, the Black Pepper

Piper peltatum (Pothomorphe)

Piper macrophyllum

Macropiper excelsum psittacorum, in Christchurch, N. Z.

Piper porphyrophyllum, also known as Cissus porph.

Piper ornatum

Piper futokadsura

Piper magnificum

Macropiper excelsum

Piper betle, the Betel-leaf, in Bali

Piper nigrum, the Black Pepper, in Brazil

Pittosporum eugenioides

Pittosporum tobira 'Variegatum'

Pittosporum tobira

Pittosporum tobira 'Variegatum'

Pittosporum tobira (25cm tub)

Pittosporum undulatum

Citriobatus multiflorus

Pittosporum eugenioides 'Variegatum', in New Zealand

Pittosporum tobira, the "Mock orange", from Japan

Pittosporum viridiflorum, "Cape pittosporum", (South Africa)

Pittosporum eugenioides

Pittosporum moluccanum

Pittosporum undulatum, with fruit

Pittosporum tobira 'Wheeler's Dwarf'

Pittosporum tobira 'Compacta'

Pittosporum undulatum, in flower

Limonium sinuatum (Statice)

Plantago nivalis

Limonium sinuatum atrocoeruleum

Limonium sinuatum (Statice)

Plumbago **indica coccinea**

Plumbago auriculata (capensis in hort.)

Polygala paucifolia (Gay Wings)

Polygala capitata

Polygala myrtifolia grandiflora

Marianthus pictus, from Western Australia

Plumbago zeylanica (Namibia and Transvaal)

Marianthus ringens

Plumbago indica coccinea

Hymenosporum flavum

Gilia androsacea

Gilia rubra, "Standing cypress"

Gilia (Leptodactylon) californica

Phlox drummondii; Annual Phlox, in several color forms

Cobaea scandens

Cantua buxifolia, the Magic Flower of the Incas, at 3,800m near La Paz, Bolivia

Gilia dianthoides

Phlox carolina 'Miss Lingard' (suffruticosa)

Phlox paniculata

Cantua quercifolia

Cantua buxifolia

Punica granatum 'Alba plena'

Antigonon leptopus, on Timor

Ceratostigma willmottianum

Polygonum capitatum, "Fleece flower"

Lewisia howellii, "Mountain rose" from Oregon

Polygala myrtifolia, "Milkwort" (So. Africa)

Aphelandra aurantiaca

Eranthemum nervosum

Plumeria rubra acutifolia

Clerodendrum thomsonae

Hoya carnosa variegata

Neomarica gracilis

Bougainvillea x buttiana 'Praetoria'

Dionaea muscipula

Nepenthes 'Superba'

Zebrina pendula 'Quadricolor'

Jacobinia velutina

Fuchsia triphylla 'Bohnstedt'

Pentaphragma philippinense (J. Bogner, Munich Bot. Garden)

Punica granatum, as bonsai (65 years), Brooklyn Bot. Garden

Coccoloba uvifera 'Aurea'

Coccoloba diversifolia

Coccoloba laurifolia (floridana)

Coccoloba rugosa (inflorescence)

Eriogonum giganteum (Santa Barbara Is.)

Ruprechtia coriacea (Mexico)

Coccoloba grandifolia (pubescens)

Coccoloba uvifera 'Aurea'

Coccoloba uvifera

Cocculus laurifolius (Menisp. fam)

Coccoloba uvifera (Sea-grape)

Coccoloba latifolia

Antigonon leptopus

Homalocladium platycladum

Muehlenbeckia complexa

Coccoloba rugosa, the "Ortegon" in Puerto Rico

Coccoloba uvifera, "Sea-grape", container-grown

Rheum palmatum, "Medicine rhubarb", in China

Punica granatum 'Nana', dwarfed tree with fruit

Rheum undulatum

Coccoloba uvifera, the 'Sea-grape'

Polygonum capitatum

Polygonum capitatum, at Christchurch, N. Z.

Antigonon leptopus, the Coral-Vine

Eichhornia crassipes (Floating Water hyacinth)

Eichhornia azurea, a Creeping Water hyacinth

Reussia rotundifolia, water-creeper in Madagascar

Eichhornia heterosperma (J. Bogner, Munich Bot. Garden)

Eichhornia paniculata

Pontederia cordata

Eichhornia martiana

Eichhornia natans, miniature aquatic in Madagascar

Eichhornia crassipes, floating "Water hyacinth", Lac Alaotra, Madagascar

Hydrostachys pinnatifolia (Madagascar)

Heteranthera zosterifolia (Uruguay)

Heteranthera dubia (graminea)

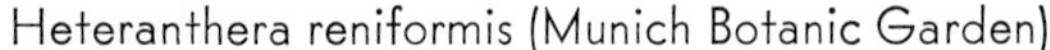
Heteranthera reniformis (Munich Botanic Garden)

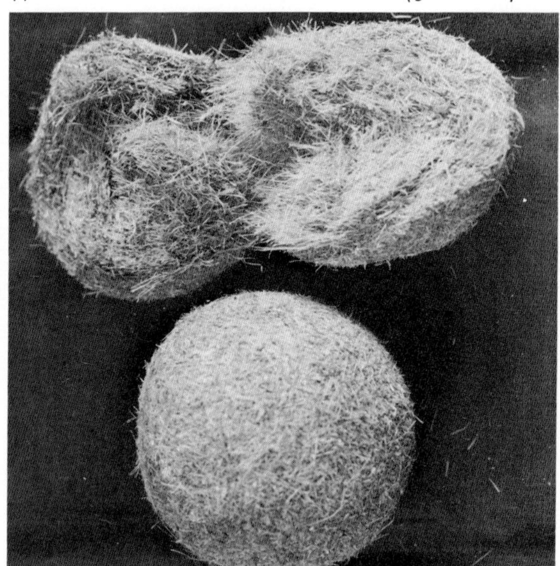
Posidonia caulinii, underwater fruit (Mediterranean)

Psilotum nudum, the epiphytic "Moa" or "Wisk-fern"

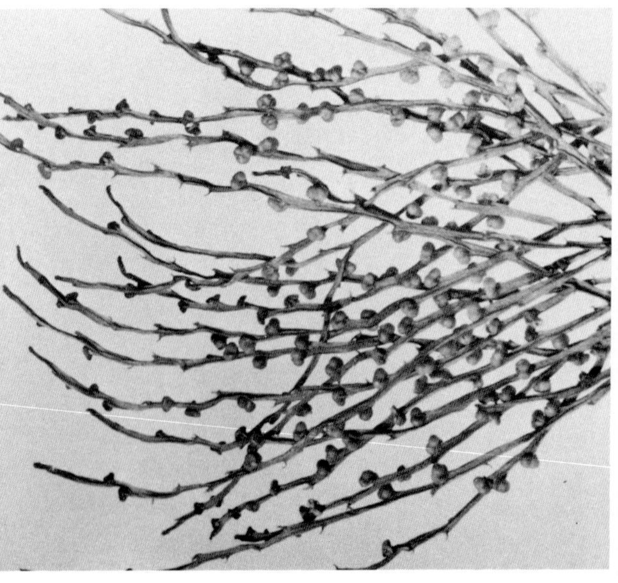
Psilotum nudum (triquetrum), primitive fern-ally

Anacampseros rufescens, "African whisker plant"

Anacampseros alstonii, in Bushmanland

Anacampseros papyracea, from Cape Province

Anacampseros fissa (South Africa)

Portulacaria afra 'Tricolor'

Portulacaria afra 'Macrophylla'

Portulacaria pygmaea (Namibia)

Portulacaria afra, in the Transvaal

Lewisia howellii

Portulaca grandiflora, the Sun plant

Anacampseros baeseckei

Anacampseros rufescens

Anacampseros meyeri

Anacampseros albissima

Portulacaria afra aurea — Talinum patens variegata — Anacampseros rufescens (arachnoides grandiflora hort.)

Portulaca grandiflora — Portulacaria afra 'Variegata' — Portulacaria afra

Anacampseros filamentosa — Anacampseros buderiana — Lewisia brachycalyx

Lewisia cotyledon (California)

Lewisia rediviva, "Bitter-root"

Talinum guadalupense

Androsace lanuginosa (Himalayas)

Lysimachia quadrifolia

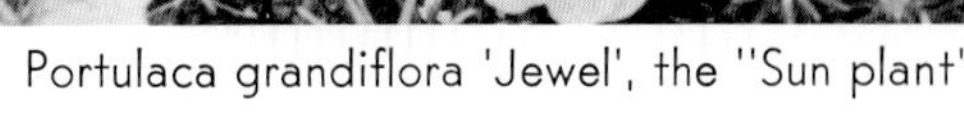

Portulaca grandiflora 'Jewel', the "Sun plant"

Anacampseros alstonii, from Southwest Africa

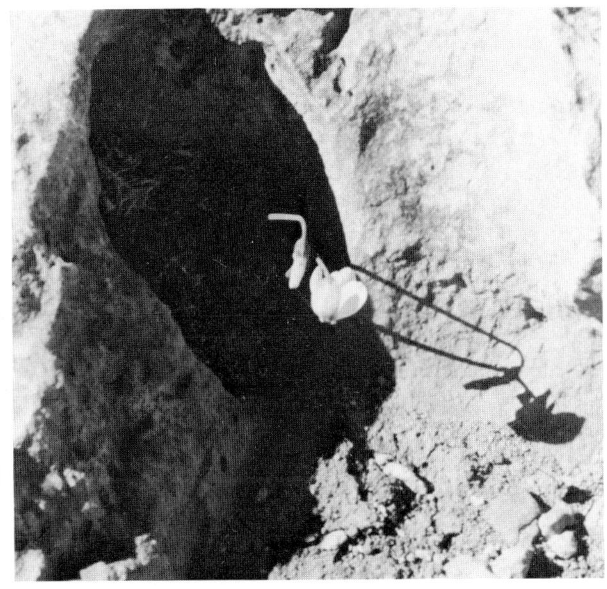

Cyclamen persicum, Acropolis, Mycaene, Greece

Cyclamen persicum (species) Cyclamen persicum cv. 'Pearl of Zehlendorf'

Cyclamen persicum 'Double Zehlendorf'

Cyclamen persicum 'Swiss dwarf'

Cyclamen neapolitanum album

Cyclamen persicum 'Fimbriatum'

Cyclamen persicum (species by Don Richardson)

Cyclamen persicum 'Rococo'   Cyclamen persicum 'Rose of Marienthal'   Cyclamen persicum 'Pearl of Zehlendorf'

Cyclamen neapolitanum

Cyclamen perscium 'Vogt's Double'

Cyclamen persicum 'Bonfire'

Cyclamen persicum 'Candlestick'

Primula obconica 'Gigantea'

Primula x polyantha

Primula auricula

Primula nutans

Primula mollis

Primula floribunda

Cyclamen persicum 'Aalsmeer double'

Cyclamen persicum 'Rococo'

Lysimachia nummularia, "Creeping Charlie"

Primula sikkimensis

Ardisiandra sibthorpoides

Dodecatheon meadia (Shooting stars)

Lysimachia clethroides

Lysimachia punctata

Primula juliae hyb.

Primula sinensis fimbriata 'Brick-red'

Primula sinensis 'Flore pleno'

Primula sinensis

Primula obconica

Primula malacoides

Primula denticulata

Primula malacoides 'Glory of Riverside'

Primula vulgaris (acaulis)

Primula veris

Primula x polyantha

Primula x kewensis

Protea cynaroides

Leucadendron argenteum (Silver tree)

Stenocarpus sinuatus

Grevillea robusta (Silk oak)

Psilotum nudum (triquetrum)

Grevillea wilsonii

Banksia australis

Banksia marcescens

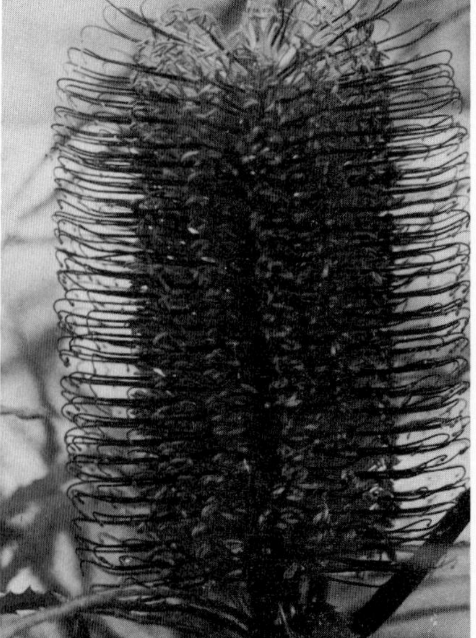

Banksia collina

Grevillea lavandulacea

Grevillea "robusta" in hort.

Grevillea thelemanniana

Grevillea banksii

Grevillea juniperina (sulphurea)

Grevillea bipinnatifida

Grevillea alpina

Grevillea asplenifolia

Grevillea vestita

Orothamnus zeyheri

Leucospermum bolusii (Paranomus reflexus)

Leucospermum lineare

Leucospermum prostratum

Serruria florida

Leucospermum reflexum, in So. Africa

Leucadendron venosum

Leucadendron discolor

Leucadendron stokoei, at Nelson, New Zealand

Leucadendron argenteum, the Silver-tree in habitat on the slopes of Table Mountain, Cape Province

Hakea laurina

Hakea suaveolens

Lambertia formosa

Leucadendron argenteum, inflorescence

Protea lorifolia (Leucad. grandiflorum)

Leucadendron salignum

Protea cynaroides

Protea barbigera

Protea compacta

Protea neriifolia

Protea grandiceps or repens hybrid, in South Africa

Leucospermum conocarpum, on the Cape Peninsula

Leucospermum nutans, at Kirstenbosch

Protea cynaroides

Telopea speciosissima (Waratah)

Macadamia ternifolia

Stenocarpus sinuatus, the "Wheel of Fire" or "Flametree" of Eastern Australia

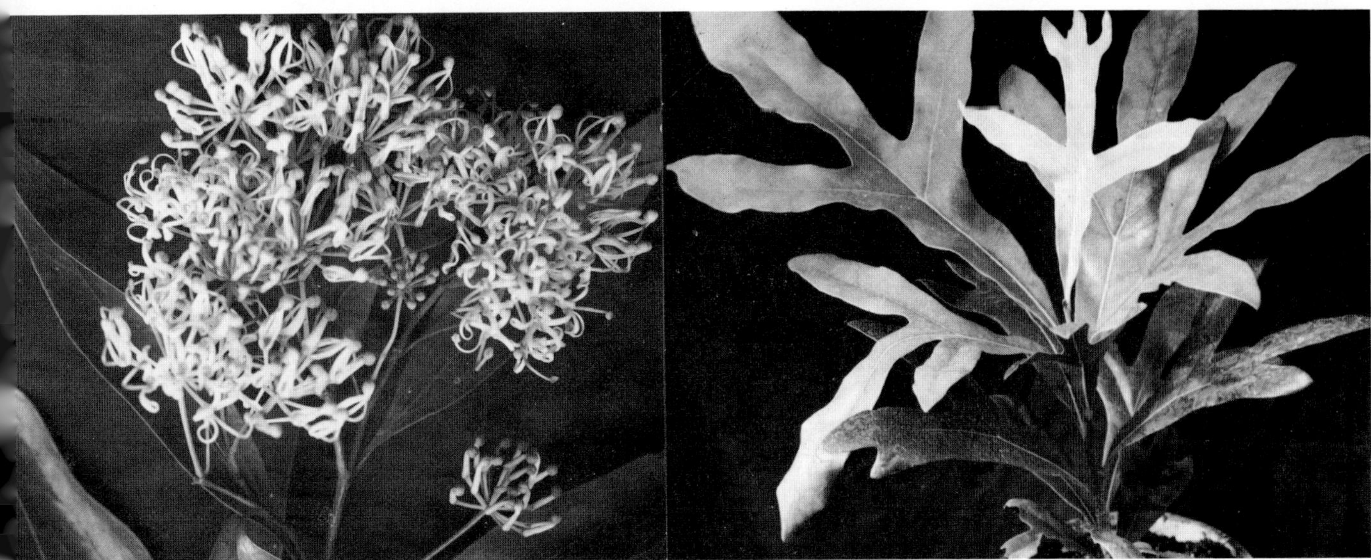

Stenocarpus salignus, flowers

Stenocarpus sinuatus, as a pot plant

Grevillea crithmifolia (W.Australia)

Grevillea punicea, "Red Spider-flower"

Grevillea rosmarinifolia

Grevillea robusta, the "Silky oak", inflorescence

Grevillea 'Noellii' (Monrovia Nursery, Calif.)

Faurea saligna (Transvaal)

Grevillea alpina (Australia: Victoria)

Banksia ericifolia, "Heath banksia"

Banksia grandis, sawtooth leaves

Banksia praemorsa (West Australia)

Banksia media (W.Australia)

Banksia serrata (J. Bogner)

Mimetes hottentotica (Cape Peninsula)

Banksia serrata (Tasmania, Victoria)

Banksia speciosa, near Perth, Western Australia

Hakea baxteri

Hakea victoriae, "Royal hakea"

Hakea cristata (Western Australia

Leucadendron adscendens, "Geelbos", Cape Prov., So. Africa

Dryandra carduacea, the "Honey pingle" in Queensla

Leucospermum ellipticum (spathulatum)

Leucadendron daphnoides, "Silvertree"

Leucospermum bolusii, a "Pincushion

Embothrium wickhamii, near Noumea, New Caledonia

Dryandra formosa, the "Showy dryandra" of Western Australia

Macadamia tetraphylla, young tree, in sunny Vista, California

Macadamia tetraphylla, the "Queensland nut", bearing fruit

Leucospermum catherinae, the "Catherine wheel", Cape Province

Leucospermum lineare, "Narrow-leafed pincushion"

Leucospermum nutans, "Nodding pincushion"

Leucospermum reflexum, "Rocket pincushion"

Leucospermum buxifolium (S.W.C

Leucospermum tottum, "Fire-wheel pincushion"

Leucospermum candicans, Cape Prov., South Africa

rotea mundii, at Kirstenbosch Botanic Garden

Protea cynaroides, the "King protea"

Protea sulphurea (Mountains of S.W. Cape)

Protea longifolia (S.W. Cape Prov.)

Protea latifolia hort. (eximia)

Protea cryophila, the rare "Snowball protea"

Protea neriifolia, "Oleander-leaf protea"

Protea susannae, at Strybing Arboretum, San Francisco

Protea compacta, the "Bot River protea"

Protea welwitschii, in the Transvaal

Protea minor, the "Ground-rose"

Protea rubropilosa, "Velvet protea" (Transvaal)

Protea speciosa, "Brown-beard"

Protea grandiceps, "Peach protea"

Protea repens, "Sugar bush"

Roupala brasiliensis

Protea lacticolor, "Baby protea"

Protea eximia

Serruria burmannii (Cape Prov.)

Telopea speciosissima, the "Waratah" (Queensland)

PSILOTACEAE: Psilotum, Tmesipteris; PUNICACEAE: Punica; RESEDACEAE: Reseda

Psilotum nudum, specimen, in Queensland

Psilotum nudum, on a treefern, in Hawaii

Tmesipteris tannensis, in N. Z.

Punica granatum; Pomegranate tree, with fruit

Punica granatum 'Nana'

Punica granatum legrellei, in flower

Reseda odorata

Anemone coronaria 'De Caen', a "Poppy anemone"

Paeonia 'Sophie', herbaceous "Peony"

Eranthis hyemalis 'Aurantiaca'

Nigella damascena (S.Europe)

Ranunculus asiaticus 'Picotee'

Phylica ericoides, in La Mortola, Italian Riviera

Helleborus lividus (corsicus), on Corsica

Ranunculus asiaticus

Anemone 'St. Brigid semi-double'

Anemone coronaria

Helleborus viridis

Helleborus orientalis x niger

Helleborus foetidus

Helleborus lividus (corsicus)

Aquilegia 'Long-spurred hybrid'

Delphinium ajacis (Larkspur)

Delphinium 'Ruysii' ('Pink Sensation')

Actaea rubra, (Red Bane-berry)

Anemone japonica

Anemone narcissiflora

Anemone blanda 'Blue Star'

Anemone coronaria

Anemone pulsatilla

Clematis x durandii

Clematis jackmanii hyb. 'Maureen'

Clematis armandii hyb. 'Appleblossom'

Clematis alpina

Clematis heracleifolia 'Davidiana'

Clematis orientalis

Clematis patens hyb. 'Sir Garnet Wolseley'

Clematis puberula

Clematis lanuginosa 'Mrs. Van Houtte'

Clematis lanuginosa 'Nellie Moser'

Clematis montana rubens

Clematis integrifolia

Clematis veitchiana

Clematis virginiana

Clematis texensis

Clematis tanqutica

Clematopsis scabiosifolia (Transvaal)

Rhamnus prinoides (Transvaal)

Clematis heracleifolia 'Davidiana'

Rhamnus alaternus 'Argenteo-variegata'

Clematis lanuginosa (China)

Clematis 'Barbara Jackman'

Clematis x lawsoniana 'Ramona', in Delaware

Clematis vitalba, "Traveller's Joy", in Europe

Helleborus niger

Helleborus orientalis atrorubens

Eranthis hyemalis

Eranthis cilicica

Eranthis x tubergenii **'Guinea Gold'**

Hepatica americana

Colletia spinosa hort., bot. prob. armata

Epidryos allenii, from Panama

Paliurus spina-christi, "Jerusalem- thorn"

Stegolepis parvipetala

Spathanthus bicolor

Ceanothus griseus horizontalis

Ceanothus griseus, "Wild lilac"

Colletia infausta (Chile)

zophora mucronata, "Mangroves", near Port Moresby, Papua

Bruguiera conjugata, "Oriental mangrove", Oahu, Hawaii

Rafflesia arnoldii, parasite on Sumatra

Rhizophora mangle, the "American mangrove", on Florida Keys

ruguiera conjugata, East Africa

Rhizophora mucronata, Leningrad

Emmenosperma alphitonioides (Taronga, Australia)

Thalictrum rochebrunianum

Paeonia lactiflora

Paeonia tenuifolia

Paeonia lactiflora 'Festiva'

Paeonia suffruticosa (Tree Peony)

Colletia cruciata

Salix matsudana 'Tortuosa'

Colletia cruciata

Malus pumila, trained as espalier

Raphiolepis umbellata ovata

Raphiolepis indica

Prunus serrulata 'Kanzan' (Jap. double-flowering cherry)

Chaenomeles lagenaria (Cydonia japonica hort.), Japanese Quince

Cotoneaster horizontalis 'Variegata'

Osteomeles schweriniae

Potentilla rupestris

Potentilla multifida

Fragaria x ananassa, the Garden strawberry

Fragaria vesca 'Albo-marginata'

Alchemilla vulgaris (Lady's Mantle)

Rubus reflexus

Rosa (hybrid perpetual) 'Ulrich Brunner'

Rosa chinensis minima 'Oakington Ruby'

Rosa 'Crimson Rambler'

Malus floribunda 'Scheideckeri'

Malus x atrosanguinea

Prunus triloba plena

Prunus laurocerasus 'Schipkaensis'

Prunus laurocerasus (English Laurel)

Kerria japonica 'Aureo-variegata'

Spiraea x vanhouttei

Raphiolepis indica

Prunus persica as Bonsai

Pyracantha x duvalii

Pyracantha koidzumii (crenato-serrata) 'Victory'

Eriobotrya japonica (Loquat)

Pyracantha fortuneana 'Graberi'

Cotoneaster apiculata

Cotoneaster horizontalis

Pyracantha coccinea 'Lalandei'

Crataegus monogyna biflora (oxyacantha)

Malus prunifolia, dwarfed "Crab-apple" in Tokyo

Duchesnea indica, "Mock-strawberry" from India

Cydonia oblonga, a "Quince" in New Zealand

Eriobotrya japonica, "Loquat", in Vista, California

Pyrus communis, "European pear", as espalier

Malus pumila paradisiaca, the "Paradise apple"

Prunus dulcis, the "Almond"

Prunus laurocerasus compacta, in Sweden

Prunus laurocerasus 'Otto Luyken', in Duesseldc

Malus baccata, grown as bonsai

·Pyrus kawakamii, "Evergreen pear" (Taiwan)

Pyrus kawakamii, in California

Prunus caroliniana 'Bright 'n' Tight' (Monrovia Nurs.)

Pyracantha x duvalii, "Red firethorn"

Heteromeles arbutifolia, "Toyon" or "California holly"

Photinia 'Fraseri' (Monrovia Nursery, California)

Kelseya uniflora, from Mountains of Wyoming

Cliffortia ruscifolia, "Climber's friend" (So.Africa)

Dryas octopetala (seed-stage)

Leucosidea sericea (So.Africa)

Osmaronia cerasiformis

Sanguisorba minor, in Europe

Petrophytum caespitosum (Spiraea)

Eriobotrya japonica 'Gold Nugget'

Photinia villosa (China, Korea, Japan)

Raphiolepis indica 'Enchantress'

Photinia serrulata, from China

Prunus caroliniana, "Carolina laurel"

Rubus reflexus, in Hongkong

Pyracantha crenulata flava

Cydonia oblonga, "Pineapple quince"

Rosa 'Better Times' (hybrid tea)

Rosa 'Golden Rapture' (hybrid tea)

Rosa 'Happiness' (hybrid tea)

Rosa (hybrid tea) 'Christian Dior'

Rosa (grandiflora) 'Buccaneer'

Rosa (grandiflora) 'War Dance'

Rosa (grandiflora) 'Ben Hur'

Rosa (grandiflora) 'Pink Parfait'

Rosa (grandiflora) 'El Capitan'

Rosa 'Magna Charta' (hyb. perpetual)

Rosa 'Mrs. W. C. Miller (hybrid tea)

Rosa 'Mothersday' (polyantha)

Rosa 'Eugene Jacquet' (rambler)

Rosa 'Double Paul's Scarlet' (climber)

Rosa 'Bonfire' (rambler)

Rosa 'Crimson Rosette' (polyantha)

Rosa 'Triomphe Orleanais' (polyantha)

Rosa 'Margo Koster' (polyantha)

Rosa (floribunda) 'Scarlet Marvel' Rosa (floribunda) 'Spice' Rosa (floribunda) 'Sarabande'

Rosa chinensis minima (roulettii)

Rosa 'Marechal Niel' (noisette)

Rosa chinensis minima 'Tom Thumb

Miniature Roses: 'Tom Thumb' 'Tinker Bell' 'Baby Gold Star'

Rosa 'Bonfire', trained Rambler rose for Easter bloom

Rosa 'Marechal Niel', fragrant climbing Noisette rose 1864

Rosa 'Rose Parade' (floribunda) (All-America 1975)

Rosa 'Red American Beauty' (hybrid tea 1959)

Rosa 'American Beauty (hybrid perpetual 1875)

Rosa banksiae, climber from China

Rosa 'Queen Elizabeth' (grandiflor

Rosa 'Golden Girl' (grandiflora)

Rosa 'Roundelay' (grandiflora)

Rosa 'Mandarin' (grandiflora)

Rosa 'La France', first Hybrid-tea 1867

Rosa 'Fashionette' (floribunda)

Rosa 'Blaze' (climber)

Rosa 'Tropicana' (hybrid tea)

Rosa 'Miss All-American Beauty' (hybrid tea)

Rosa 'Yankee Doodle' (hybrid tea 1976)

Rosa 'Mister Lincoln' (hybrid tea)

Rosa 'Starbright' (hybrid tea)

Rosa 'John S. Armstrong' (grandiflora)

Rosa 'Europeana' (floribunda)

Rosa 'Forever Yours' (hybrid tea)

Rosa 'Oregold' (hybrid tea 1975)

Alberta magna, in Zululand

Augusta grandiflora (Eastern Brazil)

Burchellia capensis

Bouvardia versicolor

Bouvardia laevis (Mexico)

Burchellia capensis rubra, "Wild pomegranate", (Natal)

Canthium huillense, "Wild coffee", in South Africa

Coprosma pumila, female "Mirror plant" with fruit

Coffea robusta; coffee harvest in the Central Highlands, Goroka, New Guinea

Alberta magna, in South Africa

Bouvardia ternifolia 'Fire Chief'

Coprosma repens 'Marginata'

Coprosma repens (baueri in hort.)

Coprosma repens 'Variegata

Coffea arabica, fruiting plant

Coffea liberica, branch with berries enclosing two beans

Coffea arabica, fruiting in Sao Paulo, Brazil

Coffea arabica in bloom

Cinchona calisaya (Quinine tree)

Nertera granadensis (depressa), the "Coral-bead plant"

Bouvardia ternifolia 'Giant Pink'

Bouvardia ternifolia 'White Joy'

Bouvardia ternifolia (triphylla)

Posoqueria latifolia

Bouvardia longiflora 'Albatross'

Bouvardia longiflora 'Humboldtii'

Mussaenda erythrophylla

Pentas lanceolata coccinea

Gardenia taitensis, Papeari Bot. Garden, Tahiti

Gardenia spatulifolia, the "Transvaal gardenia"

Rothmannia capensis, "Scented cups"

Gardenia jasminoides 'Mystery'

Damnacanthus major (Japan)

Gardenia thunbergia, in Durban, Natal

Gardenia jasminoides radicans fl.pl., "Minature gardenia

Gardenia jasminoides 'Fortuniana'

Gardenia jasminoides 'Veitchii'

Gardenia jasminoides radicans fl.pl.

Gardenia thunbergia

tailored Gardenia jasmin. 'Belmont' (Hadley)

Randia macrantha

Ixora coccinea

Carphalea kirondron (Rubia)

Ixora javanica

Myrmecodia platyrea | Hoffmannia roezlii | Hydnophytum formicarum

Hoffmannia ghiesbreghtii | Hoffmannia ghiesbreghtii 'Variegata' | Hoffmannia refulgens 'Vittata' | Hoffmannia refulgens

Serissa foetida 'Variegata'

Manettia inflata (bicolor)

Gardenia jasminoides 'Veitchii' (5½ inch pot)

Hamelia erecta, the Scarlet-bush

Ixora chinensis 'Rosea'

Hoffmannia 'Fantasia'

Hoffmannia refulgens 'Vittata'

Ixora chinensis

Ixora macrothyrsa 'Super-King'

Ixora coccinea 'Morsei'

Coffea arabica, with Coffee beans, in El Salvador

Coprosma repens (baueri), the "Mirror plant" of New Zealand

Gardenia jasminoides 'Veitchii', "Everblooming gardenia"

Pentas lanceolata, "Egyptian Star-cluster"

Schumanniophyton (Tetrastigma) magnificum (Gabon)

Warszewiczia coccinea cv 'David Auyong' in Trinidad

Pentas zanzibarensis giganteus

Damnacanthus macrophyllus

Catesbaea spinosa, "Lily-thorn"

Hoffmannia species 'Fantastic'

Hoffmannia roezlii (Mexico)

Pavetta indica (Sri Lanka)

Pachystigma thamnus, in the Transvaal

Ixora x williamsii (Kirsten)

Ixora x kewensis alba (Kew Gardens)

Ixora javanica, "Flame of the woods"

Ixora parviflora, from India

Mussaenda arcuata (Mauritius)

Mussaenda roxburghii (T. Everett, N.Y.Bot.G.)

Ixora odorata, in Botanic Garden Rio de Janeiro

Ixora borbonica (Enterospermum) (Réunion)

Ixora 'Orange King', "West Indian Jasmine"

Ixora duffii, from the Carolines, Micronesia

Luculia gratissima  | Luculia grandifolia (tsetensis) at Auckland, N.Z.  | Luculia grandifolia

Galium verum ("Yellow Bedstraw") | Mitchella rēpens (Partridge-berry)

Erythrochiton brasiliensis | Houstonia serpyllifolia ('Bluets') | Galium boreale (Bedstraw)

Morinda citrifolia 'Variegata', in Fiji

Mussaenda philippica, collected in the Finisterres, N. E. New Guinea

Mussaenda incana

Mussaenda philippica 'Aurorae', at the Botanical Gardens, Hong Kong

Mussaenda luteola

Mussaenda erythrophylla, in Thailand

Portlandia platantha, in Mexico

Portlandia grandiflora

Pentas lanceolata

Pavetta caffra

Serissa foetida 'Variegata' in flower

Rondeletia splendens

Rondeletia leucophylla, at Missouri Bot. Gardens

Rondeletia odorata

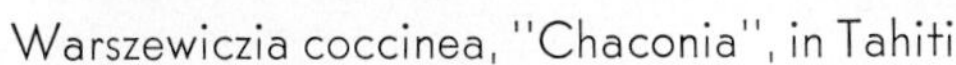
Warszewiczia coccinea, "Chaconia", in Tahiti

Warszewiczia coccinea plenissima (Trinidad)

Mussaenda erythrophylla 'Queen Sirikit', in Singapore

Myrmecodia armata, an "Ant-plant" from Malaya

Rondeletia cordata (Guatemala)

Rondeletia odorata, in Cologne

Rondeletia gratissima (Perú)

Portlandia grandiflora, "Tree-lily"

Oxyanthus natalensis (Posoqueria)

Rondeletia strigosa, in Sydney B.G

Randia maculata, from Sierra Leone, W.Africa

Mitchella repens, "Partridge-berry"

Crowea saligna (Eastern Australia)

Boronia alata, (W. Australia)

Murraya koenigii, "Curry-leaf" (India)

Murraya exotica, the "Orange-jessamine"

Calodendrum capense, "Cape chestnut"

Pilocarpus pennatifolius (Brazil)

Choisya ternata, "Mexican-orange"

Peltostigma ptelioides (Jamaica)

Adenandra fragrans

Adenandra uniflora

Boronia denticulata

Murraya paniculata

Murraya exotica

Diosma reevesii

Ruta graveolens (Rue)

Boronia megastigma

Boronia elatior

Citrus mitis, "Calamondin", potgrown for Christmas

Fortunella crassifolia, "Meiwa-kumquat", in Florida

Citrus microcarpa, an "Orangequat" in Taiwan

Citrus reticulata, "Satsuma mandarin orange"

Casimiroa edulis, "White sapote" (Mexico and Guatemala)

Aegle marmelos, "Bael fruit" (India)

Citrus aurantium, "Seville orange"

Citrus aurantium 'Myrtifolia Chinotto'

Citrus sinensis 'Valencia' (summer-bearing)

Citrus sinensis 'Washington Navel' (winter fruit)

Citrus limon 'Eureka', "Acid lemon"

Citrus aurantifolia, the "Lime", in California

Citrus limon 'Meyer', the "Meyer lemon" or "Dwarf Chinese"

Citrus sinensis 'Washington Navel' in flower

Citrus 'Temple', a "Tangor"

Citrus sinensis (Sweet Orange)

Citrus aurantium 'Myrtifolia'

Citrus mitis (Calamondin)

Citrus limon 'Ponderosa' (Wonder lemon)

Fortunella margarita (Kumquat)

Citrus x paradisi, the Grapefruit

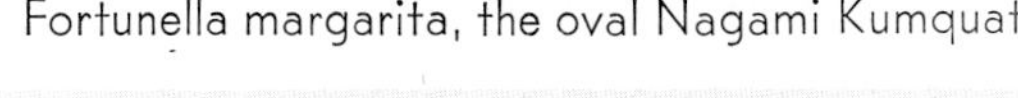

Fortunella margarita, the oval Nagami Kumquat

Citrus taitensis, the Otaheite Orange

Skimmia japonica 'Dwarf female'

Citrus sinensis 'Variegated Pineapple-orange' Citrus mitis (Calamondin) Fortunella hindsii (Dwarf Kumquat)

Poncirus trifoliata (Hardy orange) Citrus limon 'Ponderosa' (Wonder-lemon) Citrus maxima, the "Shaddock"

Correa speciosa 'Backhousiana'

Correa speciosa

equaertiodendrum magalis-montanum, the "Stemfruit" of Africa

Litchi chinensis, fruits in Taichung, Taiwan

Citrus aurantium 'Myrtifolia'

Triphasia trifolia, "Lime-berry"

Citrus limon 'Meyer', "Chinese lemon"

Glycosmis pentaphylla (Philippines)

Poncirus trifoliata, ("Hardy" orange)

Skimmia reevesiana (China)

Xanthoceras sorbifolium

Alectryon excelsum ('Titoki'), in N. Z.

Koelreuteria paniculata

Pilocarpus pennatifolius

Murraya alata

Murraya paniculata

Correa x harrisii

Crowea saligna

Dictamnus albus

Santalum ellipticum, "Sandalwood", on Maui, Hawaii

Salix matsudana 'Tortuosa', "Dragon-claw willow" of Korea

Pometia pinnata, "Langsir" on Nuku Hiva, Marquesas

Cardiospermum halicacabum, the pantropic "Balloon vine"

Mimusops roxburghiana, "Kanapalei"

Mimusops commersonii, a "Spanish-cherry" (Madagascar)

Manilkara zapota, the "Sapodilla" or "Chicle", with fruit

Manilkara (Achras) zapota, "Sapote" or "Marmelade plum"

Litchi chinensis, the "Lychee nut" of China

Nephelium lappaceum, "Rambutan" fruit in Saigon market

Licania tomentosa, the "Oiti", in Bahia, Brazil

Blighia sapida, the "Aki", Montego Bay, Jamaica

Erythrophysa transvaalensis, in South Africa

Paullinia thalictrifolia, from Brazil

Harpullia arborea, "Puas"

Casimiroa edulis 'Suebelle' (Sapote)

Dodonaea viscosa 'Purpurea', "Hop-bush"

Houttuynia cordata (Himalaya to Japan)

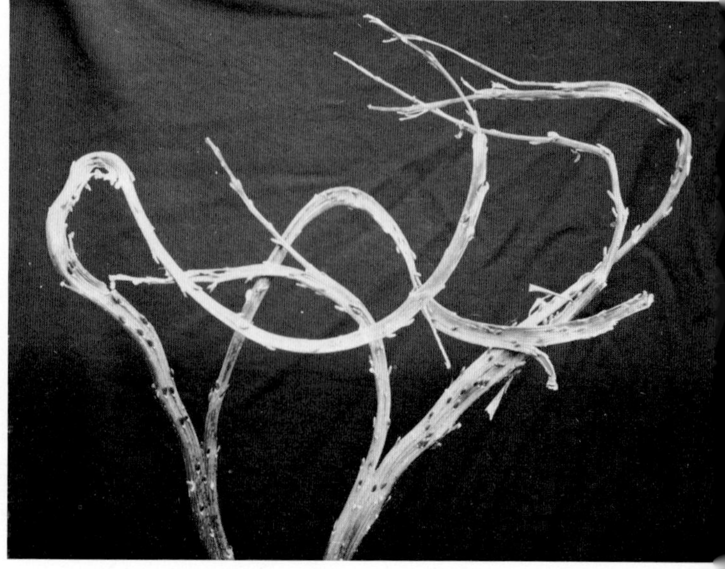

Salix sachalinensis (Northern Japan to Kuriles)

Salix discolor (Pussy Willows)

Serjania glabrata (communis)

Astilbe japonica 'Deutschland' Astilbe japonica 'Gladstone' (florists' spiraea)

Tolmiea menziesii, the Piggy-back plant

Deutzia x lemoinei

Deutzia scabra

Deutzia x rosea

Bergenia (Saxifraga) ciliata ligulata, the "Winter-begonia"

Bergenia cordifolia

Bergenia ciliata ligulata 'Rosea'

Bergenia ciliata ligulata 'Leichtlinii'

Bergenia crassifolia

Peltiphyllum peltatum

Boykinia tellimoides (Japan)

Hydrangea macrophylla 'Sensation' (bi-color)

Bauera rubioides (Tasmania)

Braxia madagascariensis (spine-tooth form)

Braxia madagascariensis

ibes speciosum "Fuchsia-flowered gooseberry"

Astilbe x arendsii, in Gotland

Deutzia gracilis (Japan)

Francoa ramosa

Itea ilicifolia

Hydrangea bretschneideri

Anopterus glandulosus

Escallonia organensis

Hydrangea arborescens

Hydrangea aspera

pot-grown Hydrangea macrophylla 'Mein Liebling' as semi-standard

root-climbing Hydrangea petiolaris adorning a window in Germany

a commercial plant of Hydrangea macrophylla 'Merveille', **forced for Easter**

Hydrangea macrophylla 'Chaperon Rouge' or 'Red Cap'

Hydrangea macrophylla 'Flamboyant'

Hydrangea macrophylla 'Ave Maria'

Hydrangea macrophylla 'Todi'

Hydrangea macrophylla 'Merveille'

Hydrangea macrophylla tricolor

Hydrangea macrophylla 'Soeur Therese'

Hydrangea paniculata grandiflora

Hydrangea macrophylla 'Alpengluehn'

Hydrangea quercifolia

Hydrangea macrophylla 'Enziandom'

Hydrangea macrophylla 'Strafford' (Mad. Cayeux)

Hydrangea macrophylla 'Kuhnert'

Hydrangea macrophylla 'Rosabelle'

Hydrangea serrata acuminata

Hydrangea macrophylla fl. pl. 'Tosca'

Hydrangea macrophylla 'Mariesii'

Hydrangea sargentiana

Hydrangea quercifolia

Hydrangea macrophylla 'Otaksa', at Lemoine's, Nancy, France

Hydrangea macrophylla 'Maculata'

Kirengeshoma palmata

Saxifraga stolonifera in bloom

Saxifraga granulata

Saxifraga stolonifera (sarmentosa)

Saxifraga stolonifera 'Tricolor'

Saxifraga cuscutaeformis

Philadelphus x virginalis

Saxifraga umbrosa

Saxifraga cotyledon pyramidalis

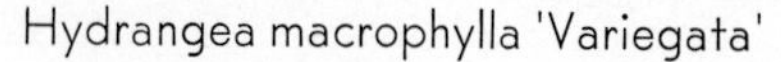

Hydrangea macrophylla 'Variegata'

Heuchera sanguinea, "Coral bells"

Dichroa fabrifuga (Himalaya)

Hydrangea serrata (thunbergii) (Japan, Korea)

Hydrangea xanthoneura var.wilsonii (W.China)

Saxifraga longifolia (Pyrenées)

Saxifraga burseriana (Eastern Alps)

Alonsoa warscewiczii (Perú)

Antirrhinum majus 'Butterfly type'

Angelonia grandiflora

Allophyton mexicanum, "Mexican violet"

Dermatobotrys saundersonii

Adenosma glutinosum (Hongkong)

Chamaegigas intrepidus, a water-plant, in Namibia

Craterostigma pumilum (Ethiopia)

Calceolaria amplexicaulis (Peru)

Calceolaria mexicana

Calceolaria teucrioides (E. Hahn)

Calceolaria integrifolia 'Red slippers'

Calceolaria scabiosaefolia (Ecuador to Chile)

Mimulus guttatus, "Monkey-flower"

Hydrotrida caroliniana

Hydrotriche hottoniifolia (Aquatic)

Chaenostoma fastigiatum (Little Stars) | Ourisia coccinea | Calceolaria herbeohybrida 'Hunt's Choicest'

Calceolaria herbeohybrida 'Multiflora nana' | Calceolaria herbeohybrida 'Grandiflora' | Calceolaria integrifolia (rugosa)

Isoplexis (Calianassa) canariensis | Castilleja indivisa | Angelonia gardneri

SCROPHULARIACEAE: Penstemon, Antirrhinum, Digitalis, Phygelius, Angelonia, Asarina

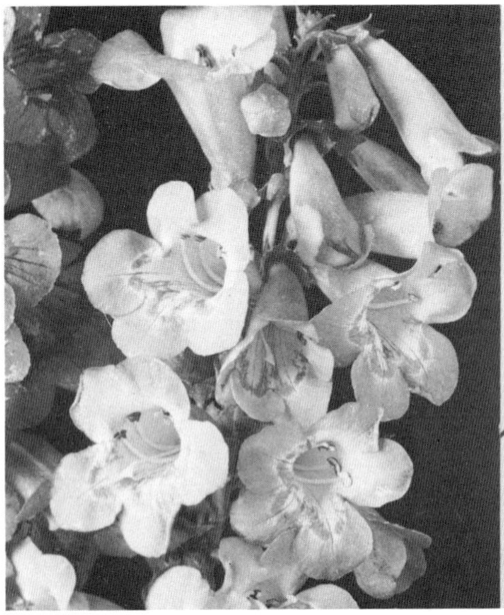

Penstemon x gloxinioides

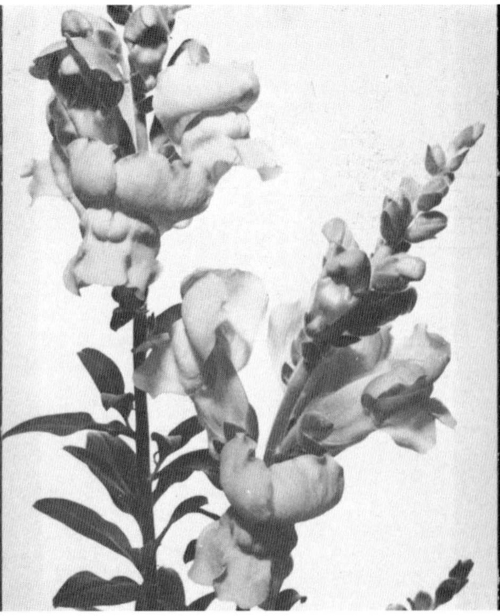

Antirrhinum majus (Snapdragon)

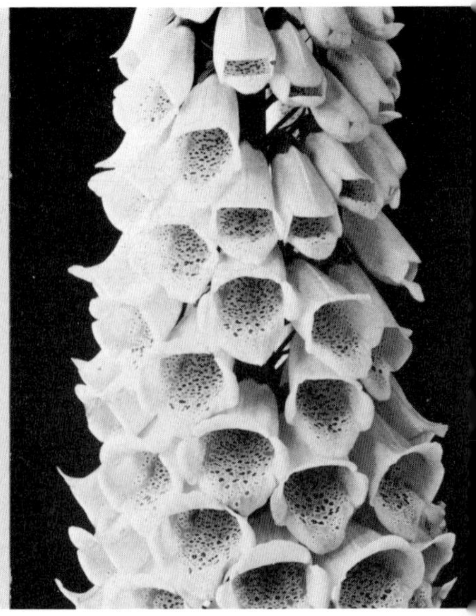

Digitalis purpurea (Foxglove)

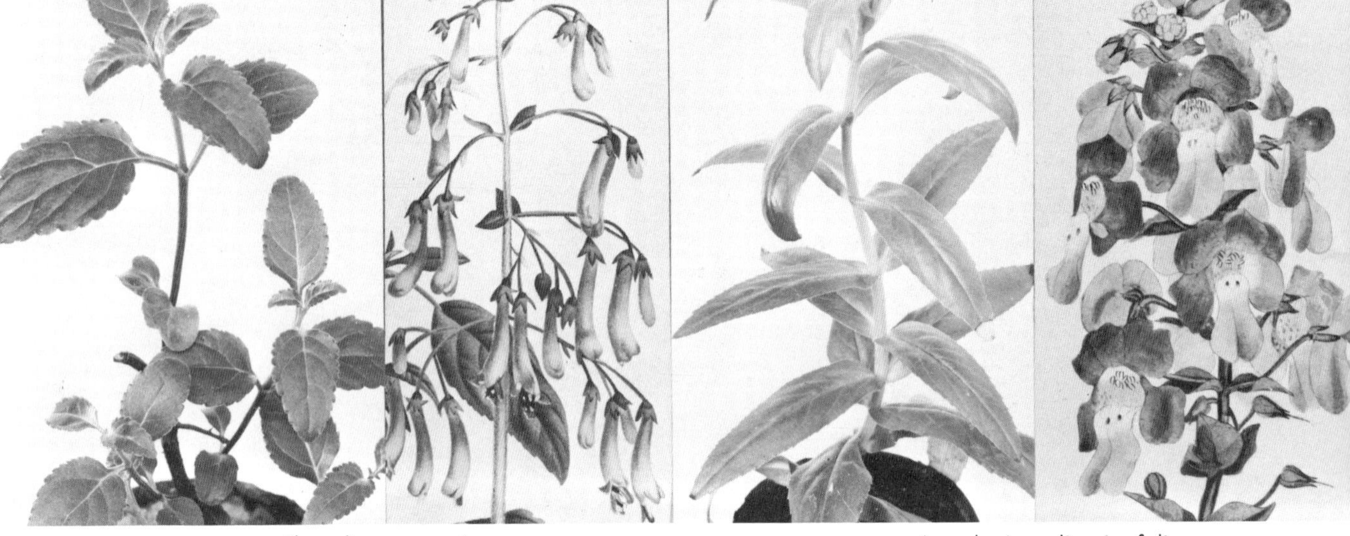

Phygelius capensis

Angelonia salicariaefolia

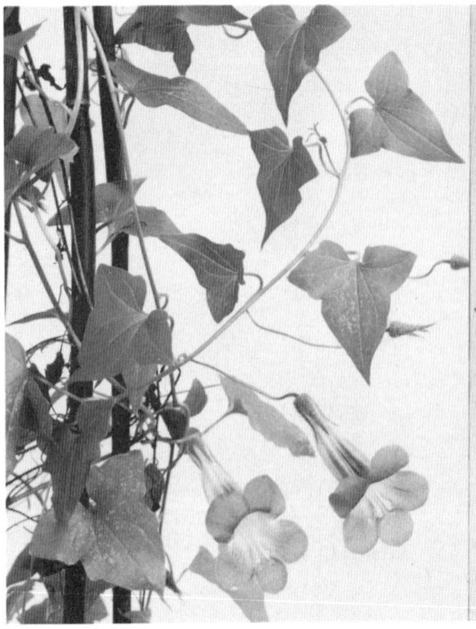

Asarina (Maurandya) antirrhiniflora

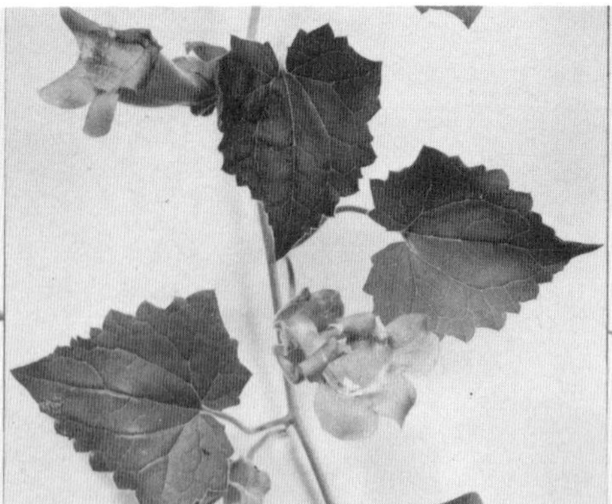

Asarina erubescens

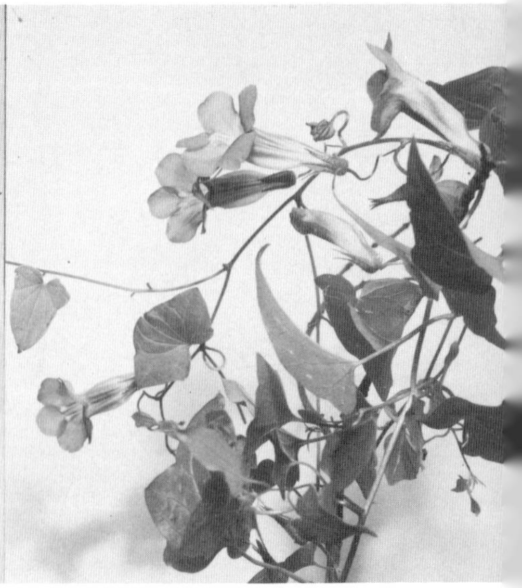

Asarina barclaiana

Hebe (Veronica) x andersonii

Veronica spicata

Hebe elliptica (Veronica decussata)

Mimulus aurantiacus

Hebe (Veronica) speciosa

Hebe 'Cranleighensis'

Hebe (Veronica) buxifolia 'Variegata'

Allophyton mexicanum (Tetranema)

Cymbalaria muralis (Kenilworth ivy)

Hebe (Veronica) x andersonii 'Variegata'

Hebe diosmaefolia

Leucophyllum texanum

Nemesia strumosa 'Blue Gem'

Digitalis ambigua

Jovellana (Calceolaria) sinclairi

Hebe (Veronica) salicifolia

Hebe x imperialis

Hebe speciosa 'Variegata'

Hebe 'Alicia Amherst'

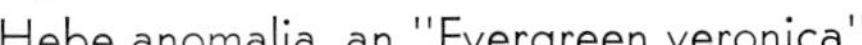
Hebe anomalia, an "Evergreen veronica"

Hebe armstrongii, in Canterbury, New Zealand

Veronica hookeriana (New Zealand)

Hebe lyallii (Milford Sound, New Zealand)

Veronica allionii (pyrenaica) (So. Europe)

Hebe subalpina, in Fiordland, New Zealand

Hebe colensoi (New Zealand)

Hebe vernicosa (N.Z.)

Hebe dieffenbachii (New Zealand)

Hebe epacridea, in Marlborough, New Zealand

Hebe cupressoides, (Otago, New Zealand)

Hebe elliptica, (New Zealand, Falkland Islands)

Hebe x andersonii 'Snowflake' (E. Hahn, Germany)

Zaluzianskya villosa

Hebe (Veronica) x andersonii

Sibthorpia pichinchensis

Hebenstretia dentata (So. Africa)

Isoplexis sceptrum (Canary Islands)

Celsia arcturus (Cretan Bears-tail)

Linaria maroccana (Toadflax)

Digitalis purpurea (Foxglove)

Charadrophila capensis

Rhodochiton volubile,

Torenia fournieri

Chaenostoma grandiflorum (Sutera grandiflora)

Nemesia strumosa

Russelia equisetiformis, the Coral plant

Russelia equisetiformis

Mazus reptans

Mimulus lowisii

Mimulus aurantiacus (Diplacus glutinosus)

Mimulus moschatus

Sibthorpia europaea 'Variegata'

Torenia fournieri

Paulownia imperialis

Nemesia strumosa 'Suttonii', "Cape jewels"

Torenia concolor

Torenia baillonii (flava of hort)

Chaenostoma grandiflorum

Russelia sarmentosa

Digitalis ambigua, "Foxglove"

Penstemon x gloxinioides

Penstemon diffusus

Penstemon x gloxinioides 'Fire King'

Selaginella wallichii, from Malaysia

Selaginella, species, on exhibition, Hibiya, Tokyo

Selaginella mariesii (Japan)

Selaginella serpens (W. Indies)

Selaginella tamariscina, in Tokyo

Selaginella flabellata (Argentina)

Selaginella x burgeffii (Wuerzburg, Germany)

Selaginella kraussiana (denticulata)

Selaginella kraussiana 'Brownii'

Selaginella emmeliana

Selaginella willdenovii

Selaginella caulescens

Selaginella martensii divaricata

Selaginella uncinata

Selaginella martensii 'Watsoniana'

Selaginella kraussiana 'Aurea'

Selaginella plumosa

Selaginella kraussiana (denticulata of the trade) the Spreading Clubmoss

Selaginella emmeliana, the Sweat plant

Selaginella martensii 'Variegata'

Selaginella lepidophylla (Rose of Jericho)

Selaginella uncinata

Selaginella martensii

Selaginella erythropus

Selaginella commutata

Selaginella biformis

Selaginella pulcherrima

Selaginella serpens

Selaginella versicolor

Selaginella cuspidata

Selaginella pilifera

Selaginella vogelii

Selaginella plana

Selaginella wallichii

Selaginella canaliculata

Selaginella delicatula

Brunfelsia pauciflora calycina

Brunfelsia latifolia hort. (australis)

Brunfelsia undulata

Brunfelsia pauciflora "Floribunda"

Browallia speciosa major

Nierembergia caerulea (hippomanica)

Browallia speciosa major

Iochroma lanceolatum

Atropa belladonna, "Deadly night-shade"

Iochroma coccineum (Perú)

Hyocyamus aureus, in Crete

Lycium ruthenicum, "Box-thorn"

Nicotiana tabacum, "Tobacco"

Iochroma warscewiczii, in Sydney

Cestrum parqui spurium, "Willow jessamine"

Iochroma tubulosum

Brunfelsia undulata (Jamaica)

Brunfelsia americana, "Lady of the night"

Browallia speciosa alba

Brugmansia suaveolens

Datura meteloides

Brugmansia arborea (Sherman)

Browallia speciosa, "Sapphire flower"

Brunfelsia nitida (West Indies)

Brugmansia candida, in the Cordilleras of Perú

Brugmansia aurea

Brugmansia sanguinea, at Nassau Bot. Garden, Bahamas

Brugmansia rosei (sanguinea hort.), Ecuador

Brugmansia suaveolens, a large flowered Angel's Trumpet

Brugmansia candida plena

Datura meteloides (in Texas)

Brugmansia candida (arborea hort.)

Datura wrightii (inoxia in hort.)

Datura metel florepleno (fastuosa in hort.)

Brugmansia mollis, at Longwood Gardens, Pennsylvania

Brugmansia suaveolens, at Longwood Gardens, Pennsylvania

Datura chlorantha

Datura meteloides, a "Thorn-apple"

Datura metel florepleno (double fl.)

Datura cornigera

Datura stramonium (Jimson-weed)

Juanulloa aurantiaca

Cestrum aurantiacum

Schizanthus x wisetonensis

Salpiglossis sinuata

Capsicum annuum 'Piccolo'

Capsicum annuum 'Christmas Candle'

Capsicum annuum 'Robert Craig'

Capsicum annuum 'Piccolo', a variegated-leaf ornamental pepper

Mandragora officinarum, the "Mandrake"

Capsicum annuum conoides 'Red Chile' (frutescens)

Solanum pseudo-capsicum (Jerusalem cherry)

Capsicum annuum cerasiforme 'Birdseye'

Capsicum annuum conoides 'Acorn'

Capsicum annuum conoides 'Celestial'

Capsicum annuum conoides 'Candle pepper'

Solanum abutiloides (T. Everett)

Vestia lycioides Chile)

Solanum glutinosum (Peru)

Solanum martii, in Rio

Solanum laurifolium (Mexico)

Nierembergia caerulea, "Cup-flower"

Solanum jasminoides (Brazil)

Solandra guttata (Mexico)

Solandra nitida, "Cup of gold"

Cyphomandra betacea, "Tomato tree"

Solanum rantonnetii, "Potato-bush"

Solanum melongena 'Moorea'

Solanum capsicastrum 'Variegatum'

Lycopersicon lycopersicum 'Tiny Tim'

Solanum quitoense (T. Everett)

Solanum pseudo-capsicum, "Jerusalem cherry"

Solanum mauritianum (So. Africa)

Nicotiana tabacum 'Kentucky'

Nicotiana x sanderae

Nicotiana alata grandiflora (affinis)

Jaborosa integrifolia

Nicotiana tabacum 'Variegata', a variegated-leaf tobacco-plant

Nicotiana glauca (Tree-tobacco)

Nicotiana tabacum macrophylla 'Variegata'

Nicotiana sylvestris

Brugmansia arborea, in the Andes near Quito, Ecuador

Nicotiana tabacum, on Rapa Nui (Easter Island) Chile

Solanum rantonnetii, "Blue potato bush" (Paraguay)

Physalis alkegenii (franchetii), "Chinese lanterns"

Cestrum purpureum (elegans)

Cestrum nocturnum, the fragrant Night-jessamine

Atropa belladonna, the Deadly Nightshade or Belladonna, with poisonous berries

Cyphomandra betacea, the Tree-tomato

Solanum auriculatum

Solanum marginatum

Petunia x hybrida fl. pl. 'Caprice'

Petunia x hybrida fl. pl. 'Sonata'

Petunia x hybrida 'California Giant'

Petunia x hybrida grandiflora 'Popcorn'

Petunia x hybrida grandiflora 'Pink Magic'

Petunia x hybrida grandiflora 'Crusader'

Petunia x hybrida grandiflora 'Elk's Pride'

Petunia x hybrida multiflora 'Glitters'

Petunia x hybrida 'Celestial Rose' (dwarf bedding)

Petunia x hybrida grandiflora 'Maytime'

Petunia x hybrida multiflora 'Satellite'

Petunia x hybrida grandiflora 'Bingo'

Juanulloa **aurantiaca**

Petunia x hybrida grandiflora 'Calypso'

Physalis peruviana edulis

Scopolia carniolica

'Potomato', the fanciful result of my grafting a tomato scion (Lycopersicon esculentum) on a sprouted potato tuber (Solanum tuberosum), at Sioux Falls, South Dakota, 1926

Schizanthus x wisetonensis 'Cherry Shades', the showy Butterfly flower or Poor Man's orchid

Lycopersicon lycopersicum 'Yellow Pear', an ornamental pear- shaped tomato

Lycopersicon lycopersicum 'Tiny Tim', an edible miniature tomato

Solanum aviculare Solanum laciniatum Solanum melongena (Egg Plant)

Solanum sodomaeum, the Dead-sea apple **Solanum crispum**

Cestrum nocturnum (Night-Jessamine) Solanum mammosum, in Java

Solandra nitida, the Chalice vine

Solandra longiflora, the Trumpet plant

Physalis alkekengi (franchetii), the Chinese Lantern plant

Streptosolen jamesonii

Capsicum annuum grossum 'Green Bell pepper'

Lycopersicon lycopersicum cerasiforme (Cherry tomato)

Solanum robustum (alatum) Solanum macrocarpum Solanum macranthum

Cestrum parqui Cestrum nocturnum (Night-Jessamine) Capsicum baccatum (Japan)

Solanum jasminoides Solanum wendlandii

Solanum pyracanthum

Solanum vespertilio

Capsicum annuum 'Weatherillii'

Solanum capsicastrum 'Variegatum', in Germany

Solanum warscewiczii

Solanum sisymbrifolium

Solanum pseudocapsicum (Jerusalem Cherry)

Solanum seaforthianum

Sterculia alexandria, "Veld chestnut", in S.E.Africa

Sterculia nobilis, from China

Brachychiton rupestris

Brachychiton acerifolium

Brachychiton diversifolium hort., bot. populr

Brachychiton populneum, "Kurrajong" in Eastern Australia

Pterospermum acerifolium, in Paris Bot.Garden, France

Brachychiton acerifolium, the "Flame tree" in tropical Northern Australia

Dombeya x cayeuxii, the "Mexican rose"

Heritiera fischeri, the "Glass tree" in Leningrad Bot. G.

Dombeya rotundifolia, in the Transvaal  Brachychiton rupestris (Sydney Bot. Garden)  Hermannia plicata

Thomasia solanacea, at Kew Fremontodendron mexicanum Abroma fastuosum

Dombeya wallichii Mahernia verticillata, the Honey-bells

Brachychiton (Sterculia) rupestris, the peculiar Bottle-tree, in Queensland, Australia

Theobroma cacao, the Cocoa tree, in flower

fruits enclosing the Cocoa seeds, borne on the trunk of Theobroma cacao, in Trinidad

Dombeya rotundifolia, "Wild pear", in the Transvaal

Dombeya viscosa, "Wedding flower" (Madagascar)

Fremontodendron mexicanum, in San Diego

Fremontodendron californicum, "Flannel-bush"

Pterospermum lancifolium, in Syc

Hermannia grandiflora (Namibia)

Hermannia candicans (So.Africa)

Thomasia pauciflora (Australia)

Mahernia verticillata (Sterc.) Theobroma cacao (Sterc.) Theobroma cacao producing fruit

Daphne odora 'Marginata' (Thym.) Tacca chantrieri, the Bat-flower Brachychiton acerifolium (Sterc.)

Eurya japonica 'Variegata' (Theac.)

Daphne odora (Thym.)

 Succulents: see Aizoaceae Amaryllidaceae Asclepiadaceae Bromeliaceae Compositae Crassulaceae Euphorbiaceae Geraniaceae Liliaceae Portulacaceae Vitaceae

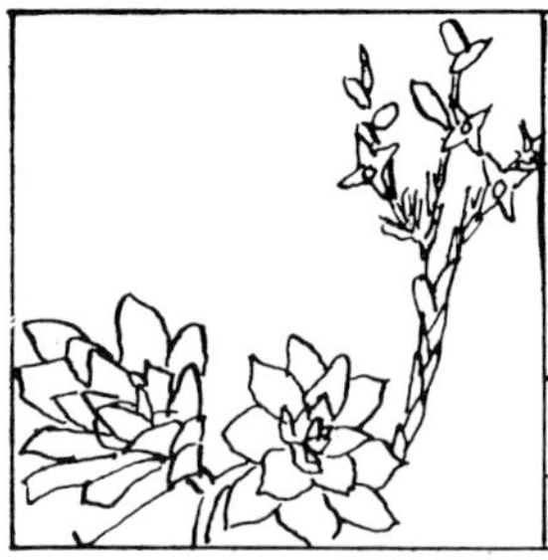

Aeonium haworthii

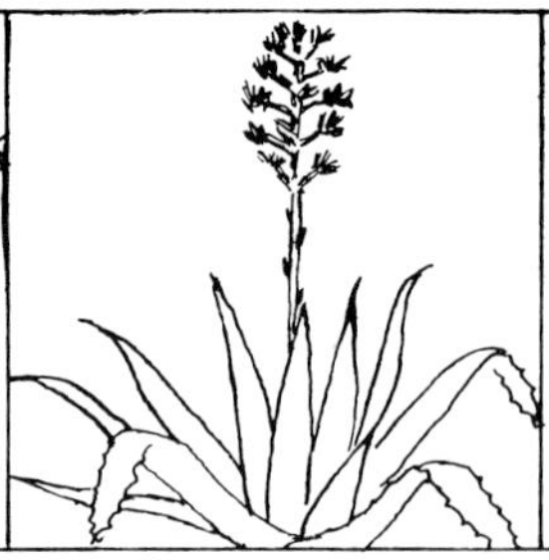

Agave americana

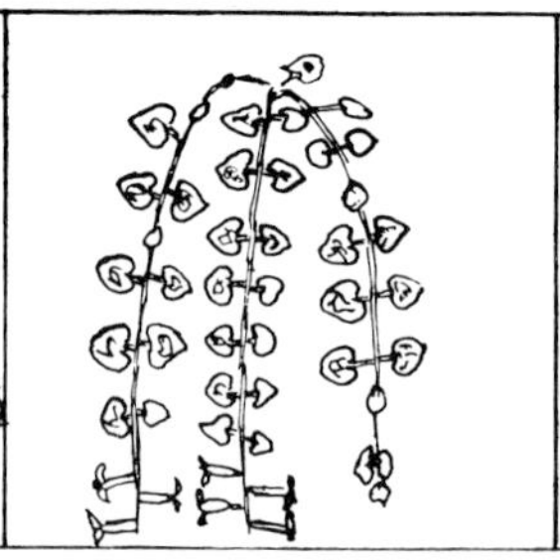

Ceropegia woodii

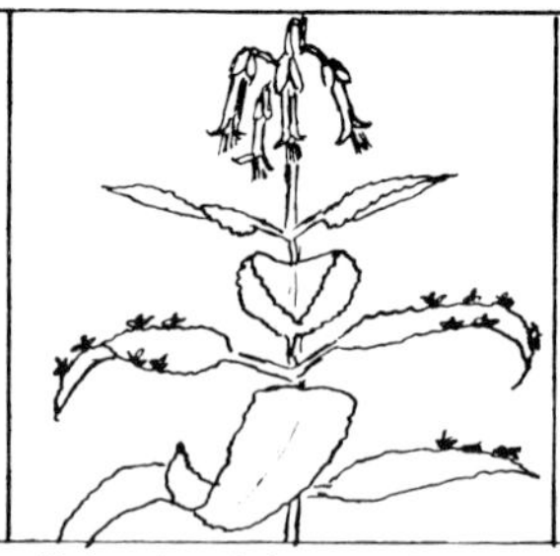

Kalanchoe daigremontianum

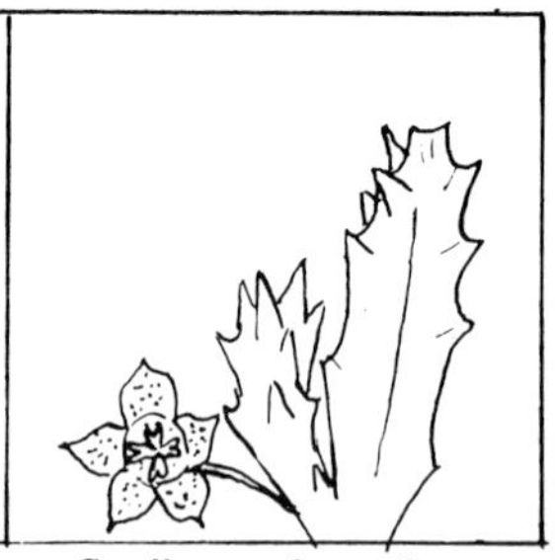

Caralluma nebrownii

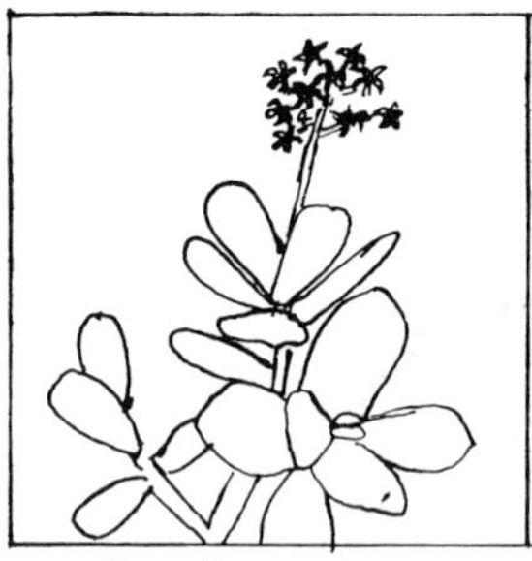

Crassula argentea

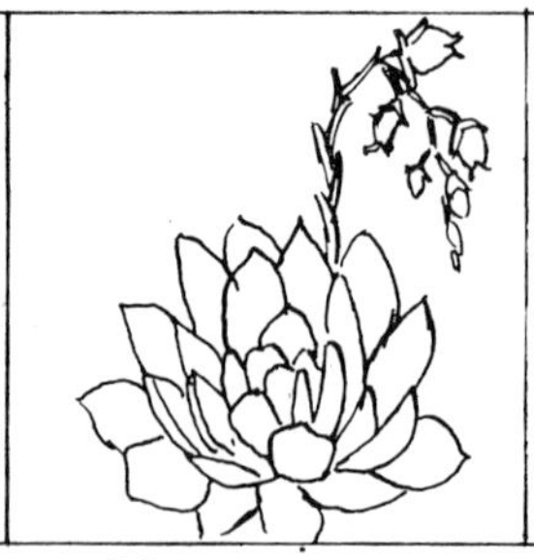

Echeveria elegans

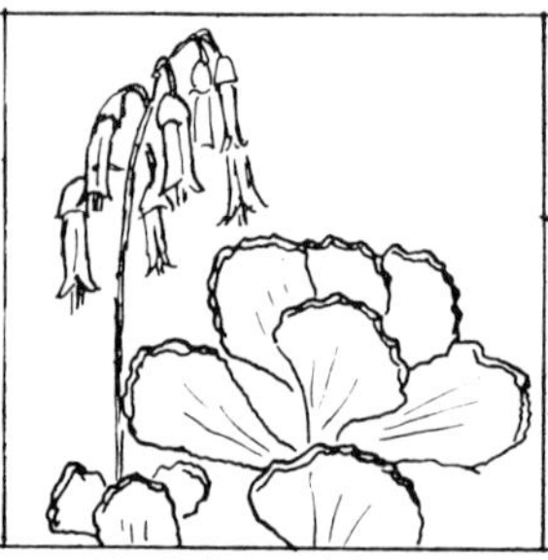

Cotyledon undulata

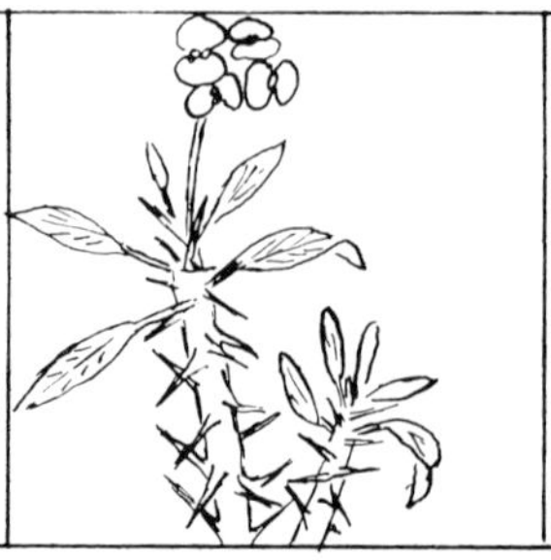

Euphorbia milii

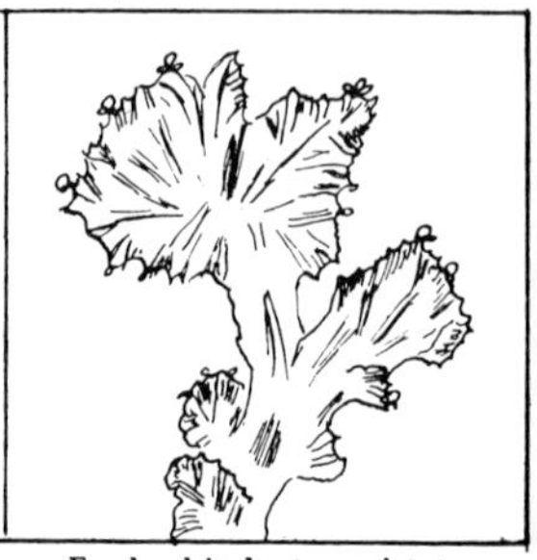

Euphorbia lactea cristata

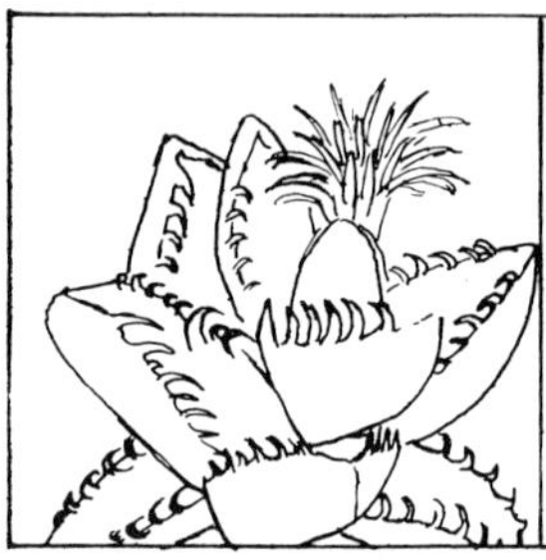

Faucaria tigrina

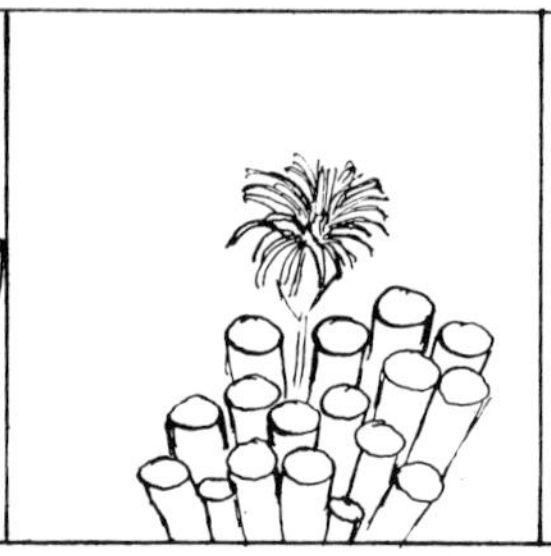

Fenestraria rhopalophylla

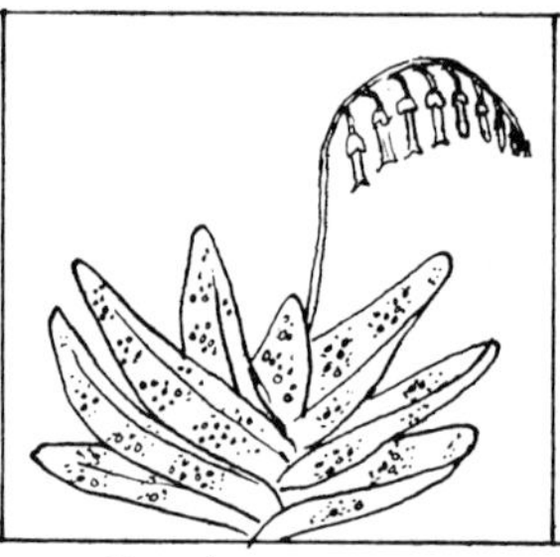

Gasteria verrucosa

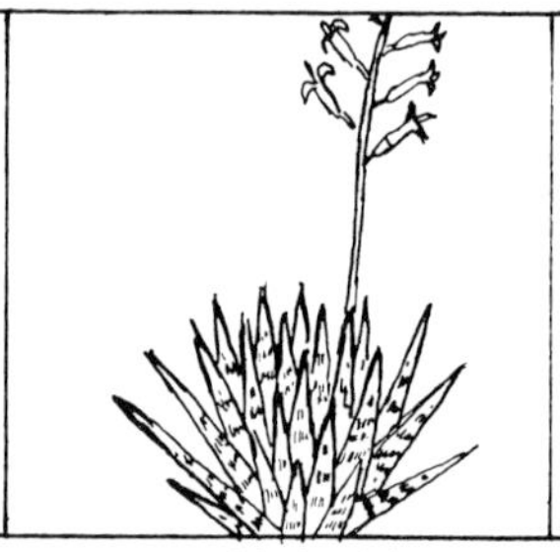

Haworthia fasciata

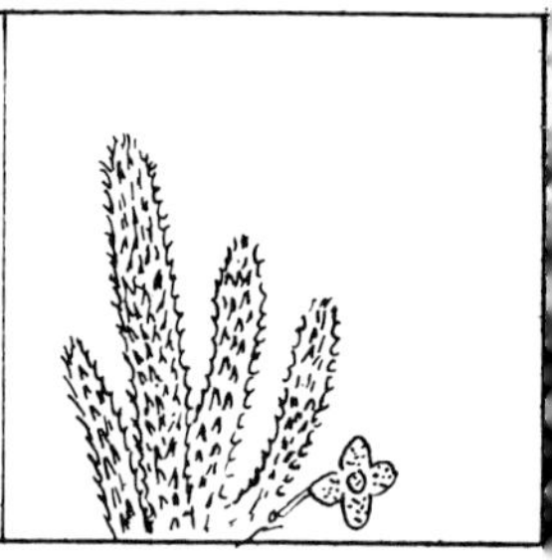

Huernia pillansii

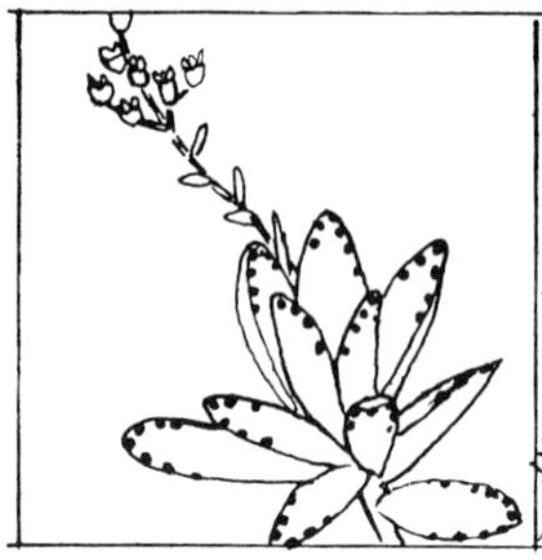

Kalanchoe tomentosa

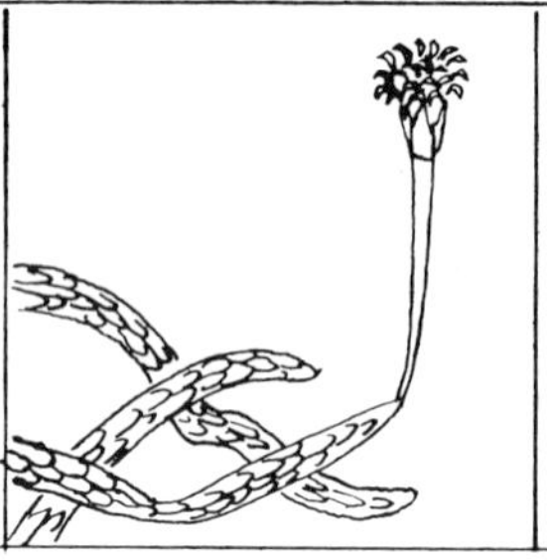

Senecio pendulus

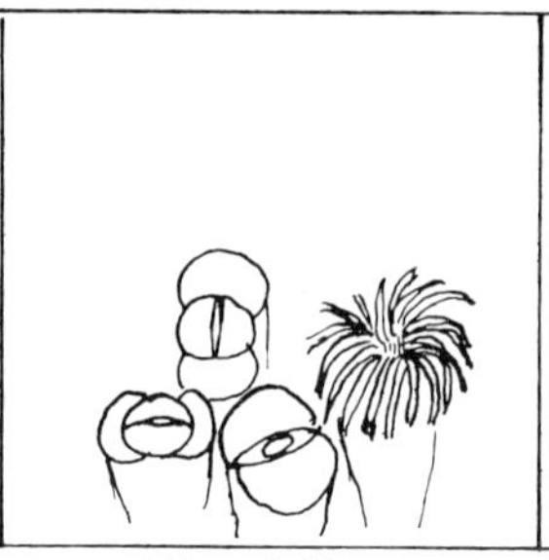

Lithops bella

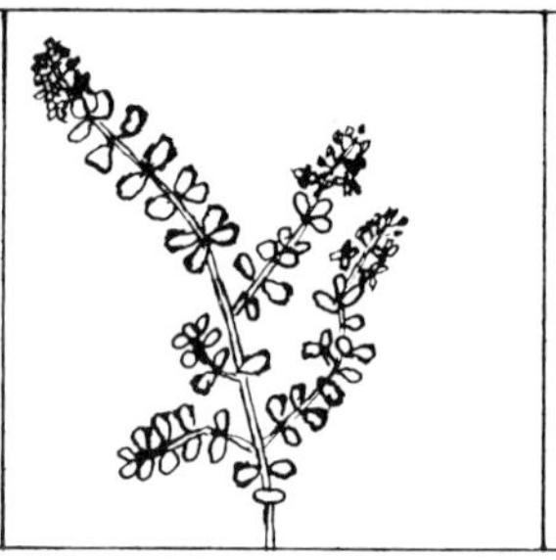

Portulacaria afra

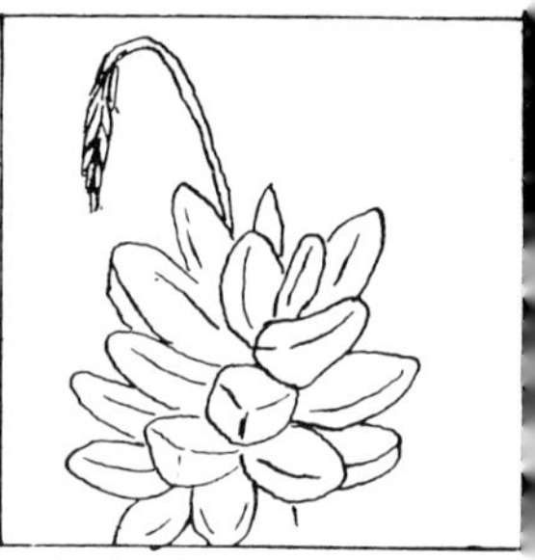

Pachyphytum compactum

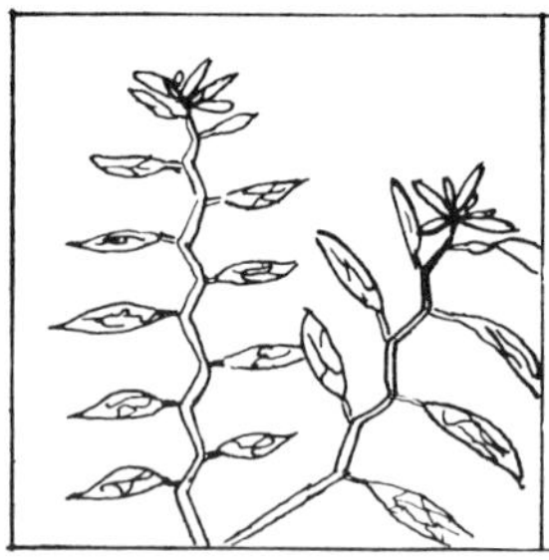

Pedilanthus tithy varieg.

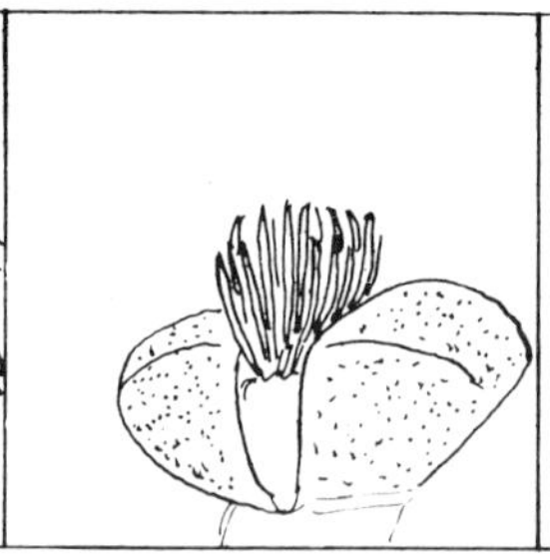

Pleiospilos bolusii

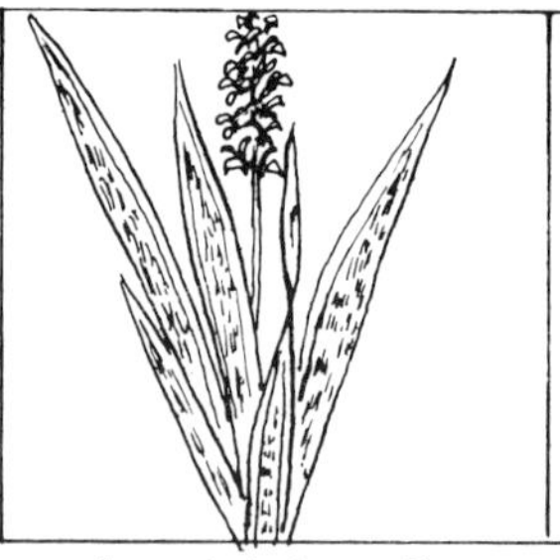

Sansevieria laurentii

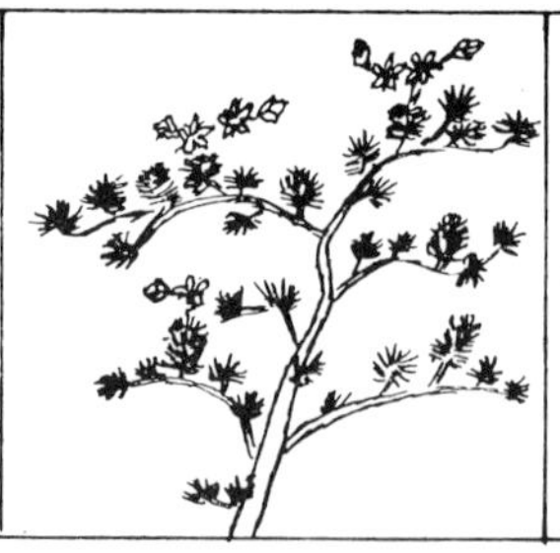

Sedum multiceps

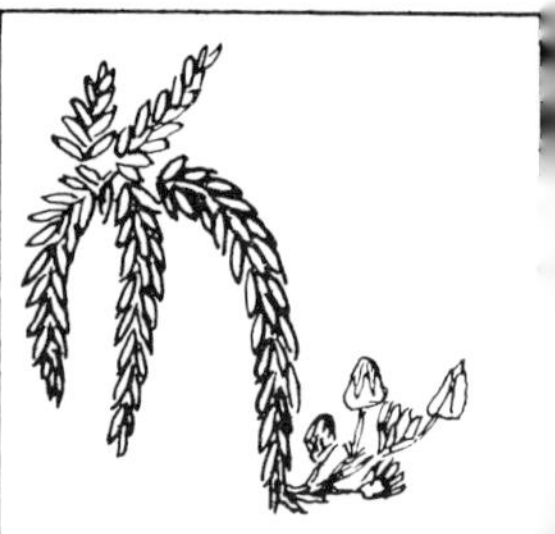

Sedum morganianum

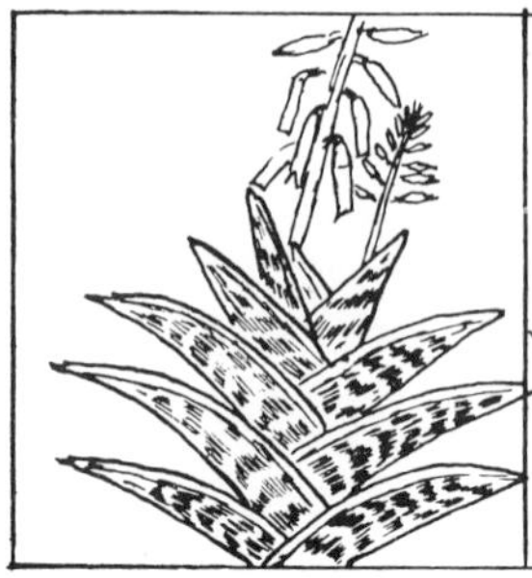

Aloe variegata

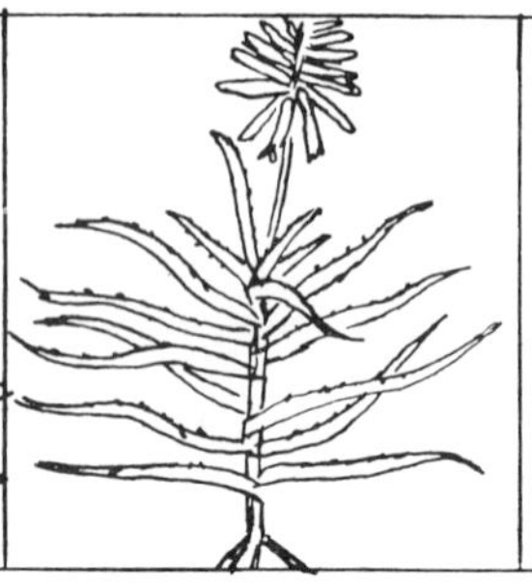

Aloe arborescens

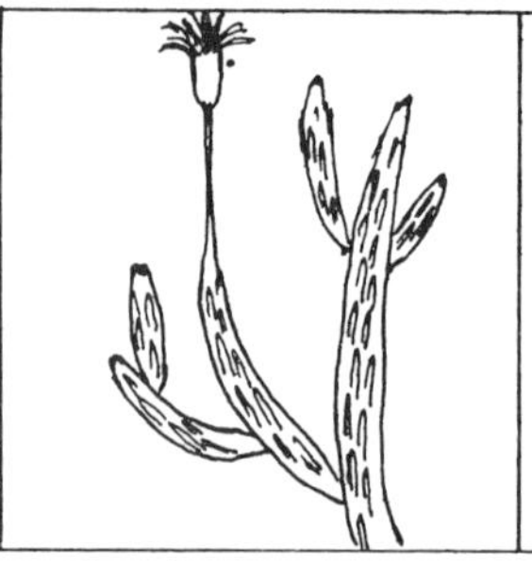

Senecio stapeliaeformis

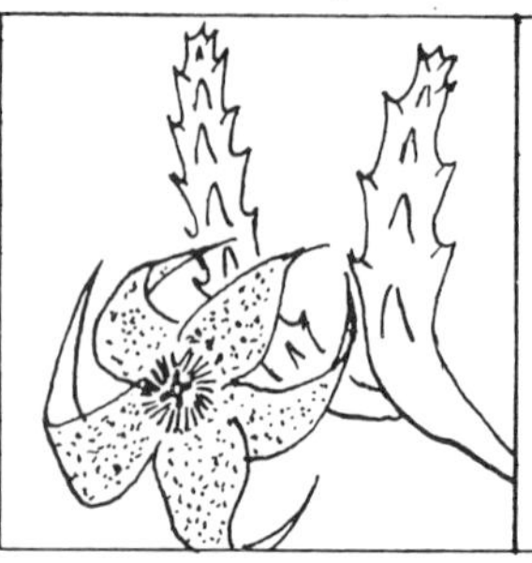

Stapelia gigantea

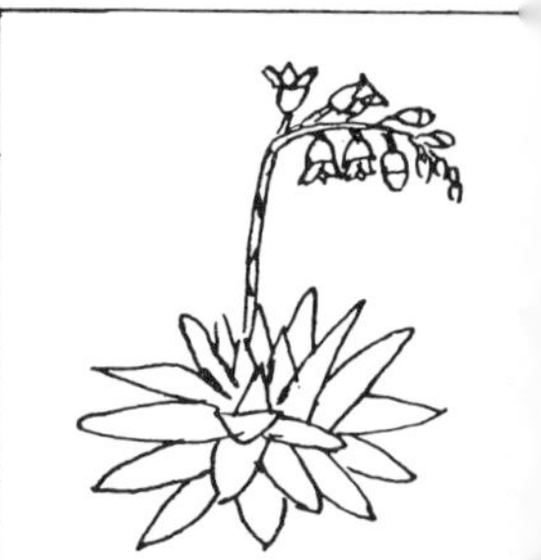

Echeveria agavoides

Rehderodendron macrocarpum, in Szechuan, China

Stachyurus praecox, "Spike-tail", in Japan

Fremontodendron mexicanum , in San Diego

Turnera ulmifolia angustifolia, "Sage-rose"

Thurnia sphaerocephala

Staphylea trifolia, "American bladder-nut"

Stylidium adnatum (Australia)

Tacca chantrieri macrantha, "Devil flower"

Tacca aspera (Burma)

Tacca cristata, a "Bat-flower"

Tacca artocarpifolia (Madagascar)

Tacca leontopetaloides (Thailand)

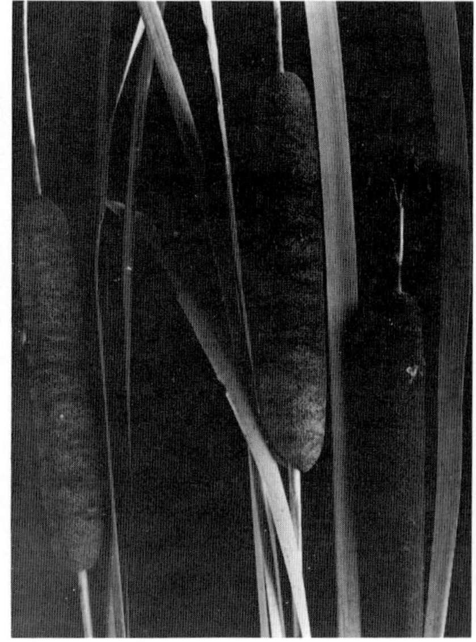

Typha latifolia, "Cat-tail"

Tacca plantaginea (South China)

Tacca leontopetaloides, "Polynesian arrow root"

Camellia sasanqua "Shishi-Gashira' in hanging basket

Eurya japonica 'Variegata' (Cleyera), in Belgium

Camellia sasanqua 'Showa-No-Sakae'

Camellia sasanqua 'Yuletide'

Camellia sasanqua 'White Doves'

Camellia japonica 'Rosedale Beauty'

Camellia reticulata, from China

Camellia japonica 'Pearl Maxwell'

Camellia japonica 'Pink Perfection'

Camellia japonica 'Alba plena'

Camellia 'Purity'

Camellia japonica 'Elegans' ('Chandleri')

Camellia 'William S. Hastie'

Camellia 'Prince Eugene Napoleon'

Camellia japonica 'Princesse Baciocchi'

Camellia 'Debutante'

Camellia 'Colonel Firey'

Camellia japonica 'Daikagura'

Camellia (Thea) sinensis

Camellia reticulata

Camellia japonica 'Debutante' ('Sara Hastie')

Camellia japonica 'Elegans' ('Chandleri')

Camellia japonica 'Jordan's Pride' ('Herme')

Camellia japonica, grown as dwarfed bonsai

Grewia caffra, "Lavender star-flower" (So.Africa)

Grewia hexamita, in the Transvaal

Tamarix pentandra, "Salt-cedar"

Sparmannia africana, in Villach, Austria

Tamarix parviflora, "Tamarisk"

Edgeworthia papyrifera, "Paper-bush" (China, Japan)

Gnidia denudata (tomentosa), in South Africa

Phaleria capitata, in Bogor Botanic Gardens, Java

Tamarix gallica, "French tamarisk" (Europe to Himalayas)

Entelea arborescens, "Cork tree" of New Zealand

Sparmannia africana, "Indoor linden" in Oberammergau, Bavaria

Daphne blagayana

Daphne longilobata

Daphne laureola

Passerina filiformis

Daphne mezereum

Daphne cneorum

Daphne odora 'Marginata'

Eurya japonica 'Variegata' (Cleyera)

Camellia japonica, in 25cm tub

Stewartia pseudocamellia

Ternstroemia japonica

Camellia sasanqua

Camellia oleifera

Camellia (Thea) sinensis, flowers

Peddiea africana

Sparmannia africana in habitat, South Africa (Til.) Luehea divaricata (Til.) Tropaeolum peregrinum (Trop.)

Entelea arborescens (Til.)

Tropaeolum peregrinum (Trop.)

Hydrocotyle rotundifolia (Umb.)

Sparmannia africana flore pleno (Til.)

Pimelea ferruginea (Thym.)

Tropaeolum azureum, "Blue nasturtium"

Tropaeolum polyphyllum (Chile)

Tropaeolum speciosum (Chile)

Tropaeolum majus nanum, "Tom Thumb nasturtium"

Tropaeolum tricolor, "Tricolored Indian cress"

Tropaeolum majus, the "Garden nasturtium"

Sparmannia africana (Indoor Linden)

Sparmannia africana in flower

Tropaeolum peltophorum

Tropaeolum majus fl. pl. 'Golden Gleam'

Tropaeolum majus

Petroselinum crispum (Curly Parsley)

Helxine soleirolii (Baby's Tears)

Tectona grandis, the "Teakwood tree", in Japan

Ulmus parvifolia, "Evergreen Chinese elm", in California

Urera baccifera, the "Cow-itch tree" (Costa Rica)

Eryngium bromeliifolium, in Botanic G. Strasbourg, France

Eryngium alpinum, in Botanic Garden Edinburgh

Lilaeopsis novae-zelandiae (New Zealand)

Aegopodium podograria 'Variegatum'

Pseudomorus brunoniana pendula

Petroselinum crispum, "Curly parsley"

Hydrocotyle umbellata, in Southern Spain

Bolax glebaria (Magellan, Chile)

Zelkova serrata (Bonsai)

Valeriana rigida (Ecuador)

Patrinia triloba (Japan)

Stachytarpheta purpurea

Valeriana sitchensis

Vaccinium cylindraceum (T.Everett)

Citharexylum berlandieri

Olmediella betschleriana, "Guatemala holly"

Agapetes hosseana (Thailand)

Elatostema latifolium acaule (Thailand)

Elatostema sessile (Trop.Africa and Asia)

Debregeasia longifolia

Boehmeria lobata (Japan)

Urera longifolia (Madagascar)

Pilea microphylla, "Artillery plant"

Pilea serpyllacea

Helxine soleirolii 'Marginata', "Baby's-tears

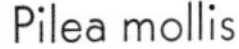
Pilea mollis

Pilea repens, "Blackleaf Panamiga"

Pilea nigrescens (W.Indies)

Pilea 'Coral' (New York Bot.G.)

Pilea crassifolia (China)

Pilea grandis (Jamaica)

Pilea cadierei 'Minima', "Silver baby"

Pilea 'Moon Valley' (imperialis), brown type

Vaccinium ovatum (Florists' greens)

Helxine soleirolii, in Strawberry jar

Pilea sp. 'Black Magic'

Pilea grandis

Helxine soleirolii 'Aurea'

Pellionia sp. 'Argentea'

Pilea sp. 'Silver tree'

Pilea depressa

Pilea cadierei 'Minima'

Pilea 'Moon Valley' (imperialis?)

Pilea spruceana 'Norfolk'

Pilea involucrata (Panamiga)

Pilea cadierei (Aluminum plant)

Pilea nummulariifolia

Pilea depressa

Pilea serpyllacea

Pilea microphylla (muscosa)

Duranta repens 'Variegata', "Pigeon-berry" in Singapore

Duranta repens, the "Sky- flower"

Vellozia elegans (Natal)

Duranta stenostachya (Brazil)

Duranta affinis (E.Hahn)

Vellozia retinervis, from the Transvaal

Barbacenia elegans (Vellozia) (Natal)

Nymphaea x daubeniana

Acacia longifolia mucronata

Gardenia jasminoides 'Veitchii'

Manettia inflata (bicolor)

Nertera granadensis (depressa)

Bouvardia ternifolia 'Giant Pink'

Medinilla magnifica

Hedychium gardnerianum

Tacca chantrieri

Ficus aspera (parcellii)

Passiflora alato-caerulea

Strelitzia reginae

Duranta lorentzii, in Argentina

Holmskioldia sanguinea 'Aurea', "Mexican hat plant"

Congea tomentosa, from India

Vellozia tubiflora, in South America

Clerodendrum x speciosum

Clerodendrum thomsonae (balfouri)

Clerodendrum speciosissimum (fallax)

Clerodendrum thomsonae variegatum

Clerodendrum bungei

Petrea volubilis

Boehmeria nivea

Myriocarpa stipitata (Boehmeria argentea)

Clerodendrum fragrans pleniflorum

Clerodendrum inerme, the Indian privet or Koyanal, carefully trained and sheared in the art of topiary, at the Feroze Mehta Hanging Gardens, Bombay (left: an elephant; right: a dinosaur)

Clerodendrum bakeri

Clerodendrum splendens, in Sydney, N. S. W.

Clerodendrum buchananii

Vitex agnus-castus (Chaste-tree)

Clerodendrum paniculatum, in Nigeria

Clerodendrum ugandense

Vitex lucens, Puriri in New Zealand

Petrea volubilis in glorious bloom, Uganda

Duranta repens

Oxera pulchella

Callicarpa rubella

Congea tomentosa

Verbena peruviana 'Chiquita'

Verbena peruviana 'Flame'

Clerodendrum nutans (Assam)

Clerodendrum splendens

Clerodendrum hastatum

Clerodendrum trichotomum, in Sydney

Clerodendrum glabrum

Clerodendrum bakeri, in fruit (Cameroun)

Verbena rigida (venosa)

Verbena chamaedrifolia

Viola tricolor, "Johnny-Jump-up"

Verbena x hortensis (Garden verbena)

Aloysia triphylla (Lippia citriodora) the Lemon-verbena

Viola cornuta 'Bluette'

Viola tricolor hortensis 'Maxima' ("Pansy")

Viola odorata (Sweet violet)

Amasonia calycina (punicea hort.)

Caryopteris x clandonensis

Viola hederacea (Erpetion)

Pellionia daveauana, older growth

Pilea pubescens 'Silver Panamiga'

Pilea repens (Blackleaf Panamiga)

Holmskioldia sanguinea

Pellionia daveauana

Pellionia pulchra

Lantana montevidensis

Lantana camara 'Red-orange'

Lantana camara nivea

Cissus adenopoda

Cissus discolor

Cissus **albo-nitens**

Parthenocissus quinquefolia vitacea

Ampelopsis brevipedunculata elegans

Cissus sicyoides

Cissus erosa Cissus albo-nitens Cissus adenopoda Cissus amazonica Cissus discolor Cissus sicyoides

Parthenocissus henryana — Cissus rhombifolia — Cissus rhombifolia **'Mandaiana'**

Cissus striata — Cissus **antarctica**

Cissus antarctica 'Minima'

Rhoicissus (Cissus) capensis — Cissus (Vitis) quadrangularis — Tetrastigma voinierianum

Vitis vinifera 'Black Alicante' under glass, at Nelson, New Zealand

Forcing of table grapes, Vitis vinifera 'Muscat of Alexandria', near Rotterdam, Holland

Parthenocissus quinquefolia in the Catskills, Ulster County, New York

Parthenocissus tricuspidata the Boston-Ivy

Parthenocissus tricuspidata 'Lowii'

Vitis coignetiae, at Botanic Gardens, Berlin-Dahlem

succulent Cissus quadrangularis, clambering over Euphorbia candelabrum, on the hot Achole Steppe, Central Africa

A grapery for forcing Vitis vinifera 'Black Hamburg', south of Brussels, Belgium. In this area some 35,000 greenhouses are devoted to the commercial production of table grapes under glass, skillfully pruned and trained.

Cissus discolor clambering over a sculptured Devata of the 12th century Khmer Ta Prohm temple, in Cambodia

Parthenocissus tricuspidata (Vitis veitchii) covering the walls of ancient Castello Verona, Northern Italy

Ampelopsis brevipedunculata elegans   Cissus **amazonica**   **Vitis amurensis**

Tetrastigma voinierianum   inflorescence of Tetrastigma voinierianum

Parthenocissus himalayana   Tetrastigma harmandii   **Leea rubra**

Cissus adenopoda

Cissus rhombifolia 'Ellen Danica'

Cissus rotundifolia (Arabia)

Ampelopsis aconitifolia

Tetrastigma obovatum (S. China)

Ampelopsis brevipedunculata

Cissus lanigeri

Cissus sicyoides, "Princess vine"

Cissus juttae, in Kirstenbosch

Leea roehrsiana — Leea amabilis — Leea coccinea

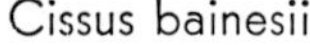

Cissus bainesii

Cissus juttae

Guaiacum officinale (Lignum-Vitae)

Cissus juttae, in Pretoria — Cissus seitziana

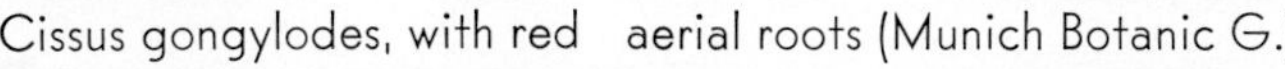

Cissus gongylodes, with red aerial roots (Munich Botanic G.)

Cissus gongylodes (Vitis pterophora, at Kew Gardens, London)

Cissus oleracea, the "Cabbage cissus" (Transvaal)

Orectanthe sceptrum, in Venezuela (J.Bogner, Munich)

Cissus gongylodes, at the Frankfurt Palmengarten

Cissus discolor, the "Rex-begonia vine"

Tetrastigma voinierianum, with woody trunk (New York Bot.Garden)

Cîssus juttae, the curious "Tree cissus", in Namibia

Alpinia sanderae, flowering on Moorea, French Polynesia

Alpinia zerumbet 'Variegata', a "Shell ginger", in Hawaii

Alpinia purpurata, the "Red ginger" from the South Pacific

Alpinia formosana

Brachychilum "horsfieldii" hort. Alpinia sanderae Alpinia zerumbet 'Variegata'

Tapeinochilos ananassae Hedychium x kewense Cautleya spicata

Globba winitii

Cautleya lutea

Nicolaia elatior (Phaeomeria magnifica), "Torch ginger"

Alpinia zerumbet (speciosa), the "Shell ginger"

Hedychium gardnerianum (Kahili ginger)

Brachychilum horsfieldii ("Alpinia calcarata" in hort.), with fruit

Costus speciosus

Costus malortieanus (zebrinus), "Stepladder plant"

Costus sanguineus

Burbidgea schizocheila

Costus igneus

Costus stenophyllus, at Turrialba, Costa Rica

Curcuma roscoeana

Amomum cardamomum Zingiber officinale  Alpinia sanderae Zingiber zerumbet 'Darceyi' Alpinia vittata

Hedychium coccineum  Curcuma roscoeana  Alpinia purpurata (Red ginger)

Hedychium flavum (Yellow ginger) Hedychium coronarium (Butterfly lily) Hedychium (Alpinia) greenei

Costus speciosus, the "Spiral ginger" in bloom

Globba atrosanguinea from Indonesia

Costus spicatus (Dr.Don Watson)

Costus malortieanus, "Stepladder plant"

Costus igneus, "Fiery costus"

Globba bulbifera (E.Himalayas)

Hedychium gardnerianum, "Kahili ginger"

Cautleya robusta (inflor.)

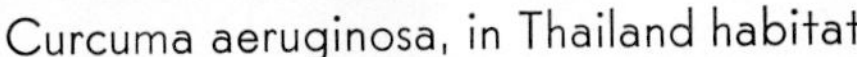

Curcuma aeruginosa, in Thailand habitat

Cautleya robusta (Himalayas)

Hedychium thyrsiforme, a "Ginger-lily" in India

Globba winitii, from Thailand

Kaempferia involucrata

Kaempferia roscoeana (Peacock plant)

Kaempferia gilbertii

Kaempferia grandiflora

Kaempferia masonii ("galanga" in hort.)

Kaempferia rotunda

Kaempferia decora

Kaempferia atrovirens

Kaempferia rotunda, in flower

Globba schomburgkii

Globba atrosanguinea

Globba winitii collected in habitat, with Somphong Lek-Aree in Thailand

Hedychium densiflorum

Curcuma roscoeana

Curcuma inodora, in Bombay State

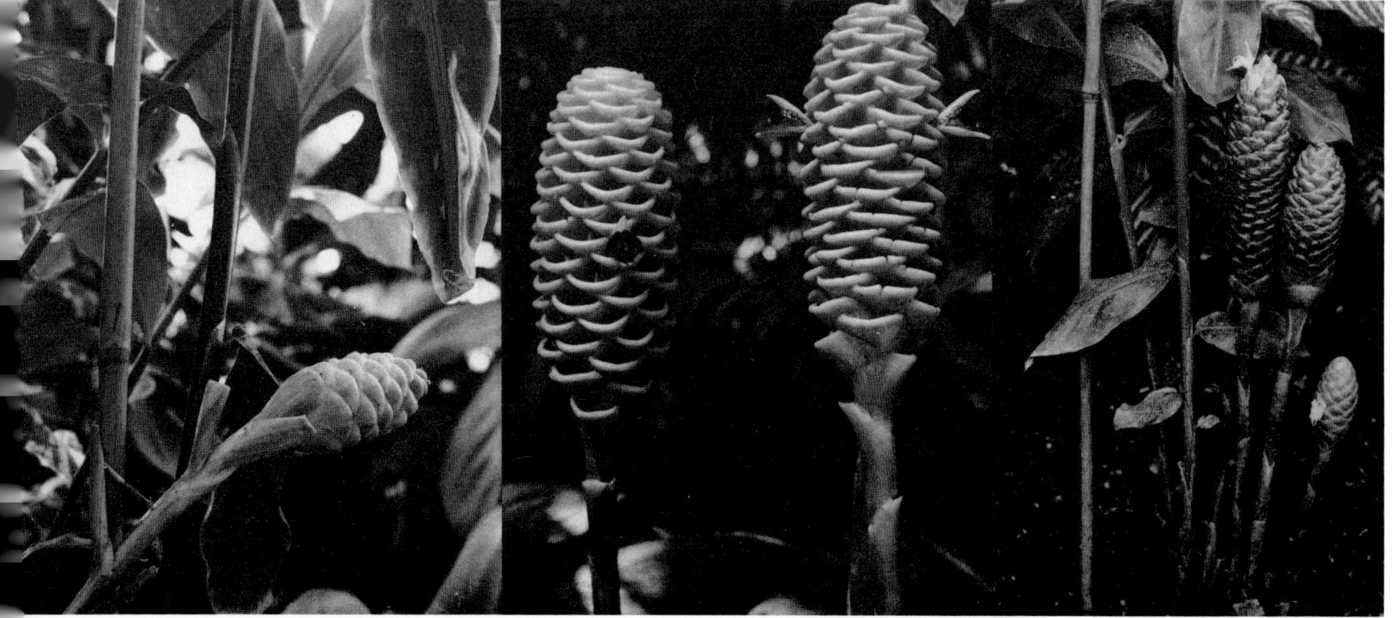

Zingiber zerumbet

Zingiber spectabile

Zingiber fairchildii

Kaempferia masonii ("galanga" in hort.)

Kaempferia galanga (Lydia Pahls - Miami)

Kaempferia decora (Mozambique)

Renealmia ventricosa (Cuba)

Kaempferia cv'Pobeda' (Korsakoff 19

Kaempferia brachystemon, from East Africa

Kaempferia pandurata, "Aromatic ginger", (India, Java)

Keampferia pulchra, "Resurrection lily" (Burma)

Kaempferia elegans, from Burma

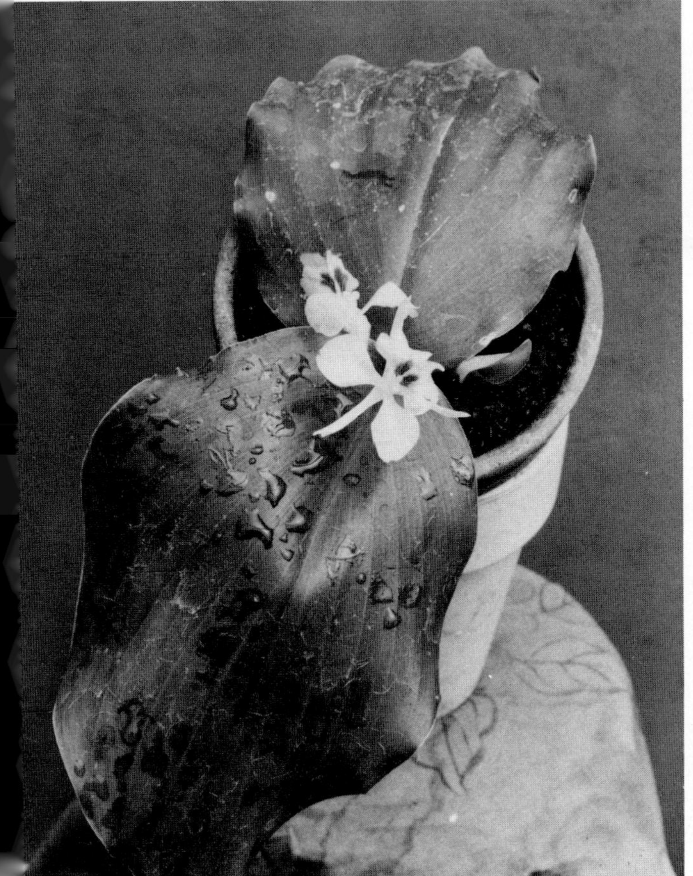

Kaempferia galanga, (India to Vietnam)

Kaempferia gilbertii, (Moulmein, Burma)

Kaempferia angustifolia (India, Malaya)

Kaempferia grandiflora, from Kenya

Roscoea humeana (Yunnan)

Tapeinochilos ananassae

Zingiber officinale, "Edible ging(

Costus englerianus (J.Bogner, Munich Bot.G.)

Kaempferia ethelae, from Natal

Roscoea alpina, Himalayan Region

Roscoea purpurea var. procera

Roscoea cautleoides, from China

Roscoea purpurea (Sikkim Himalayas)

Tribulus zeyheri, "Devil's-thorn"

Xyris bicephala, "Yellow-eyed grass"

Xyris involucrata (Venezuela)

Alpinia calcarata (India)

Amomum cardamomum, the "Cardamon ginger"

Brachychilum horsfieldii (Java)

Camptandra parvula, in Sarawak, North Borneo

Alpinia rafflesiana, from Malaya

Tapeinochilos ananassae, the "Malaysian ginger"

Zingiber zerumbet 'Darceyi', "Variegated Bitter ginger"

ngiber zerumbet, "Shampoo-ginger" at Munich Bot. Garden

Zingiber zerumbet 'Variegata', Trinidad Bot. Garden

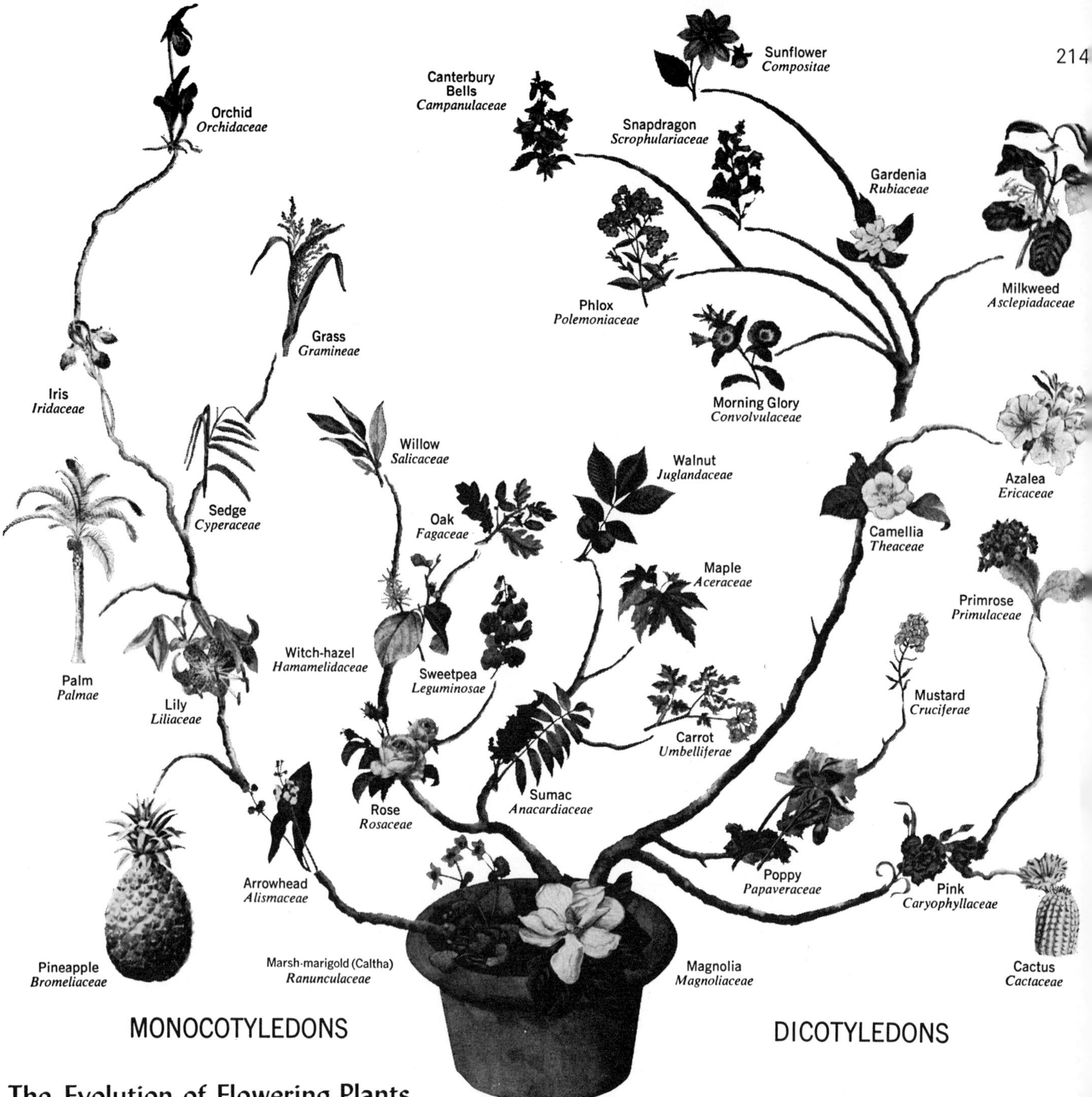

The Evolution of Flowering Plants

In the beginning, life was of an exceedingly simple nature. Through the ages, and by progressive adaptation to environmental changes in climate, the descendants of earlier organisms in both vegetable and animal life have gradually diverged from one another much as the spreading branches of a tree divide from its trunk. And so evolved the groups of individuals called families, each complex in structure and of much diversity, but the members of which are interrelated to one another by descent and similar in character.

According to Engler and Prantl's classification, the sequence of evolution in plant life passes from the most primitive and ancient toward the most specialized and modern—from the non-flowering plants collectively known as **Cryptogams**, on to the **Phanerogams**, the seed-bearing plants.

Cryptogamous plants pass from very simple, lower **algae, mosses** and **liverworts**, to the fern allies **selaginella** and **lycopodium**, and on to the true **ferns (Filices)**. These all come from minute bodies of simpler structure than seeds; **cryptogamous plants have neither stamens nor pistils.**

Phanerogamic plants, or spermatophytes, which originate from seed and bear flowers, are classed as **gymnosperms** and **angiosperms**. The **gymnosperms**, with unprotected (naked) seed, are a comparatively small and ancient group of mostly cone-bearing plants abundant in past ages, but now represented only by the various conifers, the cycads, ginkgoes, and the Gnetaceae, of which the remarkable Welwitschia is the best-known genus. The **angiosperms** or true flowering plants, on the other hand, are a great and abundant class and represent the bulk of the present world vegetation; their seeds are protected by a fruit.

Among the flowering plants it is generally understood that those whose flowers possess many separate petals, many stamens, and many separate pistils are more primitive than the ones with few such parts or those in which the parts have fused into single though compound structures. The early angiosperms have the **polycarp**, cone-type or separated arrangement of ovaries and fruiting carpels, or seed vessels. In the advanced forms of flowering plants certain organs, such as the pistils, may fuse into one—becoming **syncarp**; the sepals are joined with the ovary, the flower petals unite into tubes, and the carpels form a single fruit.

In lower orders the flowers are built **actinomorphic** or regular in fo meaning that when we face them they look round like the spokes of a wh whereas in more highly developed families the flowers, like the Snapdragon Columnea, appear irregular yet actually are bisymmetrical or **zygomorphic,** half reflecting the other half if split through the middle.

The hypothetical tree painted by Mrs. C. Burlingham for the Museum of New York Botanical Garden shows important families of flowering plants logical sequence, based on their probable phylogenetic development. These fam are thought to have as their ancestors two orders, Magnoliales and Ranales, belonging to the dicotyledons which characteristically have two seed-leaves cotyledons in their embryonic stage. The Magnolias are considered the most pr tive of those flowering plants where ligneous or woody habit is predomir while the herbaceous dicots mostly derive from the parallel Ranunculaceae which the buttercups are so typical.

In **dicotyledons,** comprising some 200 families, net-veined leaves are cal, and their floral parts are most frequently in fives though sometimes fo the trunks of woody species form annual rings. Their most highly develo families are considered to be the numerous Compositae with the zygomorphic flowers of the chrysanthemum, and the Campanulaceae with the tubular, f corolla of the bell flowers.

The **monocotyledonous plants** are thought to stem from the dicots, with Alismaceae, such as the Arrowhead, the most primitive. These arise from ar tors resembling very much the Ranunculaceae, having calyx and corolla just them. A fairly constant and most important feature of the monocots is their tary seed-leaf, but other distinguishing characters are leaves parallel-veined, c narrow, and nearly always alternate; their floral parts are usually in threes. primarily palms, are trees, and annual rings are absent in their trunks. To kinship belong about 50 families, through aroids, bromeliads, palms, lilies iris, culminating in the grasses on one branch, and the highly advanced orc on the other. Orchids are well-known for their very irregular flowers havin peculiar column in which pistil and stamens are fused into one solid organ well as the complicated, often fantastic shape and structure of the lip, which modified petal.

The Meaning of Botanical Terms

acicular — needle-like
acuminate — tapering to a point
acute — sharply pointed, but not drawn out
adventitious — other than usual place
alternate — arranged along a stem at different levels
anther — pollen bearing top of stamen
apex — the tip of an organ (as a leaf)
apiculate — with short, not stiff point
areole — cushion-like structure out of which can arise spines, branches, and flowers, a characteristic confined to cacti
articulated — jointed, separating freely by a clean scar
asexual — propagates without benefit of sex
attenuate — becoming narrow, tapered
auriculate — with ears at base
axil — the point just above the leaf where it rises from the stem
basal — at the base of an organ
bifurcate — forked
bilabiate — divided into two or equal lips
bipinnate — both primary and secondary divisions with separate leaflets
bipinnatisect — 3 times divided leafblade whose 3 parts are again several times divided
bipinnatifid — twice pinnately cut
bisexual — possessing perfect (hermaphrodite) flowers having both stamens and pistils
blade — the expanded portion of a leaf
bract — modified leaves intermediate between flower and the normal leaves, frequently colored
bristly — bearing stiff strong hairs or bristles
bulb — a growth bud with fleshy scales, usually underground
bullate — blistered or puckered
calyx — outer circle or cup of floral parts (usually green)
campanulate — bell-shaped flower with broad base
caudex — upright root stock or trunk
caulescent — becoming stalked
cephalium — woolly cap at the apex of cacti
channeled — hollowed out like a gutter
chromosomes — microscopic rodlike bodies in the plant cell, bearing the hereditary material
ciliate — fringed with eyelash hairs
clasping — leaf surrounding stem
cleft — cut halfway down
column — combined stamens and style into one body (as in orchids)
compound — similar parts aggregated into a common whole
compound leaf — a leaf of two or more leaflets
concave — hollowed out
connate — united
convex — umbrella-like
cordate — heart-shaped
corm — bulb-like but solid; enlarged fleshy base of a stem
corolla — complete circle of petals
corymb — a flat-topped open flower-cluster blooming from outside in
creeper — a trailing shoot rooting at intervals
crenate — with teeth rounded, scalloped
crested — with elevated and irregular ridge
culm — the peculiar hollow stem or stalk of grasses and bamboo
cultivar — special form originating in cultivation
cuneate — wedge-shaped, triangular
cuspidate — tipped with a sharp and stiff point
cyme — a broad, usually flat-topped flower cluster with center flowers opening first
decumbent — reclining, but summit ascending
deltoid — triangular
dentate — with coarse teeth, usually directed outward
digitately lobed — fingered and main veining radiating from more than one point
dioecious — unisexual; the male and female reproductive organs in different plants
diploid — having the basic chromosome number twice the number in normal germ-cells, characteristic of a species
dissected — several times cleft into small segments
divided — separated at the base
dorsal — back; in orchids usually a top sepal
downy — clothed with soft short hairs
elliptical — oblong, with widest point at center
elongate — drawn out in length
emarginate — notched at the end
endemic — native to a restricted region
entire — margin without toothing or division
epiphyte — air-plant; a plant growing on another, but not taking food from its host
F 1 hybrid — first generation hybrid obtained by artificial cross-pollination between two dissimilar parents (F meaning filial), each from a pure line or race, and each bearing hereditary factors (genes), which characteristics will be transmitted, according to their dominant genes, to an F 1 hybrid; as a rule imparting also greater vigor (heterosis).
F 2 generation — second generation from a given cross, usually obtained through self pollination within the F 1 hybrids, and which can then segregate into the various types present in the family lines, acording to Mendel's Law.
farinose — covered with a mealiness, or starchy matter
ferns — plants without flowers
fertile — spore bearing or seed-bearing
fibrous — with fibers, or thread-like parts
filament — thread-like stalk of an anther
filiform — thread shaped; very slender
floccose — with locks of soft hair or wool
frond — leaf of fern
funnelform — a tubular flower gradually widening upward and spreading into disk
geniculum — thickened joint or node of a stem
glabrous — smooth, not hairy nor rough
glaucous — covered with a white powder that rubs off
glochid — barbed hair, or bristle, as in cacti
glutinous — sticky
hairy — having longer hairs
haploid — having the basic chromosome number, or half the diploid number characteristic of a species
hastate — halberd-shaped, with basal lobes turned outward, or flared
head — a short dense flower spike
herb — a plant with no persistent stem above ground, usually contrasted with woody plants
herbaceous — non-woody
hirsute — hairy, with long rather stiff hairs
hybrid — a plant resulting from a cross between parents that are unlike
inferior ovary — one that is below the calyx leaves
inflorescence — the flowering portion of a plant, or more precisely the mode of its arrangement
insectivorous — plants which capture insects and absorb nutriment from them
intergeneric — hybrid between genera
internode — space between two joints
involucre — bracts surrounding flowers or their support
irregular flower — a flower which cannot be halved in any plane, or in one plane only
laciniate — slashed into narrow irregular pointed lobes
lanceolate — lance-shaped; tapering toward the tip
lateral — from the side
lenticel — lens-like corky elevations on young bark giving vent to breathing pores
lepidote — beset with small scurfy scales
limb — the border or expanded part of corolla (or spathe) above the throat
linear — narrow and flat, margins parallel
lip — the principal lobes of a bilabiate corolla; in orchids a much modified petal
lobe — any projection of a leaf, rounded or pointed
lobed — leaf cut less than halfway to the base
marginal — at the edge
membranous — thin, semi-transparent
monocarpic — a plant that flowers but once
monoecious — the stamens and pistils in separate flowers but borne on the same plant
mutant — form derived by sudden change from a species
needle-shaped — long, slender and rigid
node — a joint in a stalk where leaves or their vestiges are born
obcordate — inversely heartshaped, the notch being at the apex
oblanceolate — broad end near tip, long tapering toward base
oblique — slanting of unequal sides
oblong — much longer than broad, with parallel sides
obovate — inverted ovate, the broad end upward
obtuse — blunt or rounded at the end
opposite — opposite each other
orbicular — leaf with circular outline
ovary — that part of the pistil which contains the future seed
ovate — a leaf broadest near base, tapering upward
palmate — veins or leaflets radiating from tip of petiole
palmately compound — more than 3 leaflets borne at tip of petiole
palmately lobed — palmately divided leaf not cut to base
panicle — an open and branched flower cluster
parallel — equally distant at every part
parasite — organism subsisting on another living organism
parted — leaf cut ¾ or more
pectinate — comb-like, merely fringed, with spines
pedate — footed; palmately divided or parted
pedicel — stalk of each flower and cluster
peduncle — primary flower stalk
peltate — leaf-blade attached to stalk inside its margin
peltate-palmate — palmate leaf completely circular in outline
pendant — hanging down from its support
perianth — the calyx, or corolla, or both
perfoliate — petiole in appearance passing through the leaf
petal — a flower-leaf

petiole — the supporting stalk of a leaf; leaf stem
petiolate — furnished with a petiole
petiolule — a small petiole
phenotype — of similar physical make-up as the type species, influenced by environment
phyllodia — leaf-like stems and no blades (as in Acacia or Epiphyllum)
pilose — shaggy with soft hairs
pinnae — primary division of a pinnate leaf, its leaflets
pinnate — feather formed; separate leaflets arranged along side of leaf stalk; separation complete
pinnatifid — feathered; cut halfway to midrib
pinnatisect — pinnately divided down to the rachis; a feathered leaf cut down to the midrib
pinnule — secondary pinna or segment
pistil — the female organ of a flower, consisting of ovary, style and stigma
pistillate — flower having pistils only; female
pollen — the fertilizing powder contained in the anther
polymorphic — variable as to habit
procumbent — lying along the ground; leaning
prostrate — lying flat on the ground
prothallus — first stage of germination of fern spore into flat shield, bearing the sexual organs
pseudobulb — thickened and bulb-like portion of stem in epiphytic orchids
pubescent — covered with short, soft hairs, downy
punctate — having tiny translucent glands, appearing like dots
raceme — elongated simple inflorescence with stalked flowers
rachis — axis bearing flowers or leaflets
ray — marginal portion or floret of a Compositae flower when distinct from the disk
recurved — bent backward or downward
regular flower — with the parts in each set alike
reniform — kidney-shaped
rhizome — creeping rootstock, on or under the ground
rhombic — irregularly slanting rectangle
rosette — a cluster of leaves radiating in a circle from a center usually near the ground
rosulate — bearing a rosette, or basal cluster of spreading leaves covered with wrinkles
rugose — covered with wrinkles
runner — a slender prostrate shoot, rooting at the end or at joints
saccate — bag-shaped
sagittate — arrow-shaped, with basal ears turned straight downward or inward
salverform — slender tube abruptly expanded into disk-like flat limb
saxicolous — living on rock
scabrous — rough or harsh to the touch
scale — usually small, dry leaves or bracts
scaly rhizome — a rhizome with closely appressed, much modified leaves, scale-like in appearance
scandent — climbing, in whatever manner
scape — leafless flower stalk arising from the ground (root)
scorpioid — curved or coiled at the end
segment — one of the divisions into which a plant organ may be cleft
sepal — each segment of a calyx, or outer floral envelopes
serrate — notched like saw; finely toothed
sessile — sitting close, without stalk
setose — covered with bristles
simple leaf — one blade; opposite of compound
single flower — flower with one set of petals
sinuate — with a deep wavy margin, curved
sinus — the curve between two lobes of a leaf
slipper-shaped — tubular ventricose
sori — spore masses (in ferns)
spadix — a fleshy spike bearing tiny flowers as in aroids
spathe — partly surrounding the inflorescence a flower-like bract often colored or showy
spatulate — oblong, broadly rounded at tip but tapering to narrow base
spike — elongated flower stem, with flowers not stalked
spine — a sharp woody outgrowth from stem
sporangium — a sac producing spores — a spore-case in ferns
spore — in ferns a reproductive cell, somewhat corresponding to seed in flowering plants
spur — a tubular projection from the base of a petal or sepal
stamen — the pollen-bearing or "male" organ
staminate — flower wholly male
stellate — star-form; stellate hairs have radiating branches
stigma — that part of the pistil or style which receives the pollen
stipe — "leafstalk" of a fern
stipule — a leaf-like appendage at base of petiole
stoloniferous — sending out, or propagating itself by stolons
style — the connecting stalk between the ovary and stigma
sub-cordate — indented a trifle
subtend — to extend under, or be opposite to
subulate — owl shaped, tapering from broad or thick base to a sharp point
succulent — juicy, or storing water in stems or leaves
sulcate — grooved or furrowed
superior ovary — when all petals and sepals are inserted below it
synonym — a name rejected in favor of another
tendril — a thread-shaped shoot used for climbing
terete — circular, rounded in cross section; cylindric and usually tapering
terrestrial — plants growing in the ground
tetraploid — having four sets of chromosomes
thallus — plant body showing no differentiation into distinct members, as stem, leaves and roots
throat — the opening of the flower
tomentose — densely covered with matted wool
transverse — directed across (as on a leaf); crosswise
transversely oblong-peltate — long target-like leaf lying crosswise
trapeziform — no two lines parallel
trifoliate — three-leaved
trifoliolate — with three leaflets, as in clover—commonly, but incorrectly termed "trifoliate"
triploid — having 3 times the haploid chromosome number
truncate — as if cut off at the end
tube — the united portion of calyx or corolla
tuber — modified underground stem; the thickened portion of subterranean stem, provided with "eyes"
tubercle — a wart-like or knobby projection
tubular — having form of a hollow cylinder
turgid — inflated; swollen
umbel — inflorescence in which flower stalks or cluster arise from same point
undulate — wavy, or wavy-margined
unisexual — of one sex; staminate (male), or pistillate (female) only (see dioecious)
vaginate — sheathed; surrounded by a sheath, usually of leaf stems
ventral edge — belly side
ventricose — swollen on one side
viable — capable of germinating or living
viviparous — producing young, while attached to parent
whorled — leaves in circle around stem (above)
woolly — clothed with long and entangled soft hairs
xerophytic — growing in dry situation, subsisting with little moisture
zygomorphic — can be divided into two symmetrical halves only a single longitudinal plane passing through the axis

Descriptive Botanical Terms illustrated

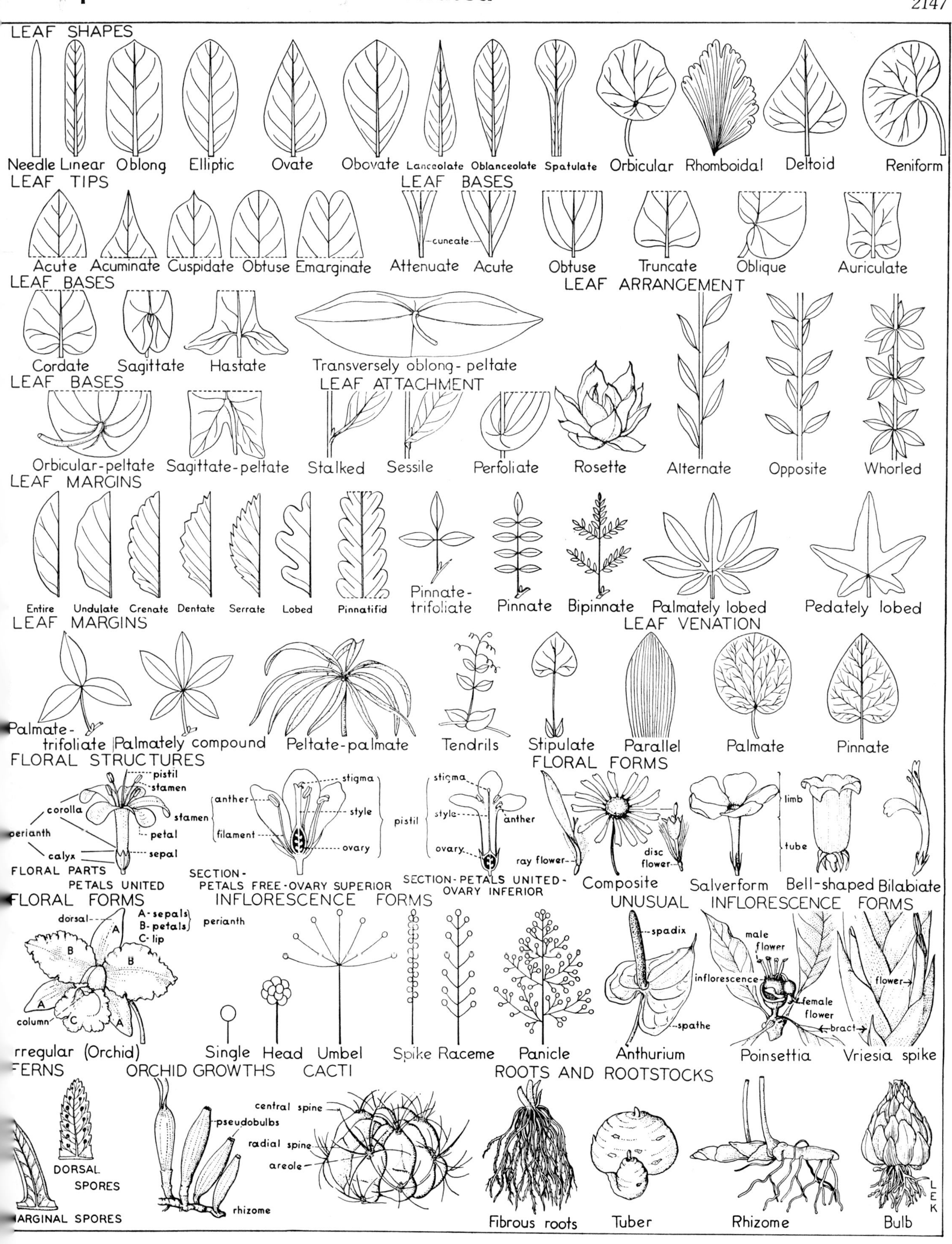

YOUR KEY TO CARE.. ..OF PLANTS

The combinations of code letters and numerals following the listing of each genus indicate, in the sequence followed below, the general environment and growing conditions which it prefers or tolerates. Species which differ in their needs or tolerance are marked individually, showing only those letters or numbers in which they are an exception to the genus as a group.

1 TEMPERATURE

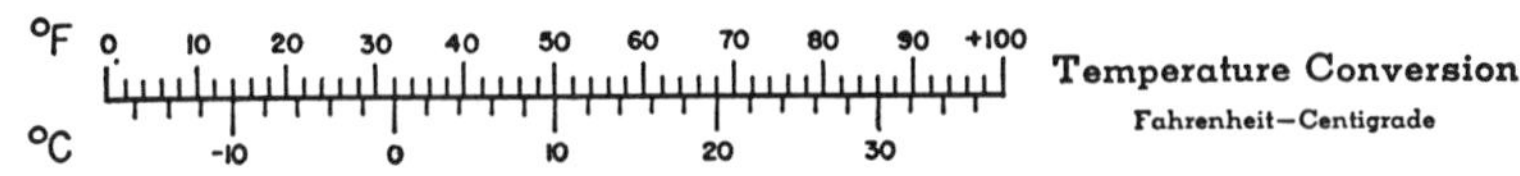

Temperature Conversion
Fahrenheit—Centigrade

(C) **Cool or cold:** 40-45°F (5-7°C) at night, rising to about 55°F to 60°F (13°-15°C) on a sunny day, with air; 50°F (10°C) in cloudy weather.

(I) **Intermediate, or temperate:** 50-55°F (10-13°C) at night, rising to 70°F (21°C) on a sunny day, or somewhat higher, with air; 60°F (15°C) if cloudy, before opening ventilators.

(S) **Warm, or 'Stove-house':** 62-65°F (16-18°C) at night; can rise to 80 or 85°F (27-30°C) in daytime before ventilators in a greenhouse must be opened. Plants that take a rest or dormancy period, should be kept a few degrees cooler during this time until active growth is to begin again.

2 LOCATION

(1) **House Plant Candidate:** Suitable for home and interior decoration, as it tolerates the reduced light of the living room or office with its artifically dry atmosphere. This class of plant would naturally prefer the ideal growing conditions of the greenhouse or at least a window site but experience has proven that it can be recommended as a good indoor subject where conditions are unfavorable.

(2) **Needs Fresh Air and Good Light:** Patio Plant, or space permitting, would be happy at a **Window** open in the summertime; a **Porch,** glassed-in during winter, or a light, well ventilated **Home Greenhouse;** in subtropical regions a sheltered **Patio.** In summer the outdoor garden, perhaps under the partial shade of a tree or a more protective lath house, will be a welcome refresher.
Hardy plants (h), garden annuals and perennials, woods plants and trees are included in EXOTICA mainly because they are occasionally forced for flower shows or in winter gardens, being fully content only when planted outdoors. Likewise, some tall climbers need a sizable greenhouse to develop fully, or perhaps the side of a building or tree trunk in subtropical climate such as in the south of the United States.

(3) **Greenhouse Plant:** Requiring a more or less controlled, relatively high humidity such as can be maintained in a conservatory. In the home, extra atmospheric moisture can be provided in a glass terrarium (converted aquarium), a Wardian (glass-enclosed) case, or even a shelter frame covered by plastic film. In humid-warm regions a moist, slatted shade-house will do for many 'conservatory' plants and with fresh air, recommended temperatures may go somewhat lower than suggested without harm

3 SOIL

(L) **Loam, clay,** or **good garden soil,** usually with decayed manure and up to 1/3 part **peat** or **humus** added. Where quick runoff is desirable, include coarse builders sand; in xerophytic plants like the desert type cacti, sand may be 1/3 to 1/2 of the loam mixture. Add agricultural lime to aggregate the clay particles in soil for good drainage and aeration, as well as to sweeten it. The **pasteurization** of potting soils is desirable to eliminate harmful bacteria, either by steaming for 1/2 hour at 80°C, or baking moist soil in an oven at 80 to 120°C for 3/4 to 1 hr. (180-250°F)

(H) **Soil rich in humus** or other organic matter such as leafmold; **peatmoss** is excellent for the root system but needs the addition of fertilizer to become fruitful; a little rough manure should be included, and a small amount of loam for structure; broken brick or charcoal, granite chips, perlite or coarse sand will improve drainage. Recently **sphagnum moss** as well as **shredded firbark** has been used with great success on such plants as Alocasia, Anthurium, and other aroids, even Christmas cactus, but additional feeding will be necessary. A good combination also is sphagnum peat 1 part to Perlite or Spongerock 1 part by volume, plus added fertilizer, or by follow-up feeding with complete fertilizer formula 1-2-1. Horticulturally sterile Perlite is a volcanic mineral exploded by heat into light-weight pebbles filled with air bubbles which can attract, and hold moisture uniformly, thereby furthering a healthy root system.

(O) **Osmunda fern fiber,** often with some **sphagnum moss** added, and lumps of charcoal and broken pot for drainage, especially in the bottom of the pots. Lately, the use of **shredded firbark** (Abies concolor) with about 1/3 peatmoss added, has given spectacular results, inducing prolific roots on many orchids, anthuriums, ferns, etc. However, this material is deficient in nitrogen and should have liquid fertilizer with every second or third watering, and must always be kept damp as it is difficult to uniformly moisten it again if once it is allowed to dry out.

YOUR KEY TO CARE..

LIGHT

Bright light or full sun. Preference for growth: 4000-8000 foot candles, for average day length. **Tolerance, for maintenance:** 500-2000 foot candles, based on 16 hr. illumination. Intense light is important to most blooming plants, shrubs and trees, also flowering bulbs. Many plants which require sunlight for normal growth can be kept in good condition in the home at much lower light intensity, with artificial light, when **maintenance** only is desired.

Filtered or diffused sunlight. Preference: 1000-3000 foot candles for average day length. **Tolerance:** 100-1000 foot candles, based on 16 hr. illumination. A simple indicator of diffused sunlight is to pass your hand over your plants and barely see its shadow. A place near a clear east window during summer is best, but a southern exposure must be lightly shaded from direct sun by slatted Venetian blinds, a bamboo screen, or curtain. For mere **maintenance** of most plants in this group in good condition in the home, light intensity may go as low as 25 foot candles, though 100 would be better.

No (direct) **sun, shady,** or **away from sun. Preference:** 50-500 foot candles for normal day length. There are very few plants which do not want some sunlight by preference; shade lovers are limited mostly to delicate plants from the forest floor, and ferns. However, a great number of subjects tolerate a minimum amount of energy-giving sunlight, and most of them are classified under the numeral 1 or starred (★). Under artificial illumination, light intensity may be as low as 10 foot candles, but the higher intensity light would be preferable to these plants provided they are shielded from the sun. High humidity is important to the well-being of plants in this group.

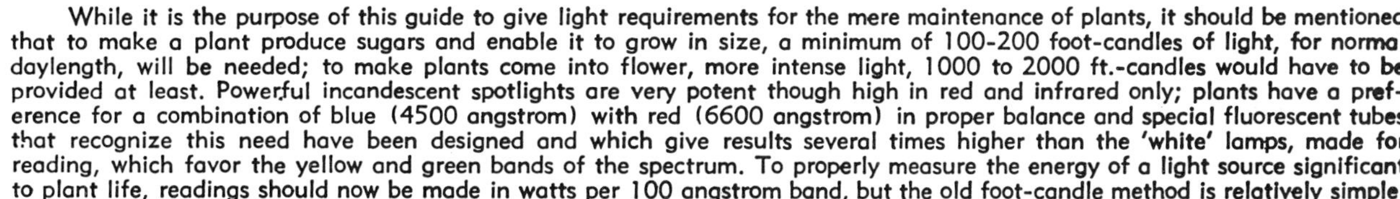

While it is the purpose of this guide to give light requirements for the mere maintenance of plants, it should be mentioned that to make a plant produce sugars and enable it to grow in size, a minimum of 100-200 foot-candles of light, for normal daylength, will be needed; to make plants come into flower, more intense light, 1000 to 2000 ft.-candles would have to be provided at least. Powerful incandescent spotlights are very potent though high in red and infrared only; plants have a preference for a combination of blue (4500 angstrom) with red (6600 angstrom) in proper balance and special fluorescent tubes that recognize this need have been designed and which give results several times higher than the 'white' lamps, made for reading, which favor the yellow and green bands of the spectrum. To properly measure the energy of a light source significant to plant life, readings should now be made in watts per 100 angstrom band, but the old foot-candle method is relatively simple.

During tests made in our office and the living room, to determine various actual light conditions, measured in foot-candles, I recorded the following:

Daylight, 30 cm distant from north window: 220 to 500 ft.-cdle.
Daylight, 1 m distant from north window: 100 to 180 ft.-cdle.
Incandescent bulb, 75 watt, 30 cm distant: 150 ft.-cdle.
Incandescent flood light, 75 watt, 1 m distant: 40 ft.-cdle.
Incandescent bulb, 100 watt, 1 m distant: 40 ft.-cdle.
Incandescent bulb, 150 watt, 1 m distant: 60 ft.-cdle.
Incandescent flood, 150 watt, 1 m distant: 90 ft.-cdle.
Incandescent spot, 300 watt, 1 m distant: 180 ft.-cdle.
Fluorescent tube, 40 watt, 30 cm distant: 120 ft.-cdle.
Fluorescent tube, 40 watt, 60 cm distant: 75 ft.-cdle.
Four fluorescent tubes, 160 watt, 2 m distant: 40 ft.-cdle.
Two 40 w. tubes 1 m 60-80, 1½ m 40-50, 2 m 30 fc.

LIGHT INTENSITY MEASUREMENTS: One footcandle is the amount of light cast by a candle, received on a white surface 1 foot (30 cm) distant, in a dark room. In metric terms 1 ft-cdle, equals 10.76 lux.

WATERING

Drench thoroughly then allow to become moderately dry between waterings. This admits air into the soil structure which, in turn, promotes development of a healthy white root system; wiry thick roots being characteristic in this group. Watering means soaking the root-ball penetratingly, holding the pot if necessary in a bucket, sink or tub of tepid water until air bubbles cease to rise. During the cold season, with steam heat in the living room, more frequent watering every day or two is required for most plants than from spring to fall. 'Feel' the soil to determine its need for water. Desert type cacti and similar succulents will stand dryness for longer periods.

Evenly moist but not constantly wet. Plants so classified generally have delicate, hair-like, fibrous roots, subject to rot if kept too wet, and equally easily burning and shrivelling if too dry, especially in hot weather. Standing in a saucer, such plants may be supplied water from the base to a degree where capillary action distributes and maintains uniform moisture throughout the root-ball, without letting the soil become water-soaked and 'sour'. During resting periods and dropping temperatures the soil-ball can be kept more on the dry side.

Thoroughly wet, or quite moist: never allow such plants to dry out. It is good practice to keep them in a saucer of gravel saturated with water, or in a jardiniere, though drainage water should be emptied every few days to keep from becoming stagnant. Such subjects may revel in moisture but resent having 'wet feet', that is having their roots left standing continuously in water. Exceptions, of course, are bog plants, and aquatics when not resting.

normally requires dormancy or rest period, during which little or no water is given, with temperatures reduced correspondingly.

winter-hardy north, sometimes with special protection from the sun, in the vicinity of New York City, where the temperatures in winter may drop to around 0°F (—18°C).

wi-winter; **sp**-spring; **su**-summer; **au**-autumn.

The Designations Tropical, Subtropic, or Warm-Temperate at end of plant descriptions in the text, are intended to serve as general guide to specific climatic area backgrounds, or temperature preference, for plants or trees usually found to grow outdoors in warmer climates:

TROPICAL: Warm surroundings; days 21-28°C (70-85°F), and balmy nights usually not below 15°C (60°F).

SUBTROPIC: Mild climate with warm, sunny days, nights frequently down to 10°C (50°F).

WARM-TEMPERATE: Warm or sometimes cool, and often rainy, in daytime; nights may drop to 5°C (40°F), with occasional frost.

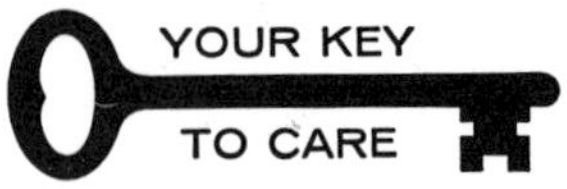

The code letters and numerals following the listing of each genus or species on the descriptive text pages indicate the growing conditions which it prefers or tolerates. For detailed key see pages 2148-2149.

Plantas para Interiores Clave para su cuido

Las letras y numerales que siguen a los nombres de cada género o especie en las paginas descriptivas indican el medio-ambiente y los cuidados que requieren para su conservación, o las condiciones que toleran dichas plantas. Para mayor información véase paginas 2148-2149.

Zimmerpflanzen Kulturschlüssel

Die Buchstaben und Nummern welche jedem Genus oder Sortennamen im beschreibendem Text folgen, deuten an welche Bedingungen die Pflanze erfordert oder erträgt. Für weitere Anweisungen siehe Seiten 2148-2149.

Plantes d'Intérieur Votre clef d'entretien

Les lettres et numéros de code qui suivent la liste de chaque genus ou variété sur les pages descriptives indiquent la condition de culture qu'ils préfèrent ou tolèrent. Pour informations aditionelles voir pages 2148-2149.

Ключ для укода за комнатными растениями

Буквы и гисла, сопрово... дающие каждое названи... рода или вида на страниц... описательного текста, обо... нагают допустимые и... предпогитаемые условия р... ста растений.

	Temperature:	***La temperatura:***	***Temperatur:***	***La température:***	**Температура:**
C	cool or cold, (40-60° F)	fresco, o frío; temperatura baja (5-15° C)	Kühl, oder kalt (5-15° C)	frais, ou froid (5-15° C)	прохладная или холодна... (5-15° C.)
I	intermediate, temperate, (50-70° F)	templado; temperatura intermedia (10-21° C)	mässig warm (10-21° C)	intermédiaire, tempéré (10-21° C)	промежуточная (10-21° C
S	stove, or warm, (62-85° F)	lugar caliente; temperatura cálida (16-30° C)	wärme-liebend (16-30° C)	chaud, serre chaude (16-30° C)	тепличная или теплая (16-30° C)
	Location:	***Colocación o situación:***	***Standort:***	***La localité:***	**Местонахождение:**
1	house plant	dentro de la casa, con luz artificial	Zimmerpflanze	plante d'appartement	комнатное растение
2	needs fresh air	balcon protegido; patio cerrado	liebt frische Luft	aime l'air frais et beaucoup de clarté	нуждается в свежем возду...
3	humid-loving	invernáculo con atmósfera húmeda	feucht-warmes Treibhaus; gespannte Luft.	plante de serre humide	влаголюбивое
	Potting soil:	***Terreno de maceta:***	***Pflanzmaterial:***	***La terre:***	**Почва для цветочны... горшков:**
L	loamy garden soil	tierra rica de jardín con abono animal	lehmige Erde, Kompost	terre grasse, ou bonne terre végétale	суглинистая садовая поч...
H	soil rich in humus	tierra vegetal de hojas, o rica en humus o turba	mit reichlich Humus oder Torf vermischte Erde.	terreau, terre de tourbe ou de bruyère	богатая перегноем
O	osmunda or fiber	fibra de osmunda o de helecho arborescente	Osmunda Farnwurzeln, poröse Fasern	osmunda, fibre, ou mousse de sphagnum	корни папоротника чис... уса или спутанное волок...
	Light preference:	***La luz:***	***Belichtung:***	***La lumière:***	**Освещение:**
B	bright light	al sol o a plena luz	helles Licht, Sonne	lumière claire, plein soleil	Яркий свет
F	filtered sun	sombra parcial; luz filtrada	leicht schattiert	ombré, sous lattis	легкое затенение
N	no sun, shade	sitio obscuro; sombra	Schattenpflanze; verträgt keine Sonne	dans l'ombre, tout à fait ombré	без солнца, тень
	Moisture in pots:	***Humedad en las macetas:***	***Feuchtigkeit der Erde:***	***L'humidité de la terre:***	**Влажность почвы:**
D	dry side	déjese secar la tierra entre reguíos	mässig giessen	arrosez seulement quand sec	суховатая
M	moist	manténgase una moderada humedad constante	gleichmässig feucht	humidité regulière	умеренно влажная
W	wet	mantenarse mojado siempre;	reichlich giessen	très humide, arrosez fréquemment	сырая
*	good house plant	estrella = planta recomendada para la casa	Stern: gute Zimmerpflanze	*étoile* = bonne plante d'appartement	хорошее комнатное растение
d	requires dormancy	necesite periodo de reposo	braucht Ruhezeit	une période de repos	требует покоя
h	winter-hardy (N. Y.)	resistente al frío	winterhart	résistant l'hiver	зимостойкое
wi	winter	invierno	Winter	l'hiver	зима
sp	spring	primavera	Frühling	le printemps	весна
su	summer	verano	Sommer	l'été	лето
au	autumn	otoño	Herbst	l'automne	осень

Descriptions of Plants illustrated, their Family, Common Names, and Code to Care

Combination Text-Index: Numerals at end of each listing indicate page numbers to plant illustrations, a short-cut to easier finding of photographs.

Plant Names other than species, in conformance with the International Code of Nomenclature, are generally distinguished as follows:

Names of Hybrids: Generic names of bigeneric hybrids, and Latinized specific names of hybrids derived from two species, are as a rule preceded by the x mark;

Cultivar names (horticultural sports or varieties, hybrids with fancy names and clonal selections) start with a capital initial letter, and are enclosed within single quotation marks (');

Names of uncertain standing, or where incorrectly used in horticulture, are shown in double quotes ("), and/or are followed by the abbreviation "hort".

Terms of measurement are generally given according to the International Metric System. Conversions to the Old English terms are:

1 centimeter (cm) = 0.4 inch; 2½ cm = 1 inch; 10 cm = 4 inches
1 metre (m) = 40 inches (or 3.28 feet). (1 cm = 10 mm; 1 m = 100 cm; 1 foot = 30 cm)
1 gram (g) = 0.035 oz; 1 kilogram (kg) = 2.2 lbs; 1 liter (l) = 1.06 quarts; 4 liters = 1.06 gal.

Temperature Conversion: Degrees Fahrenheit vs. Centigrade.
Freezing point zero deg. Centigrade = 32 deg. Fahrenheit (F.).
Boiling point 100 deg. Celsius (C) = 212 deg. Fahrenheit (F.).

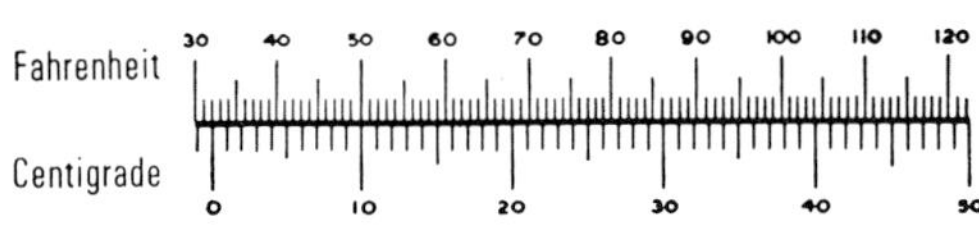

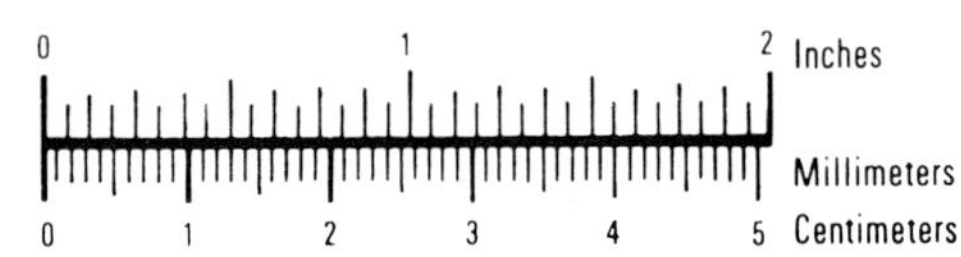

ABELIA *Caprifoliaceae* **C2LBM**

chinensis (China), "Glossy abelia"; deciduous shrub to 2m with opposite ovate, toothed leaves 4cm long; the funnel-shaped small, white flowers fragrant in terminal panicles. *p. 755*

floribunda (Mexico), "Mexican abelia"; evergreen shrub 1-2m high, with arching wiry, downy red branches; ovate, glossy green 3cm leaves; from the ends of twigs the showy pendulous trumpet flowers 4cm long, reddish purple with white throat. *Subtropic.* *p. 755*

x grandiflora (chinensis x uniflora) (China), "Glossy abelia"; attractive half-evergreen shrub with opposite ovate, glossy leaves; terminal clusters of small bellshaped fragrant flowers white flushed pink. *Warm temperate. p. 755*

ABIES *Pinaceae (Coniferae)* **I2LBMh**

balsamea (Labrador to Alberta and Virginia), "Balsam fir"; stately pyramidal conifer 15-25m high, with slender trunk, smooth grayish brown with many resin bumps; stout branches ascending; needles spreading upward 2-3cm long and notched at apex, lustrous dark green above and 2 white bands beneath, strongly scented when bruised; cylindrical cones 5-7cm long, and very resinous. Sometimes trained as dwarf bonsai in Japan. *p. 846*

ABROMA *Sterculiaceae* **S2LFM**

fastuosum (Trop. Asia, Australia); tropical evergreen tree to 3m with green, soft-hairy leaves, the lower ones 3-5-lobed, upper ones ovate; flowers with 5 petals and clawed, chocolate-purple. *p. 2088*

ABROMEITIELLA *Bromeliaceae* **I2LBM**

brevifolia (N.W. Argentina, Bolivia); small cluster-forming rosette with ovate-triangular thick-fleshy tapering leaves 2½ cm long, spineless; flowers greenish. *Subtropic.* *p. 529*

chlorantha (N. W. Argentina); cushion-forming tiny rosette, growing on rocks, with stiff-fleshy leaves 3cm long tipped by terminal spine, margins with minute teeth; flowers greenish, out of rosette. *p. 529*

lorentziana (abstrusa) (N.W. Argentina); terrestrial succulent rosette from the Andes at 1800m, forming dense cushions; tiny rosettes resembling miniature dyckias, formed by spirally arranged stiff, pointed green, gray-scaly leaves 4 to 15 cm long and tipped by sharp spine; from the center a solitary greenish flower. *p. 528*

ABRUS *Leguminosae* **S3LBM**

precatorius (E. Indies), "Crab's-eye vine" or "Weather plant"; deciduous climber to 3m, leaves with numerous pairs of oblong leaflets; flowers pale purple varying to rose and white. Seeds bright scarlet. *p. 1371*

ABUTILON *Malvaceae* **I2LBM**

x hybridum, the "Flowering maple" or "Parlor maple"; an old fashioned house plant, typical of the numerous hybrids of the tropical American species striatum, pictum and darwinii, resulting in this floriferous group of herbaceous shrubs with pubescent, soft green foliage varying from lobed to not lobed, often resembling maple-leaves, and with bell-like flowers about 5cm long, in shades from white through yellow and salmon to red; in bloom the year round. *Tropical.* *p. 1529*

x hybridum 'Apricot', "Chinese lantern"; one of the maple-leaved cultivars of the "Flowering maple", with pubescent green foliage and bell-like salmon flowers with darker red veining, flowering all year. *Tropical.* *p. 1527*

x hybridum 'Golden Fleece', a "Golden parlor maple"; showy bell-like flowers of golden yellow, and crenate, lightly lobed, soft-pubescent, green leaves; flowering over a long period throughout the summer and into winter. (A. darwinii x 'Boule de Neige'). *p. 1526*

x hybridum 'Savitzii', "White parlor maple"; colorful old cultivar of bushy habit, with its little maple-like lobed and toothed leaves grayish green and highly and irregularly variegated white from the margins in, some leaves are entirely white. A charming, colorful window-sill plant. *Tropical.* *p. 1526*

x hybridum 'Souvenir de Bonn', "Variegated flowering maple"; herbaceous shrub with soft, long-stalked, maple-like leaves a grayish green bordered in creamy-white; bell-shaped flowers salmon veined with crimson. Grows to twice the size as 'Savitzii'. *Tropical.* *p. 768A*, 1527*

megapotamicum 'Variegata' (Brazil), "Weeping Chinese lantern"; evergreen shrub of lax, graceful habit; the slender, drooping branches with small, arrow-shaped, crenate leaves fresh-green, with ivory to yellow variegation, and small pendulous flowers lemon-yellow with lantern-like red calyx. *Tropical.* *p. 1527, 1529*

x milleri (megapotamicum x pictum), a "Flowering maple"; slender, wiry branches with ovate leaves lightly 3-lobed, 8-15cm long, marbled lighter green on dark; axillary flowers 4cm long, solitary or in pairs, petals yellow with carmine veins; style and stamens prominent. *p. 1532*

pictum 'Thompsonii' (Guatemala), "Spotted flowering maple"; herbaceous shrub with slender branches; soft, maple-shaped leaves deeply 5-7 lobed, the middle lobe narrowed at base, dark green with chartreuse-yellow mottling; bell-like orange-salmon flowers; leaves not pubescent. *Tropical.* *p. 1527*

striatum 'Aureo-maculatum' (striatum spurium), "Spotted Chinese lantern"; attractive herbaceous shrub with pointedly 5-lobed and toothed foliage highly blotched and marbled, with yellow on rich green, the leaves being pubescent and smaller than thompsonii; flowers spread bell-shaped with corolla light reddish-orange with red veins. The variegation in the foliage is caused by a transmissible virus, and if a shoot of it is grafted on a green-leaved understock, this stock later becomes variegated also. *p. 1529*

striatum 'Goldprince'; bushy, dwarf German cultivar with its small lobed leaves attractively variegated moss-green, and creamy yellow. *p. 1532*

ACACALLIS *Orchidaceae* **S30FW**

cyanea (Brazil, Colombia); creeping dwarf epiphyte with small 5cm pseudobulbs and solitary leaves; arching inflorescence with relatively large 4cm fragrant flowers mauve outside, sky-blue within, lip white with purple, and yellow crest. *p. 1660*

ACACIA *Leguminosae* **C2LBD**

alata (Western Australia); flattened cladodes giving rise to small globular, yellow flower heads. *Subtropic.* *p. 1366*

armata (paradoxa) (Australia), "Kangaroo thorn"; dark green, densely branched erect shrub, to 3 m, with stems ribbed and bristly, dense phyllodia half-ovate, to 2½ cm long; flowers rich yellow in 1 cm globose heads, close to stem; willingly blooming for Easter, in the Northern hemisphere, even as a small pot plant indoors. *Subtropic.* *p. 1369*

armata pendula (Australia), "Weeping Kangaroo thorn"; of straggling habit, phyllodia longer and narrower, the small yellow ball-shaped flowers on longer stalks; April-May blooming. *p. 1369*

baileyana (New So. Wales), "Golden mimosa"; handsome spreading tree, to 10 m, with branches often pendulous, very leafy with fern-like bipinnate, glaucous, bluish-silvery leaves; the fluffy bright yellow, fragrant, globose flower heads massed in great sprays of clustering racemes, blooming in the Northern Hemisphere January into April; in Australia, June to August. *Subtropic.* *p. 1367, 1369*

cardiophylla (New South Wales), "Wyalong wattle"; shrub to 3m, with long arching branches, draped in spring with numerous small yellow flowers; soft hair on young branches; bipinnate leaflets grayish-green. *p. 1366*

cavenia (Chile); used for hedges in Algiers and elsewhere; deciduous spiny tree or shrub up to 6m; leaves bipinnate; linear leaflets scurfy downy; flowers yellow, in globose heads to 2cm dia. *p. 1365*

cornigera (South Africa), "Bullhorn acacia"; thorny-tree with small pinnate leaves, large swollen white to yellow thorns. *p. 1366*

cultriformis (New So. Wales, Queensland), "Knife acacia"; bushy shrub to 2 m, or more, with stiff, spirally set, triangular phyllodia silvery-gray and glaucous; small fluffy, bell-shaped yellow flowers in long, arching racemes forming a terminal panicle, during February-April. *Subtropic.* *p. 1367*

cyanophylla (W. Australia), "Blue-leaved wattle"; tall shrub; phyllodes linear-oblanceolate, glaucous, 15-30cm long; flowers yellow, in heads 5mm -1cm wide in axillary and terminal racemes. *p. 1366*

dealbata: see decurrens dealbata

decurrens (New South Wales to Tasmania), "Green wattle"; tree 18 m and upwards, densely leafy; leaves bipinnate, 8-12 cm long, green; flowers yellow, fragrant, in numerous globose heads 5 mm dia., forming large panicles. *Subtropic.* *p. 1366*

decurrens dealbata (Queensland, New South Wales, Tasmania), "Silver wattle" or "Tumbledown gum"; straggling tree to 4m high or more, the trunk with rough bark below, smooth and white higher up; bluish-green leaves doubly pinnate, 8-12cm long, finely cut and fern-like, covered with silvery-white down; fragrant flowers light yellow, in large panicles of 6mm globular heads, in late winter; also known as "Mimosa" in horticulture. *p. 1367, 1368*

drepanolobium (Kenya: Rift Valley; Uganda, Sudan), known in arid regions of Africa as "Whistling thorn" or "Black-galled acacia". Low tree with horizontal twigs forming a flattened top, bark blackish, with long straight white spines to 8 cm long; deciduous, bipinnate, glaucous leaves, and fragrant creamy-yellow flower heads; large hollow, black galls form at base of spines, said to be caused by ants who hollow them out, and when wind blows through the holes in the galls it sounds like a whistle. *Arid-subtropic.* *p. 1368*

drummondii (Western Australia); free-blooming shrub to 3 m, with shoots furrowed; downy, and bipinnate leaves 5 cm long; main divisions 2 or 3, each with 2-6 pairs of oblong leaflets, smooth, pale bluish-green; flowers lemon-yellow, in dense cylindrical, drooping spikes to 3 cm long, in March -April. *Subtropic.* *p. 1367*

farnesiana (found in Australia, Africa, Asia, also Mexico and Texas); thorny shrub or small tree to 6m much grown on the Riviera for the perfume obtained from the flowers; zigzag branches with glabrous bipinnate leaves, and very sweet scented globose flower heads 1cm dia., 1-3 in each leaf axil (Feb.-March). *p. 1367*

fimbriata (Australia); small tree, 6m high; phyllodes linear, 2-5cm long; flowers rich golden-yellow, in globose heads 1/2cm wide, closely packed in terminal racemes. *p. 1366*

giraffae (So. Africa), "Camel-thorn"; tree to 12m with long stout spines; leaves bipinnate; flowerheads in clusters, flowers dark yellow; pods oval half-moon shaped. *p. 1364*

karroo (So. Africa), "Sweet-thorn" or "Mimosa"; this is a widespread tree found in many parts of So. Africa to Zimbabwe; 4-6m high with round crown; globular yellow flower heads. *p. 1364*

latifolia (No. Australia), "Bush acacia"; attractive flowering shrub with glaucous leaflike stems to 15 cm long and 5 cm wide; the cylindrical flower heads, in loose spikes, to 5 cm long, yellow. *Subtropic.* *p. 1365, 1369*

longifolia (Australia, Tasmania), "Sydney golden wattle"; tree to 10 m, of willowy, spreading habit, the arching branches with long,linear, leathery dark green phyllodia to 15 cm; the bright yellow, small globose flowers in thin risps along stem during February-March, rather short-lived. *Subtropic.* *p. 1369*

longifolia floribunda (retinodes) (Australia); dense, upright tree to 8m, having most of its foliage toward the ends of its branches, with narrow linear, dark green phyllodia to 12cm long, and small globular flowers in loose racemes, blooming constantly from February into summer. *p. 1367*

longifolia mucronata (Australia), "Narrow Sydney wattle"; small spreading tree with lightly drooping branches having narrow linear, stiffly thick phyllodia only 5-8 cm long, and the lemon-yellow flowers in long, 3 cm cylindrical, fluffy spikes along the stem, March blooming. *p. 1369, 2112A*

mearnsii (Australia), "Black wattle"; black-barked, bushy tree to 6 m high, naturalized in Africa where it is considered a "beastly" wattle; I have encountered these at 2,700 m in the mountains of Kigezi, in Central Africa, with finely cut lacy, somber green foliage and attractive ball-shaped lemon-yellow clusters of flowers. *Subtropic.* *p. 1368*

neriifolia (Australia); small tree; shoots slender, glaucous when young; phyllodes linear-lanceolate, curved, 8-12cm long, strongly 1-nerved; flowers yellow, in globose heads. *p. 1364*

nigrescens (Africa: Rhodesia, Mozambique, Transvaal), "Knobthorn"; a timber tree in Africa, to 12 m high, with bipinnate, light green, deciduous leaves, and sharp, recurved thorns, which will grow into thorny knobs; sweetly scented, elongate or cylindrical flower heads pale lemon-yellow. A striking flowering tree as observed in the landscape of the dry veld of the northern Transvaal. *Subtropic.* *p. 1364, 1368*

podalyriaefolia (Queensland), "Pearl acacia"; tall, silvery-gray, pubescent shrub to 3 m, set with ovate, silvery glaucous phyllodia; flowers in axillary racemes, 5-10 cm long, carrying up to 20 globose 1 cm heads of golden yellow; December-January blooming. *Subtropic.* *p. 1367*

pubescens (Mimosa) (New South Wales), "Hairy wattle"; shrub of dense luxuriant growth, to 6m with pendant branches as if weeping, hairy stalks with bipinnate, feathery, firm green foliage; fragrant flowers bright yellow in fluffy little balls on abundant drooping racemes longer than the leaves; blooming in March. *p. 1369*

pubescens erecta (Australia); form of more upright habit, with irregular growth, and only the ends of branches arching, bearing the axillary racemes of small, lemon-yellow flowers of good lasting quality; Easter blooming. *p. 1369*

retinodes, in California nurseries as longifolia floribunda, and commonly planted on the Riviera as A. "floribunda"; (South Australia), the "Everblooming acacia"; dense, upright tree to 8 m, having most of its foliage toward the ends of its branches, with narrow linear, dark green phyllodia to 12 cm long, and small ½ cm globular light yellow, fragrant flowers in loose, clustered racemes 15-25 cm long, blooming constantly from February nearly all year. *Subtropic.* *p. 1365, 1369*

robusta (So. Africa), "Enkeldoring"; flowers borne in globose heads and not in spikes or catkins. Tree is robust and has branches rather thicker than usually found in acacias; creamy-white balls of flowers; small bipinnate leaves. *p. 1364*

saligna (W. Australia); wide-spreading large shrub or small tree with linear green phyllodes to 30cm long on willowy branches, densely set with golden-yellow ball-shaped flower heads in racemes. The Cape-Flats near Cape Town, South Africa are a never forgotten sight when in bloom there, in moist areas, during September. *p. 1368*

sieberiana var. woodii (Natal, Transvaal) "Paperbark-thorn" or "Natal Camel-thorn"; thorny tree to 8m, spreading flat crown; corky bark, flakes off in papery strips; leaves divided into small leaflets; flowers white or creamy-yellow balls. *p. 1364, 1366*

sowdenii (New South Wales), narrow-linear foliage; small globular yellow powder puffs. *p. 1366*

sphaerocephala (Mexico); tree with bipinnate, feathery leaves, armed with hollow, horn-like, ant-tenanted thorns; globose flower-heads yellow. *Subtropic.* *p. 1364, 1365*

venulosa (New South Wales, Queensland); well-shaped bush to 2½m; stiff "leaves" 5-8cm with tapered ends; yellow flowers in twos or small clusters. *p. 1364*

ACALYPHA *Euphorbiaceae* **I2LBM**

godseffiana (New Guinea), "Lance copperleaf"; profuse shrub, bushy and dense, with ovate or obovate bright green leaves having a broad cream serrate margin, flowers are greenish-yellow. *p. 1003, 1005*

godseffiana 'Heterophylla' (New Guinea); form with drooping branches and ragged foliage sometimes reduced to shreds, these narrow, lacy leaves are green with pale yellow, wavy edges. *Tropical.* *p. 1003*

hispida (sanderi) (India), "Chenille plant"; showy tropical shrub with broad ovate, bright green, hairy leaves with crenate margins; bright red flowers in long pendant spikes resembling foxtails.
Tropical. *p. 15*, 1003, 1005, 1055, 1056A**

hispida 'Alba', "Philippine Medusa"; variety having drooping tassel-like, pistillate, creamy-white spikes, tinted pink. *Tropical.* *p. 1003*

wilkesiana 'Ceylon', "Fire-dragon"; handsome tropical bush with woody stems covered toward the ends with curiously twisted roundish, coppery maroon leaves about 12-15 cm long, the margins bordered with white to bright pink lobes. *Tropical.* *p. 1004*

wilkesiana 'Hoffmannii'; beautiful ornamental shrub with woody branches displaying a dense bouquet of twisted grass green leaves, fringed by short lobes of ivory white; photographed in Honolulu. *Tropical.* *p. 1004*

wilkesiana 'Macafeana' (New Hebrides), "Copper-leaf"; robust, branching shrub dense with red ovate leaves marbled crimson and bronze, margins serrate; the slender flower spikes are red. *Tropical.* *p. 1003*

wilkesiana 'Macrophylla' (South Sea Isl.), "Heart copperleaf"; form with large pointed leaves with cordate base, russet-brown alternating with metallic bronzy green and bright copper. *Tropical.* *p. 1003*

wilkesiana 'Moorea'; spectacular tropical bush photographed on Moorea in French Polynesia with broad, blackish coppery, waxy leaves having crenate margins and twisted in coquette fashion; small greenish-red flowers in axillary spikes. *Tropical.* *p. 1004*

wilkesiana 'Obovata' (Polynesia), "Heart copperleaf"; large obovate leaves emarginate or notched at apex, green edged cream-white when young, later changing to copper with orange-rose margins. *Tropical.* *p. 1003*

ACAMPE *Orchidaceae* **S3OFM**

longifolia (India); large epiphyte allied to Vanda, with stout stems to 1m high, clothed with overlapping, long-spreading leaves, and axillary racemes of large fleshy flowers deep yellow, barred with cinnamon-brown, lip with white raised lines (Jan.-Spring). (S) *p. 1817*

papillosa (Himalayas to Burma); epiphyte resembling a small vanda in habit, with leafy stem, the thick recurving leaves 12cm long; inflorescence a short axillary raceme, or dense head of long-lived, heavy textured flowers 1cm across, the sepals and petals yellow spotted brown, the lip white with violet spots; sweetly fragrant (autumn). *p. 1660*

ACANTHOCALYCIUM *Cactaceae* **C2LBD**

violaceum (Argentina), "Violet sea-urchin"; globular cactus resembling Echinopsis, to 20 cm high, deep olive green, with 15 acute ribs lightly notched, and straight yellowish needle spines; funnel form flowers pale violet.
Arid-Subtropic. *p. 683, 692*

ACANTHOCEREUS *Cactaceae* **S2LFD**

pentagonus (horridus) (W. Indies), "Big-needle vine"; nightblooming slender clamberer 8-10cm dia., 3-4-angled, with short spines, forest green to deep green, long jointed; large white flowers. *p. 647, 654*

ACANTHORHIPSALIS *Cactaceae* **I2LFM**

monacantha (Argentina), "Spiny rhipsalis"; erect, stocky plant with mostly 3-cornered, waxy green joints, the wings notched, and usually without spines; flowers golden orange. *p. 736*

ACANTHOSTACHYS *Bromeliaceae* **I2HBM**

strobilacea (So. Brazil, Paraguay, Argentina), "Pinecone bromeliad"; epiphytic plant with long pendant, very narrow, succulent and channeled leaves deep green with gray scurf and spiny; inflorescence on reed-like stems bearing red cone-like fruit. *Sub-tropic.* *p. 512, 529, 551*

ACANTHUS *Acanthaceae* **I2LFM**

gillottii (Malaysia); erect tropical shrub to 180cm with slender stem and soft, lanceolate, slender pointed leaves shallowly lobed, the lobes spine-tipped and more so near leaf base, 25cm long; flowers lilac-rose. *p. 42*

ilicifolius (Trop. Asia); tender spiny shrub, aquatic in tropical brackish waters, to 1½ m high, forming stilt roots in bogs or shallow water; narrow oblong leaves shiny dark green with spiny lobes, 20-30 cm long.
Tropical. *p. 42*

longifolius (Greece, Yugoslavia); ornamental perennial 75-90cm high with deeply lobed leaves almost pinnate, not spiny; floral spike 30cm long, with spiny bracts and rosy, irregular tubular flowers with broad lip. (h) *p. 42*

mollis (So. Europe), "Greek acanthos"; perennial herb with large, glossy, lobed leaves cordate at base, not spiny. Flowers lilac. *Subtropic.* *p. 41, 42*

montanus (W. Trop. Africa), "Mountain thistle"; shrub with decorative, hard, black-green, pinnatifid, spiny leaves; flowers rose tinted, in terminal spike. *Tropical.* *p. 42*

perringii (Asia Minor); perennial to ½m high, with rosette of 15cm lanceolate leaves, deeply toothed and spiny; flowers in terminal spike, rosy-red corolla, and bracts silvery-green striped red. (h) *p. 42*

polystachius (Trop. Africa); spiny tropical shrub with solitary, erect stem 1½m tall, the leaves as hard as metal, arranged spirally around woody stem, deeply cut nearly to the midrib and with very sharp spines; may be grown in water culture. *p. 42*

pubescens (Kenya); attractive semi-woody bush with leathery, deeply lobed, pointed leaves armed with spines; irregular brick-red flowers in showy spikes. *Tropical.* *p. 42*

spinosus (So. Europe: Dalmatia, Greece; Asia Minor); fairly hardy perennial on lime stone soils, to 70cm high, leaves glossy green, irregularly deeply lobed, the segments with spines; flowers in dense spikes, with corolla white to purplish. The acanthus leaf is much sculptured in classical Greece, such as on the marble capital of Corinthian columns. *p. 42*

ACER *Aceraceae* **C2LBD**

buergerianum (China, Japan), "Trident maple"; deciduous small tree to 8m high, of low spreading growth, with very attractive 3-lobed glossy, rich green leaves 8cm wide, glaucous beneath. Beautiful in autumn colors varying from yellow to orange and red. Decorative patio tree and favorite Bonsai subject. (Plant in photo 80 years old). *p. 55*

palmatum 'Sansokaku'; a rare Japanese cultivar of slender habit; finely and deeply cut light green, delicate leaves, carried in contrast on striking red branches. Photographed at North Haven Gardens, Dallas, Texas.
Warm temperate. *p. 55*

ACHIMENES *Gesneriaceae* **S3HFMd**

andrieuxii; compact and shapely, hairy little plant with scaly rhizomes, forming rosette of quilted ovate leaves; from the leaf axils rise numerous 5cm stalks bearing the small, pretty violet flowers, their pure white throat lined with purple dots giving a bicolor effect and looking like miniature gloxinias. *p. 1228*

antirrhina (So. Mexico, Guatemala), "Scarlet magic flower"; erect herbaceous plant with hairy stems to 30cm or more high; opposite, ovate green leaves to 4cm long, wrinkled and hairy above and with serrate margins, reddish underneath; the hairy tubular flowers to 4cm long, straw-yellow outside, yellow with red lines inside, the flaring lobes bright scarlet. *p. 1228*

'Blue Star' (1953); seedling typical of longiflora, trailing stems with pale to dark lilac blue flowers with white eyes, yellow deep in center, the slender tubes yellow; blooming in midseason. *p. 1225*

candida (Dicyrta) (Guatemala), "Mother's tears"; low growing hairy herb with scaly rhizome; red-brown wiry stems and rugose, serrate, oblique leaves; small nodding, curved, funnel-shaped flowers white with yellow, buff outside, purple spotted throat. *Humid-tropical.* *p. 1227*

'Charm', one of the newer hybrids of the "Magic flower"; in bloom most all the time, similar to 'Little Beauty', of somewhat dwarf habit, with narrow, bright green hairy leaves and charming salverform coral-pink flowers with crimson-velvet sheen. *p. 1227, 1248A**

'Dazzler'; shapely cultivar of bushy habit, with small ovate leaves and large cardinal-red flowers. *p. 1226*

ehrenbergii (Scheeria lanata) (Mountains of Mexico); erect bushy plant with pairs of hairy, light green, ovate leaves, serrate at margins and white-woolly beneath; stalked, solitary, nodding, slipper-type flowers orchid-colored with white throat marked purple, blooming most of year. *p. 1227*

erecta (coccinea in hort.), (Mexico, Jamaica, Panama); first cultivated species imported to England in 1778; herbaceous plant of neat miniature habit with thickened scaly underground stolons, trailing stems 10-45cm with 2-3 crenate, hairy leaves together, and small axillary flowers intense bright scarlet, borne in profusion from late August into winter. *p. 1225*

flava (So. Mexico); attractive branching herb with beige stems and opposite dark metallic green, ovate leaves, puckered between veins, lightly hairy, dentate at margins, paler beneath; flowers orange-yellow. *p. 1226*

grandiflora (Mexico), an "Orchid pansy"; spreading, stiff hairy plant with ovate, toothed leaves reddish beneath, very showy, producing numerous large red-purple flowers, appearing from leaf axils. *Humid-tropical.*
p. 1225, 1227

'Leonora' (1952); a cultivar resembling 'Purple King', with dark green foliage and violet-purple flowers with yellow throat, spotted maroon; blooming in midseason. *p. 1225*

longiflora (Mexico, Guatemala); variable, tall growing plant forming pear-shaped rhizomes at the roots; resting in winter; small elliptic stiff-hairy, toothed, green leaves and solitary long-tubed, salvershaped flowers of violet blue. *p. 1226, 1227*

longiflora 'Alba' (Guatemala); known as 'Jaureguia maxima'; a graceful, free-blooming variety for hanging baskets, with large, snowy-white flowers with yellow throat marked purple, the large oblique limb 8 cm wide.
Humid-Tropical. *p. 1227*

longiflora 'Andersonii', "Monkey-faced pansy"; with slender stems distantly bearing small hairy, opposite, grass-green, ovate leaves, and axillary, short stalked, dipping salverform flowers of purplish-blue.
Humid-Tropical. *p. 1227*

longiflora 'Major', "Orchid pansy"; slender cultivar with metallic green leaves larger than the species and in greater number, and flowers lavender to pale purple, with golden throat and yellow tube. *p. 1225*

'Master Ingram'; heterophylla hybrid on sturdy red stems with hairy, nettle-like, serrate leaves and beautiful large velvety, salverform flowers strong brick-red with orange-yellow throat. *p. 1227*

misera (So. Mexico to Honduras); dwarf, weedy, branching species with softly-hairy stems and light green, ovate toothed leaves, hairy above and clammy to the touch, to 9cm long; solitary tiny flowers with flattened tubular corolla yellowish with purple flush and dots, the spreading lobes white. *p. 1226*

patens (Mexico: Michoacán), "Kimono plant"; branching herb to 45cm high, with slender brown-red stems, small oblique-elliptic dentate leaves, dark lustrous green with pale veins and short-hairy, 4cm long; small 3cm flaring oblique trumpet flowers deep violet-purple marked yellow in throat. *p. 1226, 1228*

pedunculata (Mexico, Guatemala, Honduras); hairy plant of rangy habit, with erect stems 50 to 80cm high; ovate, sharply pointed and toothed leaves to 9cm long, lightly cordate at base, on reddish petioles; handsome tubular inflated, nodding flowers 5cm long, vermilion red with orange flush below, the flaring lobes orange-red, and yellow throat lined and dotted dark red; summer-blooming. *p. 1228*

'Pulchella'; an early-blooming form of coccinea having somewhat larger flowers and less saturated red than the native Jamaican species; glowing rusty-red limb with deep yellow throat, tube yellow tinted by red hairs; hairy green leaves., *p. 1225*

skinneri (hirsuta) (Guatemala); loose grower suitable for hanging baskets, producing axillary bulbils on stems; coarse-hairy, bronzy green, ovate leaves with serrate margins and purple reverse; salverform flowers with oblique limb, light purple with yellow throat. *p. 1227*

tubiflora (Argentina); from a solid potato-like tuber rise the oblong, slender pointed downy leaves in opposite pairs, obscurely crenate; the inflorescence on erect stalks, with slender tubular white flowers 10cm long, with 5 expanded lobes 4cm across and curving upwards; summer. *p. 1228*

'Violetta'; bushy plant with drooping branches having dark foliage with red veins and orchid colored flowers with violet eye. *p. 1226*

'Vivid'; cultivar of the longiflora type known since 1875; flowers velvety purplish-red or magenta with golden throat spotted red, and distinctive orange tube; blooms midseason on trailing stems with dark green foliage. *p. 1225*

ACHRAS: see Manilkara

ACHYRANTHES: see Iresine

ACIDANTHERA *Iridaceae* **I2LBM**

bicolor 'Murielae' (Gladiolus) (Ethiopia), "Peacock orchid"; cormous plant with flat, linear leaves, in appearance between Gladiolus and Ixia; about 60 cm high; nodding fragrant flowers 4-5 cm across, with long tubes and spreading petals, creamy-white with purple star in center. The variety 'Murielae' is stronger growing than type. *Warm-temperate.* *p. 1325*

laxiflora (Ethiopia); small graceful, tender cormous plant not more than 30cm high, with flat, narrow leaves like gladiolus, and stiff-wiry stems carrying an elegant cluster of slightly pendant flowers, with long perianth tube and wide-spreading petals like a star, 5cm across, creamy-white throughout, lightly tinged with yellow, and sweetly fragrant; blooming at the end of summer. *p. 1324*

tubergenii 'Zwanenburg' (murielae x bicolor), a Van Tubergen hybrid (1957) in habit similar to murielae; the sweetly scented, large pure white flowers with larger maroon center, and 3 lower petals with more red; late July-August. *p. 1324*

ACINETA *Orchidaceae* **S3OFM**

densa (C. America: Costa Rica); stout epiphyte, with ovoid pseudobulbs having 3-4 lanceolate stalked leaves; pendulous racemes from the base of the pseudobulb, of bell-shaped, fleshy flowers bright yellow, petals covered inside with crimson spots, lip pouched at base and trilobed, with red spotted side-lobes (spring and variable). *p. 1654*

superba (Venezuela, Colombia, Ecuador); strong epiphyte with stout pseudobulbs bearing 3 leaves; 8cm flowers in pendulous racemes, reddish-brown spotted red inside, the lobed lip yellow or brown-red spotted with purple, (spring). (S) *p. 1654*

ACMENA *Myrtaceae* **I2LBD**

smithii (Eugenia) (E. Australia), "Lilly-pilly"; evergreen tree to 18 m high; with thickish ovate leaves to 9cm long, unfolding in rich bronze; terminal clusters of small snow-white flowers, followed by showy edible, pinkish or purple small berries. *Subtropic.* *p. 1606, 1607, 1613*

ACOKANTHERA *Apocynaceae* **I2LBD**

venenata (So. Africa), "Bushman's poison"; evergreen shrub 1-3m high, with opposite leathery leaves 4-10cm long; showy, dense axillary clusters of flowers 1cm across, white or pinkish and very sweetly scented, February to April; the fruit a small berry 2cm long, grape-like and very poisonous. This plant is also listed under Carissa acokanthera. *p. 136*

ACOKANTHERA: see also CARISSA

ACORUS *Araceae* **•C2LFW**

calamus (No. and C. Europe, Temp. Asia, S.E. Canada, U.S.A.), "Sweet flag"; robust water-loving perennial herb of marshlands, to 2 m high; creeping rhizome containing aromatic cells, with iris-like leaves arranged in flat, shingled fans, the linear grass-green leaves parallel-veined, 2 cm wide and with thick midrib; the inflorescence on a cylindrical spadix 5-10 cm long thickly covered with minute greenish-yellow perfect flowers. Winter-hardy. The candied rhizome was an old-time confection. *Warm temperate.* *p. 148*

calamus 'Variegatus' (N. Hemisphere), "Sweet flag"; bog plant with flat, iris-like leathery leaves, green with broad, white lengthwise variegation. *Warm temperate.* *p. 181*

gramineus (Burma, Philippines, So. China, Japan); small water-loving rhizomatous perennial with flat, narrow-linear, grass-like leaves to 30cm or more long, 5-10mm wide, grass-green and of thin-leathery texture, forming thick tufts; small 5cm spadix in catkin form, yellowish green, eventually setting small green berries containing 2-3 seeds. *p.221*

gramineus pusillus (Japan); tufted, little grass-like perennial with flat, waxy, linear, dark-green leaves to 8cm long. *p. 181*

gramineus 'Variegatus' (Japan), "Miniature sweet flag"; waterloving perennial with creeping rhizomes and tufted, linear, flat leathery leaves, light-green and white, spreading fan-like. *Tropical.* *p. 181*

ACRIDOCARPUS *Malpighiaceae* **S3HBD**

natalitius (Natal); climbing shrub with leathery obovate leaves, and pale yellow flowers with 5 crenate petals, in long racemes. *p. 1525*

ACROCOMIA *Palmae* **S2LBM**

aculeata (Cuba, Martinique); tall palm to 15m, trunk slightly thickened toward top, and with black spines; pinnate leaves to 4½m long, bright green on both sides, the rachis bearing spines. *p. 1850*

armentalis (crispa) (Cuba), the "Grugru palm"; tall, to 15m; erect trunk bulging, spindle-shaped, with alternate rings spiny and smooth; deciduous pinnate, pendant leaves to 3m long, glossy green, bluish beneath. *p. 1850, 1853*

sclerocarpa (Brazil); palm to 10m with trunk covered with persistent petiole-bases; the pinnate fronds glossy green above, gray or glaucous and finely pubescent underneath, the rachis hairy and with brown spines. *p. 1850*

totai (No. Argentina, Paraguay, Bolivia), "Gru-Gru" palm; tall palm 15 to possibly 25 m, the trunk set with stout spines, smallish pinnate fronds smooth and green on both sides, the pinnae 2 cm wide. *Subtropic.* *p. 1850*

ACRODON *Aizoaceae* **I3LBDd**

bellidiflorus (Cape Prov.); spreading succulent with recurved, 3-angled, gray-green leaves, 3-5cm long, arranged cross wise; flowers 4cm across, white bordered with red. *p. 59*

ACROSTICHUM *Polypodiaceae (Filices)* **S3LFW**

aureum (Old and New World Tropics), coarse "Swamp-fern"; 1 to 3 m high, with stout rootstock and dark green, thick-leathery pinnate fronds, only the upper pinnae fertile, smaller than the barren pinnae, and covered with the deep reddish brown coating of the spore-cases. A leather fern growing luxuriantly on the Florida Keys, in mangrove swamps and salt marshes, forming dense masses. *Humid-Tropical.* *p. 1094, 1095*

danaeifolium (excelsum) (Trop. America), "Swamp-fern"; with pinnate fronds 1-4 m high, with most or all of the pinnae fertile and bearing spores, on mature fronds. *Humid-Tropical.* *p. 1094*

ACROSTICHUM: see also ELAPHOGLOSSUM

ACROTREMA *Dilleniaceae* **S3LFM**

walkeri (lanceolatum) (Sri Lanka); ornamental small stemless tropical plant with perennial rhizome, narrow oblanceolate, bullate leaves 5-10 cm long and 2 cm wide, the margins toothed, dull red and hairy on veins beneath; yellow flowers in axillary clusters. *p. 951*

ACTAEA *Ranunculaceae* **C2LBDh**

rubra (Labrador to New Jersey, west to Nebraska), "Red baneberry"; herbaceous perennial 60cm high, with compound, lobed leaves and racemes of small whitish flowers in showy terminal clusters, followed by attractive shiny crimson-red, poisonous berries. *p. 1985*

ACTINIDIA *Dilleniaceae* **I2LBD**

chinensis (China, Taiwan), "Chinese gooseberry" or "Kiwi vine"; woody vine twining to 10 m, sparsely furnished with large 12 to 20 cm, rough, corrugated ovate leaves, dark green above, white velvety beneath; small 3-4 cm flowers cream turning to yellow in August, followed about November, in the Northern hemisphere, by pendant ovoid, brownish fruit 4-5 cm diameter; delicious to eat, with acid, gooseberry-like flavor; male and female flowers usually on separate plants. Hortus III to Actinidiaceae. *Subtropic.* *p. 81*

kolomikta (Japan, Manchuria, China), "Kolomikta vine"; shrubby twining vine to 5 m, grown for their attractive foliage; the long-stalked heart-shaped leaves 8-12 cm long, variegated green with white or pink, some are all white, others with red, more so on male plants; for colorful arbor, trellis or wall covering; cup shaped white, axillary flowers; yellow or greenish fruit on female plants. Hortus III refers this to Actinidiaceae. *Warm temperate.* *p. 81*

ACTINIOPTERIS *Polypodiaceae (Filices)* **S3HFM**
australis (Africa, Trop. Asia); attractive miniature tufted fern with palm-like fronds fanshaped with forked and linear segments, those of fertile frond longer than the barren. *p. 1094*

ACTINOPHLOEUS: see PTYCHOSPERMA

ADA *Orchidaceae* **C3OFM**
aurantiaca (Colombia); epiphyte with compressed pseudobulbs bearing 1-3 tapering leaves to 22 cm long; arching racemes of showy flowers red-orange 3 cm long, often spotted black; petals and sepals narrow, with shorter lip (Winter-Spring). *Humid-Tropical.* *p. 1654*

ADANSONIA *Bombacaceae* **S2LBD**
digitata (across Trop. Africa), the giant "Baobab" or "Sour gourd" or "Monkey-bread-tree"; one of the largest trees in the world, thought to become more than 2000 years old, and while only to 18 m tall, the swollen trunk attains a diameter of more than 10 m, is of pulpous wood without growth rings. Leaves deciduous, digitately compound with leaflets 12 cm long; large 18 cm solitary, scented, pendulous white flowers with purplish stamens; oblong, woody, hairy fruit 30 cm long, which also earns it the name "Dead rat-tree". *Tropical.* *p. 505, 507, 508*

grandidieri (Madagascar); a giant tropical Malagasy species, with smooth bottle-shaped trunks of rather symmetric form, the branches standing out like arms in the savannah landscape, leafless during dry season but with digitately compound, leathery leaves when the rains begin. *p. 506*

gregori (Northern Australia), the "Australian baobab" or "Bottle tree"; remarkable giant tree said to be of great antiquity, with stout, barrel-shaped trunk to 20m in circumference, but not more than 10-12m high, with numerous wide-spreading branches in a large tuft at top, with thick, palmate leaves, deciduous in winter; flowers white; the wood is spongy and of pith-like substance; the large 20cm seed cones contain a bready matter which is eaten by the aboriginals. *p. 506*

ADENANDRA *Rutaceae* **C2HBM**
fragrans (So. Africa), "Dwarf China flower"; small shrublet 30 cm high, green aromatic leaves 4 cm long; fragrant, bright pink flowers with 5 petals, 2 cm across. *Subtropic.* *p. 2026*

uniflora (Diosma) (So. Africa), "China flower"; small evergreen shrub with erect slender branches, 1 cm lanceolate leaves, and solitary flowers 3 cm wide, the 5 petals white with a deep rose streak, anthers brown-purple; late spring. *Subtropic.* *p. 2026*

ADENANTHERA *Leguminosae* **S2HBD**
pavonina (India), the "Red sandal-wood tree" or "Peacock flower fence"; evergreen shrub 1m high, with bipinnate leaves;glabrous leaflets ovate; small white and yellow flowers on spike-like racemes 15cm long, followed by pods with ornamental, lens-like red seeds used for beads. *p. 1370*

ADENIA *Passifloraceae* **S2LBD**
fruticosa (Rhodesia, Transvaal); striking xerophyte with club-shaped base, giving rise to a mass of whip-like scandent branches with 3-lobed, deciduous leaves, and covered with yellowish flowers. *p. 1927*

glauca (So. Africa: Transvaal, Botswana); curious xerophyte with greatly swollen stem partly above ground, with viney stems to 2m and forming tendrils, branching from the stem or from a flat surface; glaucous leaves digitately compound or deeply lobed, sessile pink flowers, followed by orange colored fruits which split into 3 or 4 valves. *p. 1927*

subglobosa (E. Africa); weird-looking succulent with massive swollen base to 1 m thick, looking like a gray-green stone, topped by pencil thick clambering gray twigs 3-4 m long, normally leafless and armed with long, stout thorns; during rains with narrow lanceolate leaves; grouped inflorescence with star-like, shining-red, odorous flowers. *Arid-Tropical.* *p. 1926*

ADENIUM *Apocynaceae* **S2LBD**
coarctatum (Tanzania: Usambara Mountains); succulent to 1m high, with thick stem, flask-shaped at base, the branches later becoming crooked, twisted and knotty; obovate, fleshy leaves smooth and green with ivory midrib, later deciduous; bell-shaped, light rose flowers becoming darker carmine toward tips. *p. 143*

multiflorum (Transvaal: Kruger Park to the Limpopo; Zimbabwe: Zambesi), the "Impala lily" is a most attractive succulent shrub with fat, swollen trunk 1-3m high, with poisonous milky sap; during the growing season the thick, stubby branches are covered with dark green, simple, alternate fleshy, deciduous, spirally arranged leaves; the funnel-shaped flowers white edged with crimson, looking like bright stars in the yellow, dusty vegetation of the steppe; much relished by elephants and monkeys. *p. 134*

obesum (coetanum) (E. Africa: Tanzania, Kenya, Uganda), the "Desert rose"; spreading succulent bush 2 m high, with thick, fleshy, twisted base and short branches; deciduous obovate, fleshy leaves glossy dark green with pink midrib, 8 cm long, when young sometimes with minute hairs; numerous showy, 5cm flowers with spreading petals pinkish edged with carmine or all carmine-rose. *Arid-Tropical.* *p. 134, 143*

somalense (Kenya, Somaliland, Aden), a "Mock azalea"; similar to obesum, with swollen stem having fleshy leaves long obovate-pointed, bluish-green, and smaller flowers white to pink. *p. 143*

ADENOSMA *Scrophulariaceae* **S3LBD**
glutinosum (China, Hong Kong); hairy herbaceous plant which may be found on Victoria Peak in Hong Kong; 30 to 50cm high, with fleshy green, wrinkled, opposite leaves having a minty aroma; tubular flowers flaring into 2 lips, orchid-purple and 3cm long. *p. 2049*

ADHATODA *Acanthaceae* **S3LFM**
vasica (Justicia in Hortus 3) (India, Sri Lanka); tropical shrub to 2 m or more high, with long-ovate, corrugated leaves to 20 cm long and covered with fine pubescence; the inflorescence in terminal spikes with tubular, two-lipped flowers to 2 cm across, white striped with red. *Tropical.* *p. 41*

ADHATODA: see also Megakepasma

ADIANTUM *Polypodiaceae (Filices)* **S3HNW**
bellum (Bermuda), "Bermuda maidenhair"; a small species with tufted fronds to 15cm long, bipinnate, and with cuneate leaflets densely set, the veins ending in the sinus. (I) *p. 1088*

birkenheadii; a horticultural tufted "species" of uncertain origin, always sterile; large, showy pinnately compound fronds 75cm long with pinnae distant, alternate, the lower bipinnate, upper pinnate, the leaflets lobed. *p. 1090*

capillus-veneris (found around the world), "Venus-hair"; creeping rhizomes produce an abundance of delicate, 2-3 pinnate fronds, the variable segments deeply lobed, with veins leading into teeth; half hardy. (I) *p. 1088*

caudatum (So. Africa, India, Indonesia, China), "Walking fern"; small tufted plant with long, simply pinnate, grayish green, hairy fronds rooting at tip, from which new plant will arise. *p. 1089, 1090*

"chilense" (Perú, Chile); underground, running rhizome, with the fronds bluish green and leathery, leaflets irregularly lobed, veins running into teeth, stalks black. *p. 1088*

cuneatum: see raddianum

curvatum (tetragonum) (So. Brazil); beautiful species from the dry mountain forest, with creeping rhizome, and 30cm fronds forked several times on black stems, with rounded, lobed, light green leaflets closely massed. *p. 1086*

decorum (wagneri) (Colombia, Perú); tufted plant with stiff brown-black stalks bearing fronds 20-25cm long, 2-4 pinnate, matte green, the leaflets rhombic to wedge-shaped, shallowly lobed. *p. 1085*

decorum wagneri (Andes of Perú); tufted plant with large fronds lacily divided into well-spaced, small, and lobed leaflets, deep green, with tapering base and veins ending in the sinus. *p. 1088*

decorum 'Weigandii'; tufted cultivar with 3-pinnate fronds triangular, larger than species, about 30cm long, pinnae and leaflets long-stalked, the leaflets ovate from a broad base, lobed, with narrow sinuses. *p. 1085*

diaphanum (Trop. Asia, Australia, New Zealand); stalks 10-20cm long, the 15cm fronds simply pinnate or with 1-3 branches at base, segments to 1cm long, with crenate edge. *p. 1090*

edgeworthii (Himalayas, China north to Manchuria); tufted fern with simply pinnate fronds like caudatum, but membrane-thin and glabrous, 25cm long, with pinnae hardly lobed; smooth stalks black. *p. 1090*

x fragrantissimum; a vigorous moorei hybrid with long-lasting, dark green fronds, long and narrow in outline, set loosely with wedge-shaped leaflets, borne on strong black stems; veins lead into teeth. *p. 1086, 1088*

fulvum (Polynesia, New Zealand, Australia); spreading species with fronds palmately compound, 22-30cm long, bipinnate, the lower pinnae branched again, and sharply toothed. *p. 1091*

gracillimum; a beautiful fern, with the tiniest of leaflets, rich green, borne in multiples on graceful, large fronds which are produced in a densely tufted crown. *p. 1088*

grossum bicolor (Colombia); handsome tropical tufted fern, 30cm high, with wiry stalks bearing pinnate fronds with waxy leaflets, broad and fan-shaped, and lobed and crisped along apex, thickly double; young growth light red, later may-green; it is a combination of these two colors that explain the varietal name bicolor. *p. 1092*

hispidulum (Australia, New Zealand), "Australian maidenhair"; handsome species with 2-3 pinnate fronds, forked at base, borne on long wiry, hairy stalks, the leaflets almost stalkless, thin-leathery, arranged along axis; veins running into teeth. *p. 1088, 1089*

hispidulum 'Tenella' (Old World tropics); delicate, pretty form with very dark, almost black-green foliage of neat shape; young expanding fronds deep coppery color. *p. 1092*

macrophyllum (Trop. America); showy fern with creeping rhizome, the pinnate fronds 30-40 cm long on shiny, black-brown stalks, the lower pinnae of barren frond 5-10 cm long, ovate, toothed, papery, yellow-green; reddish when young; the fertile leaflets narrower. *Humid-Tropical.* *p. 1090, 1091*

microphyllum (venustum) (Afghanistan, India); a sturdy Himalayan variety with wiry stalks 15-25cm long, and firm, light green, 3-4 pinnate fronds with ultimate segments 6mm across, cuneate, the upper edge rounded and usually finely toothed; almost hardy. *p. 1085, 1086*

'Ocean Spray'; very shapely cultivar between 'Pacific Maid' and 'Fritz-Luethii' with dense recurving fronds and medium-small leaflets 1cm wide, with veins running into sinuses, fresh green, also the young fronds toothed and sometimes overlapping, on brown-black stalks. From San Francisco about 1958, claimed to be a sport of 'Pacific Maid', but may be clone of 'Fritz-Luethii' from Swiss spore. *p. 1085*

pedatum (No. America), "American maidenhair"; hardy outdoors, and equally useful in the greenhouse, with fronds to 60cm high, the purplish stalks forked fan-like, each pinnate branch set with neat rows of papery, pea-green leaflets. *p. 1086*

pedatum aleuticum (Alaska to Québec, south to California), "Five-fingered maidenhair"; with palmate fronds on long near-black stalks, the 5-7 fingers in fan-shape 12-60cm dia., one or more times forked, the stalked leaflets arising from the upper side of its branches, one-sided; sori marginal, on the tips of free-forking veins. *p. 1086*

pedatum minor (Argentina); from cool regions, this charming low fern is only 8cm high, with fronds 8cm long, on black rachis; the leaves luxuriant rich green, with pinnae turned backwards on stem, forming a beautiful pattern. *p. 1092*

peruvianum (Perú); large fern with strong stalks 22-45cm long, the fronds 30cm long, simply pinnate or with 1-3 branches at base, some of these sometimes again divided, the segments 5cm or more broad, unequally ovate with cuneate base and finely lobed upper edge. *p. 1091*

polyphyllum (Venezuela, Colombia, Perú); gigantic, noble fern with creeping rhizome, having 2-3 pinnate, robust fronds to 1m long on strong black stalks, the pinnae dense with leaflets, close like a comb, fully developed on one side, and little on the other, the upper edge shapely toothed; pinkish when young, changing to metallic then pale, fresh-green when fully developed. *p. 1086*

pulverulentum (West Indies to Brazil); robust tropical fern photographed at Kew Gardens, London, with stalks 15 to 30cm long, supporting neat bipinnate fronds, the glossy green, firm pinnae, each 10-20cm long, dense with squarish, almost shingled leaflets. *p. 1092*

raddianum (cuneatum) (Brazil), "Delta maidenhair"; an old greenhouse favorite because of its tolerance, sturdiness and simple elegance of the dark green fronds with many small, firm leaflets having a wedge-shaped base, with veins running into sinus between lobes. *Humid-Tropical.* *p. 1085, 1088*

raddianum 'Excelsum'; of firm habit with long-stalked fronds of medium-fine feathering, ideal for cut; sets spores only in late autumn. *p. 1087*

raddianum 'Fritz-Luethii'; strong growing Swiss cultivar for pots, of full habit, with fronds to 50cm, much more dense than fragrans; 3-4 pinnate with medium-small leaflets somewhat overlapping, and overcast with steel-blue; veins running into sinus. *p. 1085, 1087*

raddianum 'Goldelse'; a fine cultivar of 'Elegans' and perhaps the best of the fine-feathered adiantum; strong-growing plant with fronds more compact than 'Elegans', first reddish, then of dainty yellow-green color; sterile and used for cut and pots. *p. 1090*

raddianum 'Ideal'; of larger habit than 'Matador', with unusually strong stalks bearing large fronds; pronounced variety for cut use. *p. 1087*

raddianum 'Kensington Gem'; a compact, bushy-growing plant with very hard, delta-form, pale green fronds, for cool greenhouse. *p. 1087*

raddianum 'Matador'; famous old cultivar, clone of raddianum 'Fragrantissimum'; robust-growing, hungry plant, with long-stemmed dark green fronds several times pinnate, without viable spores; used for cut. *p. 1087*

raddianum 'Maximum'; possibly a raddianum 'Fragrantissimum' hybrid, of robust growth, prolific with dark green fronds, used for cut. *p. 1087*

raddianum 'Pacific Maid' (Perú); an attractive compact plant cultivated in San Francisco, with 2-3 pinnate fronds, the pinnae stiffly set in stages above each other, satiny green leaflets, large, with veins running into sinus. *p. 1088, 1089*

raddianum 'Pacottii' (bellum); very dense form, with fronds and large fan-shaped pinnules overlapping each other to an uncommon extent. Photographed at the Los Angeles Fern Show 1965. *p. 1092*

reniforme (Canary Islands); tufted fern with stalks 20cm long and leathery rounded, kidney-shaped leaves to 6cm across, black-green, the fertile fronds lightly toothed, with sori around edge. *p. 1091*

seemanii (platyphyllum) (Central America, Bolivia, Brazil); large leaved fern with pendant, heavy fronds 22-50cm long, simply pinnate or lower pinnae compound, leaflets 8-10cm long, unequal ovate pointed; the barren ones finely serrate. *p. 1086, 1089*

subcordatum (truncatum) (Guyana, Brazil); attractive fern resembling trapeziforme, with 3-pinnate fronds 60cm long, on shining blackish stems, with lower pinnae 30cm long, but the soft, papery leaflets 5cm long, are ovate-oblique at the base on the lower side and slightly lobed on same side. *p. 1091*

tenerum 'Farleyense' (Barbados), "Barbados maidenhair"; magnificent feathery, but delicate fronds gracefully drooping, rose-tinted when young, pea-green later, the leaflets large and lacily cut and crisped, base articulated (jointed); veins run into teeth; infertile. *Humid-Tropical.* *p. 1089*

tenerum gloriosum; broad, 3-pinnate fronds with large pea green, deeply lobed leaflets, pale bronze when young, and occasionally bearing fertile spores. *p. 1089*

tenerum 'Jan Bier'; similar to gloriosum and 'Ruhm von Moordrecht' for grouping of fronds and their feathering, but more dainty and graceful, lighter green, and with more red contrast in the young growth. *p. 1090*

tenerum 'Scutum roseum' (ghiesbreghtii); a good potplant with medium size fronds beautifully tinted red when young, later dark green, on shiny black stems. *p. 1089*

tenerum 'Wrightii' (W. Indies, Mexico, Venezuela), "Fan maidenhair"; good potplant with graceful medium-size fronds of good texture, pink when young, later fresh-green, the fan-shaped leaflets growing large and lacily lobed. *Humid-Tropical.* *p. 1085, 1089*

trapeziforme (Mexico and W. Indies south to Brazil); delicate looking, yet bold-growing "Giant maidenhair" with slowly creeping rhizome and large 2-pinnate fronds on black stems, the stalked trapezoid leaflets to 5 cm long and brilliant green. *Humid-Tropical.* *p. 1091*

ADONIDIA: see Veitchia

ADROMISCHUS *Crassulaceae* ***I1LBD**

antidorcatum (hoerleinianus in hort.) (Namibia); small succulent 4 to 10cm high, with soft, turnip-like rootstock; leaves at the end of stemlets, 3 cm long, soft-fleshy, gray-green, with irregular red points; flowers grayish-violet. *p. 860*

blosianus (So. Africa: Namaqualand); succulent herb dense with thick-fleshy leaves oval almost egg-shaped, bronzy gray green, with wavy blackish red margins and apex; small tubular erect flowers pink with purple-edged star. *p. 857*

bolusii (Cape Prov.); small succulent shrub with fleshy, green spatulate 4cm leaves covered with waxy coating, margins with reddish horny edge; tubular flowers red on unbranched raceme. *p. 860*

clavifolius (Cape Province); small clustering rosette of obovate, fleshy leaves green with covering of gray dust; apex undulate or crisped. *p. 862*

cooperi (festivus: Jacobsen) (Cape Prov.); succulent with swollen 5cm leaves resembling a gloved fist, narrowed at base and flattened at the corky crested apex, gray with green blotches, purplish toward tip; rooting from leaves. *p. 859*

cristatus (Cape Prov.), "Crinkleleaf plant"; succulent rosette with stout stem covered by red aerial roots and hairy, wedge-shaped fleshy leaves with crested apex, light green and soft pubescent; tubular flowers reddish white. *p. 857*

festivus (Cape Prov.), "Plover eggs"; fascinating clustering succulent with cylindric or thick spatulate leaves flattened toward the crested apex, silvery green marbled maroon. *Arid-subtropic.* *p. 857*

halesowensis (Cape Prov.); smooth-surfaced succulent with ascending branchlets, leaves to 8cm long, terete at base then gradually widened and flattened, glossy green with waxy points toward tip and dark markings; flower reddish. *p. 874*

herrei (Cape Prov.: Namaqualand); small succulent 8-10cm high with spindle-shaped leaves spirally arranged along stem, and covered thickly with tubercles, greenish to brown-yellow, and coated with wax; long stalked red flowers; needs summer rest. *p. 862*

hoerleinianus in hort.: see antidorcatum

maculatus of hort: see rupicola

mammillaris (Cape Prov., Namibia); succulent with stems creeping or ascending, the thin brownish branches with alternate, spindle-shaped leaves bluish-green with thin waxy covering, to 8cm long; red-brown flowers. *p. 860*

phillipsiae (Cotyledon) (Cape Prov.); clump-forming shrubby succulent with leaves almost in a rosette, 4cm long, dark green with reddish reverse, fat linear and flattened at squared apex which turns red in the sun; flowers vivid orange-red. According to Jacobsen, this species is the transition to the genus Cotyledon. *p. 864*

poellnitzianus (E. Cape Prov.); attractive succulent rosettes with numerous reddish aerial roots and spatulate leaves 6-10 cm long, terete at base, flattening toward wavy apex, light green with minute pale hairs; flowers tipped red. *p. 860*

rotundifolius (Cape Prov.); small branching succulent with numerous small oblongate leaves 3 to 4cm long, glaucous green with waxy dots, and horny margins toward apex; flowers pink. *p. 860*

rupicola (maculatus of hort.) (So. Africa), "Calico hearts"; succulent rosette of few flat leaves almost round or obovate, gray-green heavily blotched with brown-purple and along margins, the edge a silvery line; flowers tipped red-white. *Arid-subtropic.* *p. 857, 859*

tricolor (Cape Prov.), "Spotted spindle"; very attractive succulent with spindle-shaped leaves pale green richly blotched maroon and marked silver; flowers pale reddish purple. Leaves don't fall off. *p. 859*

triflorus in hort. (poellnitzianus cristatus) (Cape Prov.); dense, fleshy rosette with thick obovate leaves crested at apex, silvery green with small waxy spots; flowers pink tipped white. *p. 858*

trigynus (Transvaal to Karroo); densely clustering succulent with swollen elliptic leaves, silver gray with red-brown markings. *p. 859*

AECHMEA *Bromeliaceae* ***S10FM**

amazonica (Brazil: Amazonas; Perú, Colombia); tubular spreading rosette to 1m high, with leathery leaves matte fern-green; plum-purple beneath, crossbanded with silver-white scales, the margins dense with long blackish spines; erect mealy-white stalk with bright red bracts, and laxly bipinnate inflorescence with red bracts and orange flowers. *p. 524*

angustifolia (Costa Rica to Colombia, Perú and Bolivia); sturdy rosette to 90 cm high, with strap-shaped leaves 6 cm wide, gray with brown-scurfy scales, spiny-serrate at margins; the red spike with bipinnate inflorescence of red bracts and yellow flowers, followed by white, then blue berries, long lasting. *Tropical.* *p. 523, 524*

aquilega (Gravisia), (West Indies, Costa Rica, Venezuela, Guyana, Brazil); spreading rosette with concave strap-shaped, recurving leaves almost 1 m long, gray-scaly and with marginal spines; dense inflorescence nearly globular, with deep yellow bracts and orange flowers, on erect stem with red leaf-bracts. *Tropical.* *p. 540, 550*

aquilega var. chrysocoma (Gravisia) (Costa Rica, West Indies); bold rosette of strap-shaped, shiny coppery-green, flexible leaves; the leaning inflorescence with clusters of yellow bracted purple flowers, subtended by flag-like red bract leaves. *p. 540*

areneosa (Brazil); attractive open rosette from Espirito Santo, with narrow bright green, shiny leaves to 50 cm long, and edged with brown spines; floral stem and bracts red, with branched, pyramidal cluster of numerous small prickly, greenish-yellow flowers. *Tropical.* *p. 526*

'Bert' (orlandiana x fosteriana); stocky rosette of short leathery leaves matte green marked with irregular purplish-brown crossbands, heavy dark spines; arching inflorescence with dense head of red bracts and pale flowers. *Tropical.* *p. 518, 519*

'Black Prince', showy rosette of broad, shiny blackish-green leaves; branched inflorescence with whitish berries; bracts scarlet, base and tips scarlet, on maroon stalk. *Tropical.* *p. 524*

blumenavii (So. Brazil); shapely small rosette somewhat tubular with few smooth green narrow leaves 40 cm long, the tips flushed with purple; inflorescence cylindrical with yellow flowers and rosy bracts. *p. 526*

bracteata (Mexico to Colombia); very robust plant, becoming bottle-shaped, 1-1½ m high, glossy, apple green with prominent green spines, grayish pencil lines beneath; long-lasting inflorescence an erect panicle with brilliantly red bracts and yellow flowers. *p. 516, 522*

bromeliifolia (B. Honduras, Guatemala to N.E. Argentina), "Wax torch"; large tubular rosette with variable leaves ½-1 m long, green with white-scaly coating, a few brown teeth toward apex, with tips curled under; erect, stout cylindric, long-lasting inflorescence, densely white-woolly, with leathery, broad floral bracts, the flower petals greenish-yellow soon turning black. *Tropical.* *p. 524*

bromeliifolia rubra; large, stiff erect, tubular rosette 80 cm high and 1 m spread, of scaly, reddish bronze leaves, grayish-bronze beneath, and with prominent brown thorns; the inflorescence a pinecone-like spike with rosy-red bracts and pale yellow flowers. *p. 524*

'Burgundy' (Ae. distichantha var. schlumbergeri x Ae. weilbachii var. leodiensis); soft-leathery, tubular rosette with concave leaves bronzy-green to coppery-wine-red or burgundy, glossy on both sides, margined by red-brown upcurving spines; flowers milk-white with purple petals. *p. 527*

calyculata (Brazil, Argentina); stiff rosette of deep green channeled leaves; flower spike with dense head scarlet-red, yellow flowers. *p. 518*

caudata (S.E. Brazil); robust rosette to 1 m high with leathery leaves 10-12 cm wide, glossy green, with weak marginal spines; inflorescence on wiry stem a pyramidal panicle with orange-yellow bracts and deep-yellow flowers. *Tropical.* *p. 523*

caudata 'Variegata' (Billbergia forgetii) (Brazil); big sparry rosette of rich green stiff leaves broadly banded creamy-yellow; bold inflorescence with white-mealy stem and panicle of yellow bracts and golden-yellow flowers. *Tropical.* *p. 25*, 512, 512A*, 517*

chantinii (Venezuela, Amazonas, Amazonian Perú), "Amazonian zebra plant"; colorful open rosette of hard olive-green leaves with pronounced pinkish-gray cross-bands; inflorescence on branched spike with tight red bracts tipped yellow, subtended by red bract leaves. *Tropical.* *p. 512, 516, 517, 522, 525, 531*

chantinii 'Red Goddess'; large tubular rosette with maroon-bronzy leaves barred with gray, and compact, branched inflorescence of short flattened spikes, with shingled rose pink bracts and yellow to red petals. *p. 525*

chantinii 'Silver Monarch'; beautiful colorform with foliage cross-banded silver over bronze; the inflorescence with ribbonlike floral bracts scarlet-red, the flattened spikes yellowish; collected by Lee Moore in Amazonian Perú. *Tropical.* *p. 525*

chlorophylla (So. Brazil); epiphytic or on rocks in the Organ Mountains; small species with glossy green strap-shaped leaves, covered with whitish scales; inflorescence with showy, glowing crimson bract leaves, the flowers with yellow petals, in slender cone. *Subtropic.* *p. 528*

coelestis (Hoplophytum) (S. E. Brazil); rosette of 12-20 narrow, leathery, gray-green leaves 45 cm long, with few marginal spines, the reverse with gray-white crossbands; paniculate inflorescence 30 cm long, yellowish bracts, white calyx, blue corolla petals. *p. 523*

coelestis 'Albomarginata' (S.E. Brazil); rosette of 12-20 narrow, concave, stiff gray green leaves to 50 cm long, differing from the species by having broad white margins; the reverse with gray-white cross-bands; few marginal spines; the inflorescence a branched reddish panicle, yellowish bracts, white calyx and blue corolla petals. *Tropical.* *p. 532*

comata (So. Brazil); bold tubular rosette with stiff pale green leaves turning reddish, brown spines on margins; arching spike with dense cluster of red-tinted berries, flowers yellow. *p. 516, 521*

comata 'Makoyana' (syn. lindenii); cultivar with gray-green leaves variegated with creamy-white bands lengthwise. *p. 526*

conglomerata (Brazil); tubular rosette with leathery green foliage; mealy outside; inflorescence with red "berries"; flowers tipped blue. *p. 548*

conglomerata var. discolor (Brazil); rosette with 12-20 strap-shaped leaves, 4 cm wide, 45 cm long, plain green above, claret-brown beneath in var. discolor; inflorescence densely subglobose with many small flowers, their ovary with calyx fiery-red and with petals lilac, or with blue tips. *p. 526*

cylindrata (São Paulo to Santa Catarina); hard plant tubular at base, with stiff light green leaves, some white scaly bands across the back; fine brown teeth at margins; thick, dense, cylindric inflorescence with soft, disintegrating bracts and blue flowers. *p. 516, 526*

dichlamydea var. trinitensis (Trinidad); handsome, majestic epiphyte with gray-green leaves 50-80 cm in length; long, many-branched, scandent inflorescence a rainbow of color, the pink, arching stalk and flattened lateral spikes bright coral, with densely shingled, blue bracts tipped with black-purple; flowers white with lilac, and deep blue berries. *Tropical.* *p. 524*

distichantha (So. Brazil, Bolivia to Argentina); upright dense rosette of stiff gray leaves; inflorescence a robust spike with faded rose bracts and purplish blue flowers. *Subtropic.* *p. 516, 518, 530*

'Electra'; handsome formal rosette of broad coppery-green leaves; the inflorescence a composite head of short flattened rosy spikes with wine-colored bracts and lavender flowers. *p. 527*

'Electrica'; elegant Hummel-California hybrid involving Ae. dealbata x miniata x fasciata; large rosette with leaves dominated by wine and red; the bold inflorescence a compound head of orange bracts and lavender flowers. *Tropical.* *p. 527*

'Exquisite' (x Neomea) (Ae. miniata discolor x Neoregelia tristis); bigeneric open rosette of broad purplish leaves; densely packed inflorescence of green bracts with brown-red tips, lilac flowers. *p. 527*

fasciata (Billbergia rhodocyanea) (Rio de Janeiro), "Silver vase"; stocky rosette of leathery green leaves covered with gray scales and richly tigered silver-white; blackish spines; durable inflorescence in rose-colored globose heads with blue flowers. *Tropical.* *p. 19*, 25*, 512, 512A*, 520, 521*

fasciata albo-marginata; variant with the silver cross-banded green leaves bordered by broad ivory-white bands. *p. 515, 518*

fasciata 'Silver King'; selected clone with the leathery leaves attractively and almost completely frosted with silver, exposing only occasional cross-bands of bluish-green. *p. 529*

fasciata 'Silver type' (hyb. fasciata x nallyi); handsome open rosette of broad, grayish leaves largely overlaid with silvery scales; the long-lasting inflorescence as in fasciata, with slender pointed pink bracts and lavender blue flowers. *p. 525*

fasciata 'Variegata', "Variegated silver vase"; variety with center of the channeled leaves attractively striped and banded ivory-white lengthwise through the regular green, and with silver cross-banding. *p. 517*

filicaulis (Venezuela), "Weeping living vase"; open rosette with grass-green, thin-leathery, strap-shaped, oblanceolate leaves glossy on both sides and with dark mottling; tiny soft marginal spines; long pendulous flowering panicles on snaky, string-like axis with distant, red bract leaves and white flowers. *Tropical.* *p. 516, 523*

fosteriana (Espirito Santo); striking tubular rosette of pale green to reddish green leaves with purplish brown irregular mottling and green spines; flower spike with panicle of crimson bracts and rich yellow petals. *Tropical.* *p. 518*

'Foster's Favorite' (victoriana x racinae), "Lacquered wine cup"; upright rosette with striking lacquered wine-red leaves; pendant spike of coral red pear-shaped berries tipped with midnight-blue flowers. *p. 519*

'Foster's Favorite Favorite'; a most beautiful plant, variegated sport of A. 'Foster's Favorite'; rosette with soft-leathery, glossy, strap-like leaves bordered by broad cream margins, the upper leaves tinted all over with glowing coppery rose to wine-red or maroon according to prevailing light conditions. *Tropical.* *p. 527*

fulgens (Pernambuco), "Coral berry"; loose rosette of stiff green leaves dusted gray; inflorescence in showy panicles with oblong red berries tipped with purple flowers. *Tropical.* 521

fulgens discolor (Pernambuco), "Coral berry"; free-growing rosette of soft-leathery dark olive-green leaves purple beneath, covered on both sides with glaucous gray crossbands; produces showy spikes with oval red berries tipped with violet flowers. *Tropical.* *p. 25*, 512, 521*

galeottii (C. Mexico); handsome, large rosette with scaly leaves 45 cm long with dilated base, pale green, turning red in strong sun, inflorescence a long panicle covered with white fuzz, flower petals yellow; heavily fruited with pearl-like berries. *p. 522*

gamosepala (So. Brazil, Argentina); beautiful medium-sized epiphytic rosette with smooth, glossy green leaves 50 cm long; green floral stalk with short-cylindric inflorescence of fiery red calyx bracts and lilac-blue flowers. *p. 526*

gigantea (Hoplophytum) (Chevalieria) (So. Brazil); large rosette of recurving concave leaves 1 m long, gradually tapering, with rosy sheen above, and black marginal spines; pale scaly beneath; slender-stalked branched inflorescence globular to oblong, thick white-felty with green-red bracts and white petals. *p. 529*

glaziovii (So. Brazil); elegant small rosette of some 20 recurving, concave, green leaves 40 cm long, the margins with brown spines; small erect inflorescence of loosely arranged flat, imbricated bracts with reddish-purple petals and rosy sepals. *p. 528*

gracilis (Brazil); small epiphytic rosette of dark green leaves 30 cm dia.; inflorescence a slender spike with tubular carmine red bracts tipped by blue purple flowers. *Tropical.* *p. 528*

hoppei (Perú); robust epiphyte of the Amazon region, with stiff erect, shiny green, strap-shaped leaves, the margins spiny; inflorescence with triangular boat-shaped, bright crimson bracts tipped with white; found by Lee Moore. *Tropical.* *p. 528*

'Hummel's Black Magic' (victoriana discolor x racinae); same cross as Ae. 'Foster's Favorite' only more black; large, magnificent rosette of shiny blackish wine-red leaves 5-6 cm broad. *p. 527*

hybrid 'Bert': see 'Bert'

lamarchei (Brazil: Espirito Santo, Minas Gerais); robust plant, center leaves fluted, lower leaves spreading, topside coppery, margins with purplish-red teeth, reverse beautifully maroon with pencil lines and crossbands of white; cylindric bottle-brush-type inflorescence head greenish with tight rose bract leaves on stem, and yellow flowers. *p. 516*

lasseri (Venezuela); formal rosette of broad green leaves turning reddish in the sun; inflorescence a pendulous white floccose spike with greenish-white flowers. *p. 520*

lueddemanniana (coerulescens) (So. America); stiff rosette with metallic green leaves mottled dark green and bronze base; flower spike with panicle of white berries turning a beautiful bright purple after flowering; petals lavender. *Tropical.* *p. 515, 518, 519*

magdalenae (Mexico to Venezuela, Colombia, Ecuador); rosette with lax oblanceolate linear leaves to 2 m long x 10 cm wide, smooth above, pale-scaly beneath and with marginal spines; stout inflorescence erect, mealy-white, with large compound heads, bracts red, pink or orange, the flowers inconspicuous. *p. 529*

x maginali (miniata discolor x fulgens discolor); open rosette with broad soft-leathery olive-green glaucous leaves red-purple beneath; flower spike with oblong berry-like salmon-red bracts tipped by blue flowers. p. 515, 521

mariae-reginae (Costa Rica), "Queen aechmea", robust rosette of broad, gray-green, leathery leaves, recurved and with toothed edge; stout spike with pendant, delicate pink bract-leaves, topped by cylindrical head of red-tipped berries and violet flowers. *Tropical.* *p. 520, 524*

mertensii (Trinidad, Guyana, Venez., Colombia, Perú, No. Brazil), "China-berry"; epiphytic open rosette with few green leaves to 60 cm long, covered with white scales especially beneath, and having marginal spines; slender stalk with rose bracts, the inflorescence many-flowered, bipinnate with yellow or red petals, fruit blue. *Tropical.* *p. 525*

mexicana (Mexico); large rosette of broad leathery leaves pale green with darker green blotches becoming rose-tinted in the sun; bold flower stem with long panicle of white berries and red petals. *Tropical.* *p. 520, 523*

miniata discolor (Brazil); open rosette of soft-leathery olive-green leaves, pale red reverse; inflorescence a panicled spike of orange-red rounded berries tipped by pale blue flowers. *Tropical* *p. 518, 524*

mooreana (Amazonian Perú); very showy bromeliad with branched inflorescence similar to chantinii but with lower bracts carmine-rose, the upper, flattened bracts lime green tipped flame-orange. Foliage bronzy green. *Tropical.* *p. 525*

'Nebula' (x Neomea) (Ae. miniata x Neoregelia carolinae); showy bigeneric hybrid rosette of open habit, with long spring green leaves to 40 cm; large flower head of several clustered spikes with reddish bracts, flowers white with violet tips, opening in the evening (Hummel, California 1963). *p. 527*

nidularioides (Colombia); epiphytic rosette of open habit; strap-shaped, green leaves 60 cm long, at first white-scaly, and with broad marginal spines; globular inflorescence on short stalk, red-bracted and with white flowers. *Tropical.* *p. 522, 576*

nudicaulis aureo-rosea (So. Brazil); close rosette of soft leathery, glossy deep green foliage having a natural fold near base of leaf; small flower spike with bright red bracts and flowers. *Sub-tropic.* *p. 522*

nudicaulis cuspidata (So. Brazil), "Living vase plant"; rosette more stiff and tubular at base, and with black spines; inflorescence bracts rosy-carmine; yellow flowers arranged cylindrically on red axis. *p. 515, 518*

nudicaulis var. major (Brazil); a variety from the collection of J. Marnier-Lapostolle, France; rosette larger than the species with leaves silvery over bronze; the inflorescence arching with red bracts and yellow flowers. *p. 526*

organensis (So. Brazil); spreading rosette light green dusted with gray, and scattered tiny red marginal spines, a blackish cusp at apex of leaves; pyramidal inflorescence open, cylindrical, with green sepals and blue petals. *p. 516*

orlandiana (Espirito Santo); showy rosette with bright yellow-green leaves with bizarre chocolate cross-banding and heavy black spines; arching orange spike with salmon-scarlet bracts and ivory flowers. *p. 25*, 512, 520*

ornata (hystrix) (So. Brazil); free clustering plant with erect, hard, gray-green swordlike leaves; inflorescence in dense cone-shaped spike with berry-like bracts and pale red petals. *p. 520*

pectinata (Brazil: Rio to Santa Catarina); attractive, shapely and robust, open rosette with broad, recurving leaves tapering to a point, green and shiny, faintly darker mottled, the reverse with close gray pencil lines, margins wavy with a few dark spines, the leaves become tinged reddish pink in full light; inflorescence a dense, elongate head like a small pineapple with the terminal tuft of leaves, wholly green. *p. 516, 523*

penduliflora (Costa Rica to Perú); epiphyte with straplike leaves glossy green turning maroon in strong light; inflorescence a leaning spike with spreading panicle of whitish berries with blue flowers. Syn. Ae. schultesiana. *p. 521, 522, 523*

phanerophlebia (So. Brazil); tightly closed rosette in habitat growing both epiphytic or on rocks; broad, rigid leaves to 50 cm long edged with stout black spines; erect cylindrical inflorescence with rosy-red bracts and blue flowers. Dr. L. B. Smith thinks the photo shown could be Ae. distichantha. p. 528

pimenti-velosoi (So. Brazil); small funnel-form epiphyte 30-40 cm high with erect gray-green, leathery leaves blunt at apex; the small cylindrical inflorescence is salmon-red with golden yellow flowers. *p. 528*

pineliana (S. E. Brazil); small, shapely rosette in soft tones of gray and rose with copper-lining, red-brown teeth at margin; inflorescence an upright stem covered with scarlet bracts topped with brush-like head having yellow flowers. *p. 536*

pubescens (C. America); loose rosette of brownish toothed leaves with pubescent scales; inflorescence on long branched spike with tight bracts and straw-colored petals suggesting ears of wheat. *p. 519*

purpureo-rosea (suaveolens) (Rio de Janeiro); hard tubular rosette deep green with pronounced black spines; inflorescence a mealy-coated stem with long panicle of rosy-red bracts and lavender flowers. *p. 518*

racinae (Espirito Santo), "Christmas jewels"; so called because of the striking orange-red berrylike inflorescence with yellow and black flowers, on pendant stem; shiny, friendly green, straplike leaves. *Tropical.* *p. 512, 518*

ramosa (So. Brazil); large symmetrical rosette composed of many leathery medium green leaves coated with gray scurf; inflorescence a vermillion-red spike with loose panicle of greenish-yellow berries and yellow flowers. *Subtropic.* *p. 512, 517*

recurvata (Uruguay, So. Brazil); close rosette of lanceolate, dark green rigid leaves recurving, 30-40 cm long with violet base and spiny margins, silvery-scaly beneath; inflorescence 20 cm high, protruding above foliage, nearly globular, with bracts and sepals red, petals red-purple. *p. 519*

recurvata benrathii (Santa Catarina); Tillandsia-like small rosette with narrow channeled, recurved leaves, glossy dark green overlaid with silver dust; silvery spots beneath; inflorescence in center with bract leaves dark purplish-red and lavender flowers. *p. 516*

recurvata ortgiesii (Paraná, Santa Catarina); stiff rosette with recurving narrow tapering leaves glossy green and spiny; short flower spike with shielding shiny red bracts and long, orchid-colored petals. *p. 518*

x 'Red Wing'; stunning Hummel hybrid involving Aechmea penduliflora x mutica; handsome rosette with large coppery leaves, dark purple beneath. The wine-red stalk bears an inflorescence of many berries first pink then purple, in heavy clusters; the flowers are straw-colored. *Tropical.* *p. 527*

'Royal Wine' (miniata discolor x victoriana discolor); open rosette of soft-leathery, highly glossed apple-green leaves beautifully lacquered burgundy red beneath; pendant spike with orange, pointed berries and blue flowers. *p. 520*

saxicola (So. Brazil); open rosette growing on rocks, of broad leathery yellowish-green leaves, with darker green mottling, and black teeth around edge; reverse silvery-gray; inflorescence all green, on a short but distinct stalk. *p. 523*

schultesiana: see Ae. penduliflora

tessmannii (Perú, Colombia); stiff ornamental rosette of grayish leaves with small spines; inflorescence on branched stem, the closed bracts pale orange-red each with subtended bract leaf, flowers yellow. *Tropical.* *p. 519*

tillandsioides (No. Brazil, Venezuela, Guyana); small epiphytic rosette with narrow, leathery, grayish leaves armed with marginal spines; inflorescence with serrated floral bracts green, yellowish or red; flower petals yellow, followed by berries first white then blue. *Tropical.* *p. 519, 525*

tillandsioides var. 'Amazonas' (Perú); beautiful large epiphyte of the rainforest, with gray-green leaves; the stout inflorescence similar to chantinii, with spreading, flattened spikes arranged in candelabra fashion, the closely appressed bracts lavender pink and bright red, tipped by small yellow flowers; the long pendant bract-leaves at base of spikes rosy-red; collected by Lee Moore, 1962. *Tropical.* *p. 525*

triangularis (Brazil); epiphyte from the forests of Espirito Santo; squat, fluted rosette of stiff, broad leaves 8-10 cm wide and 40 cm long, dark metallic green and scaly at margins with large black spines, the tips recurving;

inflorescence cone-like, the red stalk furnished with showy red bracts; flower petals are purple, quickly turning black. *Tropical.* *p. 525*

victoriana discolor (Brazil: Espirito Santo); attractive rosette found by Foster growing on rocks near Victoria, which differs from the all apple-green leaves of the type by its bronzy-red color on the underside; inflorescence an erect spike, with minute floral bracts, sepals yellow with red tips, and petals purple with white margins. *p. 526*

weilbachii leodiensis (Rio); attractive rosette of oblanceolate coppery-green leaves wine-red beneath, and spined; inflorescence on panicle with glowing crimson bracts and orchid-colored ovaries and flowers. *p. 520*

zebrina (Colombia); very elegant, urn-shaped rosette dense with stiff, broad leaves rounded at apex, olive green, and covered beneath by cross-bands of white scales, and with thorny margins; branched inflorescence of spreading spikes, subtended by crimson bracts, the flat flowering branches in series of yellow boat-shaped bracts, and with yellow flowers. Unlike chantinii, A. zebrina has sepals covered by the bracts. *p. 523*

AEGINETIA *Orobanchaceae* **S3LFM**

indica (India to Java, Philippines, New Guinea); curious leafless herb found growing on the roots of monocots such as Bambusa, Zingiber, Canna, Pericum, Pitcairnia, etc.; forming an erect leafless, red-striped stalk to 40 cm high, with solitary flowers nodding forward; the calyx opens in front to show the 3-5 cm corolla, white outside, purple within, and with fringed margins. *p. 1842*

AEGLE *Rutaceae* **S3LBD**

marmelos (India), "Bael fruit"; small spiny tree, with slender branches, the foliage divided into 3 slender leaflets with crenate edges; flowers with 4 or 5 narrow petals and showing numerous stamens; fruit is globular or pear-shaped, 5 to 10 cm dia., and covered with smooth, hard gray or yellow rind which contains orange, sweet aromatic pulp in 8-16 cells with seeds. The fruit pulp is used for drinks and conserves; the flowers are made into perfume in India. *Tropical.* *p. 2028*

AEGOPODIUM *Umbelliferae* **C2LBM**

podograria 'Variegatum' (Europe, natur. in No. America), "Bishop's weed" or "Goutweed"; coarse perennial herb 35 cm high, with creeping rootstock; compound herbaceous, wrinkled leaves divided into three parts, milky-green with irregular cream-white margins; flowers white; attractive hardy border plant for the garden in shady places. *Warm-temperate.* *p. 2106*

AEONIUM *Crassulaceae* **I2LFD**

arboreum (Morocco); erect succulent with thick stem to 1 m high, topped by a rosette of numerous thin, spatulate green leaves, ciliate white on margins; flowers golden yellow. *Subtropic.* *p. 861, 864*

arboreum atropurpureum, "Blackhead" or "Black tree aeonium"; striking decorative variety with coppery to deep purple leaves. The species Ae. arboreum is Mediterranean from Morocco and Portugal east to Crete; an erect bold succulent to 1 m high, little branching, topped by a flaring 20 cm rosette of spatulate light green, fleshy leaves, fringed white at margins; flowers golden yellow. *Subtropic.* *p. 858*

arboreum 'Atropurpureum cristatum'; interesting fasciation of the gray-brown fleshy stem broadened obliquely fan-like, the curved apex supporting, comblike, a dense chain of tiny, deep lacquer-red rosettes, the little oblanceolate leaves with ciliate margin. *Subtropic.* *p. 863*

arboreum nigrum, "Schwarzkopf"; striking cultivar, with tall succulent stem carrying a rosette of spatulate, soft fleshy leaves, gleaming brown-purple and almost black, gracefully recurving, 12-15 cm across; photographed in San Diego County, California. *p. 861*

bethencourtianum (Aichryson) (Canary Isl.); small shrubby succulent with brown stems, freely branching with little spatulate, spoon-like fleshy leaves, medium green, pale beneath, densely covered with white hair. *p. 858*

burchardii (Sempervivum) (Canary Isl: Tenerife); erect, beautiful succulent with stem, later branching and 20-30 cm high, bearing a flat rosette 8-10 cm across of fleshy, obovate pointed leaves, grayish green and metallic bronze, the margins ciliate; flowers soft ochre yellow; slow-growing. *p. 862*

caespitosum (simsii) (Canary Islands); attractive cushion-forming low succulent, 15 cm high, the branches tipped by broad, firm rosettes of linear-lanceolate leaves, fresh green with reddish lines, white ciliate at margins. Flowers deep yellow. *p. 860*

caespitosum x spathulatum; tiny succulent branching rosette with obovate dark green leaves having beaded margins, maroon at midrib and edge. *p. 858*

canariense (Canary Islands), "Velvet rose"; large rosette to 75 cm dia., with velvety leaves, light green, flushed red at tips. *Subtropic.* *p. 863*

decorum (cooperi) (Canary Isl.), "Copper pinwheel"; much branched shrublet topped by several open rosettes of small spatulate copper-colored succulent leaves and rose-tinted; flowers white with rose lines. *Subtropic.* *p. 858, 860, 861*

domesticum (Aichryson), "Youth and old age"; an old garden hybrid; erect, shrubby succulent plant with small, spatulate, somewhat hairy leaves; free-flowering yellow. *p. 864*

domesticum 'Variegatum' (Canary Isl.), "Youth and old age"; succulent intermediate between sedum and sempervivum; freely branching rosettes with rounded thin fleshy leaves light green with white margins; flowers yellow. *Subtropic.* *p. 885*

glandulosum (Madeira); attractive flat rosette of densely shingled spatulate and recurved leaves, green to deep coppery, sticky to the touch and with soft hairs; flowers golden yellow. *Subtropic.* *p. 862*

haworthii (Tenerife), "Pin-wheel"; bushy plant with short woody branches bearing rosettes of thick, obovate-acute gray-green leaves with ciliate, red margins; flowers pale yellow flushed rose. *Subtropic.* *p. 19*, 858, 2092*

holochrysum (Canary Islands); succulent rosette 20 cm across, of narrow spatulate, gray-green leaves tinted bronze, with red stripe and margins; stem forming; flowers golden yellow in long-stalked pyramids. *Subtropic.* *p. 861*

lindleyi (Canary Isl.); shrubby succulent with brown-woody stem, densely branching and set with rosettes of small fat, obovate, slightly keeled sticky leaves, olive green and covered with fine white velour; flowers yellow. The sap from leaves serves as antidote to Euphorbia juice poisoning if a drop is squirted into the eye or wound. *p. 858*

nobile (Canary Islands); magnificent large rosette of very fleshy, broadly channeled obovate, sticky and puckered leaves to 30 cm long, apple green; flowers coppery scarlet, in large showy clusters; a most beautiful aeonium. *Subtropic.* *p. 862*

percarneum (Canary Islands; Gran Canaria); erect branching stem bearing handsome rosettes of flat, obovate pointed, fleshy leaves, light green and grayish, tinged with red toward apex, 8-10 cm long; panicles of soft flesh-pink flowers. *p. 862*

'Pseudo-tabulaeforme' (tabulaeforme hybrid), "Green platters"; shrubby bush with distinct, thick, brown stem, with branches topped by flat open succulent rosettes, the waxy green leaves broad fan-like, ciliate at margins; golden flowers. *Subtropic.* *p.863*

sedifolium (Canary Islands), "Tiny-leaved aeonium"; twiggy shrub with tiny succulent obovate leaves brownish marked with red, shining and sticky; flowers bright yellow. *p.858*

tabulaeforme (Tenerife), "Saucer plant"; circular, plate-like rosette of small spatulate leaves arranged flat like shingles, fresh green, margins ciliate; flowers yellow. *Subtropic.* *p. 858, 862, 864*

urbicum (Canary Islands, Tenerife); unbranched, stem-forming large succulent rosette 25-30 cm dia., rather incurving, with spatulate leaves spoon-like, fresh light green and waxy, lightly keeled and with ciliate reddish margins; flowers greenish or pinkish; the plant dies after flowering. *Subtropic.* *p. 863*

AERANGIS *Orchidaceae* **S-130FM**

biloba (Angraecum)(So. Africa: Cape); epiphyte with erect stem; flowers white, tinged rose, 4 cm dia., slightly scented, spur 5 cm long and orange-red, in pendulous racemes. *p. 1653*

clavigera (Angraecum)(Madagascar); small epiphyte with large obovate leaves, and long pendant inflorescence of small greenish white flowers having very long curved spurs. *p. 1653*

coriacea (Kenya, Tanzania); vigorous epiphyte of vandaceous habit, with stem having alternate tongue-shaped, leathery leaves, widest at the apex and notched tips, glossy green and with marmoration above; floriferous with long axillary racemes of waxy star-shaped, fragrant flowers having long curving or spirally twisted spur to 18 cm long, creamy-white and tinted rose around the column, greenish toward tips, spur reddish-brown. *Tropical.* *p. 1654*

decaryana (Madagascar); epiphytic beauty with long pendant inflorescence; waxy white flowers sitting like birds with flying wings, and a long trailing tail on the thin-wiry axis. *p. 1653*

kotschyana (Kenya, Uganda, S.E. Africa, Zaire, Nigeria); epiphyte resembling phalaenopsis in habit with oblongate leathery leaves 10-25 cm long, notched at apex, grayish-green often speckled; pendulous basal racemes of handsome, fragrant 5 cm flowers, white sometimes suffused with pink, lip rhomboid, the cord-like spur to 25 cm long, spirally twisted clockwise, and light brown. *Tropical.* *p. 1654*

rhodosticta (Kenya to Kivu, Cameroun); small, almost stemless epiphyte with linear, notched 12 cm leaves; floriferous with arching zig-zag stalk, flat 3 cm star-like flowers with petals broader than sepals; creamy-white with orange-red column and forward curving spur. *p. 1654*

stylosa (Madagascar); epiphytic miniature; waxy 4 cm white flowers borne 6 to 15 on pendulous inflorescence to 30 cm long; conspicuous spur creamy white to green (summer-autumn). *p. 1653*

thomsonii (Kenya, Tanzania, Uganda); robust vandaceous epiphyte with stout stem and ranks of alternating, strap-shaped leaves notched at tip; axillary pendant racemes with bird-like, firm-textured flowers glistening white, with 15 cm spurs light bronze; finely scented more intensive after dusk. *p. 1654*

ugandense (Kenya, Uganda); strong-growing epiphyte with short succulent stem carrying 4-6 pairs of 20 cm, club-shaped, fleshy leaves obliquely notched at tip and with parallel thin veins; basal pendulous racemes with flat, star-like flowers having straight, greenish spur. *p. 1654*

AERIDES *Orchidaceae* **I-S30FM**

crassifolium (Burma), "King of Aerides"; dwarf epiphyte with erect stem clothed by thick, two-ranked leaves sheathing at base; the wax-like, fragrant flowers amethyst-purple, with lip an upturned greenish spur, in pendulous racemes, (May-June). *p. 1656*

crispum (W. India); epiphyte with two-ranked leaves; long pendant racemes with 5 cm scented flowers white suffused with rose, lip trilobed, midlobe rosy-purple and fringed. *p. 1655*

falcatum (India); striking free-growing epiphyte with 25 cm leathery bluish metallic leaves, closely ranged in 2 ranks, 1/2 to 1 m high; dense pendulous racemes of 2½ cm flowers creamy-white with a crimson spot at the apex of the sepals and petals, lip rose and ciliate (summer). *p. 1655, 1656*

falcatum houlletianum (Indochina); handsome epiphyte, similar to crassifolium, but the 2½ cm waxy flowers with petals and sepals light buff, tipped magenta, the lip lightly fringed, creamy-white with purple lines, (May-June). *p.1656*

fieldingii (Assam), "Fox-brush orchid"; epiphyte to 1 m high with fleshy leaves; racemes often 1/2 m long, crowded with white flowers beautifully dotted and suffused with bright rose, the trowel-shaped lip rosy-purple, (May-June). *Tropical.* *p. 1653, 1656*

japonicum (Japan); a pretty miniature orchid with narrow leaves 8-10 cm long, and 15 cm arching racemes with fragrant flowers greenish-white marked with purple, lip with purple ridge and spots (summer). *p. 1656*

lawrenceae (Philippines); handsome epiphyte with stems to 1 m high, and arching racemes to 45 cm long, with very wax-like, fragrant flowers, sepals and petals cream-white, tipped with crimson-purple, the lip white with purple, ending in a horn tipped green, (June-Aug.). *p. 1656*

longicornu (India, Burma); pendant spikes closely set with waxy white flowers, flushed purple on reverse (photo by T. Everett, NY Bot. Garden). *p. 1653*

multiflorum (affine) (Himalayas to Vietnam); epiphyte with short stem and arching raceme dense with many 2½ cm flowers, sepals and petals whitish flushed at tips rose-purple, the flattened lip amethyst-purple deepest in center, and with short spur, (July-Sept.). *p. 1653, 1656*

odoratum (India to China, Philippines); popular epiphyte with stems to 1 m and pendulous racemes to 40 cm long, the large flowers strongly scented, sepals and petals white with purple spot at tip, the lip white spotted with red and the middle lobe rose. (July-Sept.) *p. 1656*

quinquevulnerum (Philippines); robust epiphyte to 1½ m long, with wide, 2-ranked leaves to 30 cm long, and long, pendant racemes of 2½ cm flowers with sepals and petals white tipped and spotted with amethyst-purple; spur horn tipped green (summer-fall). *p. 1655*

vandarum (India: Himalayas); slender growing plant resembling Vanda teres, with cylindric leaves even thinner, 5 cm flowers in short racemes from the side of the stem opposite the leaves, pure white and somewhat transparent, narrow sepals and petals much frilled, lip trilobed, very fragrant, (Feb.-March). *p. 1655*

virens (odoratum majus)(Java); handsome, free-growing epiphyte with 2-ranked, bright green fleshy, broad leaves, and waxy peach-pink flowers with yellow horns, very fragrant, on long-drooping racemes (April-July). *Tropical.* *p. 1655*

AERVA *Amaranthaceae* **S3LFM**

scandens sanguinea (Java); attractive tropical more or less climbing subshrub with softly downy, ovate, dark red leaves 6 cm long; flowers very small, white or rust-colored in white-woolly spikes. *p. 81*

AESCHYNANTHUS (TRICHOSPORUM) *Gesneriaceae* **S3HFM**

boschianus in hort. (Java); rambling epiphyte with flexible vines, set with opposite pairs of fleshy ovate leaves; in the leaf axils or on branch tips the tubular flowers with purple-brown, cupped, smooth calyx, and scarlet corolla spreading at mouth. *p. 1228*

bracteatus (Sikkim, Bangladesh); tropical epiphyte with thin flexible trailing branches, clothed by small 4-6 cm fleshy light green elliptic leaves, grayish beneath; the clustered inflorescence with red-bracted flowers consisting of a showy red calyx, and scarlet corolla 4 cm long, the lower lip with lobes reflexed. *p. 1228*

grandiflorus (older and valid name parasiticus)(India); straggling epiphytic trailer with fleshy, lanceolate, dark green 10 cm dentate leaves, the curving, half-open tubular flowers 3-5 cm long, deep crimson-red tipped with orange and black-purple. *p. 1230*

javanicus (Java), "Lipstick plant"; trailing epiphyte with small ovate leaves slightly toothed; the flowers in terminal clusters, the tubular corolla pubescent, scarlet with yellow mouth, and the cup-like downy calyx purplish-red.
Tropical. *p. 1229*

lobbianus (Trichosporum)(Java); epiphytic trailer with small elliptic, fleshy, dark green leaves; tubular, two-lipped flowers with hairy calyx cup soot-red glistening like silk, the downy corolla fiery red, creamy-yellow in throat, and only twice as long as calyx. *Tropical.* *p. 1229*

longiflorus (Java); robust trailer with pendulous branches and ovate leathery leaves tapering to a slender point; erect-ascending curved, slender-tubular flowers crimson or blood-red, their mouth contracted, in clusters at ends of branches. *p. 1230*

marmoratus (zebrinus)(Thailand), "Zebra basket vine"; epiphytic trailer with beautiful waxy leaves to 10 cm long, dark green with a reticulated network of contrasting yellow-green, and maroon underneath; tubular green flowers spotted brown. *Tropical.* *p. 1229, 1230*

micranthus (Himalayan reg.); epiphytic trailer with slender flexuous branches, small opposite elliptic leaves waxy green, and with 2-3 axillary, miniature slender tubular flowers deep purplish-red edged blackish at petal tips. *Tropical.* *p. 1229*

parviflorus (ramosissimus)(Himalayas); trailer similar to grandiflorus, with deep glossy green lanceolate leaves 10 cm long; flowers scarlet, tipped yellow, the corolla 2½ cm long and scarcely contracted. *p. 1228, 1230*

pulcher (Trichosporum) (Java), "Royal red bugler"; trailing epiphytic plant with small opposite ovate, waxy light green leaves and showy tubular flowers axillary or in terminal clusters; calyx green and smooth, the bilabiate corolla 3 times longer, vermillion red with yellow throat. *Tropical.* *p. 1229*

speciosus (Trichosporum splendens) (Java); strong straggler with stems to 60 cm long and large lanceolate, waxy-green leaves; showy tubular flowers in terminal clusters, corolla flame-orange, yellow at base and beneath; throat marked brown-red on yellow. *p. 1229, 1230, 1248A**

x splendidus (A. grandiflorus or its more valid name parasiticus, x A. speciosus), "Orange lipstick vine"; robust trailer with ovate-tapering leaves 10 cm or more long; the fleshy erect, curving tubular flowers in large clusters, orange-red blotched with deep maroon. *p. 1230*

AESCULUS *Hippocastanaceae* **C2LBDh**

californica (California), the "California buckeye"; native to dry slopes of the Sierras; small deciduous tree 3 to 6 m or more high; silvery branches with rich green leaves digitately compound of 5 to 7 leaflets 8 to 15 cm long, finely toothed and with prominent ribs; showy erect, cylindrical clusters of fragrant white flowers tinged with rose and protruding stamens; large pear-shaped green fruits. Striking in spring when creamy, fragrant plumes appear like a giant candle. *p. 1321*

x carnea (hippocastaneum x pavia) (Midwestern U.S.), the "Red horse-chestnut"; ornamental flowering tree 10 to 15 m high; large compound leaves of 3 to 7 leathery green leaflets 8-15 cm long, with prominent ribs and serrate margins; in April-May a mature tree bears hundreds of 20 cm plumes of soft pink to red flowers, in center a yellow eye; brown prickly fruit 4 cm dia. *Temperate.* *p. 1321*

AETHIONEMA *Cruciferae* **I2LBD**

coridifolium 'Warley Rose', (type from Asia Minor), "Stonecress"; small subshrub 15-20 cm high with small fleshy, linear, glaucous leaves edged in pink, the flowers deep pink, in terminal racemes; rosy-purple in the species. *Subtropic.* *p. 927*

AGALMYLA *Gesneriaceae* **S3HFM**

parasitica (staminea) (Java); miniature creeping epiphyte of peculiar clinging habit, brown woody stem with waxy, oblong, dark green leaves lightly toothed, and dense axillary clusters of trumpet-shaped, deep scarlet-red flowers, the spreading petals blotched black-maroon, and a long protruding purplish style. *p. 1229*

AGANISIA *Orchidaceae* **S3OFM**

cyanea (Brazil), "Blue orchid"; small epiphyte with creeping rhizome, one-leaved ovate pseudobulbs, plaited leaves 30 cm long tapering into a furrowed petiole; basal stalks with racemes of light blue flowers with clawed, lobed lip bluish-purple with pale veins, the column streaked with red. *p. 1659*

AGAPANTHUS *Liliaceae* **I1LBM**

africanus (Cape of Good Hope), "Blue African lily"; summer-blooming plant, with basal, strap-like leaves to 2 cm wide; funnel-shaped flowers pale porcelain-blue with darker center and margins, up to 30 in large umbels, on erect stalks. *Subtropic* *p. 1416, 1417*

africanus minor, "Peter Pan lily"; a diminutive form of the "African lily"; fresh-green basal strap leaves; inflorescence on slender stalk 50 cm high, with trumpet flowers pale porcelain-blue. *Subtropic.* *p. 1417*

campanulatus (So. Africa); compact plant with leaves shorter, narrower, and more erect than in A. orientalis; deciduous; flowers sky-blue, 3 cm across, bell-shaped, spreading at mouth, on stalk 45 cm high. *p. 1417*

inapertus (Transvaal); stout creeping root-stock with linear leaves 45 cm long x 4 cm, deciduous; erect stalk with umbel of drooping, trumpet-shaped, blue flowers. *p. 1423*

longispathus albus (So. Africa); perennial herb with tuberous rootstock; deciduous basal linear leaves; with a straight stalk carrying a large cluster of white flowers with spreading segments. *p. 1417*

orientalis 'Albidus' (So. Africa); handsome perennial herb with thick-fleshy roots; rather broad, arching succulent leaves in 2 ranks, to 5 cm wide; flower stalk 60 cm long with up to 110 flowers in large umbels, in this form white, otherwise blue; summer-blooming. *Subtropic.* *p. 1416*

AGAPETES *Ericaceae* **S3LFD**

hosseana (Thailand); ornamental epiphytic evergreen shrub forming a tuberous base, on long woody branches small obovate leathery leaves, and pendant tubular light red flowers. *p. 2107*

macrantha (Thibaudia) (No. India, Bangladesh); evergreen shrub with long elliptic leathery leaves, and beautiful pendant, waxy, pointed flowers 4 cm long, creamy white and prettily marked with yellow and crimson-red lines. *p. 957*

AGATHAEA: see Felicia

AGATHIS *Araucariaceae (Coniferae)* **I2LFM**

australis (New Zealand: North Island), the famous "Kauri pine"; stately timber tree rising like a gray, straight column to 30 and 50 m high, with dia. of trunk recorded at 7 m, the thick bark peels off, tending to throw off epiphytes; leaves on young trees sparse, linear-oblong, bronze-green, to 6 cm long; the adult leaves oval 1-3 cm long; 8 cm erect ovoid cones. Produces kauri gum from resin. *Subtropic.* *p. 344*

robusta (Queensland), "Queensland kauri"; massive, resinous evergreen tree to 50 m high with variable leaves; juvenile leaves elliptic, waxy dark green. *Subtropic.* *p. 344, 346, 350, 836*

AGATI: see Sesbania

AGAVE *Amaryllidaceae* **I1LBD**

americana (Mexico), "Century plant"; large, loose open, trunkless rosette of spreading, broad and thick-succulent, glaucous gray-green leaves 2-2½ m long, sharply bend downward above the middle, with sharp brown hooks at margins, and ending in a spiny point; yellowish flowers on a tall spike to 12 m, produced when plant is 10 years or more old. *Arid-Tropical.* *p. 85, 86, 87, 2092*

americana 'Marginata', "Variegated century plant"; large rosette with the broad, laxly recurved, glaucous gray leaves with showy, broad, yellow margins. *Arid-Tropical.* *p. 85, 88, 89*

americana 'Medio-picta'; has broad yellow band down the center of leaves instead of along the margins. *Arid-Tropical.* *p. 88, 89*

americana 'Striata'; large rosette with its glaucous gray leaves lined and banded with yellow or white, to 2 m long and 20 cm wide. *p. 89*

angustifolia 'Marginata' (wilsonii, caribaea) (W. Indies), "Variegated Caribbean agave"; beautiful, freely suckering, densely formal rosette with stiff-erect, short, sword-shaped leaves to 50 cm long, bluish-gray with broad white marginal bands and little brown spines. *Tropical.* *p. 85, 86, 90*

angustissima (W. Mexico); stemless rosette dense with narrow-linear leaves to 45 cm long, flat on the upper surface, convex beneath, margins with splitting fibers, stout brown terminal spine. *p.89*

applanata (S. E. Mexico: Jalapa); stiff rosette, making few offsets; rigid erect blue-gray leaves to 1m long, long tapering, with horny edge and curved spines; inflorescence 9-12m high, with greenish flowers. *p. 99*

atrovirens (So. Mexico: Oaxaca), "Pulque agave"; large stemless rosette producing offsets; stout, fleshy smooth leaves spreading to 2m long and 25-30 cm wide, concave above, keeled convex beneath, dull dark green or blackish, margins wavy with small spines on horny base. Main source of pulque drink. *Arid-Tropical.* *p. 90*

attenuata (Mexico), "Dragon-tree agave"; rosette, on 1 m stem when old; leaves to 1 m long, wide in the middle, narrow at base, smooth, without teeth, gray-green; the beautiful inflorescence with greenish-yellow flowers in 3 m spikes gracefully arching, occasionally producing bulbils. *Arid-Tropical.* *p. 85, 86, 88*

botteri (Mexico); stemless, open rosette with broad, spatulate leaves 60 cm long, fleshy, pale green; hooked blackish marginal spines crowded; inflorescence 2 m high. *p. 89*

braceana (Bahamas); open, stemless rosette, with wide, lanceolate, gray leaves almost flat, 60 cm long, 20 cm wide, with small marginal spines and brown to gray terminal spines; inflorescence 6 m high. *p. 91*

bracteosa (N. E. Mexico: Nuevo Leon); stemless rosette making offsets, with tapering leaves spreading, recurved at tip, 40 cm long, without terminal spine, obliquely keeled, gray-green to pale green; rather rigid; margins finely dentate. *p. 90*

celsii (pallida) (Mexico), "Dwarf century plant"; symmetrical rosette with short and broad gray-green leaves with fleshy teeth. In the trade as A. miradorensis. *p. 88, 89*

cernua (Mexico); large, rather flat rosette with broad, waxy gray-green leaves 60 cm long; inflorescence 3-4 m high, gracefully arching with numerous greenish flowers. *p. 99*

cerulata (Baja California); symmetrical rosette with leaves to 35 cm long, deeply concave, gray or gray-green, hollow-grooved toward tip, terminal spine gray-brown; marginal spines brown later gray about 2½ cm apart; inflorescence to 3 m high, flowers yellow, on slender panicle. *p. 89*

dasylirioides var. dealbata (dealbata) (Mexico: Morelos); open rosette with numerous, tough-leathery, linear leaves 30-40 cm long, silvery glaucous-green with light and dark green stripes; margins rough-horny serrate, end spine needle sharp. *p. 101*

decipiens (Yucatán), "False sisal"; arborescent and bearing bulbils, with trunk to 2 m, rosette with dagger-like, glossy-green leaves with round-grooved spine. *p. 90, 91*

desertii (California: Colorado Desert); dense, stemless rosette, forming colonies; leaves broad-lanceolate, gray-green to gray, 30 cm long, with marginal spines brown to gray, on fleshy projections. *p. 90*

echinoides (Mexico); small rosette similar to striata, to 30 cm dia., dense with leaves a little more flat, very numerous, dull green to grayish, stiff, narrow linear, tipped by a 3 or 4 angled brown terminal spine. *p. 89*

ellemeetiana (Mexico); large succulent rosette 80 cm diameter, leaves spreading at base then curved up, 50-65 cm long, 10 cm wide, fresh green, finely toothed toward tip; inflorescence to 4½ m with green flowers. *p. 99*

expansa (Mexico); large, attractive rosette, with stiffly spreading leaves to 1½ m long, firm-fleshy, bluish gray-green, margins between distant spines sinuate. *p. 92*

falcata (Mexico: Coahuila); small rosette resembling A. striata, but leaves stiffer about 45 cm long, light gray to violet or red-brown, narrow-linear, sickle-shaped, with long terminal spine, margins finely horny-dentate. *p. 91*

ferdinandi-regis (N. E. Mexico), "King agave"; solitary, globose rosette with triangular, pointed leaves, dark green with converging white lines, usually terminated by three spines; fewer leaves and less compact than victoriae-reginae. *p. 90, 97*

ferox (Mexico); large, stemless, striking, open rosette with leaves to 1 m long and 30 cm wide, rigid, fleshy, glossy dark-green, the margins sinuate, with hooked black-brown marginal spines and long terminal spine. Inflorescence to 9 m. *p. 91*

filifera (Mexico), "Thread agave"; many-leaved rosette of narrow, stiff, bright green leaves, white lines along edge which split into loose filaments. Leaves 20-25 cm long. *Arid-Tropical.* *p. 88, 91*

filifera compacta (pumila hort.) (Mexico); very small, compact rosette, freely suckering at base; short, tri-cornered leaves, deep green, striped silver, with black points. *p. 88*

fourcroydes (Mexico: Yucatán), "Henequen"; furnishing fiber; rosette forming 2 m trunk, with stiff leaves to 2½ m long and 10 cm wide, grayish-green, sword-shaped, tipped by black spine, margins with small spines; inflorescence to 6 m high, with ill-smelling greenish flowers, in panicle developing adventitious plantlets. *p. 91*

franzosinii (Mexico); trunkless rosette similar to A. americana, but more imposing and beautifully colored silvery-gray or bluish-gray; leaves rough, to 2½ m long and 30 cm wide, blackish marginal hook spines; inflorescence to 12 m high. *p. 91, 92*

funkiana (Mexico); stemless rosette forming offsets, with linear leaves light green slightly glaucous, with pale central bands, the convex back with dark lines, rough reddish horny edge with small hooked spines. *p. 91*

geminiflora (Mexico); dense rosette, branching when old, with 100-200 linear, stiff dark-green reed-like leaves 50 cm long, convex on both sides, the margins with white horny edge and loose curly threads; terminal spine 3-angled, inflorescence 4 m. *Arid-Tropical.* *p. 100*

ghiesbrechtii (Mexico); stemless rosette, offset-forming, leaves 45 cm long and incurving, glossy dark green, younger leaves with pale central band; margins horny with small spines. *p. 91*

goldmaniana (Baja California: northeastern deserts); stem-forming rosette bent down and leafy for the whole length, occasionally forming colonies; smooth gray-green leaves 50 cm long, stiffly erect spreading, hollow on upper side; black terminal spine, prominent marginal spines. *p. 93*

gracilipes (W. Texas: Sierra Blanca); stemless rosette forming colonies, with smooth, light gray leaves to 30 cm long, concave above; marginal and terminal spines red-brown then gray. *p. 92*

horrida (Mexico); full rosette with hard, stiff, fleshy leaves to 45 cm long and rather wide, glossy dark green, smooth, with brown horny edge and large marginal spines curved both directions, terminal spine twisted; plant dies after flowering. *Arid-Tropical.* *p. 92*

kaibabensis (Arizona: Grand Canyon); a variety of utahensis; larger, dense rosette than the type, measuring almost 1½m in dia., with straight, stiff leaves 30 cm or more long, light green, with marginal gray hook spines. *p. 92*

kerchovei (Mexico: Puebla); incurving rosette, bent sideways, with leaves about 35 cm long, thick especially at base, light gray-green, smooth; margins with horny gray edge and irregular small spines; younger leaves with narrow central band. *p. 93*

latissima (Mexico); stemless rosette with curving leaves to 50cm long, thick leathery-fleshy; almost glossy with few gray-green zones, keeled beneath, margins with brown horny band and marginal spines. *p. 92*

lehmannii (Mexico); large gray-green rosette related to salmiana, but with longer, stout leaves; also grown in Mexico for "Pulque". According to Jacobsen, possibly a natural hybrid of A. salmiana and atrovirens. *p. 99*

leopoldii; probably a hybrid of filifera x schidigera; dense rosette with numerous leathery linear leaves, with thick base, convex on both sides, light green, with several white stripes on sides and loose fiber at margins. *p. 93*

lophantha poselgeri (lechuguilla) (No. Mexico); suckering, loose rosette with stiff, channeled, snake-like, undulate leaves, glossy green with pale green down center, and horny margins. *p. 90, 92*

lurida (Mexico); stemless rosette with flaring, recurving broad leaves 15 cm wide and 1 m long, glaucous gray-green and striped gray, rather thin, leathery fleshy; dense marginal spines on fleshy base. *p. 92*

macrantha (Mexico); compact, incurving rosette, with thick glaucous green leaves to 15 cm wide; margins with horny edge and small hook spines, tip with long brown terminal spine. *p. 93*

macroacantha (So. Mexico); full rounded rosette, forming offsets, with stiff, erect-spreading, gray-green to pale gray leaves to 60 cm long, convex to the middle, flat or concave toward tip; distant marginal spines and stout terminal spine. *p. 93*

marmorata (So. Mexico); stemless rosette with broadly lanceolate leaves outcurving, rough, green and gray banded; brown prickles. *p. 93*

mescal (crenata) (Mexico); shapely rosette, center leaves recurved and concave, soft-fleshy, bright green, the margins irregularly undulated and crenate, with brown teeth on projecting cushions. *p. 93*

micracantha (Mexico); stemless open rosette, forming colonies, with broad, long-tapering leaves 45 cm long, thick base and up to middle, soft fleshy, light green; paler reverse, slightly glaucous; terminal spine bristly, margins with small brown spines. *p. 93*

miradorensis (desmetiana) (Mexico: Vera Cruz), "Mirador agave"; large handsome trunkless rosette 1½-2 m in diameter, the spreading, leathery-fleshy leaves to 1 m long, pale gray green lightly glaucescent, gracefully recurving; finely toothed margins. This species is short-lived, blooming in Florida in 6-8 years, the 3 m inflorescence bearing numerous adventitious plantlets, also freely suckering from base. *p. 99*

nizandensis (Mexico: Oaxaca); low succulent forming suckers; rosette loosely arranged with fleshy spreading leaves 30 cm long x 2½ cm wide, dark green with pale central stripe and darker margins, these set with small whitish teeth, terminal spine red. *p. 94*

palmeri (So. Arizona, New Mexico); starry, stemless rosette with stiff, straight, hollowed leaves dull dark green to grayish; long grooved terminal spine; sinuate margins with irregular spines. *p. 94*

parrasana (Mexico: Coahuila); shapely rosette with very stiff, thick leaves to 30 cm long x 15 cm wide, concave, smooth, matte green and bluish glaucous, margins sinuate between reddish spines. *p. 94*

parryi (Arizona, New Mexico, Chihuahua), "Mescal"; trunkless, leafy rosette with leaves 30 cm long x 10 cm wide, glaucous gray, smooth, with brown to gray terminal spine and small marginal spines. *p. 94*

parryi huachucensis (Arizona); compact, slow-growing rosette, sending out stolons forming colonies; the tight cabbagey heads impress each cupped leaf firmly on its enclosing mate in beautiful pattern; leaves 30 cm long, broader than the type, thick at broadest part, beige-green to glaucous blue-green, with coarse brown or black hooked marginal teeth; inflorescence stalks to 7 m tall, with greenish-yellow flowers in heavy panicles. *p. 86, 94*

parviflora (Sonora, Chihuahua, Arizona), "Little princess agave"; striking small rosette dense with stiff leaves 10 cm long, having white lines above, the margins with white threads toward tip, lower part dentate; gray-brown terminal spine. *Arid-Tropical.* *p. 94*

patonii (Mexico: Durango); handsome formal rosette of short 30 cm leaves very broad to 20 cm, smooth gray-green and with brown marginal spines and blackish terminal spine. *p. 100*

peacockii (Mexico: Tehuacán); stemless rosette with spreading, thick fleshy, stiff, concave leaves, dark green, the margins with irregularly distant, stout brown spines large and small, and brown terminal spine. *p. 94*

picta (ingens picta) (Mexico); green plant with silvery-blue glaucescence, the margins milky gray to white, and occasionally tinted pink; marginal teeth brown. *p. 95*

polyacantha (Mexico); variable species forming colonies; with broad leaves curved inwards 60-90 cm long and 10-15 cm wide, thick-leathery beautiful clear green; prominent teeth edged by brown horny line and small blackish spines. *p. 94*

potatorum (C. Mexico), "Drunkard agave"; fleshy rosette with stiff, bluish-green leaves to 30 cm long, and lobed at margins. *p. 88, 93*

pumila (Mexico); small compact rosette 3-5cm diameter, freely suckering at base; deep green, short very stiff, triangular leaves with blackish points and silver striping, coarse fibers at margins. The smallest of the agaves. *p. 100*

purpusorum (Mexico: Puebla); stemless, full rosette with stiff, spreading, smooth leaves about 20 cm long, concave above, fresh-green, with pale central band, the margins with a horny edge and small spines; terminal brown to gray, obliquely keeled. *p. 95*

roezliana (So. Mexico); full rosette with stiff, sword-shaped leaves 30-40 cm long x 10 cm wide, glossy green with pale central stripe, well rounded beneath; margins with horny band and numerous large wavy teeth, terminal spine red-brown. *p. 94*

salmiana (Mexico); very imposing, large and broad rosette, forming offsets; leaves somewhat recurved 1 to 2 m long, gray green and with stout marginal spines and long black terminal spine; inflorescence 9-18m high. Cultivated in Mexico for obtaining the alcoholic "Pulque". Widely planted on the Riviera; somewhat winter-hardy. *p. 99*

saundersii (Mexico); compact rosette, with attractive broad leaves sinuate at the margins, to 60 cm long, quite thick, gray-glaucous; red-brown marginal spines. *p. 95*

scabra (Mexico); compact rosette with wide, gray leaves, to 20 cm long, prickly margined; inflorescence 3 m tall, with yellow flowers. *p. 88*

schidigera (Mexico); large rosette of narrow linear, incurving leaves, light green, to 50 cm long, at margins fine splitting threads; inflorescence 3½m high, with brown-red flowers. *p. 100*

shawii (Baja California); dense rosette forming clumps, short-stemmed when old; rigid leaves 25-50 cm long x 12 cm wide, dark-green glaucous; prominent lateral spines yellowish to brown; inflorescence to 3 m high. *p. 95*

sisalana (Mexico: Yucatán), "Sisal-hemp"; large rosette forming 1 m trunks developing offsets; with straight and stiff, sword-shaped leaves to 1½ m long and 10 cm wide, matte gray-green, or green, with horny edge and occasional deformed teeth, keeled beneath, and with small black-brown terminal spine; branched inflorescence to 6 m high, with greenish, odoriferous flowers. Young plants will form as suckers on the ground as well as on the flowering stalk, and plantlets or bulbils rise vegetatively from the floral bracts, according to observations I made in Tanzania. *Arid-Tropical.* *p. 87, 95*

sisalana 'Minima'; a diminutive form which I encountered in the Soviet Union, as growing in a pot, with slender woody, branching stem and several heads of narrow, rather stiff, lanceolate leaves, bluish green, concave down center and with horny edge and some marginal teeth. *p. 100*

sobria ('Baja') (Baja California); stiff, gray-green plant with gray glaucescence, the margins set with purplish hook spines, the slender tip sharp pointed. *p. 95*

striata (Mexico: Hidalgo), "Dark striped agave"; short-stemmed rosette, dense with flaccid angled, linear leaves 45 cm long, glaucous gray with dark green; brown terminal spine; inflorescence to 4m. *p. 96*

striata 'Nana' (Mexico), "Lilliput agave"; small rosette of flat, pale gray-green, linear, short leaves; suckering as a young plant. *p. 90, 96*

stricta (Mexico), "Hedgehog-agave"; roundish rosette dense with stiff, spreading and incurving, narrow linear green leaves to 35 cm long, slightly keeled on both sides, with horny edges and faint gray lines, on the margins tiny teeth, branching when old; inflorescence a raceme 2½m high. *p. 96*

stricta 'Dwarf form'; much smaller and more rounded compact rosette than type. *p. 96*

tequilana (Mexico: Jalisco), "Tequila agave"; large spreading rosette forming offsets, with rather thin, leathery, gray-green leaves 1 m long and 8 cm wide, straight margins with tiny spines curved forward, short stout terminal spine; inflorescence 6m high, with spreading branches. *p. 95*

toumeyana (Arizona); attractive small rosette with many short, dagger-shaped stiff leaves 10-25 cm long, dark green with white markings on upper surface, the margins with thin threads toward apex, lower down with translucent teeth. *p. 96*

triangularis (So. Mexico); small rosette 20 cm high, with stiff-fleshy, spreading, straight leaves, olive-gray-green and smooth, concave toward tip, margins with horny band and irregular small spines. *p. 98*

triangularis subintegra (difformis) (Mexico); spreading rosette forming offsets, with stiff-succulent tapering leaves usually dark green and occasional pale central band, 60 cm long, concave, the margins with horny edge, with very few small teeth. *p. 98*

univittata (Mexico); rosette forming offsets, with stiffly spreading concave leaves 60 cm long, long-tapering, smooth green with a darker length-stripe, 4 cm wide, hooked marginal spines on a gray horny band. *p. 97*

univittata heteracantha (Mexico); nice rosette not forming off-shoots, with rigid, rough leaves to 75 cm long and 6 cm wide, gray-green with pale midband, and horny margins indented, with larger hookspines and twisted terminal spine. *p. 97*

utahensis (So. Utah, N. Arizona, California); spiny, small clustering rosette dense with stiff, glaucous-green leaves to 30 cm long x 2½ cm wide, concave, with hooked white teeth; inflorescence 1½-2 m with yellow flowers. *p. 97*

utahensis nevadensis (California, Nevada); dwarf form with leaves glaucous green as in type and prominent teeth, but with a much longer, and wavy, terminal spine to 8 cm long. *p. 97*

verschaffeltii (potatorum verschaffeltii) (So. Mexico); attractive small rosette with broad leaves short and suddenly tapering, 18 cm long x 8 cm wide, a beautiful glaucous pearly gray, the margins sinuate, with triangular brown teeth on fleshy bases, terminal spine twisted. *p. 88, 97*

vestita (Mexico: Jalisco); small rosette dense with stiff bayonet leaves 20-30 cm long, covered when young with thin white membrane, green distinguished by rounded markings, the reverse with white lines; margins have a horny edge and loose filaments. *p. 97*

vexans (Baja California); open rosette with stiff, straight leaves 20-38 cm long, gray-green, concave, with brownish marginal spines and 3-angled terminal spine. *p. 101*

victoriae-reginae (No. Mexico), "Queen agave"; shapely dense, many-leaved rosette with keeled, dark-green leaves about 15 cm long, white margin and abrupt point, and short, blunt terminal spine. *Tropical.* *p. 90, 97*

victoriae-regina var. candida; beautiful rosette with dark green, rigid leaves, strikingly striped with white and cream. *p. 99*

vilmoriniana (Mexico); loose rosette with recurving leaves 60-75 cm long, soft-fleshy, grayish or bluish-green, concave, margins with sharp horny edge, without spines; slender terminal spine brown. *p. 98*

weberi (Mexico); stemless rosette forming offshoots, with spreading, broad leaves to 75 cm long x 20 cm wide, gray-green, with unarmed margins and dark brown terminal spine. *p. 98, 101*

AGERATUM *Compositae* **I2LBM**

houstonianum, "Floss-flower"; the popular garden bedding plant, 25 cm high, a compact horticultural form of Mexican origin; bushy herbaceous perennial grown as an annual, with tassel-like heads of clear blue tubular florets, carried nicely above the fresh green, small foliage. From seed, or occasionally cuttings. *Tropical.* *p. 803*

houstonianum 'Blue Cap'; dwarf, round-compact plant 15-20 cm high covered freely with bright orchid-blue, small flowers. *p. 803*

AGLAODORUM *Araceae* **S3HBW**

griffithii (Malaya, Sumatra, Borneo); aquatic plant found in swamps of monsoon regions, with horizontal spreading rhizomes; from internodes 6-8 cm distant, rise the oblong to oblanceolate, waxy green leathery philodendron-like leaves 25 to 40 cm long, on terete petioles with vaginate base, 10 to 60 cm long; the sheathing, greenish spathe 4 cm long; spadix bearing female flowers on lower part, the male flowers on upper end toward apex. *p. 176*

AGLAOMORPHA *Polypodiaceae (Filices)* **S3HFM**

coronans (India, Malaya, South China, Taiwan, Philippines), "Crowning polypodium"; striking epiphytic fern with thick rhizomatous base densely matted with light brown scales, and from which rise large hard leathery, fresh green fronds ½-1 m broad, in a circle, the stem with reddish midrib, at the base winged, passing gradually into a deeply lobed frond cut nearly to axis, the glossy surface having a pebbled effect. *p. 1095, 1149*

heraclea (Polypodium, Drynaria) (Java, Philippines, New Guinea), "Hercules polypodium"; giant epiphytic fern with fronds 2½m long, on thick rhizomes covered with silky light brown scales, and climbing spirally around big trees; stalks with broad wings along lower part, higher up broadening into leaves 60 cm wide, deeply lobed, light green, thin-leathery, with puckered surface, the pointed tips curled. *p. 1095, 1151*

meyeniana (Polypodium) (Philippines), "Bear's paw fern"; distinctive epiphyte with thick paw-like rhizome covered thickly with brown hair, the long pinnate, glossy fronds have broad barren segments on the lower part, while the upper third bears narrow, fertile pinnae with prominent sori on their pearly margins. (S3W) *p. 1094, 1149, 1150*

AGLAONEMA *Araceae* **•S1LNM**

brevispathum (Thailand); creeping rhizome, with long-stalked, ovate-oblong, thin-leathery leaves 10-17 cm long, glossy green; ovate spathe 6-8 cm and cylindric spadix 2 cm long. *p. 148*

brevispathum hospitum (Thailand); spear-shaped, leathery, glossy, ovate, dark-green leaves with cream-white spots, on long, wiry petioles. *p. 150*

commutatum 'Albo-variegatum'; Roehrs' sport with the green and silver leaves borne on white petioles and white stem; spathe creamy-white. *p. 152*

commutatum elegans (marantifolium hort.) (Moluccas), "Variegated evergreen"; robust-growing plant with long, lanceolate leaves deep green with greenish-gray feather design. *Humid-Tropical.* *p. 152*

commutatum maculatum (Philippines, Sri Lanka); durable plant with leathery, oblong-lanceolate leaves deep green with markings of silver-gray; waxy-white spathe; berries yellow to red. *p. 152*

commutatum 'Treubii' (Celebes); slender plant with narrow, leathery, bluish-green leaves attractively marked with silver-gray; petioles marbled. *p. 150*

commutatum 'Tricolor' (marantifolium tricolor); relatively broad deep-green leaves with silvery feathering, borne on pink petioles; waxy pinkish spathe and white spadix. *Humid-Tropical.* *p. 152*

costatum (Perak), "Spotted evergreen"; very decorative, low growing plant with stiff, broad-ovate, glossy, dark-green leaves spotted white, with band of white through center. *p. 21•, 149, 151*

costatum foxii (Malaya), a "Spotted evergreen"; short plant with leathery, shiny, cordate-pointed leaves with broad, white center band; slow-growing. *Humid-Tropical.* *p. 149, 151*

costatum virescens; dwarf plant with broadly cordate, shiny, grass-green leaf with occasional greenish-white spots. *p. 151*

crispum (Schismatoglottis roebelinii) (Malaya), "Painted droptongue"; large and showy, ovate-pointed, leathery leaves medium grayish-green, largely variegated with silver. *Humid-Tropical.* *p. 150*

cuscuaria (Malaya); robust plant with leathery, ovate, long-pointed leaves deep-green, occasionally spotted. *p. 151*

'Fransher' (A. treubii x commutatum tricolor); colorful cultivar named after Francis Scherr, originator of the Parrot Jungle in South Florida; slender plant with fleshy lanceolate leaves green to milky green variegated with cream, on white or ivory petioles. *p. 283*

hospitum variegatum, lanceolate, glossy, deep-green leaves richly marbled white. *p. 151*

Malay Beauty', also known as **'Pewter';** a free growing horticultural variation of A. 'Pseudobracteatum', less highly variegated than the type but larger in all parts; with lanceolate leafblades to 30 cm or more long, matte grass or deep green marbled with milky green and some cream. *p. 150*

marantifolium x roebelenii (Manda); broad, oblong, oblique, leathery leaf, deep-green with marbling of gray-green; lateral vein areas light gray. *p. 151*

modestum (sinensis) (Kwangtung), "Chinese evergreen"; with durable, leathery, waxy-green leaves, ovate-acuminate and, to some extent, pendant, on a slender cane. Spathe green, spadix cream. *p. 148, 149, 152*

modestum 'Variegatum'; cultivar from Pennock's Puerto Rico nursery, with the leathery, lanceolate deep green leaves dominated by creamy variegation, 12-25 cm long. *Humid-tropical.* *p. 151*

nitidum (Curmeria oblongifolia) (Malaya); slow, stiff plant with plain-green, thick-leathery, long elliptic leaves. *p. 151*

nitidum 'Curtisii' (oblongifolium) (Malaya); large, slow-growing aroid with thick stem; densely set, long, elliptic, bluish-green leaves and silver feather design. *p. 150*

'Parrot Jungle' (A. curtisii x pictum tricolor); sturdy cultivar with thin-leathery lanceolate leaves painted greenish-silver on matte deep green, green beneath; on plain green petioles; spathes ivory-white. *p. 150*

'Pewter': see 'Malay Beauty'

pictum (Malaya); dainty plant with broad-ovate, velvety leaf bluish green with irregular patches of silver gray. *p. 152*

pictum 'Tricolor' (versicolor) (Sumatra); deep green, satiny leaves with patches of silver and mixed with yellow-green blotches; difficult. *p. 152*

'Pseudo-bracteatum', "Golden evergreen"; colorful, free-growing mutation or hybrid, with long, showy leaves deep green variegated with light green and yellow, center largely cream white; stem white and marbled green; cupped, waxy, greenish-white spathe, and cream spadix. *Humid-Tropical.* *p. 15•, 149, 150, 160A•*

rotundum (Malay Peninsula). "Red aglaonema"; compact, slowly growing beauty which I found in northern Thailand; with stout stem covered by sheathing short petioles; leaves broad-ovate or rhombic 10-15 cm or more long, thick-leathery, dark metallic glossy green to coppery with pronounced midrib and lateral veins, later paling; the reverse side glowing wine-red with rosy veins. *Humid-Tropical.* *p. 149, 320A•*

'Shingii' (Pat.), "Mandalay plant"; sport of A. simplex (Mahaffey, Apopka, Florida about 1967); attractive and sharply distinct variegation of the leaf color, with yellowish chartreuse or apple-green and ivory along center, abruptly changing to dark green around outer edge of leaf, or variegated petioles; excellent ornamental plant with stocky cane and of compact habit, freely branching; ovate-pointed, leathery glossy foliage, with leaves 12-25 cm long; of good keeping qualities. *p. 151*

siamense (Thailand); long, leathery, deep-green leaves with white center vein, on slender petiole. *Humid-Tropical.* *p. 151*

'Silver King' (nitidum 'Curtisii' x pictum 'Tricolor'); striking, excellent hybrid of lush habit, freely suckering; 20 to 35 cm leaves almost entirely silver-gray; petioles marked silver. *Humid-Tropical.* *p. 150*

'Silver Queen'; very ornamental and satisfactory decorative plant, from the same Florida hybrid complex as A. 'Silver King', with leaves narrower, about 22 cm long and 3 to 5 cm wide; green with gray marbling in feather pattern, petioles more green; freely branching and suckering, for bushy effect, and of excellent keeping qualities. *Tropical.* *p. 148*

simplex (Java); similar to A. modestum but leaf is more oblong and narrow, with a twist; texture more thin and papery; deep green with depressed veins. *Humid-Tropical.* *p. 148, 149, 152*

simplex 'Angustifolium' (Penang); erect plant with long, slender, pointed, dark-green, shining leaves with depressed lateral veins and corrugated appearance. *p. 152*

AGONIS *Myrtaceae* **C2LBD**

flexuosa (W. Australia), "Willow-myrtle"; graceful evergreen shrub or tree to 12m, ultimate branches pendulous, shoots wiry, often long and slender; willow-like linear leaves 5-15cm long and fragrant; white flowers in globose clusters, pink at base. *p. 1608*

AICHRYSON *Crassulaceae* **I2LFD**

dichotomum (laxum in Hortus 3) (Canary Islands, Azores); succulent branching in pairs, with hairy stems and leaves, these spoon-shaped, bright green, often flushed purple or bronze; yellow flowers in loose corymbs. *p. 860*

• **villosum** (Madeira, Azores Isl.); small succulent annual 10-20cm high, densely branching, stem with sticky white hairs, and small spatulate leaves 2 cm long; small golden-yellow flowers. *p. 860*

AICHRYSON: see also AEONIUM, MONANTHES

AIPHANES *Palmae* **S3LFM**

acanthophylla (Puerto Rico); pinnate-leaved palm of medium height, to 10m with trunk 10-15cm thick and set with rings of long black spines; fronds 1-2m long, the square green leaflets 2½-5cm wide, regularly placed, with jagged ends. *p. 1850*

caryotaefolia (Martinezia) (Colombia, Venezuela, Ecuador), "Spine palm"; very unusual with slender trunk to 12 m ringed with long black spines, and a crown of light green pinnate leaves, with pinnae suddenly expanded and squared off and lobed at tip, clothed with long black spines beneath; yellow-red fruits. *Tropical.* *p. 1856, 1874*

erosa (Martinezia) (W. Indies); palm with leafstalks and veins thickly covered with long brown, needle-like spines, stalks mealy; wedge shaped pinnae in 2 or 3 pairs at base of the pinnate fronds, a pair of broader ones at apex, all like bitten-off toward ends. *p. 1850*

"Air Fern" see BUGULA

AKEBIA *Lardizabalaceae* **I2LBD**

quinata (China, Korea, Japan), "Chocolate vine"; hardy shrubby twiner, evergreen in warm climate, with digitately compound leaves of usually 5 oblong leaflets 8-12cm long; fragrant flowers in racemes, the males 6mm pale purple; female flowers 3 cm wide, with 3 cupped chocolate purple petal-like sepals. *p. 1361*

ALAMANIA *Orchidaceae* **S3OFD**

punicea (Mexico: Puebla); handsome dwarf Epidendrum relative, purplish glossy leaves, on cylindrical pseudobulbs less than 3 cm high; inflorescence on a leafless pseudobulb, with small 2 cm scarlet flowers having narrow sepals and petals (spring). *p. 1664*

ALBERTA *Rubiaceae* **I2LFD**

magna (Natal); evergreen shrub with willowy reddish branches and leathery, oblanceolate opposite leaves 12 cm long; erect terminal panicles of brilliant crimson flowers with long silky tubular corolla. *p. 2008, 2009*

ALBIZIA *Leguminosae* **C2LBMh**

evansii (N. Transvaal); small tree with lacy, bi-pinnate leaves, deciduous during dry season; covered by globular flower clusters conspicuous by their dense, white, long protruding feathery, filament-like stamens. *p. 1368*

julibrissin (Iran to Japan), "Silk tree" or "Mimosa"; deciduous tree to 12 m high, with large, fern-like, bipinnate leaves to 45cm long, and terminal clusters of flowers with long, conspicuous, pink stamens arranged like fluffy tassels. *p. 1368*

lebbeck (Tropics of the Old World), "Woman's-tongue"; tree to 25 m, bipinnate leaves 8-22 cm long; flowers yellowish-white, in globose heads 2 cm wide forming a terminal panicle; fruit bean-like to 30 cm long, rattling in the wind when ripe. *Tropical.* *p. 1371*

ALBUCA *Liliaceae* **I2LBDd**

major (So. Africa); bulbous plant similar to Scilla, to 1m with flat, linear basal leaves, and erect racemes of pale yellow nodding flowers with green band. *p. 1423*

nelsonii (crinifolia) (Natal); lovely bulbous perennial with concave basal leaves bright green; inflorescence on stout stalk to 1½m long, carrying raceme of white flowers with red stripe down back of each segment. *p. 1417*

ALCEA *Malvaceae* **C2LBD**

rosea (Althaea chinensis) (Asia Minor), "Hollyhock"; tall, straight, leafy-stemmed, hairy biennial to 3 m; rough leaves 5 to 7-angled; single or double flowers in long spike, red, rose, pink, yellow or white. *p. 1532*

ALCHEMILLA *Rosaceae* **C2LBMh**

vulgaris (Europe, Greenland, Labrador), "Lady's mantle"; perennial hairy herb with stout horizontal rootstock producing a clump of handsome kidney-shaped, gray-pubescent, 10-12cm leaves toothed and shallowly lobed, green beneath; small yellowish-green flowers in feathery panicles. *p. 1994*

ALECTRYON *Sapindaceae* **I2LBD**

excelsum (New Zealand), "Titoki"; handsome evergreen tree to 20m, with alternate leathery, unequally pinnate leaves 5-10cm long, the pinnae slender pointed; flowers without petals, and with red-brown anthers, in panicles; flowers, fruit and branches covered with rusty-red down; shining black seed in its scarlet envelope is a most attractive feature. *p. 2034*

ALEURITES *Euphorbiaceae* **S3LBM**

moluccana (Moluccas and South Pacific Is.), a "Candle-nut" or "Varnish tree"; large tropical tree to 10 or 12 m high, with long-stalked ovate-pointed, or lobed pale green foliage 10-20 cm long, white downy above, rusty-pubescent beneath; small whitish flowers in large clusters; the green, rough fruit 5cm dia., containing 1 or 2 jet-black seeds which are polished and made into jewelry; also oil is extracted for varnish or for lamps. *p. 1005*

ALISMA *Alismataceae* **I2LBW**

plantago aquatica (Europe, U.S.), "Water plantain"; stout bog plant 10-80cm high, with tuberous rootstock; lanceolate leaves on under-water plants, heartshaped on terrestrial leaves on long petioles; branched inflorescence with small white or pink flowers, arranged in threes; submersed leaves may be more than 1m long. *p. 80*

ALLAMANDA *Apocynaceae* **W2-3LBM**

cathartica (South America: No. Brazil, Guyana), 'Golden trumpet'; robust shrubby, tropical clamberer with whorled, long, leathery, glossy leaves to 12 cm long; large wax-like, funnel-shaped golden flowers 6-8 cm across. With its showy flowers one of the most satisfactory summer bloomers; best along walls or fences in a sunny location. *p. 135*

cathartica 'Hendersonii' (So. America: Guyana); vigorous cultivar with longer leaves to 15 cm, and extra large golden-yellow flowers 10 cm across. *Tropical.* *p. 135*

neriifolia (Brazil), "Golden trumpet bush"; erect shrub with rough, oleander-like leaves in whorls; small, light-yellow flowers, streaked orange-red and swollen at base. *Tropical.* *p. 135*

violacea (Brazil), "Purple allamanda"; weak, slender climber, branches hairy, with ovate leaves 8-12 cm in a whorl, downy above, hairy beneath; funnel-shaped flowers reddish purple, in axillary cymes. *Tropical.* *p. 135*

ALLIUM *Liliaceae (Amaryllidaceae)* **C2LBMd**

albopilosum (christophii) (Asia Minor to Iran); an ornamental onion with strapshaped leaves 4½cm wide, grown for its huge ball-like showy 20cm umbels of deep lilac flowers with metallic sheen. *p. 1420*

angulosum (C. Europe to Siberia), "Ornamental onion"; to 60cm high, with keeled, linear leaves 6mm wide and stalks topped by heads of small lilac or white flowers. *p. 1418*

cepa (Iran and Asia Minor), the "Persian onion"; large biennial bulbs, with membranous skins and edible; leaves cylindrical and hollow, and used in seasoning; floral stalks to 1m bearing dense heads of lilac to greenish-white flowers with long stamens. *p. 1419*

fistulosum (Siberia), "Welsh" or "Spanish onion"; 45cm high; clustered bulbs with hollow, cylindrical leaves about same length as hollow swollen stalk, topped by white flowers in head-like globose umbel. Used for seasoning, and as a leek in Asia. *p. 1418*

giganteum (Himalayas), "Giant ornamental onion"; striking bulbous perennial to 1 m or more high when in bloom; glaucous green, fleshy basal leaves 6 to 8 cm broad; stiff floral stalks carry a spectacularly showy, dense globular head 10 to 20 cm dia., consisting of myriads of bright lilac-purple, starry flowers with extended stamens; long-lasting as cut blooms. *p. 1419*

karataviense (Turkestan); bulbous plant with two very broad, flat leaves to 12cm across, blue-green tinged with rose, and short stalks carrying a dense 8cm globe of white flowers with purple midrib like delicate rosy stars, and long stamens; spring. *p. 1420*

moly (Mediterranean), "Lily leek"; attractive small decorative species, with clustered bulbs, blue-green flat leaves 2½cm wide; showy flowers star-like, bright yellow, in 8cm umbels. *p. 1418, 1419*

neapolitanum (Mediterranean reg.); popular bulbous plant suitable for pots, with slender linear, keeled leaves, loose-spreading, and large starry white flowers with colored stamens, becoming papery, in few-flowered umbels to 8cm across; spring. *p. 1418, 1419, 1420*

ostrowskianum (Turkestan); small but showy bulbous plant with 2-3 gray-green, flat, weak leaves; large clusters of rosy star-like flowers. *p. 1418*

porrum (of Eurasian origin); well-known "Leek" of the kitchen garden, a stout onion-like herb to 75cm high, with fleshy, flat or keeled leaves not hollow, about 5cm wide; white or pinkish flowers in dense umbels. Both the bulb and leaves are used in cooking, milder in flavor than the onion. *p. 1418*

schoenoprasum (Siberia, No. North America), "Chives" or "Schnittlauch"; hardy tufted, clustered bulbs with onion-like hollow green leaves to 45 cm high, tipped by round heads of rose-purple flowers. Use: fresh leaves in soup, salads, omelet, hamburgers, for a mild onion flavor. *p. 1418, 1419*

sphaerocephalum (W. Europe to Iran) leaves channelled; flowering stalks to 1m high, leafy in lower third; flowers dark purple, bell-shaped, in dense globular heads. *p. 1419*

triquetrum (So. Europe), "Triangle onion"; small bulbs with linear, keeled leaves, and 3-angled stalk to 30cm high, bearing umbels of large white flowers with segments keeled green. *p. 1418, 1419*

zebdanense (Lebanon); bulbous herb with linear leaves; stalks 30-60cm high, with showy white flowers. *p. 1419*

ALLOPHYTON *Scrophulariaceae* **I3LFM**

evolutum: see Ruellia blumei

mexicanum (Tetranema) (Vera Cruz, Mexico), "Mexican foxglove"; darling little plant with short stem, long obovate, dark green, leathery, flexible leaves bluish glaucous beneath, and angled purplish stalks with clusters of pretty little nodding, trumpet-shaped flowers, orchid-colored with large, lobed, whitish lip and purple-violet throat, blooming from summer on. *Tropical.* *p. 2049, 2053*

ALLOPLECTUS *Gesneriaceae* **S3HFM**

ambiguus (Puerto Rico); clambering plant with almost woody stems becoming straggly, and covered with pale hairs on new growth; unequal pairs of green leaves scalloped along margins, with short hairs; axillary flowers with yellow swollen tubular corolla almost 2½cm long, covered with red hairs; berry-like fruit cream-white. *p. 1231*

capitatus (Colombia, Venezuela), "Velvet alloplectus"; erect, 4-angled red tomentose stem to 60 cm with large velvety, olive-green, ovate leaves, reddish beneath; dense clusters of bright yellow flowers with red sepals. *Tropical.* *p. 1231*

congestiflorus (Colombia); sparry plant with waxy, somewhat hairy, olive-green, long-petioled, ovate leaves and flowers with orange-red bracts and white corolla marked with rose on the limb, in small clusters atop a pubescent stalk. *p. 1231*

nummularia (Hypocyrta, Neomortonia), (S. Mexico, C. America), "Goldfish plant"; tiny fibrous-rooted creeper on mossy tree trunks with branching, red-hairy stems and oval, crenate, 2-8cm leaves; the flowers a vermilion-red corolla tube with pouch and small yellow lobes; suitable for hanging baskets. *p. 1252*

schlimii (Andes of Colombia); erect fleshy green to woody stem with large, broad-lanceolate leaves, bristly but shimmering light green, scalloped and fringed with red hairs; small golden-yellow flowers with crimson lines. *Tropical.* *p. 1231*

teuscheri (Nematanthus) (Ecuador); attractive herbaceous plant with red stems; the lanceolate rough leaves olive-green with silver-green along the midrib and main laterals, wine-red beneath; axillary lemon-yellow flowers with crimson lobes, bracts and calyx orange-red. *p. 1257*

vittatus (E. Perú), "Striped alloplectus"; beautiful erect, fleshy plant with showy, ovate, quilted, crenate leaves bronzy moss-green with silver-white feathering along midrib, and covered with white hair; glowing red-purple beneath; yellow flowers in a cluster, orange-red calyx, and red bracts. *p. 1229, 1231*

ALLOPLECTUS: see also NAUTILOCALYX

ALLOSCHEMONE *Araceae* **S3LFM**

occidentalis (Brazil); climbing aroid with leathery, pinnatifid leaves 40-50cm long, 35-40cm wide, lobes oblong-pointed, carried on 30-60cm petioles; spathe more than 10cm long, outside white, inside rose; very rare. Line drawing by J. Bogner, Munich Botanic Garden. *p. 164*

ALLUAUDIA *Didiereaceae* **S2LBD**

adscendens (S.W. Madagascar); curious xerophyte of the dry-tropical region near Fort Dauphin; succulent erect tree 5 to 12 m tall, with thick stem and few branches, of habit like cereus; the gray columns thorny, and with tiny obcordate, dark green leaves; small stalked flowers. *p. 949*

comosa (S.W. Madagascar); succulent shrub 2 to 6 m high, the branches set with pairs of long thin 4 cm thorns; small fleshy obovate leaves to 2½ cm long. *Arid-Tropical.* *p. 950*

dumosa (S. Madagascar); succulent shrub to 2m high, with numerous erect fleshy branches, usually without leaves and few fleshy thorns 2cm long; tiny male flowers globose, female oblong. *p. 949*

procera (S. W. Madagascar); tree 3-5m, sometimes 16m high, the succulent branches ascending, and furnished with sharp, tapering spines 4cm long, the fleshy leaves obovate; new leaves turned first horizontally, later vertically. *p. 949, 950*

ALOCASIA *Araceae* **S3HFM**

affinis jenningsii: see Colocasia

x amazonica (sanderiana x lowii grandis); free and bushy grower with leaves very dark green, veins contrasting white, and white scalloped margin. *Humid-Tropical.* *p. 5*, 19*, 157, 160, 160A**

x argyraea (longiloba x pucciana); large, sagittate-peltate leaf entirely overlaid with silver. *p. 156*

augustiana (peltata), (New Guinea); vigorous, showy tropical foliage plant, the broad oval, sagittate leaves 30-45cm long, thin-leathery, green with pale ribs, on long rose-colored petioles marked with brown. *p. 161*

beccarii (North Borneo); tropical rhizomatous perennial forming clusters, with waxy green, peltate leaves 10-16 cm long and 5-7 cm wide, the lower base divided into short-pointed lobes; the inflorescence with spathe cupped in lower part and coppery greenish. *p. 154*

cadierei (Vietnam); broad, sagittate, waxy leaf rich green with gray-green veins and wavy margin. *p. 158, 159*

x chantrieri (indica metallica x sanderiana); bushy plant with deep, olive-green, peltate-sagittate leaves, leathery, with pearl-gray veins and scalloped white margin. *p. 157, 159*

x chelsonii (longiloba x cuprea); waxy, peltate pointed leaf bronzy, olive-green; veins and undulate margin silvery gray. *p. 158*

cucullata (Bengal, Burma), "Chinese taro"; shapely plant with smaller peltate, pointed leaves deep green with prominent veins, with base drawn together like a spoon. *Tropical.* *p. 160*

cuprea (Borneo), "Giant caladium"; Trop. Asian herb with large, peltate-cordate leaves with deeply depressed veins; dark, metallic, shining green; purple beneath. *Humid-Tropical.* *p. 156, 161*

cuprea x longiloba (Mauro); long, sagittate leaves shining gray-green with raised silver-gray veins and undulate margin; purple reverse; pink stem with brown stripes. *p. 158*

cuprea x lowii grandis (Mauro); bushy plant with glossy, peltate leaves olive, overcast with gray, and gray veins; purple reverse; stems pinkish with carmine stripes. *p. 158*

heterophylla (Philippines: Celebes); compact species with waxy, sagittate leaves 20-30cm long, 12-15cm wide, light metallic green with darker green veins, and greenish-white petioles 25-30cm long; spathe whitish. *p. 161*

'Hilo Beauty'; small growing species seldom reaching 1m, the stalks glaucous bluish-black with papery, medium-green leaves beautifully marked with irregular areas of pale chartreuse; gray beneath, with colored blotches translucent. *p. 154*

indica metallica (Malaya); waxy-stiff, sagittate leaves deep olive-green with metallic purple overcast, veins prominent; reverse of leaf and stalks reddish purple. *p. 154, 160*

korthalsii (thibautiana) (Borneo); stocky plant with sagittate leaves olive-grayish-green, primary veins broadly silver, and veinlets gray; purple beneath. *Humid-Tropical.* *p. 156, 159*

lancifolia (Papua); sturdy plant grown by Lecoufle with large leathery ovate leaves with cordate base, glossy deep green except for pale silvery midrib. *p. 153*

lindenii: see Homalomena lindenii

longiloba (Java); widely arrow-shaped leaf bluish-green, veined and margined silver-gray; pink stem with brown stripes. *p. 156*

longiloba x sanderiana; neatly patterned, sagittate leaf bluish-gray-green with silver veins and margin. *p. 156*

'Lowica' (lowii x amazonica); handsome tropical foliage plant from the collection of Marcel Lecoufle, France; from tuberous rootstock the red-purple petioles carry sturdy sagittate leaves of great beauty, metallic green with ivory ribs, and undulate margins, deep purple beneath. *p. 161*

lowii (lowii grandis) (Malaya); leathery leaf broadly sagittate, peltate, deep metallic bluish-green; veins silver and margin gray; purple beneath; stalks green. *p. 159*

lowii grandis; broader than type, deep metallic brownish green, veins grayish-green; has a very large leaf, the veining more silvery than A. lowii veitchii; spathe whitish-green outside. Propagates from young tubers. *Humid-Tropical.* *p. 156, 159*

lowii veitchii (Java); leaf smaller than lowii grandis, the main veins with white margins, the secondary network whitish, looking like gray marbling; stalks striped green variegated rose. *p. 159*

macrorrhiza (Malaya, Ceylon), giant "Elephant's ear"; to 4½ m high, with thick trunk, large 60 cm broadly shield-shaped, sagittate, fleshy leaves waxy green, with prominent ribs and wavy margin. *Tropical.* *p. 154, 155, 160*

macrorrhiza variegata (E. India), "Giant alocasia"; light green leaf blotched and mottled with white. *Tropical.* *p. 153, 154*

micholitziana (Philippines); beautiful, narrow-sagittate, hard leaf satiny emerald-green with white midrib; pale stalks with bizarre purplish banding. *Tropical.* *p. 158, 181*

odora (Philippines, Taiwan); glossy, light green, stiff-fleshy, sagittate leaves to 1 m long, with elevated ribs and rounded lobes on vaginate stalks from thick stem; flowers fragrant. *Tropical.* *p. 155, 157, 160*

odora var. robusta, in hort. as Colocasia indica gigantea (Philippines); gigantic "Elephant's ear"; luxuriant tropical Asiatic tree-like herb, with thick trunk, scarred from fallen leaf stems, to 6m tall, with giant thick-fleshy sagittate leaves, the quilted blade to 2m long, waxy fresh green, with prominent ribs and wavy margins, on stout sheathed petioles. *p. 223*

porphyroneura (Borneo); beautiful tropical species almost stemless; leaves triangular-sagittate, undulate at margins, from base of leaf to tip 20-25cm long, light metallic green, with center and main veins purple; dark chocolate brown beneath; long stalk pale green with violet spots; spathe greenish-yellow, striped green within. *p. 161*

portei (Schizocasia, Xenophya) (New Guinea, Philippines); large, triangular, waxy leaf deeply lobed, fresh green, on strong stem mottled brown. Bunting (Baileya Sept. 1962) refers this species to Alocasia, having the same reflexed spathe blade characteristic of that genus. *p. 157, 284*

princeps (porphyroneura) (Borneo); small plant with arrow-shaped leaves, olive-green with purplish veins, wavy margins; petioles spotted wine-red. *p. 156*

putzeysii (Java); noble species with ovate-sagittate, crinkled and wavy-edged thick-leathery leaves 30-38cm long, dark green except the silvery-white main veins and margins, purple-violet beneath; stalks reddish with brown spots pale green in upper part. *p. 159*

regina (Borneo); thick, waxy, sagittate leaves with long basal lobes and undulate margins, dark olive-green with metallic over-tone, the underside grayish maroon with prominent maroon-black veins; stem spotted brownish-purple. *p. 154*

sanderana (Philippines), "Kris plant"; tuberous plant with graceful, sagittate leaf shining metallic, silver-green with grayish-white ribs; margins deeply lobed and white; reverse purple. *Humid-Tropical.* *p. 156, 160*

sanderana 'Van Houtte' (sand. magnifica); attractive Belgian cultivar of dwarfer habit than type, with broader leaves less indented at the grayish-white margins, and almost velvety, the grayish white of the mainribs spreading over into broader adjoining areas. *p. 153*

x sedenii (cuprea x lowii); stocky plant with large, peltate-cordate leaves deep metallic-green with raised veins and wavy, gray margin; purple beneath; pale green stem. *p. 157, 160*

'Spotted Papua' (New Guinea); a robust species 1m high which we found in the steaming 32°C rainforest along crocodile-infested Brown River, with brown-marbled stalks bearing flaring hastate leathery leaves coppery green with irregular golden yellow spots, purplish beneath. *p. 159*

x 'Uhinkii' in hort.: see wentii p. 161.

vanhoutteana; large, fleshy, cordate, sagittate, intense glossy-green, puckered leaf with veins and border white, on thick stalk. *p. 158*

watsoniana (Sumatra); large, corrugated, leathery leaf blue-green with silver-white veining and margin; purple beneath. *p. 157, 159, 160*

wavriniana: see Xenophya lauterbachiana

wentii ('Uhinkii' in hort., whinckii) (New Guinea); waxy, rich-green, peltate leaves, thick veins and lightly undulate margin; light colored sturdy petioles. *p. 158, 161*

zebrina (Philippines); large, arrow-shaped, plain green leaves on slender stalk pale, with brown, zebra-like bands; spathe white. *p. 153, 156*

ALOCASIA: see also Colocasia, Cyrtosperma, Xanthosoma, Xenophya

ALOE *Liliaceae* **•I1LBD**

aculeata (Transvaal); loose rosette almost stemless, very fleshy, bluish leaves broad lanceolate to 60cm long and 12cm wide, concave above and rounded beneath, and set with reddish teeth; flowers lemon-yellow. *p. 1395, 1400*

acutissima (Madagascar); short-stemmed succulent rosette, usually creeping; leaves flat, little recurved, long tapering margins with a few dry spines; flowers red. *p. 1399*

affinis (Transvaal); rosette nearly stemless; fleshy leaves to 25cm long, green without mottling, margins dentate; flowers brick-red. *p. 1414*

africana (Transvaal), a "Spiny aloe"; a very pretty tree aloe, good compact rosette when young, though reaching 4 m or more in its habitat, the glaucous bluish leaves are hard and brown-spined at the margins; flowers yellow, tipped green. *Arid-Subtropic.* *p. 1398*

arborescens (So. Africa), "Candelabra aloe"; spreading rosette with sword-like, fleshy tapering leaves to 60cm long, glaucous pale bluish-green, edged with yellow horny teeth; on stems reaching 4½m; flowers red, in dense racemes. *Subtropic.* *p. 1398, 1403, 1408A, 1409, 1411, 2092*

arborescens 'Spineless' (So. Africa: South Cape); attractive rosette with many long tapering, narrow fleshy leaves bluish green, with smooth margins. Harry Hall told me that this could be a natural hybrid of arborescens x striata. *p. 1405*

aristata (So. Africa), "Lace aloe"; small stemless clustering rosette of densely set, slender, dark green leaves covered with white warts, white marginal teeth, the tip ending in a long pale bristle; flowers orange-red. *p. 1400, 1406*

aristata 'Variegata'; small starry rosette to 15cm dia.; dense with pointed leaves arranged in many rows, green lined with white; margins with soft white spines. *p. 1413*

bainesii (So. Africa); tree to 18 m high, with trunk to 1½ m thick and head to 6 m across, one of the largest of the genus; sword-shaped green leaves 60-90 cm long, leathery and concave, with small, marginal prickles; flowers salmon-pink tipped with green. *Arid-Subtropic.* *p. 1398, 1407*

bakeri (So. Madagascar); snaking rosette with narrow, long tapering fleshy leaves 10-15cm long x 1cm; dark green with pale green or white mottling, the margins with cream spines; in bright sun suffused with red; yellow flowers tipped green. *p. 1404*

ballyi (ballii) (Rhodesia, Kenya); tree-forming to 1.5m, with slender trunk topped by rosette of broad, recurving, light green leaves toothed at margins; flowers flame-colored. *p. 1397*

barbadensis (perfoliata vera), (Arabia, Africa, to St. Helena; West Indies to Aruba); the "Bitter aloe", known in the first century to Dioscorides; Greek herbal describes it then as having healing values; forming large rosette to 50cm high, of thick and fleshy, glaucous gray-green leaves, initially mottled; toothed at margins; tall spikes with pendant, inflated tubular flowers yellow. *p. 1397, 1411*

beguinii: see GASTROLEA

x bortiana (prob. striata hybrid); short-stemmed rosette of broad fleshy leaves 25cm long, blue with pale mottling; flowers orange-red. *p. 1411*

branddraaiensis (E. Transvaal); stemless rosette occasionally making offsets; broad green leaves 35cm long, with numerous white stripes; tips often dying back; margins dentate; flowers vivid scarlet. *p. 1414*

brevifolia (Cape Prov.); glaucous, robust 10-12cm rosette with triangular-oblong leaves twice as broad as humilis, flat on top, rounded beneath to keeled, grayish-green and with white horny teeth at margins. Suckers much more freely than var. depressa, and when full grown rarely exceeds 20cm in dia., with narrower leaves in proportion; it is also more spiny, especially on the keel below. Flowers red, in dense racemes. *Subtropic.* *p. 1396, 1404, 1408*

brevifolia depressa (Cape: Caledon), (Aloe brevifolia of the trade), "Crocodile jaws"; open rosette with broad leaves having white cartilage edge, only very few spines on back of leaf toward tip only, 12-18 cm dia., but grows to about 30-40cm, with leaves 8-10cm wide at the base. *Subtropic.* *p. 1396, 1408*

brevifolia variegata; open rosette bluish-glaucous, highly variegated and streaked with creamy-yellow; and with horny cream marginal teeth. *p. 1396*

broomii (Lesotho, So. Africa); low rosette of broad, fleshy green leaves 25cm long, indistinctly lined; flowers greenish yellow. *p. 1411*

bulbillifera (W. Madagascar); suckering, low rosette of spreading, recurving, tapering green leaves to 60cm long; numerous salmon-scarlet flowers with yellow-green tips. *p. 1412*

candelabrum (Natal); tree-like to 4m, rosette of deep green to blue leaves to 1m long, margins reddish; flowers scarlet or orange, in cylindric spikes. *p. 1411*

castanea (Transvaal: Lydensburg); forming branching stems to 4½m high, topped by dense rosettes of long, incurving fleshy, concave leaves 45cm long, grayish green, with marginal spines; red-brown flowers in long spikes. *p. 1405*

chabaudii (Rhodesia, Transvaal); clustering stemless rosettes with spreading fleshy concave leaves long tapering and curving 40-50 cm long, glaucous blue to bronze, with small marginal teeth, branched inflorescence 1m high with red flowers—a glorious sight with such plants clinging to the sheer cliffs alongside the foaming Victoria Falls, constantly bathed in the clouds of mist rising from the churning canyon of the Zambesi below. *p. 1395*

ciliaris (So. Africa), "Climbing aloe"; weak, branching and scrambling stems with open spirals of not very fleshy, 15cm leaves dark green with white teeth along the edge; flowers scarlet with green tips. *1398, 1400, 1404*

'Ciliaris hybrid'; a good commercial plant of graceful, compact habit, much more compact than ciliaris, the broader leathery, matte dark green, clasping leaves close-jointed and durable, soft marginal teeth pale cream; freely suckering. *p. 1398*

claviflora (Bushmanland); stemless rosette of fat, bluish leaves 30cm long, scattered marginal teeth; inflorescence procumbent, with orange flowers in cylindrical spike. *p. 1415*

"cleistiflora"; a compact, stiff rosette freely suckering, probably a hybrid with A. humilis echinatum, of clean habit, glaucous leaves rounded underneath, and with ivory elevations, almost flat on top, the margins with cream teeth, the tips rarely burnt; individual flowers do not open. *p. 1403*

commixta (So. Africa: Cape Peninsula); shrubby, with several erect stems in dense group, to 1m, tapering leaves 20cm long x 4cm wide, slightly concave, dark green and with white marginal teeth; flowers yellowish to orange. *p. 1404*

comosa (Cape Prov.: Great Karroo); striking rosette becoming tree-like to 2m high, with broad, fleshy, sword-shaped leaves glaucous blue, to purple in the strong sun of the Karroo, the margins with horny teeth; flowers greenish-white. *Arid-subtropic.* *p. 1404, 1407*

concinna (zanzibarica) (E. Africa); attractive scandent succulent rosette branching from base, with handsome fleshy recurving leaves 10cm long, light green with pale spots; margins dentate; flowers scarlet tipped green. *Tropical.* *p. 1413*

confusa (Tanzania); slender branching, later reclining stems with loose spirals of narrow fleshy, tapering, dark grayish-green leaves with pale green markings, to 25cm long, recurved tip and irregularly toothed, becoming reddish in the sun; tubular reddish-orange flowers. *p. 1400*

conifera (Madagascar); low rosette of bluish-gray leaves with shining red margins and small teeth; flowers yellow almost entirely covered by large bracts in cone-like inflorescence. *p. 1412*

cooperi (So. Africa), stemless rosette of elongate leaves to 50cm long, green with small white spots; flowers salmon-pink with green tips. *p. 1413*

'Crosby's Prolific' (nobilis x humilis var. echinatum); attractive small, freely-suckering rosette dense with broadly spreading fat, dagger-shaped leaves about 15cm long, deep green with scattered yellow puckers, especially beneath, and with long marginal teeth. *p. 1403*

davyana sobulifera (Transvaal); small succulent rosette, gradually forming slender stems; glaucous green tapering leaves, turning reddish in strong sun, attractively edged with prominent teeth; flowers flesh-colored. The variety sobulifera forms numerous offsets from the base. *p. 1404*

dawei (Uganda: Entebbe); stem-forming rosette branching from the base, to 1½m high, with 45cm sword-shaped, tapering fleshy leaves blue-green to purplish, sinuate-dentate along margins; flowers red. *p. 1406*

x delaetii (ciliaris x succotrina); branching from the base; broad leaves arranged spirally, 30cm long, dark green and convex above, margins with white teeth; flowers orange red. *p. 1414*

descoingsii (Madagascar); attractive small rosette to 5cm dia., forming clusters; leaves triangular, rough, dull-green, with numerous white warts; flowers orange and red. *p. 1415*

dichotoma (Cape Prov. to Namibia), "Dragon-tree aloe"; bold succulent rosette with broad fleshy leaves 25cm or more long, glaucous green edged in brownish-yellow and with triangular teeth; growing into monstrous trees to 9m high, with branches forking, on a smooth trunk; flowers canary yellow. *Arid-Tropical.* *p. 1407*

dinteri (Namibia); stemless, without offsets; rosette 35cm in dia.; leaves in 3 rows, 20-28cm long, very sharp, sickle-shaped, deeply channelled, keel and edges with horny lines, margins below middle with fine teeth, brownish-green, with flecks in transverse lines; flowers about 2½cm long, pale red. *p. 1411*

distans (So. Africa); little elongated stems with creeping branches set distantly with the thick, short, blue-green, scarcely-warted leaves tipped with a sharp point, the margins with horny teeth; tubular flowers red, tipped green. *p. 1400, 1415*

dolomitica (No. Transvaal), stem-forming rosette to 2m tall, thick-fleshy, broad leaves to 30cm long and rigid, dark green with red-brown markings and tip, margins with strong recurved teeth; flowers light red. *p. 1414*

ecklonis (S. E. Africa); nearly stemless rosette with dark green leaves to 38cm long, often reddish and without markings, margins with horny edge and a few teeth; greenish-yellow to red flowers in erect racemes. *p. 1410*

eru (Eritrea, Nubia, No. Kenya); branching rosette with stem 45cm high, very fleshy, arching leaves to 75cm long, concave above, glossy dark green striped with white, and red teeth; the 'Green form' with only faint markings; salmon-red flowers in branched racemes. *Arid-Tropical.* *p. 1405*

eru 'Maculata', "Nubian aloe"; very attractive variety with leaves smaller and narrower than the type, bluish-glaucous and very much spotted with cream; prominent pale marginal spines. *Arid-Tropical.* *p. 1401*

excelsa (Rhodesia); robust rosette becoming tree-like, to 5m high, forming a thick trunk; tapering, soft-fleshy recurving leaves to 60cm long, margins and lower surface with teeth. *p. 1410*

ferox (So. Africa), "Ferocious aloe"; bold rosette, developing a stem to 5m high, with broad, fleshy leaves bronzy-green, hollow above, curved and warty beneath, margins with brown-red teeth; flowers orange-red. The Zulus use it as an unguent, and for stomach troubles. *Arid-subtropic.* *p. 1396, 1402, 1404, 1410*

ferox variegata (S. E. Cape Prov.); a natural variety found in the wilds, and which I photographed at Kirstenbosch Botanical Gardens, Cape Town; striking, shapely rosette with broad, fleshy, upward-pointing leaves glaucous green variegated by many ivory-white longitudinal bands and stripes, marginal teeth brownish; branched raceme 60cm long, with orange flowers. *Arid-subtropic.* *p. 1395*

gariepensis (Cape Prov. to Namibia); rosette of leaves to 40cm long, dark green to reddish, lined lengthwise; flowers greenish yellow. *p. 1412*

glauca (Cape Prov.); dense rosette of tapering, spreading leaves 30-45cm long, blue-glaucous obscurely lined; margins with red-brown spines; salmon-red flowers in tall racemes. *p. 1409*

haemanthifolia (Cape Prov.); curious stemless rosette with tongue-shaped, broad fleshy leaves arrranged in two series, olive-green with red margins, 10 to 20 cm long, the apex rounded. *p. 1401*

haworthioides (C. Madagascar); stemless, pretty rosette of dark green leaves to 6cm long, densely set with soft, pale spines; flowers pale orange. *Tropical.* *p. 1413*

humilis (E. Cape Prov.), "Spider aloe"; small, shapely, dense succulent rosette forming tufts by suckering; glaucous blue-green narrow, concave leaves with white marginal teeth, and tubercles on back, giving hairy-looking appearance; flowers red, tipped with green, in long racemes. *Arid-subtropic.* *p. 1408, 1411*

humilis echinata (Cape Province), "Hedgehog aloe"; pretty rosette with pearly foliage, narrower, more concave leaves not over 1cm wide, pale fleshy spines on the upper surface and pearly warts below. *p. 1406*

humilis 'Globosa', a "Spider aloe"; a cultivar in the California nursery trade; small suckering rosette with glaucous bluish leaves more incurved and more numerous than humilis, the tips turning purplish in the sun; prominent horny teeth cream to pinkish. *Arid-subtropic.* *p. 1396*

x humvir (humilis x virens), "Needle-aloe", neat little , freely suckering rosette offered by California growers, with rich green, slender tapering leaves dotted pale green and margins with soft pale spines. *p. 1400*

jex-blakeae (E. Africa: Coast of Kenya); clustering, meandering rosette with snaking slender stems and fleshy, narrow-tapering, twisted leaves glaucous-blue, with pale marginal spines; clear lemon-yellow flowers in branched racemes. This plant was collected by Dr. Piers in Nairobi, in whose collection I photographed it. *p. 1410*

jucunda (Somaliland); small stemless, group-forming 8-10cm rosette, with broadly ovate-tapering, recurving fleshy leaves, dark green with numerous pale green to white translucent spots; margins with horny red-brown teeth; flowers pale pink. *Arid-tropical.* *p. 1402*

juveana (Madagascar); creeping succulent forming clusters, the growth ascending; short fleshy leaves along stems arranged symmetrically, 5cm dia., green with cream markings, the margins with pale teeth. *p. 1413*

latifolia (So. Africa); similar to saponaria but larger; showy rosette on short stems to 60cm with broad, fleshy leaves to 30cm long, green, often reddish, with whitish spots and brown horny teeth; flowers reddish yellow. *p. 1400*

laxissima (transvaalensis) (Transvaal); stemless rosette, suckering to form groups; leaves to 25cm, milky-green with white spots in wavy cross-bands, and horny teeth at margins; flowers coral-red. *p. 1412*

lineata (So. Africa), "Lined aloe"; large rosette on stems to 60cm with broad lightly concave leaves to 45cm long, pale glaucous blue-green, both sides with vertical green lines, the margins with reddish horny prickles; nodding red flowers. *p. 1406, 1409*

littoralis (Angola, Namibia); stout stem to 2m, rosette of sickle-shaped tapering, gray-green leaves to 90cm long; flowers coral red in many branched panicle to 5m tall. *Arid-Tropical.* *p. 1412*

longistyla (So. Africa); small stemless rosette of dense, thick-fleshy, stubby leaves bluish-green with indistinct vertical lines and soft white warts or teeth; salmon-red flowers in showy racemes; best variety for blooming in pots. *p. 1406*

macracantha (So. Africa); spreading rosette forming runners, with broad, recurving, 45cm leaves brownish-green irregularly lined and marked with white; margins with brown teeth; flowers yellow. *p. 1400*

madecassa (Tananarive, Madagascar); low compact, fleshy rosette, tapering green leaves to 30cm long, margins with pinkish teeth; flowers golden-yellow. *p. 1415*

marlothii (Botswana, Transvaal, Natal); attractive tree with single trunk, to 5m high; leaves to 75cm long and 18cm wide, in dense rosette, pale glaucous blue or greenish, concave and very spiny with short thick purplish-brown thorns; flowers red-orange. I did, however, find a double-headed old tree in the northern Transvaal. *Arid-subtropic.* *p. 1399, 1407*

melanacantha (So. Africa); short stemmed, clustering rosette of narrow green leaves convex beneath, the margins with horny white spines, later black spines curved toward the tip; flowers scarlet. *p. 1399, 1410*

melanostigma (So. Africa); attractive, incurving rosette with hard fleshy, yellow-green leaves set with large blackish spines toward apex, at the base with pale horny teeth. *p. 1400*

microdonta (Somalia); large rosette with slender stem to 1m, becoming procumbent, branching from base; leaves to 70cm, dull green to olive; whitish teeth; scarlet flowers. *p. 1415*

microstigma (So. and Southwest Africa); fleshy rosette with short stem dense with tapering, incurving leaves to 30cm long and 5cm wide, glaucous green with pink sheen, on both sides dotted with milk-white blotches, the horny margins with soft teeth; flowers greenish-yellow. *p. 1399, 1401, 1404, 1408*

millotii (Madagascar); shrub-like succulent much branched at base, slender, leaning stems with fleshy, nearly linear leaves at first in two ranks, later spirally arranged and recoiling, 8-10cm long, gray-green with some cream spotting; small white teeth; flowers red. *p. 1401*

mitriformis (Cape Prov.); clustering rosette with broad concave, fleshy incurving leaves to 15cm long and 8 cm wide, blue-green to green, with pale horny teeth; tubular flowers bright scarlet red. *Arid-subtropic.* *p. 1395, 1401, 1402, 1408*

mubendiensis (Toro, Uganda); succulent rosette freely suckering, leaves to 35cm, dull gray-green with occasional whitish spots, margins dentate; flowers brick-red. *p. 1414*

mutabilis (Transvaal); found in Kruger Park, long-leaved rosette 60cm dia., with tapering, glaucous-gray concave leaves, with indistinct lines, and with long pale teeth; flowers greenish-yellow. *p. 1410*

nobilis (So. Africa), "Gold-tooth aloe"; a small thick, attractive, nice green rosette, with later creeping stems, the leaves rounded below and with pale horny teeth at margins; flowers orange-yellow. *p. 1397, 1400*

pachygaster (Namibia); stemless rosette of leaves 12-16cm long, both surfaces convex, light gray-green with black marginal teeth; flowers red. *p. 1413*

parvibracteata (Mozambique to Zululand); attractive stemless rosette with tapering fleshy leaves 30-38cm long, green to brownish richly lined with numerous oblong whitish markings, and set with brown teeth; flowers red. *p. 1404*

parvula (C. Madagascar); attractive stemless rosette to 15cm dia., of soft-fleshy gray-green leaves, convex on both sides, covered with warts and prickly with bristle-like hairs; flowers light coral. *p. 1413*

pearsonii (Cape Prov. Namibia); elongate, stem-forming rosette to 1m high, with fat, recurved leaves 10cm long, striped red-green and with small marginal spines; flowers greenish-yellow or red. *p. 1404, 1411*

peckii (Somalia); stemless, suckering rosette with fleshy leaves to 16cm long, glossy green with pale markings, margins with brownish teeth; flowers straw-colored. *p. 1415*

peglerae (Transvaal); stemless rosette of crowded, incurving leaves to 35cm long, pale blue-green; flowers pink becoming lemon-yellow. *p. 1412*

percrassa (Ethiopia); low, stout rosette, stemless; broad leaves to 60cm long, blue-green with few spots, margins with small teeth; flowers light red. *p. 1415*

perfoliata (vera L., barbadensis) (Tenerife); stemless rosette becoming large, with thick-fleshy leaves 40-50cm long, gray-green with reddish tinge, margins with pale teeth; flowers yellow. Juice or flesh used medicinally since ancient times. *p. 1415*

petrophila (No. Transvaal); small, succulent, stemless rosette with spreading leaves 20-25cm long, light green with scattered whitish markings and dull pale lines; sinuate margins with brown teeth; flowers red. *p. 1406*

pietersii (Transvaal); hard rosette with incurving gray-glaucous concave leaves, armed at margins and keel with strong gray to brown spines; bold cylindrical erect inflorescence with orange-red flowers. *p. 1408*

pillansii (Cape Province); distinctive rosette with close-jointed thick fleshy, bluish glaucous leaves in symmetrical ranks, to 60cm long and 20cm wide at base, with yellow marginal teeth; flowers lemon-yellow; grows into a large branched tree 10m high with trunk to 2m thick. *p. 1399*

plicatilis (Cape Prov., So. Africa), "Fan aloe"; small forking tree to 5m high, with closely packed, linear, fleshy 30cm leaves of even width arranged in two ranks, tip rounded, pale glaucous blue with translucent yellow margin; large scarlet flowers in loose spike. *p. 1400, 1405, 1406, 1409*

pluridens (E. Cape Province); almost tree-like, similar to arborescens, 2-3m tall, stems branching; numerous gracefully recurved leaves to 80cm long, pale green, margins toothed; flowers salmon. *p. 1415*

polyphylla (So. Africa: Drakensberg; Basutoland), "Spiral aloe"; striking low rosette 30-40cm dia., dense with fleshy, broad leaves relatively short, but becoming 20-30cm long, pale glaucous green and with a strong, red-brown tip; the foliage spirally arranged and overlapping; branched inflorescence bearing salmon-pink flowers. A succulent of unique beauty whether large or small, with its leaves regularly arranged as in shingles on a roof, in clockwise or counter-clockwise coils. Somewhat difficult in cultivation; in habitat at 2,400m they are often under snow. *Arid-subtropic.* *p. 1413*

x principis (arborescens x ferox); tree-type to 2m freely branching from base; dense rosette of very fleshy, curved leaves to 75cm long, blue to blue-green. *p. 1412*

ramosissima (So. Africa: Cape, Namaqualand; Namibia); forms thick short-trunk, repeatedly forking, growing to 2½m high, rosettes at branch-ends with spreading, thick fleshy narrow leaves, dark gray or bluish-green, and with brown teeth; flowers yellow. *p. 1408*

x salm-dyckiana, (natural hybrid of arborescens x ferox); large rosette 2m tall with heavy, thick-fleshy leaves grayish-green; bold inflorescence orange-red. *Subtropic.* *p. 1397*

saponaria (Natal, Transvaal), "Soap aloe"; short stemmed, suckering rosette with fleshy, broad lanceolate leaves 15-20cm long, bluish-green marked with yellow-green elongate blotches arranged in transverse bands; margins with large cream to brown thorns; flowers red-yellow. *p. 1401, 1402, 1405*

saponaria x striata; a common California garden hybrid; robust rosette with incurving broad leaves concave at bottom, dark green, slightly glaucous, crossed by irregular rows of yellow-green, margins toothed and white thorny. *p. 1403*

schweinfurthii (Sudan, Zaire, Cameroun); short-stemmed, suckering rosette with fleshy gray-green leaves 50cm long, arranged vase-like, with dentate margins; teeth with brown tips; flowers orange. *p. 1414*

sladeniana (Southwest Africa); attractive stemless rosette forming clusters, with shapely pointed, short-channeled leaves to 10cm long, keeled beneath, moss-green tinted pink, and richly covered with white oblong, translucent spots and with white edge, set with small white teeth; flowers rose. *Arid-tropical.* *p. 1399*

'Soledad hybrid'; an everblooming California hybrid of close-in habit like a graceful vase; close-jointed concave, bluish-green leaves with yellow markings, the margins set with soft teeth tipped brown; flowers orange-red. *p. 1399*

somaliensis (Somalia); low, pretty rosette forming offsets, tapering leaves 20cm long, glossy brownish-green with numerous pale green markings, margins dentate; flowers light red. *p. 1415*

speciosa (Cape Prov.); tree-like, becoming 7m tall, with branching trunk, topped by rosettes of thick-fleshy, recurved spreading leaves grayish-glaucous, the margins with horny edge and small pink teeth; bright red flowers. *p. 1410*

x spinosissima (humilis echinata x arborescens), "Torch plant"; tall spidery rosette with blue-gray concave warted leaves 30cm long, spirally arranged, the margins set with horny teeth; flowers brilliant red in dense racemes. *p. 1398, 1402*

squarrosa (Socotra, Zanzibar); charming little rosette branching from base; tapering leaves 8cm long, green with pale spots in transverse bands; horny teeth; flowers red. *p. 1413*

striata (S. W. Africa, Cape Prov.), "Coral aloe"; large rosette almost stemless, of broad fleshy leaves almost 60cm long, pale glaucous gray faintly striped, the hard margins pink and without spines; pendulous coral-red flowers. *Arid-subtropical.* *p. 1399, 1400*

striata x saponaria 'Picta'; attractive variegated seedling mutation (see A. saponaria x striata); succulent rosette with broad spreading leaves incurving,dark green with yellow-green cross-markings, as well as prominent cream bands lengthwise. *p. 1410*

succotrina (Cape Prov.); branching, stem-forming rosette to 1m high; leaves to 50cm long and 5cm wide, sword-shaped, bluish-green to gray-green, lightly lined and spotted, with white prickles; flowers red with green tips. *Arid-subtropic.* *p. 1402, 1404*

suprafoliata (So. Africa: Swaziland), "Propeller aloe"; very attractive succulent plant when young, when its thick, elegantly recurved, tapering leaves are arranged in two opposing series; glaucous blue but bronzy-red toward margins and dressed with reddish marginal spines; leaves become 30cm long, set in rosettes with age; flowers coral-red with green tips. *p. 1401*

tenuior (So. Africa); branching loose rosettes with leaves to 15cm long and 1cm wide, glaucous bluish-green, thin and concave with white horny edge and minutely toothed; cylindric flowering bells yellow in dense racemes. *p. 1402*

tenuior rubriflora (E. Cape Prov.); clambering stem to 3m long and branching; glaucous-green, narrow leaves in lax rosettes, to 15cm long; flowers yellow; var. rubriflora has red flowers with yellow spots. *p. 1412*

thraskii (S. E. Africa: Natal to Zululand); stem-forming, to 2m or more high, with dense rosettes of clasping, concave leaves to 1½m long, darkish green slightly glaucous, tapering rapidly to long tip; and with fine brown thorns at margins; flowers light orange, in many-flowered racemes. *p. 1403*

tororoana (Uganda); short-stemmed rosette, 25cm dia.; lanceolate leaves 15cm long, dark green with small whitish marks; white marginal teeth; inflorescence coral-red with green tips. *p. 1414*

transvaalensis (Transvaal); stemless fleshy rosette with spreading recurved leaves to 25cm long, lightly concave, dark milky-green with numerous white-transparent ovals arranged in cross bands, and edged with light brown teeth; flowers salmon. *p. 1400*

tweediae (Kenya); solitary, stemless rosette with thick leaves to 60cm, green with pale green spots especially underside; white, horny marginal teeth; flowers red with yellow edge. *p. 1415*

vanbalenii (Zululand); short-stemmed plant with rosettes of long, channeled leaves to 60cm long, recurving and coiling, deep grayish-green with dark veins, and brown teeth; flowers reddish. *p. 1401, 1405*

vaombe (S. W. Madagascar); tree-type with stem to 6m, topped by dense rosette of dull-green leaves to 1m, dentate margins; flowers vivid crimson. *p. 1412*

variegata (Cape of Good Hope), "Partridge breast"; beautiful succulent to 30cm high with triangular blue-green leaves arranged in 3 ranks and painted with oblong white spots in irregular crossbands, the margins horny and white-warty; tubular flowers salmon red, in loose racemes. *Arid-subtropic.* *p. 1396, 1402, 1408A, 2092*

variegata ausana (Namibia); similar to A. variegata but thick tricornered, blue-green leaves arranged as a rosette, deeply channeled, and the white markings not clearly forming a crossband. *p. 1396*

vera (barbadensis) (Cape Verde, Canary Isl., Madeira), the "True aloe" or "Medicine plant"; the pulp of which is used to heal sore burns and cuts; widely cultivated; short-stemmed, suckering rosette with fleshy, dagger-shaped, channeled leaves to 60cm long, gray-green and glaucous; spotted when young; edged with soft pale spines; nodding, cylindrical, yellow flowers. *Subtropic.* *p. 1398*

vera chinensis (India, Vietnam), "Indian medicine plant"; smaller Asiatic form, the fleshy, lanceolate leaves 30cm long and recurved at tips, rounded beneath, blue-green with white markings and whitish teeth; flowers orange. *Tropical.* *p. 1400*

versicolor (Madagascar); nearly stemless, forming mats by offsets; leaves linear to 15cm, gray-green with waxy coating; whitish teeth; flowers coral-red. *p. 1415*

vigueri (Tuléar, Madagascar); stemless rosette, forming basal suckers; leaves often directed downward, 25-60cm long, whitish green with waxy coating; scarlet flowers. *p. 1414*

virens (So. Africa), "Green aloe"; stemless, freely tufting rosette of numerous lanceolate-fleshy upright tapering leaves 20cm long, light green with scattered pale spots and pale marginal teeth; flowers red. *p. 1400*

'Walmsley's Blue'; California cultivar, a small, freely suckering rosette with soft, tapering, lightly channeled bluish glaucous leaves, bronzy near base; margins with faint cream teeth. *p. 1403*

'Walmsley's Bronze'; commercial California cultivar; small branching rosette with broad-stubby, hard fleshy, channeled leaves glaucous bronzy green. *p. 1403*

wickensii (No. Transvaal); group-forming stemless rosette with leathery, tapering, rather erect leaves glaucous green to olive, to 60cm long; dark marginal spines; branched inflorescence with yellow flowers. *p. 1408*

zebrina (Transvaal, Angola); short-stemmed fleshy rosette with wide leaves to 30cm long, green, often purplish, with numerous oblong white spots connecting across the surface, edged with brown teeth; flowers strong red, in branched racemes. *p. 1400*

ALOINOPSIS *Aizoaceae* **I2LBD**

peersii (So. Africa); tiny succulent with opposite short, recurved, tongue-like leaves bluntly triangular, velvety bluish-gray-green, distinctly punctate; flowers yellow. *p. 57*

schoonesii (Cape Prov.); small clustering succulent with opposite tiny fat triangular or spatulate leaves flattened at apex, glaucous gray, top light gray dotted with small translucent windows; flowers yellow-red, shining like silk. *p. 57*

villetii (So. Africa: Bushmanland); small curious succulent with opposite erect, green, club-like, spatulate leaves covered with white or yellowish tubercles, 2-3cm high; 2cm flowers yellow tipped coppery-red, opening in the afternoon. *p. 60*

ALONSOA *Scrophulariaceae* **I2LBD**
warscewiczii (Perú), "Mask flower"; bushy herbaceous plant 60 to 90cm high, grown for its attractive scarlet-red or cinnabar winter-blooming flowers 1cm or more in dia.; 2-lipped and carried on brownish stems with fresh green, toothed leaves. *Tropical.* *p. 2049*

ALOYSIA *Verbenaceae* **I2LBM**
triphylla (Lippia citriodora) (Argentina, Chile), "Lemon-verbena"; branching shrub to 3m high with angular, wiry shoots and 8cm lanceolate, smooth leaves in whorls of 3 or 4, lemon-scented; the small reddish-white flowers in graceful pyramidal spikes and very fragrant; summer blooming. Use: leaves in finger bowls, teas, sachet, perfumes. *p. 2118*

ALPINIA *Zingiberaceae* **S3LFM**
calcarata (India), "Indian ginger"; rhizome bearing reed-stems, to 1m, with spicy leaves and terminal panicle of waxy flowers greenish white; lip yellow with maroon. *Tropical.* *p. 2142*
formosana (India, China); tropical ginger 1 to 2m high, with aromatic rhizome, and bearing slender leafy reed-stems with narrow lance-shaped, spicy leaves 30cm long and 3-5cm wide; at the apex a short 10cm terminal inflorescence with beautiful waxy, creamy-white flowers, the petal-like lip marked with pink and maroon; seed capsule red, springing open into 3 fleshy sections when ripe. *p. 2129*
purpurata (South seas from Moluccas to New Caledonia and Yap), "Red ginger"; ornamental perennial herb with leafy stems ranging from 2-5m, each ending in a showy inflorescence, with a flower spike brush-like to 30cm long, consisting of numerous large, boat-shaped bright red bracts each with a small white flower, normally erect but drooping if long; new plants germinate among the flower bracts. *Tropical.* *p. 2129, 2133*
rafflesiana (Malaya); a majestic ginger with arching, leafy stems to 2m, 30cm leaves light green with creamy variegation, downy beneath; the inflorescence a compact cluster 8cm long, with small golden yellow, waxy flowers tipped red. *p. 2142*
sanderae (New Guinea), "Variegated ginger"; very attractive ornamental ginger of dwarf habit, having creeping rhizome and clustered, leafy stems about 45cm high; the lanceolate leaves arranged somewhat in 2 ranks, pale green, edged and obliquely banded from the center to the margin with pure white. *Humid-tropical.* *p. 768A*, 2129, 2130, 2133*
vittata (Renealmia ventricosa) (South Sea Is.); handsome variegated ginger with reed-like stems from rhizomes, closely furnished with leathery, narrow-lanceolate leaves in 2 ranks, deep green with pale green, cream or yellow bars and stripes irregularly feathering from the midrib to the border; the flowers red. *p. 2133*
zerumbet (speciosa or nutans in hort.) (China, Japan), "Shell ginger"; majestic rhizomatous plant forming dense clumps of leafy, arching canes to 4m high, with smooth, long-bladed, leathery leaves arranged in 2 rows; the striking fragrant, procelain-textured flowers with bell-shaped, waxy-white calyx, the corolla white flushed with pink and tipped with red and yellow lip, in dense racemes to 30cm long, becoming nodding. *p. 2131*
zerumbet 'Variegata', "Variegated shell ginger"; a variety seen in Hawaii, with the broadly lanceolate thin-leathery dark green leaves variegated in feather design with stripes and bands of creamy yellow. *Tropical.* *p. 2129, 2130*

ALPINIA: see also Brachychilum, Hedychium

ALSOPHILA *Dicksoniaceae (Filices)* **S3HFW**
australis: see cooperi
cooperi (Cyathea australis; Sphaeropteris in Hortus 3) (Tasmania, Australia), "Australian treefern"; a noble treefern, with heavy trunk to 6m high, with well porportioned, spreading crown even when small, but requiring lots of water; the arching fronds finely divided, metallic green, on rough stalks covered with small pale brown hair-like scales. *p. 1068, 1070, 1077*
cooperi 'Robusta'; cultivated in California as a more vigorous form, with long, arching fronds, of the well-known A. cooperi, known as australis in horticulture. *p. 1069*
glauca (Java, Malaysia, Assam), "Blue treefern"; slender treefern with trunks to 15m, crowned by gigantic bipinnate fronds to 4m long, bright glossy-green above, and bluish beneath, the stalks and heart clothed with white chaffy scales. *Humid-Tropical.* *p. 1067*
kalbreyeri (Colombia); labeled as Gymnosphaera podophylla at the Leningrad Botanic Garden where I photographed this tree fern; a bold species with trunk covered with brown wool, the long-stalked fronds with brown-hairy stipes (stalks), loosely bipinnate, the long narrow-lanceolate pinnae bright glossy green and of leathery texture, the margins frilled and undulate but not lobed. Christ Index Filicum lists podophylla as from Chusan and Hong Kong. *p. 1077*
microdonta (Tropical America); treefern of moderate size, with herbaceous fronds tripinnately divided, bright green on both sides; the pinnae 30-45cm long, the segments close; slightly hairy on ribs; the base of leaf stalk (stipe) armed with thorns. With its soft leaves the plant suffers quickly and fronds will die, if pot grown and permitted to dry out. *p. 1076*

ALSTROEMERIA *Amaryllidaceae* **C2LBMd**
aurantiaca (Chile), "Lily of the Incas"; herbaceous perennial with fibrous roots from egg-shaped tubers which are attached to a common stem; showy, floriferous plant blooming in summer, with leafy floral stem nearly 1m high; lanceolate leaves, and terminal clusters of beautiful azalea-like flowers about 4cm across, orange with two upper segments streaked with orange-red, the outer ones tipped with green; long-lasting as cut flowers. *Subtropic.* *p. 104*
caryophyllaea (Brazil), "Peruvian lily"; flowering stem 20 to 30cm high, the leaves spoon-shaped oblong; two-lipped flowers scarlet red or striped with red; very fragrant. *Subtropic.* *p. 104*
'Chilensis hybrid'; herb with fleshy roots, from South American species, with glaucescent, obovate leaves, $\frac{1}{2}$-1m high, with leafy stems bearing large umbels of flowers in pleasing pastel shades from white, pink, red to orange and yellow, all beautifully marked with a yellow zone and spotted purple; spring blooming. *p. 113*
ligtu (Chile), "Inca Lily"; plant with thin linear 8cm leaves along 45cm flowering stem; the flowers with spreading perianth segments pinkish streaked with purple, and a touch of yellow. *p. 101*
pelegrina (Chile), "Lily of Lima"; 40cm high, with short, lanceolate leaves on stems, the numerous 5cm lily-like flowers with spreading segments outside lilac, spotted and lined with red-purple inside. Horticultural forms in various colors. *Subtropic.* *p. 101*
pulchella (psittacina) (No. Brazil); herbaceous perennial with leafy stem to 1m high, topped by cluster of beautiful flowers 4cm long, crimson red tipped with green and spotted brown. *Subtropic.* *p. 102*

ALTAMIRANOA *Crassulaceae* **I2LBD**
grandyi (Villadia) (Perú); small sedum-like succulent with erect stems dense like pyramids with tiny roundish, fleshy dark green leaves 5mm long; yellow flowers. *p. 862*

ALTERNANTHERA *Amaranthaceae* **S2LBM**
amoena (Telanthera) (Brazil), "Parrot-leaf"; small, bushy herb of robust growing habit with broad lanceolate leaves, brownish-red and carmine, to orange; small whitish flower. *Tropical.* *p. 82*
amoena 'Brilliantissima', "Red parrot leaf"; vigorous bushy bedding plant with ovate elliptic leaves $4\frac{1}{2}$-5cm long, coppery green overlaid with red; irregularly variegated areas mainly in center, carmine pink to red, with purplish veins; in the shade variegated yellow to pinkish. *p. 84*
amoena 'Rosea'; leaves to $4\frac{1}{2}$cm in length, long-elliptic, deep green toward bronze, and pale yellow to rosy with red veins; stems reddish. *p. 84*
bettzickiana (Brazil), "Red calico plant"; dwarf, clustering herb with twisted leaves narrow and spatulate, blotched and colored cream-yellow to salmon-red; ideal for carpet-bedding. *Tropical.* *p. 82*
bettzickiana 'Aurea', "Yellow calico plant"; a pretty horticultural variety of slightly more open habit; bushy little plant with its small $2\frac{1}{2}$-4cm spoon-shaped leaves prettily variegated pale yellow and fresh green. The green counterpart in carpet-bedding to the red A. bettzickiana, and kept in shape by shearing. *Tropical.* *p. 82*
dentata 'Ruby' (Brazil), "False globe amaranth"; red-leaf form of dentata; tall species with metallic, wine-red leaves rather flat and uniform, purple beneath; inflorescence strawflower-like, greenish-white heads. *p. 82*
polygonoides (Trop. America); attractive, herbaceous densely branching plant of low habit, to 30cm high, with narrow leaves waxy bronze green, richly splashed with yellow and red; tiny white flowers; ideal for flower bed planting. *p. 84*
versicolor (Brazil), "Copper leaf"; low compact herb with opposite broad leaves almost round and a short cusp at apex, crisped and corrugated, dark green with purplish-carmine veining edged pink and white. *p. 82, 84*

ALTHAEA: see Alcea, Hibiscus

ALYXIA *Apocynaceae* **S3LBD**
ruscifolia (Australia: No. S. Wales, Queensland), "Sea-box"; tall evergreen shrub to 2m, with small 2-3cm oval leaves glossy green, with margins turned under, and set in whorls; small white flowers with 5 windmill petals, in terminal clusters, followed by orange berries. *p. 136*

AMARANTHUS *Amaranthaceae* **S2LBM**
"atrosanguineus"; slender stems with the small leaves blood-red and red flower clusters covered with silky, white scales. *p. 82*
caudatus (South Asia), "Love-lies-bleeding"; stout plant with long, ovate green leaves and showy, red, nodding, tail-like panicles. *p. 82*
caudatus albiflorus (Tropics), "Tassel flower"; robust magnificent annual bush with spreading branches 1 to 2m high; large herbaceous, lax, ovate leaves, and terminal inflorescence of long pendulous, slender spikes, dense with tiny white or greenish flowers, without petals; very striking. *p. 81*
hypochondriacus (Trop. America), "Princess feather"; tall, glabrous plant to $1\frac{1}{2}$m tall, with lanceolate leaves purplish green to purple; flowers deep crimson, in densely packed erect spikes. *p. 81*
paniculatus (Trop. America); widely planted summer-blooming annual to $1\frac{1}{2}$m high, usually hairy, with long-ovate leaves; the inflorescence erect, with branched spikes, dark crimson or red. *Tropical.* *p. 81*

paniculatus cruentus (Tropics), "Prince's feather"; magnificent large bush 1-2m high, with dense foliage, and the plumy inflorescence with side branchlets spreading and nodding, rich blood-red; photographed on the Greek island of Rhodes. *Tropical.* *p. 81*

tricolor (gangeticus) (E. Indies), "Joseph's coat"; vigorous, erect plant with ovate, pointed leaves brilliantly colored in shades of red, green and yellow; especially the summer growth. *Tropical.* *p. 82, 320A**

tricolor 'Early Splendor'; Japanese cultivar, spectacular with its erect branches densely clothed by long ribbon-like pendant or recurving, waxy leaves brilliantly colored bright crimson, the older leaves darker to bronzy green; most showy during the warm summer season. *p. 84*

x AMARCRINUM *Amaryllidaceae* **I2LBMd**

memoria-corsii (Amaryllis belladonna or Brunsvigia rosea x Crinum moorei); this intergeneric hybrid was originally made as x Crindonna corsii, with better blooms than A. belladonna; very pretty, pink, erect funnelform, somewhat fragrant flowers with recurving segments, borne in clusters on 1m stems. *p. 104, 107*

AMARYLLIS *Amaryllidaceae* **I2LBMd**

belladonna (Brunsvigia rosea) (So. Africa), the "Cape belladonna" or "Belladonna lily", the "true" Amaryllis; a bulbous plant also known as "Naked lady" because the lovely trumpet-shaped, lily-like clear rosy-pink fragrant flowers, 10cm long, appear in clusters, on solid, reddish 60cm stalks, bare and ahead of the new strap-like leaves, in South Africa before the rains from February to April; in the Northern hemisphere in August; forming clumps. *Subtropic.* *p. 104, 105*

forgetii (Perú); small bulb with several light green leaves to 50cm long, with or soon after flowers appear; tall 50cm stalk bearing crimson-red flowers with green base about 15cm across, the segments slender pointed and with greenish white bands down center. *p. 104*

AMARYLLIS: see also Hippeastrum

AMASONIA *Verbenaceae* **S3LFM**

calycina (punicea hort.) (Guyana); subshrub with scattered oblong, toothed leaves 15-30cm long; flowers with colored bell-shaped calyx and long corolla tube, sulphur-yellow in nodding purple-hairy racemes, bracts red. *p. 2118*

AMBLOSTOMA *Orchidaceae* **S3OFW**

cernuum (tridactylum) (Brazil); epiphyte with spindle-like pseudobulbs to 30cm long, carrying a few narrow leaves; long, arching inflorescence with numerous small ½cm creamy or greenish-white flowers. (Summer). *p. 1660*

AMBROSINA *Araceae* **S3HBM**

bassii (Corsica, Sardinia); tuberous perennial herb about 10cm high, with stalked, broad-ovate fleshy brown leaves covered with thin pubescence; curious inflorescence, with a boat-shaped spathe 2cm long prolonged into a curving tail; the spadix tongue-shaped, male flowers on one side, the one female on the other, in separate compartments of the spathe; half-hardy. *p. 164*

AMHERSTIA *Leguminosae* **S23LBM**

nobilis (Burma, India), "Queen of flowering trees"; one of the showiest, most striking tropical trees when in flower; 10-20m high, with dark green pinnate leaves, unfolding brownish-pink from drooping clusters. Inflorescence in graceful racemes 60-90cm long, pendulous from every branch, with 20cm flowers, with bracts, stalks, sepals and smaller petals vermilion red, the larger petals red with white base and tipped with yellow; long protruding anthers red also. *Tropical.* *p. 1363, 1370, 1371*

AMICIA *Leguminosae* **S3LBD**

zygomeris (Mexico); woody plant 2½m high, pinnate leaves, small yellow flowers with purple splashes. *p. 1371*

AMMOCHARIS *Amaryllidaceae* **I2LBMd**

falcata (Cybistetes longifolia) (So. Africa); bulbous plant 30cm high, with long strapshaped leaves, the inflorescence on a flat stalk with umbels of rosy-red, fragrant flowers, their reflexed segments spreading and clawed. *p. 118*

AMOMUM *Zingiberaceae* ***S1LFM**

cardamomum (Java), "Cardamon"; perennial herb with creeping rootstock, and clustering leafy stems which can attain 3m, but usually grown as a durable foliage plant 60cm high; linear-lanceolate, leathery leaves deep dull green, and finely hairy, giving off when rubbed, a spicy aroma; yellow flowers in cone like spikes beneath the foliage; produces cardamon seeds. *Tropical.* *p. 2133, 2142*

AMOMUM: see also Nicolaia

AMORPHA *Leguminosae* **I2LBD**

fruticosa (S. United States), "False indigo"; shrub 1-2m high; pinnate leaves bristle-tipped; 1cm flowers purplish blue with yellow anthers, in spikes 15cm long. *p. 1371*

AMORPHOPHALLUS *Araceae* **S3LFMd**

abyssinicum (Ethiopia); handsome tuberous plant with showy spathe 22cm long and 15cm across, dark purple with flaring limb, cupped base and purple spadix; large dissected leaf after blooming. *p. 163*

bulbifer (India, Afghanistan), "Devil's tongue"; tuberous plant with inflorescence on 30cm stalk marked brown, spadix green and pink; spathe green with rose to red outside, yellow-green within; segmented leaves. *Tropical.* *p. 182*

bulbifer marmoratus (Bengal, N. E. Himalayas); inflorescence without leaves on erect marmorated, fleshy stalks; the greenish-purple, spotted spathe coiled around the thick spadix, resembling a charging cobra. *p. 184*

campanulatus (E. Indies, New Guinea); a giant aroid with tuber 25cm thick, dark green solitary lobed leaf pinnately cut; inflorescence with ovate spathe 20 x 25cm, fleshy and funnel-shaped below, green spotted white, purple inside. *Tropical.* *p. 155, 163, 303*

corrugatus (Thailand); showy spathe green with greenish-white spots and purplish margin, whitish inside, 8-10cm wide, the short spadix with female portion purple, the corrugated appendix ochre-yellow; solitary dissected leaf greenish with brown blotches, segments to 15cm long; stalk to 60cm, from 5cm tuber. *Tropical.* *p. 163*

eichleri (Trop. W. Africa); tuberous plant with green leafstalk bearing trisected leaf; inflorescence with oblique cup-shaped spathe 8-10cm long, green outside, purple in tube, margin crisped; rosy, tapering spadix. *p. 162, 163*

hewittii (Borneo); handsome, waxy spathe unfurling from a tubular base, purple inside; outside greenish, spotted with gray-green around lower part; bold spire-like whitish spadix; from the tuber the large dissected leaf on mottled stalk. *p. 163*

hildebrandtii (Madagascar, Africa, Trop. Asia); handsome dragon-lily with spathe unfurling into broad blade, white inside, greenish with purple spots outside, and long slender spiralling spadix; after bloom, a dissected leaf cut into narrow segments, arises from the tuber on a stalk handsomely marbled purple on light green. *Tropical.* *p. 163*

longituberosus (Thailand); spathe boat-shaped 8-10cm long, pale green marked with darker spots, cradling the shorter spadix with fertile, warted lower half, a smooth cone-like appendix in upper part; from the tuber 5-12cm long and 2-3cm diameter, a long stalk carrying the divided, solitary leaf 30-50cm across. *Tropical.* *p. 163*

maculatus (Equatorial Africa: Gabon); large tuberous rainforest aroid recently found by J. Bogner of Munich Botanic Garden; from large underground tuber rises the stout floral stalk with inflorescence reaching 2½m; the cupped and flaring spathe greenish to purplish brown, and a dark, erect spadix with spire-like purple appendix; the dissected leaf appearing after flowering. *p. 223*

putii (Thailand); small tuberous aroid with stiff-erect light green stalk 30cm long, carrying a boat-shaped whitish green spathe 30cm long, with club-like cylindrical yellow spadix inside; from the base unfolds a large dissected leaf. *p. 163*

rivieri (Hydrosme) (Indo-China), "Devil's tongue" or "Leopard palm"; curious tuberous plant with a 1m flower spike which carries the large reddish spadix and calla-like green and purple spathe, and with unpleasant odor; the foliage, appearing after flowering, is on a single, rose-marbled stalk with 3 palm-like branches bearing numerous elliptic segments. *p. 164, 181*

staudtii (Cameroon, Ivory Coast); small West African cormous plant with depressed-globular tuber 2cm dia; a short stalk carries the showy inflorescence; spathe 7cm long, cupped at base and flaring toward apex, red-purple inside throat, outside white; spadix 8cm long; foliage appears after flowering, umbrella-like and three-parted. *p. 148*

sylvaticus (Synantherias) (Bombay, So. India; Sri Lanka); tuberous herb, with compound palmate leaf on marbled stem; inflorescence a very long straw-colored spadix, and short, cupped spathe white inside, outside pinkish white, checkered green. *p. 294*

titanum (Sumatra); giant tuberous plant and a great curiosity with flowers on a 2m yellow spadix surrounded by the crisped 1m spathe purple inside, green outside and with disagreeable odor; 4½m leaves on 3m leaf stalk. *p. 181*

AMPELOPSIS *Vitaceae* **I1LFM**

aconitifolia (No. China, Mongolia); tendril-climbing shrub with thin stems, and fresh green leaves both sides, deeply dissected and divided leaflets to 8cm long; bluish to orange fruit. *p. 2125*

brevipedunculata (N. E. Asia); woody rambler with slender stems cordate-ovate leaves to 12cm long, with 3 coarsely toothed lobes; clusters of fruit opposite leaf axils, lilac becoming blue. *p. 2125*

brevipedunculata elegans (heterophylla) (Manchuria, Japan), "Colored grape-leaf"; attractive climber with blood-red, hairy branches and thin forking vines, variable leaves simple, 3-lobed or 5-lobed, bluish-green and prettily variegated with milky-green, creamy-white and rose. *p. 2120, 2124*

AMPELOPSIS: see also PARTHENOCISSUS

AMPHIBLEMMA *Melastomataceae* **S3LFM**
cymosum (Sierra Leone); showy shrub with large bristly, heart-shaped, rich satiny green leaves with network of depressed veins, pale beneath, tinted red; flowers bright carmine-red. *p. 1553, 1554*

AMYDRIUM *Araceae* **S3LFM**
humile (Malaysia, Indonesia); small creeping or climbing tropical plant, with cordate green leaves 5-7cm long and 3-5cm wide, on 4-7cm petioles; the inflorescence on 3-5cm stalk with 1½-2cm white spathe and sessile 1½cm spadix with hermaphrodite naked flowers. *p. 207*
medium (Epipremnopsis media in hort.) (Borneo); wiry tree climber with palmately 3-lobed parchment-like leaves deep green with faint mottling of yellow-green on puckered surface. Baileya (March 1962) puts this under Epipremnum medium. *p. 206*

AMYDRIUM: see also Epipremnum

AMYGDALUS: see Prunus

ANACAMPSEROS *Portulacaceae* **I2LBD**
albissima (Cape Prov., Namibia); small succulent herb with slender thread-like column spirally leafy with tiny silvery-white, rounded scale-like leaves appressed close to stem; flowers white. *p. 1960*
alstonii (Namibia, Bushmanland); small succulent with turnip-shaped root-stock, flattened above and 6cm dia., numerous stems 2-3cm long, 2mm thick; tiny appressed leaves in 5 rows concealed by the silvery, pointed scales; white flowers 3cm across. *p. 1959, 1962*
baeseckei (Namibia); small branching succulent 5cm high with compressed grayish, short, fleshy leaves, with white and silky hairs; flowers red edged white. *p. 1960*
buderiana (Cape Province), "Silver worms"; queer, fascinating little succulent branching with prostrate, twisting worm-like stems spirally covered with minute leaves, but hidden by silvery white membraneous stipules; flowers greenish-white. *p. 1961*
filamentosa (So. Africa: Karroo); small succulent with tuberous root, slowly creeping, dense with sessile thick, ovate leaves, and covered with fine hairs, and even longer white filaments in the axils; flowers a lovely rosy-purple. *p. 1961*
fissa (Transvaal); rosette-like succulent with flattened tuberous roots 4cm dia., numerous stems 3mm at base, covered with tiny spiralled leaves and silvery stipules (scales). *p. 1959*
meyeri (Cape Prov.: Namaqualand); small mat-forming succulent with thickened stem and erect branches worm-like covered closely with shingle-like, silver-buff leaves rounded at apex. *p. 1960*
papyracea (So. Africa: Great Karroo; Namibia); queer worm-like succulent, with thick tuberous root; short stems with many prostrate branches 5-6cm long, 8-10mm thick; leaves arranged spirally, hidden by the appressed white scales; greenish-white flowers. *p. 1959*
rufescens (arachnoides grandiflora) (So. Africa) "Love plant"; small clustering succulent with bulblike root and spiral rosettes of thick ovate-pointed leaves, green above, purplish-brown beneath, and white cobwebs in the axils; flowers deep pink, opening only in the sun. *p. 1959, 1960, 1961*

ANACARDIUM *Anacardiaceae* **S2LBD**
occidentale (West Indies), the "Cashew-nut tree"; evergreen spreading tree to 12m high, with obovate leathery leaves 20cm long; numerous small fragrant flowers yellowish-pink; the fruit a kidney-shaped nut borne on a pearshaped yellow or red fleshy receptacle. Juice from shell around seed can burn skin. *Tropical.* *p. 132*

ANACLANTHE *Iridaceae* **S2LFM**
plicata (So. Africa); clustering perennial 15cm high with lanceolate leaves distinctly plaited; flowers pale violet-blue with blue anthers and yellow stigma, and fragrant with clove-carnation scent; May-June blooming. *p. 1324*

ANACYCLUS *Compositae* **I2LBD**
depressus (Morocco); summer-flowering perennial herb with usually prostrate stems with lacy, pinnately cut leaves and terminal flower heads to 5cm across, with ray flowers dark-red on back, white above. *p. 810*
officinarum (So. Europe); annual to 25cm high, with leaves bipinnatisect into linear segments; 2½cm heads with ray florets white marked purple beneath. *p. 810*

ANADENDRUM *Araceae* **S2HFM**
microstachyum (Sumatra, Sarawak); tropical climber forming aerial roots; the internodes along the stem 5-8cm apart; ovate leaves 8 to 15cm long, the corrugated surface dark green; flaring spathe 7-9cm long, green outside, inside greenish white; cylindric yellowish, bisexual spadix. *p. 182*

ANANAS *Bromeliaceae* **S3HBM**
ananasoides (Brazil: Pará to Mato Grosso); diminutive ornamental offset-forming pineapple with narrow recurved, concave leaves 1cm wide with marginal hookspines and an erect slender, leafy stalk bearing an aggregate fruit to 15cm long, edible but not of a delicious flavor. *p. 532, 533*
ananassoides var. nanus (Venezuela, Brazil, Paraguay); a miniature terrestrial species from semi-arid regions; very attractive rosette of recurving, spiny leaves 2½cm wide, bright green; a stalk with reddish bracts carries the few-flowered inflorescence with small, colorful reddish fruit less than 10cm dia., and crowned by another leafy rosette; fruit edible but very seedy. *p. 533*
bracteatus (So. Brazil), "Red pineapple"; large terrestrial rosette with flattened leathery leaves coppery green with spines larger and more widely spaced than comosus; produces large brown edible fruit; flowers lavender. *Tropical.* *p. 530, 532*
bracteatus 'Striatus' (variegatus); open rosette of relatively broad colorful leaves predominantly cream-yellow with coppery-green center; marginal spines red. *Tropical.* *p. 512A, 530, 532*
comosus (sativus) (Bahia, Mato Grosso), "Pineapple"; large formal terrestrial rosette of stiff, tapering and spiny-edged leaves grayish to bronze-green, gracefully arching; violet flowers borne in dense heads with tufts of leaves, producing the edible fleshy fruit to 30 cm long. *p. 512, 531, 532*
comosus 'Nanus', "Dwarf pineapple"; a miniature form ideally suited for pots as everything is smaller in proportion, the leaves are shorter, with small spines, and the fruit is diminutive and cute. *p. 533*
comosus 'Porteanus' (comosus hyb.), "Golden rocket"; large and stiff rosette with olive green leaves acquiring a reddish color, and having a broad creamy-yellow center band on upper surface. *Tropical.* *p. 531*
comosus 'Smooth Cayenne variegated'; beautiful show plant; an elegant rosette of broad recurving leaves banded lengthwise with creamy-yellow and tinted rose, the margins smooth and spineless; the luscious golden yellow to red-brown fruit is topped in time by another dense rosette of variegated leaves. The 'Smooth Cayenne' was brought from Guyana to Hawaii in 1886 where it developed the big plantations. *p. 533, 561*
comosus 'Variegatus', "Variegated pineapple"; beautiful variety with the channeled leaves having broad ivory bands along the margin and red spines; center of rosette tinted rosy-red. *p. 15*, 19*, 512, 531, 532*
erectifolius (lucidus) (Brazil), "Mexican pineapple"; small wild pineapple, a rosette of thick-fleshy, concave, glossy green leaves with smooth edges, to 50cm long and 4cm wide, grooved and glaucous gray beneath; golden yellow fruit, sometimes eaten. (Bromel. Bull. 1958). *p. 533*
nanus (Brazil), "Dwarf pineapple"; miniature species to 30cm high, with recurved, serrate leaves; a slender stalk carries few-flowered small fruit less than 15cm in size, topped by leafy crown. Grown for cultivation in pots indoors. *Tropical.* *p. 532*

ANAPHYLLUM *Araceae* **S3LFM**
beddomei (South India); from creeping rhizome, carried on slender petioles 70-75cm long, the hastate to tri-parted glossy green leaves 18-20cm across; floral stalk about 35cm long, with green ovate-oblong spathe covering the spadix. *p. 164*

ANCHOMANES *Araceae* **S3LFM**
abbreviatus (East Africa); tropical aroid with tuberous rhizome from which rises a robust brownish, spiny stalk to 35cm long, topped by a cylindric spadix and a hood-like spathe 8cm long, reddish outside, the base inside purple; the foliage on spiny petiole 50-80cm long, carrying a several times divided leaf, the lobes truncate (as if cut off across end). *p. 164, 182*
difformis (Trop. Africa), large aroid with tuberous rhizome and solitary 1m pinnatisect leaf on spiny petiole, green with purple spots, 1-1½m long; fleshy spathe 15-30cm brownish, purple spotted black inside, and pale, cupped spadix on short stalk. *Tropical.* *p. 162, 164*
nigritianus (Equatorial Africa: Gabon, So. Nigeria); rare tropical aroid with tuberous root stock, sending up a giant 35-45cm hooded, fleshy, purple spathe on spiny 1½m stalk, and a separate even taller, marbled petiole 2m or more high, carrying a solitary 3-parted leaf again pinnately dissected. *p. 164*
welwitschii (Trop. West Africa); tuberous aroid from savannah country sending up a short-stalked fleshy, yellow-green spathe, shielding the stiff-erect club-shaped spadix, the clasping basis of the spathe covered with spines; later the tall foliage appears, on long fleshy stalk covered with tubercles, the leaf divided into 3 sections, each bipinnately cut into broad angled segments tipped with sharp points. *Tropical.* *p. 164*

ANCHUSA *Boraginaceae* **I2LBD**
azurea (E. Mediterranean to Caucasus), "Summer forget-me-not"; hairy perennial to 1½m, with alternate lanceolate leaves to 45cm long in the lower ones; the inflorescence on erect leafy stem with funnel-shaped flowers bright blue, 2cm across, in summer-autumn; fairly hardy. *p. 509*

ANCISTRORHYNCHUS *Orchidaceae* **S3OFM**
capitatus (Trop. Africa: Uganda); curious plant found in the Budongo forest; flat fan of leaves each 25cm long; inflorescence near base, in dense rounded clusters about 4cm across; flowers cream-colored with cream center. *p. 1653*

ANDROCYMBIUM *Liliaceae* **S3LBDd**
melanthioides (Namibia); small bulbous plant with few narrow leaves; small flowers in clusters in axils of subtended large bracts 8cm long, these white with green veins, and which form the attractive feature of this plant. *p. 1424*

ANDROMEDA: see Pieris

ANDROSACE *Primulaceae* **S3LBM**

lanuginosa (Himalayas); low prostrate, trailing perennial covered with silky-white hairs, ovate leaves 2cm long; 1cm flowers in dense clusters, rose-colored; resembling primrose; the var. leichtlinii has white flowers with crimson eye. *p. 1962*

ANDRYALA *Compositae* **C2LBD**

pinnatifida (Spain: Canary Islands); herbaceous perennial from Tenerife, with succulent stems fuzzy with white hair and with milky sap, the somewhat pubescent leaves irregularly lobed and divided; yellow daisy-like flower heads. *Subtropic.* *p. 820*

ANEILEMA *Commelinaceae* **I2LBD**

hockii (Transvaal); annual herb 30-40cm high, with small tricornered fleshy leaves, and large lilac flowers consisting of two broad lower petals and one narrow dorsal. *p. 786*

ANEIMIA *Schizaeaceae (Filices)* **S3HFM**

flexuosa (tomentosa) (Tropical America); small "Flowering fern" with long 20cm hairy stalks bearing light green bipinnate fronds, with sterile portion rather triangular in outline, 18-30cm long, curious in this genus with the fertile, spore-bearing spikes, originating from base of leafy portion, lacking expanded leaves and resembling a slender spire of flowers. *p. 1079*

phyllitidis (Trop. America: Cuba, Mexico, etc.); known as "Flowering fern"; the barren pinnate section 10-30cm long, with firm, ovate leaflets 2½-15cm, topped by a dense fertile panicle. *p. 1084*

rotundifolia (Brazil), a "Flowering fern", so-called because the fruiting panicle or portion of leaf bearing the spores is devoid of expanded leaf and looks like an inflorescence, while the sterile sections of the frond which consists of pairs of oval pinnae along the rachis, look like normal leaves; the barren portion roots at tip. *p. 1084*

ANEMARRHENA *Liliaceae* **I2LBD**

asphodeloides (C. China, Japan); creeping rhizome with glabrous grass-like leaves 38-45cm long; finely nerved; inflorescence a long raceme to 1m with small 1cm rosy-purple flowers of linear segments, greenish to brownish keeled. *p. 1460*

ANEMONE *Ranunculaceae* **I2LBMd**

blanda 'Blue Star'; with ageratum-blue flowers, one of the many color varieties of A. blanda from Greece and the Taurus Mts. in Asia Minor, a small herb to 15cm high with tuberous rhizome, with compound and cut leaves and solitary flowers 5cm across. *p. 1985*

coronaria (So. Europe to Cent. Asia), "Lily of the fields"; attractive perennial with tuberous roots, finely divided leaves both basal and sessile along the erect, hairy stalk which bears the large, solitary poppy-like, 6cm flowers, the showy sepals in combinations of red, blue, yellow, white; in spring. *Subtropic.* *p. 1984, 1985*

coronaria 'De Caen', a "Poppy anemone"; florists anemone with single flowers consisting of large round segments, in colors from white to pink, red, purple to deep blue; center black. *Subtropic.* *p. 1983*

japonica (Japan, China), "Japanese anemone"; popular garden perennial with fibrous roots, stout, branching plant 75cm high with trilobed, compound leaves, 5-8cm flowers mauve with carmine base, hairy outside, in late summer. This may be of garden origin, coming in many colorforms from white to rose, red, and purple, derived from the species hupehensis. *p. 1985*

narcissiflora (Mts. of Europe); perennial 20-60cm high with 3-5-parted, deeply toothed leaves, with 2½cm white flowers suggesting narcissus in many-flowered umbels; summer. (h) *p. 1985*

pulsatilla (Europe, incl. England); free-flowering perennial 30cm high, with black fibrous rootstock, with leaves dissected like a feather and silky-hairy; solitary bell-shaped flowers blue to purple, to 6cm across and yellow stamens, in spring. The cultivar 'Mrs. Beveridge' is a violet-blue sport, very free-blooming. *p. 1985*

'St. Brigid semi-double'; a popular strain of florists' tuberous-rooted "Poppy-anemones" for indoor flowering in late winter and spring; hybrid derived from coronaria, fulgens, and hortensis; colorful flowers with several rows of petals in shades of brilliant red, rose, purple, violet, and white; not hardy. *p. 1984*

ANEMOPAEGMA *Bignoniaceae* **S3LBM**

chamberlaynii (Brazil); vigorous climbing tropical shrub with leaves of 2 leaflets to 16cm long, and sometimes a terminal tendril; flowers funnel-form 6-8cm long, in pendant clusters, the tube constricted near base, bright yellow in throat with purple or white. *Tropical.* *p. 501*

subunculata (Brazil); woody tropical climber with long-stalked leaves consisting of two firm, leathery, lanceolate leaflets about 15cm long, the surface matte-green and quilted; tubular white flowers in clusters at leaf axils, 5-6cm long; photo taken in Jardim Botanico, Rio de Janeiro. *p. 501*

ANGELONIA *Scrophulariaceae* **I1LBM**

gardneri (Brazil); subshrubby, hairy perennial to 1 m high, with lanceolate, toothed leaves, and tall racemes with showy, 2-lipped tubular flowers purple with white center, dotted with red; upper lip 2-lobed, lower 3-lobed. *Tropical.* *p. 2051*

grandiflora (salicariaefolia), (No. South America); perennial subshrub to 50cm, sticky-hairy, with linear leaves; two-lipped 2cm tubular blue flowers in spring. *p. 2049*

salicariaefolia (Venezuela); perennial herb with opposite, lanceolate, toothed, light green, sticky leaves, and a leafy terminal raceme with showy, bilabiate, violet-blue flowers having a pale blue lip, blooming normally in August. *p. 2052*

ANGIOPTERIS *Marattiaceae (Filices)* **S3LFM**

evecta (Japan to Australia and Madagascar), "Mules-foot fern"; fleshy, robust fern from swampy places, developing a stout stem, the bipinnate leaves on swollen stalk may grow to 5 m long, the linear-oblong pinnae are succulent, dark green, and finely toothed. *Humid-subtropic.* *p. 1081*

ANGRAECUM *Orchidaceae* **S3OFM**

bidens (West Africa); pendant vandaceous stems with ranks of 5-8cm lobed leaves; the spurred flowers small, yellowish flesh-pink, almost transparent, in short, drooping 10-15cm racemes. *p. 1658*

bilobum (Zanzibar to So. Africa); long pendant racemes of white flowers flushed rosy pink, and long orange spur. *p. 1657*

capense (Mystacidium) (S. E. Africa); attractive small, but very floriferous epiphyte with short stem, oblong leaves 5-8cm long, and loose, pendant racemes of ivory-white flowers with curving, tubular, thread-like spur; summer. (I) *p. 1658*

comorense (Comores Isl.); vandaceous plant with woody stem and leathery leaves, with pendant racemes of attractive flowers of greenish lemon sepals and petals, and large white lip, and long thread-like spur. *p. 1659*

eburneum (Madagascar); epiphyte with very thick leaves on stems to 1 m high; flowers upside-down on stout spike, sepals and petals green, the broad lip ivory-white with green spur, (Dec. -March). *Tropical.* *p. 1658*

eichlerianum (African West Coast); epiphyte with scandent stems developing aerial clinging roots, thick light green leaves; often waxy, 8 cm flowers with yellow-green sepals and petals, white lip green near base and greenish spur, (June-Sept.). *Tropical.* *p. 1658*

falcatum: see NEOFINETIA falcata

giryamae (Kenya, Tanzania, Zanzibar), the biggest epiphytic orchid in Africa; stout woody stem to 1m high, with several pairs of thick-leathery, elliptical leaves 30-50cm long, and with aerial roots; inflorescence of pendant racemes of large sweetly scented 6-8cm pale green fleshy flowers with lip glistening white, and extended back into a spur. *p. 1659*

hillebrandii (Comoro Isl.); miniature epiphyte with strap-shaped leaves unequally two-lobed at apex; tiny orange-yellow flowers. *p. 1657*

infundibulare (Uganda, Nigeria, Cameroun); beautiful semi-terrestrial with long climbing stems and aerial roots, set with alternating leaves notched at apex; flowers of heavy substance and very large, 15cm down front, with sepals and petals pale green, lip snow-white, and having a rich hyacinth fragrance. *p. 1657*

longicalcar; bold epiphyte with fleshy leaves arranged fan-like on erect stem; flowers white, with very long greenish tail. *p. 1657*

magdalenae (Madagascar); choice and most beautiful small epiphyte; fan-shaped leaves with large, waxy white flowers having wide segments, and short spur (summer). *p. 1660*

ramosum (germinyanum) (Madagascar); elongate stem to 50cm, rigidly leathery leaves closely arranged; solitary, fragrant, waxy flowers white, to 10cm long, usually inverted; long-lasting (spring). *p. 1657*

sesquipedale (Madagascar), "Star of Bethlehem"; epiphyte with stems to 1 m, densely 2-ranked leaves; thick-fleshy flowers to 18 cm dia., ivory-white, with long spur; largest in the genus, (Nov.-March). *Tropical.* *p. 1657, 1658*

smithii (Microcoelia) (Tanzania); leafless epiphyte with small clusters of minute white flowers. *p. 1657*

veitchii (sesquipedale x eburneum); elegant plant; large flowers ivory-white with long greenish spur, in erect racemes. *p. 1657*

ANGRAECUM: see also Mystacidium

ANGULOA *Orchidaceae* **I3HNM**

clowesii (Andes of Colombia), "Cradle orchid"; magnificent terrestrial growing on damp rocks; the pseudobulbs bearing 2 to 4 plaited leaves; beautiful cup-shaped fleshy, golden-yellow flowers with whitish lip, to 8 cm long, very fragrant. *Subtropic.* *p. 1655*

ruckeri (Colombia); smaller plant than clowesii, with plaited leaves and large fleshy, cupped flowers olive green with crimson spots inside; midlobe hairy, on 20cm stalks; (May-June). (I) *p. 1655*

virginalis (uniflora) (Colombia), "Cradle orchid" or "El Torito"; terrestrial of bold habit, with thin plaited leaves; the solitary, sub-globose, fleshy flowers not as large as clowesii, pure white spotted and flushed with pink. (Summer). (I) *p. 1655*

ANIGOZANTHOS *Amaryllidaceae* **I2LBDd**

flavidus (S. W. Australia), "Yellow kangaroo paw"; odd perennial herb with thick rootstock; smooth lanceolate leaves; the inflorescence 1-1½ m high, with large woolly flowers having a long bent tube yellowish green, tinged red, 4 cm long, and with blue petals. *Arid-subtropic.* *p. 102*

manglesii (Western Australia), known in Australia as "Kangaroo paw"; rosette of onion-like leaves with erect, striking inflorescence 1 m tall with red -hairy stem topped by racemes of yellowish-green, woolly 8 cm tubular flowers, red at calyx, with dark green lines, the lip reflexed and tipped blue. *Arid-subtropic.* *p. 102*

ANNONA *Annonaceae* **I-S3LBD**

cherimola (Andes of Perú and Ecuador), the "Cherimoya", a custard apple; woody tree to 8m high, briefly deciduous with sappy branches and large, luxuriant, leathery leaves 25cm long, dull green with pale veins, velvety on back; fragrant fleshy flowers 3cm long, directly from woody branches, yellow or brown-tomentose outside, whitish with purple spot inside; followed by large green conical fruit, 12cm or more long, containing large black seed, the skin looking like overlapping scales or knobby warts; the flesh creamy white, tasting like custard or bananas, and is eaten with a spoon; ripening winter into spring. For best success flowers are hand-pollinated. Also known as "Fruit of the Incas". *p. 133*

muricata (West Indies), the "Soursop"; evergreen tropical fruit tree 6m high, widely planted and liked in Latin America; dark shiny green, leathery, obovate leaves 10-15cm long; large yellowish flowers with 6 fleshy petals spreading 5cm across; big ovoid or irregular oblong, pendulous fruit is the largest of the annonas, 15-20cm long and weighing as much as 3 kilos, deep green and covered with short fleshy spines. The pulp is like white cotton from which a pleasing drink, custard, or chilled sherbet is made in tropical America; in season June through November or longer. *p. 133*

squamosa (C. America, West Indies), "Sugar apple" or "Sweetsop"; tropical fruit tree to 6m high, partially deciduous with thin-leathery bluish-gray, soft oval leaves 15-20cm long; small greenish fleshy 2cm axillary flowers followed by ovoid, grayish-beige fruits 8cm long, covered with large prominent knobs, divisions falling apart much broken up by its separable sections (carpels), ripening in August to winter; the flesh is sweet, custard-like but very perishable. Greatly liked in markets from the West Indies to Rio de Janeiro. *Tropical.* *p. 133*

ANOECTOCHILUS *Orchidaceae* **S2HFM**

hispida (Sikkim Himalaya); small terrestrial with ornamental, narrow ovate, coppery leaves greenish in the center, overlaid with a pale network of veins; flowers not showy. (S) *p. 1661*

regalis (Sri Lanka), "Kingplant"; branching terrestrial with creeping stems, beautiful ovate 5cm velvety leaves bronzy-green, with network of shimmering golden-yellow veins; flowers greenish with white lip. (April-June). (S)*p. 1661*

roxburghii (Himalaya, Java), a "Golden jewel orchid"; dwarf terrestrial, with fleshy broad ovate leaves on succulent stem, beautifully reticulated in red over dark bronzy green blade with golden center; reddish flowers with white lip, on a spike, (Jan.-March). (S) *p. 15*, 1661*

sikkimensis (Sikkim Himalaya), dwarf "King of the forest"; terrestrial, with succulent stems and broad ovate, dark bronzy red leaves with velvety sheen, reticulated with a network of orange red veins. (S) *p. 1661*

ANOECTOCHILUS: see also Haemaria, Macodes

ANOMATHECA: see Lapeirousia

ANOPTERUS *Saxifragaceae* **C2LBM**

glandulosus (Tasmania), "Tasmanian laurel"; handsome evergreen shrub or small tree with alternate oblanceolate thick-leathery, serrate leaves to 20cm long, dark lustrous green; terminal racemes of waxy white flowers bell-shaped, larger than orange blossoms and often tinged pink. *p. 2042*

ANSELLIA *Orchidaceae* **S2-3HBD**

africana (Kenya, Uganda, Tanzania, Zaire to West Africa); strong growing, variable epiphyte with ribbed slightly swollen pseudobulbs to 60cm high, bearing linear leaves and an erect and rigid terminal panicle of long-lasting fleshy flowers, the spreading, linear sepals and petals about 2½cm long, yellow with cross bars of red-brown, lip bright yellow lined with brown (Winter). *Tropical.* *p. 1659*

gigantea (Natal, Mozambique, Rhodesia); similar to A. africana, with erect racemes of paler yellow flowers flecked with purplish-brown, the segments narrower; from cooler regions (Autumn-Winter). (I) *p. 1659*

nilotica (East Africa); in habit usually smaller than africana and with pendulous inflorescence, the brighter flowers yellow with chocolate flecks, golden lip marked red-brown in throat (Winter). *Tropical.* *p. 1659*

ANTHERICUM *Liliaceae* ***I2LFM**

comosum: see CHLOROPHYTUM comosum

liliago (So. Europe),"St. Bernard lily"; herb with fleshy roots; tufted basal leaves linear and channeled, to 45cm long; 60cm slender stalk with racemes of white flowers to 3cm across, spreading segments and curved style. *p. 1427*

ANTHOCLEISTA *Loganiaceae* **S2-3LFD**

macrophylla (Nigeria); small ornamental tropical tree of the rainforest, 3-6m high, with slender trunk topped by a cabbage-like rosette of spreading, broad oblanceolate leaves 60cm long, with corrugated blade and wavy margins. *p. 1516*

pulcherrima (Uganda); slender tree which I frequently found along the Kivu border of Zaire, with willowy stem to 8m high, crowned by a loose rosette of alternate long-oblanceolate leaves 60-90cm long in whorls, thin-leathery, dark green, and with wavy margins. *p. 1516*

ANTHURIUM *Araceae* **S3HNW**

acaule (W. Indies); loose rosette of short-stalked, oblanceolate leaves 60cm long, thick, leathery, dark green; linear spathe reddish inside. *p. 174*

aemulum (heptophyllum) (Mexico to Costa Rica); climber in Central American forests with soft, membranous leaves palmately compound, glossy green and depressed veins; spathe and spadix green. *p. 173*

affine (So. Brazil, Bolivia, Paraguay); large rosette of broad leathery leaves with prominent veins and crenulated margin; similar to hookeri; flaccid, long pendulous flower stems, large violet spadix. *p. 177*

andicola (huegelii) (Jamaica); in the California nursery trade as A. huegelii; sturdy selfheader with arrow-shaped, thick-leathery, highly glossy green leaves with reddish midrib, sinus partly naked, the network of lateral veins depressed; ribs red beneath; red petiole with top highly channeled and dotted yellow-green, red geniculum; leathery green lanceolate spathe and thick purple spadix. *p. 177*

andraeanum (S. W. Colombia, No. Ecuador); "Tailflower" or "Cresta de gallo" in Ecuador; erect plant with long-lobed, heart-shaped, green leaves; the showy, cordate spathe, 10-12 cm long, waxy, coral red, puckered; the pendant spadix tipped yellow with white band marking the zone where stigmas are receptive. *Humid-tropical.* *p. 21**

andraeanum album; round cordate, quilted, waxy-white spathe; spadix dipping, with base white, center area purplish-rose and tip yellow; glossy leaves. *Humid-Tropical.* *p. 21**

andraeanum 'Guatmala' (x cultorum); large-flowered cultivar from Guatemala and grown in Germany under the name spelled 'Guatmala', very popular as a potplant of compact habit, and as a cut flower because of its elegant form, broad crimson-red, glossy and firm spathe of medium size, pendant small yellow spadix, and continuous production of blooms. Very suitable for hydroculture. *Humid-tropical.* *p 179*

andraeanum rubrum (Colombia), "Wax flower"; a striking color form with large, waxy, quilted spathe of dark crimson; spadix white, yellow at tip. *Humid-tropical.* *p. 160A, 165*

angustisectum (Colombia); climber from moist forests in Cauca; leaves pendant and palmately lobed into 5 lanceolate segments with depressed veins. *p. 170*

'Anitas' (andraeanum x antrophyoides): an elegant plant with truncate-ovate, leathery green leaves and cupped, rose-colored spathe with erect spadix. *p. 167*

antrophyoides (Colombia); long, elliptic, leathery leaves with depressed, parallel veins; white spathe and spadix; blooms profusely year around. *p. 167*

'Anturio Negro': see A. watermaliense and A. 'Negrito'

araliifolium (Mato Grosso); short stem bears hard ivy-shaped leaves 20cm dia.; narrow green spathe. *p. 179*

arisaemoides (Ecuador); short-stemmed plant, with 30-40cm reddish, wiry petioles topped by tripartite leaves; the leathery leaflets 14-16cm long, green and with ribs depressed; small spathe greenish, to 8cm long. *p. 174*

bakeri (Costa Rica); on short stem, strap-like, leathery, elliptic, lanceolate leaves, deep green, with stout midrib; spathe and spadix green. *p. 160A, 172, 175*

bellum (So. Brazil); sturdy compact rosette of erect, lanceolate, fleshy leaves 14-27cm long, 5-8cm wide, glossy deep green, on short stiff, tri-cornered petiole; floral stalk reddish, 34cm long, with 7cm red spadix and small reddish-green spathe. *p. 180*

berriozabelense (Guatemala); glaucous plant with hard, sagittate leaves odd because the long basal lobes are curiously crossed. *p. 176*

bogotense (Colombia); epiphytic and terrestrial plant with fresh-green, sagittate leaves with basal lobes exceptionally large around the wide sinus; spathe yellowish, spadix reddish. *p. 178*

x bullatum (subsignatum x crystallinum); glossy green, corrugated leaf similar to subsignatum but terminal lobe much broader in relation to basal lobes. *p. 178*

calense (Colombia); climber with long sagittate, papery leaves with round basal lobes around wide sinus, fresh-green; spathe pale green. *p. 178*

caribaeum (W. Indies); robust, decorative plant; leathery-waxy, sagittate, bluish-green leaves with raised, pale-green veins, on long channeled petiole; narrow, green spathe. *p. 170*

caucanum (Colombia, Perú); stiff, decorative plant with leaves almost spoonshaped, glossy dark green with pale veins, on long, channeled petioles; spathe brown becoming green. *p. 170*

caucanum maximum (Colombia); terrestrial plant stiff-upright; glossy green, quilted leaves almost round, with interesting pattern of depressed veins. *p. 166*

x chelseaense (andraeanum x veitchii); waxy, carmine spathe widely cordate and pointed; spadix white to green; leaves ovate. *p. 167*

clarinervium (Mexico), "Hoja de Corazon"; a dwarf, ornamental species found growing in the clay of the Chiapas mist forest; dark green, velvety, heartshaped leaves with clear, silvery-gray veins; similar to A. crystallinum, but more diminutive, with leaves 12-20cm long; spathe reddish-green. *p. 169*

clavigerum (Colombia, Perú); giant climbing plant with palmately compound leaves, the broad segments pinnately parted and lobed again; very long spadix; purple fruit. *p. 168, 171*

clidemioides (Costa Rica); tropical climbing plant with rough, semi-woody stems, and internodes 6-10cm apart; the dark green leaves very decorative, of leathery texture, 6-8cm long, cordate in outline and very corrugated with ribs depressed, light green spathe 4cm long. *p. 176*

comtum (So. Brazil); small rosette of leathery, short-stalked, dark green, lanceolate leaves; narrow rose spathe and purple spadix. *p. 174*

cordatum (So. Brazil); beautiful species from the Organ Mts. with broadly sagittate leaf with wide sinus, olive-green, and pale green areas along ribs; channeled petiole. Spathe green, to 20cm long, spadix brownish-green. *p. 169*

coriaceum (So. Brazil, Argentina); creeping on rocks; upright standing, leathery, glossy gray-green, long oblanceolate leaves to 1m on short stiff stalks; spathe green, reddish inside. *Subtropic.* *p. 178*

corrugatum (papilionense in horticulture) (Colombia); ornamental leaf plant from Putumayo, the sagittate foliage light green, leathery, corrugated, with pointed basal lobes; green or greenish-white spathe; slender spadix yellowish or white. *Tropical.* *p. 171*

crassinervium (Venezuela, Panama); bold rosette with fleshy shining-green, elliptic leaves to 1m long; thick stalk 3-ridged beneath. *p. 177*

crispimarginatum (Pernambuco); rosette-type robust plant with long oblanceolate leathery leaves 60cm long, glossy green and with very wavy margins; unattractive small spathe on slender stalk. *p. 177*

crystallinum (Colombia, Perú), "Crystal anthurium"; strikingly beautiful tropical foliage plant; from the central crown with thick-fleshy roots rise wiry petioles, circular in cross-section, carrying the large decorative, heart-shaped, velvety leaves of stiff-leathery texture, glistening emerald green with contrasting network of white veins, 25 to 45 cm long, with basal lobes overlapping, acutely angled at the thickened juncture; long-stalked inflorescence with slender yellowish-green spadix and linear green spathe, followed by red-purple berries. *Humid-tropical.* *p. 19*, 169*

crystallinum illustre; a form with large, velvety, olive-green leaves largely variegated yellow and white. *p. 169*

cubense (W. Indies); bold rosette with big, obovate, short-stalked, leathery leaves and wavy margin. *p. 174*

denudatum (Colombia); moist forest plant with soft, glossy green, hastate-trilobed leaves with sunken veins, the basal lobes spreading widely; spathe brownish-green. *p. 176*

digitatum (Venezuela); climber with palmately-compound, dark green leaves; stalked segments obovate, and quite leathery; spathe green and purple, spadix purple. *p. 173*

dussii (West Indies: Guadeloupe); large, showy tropical species with slowly elongating stem; the broad, quilted leaves bright green, 35 cm long and with wide sinus; spadix dark purple, subtended by lanceolate green spathe 12 cm long. *p. 180*

eminens (Bolivia); skeleton-like radial leaf palmately compound with narrow, strap-like, leathery segments. *p. 176*

'Evans' huegelii'; large plant with leathery, elongate leaves on strong petioles, the midrib raised, the lateral veins depressed. *p. 168*

x ferrierense (andraeanum x ornatum), "Oilcloth flower"; robust climber with lobed, heart-shaped leaves; ovate-cordate, rosy spathe waxy-smooth, carried upright, and erect spadix white to rose; willing bloomer. *p. 165*

fissum (W. Indies: Martinique) slowly creeping plant with stem to 1m long, large 30 cm leaves thick leathery, deeply lobed, and divided almost to base, lobes obovate pointed, sinus wide; inflorescence with slender, brownish spadix and long linear green 15 cm spathe. Synonym of palmatum. *p. 162*

forgetii (Colombia); dwarf plant related to crystallinum but smaller, and leaves are peltate; olive-green and velvety with silver veins. *p. 169*

fortunatum (elegans) (Colombia: Rio Dagua); showy plant, with large, glossy-green, lobed leaves, the undulate, oblanceolate lobes arranged along the curving base of the sinus; reddish veins; spathe green, spadix brown. *p. 173, 176*

gladifolium (Venezuela, Brazil); short-stemmed epiphyte with long thick-leathery, strap-like pendant leaves to about 1 m long, with prominent veins, on pale, stippled petioles; narrow spathe. *Humid-tropical.* *p. 167*

gracile (Costa Rica to Perú); long, leathery, shiny emerald-green strapleaves, 3 cm wide, with edges rolled down and raised center rib. *p. 168*

grande (Bolivia); beautiful, velvety species from the Yungas; large, heart-shaped, pointed leaf with network of pale veins. *p. 169*

grandifolium (Venezuela; W. Indies); selfheading plant with large, cordate-oblong, leathery leaves on short petioles. *p. 172*

gymnopus (W. Cuba); climber with waxy-green, cordate, almost cup-like, leaves with raised, pale green veins; spathe and spadix green. *p. 168*

guildingii (dussii) (Guadeloupe); broadly sagittate, satiny green leaves with wide sinus and large basal lobes; blade corrugated and margins undulate; small lanceolate spathe 6 cm long. *p. 178*

hacumense (Costa Rica); heavy rosette with thick, leathery, oblanceolate leaves; thick spadix on short stem, and bearing bottle-shaped crimson-red fruit. *p. 168, 174*

harrisii (Brazil), "Strap flower"; leathery, glossy green, and narrow lanceolate leaves borne on slender, flat petiole; narrow spathe green or rose, spadix purple-brown. *p. 178*

hoffmannii (Costa Rica, Panama); attractive plant with large, ovate-cordate leaves satiny, emerald-green and silvery green veins; narrow spathe coppery-green, spadix purple. *p. 168*

holtonianum (Panama, Colombia); striking plant with large, palmately compound, glossy green leaves, the long segments pinnately lobed and undulate. *Humid-tropical.* *p. 171*

hookeri (huegelii) (Guyana, W. Indies), "Birdsnest anthurium"; symmetrical rosette resembling birdsnest, with broad, obovate grass-green leaves 60 cm long; spathe green. *Humid-tropical.* *p. 174, 179*

hygrophilum (Colombia, Ecuador); erect plant from the rain forests, with leathery, green, corrugated, sagittate leaves with arched base; spathe blackish-red, spadix white. *p. 176*

imperiale (Trop. America); birdsnest-like rosette with short-stalked leathery leaves lanceolate-oblong, corrugated and wavy, on thick, angled petioles; inflorescence nearly hidden, with spathe chocolate-colored inside, green outside, long spadix chocolate brown, on very short stems. *p. 162*

insigne (Colombia); stout plant with palmately trilobed leaves, glossy, friendly green, with raised veins. *p. 176*

kalbreyeri (araliifolium hort.) (C. America); climbing plant with shining-green, palmate leaves, the 5-7 broad and sinuate segments attached to base by short petioles; spathe purplish green. *p. 173*

kyburzii (So. Colombia); terrestrial plant with long, sagittate, corrugated leaves; spathe wine-red with darker venation, turning greenish toward edges; spadix white. *p. 166*

latihastatum (Costa Rica); robust plant to 1 m high; from short stem rise stiff-wiry 70-80 cm petioles, bearing dark green, hastate leaves extending to 45 cm, the basal lobes spreading wide and very long; spathe pale green. *p. 175*

leuconeurum (Mexico); handsome tropical foliage plant with velvety deep green, broad heart-shaped leaves 12-18 cm long, with silvery-white veins, glaucous beneath, and of leathery texture; spathe light glaucous green, spadix gray-green. *Humid-tropical.* *p. 179*

lindenianum (Colombia); attractive ornamental, broad, fleshy sagittate-pointed leaves with open sinus; slightly fragrant inflorescence on slender stalks with broadly ovate white spathe tipped green, similar to Spathiphyllum, and whitish spadix. Known in So. California nurseries as "Spathiphyllum cordata". *p. 177*

loefgrenii (So. Brazil); ovate, stiff, leathery leaves deep green, with pale center vein; narrow spathe. *p. 175*

longilinguum (Brazil); ornamental plant with attractive hastate leaves, leathery glossy-green, with long basal lobes, borne erect on stiff, wiry petioles. *p. 171*

lowii (Mexico); compact plant with interesting, palmately-lobed, leathery leaves, pale green and with prominent veins. *p. 168*

macdougallii (So. Mexico); small, unusual plant growing on rocks; leathery leaves sagittate, almost reniform, with wide sinus and undulate, narrow spathe brownish-green. *p. 170*

x macrolobum (leuconeurum x pedato-radiatum) (dentatum); robust plant with large, leathery, green, sagittate leaf with 5-7 pointed lobes; spathe green. *p. 171*

magnificum (Colombia); large and showy heartshaped, velvety, olive-green leaves 25-40 cm long, having prominent white veins; the petioles 4-angled; spathe and spadix green. *Tropical.* *p. 169*

maximum (Colombia: Cauca); from the Cordillera Occidental at 1400 m; large birdsnest-type species; short-stalked, broadly lanceolate leaves of leathery texture, to 80 cm long, the surface dark glossy green, with bold midrib and quilted toward margins; lanceolate, recurved spathe and cylindric bright green spadix. *p. 179*

microphyllum (Venezuela); hard plant with fleshy elliptic leaves rich green, with bold midrib, bent sideways from thick petiole, channeled at top. *p. 172*

x mortefontanense (veitchii x andraeanum); glossy, sagittate leaves with large sinus, surface as if quilted; cream-white spathe, upright, pink spadix. *p. 166*

myosuroides (Costa Rica; Colombia); tree dweller in moist rain forests, with small, ovate, papery leaves on thin petioles; slender climbing stem. *p. 175*

'Negrito' ('cabrerense') (Colombia); leathery, dark green leaves triangular-sagittate with enlarged, rounded, basal lobes; lanceolate spathe a sated copper - one of the 'black' anthuriums of smaller size from Antioquia. *p. 170*

oblanceolatum (Trop. America); rosette type at the N.Y. Botanical Garden with broadly oblanceolate, leathery-waxy, fresh green leaves on short thick stalks. *p. 174*

olfersianum (So. Brazil); numerous stiff-elliptic, larger leaves glossy green with prominent, pale midrib, on strong petiole. *p. 172*

ornatum (Venezuela); noble leaf ovate-cordate, bright green; cupped spathe white turning purplish-rose toward tip; upright spadix red-purple. *p. 167*

panduratum (No. Brazil); showy plant from the forests of Amazonas, with large, palmately compound, glossy leaves, the segments pinnately lobed and with marginal vein; spathe purple. *Humid-tropical.* *p. 171*

patulum (Ecuador); shapely, hastate, shiny leaves with spreading basal lobes, rich green with pale green veins; green spathe. *p. 178*

pedato-radiatum (Mexico); large, graceful, glossy-green leaf palmately lobed, segments slender, oblanceolate; basal lobes broader; spathe reddish, spadix green. *Humid-tropical.* *p. 173*

pendulifolium (Colombia); arboreal plant with pendulous, oblong lanceolate leaves to 1 m long; bright green with pale, prominent midrib; violet spadix. *p. 175*

pendulifolium 'Aureo-variegatum'; cultivar with magnificent pendulous leaves green variegated with pale yellow to chartreuse. *p. 172*

pentaphyllum (Colombia to Brazil); climber with large, palmately fingered, glossy-green, leathery leaves and pale veins on grooved petioles; spathe green, spadix dark green. *p. 173*

peruvianum (Perú); sturdy species with thick leathery, glossy green, triangular sagittate leaves, measuring from sinus to tip 12 cm; the slender floral stalk 40 cm long, with 5 cm green spadix and narrow ovate 5 cm spathe light green. *p. 179*

pittieri (Costa Rica); short, narrow, lanceolate, hard, leathery, dark green leaves; narrow spathe pale green. *p. 175*

podophyllum (Mexico), "Footleaf anthurium"; showy, selfheading plant from Vera Cruz; large leathery leaves digitately lobed with stiff, finger-like segments, carried on long stalks from short trunk. *p. 171, 173*

polyrrhizum (Venezuela; Colombia); robust climber with leathery, grass-green to reddish, short, sagittate, almost round, leaves on slender petioles; small, yellowish-green spathe, chocolate spadix. *p. 170*

polyschistum (Colombia: Amazonas), "Aztec anthurium"; scandent with slender stem and distantly spaced palmately compound, graceful leaves, 7-9 leaflets 10 cm long x 2 cm, matte dark green, thin-turgid, narrow, with crisped margins, on slender channeled petioles; small 2½ cm green spathe, spadix brownish. *p. 162*

ptarianum (Venezuela); a jungle species growing in mossy crevices, with glossy green, leathery, ovate leaves 25-30 cm long, 16 cm wide and with pale midrib, on long 40-60 cm petioles; inflorescence with lanceolate dull green spathe, and 9-15 cm spadix; the seed-bearing berries blood- red.*p. 180*

pulchrum (Ecuador); robust plant from Andean forests, with leathery leaves, sagittate with wide sinus, dull green, and veins depressed; spathe green, spadix red. *p. 170*

quindiuense (Colombia); terrestrial rosette of stiff, ovate-cordate leaves on wiry stems; narrow, green spathe. *p. 168*

radicans (So. Brazil); attractive creeper with small, leathery, deep, glossy green, quilted leaves, cordate-ovate, pale beneath; spathe reddish, spadix reddish-green. *p. 166*

recusatum (E. Cuba); bold rosette with broad, lanceolate-oblong, dark green, leathery leaves, pale prominent veins, margins wavy; on short stalks. *p. 174*

regale (Amazonas, Perú), "Royal anthurium"; with large, oblong, heart-shaped leaves and narrow sinus, dark olive-green with silver-green veins, pale beneath. *p. 166*

reticulatum (Colombia); tree—growing in moist forests of the Western Cordillera; thin, long, pendant lanceolate leaves, emerald green; narrow spathe, green spadix. *p. 175*

rigidulum (Costa Rica, Colombia); small epiphyte from tropical forests at 1400-1800 m; wiry, creeping stems closely set with small ovate, leathery leaves, with age 10-15 cm long; 3 cm spadix greenish-white, subtended by 2½ cm narrow spathe yellowish-green; the 5 mm fruit pale purple. *p. 180*

'Robustum'; a regal hybrid with larger, satiny leaf, iridescent, olive-green, heartshaped with open sinus and pale veining; narrow, green spathe. *p. 166*

salviniae (Guatemala), shapely rosette of oblanceolate, leathery leaves with veins depressed which gives a quilted appearance; spathe brown-purple. *p. 166*

sanguineum (Colombia); robust plant from the Central Cordillera; leaves long sagittate, satiny, bluish-green and leathery; large reflexed spathe—rosy red with green spadix. *p. 170, 176*

scandens (W. Indies to Ecuador), "Pearl anthurium"; dwarf climber with small, leathery, glossy, dark green, elliptic leaves; spathe green; purple or white fruit. *p. 172, 175*

scherzerianum (Costa Rica), "Flamingo flower"; leathery plant with lanceolate, green leaves; the long-lasting inflorescence having a golden-yellow spadix spiralling twisted, subtended by a showy, broadly ovate, brilliantly scarlet spathe 6 to 10 cm long. *Humid-subtropic.* *p. 15*, 165*

scherzerianum nebulosum; curious form with double spathe, white, dotted with red. *p. 165*

scherzerianum 'Rothschildianum', "Variegated pigtail plant"; spathe more or less red with white spots. *Subtropic.* *p. 167*

scolopendrinum (Costa Rica to Brazil); graceful, long-elliptic, leathery, strap-like leaves on slender petioles; deep green, depressed veins in center and along margin; berry-like scarlet fruit on pendant spray. *p. 175*

signatum (Ecuador, Venezuela); queer leaf hastate-trilobed with horizontal basal lobes larger than the pointed terminal, and looking like elephant ears; spathe yellow-green. *p. 178*

spathulatum (So. Venezuela); attractively waxy dark-green, small elliptic leaves on long, thin but wiry petiole. *p. 172*

splendidum (Colombia); large bullate, ovate-cordate, fleshy leaf with deep sinus, deep metallic green, pale beneath; reflexed, lanceolate, rosy spathe, green spadix, later reddish. *p. 168*

'Splendidum hybrid'; splendid tropical foliage plant with large decorative, sagittate-cordate leaves, rather fleshy, 30 cm or more long, the surface metallic green and quite wrinkled, pale beneath, on angled stalks; slender spadix deep purple-red; narrow spathe pale green. *p. 180*

subsignatum (wrightii) (Costa Rica), "Cowface"; broadly trilobed, leathery, waxy leaf, basal lobes horizontal, rounded; terminal abruptly pointed; spathe green, spadix yellow. *p. 178*

tetragonum (Costa Rica); loose rosette with ½ to 1 m oblanceolate, fresh-green leaves with bold midrib and wavy margin on 4-angled, short petiole; spathe green. *p. 174, 177*

trilobum (trifidum) (So. Colombia); short-stemmed species with leaves deeply tri-lobed into lanceolate segments to 25 cm long, thin-leathery, silky light green spathe purple, spadix purplish. *p. 177*

trinerve (Brazil, Guyana); small erect species 10 to 30 cm high, with lanceolate leathery leaves 10-18 cm long, the blade with bold mid-vein and a less noticeable vein near either margin, dark green above, pale beneath; floral stalk 3 to 10 cm long topped by the cylindrical white spadix to 5 cm long, subtended by an erect green spathe; when fertile, the spadix is covered by numerous lilac berries. *p. 179*

undatum (Brazil, Perú); climber with palmately divided leaves, the elliptic segments glossy-green, papery and with depressed veins; spathe purplish inside, spadix pale purple. *p. 173*

variabile (S.E. Brazil); climber with palmately compound, dark green, leathery leaves, strap-like narrow segments with long drawn out, tapering leaf tips; green spathe, purple spadix. *p. 173*

variegatum (Ecuador) (Bogner 913); attractive species with long cordate, leathery green leaves, and handsome inflorescence with erect spadix and ovate, glossy red-purple spathe with pale yellow stripes. Photo by J. Bogner, Munich Botanic Garden. *p. 179*

veitchii (Colombia), "King anthurium"; unusual plant with pendant, showy leaves to 1 m long, cordate at base, rich metallic green; curved lateral veins sunken, giving a quilted look; pale midrib. Inflorescence with narrow green spathe. Beautiful but difficult. *Humid-tropical.* *p. 162, 166*

venosum (W. Cuba); compact, flat rosette with leathery, cordate-ovate leaves carried on short stalks which are flat at base; spathe narrow. *p. 172*

vittariifolium (Rio Jurua, W. Brazil); interesting epiphyte with long, pendant, narrow-linear leaves to 1 m long, dark green and leathery; small linear spathe. *p. 172*

warocqueanum (Colombia), "Queen anthurium"; climbing species with showy, long tapering, velvety leaves to 1 m long; deep green with ivory veins; small spathe green to yellowish. *Humid-tropical.* *p. 15*, 169*

watermaliense (Colombia); the fabled and prized "Anturio Negro"; found at 2400 m altitude; glossy undulate, hastate leaves on slender triangular petioles, the enormous quilted spathe to 22 or 25 cm long, coppery black, with erect brown spadix. *p. 167, 170, 177*

wendlingeri (Venezuela, Costa Rica); very interesting species with long pendulous, leathery ribbon-like leaves with quilted blade, on slender arching petioles; the spadix long, thin and pendant, spirally twisted for culture in hanging basket or on walls. *p. 179*

willdenowii brevifolium (So. Brazil: Minas Geraes, Rio); stocky species with short-stalked cordate-ovate, leathery green leaves to 17 cm long, the inflorescence with purplish spadix and small green spathe. *p. 180*

ANTIARIS *Moraceae* **S3LBD**

toxicaria (Malaya), "Upas tree"; big evergreen tropical tree to 80 m tall, with poisonous milky juice, ovate-oblong, glossy-green leaves to 20 cm long, finely toothed; unisexual flowers enclosed within a fleshy purple or red fruit. *p. 1562*

ANTIGONON *Polygonaceae* **S2LBM**

leptopus (Mexico), "Coral vine"; showy tendril climber, with tuberous roots, slender zigzag stems bearing cordate-ovate, light green leaves and axillary racemes of bright rose-pink flowers with deeper center. *Tropical.* *p. 1952, 1954, 1956*

ANTIRRHINUM *Scrophulariaceae* **C2LBD**

majus (So. Europe, No. Africa), "Floral snapdragon"; normally summer-flowering, erect herb, with leafy terminal spikes of very showy, curious sac-shaped, bilabiate flowers of many colors and shades, velvety red to pink, yellow or white, the yellow mouth closed but forced open by the bees. Also known as "Dragon-jaws". *Subtropic.* *p. 2052*

majus 'Butterfly'; the "Butterfly strain" has a unique flower form, the florets are open-tubular resembling Penstemon, not closing like the dragon jaws; available in cut-flower-types, 75 cm tall and in dwarf carpet-bedding cultivars, 15-20 cm high, and grown as annual. *Subtropic.* *p. 2049*

ANUBIAS *Araceae* **S1HNM**

afzelii (lanceolata) (West Equatorial Africa: Zaire, Guinea), "Water aspidistra" or "African cryptocoryne"; bog plant along tropical rivers; creeping rhizome giving rise to petioles 25-40 cm long, bearing long-stalked lanceolate, dark green, leathery leaves 10-25 cm long and 6-12 cm wide; inflorescence with waxy spathe green and slender, folded around yellowish spadix half-covered with male and half by female flowers. *p. 181, 207*

gilletii (So. Nigeria); low stemless aroid from creeping rhizome, with 15-20 cm leaves ovate-hastate and tripartite, the short spadix partially hooded by fleshy green spathe. *p. 161*

APHELANDRA *Acanthaceae* **S1HFM**

atrovirens macedoiana; handsome foliage plant to 20 cm high, with fleshy stem closely furnished with simple elliptic, turgid leaves glossy dark green with greenish-white along midrib, purple beneath; flowers yellow. *p. 40*

aurantiaca (Mexico), "Fiery spike"; erect shrub with ovate, smooth, green leaves gray in vein areas; showy bracted spikes with brilliant, scarlet-red flowers, orange in throat and along tube. *Tropical.* *p. 15*, 39, 1952A*

aurantiaca roezlii (Mexico), "Scarlet spike"; leaves somewhat twisted, dark green, silvery between main veins; flowers orange scarlet. *p. 39*

chamissoniana (Brazil), "Yellow pagoda"; erect plant with closely set, thin, slender, pointed leaves, silver-white area along midrib and veins; flowers clear yellow; bracts yellow with green tips. *Tropical.* *p. 39, 41*

fascinator (Colombia); emerald-green, satiny leaves marked with silver, veins a silvery amethyst, purple beneath; large, scarlet flowers. *p. 15*, 39*

fuscomaculata (Trop. America); vigorous semi-woody plant with corrugated, ovate slender-pointed, glossy brownish green leaves, and a bracted inflorescence covered with fine pubescence, flowers spotted with brown, and the densely shingled bracts spirally twisted around the spike. *p. 41*

fuscopunctata (Colombia); introduced as 'Epple's Findling'; evergreen, herbaceous shrub to 1 m high with green, round stems, small ovate leaves to 15 cm long, dark green above, pale beneath, hairy and ciliate; the dense terminal spikes with overlapping red bracts and sticky, the bilabiate flowers light brown spotted dark-brown. *Tropical.* *p. 40, 41*

nitens (Colombia); upright shrub with ovate, leathery, shining, dark-olive leaves with silver center vein, purple beneath; the bracted inflorescence in spikes of orange-red flowers. *Tropical.* *p. 40*

sinclairiana (Central America, Panama, Darien), "Coral aphelandra"; compact plant with limp, ovate leaves rich glossy-green; pale, depressed veins; inflorescence clustered, the cupped bracts orange-coral, the corolla rosy-pink. *Tropical.* *p. 40*

squarrosa (Brazil), "Saffron spike zebra"; waxy, dark-green, ovate leaves with silver-white veins; pale, yellow flowers in long spike with orange bracts. *p. 39*

squarrosa 'Brockfeld'; German selection from A. sq. 'Fritz Prinsler'; habit of growth more compact, and with growth more robust than 'Dania'; the broader leaf may become 3 times the size of louisae, also broader and more blunt than 'Fritz Prinsler'; glossy black green with contrasting straw-yellow veining. Patented in Germany. *p. 40*

squarrosa 'Dania', a "Zebra plant"; very stocky Danish clone selected from A. sq. 'Fritz Prinsler', of more compact habit, with shorter internodes between the showy, white or creamy-veined leathery deep glossy green leaves, with red brown stem; every shoot pinched should form 2-5 flowering heads with showy bracts and yellow flowers. *p. 40*

squarrosa 'Fritz Prinsler' (squarrosa leopoldii x sq. louisae), "Saffron spike"; valuable cultivar combining the remarkable white to straw-yellow leaf-veining on dark olive-green of louisae with the leaf form and willingness of leopoldii but remains smaller; floral bracts deep yellow, marked green, corolla canary yellow. *Tropical.* *p. 41*

squarrosa leopoldii (Brazil); shrub with large, elliptic, glossy leaves, olive green with side-veins white, stems red; flowers yellow in red bracts. *p. 40*

squarrosa var. louisae (Brazil), "Zebra plant"; compact growing plant with shiny, emerald-green, elliptic leaves and prominent white veins; bright yellow flowers, tipped green, on fleshy, terminal spikes of long-lasting, waxy, golden bracts; fall blooming. *Tropical.* *p. 19*, 39*

squarrosa 'Louisae compacta'; a selection by European growers for its most compact, low habit, similar to the Danish cultivar 'Dania', but having foliage darker green, and with boldly contrasting veins of greenish ivory; in habit even shorter and more closely jointed; yellow flowers; most attractive as a small foliage plant with its leaves in effect arranged like a rosette. *p. 41*

squarrosa 'Uniflora Beauty'; a slow, compact growing cultivar distinguished by its small 8-10 cm leaves, which are a deep green with contrasting greenish-ivory veins; bracts and flowers yellow. *p. 41*

tetragona (W. Indies, So. America); straggling plant to 1 m, with broadly ovate, green leaves; inflorescence in clustered spikes terminal or axillary; slender tubular, bright scarlet flowers 5-8 cm long. *p. 39, 40*

APICRA *Liliaceae* ***I1LFD**

deltoidea (Astroloba) (Cape of Good Hope); small succulent close to Aloe and Haworthia, but with regular, not bilabiate, greenish flowers, and not bitter like Aloe; stem rosette with hard, smooth, almost triangular grayish green, sharp-pointed leaves, keeled beneath, arranged in a spiral column. *p. 1416*

dodsoniana (Astroloba) (Cape of Good Hope); slender erect leafy stem, later reclining, of spirally arranged, very hard, closely set metallic bluish-green leaves tapering to long point, with numerous dark green lines, keeled beneath. *p. 1416*

egregia (Astroloba) (Cape Prov.); interesting, erect columnar rosette to 15 cm high, branching from the base; short dark green tricorned leaves arranged in 5 ranks, obliquely keeled beneath, the edges warty; greenish flowers in racemes. *p. 1406*

pentagona (Haworthia) (Cape of Good Hope); erect stem rosette, to 25 cm high, with closely set, lanceolate, tricornered, pointed leaves, light green and lightly warted yet somewhat shiny; rounded beneath. *p. 1416*

spiralis (Astroloba) (So. Africa); stem forming, elongated rosette, to 20 cm high, with stiff, dark, short pointed, keeled leaves closely shingled in spiral column, lightly warted, and notched at margins. *p 1416*

APIOS *Leguminosae* **C2LBDhd**

americana (tuberosa) (E. No. America to Texas), "Ground-nut" or "Potato-bean"; tuberous-rooted twining herb, the roots with strings of tubers; pinnate leaves with 5-7 leaflets to 8 cm long; fragrant brownish-purple flowers. *p. 1370*

APLOLEIA *Commelinaceae* **S3LBD**

multiflora (Trop. America); rambling trailer with purplish, fleshy stem and long ovate, clasping leaves entirely green, waxy margins and depressed midrib; flowers scented of violets, with 3 stamens. Photographed in Botanic Garden of Zurich, Switzerland. *Tropical.* *p. 785*

APONOGETON *Aponogetonaceae* **S3LNW**

bernierianus (Ouvirandra) (E. Madagascar); submersed aquatic plant with branching tuber to 4 cm thick, growing in fresh-water rivers; the leaves ribbon-like variably from 12 to 120 cm long and 5 to 10 cm wide, the surface deep green to reddish, very corrugated and occasionally with windows, and a broad midrib; long floral stalk tipped by two opposed spikes carrying bundles of small white or rosy flowers. *p. 303*

boivinianus (N. W. Madagascar: Diego Suarez); exquisite tropical underwater aquatic, found at 50-500 m elevation in running fresh waters; tuberous root-stock with dark green, quilted, stiff leaves 12-60 cm long and 2-5 cm wide; floral stalk to 70 cm long, thickened toward apex, with white inflorescence in twin-spikes. *p. 145*

capuronii (Malagasy Rep.); tropical aquatic plant with tuberous root stock, in habitat in rapidly flowing fresh water streams about 30 cm deep, the stalked leaves narrowly lanceolate; the floral stalks to 65 cm long floating on the surface, with the white flowers in twin spikes rising above the water. *p. 145*

dioecus (Madagascar); aquarium plant grass-like, looking like Scirpus; found at 2000 m elevation in Ankaratra mountains, at water temp. of 23°C warm; tuberous rootstock, with submerged leaves light green, semi-cylindric, 20-25 cm long, with simple spike of greenish-yellow flowers appearing above the water. *p. 145*

distachyus (So. Africa), "Cape pondweed" or "Water hawthorn"; aquatic herb with tuberous rootstock, the linear-oblong, bright green solid leaves floating; white flowers hawthorn-scented, with single petal. *p. 145*

longiplumulosus (N. W. Madagascar); warm-climate aquatic with globose tuber, oblong in older plants, to 2 cm diameter; long narrow, undulate leaves 20-36 cm long and 3 cm wide, blackish to reddish-green, on 10-12 cm petioles; long 35-45 cm floral stalk with bi-forked spikes of white flowers. *p. 145*

madagascariensis (fenestralis) (Madagascar), "Laceleaf"; curious aquarium plant, from running streams; rootstock like a small potato, with leaves ascending to a little below the surface, 15 to 40 cm long, only a skeleton network of veins, pale yellow to dark olive; flower on long stalk rises a little above water, is of pinkish color, dividing into two curved hairy tufts. *Humid-tropical.* *p. 145*

APOROCACTUS *Cactaceae* ***S1LBD**

conzattii (Oaxaca); slender, clambering, dayflowering cactus with 1-2½ cm stems forming aerial roots, 8-10 ribbed with small brown spines; funnel-shaped red flowers. *p. 663*

flagelliformis (Mexico), "Rat-tail-cactus"; slender creeping or long pendant stems close-ribbed, covered with small reddish spines; small crimson flowers. *Tropical.* *p. 661, 663, 666*

x mallisonii (A. flagelliformis x Heliocereus speciosus); large-flowered hybrid with fiery-red blooms freely produced; weak creeping stems usually 6-angled to 4 cm thick. *p. 663*

x APOROPHYLLUM *Cactaceae* **S2LFD**

'Star Fire' (Aporocactus x Epiphyllum); beautiful Johnson bigeneric hybrid between Orchid cacti and Rat-tail cacti, normally epiphytic and ideally suited for baskets. This and similar hybrids are free-flowering, earlier than orchid cactus and bloom at odd times. The slender stems are ribbed and pendant but may be trained on a trellis. The large rose-red flowers are flushed scarlet outside. *Subtropic.* *p. 661*

APTENIA *Aizoaceae* **I2LBM**
cordifolia (So. Africa), "Baby sun rose"; low succulent creeper of the eastern coastal deserts; freely branching with prostrate or pendant branches, small soft-fleshy cordate, fresh green leaves to 2½ cm long, covered with glands, later gray; small 1 cm rosy-purple flowers. *p. 59*
cordifolia variegata (Mesembryanthemum) (So. Africa); soft, prostrate succulent with small, heartshaped leaves, shimmering gray-green, and cream margins; tiny, purple flowers. *p. 57*

AQUILEGIA *Ranunculaceae* **C2LFMh**
'Long-spurred hybrid', an American "Columbine"; derived from such species as vulgaris, chrysantha, caerulea, etc.; attractive hardy perennial with fibrous roots and stalked fern-like glaucous compound leaves; beautiful flowers with 5 petals each with a long straight hollow spur in shades of pink, yellow, copper and blue. *p. 1984*

ARABIS *Cruciferae* **C2LBD**
alpina 'Variegata', a variegated-leaf form of the "Mountain rockcress" native in the European Alps; low, densely clustering and slowly creeping perennial with green, pubescent obovate, crenate leaves 3-8 cm long, attractively edged in ivory-white; small white flowers. *p. 928*

ARACHIS *Leguminosae* **I2LBDd**
hypogaea (Brazil), the "Peanut vine" or "Ground-nut"; annual herb 30-45 cm high with compound leaves of two pairs of oval leaflets without tendrils; yellow flowers of two kinds: one set pealike, showy and sterile, the others fertile on lengthening stalks which touch the ground and force into it where the fertilized ovary ripens into the peanut, an oily, edible seed. *p. 1370*

ARACHNANTHE: see Arachnis

ARACHNIS *Orchidaceae* **S30FW**
flos-aeris (moschifera) (Malaya, Java, Borneo), "Spider orchid"; epiphytic; slender stems to 4 m, with scattered narrow leaves and erect spike of 10 cm blooms, greenish-yellow, heavily blotched red-brown, more so in basal flowers; musk scented. (summer). *Humid-tropical.* *p. 1662*
lowii (Vandopsis) (Borneo), "Scorpion orchid"; a giant spider orchid, epiphytic, magnificent with glossy green leaves and 8 cm flowers regularly spaced on pendulous racemes to 3 m long, the 1 or 2 lower, basal ones orange-yellow with fine red, clustered spots, the upper flowers greenish-yellow with large brown blotches, (Aug.-Nov.) (S) *p. 1650, 1662*
massoei (Malaya); robust epiphyte with slender, leafy pseudobulbs, and forming terminal racemes of yellow, waxy flowers. As customary such epiphytes are grown in Singapore nurseries in perforated clay pots in mixtures of broken brick, charcoal and bone meal, to allow good drainage in monsoon climate. *Tropical.* *p. 1650*

ARAEOCOCCUS *Bromeliaceae* **L2HBD**
flagellifolius (No. Brazil, Surinam, Venezuela, Colombia); slender rosette with few narrow brown-scaly, channeled, toothed leaves ½-1 m long; the inflorescence in erect racemes with light red bracts, and later, greenish berries. *p. 529, 532, 533*

ARALIA *Araliaceae* **C2LBD**
californica (Brit. Columbia to California), "Elk-clover"; stout herbaceous perennial 2-3 m high, with bipinnate leaves, the leaflets doubly toothed, to 30 cm long; small whitish flowers in terminal panicles 45 cm long. *p. 304, 316*
elata (Japan, Korea, N.E. China), "Japanese angelica" or "Angelica tree"; deciduous tree to 15 m high, with spiny branches, bipinnate leaves 60-120 cm long, the oval leaflets to 12 cm, pubescent on veins beneath when young and prickly; small whitish flowers borne in numerous clusters forming a large panicle; berry-like fruits. Often mistaken for A. spinosa. *p. 304, 319*
racemosa (E. Canada to Georgia and Missouri), "American spikenard"; hardy perennial herb to 2 m high, with very large herbaceous green leaves of 3 to 5 toothed leaflets to 15 cm long; small greenish whitish flowers in terminal panicles, and brown-purple berry-like fruits. *p. 304*
spinosa (U.S.: New York to Florida and Texas), deciduous tree to 10 or more meters, known as "Devil's walking-stick"; with very spiny, slender trunk and large bipinnate leaves 60-90 cm long, the ovate leaflets prickly; flowers whitish, fruit black. *p. 304*

ARALIA: see also Polyscias, Dizygotheca, Fatsia, Tetrapanax

x ARANDA *Orchidaceae* **S3OFW**
'Daniel Sato' (Arachnis flos-aeris x Vanda 'Emily Notley'); spoon-like sepals and petals lemon-yellow or cream, overlaid with purplish-brown spots; small lip (Tanaka, Honolulu 1950). *p. 1664*
maes (Arachnis x Vanda), handsome epiphyte, as seen in Fiji; of vandaceous habit, with pencil-thick leaves on climbing stem; long arching inflorescence with white sepals and petals, the lip brown with red. *p. 1664*

ARAUCARIA *Araucariaceae (Coniferae)* ***I1HFM**
angustifolia (brasiliana) (So. Brazil), the "Paraná pine"; characterizes the landscape in cooler parts of Sao Paulo and Paraná with wide spreading heads; 5 cm needles stiff and deep green. *p. 346*
araucana (imbricata) (Mts. of So. Chile, No. Patagonia), the so-called "Hardy monkey puzzle" tree; 15-30 m high, with resinous bark and whorled branches, sharp-pointed ovate, thick-leathery, dark green leaves 3-5 cm long, densely and uniformly arranged around shoot. *p. 345, 346, 347, 350*
bidwillii (Queensland), "Bunya-Bunya" or "Monkey-puzzle"; dome-shaped tree to 45 m high; the horizontal branches with thick-leathery, dark glossy-green spine-tipped leaves showing depressed parallel veining and mostly toward branch ends; the juvenile leaves narrow sickle-shaped to 5 cm long and primarily in one or two ranks; adult stage needles shorter, spiral and over-lapping; female cones huge, 8 to 12 cm long and resembling pineapples. The big seeds inside highly prized as food by the aborigines. *Subtropic to Tropical.* *p. 345, 346, 347*
columnaris (cookii) (New Caledonia), the "Cook pine"; so named because Capt. Cook discovered it on the Isle of Pines; in silhouette appearing like tall pines, with somewhat leaning trunks, said to grow as high as 60 m; difficult to distinguish from A. heterophylla as young trees in their curved, needle-like leaves; very symmetric with about 5 branches radiating around the trunk in each tier, and each branch triangular in shape; later the Cook pine develops into a narrower column than heterophylla, and on its branchlets bears overlapping more numerous, scale-like sharp-pointed leaves 1 cm long; the cones are ovoid and 8-10 cm in diam. *p. 349, 350*
cunninghamii (New So. Wales), "Hoop pine"; majestic evergreen tree to 60 m high; the juvenile leaves are short, needle-like and bluish-green. *Subtropic.* *p. 345, 346, 349*
excelsa—see heterophylla
heterophylla (excelsa in hort.) (Norfolk Is.), "Norfolk Island pine"; evergreen tree to 70 m high, from the South Pacific; when juvenile very formal with branches parallel to the ground, in tiers of bright green, soft, awl-shaped needles; best Araucaria for the home. *Subtropic.* *p. 345, 347, 348, 349, 350, 836*
hetero. 'Astrid', or 'Leopold Astrid'; a Belgian clone of compact habit with the smallest though thick needles, similar in habit to gracilis but of much more rapid growth, with very regular tiers and of nice form. *p. 346*
hetero. glauca; attractive variety with glaucous bluish-green needles, and of slower growth than the type. *p. 348*
hetero. 'Gracilis' a horticultural variety of small, graceful habit; the branches turning downward, finer needles, lighter green, and more graceful tiers, giving the plant a frilled appearance; slow grower. *p. 348*
heterophylla 'Lillianii'; a distinguished Florida cultivar by Blaine Logsdon of Port Orange, who has been raising seedlings from seed collected on Oahu, Hawaii involving heterophylla and columnaris; characterized by compactness and sturdiness in growth, and with the tiers of branches and its branchlets rather more erect than horizontal or drooping, and of rich green color; used in Florida as a living Christmas tree. *p. 349*
klinkii (bot. valid name hunsteinii) (E. New Guinea to Sepik region); a very tall and slender tree to 70 m or more, towering above the rainforest canopy, characteristic of the highlands and forested canyons near the Bulolo goldfields; leaves coarse, broadly triangular and pointed, blackish green; in younger trees in two planes, on older trees tightly pressed to the twigs and spiralled at ends of sparry branches. *p. 344*

ARAUJIA *Asclepiadaceae* **C3LBD**
sericofera (So. Brazil); the "Cruel plant" or "Bladder flower", prodigious woody twiner resembling Stephanotis, with several forms of leaves, mostly oblong, 5-10 cm long, green above, white felted beneath; salver-shaped flowers 3 cm across, white or pinkish-tawny and fragrant, fast fading; the seed pods explode with the characteristic silk of the asclepiads. Biologically interesting because the flowers are able to trap insects. *p. 353*

ARBUTUS *Ericaceae* **I2LBD**
menziesii (British Columbia to Baja California, Mexico), "Madrone"; characteristic evergreen shrub or tree from 6 to 30 m high, with smooth, reddish bark peeling in flakes; leathery, glossy green leaves, oval or elliptic to 15 cm long, finely crenate to serrate at margins; pendant, grape-like clusters of small white or pinkish bell-shaped flowers 5 mm long, followed in autumn by brilliant orange to scarlet red, pebble-skinned, 1 cm berries, lasting all winter unless eaten by birds. *Subtropic.* *p. 957*
unedo (So. Europe, etc.), the "Strawberry-tree"; small evergreen tree with rough, shreddy bark, sticky-hairy branches, oblong, shiny, toothed 10 cm leaves, and small white, or pinkish, bell-like flowers in drooping panicles; strawberry-like, orange-red fruit edible but without particular flavor. *Subtropic* *p. 958*

ARCHONTOPHOENIX *Palmae* **S2LBD**
alexandrae (Australia: Queensland), the tall-growing "King palm" or "Alexandra palm", with erect ringed trunk 15 cm thick and to 20 or even 30 m high and bulging at base; bearing a majestic crown of arching pinnate fronds, the narrow leaflets 4-5 cm wide, green above but prominently grayish-white beneath; flowers white or creamy; attractive red fruit. *Subtropic.* *p. 1849, 1851*
cunninghamiana (Australia: Queensland, N.S.W.), "Seaforthia palm" or "Piccabeen palm"; tall feathery palm with slender trunk not enlarging below

except at surface of ground; the gracefully arching fronds to 3 m long; broad leaflets dark green on both sides, 8-10 cm wide; pendulous inflorescence with lilac flowers; the coral fruit less than 2½ cm. In the California nursery trade erroneously as Seaforthia elegans; in Florida nurseries as Ptychosperma elegans. *Subtropic.* *p. 1851, 1858*

ARCTOSTAPHYLOS *Ericaceae* **I-C2LBD**

insularis (California: Santa Cruz Is.), "Island manzanita"; spreading evergreen 2 m or more, the crooked branches with dark red bark; bright green oval, 3-4 cm leaves; waxy white bell-like nodding flowers in large clusters; yellow-brown fruit nearly globose, like tiny apples. Indians chew the fruit to quench thirst. *p. 957*

pumila (California), "Dune manzanita" or "Dwarf manzanita", from Monterey Bay area; evergreen, mat-forming, leafy, creeping shrub with ascending; tiny finely pubescent young shoots 18-30 cm long; obovate leaves 1 cm long, dull green, smooth above, white pubescent below, flowers in short, dense terminal racemes, corolla white or pinkish, urn-shaped about 4 mm long, followed by small reddish-brown fruit. *p. 957*

tomentosa (Brit. Columbia to California), "Woolly manzanita"; evergreen shrub to 1½ m high with brown, shaggy bark on twisted, crooked branches, bristly-hairy when young; dense with hard, oval leaves 4 cm long, matte green on surface, downy beneath; small nodding, ½ cm urn-shaped flowers white; 1 cm brownish-red fruit. *p. 957*

uva-ursi (California north to Alaska), "Bearberry" or "Trailing manzanita"; a popular ground-cover in Pacific Northwest; prostrate spreading branches and rooting as it creeps to 5 m; bright glossy green, leathery leaves 2-3 cm long, turning red in winter; flowers white tinged pink; bright red fruit. *p. 957*

ARCTOTIS *Compositae* **I2LBD**

hirsuta (Venidium) (So. Africa: Cape Peninsula), "Hairy arctotis"; showy quick growing herbaceous annual about 30 cm high, with erect, leafy stems and soft succulent leaves, deeply lobed and wavy-toothed at margins; bright orange daisy-like flowers with shining black ring cushion around the dark center. *p. 802*

'Hybrida' (acaulis and other species), "African daisy"; stemless perennial with stout rhizome; leaves in rosettes, pinnately lobed or lyrate, green and hairy above, lower surface white woolly; long-stalked flowers 8 to 10 cm across, in many colors, cream, yellow, orange, pink, red and purple, many with central zones of contrasting colors. *Subtropic.* *p. 810*

stoechadifolia grandis (So. Africa); a tall growing annual "African daisy", 75 cm high, with spreading stems becoming woody; obovate, toothed, gray-hairy leaves to 15 cm long; ray flowers cream-white, tinted red underneath, in 8 cm heads with shiny black centers. *p. 811*

ARDISIA *Myrsinaceae* **I2LFM**

crispa (crenulata) (China, Malaya), "Coral berry"; graceful little tree to 1 m with long-elliptic, thick-leathery, shining dark green leaves having crisped margins; the fragrant white or reddish flowers in umbels, followed in winter by a tier of clustered, bright scarlet, waxy berries, often persisting until the next crop of flowers. *p. 1604*

esculenta (Trop. America), "Hen's eyes"; small evergreen shrub with ovate, smooth green, leathery leaves dotted beneath; flowers in erect clusters white dotted purple. *p. 1603*

humilis (E. Indies); evergreen shrub with softly leathery, lanceolate leaves 5-12 cm long, and umbels of small rose-pink flowers; 1 cm fruit flattened-globular, first red then black. *Subtropic.* *p. 1602*

japonica (Japan, China), "Marlberry"; small broad-leaved evergreen shrub to 40 cm high, with elliptic leathery leaves 7-10 cm long, glossy dark green and sharply toothed, and crowded at ends of branches; small white flowers in clusters, followed by red berries. *p. 1602*

japonica 'Hinotsukasa'; a tedious Japanese cultivar, with very irregular leaves, toothed, lobed and fasciated, creamy-white over a large part of the leaves; very slow, and grown in sphagnum. *p. 1604*

japonica maculata (Japan); small cool-house evergreen with broad, thick-leathery, waxy leaves dark green, strikingly marbled and variegated creamy-white; flowers white, in short axillary clusters; berries white turning bright red. *p. 1604*

japonica marginata (Japan); slow-growing, dwarf plant with thick, elliptic leaves in terminal whorls, glossy deep green, with crenate margins attractively outlined in white. *p. 1604*

japonica 'Matsu-Shima'; a fancy, named Japanese form having a pink stem and holly-like waxy leaves, deep green and beautifully variegated with a cream-white center, the margins are frilled and deeply, irregularly toothed. (Grow in sphagnum, moist). *p. 1604*

malouiana (Labisia) (Borneo: Rajah Mts.); evergreen shrub with attractive leaves, spirally arranged, 15-25 cm long, velvety dark green dominated by broad silver gray zone; reverse amaranth-red; the very small flowers light pink; pea-size red berries. p. 1602

mamillata (So. China); compact subshrub with hairy, semi-herbaceous stems, ovate leaves 5-10 cm long, dark glossy green thickly covered with raised dots, each with a single hair; flowers in axillary clusters, white, tinged rose, 5 cm long; small 1 cm rosy-red fruit. *Subtropic.* *p. 1604*

polycephala (E. Indies); glabrous shrub with leathery oblanceolate leaves 8-20 cm long, and small flowers in axillary clusters, with white or pinkish lobes; small red berries turning almost black. *p. 1602, 1603*

solanacea (Sri Lanka); small tree to 6 m, with red-brown branches; leathery narrow-oblanceolate leaves 10 cm long, pink when new; rosy-pink to purple flowers, followed by many 1 cm berries ripening red to shining black. *Tropical.* *p. 1603*

wallichii (sanguineolenta) (India), "India spice berry"; small evergreen with branches smooth except when young, obovate leaves minutely toothed, 7-12 cm; loose axillary racemes of small red flowers, and black berries. *p. 1602, 1603*

ARDISIANDRA *Primulaceae* **I2LFM**

sibthorpoides (Africa: Cameroons Mts., Fernando Po); miniature creeping herbaceous plant with meandering, round pink stems, alternate doubly-crenate, membraneous, roundish, rugose, small leaves, with cordate base, fresh-green, 3 cm dia., covered with white hairs; small axillary flowers with white corolla. *p. 1966*

ARECA *Palmae* **S2LBM**

catechu (Malaysia to Polynesia), the famed, graceful "Betel-nut palm"; a very slender, erect, dioecious palm with solitary trunk, 10 to 30 m high and 5-12 cm dia.; relatively small crown of pinnate fronds 1-2 m long, with many broad, rather soft pinnae irregularly notched at apex, the upper ones united; fragrant white flowers; fruit olive shaped to 5 cm long, reddish-orange, and housing the grooved betelnut. Much cultivated for the nut which is chewed with lime and wrapped in the leaf of Piper betel, as a mild stimulant. *p. 1853*

langloisiana (Celebes); a slow-growing, suckering palm with heavy feather fronds, the dark green, ribbed leaflets broad and leathery; showy with orange-colored crown shaft. The palm photographed at Dr. Darian's collection in Vista, California is 10 years old. *Tropical.* *p. 1856*

triandra (India, Malaya); attractive soft-leaved palm forming clusters of several green, leafy stems 1½-3 m long with recurved broad pinnae toothed at apex; olive-like orange-scarlet fruit. *p. 1852*

ARECA: see also Chrysalidocarpus

ARECASTRUM *Palmae* **S3LFW**

romanzoffianum (Cocos plumosa) (Bahia to Argentina and Bolivia), "Queen palm"; very handsome with straight smooth trunk to 12 m high and a graceful crown of long arching plumy fronds, the soft, dark shiny-green leaf segments pendant above the middle; edible orange fruit. *Humid-subtropic.* *p. 1849, 1853*

AREGELIA: see Neoregelia

ARENARIA *Caryophyllaceae* **C2LBDh**

verna (rubella) (Rocky Mts. to Alaska, Temp. Europe), the "Irish moss"; tiny cushion-forming, moss-like low creeper to 8 cm high, with narrow, flat, deep green leaves, 5-8 cm long; solitary white flowers on very slender, thread-like stalks; winter-hardy. *p.759*

ARENGA *Palmae* **S2LFM**

engleri (Taiwan), "Dwarf sugar palm"; handsome dwarf, but showy palm to 3 m high, with short multiple trunk and spreading pinnate leaves to 1 m long; dense leaflets dark green above, silvery-tomentose beneath, broadening and notched. *p. 1850, 1856*

pinnata (saccharifera) (Malaya), the "Common sugar palm"; important economic palm to 12 m high, with robust solitary trunk covered with black fibers; erect, pinnate leaves to 6 m or more, the leaflets dark green above, whitened underneath, and with jagged apex. When pierced, the young inflorescence yields sugary sap. *Tropical.* *p. 1851, 1853*

AREQUIPA *Cactaceae* **I2LBD**

leucotricha (Chile, Perú); globular to cylindric cactus to 60 cm long, becoming prostrate, grayish green covered with long yellow spines, centrals much longer than radials, on tubercled ribs, and topped by yellow wool; long and slender funnel-shaped carmine red flowers. *p.702*

ARGYREIA *Convolvulaceae* **S3LBM**

nervosa (speciosa) (India), "Elephant creeper" or "Silver Morning-glory"; elegant, robust climber reaching up to 8 m; woody stems with large, overlapping, cordate, rich green leaves prominently nerved and silvery silky beneath, 15 to 30 cm wide; showy deep rose flowers with flaring limb, 5-8 cm long, violet in throat, white-hairy outside, the base enveloped by a large white-hairy calyx. *Tropical.* *p. 854*

speciosa (India, Java, China), "Woolly morning-glory"; robust climber with large ovate-cordate leaves, white-tomentose underneath; tubular bell-shaped flowers rose, 3-8 cm long on stalks to 15 cm long. Photographed by T. Everett at Glasnevin Botanic Gardens, Ireland. *p. 854*

ARGYRODERMA *Aizoaceae* **I2LBD**

angustipetalum (Cape Prov.: Namaqualand); low succulent consisting of pairs of very thick, keeled leaves gray green, 3-4 cm long; from the cleft the sessile, clear yellow flower 3-4 cm diameter, with narrow petals. *p. 60*

aureum (So Africa: Cape Prov.), "Silver jaws"; stemless, solid succulent with 2½ cm fleshy pairs of leaves light gray, rhomboid on top; solitary golden yellow flowers from between leaves. *p. 56*

longipes (Cape Prov.); succulent with 1-2 pairs of rhomboid-eggshaped leaves; stalked yellow flowers. *p. 56*

nortieri (So. Africa: Cape Prov.); cushion-forming succulent with thick, opposite leaves; stalked yellow flowers. *p. 56*

orientale (So. Africa: Cape Prov.); clustering succulent with fat, olive-green leaves flat on top, keeled beneath; flowers pink. *p. 56*

roseum (delaetii) (So. Africa: Cape Prov.); succulent leaves 3 cm thick, bluish-green, united about halfway; flowers violet-rose, 8 cm dia., petals lax. *Arid-subtropic.* *p. 56*

villetii (Namaqualand); clustering tiny succulent, with leaf pairs united to almost globose bodies and keeled, gray-green; flowers pink. *p. 57*

ARGYROXIPHIUM *Compositae* **I2LBD**

sandwicense (Hawaii), the "Silver sword"; endemic on mountains to 3950 m altitude on volcanic cinders; narrow pointed leaves form a rosette 60 cm dia., clothed entirely with silvery-silky hair; with maturity forming a leafy stem to 2m tall, bearing a pyramidal cluster of 100 or more nodding flower heads with purplish ray florets. *Sub-tropic.* *p. 827, 832*

ARIDARUM *Araceae* **S3LFM**

burttii (Microcasia purseglovei) (Borneo, Sarawak); small tropical plant 10-20 cm high, forming clusters of long-stalked, lanceolate leathery leaves 10-17 cm long, and with stiff-erect stalk bearing large cupped, white spathe 2½-4 cm wide, shielding the spadix. *p. 180*

nicolsonii (Sarawak); small fleshy herb with bulbous base; long lanceolate dark green, recurving leaves 12-21 cm long, on stiff stalks; inflorescence a cupping spathe 6 cm long, white with green at base, soon falling; stocky yellow spadix. *Tropical* *p. 160*

ARIKURYROBA *Palmae* **S2LFM**

schizophylla (Brazil); small feather palm with trunk characteristically clothed with erect purplish-black old leaf bases; pinnate fronds dark green and gracefully arched, 2-2½ m long, the leaflets spreading in every direction; notched at apex on spiny petioles; boat-shaped spathe, orange-yellow fruit. *p. 1852, 1856*

ARIOCARPUS *Cactaceae* ***I2LBD**

fissuratus (W. Texas, Mexico), "Living rock cactus"; star-shaped succulent rosette with horny gray surface and turnip-like root; lovely pink flowers. *p. 683*

kotschubeyanus (C. Mexico); plant sprouting from the beet-like taproot, forming groups; low fleshy, star-like rosette of angular dark green rugose leaves cleft at triangular apex; flowers from the woolly center purplish-carmine. *Arid-tropical.* *p. 683*

retusus (Mexico: San Luis Potosi), known as "Seven stars"; handsome star-like rosette 10 to 12 cm across, with silvery glaucous, triangular tubercles pointed outward, like the leaves of an haworthia; with yellow wool in axils, the areole near tips; flowers whitish to pink, 5 cm dia. *Arid-tropical.* *p. 684*

trigonus (Mexico), "Living rock"; hard fleshy rosette of numerous erect leaflike tubercles, grayish green; turnip-like root; pale yellow flowers. *Arid-tropical.* *p. 683*

trigonus elongatus (Mexico), "Living star"; similar to trigonus, with longer narrow, numerous leaves; in center a cluster of yellow flowers with dark eye. *Arid-tropical.* *p. 684*

ARIOPSIS *Araceae* **S3LFM**

peltata (India); small tuberous tropical herbaceous plant somewhat of the habit of Caladium; ovoid tuber 4 cm thick, producing pale green, peltate rounded leaves of thin texture, to 15 cm long by nearly as wide, spathe ovate cup-shaped hooding the cone shaped spadix. *p. 180*

ARISAEMA *Araceae* **S-I2LFMd**

amurense (No. Korea; China: Hupeh, Manchuria; Japan); sub-tropical tuberous herb from the Yangtse Valley, with large dissected leaves, the broadly ovate segments fresh green; the tubular spathe purplish with pale green stripes and hooded at apex. *p. 185*

candidissimum (Japan, W. China); hardy tuberous plant with solitary leaf on petiole 75 cm long, the blade leathery, trifoliolate with leaflets widely ovate, each 7-20 cm wide and long; tubular spathe green at base, white tinged rose toward pointed tip and with white length-lines; slender green spadix. *Warm temperate.* *p. 185*

consanguineum (Temp. E. Asia to Yunnan); a near-hardy tuberous-rooted plant with tuber to 10 cm diameter; solitary leaf on long stiff stalk to 80 cm long, mottled pink and brown, the blade divided into 7 to 11 cuts, the lanceolate leaflets 15-30 cm long; spathe 8-18 cm long, tube glaucous green outside, striped purple inside, the blade with long thread-like tip. *p. 185*

'Exotica' (Thailand); interesting small plant with soft-leathery compound leaves on fleshy petiole greenish-cream with brown striplets, the ovate leaflets dull green with ivory spots and a creamy yellow irregular band along midrib; goes dormant. *p. 184*

fargesii (China: Szechwan); rhizome-like tuber with solitary green, trisected leaf, the three broad, smooth segments 15 to 20 cm long; spathe tube to 8 cm long, striped white or pale purple, the forward arching pointed blade greenish purple outside, deep violet inside with long slender point; spadix glossy purple, greenish and white; near hardy. *p. 185*

filiforme (Indonesia: Java); tropical tuberous-rooted herbaceous plant with large dissected leaf 15 cm long, on 50 cm mottled stalk, the segments fleshy and quilted, and painted with silver; slender tubular spathe pale green with purple blade drooping forward over the spadix, and ending in long twisted tail. *p. 185*

fimbriatum (Malaya); tuberous tropical plant with 1 or 2 leaves deeply divided in to 3 leaflets; smooth green, ovate segments 12-15 cm long, on 45 cm leaf stalk; spathe brownish-purple, striped whitish, tube funnel-shaped with extended, pointed blade; slender spadix covered with purplish threads. *p. 186*

flavum (Mediterranean to Himalaya); tuberous plant with pedately divided leaves, the segments lanceolate; spathe with yellow-green tube, blade purple with green veins. *p. 184*

limbatum (Japan: Honshu); attractive tuberous plant with glossy green herbaceous dissected leaf into 7-11 leaflets, the terminal one 10-20 cm long; the showy spathe trumpet-shaped dark purple with white stripes and a forward-arching, pointed limb. *p. 185*

negishii (Japan: Honshu); tubers depressed globose, 3-7 cm across; petioles 5-20 cm long; the leaf dissected into 9-15 leaflets, 8-20 cm long; tubular spathe pale green, the elongate pointed blade curving forward; the slender appendix to spadix purplish, 10-15 cm long. *p. 186*

ringens (Japan); leaves 3-parted, pointed segments; spathe striped green and white, with deep purple hood. *p. 184*

serratum (Temp. Asia: Japan, Manchuria, No. Korea); tuberous species with leaf dissected into 5 to 11 segments, on purple-spotted petiole; tubular spathe green to pale purple 8-11 cm long, with pointed limb arching forward; fairly hardy. *p. 185*

sikokianum (So. Japan); subtropic tuberous plant with attractive inflorescence with white club-shaped spadix; spathe trumpet-shaped outside purple, with narrow greenish bands, the upper inside white, the long lanceolate extension greenish-red with white stripes; trifoliolate leaves painted with silver, along the pseudostem or stalk carrying the floral head; fairly hardy. *Subtropic.* *p. 185*

speciosum (Himalayas); remarkable aroid with rhizome-like tuber, solitary leaf of 3 leaflets 20-40 cm long on petioles spotted purple; hooded spathe purple with pale stripes and a long slender point; spadix with purple tail to 50 cm long. *p. 183, 184*

tortuosum (India), "Cobra plant"; tuberous herb with reniform leaf pedately parted into elliptic, dark-green segments, corrugated; tubular spathe green, purple within. *p. 183, 184*

triphyllum (E. No. America), "Jack-in-the-pulpit"; tuberous woodland herb to 1 m, with usually a pair of trifoliate ovate leaflets to 18 cm long; the erect spadix is surrounded by the green spathe or "pulpit", striped with purple inside, its tip arched forward; berries red. *Warm temperate.* *p. 182*

umbrinum (Malaysia: Sarawak); tuberous-rooted tropical plant with trisected leaf, the narrow elliptic, fleshy segments glossy light green, 10-15 cm long; the long tubular spathe white flushed yellow-green, the upper part deep purplish-red; appendix thread-like filiform. *p. 185*

urashima (Japan: Hokkaido, Honshu, Shikoku); tuberous plant with usually solitary leaf on 30-50 cm petiole, cut into 11-15 leaflets in mature plants, the terminal one 10-18 cm long; trumpet-like spathe dark to bronze-purple, the blade tail-like at tip strongly arching forward; the spadix appendix filiform 40-60 cm long and pendulous, bearing at tip the floriferous parts. *p. 186*

ARISARUM *Araceae* **I2HFM**

proboscideum (Italy: Apennines), known as the "Mouse plant"; a small tuberous herb with long rhizome with arrow-shaped leaves; near ground-level the curious inflorescence resembling a mouse, a swollen tube grayish-white below and olive green above, the tip narrowed to a long curved tail; dormant in summer. *p. 184*

vulgare (So. Europe, Algeria); subtropic tuberous plant with 1 or 2 fleshy leaves triangular sagittate, deep green; the inflorescence on a spotted stalk, a light green cylindrical spathe vivid purple toward apex, and the pointed hood black-purple, curving forward. *Subtropic.* *p. 186*

ARISTEA *Iridaceae* **I2LBM**

ecklonii (So. Africa), "Blue stars"; perennial herb having a woody rootstock with long, strap-like, light green, arching leaves in basal rosette; blue, short-lived flowers with flattened lobes, 2 cm across,in loose clusters, during summer. *Subtropic.* *p. 1331, 1336*

lugens (So. Africa: Cape Prov.); perennial fibrous rooted herb to 50 cm high, with basal rosette of numerous linear leaves, and tall spikes with small 2 cm bicolored flowers; the 3 inner petals are pale blue, and 3 outer petals of darker blue; fresh bloom opening each morning but closing in the afternoon; summer. *p. 1324*

ARISTOLOCHIA *Aristolochiaceae* **S3LFM**

brasiliensis (Brazil); climber with striped stems, kidney-shaped leaves, and flowers pale purple netted and spotted dark purple, tube purple inside, two unequal lips violet. *p. 351*

cymbifera (Brazil), "Birthwort"; tropical vine with kidney-shaped leaves, green above, whitish green underneath; the curious flower 16-20 cm long, two-lipped, the lower, flared lip twice as long as the upper, pale green or creamy green, conspicuously veined and dotted with maroon, and with unpleasant odor. *p. 352*

elegans (Brazil), "Calico flower"; graceful climber with kidney-shaped leaves, and flowers a yellowish, inflated tube and expanded cup rich purplish-brown inside with white markings, to 8 cm across. *Tropical. p. 351*

fimbriata (Argentina), a "Birthwort"; stems scarcely climbing with glabrous, kidney-shaped leaves and bent, odd-shaped irregular tubular calyx simulating a corolla; tube swollen at base; one-sided limb greenish-brown outside, purple-brown inside, veined yellow, fringed. *p. 351*

gigantea (Brazil); much like grandiflora var. hookeri, but with apex of limb obtuse (rounded); big flower with smooth surface lilac with red-brown spots, inside funnel dark brown; strong climber with cordate green leaves, underside bluish green. *p. 352*

grandiflora (gigas) (Jamaica), "Pelican flower"; climber with heart-shaped, downy leaves and large flowers like an expanded bent pipe, limb veined and spotted purple, with long tail. *Tropical. p. 351,*

leuconeura (Colombia), "Ornamental birthwort"; ornamental-leaved climber with glossy, yellow-green, heartshaped leaves with wide sinus, attractively veined cream-white. *Tropical. p. 351*

sturtevantii (grandiflora var.) (West Indies, C. America, So. America), "Swan Flower"; woody tropical climber to 3 m with downy, heart-shaped leaves, and very large downy flowers up to 50 cm long, with tails 1 m long under favorable conditions; yellowish-green inflated tube, and flaring limb veined and spotted purple. *p. 352*

tricaudata (Mexico); small tree with straggling branches, wrinkled ovate leaves 12-20 cm long; flowers dark brown-purple with three long tails. *p. 351*

trilobata (West Indies to So. America); evergreen tropical twiner to 3 m; the leaves deeply trilobed into obovate segments; curious large pitchers, the basal portion inflated and bent at right angles, pale green to beige and overlaid with a netted design of brown; terminal lid red-brown and extending into long reddish twisted tail. *p. 352*

AROPHYTON *Araceae* **S3HFW**

buchetii (Madagascar); large tropical epiphyte with big heart-shaped, fleshy green leaves on stout vaginate petioles; short stalked spadix with elongate swollen column. *p. 186*

humbertii (Madagascar); tropical aroid growing on rocks; to 80 cm high; leaves pedately dissected into narrow lanceolate leaflets; slender forward-curving spathe and long slender spadix on short floral stalk. *p. 186*

rhizomatosum (Madagascar); tropical plant with arrow-shaped, broad leaves, sometimes divided into 3 segments; the spathe long-lanceolate and slenderly erect almost hiding the small spadix. *p. 186*

simplex (Madagascar); tropical jungle plant with creeping rhizome, vegetating in the humusy forest floor; triangular sagittate green leaves with broad blade, the network of veins depressed. *p. 186*

tripartitum (Madagascar); creeping rhizome 4-7 cm long; fleshy green leaves divided into 3 elliptic segments; the central one 7-14 cm long; young foliage is undivided and hastate; floral stalk 10-20 cm long, with small 4-5 cm spathe, in a concave, pointed shield behind the 3 cm spadix. *Tropical. p. 186*

ARPOPHYLLUM *Orchidaceae* **I3OFM**

giganteum (Mexico, Guatemala); epiphyte with slender compressed pseudobulb bearing solitary linear leaves; small rosy-red flowers with purple lip; cylindric erect, dense raceme to 30 cm high. (April-June). *p. 1661*

spicatum (Mexico, Nicaragua), "Hyacinth orchid"; epiphyte with long leathery leaves, forming dense, spike-like raceme of cupped, carmine-rose flowers, 8 mm dia. *Tropical. p. 1660*

ARRABIDAEA: see Saritaea

ARTEMISIA *Compositae* **C2LBDh**

absinthium (Europe), "Wormwood"; herbaceous perennial with a woody rootstock, to 1 m with lobed leaves green and nearly glabrous above, white with cottony down beneath; yellowish flower heads. *p. 815*

dracunculus (Europe), "Tarragon" or "Estragon"; hardy herbaceous perennial with green linear leaves scented like anise; panicles of whitish flowers. Use: in salads, steaks, and other cookery; yields flavor to pickles. *Warm temperate. p. 815*

purshiana (Brit. Columbia, Calif., Nebraska), "Cudweed"; herbaceous perennial with stems to 1 m, covered alike both sides of the leaf with white wool; flower heads white. *p. 815*

ARTHROPODIUM *Liliaceae* **I1LBM**

cirrhatum (New Zealand); tufted perennial herb with fleshy roots, to 1 m high; numerous spreading flexible, lanceolate, light green, clasping leaves grayish beneath, with a narrow translucent edge and parallel veins; clusters of white flowers. *Subtropic. p. 1416, 1417, 1423*

ARTOCARPUS *Moraceae* **S2LBM**

altilis (communis, incisa) (Malaysia to Tahiti), the "Breadfruit tree"; milky-juiced tree to 20 m high, with handsome huge, deeply lobed, leathery leaves to 50 cm long or more, luxuriantly green with yellowish veins; large round or ovoid prickly fruit to 20 cm dia., yellow when ripe, tasting like bread when baked; or like sweet potato when cooked. As a result of reports by Capt. Cook, Captain Bligh was given the task of bringing the nutritious breadfruit from Tahiti to the British Antilles. In 1792, on his second voyage, he took 2500 young trees, sprouted from roots, to Jamaica, and these are now widely planted in the West Indies. *Tropical p. 1566, 1576*

heterophyllus (integrifolia) (India to Malaya), the "Jackfruit"; interesting tropical tree to 15 or 20 m high related to the breadfruit, with milky juice; glossy oblong leaves, lobed on younger branches; remarkable for its enormous fruit dangling directly from the trunk and biggest branches of the tree. This fruit is one of the largest in the world, ⅓ to 1 m long and weighing up to 18 kg.; a green knobby rind encloses a soft sweet or acid pulp of unpleasant odor, and is eaten raw or cooked, the seed roasted, in tropical Southeast Asia. *Tropical. p. 1585*

ARUM *Araceae* **I2LBMd**

conophalloides (Asia Minor); robust tuberous plant with hastate leaves about 20 cm long; inflorescence on stout stalk with tubular spathe white inside with purplish margins; the flaring blade narrowing to a long point 16-30 cm long, green outside, pale mauve inside; bold cone-shaped spadix. *p. 187*

dioscoridis (Eastern Mediterranean); handsome tuberous plant with hastate or sagittate 25-30 cm leaves on long petioles; the colorful spathe pale yellowish-green with large brown-purple areas and spots inside. *Subtropic. p. 187*

dracunculus (Dracunculus vulgaris) (Mediterranean Region); tuberous herb with green leaves divided into many segments; the bold spathe flask-shaped at base pale purple, with the flaring ovate limb 25-30 cm long, inside purplish-red, the club-like spadix purple. The name botanically correct would be Dracunculus vulgaris if the plant photographed matches its description. *p. 187*

hygrophilum (Syria, Lebanon, Israel, Cyprus); sagittate, fleshy leaves dark green; the inflorescence almost as tall as foliage; the attractive flask-shaped spathe yellowish-cream, green below, margins and deep in throat purplish-red; slender spadix wine-purple. *p. 187*

italicum (Europe, No. Africa), "Italian arum"; robust, tuberous plant with hastate, fresh-green leaves with whitish veining; spathe green, white inside with reflexed purple limb; the berry-like, fleshy fruit turns scarlet red as the foliage withers and disappears. *Subtropic. p. 162, 182*

korolkowii (orientale var.) (Asia Minor); tuberous herb about 30 cm high, with fleshy, brownish-green leaves of roundish outline and cordate base; spathe tubular at base, and white inside, to flaring blade deep black-purple; club-shaped spadix with separate male and female flowers and sterile flowers between these two zones. *p. 300*

maculatum (England to S.E. Europe and No. Africa), "Lords and ladies" or "Aaron's staff"; fleshy tuberous herb 30 cm high, with arrow-shaped leaves, usually black-spotted, withering in summer; long-stalked spathe 15-25 cm long pinched at the middle, light green and purple-spotted or margined, longer than the spadix; end of July, on stiff-erect stalks, the ripening berries turn scarlet red. All parts poisonous. *p. 187*

nigrum (C. and So. Europe); from a depressed globular tuber 5 cm diameter, rise broad arrow-shaped, dull green leaves 15-18 cm long on 25-30 cm petioles; short-stalked inflorescence with spathe constricted in the lower pale green part, then flaring into wide open ovate limb of deep purple. *p. 187*

orientale (Asia Minor); an Asiatic "Jack-in-the-pulpit"; tuberous herb about 30 cm high, with brownish, arrow-shaped leaves; the oblong spathe-tube white inside, the long-ovate, pointed lip blackish-purple but variable to greenish. *p. 187*

orientale albispathum (Asia Minor); tuberous herb 30 cm high, with brownish widely hastate lance-like leaves; oblong pointed concave spathe white with greenish tubular base. *p. 182*

palaestinum (sanctum) (Israel, Syria, Afghanistan), "Black calla"; tuberous plant with arrow-shaped, green leaves, followed by flower spike with dark spadix, and spathe green outside, black-purple within and the tapering limb. *Subtropic. p. 182*

ARUNDINA *Orchidaceae* **S3HFM**

graminifolia (Assam, Burma); terrestrial orchid, reedy stems with series of plaited leaves, clusters of showy terminal flowers 5-8 cm dia., rosy-lilac with purple lip and pale disk (spring). *p. 1661*

ARUNDINARIA *Gramineae* **I2LBM**

alpina (Mountains of Africa), "Mountain bamboo"; hollow-stemmed bamboo to 15 or more metres high, spreading densely but not in clumps from woody rhizomes, the culms 5-10 cm thick, turning yellow with age; the linear leaves to 20 cm long. I photographed this species in the bamboo forest at 2,430 m on the Kivu border of Zaire, typical gorilla country. *Subtropic. p. 1307*

amabilis (So. China, No. Vietnam), the "Tonkin cane" or "Lovely bamboo"; grown commercially in Kwangtung Prov. and Kiangsi; a noble rhizomatous bamboo spreading densely, and held in high esteem because of its straight, slender stems only slightly tapering, 1 to 5 cm dia. and reaching to 10 metres or more in height, in mature canes rarely interrupted by branches and therefore widely used for fishing rods, hop poles, plant stakes and fine handicrafts; the thin-leathery, oblong lanceolate leaves to 25 cm or more long, dark green above, glaucescent beneath and showing transverse venation, on twigs pendant when mature.
Subtropic to Tropical. *p. 1311*

auricoma (Japan); suckering bamboo with round slender stems 1-2 m high, dark purplish-green, stem sheaths persistent, hairy at margins and base, leaves 5-20 cm long, rounded at base, dark green striped with rich yellow, lower surface downy. *p. 1304*

chrysantha (Japan); freely colonizing small bamboo 1-2 m high, slender reed-like culms with several branches at one joint, smooth leaves 8-17 cm long, bright green. *p. 1304*

falconeri (Thamnocalamus) (Himalayas); handsome bamboo with dark green culms from 8 to 20 m high, and 4 to 5 cm thick, at nodes forming clusters of branches; the leaves to 10 cm long, pale green and finely toothed, glaucous beneath. Photographed in Kew Gardens, London.
Subtropic. *p. 1314*

funghomii (China: Kwangtung); attractive, broad-leaved, running bamboo with slender erect culms becoming 2 m high; 3-7 branches at the nodes; leaves light green above and glaucous beneath, 8-12 cm long. *p. 1304*

hindsii (Phyllostachys, Pleioblastus) (China, Japan); to 4 m high, with stems dark olive-green, flattened above branches; sheaths deciduous on culms, leaves to 20 cm long, gradually narrowed to base, glabrous, and glaucous beneath. *p. 1304*

longifolia (E. Asia); shaggy bush with thin 1/2 cm dia. green canes, weakly bending down under the weight of foliage; the narrow linear, flaccid leaves dark green, 10-12 cm long and 1 cm wide. *p. 1314*

palmata: see Sasa

vagans (Japan); a dwarf bamboo with stems to 1 m or more, very vigorous, rapidly spreading, with leaves 5-12 cm long. *p. 1304*

viridi-striata (Pleioblastus viridi-striatus) (Japan); a small fairly hardy running bamboo 1/2-1 m high, slender stems purplish green, with leaves 4 to 15 cm long x 3 cm wide, finely toothed and pubescent beneath, usually striped yellow in spring. *p. 1304, 1314*

ARUNDO *Gramineae* I2LBM

donax versicolor (So. Europe), the "Variegated giant reed"; majestic perennial grass, only 2 m high, with knotty rootstock and stout stems almost woody; arching ribbon-like leaves gray-green striped creamy white, to 60 cm long, alternately arranged on canes, and topped by showy plume-like panicles at first reddish, then white. Very impressive with its bold, bamboo-like leafy canes; quite ornamental in containers. *p. 1311, 1315*

ASARINA *Scrophulariaceae* I3HFM

antirrhiniflora (Maurandya) (Texas, California, Mexico); perennial vine with thin stems climbing by means of coiling petioles, halberd-shaped leaves, and showy, axillary, trumpet-shaped, purple flowers white in throat and belly. *p. 2052*

barclaiana (Maurandya) (Mexico); bright-flowered perennial climbing by coiling petioles, somewhat woody at base, with halberd-shaped leaves, axillary irregular trumpet-shaped purple flowers 4-8 cm long, downy outside; in various color forms from deep purple to rose or white; tube greenish; summer. *p. 2052*

erubescens (Maurandya) (Mexico), "Creeping gloxinia"; strongly vining, hairy plant with alternate, triangular, toothed, downy leaves and twining flowerstalks, bearing large, 8 cm trumpet-shaped blossoms having broad green sepals and carmine-rose corolla with pale throat spotted rose, blooming into Nov. *Tropical.* *p. 2052*

ASARUM *Aristolochiaceae* C2LFM

maximum (China); stemless perennial herb, with spreading rhizome, heart-shaped leaves 20 cm across, dark green mottled gray; 3-lobed fleshy bell-shaped flowers maroon-purple with white basal blotch, 6 cm dia., near the ground. *p. 351*

shuttleworthii (Virginia to Alabama); a stemless, rhizomatous "Wild ginger" with 1-2 attractive kidney-shaped, soft-leathery 8 cm leaves, dark green with silvery-green marbling; resin-scented flowers near ground-level, mottled violet. *p. 352*

ASCLEPIAS *Asclepiadaceae* I2LBD

curassavica (Trop. America), "Blood-flower"; showy perennial to 1 m with woody base, stems with milky sap; oblanceolate leaves 5-15 cm long, the flowers in umbels with reflexed, 5-parted corolla brilliant red-purple, exposing the crown of 5 orange horned hoods. *Tropical.* *p. 353, 376*

incarnata (E. No. America to Colorado), "Swamp-milkweed"; perennial milky herb to 1 m; long-lanceolate leaves, and showy clusters of small rose-purple flowers; the fruit containing seeds with long silk. *Temperate.* *p. 376*

macrantha (Trop. East Africa); robust shrubby perennial 50-80 cm high with milky juice, woody stems with white, hairy, lanceolate leaves; at apex with large clusters of vivid purple flowers. *p. 353*

syriaca (cornutii) (E. Canada to Kansas); milky herb with stout stem to 1 1/2 m, ovate leaves pubescent beneath; flowers in drooping axillary umbels with purplish corolla. *p. 353, 373*

tuberosa 'Vermilion', the "Red butterfly-weed"; a red colorform of the usually orange-flowered type, native from Maine to Arizona, perhaps the showiest of milkweeds, a perennial with rough-hairy stalks 1 m high, lanceolate, thickish, rugose leaves 5-15 cm long, and numerous small flowers in terminal umbels bright orange, with 5-parted reflexed corolla lobes. *p. 353*

x ASCOCENDA *Orchidaceae* S3OFM

'Media Arnold' (Ascocentrum x Vanda); bigeneric hybrid with erect inflorescence having lovely flowers about 5 cm across, obovate petals and sepals iridescent blush-mauve with violet, the small lip yellow and rich violet-magenta, of good substance. (August). *p. 1661*

ASCOCENTRUM *Orchidaceae* S3OFM

ampullaceum (Saccolabium) (Himalayas, Burma); short-stemmed epiphyte with many linear leaves and flowers in lateral, many-flowered, short-stalked raceme, bright rose-carmine with spurred lip, (March-June). (S) *p. 1660, 1662*

miniatum (Saccolabium) (Java, Philippines); pretty, small epiphyte with short erect stem clothed with ranks of linear leaves and short cylindric racemes of small but gay red-orange flowers. (Spring and fall). *p. 1663*

x ASCOFINETIA *Orchidaceae* S3OBM

'Peaches' (Neofinetia falcata x Ascocentrum curvifolium); vandaceous plant with leaves fan-like on short stem, erect cluster of dainty flowers, peach pink to purplish with darker lip (summer). *p. 1664*

ASCOGLOSSUM *Orchidaceae* S3OFW

calopterum (New Guinea); remarkably showy epiphyte; robust stem to 60 cm long, thickly leafy; leaves rigidly stiff, bi-lobed at apex; branched raceme 60 cm long, with many small, pretty 3 cm flowers rose pink to purplish. *Tropical.* *p. 1660*

ASCOTAINIA *Orchidaceae* S3HBM

viridifusca (Tainia) (Assam, Burma); robust terrestrial, with one-leaved pseudobulbs and flowers on an erect basal raceme to 1 m high, sepals and petals brownish olive-green, the lip yellowish-white, (Feb.-March). (S) *p. 1662*

ASPARAGUS *Liliaceae* I2LFM

africanus (cooperi) (So. Africa); resembling A. setaceus, with fleshy roots, and climbing tall trees; the lacy, fern-like sprays very dark green, and the thread-like branchlets not as fine as setaceus; leaves reduced to awl-shaped, red-brown prickles; berries red. *p. 1420*

asparagoides myrtifolius (Medeola) (Cape of Good Hope), the "Baby smilax" used for wedding decorations, etc.; graceful twining vine with thread-like stems and dainty, fresh glossy-green, little ovate leaves, to 2 cm long, usually allowed to climb on strings for cutting. *p. 1420, 1422*

cooperi (So. Africa); woody vine climbing to 20 m; bare branches spreading; numerous crowded branchlets with straight prickles; firm leaves very dark green, awl-shaped to 2 cm long, making fern-like sprays; flowers white, berries red. *p. 1422*

crispus (Cape of Good Hope); climbing or drooping plant forming a tuberous rootstock; stems herbaceous and weak, with zigzag branches and needle-like, 3-angled, laxly reflexed leaves bright green, coarsely set; fragrant flowers white; berries white or pink. *p. 1420*

densiflorus cv. 'Myers' (So. Africa), "Plume asparagus"; showy, tuberous rooted plant dense with stiffly erect, plume-like branches 60 cm or more high, the dense needle-like "foliage" rich green. *p. 1421, 1422*

densiflorus 'Myriocladus' (So. Africa: Natal), "Zigzag asparagus"; erect, much branched sinuous shrub to 1 1/2 m high, from swollen roots; woody gray stems with zigzag branches, the cladodes (branches simulating leaves) thread-like 1-2 cm long, in dense clusters, bright green. *p. 1421, 1422*

densiflorus sarmentosus (So. Africa); ornamental, stiff, somewhat pendant, woody stems, with numerous square branchlets set densely with cladodes for plume-like effect, the flat, linear, rigid leaf-like cladodes 1-2 cm long and bright green. *p. 1421*

densiflorus cv. 'Sprengeri' (Natal), "Sprengeri fern"; much branched from tuberous roots, scarcely climbing, the fluffy branchlets set with soft, fresh green needles, the true leaves reduced to thorns; small fragrant flowers white, followed by bright red berries. *Subtropic.* *p. 1420, 1421, 1422*

drepanophyllus (duchesnei) (Africa: Zaire); ornamental clamberer climbing to 10 m from tuberous rootstock with linear, sickle-shaped leaves to 8 cm long, forming spiny fern-like fronds; greenish flowers and scarlet berries. *p. 1421*

falcatus (Sri Lanka, So. Africa), "Sickle thorn"; widely climbing on woody stems to 11 m; branches straw-colored, slender and with rigid spines, the clustered, firm, bright-green leaves narrow and sickle-shaped, 8 cm long. *p. 1420*

macrowannii var. zuluensis (So. Africa); tall shrub with beige-brown woody stems, bearing branches with dense tufts of awl-shaped, needle-like cladodes (simulating leaves); true leaves are reduced to scales; large clusters of tiny white flowers. *p. 1422*

madagascariensis (Madagascar); warm-loving ornamental shrubby plant with erect branches about 30 cm high; angled green stems, the 3 lanceolate leaf-like phylloclades arranged in one plane, dark olive green less than 2½ cm long; bright red berries. *p. 1421*

retrofractus (So. Africa), "Zigzag shrub"; shrubby plant with beige-gray woody stem to 2 m long, with stiff, thorny zigzag twigs at angles, bearing dense bundles of curved needle-like cladodes (branchlets) bright green; true leaves reduced to scales; small white flowers. *Subtropic.* *p. 1422*

scandens deflexus (ramosissimus) (So. Africa), "Basket asparagus"; climber, with round green stems, much branched above, the flat leaf-like unarmed, light green cladodes linear and curved, to 2 cm long. In var. deflexus the branches are deflexed and very zigzag. *Subtropic.* *p. 1421*

setaceus (plumosus of hort.) (So. Africa), "Fern-asparagus"; climber with lacy, fern-like, rich green fronds of needle-like branchlets, arranged on a horizontal plane, on thin wiry stems with sharp prickles. *p. 1420*

setaceus 'Pyramidalis' (cupressoides), "Cypress asparagus"; a curious form of the "Fern-asparagus", of dense habit, with its needle-like cladodes as well as the stems all erect and striving straight upward like a cupressus. *Subtropic.* *p. 1421*

ASPASIA *Orchidaceae* **I3OFM**

epidendroides (Nicaragua to Panama); epiphyte with 1-2 leaved, oblong, 2-edged pseudobulbs, leaves lanceolate, the 5 cm flowers in loose racemes, sepals and petals greenish-yellow streaked with brown, lip creamy-white with purple brown spots (spring). (I). *p. 1662*

epidendroides principissa (Costa Rica, Panama); epiphyte 20-38 cm high, with 2-edged pseudobulbs and large 5-8 cm flowers with narrow segments light green lined with brown, large white lip marked with mauve (spring). (I) *p. 1662*

lunata (Brazil); compact growing epiphyte 22-30 cm high, with 2-edged pseudobulbs and 12-20 cm leaves; beautiful flowers with linear sepals and petals green tipped white, barred maroon; broad, fan-like lip white with red zone (early spring). (I) *p. 1662*

variegata (Brazil, Guyana, Trinidad); showy epiphyte of medium size, compressed pseudobulbs with paired leaves, and with handsome, long lived flowers 6 cm across, green with brown bars; 3-lobed lip white, dotted with violet (winter-spring). *p. 1660*

x ASPASIUM *Orchidaceae* **I3OFM**

'Regal' (Aspasia epidendroides x Oncid. wydleri); bigeneric hybrid; compressed pseudobulbs bearing leathery lanceolate leaves, and erect basal raceme with shiny deep brown and yellow flowers 3 cm across; 5 to 6 open at a time and flowering for many months starting in spring. *p. 1661*

ASPHODELINE *Liliaceae* **I2LBD**

lutea (Mediterranean Reg.), "Jacob's rod"; "Yellow asphodel" of the ancient Greeks; perennial with fleshy roots; stems to 1 m high, with leaves linear and needle-pointed; inflorescence a slender pyramid with yellow, fragrant, starry flowers 2 to 3 cm across. Differs from Asphodelus by having leafy stalks. *Subtropic.* *p. 1417*

ASPHODELUS *Liliaceae* **I2LBDh**

albus (Mediterranean Reg.), "Asphodel"; fleshy-rooted herb with linear, 3-angled basal leaves, and 60 cm stalks bearing inflorescence of white, funnel-shaped flowers. *p. 1417*

microcarpus (Canary Islands to Asia Minor), "Asphodel"; perennial herb with fleshy roots; rosette of broad, fleshy foliage; inflorescence on branched stalks to 1 m high, bearing starry white flowers with purple line on each petal. *Subtropic.* *p. 1417*

ASPIDISTRA *Liliaceae* ***I1LNM**

elatior (lurida) (China), "Cast-iron plant" or "Parlor palm"; old-fashioned tough-leathery foliage plant with thick roots and blackish-green, shining oblong basal leaves to 75 cm long, narrowed to a channeled stalk; purple bell-shaped flowers at the surface of the ground. Ideal for cool, unfavorable locations, very tolerant of neglect. *Subtropic.* *p. 1416*

elatior 'Minor' (Japan); an attractive dwarf plant which I first saw on the bank of the Muko river at Takaradzuka in southern Japan, and which the Japanese call "Amanokawa" (Milky Way), because of the multitude of white spots in the blackish leaf. *p. 1416*

elatior 'Variegata', "Variegated cast-iron plant"; attractive variegated form having leaves striped and banded alternately green and white in varied widths. *Subtropic.* *p. 1416*

minutiflora (China); cluster-forming plant to 30 cm high, from creeping rootstock; narrow, strap-like, flexuous foliage 3 cm wide, dark green. *p. 1435*

ASPIDIUM *Polypodiaceae (Filices)* **I3LFM**

capense, bot. Rumohra adiantiforme (So. America to Africa and Polynesia); the "Leatherleaf fern"; spreading fern with creeping rhizome, the deep glossy green bipinnate fronds are triangular in outline, of leathery texture and finely cut, lasting well when cut for floral arrangements. *p. 1100*

ASPIDIUM: see also Polystichum, Rumohra

ASPLENIUM *Polypodiaceae (Filices)* **I3HNW**

adiantum-nigrum (Mountains of Europe, Asia, Africa), the hardy "Black spleenwort"; tufted fern with creeping rhizome and bipinnate or tripinnate fronds 15-30 cm long, the lower pinnae deltoid, glossy green and leathery. *p. 1096*

antiquum (So. Japan); birdsnest-type rosette densely arranged with surrounding leaves narrow lanceolate, thin-leathery glossy fresh-green, with prominent reddish midrib, and with wavy margins. *p. 1096*

bulbiferum (New Zealand, Australia, Malaya), "Mother fern"; with wiry pinnate fronds, having grooved black stem; the pinnae fresh green, and much larger than viviparum and not as deeply lacily cut, the segments becoming linear only when spore-bearing; bulbils or plantlets are produced on upper surface of frond. *Humid-subtropic.* *p. 1097, 1098*

cardiophyllum (Micropodium) (Hainan, Taiwan); attractive, rare, small fern with leathery, sagittate leaves, gradually tapering toward apex, the large basal lobes overlapping, the surface matte green and corrugated. *p. 1096*

cristatum (Trop. America); shapely tufted fern with tri-pinnate fronds 15-30 cm long. *p. 1096*

falcatum (Polynesia, Australia, Sri Lanka); pendant fronds to 45 cm long on firm grayish stalks, with 12-20 pairs of leathery pinnae in nearly horizontal position, the leaflets 5-8 cm long taper to long point, and sometimes lobed and toothed, dark green. *p. 1096*

formosum (Nigeria); neat, dense rosette of narrow, pinnate, light green tufted fronds 8-18 cm long, the 1-2 cm pinnae toothed at margins, the short lower pinnae reflexed. *p. 1093*

friesiorum (E. Trop. Africa, So. Madagascar); long dark green, gracefully arching fronds to 60 cm long; resembling Boston fern but leaves are more spreading and more or less horizontal. *p. 1093*

lucidum (obtusatum lucidum) (New Zealand, Australia), "Leather fern"; decorative tree-growing fern with grayish stems and pendant pinnate fronds of graceful habit and shining-green, reaching 1 m in length; the oblong leaflets are leathery, 15 cm long and with toothed and wavy edge. *p. 1094*

mayii hort.; a seedling probably with vieillardii from Polynesia; of tufted habit, with short, gracefully arched pinnate fronds, the dark purplish-green pinnae well spaced and deeply notched. *Humid-subtropic.* *p. 1093, 1094*

myriophyllum (Trop. No. America); tufted fern with several times pinnate, lacy fronds 15-30 cm long, the closely set leaflets deeply cut into simple or forked linear segments, and of a thin, papery texture. *p. 1096*

nidus (nidus-avis) (India to Queensland and Japan), the "Birdsnest fern"; great epiphytic rosette of simple oblanceolate, stiffly spreading, shining, friendly green fronds anywhere from 30-90 cm long, of thin leathery texture with prominent blackish midrib and wavy margins, rising from a crown densely clothed with black scales. One of the most interesting and attractive of ferns for pots, keeping surprisingly well but should be kept steadily moist and warm, or new fronds may become deformed; avoid drafts; tolerates poor light to 25 fc. *Humid-tropical.* *p. 1093, 1095, 1097*

palmatum (Hemionitis), (Spain, Canary Isl., Azores, etc.); small tufted fern with hastate fronds 10-15 cm long, on dark stalks, with two lateral lobes and triangular, long-tapering central lobe, of papery texture. *p. 1096*

paradoxum (Java, Sumatra); leathery, pinnate fronds to 60 cm long, with large oblong-rhomboid terminal and 8-12 pointed pinnae each side, slightly toothed; on gray-scaly stalks. *p. 1098*

rutifolium (Japan, China, Polynesia, So. Africa); charming small tufted fern, with light green fronds 20-30 cm long, bipinnately cut into distant, narrow linear segments with a plumy look like a carrot-leaf. *p. 1093*

squamulatum (Malaya); rosette of lanceolate, thick-leathery leaves 30-45 cm long, 5-8 cm wide, gradually narrowing to both ends, with wavy margin and stout axis, scurfy in lower part. *p. 1098*

stuhlmannii (E. Africa: West shore of Lake Victoria, Kassese); small fern with short-stalked, pinnate fronds 30-35 cm long, 5 cm wide, the thin leathery pinnae sessile, triangular-ovate and 3-5-lobed toward apex. *p. 1098*

viviparum (Mauritius), "Mother fern"; tufted plant with dark green, finely lacy, arching fronds on firm stems, the little thread-like linear segments giving rise to tiny bulblets from which develop little plants. *Humid-tropical.* *p. 109*

ASPLUNDIA *Cyclanthaceae* **S3LFM**

humilis (Carludovica humilis) (Colombia); small palm-like plant nearly stemless, forming a rosette of spreading, very broad leaves on long, slender petioles, the rich deep green blades carried like umbrellas, and fan-like pleated, with parallel ribs 30-50 cm long and 25-30 cm wide, a cleft in top center, the apex jagged. *p. 94*

x ASPOGLOSSUM *Orchidaceae* **S3OFW**

'Success' (Aspasia principissa x Odontoglossum puritonia); beautiful bigeneric; flower with broad petals burnt crimson, edged white; lip white with bold center of blood-red. *p. 166*

ASTELIA *Liliaceae* **I2HFM**
nervosa (New Zealand); herbaceous, densely tufted, terrestrial perennial, with short, thick rhizome, and numerous linear, strap-like, glossy-green leaves sheathing near base, having prominent elevated parallel ribs; forming orange-red berries on female plants. *Humid-subtropic.* *p. 1425*
solandri (New Zealand), the "Kokaha"; remarkable epiphytic herb with sword-like leaves forming immense tufts often high on lofty trees on North Island, where they store water in the thick, curved bases of their circle of foliage. Linear leaves 1/2-1 m long, olive green, silky and recurving; pendant panicles of tiny pale yellow flowers, the female plants producing wine red berries. Collospermum hastatum may be a more valid name, but this is supposed to have broader leaves and larger flowers. *p. 1425*

ASTER *Compositae* **I2LBD**
filifolius (Diplopappus) (So. Africa); low evergreen bush to 1 m high, with smooth, needle-like leaves set in dense masses; bursting into a sheet of bloom of small 2 cm lavender blue daisies with yellow center. *p. 801*
fruticosus (Felicia) (So. Africa); shrubby plant with woody stems zigzag-branched 1 m high, leaves broadly linear; 2½ cm flower-heads solitary, ray-flowers purple, tubular disk-flowers yellow. *p. 815*

ASTER: see also Callistephus

ASTERANTHERA *Gesneriaceae* **I3HFM**
ovata (Columnea) (Chile); from the cool rainforests of southern Chile, it is a vine with long woody, brownish stems rooting at the nodes and creeping on tree trunks; small ovalish, dark green leaves 1-3 cm long, sparsely white-hairy, and toothed at margins; long stalks carry the relatively large, funnel-shaped carmine-red flowers, 4-6 cm long; the 3-lobed lower lip is banded with yellow and spotted crimson. *p. 1241*

ASTERISCUS *Compositae* **I2LBD**
maritimus (Odontospermum) (E. Mediterranean); small shrubby perennial covered with silky wool, with spatulate gray leaves; yellow daisy-like flowerheads among the tufts of foliage. *p. 813*
sericeus (Odontospermum) (Canary Islands); handsome dwarf shrub dense with small rosettes of silky-hairy, obovate green leaves 4-5 cm long; in the apex of branches nestle the pretty, thistle-like golden yellow heads 4 to 8 cm across, the large cushions of disk flowers surrounded by the spreading ray florets. *Subtropic.* *p. 822, 828*

ASTEROSTIGMA *Araceae* **S3LFMd**
lividum (Southern Brazil); from a depressed-globular tuber 2 to 5 cm dia. rise fleshy petioles 30-60 cm long, handsomely marbled and puckered; the thin-fleshy, glossy green leaves pinnatisect, 15-25 cm long; the 30-40 cm stalk bears a 10-12 cm inflorescence with reddish or spotted spathe. *p. 158*
lividum lineolatum (Brazil); tropical herb with 5 cm tuber, the foliage appearing later than the flowers; the narrow-lanceolate spathe grayish green with ochre stripes outside, brownish-purple inside, spadix yellowish and rose; mature leaves cut into many segments, young leaves kidney-shaped, on pale petioles spotted and streaked with violet. *p. 188*
riedelianum (Brazil); tropical tuberous herb 60 cm high; on a spotted and variegated leaf stalk is the 3-parted leaf, the middle part pinnatisect; spathe yellowish, greenish outside, spadix slender, shorter than the spathe. *p. 188*
vermicidum (No. Argentina. Tucumán, Salta); robust tuberous herb to 1 m high; the tuber 5-15 cm diameter, with solitary fleshy light green deeply dissected leaf 30-60 cm long, appearing after the inflorescence; the hooded spathe brown purple with small cone-shaped spadix nestling inside. *Subtropic.* *p. 188*

ASTILBE *Saxifragaceae* **C2LBW**
x arendsii (chinensis x japonica), "False spiraea"; vigorous hardy perennial 60-80 cm high; herbaceous, much divided ferny leaves; plume-like airy inflorescence on slender wiry stems, small white, pink or red flowers. Photographed in Gotland, Sweden. *Warm temperate.* *p. 2041*
japonica 'Deutschland'; cultivar with long graceful, pure white plumes; late-blooming. *p. 2039*
japonica 'Gladstone' (Japan), the florists' "Spiraea"; robust, hardy herbaceous perennial easily used for forcing in pots for Easter, when its fluffy, plumy, white flower spikes, carried well above the fern-like, pinnate foliage, are very showy and attractive. *p. 2039*

ASTROLOBA *Liliaceae* **'I1LBD**
skinneri (S. Cape Prov.); spiral succulent rosette 8 cm dia., dense with short triangular leaves concave on top, dark green and keeled on bottom, with whitish tubercles; spiny point at tip; tubular greenish flowers. *p. 1425*

ASTROLOBA: see also Apicra

ASTROPHYTUM *Cactaceae* **S1LBD**
asterias (No. Mexico), "Sand dollar"; low, dome-formed, with a star-shaped depression; green tinged coppery and covered with white scales, the areoles tufted with white wool; flowers yellow with red throat 4 cm across. *Arid-subtropic.* *p. 620, 640A, 683, 685*
capricorne (No. Mexico), "Goat's horn"; hard green globe to 25 cm with some silver marking, 7 or 8 ribs with contorted spines; spreading yellow flower with red throat. *Arid-subtropic.* *p. 620, 685, 686*
capricorne major; plant larger in all its parts, with angular or flattened ashy-gray spines, mostly twisted and curved upward; flower yellow, without orange-red center. *p. 686*
myriostigma (C. Mexico), "Bishop's cap"; small globe with usually 5 prominent ribs, spines absent, covered with small white spots; flowers yellow. *Arid-subtropic.* *p. 620, 683, 685, 686*
myriostigma nudum; a green form, with no white spots or markings of any kind, and thus conspicuous amongst Astrophytum; the flower is fuller, with a double row of petals. *p. 686*
myriostigma potosinum; freer-growing plant, depressed globose, without white spots, and smaller all-yellow flower. *p. 685*
myriostigma quadrocostatum, "Bishop's hood"; a variety divided equally by four broad ribs, resembling a real 4-sided parson's cap; the little yellow flower looks pretty in the center of the plump body. *p. 686*
myriostigma virens; variety having a rather plain and rugose yet beautiful, 5-sided bishop's cap body evenly and densely covered with fine gray scales. *p. 684, 685*
ornatum (Mexico), "Monk's hood"; small and hard plant subglobose or cylindric with 8 prominent spiral folds, green and beautifully marked with silvery spots, talon-like spines; flowers lemon-yellow. *Arid-subtropic.* *p. 618, 683, 685, 686*
ornatum aureispinum; smaller plant than ornatum, the little tufts of scales smaller and in narrower bands, areoles smaller and less, smaller spines; ribbon scales are golden brown; smaller lemon flowers. *p. 686*
ornatum mirbellii; a most lovely form with golden yellow spines, and body richly covered with scales of a shining silvery white. *p. 686*

ASYSTASIA *Acanthaceae* **I-S3LBM**
gangetica (India, Malaysia), "Coromandel"; herbaceous perennial with trailing and rooting or clambering stems; the opposite, small ovate, fresh green, thin leaves 3-8 cm long; on one-sided racemes, the soft-textured bell-shaped flowers with flaring petals 2-3 cm across, orchid pink flushed with purple, and pale throat. *Tropical.* *p. 41*

ASYSTASIA: see also Mackaya

ATHERURUS *Araceae* **I3LFM**
tripartitus (Pinellia) (Japan); low tuberous herb with depressed globular tuber 2½ cm diameter, petiole 35 cm carrying a tripartite rich green leaf; the inflorescence on a 25 cm stalk with light green spathe 6-10 cm long; the long spadix 15-25 cm. *p. 188*

ATHYRIUM *Polypodiaceae (Filices)* **C3HFM**
cruciatum congestum; small hairy fern forming tufts of narrow bipinnate fronds, with pinnae irregularly cut and twisted, and very short. Photographed by T. Everett of New York Botanical Garden. *p. 1092*
filix-femina (Europe, Asia, No. America), "Lady fern"; hardy fern with tufted, graceful feathery fronds with brownish stalks, scaly below, the leaflets deeply toothed and bright green. *p. 1106*
filix-femina angustatum (W. Canada to Alaska); one of the many forms of the Lady-fern; from creeping rhizome the bipinnate, herbaceous, fresh green, thin fronds to 2 m long, somewhat narrower than the type; semi-evergreen in mild areas but dying down in winters with heavy frost. *p. 1093*
felix-femina grandiceps (So. England); distinct variety with the brittle, bright green, bipinnate fronds having the distant segments ending in small crispy crests, and with a large crest at the apex of each frond. *p. 1103*
filix-femina 'Medusae'; remarkable small cultivar with crestate fronds, the leaves bipinnately forked and spread wide, but with tips as if stopped and curled into dense heads, even each little pinnule is fasciated into crested fans. *p. 1092*
felix-femina minutissima; bushy, clustering plant with light green foliage, in habit more compact than the species, with fronds smaller and pinnae shorter. *p. 1092*
felix-femina 'Multifidum'; one of the most beautiful and graceful of the crested forms; found wild in Scotland and elsewhere in Britain; handsome bipinnate fronds 1 m long and 25 cm broad, distinguished by the tips of its leaflets being regularly tasseled and repeatedly divided and being pale green. *p. 1098*
goeringianum pictum (Japan), "Miniature silver fern"; a winter-hardy little tufted fern with pretty variegated fronds, which are spearshaped, and pinnate, the segments toothed, the stalks wine-red, and a band of gray down through the frond. *p. 1106*

ATROPA *Solanaceae* **C2LBD**
belladonna (Europe to India), the "Deadly nightshade" or "Belladonna"; perennial herb to 1 m, with ovate leaves to 15 cm; bellshaped nodding, axillary 2½ cm flowers purplish-red, blue calyx enlarging to form a shining red 1 cm berry, very poisonous. The sap yields the drugs atropine and belladonna. *p. 2067, 2078*

ATTALEA *Palmae* **I3LBW**

cohune (Orbygnia) (Honduras), the "Cohune palm"; erect slender palm with trunk 15 to 20 m tall, and 30 cm thick, usually covered by old leaf bases; ascending pinnate fronds stiffly erect on massive petioles to 10 m long; 30-50 pairs of leaflets to 45 cm long, dark green and stiff; 8 cm egg-shaped fruit in grape-like clusters. *p. 1849*

crassispatha (Haiti); massive feather palm with erect, exceptionally lengthy pinnate fronds 8 m long, the petioles straight upwards, the leaflets dark green both sides; a tree maybe 10 m tall looking like gigantic feathers before showing any trunk; 8 cm fruit in large clusters. *p. 1855*

AUCUBA *Cornaceae* **C2LFD**

japonica 'Crotonifolia'; attractive cultivar with thinner and much broader leaves than japonica 'Variegata', the margins coarsely serrate, lighter green freely marbled and blotched yellow, as compared with variegata. *Warm-temperate.* *p. 855*

japonica 'Goldiana', "Gold-leaf bush"; mutant with large leaves almost entirely golden yellow and only the margins light green. *p. 855*

japonica 'Picturata', also known in horticulture as "Goldiana", the "Golden laurel"; mutant with large leaves almost entirely golden yellow and with only the margins light green, and occasionally dotted yellow. A truly showy colorform although more easily subject to leafscorch or spotting from wetness, due to the absence of chlorophyll. *Subtropic.* *p. 856*

japonica 'Serratifolia', "Sawtooth laurel"; vigorous bushy variety; the willowy stems densely covered with rather narrow, thin-leathery lanceolate leaves 5 x 20 cm, waxy plain blackish green; the margins very much serrated. *p. 855*

japonica 'Variegata' (Himalayas to Japan), "Gold dust tree"; evergreen shrub with opposite shining leathery elliptic leaves to 18 cm long, dark green blotched yellow, and toothed above middle; purple flowers; the female plants with scarlet berries. *Warm-temperate.* *p. 855, 856*

AUGUSTA *Rubiaceae* **S3LBD**

grandiflora (Eastern Brazil); tropical evergreen shrub with glossy green, leathery ovate, slender pointed leaves; the inflorescence brush-like, with thread-like stamens from a central cushion. *p. 2008*

AVERRHOA *Oxalidaceae* **I2LBM**

carambola (India to China), the "Carambola tree" or "Oxalis tree"; evergreen 5-10 m high, with pinnate leaves of 5-9 leaflets which close when touched or at night; small fragrant flowers white marked with purple; the fleshy drooping 10 cm fruit ribbed, yellowish-brown, quince-scented and edible. *Subtropic.* *p. 1848*

AYENSUA *Bromeliaceae* **I2LFD**

uaipanensis (Venezuela); stem-forming rosette from Mt. Uaipan at 1800 m, developing cushions 40-60 cm high; stems covered with old dry leaf bases; leaves narrow triangular 3-10 cm long, light green; the inflorescence deep in center of the nesting leaves, with white flowers. *p. 528, 552*

AYLOSTERA *Cactaceae* **S3LBD**

deminuta (Rebutia) (No. Argentina); small globes freely suckering, fresh green, with numerous knobs and white to brownish rigid spines, to 6 cm dia.; free blooming even as young plant, with shimmering, coppery orange flowers. This species also described under Rebutia, but according to Backeberg placed under Aylostera. *p. 682*

AZALEA (botanically RHODODENDRON) *Ericaceae* **C-I2HBM**

AZALEA, CULTIVATED SPECIES

calendulacea (Rhododendron) (Pennsylvania to Georgia), "Flame azalea"; deciduous shrub 2-4 m high, with elliptic leaves 5-8 cm long, pubescent when young; sticky-hairy; funnel-form 5 cm flowers orange-yellow to scarlet, with long stamens, blooming after leaves unfold, May-June. *p. 973*

'Concinna' ('Queen Elizabeth'); according to Haerens Tuinbouw, probably a strong growing, erect cultivar of 'Phoenicea' which is a variety of Rhododendron pulchrum originally introduced from China. This 'Concinna' has replaced 'Phoenicea' as understock for grafting of tender Rhodo. simsii hybrids, commonly known as "Belgian Indica azaleas"; hairy branches with elliptic or oblanceolate leaves 6 cm or over, matte dark green above, glossy beneath, and thinly furnished with appressed brown hairs on both sides; flowers large when grown under glass 5-8 cm dia., wide-open, single, purplish crimson rose spotted crimson on upper petals, the margins lightly wavy. *p. 1001*

indica balsaminaeflora (Rhod. rosaeflorum) (Japan); very low growing and spreading multiple branching shrub with tiny, narrow leaves and relatively large, salmon-red double flat flowers of 40 petals, late blooming in June. *p. 973*

mollis (Rhod.) (China); deciduous shrub 1/2-1 m high, young branches hairy, 10-15 cm leaves gray pubescent beneath; flowers broad funnel-shaped, 5 cm across, golden yellow, May. *p. 973*

mucronulata (Rhod.) (No. China); shrub to 2 m with erect branches, deciduous or half evergreen, the narrow leaves 2 1/2-8 cm long, bell-like flowers appearing before leaves, rose-purple, to 4 1/2 cm dia., in profusion. *p. 973*

nudiflora (Rhod.) (Maine to Texas); deciduous shrub 1/2-2 m high, 4-10 cm leaves green on both sides; 4 cm flowers in clusters, appearing before foliage, pink to nearly white, with extending stamens, May. *p. 973*

obtusa amoena 'Purple Heart'; select cultivar with attractive small single flowers vivid purple, darker and larger than the species, very floriferous on a dense bush; flowers late; hardy. *p. 994*

obtusa kaempferi (Rhododendron) (Japan); evergreen azalea to 2 1/2 m high, much branched, leaves 2 1/2 cm long, shining green; with single funnelform 5 cm flowers, orange or brick red with darker blotch, April-May blooming, and considered one of the hardiest in the New York area; a parent of many of the salmon pot azaleas. *p. 973*

ponticum (Rhododendron) (Spain, Portugal, Asia Minor, Caucasus); evergreen shrub 4 to 6 m high, forming thick trunks, the sticky branches with rough-hairy obovate leaves 8 to 15 cm long; flowers in large trusses, light purple spotted with yellow-green, 5 cm across; blooming May-June. Parent of many fine hybrids. *p. 986*

AZALEA, EVERGREEN HYBRIDS

'Baby Jill' (Mossholder-Bristow simsii x rutherfordiana hyb.); compact growing evergreen, 8 cm hose-in-hose flowers semi-double, pastel lavender-pink with darker vein in center; midseason, holds well. *p. 1000*

'Beckii' (Plant Patent 1699, 1958); vigorous bushy evergreen described as a Kurume type, believed to be a sport mutation of Hinodegiri found at Voster's in Pennsylvania; 5 cm flowers with 3-4 telescoped corollas, deep pink; similar to 'Rose-Pericat'. *p. 1001*

'Blaauw's Pink'; a Dutch cultivar, evergreen with small elliptic leaves and small 4 1/2 cm hose-in-hose flowers light shell pink, darker salmon-rose in throat; late blooming and fairly hardy. *p. 1001*

'Christmas White'; a Yoder hybrid for commercial pot culture; compact plant with spreading branches and intense dark green foliage; semi-double medium size hose-in-hose type, star-shaped white flowers, with contrasting centers of deep chartreuse; normally forces for Christmas without controlled pre-cooling. *p. 987*

'Delaware Valley White'; form of Rhod. mucronatum; a woody, semi-evergreen plant of robust, somewhat sparry, tall habit, with obovate, shiny light green leaves and large single, pure white 6-8 cm flowers; late blooming; hardy. *p. 987*

'Desert Rose' (M-B simsii x rutherfordiana hyb.); compact evergreen with large single salmon pink blooms, the upper part of flower darker and marked red in throat; early. *p. 1000*

'Easter Bonnet' (M-B simsii x rutherfordiana hyb.) compact evergreen with large foliage, single 6 cm flowers white with rosy-lavender edge, and frilled. Easter-blooming, holding well. *p. 1000*

'Easter Parade' (M-B simsii x rutherfordiana hyb.); evergreen with large hose-in-hose flowers like simsii, pinkish-white variegated; late flowering. *p. 1000*

'Elizabeth Gable'; a Gable hybrid, indicum with poukhanense and kaempferi, very hardy; spreading bush, with medium size hose-in -hose flowers light purple, and wavy petals spotted carmine; late blooming. *p. 994*

'Esmeralda'; a Boskoop cultivar, rather straggly-growing evergreen with small 2 cm single flowers light pink; fairly hardy. *p. 998*

'Eureka'; U.S.D.A. Beltsville seedling, kaempferi x Snow, spreading Kurume type evergreen with large glossy green, obovate leaves, and covered with roundish 1 cm hose-in-hose flowers delicate lavender pink with deeper center and red spotting on upper half of throat; fairly hardy. *p. 1001*

'Gov. Meyner'; robust Bauman Kurume x kaempferi hybrid, floriferous, 3 cm single flowers fiery red; late. *p. 999*

'Hershey Red' (Hershey Nurs. about 1945); result of hybridizing with seedlings of Kurume varieties including Hinodegiri; shapely evergreen plant with glossy, olive green foliage, and beautiful full round, flaring, 5 cm hose-in-hose flowers clear rosy-crimson, blooming late, and ideal for Mother's Day mid May, Resembling a small indica it has withstood temperatures to -15°C but is apparently not bud-hardy in Pittsburgh, and foliage may "burn" if lower than -10°C. *p. 987*

'Kingfisher' (Whitewater hyb. Washington); grown by Yoder; frost-tender; habit shapely and spreading; the glossy foliage sets off clusters of large 8-9 cm carmine-rose, hose-in-hose flowers; keeping quality outstanding; early to midseason bloom. *p. 987, 992*

'Linwood Pink'; (Fischer hybrid, Atlantic City); vigorous evergreen exceptionally good but of limited hardiness; medium-large 5 cm hose-in-hose flowers soft rose, similar to 'Roehrs Tradition' but with daintily frilled margins. *p. 987*

'Louise Gable' (Gable, Stewartstown, Pa.) indicum-kaempferi hybrid of spreading sparry habit with medium small semi-double, broad petaled flowers of fine lavender-pink; somewhat deciduous; late blooming. *p. 994*

'Mrs. L. C. Fisher'; spreading sparry but pretty hardy 'macrantha hybrid', somewhat deciduous; with small hose-in-hose light carmine-rose flowers heavily marked crimson, the pointed petals recurved; midseason. *p. 996*

'My Valentine'; Brooks hybrid of simsii with obtusum; tender commercial cultivar from the West Coast, for pot culture; fast grower but does not bud too well; compact plant with large, dark green leaves; big double 8 cm flowers deep pink; similar to 'Edgard Tinel'. *p. 987*

'Penncrest'; well-branched semi-evergreen hybrid with leathery obovate leaves, covered with masses of 3 cm single flowers rose-pink shaded darker at margins, purple spotting in throat; mid-season to late; fairly hardy. *p. 998*

'Placid'; U.S.D.A. Beltsville hybrid of kaempferi x Snow; evergreen, good grower of irregular habit, 4 cm smallish flowers hose-in-hose, petals separated, pure white; fairly hardy. *p. 1001*

'Polar Bear' (Firefly x Snow), a 'Beltsville' hardy type azalea suitable for late blooming, small-flowered 4 cm floriferous, pure white, hose-in-hose with flaring petals; shining green foliage. *p. 993*

'Princess Caroline' (M-B simsii x rutherfordiana hyb.); free-blooming evergreen with shiny foliage with large 8 cm double flowers rose with spotting of red; early. *p. 1000*

'Roehrs Double Coral Bells', (Roehrs 1950) (Keller No. 27 x Coral Bells); vigorous seedling;fresh green foliage and cupped flowers larger than 'Coral Bells', having three rows of rounded petals, vivid salmon pink. *p. 994*

'Roehrs May Rose'; a 'Roehrs hardy', kurume x kaempferi cross, loaded with small hose-in-hose flowers of vivid rose, but smaller than 'Mothers Day'; late (May) blooming. *p. 993*

'Roehrs Mother's Day' (Roehrs 1956); an outstanding hybrid of the new group of hardy azaleas developed in Dr. Bauman's azalea garden, by bees, from Kurumes and the late-blooming kaempferi; vigorous habit, May flowering, with clusters of medium size, hose-in-hose, but occasionally single, frilled flowers of vivid clear rose-pink, 4-5 cm across. *p. 960A, 999*

'Roehrs Orchid'; a 'Roehrs-Bauman' hybrid of more sparry growth but pretty with its medium-size crisped, single flowers in a rare shade of rosy lavender; fairly hardy and May-blooming. *p. 999*

'Roehrs Peggy Ann'; a 'Roehrs hardy'; one of the loveliest creations the bees have brought about between kurume and kaempferi, small 4 cm wide open flowers with two rows of white petals edged in rosy-pink like apple blossoms; late blooming. *p. 960A, 999*

'Roehrs Salmon' (Roehrs-Bauman hyb. B2); Kurume-kaempferi blood, compact evergreen with glossy leaves, occasionally subject to tip-burn; single 2½-3 cm flowers rich salmon-rose with deeper shading, lighter than 'Gov. Meyner', late-blooming; fairly hardy. *p. 992, 998*

'Roehrs Tradition' (Roehrs-Bauman hyb. B3); evergreen Kurume-kaempferi cultivar of low, shapely, compact habit, with small shiny leaves which hold well through winter; hose-in-hose 3-3½ cm flowers deep carmine-pink, lighter than R. Mother's Day; fairly hardy. *p. 998*

'Rose Parade' (M-B simsii x rutherfordiana hyb.); compact growing evergreen with 6 cm very double, ruffled flowers rosy-pink shading deeper inside; Easter-blooming, good keeper. *p. 1000*

'Sun Valley' (M-B simsii x rutherfordiana hyb.); late-blooming evergreen with buds cream, opening to pure white, hose-in-hose, 6 cm flowers. *p. 1000*

'White Orchids' (M-B simsii x rutherfordiana hyb.); evergreen with 8 cm flowers usually single, white except for upper part which is speckled red suggesting an orchid. *p. 1000*

INDICA (R. LATERITIUM) HYBRIDS:

'Shinnyo-no-tsuki'; ('Moon of the real Moon'); a spectacular hybrid with large single flowers of 8 cm dia., white, with broad crimson border, May flowering; developed as one of the 'Satsuki' (Fifth Moon) race of azaleas for beauty of leaves and flowers both, from the Japanese species indicum (lateritium). *p. 973*

'Tanima-no-Yuki' (Japan) (Snow-of-the-Valley); a favorite in Japan and often grown as bonsai (dwarfed tree) with single white flowers beautifully edged orange red. *p. 1001*

AZALEA 'KURUME HYBRIDS', small-flowered evergreen azaleas originated on Kyushu Island in southern Japan during the Meiji era (1868-1912), from species involving Rhododendron obtusum, obtusum 'kaempferi' and kiusianum:

'Coral Bells' (Kirin); low, freely branching and early blooming plant with shiny, fresh green leaves, covered with a multitude of 3 cm bell-shaped hose-in-hose flowers of dainty silver-pink, shading to coral-pink in center. *p. 960A, 995*

'Coral Bells Supreme' (Plant Patent 1575, 1957); densely branching compact evergreen with small glossy leaves, sport of 'Coral Bells' with semi-double coral-pink flowers darker in center, larger than parent, about 3 cm across. *p. 998*

'Hino-crimson'; Kurume type evergreen similar to Hinodegiri but while its growth is more compact, it is an improvement over Hinodegiri in that its single flowers are a clear crimson red without the bluish overtones; late bloomer, fairly hardy. *p. 989*

'Hinodegiri' (Mist-of-the-Rising-Sun); an old favorite, bushy 'Kurume', fairly hardy with glossy foliage and small 3 cm single flowers vivid carmine-red; late blooming. *p. 960A, 995*

'Salmon Beauty'; free growing 'Kurume' with medium small 4 cm hose-in-hose flowers of an even light salmon shade, with spreading, recurved petals; early midseason. *p. 995*

'Snow'; popular 'Kurume'; willing grower with rich green, glossy foliage covered by masses of small 3 cm pure white, hose-in-hose flowers with freely spreading petals; early and midseason. *p. 995*

'Stewartstownian' (Gable-Pennsylvania); evergreen Kurume type hybrid, involving kaempferi and poukhanense blood, habit shrubby or straggly with small leathery leaves but quite hardy; single flowers 4-5 cm, brick-red. *p. 998*

AZALEA 'PERICAT HYBRIDS' (Belgian Indica x Kurume):

'Fortune'; vigorous plant with spreading branches, and relatively large 6 cm flowers semi-double and double carmine rose, with typical broad petals of good substance; midseason. *p. 997*

'Gardenia Supreme'; spreading plant with dark foliage and firm medium-size 4 cm flowers semi-double and double white with a touch of blush-pink and some violet dots; midseason. *p. 997*

'Marjorie Ann'; spreading, somewhat straggly hybrid with dark foliage and medium small semi-double to double rose-bud type flowers with broad petals, a pretty shade of salmon; midseason. *p. 996*

'Pride of Detroit'; sport of 'Mad. Pericat', an outstanding variety noted for its color and keeping quality, of spreading growth habit, with large round flaring flowers vivid fiery red, having a double row of petals but somewhat shy; midseason to late. *p. 993*

'Redwing' (Pericat hyb.); rapidly growing evergreen, requiring twice as much pinching as other Azaleas if grown for pot culture or else they will grow loose, straggly and floppy; large, wide open showy flowers, 8 cm or more, with two rows of petals, ruffled at the margins, cerise-red. Flowers larger and more frilled than 'Lentengroet', but buds normally best in older specimen. *p. 986, 992*

'Rival'; plant of vigorous upright habit, good dark green foliage and fairly large, 5½ cm lovely bright salmon rose flowers with two or three rows of broad petals, or double; rosebud type; midseason. *p. 997*

'Rose Pericat' (1931); one of the best 'Pericat' hybrids, of robust bushy growth, dark foliage and 6-7 cm pleasing clear pink double flowers with salmon sheen, center lacy and with red lines in throat, outer petals form a star; blooms early. *p. 960A, 996, 1001*

'Sensation'; vigorous variety and prolific bloomer with medium-small full round cup-like flowers of broad petals, hose-in-hose, light carmine-rose; late midseason. *p. 996*

'Sweetheart Supreme' (1931); probably the best liked of 'Pericat' hybrids, of strong spreading, irregular growth; the buds are rosy-pink unfolding like a dainty sweetheart rose, opening flat to starlike 5 cm flowers with successively smaller circles of delicate pink petals toward center; midseason to late. *p. 960A, 997*

AZALEA RUTHERFORDIANA HYBRIDS (1937), involving indica alba, Omurasaki, Belgian Indica, macrantha, Kurume and Rhododendron; many good qualities recommend this excellent evergreen pot-forcing class: vigorous growth, attractively irregular in older specimens; dark leathery foliage, and flowers borne in trusses, of long lasting quality; the result of years of breeding by Bobbink & Atkins Nurseries of New Jersey.

'Alaska' (1937), (Vervaeneana alba x Snow, with Rhododendron); very satisfactory hybrid of vigorous habit, dark elliptic foliage, and trusses of medium large 6 cm semi-double hose-in-hose pure white flowers; early forcer. *p. 960A, 988*

'Albion'; robust grower, irregular and loose in habit, with dull green leaves on erect trusses of clustered pure white flaring flowers, hose-in-hose of medium 5-6 cm diameter, with pointed petals and white anthers, and greenish throat, late. *p. 989, 992*

'Constance'; vigorous lovely variety with large trusses of medium-large single frilled flowers, vivid cerise pink; early, midseason. *p. 991*

'Dorothy Gish'; attractive variety with trusses of medium large, 6 cm flowers deep salmon, marked crimson on upper petals, hose-in-hose; midseason to late. *p. 991*

'Early Wonder'; excellent shapely variety with elegant, 'indica' type large round flowers of heavy texture, semi-double to double, bright rosy red with salmon sheen; early, and can be flowered for Christmas. *p. 960A, 990*

'Mary Corcoran'; vigorous, showy variety with lovely medium small, tubular-spreading, single flowers of apricot-pink flushed rose, and with distinct red markings on upper petals; midseason-late. *p. 990*

'Mother of Pearl'; strong grower with clusters of medium-size hose-in-hose, frilled flowers white flushed pink, spotted purple on upper petals; midseason to late. *p. 988*

'Mrs. Alice Mueller'; vigorous plant with medium size hose-in-hose or semi-double flowers bright rose pink marked red, the petals irregular and twisted; late. *p. 991*

'Orange Queen'; prolific bloomer with smaller 3 cm hose-in-hose to double flowers dense with petals, salmon-pink with purplish eye; late blooming. *p. 988*

'Pres. F. D. Roosevelt'; robust variety with medium-large 'indica' type flowers semi-double or double, bright salmon red, petals frilled; midseason. *p. 990*

'Purity'; shapely plant with dark leathery foliage contrasting with the pure white double flowers of smaller size, borne in mass in early midseason; responds to forcing for Christmas. *p. 988*

'Rhapsody'; floriferous plant with medium size, substantial semi-double flowers clear apricot salmon; late. *p. 991*

'Salmon Glow'; densely floriferous variety with trusses of medium-small semi-double flowers of beautiful bright salmon; midseason. *p. 993*

'Salmon Perfection'; floriferous variety with immense trusses of medium large semi-double to double flowers in a delightful shade of bright salmon-rose; late. *p. 990*

AZALEA 'SIMSII HYBRIDS' or **'Belgian Indica'**: descendants of Rhododendron simsii native in moist-warm subtropical Central China, Yunnan and along the Yangtse, deep rosy-red, to 4 m high. These hybrids were developed primarily for their large and showy double flowers, principally in Belgium, for forcing and flowering in pots; they are usually grafted on understock of 'Phoenicea concinna' for better growth and longer life; not winter hardy in cold climate.

'Adventgloeckchen' (Chimes) (1929), ('Paul Schaeme' x 'Fred Sander'); bushy plant with bell-shaped medium flowers glowing carmine-rose, semi-double, and of good texture; early to mid-season. *p. 982*

'Albert-Elizabeth' (1921); loosely growing variety, a unique bud sport of Vervaeneana, with large double flowers to 9 cm dia., not unlike rhododendron in form, glistening white and decorated with a salmon-red border and marked green on lower petals; midseason. *p. 960A, 984*

'Ambrosiana' (1948) ('Mad Petrick' x 'Reinhold Ambrosius'); superb early flowering, fairly new German hybrid easily forced for Christmas; vigorous grower with obovate glossy leaves and 7½ cm double flowers like little roses, glowing crimson red. *p. 980*

'Anytime'; a simsii "Belgian indica" hybrid, sport of 'Jean Haerens' with 6 cm double flowers soft salmon-rose; willing to bloom over a long period; originated by Hahn's Greenhouses, Pittsburgh, Pennsylvania. *p. 986*

'Beatrice', sport of 'Paul Schaeme'; large double, brick-red flowers, darker and richer salmon than 'Paul Schaeme'; of good substance; early and for Christmas. *p. 981*

'Blushing Bride' (1911), sport of 'Rudolf Seidel'; robust plant with very large flowers semi-double, in a dainty shade of blush-pink, of good substance; late. *p. 980*

'Brilliant'; a Southern Sun hybrid, cultivar of the group known and grown in California and the deep South as the "Southern sun azaleas"; a phoeniceum hybrid of vigorous habit, evergreen with obovate, olive green leaves, and large single, wide open funnel-flowers 6-8 cm across, carmine-red with crimson spots and lightly frilled. Much planted in Southern gardens; slightly hardy. *p. 975*

'Buergermeister Gloeckner' (1928), (Ernest Thiers x Hexe); vigorous variety very floriferous with medium size semi-double flowers burning red; midseason to late. *p. 982*

'Chimes'; grown under this name on the Pacific Coast but appears to be the same as 'Adventgloeckchen'; of full shapely habit, with leathery, glossy obovate foliage and firm semi-double flowers with rounded petals 8 cm across bright glowing rosy carmine; early. *p. 992*

'Eclaireur' (1914), (Eggebrechtii x Etoile de Noel); a sturdy grower with leathery leaves and medium-size flowers rather round and smooth, semi-double to double, rich carmine or wine-red; tends to burn; midseason. *p. 984*

'Eri' (Eric Schaeme) (1930), sport of 'Paul Schaeme'; dense habit with flowers double with small rosette in center, vivid salmon rose, variegated and margined white; early. *p. 977*

'Ernest Thiers' (1890); sturdy plant of vigorous, even growth with leathery leaves, and medium large semi-double flowers bold crimson-red, petals of good texture; late. *p. 984*

'Euratom'; a dwarf simsii hybrid similar to 'Hexe' but with frilled flowers, vivid crimson with glistening hose-in-hose funnels, on plant of compact habit with broad, dark green foliage. *p. 986*

'Fiesta' (pat. 1957), (Hexe x Mme. Chas. Vuylsteke); compact, bushy plant with firm leathery, dark leaves, and hose-in-hose, medium large flowers intense cherry-red with ruffled edges, profusely produced in large clusters; midseason to late. *p. 985*

'Haerens alba' (1921), sport of 'Avenir'; strong grower very floriferous with double white, frilled flowers, with a touch of pink in the center; midseason. *p. 980*

'Haerens Beauty' (1950); very attractive 'Paul Schaeme' seedling, similar to 'Roberta', with double flowers of good substance and frilled petals soft shell pink with outer areas silver pink; midseason. *p. 977, 989*

'Haerens rubra'; sport of 'Avenir', excellent variety, 'Haerens' habit, with large double deep salmon-red flowers; midseason. *p. 982*

'Hexe' (1888) (simsii x obtusum amoenum); excellent late season potplant, very freeblooming and of dwarf but even habit, with dark green leaves, and long lasting 5 cm flowers a glowing crimson coming alive under light, the hose-in-hose petals recurved and frilled. *p. 11*, 985*

'Hexe de Saffelaere' (1934), (Prof. Wolters x Hexe); a larger version of the popular 'Hexe', bushy variety with vivid crimson red flowers of medium size, 5½ cm hose-in-hose, with frilled petals; does well on own root; midseason to late. *p. 960A, 985*

'Ideal' (1911), early blooming (Christmas) variety of 'Mad. Petrick'; with growth similarly weak but grown because of its earliness; medium large double flowers clear lively rose bordered by tender pink. *p. 979*

'Juliet'; Roehrs 1938 hybrid, Fred Sanders, Paul Schame, and Hexe, of robust, bushy habit with fleshy medium-sized deep green leaves and substantial 6-8 cm semi-double flowers of bright and burning salmon red; spotted red in throat; mid-season. *p. 992*

'Lentegroet' (Easter Greetings) (1909), (Camille Vervaene x Hexe); similar to Hexe but with larger flowers, 2-3 times the size, crimson-red semi-double; midseason. *p. 985*

'Leopold-Astrid' ('Picotee'); simsii hybrid 1933; sport of 'Vervaeneana'; a lovely improvement over 'Albert-Elizabeth', with very pretty, 8 cm double flowers white with pink, and bordered in a rich salmon-red, the margins daintily frilled; mid-season. *p. 986*

'Lydia Haerens'; robust grower with healthy dark leaves and medium size double pure white flowers of good substance and similar habit as 'Vervaeneana'; midseason. *p. 980*

'Madame August Haerens' (1912), sport of 'Avenir'; and color similar to 'Prof. Wolters', large double flowers to 12 cm diameter, bright rose with pinkish white borders; midseason. *p. 977*

'Madame Cyrille Van Gele' (1936), (same as 'Salmon John Haerens'); sport of 'Mad. J. Haerens', robust grower with fine dark foliage and large substantial double flowers orange-red; midseason. *p. 983*

'Madame John Haerens' (1907); an excellent and free-blooming variety of vigorous habit and even growth, the large double flowers are elegant and firm, of a pleasing shade of deep rose, (midseason or late). *p. 960A, 983*

'Mme. Mestdagh'; compact simsii hybrid with dark foliage, and substantial, 6 cm semi-double flowers carmine-rose with purple spots, the margins pale pink or white. *p. 986*

'Madame Petrick' (1901); not a strong grower but is known for its dependably early bloom and forces readily for Christmas, double flowers medium large and a bright carmine rose. *p. 976*

'Mme. Robert Haerens'; a "Belgian indica" tender simsii hybrid from Ghent; bushy plant with large obovate blackish foliage, and lovely rose-pink single flowers, with broad rounded petals and carmine spots. *p. 986*

'Madame Van der Cruyssen' (1867); known for its exceptionally vigorous growth and free-blooming; with large single and semi-double flowers of good substance, carmine rose with crimson markings in upper petals; midseason. *p. 981*

'Mme. Van Oost'; a tender "Belgian indica" simsii hybrid with large, dark green foliage, and big 8 cm semi-double bell-shaped flowers soft salmon-red. *p. 986*

'Memoria Haerens'; very striking sport of Mad. Koningk, with large semi-double flowers to 10 cm dia., white or pinkish with contrasting border of cerise to fuchsia-red; against the lighter crimson of Mad. Koningk; midseason. *p. 992*

'Memoria Sander' (1923); a compact grower and good forcer for Christmas and early bloom, with substantial fully double rosy crimson, large flowers, having a purplish sheen under light. *p. 976*

'Moederkensdag'; evergreen Dutch cultivar of habit similar to 'Hexe' with short obovate leaves glossy bronze-green, and full round single flowers 6 cm dia., rich crimson-red; fairly hardy. *p. 998*

'Niobe' (1879); robust grower with blackish green leaves, and large double frilled flowers pure white with green chartreuse tint at base of petals; midseason to late. *p. 978*

'Orange Triumph'; sport of 'Triumph' with double flowers in frilled petals, vivid orange with red sheen; early to midseason. *p. 976*

'Paul Schaeme' (1912), (Vervaeneana x Pres. Oswald de Kerckhove); well-known as an early forcer for Christmas, combined with robust growth; large double flowers light salmon-red, of good texture. *p. 983*

'Perle de Swynaerde' (1935); robust grower with medium-size double flowers of good substance, the petals graduated, pure white; early to midseason. *p. 978*

'Petrick alba' (Kerstperel) (1920); sport of 'Mad. Petrick', not very vigorous but early and a dependable and willing forcer for Christmas, double flowers of good substance, white with hint of green in base. *p. 980*

'Pink Pearl'; a sturdy variety with medium size double flowers of firm texture, delicate pink spotted crimson on upper petals; form of 'Vervaeneana'; midseason to late. *p. 979*

'Reinhold Ambrosius'; (1930), beautiful German simsii hybrid for early forcing in pots to bloom during winter-time; silky, soft rosy-red, wide open double flowers 7 cm across, with satiny sheen, for midseason January, February bloom, and long-lasting. *p. 986*

'Salmon John Haerens'; sport of 'John Haerens' with the same fine shape and level growth, dependable double flowers vivid orange-red; midseason to late. Identical with 'Cyrille van Gele'. *p. 983*

'Simon Mardner' (1878); robust old variety with beautiful large double, clear rose flowers of good texture; early blooming. *p. 984*

'Southern Charm'; a typical, excellent "Southern indica" azalea, sport of 'Formosa', a phoeniceum hybrid; tall evergreen shrub with large 9 cm single flowers carmine rose with red spots, the petals rounded and half free; rough-hairy 6 cm elliptic leaves. Sun tolerant and vigorous; midseason bloom. This group of azaleas may be trimmed and trained into standard or poodle shapes. *p. 975*

'Temperance' (1890); compact grower with frilled semi-double flowers light mauve or lavender-purple spotted carmine, an unusual color possibly introduced through Rhod. ponticum; midseason. *p. 977*

'Theo. Findeisen' (1928); sport of 'Mad. Petrick', compact grower with double flowers brick-red with salmon sheen and scarlet dots; for early forcing for Christmas. *p. 981*

'Triumph' (1923) (Mad. Aug. Haerens x Lentegroet); strong grower, budding readily and early blooming; the double flowers are crimson red and beautifully frilled, holding their fresh color for a long time. *p. 976*

'Variegated Triumph' ('Candystick'); sport of 'Triumph' with double, frilled flowers carmine rose, irregularly edged with white, and dotted and striped with crimson, and a crimson eye; early. *p. 979*

'Vervaeneana' (1886); very large, rounded flowers, vivid rose with broad white margin, and spotted crimson at base of petals, nicely double; good growth of loose habit, with large green leaves; midseason. Cultivar of Rhod. simsii var. vittatum. *p. 978*

'Vervaeneana alba' (1903); sport of 'Vervaeneana', of loose spreading habit, with large double flowers pure white except for faint green dots in center; of good substance and a dependable variety; midseason. *p. 978*

'Violacea' (1833); floriferous but slow growing old hybrid with japonica blood, with the deepest warm purplish violet in the class, medium size double flowers, very unusual and attractive, but somewhat slow and of loose habit; late blooming. *p. 982*

'White Triumph'; pure white sport of 'Triumph', with large double, beautifully frilled flowers, spotted green in throat, and a few occasional red dots on petals; early. *p. 979*

AZALEA: see also RHODODENDRON

AZOLLA *Salviniaceae (Filices)* **S2-3 (water) F-BW**

caroliniana (United States to Argentina), "Floating moss" or "Mosquito plant"; moss-like aquatic fern, the floating bodies scarcely 2½ cm long, pinnately divided leaf-like stems, with root fibers, and minutely lobed, densely overlapping leaves pale green to reddish and bearing spores; forms attractive floating patches in pools or aquaria. *p. 1082*

imbricata (Sri Lanka); small floating aquatic plant from tropical fresh waters, with much branched stems bearing feathery root-fibers, the small green leaves densely overlapping and forming colonies; for indoor aquariums, or outdoor ponds in summer. *p. 1083*

BABIANA *Iridaceae* **I2LBMd**

sambucina (So. Africa, E. Cape Prov.); cormous plant 15-22 cm high, with basal leaves slightly plaited, and large bluish-purple flowers with spreading segments and yellow anthers, fragrant like elder-berry. *p. 1334*

stricta (So. Africa), "Baboon flower"; low cormous herb with hairy sword shaped pleated leaves and freesia-like fragrant flowers, 5 cm across, pale to mauve blue; winter blooming. *Subtropic.* *p. 1335*

stricta rubrocyanea; striking variety 15-20 cm high, with broad, tapered leaves downy beneath; flowers 5 cm or more across, with spreading petals, their basal half rich crimson, brilliant blue toward tip *p. 1324, 1334*

stricta sulphurea; about 22 cm high with narrow leaves, the scented flowers pale yellow and with blue anthers. *p. 1334*

BACCHARIS *Compositae* **S2LBD**

pilularis (California), "Dwarf coyote bush", "Chapparal broom"; evergreen shrub; good ground cover in dry climate; forming dense mat; small 2 cm toothed leathery leaves; small yellowish flower heads. *p. 820*

BACTRIS *Palmae* **S3LFM**

gasipaes (Guilielma utilis), (Costa Rica, Amazon), "Peach palm"; feather-leaf palm with slender ringed trunk armed with very sharp needle-like spines; graceful fronds pinnate, ½-1 m long, deep green, hairy and spiny; fruit resembling a peach, in pendulous bunches, and used as a vegetable. *Tropical.* *p. 1852*

major (Colombia, Panama, Brazil); slender palm to 7 m high, growing in clusters, with trunks 5 cm thick, spiny at first, later white-ringed and rather smooth; pinnate leaves dull green, to 1½ m long; clustered egg-shaped, purple edible fruit, and used for making wine. *p. 1854*

BAERIA *Compositae* **I2LBD**

chrysostoma (California, Oregon), "Coast Gold fields"; herbaceous, downy annual 30 cm high, with opposite, linear to thread-like leaves; flower heads bright yellow, 2-3 cm across, surrounded by two series of bracts; summer blooming. *p. 820*

coronaria (aristata) (California), "Goldfields"; annual herbaceous plant with leaves pinnately or bipinnately cut into narrow, linear segments; yellow, everlasting flower heads 2 cm across; used for bedding and as cut flowers for drying. *p. 820*

BALLYA *Commelinaceae* **S3LFM**

zebrina (Trop. East Africa); small succulent trailer with small ovate, clasping leaves velvety hairy, bronzy green with pale stripes lengthwise; flowers pale mauve. *p. 786*

BAMBURANTA *Marantaceae* **S3LFM**

arnoldiana; now identified as Hybophrynium braunianum (Zaire, W. Africa), bushy plant resembling bamboo in habit with its tall-growing, reed-like, graceful canes furnished along their length with maranta-like, ovate, short-petioled leaves. *p. 1538*

BAMBURANTA: see also Ctenanthe compressa

BAMBUSA *Gramineae* **I2LBM**

beecheyana (Dendrocalamus latiflorus hort.) (Southeastern China), "Beechey bamboo", sometimes known as Sinocalamus beecheyanus; a large running, non-hardy timber bamboo, developing thick, bright green culms to 12 m high and 10 cm thick, later turning yellow; with age and weight, gracefully arching; 6 to 10 heart-shaped leaves grouped on a twig, 10-18 cm long. This bamboo is one of the important sources of edible bamboo sprouts, cooked and eaten in China and elsewhere. *p. 1301, 1312*

'Chinese Goddess': see glaucescens riviereorum

eutuldoides (China: Kwangtung); large clump-bamboo, with short, thick rhizomes, the new shoot arising from a bud on the base of a recently developed culm, and furnished with tough, fibrous roots, about 10 m high, with stiff, erect, hollow canes far apart and straggly, 2-2½ cm in dia., olive green invariably with irregular, pleasing greenish-white or ivory stripes lengthwise; the leaves at a distinct angle, to 13 cm long, glaucous reverse. *p. 1305, 1307*

falcata (Arundinaria) (Himalayas); popular tufted clumps dense at ground level with hollow canes to 6 m high, arching outward, the sprouts are brown and hairless, the stems yellowish olive-green, with deciduous sheaths 1 cm dia.; on thicker 2 yr. culms, as many as 25-30 branches will develop at nodes in clusters, with lively glowing emerald-green leaves slightly sickle-shaped 6-8 cm long. *p. 1306, 1314*

"falcata" hort. in California trade: see B. oldhamii; in Florida nurseries: see B. glaucescens.

glaucescens (multiplex in hort.), (Indo-China), "Fernleaf bamboo"; a variable woody grass becoming 4 m high, the green reedlike hollow stems bearing graceful twigs with many very small leaves, fern-like 3-15 cm long, glabrous deep green, silver-blue beneath, and with a ring of hair at base of leaf; the older culms become 3 cm or more thick. *p. 1302, 1308*

glaucescens var. 'Alphonse Karr' (syn. B. nana Suochiku) (Japan); large and attractive hedge bamboo much like the type, however the culms and branches are bright yellow irregularly striped with vivid green and the culm sheaths have yellowish stripes; 7-12 m high. *p. 1305*

glaucescens 'Nana' (China, Japan); perennial woody grass, dense with thin woody hollow green to purplish canes and branching relatively dwarf and usually 1-1½ m high but may become 3 m tall; the small leaves are consistently the same size, 4-10 cm long and 6 mm wide, and bluish underneath. *p. 1302*

glaucescens riviereorum ('Chinese Goddess') (China); graceful bamboo of smaller size grown as a hedge in southern China, with willowy culms 1 cm thick and becoming with age 1½-3 m high; the canes are entirely green and always solid and less stiffly erect than multiplex; small dainty fern-like leaves 4 to 6 cm long, in two ranks on slender branchlets or twigs which curl down toward the tips, and with silvery green reverse. *p. 1302, 1306*

glaucescens 'Stripestem', also known as "Fern-leaf bamboo" because of its usually small, fern-like foliage; the leaves are occasionally banded with white, and the yellowish or pinkish canes to 2½ cm dia., striped, and forming clumps to 3 m high. *p. 1302*

gracilis hort. (China, Japan); tufted clumps, the stem sprouts white with blackish hairs, growing very dense, with hollow canes 2 cm dia. light blue-green, evenly tapered, to 4½ m high, stem sheaths deciduous; small leaves 6-8 cm long. *p. 1306*

gracillima hort. (China); dainty, small leaved plant from the Goddess of Mercy temple, Koon Yam Chuk; slow grower dense with slender solid stems to 2 m long and 6 mm thick, green when young, orange if older, evenly bending and arching outward all around; small leaves 1 to 2 cm long pinnately at right angles to thin branchlets. *p. 1305*

multiplex: see glaucescens

oldhamii (Sinocalamus); in nurseries as Dendrocalamus latiflorus; (China), "Oldham bamboo" or "Male bamboo"; large bamboo to 18 m high, forming open clumps; erect canes 9 cm dia., pale green, with dense foliage on pendant branchlets. *Subtropic.* *p. 1306, 1312*

polymorpha (India); attractive, feathery bamboo forming clumps 4 m high in California, the bluish waxy culms gracefully arching, 2-3 cm thick, with soft green leaves 12 cm long and 1½ cm wide. In India becoming 25 to 30 m high with basal dia. to 15 cm. *p. 1312*

textilis, (S. China; Kwangsi, Kwangtung), "Wong Chuk"; a handsome subtropical species forming compact clumps of thin-walled but tough culms with long internodes, very straight to 15 or more m tall and 5 cm thick, with nodding tips; 6-10 branches at nodes, with attractive foliage 15-20 cm long, and to 2½ cm wide. These straight, light and tough canes are split and used extensively for weaving of baskets; hardy to -10°C. *p. 1307*

tuldoides (S.E. China), "Punting pole bamboo"; used to push junks on Chinese rivers; handsome semi-hardy clump bamboo with straight culms to 18 m high and 8 cm dia., with broad, rich green leaves to 15 cm long, and green reverse. *Subtropic.* *p. 1303*

ventricosa (vulgaris var.) (China), "Buddha's belly bamboo"; so called because of the characteristic dark olive culms swollen between internodes, especially in potgrown clumps; otherwise may grow 15 m high; leaves to 18 cm long. *Subtropic.* *p. 768A, 1303*

vulgaris (Java, and wild in tropical regions of E. and W. Indies, Africa, C. and So. America), "Feathery bamboo"; widely grown ornamental bamboo because of its attractiveness and large size; forms open clump with spreading rhizomes, arching culms 15-24 m high and 10-12 cm thick, hollow with thin walls, green at first later yellow banded lengthwise or all yellow, the joints covered with deciduous brown hairs; dark green leaves 15-22 cm long borne on branches on the upper part of the stem. *Tropical.* *p. 1308, 1313*

vulgaris 'Aureo-variegata', the "Golden feathery bamboo"; giant canes of a rich golden yellow color, pencilled lengthwise with green; a beautiful sight in the tropical landscape, and very artistic with but a few culms in a container. The photo on pg. 1313 shows several sawed-off culms, with inside sections rodded through and placed into buckets of water, so they will sprout and be used for decoration, a custom seen in Hawaii and which we later used for summer display in Radio City, New York. *p. 1313*

vulgaris vittata; a variety of the "Feathery bamboo", with the thick yellow culms handsomely striped or banded lengthwise with green, the stems hollow and 4-5 cm thick and to 5 m high; the lateral branches with yellow stem and leaves bright green both sides 15-20 cm long and 2-4 cm wide. The species vulgaris has culm plain green. *p. 1312*

'Wong-Tsai' (So. China); a running bamboo photographed in New Zealand, with tall-growing, slender green culms, freely branching and arching; broad lanceolate leaves, and useful for fast growing screen. *p. 1314*

BAMBUSA: see also Dendrocalamus, Phyllostachys, Pseudosasa, Sasa

BANKSIA *Proteaceae* **I2LBD**

australis (marginata) (So. Australia to N. S. Wales), "Silver banksia"; sparry evergreen shrub 1½-4 m; with leathery 5 cm lanceolate leaves with recurved margins, deep green above, silvery beneath; greenish flowers borne in pairs in dense terminal bottle brush spikes becoming woody and cone-like. *p. 1968*

collina (Australia: Victoria, N. S. W.); handsome, dense shrub 2-3 m high with narrow 8 cm prickly saw-edged rigid dark green leaves white tomentose beneath; bronze-yellow cylindrical spikes 15 cm long with yellow or reddish-brown and purple flowers and with hooked, shining black pin-like styles. *p. 1968*

ericifolia (New South Wales), "Heath banksia"; woody shrub or tree to 4 m high; needle-like linear leaves 2 cm long, with margins turned under; cylindrical inflorescence candle-like 15-30 cm long, with long-protruding styles colored amber or chrome yellow. *p. 1975*

grandis (Western Australia), known as "Bull banksia"; handsome and curious tree 3 to 10 m high, with sparry branches, and unbelievable leaves 30 cm long, green to grayish and stiff as metal, deeply cut out to the midrib by alternating teeth like a big-edged saw, richly brown-felted at first; yellow bottle brush flowers 20-30 cm long. My photographs are of typical leaves from trees growing near Perth. *Subtropic.* *p. 1975*

marcescens (Australia); shrub 1½-2 m high with hairy shoots, oblong leaves to 3 cm long, the greenish yellow flowers in dense cylindrical spikes 8-25 cm long, wiry like a bottle-brush. *p. 1968*

media (W. Australia); bushy, woody shrub, with spatulate, stiff leaves deeply serrate at margins, cylindrical and grayish beneath; inflorescence cone-like, dense of styles light yellow to red-brownish. *Subtropic.* *p. 1975*

praemorsa (Coastal Western Australia); stiff shrub to 3 m with wedge-shaped, toothed leaves 3 cm long; cylindrical, dense brush-like spikes of brown and gold. *p. 1975*

serrata (Tasmania, Victoria, N. So. Wales); coastal tree to 10 m high, with long and narrow, stiff leaves 8-15 cm long, sharply and neatly saw-toothed along margins; big flower heads gray-green in bud, light reddish-brown when open. *p. 1975*

speciosa (Western Australia); spectacular spreading woody shrub 2-3 m tall; thick woody branches with long narrow, green to grayish stiff-leathery leaves to 30 cm long, cut to the midrib into triangular saw teeth; showy inflorescence of curving yellow styles tipped green, silvery in bud. *p. 1975*

BARBACENIA *Velloziaceae* **S3LBW**

elegans (Vellozia); (Natal); bushy plant with hard, linear-lanceolate leaves to 20 cm long, and starry flowers lilac in bud, white when open, on slender stalks. *p. 2112*

BARBOSELLA *Orchidaceae* **I3OFM**

anaristella (Costa Rica); mat-forming epiphyte, resembling a Pleurothallis. Flowers single, gold-bronze with maroon lip, over 2½ cm long. Only the lateral sepals are united to near their tips. The petals and dorsal sepal are free. Petals not club-shaped at their tips as in Restrepia. June-August. *p. 1663*

BARCLAYA *Nymphaeaceae* **S3LBW**

longifolia (Thailand, Burma); aquatic plant with rootstock growing long, narrow leaves, at first narrow and lanceolate, later oblong and arrow-shaped, red and green with transparent bluish shade; often corrugated and venation red and brown, leaves are very soft and fragile, green on the reverse; 2 cm flowers with greenish petals and purple inside; the fruit ripens under water. *p. 1626*

BARKERIA *Orchidaceae* **S3OFW**

elegans (Epidendrum) (Mexico: Chiapas); epiphyte with leafy stems; lanceolate 4 cm leaves, soon deciduous; inflorescence to 30 cm long, with handsome 5 cm flowers rosy-red, the large lip pale rose, blotched red in front. (late winter). *p. 1664*

BARLERIA *Acanthaceae* **I2LBM**

albostellata (Rhodesia, Transvaal); subshrub with gray-pubescent stems, ovate leaves to 8 cm long; white, irregular flowers 6 cm dia., in head with large, leafy bracts. *Subtropic.* *p. 43*

cristata (India), "Philippine violet"; shrub with oblong leaves covered with stiff hairs; spikes with funnel-shaped, five-lobed blue flowers. *Tropical.* *p. 43*

involucrata (India, Singapore); attractive tropical subshrub with elliptic leaves to 12 cm long and lightly yellow-bristly on surface; solitary flowers 5 cm long, lavender with white center, subtended by two leafy green bracts. *Tropical.* *p. 43*

lupulina (Mauritius), "Hop-headed barleria"; evergreen spiny shrub 60 cm high with narrow lanceolate leaves green with pink or red mid-ribs; two pairs of down-turned thorns at each node; 5-lobed tubular flowers peach-yellow from terminal hops-like spikes. *Tropical.* *p. 43*

prionitis (Tropical Asia and Africa); spreading tropical subshrub, branches furnished with 4-parted spines; elliptic privet-like leaves to 18 cm long dark green and glossy; inflorescence with spiny bracts, and apricot-yellow flowers 4 cm across. *p. 43*

strigosa (India); small herbaceous shrub to 1 m with ovate leaves somewhat leathery and bristly; 5 cm 5-lobed blue flowers in dense one-sided spikes. *p. 43*

BARLIA *Orchidaceae* **C2LBM**

longibracteata (Himantoglossum) (Spain to Greece, Algeria, Canary Islands); tuberous terrestrial rosette with broad fleshy green leaves to 20 cm; inflorescence a spike, hyacinth-like with porcelain purple 3 cm flowers with pale spotted lip, somehow reminding of lizards; to 60 cm high (spring). *Subtropic.* *p. 1664*

BARRINGTONIA *Lecythidaceae* **S3LBW**

asiatica (South Pacific islands, west to India); "Fish poison tree",with large obovate leathery leaves to 60 cm long, fragrant 18 cm white flowers with brush-like, long white stamens tipped crimson; opening in the evening, and falling in the morning; yellow-brown quadrangular fruit 10 cm long, containing one large poisonous seed. *Tropical.* *p. 1361*

BARTSCHELLA *Cactaceae* **I2LBD**

schumannii (Baja California); oval grayish-violet cactus branching into tufts, to 10 cm high, woolly at the top and in the axils, closely packed with rounded knobs, awl-shaped spines white tipped black; flowers purple. *p. 710*

BATEMANIA *Orchidaceae* **S3OFM**

colleyi (Guianas, Colombia, Trinidad); handsome epiphyte with 2-leaved pseudobulbs; pendant inflorescence of fleshy, long-lived fragrant flowers 8 cm across, deep wine-purple to brownish-red and greenish tips, lip white with reddish flush (autumn). *p. 1665*

BAUERA *Saxifragaceae* **S2LBM**

rubioides (Tasmania); attractive evergreen shrub to 2 m, with 3-parted heath-like toothed foliage 2 cm long; 2 cm flowers pink or white. *p. 2041*

BAUHINIA *Leguminosae* **S2LBM**

acuminata (India, Burma, Malaya, China), "Orchid tree"; tropical shrub to 2 m high, with smooth two-lobed leaves and showy white flowers 5-8 cm across, with spreading petals and prominent stamens; summer-blooming. *p. 1372*

blakeana, "Hongkong orchid tree"; apparently a sterile hybrid; to 5 m high, with twisted stem, leaves of two jointed leaflets and showy large orchid-like flowers of 5 spreading unequal petals carmine-rose to burgundy, with the fifth petal striped purple. As seen in Queensland, these orchid trees provide a gorgeous show for at least 5 months. *Subtropic.* *p. 1372, 1373*

bowkeri (So. Africa); small tree with leaves notched into 2 lobes; flowers white with purple eye. *p. 1373*

galpinii (Tropical Africa to Transvaal), "Pride of the Cape"; a rambling shrub clambering to 10 m; 3-8 cm leaves two-lobed, pale green; their bright flowers nasturtium-like salmon-red, with spoon-shaped petals. *p. 1372*

kirkii (Transvaal); prostrate plant to 2 m; spreading from top of a thick tuberous root; bi-lobed leaves; flowers yellow. *p. 1373*

macrantha (S. E. Africa), "Zambesi coffee"; shrub 2 m high, with bi-lobed leaves; wrinkled white flowers; seeds coffee-like, and roasted by the natives. *p. 1373*

monandra (Burma), "Pink orchid"; small ornamental tree sometimes called "Jerusalem date" or "Butterfly flower"; deciduous in winter; produces great quantities of big flowers and seldom without blossoms; flower orchid-like, white flushed rose, lip yellow marked red, changing to pink after 24 hours; leaves notched at apex. *Tropical.* *p. 1373*

picta (Colombia), "Mountain ebony"; erect small tree with roundish elliptic membranous, smooth leaves dividing into two end-lobes; flowers white, the calyx brown tomentose. *p. 1372*

purpurea (India, Burma, Vietnam), the "Butterfly tree"; small tree 2-6 m high, with broad thin-leathery leaves cleft about one third; fragrant flowers reddish-purple; with petals not overlapping, marked and shaded in other tones. *Tropical.* *p. 1372*

tomentosa (India, Sri Lanka, China, Africa), "Bell-bauhinia" or "St. Thomas tree"; shrub 2-4 m with drooping branches, hairy except 3 cm leaves above and which are two-lobed; flowers bell-shaped and pendant, lemon-yellow with 5 overlapping petals, one with purple splash at base. *p. 1372, 1373*

variegata; in horticulture sometimes as B. purpurea (India, China), the "Purple orchid tree" or "Mountain ebony"; small semi-deciduous tropical tree 4 to 8 m high, also grown as a shrub with multiple stems, with curious foliage; the thin-leathery leaves connate or cleft beyond the middle, 8-10 cm long, dull green; gorgeous 9 cm axillary flowers like a cattleya orchid, carmine-rose, the petals with dark purple center stripe, the broad lip lined with crimson, fan-like; blooming January to May. *Subtropic.* *p. 1373*

BEAUCARNEA *Liliaceae* ***I1LBD**

gracilis (Nolina) (Tehuacán, Mexico), "Bottle palm" or "Pony tail"; curious, stout xerophytic tree to 10 m, with much swollen base and branching; at apex each with a rosette of narrow, grayish-glaucous leaves ½ to 1 m long and 1 cm wide; clusters of small, off-white to reddish flowers. *Arid-tropical.* *p. 1433, 1435*

recurvata (Nolina) (Mexico), "Pony-tail"; tree-like plant with tall trunks to 10 m high, swollen at base, topped by a rosette of linear, pendulous, concave, green leaves to 2 m long, rough and thin-leathery, but not spiny-toothed; panicles of small whitish flowers. A succulent which can store a year-long water supply; related to Yuccas. *Arid-tropical.* *p. 1423, 1437*

BEAUFORTIA *Myrtaceae* **I2HBD**

sparsa, (Western Australia), "Swamp bottlebrush"; woody shrub with small ovate, hard leaves; the inflorescence a large powder puff of bright scarlet stamens. *Subtropic.* *p. 1611*

BEAUMONTIA *Apocynaceae* **S3LFM**

grandiflora (India: Himalayas), "Heralds-trumpet"; woody twiner or small tree with opposite, ovate leaves to 20 cm long, young shoots tinted rose and rusty-haired; large, fragrant, showy trumpet-shaped 12 cm flowers with 5 twisted lobes, white, with dark throat, in terminal cymes. *Subtropic.* *p. 135, 140*

BEFARIA *Ericaceae* **C2LBM**

glauca (Bejaria) (Mountains of Venezuela, Colombia), "Rose of the Andes"; handsome evergreen shrub 1 to 2 m high, from 2000 to 3000 m elevation; the branches angled, and crowded with leathery, oblong leaves 4-6 cm long, gray-green beneath; flowers of 6-7 spreading petals, salmon-rose with purple sheen, and long protruding pistil. *p. 957*

BEGONIA *Begoniaceae* **I-S2-3HFM**

'Abel Carrière', (Silver rex x evansiana); decorative branched plant with oblique, heart-shaped leaves, coloring reminiscent of a chalky-white caladium with light green veins; flowers rose. *p. 425, 454*

acaulis (New Guinea); pretty little species with rhizomatous roots oblique-ovate, glossy dark green, quilted leaves covered with bristly hairs, and with serrate margins; profusely blooming with lovely rose-pink flowers with darker eye, on red, finely hairy stalks. ("Begonian", August 1973). *p. 462*

acerifolia (Ecuador); low, shrub-like, rhizomatous plant with large leaves with several irregular points, covered with a network of sunken veins, the rough surface light green to emerald on top, light green below; flowers in loose clusters closely above foliage, blush-white, buds dark pink. *p. 443*

acetosa (Brazil); compact growing rhizomatous plant with broad, velvety heart-shaped deep coppery, olive-bronze leaves and covered with white hair, deep, wine-red beneath. *p. 414*

acida (Brazil); rhizomatous species with large, roundish leaves to 30 cm, bright green, roughly puckered; tall inflorescence with white flowers. *Tropical.* *p. 426*

aconitifolia (sceptrum) (Brazil); tall cane-stemmed species with large leaves palmately deep-lobed, green with silver streaks and reddish veins; large, waxy-white flowers. *Tropical.* *p. 427*

aconitifolia 'Faureana' (faureana) (Brazil); upright, branching plant with oblique, narrowly ovate, irregularly lobed leaves, dark green with white blotches on top, reddish below, edges saw-toothed; many quite large flowers. *p. 422*

acuminata (cubensis hort.) (Cuba), "Holly-leaf begonia"; fibrous plant with small crinkled, toothed leaves glossy green with bronze tips; white flowers in winter. *p. 390, 394, 445, 459*

acutangula; cane-stemmed, stout variety of angularis, broad-ovate leaves coarsely toothed, yellowish-green with pale veins and of smooth texture, red beneath; flowers white. *p. 407*

acutifolia (acuminata) (Jamaica), "White rhubarb begonia"; fibrous-rooted, branching plant resembling B. cubensis, with pinkish, arching stems carrying small, glossy, bristly, toothed leaves broader than cubensis, and eyelashed at margins; bronzy-green above and light maroon under; white flowers in winter. *p. 456, 459*

albo-picta (Brazil), "Guinea-wing begonia"; small, sturdy angel-wing type plant with branching, drooping stems carrying narrow, glossy, green leaves tapered and silver-spotted. Greenish-white flowers. *p. 450*

x alleryi (metallica x gigantea); tall, bushy, hirsute plant, ovate, toothed leaves brighter green than metallica, purple-veined beneath; flowers blush pink, with striking deeper pink beard. (D) *p. 419, 463*

alnifolia (Colombia); medium, branching grower with woody stems, shiny green leaves reminiscent of small-scale alder-tree; off-white flowers clustered at top of stem. *p. 431*

'Alto-Scharff' (bradei x scharffiana); beautiful, hirsute bushy plant with white-hairy, wing-shaped leaves with red, depressed veins, and red beneath; hairy pink blooms. *Humid-tropical.* *p. 415, 440*

'Alto-Scharff Ramirez'; bradei x scharffiana seedling, differing from 'Alto-Scharff' in being a taller, more robust grower with denser growth and thicker stems; leaves more rounded, and do not have the depressed veins of 'Alto-Scharff'. *p. 423*

'Alzasco' (Lucerna seedling); tall, cane-stemmed angel-wing type with blackish green, satiny, ruffled leaves with silver spots, deep purple beneath; bronzy-red flowers in drooping clusters. *Humid-subtropic.* *p. 447, 448*

'Amy' (kenworthyi x starfolia); handsome hybrid of bushy, compact habit with leaves rounded in outline, lobed and cut to appear like stars, the surface dark green with gray and painted with silver (Golding). *p. 479*

andina (Bolivia); tall, erect, fibrous-rooted plant covered with brown scurf; slender stems carry oblique-ovate pointed, green leaves; white flowers in short clusters from the axils. (I) *p. 451*

'Angie'; chance seedling from R. Shatzer 1967; rhizomatous star-type begonia with green, pedately lobed and deeply cut leaves, the pointed segments crenate at margins and crisped; prolific pink flowers in spring. *p. 466*

angularis (Brazil); tall, cane-stemmed plant with drooping branches, long, ovate-pointed, glossy green leaves with grayish-white veins, margin undulate; small white flowers. *p. 422*

'Annabelle'; tall, cane-stemmed plant with obliquely lance-shaped leaves having one basal lobe usually large, fresh green and spotted silver, margins undulate; flowers pink; maculata hyb. (I) *p. 409*

'Anna Christine' (Salmon Rubra x dichroa); angel-wing type of dwarf habit; leaves large leathery, mahogany over green, with lightly waved edges; flowers deep, bright cerise. *p. 441*

'Annie Laurie', coccinea seedling; small, erect, bushy, cane-stemmed type with ovate-lance-shaped, bright green leaves with silver spots; flowers light red with a salmon overglow. *p. 454*

annulata (Bhutan); one of the species used in breeding of rex hybrids; small, heartshaped leaves olive-green with pale green zone and covered by velvet-like rosy hairs; flowers white. (3) *p. 439, 472, 478*

arborescens (Brazil); a large-growing species with pale green, oval-pointed, ribbed, hairy leaves; cyme of small, white flowers in summer. *p. 443*

arborescens confertiflora (Brazil); long, oval, pointed, pleated leaves in dark green with bronze patina, saw-toothed margins, very rough on back; hairy flower stalk above foliage carrying close clusters of pink buds and white flowers. *p. 443*

x argenteo-guttata (albo-picta x olbia), "Trout begonia"; bushy canestem with "angelwing" leaves growing at an angle, waxy, olive green heavily spotted silver, red beneath; flowers cream with pink. *Humid-tropical.* *p. 411*

aridicaulis (Mexico); miniature rhizomatous plant with dry-looking stems; shiny, light green leaves sharply tapered; flowers white in late winter; good terrarium subject. (3) *p. 408*

'Arndt's Charlotta' (India); short-stemmed rhizomatous creeper with unpointed round leaves shiny black-green on top, vivid purple plush beneath; flowers pink. (I) *p. 420*

'Arndt's Orange Rubra'; sturdy cane-stemmed plant with larger angel-wing leaves emerald green and more bright silver spots; flowers larger than 'Orange-Rubra', warm salmon-orange in heavy, drooping clusters, in early winter. (I) *p. 409*

'Arthur Mallet', (rex 'Eldorado' x subpeltata); beautiful but difficult, fibrous-rooted, erect plant with ovate, metallic, purplish-red leaves overlaid with silver-pink dots; large, rose-pink flowers. *p. 414*

auriculata (Africa); rhizomatous species with long petioles carrying smallish, waxy leaves in coppery olive-green, marked silvery-green in center, very wavy, eye-lashed, reverse brownish red. *p. 436*

'Baby Perfection'; rhizomatous miniature; shiny, deep green, oblique-ovate leaves with chocolate-colored edges in a laced loop pattern; center chartreuse with a light eye at base and red-brown spatterings. *p. 453*

barbana (squamosa; also sold as barkeri); low-growing rhizomatous plant with medium, light green, ovate-pointed leaves, red-veined, hairy beneath; stems short and hairy. *p. 417, 431*

barkeri (Veracruz); rhizomatous; largest leaf to 75 cm, glossy green, bristly-hairy beneath; white flowers. *p. 455, 464*

bartonea (Puerto Rico); popularly "Winter jewel"; delicate, low-growing jewel with green leaves overcast with gem-like sheen; tiniest pink blossoms like an ethereal shower. (3) *p. 401, 410*

'Bayern' (Medio-picta); fibrous-rooted; of lower habit than Preussen, with long, narrow, wing-shaped leaves uniformly spotted silver; very floriferous with pink flowers. *p. 426*

'Beatrice Haddrell' (bowerae x sunderbruchii); magnificent rhizomatous plant with star-shaped leaves boldly marked chartreuse on brown; flowers in tall pink showers. *Humid-tropical.* *p. 412*

'Bessie Buxton'; rhizomatous; an upright form of erythrophylla, popularly called 'Upright Beefsteak'; leaves thinner, and with large pink flowers. (*I) *p. 399*

bipinnatifida (New Guinea); upright, branching grower with bipinnate, fern-like leaves. *p. 445*

'Black Beauty'; dwarf rhizomatous plant, leaves dark brown-green, toothed and lobed to near star-shape, veins light green; pink flowers. (I) *p. 420*

'Black Falcon' (kenworthyi x sunderbruchii); rhizomatous miniature with black, star-shaped taffeta leaves with wide, silvery-gray markings outlining the veins, red underneath; overlapping basal lobes, edges and petioles hairy; small, pink flowers in fall. *p. 453*

'Black Magic'; dwarf rhizomatous plant with irregularly shaped leaves dull-green and lighter veins, overcast to suggest iridescence; flowers pink. (I) *p. 420*

bogneri (Malagasy Republic); a most unusual new species discovered on the Isle of Masoala off the coast of Madagascar growing on mossy granite cliffs with annual rainfall of 350 cm, by J. Bogner of the Munich Botanical Garden in 1969; grass-like narrow linear leaves shiny green, 10-15 cm long and only 2 mm wide, on edges with minute teeth, on short erect stem from semi-tuberous roots; new leaves reddish; flowers are pale pink, on pinkish stalk to 15 cm high, with few male and fewer female blooms, about 2 cm across. R. Ziesenhenne reports (Begonian April 1973) that this species is an excellent terrarium plant and with supplementary, artificial light remains evergreen. *Humid-tropical.* *p. 462*

boliviensis superba; improved over boliviensis in stronger growth and nearly doubly as many flowers. Summer-flowering tuberous plant with tall, willowy stems and long, narrow, finely toothed leaves; long, nodding, orange-red flowers. *p. 491*

'Bow-arriola' (bowerae x C42); rhizomatous miniature starleaf; satiny green with intermittent purple markings at edge of leaf or along veins; flowers blush pink. *Humid-tropical.* *p. 402*

bowerae (Chiapas and Oaxaca, So. Mexico); miniature "Eyelash" begonia, rhizomatous, bushy with small, waxy ovate leaves vivid green and blackish-brown patches and erect hairs along margin; flowers pink. *Humid-tropical.* *p. 15*, 403, 416A, 435, 447*

bowerae major; larger and more robust form of bowerae with leaves almost plain and little marked but possessing a vibrant green; clumpy habit; flowers shell-pink. *p. 402*

'Bow-Joe' (bowerae x Joe Hayden); small rhizomatous plant with dark brown-green star leaves and light veins, on longish petioles; flowers pink. *p. 424*

'Bow-nigra' (sunderbruchii x bowerae); rhizomatous miniature, star-shaped, bronzy leaves with contrasting light green in center and along veins; flowers blush pink. *p. 402*

bracteosa (roezlii) (Perú), "Machu Picchu begonia"; fibrous-rooted, bushy plant, with roundish ovate, waxy leaves, bronzy and lightly toothed; flowers pale pink to lavender. *Tropical.* *p. 426*

bradei (laetevirides, laetevirens, macrocarpa pubescens), "Alto da Serra" hort.; variety with branches soft-hairy and more upright than secreta, velvety olive green leaves with red margins, reddish underneath; flowers pinkish white. *Tropical.* *p. 408, 421, 426*

'Braemar' (scharffii x metallica); hirsute, leggy plant with white-hairy stems and large, orbicular-pointed, dark, lustrous green leaves, glossy red beneath; flowers white with bright pink beard. *Tropical.* *p. 407*

brevicaulis (Khasia, Himalayas, No. India); beautiful, low, tuberous plant with heartshaped quilted leaves, coarsely hairy, deep brown-red along the veins and fresh-green between; flowers pale pink. (3) *p. 457*

brevirimosa: described under B. 'Exotica'

'Brocade'; 'Silver Star' seedling but not as starshaped and of bushier growth; rhizomatous; puckered leaves iridescent, silver-rose coloring; flowers white tinted pink. *p. 403*

bunchii: see x erythrophylla 'Bunchii'

'Calla lily': see under semperflorens

caroliniaefolia (Mexico); distinctive species with erect, thick rhizome, leaves palmately compound, the stalked, fleshy leaflets glossy green and quilted, toothed at margin; pink flowers. (3) *p. 390, 397*

'Carol Star' (caroliniaefolia x sunderbruchii); strong, spectacular plant with upright rhizome and broad, glossy, green leaves cut almost to the petiole, edges saw-toothed; inflorescence a tall, few-flowered cyme, flowers large, pale pink to rose-red. *p. 449*

carpinifolia (Costa Rica); "Beechleaf begonia"; branching, woody-stemmed plant with ovate, sparsely bristly-haired leaves with sunken veins, reminiscent of beech leaves. *p. 451*

castanaefolia (fruticosa) (Brazil); rambling, fibrous-rooted species with very oblique, arrow-shaped, pleated leaves in deep green; sparse bloomer producing single, white flowers. *p. 449*

'Catalina' (odorata x fuchsioides); slender spreading, fibrous plant with ovate, toothed leaves glossy green, silvery with pink veins beneath, petioles red; flowers pinkish. (I) *p. 409, 427*

cathayana (China: Yunnan); exquisite fibrous-rooted species to 45 cm, with obliquely cordate leaves plush-velvet resembling rex, purplish olive-green with zone of silver and smooth crimson veins; crimson velvet beneath; flowers orange-vermilion. *Subtropic.* *p. 395, 416A*

'Chantilly Lace' (bowerae x Black Shadows); lovely rhizomatous miniature plant with oblique-ovate, matte, chartreuse leaves with black stitches around edge, entire leaf often sprinkled with black dots, hairy leaf edge and petiole; clusters of pink flowers in winter. *p. 453*

x cheimantha 'Carolina', a "Scandinavian" form; (Sweden), requiring less heat, of robust growth, stiff, waxy foliage somewhat brittle, medium-large blooms vivid rose pink; winter flowering. (I) *p. 489*

x cheimantha 'Christmas White'; a freer growing form of 'Turnford Hall', which was a rather delicate mutant of 'Lorraine'; during winter, the foliage is literally snowed under by buds flushed apple blossom and opening to pure white. *p. 489*

x cheimantha 'Dark Lady Mac', "Dark Christmas begonia"; a desirable color form, and welcome variant of the old-reliable 'Lady Mac'; bushy plant with the rounded, satiny foliage overcast with burnt copper; the 4 cm flowers a deep carmine-rose, forming a large bouquet during early winter. *p. 487*

x cheimantha 'Dark Marina'; Danish sport of Solbakken, with deep rose durable flowers larger than 'Solfheim' but not quite as dark, and contrasting nicely with the yellow anthers; a medium growth habit with rich green, medium leaves; flowers from October-December. *p. 486*

x cheimantha 'Gloire de Lorraine'; from this first hybrid of socotrana x dregei developed a group of prolific, winterblooming begonias, now known as cheimantha, or the "Christmas begonia"; 'Lorraine' produces a great number of small, 4-petaled dainty pink flowers above the satiny-green, bushy foliage. *p. 489*

x cheimantha 'Lady Mac', a popular "Christmas begonia"; the bushy plant covered in winter with masses of clear pink and smallish, but long-lasting flowers; popularly called "Busy Lizzie". B. x cheimantha is an old hybrid group of socotrana x dregei introduced in France 1891 as 'Gloire de Lorraine'. *Humid-tropical.* *p. 416A, 489*

x cheimantha 'Lady Mac Supreme'; sport of Lady Mac with deep green leaves, edged in reddish bronze, young foliage red-bronze green; flowers deep glowing pink. *p. 491*

x cheimantha 'Marjory Gibbs'; flowers are larger and a darker rose than 'Lady Mac', but requires more warmth and is not quite as floriferous. *p. 489*

x cheimantha 'Melior' (socotrana x Lonsdale); 1914, older than 'Marjory Gibbs', with large flowers a softer pink, and of somewhat drooping habit; tolerates heat well. *p. 489*

x cheimantha 'Red Solfheim'; growth habit perhaps not as free as the other Scandinavian forms but the large flowers are the darkest of all, a glowing, rosy-cerise, freely produced in winter. (I) *p. 489*

x cheimantha 'Solbakken'; desirable Swedish variety of stiff bushy habit with fleshy leaves and dense head of flowers intense rose with salmon sheen gracefully above the foliage. (I) *p. 489*

x cheimantha 'Spirit of Norway'; of compact growth, similar to 'Marjory Gibbs', but a shade darker cerise-rose; blooms in September with 'short-day' treatment. (I) *p. 489*

x cheimantha 'Tove' (Skone); a Danish cultivar for cool house, with the largest flowers in the "Scandinavian" group but with fewer clusters, rich rose, blooming early from October on; leaves quite heavy and somewhat brittle. *p. 491*

x cheimantha 'White Marina' ('Snow Princess'), the "White Scandinavian begonia"; mutation of 'Marina', a color form of the winter-flowering begonias from Sweden, vigorous plant bursting with numerous large, glistening white flowers, the edges of petals flushed delicate pink, to 5 cm across, over large fresh green, somewhat brittle, waxy foliage. *p. 487*

'Chiala rosea'; fibrous-rooted, bushy plant with leaves ovate-lanceshaped, smooth, deep olive green and toothed, lightly hairy, red beneath; flowers pink, bearded white (hirsute). (I) *p. 429*

chimborazo (Guatemala); clumpy, semi-trailing rhizomatous species with thickish, glossy-green, ovate pointed peltate leaves; flowers soft pink. *Humid-tropical.* *p. 431*

'China Boy'; fibrous-rooted, low-growing dwarf plant; the reddish petioles carrying smooth, crinkled, dark green leaves with red veins above, red with darker veins beneath; flowers in pink and white. *p. 442*

'China Doll' (bow-arriola x bowerae); rhizomatous miniature, with small, obliquely pointed, irregularly lobed, chartreuse leaves with wide brown veins and wavy edges on hairy petioles; clusters of pink flowers in winter. *Humid-tropical.* *p. 453*

circumlobata (China); charming rhizomatous plant of upright and bushy habit, with palmately compound leaves of broad forest-green leaflets; showy pink flowers. *Subtropic.* *p. 420*

'Cleopatra' (Maphil x Black Beauty), "Mapleleaf begonia"; lovely hybrid distinguished by its translucent maple-leaf nile-green with chocolate-red areas toward margin; rhizomatous; clusters of perfumed, pink flowers. *Tropical.* *p. 393, 396, 416A, 464*

coccinea (rubra) (Orgãos-Brazil), "Angelwing begonia"; tall, bamboo-like canestem to 3 m high with thick ovate leaves 10-15 cm long, glossy green spotted silver, and edged red; drooping clusters of coral-red flowers blooming constantly. *Tropical.* *p. 411*

'Codelargo'; Lucerna seedling, cane-stemmed, medium tall, erect, bushy plant with long, ovate, bronzy-green, heavily silver spotted leaves, red beneath, margins toothed and ruffled; large, pink flowers in short, bunched clusters. (I) *p. 454*

compta (Brazil); tall and slender cane-stem; sharply pointed leaves green with silver stripes outlining the nerves, red beneath; bearded white flowers. *Tropical.* *p. 428*

conchaefolia (Costa Rica, Panama, Brazil); small rhizomatous plant; cupped peltate leaves glossy green, paler beneath with brown hairs; resembling a mussel shell; flowers pink. (3) *p. 422*

conchaefolia rubrimacula (Costa Rica), "Zip begonia"; miniature rhizomatous species, with petioles brown-fuzzy; waxy green, rounded, cupped peltate leaves, having red sinus spot in center; the margins slightly scalloped; veins brownish beneath; clusters of small whitish flowers. *p. 461*

confertiflora (Brazil); fibrous-rooted species of shrubby habit, freely branching with hairy, reddish stems, oblique-ovate leaves rather firm, glossy green and quilted, to 12 cm long; with hairs on mid-veins underneath; small white flowers with yellow stigma, in tight hemispherical clusters. *p. 462*

'Constance' ('Lucerna' seedling); vigorous, branched cane-stem with large dark green angelwing leaves lightly silver-dotted; pendulous clusters of light red flowers. (I) *p. 412*

convolvulacea (Brazil); rhizomatous climber with near-round, shallowly lobed, pointed, shiny green leaves; small, white flowers in spring. (I) *p. 441, 442*

'Cool Waters' (bowerae x heracleifolia pyramidalis); hardy new star-leaved hybrid with dark green leaves veined apple-green, rosy-red on the back; green petioles red-ridged. (I) *p. 423*

'Corallina de Lucerna' (Lucerna) (teuscheri x coccinea); tall, branching cane-stem with large green leaves silver-spotted; flowers droop in giant clusters. *Tropical.* *p. 395, 399, 455*

'Corbeille de Feu' (semperflorens x fuchsioides); fibrous-rooted slender plant with small ovate, glossy green leaves and nodding clusters of coral-red flowers like a "Basket of Fire". (I) *p. 450, 485*

coriacea: see 'Society'

x credneri (scharffiana x metallica); hirsute, bushy plant with broad-ovate pointed, softly white-hairy leaves olive-green, red beneath, larger than scharffiana; flowers pink and bearded. (D) *p. 415, 433*

x crestabruchii (manicata crispa x sunderbruchii), "Lettuce-leaf begonia"; rhizomatous plant with large, heavy, roundish leaves bronzy-green and very much crested, rosy petioles and nerves; flowers pink. *p. 390, 414, 446*

crispula (So. China); distinctive rhizomatous species; short-stalked round shiny green leaves deeply quilted and puckered, on short rhizome; flowers white inside, pale pink outside. (3) *p. 392*

cubensis: see acuminata

cucullata (Brazil); a fibrous-rooted relative of the semperflorens group, with green stolons creeping a short distance on the ground and later ascending into erect, succulent stems, bearing green leaves which are blunter at the apex, heavier in texture and not as flat as semperflorens, on short petioles. White or pink-tinged flowers in small, terminal clusters. *p. 445*

cyclophylla (South China); tuberous species with leaves and flower stalks arising from the tuber; leaves are oblique-ovate with doubly toothed margins and with basal lobes overlapping, green above, lighter green and flushed red beneath; rose-colored, scented flowers. *p. 491*

x cypraea; fibrous-rooted, bushy, metallica seedling, cupped leaves broad-ovate, white-hairy, olive green with darker depressed veins; flowers pinkish, bearded pink (hirsute). (ID) *p. 415*

daedalea (strigillosa) (Guatemala, Mexico); attractive, waxy, nile-green leaf with vivid red-brown markings; green petioles marked red and set with hairs; rhizomatous. *p. 393*

'Dancing Girl'; low, fibrous, angelwing variety with whirling growth of twisted leaves no two alike, olive green with silver spotting, and metallic pink along veins and margin; red flowers. *Tropical.* *p. 411*

'D' Artagnan' (epipsila x scharffiana); new hirsute hybrid dubbed "Queen of Basket begonias"; hoary-haired leaves fern-green on top, satsuma plum beneath, cupped when grown in good light. (BD) *p. 423*

'Dawn' (Abel Carrière seedling); miniature plant of low, stubby habit with small lance-shaped green leaves painted with silver between the veins. Rex derivative. (3) *p. 412*

dayii (Mexico); distinctive rhizomatous species with bold, chocolate-colored veins on light green, succulent-looking leaves; flowers ivory in tall sprays. Plant pictured may be hidalgensis. *p. 396*

decandra (Costa Rica, Puerto Rico); slender, fibrous-rooted plant with erect stems, swollen at nodes, and small ovate, toothed leaves, clear green with depressed reddish veins; pinkish flowers. (I) *p. 404*

'Decker's Select'; form of ingramii, fibrous-rooted, bushy plant with small, glossy, dark green, ovate leaves; lovely, winter flowering, rosy-red. (I) *p. 430*

decora (Assam, Vietnam, Malaya); lovely little plant with a creeping, hairy rhizome and oblique-ovate, plushy-brown leaves sharply etched with chartreuse veins, underside red with green veins, edges finely toothed; large rose-pink flowers borne high over foliage. *Tropical.* *p. 439*

deliciosa (Borneo); attractive, fibrous-rooted, smooth plant with thick red joints; palmately lobed leaves dark olive green with spotted silver gray, red beneath; pink flowers. *Tropical.* *p. 401, 427*

diadema (Borneo); fibrous-rooted, erect, fleshy plant with maple-like, deeply parted, dentate leaves, satiny green, with streaks of silver along ribs; clusters of lovely small pink flowers. *Humid-tropical.* *p. 403*

'Dianna' (Annie Laurie x dichroa); erect, bushy, angel-wing type with pleated, ruffled, bright green, heavily silver-spotted leaves; salmon-pink flowers in pendulous clusters. *Tropical.* *p. 450*

dichotoma (vitifolia) (Venezuela), "Kidney begonia"; upright rhizomatous, branched plant with oblique-ovate, smooth, green leaves with irregularly toothed edges; clusters of many small white flowers above the foliage. *Tropical.* *p. 425, 442*

"dichotoma" in hort.: see vitifolia

dichroa (Brazil); low, fibrous-rooted species inclined to be lax; ovate-pointed, glossy green leaves silver-spotted when young, wavy, dentate margins; orange flowers. (S3) *p. 400*

dichroa 'Erecta' ('upright dichroa'); cane-stemmed, less lax variety with leaves more boldly silver-spotted; pendulous clusters of large orange flowers prominent. (3) *p. 399*

'Diclata' (dichroa x undulata); bushy, smooth plant with lax or pendant branches, dense with oblique-ovate glossy green leaves undulate at margins, 22 cm long and 10 cm wide; flowers white, in pendant clusters; from J. Golding 1969. *p. 466*

'Dielytra'; variant of coccinea, cane-stemmed; typical, ovate, bright green leaves with one rounded basal lobe longer than the other; flowers blush pink. *p. 429*

x digswelliana (fuchsioides x semperflorens) (sandersii, sandersonii); low, freely branching plant with small, elliptic-ovate, irregularly biserrate leaves in shining, dark green; rosy scarlet flowers, long flowering. *p. 410, 450*

dipetala ('Mrs. W. S. Kimball') (India); delicate, stiff erect, fibrous-rooted plant rarely branched, with ovate doubly toothed grass-green leaves with scattered bristly hairs, red beneath; axillary cymes of white flowers tinged pink, like showers of luminous coins. (3D) *p. 410*

diptera (Brazil); cane-stem begonia with fibrous roots, and oblique-ovate smooth waxy green leaves with narrow sinus to petiole; large clusters of single pink flowers. The photo shows a plant that was made very true to nature from glass by artist glass-blowers Blaschka in Dresden for the Botanical Museum of Harvard University. *p. 462*

domingensis (Hispaniola); erect, cane type with medium-sized leaves, shiny green above, hairy below, and hairy stems. The pinkish flowers are rather small, but freely produced. *p. 445*

dominicalis (Dominica); bushy, fibrous-rooted plant with obliquely ovate, pointed, cupped leaves glossy green; flowers greenish white. (S) *p. 406, 450*

'Dorothy Grant'; tall thurstonii seedling, fibrous; large glossy leaves only sparsely hairy, dark metallic green and cupped, showing the blood-red beneath; flowers pinkish and red hirsute. (ID) *p. 429*

dregei (So. Africa), "Maple-leaf begonia"; semi-tuberous species with succulent, red stems annually; small angled, thin leaves shallowly lobed, bronze green with purple veins; flowers white. *Subtropic.* *p. 390, 458*

dregei macbethii, "Maple leaf begonia"; smaller leaved than dregei, more deeply cut and notched, brighter green and without purple veins; small white flowers. *p. 458*

x drostii (scharffii hybrid); tall plant with large dark green leaves deep purple beneath, overall hairy like an autumn haze; flowers pink, red-bearded or hirsute outside. *Tropical.* *p. 417*

x druryi (sanguinea x cypraea); fibrous, bushy plant similar to haageana, rough-textured, ovate leaves dark glossy green and white-hairy, maroon-red beneath; flowers white, red hirsute. (D) *p. 390, 429*

'Duchartrei' (echinosepala x scharffiana); hirsute, erect, bushy plant with large, obliquely ovate leaves with indented, red veins, upper side red and under side reddish, lobed and finely toothed; tall stalks carrying a few large, white flowers with red beard. (3) *p. 451*

'Duke of Cambridge'; fibrous-rooted, erect grower with oblique-ovate, hairy, metallic bronze-green leaves stippled silver. *p. 454*

'Duscharff' (duchartrei x scharffiana); bushy, fibrous-rooted plant with broad ovate-pointed leaves, thick textured, green and densely white-hairy; small white flowers, red-bearded. (D) *p. 415*

echinosepala (Brazil); species with red cane stems dotted with bright green spots, carrying small, obliquely lance-shaped leaves, dull satiny green on top, younger leaves bright green, shiny, reddish maroon and covered with short hairs below; irregularly crenate to serrate margins; flowers bearded, pink. *Tropical.* *p. 456*

'Echinosepala' hort.; an old hybrid begonia which has been in the trade for many years under this name; a tall, branching plant with dark green, glossy leaves with darker veins; flowers pink with darker pink hairs on the outside. (D) *p. 419*

'Edith M' (bowerae x reichenheimii); miniature plant with creeping rhizome, carrying star-shaped leaves in chocolate brown and chartreuse on red-spotted petioles. *p. 452*

edmundoi (Mexico); cane-stemmed; long lanceolate, boatshaped leaves dark olive-green and spotted, toothed, and red beneath; slow grower; greenish flowers. *p. 413*

egregia (quadrilocularis) (Brazil); fibrous-rooted species with long lanceolate, light green, puckered leaves somewhat cupped and brittle; white flowers with 4-winged seed pods. *Tropical.* *p. 390, 407, 421*

'Elaine' (Lucerna seedling); low-growing angel-wing type with narrow, curving leaves with wavy margins, blackish green with pink spots on top and deep purple underneath; bronzy red to rosy pink flowers in drooping clusters. (I) *p. 454*

elatior: see hiemalis and cheimantha

'Elithe'; tall canestem with coccinea blood; narrow pointed, dark green leaves lightly silver-spotted, wine-red beneath; free flowering pink. (I) *p. 429*

'Elsie M. Frey' (baumannii x limmingheiana); basket type plant with short stems, freely branching, and metallic-green, red-lined leaves hugging the pot; pink flowers in late winter. *p. 456*

eminii (mannii) (W. Africa); fibrous-rooted "Roseleaf begonia" with toothed, ovate leaves glossy green, pale beneath and tinged red, on long arching stems; flowers white, streaked with red, the ovaries without wings. *p. 390, 407, 451*

'Enchantment' (Missouri x Maphil); rhizomatous plant with seven-pointed star leaves in vivid reddish brown and chartreuse, underleaf red and chartreuse. Pink flowers in winter. *p. 452*

engleri (Trop. E. Africa); fibrous-rooted, succulent species with red-hairy stem and ovate leaves green with purplish veins, and coarsely white-hairy, margins toothed; flowers pink. *p. 413, 448*

epipsila (Brazil); low-growing, fibrous-rooted plant with fleshy, roundish, enamel-green leaves, reddish beneath and covered with felt; white flowers. *Tropical.* *p. 420, 422, 463*

x erythrophylla (feastii) (manicata x hydrocotylifolia), "Beefsteak begonia"; creeping rhizome, bearing great leathery, glossy, rounded leaves, 8-10cm across, dark olive green, red beneath; flowers pink. *Subtropic.* *p. 414, 432*

x erythrophylla 'Bunchii', "Curly kidney-begonia"; rhizomatous, decorative mutant, with the fleshy leaves lighter green, red-tinged, and ruffled and crested at the margins, the lobes rise and meet. *p. 390, 414, 432*

x erythrophylla helix (feastii helix), "Whirlpool begonia"; interesting form with fleshy leaves spiraled like a corkscrew in the center and with undulate margins. (*I) *p. 414, 432*

estrellensis (Costa Rica); fibrous-rooted, branching, compact plant with oblique-ovate, corrugated and deeply veined, bright green leaves recurved from base to tip; flowers white with wings and ovaries in green. *p. 456*

evansiana: see grandis

'Exotica' hort. (brevirimosa at Kew Gardens) (Baiyer River, New Guinea); magnificent, fibrous-rooted begonia with erect, reddish canes and large, oblique-ovate, corrugated leaves of shiny, iridescent taffeta in crimson on deep green, pale green beneath, both sides sparsely covered with short, red bristles, margins densely and irregularly toothed; red hairs on petioles and brown hairs on stems. Semi-dormant in winter. *Tropical.* *p. 416A, 436, 437*

'Fascination' (speculata x pearlii); rhizomatous plant with obliquely heart-shaped, pebbly-matte, brownish-olive leaves with large silvery areas around veins, new leaves silver-pink, hairy underleaf and petioles; clusters of pink flowers. *p. 452*

faureana: see aconitifolia 'faureana'

feastii: see erythrophylla.

fernandoi-costa (Brazil); fleshy, low, fibrous-rooted plant with large, roundish, soft-hairy, bright green leaves, rose-pink beneath; erect clusters of white flowers, each forming a perfect cross. *Tropical.* *p. 422, 445*

ficicola (Nigeria); called fig-loving because this small species was first discovered growing epiphytic on a fig-tree; dwarf plant with plain green peltate leaves to 12 cm long and of bullate texture; flowers bright yellow with orange tint (Begonian 1969). Also found in Gabon. *p. 462, 467*

'Fischer's ricinifolia'; pink-flowered ricinifolia seedling with low, creeping rhizome, leaves somewhat smaller and less deeply lobed, red-tinged underneath; habit bushier. *Subtropic.* *p. 405*

flava (Mozambique); bushy plant with oblique-ovate emerald-green leaves densely covered with white bristly hair, in good contrast with the orange flowers and red petioles. *p. 460*

'Fleecealba' (sunderbruchii x leptotricha); upright rhizomatous hybrid with heavy green peltate leaves lightly dusted with white, new leaves pure white fleece; flowers white. (I) *p. 419*

'Florence Carrell' (limmingheiana x incarnata); basket begonia of graceful habit with light green, waxy, ovate leaves with serrate margins, covered with drooping clusters of light coral flowers. *p. 445*

foliosa (Colombia), "Fernleaf begonia"; willowy plant with drooping branches; fibrous; small 3cm, waxy, bronzy-green, oval leaves notched toward tip; numerous tiny blush-white flowers. *Tropical.* *p. 390, 416, 424*

francisiae (Mexico), "Nasturtium leaf begonia"; rhizomatous, low and creeping; small leaves glossy deep green, the new foliage and stems strawberry-red. *p. 419*

friburgensis (Brazil); rhizomatous begonia with round thick, leathery leaves, shiny dark green on top, red underneath. New leaves show only red, folded like a cockscomb. Tall stems with clusters of white to pale pink flowers. (S) *p. 444*

froebelii (Perú); low tuberous species with roundish-cordate leaves bright green with pale veining and covered with soft purplish hairs; thick flowers scarlet; dormant in summer. *Tropical.* *p. 457*

froebelii var. strobelii (Ecuador); variety of froebelii, differing in smaller leaves and flowers, more pink than red, with a white center, and freely produced. It is more amenable to cultivation, growing at a lower altitude and tolerating warmer environment than the species. (IS) *p. 446*

frondosa (scharffii seedling); distinctive branching, bushy, hirsute plant to 1 m tall, with ovate-pointed, obscurely lobed leaves glossy dark green above, purple beneath, and of harder texture than the species; large pink flowers with red beard outside. *p. 460*

x 'Frutescans' (fruticosa seedling); low, fibrous-rooted, foliage begonia with small, thin-leathery, olive-green leaves, wavy and cupped to show red underneath; flowers white. *Tropical.* *p. 413, 451*

'Frutescaria' (fruticosa seedling); fibrous-rooted plant of low habit similar to Frutescans, but with lighter, grayish leaves, more prominent veins and without the wavy margins. Infrequent, white flowers borne high over the foliage. *Tropical.* *p. 442*

fruticosa (Brazil); rambling fibrous-rooted species with thick, deep green leaves polished to a high gloss; small single white flowers, sparse. *p. 431*

x fuchsifoliosa (fuchsioides x foliosa); slender, branched, fleshy stems with numerous, small, waxy oval toothed leaves tinged red when young, on drooping branches; fibrous; flowers red. (I2) *p. 416*

fuchsioides (Mexico), "Fuchsia begonia"; fibrous-rooted plant with slender arching stems 60-90 cm high, very small oblique-ovate toothed leaves to 4 cm long, waxy dark green; nodding fuchsia-like red flowers. *Tropical.* *p. 431, 443*

fuchsioides floribunda (multiflora) (Mexico), "Fuchsia begonia"; with arching branches full of small dark green leaves; pink flowered form of fuchsioides. *p. 416, 451*

fusca (Mexico); large plant with a rhizome which may become arm-thick, carrying large, near-round, irregularly lobed velvety leaves with lighter veins radiating from the center, and tall panicles with many whitish flowers. *p. 449*

x fuscomaculata (rubellina) (heracleifolia x daedalea); small rhizomatous, hairy plant with lobed leaves smooth, bronze-green with pale veins and chocolate spots; flowers pink. *Tropical.* *p. 399, 406, 448*

'Geneva' (Lucerna seedling); vigorous, branched, cane-stemmed plant with small, broad-ovate, dark green leaves copiously silver-spotted, purplish red beneath paling towards the margins; deep pink flowers in clusters close to the stem. (I) *p. 445*

geraniifolia (tuberosa) (Perú); tropical tuberous-rooted species with erect, angled, fleshy stems tinted purple, 30 cm high, branched above; leaves broad cordate; quilted, and dentate at margins, bright green above, bordered in red, and looking like a geranium leaf; flowers small but numerous in small pendant clusters, pinkish-white. *p. 462*

gigantea (Himalaya); many-stemmed plant swollen at internodes and base; obliquely ovate-pointed leaves light green, toothed; flowers pale pink; fibrous-rooted. *p. 407*

x gilsonii; fibrous rooted; stout stem with ovate pointed leaves shallowly lobed, glossy green, petioles hairy; floriferous, pink-flowered, the males double. (I) *p. 426*

glabra (scandens) (Brazil); attractive, fibrous-rooted species with much branched, trailing stems, and light green, ribbed, waxy leaves, cordate and nearly round, shallowly toothed; small white flowers. *Tropical.* *p. 428*

'Glacdaw' (Marjorie Daw x limmingheiana); vigorous, thickly branched, cane-stemmed begonia with triangular-ovate, pointed, attenuate, wavy, dentate leaves in green with spots of silver; few flowers in rose-pink. *p. 448*

glaucophylla: see limmingheiana

'Gloire de Jouy' (rex x incarnata); small fibrous-rooted plant with broad bronzy-green leaves marked with small silver spots with white hairs; red beneath. *Tropical.* *p. 408*

'Gloire de Sceaux' (socotrana x incarnata purpurea); a semi-tuberous hybrid, similar to socotrana but taller, the roundish leaves are bronzy-red, and flowers more vivid rose in color, flowering Jan.-May. *p. 458*

x goegocrispula (goegoensis x crispula), "Fire king begonia"; rhizomatous plant with large, shiny, puckered near-round leaves with a copper patina. (3) *p. 446*

goegoensis (Sumatra), "Fire-king begonia"; low growing gem on creeping rhizome, silky leaves round peltate, puckered, dark olive green with lighter veins, reddish beneath; pink flowers. *p. 400, 417, 436*

gracilis diversifolia (Mexico); tuberous species with erect stems and roundish leaves glossy green with brown along the veins; flowers rose-pink; forming bulblets in leaf axils. Called "Hollyhock begonia" because flowers cling to main stem. *p. 395*

grandis (evansiana) (China, Japan), "Hardy begonia"; tuberous species, with bulbils forming in leaf axils; stands some frost; on erect stems, the olive green, ovate leaves, veined purple beneath; flowers pink. Winter-hardy in parts of Canada. *Warm temperate.* *p. 434, 444, 457, 464*

'Gretchen'; bushy, well-branched plant with reddish stems streaked with white, becoming woody with age and swollen at the nodes; leaves obliquely ovate, cupped, glossy-green with lighter veins and light green beneath, margins doubly toothed; large, loose bright purplish rose to pink flower clusters from tips. *p. 448*

'Grey Feather' (angular compta); cane-stemmed; narrow gray leaves, wavy-toothed and shallowly lobed near base, with broad, silver veins; flowers white. *Tropical.* *p. 428*

'Grey Lady' (incana hybrid); upright-growing rhizomatous plant with large thick, peltate leaves dusted with white scurf; flowers white. *p. 390, 421*

griffithii: see annulata

'Gwen Lowell' (olsoniae x obscura); bushy plant to 50 cm high, with oblique-ovate, velvety leaves iridescent forest green with pale veins and toothed margins; flowers pure white. *Tropical.* *p. 465*

haageana in hort: see scharffii

handelii (China); semi-upright rhizomatous species with large ovate-pointed leaves light green, lightly covered with scarlet hairs; flowers creamy, with sandalwood fragrance. (3) *p. 431*

handroi (Brazil); fibrous, medium tall, well-branched plant with oblique-ovate, pleated, thin, soft-leathery leaves covered with white hairs, brown-red beneath, dentate margins, on thin, wiry, reddish stems; white flowers. *p. 444*

hemsleyana (China); a distinctive rhizomatous species with medium green, palmately compound dentate leaves; thinnish rhizomes somewhat erect; rose pink flowers in summer. (3) *p. 390, 405*

hepatica maculata: see squarrosa

x heracleicotyle ('Mrs. Townsend') (heracleifolia x hydrocotylifolia), rhizomatous; leaves small, fleshy, shallowly lobed, waxy green and dark edged; flowers pink. *Tropical.* *p. 406, 432*

heracleifolia (Mexico), "Star begonia"; with creeping rhizome; large, palmately lobed leaves to 30cm across, bristly-hairy, bronzy green with green ribs, flowers pink. *Tropical.* *p. 434, 455*

heracleifolia nigricans (Mexico), "Black star begonia"; handsome, rhizomatous plant smaller than sunderbruchii, the palmately lobed leaves blackish-green with contrasting pale green area along main veins. *p. 396, 406*

herbacea (Brazil: Rio); herbaceous species with thick, creeping rhizome clothed with root fibers; the fresh green, oblanceolate, minutely saw-toothed leaves arise directly from the rhizome without any petioles on long, narrowing bases. White flowers, the female blooms arising directly from the petiole on long tubes, the ovaries sitting directly on the rhizome; the male flowers grow in bunches supported by two large, fringed, green bracts; imported by Robert Wilson. (3) *p. 405*

hidalgensis (Mexico); decorative plant with fleshy, kidney-shaped, grass-green leaves with light green veins outlined in purple; white flowers. *p. 436*

x hiemalis; a class of autumn and early winter-blooming hybrids of B. socotrana with summer-flowering tuberous types, originated by Veitch (1883) and Clibrans (1908) in England, followed by Dutch specialists in Holland about 1946 as the "Elatior" begonia; semi-tuberous plants preferring cool surroundings or moderate warmth. Unfortunately dropping flowers quickly in superheated rooms. *Humid-subtropic.*

x hiemalis 'Altrincham Pink'; the original Clibran hybrid (1908) of socotrana with summer-flowering tuberous varieties, creating the class of winter-flowering, cool-loving 'hiemalis' or 'elatior' begonias so favored in northern Europe; beautiful large long-lasting rose bud flowers of bright rose pink; waxy green foliage. *p. 486*

x hiemalis 'Apricot Beauty', "Apricot winter begonia"; early winter-blooming, semi-tuberous type, free grower large and spready, and with semi-double, salmon-pink flowers flushed rosy-red. *p. 488*

x hiemalis 'Emily Clibran'; hybrid of colorful tuberous species combined with the winter-flowering habit of B. socotrana; showy, 6-8 cm double flowers rose-pink, flushed orange, and waxy, rounded leaves. *p. 490*

x hiemalis 'Emita', "Rosy winter begonia"; (Veitch 1910), vigorous, winter-flowering variety with very large, coppery-orange to rosy crimson, single flowers. *p. 488*

x hiemalis 'Exquisite' (Veitch 1910); extra large flowered single, to 10 cm across, in blush pink passing to deep clear pink at fringed margins; the large, reddish-bronze leaves show the heritage of its tuberous parents. *p. 486*

x hiemalis 'Pink Perfection'; miniature double rosebud, long-lasting flowers clear blush-pink. *p. 491*

x hiemalis 'Rieger's Schwabenland' (1964 Pat.); robust plant with pointed, oblique leaves metallic deep green, and large, glowing scarlet flowers to 5 cm dia., with contrasting yellow stamens. The new German Rieger "Elatior" strain is distinguished by its bushy, free-growing and floriferous habit, with flowers in vivid new colors of superior keeping quality, blooming for 8-10 weeks even in the home, normally in fall-winter. *Humid-subtropic.* *p. 487, 491*

x hiemalis 'Schwabenland Orange'; a lovely mutation of the original 'Rieger Schwabenland Red' with large flowers a vivid orange-salmon over the glossy, bright green foliage. *p. 487*

x hiemalis 'Snowdrop'; a Man-Holland (1911) variety with double Camellia-like, glistening snowy-white flowers, a low grower and heavy bloomer. *p. 491*

x hiemalis 'The President'; one of the most desirable commercial varieties, a good keeper, but subject to mildew; double flowers brilliant crimson-red to 8 cm across, a beauty for Christmas. *p. 488*

x hiemalis 'Van der Meer's Glorie'; sport of 'Optima', a freely branching, willing grower with smallish leaves and crowned with an abundance of large single 5-6 cm flowers of vivid orange salmon. *p. 490*

hirtella nana (cypraea nana) (Brazil); hirsute, miniature plant; pinkish stems; 5 cm serrate leaves green with bronze; numerous pink flowers. *p. 456*

hispida cucullifera (São Paulo), "Piggyback begonia"; interesting, fibrous-rooted species with large, velvety, maple-like, pale green leaves producing adventitious leaflets on top surface of the leaf along the veins; red petioles covered with white hairs; white flowers. *p. 390, 397, 404, 414, 437*

hispidavillosa (Mexico); small creeping rhizomatous species with large, variably round, thick, kidney-shaped, light green leaves with prominent veins; leaves and stems coarse-hairy; drooping flowers rosy pink. *p. 424*

holtonis (Colombia); shrub-like begonia with arching branches bearing small, oval, pointed leaves in light green. *p. 439*

huegelii (Brazil); handsome, fibrous-rooted species with broad-ovate, soft, white-hairy green leaves shallowly lobed, reddish beneath; large white flowers bearded white. (I2D) *p. 404*

hydrocotylifolia (Mexico), "Pennywort begonia"; hairy, rhizomatous plant with rounded, thick, waxy leaves, light olive green with dark veins; small rosy flowers. Called "Pennywort begonia" because of its miniature size. *Subtropic.* *p. 398, 407, 460*

'Illustrata'; imperialis hybrid; low, rhizomatous begonia with silvery gray-green, grape-like leaves with a rough surface traced with a net of reddish veins; flowers white or pale pink. (3) *p. 418*

'Immense'; rhizomatous ricinifolia seedling, with large star-like, acutely lobed, light green leaves 30cm or more wide, waxy and flat, some short bristles on surface, edge red; leafstalks with red scale-like hairs; flowers pink. *Subtropic.* *p. 406, 421, 455*

x imperiahybrida 'Hildegard Epple' (imperialis x lindleyana); stronger grower than imperialis with a creeping rhizome and oblique, heart-shaped leaves in pebbly silver with a narrow, dark green edge. (3) *p. 438*

x imperiahybrida 'Marbachtaler' (imperialis x lindleyana); more sturdy plant than imperialis, rhizomatous, with leaves netted in dark green with silvery marks. (3) *p. 438*

imperialis (Mexico), "Carpet begonia"; choice, small, rhizomatous, hairy plant with heart-shaped, velvety, pebbly leaves in dark green, about 10cm long; small white flowers. *Humid-tropical.* *p. 438, 461*

imperialis 'Gruss an Erfurt'; exquisite, small, low plant with creeping rhizome; round, pointed leaves with bubbly sparsely hairy surface, in silver-green with greenish brown markings along edges. (S3NM) *p. 438*

imperialis 'Otto Forster' (often confused with imperialis); a variety or sport of imperialis with brown leaves and light green areas along veins. (S3NM) *p. 400, 438*

imperialis smaragdina (Mexico), "Green carpet begonia"; differs from imperialis in its lighter, emerald-green leaf color. *Humid-tropical.* *p. 400, 438*

incana (peltata) (Mexico); thick-stemmed plant woolly white with scurf; fleshy peltate, white-tomentose leaves; drooping white flowers. *p. 427*

incarnata (subpeltata) (Mexico); fibrous-rooted, bushy species about 30 cm high, with erect stems; leaves oblique-ovate to 10 cm long, light green, paler beneath, and with toothed margins and somewhat quilted; large pink flowers in graceful clusters. *p. 461*

incarnata grandiflora; a variety of incarnata with larger, long-ovate, pointed leaves, semi-glossy green with lighter veins, margins dentate, wavy, eyelashed, edged in red, underside silver, and pink cast on young leaves; drooping clusters of very large, light pink flowers, ovaries green. (3) *p. 451*

incarnata sandersii (subpeltata, insignis) (Mexico); delightful, bushy, medium tall fibrous rooted plant 30-40 cm high, with apple-green leaves, lobed and crinkled at margins; graceful pink flowers larger than the type. (3) *p. 410*

x ingramii (nitida x fuchsioides); old English fibrous-rooted hybrid with small, slim, pointed leaves gleaming bronzy-green, some scattered hairs; dark pink ornamental flowers. *p. 398*

'Interlaken' (Lucerna seedling); distinctive, tall, few-branched, cane-stemmed begonia with ovate-pointed, deep green leaves, sometimes faintly silverspotted, one basal lobe sharply pointed, margins toothed and wavy; large, coppery-red flowers in drooping clusters. *Subtropic.* *p. 450*

involucrata (Costa Rica); bushy plant with brown stems; fibrous; green leaves lobed and toothed, lightly white-tomentose; flowers white and fragrant. *Tropical.* *p. 416, 461*

'Iron Cross': see masoniana

isoptera (Java); bushy, fibrous rooted plant with erect stems, leaves very oblique-ovate, shining green with toothed, red margins; flowers greenish with pink. (3N) *p. 426*

isoptera hirsuta (E. Indies); fibrous-rooted plant less robust, smaller, shining green leaves on hairy petioles. (3) *p. 407*

'It' (socotrana x rex cult.); miniature hybrid of rex with small, rex-like leaves green with silver pearling and blotching; freely flowering bright pink the year round, with a lovely fragrance. *p. 472, 478*

'Ivy Ever' (martiana x glaucophylla scandens); unusual basket plant of pendant habit, branching out from buds that resemble bulbils; green leaves with dark metallic sheen; large pink flowers. *p. 457*

'Jinnie May' (coccinea seedling); small plant, compact if kept pruned, with little, green, angelwing leaves crowded on well branched stems; bright red flowers all through the year, in short, drooping clusters. *Tropical. p. 454*

'Joe Hayden' (mazae x reichenheimii), "Black begonia"; upright rhizomatous with large, star-like, satiny, bronzy black-green, lobed leaves, red beneath; winter-flowering red. (*) *p. 403*

'Joe Hayden Junior'; seedling of 'Joe Hayden', small rhizomatous plant with leaves the same as the parents, satiny, black-brown sheen and yellow veins, but more round than star-shaped. *p. 424*

'John R' (dayii x macdougallii); rhizomatous spreading plant with large shiny, pea-green leaves pointedly lobed, on fleshy red petioles spotted with green; small and rather insignificant greenish-white flowers. *p. 465*

johnstonii (Trop. E. Africa); fibrous-rooted, branching plant of loose habit, succulent branches streaked with red, broad leaves glossy green with reddish crenate edge and overlapping basal lobes; flowers pink. (N) *p. 413*

jussiaecarpa (Tropical West Africa); long-stemmed, erect plant with oval, lanceolate leaves and axillary flowers on very short stems. (3) *p. 443, 447, 460*

'Kathy Diane' (Bow-Joe x Bow-Chancee); rhizomatous miniature with small ovate, brown leaves with chartreuse markings and lighter veins, hairy petioles and leaf margins; tiny, deep pink flowers in fall. *p. 453*

kellermannii (Guatemala), "Lily-pad begonia"; dainty, fibrous-rooted species with peltate, cupped, oval leaves yellow-green to rose-colored, and felt-like white-scurfy beneath; flowers pink. *Tropical.* *p. 408, 448*

kenworthyae (Mexico: Chiapas); distinctive slow-growing, upright rhizomatous species with smooth, fleshy, slate-colored or bluish green, 5-lobed leaves with lighter veins, looking very much like an ivy leaf, up to 25 cm in size; flowers faintly pink in winter. *Tropical.* *p. 390, 424, 435*

x kewensis; chance seedling resembling odorata, stems cane-like, long ovate leaves green with red edge; flowers greenish white, in drooping clusters. (I) *p. 427*

kraussiantha (schulziana) (Haiti); small, rhizomatous creeper with thick, smooth, maple-shaped, dentate leaves with about 7 lobes; erect inflorescence with pink flowers. Miniature. (3d) *p. 416, 448*

'Kumwha' (kenworthyae x reichenheimii); huge, vigorous rhizomatous plant with large, dull, dark green, star-shaped leaves; free-flowering habit with clusters of pink flowers above foliage. *p. 439, 465*

laciniata bowringiana (China); rhizomatous plant with sharply lobed velvety leaves in three shades of green in a Rex-like pattern; large, pink flowers. *p. 446*

'Lady Clare' (scharffiana x luxurians); hybrid with white, hirsute flowers; of the same parentage but a smaller plant than 'Mrs. Fred Scripps', with the same 5-7 lobed, hairy ovate leaves, olive green, red beneath, and frequent separate leaflets formed by basal lobe; white flowers. *p. 424*

'Lady Waterlow'; well-known x digswelliana seedling of low, spreading habit with red branches and glossy dark green undulate leaves, serrate and ciliate at margins, 8-10 cm long and 3-4 cm wide, grayish-green beneath with pink veins, on bright red petioles; large flowers white within and pink outside; winter-blooming. *p. 465*

laetevirens, laetevirides: see bradei

x langeana (possibly manicata x erythrophylla); large, rhizomatous begonia with leaves which are nearly circular and have a short point, eyelashed around the edges, often cupped. Tall, many-flowered inflorescence; the male flowers fall off as small buds. *p. 441*

'Lecco' (Lucerna seedling); cane-stemmed, tall, branched plant with ovate-pointed, olive-green leaves with silver spots and splashes, red beneath; large, deep pink flowers in drooping clusters. (I) *p. 454*

'Legacy'; robust, semi-upright rhizomatous plant with iridescent silver-bronze, star-shaped leaves often puckered, red beneath; flowers white tinged pink. (I) *p. 417, 421*

leichtlinii; charming small rhizomatous plant with oblique-peltate leaves silvery green with bold brown-red primary veins radiating from center; photographed at Palmengarten, Frankfurt, Germany, 1966. *p. 460*

'Leo Shippy'; magnificent plant with fast-creeping rhizome, large, deeply cut leaves of bronzy-green made velvety by fine red hairs, and red-hairy beneath; glowing pink blooms. (I) *p. 394, 405*

leptotricha (Paraguay), "Woolly bear"; dwarf plant with stout, felted, succulent stems and dark green, oval, thickish leaves, the underside densely felted with brown; flowers ivory; everblooming. *Subtropic.* *p. 418, 427*

'Leslie Lynn' (Lexington x dayii); rhizomatous plant with large dark lustrous, palmately lobed, star-like leaf with 5-7 pointed fingers with serrate and ruffled edges. (I) *p. 424*

'Lettonica' (heracleifolia x nelumbiifolia); thick, erect rhizome with large ovate, light green leaves with red-toothed and lobed margin, red beneath and brown-pubescent; flowers pink. (I) *p. 413, 448*

leucotricha; attractive small species photographed by T. Everett of New York Bot. Garden; with fleshy, tortuous stems, and oblique-ovate angelwing leaves deeply quilted and covered with white hairs; the blade splashed with silver and with lobed margins; inflorescence pendant with pinkish flowers. *p. 463*

liebmannii (Mexico); foliage plant with slender, fast-creeping rhizomes; leaves light green blotched silver, red-purple beneath, and pointedly lobed like a small star; flowers greenish white. (3) *p. 417, 446*

limmingheiana (glaucophylla) (Brazil), "Shrimp begonia"; trailing with slender stems; glossy light green leaves with wavy margin; coral red flowers; good for baskets. *Tropical.* *p. 400, 416A, 430, 433*

lindleyana (Colombia); low, rhizomatous plant with broad-ovate, short-pointed leaves, sparsely hairy and unevenly moss-green above and light green, crystalline below; shallow-lobed, veins in reddish brown above and bright red underneath; white flowers in clusters above foliage. *p. 439, 440, 461*

listida (So. Brazil); attractive fibrous-rooted miniature angelwing, with narrow oblique-ovate pointed waxy leaves to 15 cm long; olive green with bronzy cast; chartreuse with cream along center; red reverse, on hairy red stalks; flowers pink. *Tropical.* *p. 461*

lobata (Brazil); compact, hirsute, branching, erect begonia with pink stems carrying oblique, tri-lobed, velvety, green leaves, pink between veins underneath which shows darker on upper surface; white flowers in clusters. *p. 452*

lobata 'Variegata'; cane-stemmed, erect, branching plant with angularly lobed, silver-spotted leaves of green satin, indented veins; white flowers; sparse bloomer. *p. 446*

lobulata: see vitifolia

'Loma Alta' (scharffiana seedling); tall, vigorous grower, covered with stiff, white hairs, large oblique-ovate, olive-green leaves with overlapping basal lobes and finely toothed margins; small white or blush pink flowers with pink whiskers on loose, branched, arching stalks. (D) *p. 450*

longibarbata (Brazil); medium size herbaceous, fibrous-rooted plant of branching habit with watery stems and oblique-ovate leaves with scalloped margins, spring green, tinged red below; flowers white to pink. (I) *p. 419*

longipes petiolata (Colombia); fibrous-rooted plant with large, round-ovate, bright green leaves bristly-haired on succulent stems and red petioles; small white flowers. (I) *p. 414*

lubbersii (Brazil); lovely exotic, erect grower with rhomboid, peltate, silver-splashed, dark green satiny leaves, purple underneath; very large flowers in white to pink from hanging stems. *Tropical.* *p. 439, 444*

'Lucerna': see 'Corallina de Lucerna'

ludwigii (Ecuador); in the trade as "rigida", fibrous rooted species of deciduous habit; stout stem with digitately lobed leaves olive-green with whitish markings and red veins; flowers pinkish. *p. 406*

x lulandii (Lucerna x sutherlandii); semi-tuberous, evergreen, spreading plant with oblique, broad leaves long-pointed, deeply serrate and undulate, bright green; large pink flowers. *p. 458*

'Luwalter' (incarnata x mazae); upright, branching, rhizomatous plant of moderate habit, with crisp-looking coppery leaves fringed and pointed; flowers pink. Forms adventitious plants on stems. *p. 418*

luxurians (Chile), "Palm-leaf begonia"; ornamental, tall fibrous rooted plant sparsely rough-hairy; leaves peltate-palmate, with up to 17 narrow, serrate leaflets, reddish above; small cream, hirsute flowers. *Humid-tropical.* *p. 390, 400, 434*

lyncheana (Mexico, Central America, Perú); upright, bushy plant with oblique-ovate, shiny leaves on short petioles, red point at base of leaf, hairy, toothed leaf edges, green on top and red underneath; large, full, red bloom. From a group including roezlii, roezlii coccinea and roezlii rosea. *p. 446*

'Mac-Alice' (imperialis x macdougallii); handsome plant with procumbent rhizome; rough, pimply star-leaves with 4-5 points bluish-green overlaid with silver. (3) *p. 401*

macdougallii (Chiapas); creeping rhizomatous stem with long, reddish petioles; palmately compound, waxy leaves of 7-10 stalked segments, 50 cm or more across, the outer ones sickle-shaped, bronzy green, red beneath, and with toothed margins; small, greenish-white flowers. *Tropical.* *p. 403, 421*

macrocarpa (secreta) (or seretii cv.) (Trop. W. Africa); fibrous-rooted species with arching or drooping branches, elliptic pointed leaves glossy olive-green, sparsely hairy and toothed; flowers white tinged pink. *Tropical.* *p. 405*

maculata (Brazil); canelike stem with smooth, long ovate, green leaves marked with large silver spots, red beneath; large, pendulous pink flowers. (I) *p. 411*

maculata wightii; tall canestem with smooth, concave, green leaves freely spotted silver; flowers greenish-white. (I) *p. 411*

'Mme. de Lesseps' (argenteo-guttata x olbia); tall, branched; leaves broad-ovate, lobed, olive-green spotted silver; red beneath; flowers creamy, tinged pink. *p. 411*

'Mme. Fanny Giron' (incarnata x tuberhybrida); graceful basket plant with drooping, fresh-green, long ovate pointed toothed leaves; showy crimson flowers at frequent intervals. *p. 448, 457*

malabarica (South India); fibrous-rooted, bushy, pubescent plant with small ovate, green, dentate leaves; flowers blush pink (D). *p. 407, 410*

malabarica dipetala: see dipetala

'Manda's Eyelash'; a pretty bowerae cultivar; dwarf rhizomatous plant more vigorous than the species; small waxy oblique-ovate leaves almost peltate, chartreuse, boldly marked with black around the margins, scalloped and set with eye-lash bristles; sprays of salmon-pink flowers. *Tropical.* *p. 466*

manicata (Mexico); robust species with stout, ascending rhizome, the large, fresh-green leaves are fleshy, smooth and toothed, reddish beneath; collar of red bristles at top of leafstalk; flowers pink. *p. 428, 435*

manicata 'Aureo-maculata', "Leopard begonia"; robust plant with stout, ascending rhizome; the large waxy, fleshy green leaves are 10 to 20 cm long, smooth and toothed, and blotched yellow or ivory, and occasionally rose-red; reddish beneath; characteristic collar of red bristles at top of leaf stalk; flowers pink. The species is from Mexico. *Tropical.* *p. 428*

manicata 'Aureo-maculata crispa'; difficult but beautiful form, the waxy, fresh-green leaves blotched yellow and occasionally rose, the margin thickly crested. *Tropical.* *p. 394, 416A*

manicata 'Crispa'; slow, rhizomatous plant with large fleshy leaves waxy light green and the margins densely crested. *p. 396, 407*

mannii: see eminii

'Maphil' (bowerae seedling); colorful dwarf plant with creeping rhizome and red-scaled petioles; small star or maple-shaped leaves chocolate-brown with chartreuse markings, the veins red, margins with eye-lashes. *p. 412*

x margaritacea (Arthur Mallet x coccinea); distinctive, fibrous-rooted, delicate hybrid with metallic, purplish-pink leaves overlaid with silver; flowers pink. *Tropical.* *p. 403, 428*

x margaritae (echinosepala x metallica); bushy fibrous plant with soft-hairy, small, ovate-pointed and toothed, quilted leaves, faded bronze green, veins purple beneath; flowers bearded pink. *Tropical.* *p. 402*

'Marie B. Holley'; branching fibrous-rooted plant with thinnish maple-shaped leaves of glossy bright green, large waxy-white flowers. *p. 408*

'Marjorie Daw' (coccinea x limmingheiana); tall, vigorous fibrous-rooted old hybrid with smooth, cane-like stems and requiring support, branches lax, with waxy oblique-ovate leaves bright green; large flowers clear pink, in large trusses, on pink petioles; very decorative. *p. 466*

marnieri (Madagascar); handsome rhizomatous species with creeping stem, the leaves palmately lobed, the segments toothed, overlaid with silver and tinted rose; flowers pinkish; needs rest period. *p. 459*

martiana var. diversifolia (Mexico), "Hollyhock begonia"; tuberous plant with strongly pointed, saw-toothed dark green leaves on erect stems; pink flowers from the leaf axils. (IB) *p. 457*

masoniana (Indochina or China, introduced from Singapore), the "Iron cross begonia"; one of the most beautiful begonias in cultivation, spectacular rhizomatous plant of robust habit, with white-hairy, reddish stems and large roundish, firm, puckered leaves nile-green, marked with contrasting, bold pattern of brown-red, the older leaves overlaid with silver, and covered with bristly red hair and red-ciliate, 15-18 cm across; waxy flowers greenish-white with maroon bristles on back; flowering March-May. *Tropical.* *p. 15*, 19*, 392, 393, 416A*

'May Drew' ('Paul Bruant' x reichenheimii); vigorous hybrid with large pedately lobed leaves very dark green with veins in pale green; the lobes slender-pointed and with serrate margins on stout red, white-hairy petioles; free-blooming with dark rosy-pink flowers, almost red; (Fort hybrid). *p. 465*

'May Queen'; small, cane-stemmed plant with branches, small, lance shaped leaves bright green spotted silver; flowers greenish-white; albo-picta seedling. (I) *p. 409*

mazae (Chiapas), "Miniature begonia"; small rhizomatous plant with red and white creeping stalk; roundish satiny leaves shaded in various greens to bronzy, paler veins in center; flowers pink. *p. 398, 402*

mazae 'Nigricans'; a form with darker leaves and overlaid with bronzy-black pattern; rhizomatous. *p. 408*

mazae viridis 'Stitchleaf', "Stitchleaf begonia"; small rhizomatous plant with satiny heartshaped, light green leaves with purple marks like stitches along margin; flowers pink. (*) *p. 390, 403*

'Medora', the miniature "Troutleaf begonia"; slender canestemmed, leaves triangular lanceshaped, glossy green, spotted silver, margins wavy; large pink flowers. (I) *p. 402*

megaptera (Himalayas, Burma); unusual begonia with a base somewhat intermediate between a tuber and an erect rhizome, with flower stems and some of the petioles arising directly from it; caulescent stems and broad leaves 12-17 cm long, with irregular, sharp-pointed lobes and toothed margins, dark olive green on top, spotted grey, red beneath; 5 cm apple-blossom pink flowers in panicles slightly above foliage. *p. 425*

metallica (Bahia), "Metallic-leaf begonia"; bushy, fibrous-rooted, hairy plant with broad-ovate pointed leaves metallic olive-green and depressed purple veins, red-veined beneath; showy pink hirsute flowers. *p. 415, 419*

'Michael L. Barnes'; rhizomatous plant with large oblique heartshaped, toothed leaves light green, spotted chocolate; flowers pink. *p. 417*

micranthera fimbriata (type from Argentina, Bolivia); summer-blooming tuberous variety with short, succulent stems carrying near-round, softly hairy, shallowly lobed, green leaves with toothed, eyelashed margins; bright orange-red flowers with masses of yellow stamens. Differs from micranthera in that the involucres are hairy at the edge. *p. 443*

minor (Jamaica); small leaves to 10 cm, glossy dark green; flowers white to pink. *p. 455, 456*

mollicaulis (probably South America); small, upright branching plant covered with short, white hairs, with soft, green leaves lighter beneath, irregularly toothed, on lighter petioles; large, white flowers, few and somewhat pendulous. *p. 439*

'Morgana'; larger, improved scharffii type. The leaves have a curled point to distinguish them. Tinted white flowers carried above the foliage. *p. 447*

'Mrs. Fred Scripps'; scharffiana x luxurians characters; fibrous rooted, vigorous, hairy; leaves velvety forest-green with red veins, deeply lobed, red beneath; basal lobe sometimes forms separate leaflet, like a finger; small pinkish, hirsute flowers. *Tropical.* *p. 413*

'Mrs. Mary Peace' (ricinifolia x caroliniaefolia), "Star begonia"; rhizomatous; fleshy, green, palmate leaves with long lobes, red beneath; flowers pink. (C-I) *p. 425*

'Mrs. Townsend': see x heracleicotyle

'Mrs. W.A. Wallow'; tall, cane-stemmed, bushy plant; leaves ovate-lanceshaped, slate green, bristly-hairy, with toothed and wavy margin; glowing-red beneath; flowers blush pink. *Tropical.* *p. 430, 450*

'Mrs. W. D. Harney' (coccinea seedling); cane-stemmed, vigorous grower with slender stems and somewhat weak branches carrying long, smooth, fresh green leaves like coccinea; white flowers eight months out of the year. *p. 454*

munita; temporary name suggested by Irmscher on a variety which is close to Frutescans; low, fibrous-rooted, vigorous, compact foliage begonia with short petioles carrying leathery-satiny, medium green leaves, wavy and cupped, showing red beneath; flowers white. (I) *p. 449, 461*

natalensis (So. Africa); evergreen tuberous species with leaves more shallowly lobed and bolder than dregei, habit larger but less branching; flowers white. *p. 423*

'Neeley Gaddis'; tall viaudi seedling, fibrous, with large, triangular ovate leaves, dull olive-green and densely hairy, red beneath; large, creamy-white hirsute flowers. (IBD) *p. 404*

'Nelly Bly' (cypraea seedling); bushy fibrous plant, hairy; quilted leaves ovate, dark green and toothed, red beneath; flowers pink, hirsute, or bearded. *Tropical.* *p. 429*

nelumbiifolia (macrophylla) (Mexico), "Pond-lily begonia" or "Lotus-leaf"; rhizomatous species with large, peltate, round, green leaves, hairy on nerves; flowers pinkish. *Tropical.* *p. 390, 426*

'Niagara'; rhizomatous chance seedling of apparent heracleifolia lineage; upright growing, with thick, glossy olive leaves obliquely heart-shaped, golden-brown hairy when young; flowers white. *p. 419*

nitida (minor) (Jamaica); medium-sized begonia having cane-like shoots with weaker branches; thick, glossy leaves, ovate with irregular lobes, olive green faintly spotted silver; flowers in dull, dark pink, tinged yellow. *p. 456*

nitida rosea (odorata rosea); fine form of minor (syn. nitida) from Jamaica; erect cane-stem to 1 m high; leaves smooth and rather fleshy, oblique-heartshaped, medium green to 18 cm long; flowers clear pink. *p.459*

nurii (Malayan Peninsula); rhizomatous plant reminiscent of Rex begonias, with roundish, drab green leaves splattered with silver, irregular and wavy margins. *p. 452*

'Oadi' (odorata alba x dichroa); fibrous-rooted erect plant to 60 cm tall, with ovate-pointed leaves gleaming glossy-green; coral pink, fragrant flowers. *p. 418*

odorata (syn. nitida odorata) (Jamaica); fibrous-rooted, robust plant, to 2 m high, with fleshy, reniform, glossy green leaves; rosy-pink flower clusters, fragrant. *Tropical.* *p. 430*

odorata 'Alba'; bushy, fibrous-rooted, floriferous plant with glossy green, roundish leaves; small flowers white, in clusters and fragrant. (IB) *p. 430*

olbia (Brazil), "Bronze mapleleaf"; bushy, fibrous-rooted plant with thin lobed leaves bronzy green and black-green veins, scattered white hairy, red beneath; the surface shimmering in light; flowers greenish-white. (3) *p. 404*

olsoniae (vellozoana hort.) (Brazil); lush, low, rhizomatous species, with large fleshy leaves in changeable colors bronze to green, contrasting with striking ivory veins; flowers whitish, outer edge sometimes rosy. *Tropical.* *p. 423, 459*

'Orange Dainty'; quaint, somewhat trailing, fibrous-rooted plant with small lustrous dark green, dentate leaves and pendant clusters of dainty flowers in startling orange. *p. 410*

'Orange-rubra' (dichroa x Coral Rubra); cane-stemmed; large leaves obliquely ovate, of the angelwing type, smooth green, silver spotted when young; lacquered orange-red flowers. *Tropical.* *p. 422*

'Oriental Music' (dayii x imperialis); rhizomatous miniature with heart-shaped, pebbly, grass green leaves, new leaves chartreuse, hairy on both sides of leaf and on petiole; white flowers with pink hairs on the outside of the petals, blooming in spring and summer. (3) *p. 453*

'Orrell' (lucerna seedling); cane-stem, with large angelwing leaves fresh green and spotted silver, margins undulate; free flowering, cherry-red during winter (I) *p. 411*

'Otto Alfred' (daedalea x burkei); long-petioled rhizomatous plant with large, light-green leaves liberally liver-mottled, somewhat hairy. *p. 423*

'Otto Alvord'; compact plant with white-hairy rhizome; oblique-ovate leaves to 20 cm dia., light moss-green with small chocolate markings, the margins finely dentate, on green petioles with white bristles; small rosy, single flowers. *p. 466*

oxyphylla (Brazil); fibrous-rooted species of shrubby appearance, long oblanceolate leaves flare out from erect stems and recurve at the tip, shining like wax. (3) *p. 421, 463*

'Page Thirteen' (Mexican species); rhizomatous plant of sprawling habit, oblique-heartshaped, crenate leaves dark green with chocolate spots, of medium size, on long petioles; flowers pale pink. *p. 423*

palmifolia: see vitifolia

parilis (Brazil), "Zig-zag begonia"; fibrous-rooted, stiff, upright, well branched grower to about 1 m; branches zig-zagging between nodes, older branches covered with brown scurf; leaves long, narrow, shining green on top, red under; long, arching stems with flowers in white with prominent yellow stamens; when in bud, so tight that the cluster resembles a snow ball. *Tropical.* *p. 444, 463*

parva (Zaire); hanging basket type, not very showy, with pendant stems carrying oval, pointed leaves whose underside, like the stems, are covered with brown felt; small, scattered red flowers. *p. 442*

'Paul Bruant', (heracleifolia longipila x Frutescans); fibrous-rooted plant with stout stem; pointed leaves lobed and toothed, glossy green, on red petioles; stems with adventitious leaves; pink flowers in winter. (I) *p. 402, 410*

paulensis (Brazil); large orbicular, peltate, hairy, quilted leaves waxy, fresh-green with pale veins which are red beneath; rhizomatous; bright red, bearded flowers. *Tropical.* *p. 393, 398, 416A*

pearcei (Andes of Bolivia); low tuberous species with succulent stems finely pubescent, broad-ovate, toothed leaves velvety dark green with glistening light green veins, flushed pink beneath; flowers yellow. *p. 458*

x pearlii; rhizomatous imperialis hybrid, low, coarsely hairy, roundish leaves fresh green and pebbled, suffused with a pearly sheen. Hybrid with B. rex. (3) *p. 430*

peponifolia (Jamaica, Mexico); medium-sized begonia with a thick, creeping rhizome; long petioles covered with narrow, green scales pointing downward, carrying very large, near-round leaves with fine hairs around the undulating edges; blush-white flowers in tall panicles. *p. 449*

x perfectiflora; woody canestem, undulata hybrid, with spreading branches, small leaves triangular lanceshaped, bright green, margins undulate; summer-flowering white. *p. 402, 409*

'Perle Lorraine' (polyantha x daedalea); bushy, slender, fibrous plant with ovate, waxy leaves dark green and netted chocolate; free flowering vivid pink in winter. (I) *p. 404*

'Persian Brocade' (bowerae x Maphil); rhizomatous miniature with obliquely cordate, light green leaves edged and interlaced in black, with light green sinus and veins, upper leaf and leaf edge hairy, under-leaf splashed with red; hairy petioles, dotted with red. Pink flowers in early spring. *p. 453*

philodendroides (Mexico); named because foliage resembles Philodendron dubium. The large, tuber-like rhizcme is underground, carrying smooth, leathery, deeply lobed leaves and large white flowers in drooping clusters. Dormant 5-6 months a year. *p. 440*

x phyllomaniaca (incarnata x manicata), called the "Crazy-leaf begonia"; fibrous-rooted branching plant with narrowly oblique-ovate, twisted leaves to 17 cm, side-lobed and toothed, green on both sides; producing from stems and all over leaves many buds and leafy growths; flowers pale pink. *p. 390, 417*

picta (Nepal); handsome tuberous species introduced to England 1818; low-growing, with broad-ovate, pointed leaves deep green mottled with lighter green and metallic bronze, rugose on the surface; flowers clear pink. *p. 460*

"picta" hort; (possibly brevicaulis), low, ornamental, tuberous species with broad, puckered leaves, green, mottled light green and metallic bronze, maroon beneath; flowers pink. Grows in summer. (3) *p. 457*

'Picta rosea'; probably coccinea form, cane-stem; narrow waxy, angelwing leaves light olive green with silver spots; pendant clusters of salmon-rose flowers. *Tropical.* *p. 411*

pilifera (C. America); somewhat shrubby plant with stout erect, sometimes branched stems to 60 cm high; leaves broadly oblique-ovate to 20 cm long and 15 cm wide, covered with soft brownish hairs; the white flowers 4 cm across, in arching clusters, the white bracts at base of ovary are fringed with purple hairs. *p. 459*

'Pinafore'; seedling of 'Elaine' by Logee; low-growing, fibrous-rooted beauty with bronzy-green, angelwing leaves spotted silver, curly edged, beet-red beneath; bright salmon flowers; cane-stem. *Tropical.* *p. 422*

pinetorum (Mexico); rhizomatous species with heavy-textured, obliquely heart-shaped leaves covered with brown flannel below, fuzzy-white over lemon-green on top, frilled effect from center, scalloped edge trimmed with brown pencil line; large clusters of pink flowers in abundance high over foliage. *p. 440, 459*

'Pink Parade' (dichroa seedling); angelwing begonia of upright, branching habit with oval-pointed, wavy, bronze leaves thickly silver-spotted; shrimp-pink flowers. (S3) *p. 456*

'Pink Spot Lucerna' (Lucerna x dichroa); robust cane-stemmed plant with dark angelwing leaves accented by pink polka dots; enormous clusters of crimson flowers. (I) *p. 418*

plebeja (Nicaragua); rhizomatous plant with rounded, waxy, light green leaves and conspicuous brown spots, toothed at margin; flowers pinkish; dormant in winter. *p. 425*

plumieri var. barahonensis (Brazil); branched plant with oval, pointed, wavy leaves, smooth and green above, hairy and red below; small pinkish flowers. *p. 440*

poggei (Fernando Po); low fibrous-rooted plant with erect stems, ovate-pointed leaves dull green; greenish-white flowers, with red wingless ovaries, close to stem. *p. 407*

popenoei (Honduras); thick ascending rhizome with large, rounded, bright green leaves, sparsely hairy, the margins reddish and toothed; large, white flowers. *p. 425, 459*

'Pres. Carnot' (corallina x olbia); vigorous canestem, with ovate, green leaves sometimes silver-spotted, slightly lobed and toothed, red-tinged; trusses of large carmine flowers in constant bloom. (N) *p. 407, 440*

'Preussen'; sturdy, fibrous-rooted, bushy plant with ovate-pointed, olive green leaves spotted with silver while young; large pink flowers most of year. Old German hybrid 1848. *p. 416, 429*

princeps (Brazil); rhizomatous plant with large, leathery jade green leaves tending to curl in at the edges; flowers creamy-white tear drops. *p. 420*

prismatocarpa (Africa); miniature begonia 5 cm tall, with creeping rhizomes and obovate, waxy leaves, pleated from base, undulate margins; small, yellow flowers amongst foliage. *p. 456*

pruinata (Costa Rica and Nicaragua); fibrous-rooted, upright, branching type with oblique-cordate, smooth, glistening green leaves, glaucous green beneath; numerous flowers in flattened clusters on 30 cm long stalks. *p. 449*

x prunifolia (Viaudi seedling); fibrous rooted, hairy plant with close-set, pointed, cupped leaves dark, olive-green, deep purple beneath; white flowers, bearded white. *p. 415*

"purpurea" (Brazil); also as McDougallii var. Brazil in the trade; impressive, large, rhizomatous plant with many, fleshy, beet-red petioles carrying palmately compound leaves of up to eight leaflets, sickle-shaped, shiny deep green above and light maroon below with red veins, and frilly, dentate margins; long, erect flower stems with very large clusters of flowers in chartreuse, edged with pink. *p. 444*

pustulata (Mexico), "Blister begonia"; beautiful rhizomatous species of rambling, hanging tendencies, with pebbly leaves off-emerald green with silver veins, underside deep rose. Similar to imperialis, with fewer hairs. Likes moss-lined wire basket, with warmth and humidity. *Humid-tropical.* *p. 401*

pustulata argentea (Mexico), "Silver pustulata"; beautiful, low-growing rhizomatous plant with plush nile-green, puckered leaves richly variegated with silver; flowers greenish. (S3) *p. 393, 401*

pustulata x conchaefolia; beautiful rhizomatous, compact plant with oblique, broadly oblong leaves in pebble pattern in silver and pale green, some with bronze cast, green and maroon on black, eyelashed; green petioles covered with white hairs; good basket plant. (S3) *p. 443*

quadrilocularis: see egregia

rajah (Malaya); charming, dwarf, rhizomatous species with roundish, rich reddish green, bullate, silky leaves and contrasting veins of yellow green; under surface dull red; flowers pink. *Humid-tropical.* *p. 400*

ramentacea (Brazil); rhizomatous, compact grower with obliquely cordate leaves, shiny and green on top and scaly and red underneath; scaly petioles. Pink flowers. *p. 441*

'Ramirez'; clone of 'Alto-Scharff' (bradei x scharffiana); robust hairy, tall cane-stem type plant with dark green leaves, red in vein area; a free bloomer with hirsute, light pink flowers. *p. 466*

'Randy' (Verde Grande x Missouri); rhizomatous begonia with large, fresh green, seven-pointed, star-shaped leaves, edges stitched in brown, entire leaf often marbled brown; hairy leaf edge and petioles; pink flowers in winter. *p. 452*

'Red compta' (Tewksbury Red); low spreading, cane-stemmed plant with large lobed leaves light green, bronzy at the veins; large clear pink flowers. *p. 413*

x reichenheimii (heracleifolia x fuscomaculata); rhizomatous plant with cupped ovate leaves dark bronzy-green suffused with dark red without spots, glossy red beneath; flowers crimson. *p. 412*

repens (Vellozo) (Brazil); low rhizomatous plant with lanceolate slender pointed leaves, waxy metalic green dotted all over with silver spots, margins wavy; white flowers low in center. Photo R. Ziesenhenne, Santa Barbara, pictured in Tropica, p. 161. *p. 459*

rex cultorum; a group of beautiful, rhizomatous foliage plants with showy, oblique, oval pointed leaves, 12 to 30 cm long; originating from B. rex of Assam, and hybridized with other related species, including the deeply parted B. diadema. Flowers pale rose, autumn-blooming. (3)

rex 'Autumn'; obliquely ovate, wavy leaf in brown and russet-tan tones. (S) *p. 480*

rex 'Axel Lange'; hyb. of B. rex. griffithii, Pres. Carnot and others; upright, tree-type rex with small, satiny, cupped leaves in olive-green to bronze with dark center and circular silver blotches, brilliant red-brown beneath. (s) *p. 474, 476, 478*

rex 'Baby Rainbow'; a miniature rex with green leaves and purple center, margins purplish brown suffused with carmine-red and silver spotted. *Humid-tropical.* *p. 472, 475*

rex 'Ballet Girl'; broad and curly leaf all metallic silver, shaded green and with pinkish overtones, red-edged. *p. 474, 478*

rex 'Bearded'; named for the hoary rose-red hairs which have a pronounced bend at their apex; leaf zones in dusky, dark shades of green. *p. 470*

rex 'Bella'; sturdy grower with broad, flat leaves having a purple background, richly overlaid and dusted with silver. *p. 472*

rex 'Bertha McGregor'; upright branching type with heavy looking, lobed leaves; color zones aquamarine silver, next zoned with red, green maroon at margin. *p. 475*

rex 'Black Knight' ('Midnight'); one of the darkest color forms; thin velvety leaves red-black with stippled band of pink dots; petioles red-hairy. *Humid-tropical.* *p. 476*

rex 'Bodnant'; beautiful leaf with contrasting blood-red middle, as well as border, against broad zone of moss-green and silver. *p. 474, 478*

rex 'Calico'; rhizomatous grower with medium-sized leaves flushed crimson, brightly mottled silver. *p. 472*

rex 'Can-Can'; shapely diadema hybrid called "Oakleaf" because of the uniquely lobed and ruffled leaves, glossy silver green overlaid with blush-pink, and in younger leaf with purplish-red in center. Shimmering like crisp taffeta. *Humid-tropical.* *p. 473*

rex 'Cardoza Gardens'; mutant of 'Ranee'; large leaves with gay rainbow colors: purple, plum, silver, olive green; one of the most brilliant. *p. 390, 471*

rex 'Carmelita'; spiral type with deep green leaves marked with brown, overlaid with a broad zone of silver, and scattered red hairs. *p. 477*

rex 'Charlotte Hoak' (Pink Lady x Fireflush); enormous spiralled leaves dark green with lighter green blotches, underside red and hairy; red hairs on elevations and on wavy edge give a red-ruffled effect. *p. 477*

rex 'Chretien'; low growing, pretty plant with broad leaves bright metallic rose zoned over royal purple-black. *p. 471*

rex 'Comtesse Louise Erdoedy' (rex Alex. von Humboldt x argenteo-cupreata); first spiralled form (1883), known as "Corkscrew begonia"; large oblique-ovate, red hairy leaves light olive green zoned with silvery rose; one or both basal lobes spirally curled. *Tropical.* *p. 390, 474, 476*

rex 'Crimson Glow' (Emperor); leaves flushed crimson in the center overlaid with silver like pebbled, shimmering taffeta, giving a sanded appearance. *p. 468*

rex 'Curly Carnot'; sturdy spiral mutant of rex 'President', with leaves to 30 cm across, deep green richly overlaid with silver on raised areas between veins. *p. 470*

rex 'Curly Fireflush', "Spiral begonia"; a beautiful curly, erect mutant with the same striking red velvet leaves as 'Fireflush', the basal lobe twisted into a spiral. *Humid-tropical.* *p. 471*

rex 'Curly Silversweet'; upright grower, elaborately ruffled and curled mutant, the silvery leaves accented with garnet veins, on wine-red petioles. *p. 471*

rex 'Curly Stardust'; perfectly spiraled leaf gray-green facing up and sprinkled with silver. *p. 472*

rex 'Dew Drop'; attractive miniature with near-round leaves, above matte silver, underside and petioles strong maroon, edges curled under. *p. 472, 475*

rex 'Duarte'; leaves green with pronounced basal spirals, a silver zone in striking contrast, and densely covered with red hairs. *p. 475*

rex 'Edna Korts'; sturdy grower with leaves often doubly spiralled; between the dark center and margin a broad zone of silver reaches into the pointed tips; red underneath. *p. 470*

rex 'Emerald Giant'; a handsome, prolific plant with large leaves a harmony of dark forest-greens and browns; outstanding in the green class. *p. 470*

rex 'Eugen Hahn'; large, greenish black center with purple overtones, silver grey and moss green middle zone, black-green outer border; a vividly colored leaf. (S) *p. 480*

rex 'Fairy'; diadema hybrid, shapely, upright habit, strong; pointed leaf with silver dominant over the puckered area and tinted pink, dark gray-green along veins. *Humid-tropical.* *p. 469, 474*

rex 'Fireflush' ('Bettina Rothschild'); beautiful plant with large heart-shaped leaves metallic olive-green with darker center and edge, and entirely covered by plush-like crimson hairs glistening in the light; flowers waxy-white. *Humid-tropical.* *p. 471, 479*

rex 'Frau Hoffmann'; silver leaf with center, veins, edge and underside reddish purple. (S) *p. 476*

rex 'Frosty Dwarf' (Curly King Edward x Silver Queen); bushy and sturdy Brooklyn Botanic Garden hybrid of dwarf habit, with firm, oblique cordate leaves silvery, and outer edge olive green; pinkish when young; brown-red beneath. *Humid-tropical.* *p. 479*

rex 'Glory of St. Albans'; brilliantly colored metallic leaves of glistening, bright rose-purple overlaid with silver, but of weak growth. *p. 472, 473*

rex 'Glory Princess'; like a spiral-leaf 'Glory of St. Albans', mainly silver with pea-green center and edge; distinguished by deep rose hairs protruding from silver spots on edge. *p. 477*

rex 'Greenberry'; an American hybrid with large, sturdy leaves in soft shades of green, finely dotted a lighter green, darker zone along margin, red beneath. *p. 473*

rex 'Green Countess Erdoedy'; spiralled leaf basically shamrock green with wide zone of silver dots, surface soft and velvety. *p. 469*

rex 'Green Gold'; enormous leaf with numerous pointed shallow lobes, green-gold overlaid with silver, trimmed with deep purple center and edge. *p. 470*

rex 'Guy Fawkes' (known as 'Midnight' in Eastern U.S.); smoky black-green leaf very dark, covered entirely with small white pepper-dots. *p. 475*

rex 'Happy New Year'; same leaf pattern as 'Merry Christmas' but with bluish cast over the whole leaf, and silvery middle zone where 'Merry Christmas' is bright ruby red; the silver zone has maroon blush, stronger toward center. *Tropical.* *p. 479*

rex 'Helen Teupel'; diadema hybrid; bushy plant with long leaves sharply lobed, center and margin dark fuchsia-red, metallic green along veins, silvery-pink areas between. Probably the best of the lacy diadema hybrids. *Tropical.* *p. 390, 473, 474*

rex 'Her Majesty'; broad, tapering leaves a blackish, satiny, reddish purple with olive-green zone overlaid with rosy silver blotching. *Humid-tropical.* *p. 468, 469, 474*

rex 'His Majesty' (English hybrid 1903); long-pointed and lightly notched leaves maroon with a broad silver zone, overlaid with pinkish purple. *Tropical.* *p. 468, 472*

rex 'Huntington Lake'; deep rich green leaf marked with neat rows of silver spots radiating out between the veins. *p. 471*

rex 'Indian Summer'; delightfully ruffled leaf, background forest-green, wide zone of Indian red, edge and center deep purple. *p. 477*

rex 'Inimitable'; predominantly silver-green wth narrow purplish margins; distinguished by erect red hairs. *p. 470*

rex 'Irish Colleen'; branching type with beautiful leaves satiny vivid emerald-green with blackish veins; free flowering. *p. 478*

rex 'It': see 'It'

rex 'Joel Gillingwators' (Adrian Schmidt x rex); broad, lobed leaves mainly gray-green, vein areas darker with pale veins; glows red when lighted from the back. *p. 470*

rex 'John Russel', see rex 'L. R. Russel'

rex 'Kathleyana' (Mrs. Moon x cathayana); upright branching plant with lobed, pubescent leaves of dark green, heavily speckled silver between the veins. (N) *p. 472*

rex 'King Edward IV'; large and bushy plant with very dark satin purplish-black leaves spotted royal-red (*N) *p. 471*

rex 'King Henry VII'; dark maroon, stiff leaves overlaid with silver-pink except at veins and edge. (N) *p. 474*

rex 'Libelle'; of dwarf habit, with flat leaves silvery gray with pink sheen, iridescent like a dragonfly; brownish green along veins. *p. 474*

rex 'Lillian'; ruffled double spiral leaf with wide opening between spirals at the stems; lobed leaves mainly silver-green suffused with pink, dark center and margin, red on the underside. *p. 477*

rex 'Louise Closson'; smallish leaf in black with irregular, royal purple, iridescent zone. (S3) *p. 480*

rex 'L. R. Russel' (John Russel); hybrid of B. pictavensis x Pres. Carnot x B. rex, shallowly indented leaves in dark green overlaid with bronze, spotted silver and rose. (S) *p. 476*

rex 'Lucille Closson' (robusta x rex cult.); small plant with richly colored leaves very dark blackish-red and broad areas of purple-pink. (N) *p. 472*

rex 'Marion Louise'; distinctive rhizomatous plant with acutely 5-7-lobed leaves silvery green, the center area and margin grass-green and overcast with purplish sheen. *p. 472, 475, 480*

rex 'Merry Christmas' (Ruhrthal, Reiga, or Gundi Busch); beautiful, smooth leaf with well defined color zones; center velvety blood-red, broad adjoining area silver and pink, outer zone nile-green, edged fuchsia-red. *Tropical.* *p. 15*, 473*

rex 'Meteor'; compact plant with sturdy, well-rounded leaves deep glowing rose, entirely speckled with pearly silver. *p. 472*

rex 'Midnight'; see rex 'Guy Fawkes'

rex 'Mikado', "Purple fan-leaf"; good American hybrid of bushy habit and enduring the heat of summer; center of leaf purple spilling into metallic silver and edged silvery purple. *Humid-tropical.* *p. 416A, 469, 478*

rex 'Nigger Tree'; slender upright growing type with cupped leaves, the center and edge are a deep blackish-red with a zone of dark olive dotted white. *p. 472*

rex 'Ojai'; attractive spiralled broad leaf with ruffled edge, rich green heavily silver-spotted and overcast with royal purple. *p. 475*

rex 'Pansy'; dwarf grower with lightly lobed leaves of strange metallic green, in the center a distinct star of dark green. *p. 475*

rex 'Patsy'; shapely plant with leaves near black, with a broad silver zone tinted purple skipping the veins; brown-red beneath. *p. 477*

rex 'Peace'; of strong habit; center area of leaf along veins and margin metallic red, balance silvery with pink sheen. *p. 19*, 468, 474*

rex 'Peacock'; large brilliant leaves hugging the pot, in darkest tones of black and red except for a zone of silver. *p. 471*

rex 'Perle de Paris'; elephant-ear-like, large, shiny leaf silver metallic green, barely showing the purplish-red veins and edge. *p. 474*

rex 'President' (Pres. Carnot); easy grower; quilted leaf with base deep moss-green; raised areas a clear silver. *Tropical.* *p. 473, 474*

rex 'Prince Charming' (cathayana x Ctse. Louise Erdoedy); shapely plant with leaves olive green in the center, shading to peagreen and deepening toward the margins, red hairs on each of the many silver spots give soft hazy look. *p. 477*

rex 'Princess of Hanover'; smoky velvet, pea green leaf with broad silver zone and a double spiral at the base; the entire surface covered with tiny pink hair. *p. 470, 480*

rex 'Purple Curly Stardust'; rough-textured, quilted leaves of purplish cast heavily stippled with silver, and with a ruffled edge. *p. 476*

rex 'Purple Pettycoats'; sturdy plant having leaves covered with silver except for purple areas along veins, and purplish toward margin; foliage on short petioles forming cups and spiralling, with ruffled margins curling in on both sides like the frilled petticoats of a Spanish dancer (Sylvia Leatherman, California). *p. 479*

rex 'Queen Wilhelmina'; bushy plant with roundish sturdy leaves, the quilted surface almost entirely silver. *p. 478*

rex 'Ranee'; large broad-ovate leaves 30 cm or more long, with purplish-black center, next a broad green area suffused with metallic rose-pink, and spotted pink toward the margins which are yellowish green shading to purple. *p. 469*

rex 'Robin'; upright silver speckled maroon maple-leaf, center area ruby; outer zone silvery green. *p. 455*

rex 'Rose Marie'; sturdy dwarf variety with crisp-textured, lobed leaves soft orchid over silver, a touch of black at edge. *p. 475*

rex 'Roxanne'; medium sized rex with a reddish brown center and olive-green edge, band of silver spots. (S) *p. 456*

rex 'Rubena'; see 'Rubena'

rex 'Ruhrthal'; see rex 'Merry Christmas'

rex 'Salamander'; diadema hybrid, bushy plant with erect slender leaves olive-green, blotched and pearled with silver. *Tropical.* *p. 472, 480*

rex 'San Mateo'; strong, bushy plant with long petioles carrying medium, spiralled, ruffled and deeply lobed leaves with sharp points. Leaf design in silver overlaid with iridescent purple, blackish center, and edge with silver spots; wine-red underneath. (S) *p. 476*

rex 'Scarlett O'Hara'; branching plant with quilted leaves of burgundy, so dark and glossy that the highlights fairly shine. *p. 470*

rex 'Seed Twist'; iridescent leaf dark reddish brown, marked silver on the raised portions of the puckered surface. *p. 474*

rex 'Silver Corkscrew'; showy leaf broadly ovate with slender tip and spiral base, the depressed veins olive green while the ridges between are of purest silver. *p. 472*

rex 'Silver Dawn'; very bushy miniature with small leaves brightly speckled silver on deep green. *p. 476*

rex 'Silver Dollar'; compact plant with many small, roundish, pointed leaves to 12 cm long, the oblique point broader and more blunt than on most rex varieties; basically silver, with dark olive-green narrowly outlining the veins in center also irregularly along edge; back of leaf red-maroon. *p. 479*

rex 'Silver Queen'; flat leaf a soft silver-gray excepting along veins in center and the margin a metallic green. *Tropical.* *p. 469, 474*

rex 'Silver Sweet'; upright and much branched plant with leaves gun-metal silver, center and veinings gray black; strong and sturdier than most. *p. 471*

rex 'Solid Silver': see 'Solid Silver'

rex 'Sunburst'; broad leaves 30 cm long and doubly spiralled at base and zigzag with pointed lobes, metallic gray-green suffused with pink, dark green sunburst radiates from center. *p. 477*

rex 'Thrush' (rex x dregei); distinctly different; branching plant, with upright stem; small maple-shaped leaves crimson-red spotted with fine silver; prolific bloomer. *Tropical.* *p. 455, 468, 472*

rex 'Twisty Spot'; spiral type leaf coarsely toothed and wine-colored, with silvery spots, evenly distributed. *p. 472*

rex 'Vesuvius'; iridescent blackish-red leaf with faint, deep moss-green zone, overlaid with silvery pink spots and blotches. *p. 474, 480*

rex 'Winter Queen'; roundish leaf with lobed margin, undulate and overlapping, grass-green overlaid with silver, center and edge brown-red. *p. 474, 477*

rex 'Yuletide'; spectacularly colored leaf with reddish-black center, a well defined middle zone vivid ruby-red, outer zone with spots of red, forest green and silver, leaf edge blackish; to 20 cm long. *Tropical.* *p. 479*

rhizocarpa (Brazil); low-growing species with a short, thick, creeping rhizome with near-symmetrical, narrow-ovate, pointed, saw-toothed, often white-spotted leaves to 10 cm long, on short reddish petioles. White flowers; the female flowers have long tubes with the ovaries sitting directly on the rhizome; the male flowers are produced in a bunch, supported by two large, fringed, green bracts. Rare. *p. 456*

'Richard Robinson' (macbethii seedling); small, low plant with silvered leaves lobed and finely toothed, center green, on short petioles; flowers white; deciduous in winter. *p. 457*

richardsiana (So. Africa), "Scented mapleleaf begonia"; semi-tuberous, small, succulent plant with thin, light green leaves digitately lobed, and a red spot at the juncture of the long lobes; free-flowering white. *p. 458*

x richmondensis; (fuchsioides x semperflorens seedling); floriferous, fibrous-rooted plant with red stem and medium oblique-ovate, waxy green leaves with bronzy overtone and dentate edge, reddish beneath, 8 to 10 cm long; flowers dainty pink. *Tropical.* *p. 413*

x ricinifolia (heracleifolia x peponifolia), "Castor-bean begonia"; robust, old hybrid with erect rhizome and large, roundish leaves, deeply lobed like a maple leaf, fresh moss green with a taffeta sheen on top, reverse pale green, pale veins with red scales; petioles ringed by red, broad-scaly hairs, especially near apex; pink flowers.
Humid-subtropic. *p. 390, 421, 422, 433, 455*

'Ricky Loving' (Billy x sunderbruchii); rhizomatous plant with large, 7-pointed, black, velvet leaves with silvery-grey lacing along the green veins, underleaf and petioles densely hairy; rose-colored flowers in fall and winter. (W) *p. 452*

'Ricky Minter' (manicata crispa x mazae); robust rhizomatous plant with large round bronze to mahogany leaves with prominent pale veins, the margins crisped and frilled; spires of rose-pink flowers in winter.
Humid-subtropic. *p. 397, 405*

rigida (Ecuador); species with tall, brown, woody, branching cane stems carrying oblique-ovate, light green leaves with sunken veins 9 to 13 cm long, with a silken sheen, underneath light grey-green, edges slightly frilly and eyelashed, a red pencil mark at each lash. *p. 456*

'Roberta'; a chance seedling from Robert Shatzer 1967; rhizomatous plant with giant leaves rounded in outline, but cut with numerous pointed lobes, bronzy green and finely pubescent; clusters of pink flowers rising high above foliage, blooming in spring. *p. 466*

roezlii: see bracteosa

'Rogeri'; small form of thurstonii, fibrous-rooted; glossy olive-green, cupped leaves occasionally indented at the margin; free-flowering, with hirsute pink flowers. *Humid-subtropic.* *p. 415*

'Rondo' (mazae x hydrocotylifolia); rhizomatous hybrid spreading sideways, with leaves obliquely rounded and a somewhat cordate base; lightly hairy and moss-green on surface, amaranth-red underneath. *p. 466*

'Rosea gigantea' (semperflorens x roezlii); vigorous fibrous-rooted hybrid with roundish, bright, glossy green leaves; flowers coral-red, during winter. (I) *p. 404, 445*

'Rossii', tall, canestemmed; "angelwing" begonia with large, green leaves flushed bronzy-red toward margins, faintly silver spotted; large, pink, pendulous flowers. 'Lucerna' seedling. (I) *p. 407*

'Ross Swisher' (aconitifolia seedling); "angel-wing" type with stocky cane-stems carrying large, pointed, lobed leaves of deep, dull green, heavily sprinkled with silver; drooping clusters of lavender-pink flowers. (I) *p. 447*

rotundifolia (Haiti); low species with creeping rhizome and clusters of small roundish leaves glossy yellow-green and scalloped edge; flowers pink. A miniature begonia. *p. 422*

roxburghii (inflata) (Himalayas); slender fibrous-rooted species sparsely hairy with large, obliquely heartshaped leaves bright glossy green; fragrant white flowers. *Humid-subtropic.* *p. 404, 431*

'Rubaiyat'; canestem dichroa seedling, bushy and vigorous, with large oblique pointed leaves glossy green, occasionally spotted silver, rose-red beneath; flowers deep pink. (•) *p. 408*

'Rubena'; rhizomatous plant with large, rounded, green leaves with broad zone of silver, overlaid with a sheen of metallic red which glistens in the light. *p. 478*

rubra (Java); bushy cane-type species with small shiny oblique-ovate, angelwing leaves 8 cm long, shimmering nile-green with purplish sheen; small pinkish flowers; photographed at the Los Angeles Arboretum, Arcadia, California. *Tropical.* *p. 460*

rubro-venia (Bhutan); low species with ascending rhizome with short, erect branches; slender, oblong-pointed leaves glossy dark green, often red beneath; flowers white with red veining. *p. 404*

rubro-venia 'Maculata' (Himalayas); a variety with its narrow ovate dark green leaves corrugated, and painted with gray between the vein areas. *p. 467*

rubro-venia 'Silver'; attractive form with the leaves a metallic coppery silver, red underneath, on long, grooved leafstalks. *p. 403, 421*

rubro-venia 'Spotted'; variety with cream-colored spots and blotches. *p. 447*

x rufida (Viaudi x prunifolia); vigorous well-branched, frosted plant with large dark green toothed leaves, wine-red and densely hairy beneath; red-bearded (hirsute) pink flowers. (D) *p. 418*

rupicola, (Java); unusual small species with slender creeping rhizomes, and obliquely heart-shaped 8 cm leaves, brown-green with yellowish areas, irregularly toothed margins; flowers pale pink. *p. 424*

'Sachsen'; old German seedling; low, spreading, fibrous-rooted; small, angelwing leaves dark bronzy green, underside red; free flowering rosy red. *Humid-subtropic.* *p. 429, 435*

salicifolia (Brazil); cane-stemmed species with wide oblique-ovate leaves blue-green dotted with large silver spots. (I) *p. 412*

x sandersonii; identified as a cultivar of the same parentage as x digswelliana (fuchsioides x semperflorens), with smoother, less serrate-edged leaves. (3) *p. 456*

sanguinea (Brazil); fibrous rooted, smooth and shining plant with many reddish stems; fleshy, oval leaves olive-green, blood-red beneath; small, white flowers. *Tropical.* *p. 406*

'Sarabande' (bowerae x heracleifolia); bushy rhizomatous hybrid of low habit, with small oblique-ovate, waxy leaves, deeply lobed and with ciliate hairs along margins, deep velvety green and lighter green and ivory along main veins; in form close to heracleifolia with its larger foliage and rose-pink inflorescence. *p. 464*

'Sarabelle'; distinctive Maybelle seedling, short canestem, with small oval, flat green leaves spotted silver, flushed red beneath; pink flowers. (I) *p. 411*

sp. 'Sarawak' (Malaysia); a beautiful tropical, fibrous-rooted begonia of shrubby habit to 50 cm high; the oblique-ovate, corrugated satiny leaves metallic green, prettily spotted with silver, margins sharply saw-edged and pink, on reddish stems; pinkish flowers. Photo by J. Bogner of Botanic Garden Munich. *p. 467*

sarmentacea (Brazil); rich-looking rhizomatous plant of low habit with hairy, short-petioled, broad leaves, gold-green like iridescent satin and prominent veins above, light red below; white flowers of fair size. (3) *p. 418, 442*

scabrida (Venezuela); decorative, fibrous-rooted, erect, bushy plant with ovate, bright green, rough-hairy leaves irregularly toothed; small white hirsute flowers like pearls. (I) *p. 430*

'scandens': see glabra

sceptrum (aconitifolia 'Hild. Schneider') (Brazil); fibrous-rooted species with erect stems and large leaves digitately lobed, the segments long and finger-like, green streaked with silver; flowers pinkish-white. *p. 427*

scharffiana (Brazil); compact, spreading, densely white-hairy, fibrous-rooted species with red stems; broad ovate leaves, olive-green, red beneath; pale pink hirsute flowers. Of smaller habit than scharffii. *Subtropic.* *p. 415*

scharffii (haageana) (Brazil), "Elephant-ear begonia"; lovely, rugged, white-hairy plant wth fibrous roots, and big 25 cm ovate leaves larger than scharffiana, brownish yellow-green with red veins, and red beneath; large pinkish flowers with beards (hirsute) in clusters. Parent of many velvety beauties. *Subtropic.* *p. 412, 415, 463*

schmidtiana (Brazil); small, fibrous-rooted begonia with reddish, hairy stems and oblique, heart-shaped, olive-green, hairy, toothed leaves, beneath reddish with green margin; hirsute flowers in pale pink. *Tropical.* *p. 408, 410, 464*

schulziana (kraussiantha) (Haiti); small, rhizomatous miniature creeper with thick, smooth, maple-shaped, dentate leaves with about seven lobes; erect inflorescence with pink flowers. *Humid-tropical.* *p. 460*

secreta: see macrocarpa

semperflorens (cucullata), "Wax begonia"; originally from Brazil, but the derivatives in cultivation are grouped under B. semperflorens cultorum, or "Wax begonias"; fibrous-rooted, glabrous and more or less succulent plants with fleshy, oval leaves, and usually rose-red flowers in axillary clusters. Very popular as summer bedding plants. *Subtropic.* *p. 19•, 482*

semp. albo-foliis, "Calla lily begonia"; dainty mutant with glossy light green leaves marbled white and flushed bronzy-red toward margins, and the terminal growth a glistening white suggesting miniature calla lilies; flowers pink. *Tropical.* *p. 481, 483*

semp. albo-foliis 'Double Pink Calla lily'; mutant with more tender leaves but fully double, pink flowers; somewhat more delicate. (3) *p. 483*

semp. albo-foliis 'Maine Variety'; sturdier, heavier-leaved "Calla lily" variety, with single pink flowers; recommended for the home. (D) *p. 482, 483*

semp. albo-foliis 'Pink Jewel'; a delicate calla lily begonia with semi-double, pink flowers. (ID) *p. 482*

semp. albo-foliis 'Ruby Jewel' (Calla Lily x Bijou de Jardin); exquisite, very bushy, dwarf plant with the little waxy leaves green and white; flowers carmine-red with double center. *p. 483*

semp. 'Charm'; seedling of "Calla lily begonia" 'Nancy Etticoat', with green, often irregular leaves blotched and marbled with cream and yellow, tinged pink in sun; flowers single pink. (•I-2D) *p. 483*

semp. 'Cinderella'; bright green leaves and large, single flowers with prominent tufts of yellow stamens. *Subtropic.* *p. 482*

semp. 'Fiesta'; green-leaved, strong-growing wax begonia with many large scarlet red flowers set in center with a yellow, double stamen cluster like a tuft of gold. (ID) *p. 485*

semp. 'Flamingo'; sturdy green-leaved plant with single bicolor flowers, white edged with crimson-red. *Subtropic.* *p. 485*

semperflorens fl. pl. 'Ballet'; free-blooming, fully double white Rose-begonia with bronze-red leaves. (ID) *p. 390, 483*

semp. fl. pl. 'Bo-Peep'; fibrous-rooted plant of bushy habit, with waxy leaves mahogany-red, and an abundance of bright pink flowers so double as to resemble a hoopskirt. (•ID) *p. 485*

semp. fl. pl. 'Carlton Delight', (Indian Maid x Geneva); bronzy-wax leaves with large, densely double blush-pink flowers; propagated from bottom breaks. *p. 484*

semp. fl. pl. 'Curlilocks'; eye-catching "Thimble-type" wax begonia with deep coppery-bronze leaves and somewhat pendant clusters of large flowers, the pronounced back petals rosy red, and the center with a high crest of stamen turned into petals, first green then bright yellow. *Subtropic.* *p. 416A, 485*

semp. fl. pl. 'Dainty Maid'; compact, bushy dwarf plant with waxy green leaves, two-toned fully double flowers white in center, outer petals tipped with rose. (ID) *p. 484*

semp. fl. pl. 'Firefly'; dark coppery-black leaved wax begonia covered by high-crested, thimble-type red flowers with distinct back petals. *p. 485*

semp. fl. pl. 'Geneva Scarlet Beauty'; sturdy, green-leaved plant known as a "Rose begonia", self-cross of 'Gustav Lind', larger habit and bigger bright scarlet double flowers full and round like a pompon. (ID) *p. 484*

semp. fl. pl. 'Goldilocks'; smallish red-leaved wax begonia with thimble-type semi-double flowers; big single petals framing bright yellow tufted centers. (ID) *p. 483*

semp. fl. pl. 'Gustav Lind'; also known as 'Westport Beauty', a dwarf and bushy wax begonia with glossy green foliage and fully double pink flowers. (•ID) *p. 484*

semp. fl. pl. 'Lady Frances' (originally 'Lucy Lockett'), "Rose begonia"; endearing and enduring plant, popular in Milwaukee, with waxy, mahogany-red leaves and a profusion of ruffly camellia-type flowers fully double bright pink, with white ovary but without prominent back petals, in constant bloom. *Subtropic.* *p. 481*

semp. fl. pl. 'Little Gem' (dwarf); a pigmy plant with red-bronze leaves set with ruffled double pink flowers. (ID) *p. 484*

semp. fl. pl. 'Pied Piper', "Thimble begonia"; dwarf, bushy, somewhat lax plant with dark bronze foliage, covered with clusters of thimble type, sweet pink flowers crested in center. (ID) *p. 484*

semp. fl. pl. 'Pink Camellia'; a dwarf and bushy plant with lacquered, deep red leaves and double pink, small, camellia-like flowers. (•ID) *p. 481, 484*

semp. fl. pl. 'St. Catherine' (Patricia); freely self-branching and fairly large, robust wax begonia, popular in Pennsylvania, with polished deep bronzy-maroon leaves, freely everblooming with pendant fully double pink rosebud-like flowers. (*IID) *p. 485*

semp. 'Frosty' (Karin); dwarf, bushy growing wax begonia with dark bronze foliage and single white flowers with gold in center. (ID) *p. 485*

semp. 'Indian Maid' (Indianerin); robust, bronze-leaved German seedling, freely blooming with single flowers of warm, glowing orange cerise. (D) *p. 485*

semp. 'Luminosa'; compact variety with flowers soft scarlet, and light green waxy leaves with ciliate red border, turning deep red-brown if grown in full sun. *Subtropic.* *p. 483*

semp. 'Pink Pearl'; gracilis type, a good compact growing "bedding" variety with fresh-green waxy leaves and covered with single flowers bright rose-pink. *Subtropic.* *p. 483*

semp. 'Red Pearl'; green-leaved variety with glowing, red flowers. *Subtropic.* *p. 482*

semp. 'Scandinavia Pink'; vigorous bushy plant of intermediate habit 20-25 cm high, with glossy-green, wavy leaves, tinged bronze, producing masses of bright rose-pink flowers. Widely used for summer garden planting. *Subtropic.* *p. 482*

semp. 'Scandinavia White'; similar to Scandinavia Pink, but with white flowers; light green foliage on reddish stems. *Subtropic.* *p. 482*

serratipetala (New Guinea), "Pink spot"; beautiful, ornamental species, fibrous-rooted, freely branching with arching stems carrying small, shiny, frilled, pleated, deeply lobed and doubly toothed leaves in dark olive green with iridescent, deep pink to red spots; deep pink flowers. Name refers to the red-toothed petals of the female flower. *p. 437, 447, 467*

'Shippy's Garland'; fibrous-rooted trailer with glossy, grass-green, lanceolate leaves slightly undulate and scalloped; abundant flowers cherry rose. *p. 412, 442*

'Silver Jewel' (imperialis x pustulata); luxurious as pustulata argentea but sturdier; cordate leaves with silvery blisters, streaked with emerald green. *Tropical.* *p. 401*

'Silver pustulata': see pustulata argentea

'Silver Star' (caroliniaefolia x liebmannii); rhizomatous; star-shaped leaves, deeply lobed, olive green, largely overlaid with silver and puckered, margins toothed, red beneath; flowers white. *Subtropic.* *p. 390, 401*

'Sir Percy' (Silver Star x speculata); unique rhizomatous plant with small leaves of metallic sheen which sometimes look like silver, sometimes green, dark green edge; brick-red underneath. *Subtropic.* *p. 423*

'Skeezar' (dayii x liebmannii); rhizomatous, a favorite because of its strong bushy growth and attractive, smallish, rippled, silver-splashed leaves; flowers greenish-white. *Tropical.* *p. 397*

'Society' (coriacea florealba); bushy fibrous plant with small ovate, fleshy, cupped leaves, dark glossy green above, brown-felted beneath; flowers creamy. *p. 416, 441, 451*

socotrana (Socotra Is., Indian Ocean); bulbous, branched species with low, succulent stems and peltate, round, waxy green leaves; flowers rose-pink in erect clusters above the foliage. (S) *p. 486*

'Solid Silver'; bushy rhizomatous plant with wing-like, pointed leaves in a monotone silvery gray; good bloomer. *p. 468*

sparsipila (barkeri) (Central America); fibrous-rooted plant of medium growth, completely covered with brown scurf; the lobed, toothed, green leaves usually depressed in center; large, pink flowers. *Tropical.* *p. 431, 441*

'Spaulding' (bowerae x hydrocotylifolia); extra bushy rhizomatous dwarf with rounded leaves shading from grass to moss green into velvety black lines, underneath ox-blood red, and edged with eyelashes. (I) *p. 418, 433*

x speculata (hybrid with rex), "Grapeleaf begonia"; low, hairy, rhizomatous plant with leaves nearly round and shallowly lobed, dull gray-green, speckled gray, reddish beneath; flowers white. *Subtropic.* *p. 390, 426*

spinibaris (Brazil), "Seersucker begonia"; erect, fibrous plant with reddish stem and petioles, thickly covered with white, hair-like scales, carrying oblique-ovate, satiny, moss-green, hairy leaves, flushed purplish beneath, margins irregularly crenate; white flowers. *p. 444*

squamosa: see barbana

squarrosa (hepatica maculata) (Mexico); low-growing rhizomatous species with thick, waxy, round-ovate leaves nile green with light brown areas, on red-hairy petioles; (hepatica maculata in the trade). *p. 403*

"strigillosa" in hort., bot. tacanana (Mexico); small rhizomatous plant with waxy, oblique-ovate leaves light green with darker markings. *p. 455*

subnummularifolia (Borneo); low species of flattened habit, with creeping rhizome; small waxy, bronzy leaves nearly round, 4-5 cm across, sparsely covered with fine hairs and with obscurely crenate margins; dainty pink flowers on slender stalks. *p. 463*

subvillosa (mollicaulis) (Brazil); fibrous-rooted species with soft-hairy, succulent, pale stem and velvety, light green ovate leaves with irregularly toothed margins; large white flowers. (I) *p. 413*

sulcata (Colombia); fibrous-rooted, upright, branching, brittle begonia to 50 cm tall, of small habit, with red stems carrying obliquely-ovate, irregularly toothed, soft, fleshy, shining emerald green leaves, reddish beneath; flower in pale pink to white in loose clusters. *p. 431, 456*

'Suncana' (sunderbruchii x incana); rhizomatous plant with fairly large leaves on glossy light green elongate petioles, covered with brown tomentum; flowers white in tall inflorescence. *p. 419*

x sunderbruchii (ricinifolia x heracleifolia), "Finger leaf begonia"; a rhizomatous "Star begonia" with palmately lobed, bright and bronze-green leaves, and silver bands along nerves; flowers pinkish. *Subtropic.* *p. 406*

x superba; a large cane-stem hybrid, probably of the aconitifolia with 'Lucerna' complex; with handsome oblique-ovate waxy angelwing leaves to 18 cm long, olive-green with silver spots, reverse green to purplish, the margins deeply lobed. *p. 463*

'Superba-azella' (aconitifolia x Lucerna); one of the 'Superba' strain of these parents; tall, vigorous cane-stems with green leaves silver-shaped, the margins red; oversized pink flowers. (I) *p. 417*

sutherlandii (Natal); slender tuberous plant with drooping branches; lance-shaped, serrate, crisped leaves bright green with red veins; flowers orange. *Subtropic.* *p. 492*

tacanana: see "strigillosa"

tafiensis (Argentina); fibrous-rooted, small, bushy plant with many kidney-shaped, woolly, silvery-grey leaves, rust-colored underneath, with crenate edges; tall, silver-haired flower stalks carrying two dainty pink flowers each. *p. 456*

'Tamo' (incana x mazae); upright rhizomatous plant with rounded, fleshy, green-brown, waxy leaves, sometimes covered with satiny hair, red beneath; flowers greenish pink. *p. 402*

'Tea Rose' (odorata alba x dichroa); upright and branching fibrous-rooted plant with glossy bright-green leaves; flowers dainty, delicate pink and fragrant. (I) *p. 420, 464*

'Templinii', "Crazy-leaf begonia"; mutant of phyllomaniaca; fibrous-rooted, self-branching; leaves ovate-pointed, glossy green and blotched yellow, margins ruffled; forms adventitious leaves all over foliage; flowers pink. *Tropical.* *p. 417, 430*

tenuifolia (Java); old species with stubby rhizomes short-branched and ascending; leaves long petioled, thin-textured, obliquely broad-ovate, toothed and bright Irish green; pink flowers few. *p. 431*

'Thurstonii' (metallica x sanguinea); fibrous-rooted, bushy plant with white-haired red stems and cupped ovate leaves glossy, bronzy green, red beneath; flowers pink. *Tropical.* *p. 395*

'Tingley Mallet' (rex Eldorado x incarnata purpurea); handsome erect shrubby plant, brighter than 'Arthur Mallet' and less difficult; oblique-ovate leaves metallic maroon and red-hairy, margins toothed; flowers pink. *Tropical.* *p. 401, 465*

tomentosa (Brazil); bushy, fibrous-rooted species with smallish, cordate-ovate, somewhat cupped leaves beautifully covered with white felt; flowering white. *Tropical.* *p. 427*

'Tom Ment'; large angelwing begonia with waxy, oblique-ovate leaves, dark olive-green and blotched with silver; flowers pinkish white and rose. *Tropical.* *p. 466*

x tuberhybrida, or "Tuberous begonia"; sturdy hybrids of Andean species, with watery stems and brittle, pointed leaves; large, single and double, waxy flowers, white, yellow, orange or red, during summer; the male flowers 8-15cm across. *Humid-subtropic.*

tub. 'Bicolor' (Rosebud); double flowers in two-tone combination of yellow center and red border. *p. 494*

tub. 'Bouton de Rose' (Rosebud); exquisite double flowers resembling rosebuds, in pastel shades rose, cream, and salmon. *p. 494*

tub. 'Camelliaeflora'; double flowers slightly smaller than the "Camellia type" but in perfect camellia form with two-toned combinations, rose with contrasting white near margins; reminding of the well-known Camellia 'Chandleri elegans'. *p. 494*

tuberhybrida 'Camellia type'; giant double camellia-like flowers; crimson, pink, white, scarlet, orange, yellow. *p. 416A, 493, 494*

tub. 'Crispa marginata'; large single flowers white or yellow with contrasting crisped scarlet margin (Picotee). *p. 494*

tub. 'Crispa undulata'; large semi-single flowers with 2 rows of petals attractively crisped and wavy at margins; in scarlet, white, yellow, rose, orange. *p. 493*

tub. 'Cristata erecta'; curious flowers single but with feathery crest-like outgrowth on 4 petals, in colors white, yellow, rose, orange, copper, scarlet. *p. 494*

tuberhybrida 'Fimbriata plena' (carnation type); very double flowers with petals serrated and frilled at edges, very much resembling a carnation; red, rose, white, orange. Beautiful, but very brittle. *Humid-subtropic.* *p. 493*

tub. 'Marmorata'; abundant bloomer with double flowers with marbled petals mostly with rose base marbled with red, or reverse. *p. 494*

tuberhybrida multiflora 'Helene Harms'; miniature tuberous begonia of compact bushy habit, with smaller, canary yellow double flowers, 4-6cm across, blooming profusely through the summer; originated from the dwarf Andean species B. davisii, and the velvety marbled foliage of B. pearcei. *Humid-subtropic.* *p. 492*

tuberhybrida multiflora 'Maxima', "Dwarf tuberous begonia"; strain developed by crossing the large camellia-flowered type with multiflora; compact plants with rigid stems and dark foliage, covered with many medium-sized double blooms, red, rose, yellow, white. Ideal for bedding. *Humid-subtropic.* *p. 493*

tuberhybrida multiflora 'Tasso'; bushy, compact, tuberous begonia derived from B. davisii, with small double flowers of bright red. *Humid-subtropic.* *p. 492*

tuberhybrida pendula fl. pl. 'Orange-flowered', "Hanging-basket tuberous begonia"; tuberous begonia with drooping stems carrying triangular leaves with frilled, dentate margins and double, orange flowers with many narrow petals. Good hanging basket begonia. *p. 492*

tuberhybrida pendula fl. pl. 'Red-flowered'; tuberous begonia with pendant stems when mature, well branched, with arrow-shaped leaves in green, margins dentate; semi-double red flowers on long, thin stems. Ideal for baskets. *p. 492*

tuberhybrida pendula fl. pl. 'Scarlet Glow'; freely branching basket begonia with pendulous stems, carrying arrow-shaped leaves, veins indented, edges frilly and crenate; typical shaggy double pendula flowers with pointed petals in a rich scarlet. *p. 491*

tuberhybrida pendula 'Lloydii' (plena), the "Basket begonia"; drooping stems with narrow leaves, and numerous small double pendulous flowers produced from a single tuber; red, rose, salmon, white, yellow; derives its pendant habit from B. boliviensis. *Humid-subtropic.* *p. 492*

tub. 'Picta' (Butterfly); large double flowers with broad petals white, marbled or overlaid with rose-red. *p. 494*

tub. 'Single'; large plain, flattened single, showy flowers suggestive of the wild rose, ranging in colors crimson, scarlet, rose, pink, white, yellow, salmon, orange, copper, to 15 cm dia. *p. 493*

tuberhybrida 'Triumph' (Rosebud); double flowers white in center, and margins red. *Humid-subtropic.* *p. 494*

ulmifolia (Colombia, Venezuela), "Elm leaf begonia"; tall, rapid-growing, fibrous-rooted species with elm-like ovate leaves rough brown-hairy; small white flowers. *Subtropic.* *p. 390, 428*

'Undine'; odorata alba seedling; low, branched, fibrous; leaves small ovate, curled, fleshy, glossy green; flowers pink. (IB) *p. 416*

undulata (alba perfecta) (Brazil); tall cane-stem with spreading branches; ovate, light green leaves with undulate margins; pendulous white flowers. *p. 429*

'Universe' ('Norah Bedson' x 'Leslie Lynn'); outstanding rhizomatous hybrid becoming very bushy, with firm, smooth leaves somewhat star-shaped, 16 x 10 cm, bright green with symmetric brownish-red pattern, the margins serrate and with short white hairs, on red petioles with bristly white hairs; white flowers 2½ cm across, on long basal stalk, in spring (by T. O'Reilly, La Mesa, Calif; American Begonia Soc. award 1969). *p. 465*

valdensium (Brazil), "Philodendron-leaved begonia"; fibrous-rooted, with decorative satiny-green leaves 20 cm or more long, prominent ivory veins, and wavy margins; pinkish flowers. *Tropical.* *p. 402, 437*

vedderi; bushy, fibrous-rooted, hairy plant; compta seedling, smaller, lobed leaves shorter, olive green, reddish beneath; flowers pink. (C) *p. 425*

'Veitch's Carmine' (dregei x coccinea); cane-stemmed, bushy plant with ovate, pointed, green leaves shallowly lobed, red margins; drooping red flower clusters. *p. 390, 409, 434*

vellozoana of hort.: see olsoniae

venosa (Brazil); fibrous rooted plant covered with white scurf; stem thick; succulent cupped leaves reniform and appearing frosted; flowers white. *Tropical.* *p. 427*

'Verde Grande' (manicata x Dark Sheen); outstanding rhizomatous hybrid with large leaves velvety-green, pale green at the sinus and along the veins, and blue-black streaks along the edge. *p. 423*

x verschaffeltii (manicata x caroliniaefolia); tall like a palm tree, thick erect rhizome; glossy bright green, fleshy leaves shallowly lobed, red-edged and toothed; drooping pink flowers. (I) *p. 414*

versicolor (China), "Fairy carpet begonia"; with thick, corrugated, roundish leaves radiating a design of silver, emerald-green and bronze, and covered with red hairs; small, rhizomatous plant. Needs high humidity; good for terrarium. *Tropical.* *p. 393, 436*

'Viaudi' (duchartrei x pictaviensis); fibrous-rooted, hairy plant with thick, ovate leaves olive green, toothed and cupped; large white flowers. (D) *p. 409, 416*

'Virbob'; elfin bowerae seedling, rhizomatous, with short petioles holding foliage close to pot; small star-shaped leaf richly marked green, chartreuse, bronze, and deep red. *p. 419*

vitifolia (dichotoma, lobulata, palmifolia) (Brazil), "Grapeleaf begonia"; large, handsome begonia with upright, branching stems, hairy petioles carrying broad-ovate, pointed to rounded, shallowly lobed leaves, hairy on top, margins finely toothed; small, white flowers. Several horticultural names have been applied to what probably is this same plant. The picture of B. vitifolia (palmifolia hort.) has a shinier leaf with deeper lobes; the photo of B. vitifolia (lobulata hort.) has a more leathery leaf and more compact growth. The pictured B. vitifolia (dichotoma hort.) is often confused with the true B. dichotoma. *p. 412, 425, 426, 441*

'Washington Street', "Peachleaf begonia"; fibrous-rooted, tall and bushy, the arching stems with peach-like, serrate leaves glossy green; flowers peachy-white. *p. 390, 428*

x weltonensis (sutherlandii x dregei), "Mapleleaf begonia"; semi-tuberous bushy plant with light green leaves shallowly lobed and toothed, with purple veins, on wine-red petioles and stems; flowers pink. There is also a white form, 'Alba'. *Tropical.* *p. 457*

'Whirly-Curly'; heracleifolia-nigricans sport, small rhizomatous plant with twisted leaves, copper with green in vein areas, red beneath; foliage arranged fan-like; of dwarf habit. *p. 464*

'Winter Jewel': see bartonea

xanthina (Bhutan); rhizomatous species with large quilted leaves lobed like a maple-leaf, coppery green with velour sheen and red veins, reverse purplish-red; flowers yellow. *p. 400*

'Zee Bowman' (liebmannii x bowerae); dwarf rhizomatous plant with many small lobed and quilted leaves silvered, and pointing in all directions; flowers pink. *p. 418*

BEJARIA: see Befaria

BELAMCANDA *Iridaceae* **C2LBWd**

chinensis (China), "Leopard flower"; rhizomatous perennial about 1 m high, with flat leaves arranged fan-like; branching wiry stalks bear graceful sprays of beautiful flowers 5-6 cm across, orange-yellow, spotted crimson. *Warm-temperate.* *p. 1324*

BELLIS *Compositae* **C2LBM**

perennis fl. pl. (W. Europe, Asia Minor), "English daisy"; low perennial with obovate fleshy leaves in tufts; the short flower heads with several layers of white to rosy florets. *Warm temperate.* *p. 803*

perennis fl. pl. 'Spring Joy'; an exceptionally large and double early-flowering "English-daisy" with inner ray flowers tubular at base 5 cm dia., pure white. *p. 811*

BELLONIA *Gesneriaceae* **S3LFM**

spinosa (Hispaniola) "Clavellina"; discovered in both Haiti and Dominican Republic growing on rocks at 700 m alt., and reported in the Gloxinian, July 1966 by Ruth Katzenberger; fibrous-rooted woody shrub of pendulous habit, reaching to 2 m, the stems with small thorns, and ovate leaves 2½ cm long, with lobed margins and covered by white hairs; from the leaf axils the white or pinkish flowers, resembling a small saintpaulia. *p. 1232*

BELOPERONE *Acanthaceae* **I2LBD**

amherstiae (Brazil); spreading tropical shrub with graceful slender, arching branches, smooth ovate leaves in pairs; between them, toward end of shoots, the short spikes with tubular, split flowers rose-pink, 4 cm long, with flaring segments. *p. 44*

angustiflora (Trop. America); semi-shrubby plant with narrow, smooth leaves dark green with yellow midrib; flowers in heads, rosy-lavender with white veinings in throat. *p. 44*

californica (California, Mexico), "Chuperosa"; low spreading shrub of the Colorado desert, with branches often leafless, small 1 cm opposite leaves; flowers in spikes with overlapping bracts, deep scarlet, 4 cm long, in 4-ranked racemes. *p. 44*

comosa (Mexico); shrubby plant with hairy, ovate leaves and coppery, bracted spikes with yellow flowers marked red; lip fiery red. *p. 44*

guttata (Mexico), "Shrimp plant"; wiry stems with ovate, hairy leaves; white flowers beneath showy, overlapping, reddish-brown bracts, in drooping terminal spikes. *Tropical.* *p. 44*

guttata 'Yellow Queen'; a cultivar with the bracts yellow instead of coppery. *p. 44*

tomentosa hort.; herbaceous plant 1 m with long-ovate pubescent leaves, the two-lipped flowers cream and purple, in reddish-brown, small bracts. Probably B. violacea from Colombia. *p. 44*

violacea (Colombia); tropical bushy shrub to 30 cm high, with narrow to ovate herbaceous leaves; flowers with gaping lips in terminal spike, purple, lower lip with white netting, 2½ cm long. *p. 44*

BENINCASA *Cucurbitaceae* **S3HFM**

hispida (Indo-Malaysia: Japan to Polynesia), "Wax-gourd" or "Chinese watermelon"; annual, tendril-bearing, pumpkin-like vine with brown-hairy stem and broad lobed leaves 15-22 cm; male and female flowers yellow; fruit melon-like, cylindrical 20-40 cm long, hairy, and white-waxy, flesh white. Grown as ornamental curiosity, but in China is the source of the preserving melon and sweet pickles. *Tropical.* *p. 932*

BENTINCKIA *Palmae* **S3LFM**

nicobarica (Nicobar Islands east of South India); stately, slender feather palm 20-30 m high and 22 cm thick, with palmate fronds 1-2 m long, the linear leathery leaflets having bilobed tips; the fruit a scarlet cherry. *p. 1851, 1852*

BEQUAERTIODENDRUM *Sapotaceae* **S3LBD**

megalis-montanum, (syn. Chrysophyllum) (Trop. Africa south to Natal), the "Stem fruit" on the Transvaal veld; tree with leathery leaves brown-hairy beneath; small white flowers; sweet edible red fruit abundantly borne cauliflorous directly on and along their thick trunk and branches, and exuding a sticky latex. *p. 2033*

BERBERIDOPSIS *Flacourtiaceae* **C3LBD**
corallina (Chile); low evergreen, scrambling shrub with long cordate, smooth, toothed leaves to 8 cm long; tubular crimson flowers in pendant clusters, followed by small berries. *p. 1062*

BERBERIS *Berberidaceae* **I2LBD**
thunbergii 'Crimson Pigmy' (atropurpurea nana); a miniature form of the "Japanese barberry" from Japan; spiny shrub, deciduous in cold areas, to 40 cm high and 70 cm wide, with slender arching, spiny branches dense with roundish leaves 2-3 cm long, when mature bronzy blood-red, new leaves bright red when grown in sun; bead-like bright red berries along the branches in autumn. *p. 495*

BERBERIS: see also Mahonia

BERGENIA *Saxifragaceae* **C2LFMh**
ciliata fa. ligulata (Saxifraga) (Nepal Himalayas), "Winter begonia"; hardy perennial with broad obovate or round leathery leaves, glossy fresh green, pale beneath, and ciliate at margin; pink, begonia-like, nodding flowers in a massive raceme, blooming in spring. *p. 2040*

ciliata ligulata 'Leichtlinii'; cultivar with reddish leaves and rose colored flowers. *p. 2040*

ciliata ligulata 'Rosea', "Winter begonia"; cultivar with typical green leaves and deep rose flowers. *p. 2040*

cordifolia (obcordata) (Siberia); stout herb with thick rootstock, forming clumps, with roundish heart-shaped soft-leathery, shining grass-green leaves, veins lighter, to 30 cm across, margins slightly crenate but not hairy, base cordate, petiole channeled; flowers clear rose in dense nodding cymes partly hidden between the foliage. *p. 2040*

crassifolia (Siberia, Mongolia), "Winter begonia" or "Siberian tea"; ornamental perennial herb more or less evergreen with thick, woody rootstock, and large fleshy obovate leaves to 20 cm long, shining green and with the blade extending down the leafstalk; flowers rose-pink or lilac, in clusters above the foliage in spring. *Temperate.* *p. 2040*

BERGERANTHUS *Aizoaceae* **S3LBD**
jamesii (So. Africa: Cape Prov.); succulent 3 cm high, leaves sickle-shaped, semi-cylindrical tapering, bluish to glaucous, 2-3 cm long; yellow flowers, 2 cm diameter, opening afternoon. *p. 59*

BERTOLONIA *Melastomataceae* **S3HNM**
hirsuta (Triolena) (Trop. America), "Jewel plant"; small herb to 20 cm high, with oval, pubescent leaves vivid green, red-brown along center; flowers white. *p. 1555*

x houtteana (x Bertonerila); intergeneric hybrid of Bertolonia, Gravesia and Sonerila, happiest in a warm conservatory; with large, moss-green, herbaceous leaves veined and dotted clear carmine-red, purple underneath. *p. 1554, 1555*

lowiana (So. America); small tropical herbaceous plant with cordate, corrugated leaves dark bronze, margins finely serrate; pretty pink flowers with yellow anthers. *p. 1552*

maculata (Brazil); dwarf species with coarsely hairy, dark green leaves 5-8cm long, shaded light moss-green with reddish margin and lightly marked silver-green along center; deep red beneath. *p. 1555*

maculata 'Wentii'; an exquisite small tropical plant with corrugated leaves, velvety green with silver zones along parallel veins. *p. 1555*

marmorata (Ecuador); beautiful herbaceous plant with quilted ovate leaves velvety moss-green, painted silvery-white along the parallel veins, purple beneath; purple flowers. *Tropical.* *p.1555*

marmorata aenea, "Bronze jewel plant"; variety with leaf surface reddish-green, shimmering bronze, without markings. *p. 1555*

'Mosaica'; colorful German cultivar of low habit; strikingly beautiful, velvety green leaves with white longitudinal bands broadest along the midrib, iridescent in several colors; fairly durable. *Humid-tropical.* *p. 1555*

pubescens in hort. (bot. Triolena pustulata) (Ecuador); small branching plant; nettle-like, pointed, corrugated leaves with white bristles, emerald green with purplish-brown band down center. *p. 1555*

sanguinea; ornamental plant with hairy, bronzy leaves, silver-banded along middle, and red beneath. *p. 1555*

BESCHORNERIA *Amaryllidaceae* **I2LBD**
bracteata (Mexico); succulent rosette similar to agave, 1½-2 m high, with tuberous root-stalk, fleshy thin, lanceolate leaves 30-45 cm long, glaucous green, with rough margin; inflorescence in tall, arching raceme with funnel-form flowers at first green, becoming yellowish red, and with large reddish bract. *p. 130*

yuccoides (Mexico); succulent rosette of about 20 leaves 45 cm long x 5 cm wide, glaucous gray-green, rough on margins and beneath; flower stems coral red, to 1 m, with numerous nodding bright green flowers subtended by bright red bracts. *Tropical.* *p. 122, 130*

BESLERIA *Gesneriaceae* **S3HFM**
lutea (West Indies); herbaceous clamberer 2-3 m high, with opposite, thickish smooth, elliptic leaves with veins very prominent beneath; small tubular swollen, axillary, golden yellow flowers. *p. 1231*

BESSERA *Liliaceae (Zander), Amaryll. (Hortus 3)* **C2HBMd**
elegans (Mexico), "Coral drops"; showy bulbous plant with narrow, furrowed leaves; several floral stalks with 3 cm flowers brilliant red usually marked creamy-white, and with purple stamens. *p. 1424*

BIARUM *Araceae* **C2LFD**
tenuifolium (So. Europe, Mediterranean); from an oblong-cylindric tuber 3 cm long, rise linear-lanceolate to spoon-shaped, entire leaves, appearing after the inflorescence; cylindrical spathe tube pale, the lanceolate blade extending the spathe 15-25 cm long, dark purple inside; the spadix long and very slender lengthening into a pendant appendix. *p. 188*

BIFRENARIA *Orchidaceae* **I3OFMd**
aurantiaca (Rudolfiella) (Brazil, Guyana, Trinidad); small epiphyte with ovoid 5 cm one- or two-leaved pseudobulbs; clusters of vividly-colored, 3 cm flowers orange-yellow spotted purple; paler lip with long claw (autumn). *p. 1665*

fuerstenbergiana (Brazil: Santa Catarina); robust epiphyte with conical pseudobulbs topped by solitary, sturdy broad, ribbed leaves; flowers 6-8 cm, sepals and petals yellowish-green, trilobed lip softly hairy, flushed violet (spring-summer). *p. 1663*

harrisoniae (Brazil); sturdy epiphyte; 4-angled pseudobulbs with a solitary leathery leaf; large fleshy, 8 cm flowers, the sepals and petals yellowish, tinged with red, the lip violet-red with yellow hairy callus, (March-May). *Subtropic.* *p. 1663*

tetragona (Brazil); lovely epiphyte with 4-sided, pear-like pseudobulbs bearing a solitary leathery leaf; lateral clusters of large 8 cm fragrant, waxy flowers, greenish ivory flushed coppery pink, the lip with upturned sides richly colored yellow and purple with black-maroon lines (late summer). (I) *p. 1663*

BIGNONIA *Bignoniaceae* **I-S3LFM**
argyraea (So. America: Amazon), "Silver trumpet vine"; tropical vine with tendril-climbing wiry stems, ovate lanceolate leaves deep green, with vein areas silvery-gray; toothed at margins and with a satiny look, purplish beneath; according to Bailey's Hortus, not known in flower; cultivated in greenhouses. *p. 501*

argyreo-violescens (Amazon), "Silvery trumpet vine"; greenhouse vine with ovate leaves in pairs, violet and veined silvery-white, purple beneath, 8 to 12 cm long. *p. 498*

capreolata (Virginia, Florida, Louisiana), "Crossvine" or "Trumpet flower"; evergreen climbing shrub to 15 m with leaves of 2 ovate leaflets, each to 15 cm long; funnel-form flowers 5 cm across, yellow and brown-red, the flaring limb golden yellow, anthers cream with reddish line on each. *Warm temperate.* *p. 501*

cherere: see Distictis buccinatoria

venusta: see Pyrostegia ignea

villosa (Venezuela); gorgeous liane originally grown by Stoffregen; vines to 3 m long, with ovate leaves 10-12 cm long, dark green, veined and tesselated silver gray; the small, insignificant flowers pale yellow. *p. 501*

BIGNONIA: see also Anemopaegma, Campsis, Clytostoma, Cydista, Distictis, Pandorea, Pyrostegia, Saritaea, Tabebuia, Tecoma, Tecomaria

BILLBERGIA *Bromeliaceae* **I-S2HBD**
x 'Albertii' (distachia x nutans), "Friendship plant"; tall clustering tubular hybrid, the offshoots with narrow tapering leaves, dark green and gray-scurfy; inflorescence rosy-red with pendulous green flowers edged blue. *Subtropic.* *p. 539*

amoena (So. Brazil); fluted rosette of stiff gray-green leaves with pronounced silver cross bands; inflorescence on arching spike with rose bracts and green flowers edged blue. *Tropical.* *p. 512, 539*

amoena viridis, a "Vase plant"; fluted rosette more richly silver-banded and spotted ivory; inflorescence with rose bract leaves and petals entirely green. *Tropical.* *p. 536*

x 'Bob Manda', "Manda's urn plant"; a colorful, compact pyramidalis hybrid with broad leathery leaves in a bold rosette, highly variegated and blotched cream over copper to olive and even purple. *Tropical.* *p. 541*

brasiliensis (leopoldii) (So. Brazil: Guanabara); handsome tubular rosette of broad leaves 80-100 cm long, grayish green and grooved with white crossbands and spotted underneath, small marginal spines; the inflorescence pendulous with numerous large vivid red bract leaves subtending the pyramidal powdery floral spike, with violet petals and long protruding, awl-like stamens. *p. 541*

calophylla hort.; an attractive plant seen under this name in New Zealand, but actually a synonym of B. vittata, which see; bronzy-green tubular rosette broadly banded with silver; flowers with bright red floral bracts and recurving indigo-blue petals, showing the golden anthers. *p. 535*

decora (Brazil: Pará; Bolivia, Perú); tall tubular rosette 45-60 cm high, clasping at base, grayish green with mealy white cross-bands, and spiny margins; pendulous inflorescence spike with large bright red bracts almost hiding the greenish flowers. *p. 535*

distachia (So. Brazil); free clustering compact tubes with broad green leaves tinged with purple, heavily covered with silver-white scurf; rose bracts and pendulous flowers green tipped blue. *p. 536, 537, 538*

distachia rubra; tubular rosette, a variety having leaves like purple haze in the sky, with silver clouds shining through; pendulous inflorescence rises from the urn, with rose bracts and green flowers tipped blue. *p. 537*

distachia var. straussiana (pallescens) (So. Brazil); slender rosette of concave, linear green leaves 40-50 cm long, 4 cm wide, underside gray-scaly; pendant inflorescence with light red bract leaves and flowers entirely green, without the blue tips of the species. *p. 541*

euphemiae (So. Brazil); stiff tubular plant with gray-scurfy, green leaves and gray crossbands; inflorescence of rosy bracts and pendant blue flowers. *Tropical.* *p. 512A, 536, 538, 544*

'Fantasia' (saundersii x pyramidalis), "Marbled rainbow plant"; urnshaped hybrid with coppery green leaves highly blotched and variegated creamy white and pink; blooming with rose bracts and blue flowers. *p. 538, 539*

'Henry Teuscher' (venezuelana x pyramidalis); tall, bold tubular plant with broad olive green leaves and strong purplish teeth at margins; outside of leaf definitely turning coppery-purple and blotched ivory, also pencil lines and silvery cross bands of scales. *p. 537, 538*

x hoelscheriana (nutans hyb. x saundersii); rosette of rigid leaves neatly cross-banded with silver; inflorescence pendant, with red bract leaves, the flowers very contrasty because of the green petals with violet edging, green stigma and golden-yellow anthers. *p. 535*

horrida (So. Brazil); stocky fluted plant with stiff bronze leaves having pronounced silver crossbands; upright inflorescence with red bract leaves and spidery blue flowers. Syn. B. horrida zebrina. *p. 536, 538*

horrida var. tigrina, "Tigered urn plant"; form with brown leaves richly tiger-banded white beneath; the flower petals narrow, and 5 cm long. *p. 535*

x intermedia (nutans x vittata); olive green tubes with lighter green dots and splotches, the whole plant both inside and out dusted with silver; flowers bright green tipped with blue, in pendulous raceme. *p. 535*

iridifolia concolor (Espirito Santo); tubular plant with thin-leathery fresh-green channeled wavy leaves covered with gray scurf, margins with scattered spines; pale pink bracts, flowers yellow. *p. 536*

leptopoda (So. Brazil), "Permanent wave plant"; short tubular leaves wavy and with ends curled down, deep green with pale spots and with gray scurf; rose bracts, and flowers green with blue. *p. 536, 541*

macrocalyx (Minas Geraes), "Fluted urn"; clustering stiff green tubes with scattered silver bands; inflorescence with large rosy bracts and large pale blue flowers on mealy white stalk. *p. 536, 538*

macrolepis (pallidiflora) (Costa Rica, Panama, Venezuela, Colombia); tall tubular rosette with narrow leaves 1 m long x 3 cm wide, serrate, grey-green and marked beneath with long white longitudinal stripes and spots and pale scurfy cross bands, spines wine-red; lax, cylindric, white-mealy inflorescence with rosy bracts and sessile greenish flowers. *p. 535*

magnifica (S. Brazil, Paraguay); robust compact, tubular rosette from which rises a showy, pendant inflorescence with broad rosy bracts, and sessile flowers with blue petals spirally recurved. *p. 537*

meyeri (Minas Geraes to São Paulo); tall, slender tubular plant with narrow channeled leaves, tips coiled, bronzy-gray and scurfy, ringed and spotted gray; greenish spidery flowers. *p. 536*

'Muriel Waterman' (horrida x euphemiae); tubular plant resembling a Grecian urn; reddish purple with contrasting silvery cross bands, and prominent teeth; red bract leaves and greenish flowers. *p. 539*

nutans (So. Brazil, Uruguay, Argentina). "Queen's tears" or "Indoor oats"; slender rosette of narrow, silvery bronze foliage, forming clusters. An arching flowerstalk bears the nodding inflorescence of rosy bracts and green flowers edged violet—a tear-drop forming on the stigma. Very tolerant. *Subtropic.* *p. 512, 535, 537, 539*

'Nutans hybrid' (nutans x distachia); popular and tough plant grown in California nurseries for use in dishgardens and novelty containers; the flexible leaves 2 cm or more wide, gray green densely covered with silvery scales overlaid with bronze in good light; the arching floral stalk with green flowers edged in violet and with rosy bracts; very durable. *p. 541*

pallescens (So. Brazil); tube with few leaves, dull green covered with gray scurf, tops recurved; young plants produced on runners; rose bract leaves and blue flowers. *p. 536*

porteana (Brazil); erect tubular rosette 1 m high, dull-green tinged wine-purple and transversed by white bands; pendant spike with bright red bracts and green petals rolled spirally and showing the violet filaments, on mealy-white stalk. *p. 535*

pyramidalis x buchholtzii; sturdy hybrid with broad rose bracts and flowers with purple petals. *p. 538*

pyramidalis concolor (thyrsoidea) (Brazil), "Summer torch"; rosette shaped like a birdsnest, broad, glossy, apple-green leaves; showy but short-lived inflorescence, stem mealy-white, and head of large red bracts and crimson red flowers tipped purplish, with blue stigma. *Tropical,* *p. 512, 534*

pyramidalis var. pyramidalis (Brazil); vase-shaped rosette with thin-leathery, glaucous, dark green leaves, and faint gray banding beneath; inflorescence an upright cluster of scarlet flowers tipped blue; bract leaves red. (F) *p. 536, 537*

pyramidalis 'Striata'; an attractive seedling clone raised by M. Foster 1950, from the species collected in Brazil; has broad tomentose blue-green leaves, not glabrous yellow-green as in the type, but are striated and variegated at margins with cream; flowering in winter. *Tropical.* *p. 537, 541*

rosea (Trinidad); tall tubular plant to 1 m high, gray-scurfy and with dark thorns; pendant simple inflorescence white-mealy, with rosy bract leaves and yellow-green recurved petals. *p. 544*

x rubro-cyanea, a nutans x saundersii hybrid; the original "Rainbow plant" originated by Atkinson, Leucadia, California; with the tubular, coppery green plants very much blotched with ivory and banded silver; the inflorescence bract leaves salmon-red on a mealy stalk, the recurved petals iridescent purple-blue. *p. 538*

'Santa Barbara' (prob. pyramidalis x nutans hyb.); attractive urn-shaped rosette of compact habit and forming tight clusters; leathery, broad gray-green leaves widely banded with ivory-white along margins and flushed pink in good light; the inflorescence with rosy bract leaves and green flowers. *p. 541*

saundersii (Bahia), "Rainbow plant"; smallish tubular species with stiff olive to bronzy foliage blotched ivory and tinted pink; inflorescence bracts red and pendant blue flowers. *Tropical.* *p. 25*, 533, 539*

'Saundersii hybrid' (nutans x saundersii), "Rainbow plant"; compact tube with bronzy leaves richly blotched ivory with rose tinting; crimson bract leaves and drooping dark blue flowers. *p. 534, 536*

saundersii x nutans: see B. 'Saundersii hybrid'

x speciosa (pallida); self-cross between forms of amoena; strap-shaped purplish green leaves covered with gray scales and with miniature marginal spines; inflorescence in loose drooping cluster with rose bracts and pale green flowers tipped blue. *p. 538*

stolonifera hort.; from the collection of Merry Gardens, Camden, Maine; elegant compact, urn-shaped rosette with broad deep glossy green leaves, the underside with silvery cross bands. *p. 540*

tessmanniana (Perú), "Showy billbergia"; tall urn-shaped plant with bronzy leaves mottled gray and white; possibly the showiest of this genus for its inflorescence, which is a giant pendulous spike with red and pink flowers, the rosy bract leaves flaring out into a fabulous show. *p. 540, 541*

venezuelana (Venezuela), "Giant urn plant"; bold tubular plant with attractive coppery leaves marked with pronounced crossbands of silver; margins toothed; inflorescence with rosy bracts, sepals white farinose, and petals yellow-green. *p. 534, 536, 540*

vittata (S. E. Brazil), "Showy billbergia"; clustering, fluted species with leathery, olive to purplish-brown leaves silver-banded; leaning inflorescence of dark flowers and glowing red bract leaves. Formerly known as B. calophylla. *p. 539*

'vittata x zebrina' (rubra); tall tubular rosette green to pinkish mauve to purplish-brown freely banded silvery-gray; pendant inflorescence of salmon bracts and lighter blue petals. *p. 539*

'Windii' (decora x nutans); from the collection J. Marnier-Lapostolle, France; clustering tubular rosettes with gray-scaly, tough-leathery leaves; the inflorescence with vivid red bract leaves, and long tubular flowers tipped with flaring, recurved, brilliant blue petals. *p. 540*

zebrina (Minas Geraes to Rio Grande do Sul), "Zebra urn"; attractive species with long fluted leaves purplish bronze in strong light, heavily crossbanded silvery white, and armed with thorns; inflorescence with large rosy-red bract leaves and nodding violet flowers, the salmon calyx leaves tipped violet. *Tropical.* *p. 512, 535, 536*

BILLBERGIA: see also Aechmea

BIOPHYTUM *Oxalidaceae* **S3HBM**

sensitivum (Zaire, Malawi, E. Indies, Laos, China, Philippines, Perú, Colombia), the sensitive "Life plant"; a low perennial herb 5-20 cm high, with little stem holding an umbrella-like circle of pinnate, fresh-green leaves lightly hairy with pairs of oblique-oval leaflets on brown axis, folding back when touched or because of air currents, or in bright sun; cup-like flowers both short and long-stalked, single or in heads, pale purple changing to orange-yellow. *p. 1845, 1848*

zenkeri (Zaire), "Sensitive life plant"; a small sensitive plant with pinnate leaves 5-8 cm long, occasionally forking, the pinnae short and roundish, dark glossy-green, and which fold back when touched; small yellow flowers. *Tropical.* *p. 1848*

BISCHOFIA *Euphorbiaceae* **S2LFD**

javanica (trifoliata) (Trop. Asia: Java), "Toog tree"; ornamental evergreen tree to 25 m high, somewhat deciduous, with large alternate compound leaves of 3 ovate, fleshy leaflets deep green to bronzy, minutely toothed; small greenish flowers without petals, and reddish pea-size fruit on female flowers. *Tropical.* *p. 1054*

BISMARCKIA *Palmae* **S3LFM**
nobilis (Madagascar); majestic, dioecious fan-palm with great trunks to 60 m high, large crown with gray-green palmate, rigid leaves 3 m across, the stalk streaked with scurfy white; 3 cm plum-like brown fruit on female trees, in huge clusters. *Tropical.* *p. 1852, 1858*

BIXA *Bixaceae* **S2LBM**
orellana (West Indies), "Lipstick-tree" or "Annatto-tree"; a showy small evergreen tree 6-10 m high, with broad, smooth, heart-shaped ovate leaves to 18 cm long; 5 cm regular flowers pink, the fleshy fruit spiny and source of orange henna or Annatto dye made from its pulp. The foliage was reddish where I have seen them growing in East Africa. *p. 504*
orellana 'Variegata'; cultivar with leaves irregularly marbled and variegated with creamy white. *p. 504*

BLAKEA *Melastomataceae* **S3HFM**
trinervia (tuberculata) (Jamaica); scandent woody plant with roots sometimes springing from the stems; dark green, elliptic leaves, rusty tomentose beneath, prominently 3-nerved; flowers solitary on long stalks, pink or rose color. *p. 1559*

BLECHNUM *Polypodiaceae (Filices)* **C-S3HNW**
auriculatum (Temperate So. America); graceful rosette of slender, narrow bipinnate leaves on stout rhizome, lanceolate leathery fronds 22-45 cm long; the sterile pinnae sickle-shaped and broad, lower edge lobed, the fertile leaflets narrower. *p. 1099*
brasiliense (Brazil, Perú); coarse rosette growing on a scaly trunk to 1 m high; the leathery green fronds deeply pinnatifid, widest in the upper third, the midrib broad, with pinnae overlapping and wavy, and coppery when young. *Humid-tropical.* *p. 1099*
brasiliense 'Crispum'; a pretty cultivar, not quite so strong-growing and with smaller fronds than the type, with the edges of the more crowded pinnae very much crisped and wavy, reddish when young. *p. 1099*
gibbum (Lomaria) (New Caledonia); graceful, symmetrical rosette, developing a trunk to 1½ m high; with broad, thin-leathery, arching pinnate fronds to 1 m long, the shining green pinnae are long and narrow, and almost threadlike on the fertile fronds. *Humid-tropical.* *p. 1099, 1107*
moorei (New Caledonia); rosette forming short trunk, with simply-pinnate light green, thin-leathery fronds 20-30 cm long, on blackish hairy stalks, sterile pinnae ovate-oblong, toothed or lobed, fertile narrow-linear. *p. 1099, 1100*
occidentale (West Indies to Chile); elegant fern dense with pinnate, spear-shaped fronds 22-42 cm long on flexible, scaly stalks and creeping rhizome; the linear-pointed, leathery, entire leaflets arranged along a paler midrib. *p. 1099*
patersonii (Philippines, Queensland); tufting fern with creeping rhizome; the narrow strap-shaped, stiff green leaves 30 cm long, and 2 cm wide, broader toward the upper part, and with midrib reddish beneath, the margins wavy; young fronds bright red. *p. 1100*
penna-marinae (South Temperate Regions and Antarctic); small pinnate fern on wide-creeping rhizomes clothed with rusty scales; barren fronds 10-20 cm long with short pinnae rounded at tip, fertile fronds on stalks to 30 cm long, pinnae narrower and more distant. *p. 1099*
spicant (Alaska to California, Europe, Asia), the "Deer-fern"; from a stout, short-creeping rhizome rise the pinnate fronds 25 cm to more than 1 m long; the shorter sterile leaves in each crown surrounding the taller fertile fronds; evergreen. *p. 1100*

BLETIA *Orchidaceae* **I2HFDd**
patula (Haiti); terrestrial with flattish corm and tall plaited, grass-like leaves, the brightly colored purple, spreading flowers with throat lined white are carried on stalks to 1 m high, (April-June). (S) *p. 1662*

BLETILLA *Orchidaceae* **S-C2-3HFD**
striata, better known in horticulture as Bletia hyacinthina (Vietnam, So. China, Japan); handsome terrestrial orchid 30-60 cm high, growing leafy stems from tuberous rhizomes, bearing 3-5 rather thin plaited leaves; light purple flowers with trilobed lip lined by deep purple ridges; the blooms are 3 to 5 cm across, usually not fully opening, in terminal clusters on erect leafless stalk, rising from the center of the new shoots, mostly in June-July. A good orchid for summer on the patio. Easy to grow and fairly winter-hardy with protection. *Warm temperate.* *p. 1663*

BLIGHIA *Sapindaceae* **S2LBD**
sapida (West Africa: Guinea), the "Aki"; large ornamental, tropical fruit tree from West Africa but very common in the West Indies where it was introduced in slave days; 10-12 m high, with compound leaves of 3 to 5 pairs of glossy green oblong leaflets each about 15 cm; greenish-white fragrant flowers; the attractive oblong, ribbed fruit is orange with red cheeks, 8-10 cm long, triangular in cross-section with leathery red shell which opens when ripe, exposing firm white, nut-flavored pulp; wholesome food when ripe, eaten raw, fried or boiled; the seed coat is poisonous. *p. 2037*

BLOOMERIA *Liliaceae (Zander), Amaryll. (Hortus 3)* **C2LBMh**
crocea (So. California), "Golden-stars"; cormous herbs with basal grass-like leaves; slender 45 cm stalks with wheel-shaped flowers orange-yellow, and green stripe down center of outside of each petal. *p. 1424*

BLOSSFELDIA *Cactaceae* **C2LBD**
atroviridis (Bolivia), a "Midget cactus" from Cochabamba at 2500 m in the Eastern Andes, and which I remember as a region of everlasting spring with sunny, clear days and refreshing crisp nights; dark bronzy-green miniature globes 1½ cm dia., forming clusters, covered almost entirely with snowy white areole cushions; small pinkish-cream flowers. The plant on pg.684 is by Marjorie Wihtol, and grafted on Myrtillocactus geometrizans for better survival. *p. 684*
liliputana (No. Argentina), "Lilliput cactus"; from the Andean foothills near Salta at 2000 m, the tiniest cactus genus; clustering miniature heads only 12 mm dia., dull grayish-green with ribs barely indicated, and spineless, the tiny areoles in spirals; flowers very small creamy-white to buttercup-yellow; should be grafted for better growth. *p. 684*

BOCCONIA *Papaveraceae* **I2LBD**
frutescens (W. Indies, Mexico), the "Plume poppy", or "Tree celandine"; handsome woody shrub to 2 m high, dense with pinnately lobed leaves, 15-35 cm long, grayish-green, smooth above, densely pubescent underneath, on slender branches; small greenish-purple flowers, in panicles 30 cm long. *Tropical.* *p. 1921*

BOEA *Gesneriaceae* **S3HFM**
hygroscopica (East Asia), "Oriental streptocarpus"; lovely small, fibrous-rooted perennial herb about 15 cm high, close to streptocarpus; fleshy oval, bullate fresh green leaves 5-8 cm long, deeply veined and ribbed and covered with short white hairs, the margins pronounced crenate; small 1 cm 5-lobed flowers purplish-violet and wheel-like, showing yellow pollen; if dry, leaves will shrink and curl but spread again when watered. *Humid-tropical.* *p. 1231*

BOEHMERIA *Urticaceae* **I-S3LFM**
lobata (Japan); semi-herbaceous plant, with green, very rough and quilted leaves, some bilobed to form fishtail apex; insignificant tiny greenish flowers in axillary spikes; pollen is distributed in explosive bursts as with Pilea. *p. 2108*
nivea (China, Japan, So. Asia), "Chinese silk-plant"; herb or shrub to 2 m high with alternate, broad-ovate leaves to 15 cm long, coarsely toothed and slender-pointed, white-tomentose beneath; with clusters of small greenish flowers; the inner bark is the excellent Chinese grass-cloth fiber. *p. 2114*

BOEHMERIA: see also Myriocarpa

BOERLAGIODENDRON *Araliaceae* **S2LBM**
eminens (Philippines: Mindanao); evergreen tree 5-10 m high, glabrous throughout, large leaves to 60 cm long, palmately 10-14 lobed, lobes reaching nearly to base, irregularly toothed and coarsely incised, shining green on both sides. *Tropical.* *p. 304, 307*
novo-guineense (Papua); small willowy tree to 6 m high with sparry branches set with large palmate 60-90 cm leaves, on long petioles having thorns near base, the leaflets irregularly lobed and glossy green; the showy inflorescence caught my eye with its enormous panicle like a gigantic pincushion, of bright orange flowers and purplish fruits. *Tropical.* *p. 320*

BOLAX *Umbelliferae* **C3LBM**
glebaria (Magellan, Chile); tufted perennial herb forming low cushions; divided smooth leaves with leathery ovate lobes; white flowers in simple 4-flowered clusters. *p. 2106*

BOLBITIS *Polypodiaceae (Filices)* **S3HFM**
heteroclita (Trop. Asia); small fern with creeping rhizome, the barren fronds on stalks 15-30 cm long with simple or to 3 pairs of pinnae, the terminal lanceolate, often rooting at tip, laterals 8-15 cm long; fertile pinnae 5-8 cm long x 1 cm wide. *p. 1106*
heudelotii (Trop. Africa); handsome fern with creeping rhizome, related to Acrostichum; the long-stalked fronds with firm green pinnae; broad and lanceolate for the sterile leaflets, with margins toothed; the fertile fronds with pinnae narrow and bearing spores. *p. 1100*

BOLIVICEREUS *Cactaceae* **I-S2LBD**
samaipatanus (Borzicactus) (Bolivia); slender oblique columnar cactus light olive green deeply ribbed and characterized by a hair-ring, the ribs set with long straw-colored needle spines tinged with red, and shorter radials; lateral tubular flowers with series of petals spreading 3 cm, velvety crimson edged in gold, from pale tube. *Arid-subtropic.* *p. 647*

BOLUSANTHUS *Leguminosae* **S2LBD**
speciosus (No. Transvaal, Swaziland, Mozambique), the "Tree wisteria"; a slow-growing small tree with gray trunk, about 5 m high as I saw it in the Northern Transvaal, but may reach 12 m; with deciduous, glossy green pinnate leaves usually appearing after the flowers; these are pea-shaped, bright, purple, in pendulous 15 cm racemes resembling wisteria. *Tropical.* *p. 1363*

BOLUSIELLA *Orchidaceae* **S3LFW**
mandae (Zululand, Natal); small epiphyte about 5 cm high, occasionally growing on rocks, with short flattened stems topped by a fan of succulent, flattened, overlapping leaves; densely flowered spikes of minute white flowers. *p. 1664*

BOMAREA *Amaryllidaceae* **I-S3HFM**
caldasiana (Guatemala, Colombia); tropical twiner with oval, parallel-veined leaves 5-15 cm long; clusters of pendant, bell-shaped 4 cm flowers with outer segments orange-red, tipped green, inner segments bright yellow. *p. 120*

carderi (Colombia); tropical twining herb with oblong parallel-veined leaves 16 cm long; and 6 cm bell-flowers in pendulous clusters, the outer segments rose, inner crenulated, spotted purplish-brown. *Tropical. p. 120*

edulis (Mexico and Cuba to Perú); handsome tuberous twiner with oval green parallel-veined leaves on twisted leaf stalks; funnel-shaped flowers 2½-4 cm long, the outer segments rose or yellow tipped green, the inner yellow or greenish spotted rose, in pendulous umbels. *p. 102*

multiflora (Colombia, Venezuela); attractive vine with oblong leaves 10 cm long, and dense many-flowered umbels, corolla about 3 cm long with outer segments tinged red, inner reddish-yellow spotted claret-brown. *p. 102*

BOMBACOPSIS *Bombacaceae* **S3LBM**
fendleri (Trop. America); queer, branching plant with thick, dark gray-green stems, the bark with cracks in corky length-lines, and covered all over with prominent spine-tipped conical tubercles. *p. 509*

BOMBAX *Bombacaceae* **S2LBD**
ceiba (malabaricum) (India to Indochina), "Red silk-cotton" or "Red kapok tree", in India known as Salmalia or "Simal", the tree under which Buddha is said to have been born; big soft wooded tree 25 to 30 m high, with buttressed, spiny trunk 2½ m dia.; palmate leaves with 5-7 leaflets; huge orange-scarlet fleshy flowers of 5 petals, overlaid with glowing crimson, 20-28 cm across; in the center orange filaments with blackish stamens, from 3-lobed, black-brown, leathery calyx cup; usually blooming leafless, as seen in Delhi, India. *Tropical. p. 507, 509*

ellipticum (Mexico: Jalisco, Veracruz to Yucatán), the "Shaving brush"; a large soft-wooded tree with green trunk; the large deciduous leaves of 5 leaflets finger-like, wine-red when young, later dark green; the flower buds composed of 5 purplish petals stuck together, later bursting open and revealing a bundle of delicate, silky rose-pink stamens 8 cm long, tipped with golden anthers. *Tropical. p. 507*

BONGARDIA *Berberidaceae* **I2LBD**
rauwolfii (chrysogonum) (Syria, Iran); tuberous-rooted perennial with pinnate, glaucous leaves, each leaflet purple-spotted at base; flowers golden yellow, in pyramidal branched panicles. *p. 496*

BOOPHONE *Amaryllidaceae* **SLBMd**
haemanthoides (Cape Prov.), "Fan-plant"; large bulb thickly covered with fibrous skins; from the apex fan-like, the opposite, fleshy lanceolate leaves, glaucous green and with undulate margins; inflorescence on stout stalk, a dense, many-flowered umbel of pinkish tubular flowers with linear, reflexed segments. The bulb is poisonous, well known to Hottentots and Bushmen in Southern Africa. *p. 122*

BORAGO *Boraginaceae* **C2LBM**
officinalis (Europe, No. Africa), the "Borage"; luxuriant, hairy Mediterranean herb 30-60 cm high, with quilted, coarse oblong leaves, 9-15 cm long, gray-green and stiff-hairy; beautiful sky-blue, nodding, starry flowers 2 cm across, attractive to bees. The leaves are edible and taste like cucumbers, and may be used for iced drinks, salads, pickling, or cooked to flavor soups and stews. *p. 511*

BORASSUS *Palmae* **S2LBM**
aethiopum (Africa: No. Transvaal to Kenya, Uganda, Sudan, to Guinea coast), "African fanpalm"; stately palm to 25 m high, with spindle-shaped trunk swollen above the middle, the bark gray and smooth; leaves fan-shaped, to 4 m long including petiole, divided to middle; 15 cm orange fruit. *Tropical. p. 1869*

flabellifer (India, Burma, Malaya), the widely cultivated and fabled "Palmyra palm" or "Toddy palm" of India where it finds hundreds of uses, for food, black timber, sugar and toddy; trunk 20-30 m tall sometimes swollen above the middle, to 1 m thick; rounded head of palmate gray-green leaves to 3 m across rather folded, rigid and with stiff tips, the stalk with horny thorns. Female trees with big 12-20 cm edible fruit yellow to brown and black. The intoxicating toddy is taken from the dense flower spikes. *Tropical. p. 1849, 1852, 1869*

BORDEREA *Dioscoreaceae* **C2LBM**
pyrenaica (Dioscorea) (Pyrenées); small tuberous plant related to Dioscorea but not climbing; the small tuber 2 cm dia., forming several annual branched stems about 10 cm long; smooth green, heart-shaped leaves; inconspicuous flowers, on male plants in elongate racemes, female plants solitary and short-stalked. Hardy. *p. 952*

BORONIA *Rutaceae* **I-C2HFM**
alata (W. Australia), "Winged boronia"; shrub of the coast near Perth; aromatic small, ferney, somewhat glaucous pinnate leaves, with leaflets 1 cm long; umbels of rose-pink flowers with pointed petals; flowers and foliage delightfully fragrant and slightly sticky. *p. 2025*

denticulata (Western Australia); attractive small shrub 1 m high with narrow 1½ cm foliage minutely toothed and with strong aromatic scent, smothered in charming, starry, long-lasting lavender flowers, in flat-topped heads. *p. 2026*

elatior (Western Australia), "Scented tall boronia"; leafy evergreen dense shrub to 1-1½ m high, the shoots thickly furnished with spreading hairs; lacy, fresh-green pinnate foliage with needle-like leaflets, and numerous attractive nodding globose 6 mm fragrant flowers along the stem, carmine-red and often of different colors on the same plant, in May. *Subtropic. p. 2026*

megastigma (Western Australia), "Scented boronia"; slender, hard-wooded, evergreen 60 cm shrub with downy shoots; sessile, fresh-green, needle-like leaflets having transparent dots; small 1 cm, sweetly scented, axillary flowers with globose brown-purple corolla, yellow inside, in spring. *Subtropic. p. 2026*

BORZICACTUS *Cactaceae* **I-S2LBD**
humboldtii (listed in Hortus 3 as synonym of B. icosagonus) (Binghamia) (Perú); erect stems to 1 m long and 5 cm thick, dull green dotted white, with yellow wool and needle spines; night-blooming pink to crimson. *p. 645*

icosagonus (Binghamia) (Ecuador); cylindric stems erect or semi-prostrate, rather slender and branching from the base, with 18-20 ribs dense with pale yellow spines; night-flowering orange-red. *p. 645, 655*

sextonianus (Maritimocereus gracilis, Loxanthocereus nanus) (So. Coastal Perú: Mollendo); small cylindrical cactus of prostrate habit, with few ribs, the knobby elevations set with yellow needle spines and numerous coarse radials, the small tubular flowers with spreading petals white. *p. 650*

BORZICACTUS: see also Bolivicereus

BOUGAINVILLEA *Nyctaginaceae* **I-S2LBD**
x buttiana 'Barbara Karst' (peruviana x glabra clone); rather bushy grower with cascading masses of large brilliant red floral bracts borne almost continually, blooming at an early age. Very popular in California gardens. *Tropical to subtropic. p. 1616, 1617*

x buttiana 'Mrs. Butt'; known in the U.S.A. as 'Crimson Lake' (peruviana x glabra); vigorous, pubescent clamberer with large recurved spines, with broader and thicker, ovate leaves than glabra; flowers in big panicles with larger cordate bracts of clear bright crimson. *p. 1616*

x buttiana 'Praetoria'; bracts peach yellow turning to golden salmon. *Tropical. p. 1616, 1952A*

x buttiana 'San Diego Red'; very vigorous cultivar also known as 'Scarlett O'Hara'; bold branches with green leaves carry heavy masses of large bracts of glowing crimson. *Subtropic. p. 1617*

x buttiana 'Temple Fire'; desirable, warmth-loving variety of low, compact, bushy habit, about 60 cm high, non-vining; during the sunbright, warmer season constantly covered with brick-red flower bracts, later turning cerise. *p. 1616*

glabra (Brazil), "Paper flower"; strong woody rambler with bright green, smooth leaves slender pointed and with narrow base; flower clusters smaller than spectabilis, the branchlets with acute purplish-pink bracts in threes, blooming in summer; more compact than spectabilis. *Tropical. p. 1616*

glabra 'Sanderiana', "Paper-flower"; floriferous form of glabra; strong climbing, glabrous shrub to 6 m high, with thorny branches, oval-pointed, bright green leaves, and inconspicuous yellowish flowers enclosed by showy, papery, cordate bracts of vivid rose in threes. *p. 1616*

glabra 'Sanderiana variegata', "Variegated flowering bougainvillea"; the smooth foliage attractively bordered or variegated with creamy white. *p. 1620*

'Harrisii'; a strikingly beautiful, though delicate, variegated foliage plant, probably a form of glabra; of low bushy habit, freely branching, with dense ovate, thin leaves, friendly green with cream when young, grayish green with age, liberally splashed with glistening white inward from the margins. Flowers white, subtended by purple bracts. *p. 15*, 1615, 1616, 1620*

spectabilis 'Double Rose'; a lovely double-flowered form dense with numerous bracts bright carmine-red, resembling roses in form and color; photographed in Bangkok, Thailand. *p. 1621*

spectabilis 'Manila Red' (Pat. Monrovia Nurs., Calif.); one of the showiest cultivars brought from the Philippines; handsome huge clusters of frilly double-bracted flowers in warm magenta red. *p. 1617*

spectabilis 'Mary Palmer'; unique cultivar observed in Nairobi, Kenya and Bangalore, Mysore, India; bushy plants with scandent branches, and flowers some with carmine-red bracts, and others with white bracts on the same plant. *Tropical. p. 1617*

spectabilis 'Miggi Ruser'; a German cultivar with floral bracts a unique shade of orange-yellow. *p. 1617*

spectabilis 'Milflores' (Philippines); from Ilo-Ilo, Visayas Province; a spectacularly beautiful cultivar profusely blooming, with double flower bracts a glowing crimson-red, in large dense clusters; on vigorous woody clambering stems. *Tropical. p. 1617*

spectabilis 'Tahitian Maid' (Pat. Monrovia Nursery, Calif.); bountiful double floral bracts of blush pink; darker rose when opening. *p. 1617*

BOUVARDIA *Rubiaceae* **I2LBMd**

laevis (Mexico); evergreen bush with arching, thin woody branches, set with pairs of slender-ovate, soft green leaves, dull on upper side, glossy beneath; at branch tips the clusters of slender-tubular flowers 4 cm long, apricot-salmon. *p. 2008*

longiflora humboldtii (Mexico), "Sweet bouvardia"; beautiful fall-to-winter-flowering shrub with woody and flexible branches, opposite, smooth, fresh-green leaves, and bearing toward the tip several waxy, salver-form, fragrant flowers having long, slender, 6 cm tubes opening into lobes of purest white. *Subtropic. p. 2011*

longiflora humboldtii 'Albatross'; horticultural form developed at San Francisco, distinguished by snowy-white flowers larger than humboldtii, and sweetly fragrant, for fall-winter cut. *p. 2011*

ternifolia (triphylla) (Mexico, Texas), "Scarlet trompetilla"; straggling shrub with thin, woody branches; the whorled, ovate, pubescent leaves opposite on the branchlets, which are terminated by clusters of 3 cm, tubular flowers of fiery scarlet-red, blooming most of the year; horticultural varieties are 'Christmas Red' and 'Fire Chief'. *Subtropic. p. 2011*

ternifolia 'Fire Chief'; low growing woody evergreen shrub with willowy branches bearing clusters of bright red tubular flowers with 4 spreading lobes, in terminal cymes. *p. 2009*

ternifolia 'Giant Pink'; a favorite florist's form for cut flowers, with clusters of larger, rose-pink flowers with salmon sheen. *Subtropic. p. 2011, 2112A*

ternifolia 'White Joy'; pretty albino form with clusters of numerous, small, pure white flowers, and with pubescent foliage. *Subtropic. p. 2011*

versicolor (So. America); small shrub 50 to 80 cm high, with thin-wiry branches becoming pendant; small narrow ovate dark green leaves 4 cm long; terminal clusters of charming slender tubular flowers 3 cm long, orange-red and prettily tipped yellow; blooming from July to September. *p. 2008*

BOWENIA *Cycadaceae* **S2LFM**

spectabilis (North Queensland); remarkable, very attractive small cycad, with its unusual bipinnate foliage; forming a clump, with edible tuberous base, and a long wiry stalk bearing a large palmately compound leaf about 60 cm across, the pinnate segments with sickle-shaped, leathery, glossy-green leaflets finely toothed and slender pointed; used for cut. *Tropical. p. 942*

BOWIEA *Liliaceae* **I1LFMd**

volubilis (Schizobasopsis) (So. Africa), "Climbing onion"; grown as a curiosity; succulent, light green bulb, to 20 cm diam., above ground, sending up a twining fresh-green branched stem with few linear deciduous leaves; small greenish-white flowers. *Subtropic. p. 1423, 1452*

BOYKINIA *Saxifragaceae* **C2HBD**

tellimoides (Japan), perennial with creeping rootstock, to 1 m high, decorative 7-to 9-lobed leaves; flowers greenish; a rock garden plant. *p. 2041*

BRACHYCHILUM *Zingiberaceae* **S2LFM**

horsfieldii (Alpinia calcarata) (Java); a slender ginger with leafy stems 1-1½ m high, furnished with sessile, long-sheathed, lanceolate leaves to 30 cm long, glossy green and leathery; flowers with greenish-white corolla and white lip; the fleshy fruit a 3-celled red capsule, showy orange when open, with crimson-red seed masses. *Tropical. p. 2130, 2131, 2142*

BRACHYCHITON *Sterculiaceae* **I2LBM**

acerifolium (New S. Wales, Queensland), "Flame tree"; to 30 m high, resembling Trevesia but without thorns; the attractive, glossy green, palmate leaves deeply 5-7-lobed, to 30 cm across, on long petioles; flowers without corolla, but a rich-red, bellshaped calyx. *p. 2086, 2087, 2091*

diversifolium: see populneum

populneum (Sterculia diversifolia) (Australia: Victoria, to Queensland, No. Terr.), "Kurrajong"; handsome upright-growing tree to 20 m, with shining 8 cm leaves which vary considerably in shape, from ovate poplar-like, to deeply cut into linear segments; showy bell flowers in profusion, yellowish-white spotted brown, reddish inside; followed by 8 cm boat shaped pods. *p. 2086*

rupestris (Sterculia) (Queensland), the peculiar "Queensland bottle-tree"; semi-deciduous, 6-15 m high, with a huge bottle-shaped trunk 3½ m in dia., and storing water; the spreading branches with variable blackish-green leaves lanceolate or palmately divided; tomentose bell-shaped flowers. *Tropical. p. 2086, 2088, 2089*

BRACHYCORYTHIS *Orchidaceae* **S-I3HNM**

kalbreyeri (Sierra Leone, Liberia to Cameroun, Zaire to W. Kenya); small terrestrial with potato-like tuber, sending up a weak leafy stem to 30 cm high, the well-spaced leaves narrow-elliptic, and terminal raceme of lilac-mauve 5 cm flowers with royal purple lip, scented like rich spice. *Tropical. p. 1667*

BRACHYSTELMA *Asclepiadaceae* **I-S3LFD**

barberiae (Transvaal, Oranje Free State); small succulent with large tuber; large soft, linear oblong, velvety-hairy leaves arranged like antlers on short branches, and bird-cage-like crimson-brown flowers, speckled yellow. *p. 354*

campanulata (So. Africa); tuberous, somewhat succulent small plant with stalked oval, hairy leaves; the stapelia-like cupped star-flower beautifully marked and striped with purplish-brown. *p. 354*

foetidum (Transvaal), "Hottentot's-bread"; small succulent bush with procumbent branches from an underground tuber; ovate leaves rough pubescent and with wavy margins; flowers star-like, similar to Stapelia, with yellow mouth spotted red, and the 5 spurs blackish-red. The natives eat the tubers. *p. 354*

galpinii (Transvaal); small tuberous subshrub with folded deciduous leaves, hairy beneath; branched inflorescence with parachute-like greenish-yellow flowers divided into linear segments, resembling some Ceropegias. *p. 354*

pulchellum (So. Africa: Transvaal, Natal); shrubby succulent with large potato-like 7 cm tubers with prostrate stems tinged purple, 6-11 cm long, and spreading; small ovate leaves in pairs, purplish above; solitary starry flowers in the axils to 1½ cm across, purple maroon. *p. 354*

BRAHEA *Palmae* **S2LBD**

armata (Erythea) (Mexico: Baja California), "Mexican blue palm"; stout fan-palm to 12 m; the trunk naturally covered by a dense petticoat of dead leaves; stiff, palmate fronds waxy-blue in heavy crown, deeply cut into many segments, 1-1½ m across, the petiole armed with curved white spines; handsome arching spadices to 5 m long. *Tropical. p. 1866, 1872, 1873*

brandegeei (Erythea), (Mexico: Baja California), "Daughter of the West", or "Hesper palm"; tall, sturdy fan palm to 30 m or more tall, comparatively slender trunk with persistent leaf bases; heavy crown of green, palmate leaves 1-1½ m dia., on long petioles heavily armed with recurving spines; blade divided in center, segments deeply split, waxy white beneath; shining brown, 1 cm fruit. *Tropical. p. 1873*

edulis (Erythea) (Mexico: Guadalupe Is., Baja California), "Guadalupe palm"; robust, squat-growing, about 10-12 m high, trunk to 40 cm thick and ringed with scars; palmate, rigid leaves 2 m across, green on both sides, the numerous segments deeply cut and cleft or torn at apex. *p. 1872, 1873*

elegans (Mexico: Sonora), "Franceschi palm"; beautiful small, slow-growing fan palm; glaucous leaves 50 cm across, and deeply cut, with few filaments, on long bluish, armed petiole with sharp spines; blooming profusely, followed by pear-shaped fruit. *p. 1886*

x BRAPASIA *Orchidaceae* **I3OFM**

'Panama' (Brassia caudata x Aspasia principissa); small bigeneric epiphyte with 2-leaved pseudobulbs, and flowers with long-pointed sepals and petals green and yellowish-white, and broad lip; autumn. *p. 1661*

BRASSAIA *Araliaceae* **S1LBD**

actinophylla (Schefflera macrostachya) (Queensland, New Guinea, Java), the "Queensland umbrella tree"; an attractive ornamental tub plant in U.S.A. where it is generally known as "Schefflera actinophylla"; in Queensland becoming a tall tree 30 m or more high; in New Guinea I have seen them growing epiphytic 30 m up on rainforest trees 5 m high; the sparry, willowy brownish, later woody branches each end at their top with a rosette of successively larger, palmately compound leaves forming umbrella-like symmetrical heads; lacquered-green, soft-leathery oblong, stalked leaflets, having about 5 prominent lateral veins each side of the ivory midrib;the young leaves with 3 later 5, in older plants 7 to 12 and 16, to 30 cm long; with irregularly spaced, sparse teeth on juvenile plants, entire on mature stage leaves. Terminal inflorescence of several 1-1½ m straight spikes set with sessile round, dense clusters of honey-laden flowers with fleshy wine-red petals, and which form into the purple fruit. Very satisfactory decorator if kept warm and fairly dry. *Tropical. p. 5*, 308, 309, 311, 312*

actinophylla 'Chisae'; stocky little plant with thick leaves 10 cm dia., palmately compound of 5-7 short oval segments, glossy light green; seen in Honolulu nursery. *p. 314*

actinophylla var. compacta (Philippines); evergreen tree with palmately compound leaves, the short-stalked, bold segments are broad-elliptic and leathery; a slow-growing form and a durable plant. Planted in South Florida where this compact Philippine form is readily distinguished from the faster growing type. *p. 311*

actinophylla 'Variegata'; interesting sport with leaves more or less variegated creamy-white or pale yellow, some leaflets being entirely white, others green. *p. 312*

BRASSAIA: see also Schefflera

BRASSAVOLA *Orchidaceae* **S-I3OND**

acaulis (Guatemala, Costa Rica, Panama); pendulous epiphyte with 1-leaved cylindrical stems; leaf terete to 70 cm long; basal inflorescence of fragrant, heavy flowers 10 cm across, greenish white and purplish brown reverse, white lip. *Tropical.* *p. 1666*

cordata (subulifolia) (West Indies); small epiphyte with long linear, pendant, channeled leaves on cane-like pseudobulbs; fragrant flowers white, the porcelain-white heart-shaped lip with its tube-like base marked purple; summer. *Tropical.* *p. 1666, 1667*

cucullata (Trop. America); epiphyte with cylindric pseudobulbs, and fleshy cylindric leaves; flowers with linear white sepals and petals, to 8 cm long, and white lip. *Humid-tropical.* *p. 1667*

digbyana (Laelia) (Honduras); white-mealy epiphyte, in habit resembling cattleya, the pseudobulb bearing a solitary, rigid, glaucous leaf; large, showy, fragrant flower, the narrow petals and sepals greenish-white, tinged purple, the rounded lip cream-white with green throat, fringed at the margin with a long beard, (May-July). *Tropical.* *p. 1667*

flagellaris (flagelliformis hort.) (Brazil); epiphyte with cylindric stems and single terete, fleshy leaves; fragrant flowers to 8 cm dia., yellow-white and long-lasting, lip white with green in throat (spring). *p. 1666*

glauca (Laelia) (Mexico, Guatemala); small, bluish-gray epiphyte with slender pseudobulbs bearing a stiff, glaucous leaf; fragrant flowers with linear sepals and petals white, often tinted green, the large lip cream-white sparsely marked with pink, (Dec.-March). *Tropical.* *p. 1667*

martiana (Bletia) (Brazil, Guyana); epiphyte with semi-terete leaves; the inflorescence with numerous very fragrant long-lasting flowers to 8 cm across, linear sepals and petals yellowish-white, lip white with green blotch in throat (summer). *p. 1666*

nodosa (Jamaica, Costa Rica, Colombia to Surinam), "Lady of the night"; epiphyte with stemlike pseudobulbs bearing a solitary, stout, channeled leaf; flowers solitary or in clusters, linear sepals and petals greenish-yellow and broad, pointed, white lip, (Sept.-Dec.). *p. 1667, 1668*

perrinii (Brazil); tufted epiphyte with short, narrow pseudobulbs and terete foliage; flowers about 5 cm across, with narrow greenish white segments and white heart-shaped lip (summer). (I) *p. 1667*

subulifolia hort. (bot. cordata) (West Indies); see cordata.

BRASSIA *Orchidaceae* **I3OFM**

allenii (Panama); pseudobulbless epiphyte with stiff vandaceous, overlapping foliage and showy flowers having long narrow tapering sepals and petals cinnabar red, greenish-yellow toward base, and a broad, almost square yellow lip and spotted brown in front of the white callus. (Spring). *Tropical.* *p. 1668*

antherotes (Ecuador); very ornamental epiphyte to 45 cm high, with oblong 1-leaved pseudobulbs; basal racemes of large firm-textured flowers, the long narrow, threadlike sepals and petals deep yellow, with purple-brown blotches at base, the lip brighter yellow (early summer). *p. 1666*

bidens (Venezuela); epiphyte with long lanceolate leaves, arching inflorescence of spidery flowers 12 cm across, long thread-like sepals and petals buff yellow with purple dots, lip yellow. *p. 1666*

brachiata (Guatemala); strong-growing epiphyte with stout, ovoid pseudobulbs bearing two linear-lanceolate leaves to 30 cm long; racemes more than 1 m long with large 15 cm flowers green, tinted with yellow, lip yellowish, all segments spotted brownish-green, on the lip wart-like; early summer. (I) *p. 1669*

caudata (W. Indies, C. America); robust epiphyte with large pseudobulbs having 2 tongue-like leaves; freely producing arching spikes of flowers having tail-like, greenish-yellow sepals with chocolate spots on basal half, petals shorter, the pointed lip yellow, spotted with greenish-brown, (Jan.-Aug.). (I) *p. 1668*

chloroleuca (Costa Rica and Panama); epiphyte with flattened, 2-leaved pseudobulbs; flowers in an arching raceme, pale yellow, fragrant; petals and lip brown-spotted, lower sepals tail-like to 15 cm long. Resembles B. longissima but the pseudobulbs are one-leaved in B. longissima — and the upright, white teeth in front of the crest of the lip are missing in B. longissima — setting it apart; May-June. (I) *p. 1669*

chlorops (Costa Rica and Panama); epiphyte with flattened, usually 2-leaved pseudobulbs; flowers in an upright, few-flowered raceme, sepals and petals greenish with brown spots, lip golden-yellow in front, the crest of the lip a round, hairy cavity with two-spotted teeth in front of it, column dark green, flushed maroon at the tip; January-March. (I) *p. 1669*

gireoudiana (Costa Rica, Panama), "Spider orchid"; epiphyte with flat pseudobulbs bearing 2 oblong leaves; long arching racemes to 60 cm with spidery flowers, the sepals and petals yellow tinted green, spotted brown-red, the pale lemon lip marked purple, (Dec.-May). (I) *p. 1668*

lanceana (Surinam, Guyana); free-blooming epiphyte with compressed pseudobulbs bearing two long-tapering leaves 15-30 cm long; lateral raceme set with fragrant flowers bright yellow blotched red-brown, the undulate lip yellow and slightly spotted at base; summer. (S) *p. 1669, 1681*

lawrenceana (Guyana, Brazil); handsome epiphyte with two-leaved pseudobulbs; long racemes of very fragrant flowers, with sepals much longer than the petals, bright yellow tinged with green at the base and spotted cinnamon; summer. (S) *p. 1669*

lawrenceana longissima (antherotes longissima) (Costa Rica); 1-2 long-leaved pseudobulbs; the wiry, arching racemes to 60 cm long, with flowers having long thread-like petals, and lateral sepals to 30 cm long, bright yellow to buff, marked brown-purple at base, pointed cream-colored lip spotted red-brown, (Febr.-Oct.) *p. 1668*

maculata (W. Indies, Guatemala); epiphyte with single-leaved pseudobulbs, and erect spike with waxy flowers, the narrow sepals and petals pale greenish-yellow barred with brown, the white lip marked red-brown, (April-Oct.). *Tropical.* *p. 1668*

mexicana (Mexico); epiphyte to 45 cm high, with long, flattened pseudobulbs bearing strap-like, oblanceolate leaves; the flower stem densely set with lemon-yellow flowers, sepals and petals narrow and marked with bronze; the pointed lip white, marked purple (summer). *p. 1666*

verrucosa (Mexico, Guatemala, Honduras, Venezuela), "Queen's umbrella"; vigorous epiphyte with pseudobulbs bearing 2 oblong leaves; arching, wiry flower stems with long threadlike, 12 cm sepals greenish-yellow, 8-12 cm long, spotted at base with purple, as are the petals; the finely brown-warty lip white. *Tropical.* *p. 1668*

BRASSICA *Cruciferae* **C2LBM**

oleracea acephala; very popular for outdoor planting in Japan and China, also grown in pots for ornament, and known as "Flowering cabbage"; thick-leaved, glaucous perennial, a form descended from the European type; with spreading leaves forming a green rosette which with the advent of colder weather develops in its center striking shades of ivory to rose, imitating a showy flower. Good commercial cultivars are 'Red Crown' (Kokan) deep green with purplish center and purple ribs; and 'White Ripple' (Ginpa) ivory-white on green. *Warm-temperate.* *p. 928*

oleracea acephala crispa, the "Miniature flowering kale"; grown as an ornamental pot plant, reported to be a hybrid between "Flowering cabbage" and ordinary Kale, forms a big rosette of large frilled and fringed foliage, glaucous-green in the younger stage, but in autumn as the season advances and they are kept cold, (under 10°C for an extended period), remarkably beautiful colors begin to appear with the center blossoming forth in shades of ivory, yellow, rose and purple. These plants are used as Christmas and New Year's pot plants in Japan, and have equally been used in flower arrangements in New York. *Warm-temperate.* *p. 928*

oleracea acephala fimbriata, "Flowering kale"; a Japanese cultivar with the soft-leathery foliage in a showy rosette, with fewer leaves when young, later more full and double but non-heading; the leaves undulate and pale along ribs and center, the margins deep green, and flushed carmine-rose in center of rosette; ribs purple. *p. 928*

x BRASSIDIUM *Orchidaceae* **I3OFM**

'Supreme' (Oncidium papilio x Brassia maculata); narrow linear sepals and petals cream with black cross-bars and blotches, broad lip and tiny yellow heart (Moir 1960). *p. 1670*

x BRASSOCATTLEYA *Orchidaceae* **I3OFD**

cliftonii magnifica (Bc. digbyana-mossiae x C. trianaei); an elegant example of inter-generic breeding combining the size of a large cattleya with the bearded or fringed lip of brassavola; pure white with purple lip except for a white fringe (spring fl.). (I) *p. 1682*

'Heatonensis' (B. digbyana x C. hardyana); very handsome bigeneric hybrid with large flowers to 16 cm across; pure white with tinge of green on outer sepals, lip beautifully fringed, and delicate yellow-green inside. *Tropical.* *p. 1665*

lindleyana: see Laelia lindleyana

veitchii (Brassavola digbyana x Cattleya mossiae); first bigeneric hybrid between these genera (1889), with large delicate rose-pink flowers having a large, beautifully bearded lip and crimson in throat changing to yellow and fading out to cream. *Tropical.* *p. 1682*

x BRASSOEPIDENDRUM *Orchidaceae* **I-S3OFD**

'Alex Hawkes' (Brassavola nodosa x Epidendrum mariae); pretty bigeneric with stiff-leathery, narrow, folded leaves deep green; flowers with long linear lemon-yellow sepals and petals and broad white lip. *p. 1670*

'Phoenix' (Brassavola nodosa x Epidendrum phoeniceum); beautiful bigeneric hybrid, 25 cm high; fleshy leaves deeply concave; 8 cm flowers creamy-white freely spotted purple. *p. 1677*

x BRASSOLAELIA *Orchidaceae* **I3OFD**

'Charles J. Fay' (Brassavola nodosa x Laelia crispa); showy bigeneric with its short stem-like pseudobulb bearing a fleshy leaf, and flowers with large white sepals and petals; white with purple spots in radiating lines on broad lip, yellow in throat, winter. (I) *p. 1669*

x BRASSOLAELIOCATTLEYA *Orchidaceae* **I-S3OFD**

'New Moon'; a typical trigeneric hybrid (Brassia x Laelia x Cattleya), with lovely large flowers rose-pink, ruffled petals and characteristic broad fringed lip; shown on photo with Miss Stewart at Rodney Jones, New York. *p. 1665*

BRAVOA *Amaryllidaceae* **I2LBDd**
geminiflora (C. Mexico), "Twin-flower"; deciduous tuberous herb with linear-sword-shaped basal leaves pale green, and 60 cm long racemes of nodding tubular rich orange-red flowers 3 cm long, summer blooming, in pairs. *Tropical.* *p. 131*

BREDIA *Melastomataceae* **I2LFD**
hirsuta (Japan); floriferous, decorative shrub with bristly stems, ovate, slender pointed, 5-nerved, unequal, hairy leaves, and rose-pink flowers in terminal cymes, in autumn. *p. 1554*
tuberculata (China: Yunnan to Kwangtung); erect branching herbaceous plant with reddish stem covered with bristles and hair, ovate leaves cordate at base, green above, purple and green beneath; dentate margins, every tooth ending in a long crimson bristle; inflorescence in umbels, the sepals linear, the 4 petals pink to cerise, glabrous, and with creamy white stamens and anthers. *p. 1554*

BREVOORTIA *Amaryllidaceae* **I2LFDd**
ida-maia (Brodiaea coccinea, Dichelostemma) (Oregon, California), "Fire-cracker flower"; cormous herb with linear basal leaves, and a tall stalk to 1 m high with an umbel of nodding tubular 3 cm long lasting flowers, scarlet tipped with green, in early summer. *p. 120, 130*

BREXIA *Saxifragaceae* **S3LBW**
madagascariensis (Madagascar); tropical tree to 6 m; ornamental, leathery leaves obovate, or long-narrow, spine-toothed at margins; flowers pale green, anthers orange. *p. 2041*

BREYNIA *Euphorbiaceae* **S3LFM**
nivosa (disticha, Phyllanthus) (South Sea Isl.), "Snow-bush"; loose growing, green-stemmed pendant branches with alternate, small, fern-like oval leaves, 5 cm long, richly mottled and variegated white. *Tropical.* *p. 1003, 1056A*
nivosa roseo-picta, a form known as "Leaf-flower" because the little oval, papery leaves are attractively mottled or variegated green, white and pink, looking like flowers, with red stems and petioles. *p. 1003, 1005*

BRIGGSIA *Gesneriaceae* **C2HFD**
agnesiae (China: No. Yunnan); basal rosette with ovate leaves 4-5 cm long, densely gray hairy on both sides and crenate margins; solitary nodding flowers deep rose, inflated tube with pointed lobes; hairy outside. *p. 1242*
aurantiaca (S. E. Tibet); rosette of green, quilted leaves covered with shaggy red-brown hairs, from slender rhizomes; stalked tubular flowers usually 1 or 2 on stem, with corolla under 2 cm long and blunt lobes, deep golden yellow, spotted and striped on the inside with reddish-brown. *p. 1242*

BROCCHINIA *Bromeliaceae* **S3LBD**
acuminata (Venezuela, Colombia); large terrestrial with strap-shaped leaves dark bronze, covered by white powder, 80 cm long and 2-4 cm wide, forming at base an elongate bulb-like rosette; the leafy floral stalk to 2 m high and branched, with tubular white flowers. *p. 552*
reducta (So. Venezuela); terrestrial plant with the inflorescence 50-70 cm high, from moist summits to 2000 meters; leaves light green and 60 cm long, arranged in a cylindrical rosette forming a very long funnel, green on surface, dark bronzy outside; inflorescence branched with small white flowers. *p. 552*

BRODIAEA *Amaryllidaceae* **C2LBMd**
coronaria (grandiflora) (Brit. Columbia to California), a "Triplet lily"; to 45 cm high, with linear leaves grooved above, and a loose umbel of glossy violet funnel-shaped flowers of lasting quality; late spring. *p. 119*

BRODIAEA: see also Ipheion

BROMELIA *Bromeliaceae* **I-S2LBM**
antiacantha (fastuosa) (So. Brazil, Uruguay); formidable terrestrial rosette with vicious hooked spines on narrow leaves, inner leaves along inflorescence stalk colored orange-red; showy spikes with bracts mealy-white, and lavender flowers. *Subtropic.* *p. 530, 533*
balansae (Brazil, Argentina), "Piñuela"; large and vicious terrestrial rosette used for fencing; stiff green leaves to 1½ m long, with dangerous hook spines facing both directions; center turning red before bloom; flowers white, in paniculate inflorescence forming branches of small, ovoid orange-yellow fruit with pineapple flavor. Easily confused with B. pinguin, but balansae has broad sepal tips, pinguin needle-like tips and loose inflorescence. *Subtropic.* *p. 512A, 542, 569*
balansae variegata (serra); form of the Brazilian balansae; large showy plant but dangerously spiny; the spreading leaves grayish-green with broad ivory margins; when flowering, center turns bright red, and spike with red bract-leaves and maroon flowers. *p. 512*
fastuosa (Brazil); robust basal rosette of numerous thick-leathery, recurving, concave leaves to 1½ m long, 4-5 cm wide, deep green with gray scurf, the margins with sharp yellowish spines; erect inflorescence 60 cm high, with numerous purple flowers and rosy-red bracts. Possibly identical with B. antiacantha. *Subtropic.* *p. 533*
karatas (West Indies); large terrestrial rosette 60 cm high and to 3 m across, of numerous concave, linear lax leaves to 2 m long x 5 cm wide, dangerously armed with sharp-pointed marginal spines; inflorescence in a dense contracted panicle deep in the center, with pink flowers surrounded by scaly bracts. *p. 542*
pinguin (W. Indies, So. America), "Pinguin"; bold basal rosette of many spreading rigid, light green leaves 1½-2 m long, 3-4 cm wide, armed with large hooked brown spines; flowers with reddish petals, needle-like sepal tips and white-tomentose at apex, in erect mealy panicles shorter than leaves, and more loosely arranged than B. balansae. *Tropical.* *p. 542*
"pumila" hort.; a relatively small and shapely rosette with light green leaves paler in center and covered lightly with silvery powder, silvery longitudinal stripes on back, and with brown marginal teeth; cultivated under this name in Florida gardens as an ornamental; leaves turn scarlet in center at flowering time. *p. 542*
serra 'Variegata', known as "Heart of flame"; large showy plant but dangerously spiny, the spreading leaves grayish-green with broad ivory margins; when flowering, center turns bright red, and spike with red bract-leaves and maroon flowers. Produces orange-colored fruits. Inflorescence globose, unlike the elongate inflorescence of balansae. *Tropical.* *p. 542*

BROMHEADIA *Orchidaceae* **S3HBM**
aporides (Thailand); stems to 12 cm high bearing in 2 ranks fleshy, flattened leaves 10 cm long; solitary flowers terminal, 4 cm across, yellowish white with rosy veining and yellow blotch on lip; short-lived flowers fading by noon (spring). *p. 1665*

BROMINIANA *Orchidaceae* **S3OFW**
citrina (Botanic Garden Mayence, Germany); clustering epiphyte with short 2-leaved pseudobulbs; basal, long-stalked flowers lemon-yellow. *p. 1665*

BROSIMUM *Moraceae* **S3LBD**
galactodendron (Tropical America), "Cow-tree", "Milk-tree" or "Palo de Vaca"; large evergreen tree 30 m high with a trunk 2-2½ m dia.; the leaves leathery, oblanceolate; inflorescence curious with one female and many male flowers in a spherical head, the female sunk in center. The natives make incisions in the trunk and drink the abundant milky sap as a substitute for animal milk. *Tropical.* *p. 1562*

BROUGHTONIA *Orchidaceae* **I3OFM**
sanguinea (Cuba, Jamaica); small epiphyte with flat, 1-2-leaved pseudobulbs crowded; the roundish, flattened flowers crimson-scarlet, in terminal panicle, (Jan.-June & autumn). (I) *p. 1665, 1671*

BROWALLIA *Solanaceae* **I2HFM**
speciosa (Colombia), "Amethyst flower" or "Sapphire flower"; attractive herbaceous plant with shrubby base, and sprawling slender branches; small glossy, fresh green leaves; profusely blooming with dark purple flowers to 5 cm across, pale lilac beneath. Graceful in hanging baskets. *p. 2068*
speciosa alba; horticultural form with pure white flowers, contrasting effectively with the fresh green foliage. *p. 2068*
speciosa major (Colombia); straggling herb with small lanceolate, dark green leaves, and large, solitary, salverform flowers having slender tube and spreading limb, violet-blue with white edge, pale lilac beneath; blooming almost continuously. *p. 2066*

BROWNEA *Leguminosae* **S3LFD**
coccinea (Venezuela), "Scarlet flame-bean"; beautiful tropical evergreen shrub 2-3 m high with oblong leathery pinnate leaves, and very showy scarlet flowers with stamens protruding, in dense clustering heads; July-August. *Tropical.* *p. 1370*
coccinea x latifolia; small evergreen tropical tree with pinnate leathery leaves, bright colored when young; showy orange-red flowers forming crowded round heads with protruding stamens. *p. 1371*

BRUCKENTHALIA *Ericaceae* **I2HBM**
spiculifolia (S. E. Europe: Balkans, N.W. Asia Minor), "Spike-heath"; small evergreen erica-like shrub 15-25 cm high, downy young growth, crowded with tiny linear, ciliate leaves 3-6 mm long; small bell-shaped, 4-lobed magenta-pink flowers 3 mm long in terminal racemes, in summer. *p. 960*

BRUGMANSIA (DATURA) *Solanaceae* **I-S2LBW**
arborea (Peruvian Andes), "Angel's trumpet"; small, pubescent tree to 3 m high, with soft-hairy, ovate leaves; the nodding, trumpet-shaped flowers not over 18 cm long, white with green nerves and recurving pointed lobes, the long green calyx spathe-like, tapering to one tip. *p. 2068, 2077*
aurea (Peru); sparry shrub with brittle, woody branches; large corrugated leaves 30-40 cm long; handsome pendant flowers 15 cm long, calyx with 2 to 4 lobes, and corolla a rich apricot yellow. Seen at Botanical Gardens in Ghent (Belgium), Dortmund and Tubingen (Germany). *p. 2069*
candida (arborea of hort.) (So. America), "Tree datura"; with large pendant white flowers 20 cm or more long; commonly in cultivation as D. arborea. *p. 2069, 2070*

candida plena (So. Perú, Chile); this tree which I photographed at the Kebun Raya in Java, is a double-flowering form, with the beautiful, hanging white trumpets with long recurving lobes very large, the green calyx spathe-like, tapering to one point like arborea, and the dark green, smallish, velvety-hairy leaves with an oblique base like suaveolens. Flowers fragrant. *p. 2070*

mollis (Ecuador); extremely showy tree-like shrub with herbaceous, ovate leaves and delicately tinted, large nodding trumpet-like flowers, vivid salmon-pink suffused with orange, and a long spathe-like calyx. *p. 2070*

rosei (sanguinea hort.) (Ecuador); small tree-like shrub with rough hairy, angular foliage; pendant trumpet flowers 18 cm long deep crimson red with white base, and the green calyx with single lobe. Photographed at St. Jean-Cap-Ferrat, France. *p. 2069*

sanguinea (Perú); showy tropical shrub becoming 4-5 m high, the brittle branches with clustered, long-ovate soft-hairy foliage 16 cm long, and carrying the weight of large pendulous 25 cm trumpets like so many bells, flesh pink to orange red toward apex, with yellow veins, calyx with two or more pointed lobes. Photographed at Nassau Botanic Garden, Bahamas. *p. 2069*

suaveolens (Datura in hort.) (Brazil), "Angel's trumpet"; tree-like shrub to 4½ m high, with heavy canes, large lanceolate, 30 cm leaves, oblique at the base, glabrous green, thin and quickly wilting; the large, nodding, funnel-shaped flowers with a tubular, 5-toothed calyx and a showy, white corolla to 30 cm long and fragrant. *p. 2068, 2070, 2071*

BRUGMANSIA: see also Datura

BRUGUIERA *Rhizophoraceae* **S3LBW**

conjugata (gymnorhiza), (Africa, Malaya and India to So. China and Pacific), "Oriental mangrove" or "Many-petaled mangrove"; spreading shrub with jointed branches, sending out aerial stiltroots into shallow water of tropical tidal shores and lagoons, forming dense interconnected tangles; large shiny green, thick-leathery pointed leaves on erect brown branches; pink, yellow or red flowers with 10 or more calyx lobes and short woolly petals. *Tropical.* *p. 1991*

BRUNFELSIA *Solanaceae* **S-I2LFM**

americana (West Indies), "Lady of the night"; evergreen shrub to 2 m high, the leathery leaves oval to obovate, 8-10 cm long; exquisite flowers white, fading to pale lemon yellow with age, usually solitary, with a slender tube to 10 cm long and spreading limb to 6 cm across; very fragrant especially at night; blooming in spring and summer. *Tropical.* *p. 2068*

latifolia in hort. (B. australis in Hortus 3) (Franciscea) (Trop. America), "Kiss-me-quick"; shrub 60-90 cm high, with broad, leathery, obovate leaves to 10 cm long, slightly pubescent beneath; flowers pale violet with white eye at first, changing in a day or so to white, and very fragrant; blooming freely in winter and early spring. *Tropical.* *p. 2066*

nitida (undulata) (West Indies); evergreen shrub with obovate, shining 8 cm leaves; flowers with whitish tubular corolla thread-like on slender tube to 10 cm long, and with spreading lobes. *p. 2068*

pauciflora calycina (Franciscea) (Brazil), "Morning-noon-and-night"; handsome spreading shrub with long lanceolate, shining livid-green leaves and large 6 cm salver-shaped flowers with wavy margins, rich dark purple, blooming successively throughout the year. *Tropical.* *p. 2066*

pauciflora 'Floribunda', "Yesterday, today and tomorrow"; floriferous evergreen shrub with spreading branches; dark green, long elliptic, leathery leaves and large, 5 cm rich violet to lavender flowers with small white eye, quickly fading to white, blooming from January to July. *Tropical.* *p. 2066*

undulata in hort. (Jamaica); Timothy Plowman of Harvard refers this to B. nitida; "White raintree"; magnificent, strong-growing evergreen shrub, flowering freely when quite small; light green, elliptic leaves, the pendant, salverform flowers with long slender tubes, fragrant, white, changing to creamy-yellow with age, the petals undulate. *p. 2066, 2068*

BRUNIA *Bruniaceae* **I3LBD**

nodiflora (So. Africa); heath-like shrub with branches in whorls, 30-90 cm high; small overlapping, awl-shaped tricornered or needle-like green leaves; the inflorescence in clusters of 2 cm "ball-button" flowers at the tips of branches, grayish white little balls as large as a cherry, before opening into white flowers. *p. 615*

x BRUNSDONNA, bot. **x AMARYGIA** *Amaryllidaceae* **I2LBMd**

parkeri (Brunsvigia or Amaryllis x parkeri), the "Naked lady lily"; hybrid of the So. African Amaryllis belladonna and Brunsvigia josephinae; handsome bulbous plant 50 cm high; stalked cluster of funnel flowers exquisite pink with yellow throat, in summer; very fragrant. *p. 113*

BRUNSVIGIA *Amaryllidaceae* **I2LBMd**

josephinae (So. Africa: Cape Prov.), "Josephines-lily"; showy bulbous plant with strap-shaped, glaucous leaves 60-90 cm long, from bulb 15 cm thick; floral stalk 45 cm high, topped by a large umbel of long-stalked trumpet flowers 6 cm long, in vivid scarlet red, the filaments purplish, anthers white; late summer blooming. *Subtropic.* *p. 117*

racemosa (So. Africa); attractive bulbous plant with broad basal leaves, and stout stalk topped by a large umbel of starry, lilac-rose flowers with flaring stamens. *p. 117*

BRUNSVIGIA: see also Amaryllis

BRYONIA *Cucurbitaceae* **C2LBDh**

dioica (Europe, No. Africa, W. Asia), "Bryony"; hardy tuberous-rooted tendril-climbing plant 3 m or more high, with annual stems, leaves palmately 5-lobed and rough-hairy; greenish-white flowers 1 cm across, followed on female plants by small 2 mm red berries. *p. 932*

BRYONOPSIS *Cucurbitaceae* **S3LBM**

laciniosa (Trop. Africa to Asia, Pacific Islands); annual vine with slender stems tall-climbing with tendrils, green leaves deeply 3-lobed, axillary flowers small and greenish; the ornamental fruit a small gourd, gooseberry-like, yellow green to reddish with white lines, 2 cm dia. *p. 932*

BRYOPHYLLUM: see Kalanchoe

BUCEPHALANDRA *Araceae* **S3HFW**

motleyana (Sarawak, Borneo); small tropical aroid from wet areas forming clusters; from base the slender petioles carry elongate-elliptic leaves 4-7 cm long and 2-3 cm wide, dark waxy green; reddish stalks topped by inflorescence with flaring spathe, pale green in lower part and white toward apex; short club-shaped spadix. *p. 184*

BUCIDA *Combretaceae* **S3LBM**

buceras (Florida, West Indies to Panama), the "Black olive"; handsome tropical evergreen tree becoming 18 m high; as a younger shrub of very symmetrical growth habit, and sculptured shape, with branches laterally in tiers; small leathery obovate leaves 5-8 cm long, at the end of twigs; insignificant greenish flowers lacking petals, displaying long stamens; followed by small ovoid 1 cm black berries. *p. 777*

BUDDLEJA (BUDDLEIA in Hortus 3) *Loganiaceae* **I-C2LBM**

alternifolia (China); deciduous shrub becoming 3-6 m high, with gracefully pendulous branches bearing alternate, lanceolate green leaves to 10 cm long, gray-scurfy beneath; 6 mm flowers lilac-purple, in dense racemes, on last year's growth; June-July. *p. 1516*

asiatica (E. Indies), "Butterfly bush"; evergreen shrub with narrowly lanceolate leaves white downy beneath, on round stems; sweet scented white flowers in long panicles, during winter and spring; grown under glass as a cut flower. *p. 1515*

auriculata (Transvaal); evergreen shrub of lax habit, with oblong leaves 5-10 cm long, white-felted beneath; flowers very fragrant, crowded in rounded panicles 5 cm across; corolla 1 cm long, creamy white with yellow throat. *p. 1517*

crispa (paniculata) (No. India: Himalayas); deciduous shrub 2-5 m high with woolly branches bearing lanceolate, opposite leaves to 12 cm long, coarsely toothed, woolly above, white or yellow tomentose beneath; fragrant flowers lilac with white eye, in short panicles; summer. *p. 1516*

davidii (Buddleia) (China), "Butterfly bush" or "Summer lilac"; deciduous, strong growing shrub to 4 m, with 4-angled downy shoots and long lanceolate, toothed leaves white-felted beneath; fragrant flowers lilac with orange eye, in slender panicles, in July to October. *Subtropic.* *p. 1515*

davidii alba; white-flowering form of this free growing, spreading and showy bush. *p. 1515*

davidii 'Empire Blue'; cultivar with flowers deep violet-blue, in beautiful, dense erect, pyramidal spikes. *p. 1516*

x farquhari (officinalis x asiatica); shrub with narrow lanceolate leaves yellow-woolly beneath; flowers pale pink, in slender spikes. *p. 1516*

globosa (Chile, Perú); semi-evergreen shrub 3-5 m high, with loosely felted branches, opposite lanceolate leaves 10-25 cm long, wrinkled above, tawny-felted beneath, and wavy-toothed; bright ochre-yellow, fragrant flowers in dense round heads; June. *p. 1516*

madagascariensis (Madagascar); evergreen shrub of tall, lax habit to 6 m high, with branches downy, 12 cm lanceolate leaves dark green above, pale-woolly beneath; orange-yellow flowers in slender terminal panicles, in winter. *Subtropic.* *p. 1516*

x pikei (caryopteridifolia x alternifolia); hybrid shrub not as lax as alternifolia but more vigorous than caryopteridifolia; covered with stellate hairs; ovate to oblong leaves to 15 cm long; the inflorescence a collection of clusters to 60 cm long, of strongly scented flowers 6 mm across, in shades of lavender-pink; long-lasting. *p. 1516*

salvifolia (S. Africa); semi-evergreen shrub to 5 m in nature; 4-angled, downy, slender shoots with lanceolate leaves to 10 cm long, wrinkled and sage-like; 15 cm panicles with fragrant white to pale lilac flowers; orange at mouth of tube. *p. 1517*

tubiflora (Brazil); densely tomentose shrub with rusty hair; leaves ovate, rugose, toothed, velvety above, woolly beneath; flowers in dense clusters forming a spike; corolla tubes 2 cm long. *p. 1517*

BUGULA *Ectoproctaceae*

species (off English and Norman coasts), the "Airfern" or "Neptune plant", as sold in department stores; a curious fern-like plume to 30 cm long, by early naturalists (Rondelet 1558) considered as of the nature of plants and grouped as a Zoophyte or "Sea plant", at a time when sea coral was regarded as a "Stony plant". Now recognized to be a lowly moss-animal of the genus Bugula, it is found growing under water on rocks or floating wood. The fan-like structure is produced by the labor of invertebrate polyps which build colonies, sceletal cases of gelatinous material of their own secretions, originally a translucent brownish gray, but dyed a luminous green and sold for decoration like lacy ferns, never requiring water or soil. p. 954

BULBINE *Liliaceae* **I2LBD**

caulescens (Cape Prov.); tuberous-rooted branching succulent with ranks of very soft-fleshy, semi-cylindrical, light green leaves 25 cm long, and bright yellow flowers with bearded stamens, in dense racemes. *p. 1425*

latifolia (Natal); rosette of broad and fleshy, fresh-green leaves; inflorescence on slender stalk, with spike of yellow flowers. *p. 1424*

natalensis (Natal); low but spreading succulent rosette which I found growing at the old fort in Durban; few concave, very soft-fleshy, fresh yellow-green leaves broad at the base and gradually tapering to a long point and recurving; small bright yellow flowers in a dense raceme on a long snaking wiry stalk. *Subtropic.* *p. 1424, 1425*

BULBINELLA *Liliaceae* **I-C2LBMd**

floribunda (So. Africa); perennial with fleshy roots, linear basal leaves, and tall 75 cm spikes of small flowers a shining daffodil yellow or orange; resembling miniature kniphofia; dormant in summer. *Subtropic.* *p. 1424*

robusta (So. Africa), "Florist's bulbinella" or "Cats-tail"; perennial herb with fleshy tuberous roots; linear basal leaves deeply grooved down the center; floral stalk 50 cm high bearing a thick 12 cm poker of small glittering yellow flowers; popular as a cut flower. *p. 1424*

setosa (hookeri) (New Zealand), "Maori onion"; perennial with tuberous roots, linear leaves, and small bright yellow flowers in erect racemes on stalks to 1 m high. *p. 1424*

BULBOCODIUM *Liliaceae* **C2LBDd**

vernum (Colchicum) (Pyrenées, Alps to Russian Caucasus), "Spring-meadow saffron"; crocus-like cormous herb with 2-3 broadly strap-shaped, concave, basal leaves, preceded by short-stalked tubular-funnel-shaped flowers with split, clawed perianth segments, rosy-purple with white spot on claw. *p. 1425*

BULBOPHYLLUM *Orchidaceae* **I-S3OFM**

affinis fletcheranum (New Guinea); epiphyte with heavy, lanceolate, lax leaves 30-40 cm long; pendant inflorescence of flesh-colored flowers, bristly hairy and evil-smelling. *p. 1670*

ambrosia (Hong Kong); free-flowering epiphyte with small cylindrical one-leaved squarish pseudobulbs bearing fleshy leaves to 5 cm long x 2 cm wide; solitary erect flowers 2½ cm long, creamy-white veined with purple; mobile lip tipped purple, and slightly fragrant; Dec.-March. *p. 1672*

barbigerum (West Africa: Sierra Leone); curious dwarf, creeping epiphyte with flattened pseudobulbs 2½ cm across bearing solitary leaf 8 cm long; flowers in lateral racemes, sepals and petals greenish brown, the lip green with yellow markings and tipped with a long tuft of chocolate hairs, so jointed that it oscillates in every movement of the air; summer. (S) *p. 1672*

elatius (Borneo); short stem bearing broad obovate leathery leaves to 45 cm high; the slender, erect raceme crowded with tiny cream-colored flowers; autumn. (S) *p. 1672*

'Fascination' (Cirrhopetalum) (fascinator x longissimum); charming small plant with characteristic inflorescence, the flowers with showy sepals connate (united), brownish to greenish-white heavily spotted purple, arranged fan-like on slender stalks. *p. 1670*

fascinator (Cirrhopetalum) (Vietnam); remarkable epiphyte with broad leaves and pendant inflorescence, bearing the curious light green flowers suffused, striped and marbled with purple; the upper sepal and small petals heavily fringed with purple hairs; the lower, lateral sepals to 20 cm long and long-tailed. *p. 1675*

gamosepalum (Cirrhopetalum) (Burma); small epiphyte with pseudobulbs 3 cm high, and 2 to 4 leaves; pendant flowers 3 cm across, red with purplish markings on the lateral sepals. *p. 1670*

grandiflorum (New Guinea); probably the most remarkable orchid it has been my privilege to see in New Guinea; the large flowers solitary, olive-green with pale chartreuse spots and netted with brown, the sepals 10-12 cm long, strongly arching over at base with the dorsal hanging down in front hood-like, petals and lip very small and almost hidden, the lip greenish dotted with red-brown; flowering in autumn in the north, in New Guinea in May-June; short 4-angled pseudobulbs with solitary leaves, on creeping rhizome. *Humid-tropical.* *p. 1671, 1673*

guttulatum (Cirrhopetalum) (India); small epiphyte from the subtropical Himalaya; pear-shaped pseudobulbs with leaves to 20 cm; wiry stalks bearing clusters of small 2 cm yellow-green flowers; speckled with bright purple, and purple lip. *p. 1675*

leopardinum (Khasia Hills); small epiphyte with close, flat pseudobulbs and fleshy leaf; the fleshy, somewhat globose flowers borne in clusters, sepals and petals yellow thickly spotted with crimson-red, grooved, very fleshy lip bright crimson, (summer) (I) *p. 1671*

lepidum (griffithii) (Malaya, Java); miniature terrestrial with solitary leathery leaves on pear-shaped pseudobulbs; clusters of small cupped flowers pinkish, greenish at edge overlaid with dark red; small white lip (summer). *p. 1670*

lobbii (Indonesia to Burma); epiphyte with creeping rhizome and small, single-leaved pseudobulbs; large solitary flower with sepals and petals buff-yellow, marked with red, the lip golden-yellow, (May-June, Nov.). *p. 1671*

longisepalum (New Guinea); small epiphyte with angular, one-leaved pseudobulbs on creeping rhizome, leaves thick-fleshy; solitary flowers on short reddish stalks, with creamy sepals spotted and veined dark red, 10 cm long and narrow tapered, the dorsal arched over the column and small petals, small lip hairy; summer. (S) *p. 1672*

longissimum (Cirrhopetalum) (Malaya); remarkable epiphyte with 4-angled pseudobulbs bearing a fleshy pointed leaf 10-15 cm long; the fascinating inflorescence pendant on arching stalks with long, gradually tapering lateral sepals 15-30 cm long, soft pink buff with deeper lines, the upper sepal and petals short, concave and ciliate lined with purple, lip yellow (winter). (I) *p. 1679*

makoyanum (Cirrhopetalum) (Malaya); beautiful little epiphyte with 3 cm pseudobulb and solitary leaf; the unusual 3 cm flowers 12-14 in a radiating, wheel-like umbel, pale yellow shading to deep crimson toward base, the whole inflorescence looking like a pretty daisy (winter). *p. 1672*

mastersianum (Cirrhopetalum) (Malay Archipelago, Moluccas); very interesting and handsome small epiphyte with angled pseudobulbs and solitary leaf 10-20 cm long; flowers at the apex of the wiry stalk in a semi-circle fan-like, the lateral sepals united and drooping downward, rich yellow veined at the base with brown-red, the very small lip brown-purple. (I) *p. 1673*

medusae (Cirrhopetalum) (Malaya, Thailand, Borneo); phenomenal epiphyte because of its compact heads of curious flowers, with 2 of the 3 sepals lengthened into numerous threads to 15 cm long, greenish-white or straw-colored, dotted with red; small pseudobulbs with solitary leaves, (Jan.-Feb. bl.). (S) *p. 1671*

ornatissimum (Sikkim Himalaya, Philippines); pretty, dwarf epiphyte, with small ovoid pseudobulb and leathery 15 cm leaf; lateral stalk bearing an umbel of flowers 8-10 cm long, yellowish or pale purplish-brown striped and netted with dark purple, lip crimson-purple; autumn. (I) *p. 1673*

picturatum (Cirrhopetalum) (Burma); epiphyte with pseudobulbs, carrying on a stalk a series of beautiful flowers arranged as in a fan, with 2 long-oblong, greenish-yellow basal sepals, spotted red, folded alongside each other and carried upward like a semaphore, the dorsal and the rounded pouch brown-red, (August). (S) *p. 1671*

porphyroglossum (Zaire); small, not particularly attractive species from Central Africa, with short rounded pseudobulbs bearing a broad fleshy leaf; the inflorescence a lateral wiry stem with an arching raceme of small flowers purplish pink and pale green. (S) *p. 1672*

pulchellum (Cirrhopetalum) (Malaya, New Guinea), "Walnut orchid"; small epiphyte having pseudobulbs bearing a solitary leaf; a basal stalk carries about 5 very remarkable flowers with tiny striped petals and small dorsal sepal, but the two lower sepals are long lanceolate, folded over in front and ending in a long tail, the dark lip a small pouch, (early spring). (S) *p. 1671*

pulchrum (Malaya); small epiphyte with 4-angled pseudobulbs bearing leaf 10-15 cm long, on creeping rhizome; flowers in umbels arranged fan-like, the long lateral sepals united and almost 5 cm long, yellow spotted with purple, upper sepal concave, thickly spotted red and hairy; petals and lip small; summer. (I) *p. 1673*

purpurascens (Cirrhopetalum) (Malaya, Java, Sumatra, Borneo); miniature species with tiny rounded pseudobulbs on creeping rhizome, small fleshy, purplish leaves; fragile inflorescence of pale yellow flowers in a spreading whorl on slender, but stiff stalk. *p. 1670*

purpureorhachis (Megaclinium) (Zaire), the "Cobra orchid"; a sinister-looking epiphyte from inner Africa, with clustered pseudobulbs and paired, rigid leaves to 15 cm; the curious inflorescence 30 cm long, the stalk a singular flattened green axis, densely spotted and overlaid with deep red; tiny 1 cm deep brown flowers borne in a single row on the flat sides (August into winter). *p. 1677*

rothschildianum (Cirrhopetalum) (India); fine epiphyte with angled pseudobulbs bearing a stout leathery leaf to 15 cm long, and arching, wiry stem with a spreading umbel of bright crimson-purple flowers blotched with yellow on the drooping sepals 10-15 cm long, the dorsal greenish-yellow lined red, the margins with purple hairs; the small lip crimson-purple; summer and various. (I) *p. 1673*

roxburghii (India); attractive dwarf epiphyte with small pseudobulbs and solitary leaves 5 cm long; slender stalks with umbellate inflorescence of small but pretty flowers, the dorsal and petals pale yellow lined with purple, the longer lateral sepals flecked with red-purple, lip darker yellow lined with red; summer. (I) *p. 1672*

vaginatum (Cirrhopetalum) (Malaya: Penang); miniature epiphyte resembling B. medusae; conical pseudobulbs bearing 5-10 cm leaf, on stout, matting rhizomes; the flowers with sepals drawn out into long threads at the apex, pale yellow; summer. (I) *p. 1673*

virescens (Amboina, Java), "Windmill orchid"; very striking epiphyte, with flattened, one-leaved pseudobulbs carried at intervals on creeping rhizome; the flowers arranged in a circle with long-tapering 12 cm, greenish sepals, the fleshy lip red-purple with a white waxy center, (summer). *p. 1671*

wrightii (So. Cameroons: M'Bong); small African species not spectacular, with angled pseudobulb bearing solitary leaf; lateral stalk with dense raceme of tiny flowers lemon-yellow and brown, with persistent bracts brown above, light gray beneath. (S) *p. 1672*

BULBOSTYLIS *Cyperaceae* **S3LBM**

paradoxa (Trop. South America); small grass-like tufts from tropical savannas, with thread-like, rich green leaves 15-25 cm long; the tiny flowers in spikelets at their tips. *p. 948*

BURBIDGEA *Zingiberaceae* **S3LFM**

schizocheila (Malaysia); showy perennial herb 22-40 cm high, with creeping rhizome, wide leathery leaves dull green above, reddish-brown beneath, on a fleshy stem; inflorescence an erect terminal cluster of orange-yellow flowers, the lip hairy at the tip. *p. 2132*

BURCHELLIA *Rubiaceae* **I3LBM**

capensis (So. Africa: Cape to Natal), "Wild pomegranate"; small evergreen shrub to 1½ m, becoming tree-like; with ovate, bristly-hairy dark green, 10 cm leaves; pretty, thinly-hairy, swollen tubular flowers 3 cm long, bright coral, in clusters at branch tips. *p. 2008*

capensis rubra (So. Africa: Transvaal), "Buffalo horn"; leafy bush of luxuriant appearance; at branch ends the handsome clusters of inflated-tubular, velvety 3 cm flowers rich scarlet red, with yellow styles. Known by Boers as "Buffelshoorn", for the horn-like calyx which remains when the woody berry is formed. *p. 2008*

BURLINGTONIA: see Rodriguezia

BUTEA *Leguminosae* **S2LBD**

frondosa (India, Burma), "Flame of the forest"; showy tree to 15 m, bearing masses of scarlet-red flowers 5 cm long; appearing before the leaves, these consisting of 3 leaflets. *p. 1371*

BUTIA *Palmae* **I2LBM**

bonnetii (So. Brazil), "Acorn butia"; a robust feather palm of smaller habit, trunk short and thick; very arching leaves with leaflets equally distant on the stalk; narrow inflorescence to 60 cm long; orange fruit egg-shaped 2 cm long, edible. *Tropical.* *p. 1855*

capitata (Cocos australis) (Brazil, Uruguay, Argentina), "Jelly palm"; short, stocky, rather coarse palm, slowly reaching 5 m, with thick trunk, covered with persistent leafbases; the long pinnate bluish-gray leaves stiffly recurving, whitish underneath, spiny at base; tough pinnae often 2-3 together; orange fruit with edible pulp. *Subtropic.* *p. 1855, 1874*

yatay (Argentina, Uruguay), "Yatay palm"; stout palm to 8 m tall; trunk with leaf bases long persistent, to 45 cm thick; stiff pinnate fronds 3 m long, arching forward and recurving, blue glaucescent; petiole armed; flowers yellowish; large clusters of ovoid fruit 4 cm long, dark yellow or orange, edible. *Subtropic.* *p. 1855*

BUXUS *Buxaceae* **C2LBM**

microphylla japonica (Japan), "California boxwood" or "Japanese little-leaf boxwood"; evergreen densely branching shrub to about 2 m high, the wiry shoots with small 1 to 2 cm obovate leathery leaves closely set, and a glossy bright green to deep green. Clipped into hedges, or globes, pyramids or other topiary shapes in containers. Tolerates the dry heat of a California patio, and alkaline soil, but not fully frost-resistant. *Warm temperate.* *p. 615*

sempervirens (Europe, No. Africa, Asia Minor), "Common boxwood" or "English boxwood"; winter-hardy evergreen shrub or tree 2 to 5 m high, much used for sheared hedges or topiary; of dense habit, with quadrangular branches, small leathery obovate leaves lustrous dark green, 2-3 cm long; small axillary flowers without petals. *Temperate.* *p. 615*

sempervirens marginata (No. Africa to Asia Minor); evergreen of loose, sparry habit, with small hard, elliptic leaves glossy dark green with broad, creamy-yellow border. *p. 615*

sempervirens suffruticosa; the "Edging box", permanently dwarf and dense variety used for centuries to edge beds and in formal gardens; leaves mostly obovate and smaller than the species, usually 1-2 cm long; can be propagated by division. *p. 615*

BYBLIS *Byblidaceae (Carnivorous plants)* **I-S3HBM**

gigantea (Western Australia); from swampy, sandy places of the Swan River near Perth; semi-shrubby plant 30-50 cm high, with woody rhizome, a stem with several branches with long filament-like yellow green leaves 10-20 cm long, clothed with numerous mucilage glands, secreting viscous glue to hold and eventually digest insects; large rosy or violet flowers. *Subtropic.* *p. 764*

liniflora (Western Australia); a tropical insectivorous plant smaller than B. gigantea, with linear, filament-like leaves 6-8 cm long, densely covered with mucilage glands secreting honey-like sap to catch and hold insects for gradual digestion; small pale purple flowers. *p. 764*

CABOMBA *Nymphaeaceae* **S3LFW**

aquatica (So. America), aquatic "Fanwort"; easy to grow aquarium plant with richly branched stem which frequently attains a length of 2 m below the surface of the water; leaf blade divided into fine green segments, 4-5 cm long and repeatedly divided, forming a rosette below the surface; floating leaves are round when blooming; flowers bright yellow. One of the best underwater oxygenators for aquaria to keep water at healthful level. Plants exude oxygen utilized by fish in their breathing, and in turn give off carbon dioxide assimilated by water plants. *p. 1622, 1626*

CACALIA *Compositae* **I2LFM**

adenostyloides (Senecio) (Japan: Honshu, Shikoku); perennial herb from wooded mountains, 60 to 100 cm high, with slender stems and membranous, kidney-shaped leaves 10-20 cm wide, irregularly toothed or lobed; the inflorescence in loose racemes on slender stalks, with whitish-yellow, tubular florets 3-4 cm long. *p. 804*

CADETIA *Orchidaceae* **S3OFW**

ceratostyloides (New Guinea); epiphyte or rock-dwelling; slender, stem-like pseudobulbs with solitary, rigid leaves; small 2 cm flowers between the foliage from the leaf base, creamy white and very short-lived, often withering after a few hours (summer). *p. 1677*

karoense (Solomon Islands: Bougainville Is.); small epiphyte 10 cm high; pseudobulbs stem-like, single-leaved; 1 cm flowers in small clusters from leaf base, white with cream lip and violet-tipped column, very fragrant; adventitious roots develop at base of flower stalk. *p. 1677*

CAESALPINIA *Leguminosae* **S3LBM**

coriaria (Aruba), "Divi-Divi"; thorny tree generally with wind-blown branches; numerous small leaflets; flowers yellow; curved 3 cm pods. *Arid-tropical.* *p. 1375*

gilliesii (Argentina, Uruguay), "Bird-of-paradise shrub"; straggling shrub with bipinnate leaves, the leaflets very small; terminal inflorescence with pale yellow flowers and long red stamens. *Subtropic.* *p. 1375*

pulcherrima (Poinciana) (W. Indies and other tropics), "Dwarf poinciana" or "Pride of Barbados"; prickly, glabrous shrub with delicate bipinnate, mimosa-like leaves, and very gaudy orange-red flowers with crisped, golden-edged petals and red stamens, 6 cm long. *Tropical.* *p. 1378*

pulcherrima flava (Poinciana) (East Africa, widespread in Tropics), "Pride of Barbados" or "Peacock flower"; spiny, handsome-flowered bush to 5 m; with bipinnate fern-like leaves and bright yellow flowers. *p. 1389*

sepiaria (India), the "Mysore-thorn"; prickly shrub with bipinnate leaves, oblong leaflets, and erect racemes of yellow cup-shaped flowers, later forming beaked pods. *p. 1378*

CAIOPHORA *Loasaceae* **I2LBD**

lateritia (Blumenbachia) (Chile); perennial twining or prostrate herb with stinging hairs, with opposite, pinnate leaves, and showy, axillary orange-red flowers to 5 cm across, on long stalks, forming capsular twisted fruits. *p. 1522*

CALADIOPSIS *Araceae* **S3LFM**

atropurpureum (Ecuador); tropical ornamental tuberous rainforest plant related to Colocasia, with purplish petioles grooved on upper part, vaginate toward base; the leaves broadly hastate, matte green and corrugated 25-30 cm long; inflorescence on mottled stalk, with slender elongate spadix and narrow pinkish cream spathe. *p. 189*

CALADIUM *Araceae* **S3HFM**

bicolor (Trinidad, Guyana, Brazil), "Heart of Jesus"; tuberous, stocky plant with sagittate-ovate, firm leaves mostly green, red veins and scattered white spots; variable; spathe green, top white to yellow. The most important parent of most of our present horticultural forms. *Tropical.* *p. 188, 191*

bicolor rubicunda (Amazonas); rather heavy leaf, broadly heart-shaped, color intense purplish-amethyst with pale lavender blotching, and wine-red veins. *p. 191*

bicolor 'Speciosum'; ornamental tuberous tropical herb with very attractive foliage; the leaves broadly arrow-shaped, quilted and green with bold white mid-rib and greenish white lateral veins. *p. 188*

bicolor 'Venosum', magnificent tropical foliage plant from tuberous root; the triangular, dainty herbaceous leaf rich green, the central rib, lateral veins and a nerve-line inside the margins white to greenish-white. *p. 188*

bicolor wightii (Brazil: Central Amazonas); sagittate leaves smallish in cultivation but becoming 25 cm long if planted out; blade olive-green with large red-purple blotches and smaller white spots, veins green. *p. 191*

'Changjur' (Java); small, ovate, slender-pointed, firm leaves, pendant, light green shading to dark, with prominent white ribs and borne on white stems. *p. 203*

hortulanum, "Fancy-leaved Caladium"; tuberous herbs with membranous leaves varying from 15-30 cm long, mostly beautifully marked in many colors and patterns, on slender petioles; widely hybridized; the larger peltate-heartshaped leaves have C. bicolor blood; the lanceolate strap-leaved hybrids go back to C. picturatum. *Tropical.*

'A.B. Graf'; an improved 'Scarlet Pimpernelle', with more leaves, sturdy, and more crimson, with a broad margin of contrasting lemon-yellow or nile green. *p. 195*

'A. J. Barnes'; firm leaves of a lively red color with bronzy-green outer area and brilliant scarlet-red main ribs. *p. 206*

'Aaron'; turgid-sturdy, rugged plant with leaves milky-white in center area and deep green toward margins, the main veins forming a bold pattern of white. *p. 206*

'Ace of Hearts'; beautiful leaf, center area transparent-rose to crimson, moss-green toward margin; strong, blood-red ribs. *p. 190, 193*

'Ace of Spades', "Lance leaf"; a glorious lance leaf, with broad cordate base, on long petioles, the dominant red veins over rose and white marbling, the margin dark green. *p. 205*

'Ann Greer'; heavy plant with large leaves in red-bronze, with dark emerald-green tracings and border area. *p. 192*

'Appleblossom'; attractive delicate transparent apple-blossom shade, narrow dark green border and ribs. *p. 200*

'Attala'; large colorful leaf irregularly variegated pink and dark green, with clear red main ribs. *p. 193*

'Billy'; large, delicate leaf transparent pink, with much mottling of deep green, main veins deep green. *p. 193*

'Bing Crosby'; robust, attractive, large heavy-textured leaves white in the center area gradually marbling into broad borders of forest green; main veins red. *p. 192*

'Bleeding Heart'; heartshaped, pointed leaf transparent rose in center, followed by zone of white marbling and green border, veins boldly crimson. *p. 200*

'Brilliantissimo'; large satiny leaves with large areas of translucent carmine red, the main veins deep blood red, marbled with moss-green and whitish, border light green; stems blackish. *p. 190*

'Buck'; smallish, firm, glossy leaves with deep crimson-red center and purplish veins, outer area grass-green; stem marbled brown. *p. 192*

'Caloosahatchie'; broad lance leaf of almost cordate shape; pale ivory and red-brown with olive-green border and thin carmine veining; bushy and good keeper. *p. 190*

'Candidum', "White caladium"; showy, white leaf traced with dark green veins and green border; delicate, yet a good keeper. Ideal for Easter; 20-30 cm foliage. *p. 191, 193, 200*

'Caro Nome'; large ivory leaves dissected by contrasting broad crimson-red veins and faint tracings of moss-green, the center of leaf bronzy rose-colored, margin green; stalks brown marbled. *p. 206*

'Carolyn Whorton'; colorful variety dominated by a pink to blush transparent blade, crossed by the crimson main veins, with green marbling toward green edge. *p. 193*

'Cheerio'; deep green, corrugated leaf marbled rose and white toward center, ribs crimson. *p. 193*

'Cinderella'; sturdy lanceleaf with greenish to cream-white leaves, green veins and spotted purplish-red, margin wavy. *p. 205*

'Citation'; shapely variety; the long lanceolate leaves sturdy, pink to milky white, dark green at undulate margin, a touch of rose at base. *p. 205*

'Cleo' (Texas Wonder); tall, sturdy variety, red in center, background green with pink marbling and spots; veins contrasting red. *p. 200*

'Coral Glow'; leaf with center area rose to flesh-pink; white mottling toward green border, and carmine ribs. *p. 201*

'Crimson Wave'; luminous leaf transparent rose-red marbled with white and green toward margins; veins and stems purple. *p. 190, 193*

'Davy Crockett'; low bushy plant with crinkled leaves white and transparent lavender-pink with bold blackish-green ribs and green edge. *p. 195*

'Debutante'; bright, colorful leaf regularly marbled white on green, the center and vein area rosy to red. *p. 193*

'D.M. Cook'; leaf somewhat rumpled, brownish-red with crimson markings, margin deep green. *p. 190*

'Dr. Groover'; shapely plant with leaves translucent pink in center, border area irregularly bronzy-green, narrow main ribs bright crimson. *p. 190*

'Dr. T. L. Mead'; rosy-red leaves with translucent areas increasingly marbled green toward margin; veins purplish-red. *p. 193*

'Dutch Frill'; delicate, narrow, lanceleaf with ruffled margins; maroon-red with transparent spots. *p. 203*

'Edith Mead'; sturdy plant with medium-small leaves glistening white in center and dark green toward margins, thin red veins. *p. 190, 194*

'Edna'; large glossy leaves translucent red, metallic green toward edge, thick ribs dull red. *p. 194*

'Elizabeth Dixon'; showy leaves basically deep green but more or less variegated white, more so in center where there is a flush of transparent pink; main ribs crimson. *p. 194*

'Elizabeth Lou'; large heartshaped leaf with deep green ribs and broad edge, the area between transparent lavender pink. *p. 205*

'E.O. Orpet'; lanceolate strapleaf, almost leathery; a glossy, bright red, shading to blood-red with narrow green border; low habit, and good keeper. *p. 203, 205*

'Evening Pink'; large leaves dominated by blush-white, with center area of transparent pink, and a network of thin green veins. *p. 201*

'Festivia'; pretty leaf largely translucent bronzy to salmon-red with green toward margin, and deep green ribs. *p. 194*

'Firebrand'; short plant with small leaves, nile green blade, to transparent pink, spotted red toward center, veins pink. *p. 200*

'Fire Chief'; large leaves delicate pink to transparent rose, mottled in outer area with dark green, ribs purplish-crimson. *p. 194*

'Fire Nymph'; large but delicate leaves transparent pink, marbled green toward edge, and with dark veins. *p. 200*

'Frieda Hemple'; top red variety, bushy, compact and sturdy; medium size leaves clear bright red with primary ribs scarlet, the outer edge deep green. *p. 194*

'Gail Dee'; a pink Caladium making numerous leaves with transparent rose-pink center areas and deep rose veins, narrow border mottled light and deep green. *p. 206*

'Gray Ghost'; bold leaves with center area and veins cream to creamy-gray, changing to grass-green toward margins. *p. 192*

'Grey King'; tallish variety, medium size smooth leaves with milky-white center area and white ribs, mottling into blackish-green toward margins. *p. 201*

'Highland Pride'; bushy plant with smallish leaves having the outer half dark green, the inner salmon-rose or pink, with rose to red main ribs. *p. 194*

'Horatio Cid'; strap-leaved, with blackish petioles and broad leaves green and ivory-white variegated, veins and base of leaf purple, with a few transparent pink spots. *p. 205*

'Hortulania'; entire leaf transparent, almost shimmering, pink or rose, with narrow green border; veins scarlet; very showy. *p. 195, 200*

'Itacapus'; early forcer with large leaves almost entirely metallic-red with a netting of green between, and dark green border. *p. 190, 195*

'Jacqueline Gireaud'; vigorous medium tall plant with leaf area and veins light yellow-green mottled with pale areas, all over splashed with irregular shapes of crimson and minute red dots. *p. 200*

'Jequintinhonha'; bushy plant with leaves light green, the center and veins reddish brown. *p. 200*

'Jessie Thayer'; large leaves with unusually bold, scarlet ribs which stand out conspicuously against metallic green, which changes to bronzy-white with pink except for border. *p. 190, 195*

'John Hachmeister'; few but giant, smooth leaves of dull crimson, the margins are deep sea-green which extends irregularly inward between the deep red of the veins and veinlets. *p. 202*

'John Peed'; sturdy variety with firm, waxy, warm moss-green leaves with metallic orange-red center area and scarlet-red veins; purplish stem. *p. 190, 195*

'June Bride'; beautiful large, all-milk-white, flat, fleshy leaf, with ribs white also, and a narrow dark green border. *p. 195*

'Juno'; bold strap variety with dark green to brown leaves wavy margined, the center white, and pink or watery buff-transparent, veins green or brownish. *p. 205*

'Kabootie'; marbled leaf with outer area dominated by dark green, inner by rose-pink; thin crimson veins. *p. 195*

'Kathleen'; pointed leaf mostly transparent rose to flesh-pink, dark green along margins, the ribs carmine-rose. *p. 195*

'Keystone'; large leaf deep forest-green with white spotting; bold orange-red veins. *p. 202*

'Lady Chrys'; very showy leaves with wavy blade creamy white, the main ribs green, and with blood-red blotches, edged with a fine deep green border line. *p. 192*

'Lady-in-Pink'; bushy plant with transparent rose-pink leaves somewhat curled, dark green ribs and sometimes green margined. *p. 197*

'Lee Stokes'; large forest-green leaves irregularly marbled and variegated white, main ribs greenish-white. *p. 197*

'Little Rascal'; small lance-leaf, pink to light red, transversed by red to purplish veins, outer edge green and frilled. *p. 205*

'L.L. Holmes'; an improved 'Marie Moir' by Joyner with more but narrower leaves and the corrugated leaves more white, traced by blackish main ribs, and scattered red blotches. *p. 197*

'Lord Derby'; bushy plant with transparent, quilted leaf with wavy edge, delicate rose-pink with network of thin, green veins and green margin. *p. 190, 197*

'Lord Rosenberry'; bushy plant with sturdy deep green leaves, a zone of yellow-green and a rosy center; main veins carmine. *p. 197*

'Luella Whorton'; large pink leaf with a fine network of dark green and green edge, main ribs carmine-red. *p. 197*

'Macahyba'; large, showy leaves, the center area transparent with marbling of white to rose, scattering out into the moss-green blade reticulated with occasional yellow green; primary ribs crimson to purple. *p. 190, 197*

'Mad. Truall'; lacquered, firm leaf blackish-red to blackish-green with network of scarlet-red veins. *p. 202*

'Maid of Orleans'; colorful variety deep green richly marbled with rosy-pink and some white; ribs bright red, on red stems. *p. 201*

'Mandago'; odd in variegation through in general quite greenish; veins outlined cardinal red, the remainder of leaf divided between white and green. *p. 202*

'Marie Moir', "Blood spots"; a beautiful variety because of its simplicity, pure white with a network of green tracings, and dark green ribs, and a sprinkling of showy blood-red blotches. *p. 197*

'Mary Queen of Scots'; unique; leaves irregularly mottled dark moss-green, gray green, gray, and deep red; netted and veined deep maroon, occasional spots of transparent red. *p. 202*

'Midget Princess': see 'Miss Muffet'

'Miss Chicago'; variegated leaf transparent rose and white, with dark green toward margin, main ribs crimson. *p. 197*

'Miss Frances'; variegated leaf deep green toward outer half, through pink marbling leading into a solid pink center; ribs crimson. *p. 196*

'Miss Marvene'; low growing plant with leaves delicately tinted pink, narrow green veins and fine green edge. *p. 192*

'Miss Muffet' (Midget Princess), "Baby elephant-ear"; wonderful little miniature with intriguing leaf, sturdy, compact, nile green or chartreuse, with white primary ribs and deep blood-red blotches and heart. *p. 196, 201*

'Mrs. Arno Nehrling'; elegant large white leaf traced with a network of fine dark green and the distinct main ribs deep crimson, border green. *p. 196*

'Mrs. Fannie Munson'; compact variety with large rosy leaves, crimson ribs, and narrow dark green edge. *p. 194*

'Mrs. F. M. Joyner'; a rich looking, bushy plant with large white leaves changing into pinkish, overlaid with a network of bold red veins and a narrow green edge; good keeper. *p. 196*

'Mrs. F. Sanders'; leaves medium green with rose-pink marbling, and purple main ribs. *p. 196*

'Mrs. Martin Miller'; large crinkled leaf transparent glowing rose-pink, with dark crimson ribs, and dark green at margin. *p. 196*

'Mrs. W.B. Halderman', "Coloradium"; beautiful cultivar with medium leaves more lightly variegated than 'Gen. W.B. Halderman'; translucent rose with red along veins; green along margins. *Humid-tropical. p. 190, 196, 202*

'Mumbo'; large lance leaves on long petiole, the main area rosy to milky, fanning ribs red, and broad green wavy margin. *p. 205*

'Myrt'; large smooth leaf almost entirely rosy pink, some leaves olive green at margin; ribs rose to carmine red. *p. 199*

'Okeechobee'; tall, strapleaf variety with leathery, deep green, narrow, pointed leaves alternating with lighter green areas. *p. 203*

'Our Red'; mature leaf medium size, crinkly, transparent clear rose, with green veins and edge; when in middle growth, the rose and green are dotted white; needs warmth. *p. 202*

'Patience'; broad lance leaf light green to almost white; strong habit. *p. 203*

'Paulo Lietz'; robust strap leaf variety with very long, pointed, pendant leaves marbled bronze and gray-green, even tan, and flushed pink. *p. 203*

'Pink Beauty'; blush pink, marbled green; red ribs. *p. 196*

'Pink Blush'; glossy, crinkled leaves of translucent carmine-rose, occasionally marbled with cream, the main ribs blackish crimson, and a very narrow edge of dark green; dark brown stems. *p. 198, 206*

'Pink Bonnet'; pretty and pleasing variety with large area of leaf transparent pink and mottled white, toward the margin increasing green, while ribs are crimson. *p. 201*

'Pink Charmer'; broad lance leaf, bright, soft pink with green border and red veins; ruffled edge. *p. 204*

'Pink Cloud'; large variegated leaves very dark green, with transparent marbling of lavender rose, and white to pink along main ribs. *p. 198*

'Pink Delight'; bushy plant, crazily speckled and marbled transparent pink on dark green leaf, ribs light red. *p. 201*

'Pink Glow'; bushy lance leaf, the broad leaves creamy white, the ribs white or green, with mottling in between and rosy splotching, the wide margins deep green. *p. 203*

'Pinkie'; prolific grower with delicate, mostly transparent pink leaves with red veins, some more or less with deep green border. *p. 198*

'Pink Radiance'; bushy plant with curled, transparent blush to rose-pink leaves with red veins, more or less with deep green border. *p. 198*

'Poecile Anglais'; bushy plant with smaller leaf, crimson-red, with broad, moss-green border; veins scarlet. *p. 198*

'Postman Joyner'; bushy, compact variety with medium leaves light red with darker scarlet veins and a narrow margin of forest green. *p. 198*

'Pothos'; sturdy lance leaf with thick milk-white leaves marbled with dark green; tracings of purple in veins. *p. 204*

'Puerto Rico'; compact, low growing, bushy variety with medium leaves of sturdy habit, bright transparent crimson, marbled green in margin area. *p. 202*

'Queen's Delight'; long strapleaf with greenish cream-white center and pink transparent blotches, margins green. *p. 204*

'Red Ace'; large, sturdy leaves dominated by rosy red, the ribs somewhat more red, the border area deep green. *p. 198*

'Red Calla'; sturdy leaves broad-lance-shaped, blade translucent vermilion and pink, with striking leaf pattern cream and green, border area green. *p. 206*

'Red Chief'; short but sturdy lance leaf boldly rosy-red with dark green margin and bright red main veins. *p. 203*

'Red Ensign'; sturdy, almost glossy leaf, boldly carmine red, deep green toward margin; main ribs scarlet. *p. 198*

'Red Flare'; interesting leaf rosy to purplish in center, outer zone white, or greenish variegated green, ribs crimson. *p. 198*

'Red Frill'; small, sturdy strapleaf, rosy-red with main ribs scarlet fanning out toward deep green, wavy margin. *p. 204*

'Red Polka'; large sturdy leaf bluish green mottled milky green, the center rose, main ribs carmine, and blotches of blood-red. *p. 199*

'Ripple'; bushy, prolific lance leaf with large, fleshy leaves white, transparent areas of lavender pink, green toward apex, and some veins green. *p. 204*

'Roehrs Dawn'; a great caladium with large, dainty, quilted, transparent leaves of shimmering creamy-white contrasting with the rosy red veins and a narrow green edge. *p. 160A, 201*

'Rosalie'; dwarf lance-leaf, glossy metallic rosy-red with red veins and green margins. *p. 204*

'Rose Envy'; low-growing "pink" Caladium; rosy-pink leaf-blade traced with green veins and edge, darker red blotches in between; stalks brown marbled black. *p. 190*

'Ruby Smith'; showy leaf mainly transparent red except for deep green veins and increasing green toward margin. *p. 199*

'Scarlet Beauty'; bushy plant with large leaves mainly transparent rosy-red, main veins red, outer edge deep green. *p. 199*

'Scarlet Pimpernelle'; large leaves bright carmine-rose, mottled grayish green, outer area straw colored, heavy red ribs. *p. 202*

'Scotch Plaid'; mottled leaf dark green and grayish-green and spotted scarlet; maroon ribs. *p. 190*

'Seagull'; greenish white center area, mingling with dark, bluish-green toward edge; veins usually white. *p. 190, 199*

'Southern Belle'; bushy variety with pretty leaves largely rose-pink or blush-white, toward margin more or less green, the main ribs rosy to crimson. *p. 201*

'Spangled Banner'; bushy variety with solid leaves red in center, the carmine main ribs radiating star-like into the dark green leaf which is marbled lavender-pink. *p. 199*

'Stacy'; large white leaf with blush-pink transparent undertones and black-green veins and thin edge. *p. 199*

'Surprise'; white leaf with dark green main ribs, and border, in older leaves a network of fine green tracings; holds up well. *p. 199*

'The Thing'; tall, vigorous plant with large stiff leaves to 45 cm on light stalks, with ivory-white center, soft green outer area, and blotched salmon-red. *p. 192*

'Thomas Tomlinson'; compact, bushy plant with shiny, moss-green leaves transparent lacquer-red in center; green ribs. *p. 199*

'Token'; sturdy strapleaf, milky-white to milky-green, with broad blackish-green wavy edge, the ribs green to purple, purplish at base, on blackish petioles. *p. 204*

'Triomphe de l'Exposition'; bushy plant with smaller leaf yellowish-green with scarlet veins shooting star-like from the red center; blue stem. *p. 190, 196*

'Twenty Grand'; tall lance-leaf with broad blade marbled and mottled light green, white, pink and bronze, the border area green. *p. 194*

'Twinkles', substantial leaf almost waxy, bronzy red over green and margin metallic green; ribs clear red. *p. 190*

'White Christmas'; a promising "white" cultivar with large 25-30 cm leaves turgid-firm, the blade essentially pure glistening white with veinlets of deep green and the ragged main ribs, more bold than in Candidum, also deep green. *p. 191*

'White Glory'; fleshy lanceleaf creamy-white with increasing fine mottling of medium green toward green, wavy margin. *p. 204*

'White Princess'; bushy, small growing variety with slender, membranous leaves pure white, with main veins deep green as well as green toward border. *p. 190*

'White Queen'; stunning introduction with pure white, lightly crinkly leaves contrasted by clear crimson primary veins, with a tracing of green laterals and a fine deep green edge. *p. 190*

'White Wings'; lance leaf; substantial leaves of good texture, white with fanning pink veins, dark green at edge. *p. 203*

humboldtii (argyrites) (Pará, Brazil), "Miniature caladium"; smallest and daintiest of genus; the tiny leaves 9-12 cm long, light green with transparent white areas between veins. Prefers dormancy period at warm 18°C. *Humid-tropical.* *p. 191, 192, 203*

macrotites (Brazil, Bolivia); robust tuberous plant forming clusters; stiff petioles measuring to 1 m, vaginate toward base; leaves arrow-shaped about 50 to 100 cm long, rich green with prominent ribs; the bold inflorescence with rolled, cream-colored spathe, inflated and green at base, and concealing the slender white spadix. *p. 189*

marmoratum (Ecuador); tuberous tropical plant very ornamental, with stiff 30-40 cm petiole carrying a handsome peltate leaf 20-25 cm long and 12-15 cm wide, dark green with whitish spots. *p. 189*

plowmanii (Ecuador); stem-forming small aroid developing aerial roots; 8-10 cm green petioles with hastate, arrow-shaped leaves 10-12 cm long and 7-8 cm wide, dark green and iridescent velvety, transversed by prominent veins; inflorescence with erect spadix appended by constricted spathe tinged with red. *p. 191*

sagittifolium (picturatum) (Brazil; Perú), "Strapleaf caladium"; leaves lanceolate, red flushed to buff and green; undulate margin; on long, firm petioles. *p. 203, 204*

steudnerifolium (Colombia); waxy, peltate-cordate leaf emerald green with grayish-white blotching which does not show through; leaf green beneath; stem buff with purple cross-banding. (S3HFM) *p. 208*

striatipes (Brazil); handsome tuberous ornamental species, carrying on long 40-50 cm petioles, fountain-like, the lanceolate, thin-leathery leafblades 30 to 40 cm long and to 9 cm or more wide, bluish-green with midrib and lateral veins in contrasting ivory-white; the inflorescence with spathe constricted, 18 cm long, green below, toward apex yellow, and yellowish spadix. *Tropical.* *p. 191*

CALAMUS *Palmae* **S3LFW**

ciliaris (Borneo, Java, Sumatra), "Rattan palm"; very long thin and tough stems, with vivid green leaves pinnate with numerous narrow, hairy segments, climbing by leafless branches with hooked spines appearing under each leaf. *Tropical.* *p. 1858, 1876*

dealbatus (Brazil), a "Rattan palm"; slender tropical fan palm with scandent stems thickly armed with brown spines, and climbing over nearby trees and shrubs, forming thickets; the leaflets spread out flat, the petioles and midrib of the leaf set with dangerous hooks. *Tropical.* *p. 1863*

siphonospathus, or more correctly C. maximus (Old World Tropics: Malaysia, Philippines), "Rattan palm"; a climbing featherleaf palm whose flexuous stems scramble 30-60 m high into the tree tops by means of hooks on the pinnate leaves, these hooks being modified pinnae; the spiny, bamboo-like stems are used as furniture rattans and for canes. *p. 1854*

CALANTHE *Orchidaceae* **C-S3LFMd**

x bella (turneri x veitchii); squarish, silvery-gray pseudobulbs with broad-lanceolate plaited leaves developing after flowering; the inflorescence in long arching raceme with large flowers having white sepals, the petals blush, the four-lobed lip blush-pink with crimson blotch edged in white; winter. *p. 1674*

elmeri (Philippines); attractive terrestrial with large pseudobulb constricted in the middle; leaves absent at blooming time; flowers clear rose-pink with brown-red center, on erect stalk, (winter). (S) *p. 1674*

'Florence' (sedenii x veitchii); terrestrial hybrid having pseudobulbs with ribbed leaves and spikes of large, rosy-purple flowers, cream-white to lemon in lip, (winter). *p. 1674*

furcata (Philippines); evergreen terrestrial, with plaited green leaves in a rosette; the flowers in dense raceme on 1 m, erect spike, white turning blue; the lip resembles a dancing girl, (June-Aug.). *Tropical.* *p. 1674*

masuca (India); handsome evergreen terrestrial with broad green leaves 30 cm long; erect spikes 45 cm high, carrying 5 cm flowers with long spur, rosy purple with orange blotch on lip. *p. 1677*

reflexa (Japan, W. China); terrestrial with small pseudobulbs hidden when plant is in growth; up to 8 emerald-green 17 cm leaves; flowers on erect, hairy stalks, reflexed sepals and spreading petals pale pink, lip violet-mauve, without spur; Sept.-Nov. *p. 1674*

striata (sieboldii) (Japan); elegant dwarf evergreen species 45 cm high, with broad dark green plaited leaves and erect raceme of large yellow flowers tinted coppery orange, the lip dark yellow marked crimson (summer). (C) *p. 1674*

triplicata (Malaya); similar to furcata; terrestrial without pseudobulbs, leaves to 30 cm long; flowers 3 cm across, on erect stalk, pure white with small area of pink on lip (Kew Gardens). *p. 1677*

x veitchii (rosea x vestita); winter-flowering terrestrial hybrid; pseudobulb with plaited leaves and long raceme of carmine-rose flowers with a white spot at base of lip, (winter-early spring). (S) *p. 1674*

vestita (Burma, Malaya); terrestrial with large, whitish pseudobulb, ribbed leaves broad-lanceolate, and deciduous; large white flowers with yellow eye and slender spur, on nodding spikes to 75 cm long, (Nov.-Dec.). (S) *p. 1674*

'William Murray' (vestita x williamsii); terrestrial hybrid with graceful spray of large flowers from alongside the pseudobulb, petals white and lip carmine-red with darker throat, (winter fl.). *Tropical.* *p. 1674*

CALATHEA *Marantaceae* **S3HFM**

"acuminata"; listed by Merkel, of undetermined standing; compact plant branching at base; with narrow lanceolate leaves 30 cm by 4 cm dark olive green above and somewhat glossy, maroon beneath, and slightly pubescent on both sides; long maroon, pubescent petioles with green patches, sheathing at base. *p. 1534, 1540*

aemula (Brazil); sturdy plant with oblique-oval 15 cm leaf on short petiole, glossy dark grayish-green with broad flame-like irregular band of greenish yellow through the center; reverse gray with purple tinge and soft pubescent. *Tropical.* *p. 1542*

albicans (Guyana, Colombia, Nicaragua); handsome bushy, tufting plant with somewhat quilted, broad-oval, unequal-sided leathery leaves 15 to 18 cm long, glossy light green to grayish, and dark green feathering along lateral veins; underside grayish green. *Tropical.* *p. 1538, 1545*

altissima: see princeps

argyraea (Brazil), "Silver calathea"; sturdy plant with foliage borne on stiff-erect, winged stalks; leaves oblanceolate, unequal-sided, glossy, the feathered vein areas grass-green, silvery-gray between; reverse wine-red; from the collection at Paris Museum. *Tropical.* *p. 1542*

"argyraea" hort.; short bushy plant with obliquely heartshaped, leathery leaves borne more or less horizontally, silver-gray with dark green, almond-shaped blotches and lateral veins from either side of midrib; gray-green beneath. *p. 1539*

aurantiaca (Brazil); sturdy, showy plant with large leathery, oblique-ovate leaves glossy gray-green to yellowish, with dark green herringbone feathering. *Tropical.* *p. 1545, 1546*

bachemiana (trifasciata) (Brazil); small plant with slender stalks and oblique, narrow tapering, leathery leaves pale greenish-gray, with dark green, almond-shaped blotches alternately fanning out from midrib, and a narrow border of the same deep color; green beneath. *Tropical.* *p. 1536, 1539*

sp. 'Burle Marx' (Brazil); grown by Fantastic Gardens, Miami; erect growing, sturdy plant with oblique broad-ovate, thin-leathery leaves 20 cm long, shining dark green with lighter feathering; reverse in part purple. *p. 1545*

carlina (Brazil); species resembling kegeliana but the leathery leaves are shorter and broader, oblique ovate 18 cm by 12 cm, glossy gray with dense net of yellow reticulations or cross veinlets, and a fish bone design of grass green and regular thin green veins between, as well as a narrow green border; grayish green beneath reticulated green. *Tropical.* *p. 1542, 1544*

clossonii (Maranta) (Brazil); slender bushy plant with thin-leathery narrow-lanceolate leaves, the lightly quilted surface yellow-green, with short almond-shaped medium-green blotches on each side of midrib. *Tropical.* *p. 1539*

concinna (Acre, W. Brazil); bushy plant with very pretty, glossy, ovate leaves larger than leopardina, the yellow-green blade marked with not as bold but more numerous, usually opposite, narrower bands of dark green, tapering to a narrow line and reaching to the marginal deep green border, dark green lateral veins between; purple reverse. *Tropical.* *p. 1536A, 1539*

crotalifera (insignis Petersen) (Mexico, Panama, Ecuador); tall-growing, coarse plant 1-2 m high, with large oval leaves to 60 cm long, satiny, friendly green above, pale along midrib, and grayish beneath; elongate, compressed flower spikes, the boatshaped, greenish-orange bracts 2-ranked, with yellow flowers. *p. 1541, 1543*

cylindrica (Brazil); robust plant to 1½ m high, the long stalks bearing elliptic or lanceolate, thin leaves 45 cm long, pale green; flowers white in cylindrical, club-like spike 15 cm long. *p. 1543*

eximia (Central America); tuberous-rooted plant with oblique-ovate leaves 15-30 cm long, on short stalks, the channeled midrib pale yellowish-green; the feathering lateral veins olive green, the areas between grayish silver; underneath wine-red and softly-brown-hairy; inflorescence an elliptical spike with brown hair and violet bracts. *p. 1542, 1546*

fasciata (Brazil: Bahia); with beautiful foliage, as pictured Gartenflora 1859, Berlin; now referred to C. rotundifolia var. fasciata, which see. *p. 1546*

grandiflora (Brazil); robust plant to 75 cm high, with large 30 cm oblique-oblong leaves shiny grass-green, closely corrugated by its prominent veins, on winged stalks, brown at base of leaf; grayish beneath; flowers yellow. *Tropical.* *p. 1538, 1541, 1546*

insignis Bull (Brazil), "Rattlesnake plant"; very pretty, bushy species with narrow, tapering, almost linear stiffly erect foliage wavy at the margins, yellow-green with lateral ovals alternately large and small of dark green; underside a showy maroon red; while slow growing at first, I have seen it measure 60 cm or more as growing in Brazil. *p. 1534, 1536*

kegeliana (Brazil); robust, durable plant to 45 cm high with wiry stalks bearing heavy, thick-leathery oblique-ovate leaves having cordate base, laxly pendant; the surface silvery gray attractively patterned with lateral veins and lance-shaped bands of yellowish to dark green; grayish green beneath with midrib showing yellow. *Tropical.* *p. 1536A, 1539*

leonii (Ecuador); showy plant with elongate ovate leaves on long-stalked petioles, the blade velvety moss green, except for bands of greenish silver along midrib and lateral veins; reverse red; flowers white within green bracts. *Humid-tropical.* *p. 1540*

leopardina (Brazil); attractive species to 40 cm high with beautiful oblique-lanceshaped, waxy leaves on slender stalks, the blade is nile-green marked with bold dark green triangles, alternately on both sides of the midrib, and not reaching the margin; underside tinted bronzy purple. *Tropical.* *p. 1539*

leucostachys (Costa Rica); robust plant about 45 cm high, with large 25 cm downy, oblong leaves green above and reddish purple beneath; inflorescence a spike with white flowers, and yellow bracts white at apex. *p. 1545*

lietzei (Brazil); pretty plant with narrow-ovate, thin-leathery leaves deep green with sharply contrasting, alternate lateral bands in silvery green to margin, and purple beneath; sending up erect runners bearing young plantlets. *Tropical.* *p. 1534, 1537*

lindeniana (Brazil); vigorous plant to 1 m high, broad oval leaves deep green, with a feathery, pale olive zone either side of midrib and near the border, a darker zone between, purple underneath except near midrib. *Humid-tropical.* *p. 1537*

louisae (albertii) (Brazil); tufted plant somewhat similar to lietzei but makes no runners, leaves are larger and more broadly ovate, dark green with light yellowish-green, irregular feathering along the midrib; purple underneath; flowers white out of pale green bract head. *Tropical.* *p. 1534, 1537, 1543*

lucianii (Trop. America); tufting plant to 1 m high, slender stalks; the thin leaves are broad-ovate, oblique, metallic bronzy green, wrinkled on the surface, rusty-red reverse; flowers yellow. *p. 1544*

lutea (Venezuela); robust plant with large, gracefully recurving, thin-leathery, broad oval leaves vivid green and corrugated by its numerous raised lateral veins, gray beneath; the top, swollen section of the long stem, and the midrib underneath is a pretty golden yellow. *p. 1536*

magnifica (Panama); attractive plant with large oblique, elliptic leaves of firm texture, nile green with peacock-feathering of dark green bordered grayish; gray-green beneath. *p. 1535, 1545*

makoyana (Minas Geraes), "Peacock plant"; bushy plant 20-40 cm high stunningly beautiful on both sides of its oval 15-20 cm leaves, the surface with a feathery design of opaque, olive green lines and ovals alternately short and long in a translucent field of pale yellow-green; this pattern of lines and ovals is purplish-red beneath. *p. 15*, 19*, 1534, 1535, 1536A, 1539*

medio-picta (Brazil); bushy plant to 50 cm high, having oblique oblong, recurving, olive green leaves with lightly ribbed surface, and a greenish-white feathered band following the midrib, grayish beneath; short brown stalks. Inflorescence blush-white. *p. 1534, 1535*

metallica (picturata) (Colombia, Amazonas); bushy plant 38 cm high with short stalks and large oblique-elliptic leathery leaves, dark green, irregularly banded silvery white in center as well as lightning-like, white, zigzag bands two-thirds toward margins, usually purple beneath. *p. 1540*

metallica 'Undulata' (Brazil); large plant with oblique-oblong pointed leaves 40 cm x 16 cm, corrugated undulate throughout the blade to the margins, the surface iridescent satiny-silky forest green with paler midrib, royal purple beneath. *Tropical.* *p. 1542*

micans (Brazil, Perú); perhaps the tiniest of Calatheas; narrow, pointed leaves, shining medium-green with a flame-shaped silvery-white center band above, gray-green beneath. *Tropical.* *p. 1537*

musaica (Espirito Santo); a beautiful species which I have found in Brazil; of low habit; the broad arrowshaped leaves are leathery, glossy yellow green with a network of deep-green bars at right angles to the likewise dark green lateral veins; underside green. *Humid-tropical.* *p. 1536, 1536A*

orbiculata (Ischnosiphon) (Brazil); fleshy stalked leaves, almost round, with corrugated, shining surface, pretty when young, pale green with silver-gray lateral bands while midrib is yellow-green; blade turning entirely green with age, large and heavy, to 30 cm long by 25 cm wide. *p. 1537*

ornata (Guyana, Colombia, Ecuador); variable, slender plant, growing from 45 cm to 2½ m tall, with long-stalked, papery leaves often striped with pink or white when juvenile, the adult stage plain metallic coppery-green, pale wine-red underneath. *p. 1541*

ornata 'Roseo-lineata'; long narrow-ovate, unequal-sided, metallic olive-green leaves, 15-20 cm long, later stage to 60 cm, in the juvenile stage nicely marked with closely-set pairs of rosy-red lateral stripes, later turning white in older leaves; purple beneath. *p. 5*, 1534, 1535, 1536A*

ornata 'Sanderiana'; showy form with erect, leathery, rather broader leaves a glossy dark olive green, with boldly contrasting pink or white stripes curving across the blade in groups of two or more; reverse rich purple-red. *Tropical.* *p. 1535*

pavonii (tubispatha) (Perú); tufted plant with oblique-elliptic 15-25 cm leaves covered with weak hairs, bright green marked in peacock pattern with purplish-brown blotches, greenish beneath; petioles with sheathing bases; large yellow flowers with 3 petals, on long stalks. *p. 1544*

picturata 'Argentea' (Venezuela); dwarf plant similar in habit to vandenheckei but with short-stalked leaves almost entirely shining silver except for a border of dark green; wine-red beneath. Cv. 'Wendlinger' may be the same plant. *Tropical.* *p. 1534, 1536A, 1537*

picturata 'Vandenheckei' (Amazonas, Colombia); juvenile form of metallica (picturata); dwarf plant with oblique, glossy leathery leaves, deep olive to blackish green, with feathered silver white band in center and two-thirds toward margin; wine-red beneath. *Tropical.* *p. 1534, 1537*

princeps (Amazonas); large oblong, showy leaves of yellow-green, and a feathery center band of blackish-green, with dark veins running to the dark border, violet-purple beneath; I was surprised to see it grow in a rock-hard floor of the primeval forest north of Manaus in Brazil. According to Kyburz, princeps is the juvenile form of altissima, which grows to 2 m tall and becomes plain green. *Tropical.* *p. 1534, 1536*

sp. 'Putumayo' (Perú); sturdy plant with leathery, oblanceolate 15 cm leaves silver gray with dark green feathering; reverse black-purple; grown by Fantastic Gardens, Miami. *p. 1546*

roseo-picta (Brazil); low plant with short-stalked, large 22 cm rounded, unequal-sided leaves dark olive-green above with red midrib and narrow zone of bright red near margin, changing to silver pink when old; underside purple. *Tropical.* *p. 1536A, 1537*

rotundifolia 'Fasciata' (Bahia); showy variety of low habit, with large thick leathery leaves 22 cm long and almost as wide, on thick brownish stalks; blade glossy green with broad lateral bands of silvery gray, transversed throughout by dark lines; underside gray tinged purple. *Tropical.* *p. 1536A, 1539, 1542, 1546*

rufibarba (Brazil); stout plant to 50 cm high, forming clusters; the pale-spotted petioles covered with purplish-brown hairs, and carrying long oblanceolate, unequal-sided leaves to 20 cm long, on surface glossy olive-green, shading to yellow-green along midrib, the blade corrugated, and purplish-maroon underneath; margins ciliate and underside covered with dense brown hair; spike of yellow flowers with violet bracts. *p. 1538, 1542*

"splendida" hort. (Brazil); a pretty, small clustering species from Espirito Santo with narrow lanceolate leaves glossy yellow-green with lateral, almond-shaped markings of dark green and deep-green margin, purplish beneath, except for green feathering; reddish sheaths over wiry green petioles. *p. 1537*

stromata (Brazil); attractive low bushy plant of stiffish, thin-leathery foliage; leaves broad oblong, 10-12 cm long, with squared-off apex, silver-gray with dark-green herring-bone pattern; reverse deep purple. *p. 1545*

'Tuxtla' (So. Mexico); nice species with glossy, obliquely broad-ovate leaves, medium green with a silvery zone along the midrib, and a second silver zone just inside the margin; gray-green underneath. *p. 1538*

undulata (Perú); tufted small plant 20 cm high, with thin-leathery, oblique-ovate leaves on short petioles with waxy undulate ridges following lateral veins to margins; metallic dark green with bluish sheen when young, and a jagged band of greenish silver along midrib, purple beneath over green; flowers white with green bracts margined and dotted white. *Tropical.* *p. 1534, 1540*

vandenheckei: see picturata

varians (vestita) (Guyana); tufting plant with stiff erect, long stalks spotted red-brown and green covered with hairs, leaves linear-lanceolate to 40 cm long, green above, red beneath and glabrous; hairy brown bracts. *p. 1544*

veitchiana (Ecuador, Perú), "Peacock plant"; strikingly beautiful plant from the Jivaro country; with large, stiff-leathery, glossy leaves to 30 cm long, obliquely broad-ovate, in four different shades of green with a peacock-feather design outlined in yellow green, encircling brownish-green halfmoons which adjoin the pale bluish green feathered center zone; marginal area bright green; the peacock-feather design outlined in red over bluish green underneath also. *Humid-tropical.* *p. 1535, 1536A*

vittata (Colombia); bushy plant with short-stalked, lanceolate leaves light grass green, and symmetrical stripes of silver-green to white between the lateral veins; yellowish-green beneath. *p. 1536, 1540*

warscewiczii (Costa Rica); heavy plant to 75 cm high, with short-stalked, oblong leaves undulate at margins, velvety deep green except for yellow-green midrib feathering into pale green lateral veins; underside wine-red. Inflorescence a short spike with tubular, leathery white bracts, white flowers. *Tropical.* *p. 1535, 1543*

wiotii (Phrynium brachystachyum) (Brazil); dwarf plant with thin-leathery short-ovate leaves 10 cm long, glossy light green with elevated oval blotches of dark green on either side of midrib; reverse mostly gray-green tinted purple. *Tropical.* *p. 1536*

zebrina (Rio, São Paulo), "Zebra plant"; bold, vigorous plant to 1 m high, with magnificent, thin leaves deep velvety green, the midrib and lateral veins pale or yellow-green, purplish beneath. *Tropical.* *p. 19*, 1535, 1536A*

zebrina 'Binotii' (Brazil); large form having long 1 m leaves, fresh velvety green with pale midrib and short lateral dual bands of dark brownish-green half way to margin only; grayish green beneath. *Tropical.* *p. 1534, 1542*

zebrina humilior (tigrina, pulchella) (Bahia, Goyaz); compact plant having much smaller, fresh-green, velvety leaves, with broad lateral bands of blackish-green toward margins; light grayish-green reverse showing veins of olive-green. *p. 1535, 1542*

CALATHEA: see also Maranta, Ctenanthe, Stromanthe

CALCEOLARIA *Scrophulariaceae* **C2HND**

amplexicaulis (Perú); herbaceous plant with shrubby base to 75 cm high, hairy stems with ovate, wrinkled green, toothed leaves 8 cm long; small 2 cm pouched flowers clear yellow, in terminal clusters. *p. 2050*

herbeohybrida 'Grandiflora', "Pocketbook plant"; herbaceous cultivar derived principally from C. crenatiflora which grows in the cool Andes of Chile and north, developed for use as potplants, with thin, fresh-green leaves, and clusters of showy, membranous flowers, 5-8 cm across, distinguished by a large inflated lower lip resembling a handbag, 6 cm or more across, in shades of yellow or red, often brilliantly spotted or tigered orange-red to maroon, blooming in spring. *Humid-subtropic.* *p. 2051*

herbeohybrida 'Hunt's Choicest'; a select 'Grandiflora' strain with pouched flowers very large and of brilliantly tigered colors. *p. 2051*

herbeohybrida 'Multiflora nana'; a herbaceous crenatiflora form of dwarf, bushy habit, ideal as a potplant, with thin ovate, toothed and quilted leaves, and clusters of numerous, smallish pouch-like flowers, 3 to 5 cm across, most often yellow or orange or red, usually spotted or tigered with crimson. *Humid-subtropic.* *p. 2051*

integrifolia (rugosa) (Chile), "Chilean pouch flower"; shrubby perennial of bushy habit, with woody, hairy stems, small, wrinkled, toothed leaves, and clusters with masses of small 1 cm pouch-flowers, yellow to red-brown. *Humid-subtropic.* *p. 2051*

integrifolia 'Red Slippers' ('Pauline'); a new German strain of this small-flowered bedding plant, with masses of flowers 2 cm dia. in vivid red. *p. 2050*

mexicana (Mexico, C. America); small, bushy herbaceous plant to 30 cm high, sticky-hairy, with slender reddish stems; deeply lobed and sliced and toothed leaves 8 cm long; small 1 cm pale yellow pouch flowers clustered at apex; summer-blooming. *p. 2050*

scabiosaefolia (Ecuador to Chile); pubescent herbaceous bushy plant to 60 cm high, with pinnate green leaves to 20 cm long, the leaflets toothed or incised; small yellow flowers 1 cm across. *p. 2050*

teucrioides (South America); shrubby plant with opposite sessile, pubescent leaves narrow ovate, and with undulate, crenate margins; at the apex a branched inflorescence of pale yellow flowers with small petals and elongate, narrow pouch, in loose clusters. *p. 2050*

CALENDULA *Compositae* **C2LBM**

officinalis 'Apricot Queen'; a highly developed type of "Pot marigold"; originating in So. Europe, annual with brittle fleshy leaves and large golden to orange double flowers. *p. 803*

officinalis 'Ball Gold'; showy annual herbaceous plant with bright green, brittle, slightly sticky leaves; large double 10 cm flowers deep golden yellow with lighter eye; blooming winter to spring in mild climate, spring to mid summer in colder areas; effective in borders, but also for containers. *p. 804*

CALIANASSA: see Isoplexis

CALLA *Araceae* **C2LBWh**

palustris (Atlantic No. America, No. Europe, Lapland, Siberia), the "Water-arum", or "Wild calla"; bog-aquatic with creeping or floating stems or rhizomes with heart-shaped 15 cm leaves; the inflorescence with 5 cm spathe green outside, white inside and thread-like stamens; forming clusters of red berries. *Temperate.* *p. 162*

CALLA: see also ZANTEDESCHIA

CALLIANDRA *Leguminosae* **I-S2LBM**

emarginata ('Minima' in hort.) (Mexico, Guatemala), "Miniature powder-puff"; small shrub with leaves compound of several uneven leaflets; small inflorescence a globular head of red stamens. *p. 1374*

eriophylla (Texas to Arizona); low woody shrub to 50 cm; bipinnate small leaflets hairy beneath; pubescent purple flowers with long conspicuous stamens; flat pods. *p. 1375*

haematocephala (Inga pulcherrima) (So. Brazil), "Pink powder puff"; rambling shrub with branched pinnate, silky leaves and powder-puff-like balls of conspicuous dark crimson stamens. *Subtropic.* *p. 1374*

harrisii 'Minima' in hort. (Mexico), "Powder puff"; woody shrub with scandent willowy branches; more compact than inaequilatera; leathery leaves; inflorescence 5 cm dia. brush-like heads of crimson-red stamens, white at base. *p. 1375*

"inaequilatera" in hort. (bot. prob. haematocephala) (Ecuador, Bolivia), "Red powder puff"; foliage pinnate; globose inflorescence larger and more dense than tweedii, with showy, long silky bright red stamens. *Subtropic.* *p. 1374*

'Minima' hort.:see emarginata

portoricensis (caracasana) (Central America); shrub to 2½ m, shoots grooved, downy; leaves bipinnate; flowers white in globose heads, the long stamens spreading like a powder puff 5 cm dia. *Tropical.* *p. 1375*

surinamensis (Surinam); low, spreading shrub or woody climber resembling an inverted umbrella, with pinnate leaves always in forked pairs, smothered with pretty, pink brush-like flower heads composed of numerous long, thread-like, silky stamens reddish in the upper part and white below. *Tropical.* *p. 1374*

tweedii (Inga pulcherrima) (S. Brazil), "Mexican flame-bush"; shrub with bipinnate leaves, the numerous leaflets almost linear, 4-6 cm long, silky when young; the long stamens red-purple; somewhat cold-resistant. *Subtropic.* *p. 1374*

CALLICARPA *Verbenaceae* **I2LBD**

rubella (China, Burma, Assam), "Beauty-berry"; deciduous shrub of loose habit, with obovate-cordate leaves lightly toothed 10-15 cm long; numerous tiny 4-lobed pink flowers, tubular at base, in clusters, followed by profusion of lavender berries. *p. 2116*

CALLIOPSIS: see Coreopsis

CALLISIA *Commelinaceae* ***I2LFM**

elegans (Setcreasea striata) (Oaxaca), "Striped inch plant"; vigorous little creeper hugging the ground, with succulent triangular, clasping leaves olive green and lined with white stripes, deep purple beneath, and arranged like shingles; flowers white. (F) *p. 779, 780*

fragrans (Spironema, or Trad. dracaenoides) (Oaxaca); fleshy rosette sending out long runners with young plants, fresh glossy-green lanceolate clasping leaves turning reddish-purple in strong light, margins smooth and pale green; fragrant white flowers. (S) *p. 780, 787*

fragrans 'Melnikoff'; fleshy creeper with closely grouped clasping ovate leaves fresh green, striped lengthwise with yellowish bands. (I) *p. 5*, 780*

CALLISTEMON *Myrtaceae* **I2LBD**

acuminata (Australia); shrub with narrow lanceolate leaves and small axillary, scattered, brush-like inflorescence showing prominently the red stamens, with yellow anthers. *p. 1612*

brachyandrus (South Australia, Victoria, New South Wales), the "Prickly bottle-brush"; tall shrub of stiff habit, with needle-like leaves spiny-pointed, the brush-like spikes with short 1 cm stamens deep-red, dusted as if with gold from the yellow anthers. *p. 1612*

coccineus (So. Australia); small woody, glabrous shrub with shoots silky while young, shorter 5 cm leaves narrow lanceolate and stiff, and dense, bottle-brush flowers of scarlet-red tipped by yellow anthers. *p. 1609*

lanceolatus (Metrosideros floribunda) (New South Wales), "Bottle-brush"; tree-like shrub of sparry, bare habit, with hard heavy wood, sun-loving and drought resistant; the silky twigs with rigid, long-linear 8 cm leaves and cylindrical flower spikes with masses of brilliant crimson brush-like stamens with dark yellow anthers, out of a grayish, felted calyx. *p. 1609*

macropunctatus (supposedly C. rigidus x lanceolatus); sparry shrub with rigid, narrow-lanceolate leaves, and a showy, bottle-brush-like inflorescence spike of red stamens with yellow anthers. *p. 1612*

montanus (Western Australia); woody shrub of sparry habit; short, dark green, sharp-pointed sessile leaves; the showy inflorescence axillary. a dense bottle brush of carmine-red filaments; photographed near Perth, W.A. *Subtropic.* *p. 1611*

paludosus (Western Australia); xerophytic shrub 2 to 3 m high, with smooth, thickish, narrow-linear leaves, and cylindric inflorescence of brush like bundles of creamy yellow to pale pink stamens 6 cm long. *p. 1611*

phoeniceus (W. Australia), "Fiery bottle-brush"; bushy shrub to 2½ m; grayish, thick and smooth, narrow oblanceolate leaves to 10 cm long; inflorescence in rich scarlet bottle brushes with stamen bundles tipped dark red. *Subtropic.* *p. 1611*

rugulosus (probably C. coccineus) (So. Australia, Victoria, N. S. Wales); known in Australia as the "Pink bottle-brush"; shrub to 5 m high, with rigid, rather narrow, sharp-pointed leaves 4-5 cm long, and cylindric brush-like spike dense with showy red stamens tipped by golden anthers; giving the inflorescence a pinkish appearance. *p. 1612*

salignus viridiflorus (Tasmania); tall shrub with willowy linear-lanceolate leaves 5-8 cm long, thin but firm; the inflorescence spike not very dense, with greenish-yellow stamens; yellow in the type species. *p. 1612*

CALLISTEPHUS *Compositae* **C2LBM**

chinensis 'Ball's Purple Aster'; excellent annual "Florists aster" bred for growing under glass, wilt-resistant, large 9- 10 cm extra double incurved flowers bright purple on stiff stems; this strain also comes in shades of pink, blue and white. *p. 805*

chinensis 'Crego Aster'; a form of annual "China aster" which has ostrich-feathered shaggy flowers, from violet through rose to white, early blooming and bushy. *p. 805*

chinensis 'Dwarf Queen Aster'; a very dwarf "Aster" suitable for pot culture, with fully double flowers 5-8 cm dia. in various colors pink, rose, red, to blue. *p. 805*

CALLOPSIS *Araceae* **S3HFM**

hallaei: referred to Nephthytis hallaei

volkensii (Tanzania), "Miniature calla"; short-branching little plant with underground rhizome, resembling a calla-lily, but only 10 cm high, from Mt. Msasa near the Sigi river; cute, cupped spathe waxy-white, with an attractive yellow spadix; quilted, leathery, heart-shaped leaves; winter flowering. *Tropical.* *p. 208*

CALLUNA *Ericaceae* **C2HBMh**

vulgaris hypnoides (No. Europe), "Heather"; evergreen bushy shrub differing from Erica in having a colored calyx longer than the corolla, in this species both purplish, in late summer. The variety hypnoides has deep pink flowers, grows 30 cm high. *p. 963*

vulgaris 'Mrs. H. E. Beale'; a double-flowering Scotch heather, vigorous upright branches to 75 cm high, with long arching sprays of comparatively large fully double, pale rose-colored flowers July to October. *p. 962*

vulgaris 'Mrs. R. H. Gray'; very low-growing, horizontally spreading heather only 8 cm high, this interesting variety forms a thick carpet of matted growth deep emerald green, with spikes of lavender-pink flowers arching over it in late summer. *p. 962*

CALOCEPHALUS *Compositae* **I2LBD**

brownii (Australia), the "Cushion-bush"; rigid, white-woolly dwarf shrub about 30 cm high, with tiny alternate, linear silvery-gray leaves, and round terminal clusters of yellow composite tubular flowers. *p. 820*

CALOCHORTUS *Liliaceae* **C2LFMd**

amabilis (Northern California), "Golden fairy-lantern"; charming bulbous perennial plant; stout, branched, leafy stems to 50 cm tall, carrying linear-lanceolate leaves; pretty, nodding flowers triangular in outline, 3 cm long, the deep, clear yellow globular petals bearded and ciliate. *p. 1428*

uniflorus (California), "Star-tulip" or "Mariposa lily"; cormous herb to 25 cm, with linear lanceolate leaves borne on the stem, and bulblets at its base; 3 cm flowers lilac. *p. 1427*

CALODENDRUM *Rutaceae* **I2LBD**

capense (So. Africa to Zimbabwe), "Cape chestnut"; tall, semi-evergreen tree to 18 m, with oval 15 cm, ruffled leaves, and very conspicuous when it bears its large clusters of dainty pinky-mauve flowers; the five slender and recurving petals marked with crimson, measuring 8-10 cm across; of 10 pale pink stamens, five resemble thin petals and are spotted with red; the brown fruits are knobby and split to release the seed. *Subtropic.* *p. 2025*

CALONYCTION *Convolvulaceae* **S2LFMd**

aculeatum (American and other Tropics), the legendary tropical "Moonflower"; perennial twiner related to morning-glories (Ipomoea), but blooming at night instead of in sunshine; stems more or less prickly, with milky juice, climbing to 5 m high; cordate, smooth leaves 15 cm long, and large salver-shaped flowers 12-15 cm wide, pure white, and fragrant, opening toward evening and closing in the morning. *Tropical.* *p. 854*

CALOPHYLLUM *Guttiferae* **S3LBD**

inophyllum (native on shores of the Indian and Western Pacific Oceans), the "Beauty leaf", "Kamani" or "Alexandrian laurel"; handsome, low-branching crooked or leaning tree such as the one I photographed on Moorea in French Polynesia; to 20 m high, with rough gray bark, and shiny green, leathery, oblong leaves 8-20 cm long and with yellow midrib; the white flowers suggest orange blossoms and are very fragrant; the 3 cm green fruit in pendulous clusters; thin leathery skin covers a bony shell, containing an oily kernel yielding "dilo oil", used medicinally and for lights. *Tropical.* *p. 1319*

CALOTHAMNUS *Myrtaceae* **C2LBD**

chrysantheros (W. Australia), "Claw flower"; dense shrub to $1\frac{1}{2}$ m, with thick brown stems often corky; long pencil-like thin dark green leaves 5-10 cm long; the inflorescence an axillary group of stout crimson stamen bundles feathering at apex into slender filaments; seen at King's Park, Perth. *Subtropic.* *p. 1611*

gilesii (Western Australia); interesting evergreen, photographed at King's Park Botanical Garden, Perth; stout stem bearing rosette of long-lanceolate, hairy leaves 45 cm long, with depressed veins; the inflorescence 3 m tall, with bright red claw-like flowers on the older stems. *p. 1611*

homalophyllus (Western Australia), "Claw-flower"; lovely spreading shrub 1-2 m, with flat, leathery, grayish 5 cm leaves, loosely arranged; the inflorescence one-sided, the stout staminal bundles or united stamens rich crimson, dividing brush-like at apex; photographed at Perth. *p. 1611*

villosus (W. Australia); bushy shrub to 2 m; the woody stems dense with grayish woolly needle leaves crowded into terminal clusters; axillary inflorescence of numerous red stamen bundles, the floral petals inconspicuous. *p. 1611*

CALOTROPIS *Asclepiadaceae* **S2LBD**

gigantea (Iran, Tibet, India, China), the "Crown plant"; lush shrub with white glaucous stem containing milky juice; large obovate leaves 15-20 cm long covered with white down, and with pale veins; axillary inflorescence clusters of star-like flowers lavender to purple, with a crown of 5 narrow, fleshy scales. Sacred to Hanuman, the Monkey-god, in India. *p. 372, 373*

procera (India, Syria, No. Africa to Morocco), "Felt plant"; handsome hairy shrub to 5 m high, with large opposite, almost sessile leaves 15 cm or more long, white-woolly and with prominent pale ribs; the fragrant crown-like flowers white to lavender with purple spot at base, in clusters. Fiber from the stems is used for rope or fishing lines. The milky juice is poisonous and may irritate the skin. *Arid-tropical.* *p. 353*

CALYSTEGIA *Convolvulaceae* **C2LBM**

sylvestris rosea (silvatica) (Hungary to No. Africa); vigorous twiner with smooth, wiry, angled stems, and sagittate leaves, sinuate at margins, on long petioles; flowers wide-funnel-shaped soft rose-pink; distinct from Convolvulus by the large bracts below the calyx. *p. 853*

CAMAROTIS *Orchidaceae* **S3OFM**

purpurea (rostrata) (India); vandaceous type epiphyte, with alternate leaves in two ranks along scandent stem; axillary racemes of pale rose-colored $2\frac{1}{2}$ cm flowers, thick-fleshy lip deep rosy-crimson hollowed out near tip; March-May. *p. 1663*

CAMASSIA *Liliaceae* **I2LBM**

esculenta (Pennsylvania to Georgia and Texas); bulbous herb with linear basal leaves, and floral stalks to 60 cm high, bearing starry flowers in shades from light to deep blue. *Warm temperate.* *p. 1424*

leichtlinii (Brit. Columbia to California); bulbous herb with linear basal leaves and tall stalks 60 cm high with terminal bracted racemes of dark blue to creamy flowers $2\frac{1}{2}$ cm long, with spreading segments. *p. 1428*

CAMELLIA *Theaceae* **C2HFM**

japonica (Mountains of Japan and Korea), the "Common camellia"; a fine ornamental evergreen tree to 12 m high, well-shaped with woody branches and dark green, glossy, leathery, ovate leaves to 10 cm long, finely toothed; axillary flowers 4 to 12 cm across, variably single to double, white, pink, red, or variegated and listed under various cultivar names. *Subtropic.* *p. 2097, 2101*

japonica 'Alba plena'; fine cultivar; evergreen tree to 10 m high, with rather erect, woody branches; handsome, alternate, leathery, ovate, slender-pointed leaves deep shining green, with finely toothed margins; large round, sessile flowers of the formal type, 9 cm across;snow-white, double, early blooming and long lasting, Oct.-Jan. *Subtropic.* *p. 2096*

japonica 'Colonel Firey' (C.M. Hovey); compact grower with twisted, narrow, dark green leaves, and perfectly formal, very double, large flowers of brilliant crimson, blooming midseason to late. *Subtropic.* *p. 2096*

japonica 'Daikagura'; an early variety from California, slow-growing, of open, willowy habit, but blooming freely when quite young; dark green foliage, and large, peony-type flowers rosy-red splashed with white, October through December blooming. *Sub-tropic.* *p. 2096*

japonica 'Debutante' (Sara Hastie); originating in South Carolina; this is a shapely, fast-growing beauty, ideal pot plant; early and free-flowering, with exquisite, full peony-form, firm, small 4-6 cm flowers of clear rose-pink, from October to January and later. *Subtropic.* *p. 1824A, 2096, 2097*

japonica 'Elegans' (chandleri); an old variety; wide-spreading tree with long, glossy foliage and very large flowers of the peony type, 10 cm across,variegated cherry-red with white, borne in profusion in late January. *Subtropic.* *p. 2096, 2097*

japonica 'Jordan's Pride' (Herma); free-blooming, dependable variety with large formal semi-double 8 to 10 cm flowers of soft shell pink, irregularly streaked deep pink and bordered white, occasionally altogether pink (midseason to late; January to March). *Subtropic.* *p. 2097*

japonica 'Pearl Maxwell'; large formal, double flowers soft shell pink; looks like a glorified 'Pink Perfection' (midseason to late). *Subtropic.* *p. 2095*

japonica 'Pink Perfection'; popular variety of symmetrical, vigorous growth; small, well-formed double, rather flat flowers of delicate shell-pink, free flowering from November-April. Earlier name: 'Frau Minna Seidel.' *Subtropic.* *p. 2096*

japonica 'Prince Eugene Napoleon' (Pope Pius IX); vigorous grower and good bloomer, with large, high-centered, double flowers of glowing deep red, in profusion from January through March; good pot plant. *p. 2096*

japonica 'Princesse Baciocchi'; a late-flowering, tall-growing beauty from Savannah, with full double flowers of the rose type, dark red marbled with white; blooms freely from February into May. *Subtropic.* *p. 2096*

japonica 'Purity'; well-known variety of slender habit, free-blooming while quite young, with glossy, pointed leaves, and exquisite white, double flowers of the formal type, of porcelain texture and long lasting, Nov.-April. *Subtropic.* *p. 2096*

japonica 'Rosedale Beauty'; outstanding trademarked hybrid, profusely blooming with big double, formal flowers crimson-red about 10 cm across; of vigorous growth and compact habit with broad, dark green leaves (midseason). *p. 2095*

japonica 'William S. Hastie'; outstanding variety of slender habit with long pointed, dull green foliage, and freely bearing large, perfect, rose-form flowers of brilliant crimson, from February-April. *Subtropic.* *p. 2096*

oleifera (China); freely flowering shrub to 6 m high, with young branches brown-hirsute; leathery leaves elliptic to obovate, minutely toothed, 5-8 cm long; single flowers white, drooping quickly; larger, thicker leaves than sasanqua, also larger fruits. Cultivated in China for the "tea-oil". *p. 2101*

reticulata (China); "Temple flower"; sparry shrub to 6 m high, with scattered rigid foliage having prominent veins; large single flowers 8 to 15 cm and more across, vivid rosy-red, with wavy petals, blooming in February. *Warm temperate.* *p. 2095, 2096*

sasanqua (China, Japan), "Sunlight camellia"; evergreen shrub of loose habit and with branches pubescent when young; small, thin-leathery leaves elliptic and toothed, shining dark green and hairy on the midrib above; very floriferous with small, 4-5 cm single, slightly fragrant blossoms white in the type, with 5 or more petals and with yellow stamens, but running into many forms semi-double, white, pink to cherry-red; more hardy than japonica, but the flowers shed easily; Oct.-April. Winter-hardy in So. N.J. (Zone 7). *Warm temperate.* *p. 2101*

sasanqua 'Shishi-Gashira'; vigorous Japanese cultivar with spreading branches with dark foliage and semi-double bright carmine-rose flowers 6 cm across; ideal in hanging baskets; free-blooming. *p. 2095*

sasanqua 'Showa-No-Sakae'; charming Japanese form of compact habit with small 6 cm dark green leathery leaves on willowy branches; semi-double to peony form. *p. 2095*

sasanqua 'White Doves'; vigorous, spreading grower and free bloomer; relatively large semi-double to loose peony-form flowers pure white, indented at margins; like most sasanquas, buds and flowers drop easily but are replaced by others; effective trained on espaliers. *p. 2095*

sasanqua 'Yuletide'; striking flowering plant for the winter season; erect bushy plant with dark green small foliage finely crenate; brilliant fiery red to maroon single blooms shaped like cups, in the center a nest of bright yellow stamens in charming contrast; flowering from autumn on into the Christmas season. *Warm temperate.* *p. 2095*

sinensis (China, India), "Tea plant"; evergreen, tree-like shrub to 10 m high, with alternate, waxy, thin-leathery, elliptic leaves finely serrate, and small, white, fragrant flowers; makes a handsome plant for tubs; where I have seen tea cultivated in Sikkim, Sri Lanka, Java, or Japan, the bushes are kept low for women to pick each tender tip every 3 weeks, and gentle heating, rolling and fermenting produces the aromatic black tea of commerce; fruit a woody capsule. *p. 2096, 2101*

CAMOENSIA *Leguminosae* **S3LBD**

maxima (Angola); shrubby climber; shiny leaflets obovate pointed; flowers pale cream, edges of petals frilled; standard projecting about 10 cm. *Tropical.* *p. 1375*

CAMPANULA *Campanulaceae* **I-C2LBM**

aucheri (Armenia, Caucasus, Iran); small hardy perennial forming clump, 10-12 cm tall, with spatulate pubescent leaves 5-8 cm long; large erect violet bell-flowers. *p. 748*

elatines 'Alba plena', the "Double white star of Bethlehem"; a pretty hanging basket plant with glossy green leaves and double white flowers blooming in summer; a selected clone of the C. elatines complex which is native in S. E. Europe and the Adriatic region. *p. 749*

elatines florepleno (hyemalis); hanging basket plant with small, toothed leaves and pretty, full-double, rather flat flowers lavender-blue; summer blooming. *p. 749*

fragilis (Italy); small vine-like trailer with little spoonshaped, crenate leaves glossy green; large star-like flowers not as flat as isophylla, petals grooved, purplish blue with white center. *p. 748*

isophylla 'Alba' (Italy), "Star of Bethlehem"; dainty trailer for hanging basket; small green ovate toothed leaves on thin stems, and white star-like, saucer-shaped flowers. *Subtropic.* *p. 749*

isophylla mayii, "Italian bellflower"; variety with larger, heavier, white-hairy leaves, and pale blue flowers larger than isophylla. *Subtropic.* *p. 749*

isophylla 'Variegata'; leaves not hairy as in type, and the normally green foliage attractively variegated with white. *p. 748*

lanata (S. E. Europe: Thrace); hairy biennial 60-80 cm high, with thick rhizome producing numerous stems with silky-hairy leaves, lower ones cordate, 5 cm long, the upper ones ovate and smaller; large bellflowers yellow or peach pink according to Hortus and Sanders, but apparently variable as it is reported by Royal Hort. Dict. as having blue flowers. *p. 750*

malacitana (S. E. Spain: Andalucia); pendant, wiry branches with small ovate, crenate leaves, and starry flowers light blue with pale throat. *p. 750*

medium (So. Europe, France), "Canterbury bells"; hairy biennial with tall branched stem bearing numerous large bell-shaped flowers violet-blue. *Warm temperate.* *p. 748*

medium 'Dean hybrid'; a hardy perennial with showy bell-shaped flowers of exceptional size, some measuring to nearly 12 cm, in shades from pale lavender to dark blue, and pink to carmine-rose. *Warm temperate.* *p. 748*

medium florepleno; the double-flowered form with 2 to 4 bellshaped corollas telescoped within one-another, in colors blue, pink, or white. *p. 748*

mirabilis (Caucasus); hardy biennial with fleshy rootstock, 40 cm high, with ovate, leathery leaves coarsely toothed; erect bellflowers pale lilac 5 cm across, in pyramidal clusters; late summer. *p. 748*

punctata (Siberia, Japan); hardy perennial 45 cm high, with underground running root-stock, ovate toothed leaves to 12 cm long; nodding bell flowers creamy pink, dotted purple inside, 6 cm long; summer. *p. 748*

pyramidalis (So. Europe), "Chimney bell-flower"; erect biennial 1 m high, with lower leaves ovate and stalked, upper lanceolate and sessile; flowers in dense pyramidal panicle, broadly saucershaped, pale blue with dark base 2½ cm long. *p. 748*

saxifraga (Caucasus); tufted hardy perennial 8-10 cm high, with linear or oblanceolate leaves, the stem-leaves linear, topped by numerous violet-blue bell flowers 2 cm long. *p. 752*

vidalii (Azores); perennial subshrub 30-60 cm high with spatulate toothed, thick-fleshy, clammy leaves; nodding white flowers with yellow base, wax-like, urn to bell-shaped, 5 cm long, in arching racemes. *p. 750*

CAMPELIA *Commelinaceae* **S3LFM**

zanonia 'Mexican Flag' (long known as Dichorisandra albo-lineata), a striking cultivar of the green species (Mexico to Brazil); attractive and vigorous foliage plant, with erect, thick-fleshy stalk to 90 cm high, and large thin-fleshy, lance-shaped, light green leaves 20-30 cm long in a rosette, striped white lengthwise in center and broad, cream-white marginal bands edged red; flowers purple and white, in cluster, from leaf axils. *Tropical.* *p. 5*, 19*, 779*

CAMPSIS *Bignoniaceae* **I2LBD**

grandiflora (chinensis) (China, Japan), "Chinese trumpet-creeper"; climbing by aerial rootlets; related to Bignonia but without tendrils and with opposite leaves, pinnate, deciduous; the 7-9 ovate leaflets toothed; terminal clusters of large funnel-shaped orange and scarlet flowers 8 cm across. *Subtropic.* *p. 500, 501*

radicans (Pennsylvania to Florida and Texas), "Trumpet-vine"; high climber to 12 m, by means of aerial roots; pinnate leaves with 9-11 oval leaflets partially pubescent; trumpet-shaped flowers in terminal clusters, orange with scarlet limb, 5 cm across. *Warm temperate.* *p. 504*

CAMPTANDRA *Zingiberaceae* **S3LFM**

parvula (Borneo: Sarawak); low, bushy tropical plant with rhizomatous roots; the sheathing thick, short petioles bearing broad-ovate, unequal-sided fleshy leaves 7 to 10 cm or more long, the surface glossy light green; small waxy tubular flowers yellowish ivory. *p. 2142*

CAMPYLOCENTRUM *Orchidaceae* **S3OFM**

micranthum (Surinam, Brazil); epiphytic species with flexuous leafy stems that root into the bark of trees; alternate leaves 5 cm long, the tiny flowers borne profusely in short one-sided spikes from leaf axils; spikes 3-4 cm long; flowers in two up-turned rows; the tube olive green, petals white. *p. 1677*

CAMPYLONEURON: see Polypodium

CANANGA *Annonaceae* **S3LBD**

odorata (Burma to Malaya and Australia), "Ylang-ylang" or "Perfume tree"; charming tropical tree with crooked trunk, to 25 m tall, and pendant brittle branches; oblong pointed, soft-leathery foliage 12-20 cm long; large axillary clusters of peculiar greenish-yellow flowers with long lanceolate drooping, twisted petals of soft-leathery texture 5-10 cm long, and intensely fragrant, strongest in early morning. The flowers are worn for their perfume or used in leis as in Tonga; and distilled for their fragrant essential oil in perfume. *Tropical.* *p. 132*

CANARINA *Campanulaceae* **I3LFWd**

campanulata (Canary Islands), "Canary bellflower"; beautiful herbaceous perennial arising from a tuber, the branches with ovate, glaucous leaves irregularly toothed; open bell-shaped flowers 5 cm long, yellowish purple or orange with red lines. *Subtropic.* *p. 750*

CANAVALLIA *Leguminosae* **S3LFM**

ensiformis (Tropics), "Jack-bean" or "Chickasaw Lima-bean"; bush or climber; leaflets ovate, 12-20 cm long, strongly veined, dull green; flower small, light purple, keel curved; long pendant green beans; ripe seeds used as substitute for coffee. *Tropical.* *p. 1375*

CANISTRUM *Bromeliaceae* **S1HFM**

fosterianum (Brazil: Bahia); tubular rosette partially covered with scurfy scales, and heavily mottled with chocolate brown, margins with tiny spines; long slender stalk with clustered inflorescence of red bracts and white flower petals. *Tropical.* *p. 552*

lindenii exiguum variegatum ('Francois Spae striata'); stiff upright variegated sport with rich green leaves dark mottled and broad ivory-white stripes and bands through center of leaves, spines more sparse than innocentii. *p. 566*

lindenii roseum (So. Brazil), "Wine star"; stocky, open rosette with broad leaves waxy yellow-green on both sides, and with darker mottling, the underside with rosy wine-red bands and lines, soft scattered teeth at margins; the erect-stalked inflorescence in a dense head like a basket with rose red bracts and white and green flowers. *p. 512, 549*

x CANMEA *Bromeliaceae* **S3LBD**

species, a bigeneric Canistrum x Aechmea hybrid by Mulford Foster; attractive, bold tubular plant with leathery leaves 50 cm long and 6-8 cm wide, grayish-green overlaid with silvery scales, purple in younger foliage; black-purple edge and spines; inflorescence with showy, broad orange-red, leathery bracts. *p. 574*

CANNA *Cannaceae* **S2LBM**

coccinea (W. Indies to S. America), "Scarlet Indian shot"; growing from tuberous rhizome, slender stalks with large oblong pointed leaves, and raceme with small green bracts, the flowers with sepals green, petals scarlet, lip spotted yellow. *p. 753*

generalis 'Cleopatra'; a fancy cultivar from Texas, with flower heads 20 to 25 cm across, huge yellow petals with contrasting red spots and others solid red; foliage green with purple streaks and also leaves solid purple on same floral stalk. *Tropical.* *p. 752*

generalis 'Grumpy'; a miniature canna of the "Seven dwarf" series; compact plant to only 50 cm high, with luminous flowers a brilliant rosy red, blooming constantly all summer; suitable for pot culture (Park Seed Co.). *p. 753*

generalis 'King Humbert', "Bronze garden canna"; striking perennial tropical herb with thick branching rootstocks and large bronze-red leaves, with a showy truss of large orange-red flowers; to 1 m high. *Tropical.* *p. 752*

generalis 'Lucifer'; spectacular cultivar of dwarf habit to 60 cm high, with glossy deep green foliage; from the center a stout stalk bearing a cluster of numerous bicolored flowers Chinese-red, with bright yellow along margins; ideal for growing in planters (Park Seed, S.C.). *Tropical.* *p. 752*

generalis 'President', an old "French canna"; variety with large green leaves and a terminal cluster of large and showy scarlet flowers; to 1 m high. *Tropical* *p. 752*

generalis 'Scarlet Beauty' (Dwarf Pfitzer strain); hybrid of low bushy habit originated by Wilhelm Pfitzer, Stuttgart, Germany, only 60 to 80 cm high; from tuberous rhizomes rise bold stalks with glossy green leaves, and profuse clusters of huge, scarlet-red flowers, often edged with a fine border of golden yellow. *Tropical.* *p. 752*

indica (Trop. America), "Indian shot"; tall perennial herb to 1 m, with thick rootstock and green stem, lanceolate leaves 20-60 cm long, and bright red flowers, the lip orange spotted with red. *p. 753*

iridiflora (Perú) (photo possibly humilis); to 3 m tall; lanceolate leaves ½-1 m long, woolly beneath at first; flowers rose, in racemes, the nodding corolla 6-12 cm long. *Tropical.* *p. 753*

limbata (Brazil); pretty species to 1 m high, with lanceolate, pointed leaves glossy grass green, 30 cm long, on slender canes; flowers in branched inflorescence, green sepals and lanceolate petals red with throat and base yellow. *Tropical.* *p. 753*

orchiodes, "Orchid-flowered canna", of hybrid origin; foliage green or bronzy, topped by large flowers 15 cm across, tubular at base, yellow to red, striped and splashed, the petals reflexed. *p. 753*

palustris (Tropics) swamp-loving tuberous plant with lanceolate green leaves, and slender yellowish flowers. *p. 753*

'Striped Beauty'; striking beauty of stocky habit found in Thailand, probably a mutation in the C. generalis group, with beautiful foliage brilliant green, having the broad midrib and lateral veins in contrasting yellow to ivory-white; topped by a large truss of deep scarlet flowers. *p. 752*

CANNABIS *Moraceae* **I2LBD**

sativa (India), "Hemp-plant", "Marijuana" or "Hashish"; handsome annual herb to 3 m tall; large long-stalked digitate leaves of 5-7 leaflets, coarsely toothed and grayish-green; flowers small, dioecious, the males with 5 sepals and 5 drooping stamens, in axillary panicles, the females in spikes. Cultivated in India for the fiber (hemp) used in rope-making. The resin which exudes from the dried leaves when smoked, has a powerful narcotic effect, especially from the flowering tops of the female plants which are rich in the drug marijuana. Cultivation in the U.S. is controlled by the Federal Marijuana Tax Act of 1937 and must be registered with the Federal Bureau of Narcotics. *p. 1562*

CANTHIUM *Rubiaceae* **S3LBD**

huillense (So. Africa), "Wild coffee"; woody evergreen shrub or small tree, with leathery oval and ovate, concave leaves; white flowers in clusters along the sparry branches on short spurs or near leaf junctures, followed by green to black berries. *p. 2008*

CANTUA *Polemoniaceae* **C2LBM**

buxifolia (Perú, Bolivia, N. Chile), "Sacred flower of the Incas"; beautiful flowering, dense bush which I saw growing 2½ m high in Puna climate at 4,000 m in the Cordilleras of Bolivia; the woody shrubs with small leaves; colorful, pendant, 8 cm tubular flowers, pale green calyx, yellow tube striped red, the lobes inside rosy-red, outside crimson. *Subtropic.* *p. 1951, 1952*

quercifolia, (Perú: Andes); small tree with woody branches, densely set with gray-green 8 cm leaves, covered with thin white hairs, the margins sharply lobed like a saw; terminal clusters of cupped white flowers with long-protruding stamens. *p. 1952*

CAPPARIS *Capparidaceae* **S3LBD**

jamaicensis (West Indies); rambling evergreen shrub with ovate leathery leaves on woody branches; the white flowers with prominently spreading stamens. *p. 754*

spinosa (So. Europe, Egypt), the "Caperbush"; straggling spiny, deciduous shrub to 1 m high, with thick roundish or ovate leaves to 5 cm long on flexible branches; white flowers 2-3 cm long red outside, with large ovary, and prominent red stamens; solitary in leaf axils, and fading before noon; the fruit a berry. The pungent flower buds are pickled and sold as "Capers". *p. 754*

transvaalensis (So. Africa); woody, scrambling shrub with small spines, and narrow elliptic leathery leaves; toward the end of branches with flowers red brown at base, and white petals, the stamens and filaments protruding; berry-like fruit. *p. 754*

CAPSICUM *Solanaceae* **S2LBM**

annuum cerasiforme 'Birdseye', "Christmas pepper"; small tropical shrub originally from South America, mostly grown as a herbaceous annual pot plant, much branching, the twigs dense with small lanceolate, fresh-green, thin leaves bearing a multitude of small white flowers, followed by small, rounded, waxy, 1 cm, berry-like fruit first green then scarlet red, beginning in autumn and keeping well for Christmas. *p. 2073*

annuum 'Christmas Candle', a "Christmas pepper"; a Craig clone of robust, broadly spreading habit, with erect slender conical yellow to red fruit, 6-8 cm long. *p. 2072*

annuum conoides 'Acorn'; very shapely potplant of low habit, forming a flattened top with a canopy of rich green leaves, above which are borne the small oval, waxy fruit which changes from green and purple to crimson red, usually keeping to Christmas. *p. 2073*

annuum conoides 'Candle pepper'; this robust "Tabasco pepper" is grown as a herbaceous annual potplant, spreading rather broadly, full of small ovate leaves and heavily set with slender, erect, conical fruit 2½ cm high like candles and looking like them when still white, later turning a brilliant orange-red; an exceptional keeper for the Christmas holidays; edible but very pungent. *p. 2073*

annuum conoides 'Celestial'; compact, bushy potplant with deep green ovate leaves and broadly conical fruit under 2½ cm high, wide at base, coloring first green then purple and finally orange-red; ready in early fall, and fruits will usually shrivel before December. *p. 2073*

annuum conoides 'Red Chile'; actually an edible vegetable with its sweet-spicy, large conical, 5 cm fruit, but also an attractive annual potplant with white star-like flowers and fruits beautifully lacquered cardinal red, born stiffly above the rich green, scattered foliage on few, wiry branches. *Tropical.* *p. 2073*

annuum grossum, the "Italian bell-pepper", also known as "Sweet-pepper"; stout plant about 60 cm high, little branched, with large turgid leaves 10-12 cm long; white flowers, and producing large oblong, puffy fruit wrinkled on the sides, and lacquered red; the "Green Bell-pepper" is waxy dark green, and of a mild flavor. *Tropical.* *p. 2083*

annuum 'Piccolo'; variegated leaf ornamental pepper, with some of the foliage almost entirely cream-white, others cream, milky-green, and glossy deep green; small starry flowers lavender, followed by 2½ cm globular fruit black-purple. *p. 2072*

annuum 'Robert Craig'; shapely ornamental pepper, densely branching sport of "Hollyberry" or "Birdseye", fruits short-conical 1-2 cm long, at first cream with purple blotches, later red. *p. 2072*

annuum 'Weatherillii'; large 10 cm leaves shining green above; flowers white; slender, large conical fruit yellow to scarlet, long persistent. Listed in Europe as a form of Solanum pseudocapsicum. *p. 2085*

baccatum (frutescens baccatum) (Japan); an ornamental pepper similar to frutescens but not as tall and more erect, with branches upward-parallel; ovate leaves deciduous, and small nearly round 6 mm red fruit. *p. 2084*

CARAGUATA *Bromeliaceae* **S2LFM**

magnifica (Guzmania); low plant 35 cm across, purplish, or green suffused with wine-red; central bracts bright scarlet. Photographed by T. Everett of N.Y. Botanic Garden. This genus is now referred to Guzmania. *p. 552*

CARAGUATA: see also Guzmania

CARALLUMA *Asclepiadaceae* **I2LBD**

baldratii (Arabia, Eritrea); fat succulent with 4-angled, short stem greenish-white spotted with red, and with fleshy teeth; solitary flower to 3 cm across, mahogany-brown with red spots, and finely white-haired. *p.355*

bredae var. bredae (Cape Prov.: Beaufort); succulent with creeping rhizome, 4-angled stems to 5 cm high, warty along the angles; 1½ cm starry flowers brown-red to wine-colored, the center cup-shaped. *p. 355*

burchardii (Canary Islands); tufting succulent with 4-angled, gray-green or olive-green, irregular stems to 20 cm long, with small teeth pointing downward; the tiny flowers in clusters, whitish inside, olive-brown outside. *p. 356*

caudata (Mozambique, Malawi, Zimbabwe, Namibia); succulent with grooved stems to 10 cm tall, having star-shaped flowers at base of branches, almost 10 cm across, yellow with reddish spots and brown center, the margins with red hairs. *p. 355*

deflersiana (S. W. Arabia); succulent with crowded stems 5-7 cm long, gray-green with brownish spots and with fleshy teeth; tubular-bell-shaped flowers grayish outside with brownish spots; the lobes warted and purplish-brown. *p. 355*

europaea (Mediterranean); succulent, four-angled, leafless stems with blunt teeth, gray-green and branching; flowers greenish with brown lines. *Subtropic.* *p. 356*

europaea gussoneana (So. Spain and around Mediterranean); succulent with angled, spreading or ascending stems, gray-green with reddish spots, 1½ cm thick; small 1½ cm 5-cleft flowers greenish-yellow with red-brown cross-stripes, tips brown-red, corona black-brown. *p. 355*

hesperidum (Morocco); attractive succulent with very fleshy, spiny-pointed, angled leaves greenish-white and spotted with red; small flowers 2 cm dia., velvety chocolate-brown with tiny cream center. *p. 357*

knobelii (So. Africa: Kalahari); succulent with spreading stems 10 cm high, angled and with curved fleshy teeth; 5-lobed flowers 3½ cm across, white, spotted with black-purple, and with dark hairs. *p. 355*

lugardii (Botswana, W. Cape Prov., Namibia); succulent with prostrate or ascending, grooved stems 10-15 cm long, gray-green with brown spots or stripes and small fleshy teeth; flowers with spreading, linear, tapering segments, 5-6 cm across, brown inside at base, green-yellow toward tips and ciliate at margins. *p. 355*

lutea (So. Africa); thick, 4-angled and sharply toothed, tufting, gray fingers mottled with purple; starlike flowers yellow, with long hairs. *p. 356*

mammillaris (South Africa: Great Karroo, Namaqualand); mat-forming stems with 5-6 angled columns 3 cm thick, the angles with spreading teeth, bronzy green overcast with glaucous purple; flowers inside black-purple, tube whitish, dark spotted. *Arid-subtropic.* *p. 356*

melanantha (Transvaal); procumbent succulent forming clumps, the 4-angled stems 5-7 cm high and with spreading teeth; flowers from the middle of the shoots, 5 cm across, the corolla rounded, with 5 lobes, inner surface black-brown, with transverse wrinkles; very variable, some flowers ciliate with marginal hairs. *p. 355*

nebrownii (S.W. Africa), "Spiked clubs"; fat, 4-angled, branching stems with prominent, distant toothing, gray-green, mottled dull-red; flowers dark, red-brown. *p. 355, 356, 2092*

nebrownii var. pseudonebrownii (Namibia); fleshy 4-angled stems 15-18 cm long green or gray-brown and marbled dull-red; starry flowers 7-11 cm across, red-brown with yellow spots on the thick-warted surface. *p. 355*

penicillata (So. Arabia: Yemen); branching, succulent 4-angled stems 2-3 cm thick, and 40-100 cm tall, light green; the angled crest horny; flowers in clusters, the corolla 12 mm across, with 5 lobes, light brown with pale yellow spots and with red hairs. *p. 357*

retrospiciens (Kenya, Sudan, Ethiopia, Somalia); striking, tall, stout succulent freely branching;fleshy stems with 4 compressed angles and small teeth; shoots from angle to angle 8 cm dia., clusters of numerous flowers from tips of branches, the corolla 2 cm across almost black-brown, with violet ciliate hairs. *p. 357*

retrospiciens var. timbuctuensis (tombuctuensis) (Mali, Mauritania, Sudan, Nigeria); clump-forming large succulent from the Sahara desert to 1½ m tall, the 4-angled stems of 3-4 cm dia., pale apple-green, often with blue-glaucous waxy coating, and small 1½ cm flowers black-purple, the lobes wrinkled and with red marginal hair. *p. 357*

rogersii (Botswana); succulent 4-angled, toothed, greenish stems erect or scandent, about 10 cm high, and forming clusters; flowers with wide-spreading lobes, to 3½ cm across, yellow, and with fine hairs. *p. 355*

speciosa (Somalia, Kenya, Tanzania); large succulent 1 m or more tall, with 4-angled, finely-toothed stems glaucous blue; flowers 4½ cm across with cup-shaped corolla lobes deep brown, and yellow tube, in large clusters 12 cm from tip to tip. *p. 357*

x suaveolens (nebrownii x ausana); succulent angled gray column 10 cm high, with prominent soft teeth, marbled maroon to purple. *p. 356*

ubomboensis (Natal, Swaziland); branching succulent with 4-angled stems 4 cm high, and with small teeth; small 1 cm wrinkled flowers dark red-brown. *p. 355*

vibratilis (Kenya, Uganda, Tanzania); succulent with persistent underground stolons; stems 5-8 cm high, deeply grooved and with fleshy teeth, in habitat dying off; bell-shaped flowers red-purple with small yellow spots, the 5 lobes hairy. *p. 357*

CARDIOSPERMUM *Sapindaceae* **I3LBD**

halicacabum (Pantropic to India, Africa, America), the "Balloon vine" or "Heartseed"; tendril-climbing herb to 3 m, with twice 3-parted thin leaves 10 cm long, and small white flowers; fruit a brown, thin-shelled inflated, angled capsule 3 cm dia. containing 3 black seeds each with a white, heart-shaped scar. *Tropical.* *p. 2035*

CAREX *Cyperaceae* **C-I2LFW**

elegantissima: see foliosissima 'Albo-mediana'

foliosissima 'Albo-mediana' (elegantissima) (Sakhalin, to Japan); grass-like tufted plant with elegant, flat leaves bright green with a white stripe near each margin, of stiff-erect habit. *Warm-temperate.* *p. 946*

kobomugi, (Japan), "Japanese sedge"; small rosettes of soft-leathery, rich green, strap-shaped channeled leaves recurving and 45 cm long, to 3 cm wide, travelling and spreading by means of underground rhizomes or stolons; the inconspicuous flowers in dense spikes. Photographed in the sand dunes of Barnegat along the Atlantic Ocean shore of New Jersey, planted there for colonizing and holding the dunes. *p. 948*

morrowii 'Variegata' (Japan), "Variegated sedge grass"; attractive, tufting, grass-like plant with narrow-linear, 6 mm wide concave leaves recurving, very colorful ivory-white to pale yellow, edged with green margins. *Subtropic.* *p. 946, 948*

CARICA *Caricaceae* **S2LBM**

papaya (Colombia), "Melon tree"; dioecious succulent tree to 8 metres high, with leaves digitately 7-lobed; flowers greenish-yellow, the hanging fruits to 30 cm long resembling a melon and with sweet almost peach-like flavor. In tropical plantations, only female seedlings are planted for fruit production; these are recognized by their split mainroots, while male seedlings have a straight tap root. Papaya fruits twice yearly in Tahiti, in December-January and in July. *Tropical.* *p. 754, 761*

quercifolia (So. America); unbranched evergreen tree containing acrid, milky juice, leaves oak-like, palmately 5-lobed, on long stalks. Whitish male flowers salver-shaped, female flowers with 5 erect petals. *p. 754*

CARISSA *Apocynaceae* **I2LBM**

acocanthera (Acokanthera venenata) (So. Africa: Cape), "Bushman's poison"; evergreen shrub with large 10 cm leathery, long elliptic, glossy green leaves; axillary panicles of tubular shining white flowers with star-like spreading lobes, and lightly hairy outside; very fragrant. *p. 135*

arduina (bispinosa) (So. Africa), "Hedge-thorn"; evergreen spiny shrub to 3 m, oblong leathery leaves, small white flowers 1½ cm dia., small 1½ cm red fruit. *p. 135*

grandiflora (macrophylla) (Natal), "Natal plum"; woody shrub to 9 m, armed with massive forked spines, lustrous green, ovate leaves, and large 5 cm white, fragrant flowers; big plum-like scarlet fruit to 5 cm long, and edible. *Subtropic.* *p. 139*

grandiflora 'Horizontalis', "Natal creeper"; trailing evergreen shrub of dense habit, ideal for ground cover; small, bright green foliage on wiry twigs with beige thorns, the fragrant white flowers followed by fiery scarlet fruit 3 cm diameter. *p. 136*

grandiflora 'Nana'; low evergreen subshrub without thorns, leathery glossy leaves, and tubular pure white flowers with rounded lobes spreading like a pinwheel. *p. 135*

humphreyi 'Variegata'; very decorative little bush dense with oval, leathery leaves 2 cm long, tipped with short spine, rich green variegated and edged with ivory-white; holding variegation well. *Subtropic.* *p. 136*

spectabilis (Acokanthera) (So. Africa), "Wintersweet"; evergreen shrub with narrow-oval, leathery, glossy leaves and clusters of sweetly-scented, pure-white flowers. *p. 137*

CARLEPHYTON *Araceae* **S2LFM**

diegoense (Madagascar); tropical plant with depressed tuber 3 cm dia.; reddish-green floral stalk 4-5 cm, with 3½ cm boat-shaped spathe reddish-green outside, inside deep purplish red; fleshy petioles 13-20 cm long, vaginate in lower half, the leaf cordate 10-13 cm long and 8-9 cm wide, green, occasionally with red spots. *p. 209*

glaucophyllum (Madagascar); tuberous plant of Diego Suarez Province; tuber to 6 cm dia.; after a period of rest appears a glaucous green leaf, usually solitary, broadly heart-shaped on reddish petiole 25-50 cm long; boat-shaped 8-10 cm spathe, pale lemon-green inside, white outside on upper part; long slender spadix. *Tropical.* *p. 224*

madagascariense (Madagascar); tropical tuberous plant, with inflorescence appearing before or with new foliage; the short-stalked spathe yellowish-green to purplish red, constricted in lower part, and flaring wide toward apex; the usually solitary fleshy leaf light green, to 40 cm wide and long; ripe fruits orange-red. *p. 209*

CARLINA *Compositae* **C2LBD**

acaulis (Europe); stemless perennial thistle with spiny leaves in a rosette, very deeply incised; solitary heads silvery, to 12 c m across. *Temperate.* *p. 832*

CARLUDOVICA *Cyclanthaceae* **S1LFM**

laucheana (Ludovia) (Colombia: Antioquia); nearly stemless, unarmed palm-like plant with large sickle-shaped, glossy-green leaves to 30 cm long, two-lobed to middle or below, plaited with parallel veins, the segments linear-oblong, 5 to 7-ribbed; inflorescence with cylindric, cream spadix and whitish spathe. *p. 945*

palmata (Colombia, Ecuador, Perú), "Panama hat plant"; stemless plant to 2-3 m high, with friendly green, fan-shaped, palm-like leaves to 1 m long, usually cut into 4 parts, the lobes cut again; used for making of hats. *Tropical.* *p. 945*

CARMICHAELIA *Leguminosae* **I2LFM**

enysii (New Zealand); much-branched shrub a few cm high, forming a compact thicket of flattened branches; flowers 1/2 cm long, violet. *p. 1375*

CARNATION: see Dianthus

CARNEGIEA *Cactaceae* **S2LBD**

gigantea (Cereus) (So. Arizona, No. Mexico), "Giant saguaro"; tall tapering column to almost 18 m, branching with age, close-ribbed; the ribs with strong light brown spines; white flowers 10 cm long, will open in daylight. One of largest tree-like cacti known. *p. 637, 648, 659*

gigantea 'Monstrosa'; a spectacular crested form of the giant saguaro, photographed in Saguaro National Forest south of Tucson, Arizona; the crest fan-like on top of a 6 m column. *Arid-subtropic.* *p. 658*

CARPHALEA *Rubiaceae* **S3LBM**

kirondron (Rubia ornamentale hort.) (introduced to the Philippines from Madagascar in 1957), popularly known as "Rubia"; handsome, floriferous shrub to 2 m or more high, dense with willowy branches; opposite ovate or lanceolate glossy green leaves 6 to 12 cm long, the midrib ivory to reddish; the showy inflorescence in globular heads 8 to 10 cm across, of flowers with velvety, linear, glowing red petaloid bracts or sepals, and tiny white 4-lobed white corolla under 1 cm across, on long protruding slender red tube, and blooming the year round. *Tropical.* *p. 2013*

CARPINUS *Betulaceae* **I2LBD**

japonica (Japan), "Japanese hornbeam"; hardwooded deciduous small tree of the birch family, to 12 m high, with smooth gray bark, spreading branches with lanceolate leaves 5-10 cm long and more or less two-ranked; the male flowers in pendant catkins, blooming before the leaves unfold; ribbed nutlets sheltered by leaflike bracts in attractive, drooping clusters. Often used as dwarfed bonsai tree with contorted trunk in Japan. *p. 504*

CARPOBROTUS *Aizoaceae* **I2LBD**

edulis (So. Africa), "Hottentot-fig"; creeping, freely growing, branching succulent, often planted as a sand-binder along sub-tropical seashores; branches angled, to 1 m long, with long linear 3-angled fleshy, grass green or glaucous leaves 8-12 cm long, keel minutely serrate; large flowers 8-10 cm across with narrow, silky rays opening with the warming sun, yellow or purple; large fruits edible. In South Africa, I have observed the purple form primarily on the cool Cape Peninsula, the yellow in the glaring hot Karroo. *Arid-subtropic.* *p. 61*

CARRUANTHUS *Aizoaceae* **I1LBD**

caninus (Cape Prov.); much branched short-stemmed succulent with clustered triangular keeled leaves 6 cm long, glossy deep green to grayish, the margins dentate toward tip; 5 cm flowers yellow, reddish outside, with linear petals. *p. 77*

CARYA *Juglandaceae* **C2LBD**

pecan (olivaeformis) (Indiana to Alabama, Texas and Mexico), the "Pecan nut"; handsome partially deciduous hard-wooded tree to 25 m high, planted by the millions in the South for their delicious nuts; Thomas Jefferson brought the first pecans from the Mississippi Valley to George Washington where he planted them at Mt. Vernon, Virginia in 1775. Wide-spreading, with grayish, deeply furrowed bark and graceful pinnate foliage; thin-leathery fresh green, crenate leaflets with yellow midrib 10 to 15 cm long; the male flowers in pendulous catkins, the female flowers in terminal spikes, producing clusters of oblong, angled green husks 4-8 cm long which split into 4 sections, and holding the edible, and sweet-tasting kernel or nut; ripening in autumn. *Warm-temperate.* *p. 1340*

CARYOPTERIS *Verbenaceae* **C2LBD**

x clandonensis (mastacanthus x mongholica), "Bluebeard"; deciduous shrub of Japanese and Chinese parentage, with opposite lanceolate, toothed leaves 5-9 cm long, underside and stalks gray-white; bright blue flowers with 5-lobed corolla including one larger fringed one. *p. 2118*

CARYOTA *Palmae* **I-S1LFW**

maxima (Java); a tall "Fishtail palm" with pinnate leaves; the broad almost triangular, leathery leaflets rigid and spread out like green fans, jagged along apex. *p. 1856*

mitis (Burma, Malaya, Indonesia), "Clustered fishtail palm"; with numerous suckers growing up in clusters; green-gray trunks 7 m high topped by dense tufts of irregularly bipinnate dull-green leaves, the pinnae fan-shaped, jagged at apex and many-veined, nodding at the tips; fruit blackish-red. *Tropical.* *p. 1854, 1857*

obtusa (ochlandra) (Upper Assam); a Himalayan fishtail palm similar to urens but with leaflets more rounded at the tips, also found in the mountains near Canton, growing about 8-10 m tall; this northernmost of the genus tolerates some frost. *p. 1857*

ochlandra (China), "Chinese fishtail palm"; handsome palm with slender trunk, the bipinnate arching fronds arranged like a bouquet; the long triangular green leaflets lobed and pointedly jagged at apex. *p. 1856*

"plumosa" (Ceylon), a "Fishtail palm" more handsome than mitis when mature, differing in having a dominant trunk with few and much smaller suckers whereas mitis has many suckers more or less equal; the leathery fronds with fan-shaped segments fresh-green and almost glossy. *p. 1857*

rumphiana (Indonesia, New Guinea, No. Australia); a handsome "Fishtail palm" with columnar solitary trunk, to 20 m high and 45 cm thick, prominently ringed; arching fronds doubly pinnate to 6 m long, the leaflets obliquely fan-like, leathery-rigid, folded and toothed; spadix to 3 m long; purple, fleshy, globular fruit. *p. 1854, 1856*

urens (Himalayas, India, Burma, Ceylon, Malaya), "Wine palm" or "Fishtail"; I remember these majestic, solitary palms giving special character to the beautiful, verdant landscape of the mountains of Ceylon; glossy gray trunk more than 30 m high, topped by bipinnate, arching leaves with thick wedge-shaped, loosely spaced segments; yields wine. *Tropical.* *p. 1857*

CASIMIROA *Rutaceae* **I2LBM**

edulis (Mexico, C. America), the "White sapote" or "Mexican apple"; fast-growing tropical fruit tree to 15 m high, treasured by the Aztecs; shiny green leathery leaves, palmately compound of 5-7 leaflets 12 cm long; small greenish or whitish flowers; the handsome apple-shaped fruit to 10 cm dia. pendant on long stalks, yellow-green with thin waxy glaucous cover; the edible soft and juicy, cream-colored flesh very sweet resembling mango, and with fragrant aroma, but may have a bitter after-taste. The seeds are used medicinally in Mexico to induce sleep. Planted in South Florida and So. California in several good-flavored varieties; eaten fresh or in sherbets. *Subtropical.* *p. 2028*

edulis 'Suebelle', "White sapote"; a favored cultivar of medium size for the home garden, because of its sweet, rich, soft pulp and small seeds; ripening most in November, turning yellow; fruit has musky sweet flavor and does not keep long. *Subtropic.* *p. 2038*

CASSIA *Leguminosae* **I2LBM**

alata (Trop. America), "Candle-bush"; short-lived big bush 1 to 4 m high, with pinnate foliage; 6 cm leaflets; erect candle-like spikes of golden yellow flowers. *Tropical.* *p. 1376*

artemisioides (Australia), "Feathery senna"; bushy shrub 2-3 m high, covered with silky-gray pubescence, with leaves of 6-8 stiff linear needle-like leaflets, and bright yellow, showy flowers with black anthers. *p. 1378*

bicapsularis (bot. pendula) (bicuspidata in hort.) (Trop. America); showy, robust bush to 3 m high, with pinnate leaves, the oval leaflets leathery; erect terminal inflorescence with large cupped golden yellow flowers 4 cm across. *Tropical.* *p. 1376*

closiana (Chile); flowers deep golden-yellow, each about 3 cm across; foliage slightly bluish green. *p. 1376*

corymbosa (Argentina), "Flowering senna"; sunloving shrub with pinnate foliage of 3 pairs of leathery leaflets, and showy clusters of nearly regular, rather cupped flowers of golden yellow. Sometimes listed as "marilandica" in horticulture. *Subtropic.* *p. 1378*

didymobotrya (nairobensis), (Trop. Africa), "Popcorn-bush"; bushy shrub or small tree to 3 m, young shoots and leaves finely downy; leaves 35 cm long; leaflets in 4-18 pairs; flowers in erect, showy racemes 15-30 cm long, several borne near end of shoots; large cupped golden yellow flowers. *Tropical.* *p. 1377*

excelsa floribunda (E. Brazil), "Crown-of-gold tree"; tall shrub or tree to 10 m, with branchlets softly pubescent; pendant foliage with 10-20 pairs of oblong leaflets 4 cm long; inflorescence in axillary or terminal clusters of fragrant bright yellow flowers. *p. 1376*

fistula (India, Sri Lanka); "Golden shower" or "Pudding pipe tree"; beautiful tree of moderate size; leaves with leaflets in 4 to 8 pairs, 5-15 cm long; fragrant flowers golden yellow, in drooping racemes to 30 cm long, resembling huge bunches of grapes. *Tropical.* *p. 1376, 1377*

leptophylla (Brazil); very ornamental 10 m tree widely planted in Brazil; bearing great quantities of purplish-rose flowers in large heads on long flexuous branches; glaucous leaves pinnate, with crenate leaflets. *p. 1376*

marilandica (S. E. United States), "Wild senna"; subshrub sending up erect, pithy shoots from a woody rootstock to 1 m; pinnate leaves glaucous beneath, flowers with corolla 1 cm wide, petals yellow, anthers purple, in axillary racemes. (b) *p. 1376, 1378*

multijuga (W. Indies, So. America), "November shower"; small tree to 6 m high, pinnate foliage; golden yellow flowers 5 cm dia., in erect clusters. *Tropical.* *p. 1376*

'Rainbow Shower' (fistula x javanica); beautiful hybrid tree and the landmark of Honolulu; very spectacular, with showy masses of flowers from cream to orange and red, dominating the landscape from March to August almost obscuring the luxurious pinnate foliage. *Tropical.* *p. 1377*

roxburghii (marginata) (Sri Lanka), "Red cassia" or "Ceylon senna"; large, showy, spreading tree with dense ranks of pinnate leaflets along a willowy axis; the arching branches beautifully set with masses of axillary flowers, salmon rose. *Tropical.* *p. 1377*

spectabilis (Trop. America), "Popcorn bush"; showy spreading tree to 12 m high, with long pinnate leaves, the leaflets lanceolate and bright green; branches bearing spectacular erect 30-60 cm racemes of large beautiful, cupped golden-yellow 4 cm flowers like shining lamps. *Tropical.* *p. 1378*

splendida (Brazil), "Golden wonder senna"; floriferous shrub to 3 m high, leaves pinnate with oval leaflets, and large yellow flowers in clustered racemes. *p. 1378*

surattensis (glauca) (Marquesas, India, Sri Lanka); "Scrambled eggs"; tall shrub or tree, shoots angular; leaves 15-22 cm long; leaflets in 6-9 pairs, very glaucous beneath, 4-6 cm long; flowers in a fine, erect cluster of axillary and terminal racemes 10 cm long; corolla 3 cm across, yellow; pod 15-20 cm long, wide, flat. *Tropical.* *p. 1376*

CASSINE *Celastraceae* **S3LBD**

orientalis (Madagascar, Mauritius), "False olive"; handsome tropical shrub or small tree with ornamental waxy, bluish green foliage on reddish stems, the opposite leaves long-linear in the juvenile stage; in the maturity stage shorter obovate 5-8 cm long with scalloped edges; small greenish and white flowers in axillary clusters, followed by the olive-like fruit. *p. 759*

CASSINIA *Compositae* **I2LBD**

fulvida (New Zealand); evergreen shrub with yellow-downy shoots, erica-like 1 cm leaves dark green and sticky above, yellow-tomentose beneath; tiny white disk flowers with tubular florets, borne in whitish chaffy bracts, in clusters. *p. 820*

CASTANOSPERMUM *Leguminosae* **C2LBM**

australe (New So. Wales), "Moreton Bay chestnut"; evergreen tree 12-18 m; leaves 30-45 cm long; leaflets 10 to 15, ovate to oblong, pointed, 8-12 cm long; flowers orange-yellow in axillary racemes 10-15 cm long; fruit a pod 20 cm long, spongy inside, containing seeds as large as a Spanish chestnut, which is eaten when roasted. *p. 1379*

CASTILLEJA *Scrophulariaceae* **I2HFD**

indivisa (Texas), the "Texas painted-cup", or "Indian paint-brush"; annual herb to 60 cm which prefers to live parasitic on roots of other plants; leaves linear-lanceolate, usually margined red; the inflorescence with showy bright red bracts, red calyx and greenish-yellow 2-lipped tubular flowers. *p. 2051*

CASUARINA *Casuarinaceae* **I2LBM**

equisetifolia (No. Australia, Queensland), the "Horse-tail tree" or "Australian pine"; hardwooded tree to 25 m high, with pendulous branches swaying in the breeze; wirelike branchlets with apparently leafless twigs, the leaves reduced to scales and suggesting the horsetail (Equisetum). Adaptable as a patio tree, or the sunny, airy greenhouse, when sheared into compact shapes or imaginative topiary forms. *Tropical.* *p. 756, 761*

stricta, (So. Australia, Tasmania), "She-oak"; tall dense shrub or tree to 10 or 20 m high, the green branchlets drooping and ribbed, the leaves reduced to scales; lined along the larger branches are the dioecious flowers, the females producing the 3-5 cm ovoid fruit-cones. *p. 756*

CATALPA *Bignoniaceae* **I2LBD**

bignonioides (Georgia, Florida, Mississippi), the "Indian-bean"; tree 8-18 m high, of rounded, spreading habit, with ovate leaves 15-25 cm long, pale green, downy beneath; inflorescence a broad erect panicle with bell-shaped flowers, and spreading, frilled lobes, white, with two yellow stripes and purple spots, 5 cm across. *Warm-temperate.* *p. 496*

x CATAMODES *Orchidaceae* **S3OFM**

hybrida (Catasetum inornatum x Mormodes buccinator); interesting bigeneric with hooded flowers light chartreuse or linden-green with yellow sheen, the wings yellow-green, irregularly and weakly spotted chestnut brown; from the Hamburg Bot. Garden. *p. 1680*

CATASETUM *Orchidaceae* **S3OFM**

appendiculatum (Brazil: Amazonas); long lanceolate leaves with depressed longitudinal ribs, the inflorescence in many-flowered pendant racemes, the slender green and brownish flowers sitting like birds in flight. *p. 1676*

barbatum (bicallosum) (Demerara); unusual terrestrial with papery plaited leaves on long swelling bulbs, cluster of greenish flowers with narrow segments marked brown, lip with long fimbriate beard. (S) *p. 1678, 1680*

bicolor (Panama); epiphyte with swollen pseudobulb and plaited leaves; curious inflorescence with female flowers on short spikes with upright, helmet-shaped lip greyish-green, while the male flowers are on long pendant racemes, with chocolate-brown sepals, greenish-brown petals and a white, purple-spotted and purple-margined lip, (Sept.-Oct.). (S) *p. 1679*

callosum (Venezuela, Colombia); robust epiphyte with spindle-shaped, conical pseudobulbs, and deciduous, folded leaves; from the base either the erect female inflorescence; or the arching, pendant, many-flowered and pollen-spraying male raceme; 6 cm flowers inverted, brownish with red-dotted green lip (winter). *p. 1675*

cernuum (Brazil); inflorescence arching to pendant; flowers nodding, 4 cm long, sepals and petals green spotted black brown, lip green. *p. 1676*

cristatum (Brazil); epiphyte 60 cm high; pseudobulbs with fresh green foliage; from the base the arching inflorescence with flowers 6 cm across, greenish, and speckled purple brown; lip bright green, coarsely fringed (August). *p. 1677*

discolor (Brazil: Pernambuco); small epiphyte with tapering pseudobulbs bearing ribbed leaves; erect racemes from base, with flowers attached upside-down; greenish sepals and petals, the cup-shaped lip yellow outside, hairy and lined with brown inside, with two purplish lateral fringes; summer. (S) *p. 1680*

discolor rosea-album (Brazil); foliage light green; inflorescence from base of last year's pseudobulb, 75 cm long, bearing buff-yellow flowers, with reddish tinge to lip, and red inside; lip a deep pouch fringed at margins; male flowers 3 cm across. *p. 1676*

fimbriatum (Brazil, Paraguay); epiphyte with pseudobulbs bearing several lanceolate ribbed leaves; fragrant, fleshy flowers in semi-erect to pendant racemes, yellowish-green with reddish spots, the lip fan-like, yellowish and fringed, (August). (S) *p. 1676, 1678*

hookeri labiatum (Brazil); variety of hookeri with smaller and rounded flowers concave and incurving, sepals and petals green, lip pale yellow, midlobe tongue-like and incurved. *p. 1680*

integerrimum (Mexico, Costa Rica to Venezuela); robust epiphyte with spindle-shaped pseudobulbs to 40 cm tall; topped by large folded, deciduous leaves; erect inflorescence to 35 cm; fleshy, fragrant flowers 6 cm long, not opening fully, yellowish green to purplish, often spotted with deeper color. *p. 1676*

macrocarpum (Trinidad, N.E. So. America); remarkable orchid with keeled leaves on striated 20 cm pseudobulbs; an arching inflorescence to 30 cm tall, with 5-14 flowers on male spike, sepals and petals yellow-green spotted with red inside, hooded lip yellow with greenish apex, spotted purple, with 3 teeth. (S) *p. 1676*

mooreanum (Amazonian Perú); newly discovered species with broad foliage, and heavy, arching racemes of chartreuse green flowers (Lee Moore 1965). *p. 1677*

oerstedii (Nicaragua, Costa Rica, Panama); similar to macrocarpum; inflorescence to 50 cm tall, usually arching; 5 cm flowers heavily scented; sepals and petals greenish brown marked with purple, yellow lip spotted brown. *p. 1678*

pileatum (Trinidad, Venezuela, Brazil, Ecuador); handsome epiphyte with cylindrical pseudobulbs bearing plaited leaves; 30 cm stalks with large 6 cm flowers, pale yellow sepals and petals, the lip nearly kidney-shaped, and pouched in back, inside orange-red; autumn. (S) *p. 1680*

platyglossum (Ecuador); stout terrestrial with swollen pseudobulbs and a series of plaited leaves; short, arching inflorescence of numerous flaring and hooded flowers; the female flower with upright, helmet-shaped lip is green; the male flower greenish-yellow, with lip at first fresh-green but changing to yellow, callus and cavity bright orange (July-August). (S) *p. 1678*

roseum (Mexico: Oaxaca); a small, very pretty epiphyte with short pseudobulbs and deciduous leaves; numerous showy and long-lasting, cupped star-like waxy flowers on short, pendant raceme, cream flushed rose, petals and lip fringed with rosy hairs; lip greenish inside (early spring). *Tropical.* *p. 1678*

russellianum (Guatemala); robust epiphyte with pseudobulbs bearing plaited leaves; showy, pendant racemes with numerous flowers having pale green petals and sepals lined dark green, and a white, sac-like lip with fringed margins, (Aug.-Sept.). (S) *p. 1678*

saccatum christyanum (Brazil: Amazon); curious epiphyte with spindle-shaped stems set with plaited leaves, and strong racemes of large 10 cm flowers, the sepals reddish-brown, petals lighter brown pale-spotted at base, lip green marked purplish at base, the lateral sack-like lobes with long purple fringes; summer-autumn. (S) *p. 1680*

sodiroi (Ecuador); arching stem bearing 5 fragrant flowers each to 8 cm across; petals pale green, lip deep green with conspicuous orange yellow blotch around sac. *p. 1676*

x splendens (pileatum x macrocarpum); beautiful epiphyte with spindle-shaped pseudobulbs topped by narrow lanceolate leaves; erect racemes bearing large waxy flowers with yellowish-white sepals and a rounded, oyster-shell like lip of porcelain-white, (June). (S) *p. 1678*

suave (Costa Rica, Panama); epiphyte with thick cylindrical pseudobulbs which shed their ribbed leaves during their period of rest; the fleshy, waxy-white, bisexual and strongly spicy-fragrant flowers are produced on an arching or sometimes upright rather dense raceme; March-May. (S) *p. 1680*

trulla (Brazil); pseudobulbs bearing broad leaves; the inflorescence on arching racemes with 5 cm flowers having greenish sepals and petals, the lip spoon-shaped, concave, fringed at margins greenish-white with brown tip; September. *Tropical.* *p. 1680*

viridiflavum (Cent. America to Perú); terrestrial with plaited leaves 30 cm long, the inflorescence shorter than the foliage, with up to 12 flowers, petals wider than sepals all yellow-green and concave, lip marked with yellow inside, conical-saccate and hooded (summer). *Tropical.* *p. 1678*

warscewiczii (scurra) (Costa Rica to Venezuela); dwarf species with egg-shaped pseudobulbs, 4-5 leaves to 45 cm long, deciduous in time; inflorescence pendant, with fragrant, long-lived 4 cm turgid flowers, creamy white or pale green with brown lines and fringed lip. *p. 1676*

CATESBAEA *Rubiaceae* **S3LBD**

spinosa (Cuba, Bahamas), "Lily-thorn"; spiny evergreen shrub to 4m high, with small leathery leaves in clusters; the spines above the leaf axils; flowers funnel-shaped with a very long tube, 8-15cm long, gradually widening; the corolla pale yellow and drooping; orange-yellow fruit. *Tropical* *p. 2017*

CATHARANTHUS *Apocynaceae* **I2LBM**

roseus (Vinca rosea) (Java to Brazil), "Madagascar periwinkle"; erect, fleshy plant with oblong leaves glossy green with white center vein; showy 4cm flowers rosy-red with purple throat. *Tropical* *p. 141*

CATOBLASTUS *Palmae* **I3LBM**

praemorsus (Venezuela, Colombia), "Prapa stilt palm"; handsome cluster-forming feather palm of the Andes, 10 to 15 m high, the slender 8 cm dia. trunks covered by black bark, and supported on a cluster of short stilt roots; mature pinnate leaves to 1 m or more long, glossy green on both sides; leaflets are premorse (as if bitten off at ends), the terminal ones usually united and wedge shaped; the 3 cm fruit is beautiful, in lustrous black. *Subtropic.* *p. 1858*

CATOPSIS *Bromeliaceae* **I2HBM**

berteroniana (Florida, Bahamas, Greater Antilles, C. America, Trinidad, Venezuela, Guyana, E. Brazil); rigid symmetrical epiphytic rosette, 45-90 cm high, with concave leaves gradually spreading, white-chalky; inflorescence on stout erect stalk with lower bracts overlapping, broad green floral bracts and lax flowers with white petals. *p. 548, 562*

floribunda (Puerto Rico and W. Indies); small stiff rosette of pea-green leaves tapering sharply to point; inflorescence on branched stem with white flowers. *p. 548*

morreniana (So. Mexico, Guatemala, and C. America); small epiphytic or terrestrial rosette with strap-like glossy green leaves 10-20 cm long; the inflorescence tall, erect and branched, with pale yellow bracts and tiny white flowers. *p. 548*

nitida (Greater Antilles, C. America, Panama, Guyana); epiphytic rosette 45 cm high, fluted below, the few concave leaves shining green and spreading above; green inflorescence laxly compound, with tiny bracts and minute flowers. *p. 548*

nutans (Greater Antilles, C. America to Panama, Venezuela, Ecuador); epiphytic rosette rather open, broad leaves tapering to apex; arching inflorescence with short floral bracts and small flowers with three yellow petals. *p. 548*

sessiliflora (West Indies, So. Mexico to So. Brazil, Colombia, Perú); small epiphytic rosette, 12-30 cm high, with green leaves curving outward; the slender erect inflorescence stalk topped usually by a spike bearing small flowers with white petals, almost hidden by the broad green floral bracts. *p. 548*

CATTLEYA *Orchidaceae* **S-I3OFD**

amethystoglossa (Brazil); tall plant 60-90 cm high with long terete stems topped by 2 leaves, and clusters of 3-20 flowers 8-10 cm across, sepals and petals bright rose and spotted with purple, lip with whitish side lobes and violet middle lobe (Nov.-July). *Tropical* *p. 1682*

aurantiaca (Epidendrum) (Guatemala, Mexico); robust epiphyte with slender club-shaped cane-type pseudobulbs topped by two stiff leaves; small 8 cm flashy flowers fiery orange-red, seldom fully expanding, in dense clusters. (Dec.-May). (I) *p. 1684*

bicolor (Brazil); epiphyte with long cane-like pseudobulbs bearing 2 leaves; flowers with linear petals and sepals brownish green, the narrow lip rosy-purple sometimes edged with white. (Sept.-Nov.). *Tropical* *p. 1687*

bowringiana (Honduras); prolific epiphyte with long, cane-like 2-leaved pseudobulbs, topped by clusters of numerous smallish 8 cm flowers, sepals and petals rosy-purple, lip much darker maroon-red. *Subtropic.* *p. 1685*

chocoensis (Colombia: Choco); handsome epiphyte with oblong pseudobulbs and solitary leaves, and large fragrant flowers not fully expanded, with wide petals pure white, and yellow lip stained in front with purple (fall, winter). (I) *p. 1682*

citrina (Mexico), "Tulip cattleya"; beautiful epiphyte with silvery, globular pseudobulbs and strapshaped leaves; the fragrant, bell-like flowers are borne singly and pendant, bright lemon-yellow, lip edged white and crisped, (April-June). *Tropical* *p.1684*

dowiana (Costa Rica), "Queen cattleya"; epiphyte with stout pseudobulbs bearing solitary leaves, and beautifully colored, fragrant flowers widely used for hybridizing, the crisped petals golden yellow, the sepals yellow shaded buff, and a great, frilled lip deep crimson-red streaked with old gold, (May-Aug.). *Humid-Tropical.* *p. 1685*

dowiana aurea (Colombia), "Queen cattleya"; a superb epiphyte with stout pseudobulbs bearing solitary leaves, and beautifully colored, highly fragrant flowers to 15cm across, the crisped petals and sepals golden yellow, and a great, frilled lip deep crimson-red distinctly streaked or banded with old gold; blooming from May to Autumn. *Tropical* *p. 1681*

eldorado var. virginalis, (Brazil: Amazon); small epiphyte with pseudobulbs bearing a solitary large leaf; the flowers with narrow sepals and petals 10-15 cm across, pink with purple on the lip in the species, the variety virginalis a chaste pure white with frilled lip and orange disk; sweet-scented; August-September. (I) *p. 1686*

elongata (Brazil); small epiphyte with 2-leaved pseudobulbs, small waxy flowers on long stalk, narrow sepals and petals variable, red-brown or greenish, lip rose with darker lines; March, October. (I) *p. 1686*

'Enid' (gigas x mossiae); robust, elegant hybrid with big, purplish-mauve flowers of firm texture, the lip overlaid with purple, yellow in the throat; blooming at various times, often twice a year. *Tropical* *p. 1683*

forbesii (Brazil), a "Cocktail orchid"; clustering epiphyte, and a sight to see it nesting in small trees, loaded with medium-size flowers, the sepals and petals yellow-green, lip white outside, yellow streaked with red inside, borne on stem-like, 2-leaved pseudobulbs, (May-Oct., and various). *Tropical* *p. 1684, 1685*

gaskelliana (Venezuela, Brazil), "Summer cattleya"; epiphyte with 1-leaved pseudobulbs; fragrant flowers in clusters of 3-5, petals and sepals lavender, the fringed lip purple with yellow throat, (May-July). *p. 1683*

gigas: see C. warscewiczii

granulosa (Guatemala and Brazil); free-growing species with slender terete 2-leaved stems 40-50 cm high, and olive green, fleshy 10 cm flowers spotted with brown, the spreading lip white dotted with purple (Aug.-Sept.). *Tropical* *p. 1687*

x guatemalensis (Guatemala); epiphytic, natural hybrid between skinneri and aurantiaca; flowers of medium size in large clusters, sepals and petals pale rosy-purple and buff, lip reddish-purple and orange, with crimson lines, (spring). (I) *p. 1684*

guttata (Brazil); beautiful waxy, fragrant 10 cm flowers in clusters, sepals and wavy petals reddish-brown on green and spotted crimson, hooded lip white with purple (autumn). *p. 1681*

guttata leopoldii (Brazil: Bahia); interesting variety with terete pseudobulbs 50 cm long and a pair of short leaves; bold inflorescence carrying as many as 30 fragrant, waxy 8-10 cm flowers, sepals and petals bronze spotted crimson, small lip rich crimson-purple; free-blooming (summer). (I) *p. 1687*

x hardyana alba (dowiana x gigas) (Colombia); natural epiphytic hybrid with showy white flowers having a beautiful, large frilled lip of crimson veined with gold, and two yellow eyes in the throat. (June-Aug.). (I) *p. 1684*

intermedia (Brazil); epiphyte with 2-leaved, slender, cane-like pseudobulbs; slender flowers to 12 cm, usually 3-5 together in clusters, pale rose, with middle lobe of lip purple and crisped, (April-Nov.). *p. 1685*

intermedia alba (parthenia) (Brazil); variety with pure white flowers on cane-like pseudobulbs much longer than the species; summer. *p. 1687*

intermedia var. aquinii; a curious variety in which the normally irregular flower becomes regular because petals imitate the lip; sepals and petals soft rose, the midlobe of lip and tip of petals purple. *p. 1687*

labiata (Trinidad, Brazil); epiphyte with pseudobulbs bearing a solitary leathery leaf, the showy flowers 15-18 cm across, 3-7 in a cluster, sepals and petals bright rose, the latter broad and wavy, large lip deep velvety-crimson, throat marked yellow. (Aug.-Nov.). (I) *p. 1683*

lawrenceana (Guyana, Venezuela); free-blooming epiphyte with tall, furrowed pseudobulbs 30-38 cm high, bearing solitary leaves; flowers 10-12 cm across, rosy-purple, lip deep purple with maroon band, and whitish throat, early summer. (S) *p. 1686*

loddigesii harrisoniae (Brazil); noble, free flowering epiphyte with long cane-like pseudobulbs bearing 2 leaves; the waxy flowers of medium size, 2-5 together, a beautiful rose-lilac, the fringed middle lobe of lip cream-white and edged yellow. (Jan.-Feb., July-Oct.). (I) *p. 1685*

loddigesii violacea (superba) (Guyana to Perú); slow-growing, distinctive epiphyte with club-shaped stems and a pair of thick leaves; firm, fragrant 10-12 cm flowers deep rose with lip crimson and yellow center, long-lasting (summer). (S) *p. 1682*

lueddemanniana (Brazil, Venezuela); epiphyte with solitary leaves; large 15 cm flowers, 2-5 together, with broad petals delicate purplish-rose, the front lobe amethyst-purple and crisped, throat yellow, lined purple, (July-Sept.). (I) *p. 1685*

luteola (Brazil, Ecuador, Perú, Bolivia); dwarf epiphyte, with solitary leaves on clustered pseudobulbs; small flowers in clusters, lemon-yellow, the middle lobe of lip white and wavy, the side lobes sometimes streaked with purple, (Nov.-Aug.). *Tropical* *p. 1684*

x mantinii (bowringiana x dowiana); showy epiphytic hybrid with large clusters of medium-size flowers, the sepals lavender-rose, the broader petals purplish-rose, lip deep red-purple marked with yellow in throat. (Fall bl.). (I) *p. 1684*

maxima (Colombia, Ecuador, Perú); magnificent species with furrowed club-shaped 1-leaved stems, and large 12-15 cm flowers pale at first, gradually becoming deeper to a bright rose, the darker lip beautifully ornamented with crimson veins (winter). (I) *p. 1686, 1687*

mossiae (Venezuela), "Easter orchid"; epiphyte with pseudobulbs bearing solitary leaves; the handsome flowers 12-15 cm dia., 3-5 or more in a cluster, blush or light rose, large frilled lip crimson and rose with golden yellow markings, often on a suffused white ground, (March-June). *p. 1683*

nobilior hort. (walkeriana) (Brazil); epiphyte with firm, paired leaves 12 cm long, and 10 cm flowers orchid-pink; lip with cream blotch veined violet. See C. walkeriana. *p. 1681*

percivaliana (Venezuela, Colombia); epiphyte growing on rocks, with 1-leaved pseudobulbs; flowers 10-12 cm smaller than mossiae but darker and richer in color, sepals and petals deep rose, frilled lip intense magenta-crimson, throat marked crimson and gold, (Nov.-Jan.). (I) *p. 1683*

rex (labiata var.) (Perú); distinctive Andean epiphyte with 1-leaved pseudobulbs, and striking flowers 12-15 cm across, sepals white tinged primrose, petals creamy-white and wavy, lip crimson with yellow in upper throat and frilled (summer). *Tropical.* *p. 1682*

schilleriana (Brazil); epiphyte with 2-leaved cane-like pseudobulbs tinged with red; the beautiful flowers are fleshy and of medium size, usually two on a stem, the narrow sepals and petals wavy-margined, rose-green spotted with brown, lip rose-red with darker lines, yellow inside, (April-May, Sept.-Oct.). (S) *p. 1685*

schroederae (Colombia); epiphyte with single-leaved pseudobulbs; large, sweet-scented flowers of dainty pink, the petals and lip crisped, throat purple in front and orange inside, (Feb.-May). (I) *p. 1683*

skinneri (Guatemala); epiphyte with long, twin-leaved pseudobulbs; the small 5-8 cm flowers in clusters, sepals and petals rose-purple with lightly pointed dark lip, yellowish-white in throat, (April-June). *p. 1685, 1687*

skinneri autumnalis (deckeri) (Brazil); like skinneri but smaller, with cylindric stems and short fleshy leaves, and a large cluster of rose-pink flowers with lip carmine rose, the throat rosy-red bordered by purple zone (early summer). (I) *p. 1687*

'Thayeriana' (intermedia x trianaei); charming flowers pale rose, tipped with purple. *p. 1681*

trianaei (Colombia), "Christmas orchid"; epiphyte with 1-leaved pseudobulbs, bearing showy flowers to 17 cm dia., 2-3 together, sepals and broad wavy petals rose, the frilled lip purple-crimson with yellow throat, (Dec.-March). *Tropical.* *p. 1683*

walkeriana (Brazil, Bolivia); elegant dwarf epiphyte, with egg-like pseudobulbs bearing a solitary leaf; sweet-scented flowers to 12 cm across, with rosy petals and sepals, the broad lip purplish-rose with red veining, yellow at base; winter. (I) *p. 1686*

warneri (Brazil); one of the finest species cattleyas, with large flowers 15 cm across, the wavy sepals and petals beautiful rose, the large lip rich crimson with yellow throat and finely fringed (summer). (I) *p. 1682*

warscewiczii alba (gigas alba) (Colombia); the beautiful pure white species which was sold by Lager in 1910 for $10,000; large flowers all white except for two yellow eyes in the throat; epiphytic, with solitary leaves, (summer bl.). (I) *p. 1684*

warscewiczii alba 'Firmin Lambeau' (gigas); a selected clone with large flowers 18-22 cm across, pure white except for trace of pale yellow in throat, borne on tall, solitary-leaved pseudobulbs. Valuable because it breeds all-white without the occasional colored lip. *p. 1686*

CATTLEYOPSIS *Orchidaceae* **S3OFW**

ortgiesiana (Cuba, Bahamas); miniature epiphyte resembling a small cattleya; elongate pseudobulbs; rigidly leathery leaves with unique saw-toothed margins; the inflorescence on long stalks, brilliant rose-carmine, lip marked strong purple and yellow (spring). *p. 1681*

x CATTLEYTONIA *Orchidaceae* **I3OFD**

'Rosy Jewel' (Cattleya bowringiana x Broughtonia sanguinea); compact bigeneric with narrow leaves 12-15 cm long on short pseudobulbs; wiry stalk bearing clusters of small cattleya-like flowers 5 cm across, a lovely rose-red. *p. 1663*

CAUTLEYA *Zingiberaceae* **I3LFD**

lutea (Roscoea) (Nepal, Sikkim, Darjeeling); rhizomatous Himalayan herb with clusters of fleshy roots, sometimes growing epiphytic, erect leafy, sheathed base and 4-6 sessile lanceolate leaves, purple underneath; yellow flowers in loose spike, with red-purple calyx. *p. 2130*

robusta (Himalayas); herbaceous perennial with long lanceolate fleshy leaves; inflorescence in bracted reddish spikes, with pale yellow flowers. *p. 2134, 2135*

spicata (Simla Himalaya); growing in habitat at an elevation of 1500-2400 m; rhizomatous herb 75 cm high, with dark leafy stems, broad-lanceolate, sessile leaves, and terminal spikes with crimson-maroon bracts appended to light yellow flowers with tubular corolla, the upper lobe erect, concave, lateral lobes broader and reflexed; calyx red, slit on one side; capsule red, when ripe the 3 valves are reflexed exposing their red lining and numerous small seeds. *p. 2130*

CAVANILLESIA *Bombacaceae* **S2LBM**

platanifolia (Panama, Colombia), the "Quipo"; tall tropical tree to 30 m high; the thick, smooth grayish trunk with soft wood of lighter weight than balsa; large 5 to 7-lobed leathery leaves, deciduous before blooming; small flowers with 5 narrow red petals 2 cm long, the longer stamens in clusters; hard spindle-shaped orange-colored ornamental fruit with 5 wings, 6-8 cm dia., very attractive on bare branches. *Tropical.* *p. 506*

CAVENDISHIA *Ericaceae* **I3LBD**

acuminata (Colombia, Ecuador); evergreen shrub at home in the Andes, with pendulous branches; leathery leaves 5-8 cm long; showy inflated flowers 2 cm long, bright crimson red with pale green tips, covered in bud by large scarlet bracts. *Subtropic.* *p. 957*

CEANOTHUS *Rhamnaceae* **C2LBD**

griseus (No. California), "Wild lilac"; low spreading shrub or upright to 2½ m; scandent branches with shiny dark green, corrugated leaves 3-5 cm long, gray-hairy beneath; violet-blue flowers. *p. 1990*

griseus horizontalis (No. California), "Carmel creeper"; shrubby ground cover from Monterey; low and creeping; dark green oval, glossy leaves to 5 cm; blue flowers in dense clusters. *p. 1990*

CECROPIA *Moraceae* **S2LBM**

peltata (Puerto Rico to Jamaica), "Guarumo"; noted tropical tree to 18 m high, of sparry habit and with milky juice, its hollow branches often inhabited by vicious ants; the large decorative, peltate, long stalked leaves are palmately 7-9-lobed, rough hairy above and shimmering white-downy beneath, flashing like silvery mirrors when turned up by a breeze. *Tropical* *p. 1566*

CEDRELA *Meliaceae* **I2LBM**

toona (New South Wales, Queensland), "Australian red-cedar"; large, partly deciduous tree to 30 m, with colored wood; and with fern-like pinnate 30 cm leaves opening bronze; fragrant honey-scented white or pink flowers in large panicles; winged seed. *p. 1551*

CEDRUS *Pinaceae (Coniferae)* **C2LBM**

atlantica (Morocco, Algeria), "Atlas cedar"; slow-growing, large evergreen tree to 30 m high, with wide-spreading branches; stiff, bluish-green needle-shaped, 4-angled leaves to 2½ cm long, softer than C. libani, clustered on short stout, lateral spurs; ovoid male cones erect, 8 cm long; female cones smaller. *Warm Temperate.* *p. 838, 845*

atlantica 'Glauca pendula', "Weeping blue cedar"; a variety of weeping habit, with the lateral pendulous branches drooping like a bluish curtain 3 m or more from limbs. *Warm temperate.* *p. 841*

deodara (Himalayas), "Deodar cedar"; outstandingly graceful, tall tree of pyramidal habit, with branches and leading shoots pendulous; slender, needle-thin leaves to 4 or 5 cm long, dark bluish green. *p. 838, 845, 846*

libani (Syria, Lebanon), "Cedar of Lebanon"; aristocratic conifer; when young with branches erect; tufted needles, very stiff and sharp, on short lateral shoots, to 2 cm long, green or glaucous; with age trees will branch and grow from 15 to 30 m high, with branches horizontal and fan-like. *Temperate.* *p. 841, 845*

CEIBA *Bombacaceae* **S2LBD**

pentandra (Tropics of America, Africa, Asia), the "Kapok tree" or "Silk-cotton"; large deciduous tree to 40 m high, with widely spreading branches, trunk to 3 m thick and often prickly, and forming board-like buttresses; digitately compound leaves, of 5-7 elliptic leaflets, and large dense clusters of small fragrant flowers 2 cm long, with fleshy calyx, rosy outside, yellowish inside; the fruit a leathery capsule 10-12 cm long with the seeds embedded in long cotton-like fiber or kapok. *Tropical.* *p. 505, 506*

CELMISIA *Compositae* **C2LBDh**

coriacea (New Zealand), the "Mountain daisy"; noble rosette, at home along the Southern Alps and to the Fiordland, with stiff-leathery sword-like leaves 30-60 cm long, beautifully covered with silver skin above when young, later dark green and shining; beneath dense with silvery wool; large daisy-like rayflowers 8-10 cm across, white with golden center, on woolly stalks. *Warm-temperate.* *p. 815*

CELOSIA *Amaranthaceae* **S2HBM**

argentea (Trop. Asia), "Chinese wool-flower"; showy herbaceous tropical annual 30-50 cm high, succulent angled stems with narrow ovate fresh green leaves; toward apex the branching inflorescence of numerous plume-like spikes a glistening silvery-white. *p. 84*

argentea 'Castle Gould'; a beautiful cultivar of C. arg. childsii from Johore; with immense heads of loosely twisted, pendant, feathery plumes in shades of red or yellow. *Tropical.* *p. 83*

argentea cristata 'Red and Gold'; curious form showing both yellow and red in its crest. *p. 83*

argentea plumosa 'Flame', "Burnt plume"; herbaceous annual from Tropical Asia with fresh-green ovate leaves, and with stem and branches terminated by dense chaffy spikes highly colored as fiery red plumes. *Tropical.* *p. 83*

argentea plumosa 'Golden Fleece'; fleshy herb with light-green lanceolate leaves and showy, feathery flower spike in yellow. *p. 83*

argentea pyramidalis (Trop. Asia), "Plume celosia"; a taller growing annual ½-1 m high, with erect stems bearing spectacular pyramidal plumes with silky threads, and looking like the feathery inflorescence of Pampas grass, but in brilliant colors of luminous crimson-red, bronze, copper or golden yellow, carried well above the fresh-green foliage. Useful cut flowers in late summer; may also be dried for winter bouquets. *Tropical.* *p. 83*

argentea thompsonii, compact plant with numerous, plumy, red flower heads. *p. 83*

CELSIA *Scrophulariaceae* **C2LBD**

arcturus (Crete, Asia Minor), "Cretan bear's tail"; erect biennial or half-hardy perennial herb with basal leaves lobed and a single hairy stem 20-45 cm high with ovate, crenate foliage, bearing a loose raceme of large clear-yellow, stalked flowers with purple anthers; July-Sept. *p. 2058*

CENTAUREA *Compositae* **I2LBM**

americana (Missouri to Louisiana, Mexico), "Basket-flower"; annual herb 1-2 m high, with oblong-lanceolate leaves on stout stem; flower heads 8-12 cm across, rose or flesh-colored or purplish, the bracts surrounding flowers are fringed. *p. 811*

candidissima (Sicily), "Dusty miller"; small perennial densely covered with white matted wool; leaves pinnately parted into broad lobes in maturity; inflorescence golden yellow. *Subtropic.* *p. 819*

cineraria (gymnocarpa) (Capri), "Dusty Miller"; perennial used for bedding, densely white-woolly, leaves 2-pinnate into linear entire lobes; inflorescence a large head of thistle-like lavender flowers with purple style. *p. 819*

moschata (suaveolens) (E. Mediterranean), "Sweet sultan"; popular annual herb to 60 cm; smooth leaves toothed or pinnately cut; fragrant solitary 5 cm flower heads white, yellow, purple, red or pink in horticultural forms; summer. *p. 812*

ragusina (Crete); half-hardy subshrub 60 cm or more high, with silvery stems and foliage covered with fine white hairs, the fleshy, oblong leaves deeply lobed, to 12 cm long; bright yellow flower heads. *p. 821*

CENTAUREA: see also Senecio

CENTRADENIA *Melastomataceae* **S2LBM**

floribunda (Guatemala, Mexico); evergreen shrub with red stems; opposite thin, 3-nerved, oblique-ovate leaves in pairs; flowers lilac rose. *p. 1552*

grandifolia (Mexico); attractive subshrub with 4-winged branches; broad ovate leaves with depressed veins, bright red beneath; flowers light rose in flat-topped clusters or cymes. *p. 1552*

inaequilateralis (Mexico); small semi-shrubby plant 30 cm high, with narrow-lanceolate, oblique leaves reddish beneath and fringed with eyelash hairs; flowers pink. *p. 1552*

CENTRATHERUM *Compositae* **I2LBM**

intermedium (Brazil), "Brazilian button flower"; herbaceous bush with serrate leaves, bearing at the ends of branches long-lasting, bluish-lavender, fluffy button flowers 2½ cm across, over a long blooming period. *p. 815, 822*

'Manaos Beauty' (Brazil); tropical herbaceous plant grown as an annual, to 60 cm high, with bluish-green, serrate leaves topped by interesting tassel-blossoms deep lavender blue and 3 cm across, blooming all season long; of uniform shape and growing like a clipped hedge planted in a row (Park Seed Co., Greenwood, S.C. 1975). *p. 820*

CENTROPOGON *Lobeliaceae* (Hortus), *Campanulaceae* (Zander) **S3HBD**

cornutus (C. America to Bolivia); handsome shrub with ovate 7 cm leaves; tubular constricted flowers 5 cm long, bright red, inside yellow and white. *p. 1514*

x lucyanus; tropical herbaceous plant raised in Marseilles 1856, said to be a hybrid of Centropogon fastuosus of Mexico x Siphocampylus betulaefolius from Brazil; a good basket plant; prostrate herbaceous branches with ovate, toothed, green leaves, and long tubular, bilabiate flowers rosy-carmine or burnt red, 4 cm long; winter-blooming. *p. 750*

CEPHALOCEREUS *Cactaceae* ***S1LBD**

chrysacanthus (Pilocereus) (Mexico: Puebla, Oaxaca); lovely tree-type column cactus branching from the base to 3 or 4 m high, and 6-8 cm thick, deep glossy green with 10-12 acute ribs, and golden spines, the upper part covered with dense, shaggy pale yellow hairs; the funnel-shaped flowers rosy-red and 8 cm long, blooming at night. *p. 620, 651, 656*

chrysacanthus cristatus; attractive crested form with its glossy green ribbed body beautifully covered with short golden yellow hairs. *p. 620*

collinsii (Mexico: Oaxaca); spiny column to 3 m high and nearly 5 cm thick, with 6-8 ribs, woolly areoles and dense with needle spines. *p. 652*

cometes (Mexico); tall columnar branching species 10 cm thick, dull green or grayish green, with 9-15 ribs; the growing tips have yellow spines and copious tufts of yellow hair, more abundant on the flowering side of the stem, like a mane. *p. 636*

dybowskii (Brazil, Bolivia); lovely species with erect, slender stems to 4 m high and 8 cm thick, very even and cylindrical, branching from base, up to 26 ribs, entirely covered with matted silky yellow-white wool, and yellowish needle spines; flower petals white. *p. 620, 646*

euphorbioides (Neobuxbaumia) (So. America); 10 cm thick, looking like a euphorbia, column to 5 m high, glaucous green, with 8 sharp ribs, and areoles close together and felted with white; day-flowering rose-red. Dr. Bravo (Mexico) refers this to Neobuxbaumia. *p. 636, 651*

fluminensis (S.E. Brazil); sprawling columns branching from the base, often coiling like a snake but branches erect, ascending or pendant, to 10 cm thick, with 10-17 ribs, the areoles with yellow spines and abundant white wool; flowers pink outside, white within. *Arid-tropical.* *p. 637*

glaucochrous (Bahia); beautiful, slender column of dwarf habit, bright blue, areoles with yellow wool and short spines; flowers with inner perianth segments pink to whitish. *p. 639*

hoppenstedtii (So. Mexico); slender many-ribbed column covered with coarse white spines; flowers white, tipped with rose. *p. 651, 654*

leucostele (Stephanocereus) (Brazil); from the deserts of Bahia, normally single columns to 5 m tall and with 12-18 shallow ribs, and dense wool covering the stem; cephalium densely white-woolly with a peculiar collar of yellow bristles 8 cm long; flowers white. *Arid-tropical.* *p. 636*

mezcalensis (Neobuxbaumia) (Guerrero); fresh green column with white spines, and short woolly at areole, globular as seedling, with the many ribs spirally twisted; flowers pale pink. *p. 651*

nobilis (W. Indies); erect branching, skinny cylindrical stem, dark green, 5-11 rounded ribs, areoles with yellow wool and reddish spines; flowers purplish. *p. 654, 656*

palmeri (E. Mexico), "Woolly torch cactus"; tree type to 8 m; slender columns, dark green, glaucous and bluish when young; 7-9 rounded ribs, white-hairy at top; flowers purplish. *Arid-tropical.* *p. 651*

polylophus (Neobuxbaumia) (Mexico); fat column to 12 m; close-ribbed, deep green, yellow-spined; dark red flowers to 8 cm long. *Arid-tropical.* *p. 651*

robustus (ulei) (Brazil: Rio and Cabo Frio); tall column to 6 m high, thick stem with ribbed branches 10 cm dia., covered with a pale whitish-blue glaucescence, and densely woolly at the top; on the flowering side near the top is a silvery mane of long hair; flowers white with purple anthers. *p. 644*

royenii (West Indies); strong columns to 6 m high branching near base, to 8 cm thick, bluish green, with 7-11 ribs, the areoles with white hair tufts, and long light brown spines; small shell-pink tubular flowers brownish outside. *Arid-tropical.* *p. 639*

russellianus (Colombia, Venezuela); attractive column growing into trees, 7 m high branching at top, satiny moss-green or glaucous, 4-6 ribs, with channels curving back from the notched rib, the areoles set with white hair and short brown spines; flowers cream. *p. 646*

senilis (Mexico), "Old man cactus"; slender column to 6 m or more high, and to 30-40 cm thick, closely ribbed, and covered with long gray hairs; nocturnal flowers rose-colored, to 9 cm long. *Arid-tropical.* *p. 19*, 618, 620, 637, 646, 651*

senilis cristatus; curious crestate form in form of a fan, entirely covered with snowy-white hairs. *p. 651*

smithianus (Venezuela, Trinidad), erect or clambering stem simple or branched, glossy green, purplish at the top, to 8 cm thick, with 9-11 ribs, notched, and felted with areoles; night-blooming reddish into white. *p. 636*

CEPHALOPENTANDRA *Cucurbitaceae* **S3LBD**

ecirrhosa (Momordica) (Kenya); curious succulent with short fleshy thick trunk of irregular conical shape, sprouting slender, wire-like stems climbing by tendrils, leaves oval or arrow-shaped; yellowish flowers; fleshy, warted fruit, bursting when ripe into irregular valves. *p. 933*

CEPHALOPHYLLUM *Aizoaceae* **I2LBD**

alstonii (Cape Prov.: Karroo), "Red spike"; striking succulent forming dense cushions of erect, and glaucous green leaves 7 to 10 cm long, and usually angled-cylindrical; showy flowers ruby-red. According to Herre of Stellenbosch, the "Diamond" among the Mesembryanthemums. Known also as Cylindrophyllum in hort. *Arid-subtropic.* *p. 59*

aureorubrum (Cape Prov.: Namaqualand); spreading succulent with bold leaves 5-6 cm long, flattish above, glaucous gray green; 4 cm flowers golden yellow inside, magenta red toward tips. *p. 59*

ceresianum (Cape Prov.); trailing succulent with soft 3-angled leaves in opposite pairs, 4-8 cm long; yellow flowers 4 cm across. *p. 59*

gracile (Cape. Prov.); trailing succulent with 3-angled yellow-green leaves, flat above, round below, to 4 cm long; solitary flowers 3-4 cm across, lemon to deep yellow. *p. 59*

CEPHALOTAXUS *Cephalotaxaceae (Coniferae)* **I2LFMh**

drupacea pedunculata (harringtoniana) (Japan), "Plum-yew" or "Cows-tail pine"; small ornamental evergreen rarely higher than 10 m, arching branches with 2-ranked linear leaves 4-6 cm long, glossy green, with 2 grayish bands beneath, and abruptly pointed; on female plants the pendulous greenish, spindle-shaped fruit 2-3 cm long. *p. 850*

CEPHALOTUS *Cephalotaceae (Carnivorous Pl.)* **I3HFM**
follicularis (Western Australia), the "West Australian pitcher plant"; a curious herbaceous perennial, rosette only 5-8 cm high, earth-hugging, with two types of leaves, one normal ovate-flat, green and fleshy in the center of the rosette; the other type in form of a curious little pitcher 2½-5 cm long, on the outer margins of the plant, with down-pointed teeth inside the trap mouth, holding water, and carnivorous, pale green with maroon tinting, and shielded by a red-veined lid; tiny buff flowers on 60 cm stalk. *p. 764*

CERATONIA *Leguminosae* **I2LBD**
siliqua (Eastern Mediterranean Reg.), "St. John's bread" or "Carob"; evergreen tree 12-15 m, with stout trunk and rounded head of branches; leaves pinnate, 15-30 cm long, leathery; flowers in cylindrical racemes to 15 cm long; fruit a brown pod 12-30 cm long, the pulp of which is sweet and much valued in S. Europe as animal food, or for chewing. *Subtropic. p. 1379*

CERATOPETALUM *Cunoniaceae* **I2LBD**
gummiferum (Australia: New So. Wales), "Christmas bush"; handsome evergreen resinous tree 6-12 m high, with opposite 8 cm leaves of 3 narrow leaflets; numerous small flowers with deeply lobed petals, in loose clusters, white at first, turning coral red; when petals drop the calyx enlarges, turning brilliant red at Christmas time (in Australia). *p. 934*

CERATOPTERIS *Parkeriaceae (Filices)* **S3LFW**
thalictroides (in quiet waters of the Tropics), "Water fern"; a true aquatic fern with rosettes of light green, succulent fronds, barren ones floating and forming young plantlets along the lobed margins, the fertile fronds divided into linear segments. The leaves are widely eaten in the Orient as a vegetable. *Humid-tropical. p. 1078, 1083*

CERATOSTEMA *Ericaceae* **I2LBD**
callistum (Perú); attractive woody epiphyte with branches to 5 m long, the leathery ovate-pointed leaves arranged like shingles along the pendant stems; tubular flowers 3 cm long, scarlet red with yellow crowns, in small terminal clusters. *p. 957*

CERATOSTIGMA *Plumbaginaceae* **I2LBD**
willmottianum (W. China), "Chinese plumbago"; low spreading shrub to 1½ m high, with angled branches; obovate dull green leaves 5 cm long, bristly on both sides; salver-shaped flowers 2 cm across; limb sky-blue with white eye and with rosy tube; summer-blooming. *Subtropic. p. 1952*

CERATOSTYLIS *Orchidaceae* **S3OFW**
rubra (Philippines); charming small epiphyte; clustered stems with glossy green, fleshy semi-cylindrical, grooved leaves to 12 cm long; showy short-stalked flowers opening flat, brilliant salmon-red, 3 cm across. *Humid-tropical. p. 1681*

CERATOZAMIA *Cycadaceae* **I-S1LBD**
kuesteriana (Mexico); short globose or branching trunk 25 cm thick, supports a head of finely pinnate leaves 1 m or more long, on tomentose, spiny petioles; the well-spaced rigid, lanceolate leaflets 20 cm long, shining dark green or olive on surface, brownish beneath. *p. 938*

mexicana (Mexico), "Mexican horncone"; palm-like cycad with stiff pinnate glaucous and hairy leaves borne in a whorl on a short hairy trunk, to 2 m high, with up to 150 leathery leaflets, the stalks spiny; the flowers in cones. *Tropical. p. 936, 940*

sp. 'Hilda' (Mexico), "Bamboo zamia"; palm-like cycad with only short trunk, bearing stiff pinnate fronds 1-1½ m long, in shade even 2 to 3 m tall; the bamboo-like axis beige and lightly armed with prickles; thin-leathery, shiny grass green leaflets 15 cm long, whorled in pairs nearly around stem. Quite unusual in its type. *Tropical. p. 938*

spiralis (Macrozamia) (New South Wales); cycad with thick trunk usually below surface and ovoid but sometimes above and cylindrical to 2 m or more, with 1-2 m pinnate leathery leaves, the linear, flat leaflets spine-tipped and sickle-shaped, shiny deep green. *p. 944*

CERBERA *Apocynaceae* **S3LBD**
manghas (Polynesia, Hongkong, Malaya, India); evergreen shrub or small tree to 6 m high, belonging to the mangrove swamp flora, with milky latex; alternate leathery ovate leaves 15-30 cm long crowded on young branches; fragrant white tubular flowers with 5 spreading lobes and rose-pink center, 3-8 cm across; the pink to black roundish fruit 5-10 cm long. *p. 136*

CERCESTIS *Araceae* **S3LFM**
afzelii (Trop. West Africa); low creeper and climber with dull green leaves hastate triangular in outline, with big midlobe, somewhat similar to Nephthytis, 15-20 cm long and 20-30 cm wide. *p. 209*

CERCIS *Leguminosae* **I2LBD**
siliquastrum (S. Europe and the Orient), "Judas tree" or "Redbud"; tree to 12 m, usually smaller and more shrubby; leaves deeply cordate, 6-10 cm wide, glaucous green; flowers bright purplish-rose 1-1½ cm long, in clusters of 3 to 6, produced in immense quantities directly from branches young and old, often appearing before the leaves. *p. 1379*

CEREUS *Cactaceae* **S-I1LBD**
azureus (No. Argentina, So. Brazil); slender column to 3 m high, glaucous blue with a metallic sheen, 6-7 notched ribs with woolly areoles and thin black spines; day-blooming white, brown outside. *p. 640*

caesius monstrosus (Brazil); glaucous silver-gray column of irregular growth with high ribs and forming several heads; small spines few. *p. 654*

childsii (Brazil); handsome branching bluish columns to 15 cm thick, with 4-6 compressed ribs and long needle spines; flowers large and one of the few of deep rose coloring; sweetly fragrant. *p. 658*

dayamii (Argentina: Chaco); erect or leaning on trees, to 20 m long, much branched, stems to 20 cm thick, dull green, with 5-6 ribs; areoles with brownish wool and short spines; flowers white inside. *p. 652*

x gonianthus (dayamii hyb.), attractive glaucous blue "Flowering tree-cereus"; branching from base to 5 m high, the deeply 5-6 angled stems constricted into short joints; flowers with white inner petals, reddish outer petals; red, edible sweet fruit; similar in appearance to 'peruvianus' but spineless. *p. 635*

hexagonus (Colombia), "South American blue column"; tall tree type to 15 m, branching near base; glaucous blue-green fleshy columns, with 4-6 high ribs, and few spines; white flowers 20-25 cm long; reddish fruit to 12 cm. *Tropical. p. 641*

hildmannianus (Brazil: Guanabara); treelike column cactus, freely branching, to 5 m high, with stems 10-12 cm dia, at first bluish then passing to grayish green, with 5 or 6 winglike acute ribs, notched at 2 to 3 cm, nearly spineless; funnel-flowers to over 20 cm long, greenish outside, white inside; large red, edible fruit. *Tropical. p. 659*

hoppenstedtii: see under Cephalocereus

jamacaru (Brazil); branching tree type to 10 m; slender column quite blue when young, deeply 4-6-ribbed, spines yellow to brown; flowers white. *Tropical. p. 643, 654*

jamacaru monstrosus; monstrose form, a slender glaucous blue column of irregular growth and knobby; almost spineless; very slow-growing. *p. 654*

obtusus (S. E. Coast of Brazil); stem erect or semi-prostrate, branching at base, dull green and glaucous, branches at first strongly ribbed with notches, but in age simply angled, few yellowish spines; flowers with inner petals white. *p. 636*

pernambucensis (Brazil coast, Uruguay); clustering clump of slender columns, pale green, sometimes nearly white; 3-5 prominent ribs strongly crenate, white wool at areoles; flowers white, tube red. *p. 654*

peruvianus (C. Brazil); thought to be the true species; sparry tree type with slender columns, powdery blue; tan spines. *p. 618, 654*

peruvianus hort.; the commonly cultivated tree-cereus in the trade, possibly a hybrid; fleshy columns 6-9-ribbed, glaucous bluish-green, free branching; variable, usually the older portions with long brown spines, upper or younger sections often nearly spineless; showy nocturnal flowers to 24 cm long, the inside petals white to greenish, outside tinged with copper; the crimson-red fruit is edible. *Tropical. p. 19*, 635, 639*

peruvianus glaucus; a blue form, slender fleshy column with few ribs and more powdery blue, areoles short-woolly; gray spines. *p. 654*

peruvianus 'Monstrosus', "Curiosity plant"; an irregular growing monstrose form constantly forming new heads; glaucous bluish, slow growing but always retaining its habit. *Tropical. p. 635, 639*

peruvianus 'Monstrosus minor'; a branched monstrose form remaining dwarf, deep green, with woolly cephalia and fine, needle-like light brown spines. *p. 646*

sublanatus (Cephalocereus arrabidae) (Brazil: Bahia, Pernambuco); slender column cactus with many branches to 3 m high but often procumbent, 6-10 cm thick, green to bluish with 6-8 prominent ribs and small spine clusters; flowers 7 cm long, green on outside, greenish white inside. *p. 657*

tetragonus (Rio de Janeiro); freely branching green columns to 2 m with 4-5 high ribs, spines nearly black; reddish funnel-form flowers. *p. 636*

validus (Argentina); branching columns to 2 m, glaucous when young, 4-8 ribs, long spined; large nightblooming flowers greenish-white inside, brownish-red outside. *p. 636, 641*

variabilis (Coast of Brazil); creeping over rocks or clambering into trees, short thick joints, 3-5 ribs strongly indented, yellow spines; nightblooming lemon-white flowers. *p. 641, 654*

CEREUS: (see also Acanthocereus, Carnegiea, Cephalocereus, Cryptocereus, Echinocereus, Espostoa, Haageocereus, Hylocereus, Lemaireocereus, Lophocereus, Monvillea, Myrtillocactus, Nyctocereus, Oreocereus, Pachycereus, Selenicereus, Trichocereus)

CEROPEGIA *Asclepiadaceae* ***I1HFD**
ampliata (Mozambique, Natal, Namibia); climbing plant with rather thick branches, small leaves soon falling, but flowers large and beautiful, to 6 cm long, tubular with inflated base; tube near white inside with green nerves; violet hairs in the swollen base, the petals purple and united at tip. *p. 360*

aristolochioides (Trop. Africa: Sénégal to Ethiopia); slender stems slightly succulent, with ovate glossy green leaves; flowers a whitish curved tube to 15 mm long, the lobes inside yellow, outside burnt crimson. *Tropical. p. 358*

armandii (S.W. Madagascar); succulent stems stapelia-like to 2 cm thick, sprawling 10-15 cm long, the flowering stem sections much prolonged and twining to over 1 m long; 7 mm ovate leaves; flowers lantern-like, beige with greenish 12 mm lobes. *Tropical.* *p. 358*

ballyana (Kenya); robust, twining pencil-like stems, with fleshy leaves, and canary-cream flowers with red-brown spots 6-7 cm long, the blackish lobes twisted together. *Tropical.* *p. 358*

barkleyi (Cape Province); slender vine from corm-like roots, ovate, green, succulent leaves with silver-white veining; flowers greenish veined with purple. *p. 359*

caffrorum (Eastern So. Africa), "Lamp flower"; wiry vine with small, grass-green, ovate leaves in pairs, with red veins and petioles; flowers green with purple lines. *p. 359*

debilis (Malawi), "Needle vine"; threadlike vine with corm-like roots, the small leaves narrow-linear, and flowers greenish marked with purple. *p. 359, 360, 361*

de-vecchii (Ethiopia, Yemen); very succulent twining or creeping stems almost leafless, with flowers tinged pale green or pink, spotted red-brown, with 2-3 cm tube and spreading petals 1-2 cm long. *p. 361*

dichotoma (Canary Islands); succulent, upright, forked gray stems with scattered linear leaves; flowers yellow. *p. 358, 359, 360*

dimorpha (S. W. Madagascar); stapelia-like succulent with fleshy non-flowering stems 1½ cm thick and 15 cm high; the slender flowering segments with linear leaves ½-8 cm long; flowers with inflated tube marked with purple. *p. 361*

distincta (Zanzibar); twining plant with ovate leaves 5 cm long; flowers a curved, fluted funnel 2½ cm long, rose-pink spotted purple; apex lobes curved inward to form 5-angled cover, dark purple. *p. 362*

elegans (India: Malabar; Ceylon); trailer with elongate or oval leaves minutely ciliate, not fleshy; flowers a tube expanded funnel-like, near white and blotched with purple; apex lobes united in the center, and edged with long dark hairs. *p. 362*

fimbriata (So. Africa: S. E. Cape); very succulent twining stems, leaves when present reduced to scales 1 cm long; flowers with tube 3-5 cm long, topped by an umbrella-like canopy. *p. 358*

fusca (Canary Isl.), "Carnival lantern"; succulent shrub with upright, forked, cylindrical columns constricted at joints, gray to purplish; flowers brown and yellow. *Subtropic.* *p. 359, 361*

galeata (Kenya); twining, leafless stems very succulent; flowers interesting with tubular corolla inflated balloon-like at base, 4 cm long, yellow-green with brown blotches, toward top funnel-shaped and covered by a canopy fringed with purple hairs. *p. 361*

haygarthii (Natal), "Wine-glass vine"; twining, succulent stem with small ovate leaves; flower like a fluted wineglass with bent stem, cream with specks of maroon, covered by maroon parachute; from center rises a maroon stalk topped by red knob, sparsely covered by white hair. *Subtropic.* *p. 360, 362*

haygarthii fa. lugardae (Kenya, Tanzania, Mozambique, Zimbabwe, Botswana); robust twiner with flowers a bent, flaring trumpet pinkish with brownish blotching, tipped by stalked reddish knob. Photo plant in collection Marnier-Lapostolle. *p. 362*

mozambicensis (So. Zaire, East Africa to Mombasa); twiner with smooth elliptic leaves and axillary flowers constricted above base, expanded toward apex, greenish-white spotted red, lobes recurved and hairy. *p. 360*

multiflora (Cape Prov., Transvaal, Namibia); slender vine from turnip-like tuber, twining stem with linear leaves 2-3 cm long; flowers swollen at base, cylindric greenish-white tube to 2½ cm long, tipped by threadlike lobes joined at apex. *p. 358*

nilotica (Ethiopia, Uganda); tuberous-rooted twiner with 4-angled stems, ovate fleshy leaves dentate; flowers with corolla to 4 cm long, club-shaped, dark brown; triangular lobes with brown hairs inside, yellow spots at base. *p. 362*

peulliorum var. breviloba (Central African Republic); twining succulent stems usually leafless, with attractive flowers a curving trumpet, whitish with purple spots, the closed, winged apex forming a small lantern. *p. 361*

pygmaea (Transvaal, Namibia); small succulent from a big tuber 5-7 cm broad, the erect stalk 10-15 cm high, lanceolate 6-7 cm leaves; the flowers to 8 cm long, from cylindrical base to spreading lobes covered with white, bristly hairs. *p. 361*

radicans (So. Africa), "Umbrella flower"; succulent, prostrate creeper with small ovate, dark green leaves; flowers a slender tube, expanding into joining lobes zoned in purple, white and green. *p. 359*

rendallii (Transvaal); climber with smooth ovate to linear leaves, and flowers with white curved tube, swollen at purple base and expanded toward mouth, the green lobes claw-like, united at tips like an umbrella. *p. 358, 362*

robynsiana (West Africa, Zaire); climber with fleshy pointed leaves; curious flowers 5 cm long, inflated balloon-like near base, above it an expanding whitish-green funnel with red-brown spots and tipped by long beak-like pointed lobes. *p. 362*

sandersonii (Natal), "Parachute plant"; twining succulent with small ovate, fresh green leaves on younger tips; flowers like a parachute mottled light and dark green. *Subtropic.* *p. 359, 363*

sororia (So. Africa: E. Cape Prov.); curious succulent with erect branching wire-thin stems and long-linear leaves; the flowers a long tube inflated in lower part and striated, at apex the thread-like lobes not joined and hanging free. *p. 358*

stapeliaeformis (Cape Province); succulent stems stout, short jointed, gray-green with purple, leaves reduced to slight knobs as in Stapelia; flowers funnel-like. *p. 359, 362*

variegata cornigera (syn. Adelaide) (Kenya); a variety of C. variegata from Arabia, with stout succulent, snaky stems and axillary flowers a slender tube swollen at base, whitish-green and marbled brownish, the 5 lobes spreading wide, concave-linear and horn-like. *p. 360*

woodii (Natal), "String of hearts"; so called because of the trailing, threadlike stems set with pairs of succulent, heartshaped, bluish leaves 1-2 cm across, marbled with silver, purple beneath; corm-like roots; flowers purplish. *Subtropic.* *p. 359, 360, 361, 363, 2092*

CEROXYLON *Palmae* **I2LFD**

andicola (Colombia); "Waxpalm" of the Andes, found at altitudes above 3000 m; tallest amongst palms, with straight trunks to 65 m tall, covered with a layer of wax and looking like marble columns to 60 cm thick, slightly swollen in the middle; crown of pinnate fronds to 6 m long; linear dark green leaflets split at end, whitish powder underneath. *Subtropic* *p. 1856*

quindiuense (Venezuela, Colombia: Antioquia), "Andean Wax-palm"; majestic very tall palm, at home in high valleys of the Central Andes to an altitude of 3000 m; the straight, slender trunk 60 m or more high, covered with silvery gray wax, smooth except for prominent rings from old leafscars; crown of graceful, pinnate fronds 5 m or more long, the rigid, dark green leaflets pendant, and powdery white beneath; large pendulous clusters of brown fruit 3 cm long. The wax is used in making candles and polish. *Subtropic.* *p. 1869*

CESTRUM *Solanaceae* **S2LBM**

aurantiacum (Guatemala); rambling or half-climbing shrub with matte green ovate leaves 5-8 cm long, and leafy pyramidal clusters of bright orange-yellow 2½ cm flowers with reflexed lobes. *Subtropic.* *p. 2072*

nocturnum (West Indies), "Night jessamine" or "Queen of the Night"; evergreen shrub to 2 or 3 m high with wiry, brownish branches; shining, thin-leathery, 8 to 15 cm ovate leaves, and small, greenish or creamy-white, slender tubular flowers with pointed lobes, to 3 cm long, axillary in profuse clusters, intensely perfumed at night, and blooming mostly from July to September, but at intervals throughout the year. *Tropical.* *p. 2078, 2082, 2084*

parqui (Chile), the "Willow-leaved jessamine"; deciduous shrub 2-4 m high, with lanceolate leaves 5-12 cm long, and greenish-yellow tubular flowers with spreading lobes, in profuse clusters, intensely fragrant at night. *p. 2084*

parqui spurium (Chile), "Willow-jasmine"; partially evergreen shrub with willowy, erect stems, to 2 m high, small ovate fresh-green leaves 5-12 cm long; at branch ends the heavy clusters of slender tubular flowers 3-4 cm long, yellow, and strongly perfumed at night. *Subtropic.* *p. 2067*

purpureum (elegans) (Mexico); rambling evergreen shrub to 3 m or more, with soft-hairy branches and ovate leaves to 10 cm long, the flowers in nodding clusters, slender tubular corolla with spreading lobes, glowing wine-red. *p. 2078*

CETERACH *Polypodiaceae (Filices)* **I3LFD**

officinarum (C. and So. Europe to N. Asia and Africa), the "Scale-fern"; small tufted xerophyte, rhizome covered with black hairs, the pinnate or lobed fronds 15 cm long, thick-leathery, dark green and smooth above, underneath dense with yellow-brown scales. *Warm temperate* *p. 1100*

CHAENOMELES *Rosaceae* **C2LBDh**

lagenaria (Cydonia japonica hort.) (China; cult. in Japan), "Japanese quince"; deciduous shrub to 3 m high, of dense habit, more or less spiny with sharply toothed, glossy green, ovate leaves; the showy, waxy flowers red, to 5 cm across, in spring before the leaves; roundish fruit greenish-yellow and fragrant. *p. 1993*

CHAENOMELES: see also Cydonia

CHAENOSTOMA *Scrophulariaceae* **I2LBD**

fastigiatum (So. Africa), "Little stars"; a low much branched perennial with small 1cm oblong leaves and profuse masses of small 1 cm pink to white, starry flowers at all times, mainly from July to October, in head-like racemes. *p. 2051*

grandiflorum (Sutera) (So. Africa), "Purple glory tree"; sticky pubescent small subshrub with 2½ cm toothed leaves, and terminal racemes of deep purple tubular flowers with spreading petals. *p. 2058, 2060*

CHAMAEALOE *Liliaceae* **I2LBD**

africana (Cape Prov.), "False aloe"; low, mat-forming stemless rosette of numerous fleshy leaves, broad at lower end and together forming a bulb-like base, narrow-linear to awl-shaped toward apex, 10 cm long, the upper surface grooved, pale green with distinct lines lengthwise; margins with white teeth; small tubular white flowers. *p. 1414*

africana x Aloe parvula; beautiful bigeneric hybrid by Hummel; a dense glaucous-green succulent rosette of slender, soft-fleshy erect spreading leaves arranged spirally; leaves rounded on bottom, flat on top, and decorated all over with long, soft, creamy spines. *p. 1403*

CHAMAECEREUS *Cactaceae* **I1LBD**

'Hummel's silvestri hybrid' (C. silvestri x Lobivia aurea); freely suckering little plant with branches more plump and densely covered with soft white spines. *p. 669*

silvestri (Argentina), "Peanut cactus"; little clusters of short cylindric, fresh green branches with soft white spines; flowers orange-scarlet. *Subtropic.* *p. 618, 669*

silvestri crassicaulis cristatus; a form with stems fasciated and monstrose, beautifully covered with soft white spines; blooms freely with larger orange-scarlet diurnal flowers which set good seed. *p. 669*

silvestri 'Crested'; a curious form with stems thickened and crested like a little green fan clothed with soft white spines. *p. 669*

CHAMAECYPARIS *Cupressaceae (Coniferae)* **C2LBMh**

obtusa (Japan), "Hinoki cypress"; coniferous, slow-growing evergreen tree to 30 m or more high; handsome with glossy dark green, scale-like leaves in flat, fan-like branchlets. *Temperate.* *p. 842*

obtusa nana compacta (Japan), "False cypress"; tough, slow growing, dwarf and compact form of an otherwise large tree, with glossy dark green, scale-like leaves in flat, fan-like horizontal branchlets. *p. 839*

pisifera plumosa (Japan); a soft-leaved form of the "Sawara cypress"; dense conical evergreen with feathery branchlets flattened and slightly drooping; small awl-shaped sharp needles, glossy green above and with silvery-white lines beneath. *p. 842*

CHAMAEDOREA *Palmae* **•S1LNM**

brachypoda (sometimes grown as stolonifera in hort.) (Guatemala), "Fishtail rattan"; stoloniferous small palm to 2 m high, covering in time large areas by running stolons; the thin rattan-like canes toward top carry the plaited satiny green leaves to 15 cm long and 10 cm wide, 11 to 13-ribbed on each side, the blade remaining undivided except for the bifid, deeply cleft apex, satiny green with pale axis beneath; male flowers yellow; the shingled female flowers followed by tiny oblong black fruit. Photographed in the collection of David Barry, California Jungle Gardens, West Los Angeles, 1958. *p. 1859*

cataractarum hort. (Mexico); one of the loveliest dwarf palms, compact and robust, of full habit, with single trunk bronzy green peppered with ivory-green dots, furnished with a well-leafed crown of numerous dark green fronds, only 40 cm in diameter when fully developed; female plants very pretty when loaded with scarlet fruit. *p. 1859*

concolor (Mexico); small clustering palm with slender canes from creeping rhizomes, the fronds pinnate, the leaflets broad rhombic-oblong with curved slender tips, shining green; fruit yellow. *p. 1860, 1863*

costaricana (C. America), "Showy bamboo palm", a clustering palm of great beauty, with bamboo-like dark green canes to 3 or even 6 m high, furnished from bottom to top with graceful pinnate fronds, to 50 cm long, each with about 40 pinnae, solid green, not glaucous, and tipped by a pair of broad-obovate leaflets as in a fishtail; long-stalked inflorescence bearing globular fruit. *Tropical.* *p. 1861*

elatior (Mexico), a "Rattan palm"; slender stems more or less climbing to 2½ m, the green cane to 2 cm thick; pinnate pendant leaves to 50 cm with lanceolate, thin-leathery leaflets spaced distantly in pairs, 25 cm long diminishing to 12 cm, and 2-3 cm wide, in mature specimen to 60 cm long; prominently ribbed and shining dark green; young leaves bifid; the inflorescence in basal panicles. *p. 1858*

elegans ((Collinia) (Mexico), "Parlor palm"; small graceful, relatively fast grower with thin stem to 3 m high, 3 times as high as Neanthe bella and eventually forming clusters; pinnate leaves loosely spirally arranged, broadly lanceolate, thin-leathery segments dark green; good keeper in shady locations; fruit yellow to white. *Tropical.* *p. 1859, 1861*

elegans 'Bella' (Neanthe bella) (E. Guatemala); a tree palm in miniature, from mountain forests of Mayaland, more dwarf in habit than Chamaedorea elegans and slow-growing; thin stems bearing near the top a graceful rosette of small, pinnate fronds, with narrow, hard-leathery dark green pinnae; will flower as a youthful plant in pots. *p. 1859, 1886*

ernesti-augusti (Eleutheropetalum) (Colombia); slender reed-like stem to 1 m high bearing a rosette of broad, simple, plaited leaves 60 cm long, deeply split at apex, dark green and serrate; showy inflorescence spikes bright orange-scarlet. *p. 1868*

erumpens (Honduras), "Bamboo palm"; suckering dwarf palm, forming bushy, erect clusters of thin, bamboo-like reed-stems, loosely furnished down to the base with short pinnate, drooping leaves, the segments are broad, almost papery, dark green and recurved; a good keeper when well established. *Tropical.* *p. 1859, 1863*

glaucifolia (Guatemala), "Blue leaf Chamaedorea"; slowly ascending, solitary trunk to 7 m high, draped with slender pinnate fronds 1 to 2 m long, the many well separated long and narrow leaflets glaucous gray over dark green; inflorescence between the foliage. *p. 1858*

klotzschiana (Mexico?); small palm with slender solitary stem bearing fronds with pinnae sigmoid, or S-shaped curved in opposite directions, and arranged in groups of 4 to 6 along the axis. *p. 1860*

martiana (Mexico: Chiapas); dwarf, spreading palm with many small forked reed-like stems, the fronds pinnate with pendant 15-20 cm leaflets narrow, deep green and widely separated. The palm pictured may be C. elatior. *p. 1860*

metallica, introduced in hort. as tenella (Mexico), the "Miniature fishtail"; one of the smallest of palms, slowly developing a stiff stem to 1 m high, and which bears a rosette of broad, entire leaves forked only toward apex. *Tropical.* *p. 1860*

nana (Costa Rica); very dwarf cane-type species with broad leaves; glossy green, thin-leathery and strongly ribbed, and bifid (divided to middle) like a pair of wings. *p. 1858*

"pacaya" of hort, (Panama, Costa Rica, Guatemala); slender cane-like trunk to 3 m high, with pinnate leaves about 1 m long, the leaflets long pointed S-shaped, shiny green on red rachis, fruit black; close to tepejilate but trunk more yellow-green with broad, stepped leaf-scars, broader pinnae and more papery. *p. 1860*

radicalis (Edanthe) (Mexico); slender, ringed 4 cm stems to 3 m tall, with arching pinnate fronds to 1 m long, close with numerous deep green leaflets, the rachis channeled; flowers yellow. *p. 1858, 1860*

seifrizii (graminifolia) (Mexico: Yucatán), "Reed palm"; small stoloniferous palm with clustering slender cane-like stems alternately furnished near the top with broadly spreading pinnate fronds, their pinnae long and narrow and spaced apart, giving the plant a lacy appearance; withstands some cold. *Tropical.* *p. 1859*

stolonifera (So. Mexico), "Climbing fishtail palm"; from the mountains of Chiapas; curious small palm with creeping stolons forming new plants with slender rattan-like canes about 1 cm in dia. and clambering to 2 m high; the broad plaited thin-leathery leaves with entire margins and not pinnate, satiny green and slightly glaucous, remaining undivided except for a fish-tail-like deep cleft at apex, short inflorescence below leaves with orange flowers, followed by small black fruit. *p. 1858*

CHAMAEGIGAS *Scrophulariaceae* **S3LFW**

intrepidus (Namibia); a stringy under-water plant with pretty, light pink flowers floating on the surface. *p. 2049*

CHAMAELAUCIUM *Myrtaceae* **C2LBD**

uncinatum (Western Australia); the "Geraldton wax-plant"; a heather-like shrub 1½-2 m high or more, with tiny linear leaves hooked near apex; the nodding branches with masses of 6 mm pink or lilac flowers of long-lasting quality. *p. 1605, 1613*

x CHAMAELOPSIS *Cactaceae* **S3LBD**

'Firechief' (Chamaecereus x Lobivia); striking bigeneric hybrid by Harry Johnson of California; small olive-green finger-like, 9 to 10 ribbed columns bearing needle spines and white radials, forming clusters; free-blooming with brilliant flame-red flowers to 8 cm across. *Arid-subtropic.* *p. 675*

CHAMAERANTHEMUM *Acanthaceae* **S3LFM**

gaudichaudii (Brazil); herb with creeping stem, small, oval leaves dark green, center silver gray; small lavender flowers with white star in center, in short raceme. *p. 46*

igneum (Xantheranthemum) (Perú); low, spreading herb with beautiful, dark brownish-green, oblanceolate, veloured leaves, and vein pattern in red to autumn-yellow; bright yellow flowers. *Tropical.* *p. 15*, 52*

venosum (Brazil); dwarf plant with wiry stems spreading close to the ground, its small, hard-leathery 5-8 cm ovate leaves grayish, and attractively marked with a network of silver along veins. *Tropical.* *p. 46*

venosum cv. 'India Plant' (Brazil); introduced by Mulford as Daedalacanthus, an attractive plant with oval, leathery leaves about 12 cm long, deep gray-green marked with beautiful silvery vein pattern; star-like flowers lavender with white center. Close to C. venosum but this has leaves generally only 5-6 cm long and the leafbase more obtuse. *p. 47*

CHAMAEROPS *Palmae* **•I2LBD-W**

humilis (Mediterranean, So. Europe, No. Africa), "European fan palm"; usually dwarf, clusterforming, sometimes to 6 m in arborescent forms; trunk rough, clothed with fiber; tough leaves relatively small, stiff and folded, with many narrow segments nearly to the base, on spiny, flat stalks; small red-brown fruit. *Subtropic.* *p. 1863, 1866, 1876, 1909*

humilis 'Nana'; one of the scrubby forms remaining low and compact, freely suckering and becoming bushy. Grown in California nurseries for planting in containers; very similar to the bushy forms in habitat in northern Morocco and in Andalusia, Spain. *p. 1866*

CHAMAEROPS: see also Trachycarpus

CHAMBEYRONIA *Palmae* **S3LBD**
macrocarpa (Australia, New Caledonia); beautiful, unarmed feather palm with trunk to 20 m tall, the pinnate fronds to 1 m or more long; alternate dark green leaflets, prominently ribbed, on yellow or brown petiole; attractive with young unfolding leaves deep blood-red; ovoid fruit 3 cm long. *Tropical.* *p. 1864*

CHARADROPHILA *Scrophulariaceae* **I3HFM**
capensis (South Africa: S. W. Cape); in habitat on moist rocks; a beautiful fibrous-rooted plant, velvety greenish-coppery leaves with pale midrib and crenate margins; the flowers with bilabiate axillary, sinningia-like blue corolla tube spreading into 5 broad lobes, white inside. Placed by Engler 1899 with the Gesneriaceae, but Moore refers to Scroph. *p. 1233, 2058*

CHASMANTHE *Iridaceae* **I2LBDd**
aethiopica (So. Africa); cormous plant with flat, gladiolus-like linear basal leaves and erect spike of reddish-yellow flowers with curved tubular 6 cm corolla, the large upper lobe hooded and contracted below middle. *p. 1334*

CHEILANTHES *Polypodiaceae (Filices)* **I2HFD**
bergiana (So. Africa, Malawi); small tufted, somewhat brittle, rock-loving fern with short rhizome, erect fronds, 30-45 cm long 3 to 4 pinnatifid, on tomentose stalks. *p. 1101*
gracillima (Brit. Columbia to California), "Lace-fern"; a tiny rock-fern with bipinnate, bronzy green, thin-leathery fronds under 5 cm long, but growing to 25 cm; brown-woolly beneath, margins recurved, on brown stalks. (h) *p. 1101*
myriophylla (Mexico to Chile); densely tufted fern with wiry brown, woolly stems and leathery 10-15 cm fronds 3-4 pinnate, the ultimate segments very small, roundish and bead-like, bright green above, woolly and scaly beneath. *p. 1101*
pulchella (Madeira, Canary Islands); attractive tufted fern, with shining brown stalks bearing fronds 8-30 cm long, finely cut in tripinnate fashion, the leaflets dense and feathery; preferring a cool location if grown indoors. *p. 1100*

CHEIRADENIA *Orchidaceae* **S3OFW**
imthunii (Venezuela); terrestrial species with straplike fleshy leaves; cupped, waxy flowers white, purple inside; lip pocket-like. *p. 1681*

CHEIRANTHUS *Cruciferae* **C2LBD**
cheiri (So. Europe), "Wallflower"; woody perennial, but grown as a biennial, blooming in spring; sweetscented flowers on terminal racemes like stocks, but in yellow-brown shades; narrow leaves slightly pubescent. *p. 927*

CHEIRIDOPSIS *Aizoaceae* **S2LBD**
candidissima (So. Africa), "Victory plant"; tufted succulent with pairs of long, boat-shaped, silver-gray leaves, 8-10 cm long; flowers pale pink. *Arid-subtropic.* *p. 57, 63*
gibbosa (Cape Prov.), clustering succulent with 1-2 pairs of keeled leaves, blush gray-green with darker green dots. *p. 63*
peculiaris (Cape Prov.: Namaqualand); low succulent with 1 or 2 leaf pairs, united at base, 4-5 cm long and wide, upper surface flat, gray-green with dark dots; flowers yellow 3-4 cm across. *p. 59*
rostrata (Cape Prov.); mat-forming succulent with spreading, tapering leaves 5-8 cm long often curved sideways, the lower portion united into a cylindric body, gray-green, keel and margins rough; large flowers lemon-yellow. *p. 63*
summitata (So. Africa); tufting succulent with paired, linear, keeled leaves and masses of long-stalked yellow, daisy-like flowers. *p. 63*
truncata (Cape Prov.: Karroo); clustering succulent with fleshy, split bodies, to 4 cm long, pale glaucous and velvety hairy; 6 cm yellow flowers. *p. 60*

CHELIDONIUM *Papaveraceae* **C2LFW**
majus fl. pl. (Europe, W. Asia to Iran), "Celandine" or "Swallow-wort"; perennial herb to 60 cm high, with erect, brittle, hairy stems having orange-colored juice; lobed leaves; double yellow 2 cm flowers in clusters, single in the species. *p. 1992*

CHELONISTELE *Orchidaceae* **I-S3OFW**
sulphurea (S. E. Asia), rock-dwelling species allied to coelogyne, the small pseudo-bulbs with broad, flaccid leaves, and racemes of small yellow flowers. *p. 1681*

CHIASTOPHYLLUM *Crassulaceae* **C2LFDh**
oppositifolium (Cotyledon simplicifolia hort.) (W. Caucasus); creeping forest perennial with roundish-ovate succulent leaves coarsely crenate, the inflorescence a pendulous raceme of tiny yellow campanulate flowers. *p. 905*

CHILENIA: see Neoporteria

CHILOGLOTTIS *Orchidaceae* **I3HFM**
trapeziformis (Australia); small terrestrial orchid growing from subterranean tubers; the very short stem carries paired, fleshy basal leaves, ovate to broadly lanceolate, nearly hugging the ground and to 20 cm long, light green with dark network of veins; flowers solitary and widely expanding, 3-5 cm across, greenish and tinted with copper, the lip with purple lobes. *p. 1704*

CHILOSCHISTA *Orchidaceae* **I-S3OFM**
lunifera (Sarcochilus) (Sikkim to Burma); dwarf leafless epiphyte consisting of tangled masses of roots, from the center of which rises an inflorescence bearing leaflike bracts and small 1 cm flowers, yellow with purple spot. (autumn). *p. 1693*

CHIMONANTHUS *Calycanthaceae* **I2LBD**
praecox (fragrans) (China), "Wintersweet"; deciduous shrub to 3 m high, blooming early winter from November on to March in the Northern hemisphere, long preceding the foliage; waxy 2 cm flowers with outer sepals and petals yellow, inner petals smaller and brown-purple; followed by the lustrous green lanceolate leaves 8-15 cm long. *p. 752*

CHIMONOBAMBUSA *Gramineae* **I2LBD**
marmorea (Arundinaria) (Japan); bushy dwarf bamboo with creeping rootstock, used in California for outdoor planting, 1 to 2 m high, and forming dense bush; slender coppery yellow stems 2 cm dia. with squarish knobs; green leaves 6-8 cm long, 1 cm wide. *p. 1312*
quadrangularis (Bambusa) (China, Japan); a tall running bamboo 6 to 10 m high, with square, coppery, hollow canes, 2 cm thick, wide-spreading and forming dense clusters; leaves 5-15 cm long, 2 cm wide, green with parallel veins, corrugated lengthwise. *p. 1312*

CHIONANTHUS *Oleaceae* **C2LBD**
retusa (China), the "Chinese fringe-tree"; deciduous small tree 3-6 m high with elliptic 10 cm leaves downy beneath, and numerous small white flowers with 4 narrow petals in showy pendulous panicles; dark blue fruit. *p. 1632, 1633*
virginicus (Pennsylvania to Florida and Texas), the "American fringe-tree"; deciduous tree to 10 m, with oblong leaves to 20 cm, veins downy beneath; white flowers with usually 4, sometimes 5-6 narrow linear 2½ cm petals, in drooping panicles; dark blue fruit. *Warm temperate.* *p. 1632*

CHIONODOXA *Liliaceae* **C2LBMd**
luciliae (Asia Minor, Crete), "Glory-of-the snow"; early spring-blooming, small bulbous plant to 20 cm high, related to Scilla, with narrow basal leaves and attractive, waxy, funnel-shaped flowers expanded star-like, of an intense blue, shading to white in the center. *p. 1428, 1447*
sardensis (Asia Minor), "Glory-of-the-snow"; bulbous herb with rolled channeled leaves, and all-blue flowers with long spreading lobes on nodding stemlets, 3 to 6 on each short stalk, in early Spring. *Subtropic.* *p. 1428*

CHIRITA *Gesneriaceae* **S3HFM**
hamosa (India); erect succulent plant of variable height, to 50 cm; very light green, opposite toothed leaves, waxy and lightly hairy, ovate and from 3-15 cm long; near apex the charming slipper flowers delicate pale pinkish lavender with whitish throat, 2-3 cm long. *p. 1232*
horsfieldii (Java); tropical herbaceous plant to 60 cm high, with fleshy ovate, hairy leaves in opposite pairs, and with crenate margins; at apex the clustering short, slipper-shaped flowers pale lavender-blue with yellowish white throat. *p. 1232*
lavandulacea (Malaya), "Hindustan gentian"; erect, branching, rather succulent plant with large ovate, soft hairy, opposite leaves with toothed margins, and whorls of axillary flowers with white pouchlike corolla tube and spreading limb of pale lavender blue, marked yellow in throat. *Humid-tropical.* *p. 1233*
micromusa (Thailand); large cordate leaves green and softly hairy; small flowers bright orange-yellow. *p. 1233*
pumila (No. India); erect herbaceous plant with bright green, fleshy, ovate quilted leaves with crenate margins; the nodding funnel-shaped hairy flowers 4 cm long, cream with flaring limb purplish lavender. *p. 1232*
sinensis (So. China), "Silver chirita"; attractive stemless plant to 15 cm high, with tuberous roots, and large quilted thick-fleshy ovate leaves set crosswise, white-hairy over deep green and silver variegation, crenate margins, on flat petioles; lavender-lilac flowers gloxinia-like, in stalked clusters. *Humid-tropical.* *p. 1232, 1233*

CHIRONIA *Gentianaceae* **I2-3LBD**
baccifera (Trop. Africa); ornamental herb to 60 cm high with opposite linear leaves on angled branches, and terminal cymes of rose-pink salver-shaped flowers with narrow tube and spreading limb 2 cm across. *p. 1168*

CHLIDANTHUS *Amaryllidaceae* **I2LFDd**
fragrans (Andes of Perú to N.E. Argentina), "Perfumed fairy lily"; bulbous plant with basal strap-shaped sheathing leaves, and fragrant yellow 8 cm trumpet flowers, appearing before the leaves, in umbels on solid stalks; summer. *Subtropic.* *p. 106*

CHLORAEA *Orchidaceae* **C-I3HFM**
membranacea (Argentina); handsome terrestrial rosette to 75 cm high, of leaves produced from finger-like subterranean tubers; large creamy-white flowers veined green on erect spike. *p. 1693*

CHLOROPHYTUM *Liliaceae* ***I2LFM**
bichetii (Trop. W. Africa), "St. Bernard's lily"; small tropical herb with broad, grass-like but thin-leathery leaves fresh-green with yellowish white stripes, forming bushy tufts. *Tropical.* *p. 1426, 1427*

capense (elatum) (South Africa: E. Cape Prov.); elongate rosette of firm, glaucous, narrow-concave leaves with parallel veins, and long much branched raceme with small flowers, on compressed stalk; not forming young plantlets on inflorescence stems. *p. 1426*

comosum (Anthericum) (So. and Central Africa); tropical herb with fleshy roots; green, strap-shaped, lax leaves 2-3 cm wide and 30 cm long; small white flowers in scandent leaf-tipped racemes. Differing from Anthericum mainly by broader leaves and 3-angled seed capsule. *p. 1427*

comosum 'Mandaianum'; Manda cultivar 1915, a small Spider-plant with narrow dark green leaves 10-12 cm long and 1 cm wide, featuring a bright yellow stripe instead of white center stripe; ideal basket plant. *p. 1426*

comosum 'Milky Way'; a beautiful cultivar with broad-linear recurving foliage; cream-white and with friendly green edging; very attractive in a hanging basket. *Subtropic.* *p. 1427*

comosum 'Picturatum' (Anthericum, Phalangium) (So. and Cent. Africa); ornamental perennial with fleshy roots and a loose rosette of succulent, strapshaped, lax leaves 30 cm long, fresh-green with yellow center bands; small white flowers on slender racemes later giving rise to new plantlets. *p. 1426*

comosum 'Variegatum', "Ribbon plant"; or "Walking anthericum"; large rosettes of arching, fresh green, linear leaves 25-40 cm long, 2-3 cm wide, having margins edged in white; long racemes appearing from the center will first bloom with small white flowers, then develop tufts of leaves with aerial roots. *Subtropic.* *p. 1426*

comosum 'Vittatum' (C. elatum vittatum) (Cape of Good Hope), "Spider plant"; low clustering rosette with channeled narrow-linear, recurving leaves, dark green banded white in center; successive plantlets develop from the long flowering racemes which become pendant if used in baskets; leaves only 10-20 cm long, 1 cm wide. *Subtropic.* *p. 1426*

ignoratum (Trop. Africa); fleshy lanceolate green leaves 30 cm long; inflorescence on erect stalks with small green flowers salmon-pink in center. *Subtropic.* *p. 1427*

macrophyllum (Ethiopia); growths clustered from tuberous roots; leaves to 45 cm long, elliptic, smooth, somewhat glossy, tapering to deeply channeled short petioles; floral stalks to 45 cm, very erect, unbranched; small flowers white with strongly reflexed petals; filaments white with yellow anthers. *p. 1427*

triflorum (So. Africa); leafy herb with green, sword-shaped, lax leaves, and leafy stalks with starry white flowers, each petal with a green center line. *p. 1427*

CHLOROSPATHA *Araceae* **S3HFM**
maculata (Colombia); compact plant of the rain forest with pedately 3-lobed leaves of firm texture, the basal segments oblique, glossy, black-olive-green with cream-white blotching; purple beneath, also petioles. *p. 208*

CHOISYA *Rutaceae* **I2LBD**
ternata (Mexico), "Mexican-orange"; evergreen shrub to 3 m high, with lustrous, yellow-green trifoliate leaves, held toward the end of the branches, each leaflet to 8 cm long, and forming fans giving the plant a dense, massive look; fragrant white flowers 3 cm across, like small orange blossoms, in clusters above the foliage; fruit of 8-10 cm dia.; leaves are strongly scented when bruised. *Tropical.* *p. 2025*

CHONDRORHYNCHA: see Cochleanthes

CHORISIA *Bombacaceae* **S2LBD**
insignis (Perú, N.E. Argentina), "White floss-silk tree" or "Drunken tree"; big tree to 15 m high, with fat, flask-shaped green trunk to 2 m thick, big spines on the younger trunk and branches, the sparry branches with palmately compound leaves of 5-7 obovate, waxy green leaflets 6-8 cm long and usually toothed near apex; beautiful, lily-like, large waxy flowers to 14 cm long, with undulate petals at first yellow with purple markings toward base, later fading to cream or white. *Subtropic.* *p. 509*

speciosa (Brazil, No. Argentina), "Floss-silk tree"; large tree about 15 m high, its trunk usually studded with stout sharp thorns, digitately compound toothed leaves, and showy, variable, usually pinkish 5-petaled flowers; pear shaped fruits containing silky floss on the seeds. *Tropical.* *p. 507, 509*

CHORIZEMA *Leguminosae* **I2LBD**
cordatum (ilicifolium) (Western Australia), "Australian flame pea"; shrub with weak, wiry branches, and small leathery, ovate or cordate 3 cm leaves sharply toothed and spine-tipped; small flowers red-orange with a yellow blotch, and purplish keel. *Subtropic.* *p. 1372, 1379*

CHRISTIA *Leguminosae* **S2LBM**
vespertilionis (Lourea) (Brazil); evergreen bush with scandent, rambling, wiry branches, and leaves with two long lobes, set at an angle like swallow-tails spreading 15 cm, green with silvery-gray or ivory ribs; small white flowers. *Tropical* *p. 1380*

CHRYSALIDOCARPUS *Palmae* ***S1LFW**
cabadae (Madagascar), "Cabada palm"; fast-growing clustering graceful feather palm to 10m tall; slender trunks with swollen base; the leaves are arranged in vertical rows of three as seen from below; slender, glossy green leaflets in one plane held at an open angle, on thin wiry petioles; small 2cm red fruit. *Tropical* *p. 1866, 1884*

decipiens (Dypsis), (Madagascar); a "Butterfly palm"; small cluster-forming feather palm with slender trunks, without spines; the gracefully arching fronds with long, well-spaced leaflets, strongly ribbed. *p. 1864*

lucubensis (N. W. Madagascar), slender "Feather palm" with solitary, ringed trunk to 10 m, gracefully arching pinnate fronds, 2½ m long, the glossy pinnae in clusters along the midrib, broader than lutescens. *p. 1860*

lutescens (Areca) (Madagascar), "Butterfly palm"; with slender, graceful, yellowish stems, forming an attractive clump to 8 m tall, with pinnate foliage nearly to the base; the narrow, thin-leathery pinnae glossy yellow-green and well spaced, on yellow, willowy, furrowed stalks; fruit violet-black. *Tropical* *p. 1860, 1861, 1874*

madagascariensis (Dypsis) (Madagascar); clump-forming slender-trunked feather-palm with 3 m pinnate fronds arranged in a denser head than lutescens, about twice as many, but weaker leaflets, with tips drooping. *p. 1860*

CHRYSANTHEMUM *Compositae* **C2LBM**
balsamita (W. Asia); aromatic herbaceous hardy perennial 60 cm or more high, with oblong, serrate leaves 12-25 cm long; small 1 cm flower heads yellow with tiny white rays, in large clusters; persistent plant grown for its sweet-smelling foliage, sometimes called "Lavender" and also known as "Mint geranium". *p. 802*

carinatum (Morocco), "Tricolor mum" or "Annual marguerite", smooth herbaceous plant sparsely branched, 40 to 80 cm high, with ferny, fleshy grayish green foliage, pinnate or bipinnate into short linear segments; colorful inflorescence with large heads 6 to 8 cm across; the tubular disk flowers forming purple cushion; ray flowers white, yellow, vivid red or two-tone purple, at base yellow and forming a contrasting ring around center; blooming late summer. *Subtropic.* *p. 809*

coccineum (Pyrethrum) (Caucasus, Iran), the "Pyrethrum" of gardens or "Painted daisy"; perennial to 60 cm, with fern-like bipinnatifid vivid-green foliage, and showy daisy-like flower heads in shades of red, also pink, lilac, and white, with yellow disk. *p. 813*

foeniculaceum (Canary Islands: Tenerife); semi-shrubby plant woody at base, 60 cm to more than 1 m high, densely branched with fleshy bluish, finely cut, leathery leaves, and marguerite-like white flowers 5 cm across with yellow cushions. *p. 802*

frutescens (Canary Islands), "White marguerite"; bushy branching herbaceous plant with lacy, divided grayish-green leaves, and single white flowers 4-6 cm across, with yellow disk. *Subtropic* *p. 801*

frutescens chrysaster, "Boston yellow daisy"; form with fleshier stem; fresh green, divided leaves, and lemon-yellow rays heavier and not as free flowering as the type. *Subtropic* *p.801*

frutescens 'Mary Wootten'; a famous "Tree-marguerite" named after a lovely Miss New Zealand; (Pink Beauty x Mrs. Sanders); 8-10 cm flowers, pleasing rose-pink, the high cushion center with the outer fringe darker, center more soft pink; very desirable in this color range; blooming over a long period. *Subtropic* *p. 801*

frutescens 'Mrs. Sanders'; herbaceous shrub of the group grown in New Zealand as "Tree-marguerites"; wide-branching plant with lacy-pinnately cut bright green leaves and double flowers with large pincushion centers, pure white; widely used by florists for cut and grown in gardens. *Subtropic* *p. 801*

frutescens 'Snowflake', "New Zealand tree-marguerite"; rambling sub-shrub with pure white somewhat shaggy, double flowers glistening white, about 6 cm dia. *Subtropic* *p. 801*

frutescens 'Wellpark Beauty'; an English "Tree-marguerite," with waxy green, irregularly cut bipinnatisect foliage, and soft lilac-pink flowers with anemone type double cushion soft pink, darker red in center. *p. 801*

maximum 'Wirral Supreme'; a large-flowered "Shasta daisy", originally from the Pyrenees of Spain; robust, hardy perennial to 75cm and more high, often grown as biennial; with lanceolate, serrate, deep green foliage, the stems topped by large 5 to 10 cm marguerite-like white flowers with a double row of ray-flowers, and a white and yellow anemone center cushion; late summer blooming. *Warm temperate* *p. 802*

morifolium (hortorum), the "Florists' chrysanthemum", known in slang as "Mum"; cultigen of Chinese origin and cultivated in China and Japan for 3000 years; perennial herb ½-1 m or more high, and much-branched, with succulent stems becoming woody, and strong-scented lobed leaves gray pubescent; flowers in showy terminal heads of various colors except blue, the florets modified by long cultivation into petal-like marginal ray-flowers and small, usually tubular disk-flowers forming center cushions; developed into several groups such as single, cascade, anemone (with center cushion), pompon (globular), decorative (aster-like), spider, incurved, and large exhibition; their growth habit is regulated by pinching, or chemical growth retardant. *Warm temperate*

mor. 'Alex Colson', large "decorative" with aster-like flowers vivid orange bronze, with excellent foliage, for pots (Nov. 1). *p. 796*

mor. 'Anna'; white daisy type "cascade" of single flowers with golden yellow center, about 5 cm in diameter with double row of petals , blooming early November (Nov. 5). *p. 798*

mor. 'Beautiful Lady', "Anemone-mum"; large "anemone" of bushy habit with strong stems and good foliage, flowers semi-double lavender pink, lighter toward center, and a yellow cushion (Nov. 25). *p. 794*

mor. 'Bonaffon Deluxe', "Incurved"; well-known pot plant variety, with numerous medium-large deep lemon yellow flowers of good lasting quality, on wiry stems, and with foliage of good substance (Nov. 20). *p. 789*

mor. 'Bridesmaid', large "spider" type for pots, light lavender pink, of dwarf, compact habit with rigid stems stronger than the 'Lace' varieties (normally blooming Nov. 1). *p. 790, 796*

mor. 'Bronze Palmero', a large "semi-incurved", robust grower with coral-bronze flowers. (Oct. 28). *p. 790*

mor. 'Capricorn', large "decorative" standard type for pots, yellow turning bronzy in cold temperature, but fully double not revealing center like 'Yellow Delaware' (Nov. 5). *p. 791, 796*

mor. 'Carnelia', large "single" type 8 cm flowers with broad, flattened petals rusty red with golden undertones and eye, and green center cushion, reverse yellow; good pot plant of stiff-habit. Normally blooms Nov. 20 in latitude 40-45. North. *p. 793*

mor. 'Charm', intermediate "anemone" of short habit and good spread for pots; bright pink petals and large cushion. (Nov. 15). *p. 796*

mor. 'Cherry Blossom', a "Cascade anemone" with 4 cm flowers, the ray flowers with an outer ring of dark cerise, white toward base, the center cushions red. (Oct. 25). *p. 790*

mor. 'Delaware', "Incurved type"; a typical good commercial, free branching pot plant with firm foliage and semi-incurved, deep amaranth-red bleaching to bronze; reverse yellow, 10 to 12 cm dia. *p. 794*

mor. 'Desert Song'; bushy duplex semi-incurved "pot" variety in apricot-salmon, flowers with several rows of broad petals showing an open center, on strong, stocky stems (Oct. 25). *p. 792*

mor. 'Dolli-Ette', intermediate sized "spoon" type flowers with long tubular petals opening at the tip into an open 'spoon' of golden bronze; shapely habit, prolific and durable (Oct. 10). *p. 797*

mor. 'Dwarf Jane Harte', small-flowered "cascade" variety with 2½ cm golden yellow flowers having 2 rows of petals, in long-lasting dense clusters, their long stems ideally suited to training on trellis (Nov. 1). *p. 799*

mor. 'Ethrelda', an intermediate "anemone" with several rows of recurving orchid-purple petals framing a raised golden cushion; dwarf, freely branched pot plant (Oct. 25). *p. 793*

mor. 'Golden Cascade', "Daisy-cascade"; commercial "Cascade" variety of the single daisy type very floriferous with light yellow ray-petals around a golden yellow center disk; earlier than 'Jane Harte'; its dense habit with long wiry branches is equally adaptable to training to forms as well as broad bushy globes. (Oct. 30). *p. 799*

mor. 'Golden Lace', "Fuji-mum"; morifolium cultivar of the spider type; large flowers with graceful threadlike, golden yellow quilled florets hanging from the double center, the tips are open and curled (Oct. 25). *p. 797*

mor. 'Golden Princess Ann'; large "decorative" type of the same sturdy habit as 'Princess Ann' with full 10 cm flowers yellow; top-rated pot plant for year-round production. (Nov. 10). *p. 791*

mor. 'Golden Seal', large "semi-double" variety suitable for pots, 8 cm flowers deep yellow with several layers of petals (Dec. 1). *p. 792*

mor. 'Gyokuhai', a "Cascade anemone", with large 5 cm flowers clear yellow, the cushion center dark golden yellow. (Oct. 25). *p. 790*

mor. 'Handsome', full "pompon" type, of large size flowers purplish rose, in sprays on stiff stems with closely internoded foliage, and erect bushy habit ideal for pots or cut (Nov. 1). *p. 793*

mor. 'Humdinger', a "formal pompon" and shapely plant with stiff erect stems, with clusters of 8 cm flowers with broad petals velvet purplish crimson, pale red beneath (Nov. 10). *p. 793*

mor. 'Illini Bonbon', "Cushion anemone"; small but attractive "Anemone" of short, bushy habit ideal for pots, the stiff stems with massive clusters of 4 cm flowers of daisy like flat petals lemon yellow, surrounding a high center cushion of golden yellow tubular petals (Nov. 18). *p. 795*

mor. 'Illini Spinwheel'; vigorous, rounded, densely branched plant with different-looking daisy-like flowers 4-6 cm in dia., spoon-shaped ray petals pure white, the central disks bright yellow (Yoder 1972). *p. 788*

mor. 'Imperial'; a "Decorative" form of 10 cm aster-like flowers with boat-shaped petals carmine pink with darker streaks and pale reverse, the double center attractively tipped with pale gold; free-blooming, medium-tall pot plant (Nov. 20). *p. 795*

mor. 'Inca', intermediate "anemone" type of fairly large flowers with broad, reflexed petals amber-bronze turning to bright yellow at high temperatures; good pot plant (Oct. 10). *p. 800*

mor. 'Incurved Delaware'; mutation from the deflexed 'Delaware', with petals tightly incurving, red-bronze showing the contrasting yellow reverse, flowers hold their form concealing the open center well past maturity; stiff upright, good pot plant (Nov. 8). *p. 794*

mor. 'Indianapolis Cream', large "incurved" for pots, cream-yellow, taller and more vigorous than 'Ind. Yellow' (Nov. 5). *p. 789*

mor. 'Indianapolis White', large "incurved" pure white pot plant variety, (normally blooms Nov. 5). *p. 796*

mor. 'Indianapolis Yellow', large "incurved"; dependable type, assuring good buds and elegant flowers, with rich yellow petals in part tubular, bleaching to pale yellow with age, but of long-lasting quality; a rather tall variety for pots, very vigorous (Nov.). *p. 795*

mor. 'Jane Harte', "cascade" type derived from C. indicum x morifolium; the deep yellow daisy-like flowers are small and dainty, 4 cm dia., with double rows of wavy florets produced in mass on thin wiry, trailing stems which allow them to be trained to variously shaped supports; Sport of 'Anna', with flowers of good lasting quality (Nov. 1). *p. 800*

mor. 'Joybringer', an early garden variety, "Pompon" salmon-rose with rather open flowers. (Oct. 10). *p. 790*

mor. 'Lavender Beauty', daisy type "cascade" in a beautiful lavender pink, extremely free-flowering and lasting; suitable for training (Oct. 20). *p. 800*

mor. 'Lee-Ette', unique "small spider" type with double flowers of tubular petals appearing silver bronze because only reverse is displayed (Oct. 23). *p. 797*

mor. 'Lipstick', shapely "cushion pompon" with small aster-type flowers amaranth or burgundy-red; a dense low bush ideal for pots (Oct. 5). *p. 793*

mor. 'Lorraine'; a good true "Spider mum"; very floriferous with thin but wiry stems; large 15 cm flowers as growing in pots; long tubular petals with quilled spoon at tips, clear lemon yellow (Nov. 15). *p. 797*

mor. 'Loubens', elegant "incurved" standard type of short habit for pots, with large flowers deep lavender pink (Nov. 5). *p. 789*

mor. 'Louisa Pockett', an "Exhibition incurved" chrysanthemum formed like a large round ball of tightly interlaced narrow petals of pure white; usually grown for shows on single stem (Nov. 10). *p. 798*

mor. 'Monument', an "incurved" globular flower of large size, ivory white, with petals incurving but rather open (Nov. 10). *p. 798*

mor. 'Mrs. Wolfe', large "incurved" pot variety, lemon yellow, almost an exhibition type of short habit (Nov. 1). *p. 796*

mor. 'Orange Aglow'; compact plant with large single, daisy-like flowers bright orange-bronze with an attractive green eye (Yoder 1972). *p. 788*

mor. 'Oregon', "semi-incurved" variety exclusively for pots; stronger habit and larger flower than 'Wilson's White', compact stiff growth with healthy foliage, and double white flowers incurved at first but becoming shaggy without showing center (Nov. 5). *p. 792*

mor. 'Oregon Trail', large "semi-incurved" for pots, sport of 'Oregon', a pleasing shade of light yellow resistant to fading (Nov. 5). *p. 796*

mor. 'Paloma', large-flowered "single" with shaggy petals mahogany red, reverse yellow (Nov. 1). *p. 798*

mor. 'Paragon'; pot plant variety with large decorative type flowers 10-12 cm across, pure paper white; never turns pink when grown cool (Yoder 1972). *p. 788*

mor. 'Peggy Ann Hoover'; attractive "Spider" mum of the "Fuji" type, large fine mauve pink flowers with thread-like tubular petals, a tint of pale yellow in center; thin-necked but wiry stems and good in pots (Oct. 20). *p. 797*

mor. 'Pink Deluxe', large "decorative" aster type 12 cm flowers with shaggy recurving petals and full high center lavender pink, on heavy stems with short internodes; ideal for pots (Nov. 10). *p. 794*

mor. 'Pink Turner', an old "Exhibition incurved" type of show chrysanthemum, with large globular, pink flowers with loosely incurved broad petals, usually grown on a single stem. In England, such types, when disbudded, have produced giant heads 20 to 25 cm in dia. (Nov. 10). *p. 798*

mor. 'Precose', large "anemone" type spreading flower 11 cm across lemon-yellow in bud opening to white with greenish center, with several rows of petals; bushy pot plant (Nov. 10). *p. 792*

mor. 'Princess Ann', "Decorative" type, and excellent pot plant of compact, shapely growth habit with firm foliage and substantial flowers 10 cm across, broad-petalled, peach-pink slightly darker in center, paling to light pink at edges. (Nov. 10). *p. 791*

mor. 'Queen's Lace', true "spider" mum with slender pure white filament-like tubular petals slashed open at ends (Nov. 1). *p. 797*

mor. 'Real Mackay', "Cascade-mum"; a dependable "Cascade" type branching bush, with flexuous branches bearing the numerous large daisy-like 5 cm flowers fine rose to pale pink, with yellow cushion center. *p. 791*

mor. 'Red Gem', button-size "cascade" variety with thin-wiry branches suitable for training; of floriferous habit with 2½ cm flowers ruby-red and protruding yellow center (Oct. 25). *p. 800*

mor. 'Red King'; large "Anemone" type 9 cm flowers with half dozen layers of recurved boat-shaped petals rusty-red, and contrasting yellow beneath; a robust pot plant (Nov. 13). *p. 793*

mor. 'Red Star'; compact plant with shiny green foliage, and decorative, aster-type double flowers with flat petals yellow to bronze, cinnamon beneath. *Warm temperate.* *p. 788*

mor. 'Scepter', large "decorative" type with spreading petals, deep golden yellow, and will tinge golden bronze at low temperature; ideal for small pots (Nov. 10). *p. 796*

mor. 'Shimo-Bashira', an excellent Japanese "Cascade" variety whose name means "Spiny frost"; with several layers of pure white florets making this a "double" form; 3 cm flowers (Oct. 30). *p. 800*

mor. 'Snow Crystal', a "spider" type, grown as a pot plant, dense with medium size spidery flowers ivory-white. (Nov. 5). *p. 791*

mor. 'Sundial', intermediate "feathered spider" type for pots, of short habit and with excellent foliage, deep lemon yellow (Oct. 25). *p. 796*

mor. 'Sungold'; vigorous "Incurved" type with large flowers deep lemon yellow, fully double and of good keeping qualities, some petals tubular; strong stems and good commercial pot plant for Thanksgiving (Nov. 25). *p. 799*

mor. 'Sunnyside', "Pompon" type (morifolium x indicum); top quality yellow in this neat, small flowered but densely double, and nearly globular class, with quilled florets in many series (Nov. 20). *p. 798*

mor. 'Sunnyslope Splendor', a morifolium cultivar of the "Japanese Fuji" type, with full centered large flower and quilled florets of various lengths in glistening white with green tinting (Oct. 15). *p. 797, 798*

mor. 'Sweepstake', "Pompon-mum"; typical small-flowered "Pompon" with full round golden-yellow $4^1/_2$ cm blooms, of dense, bushy habit with small, dark green foliage; used for cut, pots or garden (Oct. 7). *p. 795*

mor. 'Thos. Pockett', perfect example of the best "Japanese incurved exhibition" type, with enormous flowers of deep pink and silvery pink reverse, 15 cm or more in dia. (Nov. 8). *p. 798*

mor. 'Venoya'; listed as a "Large anemone" but with its thick layers of shaggy petals appearing like a decorative type, except for its green-eyed cushion, framed by blush to lavender pink petals; a tall pot plant (Nov. 22). *p. 792, 795*

mor. 'Vulcan', a "decorative" type for pot plant culture, of beautiful crimson-red, heavy-textured flowers, in habit somewhat sparry and difficult to break. (Nov. 5). *p. 790*

mor. 'Warhawk'; striking pot plant variety with large and showy incurved, double flowers 12 cm across, burnt brown-red with amber-yellow reverse; firm leathery foliage. *Warm temperate.* *p. 788*

mor. 'White Beautiful Lady'; large "anemone" type, a morifolium-indicum cultivar, with white rays flat and horizontally arranged, as in a single flower, but with a rounded center disk of long yellow tubes; good keeper (Nov. 25). *p. 794*

mor. 'Wild Honey'; compact plant of upright habit for pots, with semi-incurved, fully double flowers 10-12 cm dia., golden yellow; will tinge bronze under finishing temperature of less than 15°C. (Yoder 1972). *p. 788*

mor. 'Wilson's White'; intermediate "Semi-incurved" pot variety with small foliage and broad-petalled pure white flowers tinted greenish in the center (Nov. 1). *p. 792*

mor. 'Woking Scarlet', large "decorative" standard type, elegant flowers with boat-shaped petals brilliant scarlet-bronze, an exciting combination of vivid color and vigorous habit for pots (Nov. 10). *p. 789*

mor. 'Yellow Delaware', intermediate "Semi-incurved" sport of 'Delaware', rich yellow 10 cm flowers (pot-grown), the lower petals turning outward and center opens; (Nov. 8). *p. 11*, 794*

mor. 'Yellow Gem'; shapely, compact branched bush with small "button" type anemone 2 cm flowers with large golden cushion and short lemon yellow rays. *p. 791*

mor. 'Yellow Puritan'; stocky pot plant variety, with medium-sized decorative type flowers 8-10 cm across, bright yellow; (Yoder 1972). *p. 788*

mor. 'Yellow Umbrella', a small-flowered "pompon" type of deep yellow flowers in a dense, compact head of small green leaves and wiry branches lending itself to growing as a semi-standard little tree. (Nov. 1). *p. 790*

parthenium (Matricaria capensis) (S.E. Europe to Caucasus), "Feverfew"; old-fashioned erect bushy, aromatic perennial 30 to 60 cm high, once favored in Victorian gardens as cutflower; the leafy stems with strongly scented foliage to 8 cm long, more or less deeply cut or lobed; in summer a profusion of small button-like yellow floral disks fringed by short white rays, 2 cm across. Dried flowers are used medicinally. *p. 802, 805*

ptarmicaeflorum (Canary Isl.), "Silver lace"; white tomentose, shrubby plant with lacy, silvery leaves bipinnately parted, inflorescence with white rays. *p. 819*

CHRYSOCOMA *Compositae* **I2LBD**

coma-aurea (So. Africa); evergreen subshrub to 60 cm with small linear leaves, and erect branches successively branching, and terminating in yellow roundish 1 cm heads composed only of disk flowers. *p. 814*

CHRYSOLARIX: see Pseudolarix

CHRYSOTHEMIS *Gesneriaceae* **S3HFM**

friedrichsthaliana (Alloplectus lynchii, Tussacia) (Guatemala, Trinidad, W. Indies); erect, tuberous-rooted, succulent plant with waxy green, hairy, lanceshaped, crenate leaves to 30 cm long; axillary flower clusters, the short orange corolla with dark-striped lobes peeking out of large greenish-yellow calyx. *Humid-tropical.* *p. 1243*

pulchella (Trinidad), erect succulent herb producing tubers with age; large fleshy opposite, rough-bristly, puckered 15 cm leaves shiny bright green, with crenate margins; the flowers in the leaf axils are small bristly 1 cm tubes buttercup-yellow with red stripes and markings inside, but curiously interesting for the cluster of large flame-red calyces which appear well before the blossoms and keep long afterwards, giving the plant a colorful appearance over a long period. Blooms in spring; allow to go dormant when too tall. *Humid-tropical.* *p. 1232*

CHYSIS *Orchidaceae* **I3OFD**

aurea (Mexico, Colombia, Venezuela); bright colored epiphyte with spindle-like stems bearing 3-5 deciduous leaves; the thick-waxy 5 cm flowers closely clustered in short raceme, petals reddish-buff with golden yellow edges and base, throat yellow, marked red. (March-Aug.) *p. 1688*

bractescens (Mexico, Guatemala); epiphyte with compact pseudobulbs and deciduous leaves; the fragrant waxy, large 8 cm flowers in arching raceme, ivory-white with yellow lip marked red. (Feb.-May). *p. 1688, 1693*

x chelsonii (bractescens x laevis); epiphyte with pendulous stems and 5-7 fleshy flowers 6 cm wide, sepals and petals yellow shaded red-brown toward apex, lip white finely spotted with red. (spring). (I) *p. 1688*

laevis (Mexico, Guatemala); a beautiful epiphyte of robust habit, with spindle-shaped, arching stems, and pendulous racemes of showy creamy-yellow, fleshy flowers flushed with copper-brown toward apex of each petal and sepal, the lip red-veined at base, cinnamon-crimson at tip and frilled, the column spotted with cinnamon; June. (I) *p. 1688*

CIBOTIUM *Dicksoniaceae (Filices)* ***S1HFM**

barometz (So. China, Assam, Malaya), "Lamb of Tartary"; from a hairy rhizome rise the handsome, fragrant, light green fronds of leathery texture, bipinnately toothed, and bluish beneath, on wiry stalks covered with light brown hairs. *Humid-tropical.* *p. 1068*

chamissoi (menziesii in hort.) (Hawaii), "Man fern" of the islanders; with a short, stout, fibrous trunk to 8 m tall, and handsome, massive, tripinnate fronds, delicate, glossy nile-green and of a smooth leathery-hard texture, on stalks covered with blackish woolly hair. *Humid-tropical.* *p. 1072, 1077*

glaucum (chamissoi in hort.) (Hawaii), "Blonde treefern" of the rainforest; with stout, fibrous trunks, consisting of a mass of aerial roots around a core of starch, and capable of storing moisture, with heads of large, soft-textured, tripinnate crinkled fronds luxuriously green, the stalks covered with soft pale hair. *Humid-tropical.* *p. 1070, 1072*

regale (Mexico); a gigantic, slow growing fern, gradually forming a stout trunk to 10 m high; strong erect, hairy stalks with large, fresh green, elegantly arching, tripinnate fronds to 3 m long. (3) *p. 1070, 1072*

schiedei (Mountains of Mexico and Guatemala), "Mexican treefern"; favorite decorator of florists, when grown in tubs; with shapely crown of graceful, light green fronds, thin-leathery and dainty yet durable, lacy tripinnate, and glaucous beneath; will eventually, over many years, form a fibrous trunk to 5 m high. *Humid-tropical.* *p. 1072, 1075*

CINCHONA *Rubiaceae* **S3HFM**

calisaya (Bolivia, Perú); Andean tree to 12 m tall, of medicinal importance as well as ornamental; large obovate, 18 cm satiny leaves olive-green with beautiful red veining and red beneath, on red-purple stems; small, pink, tubular flowers; the bark stripped from young trees produces quinine. *p. 2010*

CINERARIA: see Senecio, Centaurea

CINNAMOMUM *Lauraceae* **S2LFD**

cassia (Indo-China, China), the "Cassia-bark-tree"; aromatic evergreen tree to 12 m with brittle-leathery lanceolate, opposite light green leaves strongly 3-nerved, to 15 cm long; the surge of young leaves a showy cream or flushed red; small flowers in panicles; the bark is used as a substitute for cinnamon. *p. 1359*

CIRRHOPETALUM: see Bulbophyllum

CIRSIUM *Compositae* **I2LBD**

diacanthum (Asia Minor: Syria), the "Fish bone-thistle"; biennial herb, a rosette of skeleton leaves 30 cm long, consisting of a winged midrib with 3-parted linear remnants shining green with silvery lines and tipped with ivory thorns; the purplish disk flowers in dense, spike-like clusters. *p. 814*

eriophorum (C. Europe, Russia), a "Plumed thistle"; biennial to $1^1/_2$ m with strong branches, white-tomentose pinnatisect leaves with thorns; large white-woolly flower receptacle tipped with spines, and topped by purple ray flowers. *p. 814*

CISSUS *Vitaceae* **I-S1-3LFD-M**

adenopoda (njegerre) (Usambaras, Uganda), "Pink cissus"; rapid herbaceous climber, with tuberous roots, the slender vines with large trifoliolate, green leaves having a coppery sheen and covered with purple hairs, the stalked leaflets coarsely serrate and with sunken veins, wine-red beneath; flowers pale yellow. *p. 2120, 2125*

albo-nitens (Brazil), "Silver princess vine"; rapid tropical climber, with small, herbaceous, arrow-shaped leaves shining metallic silvery-gray on the surface, veins green, green beneath. Prob. cv. of sicyoides. *p. 2120*

amazonica (Amazonas); very attractive tropical climber with string-like vines, and closely set, alternate, narrow-lanceolate, somewhat fleshy leaves in two ranks, becoming broader with age, the glossy surface deep metal-gray with contrasing silvery vein area and brown midrib, the margins remotely toothed, and maroon beneath. *Tropical. p. 2120, 2124*

amazonica hort. (adenopoda); tall tropical climber with tendrils and aerial roots; thin woody stems with leaves of 3 ovate leaflets, crenate at margins; coppery-green leaves purplish beneath and covered with hairs; photographed under this name at Royal Botanic Gardens, Kew, London, but should probably be referred to C. adenopodus (adenopoda). *p. 2125*

antarctica (Rhoicissus) (New So. Wales), "Kangaroo vine"; attractive plant with shrubby base and flexuous, slowly climbing, tomentose branches, the elegant, firm leaves almost leathery, bright shining green to a deep metallic shade, and light brown veins, the base cordate, and margins sinuately toothed, becoming 15 cm long; a good keeper. *p. 19*, 2121*

antarctica 'Minima', "Miniature kangaroo treebine"; (Manda 1950), slow-growing, dwarf, self-branching form of excellent keeping qualities, dense with small, ovate, stiff-leathery, 8 cm leaves irregularly toothed, the waxy surface a deep green; long remaining compact. (ID) *p. 2121*

bainesii (So. West Africa), "African tree-grape"; bold succulent with thick bottle-shaped trunk to 25 cm thick, skin yellow-green becoming papery and peeling with age; green leaves coarsely serrate and woolly; globular red fruits. *p. 2126*

discolor (Java, Cambodia), "Rex begonia vine"; beautiful tendril-climber, with thin angled, dark-red veins and petioles, the strikingly colored, oblong-cordate, quilted leaves to 15 cm long, the sunken network of veins moss-green, with elevated ridges painted shimmering silver, and the center variegated violet and red-purple with velvet sheen; toothed margin and reverse glowing maroon. *p. 1824A, 2120, 2123, 2128*

erosa (Puerto Rico); rambling tendril climber along the waysides over hedges and small trees, with thin wiry vines bearing compound, stiff-succulent, trifoliate, glossy leaves waxy fresh-green, the obliquely ovate, stalked leaflets coarsely toothed at the margins, and pale beneath. (*SIL) *p. 2120*

gongylodes (Brazil, Paraguay, Perú); robust liane for the large conservatory; rapid climber with 4-angled stems, large trifoliolate rugose leaves to 20 cm long; hairy at the nerves and at the margins; the tendrils with suction cups. Most attractive are the long pendant, red aerial roots looking like a bead curtain. At end of growing season the ends of branches produce a terminal fleshy tuber which drops and develops into a new plant. *Tropical. p. 2127, 2128*

juttae (S. W. Africa), "Tree cissus"; queer-looking succulent with thick-fleshy, stubby, pale gray, smooth trunk 1-1½ m high, dividing into a few thinner branches toward apex, sessile oval, serrate leaves 10-15 cm, shining waxy green above, translucent hairs beneath, soon falling; panicles of small flowers followed by attractive clusters of red berries. *p. 2125, 2126, 2128*

lanigeri (So. Africa); vigorous tropical vine, softly hairy; leaves of 3 coarsely toothed leaflets, with center leaflet largest and 14 cm long; minute yellowish flowers in 2-ranked inflorescence. *p. 2125*

oleracea (Transvaal), the "Cabbage cissus"; strikingly handsome spreading shrub, with large, softly succulent, glaucous leaves looking like cabbage, standing erect along the branches, as can be seen in the Kruger National Park area. *p. 2127*

quadrangularis (Vitis) (Trop. Africa, Arabia, India, Moluccas); odd succulent with thick, fleshy, rich green, 4-winged stems much constricted at the nodes, climbing, mostly glabrous, often nearly leafless, looking like a spineless cactus; small herbaceous, 3-lobed, green leaves; green flowers and berried red. I have seen this plant clambering over euphorbias and various scrub on the steppes in Uganda, Tanzania and northern Transvaal. *Arid-tropical. p. 2121, 2122*

rhombifolia (Vitis, Rhoicissus) (West Indies, N. So. America) "Grape-ivy"; scandent, herbaceous plant with vine-like, flexuous, brown-hairy branches having coiling tendrils, and compound leaves of 3 rhombic-ovate, stalked, thin-fleshy leaflets wavy-toothed, the glabrous surface fresh green to metallic deep green and with brownish veins and petioles, pubescent underneath; the young growth covered with white hairs. Small flowers with 4 petals, unlike Rhoicissus which have 5-7 petals. *Tropical. p. 2121*

rhombifolia 'Ellen Danica'; excellent, vigorously growing grape-ivy; mutation of 'Jubilee' (Nielsen-Denmark) found in Odense about 1965; of bushy habit with foliage divided and larger than the species, the leaflets like deeply lobed and incised oakleaves, rich glossy green, on brownish branches. Suitable for larger containers or for pyramids. *Subtropic. p. 2125*

rhombifolia 'Mandaiana' (Vitis); meritorious sport introduced by Manda in 1935, of more upright, compact habit, thicker stems and substantial, fleshy, deep green leaves, the leaflets broad and firm, almost leathery, lightly quilted and recurved, shining like polished wax; very attractive and a good keeper. *Tropical. p. 2121*

rotundifolia (E. Africa: Tanzania, to Yemen), "Arabian wax cissus"; climbing plant with green, 4-angled stems having sharp corky edges in older specimen; rounded waxy-fleshy leaves 6-8 cm dia., distantly toothed at margins, glossy fresh green to olive; inconspicuous green flowers, followed by red berries. *Arid-tropical. p. 2125*

seitziana (S. W. Africa); tree-like succulent with fat, swollen trunk 1½ m high, branching into divided head topped by fleshy gray-felted long-ovate leaves, dentate and brownish at margins. *p. 2126*

sicyoides (Brazil), "Princess vine"; tall, prolific tendril climber of the tropical rainforest, for the conservatory where, with high humidity, it will send down a multitude of stringlike aerial roots 3 m long or more, forming a veritable curtain; the light green, cordate leaves are somewhat fleshy with serrate margins. *p. 2120, 2125*

striata (Vitis) (Chile), "Miniature grape-ivy"; cute little plant with thin reddish shoots climbing by tiny tendrils, dense with small, palmately compound leaves to 4 cm across, with 5 obovate leaflets toothed toward the apex, bronzy-green above with pale midrib, and wine-red beneath. Has been listed in Europe as Vitis orientalis. *p. 2121*

CISSUS: see also Piper, Parthenocissus, Rhoicissus, Tetrastigma

CISTUS *Cistaceae* **I2LBDd**

x purpureus (ladanifer x villosus), "Orchid rock-rose"; flowering evergreen shrub to 1 m or more high, with sticky-hairy twigs; dark green, rough leaves 3-5 cm long, gray-hairy beneath; showy purple, crepy flowers 6-8 cm across, yellow at base with maroon blotch on each petal. *p. 926*

salvifolius (S.E. Europe), "Sageleaf-rock-rose"; low spreading shrub to 60 cm high, photographed amongst ancient Greek ruins on the island of Rhodes; with small gray-green rugose leaves 3 cm long, and flowers like wild roses, with white or pinkish petals of crepy texture, with yellow spots in base, 4 cm across; blooming very profusely in spring. *Subtropic. p. 926*

CITHAREXYLUM *Verbenaceae* **I-SLFM**

berlandieri (Mexico); cool-growing evergreen shrub; 4-angled branches with elliptic to obovate opposite leaves 4 cm long, finely ciliate and with hairs on veins beneath; flowers white in terminal spikes 1 cm across, with green center. *p. 2107*

CITRIOBATUS *Pittosporaceae* **I2LBD**

multiflorus (New So. Wales, Queensland); dense, thorny shrub with tiny roundish dark green leaves and small white flowers, followed by reddish berries. *p. 1947*

CITRUS *Rutaceae* **I2LBD**

aurantifolia (Malaya, India), the "Lime" or "Key lime"; small thorny tree to 5 m tall, very tender; with aromatic small 6-8 cm glossy green, oval leaves; waxy-white, fragrant, axillary flowers; small oval, green to greenish yellow fruit 3 to 5 cm dia. usually in clusters; smooth, thin-skinned with very acid seedy pulp; used in drinks, on seafood or in preserves. *p. 2029*

aurantium (Vietnam), "Sour Seville orange"; vigorous tree with slender-pointed leaves on broadly winged petioles; large fragrant, white-waxy flowers; fruit orange when ripe, of tart taste; in Curacao the peel of unripe fruit is used for its aromatic oils to flavor the famous liqueur. *Subtropic. p. 2028*

aurantium 'Myrtifolia' (China), "Myrtleleaf orange"; dwarfish, thornless tree with dense, deep green, stiff, little 2 cm leaves; waxy flowers and small, sour, bright orange fruits; while blooming in April in the northern hemisphere, I remember the strikingly impressive sight of these trees in Uruguay and Argentina in October, when literally covered with fragrant white flowers. *Subtropic. p. 2030, 2033*

aurantium 'Myrtifolia Chinotto', "Chinotto-orange"; dense, small, thornless tree to 3 m high, with small sharp-pointed leathery, green leaves 6 cm long; the bright orange fruit 4 cm or more in dia., with thin rind, and with solid pulp, of sour but characteristic flavor; season November-December. A broadleaf clone of C. myrtifolia, resembling in appearance the Myrtus boetica. *p. 2028*

limon 'Eureka', "Acid lemon"; medium size tree, open and spreading, almost thornless; large dark green leaves; fragrant waxy white flowers; oblong fruit with protruding apex, lemon-yellow, 8 cm or more long; very juicy and acid. *Subtropic. p. 2029*

limon 'Meyer' (hybrid of lemon with sweet orange), "Meyer lemon" or "Dwarf Chinese"; semi-dwarf, spreading tree, nearly thornless, with small leaves, often grown in pots as it produces sweetly-scented, lavender to white flowers while young, and bears good-looking, roundish lemons of table quality, 6-7 cm long furnishing excellent acid juice almost the year round; of somewhat sweeter or milder flavor than the typical Eureka lemon. *Subtropic. p. 2030, 2033*

limon 'Ponderosa' (Maryland hybrid 1887), "American wonder-lemon"; ornamental tree 2½-3 m high, often grown in tubs; with irregular branches and short, stout spines, large oblong leaves on short petioles nearly wingless; the large waxy flowers white; the somewhat pear-shaped, enormous fruit lemon-yellow, almost 12 cm long, weighing 1 kg, and while edible, its juice is sour. *Subtropic. p. 2030, 2032*

maxima (grandis), the "Shaddock" or "Pummelo", probably from So. China, Malaya and Polynesia; tender tropical spiny tree to 9 m, with angular twigs and large oval 10-20 cm leaves slightly pubescent beneath, the petiole widely winged; large white flowers; fruit 15 cm large and pale yellow, broadly pear-shaped, the acid flesh coarse-grained and separating readily. *p. 2032*

microcarpa (South China), "Four-season tangerine"; possibly hybrid of Mandarin x Fortunella; depressed globose fruit 3 cm dia., with thin peel and with intensely acid pulp. *Subtropic.* *p. 2027*

mitis (x Citrofortunella) (Philippines), "Calamondin"; a small, spineless tree with upright slender branches dense with broad-oval, leathery leaves on narrowly-winged petiole; small white, fragrant flowers borne singly at the tips of twigs; small 3 to 4 cm round fruit somewhat flattened, deep orange-yellow, loose skinned. Probably a hybrid of lime with kumquat; strongly acid, pleasant flavor like lime; season Nov.-Dec., but occasionally everbearing. Popularly grown in pots for Christmas. Fruit, including rind is used for making marmalade. *Subtropic.* *p. 320A, 2027, 2030, 2032*

x paradisi (West Indies), "Grapefruit"; spreading tree with big leaves on broadly winged petioles, and large white flowers, the smooth branches bending under the weight of the large and heavy, pale lemon-colored, round fruit, 10-14 cm dia., much grown for its juice. C. paradisi of the West Indies is a satellite species rising from the tropical C. grandis (maxima) of S.E. Asia. *Subtropic.* *p. 2031*

reticulata (Southeast Asia), "Mandarin orange"; small spiny tree with slender branches; lanceolate leaves; flowers white and fragrant; fruit deep orange-yellow depressed globose, to 8 cm dia.; loose thin skin, sweet pulp. *Subtropic.* *p. 2027*

sinensis (Kwangtung, Vietnam), "Sweet orange"; tree to 10 m high with regular branches, flexible spines, dark green, ovate, leathery leaves on narrow-winged petioles; fragrant, waxy-white flowers smaller than aurantium, the nearly round fruit golden yellow with sweet pulp; the Navel orange belongs here. *p. 2030*

sinensis 'Valencia' (Spain), "Valencia orange"; large vigorous tree to 10 m high, fuller growing than Washington Navel, with regular branches and rounded top; flexible slender spines sometimes absent; dark shining green, ovate leaves narrowly winged; waxy white, sweetly fragrant flowers; fruit nearly globose, golden yellow 7-8 cm dia., and with sweet pulp, ripening March to July and lasting on the tree for months, improving in sweetness. It is the most widely planted juice orange in the world. Known in California since 1876, it had its origin in Spain under the name "Naranja tarde de Valencia". *p. 2029*

sinensis 'Variegated Pineapple-orange'; a midseason sweet orange, with elliptic leaves 9 cm or more long, gray-green to milky, with margins variegated creamy-white, and of ornamental value. *p. 2032*

sinensis 'Washington Navel' or 'Bahia', from Brazil, "Winter orange"; excellent, large commercial sweet orange, early-ripening, and seedless, to 8 or 10 cm dia., from November to April (Valencia from March to Nov.); best adapted to California and Arizona climate and produces low yield and poor fruit in tropical regions; it derives its name from the characteristic rudimentary secondary fruit imbedded in the apex of the primary fruit, and which serves as a trademark; deep orange in color, and easy peeling; flowers in large clusters, waxy-white and sweetly fragrant. *Subtropic.* *p. 2029, 2030*

taitensis (otaitense), "Otaheite orange"; dwarf tree grown as an ornamental pot plant, with glossy-green, dense foliage and few spines; the waxy-white, very fragrant flowers tinged with pink, appearing in January, followed toward Christmas by golden orange fruits; a miniature version of the sweet orange, except that the juice is tart, more resembling a lime; the best for pots. Probably a lemon (or lime) x mandarin (aurantifolium x reticulatum) hybrid, possibly of garden origin in South China. *p. 2031*

'Temple' (reticulata x sinensis), a beautiful, highly flavored, juicy "Tangor" (tangerine x sweet orange hyb.) originated in Florida; loose-skinned mandarin-type orange maturing January to Spring; 7 to9 cm dia. with reddish-orange peel and flesh; bushy, thorny tree with medium-size leaves and waxy white, fragrant flowers; bearing freely when very young, ideal for the home garden and lending itself to culture in tubs; more tender than sweet orange. *Subtropic.* *p. 2030*

CLADANTHUS *Compositae* **I2LBD**

arabicus (S. Spain, Morocco); strongly aromatic annual herb to 1 m with finely divided leaves, and heads of yellow ray and disk flowers. *p. 820*

CLARKIA *Oenotheraceae* **C3LBM**

amoena (Godetia) (California to Brit. Columbia), "Farewell-to-spring"; showy herbaceous annual to 80 cm, with linear leaves, and satiny flowers 3-5 cm across, in shades of purplish carmine or rose-pink in loose clusters; day-blooming. *p. 1628*

amoena plena (Godetia) (California to Brit. Columbia), double "Farewell-to-spring" or "Satin flower"; slender annual, branching herb, 30-75 cm high with narrow leaves, often with smaller ones in the axils; profuse with double flowers 2½-5 cm wide, the satiny petals lilac-crimson or reddish-pink; July-October. *p. 1648*

elegans (California); showy annual herb with alternate narrow leaves and handsome purple or rose-colored flowers often double in few-flowered clusters, on erect, reddish glaucous stems; 45-65 cm high; summer. *p. 1648*

grandiflora (Godetia, Oenothera); amoena lindleyi in Hortus 3; compact, leafy, summer-flowering annual to 30 cm high, with stout stem and narrow, alternate leaves, and satiny, 8-12 cm flowers, rosy-red varying to white, with a darker shading in the center of petals. *p. 1648*

CLARKIA: see also Godetia

CLAVIJA *Theophrastaceae* **S3LBD**

tarapotana (Perú, Bolivia); evergreen palm-like subtropical tree with unbranched stem, bearing a rosette of large obovate, leathery leaves blunt at the tip, about 40 cm long; axillary from near the apex the pendant inflorescence; numerous racemes of small very fragrant orange-red flowers, followed by grape-like clusters of red berries. *Subtropic.* *p. 1607*

CLEISOSTOMA *Orchidaceae* **I3HFM**

paniculatum (Taiwan); a charming dwarf, terrestrial orchid which I photographed in Taipei growing in a terracotta bowl; long-linear glossy green leaves and branching, wiry stems bearing a cascade of small waxy flowers 1 cm dia., with light brown sepals and petals, the lip yellow, densely set on pendant racemes. *p. 1704*

CLEISTOCACTUS *Cactaceae* ***I2LBD**

baumannii (Argentina, Paraguay), "Firecracker"; thin, ribbed column clambering and branching at base, covered with white or brown spines; flowers scarlet, 6-7 cm long. *Arid-subtropic.* *p. 650*

baumannii flavispinus; stem more slender, 2½ cm thick, the areoles yellow and all spines pale yellow. *p. 650*

buchtienii (Bolivia); possibly a variety of herzogianus; tree-like, to 1½m high, with stiff erect column, many (11) rounded ribs, deep green, set closely with clusters of reddish spines; flowers wine-red. *p. 638*

candelilla (Bolivia: Cochabamba), aptly named the "Small candle in the Andes" because of the flame-like tubular red flowers, tipped with yellow, that appear near the apex of the slender ribbed columns of this natural fence or thicket-forming cactus, branching from the base, and ½-1m tall; spreading radial spines yellowish, and 3-4 needle-like central spines. *Arid-subtropic.* *p. 647*

hyalacanthus (Argentina: Jujuy); branching columns to 3 m high, with 12 ribs deeply furrowed, densely covered by straight bristly, creamy spines. *p. 650*

parapetiensis (Bolivia); erect column to 60 cm high, 4 cm dia., fresh green to bluish, densely ribbed; starlike, small beige-colored stellate hairs and one central spine; tubular flowers 3½ cm long, yellow-green with rosy-red base; 1 cm purple fruit. *p. 658*

smaragdiflorus (Argentina, Uruguay, Paraguay), "Firecracker cactus"; slender, erect stems with 12-14 ribs, 5 cm thick, 2 m high, later leaning; closely set yellow areoles and numerous thin yellow to brown spines very sharp; flowers orange red inside but remaining closed. *p. 650, 658*

strausii (Bolivia), "Silver torch"; slender, light green, clustering, many-ribbed column to 2 m high and 6 cm thick, covered with bristle-like white spines, central spine pale yellow; flowers red, to 9 cm long. *Arid-subtropic.* *p. 618, 650, 659*

strausii jujuyensis (Argentina), "Silver torch"; form with areoles bearing white bristly spines and one brown central spine. *Arid-subtropic.* *p. 650*

CLEMATIS *Ranunculaceae* **C2LFD**

alpina (N. Europe, Siberia); woody deciduous climber with compound, toothed leaves, and nodding bell-shaped flowers 4 cm long, violet-blue, in spring. *p. 1986*

armandii hyb. 'Appleblossom'; cultivar of the white-flowered armandii from W. China; robust evergreen climber with 3 leathery shining leaflets, and rosy flowers strongly fragrant, 6 cm dia., in April-June. *p. 1986*

'Barbara Jackman'; a popular cultivar of the lanuginosa and viticella hybrid group; large 10-12 cm flowers orchid-purple with dark purple in center; not as deep violet-purple as C. x jackmanii; 3-foliolate leaves. *p. 1988*

x durandi (jackmanii x integrifolia); deciduous climber with ovate leaves, and large violet-blue flowers 8-12 cm across, and with yellow stamens, in June-Sept. *p. 1986*

heracleifolia 'Davidiana' (China); deciduous subshrub with woody base and herbaceous stems, leaves of 3 coarsely toothed leaflets, and tubular flowers with spreading, recurved segments, deep blue and fragrant; Aug.-Sept. *p. 1986, 1988*

integrifolia (Eurasia); erect subshrub with thin, ovate leaves, and violet-blue flowers with yellow stamens; June-July. *p. 1987*

x jackmanii 'Maureen' ; the jackmanii group (lanuginosa x hendersonii) is one of the best of "Virgin's bowers" for size of flower, vigorous in growth, and profuse in bloom; climber to 3 m, with pinnate or 3-foliolate leaves; flowers 10-15 cm across, violet-purple, and long-lasting, in July to October; fairly hardy. *p. 1986*

lanuginosa (China); woody climbing vine to 2 m high; leaves simple or of 3 entire leaflets; flowers 10-15 cm across, white or pale lilac, of 6-8 obovate, overlapping sepals, downy beneath. *p. 1988*

lanuginosa 'Mrs. Van Houtte'; climber, originally from China, with simple or 3-foliolate leaves, the flowers 10-18 cm wide, lilac in the type, pure white in this cultivar. *p. 1987*

lanuginosa 'Nellie Moser'; a free-blooming cultivar with flowers pale mauve-pink, and with a carmine-red bar down the middle of sepals; June-Sept. *Warm temperate.* *p. 1987*

x lawsoniana 'Ramona'; a "Virgin's bower" vine of the lanuginosa (China) x patens (Japan) hybrid complex; shrubby deciduous winter-hardy climber with leaves of 3 leaflets, and striking flowers with spreading petals 15 cm or more across; in the clone 'Ramona' lavender blue with purple stamens, blooming during summer. One of the most beautiful of flowering hardy vines. *Temperate.* *p. 1988*

montana rubens (Himalayas); vigorous deciduous climber with 3-foliolate leaves, purplish when young, and fragrant 5 cm flowers rosy-red (white in the type); in May-June; fairly hardy and stands up well. *p. 1987*

orientalis (Iran to Himalayas); deciduous climber with ribbed shoots and pinnate or bipinnate leaves; 5 cm yellow flowers; Aug.-Sept.; and feathery fruit. *p. 1986*

patens hyb. 'Sir Garnet Wolseley'; deciduous climber with leaves of 3-5 leaflets, and large 10-15 cm wide-spreading flowers white to violet in the type from Japan; bronzy-blue with a plum-red bar in the cultivar; May-June. *p. 1986*

puberula (W. Himalayas, Nepal); woody vine with grooved stems, pubescent, pinnate, membranous leaves, and bell-shaped slightly hairy, pinkish flowers filled with protruding yellow stamens, silky outside. *p. 1986*

tangutica (N. China, Mongolia); deciduous climber with glaucous green, pinnate or bipinnate toothed leaves, and nodding flowers with golden-yellow petal-like sepals to 5 cm long; June-July; fruit plumed. *p. 1987*

texensis (Texas), the "Scarlet clematis"; a semi-woody climber, with glaucous, pinnate leaves, and nodding, urn-shaped flowers to 3 cm long, scarlet or carmine-rose, June to August; fruit feathery; fairly hardy. *p. 1987*

veitchiana (China); vigorous deciduous climber with bipinnate leaves silky beneath; fragrant, nodding, bell-shaped 1 cm flowers yellowish, in September-October. *p. 1987*

virginiana (Nova Scotia to Kansas), the "Woodbine"; deciduous vine with leaves coarsely toothed or lobed, and small 2½ cm flowers white, in leafy panicles; the male and female flowers on separate plants; Aug.-Sept. *p. 1987*

vitalba (Europe, N. Africa, S.W. Asia), "Travellers-joy" or "Old man's beard"; climbing to 10 m; leaves of 5 entire toothed or 3-lobed leaflets; fragrant flowers greenish-white, to 2½ cm across; very floriferous, in massed clusters. *Subtropic.* *p. 1988*

CLEMATOPSIS *Ranunculaceae* **S3LFM**

scabiosifolia (stanleyi) (Transvaal); attractive hairy, herbaceous plant with shrubby base to 1 m; bipinnately lobed leaves to 35 cm; pretty nodding flowers 4 cm long, pink, pale purple or white, and sweetly scented. *p. 1988*

CLEOME *Capparidaceae* **S2LBM**

spinosa (pungens) (W. Indies), "Spider flower"; pubescent strong-scented annual with spiny stem, palmately compound leaves, and large rose-purple flower clusters having long spidery stamens. *Tropical.* *p. 757*

CLERODENDRUM *Verbenaceae* **I-S3LFM**

bakeri (Trop. Africa); woody shrub to 1 m with obovate toothed leaves to 20 cm, or more long; fragrant white flowers with slender tube and spreading lobes, in large clusters from main stems, often near soil level. *p. 2115, 2117*

buchananii (East Indies); large palmately lobed leaves, and showy erect terminal clusters of bright red flowers similar to C. fallax. *Tropical.* *p.2115*

bungei (China); erect-growing shrub with wiry branches to 2 m high, with large, broadly ovate, quilted leaves to 30 cm long and coarsely toothed, dark green on the surface; fragrant flowers rosy-red in a head-like cluster 10-20 cm across from June to September. *Subtropic.* *p. 2114*

fragrans pleniflorum (China, Japan), "Glory tree"; shrubby plant with stiff stems covered with white hairs; broad ovate, opposite leaves light green and hairy on the surface, green beneath; with margins toothed; the fragrant, 2 cm flowers in a dense terminal cluster, delicate peach-white and fully double, calyx purplish-red. *Subtropic.* *p. 2114*

glabrum (So. Africa); shrub or small tree 1 to 5 m high, with young branches downy; glossy or ovate leaves 5-10 cm long, opposite in whorls; the numerous white or pinkish fragrant flowers with 1 cm tube in tight clusters, followed by blue-green metallic looking fruits. *p. 2117*

hastatum (India); evergreen shrub to 2 m high, with 4-angled branches softly downy; the leaves 20 cm long, and 15 cm wide, deeply 3 or 5-lobed; the terminal, erect inflorescence of numerous white, fragrant flowers with inflated purple calyx, and long thin, arching tubes 10-15 cm long, 4 cm across the twisted lobes. *p. 2117*

inerme (India: Bombay), the "Indian privet"; evergreen branching shrub with hard-leathery, small boxwood-like shiny deep green leaves, and small white flowers with purple stamens; indigenous to mangrove areas near Bombay, and planted at the Hanging Gardens of Bombay, trained over wire frames, into topiary shapes of animals; sheared every 2 weeks. *Tropical.* *p. 2115*

nutans (Assam); tropical evergreen shrub 1-2 m high, with spreading, quadrangular branches; dark green quilted, oblanceolate leaves 20 cm long; inflorescence in lax terminal clusters of creamy-white flowers 3½ cm across limb; followed by small purple berries. *p. 2117*

paniculatum (E. Trop. Asia), "Kashmir bouquet"; robust bush with broad, shining green, 5-lobed leaves, and showy terminal panicles to 30 cm high, of scarlet red flowers. *Tropical.* *p. 2115*

speciosissimum (fallax) (Java, Ceylon), "Glory bower"; a magnificent shrub I remember from the mountains of Java and Ceylon, the 30 cm flower clusters a blaze of fiery scarlet above white-pubescent, heart-shaped foliage, on white-hairy, angled stems to 1 m high. *Tropical.* *p. 2114*

x speciosum (splendens x thomsonae); shrubby plant of semi-erect habit with scandent branches, dark green glossy leaves, and terminal clusters of flowers having a pinkish calyx and deep crimson corolla shaded violet, blooming in summer. *Tropical.* *p. 2114*

splendens (W. Africa: Senegambia to Angola); twining shrub with large, oblong or elliptic, corrugated, leathery leaves to 15 cm between which show large clusters of brilliant scarlet 2 cm flowers. *Tropical.* *p. 2115, 2117*

thomsonae (Trop. West Africa), "Bleeding heart vine"; twining evergreen shrub, climbing to 4 m, with ovate, quilted, glossy, papery leaves to 12 cm long, deep green; showy flowers in forking clusters, the inflated calyx pure white changing to pink, corolla deep crimson; spring-blooming. Often grown under the synonym C. balfouri, but this has larger flowers. *Tropical.* *p. 1952A, 2114*

thomsonae variegatum; fairly common form distinguished by its thin, variegated leaves, pale yellow-green at the margins with the center marbled in shades of light and dark green. *p. 2114*

trichotomum (Japan), "Harlequin glory bower"; hardy shrub or tree 3 to 6 m high, deciduous in colder regions, with pithy, downy branches and dark green ovate leaves to 20 cm long, downy beneath; in upper leaf axils the clusters of small white, fragrant flowers with spreading petals 4 cm across, from inflated, fleshy crimson red calyx; small blue berries. *Warm temperate.* *p. 2117*

ugandense (Uganda to Zimbabwe); smooth climbing shrub to 3 m high; bright green elliptic or obovate leaves 10-12 cm long, toothed at margins; flowers to 3 cm long, calyx lobes crimson, corolla with 3 lobes pale blue and 1 lobe violet-blue, filaments purple and anthers blue. *Tropical.* *p. 2115*

CLETHRA *Clethraceae* **I2LBD**

arborea (Madeira), "Lily-of-the-Valley tree"; beautiful small evergreen tree to 8 m, with rusty-pubescent young shoots; glossy bronzy green elliptic leaves 8 to 10 cm long, at tips of branches the lovely erect inflorescence in spikes of ranked nodding, waxy bell-flowers creamy white and sweetly fragrant. *Subtropic.* *p.755*

CLEYERA: see Eurya

CLIANTHUS *Leguminosae* **I2LBD**

formosus (dampieri) (Australia), "Glory pea"; a striking clambering shrub to 3 m high covered with long white, silky hairs ; with glaucous-gray pinnate leaves feather-fashion, and pendant, showy clusters of scarlet, pea-shaped flowers to 8 cm long, and a parrot-bill-shaped keel-petal, blooming from March on. Young plants may flower from August into winter; silky-hairy pods follow blooms. *Tropical* *p. 1370, 1381*

puniceus (New Zealand), "Parrot's-bill" or "Red kowhai"; evergreen scandent shrub to 3½ m; leaves pinnate; flowers in axillary clusters on a pendulous stalk wholly brilliant red; keel canoe-shaped, 6 cm long. *p. 1381*

CLIFFORTIA *Rosaceae* **S3LFM**

ruscifolia (So. Africa: Cape), "Climbers friend"; sprawling, robust evergreen shrub to 2 m high, dense with rigid, sharp-pointed leaves; small red flowers without petals, in leaf axils, the male flowers with many filaments. *p. 2000*

CLITOREA *Leguminosae* **S2LBM**

ternatea (Pantropic: Panama to India and Moluccas), "Butterfly pea"; tropical annual or biennial slender twiner with pinnate leaves, and pea-like solitary, showy flowers 5 cm long with broad, fan-like lip narrowing to the base, bright blue with beautiful markings in the throat, blooming all summer. *Tropical.* *p. 1381*

CLIVIA *Amaryllidaceae* **I2LFD**

miniata (Imantophyllum) (Natal), "Kafir lily"; bulb-like plant with fleshy roots, with long, waxy, straplike, arching leaves; broad, fleshy bell-shaped, erect, orange-red flowers to 8 cm long, yellow toward center, in stiff umbels. *Subtropic.* *p. 112, 1824A*

miniata 'Grandiflora'; a highly developed commercial cultivar with broad, dark green leaves and extra large fiery-red flowers. *p. 112*

nobilis (So. Africa), "Greentip Kafir lily"; inflorescence with many drooping, narrow, funnel-shaped flowers salmon red with green tips. *Subtropic.* *p. 112*

CLUSIA *Guttiferae* ***S1LFM**

grandiflora (Guyana), "Scotch attorney"; tropical evergreen shrub 3-6 m high, usually beginning life epiphytically on another tree; after the roots reach the ground, it begins to strangle its host and replaces it; branches thick and spreading, with large leathery, obovate leaves 15-30 cm long; cupped white to rosy flowers 5 cm wide. *p. 1321*

"lanceolata" (Venezuela); succulent evergreen shrub from Cerro Cipapo, with brown-hairy stem and long-pointed, narrow, fleshy, green leaves without consipicuous lateral veins broadening in older plants; on milky stem. *p. 1317*

rosea (W. Indies, Panama, Venezuela), "Fat pork tree"; evergreen tree 6 m or more high, growing naturally on rocks or epiphytic on other trees; with obovate thick leathery, deep green, opposite leaves to 20 cm long, without lateral veins; large rose flowers. *Tropical. p. 1317, 1321*

rosea 'Aureo-variegata', "Variegated balsam apple"; unusually showy variety having the broad obovate leaves beautifully variegated dark green, light green and creamy to golden yellow. *Tropical. p. 1317*

CLYTOSTOMA *Bignoniaceae* **I3LBM**

callistegioides (Bignonia) (Brazil, Argentina), "Argentine trumpet vine"; climbing shrub with opposite oval leaves and simple tendril; large funnelshaped flowers in pairs, with spreading lobes, lavender and streaked. *Tropical. p. 498*

COBAEA *Polemoniaceae* **I2LBM**

scandens (Mexico), "Monastery-bells"; attractive climber with pinnately compound leaflets terminating in a branched tendril used for climbing, and with large bell-shaped flowers to 5 cm long, having a violet calyx, and a corolla first greenish, then violet. *Subtropic. p. 1951*

COCA: see Erythroxylum

COCCINEA *Cucurbitaceae* **S3LBM**

sessilifolia (So. Africa, Namibia), an "Ivy-gourd"; herbaceous tendril climber with tuberous roots; pleasing dark green, lobed leaves; the insignificant male and female flowers on different plants; cylindrical oblong fruit about 10 cm long, attractively red and marbled with white. Grown for the ornamental fruit; its flesh has an insipid flavor. *p. 929*

COCCOLOBA *Polygonaceae* **•S1LB-FM**

diversifolia (floridana) (So. Florida, Bahamas, to Jamaica), "Dove-plum", also known as "Pigeon-plum"; evergreen tree 3 m high, but on occasion to 20 m, with light gray bark; thin-leathery, ovate leaves to 10 cm long, shining bright green; small yellowish-green flowers followed by small clusters of 1 cm dark purple edible berries. *p. 1953*

grandifolia (pubescens) (Trop. America); great tree to 24 m high, with woody stems and giant round, leathery sessile leaves to 1 m across, fresh green and with sunken veins, the margins turned down, with rusty hairs beneath, especially on the prominent ribs. *p. 1954*

latifolia (South America); evergreen tree with large, dark green broad-obovate, almost round leaf with cordate base, to 45 cm wide, the alternate veins deeply depressed resulting in a net-like quilted surface and with wavy edge. *p. 1954*

laurifolia (floridana) (So. Florida, Bahamas, No. coast of So. America), "Pigeon plum"; evergreen growing into a tree 8-10 m high, with thin-leathery, glossy green long elliptic 5-10 cm leaves transversed by 3 depressed parallel veins, on petioles purplish at base of leaf; greenish flowers and small pear-shaped, edible berries. *p. 1953*

rugosa (Puerto Rico, W. Indies), the "Ortegon"; at home in the Sierra Luquillo; a magnificent sparry, tall-growing evergreen tree with stiff-erect, many-angled woody brown stems to 10 m high; big clasping, roundish leaves to 60 cm dia., dull-green and deeply wrinkled, of a heavy texture as if made of aluminum; the sinus of the leaf circling the stems; at the apex a long pendant raceme crowded with tiny salmon-rose flowers. *p. 1953, 1955*

uvifera (South Florida, W. Indies), the familiar "Sea-grape"; along sandy tropical shores, a good decorative shrub or tree to 6 m with flexuous branches and stiff-leathery, rounded leaves to 20 cm across, glossy yellowish to olive green, with prominent crimson-red veins on young growth, later changing to ivory; the flowers white; fruits purple, resembling bunches of grapes, used for jelly. *Tropical. p. 1954, 1955, 1956*

uvifera 'Aurea' (Florida); spectacular sport with large, almost sessile, leathery leaves largely variegated with creamy yellow. *p. 1953, 1954*

COCCOTHRINAX *Palmae* **S3LFM**

argentata (So. Florida, Bahamas), a small "Silver palm" to 6 m; with small, very deeply divided star-shaped leaves which appear peltate, the segments narrow and more or less pendant, glossy green above and silvery-white beneath. *Tropical. p. 1862, 1864, 1876*

argentea (Haiti, Dominican Rep.), "Silver palm"; a small unarmed fan palm with medium large palmate leaves, divided nearly to the base into slender arching green segments, decidedly silvery underneath; brown-black fruit. *p. 1862*

dussiana (Thrinax barbadensis) (Barbados); a beautiful, stately fan-palm with tall, slender trunk bearing a crown of palmate leaves, glistening silvery underneath, the segments not very deeply cut; fruit blackish (Thrinax fruit is white). *p. 1862*

fragrans (Cuba, Haiti, Jamaica), "Cuban silver palm"; slender palm to 5 m, with solitary, smooth trunk, and near circular 1 m palmate fronds with narrow segments deeply cut and recurving, glossy green above and bluish beneath; the spadix with yellow, very fragrant flowers. *p. 1862, 1864*

martii (Cuba); slender fan palm with palmate leaves of about 30 segments 75 cm long, deeply cut, glossy green above, silvery beneath; short hanging inflorescence, and blackish fruit. *p. 1862*

miraguama (Cuba); handsome palm to 12 m tall, with slender trunk often covered with woven fiber, the rigid, smallish, fan-leaves roundish, leaves about 60 cm across, split into many narrow segments lustrous green above, gray-pubescent beneath. *p. 1862, 1864*

COCCULUS *Menispermaceae* **I1LBD**

laurifolius (Himalayas), "Platter-leaf"; decorative, sparry shrub to 5 m high, with wiry green branches and alternate stiff-leathery, ovate to narrow-elliptic leaves 12-15 cm long, shining forest green, concave with prominently raised yellow-green parallel veins. *p. 1548, 1551, 1954*

COCHEMIEA *Cactaceae* **S2LBD**

poselgeri (Baja California), "Long hooks"; sprawling cylindric plant with numerous stems, to 2 m long and 4 cm thick, bluish green, with conical warts, and white-woolly in axils, reddish radials and solitary hooked central spine; small, glossy scarlet flowers. *Arid-tropical. p. 713*

setispina (Baja California); cylindric plant to 30 cm high, with olive green knobs, woolly in the axils, radials white with black tips, some spines hooked; flowers scarlet red. *p. 710*

COCHLEANTHES *Orchidaceae* **I3OFM**

aromatica (Warscewiczella wendlandii) (Costa Rica, Panama); tropical epiphyte without pseudobulbs; pale green, tufted leaves to 25 cm; short-stalked, very fragrant, heavy-textured flowers 8-12 cm across, long-lasting; sepals and petals white to yellow-green, lip violet through the center with frilled white margins. (Summer). *p. 1832*

discolor (Chondrorhyncha, Warscewiczella) (Cuba, Costa Rica, Panama); tufted epiphyte with lanceolate leaves to 60 cm long and flowers with pale yellowish sepals, petals pale yellowish at base and pale violet on their upper half and a yellow spot at apex, lip deep violet with whitish front; (spring-early summer). *Tropical. p. 1693, 1700*

COCHLIODA *Orchidaceae* **C3ONM**

rosea (Andes of Perú); epiphyte with flattened pseudobulb 8 cm long, solitary linear soft leaf; inflorescence gracefully arching, to 40 cm long, 4 cm flowers dark rose-red. *Subtropic. p. 1690*

COCHLIOSTEMA *Commelinaceae* **S3HFW**

odoratissimum (jacobianum) (Brazil and Ecuador); large epiphyte of the habit of a billbergia, 30-75 cm high; oblong lanceolate leaves to more than 1 m long, and 10 cm wide, rich green above and purplish red with violet lines beneath, sheathing at the base and forming a rosette; numerous beautiful, deep violet-blue flowers of three petals and large white claw, and leaf-like hairy yellow-green sepals with reddish tip. *Tropical. p. 782, 784, 786*

COCHLOSPERMUM *Cochlospermaceae* **S3LBM**

vitifolium plenum (Maximilianea) (Mexico, C. America, Puerto Rico, So. America), "Brazilian-rose" or "Rosa amarilla"; magnificent tropical tree to 12 m high, deciduous during the dry season; with palmately lobed leaves to 30 cm across, and showy yellow, fully double rose-like flowers of 8 cm dia., appearing before the foliage. The velvety, globular seed capsules bear an abundance of silky white cotton. *Tropical. p. 926*

COCOS *Palmae* **S3LFW**

nucifera (Indian Archipelago), "Coconut palm"; widely spread into all tropical regions, especially along the sea where its curving-erect swaying trunks, to 30 m high, leaning toward the water, and topped by majestic crowns of glossy, feathery fronds are a feature of tropical shores; producing its edible nuts inside a large yellow-brown, tough, fibrous husk, 20-30 cm long. This "Tree of life" is of greatest economic importance in most tropical regions; the meat of the coconut is dried into copra, used to manufacture palm-oil, fats and soap. *Tropical. p. 1851, 1854, 1864, 1870, 1871*

nucifera 'Dwarf Golden Malay'; originated from seedlings of the dwarf King-coconut from the Andaman Islands; more diminutive and more slender-trunked than 'Dwarf Samoan'; and smaller-fruited (yellow, green, or red); starts producing in about three years, in time 100 or more nuts per year as against 30 to 40 of the common coconut palm, and has a trunk so low that the clusters may need props. *p. 1854*

nucifera 'Dwarf Green', (Malaya), "Green Malay coconut"; a strain brought in from Malaysia having shorter trunk and starting to produce its green fruit earlier (3 years on) than the larger species; also has been found more resistant to the "lethal yellowing", probably caused by microbes or bacteria, and an epidemic disease that has killed more than 6,000,000 coconuts in Florida and the Caribbean since 1970. *Tropical. p. 1867*

nucifera 'Dwarf Samoan' (Marquesas); a dwarf growing coconut forming stout but short trunk, to 8 m high, and bearing fruit larger and more rounded than that of C. nucifera typica; begins to bear at 5 years from planting seed while var. typica takes 8-10 years; husk color either green or red, with average 550 gm of fresh meat per nut against the normal 350 gm in the type coconut. *Tropical.* *p. 1854*

nucifera 'Nino'; a graceful, very decorative feather palm of compact habit, with elegant pinnate fronds set closely with long, narrow leaflets, glossy green; said to produce smallish fruit (at Dr. Darian's Palmatum, Vista, California). *p. 1867*

weddelliana in hort., bot. Syagrus (Brazil: Guanabara); miniature "Terrarium palm"; small graceful feather palm to 2 m high in habitat, with slender trunk to 5 cm thick; pinnate leaves to 1½ m, gracefully arching; narrow, slender 12 cm leaflets light green; fragrant yellowish flowers. In horticulture grown in small pots as miniature for terrarium planting. (See Syagrus). *p. 1864*

COCOS: see also Arecastrum, Syagrus

CODIAEUM *Euphorbiaceae* **S2-3LBM**

aucubaefolium (Polynesia), "Aucuba leaf"; bushy plant with small elliptic thin leathery 8-10 cm leaves bright glossy green blotched and spotted yellow. *p. 1009, 1010*

bogoriense (Java); compact shrub with stiff leathery, broad stubby linear leaves with truncate base, simple but highly veined and variegated yellow on green base. *p. 1010*

spirale (Malaysia); compact plant with stiff linear leaves spirally twisted like a corkscrew, and checkered red, yellow and green. *p. 1010*

variegatum pictum (So. India, Ceylon, Malaya, Sunda Isl.); "Crotons" are beautiful tropical shrubs with highly ornamental leaves, thick leathery, glabrous, ovate to linear, entire or lobed, or spirally twisted, 10-30 cm long, variegated in beautiful colors, the greens and yellows of the leaves later often change to shades of red; small female and male flowers, the latter with white petals; developed into many varieties and hybrids; some of the better known cultivars are listed below. *Tropical.*

'A. B. Cartledge'; large leathery lobed leaves of a tender but intense pink over green, the veins scarlet-red. *p. 1012*

'America'; fast growing plant with large leathery leaves broadening from the base but constricted near apex, strikingly colored copper to maroon and a network of veins shading from pale yellow to red. *Tropical.* *p. 1007, 1016*

'Andreanum' (1910); thrifty plant of compact habit with oval pointed leaves coppery green with rich yellow veins turning orange red, and variegated yellow toward margins. *p. 1010, 1015*

'Angustissimum'; long strapshaped leaves broadest at base, fresh to deep green with distinctive lemon-yellow midrib and margin. *p. 1016*

'Anietumense' (1910); narrow and long lanceolate leaves gracefully arched, light green with network of yellow veins. *p. 1014*

'Annie Rutherford', long, rather large leaves lightly lobed, rich pink to orange and blue-black. *p. 1012*

'Appendiculatum'; an old and peculiar variety with 10-20 cm leaves narrow-lanceolate or linear, entirely dark green; the blade interrupted in the middle and held together by the thread-like midrib only; apparently introduced from Polynesia. *p. 1017*

'Applause'; robust grower with broad, lightly lobed leaves dark green with edges yellow to delicate pink; veins scarlet. *p. 1013*

'Appleleaf' see 'Imperialis'

'Arthur Howe'; recurving lobed leaves orange-pink and ranging from apricot to scarlet-red, with dark bluish-green. *p. 1015*

'Baronne de Rothschild'; compact variety with ovate or lanceolate leaves wavy at margins; young foliage green and yellow, older leaves rich in red. *Tropical.* *p. 1010, 1014, 1016*

'Beautiful Lady'; large, lobed leaves blackish-green with scarlet and yellow; new growth leaves yellow and green with vivid scarlet edge. *p. 1015*

'Big Dipper'; large, bushy plant with broad obovate leaves nearly blue-black, variegated with orange and deep green; a Cutler hybrid, Florida. *p. 1018*

'Bimbo'; stout plant with leathery, large, lobed leaves blackish-green and vivid scarlet, older leaves pale yellow at tips. *p. 1013*

'Black Prince'; leathery broad-ovate or oval leaves deep blackish-green, only occasionally speckled red or orange. *p. 1017*

'Bravo'; a showy new Cutler hybrid of compact habit with large, thick leaves somewhat oakleaf-shaped, the golden-yellow to rosy-red vein areas in striking contrast to the dark green background. *p. 1008*

'Bruxellense'; vigorous growing variety with lanceolate bronzy leaves with yellow veins turning red. *p. 1014*

'Buena Vista'; large leaves lightly lobed and crowded, deep green with brilliant yellow ribs and spots. *p. 1013*

'Butterball'; large obovate or elliptic leaves somewhat crimped, rich green with yellow ribs, to mostly yellow with green marking on younger foliage. *p. 1013*

'Capt. Kidd'; strapshaped or narrow lanceolate leaves deep green mottled with yellow, orange and red. *p. 1017*

'Caribbean Star'; an excellent Cutler hybrid being a consistent colorer, with broad elliptic, quilted leaves green, shading into bronzy-black while the center area and lateral veins are yellow to orange red, and red midrib. *p. 1011, 1016*

'Clipper'; an elegant and vigorous new Cutler hybrid descended from 'Monarch', with large lanceolate waxy leaves to 45 cm long, shining green with prominent lemon-yellow veins and margins turning rosy with age. *p. 1008*

'Columbiana Gold'; large elliptic or obovate leaves with ribs or central area of blade yellow, sometimes almost all the leaf, the balance or outer area glossy green. *p. 1013*

'Commotion'; colorful Florida hybrid with heavy leaves lightly lobed or in fiddle-fashion; deep bluish green and bright green with pink, yellow and cream, changing to scarlet. *p. 1018*

'Comte de Castelaine'; thick, medium-wide coppery-red leaves, pink through center. *p. 1014*

'Confucius'; large, undulate, waxy leaves of irregular shape, occasionally lobed, and multicolored olive-green, shading to maroon, the center along veins yellow to pink and autumn colors. *p. 1011, 1016*

'Corkscrew'; sturdy plant dense with stiff erect, strap-shaped leaves typically twisted and spiralled, deep green and metallic red with yellow in shady location, but becoming more vivid in strong light, in shades of golden yellow, pink, red, bluish black and green, the midrib usually yellow. *p. 1015*

'Craigii'; (1910); attractive plant with stiff, deeply trilobed leaves, bright green with yellow veins. *p. 1007, 1009, 1014*

'Craigii Supreme'; a variety with very fine trilobed leaves highly variegated yellow along the veins and along edge, over a waxy fresh green base. *p. 1016*

'Cronstadtii'; remarkable variety with narrow, long strap-shaped leaves variously flat, or spirally twisted and crisped at margins, sometimes with interruptions in the leaf blade, variegated green and yellow; listed by Dreer 1884. *Tropical.* *p. 1018*

'Cutler's Supreme'; large, deeply lobed leaves to 30 cm long, basically green, but with veins and margins yellow and red, blotched with pink. *p. 1012*

'Daisy-O'; broad elliptic, shiny leaves deep copper to metallic black, irregularly variegated and shaded orange-red. *p. 1016*

'Daisy's Pride'; bushy plant with puckered, leathery, ovate leaves with ribs usually yellow, the blade in colors bluish black, scarlet, orange and some yellow. *p. 1012*

'Davis Compacta'; of bushy, compact habit, with medium-sized deeply lobed leaves green and bluish-black marked with pink; the young foliage dominated by brillant yellow. *p. 1012*

'Dayspring'; long, narrow-lance-shaped leaves bronzy green mottled red and yellow. *p. 1017*

'Delicatissimum'; elegantly arching linear leaves, dark green with yellow center, turning red toward apex. *p. 1014*

'Disraeli'; trilobed oakleaf-type with slender fingers green with yellow ribs and markings. *p. 1017*

'Don Quixote'; heavy leaves lobed and somewhat irregular, deep green with numerous yellow veins, older leaves orange to scarlet and strong pink with green. *p. 1012*

'Dreer No. 7'; a fine old hybrid of dense habit with medium large oak-type leaves, pleasing green and turning red toward apex, yellow veining and mottling turning pink and red in older leaves. *p. 1011, 1016*

'Duke of Windsor'; a good, robust, resistant, standard variety, always colorful, with wide linear leaves slightly broader near base, deep green, with gold to orange center, red midrib and red-orange margin. *p. 15*, 1011, 1016*

'Eburneum'; large ovate leaves contracted or indented toward apex, silvery-green with yellow border areas, sometimes creamy-yellow over large portions of the blade; photo by G. Roof of Miami. *Tropical.* *p. 1018*

'Echo'; sturdy plant with bold, broad, elliptic leaves barely indented to 40 cm long, vivid pink and bluish black, veins often scarlet in older foliage. *p. 1013*

'Edmontonense' (1910); slow growing spirally twisted linear leaves almost entirely bronzy red, with dark crimson midrib, and some yellow variegation. *p. 1014*

'Edwin T. Meredith'; long narrow leaves, tall and stiff, green with yellow ribs and margins, more color than anietumense. *p. 1014*

'Elaine' (1910), "Lance-leaf croton"; a good variety with stiff upright lanceolate leaves, shallowly lobed, smaller than 'Reidii', fresh green with bright yellow veins tinted into pink and red. *Tropical.* *p. 1009, 1014*

'Evening Embers'; robust plant dense with lightly lobed leaves to 25 cm long, shining bluish-black blotched red and green; vivid fiery-red veins. *p. 1012*

'Excurrens'; leaves very variable from narrow-linear to small oval or obovate; waxy leaves fresh green with part of blade creamy yellow and midrib yellow or red; with age shading more into reds. Known in England since 1884. Glenn Roof of Miami tells me that this variety in cultivation can have leaves both broad and oval as well as narrow-strap-shaped, twisted or with interrupted sections of leaf blade, all on the same bush. *Tropical.* *p. 1018*

'Exotica'; a beautiful Florida (Cutler) hybrid with giant halberd-shaped leaves to 35 cm long; blackish-green with cherry-red vein areas, later autumn-colored in bronzes and salmons. *p. 1006*

'Fascination'; bushy plant with clustered branches of threadlike narrow leaves red and green with yellow variegation. *p. 1014*

'Franklin Roosevelt'; strap-shaped or narrow-lanceolate leaves deep green to red, blotched with pinkish-orange. *p. 1017*

'Fred Sander' (1910); yellow stems with leaves distinctly 3-lobed, yellow central area and fresh green margins, soft stem often yellow; delicate and susceptible to checks. *Tropical.* *p. 1014*

'Gen. Marshall'; sturdy and showy hybrid with large linear and unusually long, wavy leaves, pleasing green with yellow center when young, later changing to blackish maroon with orange, midrib red. *p. 1011, 1016*

'Gen. Paget'; distinct variety with broad, large and wavy, oblanceolate leaves deep green with bright yellow ribs and marbling, some entirely creamy-yellow. *Tropical.* *p. 1017*

'Gloriosa'; an excellent hybrid, fast growing yet tough, and colors well; the large oval glossy leaves are rich green with yellow veins when young, later olive green to maroon with veins golden yellow to red. *p. 1016, 1056A*

'Gloriosum superbum', "Autumn croton"; dependable variety with long leathery leaves lobed near the apex, nicely variegated according to age of leaf with yellow veins and margins changing to autumn and crimson, the blade fresh green to almost red-black; good keeper. *Tropical.* *p. 1009*

'Golden Ring'; a fine variety that can be grown as a standard 2 m high like warrenii, the long twisted pendant leaves are narrower, highly variegated golden-yellow and green, and of good keeping quality. *p. 1010*

'Graciosum'; graceful little plant with arching narrow linear leaves of dark copper with small yellow spots. *p. 1014*

'Grusonii'; narrow linear, waxy-smooth, yellowish green leaves with rosy-red midrib, the margins narrowly colored yellow and shading to red. *p. 1016*

'Harvest Moon'; vigorous grower of excellent coloring even in shady location, broad, stiff leaves, constricted near apex, waxy grass-green with bold lemon-yellow veins and margin. *p. 1011, 1016*

'Hookerianum'; narrow oblanceolate leaves glossy bright to blackish-green, irregularly variegated down the center. *p. 1017*

'Imperialis' (Appleleaf); small, compact plant and good keeper, with simple, elliptic leaves almost entirely colored yellow, shading to peach and turning rose and red, green midrib and apex turning metallic purple. *Tropical.* *p. 1006, 1009, 1016*

'Indian Headdress'; bushy plant with elliptic leaves undulate at margins, green with bronze, yellow and red. *p. 1012*

'Interruptum' (Polynesia), a "Garden croton"; long linear leaves red and yellow, with midrib extending beyond the blade. *Tropical.* *p. 1014*

'Irene Kingsley; a tropical showpiece with medium size, deeply trilobed leaves blackish red contrasting against the lighter red veins and margins. *p. 1016*

'Irregularis'; old variety from the South Sea Islands, with variable leaves long and narrow but broader toward the apex, green with yellow or red ribs and spotted yellow and red. *p. 1017*

'Jan Bier' ("Croton"); European hybrid with showy leaves rich yellow in center, the ribs spreading out yellow in herringbone pattern. *p. 1006*

'Johanna Coppinger', "Strap-leaf croton"; vigorous, bushy strap-like leaves dark green with yellow to orange-red, ribs red. *p. 1006, 1015*

'Jungle Queen'; large ovate to oval leaves to 40 cm long, deep green and yellow with red veins; older leaves deep blue-black with scarlet blotches. *p. 1015*

'Katonii'; lobed leaves deep dull green dotted and blotched with yellow; medium-sized leathery foliage to 15 cm long. *p. 1017*

'Kentucky'; large leaves of stiff texture, lightly lobed, coppery green with gold when young, black when older, with orange to crimson variegation. *p. 1016*

'King George'; broad, ovate leaves fresh green with contrasting ribs and veinlets in yellow, turning to red. *p. 1017*

'Lillian Staffinger'; fine standard hybrid of sturdy growth, with long oblong waxy leaves pretty forest green with sharply defined, broad yellow veins and yellow border. *p. 1011, 1016*

'Linearis nigrescens'; very dark reddish, stiff strapshaped, linear leaves blackish red with lighter red center. *p. 1014*

'L. M. Rutherford', "Giant croton"; large heavy, undulate semi-oakleaf, consistent pink color, with gold and crimson on green. *p. 1016*

'MacArthurii', also known as 'Sir William'; vigorous bush with large and heavy long-ovate leaves, light moss-green richly variegated with yellow. *Tropical.* *p. 1018*

'Mad. Fernand Kohl' (1910); large leaves lightly lobed, narrow deep yellow veins in reddish blade. *p. 1014*

'Mad. Juliette Delarue'; erect long finger-lobed thin leaves mostly bright yellow on fresh-green. *p. 1014*

'Majesticum'; a Polynesian variety of drooping habit, with very long, narrow-linear recurving leaves to 45 cm or more long, deep green with yellow ribs when young, changing to olive with age, the yellow becoming crimson in sunlight. *Tropical.* *p. 1017*

'Mark of Gold'; sturdy plant with large oval leaves rich green with bold light yellow ribs and spots. *p. 1015*

'Martha Francis'; large elliptic leaves green when young turning red with variegation of yellow, pink and autumn colors. *p. 1011, 1016*

'Maryland'; medium broad, pearshaped leaf of a bold red, the veins rosy or in autumn color. *p. 1014*

'Masterpiece'; shapely plant with upright, tightly spiralled linear leaves resembling a corkscrew, yellow turning to red, edged green. *p. 1014*

'Mona Lisa', "White croton"; outstanding Bachmann cultivar with large, broad ovate leaves lobed or constricted toward apex, the young growth almost entirely a waxy creamy-white edged in green, later the center area and ribs with reddish tints, the green turning into olive or coppery. *p. 1007*

'Mons. Ernest Delarue'; trilobed leaves light green attractively colored by golden yellow blotching and broad yellow veins. *p. 1014*

'Mons. Florin'; compact grower with hard, medium large, broad elliptic or obovate leaves, apple green with contrasting yellow veining traced in lacy network pattern. *Tropical.* *p. 1011, 1016*

'Mortefontenense'; bushy plant with small leathery, deeply lobed leaves olive green to coppery with yellow to reddish veins and margin, and lightly spotted. *p. 1016*

'Mortii'; well-known old variety, tall-growing, with long-lanceolate leaves olive-green with contrasting fishbone design of yellow veins; later the greens change into dull red, and the yellows into orange. *p. 1014, 1015*

'Mortimer'; generally known as 'Piecrust'; narrow-lanceolate leaves 15-20 cm long shiny green, brilliantly blotched yellow and cream, turning crimson-rose to dark blood-red; unusual because the margins are undulate and frilly (Royal Palm Nurs., Oneco, Florida). *Tropical.* *p. 1006*

'Mosaic'; pastel colored, attractive hybrid with large obovate, undulate leaves light green to blackish, veined and spotted yellow, bronzy red and pink. *p. 1016*

'Mrs. Colette' (Kentucky x Polychrome); a new Cutler hybrid of loose habit, with long, trilobed leaves in riotous variegation of golden yellow, dark green, crimson-red and copper. *p. 1008*

'Mrs. Iceton'; smallish, obovate leaves blackish-green variegated between the veins, especially in the central area, with deep pink and red; the juvenile growth with cream. *p. 1006, 1017*

'Mrs. Wm. F. Dreer'; lanceolate leaves with deep yellow to red center and lateral veins, balance of blade fresh green. *p. 1014*

'Norwood Beauty' (1924); small and tough 3-lobed leaves of the oakleaf type, dark green with bronze to brown-red and rosy edge, yellow in vein areas, 15-20 cm long. *Tropical.* *p. 1009, 1014*

'Philadelphia'; small leathery lobed oakleaf type with yellow veins in fresh-green leaf. *p. 1009, 1014*

'Polychrome'; large, stiff leaves lightly lobed above the middle, largely pinkish yellow shading to autumn gold and rose, with olive green, midrib pink. *p. 1010, 1016*

'Prince of Monaco'; long linear, strap-shaped leaves olive green with yellow variegation and tinted with red. *p. 1006*

'Puccini'; old hybrid of compact habit and slow growth, the medium size leaves somewhat irregular in outline, olive-green to blackish with red veining. *p. 1016*

'Punctatum aureum'; densely bushy, free branching shrub with narrow linear, dark glossy green leathery leaves freely spotted yellow; good as miniature plant. *Tropical.* *p. 1009, 1010*

'Rapture'; large lightly lobed leaves to 50 cm long deep green to bluish-black with marbling in vivid orange to red, veins and margins scarlet. *p. 1013*

'Reidii'; an old and good variety with medium large obovate leaves, green shading to yellow, pink and red, with contrasting yellow to orange red veins; holds color well. *p. 1006, 1010, 1016*

'Rex'; handsome variety with long, narrow leaves occasionally spiralling; when young, green with yellow veins and mottling, with age the yellows turn red and underside of leaf dark red. *p. 1014, 1017*

'Robert Craig'; oblanceolate leaves subtly green and blue-black contrasting with orange and red shades. *p. 1013*

'Robert Lavalois'; erect, oblanceolate, fresh green leaves with contrasting design of yellow veining and around margin. *p. 1014*

'Rosette'; as its name indicates, this is a dense rosette of medium large, richly autumn colored leaves, rosy red with dark green, and blotching of orange-yellow. *p. 1008*

'Sanborn Jr.'; consistently colorful hybrid of lanky habit, with leaves rather narrow and lightly lobed, the black background nicely variegated with yellow to orange, and pink to red. *p. 1016*

'Sanderi'; broad, oblanceolate, bright green leaves with irregular blotches and center of pale yellow. *p. 1014*

'Schattii'; thick leathery, broad-obovate leaves medium green, with prominent yellow veins and border, turning to pink. *p. 1014*

'Seminole Queen'; large oval leaves occasionally lightly lobed, green and blue-black veined and marbled with orange and strong pink. *p. 1013*

'Show Girl'; wide, lobed leaves deep green to bluish-black with veins and marbling of orange and red. *p. 1015*

'Souvenir de Thos. Rochford'; erect narrow linear leaves olive-green to red with contrasting pale yellow midrib. *p. 1014*

'Souvenir Ernest Delarue' (1924); broad leaves light olive green with rich yellow veins and blotching, turning to red. *p. 1010*

'Stewartii'; an old well-known variety from New Guinea; the leathery, obovate leaves deep bronzy-green with contrasting veins and blotching of yellows, the midrib and petiole red; tolerates cooler temperature. *Tropical.* *p. 1017, 1018*

'Stoplight'; bushy plant of broad linear, leathery leaves a blackish-red, the center and undulate margins yellow to salmon-red. *Tropical.* *p. 1008*

'Sunrise'; sturdy variety with narrow lanceolate leaves green, veined and edged in orange to red, the juvenile growth green with yellow. *p. 1017*

'Sybil Griffin'; a Cutler hybrid of 'Kentucky', with tremendous leaves, deeply lobed oakleaf type, blackish red with areas along the veins salmon-rose shading to autumn colors and pink. *p. 1008, 1016*

'Tapestry'; strikingly colorful plant of compact habit, with long narrow, barely lobed leaves nearly obtuse at apex; new growth intermingled green and yellow with red veins, with age becoming coppery-green and lovely rose, with lavender tinting. *Tropical.* *p. 1018*

'The Queen'; large, lanceolate leaves glossy fresh green with veins and basal area in cream and yellow. *p. 1017*

'Tortilis'; linear strap-shaped, twisted leaves similar to 'Corkscrew' but larger, dark green with orange to red markings. *p. 1017*

'Undulatum'; long, narrow-lanceolate leaves with wavy edge, green with red speckling and veining; underside bronze with vein pattern pale green. *p. 1017*

'Veitchii'; long, narrow-lanceolate leaves green with pronounced vein pattern and margin in creamy-yellow, later changing to rose and carmine. *p. 1017*

'Volutum' (Polynesia), "Ramshorn"; short recurved, linear leaves; veins and midrib yellow. *Tropical.* *p. 1017*

'Vulcan'; magnificent hybrid cultivar with obovate pointed leaves, similar to 'Apple leaf' but more colorful; the younger foliage creamy-yellow with pink fringe, green at tip and midrib; older leaves almost bright wine-red. Photographed at Rochford Nurseries near London. *p. 1018*

'Warrenii' (Polynesia); robust tall growing stem topped by a crown of long linear, pendant leaves only 2-3 cm wide, spirally twisted or undulate, red in center with yellow blotches, margins coppery green. *p. 1010*

'Weismannii' (1873); broad wavy leaves with yellow midrib and veins and green blade, red petioles. *p. 1014*

'William Craig'; a favorite so colorful it has been compared with 'Joseph's Coat'; large thin-leathery leaves metallic green with contrasting autumn coloring of orange to bright crimson, older leaves almost black, with orange-red center. *p. 1016*

'Wotan'; large foliage, first green with yellow veining, older leaves bluish-black with orange variegation. *p. 1012*

'Yellow Imperialis' (Apple-leaf); attractive old variety with elliptic, bright green, shiny leaves 8-12 cm long, highly variegated with creamy-yellow from base of leaf upwards. *p. 1006*

CODONANTHE *Gesneriaceae* **S3HFM**

crassifolia (Costa Rica, Panama, No. South America); branched creeping stems rooting below nodes, with stiff-waxy elliptic leaves light olive green, underside red-spotted and with red midrib; slipper-shaped flowers with tube 3-4 cm long, creamy-white spotted orange in throat. *p. 1233, 1243*

gracilis (Brazil); small epiphytic clamberer found in the wooded Organ Mountains, with thin purplish branches, rooting below nodes, with pairs of glossy, deep green elliptic leaves, reddish beneath; tubular flowers with spreading lobes, creamy white spotted with purple in throat. *Tropical.* *p.1232*

macradenia (Cent. America), "Central American bell-flower"; tropical vine, in habitat creeping over rocks and trees, the flexuous stems rooting below the nodes; small opposite ovate, thick shiny leaves similar to Aeschynanthus, but with red spots on the underside; axillary slipper-shaped, oblique flowers waxy-white with red markings inside the tube, and ever blooming, followed by long-lasting white berries. Similar to crassifolia but this has red berries. *p. 1232*

CODONOPSIS *Campanulaceae* **C2LBM**

ovata (Kashmir); small perennial 15-30 cm high, lower part of stems spreading, upper erect, with ovate hairy leaves 2 cm long; solitary bell-shaped flowers pale blue with darker veins, 3-4 cm long. *p. 751*

COELOGYNE *Orchidaceae* **I-S3OFD**

carinata (New Guinea); small epiphyte with 4-angled pseudobulbs bearing 2 leaves; flower stem erect, or arching, appearing with the young leaves, sepals and petals greenish-white, the trilobed lip marked with brown. (Autumn). (S) *p. 1690*

corymbosa (Himalayas: Sikkim); small epiphyte with 2-leaved pseudobulbs, and arching raceme of 8 cm flowers white, the pointed lip with two golden blotches edged in brown; summer. (C) *p. 1702*

cristata (Nepal, Himalayas); small easy-growing epiphyte with branching rhizome forming mats of fleshy pseudobulbs with thin twin leaves; large 8-10 cm crystalline, fragrant flowers in drooping clusters, snow-white with five golden-yellow, fringed keels down the middle of the lip. (Feb.-April). *Humid-subtropic.* *p. 1688, 1690, 1692*

dayana (Borneo, Sumatra), "Necklace orchid"; decorative epiphyte with pseudobulbs having 1-2 narrow leaves; pendulous racemes 1 m long, loosely many-flowered; 6 cm flowers with narrow lemon-yellow sepals and petals, and broad, lobed lip blotched with chocolate and with white keels. *p. 1690*

dayana grandis; long, drooping inflorescence with showy blooms arranged in 2 ranks; flowers to 4 cm across, sepals and petals buff yellow, cream lip heavily blotched with chocolate. *p. 1691*

fimbriata (Vietnam, So. China, No. India); small pseudobulbs carrying 2 thin-leathery leaves; inflorescence from top of the pseudobulb; long-lasting flowers musk-scented, sepals and petals greenish yellow to tan, 4 cm across, the fringed yellowish lip streaked with brown (autumn). *p. 1691*

flaccida (Nepal, Himalayas); epiphyte with dark green twin leaves; the small flowers in graceful pendulous racemes and of heavy odor, cream-white with lip having brownish streaked side lobes and yellow in the middle. *Tropical.* *p. 1689*

glandulosa (Nilghiris, So. India); flowers pure white, 4 cm across, in a nodding raceme; marked on disk of lip with yellow lines. *p. 1691*

graminifolia (Burma, Assam); small pseudobulbs bearing two grass-like leaves; raceme of 5 cm flowers with creamy white sepals and petals; the lip recurved and streaked with brown; winter. (I) *p. 1689*

huettneriana lactea (Burma); free-blooming epiphyte with furrowed pseudobulbs bearing pairs of leathery leaves; basal arching raceme with 4 cm flowers white, the lip creamy-white tinged with yellow; April-June. (I) *p. 1689*

lawrenceana (Viet-Nam); fine epiphyte with 2-leaved oval pseudobulbs and 1-3 large showy, 10 cm flowers on erect stalk, broad sepals and linear petals buff-yellow, large lip with white center lobe and brown side-lobes, disk orange with brown keels. (June). (I) *p. 1690*

massangeana (Assam to Java); epiphyte with oval 2-leaved pseudobulbs; numerous 6 cm flowers loosely spaced on long pendulous racemes, sepals and petals pale yellow, chocolate lip veined yellow and edged with white. (March-July). *Tropical.* *p. 1688, 1690*

meyeriana (Trop. Asia: Malaysia); epiphyte with rounded, two-leaved pseudobulbs on creeping rhizome; leaves comparatively large; flowers in an arching raceme produced from the young shoot, sepals and petals olive green, lip undulate, and marked with blackish-brown; June-August. (S) *p. 1692*

mooreana (Vietnam); clusters of pseudobulbs from creeping rhizome, each bearing 2 glossy leaves 30 cm long; inflorescence erect or arching, carrying attractive, fragrant flowers 8 cm across, snow-white with yellow blotch in lip (spring). *p. 1691*

nitida (Thailand to Bhutan); two-leaved pseudobulbs; short racemes of fragrant lemon-white 4 cm flowers, the lip with two yellow blotches, lined with purple; brown markings in throat (spring). *p. 1691*

ochracea (High Himalaya); floriferous epiphyte with ovoid pseudobulbs topped by two stalked leaves; inflorescence produced from the unfolding leaves; fragrant 4 cm heavy-textured flowers white with 4 orange-red keels on lip (spring). *p. 1691*

ovalis (Himalayas); small plant with short, tapering pseudobulbs and $2\frac{1}{2}$ cm flowers having broad greenish-yellow or brownish, recurved linear petals and fringed lip yellow, streaked with red-brown (June-July). (C) *p. 1689*

pandurata (Borneo, Sumatra), "Black orchid"; straggling epiphyte with large pseudobulbs and shining leaves; the large flowers to 10 cm, in pendulous sprays 60 cm long and very fragrant, sepals and petals lovely green, lip greenish-yellow with black raised ridges. (May-July). *p. 1664A, 1689*

parishii (So. Burma: Moulmein); small epiphyte with squarish pseudobulbs and several 8 cm flowers resembling small pandurata, with slender pointed sepals and petals pale nile-green, the crested lip marked with black (spring). *Tropical.* *p. 1689*

sparsa (Philippines); dwarf epiphyte with tapering pseudobulbs and 8-10 cm glaucous leaves; short racemes of small $2\frac{1}{2}$ cm fragrant flowers white tinted green, and white, lobed lip with sides dotted purple and brown cross-bar on front lobe (Jan.-May, Nov.). *Tropical.* *p. 1690*

speciosa (Java); small epiphyte, with ovate pseudobulbs bearing a solitary broad, ribbed leaf; large short-stalked 8-10 cm long-lasting flowers with sepals and petals brownish or olive-green, fringed lip yellow outside, with white apex, base brown, and veined with red (Feb.-July, Sept.). (I) *p. 1690*

sulphurea (Sumatra, Java); epiphyte with single-leaved pseudobulbs; flower stalk from the young growth; small flowers greenish-yellow, with orange-red blotch on lip. April-May. (S) *p. 1688*

COFFEA *Rubiaceae* **I-S2LFM**

arabica (Ethiopia, Angola), "Arabian coffee"; evergreen shrub to 5 m high, with willowy branches bearing shining dark green, ornamental, elliptic foliage to 15 cm long, and wavy at the margins; the pure white, fragrant flowers, in axillary clusters at the base of leaves, are followed by brilliant crimson, pulpy, 1½ cm berries containing the two seeds or "beans", which are roasted into coffee. Superior type of 'Blue Mountain' coffee, grown at higher altitudes or cool climates. C. arabica is the "Brazilian coffee" grown in Sao Paulo state since 1727. *Subtropic.* *p. 2010, 2016*

liberica (West Africa: Liberia), "Liberian coffee"; more robust than arabica, with longer, wider obovate, shining leaves to 30 cm long, and with a shorter point; flowers in a dense cluster of 15 or more; fruit black 2 cm long; a chief source of coffee, thriving in hot climates where C. arabica will not grow well. *Tropical.* *p. 2010*

robusta (canephora in Hortus 3) (Zaire), "Robusta coffee"; vigorous, small evergreen tree of luxuriant habit, with willowy branches furnished with large ovate-elliptic, sharp-pointed leaves shining dark green and distinctly corrugated or wavy between the veins; the axillary flowers pure white, later developing large brownish-red berries and containing a pair of coffee beans; not as exquisitely flavored as C. arabica but a better producer in the tropics. *Tropical.* *p. 2009*

COIX *Gramineae* **S3LBM**

lacryma-jobi (Trop. Asia), "Job's tears"; perennial or annual grass 1-2 m high, with leaves 30-50 cm long, sword-shaped and with prominent midrib; the stems curiously jointed, grown for the interesting female spikelets which develop the peculiar beads 4 cm dia., hard and shining pearly white, containing the kernel; source of the cereal food adlay in East Asia. *p. 1316*

COLAX *Orchidaceae* **S3OFW**

jugosus (So. Brazil); beautiful epiphyte related to Zygopetalum, with clustered pseudobulbs each bearing 2 leathery, lance-shaped leaves dark glossy green, to 22 cm long; inflorescence with 2-4 fleshy, fragrant flowers pinkish green to creamy white, with petals and lip liberally streaked and spotted chocolate purple (late spring). *p. 1693*

COLCHICUM *Liliaceae* **C2LBWd**

autumnale (Europe, No. Africa), "Autumn crocus"; with long tubed lilac-violet flowers resembling slender-stemmed goblets produced from the corms without foliage in August-September, the broad basal leaves appear the following spring. Widely planted for naturalizing in gardens or woods. *Warm temperate.* *p. 1428*

autumnale florepleno 'Water lily'; double flowers pale violet, attractive with series of narrow linear petals as in a bouquet; in autumn. Likely parentage C. autumnale album plenum plus C. speciosum. *p. 1428*

COLEUS *Labiatae* **S2LBM**

blumei (Java), "Painted nettle"; gorgeous herbaceous foliage plant having succulent, square stems, with very decorative foliage; the opposite, generally ovate leaves 10 to 15 cm or more long, now grown in many cultivars beautifully painted and variegated in brilliant colors; the inflorescence in a spire of small lilac blue flowers with two-lipped corolla. *Tropical.* *p. 5**

blumei 'Beauty of Lyon'; attractive cultivar with closely-set medium small ovate-pointed leaves undulate and deeply-lobed; coloring in various shades of red, blackish-maroon when young, turning into brighter crimson later, margins first green, later yellow; stems green. *p. 1344*

blumei 'Beckwith Gem', a beautiful "Painted nettle"; tropical, herbaceous plant originally from Indonesia, with velvety soft foliage 10-15 cm long, and spires of small lavender flowers; in this cultivar leaves blackish-red at the base and center, bronzy scarlet alongside, and yellow along the crenate margins. *Tropical.* *p. 1342*

blumei 'Brilliancy'; horticultural cultivar of the "Painted nettle" from Java, a soft but showy-leaved herb with square, succulent stems and blue flowers; the leaves of 'Brilliancy' are boldly crimson red, marked gold on finely crenate edge. *Tropical.* *p. 1343, 1344*

blumei 'Butterfly'; large wavy leaves purplish-red, on pale green base, light carmine-red along veins and yellow at base. *p. 1345*

blumei 'Candidum', "White coleus"; striking new hybrid with large, broad wavy leaves featuring a central area of creamy white framed yellow, spreading into the outer zone of friendly light green. *p. 1342*

blumei 'Christmas Cheer'; showy, broadleaved plant with foliage mostly wine-red, alternating with deep blood-red, narrow border yellow-green. *p. 1342*

blumei 'Christmas Gem'; unusual design with basal half of leaf and edge light green and yellow, upward, toward tip, blood red with purplish mottling. *p. 1345*

blumei 'Copper Mine'; robust, nettle-like plant with large ovate, concave, velvety leaves with prominent, saw-like pointed lobes primarily coppery-red with basal area dusky, brassy yellow-green; veins, underside, petiole and square stem dark carmine. *p. 1344*

blumei 'Defiance', "Painted nettle"; showy standard variety with lanceolate leaves brownish-red bordered with broad yellow margin finely crenate. *p. 1343*

blumei 'Ella Cinder'; beautifully marbled leaf in a riot of bright shades, carmine-red, pink, green, yellow, and deep blood-red. *p. 1345*

blumei 'Elwood Kalin'; beautiful red plant with center of leaves crimson, the outer zone purplish-red, on purple stem. *p. 1345*

blumei 'Firebird'; an attractive cultivar with leaves variously colored cream, apple green, dark green, rose and purple, finely dissected into long lobes. Photo from Merry Gardens, Camden, Maine. *p. 1341*

blumei 'Firebrand' ('Red Verschaffeltii'); attractive, all-red, self-branching plant with medium-sized ovate leaves having a narrow center area feathered in carmine, the outer area dark blood-red occasionally with a green blotch; underside and stem maroon. *p. 1346*

blumei 'Forest Park'; showy plant with carmine center and spreading into the wide outer zone of rusty red, light green crenate edge. *p. 1342*

blumei 'Frilled Fantasy'; outstanding cut-leaf variety, with leaves deeply lobed and scalloped, in various shades of red and pink with narrow green or yellow edge, veins lavender. *p. 1344*

blumei 'Goldbound'; leaves rather narrow and crinkled, brown-red and green in center, orange-red toward edge, deeply crenate margin nile-green. *p. 1343*

blumei 'Golden Bedder'; ovate, crenate leaves entirely lemon-yellow, changing to gold in full sun; simple but desirable for contrast. *p. 1343*

blumei 'Hollywood Red'; wavy, pointed leaves in shades of crimson and blood-red, with scalloped golden edge. *p. 1345*

blumei 'Klondyke', "Butterfly coleus"; robust variety wildly streaked and variegated brownish-red and yellow. *Tropical.* *p. 1345*

blumei 'Laciniatus'; attractive variety with lacy, deeply cut and lobed leaves light green variegated with creamy-yellow. *p. 1344*

blumei 'Lord Alverson'; unusual cultivar with ovate leaves dark red, irregularly blotched or marbled with green or yellow. *p. 1346*

blumei 'Majesty'; frilly leaf carmine-red in center and following the veins, on blackish red base, deeply crenate edge green. *p. 1345*

blumei 'Max Levering' ('Butterfly'); similar to Klondyke; attractive plant with long-ovate leaves variegated alternately, clown-like, with greenish-yellow and rich brown-red; stem green. *p. 1346*

blumei 'Mrs. Harding'; attractive leaves deeply crenate, the center light red, zoned with dark bronze, broad light green margins. *p. 1345*

blumei 'Pink Rainbow', "Showy coleus"; large, showy new hybrid with broad, wavy leaves painted in copper, rusty-red, and moss green, carmine-red along veins, the crenate edge outlined in green. *p. 1342*

blumei 'Pride of Autumn'; most attractive cultivar with ivory white stem and medium-sized ovate leaves having bright carmine center, outer area chocolate brown, and a contrasting margin lightly crenate; underside pale green with carmine center showing through. *Tropical.* *p. 320A, 1346*

blumei 'Pyrenees Gold'; French cultivar with leaves rather narrow and irregularly lobed and toothed, yellow with reddish ribs. *p. 1344*

blumei 'Rainbow Amber Beauty'; bushy plant of dwarf habit, branching easily; resembling 'Gold Dust' but leaves are amber-colored, mottled with green; reverse and stems reddish; listed by Sakata of Yokohama, Japan. *p. 1341*

blumei 'Rainbow Red'; also known as 'Red Verschaffeltii'; voluptuous, highly colored cultivar of Rainbow strain character, resembling 'Verschaffeltii' except for its green stems shaded or dotted purple; large ovate leaves fuchsia-red in middle area, veins and outer zone velvety blackish-crimson, lobes tipped yellowish; underside also deep red; flowers tipped violet. *p. 1346*

blumei 'Rainbow Salmon Flame'; colorful cultivar of vigorous habit growing to 60 cm high; the broad ovate leaves exquisitely painted deep salmon rose, bordered by a crimson-red zone and edged in green; listed by Sakata of Yokohama, Japan. *p. 1341*

blumei 'Red Croton'; attractive variety with narrow, arrow-shaped leaves 9 cm long, irregularly scalloped and lacily lobed; brown-red with center glowing rose-pink, ribs carmine on surface of leaf. *p. 1341*

blumei 'Sunset'; attractive broadleaved variety with center of salmon-rose spreading into the broad moss-green outer zone, the crenate teeth light green. *p. 1345*

blumei 'The Chief'; outstanding variety with ruffled leaves entirely bright red, except for a narrow line of yellow-green following the scalloped margin. *p. 1342*

blumei 'Turner'; loose growing variety with comparatively narrow, long pointed leaves brownish-red, with yellow-green irregular border. *p. 1342*

blumei 'Two-tone Red'; robust, old-time variety with ovate leaves all red in shades of coppery red to blackish maroon; purplish-red beneath with pale green veins; stem dotted red. *p. 1346*

blumei 'Verschaffeltii' (Java), "Painted nettle"; most beautiful variety with large, glowing crimson-red leaves, purple in center, and narrow, nile-green border, underside purplish-red also; stems and petioles white to purple; flowers pale blue. *Tropical.* *p. 1342*

blumei 'Victoria'; also known as 'Goldbound', 'Gold-banded', 'Setting Sun'; fine variety with broad leaves entirely rich maroon, the ribs purplish-crimson, the marginal lobes chartreuse; stem light green with maroon bands at nodes. *p. 1346*

comosus hort. (Ethiopia); shrubby plant with thick, green, roundish leaves with crenate margins, of fleshy texture and clammy to the touch, densely shingled in alternate pairs; long-stalked inflorescence of purplish bracts in cone-like heads, and long bilabiate blue flowers. *p. 1341*

lanuginosus (Central Africa); woolly-white nettle-like plant with roots bearing tubers; the succulent brown stems and fleshy ovate velvety leaves to 8 cm long, olive green and crenate at margins, silvery pubescent beneath; flowers white in spike-like racemes. *p. 1341*

pumilus (Philippines), "Dwarf creeping coleus"; rather weak species with lax stems more or less reclining and rooting at lower joints, leaves small, broad, blackish-red, lighter along veins, and marked nile-green along the crenate edge. *p. 1343*

rehneltianus (Sri Lanka); vigorous little branching creeper with square stems, and small roundish, nettle-like, deeply crenate leaves purplish-brown in center and broad, sea-green margin and white base; flowers lavender tipped violet. *p. 5*, 1343*

rehneltianus 'Lord Falmouth', "Red trailing nettle"; beautifully colored creeper with small ovate, long-stalked crenate leaves glowing carmine red with rosy center. *p. 1343*

rehneltianus 'Red Trailing Queen'; robust creeper with small, broad-ovate leaves, the center purple carmine, outer zone deep blood red, broad border of dull green into lobes. *Tropical.* *p. 1343*

rehneltianus 'Trailing Queen'; a popular commercial cultivar densely branching especially if pinched, with somewhat larger 4-6 cm, ovate leaves chartreuse to emerald green along margins, prominently overlaid and marbled with brownish purple, carmine center near base. *p. 1342, 1344*

spicatus (India, Madagascar); succulent shrub to 50 cm high, with freely spreading red branches, and broad elliptic fleshy leaves 5 cm long, with upturned margins coarsely toothed, and clammy hairy; inflorescence in erect elongate cluster of terminal spikes of rosy-lavender flowers 2 cm long, each subtended by deciduous bracts tinged lavender. *p. 1341*

thyrsoideus (Central Africa), "Flowering bush-coleus"; tender shrub 60-90 cm high, with 4-angled pubescent stems dense with cordate-ovate, plain green leaves up to 18 cm long and coarsely lobed, and bright blue flowers in long, spike-like racemes. *p. 1342*

COLLETIA *Rhamnaceae* **I1LBD**

cruciata (So. Brazil, Uruguay), "Anchor plant"; curious rigid glossy green spiny shrub with flattened branches, armed with flat triangular spines which are really modified branches, borne in pairs, each pair set at right angles to its neighbor, and sharply pointed; tiny deciduous leaves, and small tubular yellowish-white flowers, in autumn. *Subtropic.* *p. 1992*

infausta (Chile); vicious shrub to 3 m high, stiff green branches with dagger-shaped spines to 3 cm long, leaves small if present, and tiny 5 mm flowers dull white suffused with red. *p. 1990*

spinosa hort., bot. prob. armata or infausta (Chile); spiny stiff shrub to 3 m high, branches usually pubescent; the rigid spines to 3 cm long are really modified branches borne in pairs, the minute leaves soon falling except on seedlings; tiny fragrant waxy white tubular flowers; fruit in 3 rounded capsules. *p. 1990*

COLLETOGYNE *Araceae* **S3LFM**

perrieri (Madagascar); curious small tropical plant with short-stalked inflorescence, the waxy cupped spathe pale foam green spotted black inside, and forming a shield for the short, brownish-purple spadix with white flowers ringed purple-brown; the broad hastate, horizontal leaves standing like an umbrella over the clustered flowers. *Tropical.* *p. 209*

COLLINIA: see Chamaedorea

COLOCASIA *Araceae* **S3LFW**

affinis jenningsii (Trop. Himalayas), "Black caladium"; tuberous herb with soft, peltate leaves dull, emerald green with purple blotches between veins; pale stalks marked brown. *p. 154, 158*

esculenta (Hawaii and Fiji), "Elephant's ear", "Yam", or "Taro"; soft, fleshy herb with edible tuber and large peltate, quilted leaf to 1 m, bright, satiny green. A popular vegetable in the West Indies; the tubers, which are 8-40 cm long and to 20 cm thick, are also a staple food in South China, and known as "Yam" in Hong Kong. *Tropical.* *p. 208*

esculenta 'Fontanesii' (antiquorum fontanesii in hort.) (Ceylon), "Taro"; tropical bog plant with soft, peltate-heartshaped leaves satiny, happy green with purple edge on succulent purplish-brown stems; spathe pale yellow. *p. 208*

esculenta 'Illustris' (antiquorum illustris hort.) (E. Indies); the soft, peltate, heartshaped leaves are fresh, spring-green, especially in vein areas, the balance brownish-purple which shows through to grayish reverse; stems green or violet. *p. 208*

fallax (Sikkim); shield-shaped leaf metallic, fresh-green with lighter veins. *Subtropic.* *p. 154*

gigantea (indica) (Malay Penin., Java), an "Elephant's ear"; large herb forming trunk-like stems to 60 cm or more; the big sagittate-peltate leaves fresh-green above, white-glaucous beneath, 60 cm or more long, undulate at margins; hooded white spathe to 20 cm long. Photo by J. Bogner, Munich Botanic Garden. *Tropical.* *p. 213*

marshallii (Alocasia); broad sagittate-peltate, thin leaf deep, dull green with white transparent variegation, on buff stalks. *p. 154*

COLPOTHRINAX *Palmae* **S2LBM**

wrightii (Cuba), the "Barrel palm"; to 12 m high, with trunk swollen at or below the middle; palmate fronds of circular outline to 1½ m across, with numerous firm blue-green segments. *p. 1868*

COLUMNEA *Gesneriaceae* **S3HFM**

affinis (Venezuela); by nature often epiphytic, with long stout stems densely covered with red-purple velvety coat; unequal leaves to 22 cm long, in pairs, dark green and covered with purple hairs; axillary flowers with deep yellow corolla covered by orange hairs, the bracts and sepals orange. *p. 1236*

allenii (Panama); slender hanging, pale-hairy stems with elliptic 2 cm leaves shining dark green; and axillary flowers with reddish calyx and 2-lipped corolla red or orange. *p. 1234*

arguta (Panama); epiphytic trailer with dense pendulous strands covered with maroon bristles and densely set, waxy, ovate, very sharp pointed leaves; wide open, large salmon-red flowers marked yellow during the leafless state in its native habitat. *p. 1241, 1242*

aureonitens (Colombia); large species with stout stems covered with white or purple hairs; the lanceolate green leaves in pairs of unequal size, densely covered with silky golden or purplish hairs; flowers yellow with red hairs, the calyx lobes scarlet and very hairy. *p. 1240*

x banksii (oerstediana x schiedeana); trailing plant as showy as oerstediana, with small waxy ovate leaves red beneath, with downy, vermilion-orange, slender, bilabiate flowers. *p. 1234, 1235*

brenneri (Trichantha) (Ecuador); epiphytic plant with flexuous fleshy, brownish stems covered by thin-bristly hairs; the waxy, brittle green leaves long ovate, and pubescent especially on the red ribs beneath and along the lightly crenate margins; flowers on hairy stalks, the corolla slender tubular to 5 cm long, creamy-yellow and striped with red, the small spreading lobes edged in purple. *p. 1236*

'Campus Sunset'; very showy Cornell University hybrid 1959; trailer with red, hairy stems; dense with nearly shingled, ovate leaves 5 cm long, hairy on both sides, upper surface olive green, lower red; axillary bilabiate flowers 5-6 cm long, the tube canary yellow, and limb orange red. *p. 1240*

'Canary'; Cornell hybrid 1959 of yellow verecunda x moorei; semi-erect plant with thickish rambling stems, constricted at nodes; dark green, smooth leaves in pairs, one of each twice as large as the other, 3 to 5 cm long, wine-red with green veins beneath; the medium-small 4 to 5 cm flowers bright canary-yellow, covered with silky white hairs; blooming from October to March. *p. 1240*

'Cayugan'; a clone from the Cornell 1959 hybrid crassifolia x hirta, intermediate between the two parents; erect-spreading, shrubby habit; stems with reddish hairs set with unequal pairs of all-green narrow leaves 4 and 5 cm long; from each joint the vivid reddish orange flowers 6 to 8 cm long, intensified by dense red hairs. Although in bloom only in winter and spring, the abundance of flame-colored flowers creates a striking effect while in season. *p. 1240*

'Cornellian'; an outstanding hybrid clone produced at Cornell University, Ithaca, New York 1959, from a yellow-flowered C. verecunda with the orange-red crassifolia; a more or less erect-growing, somewhat shrubby plant, with glossy dark green narrow-elliptic leaves, red beneath, in unequal pairs, 8 and 12 cm long; profuse with 5 cm flowers dark reddish-orange with yellow throat; tested as a good house plant blooming throughout the year. *p. 1240*

crassifolia (Mexico, Guatemala); erect, succulent plant with long linear, fleshy, glossy-green leaves and nearly erect, orange-red, spread-open, tubular flowers, covered with erect red hairs. *Humid-tropical.* *p. 1238*

crassifolia 'Stella Nova'; a tetraploid, result of colchicine-treated C. crassifolia 1955; stiff plant of slower habit than parent, thicker stem, larger leaves to 15 cm long; stronger flower darker orange-red. *p. 1237, 1238*

glabra (Costa Rica); handsome semi-erect tropical shrub with scandent or trailing branches, rooting at nodes, the fleshy, ovate leaves glossy dark green marked with pink; large erect, bilabiate tubular flowers scarlet, with white stamens. *p. 1239*

gloriosa (Costa Rica); epiphytic trailer with rooting and pendulous stems; small oblong leaves covered with brown-red hairs, and large, solitary, bilabiate, fiery red flowers to 8 cm long, with wide open yellow throat, and broad, helmet-like upper lip; good in baskets. *p. 1234, 1241*

hirta (Costa Rica), "Goldfish plant"; epiphytic creeper with rooting stems covered with red hairs; small ovate, red-satiny leaves; vermillion red, bilabiate flowers marked with orange, solitary from axils; smaller than gloriosa but more floriferous. *p. 1233, 1236, 1243, 1248A*

illepida (Trichantha in hort.) (Peru?); robust, ungraceful herb with ascending stems covered with brownish hairs, opposite hairy leaves in unequal pairs light green splotched red beneath. Axillary 8 cm flowers yellow with dark brown stripes on tube and limb, almost always in bloom. *p. 1240, 1295*

'Ithacan'; type selection of 1953 Cornell University hybrid of C. x euphora (gloriosa x lepidocaula); very vigorous plant with scrambling branches, small opposite leaves, and huge curved tubular, bilabiate, orange-red flowers 8 cm long, similar to gloriosa. *p. 1240*

x kewensis 'Variegata'; a variegated-leaf cultivar known as 'Andenken an Rosalinde' (C. glabra x schiedeana); herbaceous plant with scandent branches, long-elliptic leaves 5-8 cm long, shining dark green variegated with pink and white, nerves underneath red-violet; long bilabiate axillary hairy flowers vivid orange or scarlet, 5-6 cm long, in Feb.-May. *p. 1234, 1239*

lepidocaula (Costa Rica); erect, shrubby herb with succulent stems becoming woody with age; fleshy, glossy deep green elliptic leaves 9 cm long; axillary flowers with green calyx, the 8 cm corolla orange, shading to yellow at throat and lower side of tube, and covered with hair. *p. 1236*

linearis (Costa Rica), "Pink goldfish plant"; bushy trailing epiphyte with long narrow, shiny leaves and axillary rose-pink, bilabiate flowers about 6 cm long, with flattened throat, covered with silky-white hair. *Humid-tropical.* *p. 1235, 1239, 1243*

'Magnifica' ('Vilmoriniana'); a triple hybrid, shrubby plant, rooting at nodes of flexible stems, with light green, ovate, downy leaves and large, fan-like flowers brilliant scarlet-red with yellow veining. *p. 1235*

microphylla (diminutifolia) (Costa Rica),"Goldfish vine"; soft trailing plant with tiny rounded or broad-elliptic, coppery hairy leaves,and relatively very large, spread-open bilabiate flowers burnt-red with yellow along bottom of tube,similar to gloriosa but smaller. *Humid-tropical.* *p. 1235, 1238, 1242*

moorei (Panama); beautiful new species first described 1959, with flexible trailing branches and small ovate, waxy leaves; remarkable flowers with extra long tube of vivid red, with bright yellow faces, entirely covered by long, silky red hairs. *p. 1239*

mortonii (C. America); bushy tropical red-hairy plant with stiff, upcurving branches densely covered with small, fleshy ovate leaves; the axillary, curved tubular bilabiate flowers deep red, about 6 cm long and shorter than in hirta, which it resembles. *p. 1239*

nicaraguensis (localis) (C. America); profusely blooming, stiff-stemmed, epiphytic trailer with large lanceolate, corrugated, satiny green leaves red beneath, and axillary, brilliant red flowers, often yellow at the throat. *Humid-tropical.* *p. 1233, 1238*

nicaraguensis 'Marginata'; handsome variation with the pendant vines dense with lanceolate, waxy leaves 8-10 cm long, prettily variegated and edged with white; the curved tubular, bilabiate, hairy flowers 5 cm long and carmine red. *p. 1239*

percrassa (Panama); succulent green stems with thick-fleshy, glossy dark green elliptic leaves, pale beneath, to 4 cm long; axillary flowers with scarlet corolla with orange and yellow inside. *p. 1235*

pichinchensis (Ecuador); erect herbaceous shrub with corrugated, ovate leaves olive green above, wine-red beneath; numerous small axillary flowers lemon-yellow. *p. 1241*

pilosissima (C. America); softly hairy trailer, the stems dense with fleshy, narrow leaves glossy green, to 3 cm long; bilabiate flowers 7 cm long, reddish tangerine with yellow in throat, pistil and stamens yellow; ideal for hanging baskets. *p. 1239*

purpureovittata (Trichantha) (Perú) wide-spreading gesneriad with long, flexible, hairy branches; long lanceolate, fleshy, wrinkled leaves with unequal sides, 10-14 cm long, glossy deep green, dark red underneath; pendulous tubular flowers yellow with purple stripes; followed by red berries. *p. 1292*

'Royal Tangerine' (Cornell hybrid 1959); very attractive basket plant with spreading branches, dense with narrow ovate waxy leaves 3-5 cm long; the curved-tubular, bilabiate flowers 8 cm long, bright tangerine orange-red, more pale in throat, and with reddish-orange hairs on outside. *p. 1240*

sanguinea (Alloplectus) (West Indies); sparry, densely hairy shrub with strong stems, looking like an alloplectus; opposite, short-stalked, 20 cm lanceolate leaves emerald green, blotched blood-red beneath; small, furry, pale yellow flowers. *p. 1236*

schiedeana (E. Mexico); large upright or climbing shrub with long lanceolate green leaves covered with white plush, burgundy-red beneath; bilabiate flowers orange-yellow, striped and spotted crimson. *Humid-tropical.* *p. 1234, 1241*

'Splendens'; a phenotype of C. x banksii, epiphytic trailer with small corrugated waxy, ovate leaves dark olive green, and axillary, bright red, tubular flowers opening into a flattened throat. *p. 1235*

'Stavanger' (microphylla x vedrariensis), the "Norse fire plant"; (Haualund 1949), free-growing Norwegian diploid trailer with pendant branches, leaves rounded or broad-elliptic, dark green, smooth and fairly shiny; willing bloomer with bilabiate tubular, erect, hairy flowers 8-10 cm long, fiery cardinal-red from orange base, with a little yellow in throat. *p. 1235, 1237*

teuscheri (Trichantha minor in horticulture) (Ecuador); rambling creeper with long thread-like vines set with lance-shaped blackish-green leaves shiny above and hairy beneath; from the leaf axils the very unusual tubular 5 cm flowers dark purple, with 4 stamens, the calyx a feathery cluster of carmine bristles, and the face of the corolla contrasting yellow and black, with 5 curious yellow horns at the mouth; blooming for 4 months, starting in summer. *Humid-tropical.* *p. 1295, 1330*

tulae 'Flava' (Puerto Rico, Haiti); climbing and trailing plant from mountainous areas, with aerial roots and pubescent, soft green leaves; hairy, bilabiate flowers bright yellow, with long tube and spreading lobes. *Humid-tropical.* *p. 1241*

'V. Covert'; (linearis x tulae); hybrid registered 1958; densely and freely branching with long scandent stems with small, narrow ovate leaves of waxy texture; bilabiate flowers only 4 cm long, but freely blooming, opening yellowish but becoming completely salmon-pink. *p. 1240*

x vedrariensis (magnifica x schiedeana); erect, vigorous shrub with dark waxy, elliptic leaves, and downy tubular flowers wide-spread at opening, bright scarlet with network of pale yellow veining. *Humid-tropical.* *p. 1235*

'Vega' (C. Stavanger x vedrariensis), "Goldfish bush"; 1956 diploid bush with erect or arching wiry branches first light green, later reddish; fresh green round-oval, smooth leaves 3 cm long; the erect bilabiate flowers 6-8 cm long and evenly cox-comb red; of stiffer habit than Stavanger, flowering 3 weeks earlier; set buds by chilling, cool and dry in Sept., after 6 weeks give warm 18°C. *Humid-tropical.* *p. 1237, 1238*

verecunda (Costa Rica); compact, shrubby, erect plant with waxy, deep olive-green, lanceolate, convex leaves red beneath, shielding the axillary, flattened, bilabiate, lemon to golden-yellow flowers, beautifully wine-colored below. *Humid-tropical.* *p. 1234, 1235*

x woodii (crassifolia x nicaraguensis); robust branching plant with strong, stiff stems; long lanceolate leaves; from the leaf axils the dark reddish orange flowers with flaring lobes. *p. 1239*

COLVILLEA *Leguminosae* **S2LBD**

racemosa (Madagascar); spreading, showy tree to 15 m, with fern-like bipinnate foliage and robust, curving whips of branches bearing masses of pendant floral racemes to 60 cm long; brilliantly fiery-red flowers with yellow stamens; opening from burnt red berry-like buds; the round seed pods to 15 cm long. *Tropical.* *p. 1378*

COMATOPHYLLUM *Liliaceae* **S3LFD**

prostratum (Madagascar); unusual plant resembling bromeliad in foliage; rosette of broad fleshy leaves with marginal teeth, and short-stalked inflorescence of long tubular flowers. *p. 1452*

COMBRETUM *Combretaceae* **S2LBD**

coccineum (Madagascar); magnificent scandent woody shrub with clambering branches to 6 m; oblong leaves to 10 cm long, dark shining green; toward branch tips dense racemes of bright scarlet bell-flowers with spreading segments, the stamens long protruding. *p. 777*

erythrophyllum (So. Africa), the "Bush willow" along rivers in the Transvaal; a tree with spreading branches and narrow leaves; along the twigs the pretty puffs of yellow stamen-flowers, followed by russet-brown 4-winged fruits: very striking in the landscape in autumn when the foliage turns red. *p. 777*

microphyllum (Zimbabwe, Transvaal, Mozambique), the "Burning bush"; spectacular rambling shrub with whip-like branches, set with small, deciduous leaves; and the numerous clusters of tiny flowers along branches, conspicuous because of their puffs of brilliant-red stamens; often found high in trees covering them as if with a sheet of flame. *p. 778*

mozambicensis (Trop. E. Africa); showy shrub, the rambling, slender branches with oval leaves; on short branchlets the powderpuff-like inflorescence of clustered pale yellow flowers spreading wide their prominent stamens. *p. 778*

zeyheri (So. Africa, Tanzania); a common tree of the Transvaal bush veld, to 8 m high, with spreading branches; green, oval leaves; from between leaf axils small spikes of insignificant cream colored flowers, followed by conspicuous light-brown, 4-winged fruits. *p. 777*

COMMELINA *Commelinaceae* **I2HFM**

benghalensis variegata (Trop. Asia, Africa), "Italian dayflower"; delicate creeper with watery stems and soft fleshy, pale grayish green, narrow leaves striped and edged in white; flowers, with 2 reniform petals, sky blue. *p. 783*

coelestis (Mexico), "Dayflower"; a rank creeper with soft fleshy, obliquely ovate leaves glossy-green, purple when older, especially underneath, on hairy purplish stems; flowers sky blue open only mornings of sunny days. *p. 783*

communis aureo-striata, "Widow's tears"; a variegated-leaf form found in New Jersey, probably a form of the variety ludens; annual creepers with succulent stems and lanceolate 5-10 cm leaves bright glossy green, banded and striped with cream; the flowers with 2 large blue petals and one smaller white petal, the margins of spathe free at base; the green species is from N. E. U.S. and E. Asia. *p. 784*

eckloniana (So. Africa); annual herbaceous plant with hairy stems, to 20 or 30 cm high, the long lanceshaped, concave leaves clasping and sheathing at base, lightly hairy; flowers blue, of 3 petals with dark blue in base. *p. 786*

latifolia (Uganda); low creeper with fleshy, narrow-linear bronze-green leaves and tiny lavender flowers. This may be more correctly a Cyanotis. *p. 782*

COMPARETTIA *Orchidaceae* **S3OFW**

falcata (Mexico, West Indies, No. So. America); pretty, dwarf epiphyte with clusters of small pseudobulbs each with single 10 cm leathery leaf; branched floral stems with purple 2 cm flowers, the lip scarlet; interesting in structure as the connate lateral sepals are prolonged into a long spur and protecting the throat (autumn). *p. 1693*

speciosa (Ecuador); beautiful small epiphyte with one-leaved pseudobulbs, and pendulous racemes of numerous flowers, sepals and petals light orange, lip cinnabar-red, orange at base, and with long spur. Summer. (S) *p. 1693, 1738*

CONANDRON *Gesneriaceae* **C-I3HFD**

ramondioides (Japan); herbaceous rosette with tuberous roots; oblong pointed, wrinkled, thin green leaves 10-18 cm even 40 cm long, irregularly toothed at margins; inflorescence on erect stalk bearing 6-25 flowers in loose cluster, with lilac or white, wheelshaped corolla spotted orange in center. *p. 1242*

CONGEA *Verbenaceae* **S-I2LBD**

tomentosa (India), "Shower orchid"; climbing shrub with opposite ovate entire, 8 cm leaves hairy beneath; white flowers subtended by lilac leaf-like, hairy bracts. *Tropical.* *p. 2113, 2116*

CONICOSIA *Aizoaceae* **I2LBD**

communis (South Africa); ground-covering spreading succulent, with long-linear, 3-angled soft leaves 10-15 cm long without dots, arranged in spirals on the stem; yellow ray flowers on pedicels which die after fruiting. *Arid-subtropic.* *p. 61*

CONIOGRAMME *Polypodiaceae (Filices)* **I3HFM**

japonica (Japan, Taiwan), the "Bamboo-fern"; with creeping rhizome, mostly pinnate fronds of stiff habit resembling Pteris cretica, to 60 cm long, the dark green pinnae finely toothed. *p. 1101*

CONOCARPUS *Combretaceae* **S2LBD**

erectus sericeus (West Indies), "Silver tree"; attractive evergreen shrub to 2½ m with alternate oblong, thickish leaves persistently covered with silvery white down; white flowers without petals. *p. 777*

CONOPHYLLUM *Aizoaceae* **I2LBD**

grande (Namaqualand), succulent with opposite 2-angled keeled sterile 10 cm leaves, flat on the upper surface, light green, smooth, to 20 cm high; the flowering growth with elongated internodes, to 75 cm tall, bearing leaves connate during resting; splitting later; flowers shining white. *p. 58, 79*

latisectum (So. Africa); small shrubby succulent, in dormant stage resembling a pale grayish-green cone, of two united (connate) leaves rounded on the outside; the new growth splitting to allow young lingui-form growth of new leaves, and flowering stalks. *p. 58*

tenuifolium (So. Africa); branching succulent with long linear, fleshy, angled, sterile leaves glossy green, splitting into forks from the middle up. *p. 58*

CONOPHYTUM *Aizoaceae* **I2LBD**

aureum (So. Africa); clusters of grayish little clubs dotted green; notched apex with tiny translucent windows; large purple flowers with pale center. *p. 58*

calculus (W. Cape Prov.), "Flowering Easter-egg"; curious clustering sun-loving succulent of little egg-shaped bodies 2 cm diameter, glaucous gray-green, with small 12 mm flowers yellow, tipped with brown. *p. 59*

elishae (So. Africa); small, clustering succulent with thick, club-like, two-lobed leaves grayish-green with purple; flowers yellow. *Arid-subtropic.* *p. 58*

giftbergensis (So. Africa); smooth green, lightly split globes dotted with dark spots; small shimmering flowers from cleft, the pale canary-yellow petals thread-like, deep golden center. *p. 58*

griseum (Southwest Africa), "Silver stars"; clusters of tiny flattened, split clubs coppery-rusty with surface windows and blackish dots; masses of small white, daisy-like flowers showing yellow anthers. Prob. form of fenestratum. *Arid-subtropic.* *p. 58*

minutum (Cape Prov.); tiny clustering succulent, with pear-shaped little bodies to 1 cm diameter, bluish gray-green; light purple 2 cm star flowers; blooming regularly; good subject for pot culture. *p. 60*

muscosipapillatum (Cape Prov.); succulent growing in clusters of 5-10 flattened leaves, gray-green and dotted, at the margins velvety hairy and reddish; stalked flowers shimmering golden yellow. *p. 58*

nelianum (So. Africa: Namaqualand); mat-forming succulent with heart-shaped little bodies to 4 cm high, glossy grayish green with numerous dark green dots; flowers yellow. *p. 77*

obcordellum (Cape Prov.); clustering succulent with small obconical bodies, glossy bluish-green with brown-purple flecks, and a small split in center of the flattened or concave top; flowers creamy-white. *p. 77*

simile (So. Africa: Cape Prov.), "Cone plant", very small succulent 2 cm high, forming clumps similar to Lithops but smaller; the fat little bodies heart-shaped, with the notch on top, smooth and bluish green or gray-green, dotted with dark green all over; large 2½ cm yellow flowers. Conophytum belong to the pigmies amongst the mimicry plants; resting in summer, blooming in winter, a joy in the window. *p. 60*

tischeri (Cape Prov.); low succulent, forming mats; bodies oval, deepened above, to 1 cm wide, with fissure gray green with darker dots; producing small stems when old; 1½ cm flowers pale lilac. *p. 60*

truncatellum (So. Africa); densely clustered gray green plastic-like plant bodies 2 cm thick, marked with tiny dark green dots and small split centers; 2 cm flowers pale yellow. *p. 60*

wiggettae (Cape Province); clustering succulent with squat, club-shaped bodies, fairly flat on top except for small sunken cleft, gray green with numerous dark green dots, sides reddish; flowers whitish. *p. 58*

CONSOLEA falcata: described under Opuntia

CONVALLARIA *Liliaceae* **C2LFWdh**

majalis (Europe, temp. Asia), "Lily-of-the-valley"; small perennial herb with horizontal slender creeping rootstock, the upright parts called pips, with 2 basal, fresh green lanceolate leaves, and stalk with nodding little bells of fragrant, waxy-white flowers. *Temperate.* *p. 1428*

majalis 'Rosea', the "Pink lily-of-the-valley"; dainty and more dwarf than the white species, leaves slightly glaucous; waxy, bellshaped flowers 6 mm long, delicate ivory flushed pink, and more reddish at base, in erect, one-sided racemes. (h) *p. 1408A, 1428*

CONVOLVULUS *Convolvulaceae* **C2LBM**

althaeoides (Mediterranean Reg.); deciduous perennial "Bindweed", with twining stem to 1 m; leaves shining silvery; palmately divided into narrow segments in the upper leaves, the lower ovate-cordate; large rose or lilac flowers, 3 cm long, during summer. *p. 853*

cneorum (So. Europe), "Bush Morning-glory"; charming subshrub 60-80 cm high, with ascending stems, the lance-shaped leaves covered with silvery silky hairs, 6 cm long; wide-open morning-glory-flowers pale pink, with yellow throat; flowering most prolific in full sun. *p. 853*

mauritanica (No. Africa; Spain); twining perennial covered with soft white hair; small ovate leaves and 2½-5 cm flowers lilac blue or violet, and yellow anthers. *p. 853*

soldanella (Calystegia) (seashores of Britain and France); procumbent creeper with decorative kidney-shaped leaves, and solitary pretty, salver-shaped pink or purple flowers to 6 cm across. *p. 854*

COPERNICIA *Palmae* **S2LFM**

australis (Paraguay, Argentina); beautiful fan palm to 20 m tall, the trunk covered with glossy brown leaf bases in a spiral, geometric pattern; the glaucous-green palmate leaves are firm and erect, to 1 m dia. and deeply divided; petioles armed with dark brown teeth; much branched inflorescence with olive-shaped, 2 cm brown fruit. *p. 1864*

baileyana (Cuba); robust fan-palm, to 15 m, with smooth, thick trunk, and numerous large 1½ m, glossy green hard-leathery leaves in a dense, roundish crown, on thorny stalks. *Tropical.* *p. 1862*

curbeloi (Cuba), a "Wax palm"; bold fan palm with dense crown of palmate leaves, and developing a stout trunk that may become 6 to 12 m tall; the leaves silvery, 1½ m across, with drooping segments, on stout, spiny, flat petioles. *p. 1867, 1886*

macroglossa ("torreana" of hort.) (Cuba), the "Cuban petticoat palm", so called because of the dense cylindrical hanging growth of dead persistent leaves covering the trunk of this fan palm; growing to about 8 m; the stiff, folded, lustrous deep green leaves 1½-2 m across, on short thorny stalk. *Tropical.* *p. 1871*

pauciflora (Cuba); a petticoat palm similar to macroglossa, with stiff fan-leaves on longer petioles about 1 m long. The palm shown under this name may represent C. macroglossa. *p. 1862*

rigida (Cuba); curious-looking fan palm with long and narrow wedge-shaped palmate, plaited leaves arranged in densely packed, erect layers as if tied together, the long segments stiff-erect, on short 30 cm petioles. *Tropical.* *p. 1862, 1865*

sueroana (Cuba); strange-looking palm with densely shingled, palmate, fan-like leaves, deeply cut; erect petioles covering and hiding base of trunk; in appearance like a bursting fountain. *Tropical.* *p. 1865*

COPIAPOA *Cactaceae: Echinocactanae* **I2LBD**

dura (Northern Chile); small globular cactus to 12 cm dia, with age branching and elongate to possibly 1 m high; brownish-green with 11-15 ribs covered by strong spines; fragrant sulphur-yellow, small flowers 2 to 4 cm long; the fruit a short dry berry with open top. Similar to Wigginsia but this has wool on the perianth tube, and fruit is oblong. *p. 690*

COPROSMA *Rubiaceae* **I1LFM**

pumila (New Zealand), the "Creeping coprosma"; small shrub with prostrate and rooting gray branches; bright green oval leaves, and greenish-white flowers; attractive with round, juicy orange-red berries. *p. 2009*

repens (baueri in hort.) (New Zealand), "Mirror plant"; flexible densely leafy dioecious shrub with opposite, roundish, soft-leathery leaves 6-8 cm long, bright green and glossy as if varnished; small flowers greenish, the berries on female trees orange-yellow; I remember planting this evergreen along the seashore in Southern California because of its resistance to salt spray. *p. 2009, 2016*

repens 'Marginata'; the "Variegated mirror plant"; with lacquered vivid green to milky green leaves prettily edged in creamy-white. *p. 2009*

repens 'Variegata' (picturata), cultivated form with undulate oval leaves glossy happy-grreen with nile-green and golden yellow center variegation. *p. 2009*

CORALLODISCUS *Gesneriaceae* **C3HFD**

lanuginosus (Himalayas); handsome gesneriad, rosette of obovate, hairy, scalloped leaves to 75 cm long, with fibrous root-stock; stalked clusters of hairy, tubular flowers with spreading lobes pale blue or purplish, 2 cm across. *p. 1242*

CORDIA *Boraginaceae* **S3LBD**

myxa (dichotoma) (Egypt to India and No. Australia), "Sebesten plum"; tropical shrub or tree to 12 m high, with glossy, oval leaves 5-12 cm long, lightly lobed or toothed; small white flowers 1 cm wide with narrow, reflexed lobes in loose clusters, followed by pinkish or yellowish cherry-like 2 cm fruit with edible pulp; at home in dry tropical regions. *p. 511*

sebestena (Florida Keys, Bahamas, West Indies to Barbados), "Geiger tree"; small evergreen tropical tree to 8 m, with rough brown bark; dark green, oval leaves 8 to 20 cm long, with pale veins, in clusters at ends of branches; flowers to 5 cm across, brilliant orange-scarlet, quilted and ruffled and of a crepy texture; small white 2 cm fruit sweet and edible. *Tropical.* *p. 509, 511*

superba (Brazil); large tropical shrub with stout young shoots; long obovate, rough leaves 15-20 cm long, clustered at ends of branches; white, crepy, bell-shaped flowers 5 cm wide, in long-stalked clusters. *p. 511*

CORDYLINE *Liliaceae* **S2LFM**

australis (New Zealand), "Dracaena indivisa" of florists; palm-like tree to 12 m high, with single erect stem crowned by a dense cluster of flat and narrow, arching leaves tough-leathery, bronzy-green with fresh-green midrib, 6-8 cm wide in maturity; fragrant white flowers, following which the head will fork. Small plants in pots grown from seed by florists have slender leaves only 1-2 cm wide. Known as "Grass palm", or in New Zealand as "Cabbage tree"; an ancient monocot. Roots are typically white in Cordyline (yellow in Dracaena) *Subtropic.* *p. 1429, 1430*

australis 'Atrosanguinea'; a culture form in California nurseries; tough-leathery, narrow lanceolate leaves bronze, suffused with deep purplish-red. *p. 1432*

australis 'Aureo-striata'; elegant small tree with slender trunk and a crown of narrow-linear, leathery, graceful leaves olive green, variegated with broad longitudinal bands and margins of creamy-yellow. *p. 1429*

australis cuprea; dark-leaved form with the slender leaves entirely a coppery reddish brown. *p. 1426*

australis 'Doucetii'; horticultural variety originated in Belgium; dense rosette of narrow leathery, strap-shaped leaves dark olive-green, strikingly variegated with cream-white, margins tinted pink; the sub-variety 'Albertii' has red midrib. *p. 1426*

australis 'Marginata'; a decorative variety with leathery, olive green leaves prettily edged in creamy-white. *p. 1433*

banksii (New Zealand); slender stems to 3 m high, often clustering and sometimes branched, dense with 1 m long recurving strapshaped leaves dark green with pale yellow midrib, to 8 cm wide, veins often red; flowers in pendant panicle. *Subtropic.* *p. 1429*

indivisa (New Zealand); slender tree to 8 m high, usually with single, flexible stem, with a large head of sessile, flat, tough leaves, matte green with raised orange midrib, glaucous blue beneath, to 20 cm, or twice as wide as australis; not branching after flowering. *p. 1429, 1430, 1433*

indivisa 'Purpurea'; found in California; tree-forming with woody trunk usually clothed with foliage, toward apex a dense crown of broad, flexuous leathery leaves entirely suffused with bronzy purple; young growth sprouting from base has foliage much narrower. *Subtropic.* *p. 1438*

indivisa 'Rubra', "Red palm-lily"; tree-like with erect stem bearing a fountain of broad, flexible leathery leaves, entirely colored dark bronze; the inflorescence a beautiful erect panicle of fragrant white flowers. *p. 1432*

rubra 'Bruantii'; form with gracefully recurved, coppery-red leaves, of this Australian, slender tree-like species, intermediate between terminalis and stricta, growing to 5 m; leaves continually ascending, closely set, narrow oblanceolate and thick, normally dull green, reddish reverse when young, prominent midrib, on broad grooved petiole. *Subtropic.* *p. 1430*

stricta (Drac. congesta) (Queensland, New So. Wales); treelike, with slender stem to 4 m high, occasionally branched; narrow clasping leaves swordshaped, leathery, matte green with rough edges, inconspicuously toothed, narrowing toward a constricted base; young growth reddish. *Subtropic.* *p. 1436, 1442*

stricta 'Rubra'; slender wiry stems and lax, soft-leathery, lanceolate leaves of coppery-red coloring. *p. 1432*

terminalis (India, Malaysia to Polynesia), "Tree of kings"; a commercial "Red dracaena" with rather slender, leathery, swordshaped leaves in a cluster of erect habit, on a cane to 3 m high; the normal leaves are copper-green shading into red, the young winter growth intense rosy crimson; flowers lilac-tinted, in panicles, followed by red berries. *Tropical.* *p. 1431, 1436*

terminalis 'Amabilis', "Pink dracaena"; strong growing form with broad, shining green to bronze foliage prettily variegated or edged with cream suffused with pink. *Tropical.* *p. 1431*

terminalis angusta (Java); attractive variety from the Sunda Islands with long narrow, leathery leaves coppery green edged red, purplish beneath. (3) *p. 1431*

terminalis 'Baptistii'; robust variety with broad, somewhat recurved leaves dark green to bronzy, diffused with red, variegated with pink and creamy yellow stripes. (3W) *p. 1430*

terminalis 'Bicolor'; robust, shapely hybrid deep metallic green attractively edged and variegated with pink. (3W) *p. 1430*

terminalis 'Calypso Queen'; very compact plant, with small leaves deep bronzy red; the center purplish. *Tropical.* *p. 1432*

terminalis 'Firebrand', excellent commercial "Red dracaena", which in addition to being a compact rosette, also holds its foliage well; slender stiff, gracefully recurving leaves a satiny purplish-red with glaucous sheen, the younger foliage mahogany red with crimson midrib. *Tropical.* *p. 1431*

terminalis 'General Pershing'; compact cultivar with leaves to about 30 cm long by 10 cm wide, dark green with carmine-pink and red margins, the variegation being usually broadest toward base of leaf. *p. 1432*

terminalis 'Hawaiian Bonsai'; dwarf form of C. terminalis, with red petioles, and leaves rather narrow and stiff, bronzy green with red and pink variegation. *Tropical.* *p. 1432*

terminalis 'Kilimanjari'; a Florida cultivar, very compact with broad, stiff-leathery oblanceolate leaves a blackish-crimson. *p. 1432*

terminalis 'Mad. Eugene André', "Flaming dragon tree"; showy commercial variety of spreading habit, with broad leaves deep green to coppery, and red border; the new growth in winter a beautiful shocking pink, indicating the flowering season, after which the lower leaves tend to drop if disturbed. *Tropical.* *p. 1431*

terminalis 'Margaret Storey'; good variety quite similar to Andre, more compact, leaves shorter and wider; color quite attractive having pink and red splashes with the green to coppery-red foliage. (3W) *p. 1430*

terminalis minima 'Baby Ti' (Hawaii); one of the tiniest of "Red dracaenas"; miniature rosette with narrow, concave, gracefully recurved leaves deep metallic green suffused with copper, and a red border. (3W) *p. 15*, 1431*

terminalis 'Negri', known in horticulture as Dracaena Negri, the "Black dracaena"; a striking cultivar from Louisiana, outstanding for its big leathery, glossy coppery maroon leaves almost black, ¾ to 1½ m long and 12 cm wide, in graceful rosette on slender canes. *Tropical.* *p. 1432*

terminalis 'Stricta grandis'; robust, stiff variety with wide leaves of a medium green to metallic bronzy-red color, on long, constricted petioles, the young growth edged with white and pink. (3W) *p. 1430*

terminalis var. 'Ti' (Taetsia fruticosa) (Hawaii to New Guinea), "Tree of kings" or "Hawaiian good luck plant"; palm-like, robust, with slender cane to 4 m high, topped by a cluster of oblong leaves to 60 cm long spirally arranged, smooth, flexible and plain green; this foliage is used for hula skirts; sections of cane will sprout young plants. *Tropical.* *p. 1430, 1431, 1433*

terminalis 'Tricolor', "Tricolored dracaena"; very colorful rosette of broad leaves beautifully variegated red, pink, and cream over a base of fresh green and a good keeper. *Tropical.* *p. 1408A, 1431*

'Volckaertii'; a Belgian terminalis cultivar 1929, with broader, somewhat spatulate leaves light and dark green, grayish beneath; in habit more vigorous and more tough and durable than terminalis. *p. 1432*

COREOPSIS *Compositae* **C2LBM**

auriculata nana; low growing herbaceous perennial forming mats; dwarf variety of the species at home from Virginia to Florida, with spreading branches, 5-10 cm spatulate leaves; flowers 3 to 6 cm across, the petals fringed at apex, bright yellow with darker lines. *p. 802*

gigantea (So. California coast); succulent shrub to 2 m, with thick-fleshy stem leafy only toward top; leaves finely cut into fern-like threads; flower-heads yellow, 4 cm across, in short clusters. *p. 802*

maritima (So. California, Mexico), the "Sea dahlia"; perennial to 1 m, with leafy hollow stems, divided leaves, and long-stalked 8 cm daisy-like flower heads vivid yellow, in autumn. *p. 802*

tinctoria, "Calliopsis" in hort. (Minnesota to Arizona); herbaceous summer-flowering biennial with divided leaves and long-stalked flowers with toothed yellow florets and crimson base, disk brownish-purple. *Temperate.* *p. 809*

CORIARIA *Coriariaceae* **I2LBD**

terminalis xanthocarpa (Sikkim, Tibet, China); small subshrub spreading by underground rhizomes, with 4-angled twigs, small ovate leaves, and terminal racemes of small greenish flowers, later forming into black berries in the species, translucent yellow fruit in xanthocarpa. *p. 851*

CORNUS *Cornaceae* **C2LBD**

alba 'Spaethii', "Tartarian dogwood"; attractive, large tree-like shrub with red twigs, deciduous ovate 12 cm leaves glaucous-bluish beneath and minutely hairy with broad yellow margins; small yellowish flowers; the species is from Siberia. *p. 856*

canadensis (No. America: Newfoundland to Alaska, W. Virginia; E. Asia), "Bunch berry"; woody perennial herb with creeping rootstock, to 25 cm high with whorled leaves; purplish flowers in dense heads surrounded by 4 white petal-like bracts; fruit red. *p. 855*

capitata (Himalayas); attractive evergreen tree dense with leathery 10 cm elliptic leaves, reverse grayish and finely pubescent, on willowy branches; inconspicuous flowers subtended by fleshy, 4 cm sulphur-yellow bracts; fruit puckered strawberry-like, salmon-red to crimson. *Subtropic. p. 856*

florida (Maine to Florida and Texas), "Flowering dogwood"; popular deciduous flowering tree to 12 m high, with spreading branches, and blooming on bare wood; the small inconspicuous yellow flower cluster surrounded by 4 large, gleaming petal-like white bracts 4-6 cm long, notched at apex, turning pink with age; the 8-12 cm ovate green leaves will turn red in late autumn; berry-like fruit scarlet. *Temperate. p. 856*

florida 'Rubra' (Maine to Florida and Texas); deciduous tree to about 10 m high, with ovate leaves 10-15 cm long and small greenish flowers in dense heads, subtended by 4 large showy, notched rosy, petal-like bracts; white in the species florida; fruit red. *Warm temperate. p. 855*

florida 'Welchii'; variety with ornamental leaves green, variegated or edged yellow and red. *p. 855*

florida 'White Cloud' ('Cloud Nine'); a dwarf "Dogwood" of shrubby dense habit without a leader, full of flowers, with 4 white bracts much more rounded in form and borne more horizontally than those of florida, of which it is a cultivar; flowering at an early age. Photographed at North Haven Gardens, Dallas, Texas in spring 1971. *p. 856*

mas (C. to So. Europe, Asia Minor, Armenia, Caucasus), "Cornelian cherry"; small deciduous tree of spreading habit, 10 cm ovate, dull green, lightly hairy leaves; small yellow flowers in umbels, enclosed in 4 downy, yellowish bracts; in spring before the leaves; fruit scarlet. *p. 856*

nuttallii (Brit. Columbia to No. California), "Pacific dogwood"; spectacular flowering tree 5 to 25 m high, often encountered in Sequoia National Park and the Sierra Nevada, blooming on bare branches, the flowers with 4 to 6 or 8 glistening white bracts 4-6 cm long, later turning pink, around a center cluster of tiny flowers; the downy foliage 8-12 cm long and glaucous beneath. *Warm temperate. p. 856*

COROKIA *Cornaceae* **I2LBD**

cotoneaster (New Zealand), "Golden koroko" or "Zigzag bush"; slow-growing stiff evergreen shrub to 3 m high; the numerous slim, nearly black branches contorted and so interlaced as to make an intricate, bizarre pattern; the little 2 cm leaves dark green above, white-tomentose underneath; tiny yellow, starry 1 cm, jasmine-like flowers in spring to summer, followed by small bright yellow to red fruits. Thrives in containers, best in sun. *p. 856*

CORONILLA *Leguminosae* **I2LBD**

emerus (Central and So. Europe), "Scorpion senna"; deciduous shrub with angled shoots; unequally pinnate leaves with 3 cm leaflets, yellow, 2 cm flowers with long claws, the standard petal marked with red. *Warm temperate. p. 1380*

glauca variegata (So. Europe); evergreen shrub to 1 m with odd-pinnate leaves, 5-7 variegated leaflets; rich yellow flowers 2 cm long, petals with long claws; fragrant by day. *p. 1380*

COROZO *Palmae* **S3LBM**

oleifera (C. America, Panama, Colombia, Amazon), the "American oil palm"; with trunk inclined to lean and creep along ground before turning upright; large and graceful pinnate leaves 4 m long; small 2½ cm orange to black fruit of which the flesh yields oil. *p. 1868*

CORPUSCULARIA *Aizoaceae* **I2LBD**

algoense (So. Africa), "Grayhorns"; dwarf succulent with slender, keel-shaped, opposite, gray-green leaves. *p. 57*

lehmannii (Delosperma) (Cape Prov.); with opposite 3-angled gray-green leaves arranged alternately at right angles, 2-4 cm long; 4 cm pale yellow flowers opening in afternoon. *p. 59*

CORREA *Rutaceae* **C2HBM**

x harrisii (speciosa hybrid), "Australian fuchsia"; evergreen shrub with opposite simple, downy leaves, and nodding, tubular 3 cm flowers scarlet red with protruding stamens and yellow anthers. *p. 2034*

speciosa (reflexa) (So. Australia to Queensland, Tasmania), known in Australia as "Native fuchsia"; evergreen shrub to 1 m; small ovate leaves tomentose beneath; tubular 4 cm flowers red with green tips. *p. 2032*

speciosa 'Backhousiana'; with oval leaves and cream colored flowers like little weeping bells. *p. 2032*

CORRYOCACTUS *Cactaceae* **I-S3LBD**

melanotrichus (Cereus) (Bolivia); column cactus from the Andes near La Paz at 4000 m; branching, 1-2 m high, with yellowish-green 7 to 9-ribbed stems 5-6 cm thick, with yellow radial spines and 1 to 3 central spines 3-5 cm long; funnel-shaped glossy pink flowers 7 cm across. *p. 656*

CORTADERIA *Gramineae* **I2LBM**

selloana (argentea) (Argentina), the "Pampas-grass"; gigantic tufted grass 2-3 or even 6 m high, forming great clumps; the leaves 1-3 m long and 2 cm wide, with rough edges; female spikelets borne in panicles; beautiful silvery-white, silky plumes to 1 m long. The plumes can be dried for indoor decoration. *Subtropic. p. 1311*

selloana pumila; forming compact clumps only 1 m high, of long, narrow grass-like leaves and masses of decorative white, silky plumes. *p. 1310*

CORYANTHES *Orchidaceae* **S3OFM**

bicalcerata (Perú), "Bucket orchid"; curious epiphytic orchid related to Stanhopea; conical pseudobulbs topped by thin-leathery leaves; from the base a pendulous stalk with 2 or 3 very complicated hooded flowers, white with purple markings and with strong, penetrating odor; the lip is thick-fleshy, wax-like in texture. *Humid-tropical. p. 1694*

bungerothii (Venezuela), "Bucket orchid"; a wondrous epiphyte with large waxy flowers whitish green dotted with red purple, the lateral sepals 15 cm long; yellow hood spotted red inside; bucket 5 cm deep, yellowish marked with crimson-brown spots. Insects fall into the bucket filled with odorous liquid and carry pollen in their struggle to escape. *p. 1694*

leucocorys (Amazonian Perú); distinct species with large flowers, waxy-white with deep red spots; the lateral sepals 10 cm long and 5 cm wide, petals narrow; sepals greenish yellow marked with red spots, petals with fainter purple markings. *Tropical. p. 1694*

macrantha (Trinidad, Venezuela, Guyana), "Helmet orchid"; epiphyte of the habit of Stanhopea, pushing out from the base of its pseudobulbs a pendulous stem with large odorous flowers, the delicate sepals and petals are yellow spotted purple, the helmet-shaped wax-like lip orange spotted with red. *Tropical. p. 1692*

macrocorys (Perú), "Helmet orchid"; from the upper Amazon; flowers of medium size, the lateral sepals concave and arranged to form a shield to the lip; sepals and petals greenish white marked with cinnamon-red; purplish hood with large horns and suffused with purple (summer). *Humid-tropical. p. 1694*

maculata (Demerara, Guyana), "Helmet flower"; remarkable epiphyte with curious pendulous flowers having membranous sepals and petals greenish yellow spotted with crimson, the hood yellow, bucket suffused and spotted with crimson. (May-July). (S) *p. 1692*

maculata punctata (Guyana); colorful form with sepals and petals yellowish and spotted red, hypochil (basal part of lip) flushed with orange-red and spotted purple. *Humid-tropical. p. 1694*

CORYMBORCHIS *Orchidaceae* **S3OFW**

flava (Panama, W. Indies); reed-like terrestrial plant with ribbed leaves; terminal flowers nearly white. *p. 1695*

CORYNOCARPUS *Corynocarpaceae* **C2LBDh**

laevigata (New Zealand), the "Karaka" of the Maori, and "New Zealand laurel"; handsome evergreen tree 6-15 m high, with laurel-like glossy green leaves 8-16 cm long; tiny 5 mm white flowers in clusters, followed by orange, edible fruit 4 cm long, but its seed is very poisonous. *p. 753*

CORYPHA *Palmae* **S2LBD**

elata (Bengal, Burma, Pacific Is.); robust fan palm to 20 m high; trunk more slender than the 45 cm dia. related Talipot palm, and covered with leaf bases; the bright green fan-leaves 2-3 m across, segments divided halfway, end of leafstalk extended into the leaf forming a rib; at maturity the 6 m monocarpic inflorescence appears above the crown, the palm then dying. *Tropical. p. 1865*

umbraculifera (Ceylon, So. India), the "Talipot palm"; slow-growing to 30 m high, with straight trunk and a great crown of fan-shaped, plaited bright green leaves about 4 m wide, on spiny stalks; pyramidal terminal inflorescence of creamy-white flowers, and small olive-colored fruit appear when palm is 25 to 80 years old; after fruiting the tree will die. *p. 1865, 1869*

CORYPHANTHA *Cactaceae* **I2LBD**

andreae (Mexico: Vera Cruz); small globe of 8 cm dia., dark glossy green, woolly on top, with plump grooved knobs set with yellowish radials and stiff curved central spines; flowers light yellow. *p. 709*

asterias (Mexico); globular to short cylindric plant to 12 cm high, grayish-green, with thick knobs set with yellow spines arranged like stars, axils with white wool; flowers white to pink. *p. 709*

bumamma (Mexico), "Starry ball"; globular plant to 15 cm high, with few very large bluish-green tubercles with recurved brownish radial spines, and yellow flowers. *p. 709*

clava (Mexico: Hidalgo); club-shaped, to 30 cm high, with big elongate, olive green nipples tipped by a rosette of white to brown spines; flowers yellow tinged red. *p. 711*

compacta (Mexico: Chihuahua); small solitary globes to 6 cm high, tubercles in 13 rows closely packed, with stiff, flattened down, whitish radials; flowers yellow. *p. 709*

cornifera (Mexico: Hidalgo); pale green, small globe to 12 cm high, wooly at top, with short, broad grooved knobs, set with all radials yellowish tipped red; flowers yellow tinged red. *p. 709*

echinus (W. Texas); solitary small, ball-like globe to 5 cm, covered with many spine-bearing tubercles, flat pressed radials white; flowers yellow. *p. 710*

elephantidens (Mexico: Michoacán), "Elephant-tooth cactus"; beautiful globose plant to 15 cm high and broader to 20 cm; blue-green obtuse knobs 5 cm long, densely white-woolly in axils; 6-8 brownish spines and all radial; large showy flowers about 10 cm across, and yellowish to salmon-rose colored with crimson-red center and red tips. When old, freely sprouting from the warts, or knobs, and extending. *Arid-tropical.* *p. 708*

macromeris (Mexico, Texas, N. M.); globose plant with very high, dense knobs to 12 cm long, pale grayish green, tipped with woolly areoles, awl-shaped white radials and long black central needle-like spines; flowers purple. *p. 711*

muehlenpfordtii (No. Mexico, N. M., Texas); globular plant to 20 cm high with pronounced knobs to 2½ cm long and grooved, set with yellow to reddish spines; flowers yellow. *p. 709*

neomexicana (W. Texas, N. M., Chihuahua); small globe or short-oblong to 10 cm, very spiny with numerous white radials and thicker central spines tipped black; flowers purplish inside. *p. 709*

radians (Mexico: Hidalgo); small green globe 8 cm wide, woolly at top, the ovoid tubercles covered with yellowish radials spreading comblike; flowers lemon ringed red outside. *p. 709*

roederiana (Mexico: Coahuila); glossy-green, oval plant 12 cm high, slowly clustering, woolly and spiny at the top; tubercles conical, the areoles very woolly when young; radials needle-like and one stiff brown central spine; flowers pale yellow, red at base. *p. 709*

vivipara (from Manitoba and Alberta to Kansas, Colorado, Texas), "Spiny stars"; olive green globes 5 cm thick, clustering, dense with high woolly nipples covered with spreading white radials and central spines; flowers flushed rose. *Temperate.* *p. 710, 711, 727*

CORYPHANTHA: see also Escobaria

CORYTHOLOMA: see Sinningia

COSMOS *Compositae* **S2LBM**

bipinnatus (Mexico), "Garden cosmos"; showy summer and fall-blooming annual that may grow to 2 m and more, of open branching habit, with light green bipinnate leaves finely cut into lacy segments, and daisy-like heads 5 to 8 cm across, with broad petal-like ray flowers in white, shades of pink, rose, lavender, purple or crimson, with tufted yellow centers. *Tropical.* *p. 804*

COSTUS *Zingiberaceae* ***S1LFM**

englerianus (West Africa, Equatorial Africa, Gabon); creeping rhizomatous plant with large fleshy, glossy leaves; trumpet flowers white with yellow throat sessile with leaf base. *p. 2140*

igneus (Brazil), "Fiery costus"; stout leafy stems maroon with 15 cm leaves green above, reddish beneath, spirally arranged; large 6 cm flowers deep orange. *Tropical.* *p. 2132, 2134*

malortieanus (zebrinus) (Costa Rica), "Stepladder plant"; showy, suckering plant with stout stalks to 1 m high in spirals, with broad, recurved, fleshy leaves to 30 cm long, bright emerald green, banded lengthwise with dark zones and covered with glistening hair; flowers yellow marked with red. *Tropical.* *p. 2132, 2134*

sanguineus (C. America), "Violet spiral flag"; beautiful "Spiral flag" with coppery green stems clasped by wine-red petioles bearing in spiral order, the gracefully recurving, oblique-elliptic, fleshy leaves of shimmering velvet-bluish-green, marked with a central band of silver, thin gray lines, and a zone of yellow-green toward the margin; deep blood-red beneath. *p. 15*, 2132*

speciosus (India), "Spiral ginger"; perennial herb with heavy rootstock; clustering, slender reed-like, green, leafy stems to 3 m long, growing upward in loose spirals or drooping in graceful curves, set in spiral order with fresh-green, oblanceolate, glossy, succulent, slender-pointed leaves, silky beneath; flowers in dense spike, white with yellow center and red bracts. *Tropical.* *p. 2132, 2134*

spicatus (West Indies), "Indian head ginger"; stout perennial herb with leafy stems to 2½ m tall; smooth, thick ovate leaves to 15 cm; club-like cylindrical inflorescence of overlapping red bracts, and yellow flowers. *Tropical.* *p. 2134*

stenophyllus (Costa Rica); tall clustering plant with bamboo-like canes green with pale cross-bands, and long linear leaves; the flowers from the base, yellowish. *p. 2132*

COTONEASTER *Rosaceae* **C2LBM**

apiculata (China), "Cranberry cotoneaster"; spreading shrub with tiny roundish dark glossy green leaves set with solitary, pink flowers all along the sparry, woody branches, followed by red berries, retained well into winter. (h) *p. 1996*

horizontalis (China), "Rock cotoneaster"; low, semi-evergreen shrub spreading horizontally over rocks, branching herring-bonelike, and set with dark glossy green, leathery, rounded leaves, small pinkish flowers and later, with coral-red fruit. *p. 1996*

horizontalis 'Variegata'; attractive horizontally spreading shrub with the little 1 cm leaves dark green edged in creamy-white. *p. 1993*

COTTENDORFIA *Bromeliaceae* **S3LBD**

guianensis (Venezuela, Guyana); a rather primitive terrestrial from the Guyana highlands, in habitat living on rocks or the savanna; long-linear stiffish, unarmed leaves to 120 cm long, with spiny apex, white-scaly beneath; the small inflorescence on long cone, flowers white. *p. 540*

guianensis var. vestita (Venezuela); small terrestrial sunlover from swampy savanna in Bolivar state; rosette of firm narrow grass-like leaves 30 cm long and 5 mm wide, covered with silvery scales beneath; slender inflorescence with small cluster of white flowers shielded by straw-colored bracts. *p. 540*

COTYLEDON *Crassulaceae* **I-S2LBD**

barbeyi (Eritrea, Arabia), "Hoary navelwort"; bold succulent with large, thick, shovel-shaped leaves, hoary-white on light green; flowers olive-green and red. *p. 864*

buchholziana (Cape Prov.); low branching succulent shrub with cylindrical branches gray-green, at first with reddish scale-leaves, which soon disappear; the forked lateral shoots with tiny linear leaves, and lilac flowers. *p. 866*

coruscans (So. Africa); short-stemmed succulent with long smooth, incurving wedge-shaped leaves 4-10 cm long, arranged at base in a rosette; tall stalk 20-45 cm high, with orange-red flowers greenish at base. *p. 869*

decussata (flanaganii) (Cape Prov. to Namibia); shrubby plant with loose rosettes of succulent, spatulate leaves gray-green with silvery glaucescence, flattened at tip, margins jagged or irregular, apex edged purple-brown; flowers yellowish, striped red. *p. 866*

gracilis (Morocco?); succulent with trailing stems, small 2½ cm obovate fleshy leaves with acute margins, glaucous white but turning beautiful bronze-red in full sun; long inflorescence with little red flowers tipped pink, looking like miniature tiger-lilies. *p. 864*

ladismithiensis (Cape Prov.), "Cub's paws"; attractive branching succulent with small and thick-fleshy leaves yellowish green and covered with white hair, apex claw-like and maroon; shiny flowers pale yellow tinged apricot, darker outside. *Subtropic.* *p. 865, 867, 880*

macrantha (E. Cape Prov.); showy and beautiful succulent to 1 m high, much grown on the Riviera; stout stem with erect branches, dense with fleshy, fresh green obovate, concave leaves edged in red, to 10 cm long; inflorescence on stiff stalk with inflated tubular, nodding flowers intensely red, inside greenish. *Subtropic.* *p. 867*

macrantha virescens (Cape Prov.); shrubby succulent with thick stems set with thick-fleshy obovate leaves dark green and still darker spots, margins red; flowers yellow-red. *p. 874*

orbiculata (Namibia); large robust succulent with thick, obovate leaves covered with waxy silver-white bloom and with red margin; flowers yellowish red. *Arid-subtropic.* *p. 864, 865, 866, 868*

orbiculata ausana (Namibia); smaller than the species, the silvery waxy leaves strongly edged with red, the smaller flower orange-red. *p. 874*

orbiculata oophylla (Namibia); elongate rosette of thick-fleshy obovate gray-green leaves covered with silvery blue powder, the apex edged in brown-purple; nodding bell-shaped flowers orange red. *p. 866*

paniculata (Namibia to Karroo and to Cape of Good Hope), the "Botterboom" of the Boers; thick-stemmed succulent tree-like to 3 m high, with swollen trunk covered with papery yellow-brown skin, few branches with obovate leaves 5-10 cm long, gray-green with yellow margin, deciduous during resting time. Red flowers with green stripes. *p. 866, 867, 868*

teretifolia (Cape Prov.: Karroo); shrubby plant with stems covered with white hair, obovate-linear leaves to 12 cm long, rather flat, light to dark green covered with gray-white hairs; flowers yellow. *p. 866*

tomentosa (Cape Prov.); attractive succulent with thin branches but thick obovate, like a paw, egg-shaped 3 cm leaves, red-warted at the squarish apex like toenails, the entire plant covered with white down; erect clusters of red furry flower buds open into dainty honey-colored blossoms with red around the edges. *p. 865*

undulata (Cape Prov.), "Silver crown"; interesting succulent with opposite, broad wedge-shaped leaves covered with silver-gray bloom, the crimped apex pure white; flowers orange. *p. 19*, 64A, 864, 865, 2092*

wallichii (South Africa); branching succulent with pencil-like, subcylindrical leaves grooved on top, and incurving, glaucous gray, bronzing in the fierce sun, and deciduous; flowers green, dotted red; very poisonous. *Arid-subtropic.* *p. 866*

COUROUPITA *Lecythidaceae* **S2LBD**

guianensis (Guyana), the "Cannonball-tree"; tall, soft-wooded, deciduous tree with armed branches; obovate, serrate 30 cm leaves, and fragrant 12 cm waxy flowers rose-colored inside, orange-yellow outside, borne on the tree-trunk on tangled stems, later followed by the large round 15-20 cm brownish fruits. *Tropical.* *p. 1361*

CRASSOCEPHALUM *Compositae* **S2LBD**

mannii (Gynura) (Uganda); branching small tree to 8 m, with green to purple stems, and rosette of large oblanceolate leaves 45 to 75 cm long, prominently toothed at margins; yellow flowers in terminal inflorescence. *Tropical.* *p. 816*

CRASSULA *Crassulaceae* ***I2LB-FD**

acinaciformis (Zimbabwe, Transvaal); woody root stock bearing annual shoots , forming aloe-like rosette of soft-fleshy leaves a beautiful wine-red in sun; inflorescence 50-70 cm high, with large clusters of whitish flowers. *Arid-subtropic.* *p. 867, 869*

"albiflora" hort. (Cape Prov.); erect succulent with wine-red stem and matte green sessile obovate leaves reddish toward margins, and twisted upward parallel with other side; flowers white. *p. 881*

alstonii (Cape Prov. and Namibia); small succulent, slowly clustering, with thick-round gray-green leaves in four ranks tight like shingles and curved inward; flowers white. *p. 872*

arborescens (So. Africa: Namaqualand to Natal), known commercially as argentea or "Silver dollar" or "Silver jade plant"; heavy, branching succulent growing tree-like with thick trunk to 4 m high, the robust branches with boldly fleshy, broad obovate, opposite leaves 4-8 cm long, united at the base, silver gray with reddish dotting and contrasting red margin; starry flowers white, turning pink. Slow growing and rarely blooming; excellent in pots. *Arid-subtropic.* *p. 878, 879*

"arborescens" of horticulture: see argentea

argentea by some taxonomists referred to C. obliqua (Cape Prov., Natal), known as C. arborescens, the "Jade plant", in the trade; Toelken gives priority to C. ovata (Cact. and Succ. Journ. 5-81); freely-branching or forking succulent growing to 3 m; leaves spatulate, thick-fleshy, 4-6 cm long, upper surface convex, lower flat, glossy jade-green, turning reddish in the sun, edged red; an old house plant; with age blooming with clusters of small starry, pinkish-white flowers. *Subtropic. p. 877, 878, 879, 881, 2092*

argentea 'Crosby's Compact'; a dwarf form grown in California nurseries specializing in succulents for dishgardens; the plump, roundish leaves average 2 cm long and are of a bronzy-purple color depending on sunshine; slow growing. *p. 869*

argentea 'Dwarf Ruby'; cultivar of the commercial "Jade plant", of more compact habit with smaller leaves dark green and colored wine-red toward apex, especially when grown in sun. *p. 879*

argentea minima (So. Africa); a small-leaved variety collected by Bernard Carp, forming a densely branched, compact bush with small fleshy leaves shining green and edged in red. *p. 878*

argentea 'Sunset', ('Hummel's Sunset'); a California cultivar grown by Hummel, with three-tone leaves in glossy green variegated with yellow, and a contrasting red margin; best under cool growing conditions. *p. 878*

argentea variegata, "Variegated jade"; with green and grayish leaves variegated cream to orange-yellow and with an orange-red edge; tends to revert to green. *p. 879*

arta (Cape Prov.); small succulent column of light green, fat triangular leaves with projecting gray markings, 1-2 cm long, arranged in 4 dense rows; flowers white. *p. 871*

barbata (So. Africa); clustering 4 cm rosettes from the dry Karroo, with broad, almost round leaves except for small point at apex, green and fringed with long white hairs, which feel hard to the touch like a thistle; small white flowers. Monocarpic, the growth dies down after flowering, but new growth starts from base. *p. 880, 883*

brevifolia (So. Africa); small succulent creeper, branching from base, stem later woody; light green, thick roundish leaves 6-10 mm long, united at base, the upper surface red-dotted and with red edge; flowers lemon-yellow. *p. 871*

cephalophora (So. Africa); branching succulent forming flat rosettes of ovate fleshy leaves to 8 cm long, rather flat on top, and covered with whitish hairs, the margins white-ciliate; flowers yellowish. *p. 875*

columella (Cape Prov.); small branching succulent with columnar branches 8-10 cm high, formed by small tightly compressed leaves velvety olive green turning bronzy, and with minute hairs; flowers greenish-white. (F) *p. 875*

columnaris (Cape Prov.: Karroo); low succulent; with clasping, cupping, green leaves in 4 ranks forming 4-angled columns, brownish during rest period, ciliate at margins; scented yellow-orange flowers. *p. 871, 875*

comptonii (Cape Prov.); tiny rosette of succulent, obovate leaves covered with minute gray hairs; yellow flowers. *p. 882*

conjuncta (E. Cape Prov.); branching succulent similar to C. perforata; scandent, wiry stems with opposite, sessile triangular, bluish leaves, puckered and ciliate at margins; flowers white. *p. 884*

cooperi (Transvaal); dainty low succulent herb forming mats, with tiny lanceolate, keeled leaves 1-1½ cm long, light green with ciliate margins; pale salmon flowers. *p. 870*

cordata (S.E. Africa, to Natal); shrubby succulent with heartshaped, smooth, white-waxy leaves 2 cm long, reddish at margins; white flowers. *p. 884*

cornuta (Namibia), "Horned crassula"; small gray column of snugly fitting opposite gray puckered leaves, short keelshaped, glaucous silver gray; flowers white. *p. 883, 884*

corymbulosa (S.E. Cape Prov.); erect-growing plant with gray green, triangular leaves to 5 cm long, densely shingled in 4 ranks, shorter and more separated upward on floral stalk; inflorescence 30 cm long with starry white flowers. *Arid-subtropic.* *p. 884*

cultrata (Cape Prov.), "Propeller plant"; small shrubby succulent with well spaced small pairs of obovate, light green leaves twisted like a propeller; whitish flowers. *p. 879*

dasyphylla (E. Cape Prov.); small cushion-forming perennial with prostrate, rooting branches set with tiny 5 mm pale green, rough, mealy-white leaves dark dotted; flowers white. *p. 880*

deceptrix (Cape Prov.); dwarf clustering succulent with stubby thick leaves closely overlapping and keeled beneath, silvery gray, marked with raised buff and brown dots; tiny pinkish flowers. *p. 881, 883*

deltoidea (Cape Prov.), "Silver beads"; tiny succulent shrub with red stems and little fleshy keeled leaves mealy gray and speckled red. *p. 881*

densa ('cephalophora') (So. Africa); small succulent with crowded, depressed leaves bluish gray, and covered with white hairs; flowers yellowish. *p. 881*

dregeana (Cape Prov.); attractive, shrubby branching succulent with fat, long-pointed channeled leaves obliquely keeled, dark green and entirely covered with tiny white pebbles, and arranged as in a cross; tiny flowers carmine red to whitish. *p. 885*

dregeana x trachysantha; very attractive hybrid succulent dense with thick-pointed, boat shaped green leaves appearing rough and gray from dense short white hairs, and symmetrically arranged alternately crosswise. *p. 885*

falcata (Rochea) (Cape Prov.), "Scarlet paintbrush"; handsome succulent with wide, flattened and sickle-shaped curved leaves arranged like parallel shingles, rough gray-green, and sending up fleshy stalk with showy terminal cluster of bright crimson flowers. *Subtropic.* *p. 64A, 877, 885*

'falcata x deceptrix'; an attractive Hummel hybrid resembling cornuta with thick-fleshy, short keelshaped leaves velvety grayish green. *p. 885*

'Falcata x rosularis hybrid'; can be in flower from January into summer; handsome succulent flowering plant with dense rosette of shingled, gray-green, concave leaves 8-10 cm long, united at base and arranged in form of a cross; large and striking cluster of brilliant red flowers; more compact than falcata and with larger flowering head. *p. 871*

flava (So. Africa); low xerophytic succulent from Cape Town's Table Mountain, spreading with numerous branchlets, dense with narrow leaves, ciliate with white bristly hairs; flowers creamy-white. *p. 868*

'Franken' (schmidtii x bolusii); bushy, small succulent, dense with leafy branches, the small foliage shiny gray-green, and covered with a multitude of carmine-red small flowers; an attractive pot plant, by A. Graeser-Nuremberg, Germany. *p. 868*

'Giant Pagoda'; a Hummel introduction and probably the most attractive of the 'pagoda' group as it is most robust with sets of leaves to 8 cm across, deep green with red border. Probably a perforata cultivar. *p. 873*

x graeseri (schmidtii x cooperi); compact little succulent hybrid with pointed leaves and flower stalks brown-red, spotted and striped, free-blooming with many clusters of pink to purplish-red blooms, from Feb.-Aug. *p. 872*

hemispherica (Namibia), "Arab's turban"; small round plant forming cushions, the rounded leaves are close together, overlapping and curving downwards, dark gray green and finely fimbriate at edges; flowers white. *Arid-subtropic.* *p. 881*

hottentotta (Namibia); small clustering succulent with columnar branches dense with short pointed, fleshy leaves in four ranks, silver gray with brownish edges and green spots; sometimes confused with C. cornuta. *p. 877*

x imperialis (pyramidalis x lycopodioides), "Giant's watch chain"; similar to lycopodioides but the stems are more robust and thicker, the leaves much larger and rich green. *p. 873*

justi-corderoyi; branching succulent, possibly a cultivar, with thick-fleshy, lanceolate leaves flat on top, dark green with red spots and covered with white hairs arranged in lengthwise rows; pink flowers. *p. 882*

lactea (Natal, Transvaal), "Tailor's patch"; succulent with broad, flat, opposite leaves smooth dark green and spotted white at margins; flowers white and fragrant, in a paniculate cyme. (F) *p. 880, 885*

'Lactea hybrid'; cultivar with a small-leaved crassula, an attractive open rosette of short-ovate, closely set flat leaves smooth glossy green without the typical marginal dots, and edged in red. The species lactea is lightly covered by scurfy scale. *p. 884*

lycopodioides (Namibia), "Skinny fingers" or "Toy cypress"; spreading lycopodium-like with string-like brittle branches covered tightly with scale-like pointed leaves in 4 ranks, fresh yellowish-green; minute whitish flowers. *p. 873*

marginalis (Cape Prov.); weakly prostrate succulent, ideal for baskets, with branches rooting at nodes, tiny rounded leaves sessile, grayish green with a row of red spots along the margin; flowers tinged reddish. *p. 873*

marginalis minuta; dainty miniature form with tiny heart-shaped leaves edged with red spots, on numerous prostrate branches; when in flower the plant is smothered with tiny white blossoms, each petal lined with red. *p. 882*

marnieriana (Cape Prov.); branching succulent with pencil-like cylindrical stems formed by the closely surrounding tiny, smooth, bluish leaves, edged in red; flowers white. *p. 876*

marnieriana 'Jade Necklace' (marnieriana x falcata); twisted stems dense with plump, broad-ovate succulent leaves 1 cm long, opposite and united at the base, densely arranged as in a chain, grayish with pronounced red edge; flowers white, clustered at tips. *p. 868*

mesembryanthemopsis (Namibia); clustering rosettes of 4-5 succulent pairs of squared-off, oblique angular leaves, flat on top, grayish green with white etching; white flowers in sessile head. *Arid-subtropic.* *p. 871*

'Morgan's Beauty' (C.°mesembryanthemopsis x falcata); pretty little clustering plant dense with irregularly wedge-shaped thick leaves covered with pearly gray puckers, bearing a tight cluster of rosy-salmon fragrant flowers with yellow anthers, lasting a long time. *Subtropic.* *p. 883*

multicava (Natal, Transvaal); spreading succulent with flat oval leaves grass-green tinged reddish and finely dotted; young plantlets rise within the pinkish inflorescence. *p. 881*

namaquensis (W. Cape Prov.: Karroo); branching succulent, thick, obovate leaves with rough surface; small white flowers. Dropping leaves are equipped with tiny rootlets to form new plants. *p. 880*

nodulosa (Mozambique, Transvaal, Namibia); succulent perennial branches from base, with flat, ovate leaves 2-7 cm long and with translucent marginal hairs; white flowers in erect spikes. *p. 868*

obliqua variegata (argentea), "Variegated jade plant"; variegated variety of obliqua, freely forking succulent with fleshy or corky stem, and obovate, thick leaves green and grayish, variegated with cream to orange-yellow and edged in orange-red; tends to revert to green; small pinkish-white starry flowers in large clusters. This appears to be the same plant as C. argentea variegata which see. C. obliqua is a name preferred by some authorities, but Jacobsen (1974) still lists it as C. argentea. *p. 869, 877, 879*

obvallata ('tomentosa') (Namibia); interesting succulent with fleshy, oblique obovate leaves flat on the surface, rounded beneath, and arranged diagonally like propeller blades, grayish green and covered with fine white felt. *p. 880, 885*

orbicularis (So. Africa to Natal); small flattened rosettes hugging the ground with obovate, waxy yellow-green deflexed leaves and sprinkled with pale pepper dots, ciliate at edges; clustering by sending out thread-like runners; flowers white. *p. 880, 883*

perfoliata (Cape Prov., Natal); elegant erect plant with tapering, fleshy leaves in 4 rows, gradually broadening near base and becoming lanceolate, deep grayish green covered with a silvery roughness; flower heads brilliant scarlet. *Subtropic.* *p. 873*

perforata (So. Africa), "Necklace vine"; thin wiry stems more scandent and creeping, the opposite triangular leaves somewhat thin and recurved, dark green, finely dotted gray and with white ciliate edges; little yellow flowers. *p. 873*

perforata 'Pagoda', "Pagoda plant"; more stiffly upright and with fleshier, larger leaves than perforata which seems to be one of its parents as it has the same rich green color and white ciliate margins. *p. 873*

perfossa (So. Africa), "String o'buttons" or "Necklace vine"; attractive succulent of erect habit with thin woody stem on which are, as if threaded, pairs of united thick, keeled leaves glaucous bluish-gray with purplish-red dotting and edging; small yellow flowers. The branches later fall over. *p. 872, 873*

portulacea (argentea x lactea), "Baby jade"; type of "Jade plant" with fleshy obovate pointed leaves somewhat smaller than argentea and entirely green; upper surface flat, rounded beneath. *Subtropic.* *p. 879*

pseudohemisphaerica (So. Africa, Namibia, Madagascar); interesting succulent forming mats, the flat, rounded leaves in dense rosette 5-6 cm dia., ivory-white to pale green with brown markings, the margins ciliate with white hairs; the 12-15 cm floral stalks with clusters of small whitish flowers. *p. 870*

pseudolycopodioides (Namibia), "Princess pine"; similar to lycopodioides but more vigorous and freely branching, leaves rich green and spread away from stem which is lax and rambling. *p. 873*

punctulata (Cape Prov.); small branching succulent with stiff brown twigs, tiny glossy green, awl-shaped leaves thickly powdered silvery-white, punctured with tiny spots; small white, bell-shaped flowers. *p. 882*

pyramidalis (Cape Prov.: Namaqualand); very attractive little succulent, grass green with tricornered flat leaves of equal size arranged in four ranks close above each other as in a perfect pyramid, over 2 cm dia., apex tinted red in the sun; flowers white. *Subtropic.* *p. 879, 882*

radicans (Cape Prov.); branching, shrubby succulent with 1 cm flattish obovate leaves mostly smooth; masses of small white flowers. *p. 882*

rogersii (Cape Prov.); branching succulent with woody stems, set in ranks with oblongate, soft-hairy leaves convex on both sides. *p. 875*

rosularis (Cape Prov., Natal); succulent perennial with flat, basal rosettes producing branches; thin-fleshy leaves linear-spoon-shaped to 8 cm long, glossy green, edges white-horny ciliate; flowers white. *p. 875, 884*

rubicunda (S.E. Africa to Mozambique); showy succulent rosette of concave, lanceolate tapering leaves, silvery gray tinted with purple, the lower ones 5 to 20 cm long; leafy stalk with terminal inflorescence in flat clusters of tiny flowers brilliant red. *Arid-subtropic.* *p. 869*

rubicunda in hort: see Rochea coccinea

rupestris (monticola) (Cape Prov.), "Rosary vine"; shrubby succulent with scandent branches, the thin wiry stems set with opposite, sessile fat triangular leaves united at the base, to 2½ cm long, glaucous light gray-green, the margins tinged red; clusters of yellowish flowers. *Arid-subtropic.* *19*, 873, 880*

rupestris 'White form'; small shrubby succulent with scandent branches; small, fat, cupped leaves silver glaucous except at margins; flowers white with pink center, as grown by M. Shields, Christchurch, N.Z. According to E. A. Alexander of N. Y. Botanical Garden, this may be an earlier flowering Hummel hybrid. *p. 881*

sarcocaulis (Cape Prov.); shrubby succulent successively branching, with fleshy stem and tapering lanceolate leaves; flowers whitish. *p. 884*

sarmentosa (S. E. Africa, Natal); succulent perennial with leaning branches, ovate-pointed shining green leaves coarsely toothed and cut at margins; flowers pinkish. *p. 884*

sarmentosa variegata; attractive branching small succulent with wiry stems; small fleshy, opposite ovate, 3 cm leaves olive-green, with yellowish variegation in center; tall clusters of starry pinkish flowers. *p. 869*

schmidtii (S. W. Africa, Transvaal, Natal), "Red flowering crassula"; small mat-forming floriferous succulent 8 cm high, sometimes grown as 'Crassula rubicunda', which is a taller plant; fleshy needle-like channeled leaves gray green with darker dots and ciliate; reddish beneath; freely sending up clusters of carmine-red flowers. *p. 879*

sericea (Cape Prov.); small branching succulent to 12 cm high with short, thick, boat-shaped leaves, covered with fine white velvety hairs becoming brownish; flowers white in long-stalked clusters. *p. 870*

sladenii (Cape Prov.); attractive succulent with elongate stems, roundish fleshy grayish-green leaves with flat surface, bottom rounded; small white flowers in inflorescence. *Subtropic.* *p. 882*

socialis (Cape Prov.); low, branching succulent forming mats; tiny leaves densely crowded in small rosettes, ovate-triangular; upper surface concave, rounded below, light green with horny margins; flowers white. *p. 882*

susannae (Cape Prov.); odd-shaped low succulent with turnip-shaped root; rosette of short 1 cm leaves cut off squarely at top, hollow in upper third, almost right-angled, the blunt edges covered with translucent warts and projecting above soil level; flowers white. *p. 871*

tabularis (Namibia: Hereroland); low succulent with turnip-like roots, sprouting with many slender stems, dense with shingled triangular leaves 2-3 cm long, arranged as in a cross, the upper side with dark green spots, the margins with ciliate hairs; small white flowers. *p. 870*

tecta (Cape Prov.); low, branched plant with closely set, short fleshy boat-shaped leaves, green and densely covered with short and thick white hairs; flowers white. *p. 885*

teres (So. Africa), "Rattlesnake"; dwarf clustering plant with roundish columns, closely appressed, pale green leaves, having a pale-translucent margin, which gives them a glazed appearance; flowers white. *p. 871, 885*

tetragona (Cape. Prov.), "Miniature pine tree"; erect shrub with opposite, thin spindle-shaped, glossy green leaves 3-5 cm long; small white flowers. *Subtropic.* *p. 881*

'Tricolor Jade' (argentea x lactea); habit upright, foliage somewhat pointed and a true green; the glossy leaves are beautifully variegated rich green, gray, white and pink, shading to purplish towards margin, surface flat, round beneath. Has the typical needlework patch of lactea along margins. *Subtropic.* *p. 19*, 64A, 879*

triebneri (Namibia), "St. Andrew's cross"; low succulent rosettes forming carpets, with crosswise opposite pointed leaves fresh green with darker spots; erect racemes with numerous white flowers of honey aroma and green bracts. *p. 883, 884*

turrita (So. Africa: Cape Prov.); low succulent with elliptic or linear, thick fleshy leaves 2-3 cm long, channeled on surface and hairy along margins, arranged in a 4-sided rosette; the leafy floral stalk to 60 cm long, topped by small clusters of tiny white flowers. *p. 869*

umbella (Cape Province); low succulent from tuberous root; the annual branches with opposite, rounded leaves 2 to 7 cm long, united at base and forming a plate-shaped disk, and with crenate margins; small whitish flowers. *p. 870*

'Zabo' (schmidtii x bolusii); charming small clustering succulent branching and spreading; many short stems with grayish green, pointed leaves, topped by clusters of numerous carmine-rose flowers. Photographed at Graeser's, Nuremberg, Germany. *p. 868*

CRASSULA: see also Rochea

CRATAEGUS *Rosaceae* **C2LBD**

monogyna biflora (oxyacantha), the Glastonbury form of the "English hawthorn" of Europe, producing two crops of flowers, in midwinter and in spring; spiny deciduous shrub to about 5 m high, with 5 cm leaves deeply 3-7-lobed; white flowers in small clusters with red anthers, and fruit resembling a miniature apple 1 cm long, bright red in autumn. p. 1996

CRATEROSTIGMA *Scrophulariaceae* **S3LBD**

pumilum (Torenia) (Ethiopia); low perennial herb spreading and forming tufts; the broad ovate parallel-veined leaves forming a fleshy rosette; numerous slender-stalked flowers 2 cm dia., pale lilac blotched purple, in the throat yellow and veined with white. p. 2049

CREMNOPHILA *Crassulaceae* **I2LBD**

nutans (Mexico); smooth succulent rosette 6-8 cm across, with broad rhombic, turgid leaves having rounded margins and keeled beneath, grayish with coppery tints; the inflorescence a nodding cluster of small yellow flowers. p. 898

CRESCENTIA *Bignoniaceae* **S3LBD**

cujete (Trop. America), the "Calabash tree"; small tree to 12 m high, with sparry, spreading branches; simple oblanceolate usually clustered leaves to 15 cm long, borne in groups of 2 or more on spurs from axillary buds on thick gray branchlets; flowers bell-shaped 5-8 cm long, yellow with brownish markings; interesting are the melon-like smooth, yellow to black fruit 12-30 cm or more dia., like a hard-shelled gourd, on its trunk and older branches; like gourds they can be tied around their girth as they mature to produce unusual forms, for making into cups or other vessels in tropical lands. *Tropical.* p. 499

x CRINDONNA memoria corsii—see x Amarcrinum

CRINODENDRON *Elaeocarpaceae* **I-S2LFD**

dependens (Tricuspidaria hookerianum) (Chile), "Lantern tree"; evergreen tree 3 to 10 m high, with narrow-elliptic, leathery leaves 4-12 cm long, hairy beneath; the bell-like, 2 cm nodding crimson-red flowers with petals curving inward. Not winter-hardy in very cold regions; but grown in California. p. 954

patagua (Tricuspidaria lanceolata) (Chile), "Lily-of-the-Valley-tree" or "Flowering oak"; evergreen tree 6 to 10 m or more high, with leathery elliptic leaves 3 to 8 cm long, dark green above, gray beneath, and with toothed margins; the charming, nodding, waxy flowers cup-shaped, with petals white, not curving inward, 2 cm long. p. 954

CRINUM *Amaryllidaceae* **I-S2LBMd**

amabile (Sumatra), "Giant spider lily"; large bulbous plant with neck to 30 cm long, crowned by rosette of fleshy leaves shaded purple, 10 cm wide and 1 m long; robust floral stalk bearing fragrant flowers with red tube, and red down center of the white segments 12 cm long. *Tropical.* p. 107

americanum (Florida to Texas), "Swamp-lily"; bulbous plant with 6-10 arching leaves 4-5 cm wide; 45-60 cm stalk bearing umbel of fragrant, creamy-white flowers with greenish tube, linear segments, and purplish anthers; in winter and spring, usually preceding leaves. p. 106

americanum var. robustum; a larger, more robust form of the "Florida swamp-lily", with leek-like foliage and flowers with creamy-white segments on long green tube and with white filaments; on rust colored stalk; spring and summer-blooming; quite stoloniferous and better for garden planting; should have spring rest. p. 109

asiaticum (Trop. So. Asia, Melanesia), known as "Poison-bulb"; showy, large rosette with bulb-like roots, very decorative alone for its numerous broad, sword-like, fleshy, yellow-green leaves 8-12 cm wide, with broad clasping base, center rib depressed, 1-1½ m long; the white waxy flowers between foliage, with narrow, pointed petals inside purple-red; Melanesian maidens wear these fragrant blooms in their black hair. *Tropical.* p. 106

augustum (amabile hort.) (Sumatra), a "Crinum lily"; sturdy plant with bulb sometimes 15 cm thick and 30 cm neck; many leaves 8-10 cm broad; numerous fragrant flowers on 1-1½ m stalk, the lanceolate segments deep wine-red outside, lighter inside. *Tropical.* p. 106, 108

bulbispermum (capense, longifolium) (So. Africa), probably the commonest Crinum, with relatively narrow leaves and funnel-form flowers white, flushed rose, with straight tube, to 12 blooms in umbels. p. 107

bulbispermum rubrum (So. Africa: Oranje River), "Orange River lily"; type species from semi-arid regions, with dark red funnel flowers with curved tube 8-10 cm long and segments 10 cm, and with red filaments; resembling amaryllis in shape; long-necked bulb with glaucous leaves; winter-deciduous. p. 109

'Cape Dawn' (burkanii hybrid x bulbispermum rubrum); a large polyploid hybrid by L. S. Hannibal (California), producing several floral stalks 1½-2m tall during summer, from giant bulb 15-25 cm diameter and with long neck, broad foliage 8-12 cm wide and to 2 m long; flowers in large umbels near 50 cm spread, chalice-shaped, coral red to vivid pink; a gorgeous sight commanding attention in the garden. p. 110

'Catherine' (americanum hyb.); found in an old Natchez, Louisiana garden; tender bulbous plant producing numerous offsets, with erect foliage tapering to a point, the floral stalk 85 cm tall, carrying 5-6 erect, white flowers with purple filaments. p. 109

crispum (So. Africa: Transvaal); dwarf bulbous species with rosette of deeply channelled leaves 25 to 45 cm long; waxy white funnel-form flowers pinkish outside, with 9 cm tube and 5 cm segments, and having spicy fragrance, on short 15-25 cm stalk; fairly hardy. p. 108

'Ellen Bosanquet'; "Red angel lily"; one of the best hybrid Crinum, and can be grown in pots, September flowering; stocky plant with broad, fleshy, spreading leaves and an umbel of large amaryllis-like deep wine-red flowers; best for cool-growing. p. 107

erubescens (So. Mexico, C. America, to Brazil); attractive bulbous plant related to americanum but larger; thin strap-like foliage; salver-form flowers with spreading segments 5 to 8 cm long, white inside, keeled bright wine-red outside, on long tube and with bright red filaments, in umbels on stalks 60 cm long; blooming midsummer to autumn. p. 109

giganteum: see C. jagus

"giganteum" of hort., "Giant spider lily"; bulbous plant with wide, strapshaped leaves, and white flowers with linear segments, in large umbels. The true West African species C. giganteum has lily-like white, bellshaped flowers, strongly scented. p. 106

x grandiflorum (bulbispermum x careyanum); charming old (1894) hybrid with long-necked bulb, a rosette of broad, basal leaves almost 1 m long; robust stalk 75 cm or more tall, carrying 8-15 fragrant trumpet flowers spanning 16 cm, white with each segment striped with red down center, opening at night; freely forming offsets; somewhat hardy. p. 108

'Gulf Pride' (x herbertii), (scabrum x bulbispermum); a broad-petal "Milk and wine lily"; beautiful, spicy fragrant flowers, trumpet-shaped with nicely rounded petal tips, white, the keels marked with rosy stripe. p. 110

humile (amoenum in hort.) (India, Sikkim); small tropical species with short-necked green bulb, linear leaves 25 cm long; floral stalk 30 cm carrying clusters of spidery white flowers with green tube and spreading, narrow-linear segments 5 cm long, the slender filaments bright red; autumn-blooming. p. 109

jagus (giganteum) (Trop. Africa: Kenya); showy bulbous species with large, somewhat tulip-shaped snow-white blossoms with vanilla fragrance, curved corolla tube 10-16 cm long, segments 8 cm and reflexed at tips; autumn and winter-blooming, opening to cupshape in the evening and expanding in daytime; stalk 50-75 cm tall; leaves on short petioles and 30-50 cm long, 8-10 cm wide. p. 108

japonicum 'Variegatum' (asiaticum hort.) (Japan: Honshu); striking for its foliage; broad fleshy leaves, swordlike, with clasping base, grass green alternating lengthwise with creamy-white bands and stripes; the succulent spreading leaves to 60 cm long, and 5-12 cm wide, from columnar bulb; floral stalks 30-50 cm tall, bearing to 20 blossoms, with 8 cm tube and spreading white ray-like segments 8 cm long; summer-blooming; semi-hardy. The species grows as far north as Tokyo; photographed at Kosobe University gardens, Osaka. p. 110

kirkii (Zanzibar); large globose bulb with 1 m strapshaped leaves with white ciliate, crisped margin; funnelform flowers white keeled red on back of segments, the tube greenish, in 12-15 flowered umbels, during summer. p. 107

kirkii 'P. F. Reasoner' (kirkii x bulbispermum); a typical "Milk and wine lily"; robust sterile hybrid for garden planting, with large fragrant funnel-form, open-faced white flowers, the overlapping segments with bright red keels, and 10-12 cm long; bulbs 12-15 cm diameter with long neck, foliage strap-like more than 1 m long. Developed by Reasoner of Royal Palm Nurseries, Florida, in 1895. Hybrid name proposed by L. S. Hannibal of California and published by Louisiana Society for Hort. Research 1972. p. 109

latifolium (India); bulb almost globose, to 20 cm thick, with short neck; numerous vivid green strap-shaped leaves 60-90 cm long; floral stalk 30-50 cm tall, topped by large clusters of lily-like white flowers tinged red in middle of broad, reflexed segments form curving greenish tube, blooming in summer. Much planted in Florida. p. 108

macowanii confusum (macneilii), (So. Africa); a charming crinum of the dry Karroo, with tulip-shaped blossoms a lovely rose-pink, keels striped with green and red, tube 5-8 cm long and segments 8 cm, anthers turn black after loss of pollen; bulb 10-20 cm diameter, leaves channelled and glaucous, sprawling along ground; summer-blooming. p. 110

"meldensis" hort.: see 'Miss Elsie'

'Miss Elsie' (americanum x bulbispermum); "meldensis" in Europe; plant knee-high, with strap-shaped, wide, glaucous leaves; the flowers in large clusters on erect stalk, the linear petals 10 cm long, white inside, outside flushed reddish-brown. p. 106

moorei (So. Africa: Natal), "Longneck swamp lily"; herbaceous plant from a large bulb with stem-like neck to 30 cm; broad and thin, smooth-edged, somewhat wavy, bright green leaves 60-90 cm long; showy, lily-like, soft rose bell-shaped fragrant flowers 12 cm or more across, very attractive with pink filaments, 6 to 8 blooms to a cluster, on stout stalk, during summer; free bloomer. *Subtropic.* p. 107

'Pam's Pink' (bulbispermum x powellii); large Pam hybrid with foliage to 1½ m long, and tall 1 m stalks bearing 10-12 large rose-pink, trumpet-shaped blossoms on curved tubes, summer-blooming; produces numerous offsets; fairly hardy. p. 110

'Peach Blow' (submersum hybrid); the Queen of hybrid crinums according to L. S. Hannibal; an attractive Mead hybrid with blossoms lavender-pink, the slender recurving segments soft pink inside and darker outside, and with wonderfully spicy fragrance; the clusters carried on a flattened stalk; near evergreen strap-like foliage from a large globose bulb. *p. 109*

x powellii (bulbispermum x moorei), "Powell's swamp lily"; a spectacular old English hybrid (1732), with globose bulb, carrying abundant, decorative foliage, about 20 sword-shaped leaves to 120 cm long; a 60-90 cm firm floral stalk appears in summer, crowned by a cluster of up to 10 trumpet-shaped flowers 10 cm long, generally deep rose, and opening in succession; blooming at a time when there are few other bulbous plants of its stature or beauty in flower. Slightly hardy. *Subtropic.* *p. 107*

x powellii 'Album'; chaste form of pure white, large lily-like flowers 10-12 cm long, on stiff-erect stalks over shining green foliage. *p. 107*

procerum (Trop. Asia), "Asiatic poison-bulb"; probably a variety of C. asiaticum; robust bulbous plant with basal stump to 30 cm thick, and broad, fleshy, bluish-green leaves to 2 m long and 15 cm wide; the spidery, fragrant white flowers with 10 cm tube and 6 narrow segments 12 cm long tinged red, and with red spreading stamens, blooming almost continuously. The giant bulb is poisonous, and used medicinally in Asia as an emetic. *p. 108*

procerum var. splendens; a form closely allied to C. asiaticum but with a massive bulb to 30 cm diameter and 50 cm high; like amabile it has flowers bright red outside, lighter inside, carried in a large rounded umbel, with a compact group of buds in the central area. *Tropical.* *p. 108*

roozenianum (Jamaica); a white "Swamp-lily"; robust plant rather compact in habit, with 8-10 cm bulb; strongly channelled deciduous leaves to 45 cm long; stiff floral stalks each with large clusters of 5-7 white flowers 12 cm long with slightly curved purple-crimson tubes, the back of the segments crimson and anthers cream, blooming in spring. *p. 108*

speciosum: see Hymenocallis harrisiana

'St. Christopher' (jagus or giganteum x bulbispermum); snow-white, fragrant blooms like tulips; the cup-shaped flowers with dark anthers, on 50 cm stalks 5 to 6 to a cluster, erect stalks; ovoid bulb 5 cm diameter, with neck 30 cm long, foliage thin and leek-like; semi-hardy; blooming in mid-October, St. Christopher's day; numerous offsets. *p. 110*

submersum (Brazil: Serra do Mar, Rio); very showy tropical species; oblong 8 cm bulb with tapering neck, foliage near evergreen, and straplike; floral stalk to 60 cm tall carries 5-8 spicy-fragrant flowers 16 cm across, having long curved tube and spreading white segments keeled with red on back, and with red filaments; late summer bloom. *p. 109*

x virginicum (scabrum x bulbispermum album); an early hybrid possibly dating back to 1820, common in Florida gardens; a choice plant with large white, fragrant blossoms with rose-pink markings, the margins ruffled, the keels warm pink, on long stalks to 1 m high; foliage glossy deep green; fairly winter-hardy. *p. 109*

yemense (latifolium), (South Arabia); bulbous plant with numerous shining green strap-shaped leaves 60-80 cm long; trumpet-shaped pure white flowers, the tube 8-10 cm long, with petals reflexed at tip; 10 to 20 blooms on long 30 to 60 cm stalk. *Arid-tropical.* *p. 108*

CROCOSMIA *Iridaceae* **I2LBMd**

masonorum (Tritonia) (So. Africa: Transvaal), "Golden swan tritonia"; magnificent cormous herb forming clumps of ribbed, sword-shaped basal leaves 75 cm long and 5 cm wide; branched arching stems bearing two-tiered spike-like clusters of starry flowers glowing orange-scarlet, 4 cm across, and blooming July or August; similar to Tritonia crocosmaeflora, the "Montbretia" of gardens, but with broader foliage, broader flower segments of deeper red, and inflorescence more pendant. Goes dormant during winter. Not winter-hardy. *Subtropic.* *p. 1332, 1333, 1339*

CROCOSMIA: see also Tritonia

CROCUS *Iridaceae* **C2LBMd**

moesicus (S. E. Europe, Asia Minor); in cultivation as the "Dutch yellow crocus"; with large corm, grasslike leaves and bright yellow tubular flowers 10 cm long, blooming in spring. *p. 1335*

sieberi purpureus (Greece, Crete); small cormous herb with basal grass-like leaves, and showy erect funnel-shaped, purple-blue flowers with yellow throat; spring flowering. *p. 1335*

'Vernus hybrid', "Alpine spring crocus"; typical commercial spring-blooming cormous herb with large, erect, funnel-shaped lilac or white flowers; the spreading lobes faintly striped purple; other colors from yellow to blue, and much larger than the original So. European species; throat never yellow. *p. 1335*

CROSSANDRA *Acanthaceae* **S3HFM**

guineensis (Trop. West Africa); low plant with red, furry stem rarely branched, large thin-leathery obovate leaves in 2 to 4 pairs, 8-12 cm long, with deep pink netting, underside deep purple; flowers white, tinged pink, with long slender tube, from solitary bracted, green spike. *p. 45*

infundibuliformis (undulaefolia) (India), "Firecracker-flower"; shrubby plant with glossy, ovate leaves; showy salmon-red tubular flowers with split limb, in angled, bracted spike. While grown in our greenhouses as a small 10 cm potplant, I have seen these in India and Ceylon as an ever-blooming 1 m bush. *Tropical.* *p. 45, 768A*

infundibuliformis 'Mona Wallhead'; a Swedish cultivar of compact habit about 1/2 m high, with shining, black-green leaves and flowers salmon-rose. *Tropical.* *p. 45*

pungens (Tanzania: Usambaras); attractive, bushy plant to 60 cm high, with oblong leaves olive-green, with creamy-white veins; flowers orange, set in bracts hairy at margins. *Tropical.* *p. 45*

CROTALARIA *Leguminosae* **S3LBD**

agatiflora (ageratifolia) (Trop. E. Africa), "Canary-bird bush", "Rattle-box", "Lion's claw"; shrub of 1 m, with green branches; leaves 3-foliolate; flowers very large, pale greenish-yellow, keel dull brownish-purple at tip. *p. 1379*

CROTON *Euphorbiaceae* **S3LBM**

poilanii (Vietnam: Trang Bom); small tree to 5 m high with slender gray trunk and willowy branches, dense with small 8-10 cm elliptic, plain dark green, leathery leaves crenate at margins; the female flowers usually without petals, the male flowers with 5 petals and inconspicuous; croton-oil is made from seeds. I found this species in ironwood forest 51 km northeast of Saigon. *Tropical.* *p. 1007*

reflexifolius (San Salvador), "Copalchi"; a great tree of the temperate mountain forests, with willowy, spreading branches; shining green, ovate leaves with yellow veins; small whitish flowers without petals, in slender racemes; the globular fruits are dry and spiny. Used medicinally locally, and also as shade protection for coffee fincas. Of no particular ornamental value horticulturally, but shown to point out the difference between true croton and the so-called "Croton" of hort., which are Codiaeum. *p. 1004*

CROTON: see also Codiaeum

CROWEA *Rutaceae* **I2LBD**

saligna (Victoria, New South Wales, Queensland); evergreen shrub of erect habit with narrow lanceolate leaves 2 1/2-5 cm long, on angled branches; rosy-red flowers with spreading petals, and yellow anthers. *p. 2025, 2034*

CRYOSOPHILA *Palmae* **S3LFM**

warscewiczii (So. Mexico, Panama), "Rootspine-palm"; slender fan-palm with lower part of trunk covered by spine-like aerial roots, the lowest reaching into the ground; the palmate leaves to 2 m divided to the base, the segments often split again, green above, gray beneath. *p. 1868*

CRYPTANTHEMIS *Orchidaceae* **S3OFW**

slateri (Australia), "Underground orchid"; unique subterranean rhizomatous species; minute 1/2 cm flowers waxy white, maturing below the surface of the soil, but becoming purplish-brown when breaking the surface and exposed to light. *p. 1695*

CRYPTANTHUS *Bromeliaceae* ***S1HFD**

acaulis (Rio), "Earth stars"; small, flattened, suckering , terrestrial rosette with waxy, prickly margins, medium green and covered with pale gray scurf; white flowers low in center. *p. 544, 545*

acaulis ruber (Brazil), "Miniature red earth star"; green with purplish-bronze center and margins, covered with beige scurf. *p. 543*

bahianus (Bahia); stiff succulent flaring rosette with linear recurved leaves apple-green with margins turning bronzy red, wavy edge and spiny, silvery beneath; flowers white. *p. 545*

beuckeri (Brazil), "Marbled spoon"; irregular rosette of flat, thin leathery spoon-shaped leaves with slender point, rich green marbling on pale green; flowers whitish. *Tropical.* *p. 543, 545*

bivittatus lueddemannii (Brazil), "Large rose-stripe star"; leaves much longer, strapshaped and undulate margined, thick and fleshy, with two pale green bands; flat habit. *p. 543*

bivittatus minor (roseus pictus) (Brazil), "Rose-stripe star"; flattened, small, star-like, terrestrial rosette satiny olive-green with two pale bands, overcast with salmon rose, turning coppery red in strong light; finely toothed. *Tropical.* *p. 512, 544, 545*

bivittatus 'Pink Starlite'; beautiful small, flat rosette, patented in Florida, averaging 6-8 cm across and nearly a perfect star in shape, the almost triangular leaves moss-green along center, toward margins a contrasting cream in wide bands, the finely toothed edges a vivid, pleasing rosy-red; probably a bivittatus cultivar; ideal for small dishgardens and terrarium planting. *Tropical.* *p. 547*

bromelioides (terminalis) (Espirito Santo, Rio); flaring rosette with long-elliptic tapering, smooth wavy-edged leaves, olive green to bronze; white flowers deep in center. *p. 545*

bromelioides 'Racinae'; a charming hybrid by Mulford Foster of Orlando, Florida, named after his wife Racine; attractive star with wide-spreading, stiffly lanceolate leaves 12-18 cm long, coppery bronze with irregular, silvery crossbands, the margins undulate or crisped; pure white flowers from the center cup; photographed in Palmengarten collection, Frankfurt, Germany. *Tropical.* *p. 546*

bromelioides 'Tricolor', "Rainbow star"; rather large, flat rosette, strikingly variegated with the fleshy, fresh-green leaves edged and striped ivory-white, the margins and base tinted carmine-rose. *p. 15*, 512, 512A, 544*

sp. 'Café au Lait'; miniature species forming clusters, photographed at Bob Wilson's Fantastic Gardens, Miami in 1959; narrow, undulate leaves brown and pink over green on the surface, silvery underneath. *p. 547*

diversifolius (Brazil), "Vary-leaf star"; larger rosette with arching, wavy-margined leathery leaves of diverse shape: broad-ovate, long-oblanceolate and spoon-shaped; dark bronze-purple covered with silvery scales. *Tropical.* *p. 543, 547*

farinosus (S. America); small rosette similar to praetextus but not as flat, of smaller habit, leaves harder and darker green, less glossy. *p. 545*

fosterianus (Pernambuco), "Stiff pheasant-leaf"; large rosette to 85 cm across, marked similar to zonatus but leaves much thicker and very stiff, habit very flat, coppery green to purplish brown, with tan zebra banding. *Tropical.* *p. 545*

'Gruensilber'; an attractive hybrid by Richter in Germany, with thick leaves 10 to 15 cm long, 3 to 5 cm wide, sea green with irregular cross bands of silvery scales, the margins finely toothed. *p. 547*

incrassatus (Brazil); long, narrow-lanceolate leaves 2 cm wide, smooth and bright green above, underneath covered by appressed white scales. *p. 544*

x 'It'; aptly known as "Color-band"; spectacular mutant developed from a Foster hybrid probably involving C. bivittatus lueddemannii. Terrestrial rosette with strap-like leaves to 45 cm long and 4 cm wide, coppery green with longitudinal striping and broad outer bands of ivory, the margins a glowing rosy-red intensified by good light. *Tropical.* *p. 546, 547*

lacerdae (Brazil), "Silver star"; flat rosette of thin leathery leaves emerald green with silver borders and broad center stripe; finely toothed; whitish flower. *p. 512, 543*

x lubbersianus (bivittatus x beuckeri); low rosette of oblanceolate leaves about 30 cm long 4-5 cm wide, fairly firm, green or tinged with brown on surface, with darker green blotches, and two indistinct pale vertical bands; thinly white-scurfy beneath, small marginal teeth; flowers white. This may be merely a variety of bivittatus. *p. 546*

x makoyanus (acaulis x bivittatus); short rosette with oblanceolate leaves 15-22 cm long, of moderately firm texture; on the surface with a pale sea-green vertical band on each side of the darker green middle, thinly white-scurfy beneath; flowers white. *p. 546*

x mirabilis (beuckeri x osyanus); handsome Richter hybrid with broad-ovate, recurving, undulate leaves in various shadings light green, olive and copper-brown, more pronounced in blotches or cross bands in cream, and shading into glowing rose. Photographed in the collection of Leningrad Botanic Garden, U.S.S.R. *Tropical.* *p. 547*

'Morgenrot'; handsome cultivar developed by Richter in Germany; vigorous, flat rosette dense with broad, undulate leaves, basically green with pale marbling and red midband; with strong light the plant turns completely red in remarkable coloring; freely suckering. *p. 546*

x osyanus (beuckeri x acaulis), "Mottled earth star"; irregular rosette of broad leathery leaves warm green, pale mottled and tinted pink to coppery red; white flowers. *p. 543*

'Patina'; a Richter cultivar from Germany; loose medium-large, flattened rosette of strap-shaped, linear leaves a shimmering greenish pink in varying lengthwise bands; in strong light the dense scales will form a silver gray cover. *p. 546*

praetextus (Espirito Santo); large thick-fleshy, flattened rosette with glossy, pea-green leaves and wavy margins finely toothed; gray beneath; flowers white. *p. 545*

pseudoscaposus (Brazil), "Trailing earth-star"; photographed at Hummel's, Carlsbad, California: small star of glossy coppery-green leaves with margins purplish-red and finely toothed, coppery with silver scales beneath; from the base emerge the long rhizome-like suckers, trailing, or pendant when in hanging basket. *p. 547*

'Riesen-Erdstern'; spectacular German cultivar, a low rosette to 80 cm across, with few linear-lanceolate, curving leaves to 3 cm wide, vivid red-brown with irregular cross-bands of contrasting silver-gray. *p. 574*

x rubescens, "Brown earth star"; low rosette of leathery, obovate, wavy leaves predominantly purplish-brown, the center covered with silvery scales becoming more scattered toward apex; whitish flowers. *p. 543*

sinuosus (undulatus) (Brazil: Guanabara); small rosette of leathery leaves only 5 cm long, green, and undulate at margins, edged by soft teeth, white-scaly beneath. *p. 547*

sinuosus 'Major' (in hort. as C. diversifolius) (Brazil: Rio); large open terrestrial with broad leaves spreading 30 cm or more, green with bronze cast, somewhat vary-colored, and covered with scales, the margins undulate and with minute soft teeth; flowers white. *p. 546*

zonatus (Pernambuco), "Zebra plant"; attractive spreading rosette of wavy lanceshaped soft-leathery leaves, brownish green to copper and with tan to light brown, irregular crossbands; silvery-scurfy beneath; translucent white flowers; growing terrestrial. *p. 512, 543*

zonatus 'Fuscus' (Brazil); a form with leaves reddish-brown above, with cross bands of silver-gray scale; underside gray. *p. 546*

zonatus 'Viridis' (Brazil); large rosette with leaves bronzy and green with silver cross-bands, underside green, without scale. *p. 544*

zonatus 'Zebrinus' (fuscus), "Zebra plant"; strikingly beautiful form with bronzy-purple long wavy leaves, the pronounced silvery to beige crossbanding resembling those of a zebra. C. zonatus is from Pernambuco, a rosette to 45 cm across. *Tropical.* *p. 5*, 19*, 25*, 543*

x CRYPTBERGIA *Bromeliaceae* ***S1HFD**

meadii (Cryptanthus beuckeri x Billb. nutans); small upright rosette with leathery, narrow, tapering leaves, olive green to coppery, with dark mottling and gray reverse; greenish flower cluster. *p. 512, 536*

rubra (Crypt. bahianus x Billb. nutans), "Cryptanthus-Billbergia hybrid"; small open rosette with thick, narrow, recurved leaves, bronzy green shading to wine-red in center, soft-spiny margins; raised cluster of whitish flowers. *p. 544*

CRYPTOCEREUS *Cactaceae* **S3HFM**

anthonyanus (Mexico: Chiapas), "Anthony's rickrack"; nightblooming climber of the rain forest, using aerial roots; remarkable, deeply lobed stems looking like fish bones; beautiful intensely fragrant flowers 8 cm long, the inner petals peachy-white, outer sepals pointed, rose to burning maroon, lasting only a single night and closing in the morning. *p. 640A, 661, 665*

CRYPTOCORYNE *Araceae* ***S3LNW**

albida (Burma); tropical rhizomatous plant growing in warm 23 to 28°C, shallow water; long-stalked lanceolate, light green quilted leaves 7-12 cm long and 1-1½ cm wide; a 7-10 cm spathe with twisted tube, opening into long lanceolate blade white or yellowish with purple spots. *p. 210*

balansae (Vietnam, Thailand); a pretty aquarium plant for shady locations; small ribbon-like leaves prominently quilted and undulate, 5-50 cm long and 2 cm wide; velvety green in clustering rosettes from stringy, branching rootstocks; inflorescence with spathe dark olive green 7-15 cm long and twisted toward tip, inside yellow-green spotted or striped with red. *p. 210*

beckettii (Sri Lanka), formerly known as ciliata; tropical aquarium plant, with long-trailing rootstock, sprouting shoots and leaves, long-stalked lanceolate 8-15 cm long, 3-4 cm wide, dark brownish-green, brownish-violet on the underside; inflorescence appears only above water, tubular spathe 9-13 cm long, with twisted point, inside dark purple-brown, yellowish outside and toward apex; in habitat along the shores of slowly flowing waters. *p. 210*

ciliata (Monsoon India: Bengal to Malaya), "Fragrant tape grass"; tropical aquatic herb or bog plant to 40 cm high, with creeping rhizome and stalked lance-shaped leaves of firm texture, usually growing under water, fresh to yellowish-green with undulate margins, the depressed midrib dark green. Inflorescence submerged with the enclosed spadix bearing female flowers on the lower part, male flowers on the upper, only the extended spathe above water surface. *Humid-tropical.* *p. 210*

ciliata minor (India, Malaya); aquatic herb or bog plant, with creeping rhizome and stalked linear-lance-shaped leaves of firm texture, usually growing under water, fresh green with undulate margins, the depressed midrib dark green. Inflorescence submerged with the enclosed spadix bearing female flowers on the lower part, male flowers on the upper, only the extended spathe above water surface. C. ciliata is 40 cm high, minor 15-22 cm. *p. 212*

cordata (Malaya: Borneo; Java); aquatic herb with creeping rhizome; the leaves to 10 cm long, olive green, reddish-purple beneath; in mature stage broadly elliptic or cordate; in the juvenile phase usually seen in aquaria, it has leafblades oblong-lanceolate. *p. 212*

didericii (Malay Peninsula, Sumatra), a "Water trumpet"; small rhizomatous aquatic plant; from a fleshy base rises a rosette of channeled petioles bearing the broad-ovate, dark green to reddish leaves, to 7 cm long and with cordate base; the trumpet-like, fluted spathe 10 cm long, expanding at top and running into a pointed tip, reddish brown with yellow throat. *p. 210*

griffithii (So. Malaya); aquarium plant with ovate leaves dark green, marked purple beneath; tubular part of spathe rosy; blade blood-red. *p.212*

lingua (Borneo); rather stocky, compact aquarium plant 5-12 cm high, fleshy leaves tongue-or spoon-shaped, vivid green, 5 cm long, on broad petioles; relatively large tubular spathe 7 cm long with purple-dotted yellow throat, toward pointed apex deep purple and twisted. *p. 210*

longicauda (Borneo); attractive aquatic with very broad, heartshaped leathery leaves almost 8 cm wide, of firm texture, deep metallic green with copper sheen, lightly puckered and crinkled, the reverse lighter green. *p. 212*

lucens (Sri Lanka); cultivated aquarium plant with strong rootstock freely branching, long 10-17 cm petioles with slender lanceolate leaves 6-12 cm long, glossy green with prominent midrib; spathe with flaskshaped base with 3 cm tube and brown-purple pointed blade spirally twisted. *p. 210*

nevillii (Sri Lanka); rapid-growing underwater aquarium plant, a miniature amongst cryptocorynes, by runners forming regular fields; fresh green, long-stalked, spoon-like or ovate leaves 4-7 cm long; tubular spathe 5-8 cm long with flask-like base opening toward apex, purple above with yellow inside. *p. 210*

nurii (Malaysia); aquatic tropical rosette dense with stalked, narrow-lanceolate vivid green leaves 10-18 cm long, the margins more or less undulate or crisped; the spathe on a 7-12 cm slender stalk, with swollen base, tubular toward top 6-12 cm long, coming to a long point, and blackish-purple. *p. 211*

parva (Sri Lanka); small tropical aquarium plant with creeping rhizome and strong roots, and rosettes of small long stalked, spoon-shaped grass-green leaves 2-3 cm long; tubular spathe 2½ cm long, constricted toward apex white or purple, the obliquely open limb dark purple. *p. 211*

petchii (Sri Lanka: Ratnapura); aquatic tropical plant with robust rootstock, forming a rosette of long-stalked lance-shaped green leaves 15-20 cm long, 2 cm or more wide; attractive tubular spathe 7-10 cm long, the 4 cm tube opening into a long pointed, fleshy and warty limb, olive green to brown, the inside of tube rich purplish-brown. *Tropical.* *p. 211*

retrospiralis (Trop. S. E. Asia: India, Laos, Vietnam, Burma, Thailand, So. China); robust water plant with stout, winged petioles and narrow lanceolate deep green leaves 15-50 cm long, to 1½ cm wide; spathe 12-30 cm long, tubular at base gradually opening and tipped with spiralling point, primarily purplish. *p. 211, 212*

retrospiralis var. costata (Thailand); attractive variety forming graceful rosette with narrow leaves undulate along margins, the spathe tube more open and flattened, and spirally turned in upper part. *p. 211*

schulzei (Malaysia: Johore); aquatic plant 10 cm high, with long lanceolate green leaves undulate at margins, the spathe flask-shaped at base, long tubular and with broad, pointed limb curved forward or oblique. *p. 211*

spiralis (India: Bengal, Bombay, Koromandel); tropical aquatic plant with stout rootstock, the petioles with long vagina, broadening into the narrow lanceolate or ribbon-like, light green leaves 10-20 cm long and more, 1-2 cm wide, with prominent midrib; the stalked spathe flask-like at base; slender above with spiralled narrow blade 8-15 cm long, red-purple and with warty cross furrows above. *p. 211*

versteegii (New Guinea); sturdy aquatic with short-stubby, spade-shaped, thick-leathery leaves 6 cm long, on fleshy petiole; blade light green with yellow sheen both sides, without prominent midrib. *p. 212*

wendtii (Thailand); tropical aquarium plant for both under water and above surface culture, with sturdy roots and branching; stalked leaves spear-shaped 8-11 cm long, and 3 cm wide, glossy green with brownish purple in habitat; spathe 8 cm long, tubular with twisted mouth and tail on top, brown purple. *Tropical.* *p. 211*

willisii (Trop. S.E. Asia), "Water trumpet"; aquatic plant with narrow lanceolate leaves, when young reddish-brown marked with greenish-black; curly margin. *Tropical.* *p. 212*

CRYPTOCORYNE: see also Lagenandra

CRYPTOMERIA *Taxodiaceae (Coniferae)* **C2LBM**

japonica 'Globosa nana'; a "Japanese cedar" of slow-growing, dwarf prostrate, spreading habit, over the years forming a rounded bush 1 m or more high; stout, pendant branchlets clothed with flexible, rich bluish to moss green, glossy needles down to the ground level. *p. 850*

japonica 'Nana'; a dwarf form of the normally tall, somber tree at home in Japan and Central China; in this cultivar of pyramidal habit to 2 m high, with reddish-brown bark, the branches dense and clothed with spirally arranged, short 1-2 cm needle-like metallic green leaves. *p. 839*

CRYPTOPHORANTHUS *Orchidaceae* **S3ONM**

nigriflorus (Trop. America), "Window orchid"; diminutive epiphyte with oval leaves; queer flower from leaf base; the sepals are joined to form a sac, in which the small petals and lip are enclosed, black maroon and covered with translucent bristles. *Tropical.* *p. 1695*

CRYPTOSTEGIA *Asclepiadaceae* **S3LFM**

grandiflora (Mascarene Islands), "India rubber-vine"; scandent tropical shrub with willowy, climbing branches, bearing opposite, glossy green soft-leathery leaves with ivory midrib, 10 cm long; large bell-shaped flowers 5 cm across, white inside, and reddish-purple outside, changing with age to pink. Cultivated in India for rubber-yielding latex; plants however, are poisonous. *Tropical.* *p. 372*

madagascariensis (Madagascar); woody tropical evergreen vining plant with dark green shining foliage, pubescent underneath; pink or whitish trumpet flowers having corolla segments divided. *Tropical.* *p. 372*

CRYPTOSTEPHANUS *Amaryllidaceae* **S3LBM**

vansonii (Zimbabwe); semi-bulbous plant somewhat like Clivia; leaves strap-shaped, 2 cm wide; the fleshy floral stalk flattened and winged; clusters of waxy white flowers tinged with pink, the stamens flat along petals. *p. 120*

CTENANTHE *Marantaceae* **S3LFM**

compressa (pilosa) (Pernambuco, Brazil); erroneously called "Bamburanta" in California nurseries; waxy-green, unequal-sided, leathery leaves oblong, grayish-green beneath, borne at an angle on wiry petioles, the plant is bushy but throws up bare stems bearing 2 to 4 small plants at the top forming a heavy tuft of foliage; flattened, hairy bracts. *Tropical.* *p. 1541*

compressa luschnathiana (Petropolis, Brazil); slender perennial herb to 1 m high with reedlike stalks topped by stiff, thick-leathery, narrow, light green leaves faintly marked with darker feathering; bracts ovate-acute. (2) *p. 1541*

glabra (Brazil); bushy plant with thin-leathery, oblique-ovate, almost rectangular leaves, shining yellowish-green with indistinct dark green veining, shining green beneath, on flattened petioles with long reddish sheaths. (2) *p. 1538*

humilis (Stromanthe) (Perú); perennial herb with rather leathery forest-green leaves, obliquely elongate-linear with short point, lightly quilted, reverse grayish green; throws up erect stalks bearing tufts of short-stalked narrow leaves. *p. 1541*

kummeriana (Brazil); clustering leafy bush becoming 75 cm high and sending out stolons; lanceolate leaves papery when young and dark green with attractive lateral bands of silver along the nerves, shimmering purple beneath; the silvery variegation disappearing with age. *p. 1538, 1540*

lubbersiana (Phrynium) (Brazil); spreading herb with forking stems, the oblique linear-oblong leaves are firm; green, variegated and mottled with yellow above, paler beneath. *Tropical.* *p. 1534, 1541*

oppenheimiana (Brazil); strong, compact, branching plant forming a dense, broad bush up to 2 m high, the narrow lanceolate leaves are leathery and firm, 30-50 cm long or more, dark green with lateral bands of silver, and wine-red beneath, attached at an angle to downy stalks. *p. 1534, 1536*

oppenheimiana 'Tricolor', "Never-never plant"; very colorful, tufted variety with narrow leaves, highly variegated white over green and silver gray, their wine-red underside in vivid contrast, and glowing through the surface. *Tropical.* *p. 1536, 1536A*

setosa (Brazil); slender plant with thin, narrow lanceolate leaves attached at an angle to reed-like, hairy stalks; blade almost all yellowish-silver with broad lateral bands on metallic green base; reverse purple. *Tropical.* *p. 1540*

CUCUMIS *Cucurbitaceae* **S2LBD**

anguria (So. U.S.: Florida and Texas), "West Indian gherkin" or "Gooseberry gourd"; cucumber-like vine with slender angled, rough stems and palmately lobed 10 cm leaves; yellow flowers; the females producing spiny ovoid, yellowish-green fruits 5-8 cm long, and which can be used for pickles. Interesting for the conservatory. *Subtropic.* *p. 931*

sativus (W. Trop. Asia), the "Cucumber"; rough-hairy annual trailing or tendril-climbing vine with herbaceous, lobed leaves; male and female yellow flowers 2-3 cm across; cylindric oblong edible fruit, smooth or prickly, green with pale marbling; used for salads and pickles. The pictured cultivar 'Patio Pik' (Geo. Ball, W. Chicago 1973) is adapted for growing on trellis in containers on the patio, for both ornamental and culinary purpose. *Tropical.* *p. 929*

sativus sikkimensis (Himalayas); long-running, prickly herbaceous vine with tendrils, and large 7-to 9-lobed leaves; the fruit cylindrical-club-shaped, and much cultivated in Asia; attractive also as an ornamental for its orange-brown fruit 30 cm long; sometimes grown under glass. *p. 929*

CUCURBITA *Cucurbitaceae* **S3LBM**

pepo (Trop. America), "Winter squash"; herbaceous annual with prickly vines and harsh, rugose lobed leaves; producing hard-shelled, so-called winter squash with woody rinds and firm, close-grained, fine-flavored flesh, and used for baking and pies. They come in various shapes, turban, warted and banana, as in the var. melopepo or the "Banana squash" shown on pg 929, with curved cylindric, pale yellow fruit 30-40 cm long, photographed in Vista, California. *Tropical.* *p. 929*

CULCASIA *Araceae* **S3LFM**

angolensis (W. Africa: Sierra Leone, Cameroun, Zaire, Angola); climbing aroid with vining stem forming aerial roots; long ovate, matte green leaves 25-35 cm long, 13-25 cm wide; small cupped spathe greenish white. *p. 213*

mannii (Aglaonema) (Cameroun: Mt. Victoria); tropical aroid with slowly growing stem 30-50 cm long, dense with thin-leathery, long-elliptic leaves dark green on surface, pale beneath, 20 cm or more long, and carried on stout petioles vaginate at base; spathe 5 cm long white inside, greenish outside. *p. 213*

panduriformis (Equatorial Africa: Cameroun, Gabon); tropical terrestrial aroid, newly found in habitat by J. Bogner, Munich Botanic Garden; slowly creeping with long oblanceolate thin-leathery green leaves 25 to 40 cm long, with prominently depressed ribs; the inflorescence forming pendant clusters of red berry-like fruit. *p. 213*

scandens (Trop. West Africa); climbing plant with thin stem forming numerous short aerial roots; the leathery green leaves broadly oblique elliptic 10-17 cm long and 5-8 cm wide; inflorescence singly or in pairs, with spathe 3 cm long. *p. 213*

CUNNINGHAMIA *Taxodiaceae (Coniferae)* **C2LBM**

lanceolata (China), "China fir", or "Mao Chia" in Taiwan; when visiting China I confused this handsome tree with Araucaria bidwillii which it closely resembles, but the glossy dark green needles are narrower, more close, and finely serrate. Picturesque evergreen 10 to 25 m high, with heavy trunk, stout whorled branches and drooping branchlets; interesting brown cones 3-4 cm across. *Warm Temperate to Subtropic.* *p. 838*

CUNONIA *Cunoniaceae* **C-I1LFD**

capensis (So. Africa), "African red alder"; small evergreen tree with pinnate, leathery glossy green leaves with toothed margins, on reddish petioles; dense feathery axillary racemes of white flowers; attractive cool house decorator. *Subtropic.* *p. 934*

CUPHEA *Lythraceae* **I2LBM**

hyssopifolia (Mexico, Guatemala), "False heather"; small woody shrub crowded with tiny linear, leathery leaves, the small flowers with green calyx and 6 purplish-rose petals. *p. 1522*

lanceolata (Mexico); ascending annual, 45 cm high, clammy and set with brown hairs, leaves lanceolate; flowers bluish in a spike-like raceme. *p. 1523*

micropetala (Mexico); much-branched shrub 30 cm high; leaves lanceolate, rigid and scurfy, to 12 cm long; tubular flowers with yellow and red calyx and small white petals, filaments red. *p. 1523*

platycentra (ignea) (Mexico), "Cigar flower"; low herbaceous plant with slender stems, lanceolate leaves and solitary axillary flowers having a slender, bright scarlet calyx 2½ cm long, with white mouth and dark ring at end, without petals. *Tropical.* *p. 1522*

x CUPRESSOCYPARIS *Cupressaceae (Coniferae)* **C2LBD**

'Leylandii' (Chamaecyparis nootkatensis x Cupressus macrocarpa); very ornamental with red stems, and striking green, flattened branchlets; cones 1.5-2 cm dia. *Warm temperate.* *p. 842*

CUPRESSUS *Cupressaceae (Coniferae)* **I-S2LBD-M**

arizonica (Arizona, Mexico), "Arizona cypress"; evergreen tree with small scale-like leaves glaucous bluish-green; good for dry-warm locations. *p. 839*

arizonica pyramidalis (glabra 'Pyramidalis'); the most pyramidal form of the species, handsomely compact and symmetrical, their scale-like needles having an intense silvery blue-glaucous color; drought resistant and tolerant to dry heat, a fairly good indoor container plant; as small plants in dishgardens. *p. 842, 843*

cashmeriana (Himalayas, Tibet), "Kashmir cypress"; considered the most beautiful and elegant of all cypresses, with graceful weeping branchlets of silvery gray green, from a pyramidal tree; not for cold climate. *p. 842,843*

lusitanica (Mexico, Guatemala); "Portuguese cypress" or "Mexican cypress"; evergreen tree to 30 m, with red-brown bark splitting in long strands; branches widely spreading, with branchlets more or less pendulous; small appressed, pointed needles glaucous green; cones 1 cm dia. and glaucous. *Subtropic.* *p. 842*

macrocarpa (California), "Monterey cypress"; beautiful evergreen tree to 20 m high, pyramidal when young and with bright green opposite, linear needles; spreading and picturesque in old age, and with leaves appressed and scale-like; the globular brown female cones 3 cm dia. *p. 839, 843*

sempervirens (So. Europe, W. Asia, No. India), "Mediterranean cypress"; the classic conical cypress of the Greek and Roman writers, with very short branches, usually, but not always forming a dense, narrow column slowly to 20 m or more high; the stout branchlets with scale-like leaves dark green with grayish cast in 4 ranks; small 3 cm woody cones. Esteemed for formal effect because of its stiff, picturesque outline. Suitable in containers for warm, sunny places; cool in winter. *Subtropic.* *p. 839, 842*

sempervirens var. pyramidalis (stricta) (Mediterranean Reg. to Black Sea coast), "Columnar Italian cypress"; the most pyramidal form of Italian cypress; photographed at Yalta in the Crimea, Russia; bearing brown cones 2-3 cm across; needles dark green to grayish, and while typical trees are very slender, to 20 m high, I observed others apparently of the same clone much broader; my guide told me in Turkey that the difference was in "male" and "female" trees. *p. 843*

CURCULIGO *Amaryllidaceae* ***S1LFW**

capitulata (recurvata) (Java), "Palm grass"; stemless plant with long, recurved, ribbed, palm-like leaves; small flowers near base. *p. 101, 129*

orchioides (East Indies); stemless perennial with tuberous rhizome, which can be eaten if candied; dense with narrow linear tapering, recurved, ribbed leaves; small yellow flowers with red overtones. *p. 130*

rhizophylla (Seychelles); interesting small tropical plant with tuberous rhizome, the somewhat fleshy lanceolate leaves lightly plaited; star-shaped, dark flower from the base; when the leaf tips touch the soil they will root and produce plantlets on leaf-ends. *p. 100*

CURCUMA *Zingiberaceae* **S3HWd**

aeruginosa (Thailand, Burma); tropical perennial with tuberous root, short leafy stem, and interesting inflorescence, appearing before the leaves, a spike to 20 cm long with fleshy shingled bracts red on upper half and greenish on lower, the nesting flowers yellow; sessile, lance-shaped leaves 50-90 cm long. *p. 2135*

inodora (India: Maharashtra); showy plant which I collected in rainforest east of Bombay, with large, fresh green, ribbed leaves, and erect cane-like inflorescence with cup-like green lower bracts tipped pink, topped by a tuft of colored floral bracts deep rose. *Tropical.* *p. 2137*

roscoeana (Burma), "Hidden lily"; robust, perennial herb with tuberous roots, sending up 6-8 long-stalked, lanceolate, ribbed, handsome leaves with dark green nerves; the inflorescence a splendid spike about 20 cm long, with cone-like, showy bracts gradually changing from green to vivid scarlet-orange; corolla yellow, with rich golden lip. *p. 2132, 2133, 2137*

CURTONUS *Iridaceae* **S3LFMd**

paniculatus (Antholyza) (Transvaal, Natal), known as "Pleated leaves" in South Africa; cormous plant with distinct and decorative foliage, arranged in flat tufts and grow stiffly to nearly 1 m, tapering toward both ends, 8 cm wide and deeply knife-pleated and a pleasant green; tubular flowers deep rusty or orange red on zigzag spikes; blooming in South Africa's autumn February-March, in the Northern hemisphere in August-September; dormant during winter. *p. 1324*

CUSSONIA *Araliaceae* **I-S2LFM**

holstii (E. Africa: Kenya), "Cabbage tree"; small shapely tree with slender stem and handsome leathery foliage deep glossy-green, stalked ovate leaflets with crenate margins, palmately compound and carried on long wiry petioles. *Tropical.* *p. 305*

paniculata (So. Africa), "Cabbage tree"; evergreen small tree forming rosette of heavy fleshy leaves palmately compound, the 7-12 grayish leaflets 15-30 cm long, having serrate and lobed margins, and covered with silvery bloom; on single trunk to 3 m high. *Subtropic.* *p. 306, 319*

spicata (Transvaal), "Spiked cabbage tree"; evergreen tree with handsome leathery leaves palmately compound of 5 to 9 leaflets, each 8 to 12 cm long; the smooth, grayish-green segments dentately cut or lobed again, and arranged in flat rosettes. *Subtropic.* *p. 305, 306, 317*

CYANASTRUM *Cyanastraceae* **S3LFM**

cordifolium (West Tropical Africa); tuberous-rooted perennial related to the lily family; glossy green, cordate-ovate leaves on fleshy petioles, the veins in curves depressed into the blade; the bracted blue flowers close to the base; for the warm greenhouse. *p. 934*

CYANOTIS *Commelinaceae* **I2LBD**

arachnoidea (So. India); rambling tropical herbaceous plant with succulent stems and leaves covered by fine white downy hairs; small clear blue flowers with blue-bearded filaments and orange-colored anthers. *p. 786*

kewensis (Malabar), "Teddy-bear plant"; succulent creeper with brown woolly stem and small fleshy triangular leaves, olive green wholly covered with woolly brown hair, underside violet; flowers violet blue. *p. 780*

nodiflora (So. Africa); fleshy plant 20 cm high, with spreading, slowly trailing branches, dense with long lanceolate, cobwebby or woolly leaves, later becoming smooth and glossy, ciliate at margins and stem-clasping at base; flowers of 3 blue equal purplish-blue petals; the fibrous roots terminating in tubercles. *p. 786*

somaliensis (Somalia), "Pussy ears"; succulent little creeper with linear, clasping, glossy green leaves covered with soft white hair; flowers purple and orange. *p. 780*

CYATHEA *Cyatheaceae (Filices)* **I-S2-3HFW**

arborea (mountains of Puerto Rico to Jamaica), "West Indian treefern"; slender treefern to 15 m high, with mostly bare brown trunk, the upper part covered with pale brown scales, and crowned by bipinnate, finely toothed, ample fronds soft-textured, fresh green, paler below, and without spines. Very graceful in appearance. *Humid-tropical.* *p. 1068, 1071*

cooperi: see Alsophila cooperi

dealbata (New Zealand, Lord Howe Is.), the "Ponga" or "Silver king fern"; noble tree-fern with trunk 3-10 m high, the upper part covered with leafbases, the lower with shining brown scales; apex with yellowish-brown hairs. Large tripinnate fronds spreading horizontally 2-4 m long, green or yellow-green above, powdery white below. *p. 1069*

dregei (So. Africa); robust treefern seen at Kirstenbosch, with blackish trunk and stiff erect, smooth green fronds on yellow axis, bipinnate into fine serrate leaflets. *Humid-subtropic.* *p. 1076*

medullaris (Sphaeropteris in Hortus 3) (New Zealand, S.E. Australia), the "Black tree-fern" or "Mamaku"; tallest of N.Z. tree ferns to 20 m or more, slender black trunk, at base covered with matted aerial roots, on top a great crown of spreading, curving, feathery fronds 2-6 m long, firm, tripinnate, deep green above, paler beneath; the apex and leaf bases clothed with black scales. *Humid-subtropic.* *p. 1069, 1070, 1076*

suprastrigosa (conspicua) (Hemitelia) (Costa Rica); a mountain treefern from 2000 to 2400 m altitude; slender erect trunk with aerial roots at base, the upper portion with lustrous bright brown scales; fronds rather small, the base of the stalk clothed with brown scales and small spines; the leathery fronds deeply tripinnatifid dull green above, paler below, the pinnae 50 cm long. *p. 1076*

CYBISTAX: see Tabebuia

CYCAS *Cycadaceae* ***I1LFD**

circinalis (India, Madagascar, New Guinea), "Fern palm"; palm-like tree with stout trunk to 3½ m or more high, topped by a graceful rosette of stiff-glossy leaves pinnately divided, the leaflets flat on edges; male and female inflorescence on separate plants. I have seen colonies of this species in the Bulolo highlands in New Guinea, at 1,200 m in tall Kunai grass. *Tropical.* *p. 935, 936*

media (No. Australia, Queensland), "Australian nut palm"; slender trunk to 6 m high, reported to be one of the tallest of the cycads; topped by a handsome crown of fronds, 1 m or more long, shorter than circinalis, with numerous flat leaflets, narrowed to a spiny tip; the scales of male cones tapering into long spines. *Tropical.* *p. 935, 936, 941*

neo-caledonica (New Caledonia), "Bread palm"; graceful large cycas with the trunk 18 cm thick, the arching fronds 2 m long, the narrow, closely set leaflets shining green. *Tropical.* *p. 937*

revoluta (So. Japan to Java), "Sago palm"; dioecious palm-like tree slowly forming hulking trunk to 3 m or more high, usually solitary but sometimes branched, topped by a terminal crown of stiff, deep glossy green, feathery pinnate fronds 1 to 2 m long; the leathery leaflets are spine-tipped and rolled down at margins: the petal-less flowers are in terminal clusters of brown-woolly carpels, in female trees containing the orange fruit, covering nut-like poisonous seeds. *Subtropic.* *p. 936, 942, 943, 944*

revoluta 'Mako', a very dwarf form of the "Sago palm", with contorted trunk, and dark green, rigid pinnate leaves only about 40 to 50 cm long, and recurving; ideal as a durable and frugal container plant on the patio; photographed in Honolulu, Hawaii. *p. 943*

CYCLAMEN *Primulaceae* **C3HFM**

neapolitanum (hederifolium) (So. Europe, France to Greece), "Baby cyclamen"; lovely little plant with black, flattened tuber, green, angled leaves lightly marked, and tiny, sweet-scented flowers appearing mostly before the foliage, rosy-lavender with deep carmine blotch at eared base, the stalks coiling when with seed pod. (2) *p. 1964*

neapolitanum album; charming miniature, with flattened tuber forming roots only on the upper side; color form with pure white flowers, the recurved petals 20 to 28 mm long, blooming before the foliage appears. *p. 1963*

persicum (indicum) (Greece and Mediterranean islands to Syria); charming low, fleshy herb with large, hard tuberous roots; heart-shaped basal leaves in a rosette, prettily patterned with silver; and long-stalked solitary, 4 cm nodding, fragrant flowers; with purplish-rose flaring corolla lobes elegantly reflexed. *Humid- subtropic.* *p. 1963*

persicum 'Aalsmeer double'; a very special Dutch strain with large fleshy leaves, and heavy salmon-pink flowers very double, with up to 38 petals. *p. 1965*

persicum 'Bonfire', florists' "Alpine violet"; elegant clone, of compact habit and somwhat slower, but sturdy growth, the noble flowers borne well above the foliage, in brilliant salmon-scarlet, the petals stand erect except for one, being pendant, and 5-6 cm long. *Subtropic.* *p. 1964*

persicum 'Candlestick'; interesting form, flowers with spreading petals blush pink more or less striped and banded with rosy-red. *p. 1964*

persicum 'Double Zehlendorf'; large double flowers with several rows of petals vivid salmon red; leaves handsomely patterned with silver. *p. 1963*

persicum 'Fimbriatum'; a cultivated form with richly patterned leaves, and large flowers with spreading petals fringed at margins, soft pink with carmine-red eye. *Subtropic.* *p. 1963*

persicum 'Pearl of Zehlendorf'; the favorite color form, with elegant flowers vivid salmon-red, deeper toward eye, shading to lighter salmon at margins, free-blooming. *Subtropic.* *p. 1963, 1964*

persicum 'Rococo'; curious fleshy flowers rather flat and wheel-round with margins beautifully frilled, usually light salmon pink with darker eye; not free-blooming. *Subtropic.* *p. 1964, 1965*

persicum 'Rose of Marienthal'; popular old variety with flowers soft rose with deep carmine-red eye. *p. 1964*

persicum 'Swiss dwarf'; diminutive cultivar of persicum, with attractive foliage marked silver; flowers on slender stems with petals 3 cm long; developed in Switzerland for lilliputian effect as house plant. *p. 1963*

persicum 'Vogt's Double'; beautiful, double-flowering, American strain developed since 1920, with heavy blooms with numerous petals, in shades of salmon-pink. *Subtropic.* *p. 1964*

CYCLANTHERA *Cucurbitaceae* **S3LBM**

explodens (Colombia), "Exploding cucumber"; herbaceous tropical tendril-climbing vine to 3 m, with triangular lobed or angled leaves 5-8 cm long; small yellowish flowers; and curved helmet-shaped 3 cm fruit with stout spines on one side, bursting suddenly and forcibly to discharge seed when ripe. *p. 929*

pedata (Mexico), "Climbing cucumber"; smooth herbaceous vine with forked tendrils, climbing to 6 m and grown as an annual; palmately deeply cut leaves, the segments toothed; small greenish-white, inconspicuous flowers, the male and female separate but on the same plant; oblong conical fruit 5 cm long, the yellowish-glaucous husk covered with soft, scattering prickles. *p. 929*

CYCLANTHUS *Cyclanthaceae* **S3LFW**

bipartitus (Guayana), "Splitleaf cyclanthus"; stemless, palm-like plant with a cluster of milky-juiced, large leathery, quilted leaves forked at top; scented flowers. *p. 945*

CYCLOPHORUS *Polypodiaceae (Filices)* **I3LFM**

heteractus (No. India); low creeping fern with woody rhizome, forming a succession of stalked lanceolate fronds 20-30 cm high, the blade glossy green and leathery, with pale midrib, and quilted or puckered blade. *p. 1093*

CYCLOPHORUS: see also Pyrrosia

CYCLOPOGON *Orchidaceae* **S3HNM**

variegatum (Brazil), "Jewel orchid"; terrestrial with fleshy roots; very ornamental small ovate leaves marbled with pink; inflorescence an upright spike with pinkish bracts and small pale green flowers. (S) *p. 1663*

CYCNOCHES *Orchidaceae* **S3OFM**

aureum (Costa Rica, Panama), the "Golden swan orchid"; probably a variety of egertonianum; very attractive epiphyte with thick pseudobulbs and broad plaited leaves, and male and female flowers; the large ones with short thick column are the females, green with a white lip; male flowers in a long pendant raceme, looking like yellow birds with their recurved, greenish-yellow segments tinted brown, and prominent curved column, the lip is white with green markings in the center (Sept.-Oct.). (S) *p. 1679*

chlorochilum (C. America, Colombia, Venezuela); epiphyte with tall pseudobulbs and plaited leaves, and clusters of large waxy flowers greenish yellow, lip creamy-white with a blotch of black-green at base. (Oct.-April). *Humid-tropical.* *p. 1696*

egertonianum (Mexico, Guatemala); epiphyte with long, leafy pseudobulbs, and greenish flowers suffused with purple; male flowers in long pendulous racemes, the lip with purple fringe-like filaments; female flowers yellowish-green with creamy lip; summer. (S) *p. 1696*

loddigesii (Surinam), "Swan orchid"; curious epiphyte with pendant raceme of brownish green flowers suffused and marked with purplish brown and rosy lip, bearing some resemblance to the expanded wings of a swan. (summer). (S) *p. 1696*

pentadactylum (Brazil); curious species with spindle-shaped leafy pseudobulbs and plaited leaves; large flowers yellowish-green, banded transversely with brown, the lip whitish spotted red, and is divided into five parts like a hand; summer. *Humid-tropical.* *p. 1696*

ventricosum (Guatemala), "Swan orchid"; striking epiphyte; stout pseudobulb with arching raceme of sweet-scented, waxy flowers greenish-yellow, a white lip, and an arched slender column resembling a swan's neck. (July-Nov.). *Humid-tropical.* *p. 1664A, 1696*

CYDONIA *Rosaceae* **I2LBD**

oblonga (No. Iran, E. Turkey), "Fruiting quince"; sparry, thornless tree to 6 m high, deciduous in colder regions; with attractive ovate 5-10 cm leaves, dark green above and whitish tomentose beneath; yellow in autumn; 5 cm, white to pink flowers at young branch tips; the fruit apple-like, greenish-yellow, somewhat wrinkled, and covered with light brown felt, 6 cm or more dia. and showing a woody calyx. The large, fragrant fruits are inedible when raw, being quite acid and harshly astringent when uncooked, but used for making jams and jellies. For flowering quince, see Chaenomeles. *Subtropic.* *p. 1997, 2001*

CYDONIA: see also Chaenomeles

CYLINDROPHYLLUM *Aizoaceae* **S3LBD**

tugwelliae (Cape Prov.); low branching succulent forming dense mats, with cylindrical thick glaucous leaves, two per shoot, tapering at end, 8 cm long; solitary flesh-color flower 5 cm across. *p. 74*

CYLINDROPUNTIA *Cactaceae* **S3LBD**

pallida (Mexico: Hidalgo); a cylindropuntia with cylindric stems freely branching, to 1 m high; stems 5 cm thick and tubercled; old areoles very spiny 3-4 cm long with white, papery sheaths; flowers pale rose with 15 mm petals. *p. 634*

CYMBALARIA *Scrophulariaceae* **C2LFM**

muralis (Linaria cymbalaria) (Germany, France, Switzerland), "Kenilworth ivy"; creeping, perennial, herbaceous ground cover naturalized in Ontario to Pennsylvania, an old-fashioned basket-plant, with thread-like stems rooting at the nodes, small kidney-shaped, fresh-green, waxy leaves irregularly lobed, purplish beneath; tiny lilac-blue flowers with yellow throat, like miniature snapdragons. *p. 2053*

CYMBIDIELLA *Orchidaceae* **S3OFM**

humblotii (Madagascar); remarkable cymbidium-like species, with cylindric pseudobulbs and numerous narrow, strap-shaped leaves arranged fan-like; erect inflorescence to 80 cm tall, with cluster of long-lasting waxy, 8 cm flowers yellow-green, petals and lip bordered with black (winter). *Tropical.* *p. 1695*

rhodochila (Madagascar); epiphyte often classified as Cymbidium; almost always growing together with Platycerium; the folded leaves grow from the axils of the older ones creating a braided effect; floral stalks from base of pseudobulbs, to 1 m high, bearing 20 or more yellowish green flowers, with brownish spots on petals, and crimson lip with yellow stripe (autumn). *Tropical.* *p. 1695*

CYMBIDIUM *Orchidaceae* **C-I2HFM**

x alexanderi (eburneo-lowianum x insigne); well known commercial white with pink hybrid of robust habit; terrestrial with bold, arching raceme of waxy, long-lasting flowers flushed pink, with a purple horseshoe on the lip; the form alba has pure white flowers. *Subtropic.* *p. 1698*

aloifolium (Himalayas, Burma); a small-flowered epiphyte which I have seen growing in the forking branches of hardwood trees at 2400 m in the Sikkim Himalayas; clustering plant with leathery, linear obtuse leaves nearly without pseudobulb, the flowering racemes becoming pendant, linear sepals and petals yellow with purple center stripe, lip brownish-red with yellow center, (May-Aug.). The plant pictured on page 1698 may be C. simulans. *p. 1698*

'Bo-Peep' (purpureum x pumilum) (Stewart 1955); miniature of compact habit; buff-yellow flowers shaded purplish brown along center of each petal, lip white marked crimson. *p. 1697*

'Brentwood' (Midas x Irina); a robust exhibition plant with arching racemes of 10 cm flowers having sepals and petals a bright luminous green, the lip edged in brick red; March. *p. 1700*

canaliculatum (Queensland); distinctive small terrestrial almost pseudobulbless with rigid, gray keeled leaves to 30 cm long, and stiff, arching raceme with numerous small waxy flowers intensely dark maroon-brown, almost black, edged lemon-yellow; lip pink and green spotted crimson. (April-May). *Tropical.* *p. 1698*

'Candeur' var. Dos Pueblos (brugense x Emu); a striking, very productive diploid clone with large 12 cm flowers of excellent commercial value, pure white with handsome deep red markings on the lip, and of extreme substance, in big, cascading racemes. (C) *p. 1699*

'Doris' (insigne x tracyanum); well-known commercial primary hybrid 1912, with large, fleshy, long-lasting flowers; light yellow sepals, petals closely veined with red, the lip spotted with red-brown on front lobe and veined in same color on side lobes. *Subtropic.* *p. 1664A, 1700*

eburneum (No. India, Burma); handsome terrestrial from the Himalayas and the Khasia Hills at 1,500-1,800 m, of compact habit forming tufts of 2-ranked linear foliage, and short racemes of 1-3 large waxy, fragrant flowers 10-12 cm across, blush-white, the lip yellow inside and with hairy keels (March-June). *Subtropic.* *p. 1700*

ensifolium (Japan, China); species without pseudobulbs; nerved linear leaves 1 cm wide, grass-like in tufts, to 30 cm long; inflorescence erect to 30 cm high, with firm, waxy, fragrant flowers 5 cm across, greenish-yellow sepals and petals with reddish-brown lines; lip dotted; long lasting (summer). *p. 1697*

ensifolium estriatum (Assam); erect raceme with firm flowers very fragrant, the sepals green, and whitish petals, without the prominent brown lines in the species from China (spring). *p. 1697*

erythrostylum (Vietnam); very attractive species with several-leaved 3 cm pseudobulbs; leaves to 40 cm long; arching inflorescence with white flowers having sepals 5 cm long; lip yellowish, lined with red-purple (November). *p. 1697*

'Flirtation' (pumilum x 'Zebra'); attractive, variable semi-miniature recently developed, ideal as a shapely, compact flowering pot plant, blooming successively twice a year, usually Nov. through April; arching racemes with flowers spreading 5 cm, pale pink to greenish ivory, shaded to coppery purple and striped orchid, lip white in throat spotted and blotched maroon. *Subtropic.* *p. 1698, 1699*

'Gyokuchin Unge-Kwannon' (China); miniature terrestrial, with narrow lanceolate leaves, and flowers with sepals and petals yellowish green, tubular yellow lip. *p. 1697*

insigne (Vietnam); beautiful terrestrial with globose pseudobulbs sheathed by narrow strap-shaped, glaucous green leaves to 1 m long; strong erect 1 m raceme of numerous fleshy 8 cm flowers, sepals and petals pale rose, lip white flushed and dotted with crimson and two thick yellow lines. (Feb.-March) (C) *p. 1698*

lancifolium (Himalayas at 2000 m; India to Japan, south to Malaysia); charming, terrestrial forest dweller of low habit; spindle-shaped pseudobulbs clothed with 3 to 5 ribbed thin-leathery leaves 20 cm long; stiff-erect stalks bearing inflorescence 30 cm high of scattered, fragrant and long-lasting flowers 4 to 5 cm across, greenish-cream with purple spots, the lip white boldly marked with maroon, blooming in spring and early summer. *Subtropic.* *p. 1697*

'Madonna' (alexanderi 'Westonbirt' x Mem. P.W. Janssen); magnificent robust plant of splendid habit, with stiff erect spikes carrying numerous large 10 cm open flowers, glistening white with unique green overcast, the blush pink lip spotted bright maroon-purple along margin; free-blooming in Feb.-March every year. *Subtropic.* *p. 1699*

mastersii (Cyperorchis) (Assam); handsome species with tufted, recurving linear leaves to 80 cm long, the flowers on erect raceme ivory-white, the 3-lobed lip white with rose-purple spots and orange in center; almond-scented; winter. (C) *p. 1701*

'Moira' (pauwelsii x tracyanum); popular hybrid, a good grower and free-flowering, typical of the greenish flowering kinds; terrestrial with heavy, gracefully arching spike of greenish-yellow waxy, well-shaped flowers with buff stripes, lip yellow, spotted red. (Jan.-Feb.) (C) *p. 1698*

'Nikki' (Erica Sander x Radak); vigorous hybrid very productive with 12 cm flowers white tinted slightly blush-pink, the lip marked with deep red. *p. 1700*

'Peter Pan' (ensifolium x Miretta 'Dos Pueblos'); one of the newer semi-miniatures of low habit, very floriferous with short racemes of comparatively large fleshy, durable flowers 5-6 cm across, and of a pleasing shade of green to yellow-green, the lip spotted with carmine or brownish-red. (C) *p. 1699*

'Pixie' (Ceres x Landrail) (1955); large-flowered seedling with petals and sepals buff greenish-yellow lined with purplish brown, the lip cream-white with attractively contrasting band of bold crimson along pointed lip, lemon in throat. *Subtropic.* *p. 1700*

'Priscilla' (insigne x 'Yellow Hammer'); good standard bronze type with large, durable flowers coppery yellow, the lip yellow, heavily marked with crimson inside margin. *Subtropic.* *p. 1698*

pumilum albo-marginatum (Taiwan, So. China); small terrestrial with strap-like leaves to 30 cm long, and edged in white, the small 3 cm flowers in a dense raceme, sepals and petals light reddish-brown, the lip white with red spots. (Feb.-May). (C-I) *p. 1701*

pumilum 'Shuo-Lan' (Taiwan); miniature epiphyte with narrow, grass-like but leathery leaves, and raceme of flowers with 3 linear brown-green sepals and short petals, the small lip yellow marked with red. (I) *p. 1701*

tigrinum (Burma, Vietnam); pretty little rock-dweller with ovate pseudobulbs, leaves to 15 cm long; 5 cm flowers in racemes with sepals and petals olive-green, lip 3-lobed, side lobes yellow marked with red, midlobe white, spotted red; summer. (C) *p. 1701*

virescens (Japan); miniature terrestrial, esteemed and cultivated in Japan in hundreds of named varieties varying in color of flowers and striping of leaves; clustering plant with narrow leaves and small solitary, fragrant, but not conspicuous flowers, sepals and petals green marked with red, lip white dotted red. (March). (C) *p. 1701*

virescens angustifolium (Japan); tufted, grass-like plant with linear leaves to 25 cm long; stalked flowers 5 cm dia., vivid green with faint purple stripes, two petals join over lip to form a hood, lip curved under, creamy-white with yellow throat and purple markings; winter. *p. 1701*

virescens var. 'Teikwan'; dwarf, bushy terrestrial with glossy dark leaves beautifully margined white; flower sepals and petals green with contrasting white edges, the lip white with dots of red; grown in Japan principally for their leaves as "all flowers are temporal while the leaves are permanent". (C) *p. 1701*

'Virginia Knight' (eburneo-lowianum 'Concolor' x Rosanna 'Pinkie'); vigorous productive Dos Pueblos hybrid with flowers spreading over 12 cm, white with slight blush tint, yellow area in throat. *p. 1700*

CYNANCHUM *Asclepiadaceae* **S3LFM**

macrolobum (S. W. Madagascar); succulent climbing shrub with fleshy branches to 40 cm tall and 6 mm thick, partly leafless or with small deciduous leaves, and with whitish waxy coating; flowers brownish. *p. 357*

CYNARA *Compositae* **I2LBD**

scolymus (So. Mediterranean Reg., Canary Islands), the "Artichoke" or "Globe artichoke"; robust ferny-looking perennial of irregular, fountain-like form, to 1 m or more high; silvery green leaves deeply dissected and somewhat spiny, white cottony beneath; heads with purple disk flowers resembling a thistle, 15 cm across with a nest of fleshy scales beneath. The fleshy buds are cut before they open, and are edible when cooked. Flowers may be cut for fresh or dried arrangements. *Subtropic.* *p. 827*

CYNORCHIS *Orchidaceae* **S3OFW**

angustipetala (Madagascar); leafy plant partially deciduous; arching inflorescence of small whitish flowers with flaring greenish sepals, large divided lip lavender pink marked purple near base. *p. 1693*

uncinata (Madagascar); terrestrial with fleshy roots and broad pendant, solitary leaf; the inflorescence in terminal raceme of rosy lavender flowers each 3 cm across, a white spot on lip. *p. 1693*

CYPELLA *Iridaceae* **C-I2LBDd**

herbertii (Brazil, Uruguay, Argentina); bulbous plant about 30 cm high, with linear, plaited basal as well as stem-leaves; few flowers iris-like with spreading perianth segments, yellow varying to deep chrome, with spurs in center barred deep yellow; late summer. *Subtropic.* *p. 1338*

CYPEROCYMBIDIUM *Orchidaceae* **I3OFM**

x gammieanum (Sikkim) (C. longifolium x Cyperorchis elegans); bigeneric natural hybrid, epiphytic in cool altitudes of the Himalaya; in appearance like cymbidium aloifolium with strap-shaped leaves to 90 cm long; basal inflorescence with bell shaped, nodding flowers 4 cm long, pale yellow flushed with brown and with brown lines. *p. 1697*

CYPERUS *Cyperaceae* ***I1LFW**

alternifolius (Madagascar), "Umbrella plant"; clustering perennial bogplant with ribbed stalks to 1 m high, bearing a crown of bright-green, grass-like leaves around a head of small green flowers. I have seen this also along the Athi River in Kenya. *Tropical.* *p. 946*

alternifolius 'Gracilis' (Australia), "Dwarf umbrella plant"; dwarf form in all parts smaller, only 45 cm high, with wiry slender stems and narrower leaves. *p. 946*

alternifolius 'Variegatus', "Variegated umbrella plant"; a fugitive variety with stems and leaves striped and banded lengthwise with creamy-white contrasting with shiny green. *Tropical.* *p. 946*

brevifolius (Kyllinga) (S.E. United States and tropics elsewhere); densely bushy small perennial herb with grass-like leaves succulent green, and freely branching from the base, the thin reed-like triangular stalks are topped by a white, cotton-like flower head, subtended by only three folded leaves. *p. 946*

diffusus (laxus) (Mauritius), "Broadleaf umbrella plant"; compact bushy plant sending out runners with suckers which are used for propagation; sturdy, 3-angled stalks with a crown of broad, matte green, rather rough leaves and long, pale brown spikelets. *Tropical.* *p. 947*

diffusus 'Variegatus', "Striped umbrella palm"; compact-growing variety having its broad green leaflets striped and banded pale yellow or cream. *Tropical.* *p. 947*

elegans (Trop. Africa); according to Bailey, this is a more rigid plant with narrower leaves than diffusus. *p. 946*

haspan viviparus (Africa to Surinam); small tufted plant with slender 3-angled stalks and small crowns of ray-like leaves and reddish spikelets. Correct name may be C. prolifer. *p. 947*

papyrus (Egypt), "Egyptian paper plant"; a stately plant for pools, with stout dark green stalks to 2 m high, topped by brush-like umbel of drooping, threadlike leaves. Along the shores of Lake Victoria in Africa I have seen them 5 m tall. Used in Egypt for making "papyrus" since 2750 B.C. *p. 947*

strigosus (Québec to Dakota, Pacific Coast, Florida and Texas); tufted hardy perennial with stout 3-angled stems 30-90 cm high on bulbous base, rough linear leaves, and greenish to straw-colored cylindrical inflorescence of bulbous spikelets. *p. 947*

CYPHOMANDRA *Solanaceae* **I-S3LFD**

betacea (So. Brazil), the "Tree-tomato" or "Tamarillo"; tree-like shrub somewhat woody, to 3 m, with heartshaped ovate 30 cm soft-hairy, fleshy leaves, and fragrant 1 cm flowers in pendulous raceme, the 5-lobed corolla greenish pink with a dark stripe on back of each segment; the egg-shaped, edible, reddish 8 cm fruit resembling a tomato in looks and flavor, but is much sweeter. *Subtropic.* *p. 2075, 2078*

CYPRIPEDIUM *Orchidaceae* **C2HFMhd**

acaule (Newfoundland to N. Carolina), "Pink ladyslipper"; terrestrial of the temperate zone, with two light green plaited leaves and large solitary flowers with hairy sepals and petals greenish-brown, the divided, pouch-like lip rose veined with crimson. (May-June). *Temperate.* *p. 1703*

arietinum (Québec to Mass., Ontario, New York to Minnesota); small hardy terrestrial to 15-30 cm and solitary flower resembling a ram's head, with greenish-brown dorsal and petals, conical pouch white veined with crimson (May-June). (C) *p. 1703*

calceolus (Europe, No. Asia), the "Yellow lady-slipper" of Eurasia; hardy terrestrial with short rhizome and stems to 60 cm, with plicate (folded) leaves; at the apex usually 1-3 showy flowers with narrow petals green and marked purple, the yellow lip shaped like a large pouch. *p. 1704*

calceolus pubescens (No. America), "Yellow ladyslipper"; terrestrial orchid with leafy stem bearing 1-2 flowers, the broad leaves soft-hairy, sepals and petals purplish-brown to green, petals more or less twisted, the rounded pouch yellow veined with red. (April bl. in south, Aug. in north). *Temperate.* *p. 1703*

japonicum (Japan, China); stalks with large fan-shaped, ribbed twin leaves to 15 cm long, with veins radiating to margins; solitary 6 cm flowers, sepals greenish spotted red, petals whitish, lip white stained with crimson; summer. (C) *p. 1703*

macranthum (Tibet, Siberia); stems 3-4-leaved, foliage elliptic, bright green, and attractive, solitary flowers, the large dorsal and narrow petals purple with darker netting, the inflated lip rose-pink; May-June. (C) *p.1703*

montanum (California to Washington); the "Mountain-lady-slipper"; handsome pubescent, hardy terrestrial growing in clumps 30-60 cm high, with broad plaited leaves along the stems, topped by 1-3 flowers to 10 cm across, the wavy-twisted petals reddish-brown, pouch white veined with purple (May-July). (C) *p. 1703*

reginae (Canada to Missouri), "Showy ladyslipper"; beautiful terrestrial to 75 cm tall,densely hairy, stems leafy, bearing 1-2 flowers, the ovate sepals and petals white, or flushed rose, the round pouch white or pink striped with rose. (June-Aug.) (C) *p. 1703, 1704*

CYPRIPEDIUM: see also Paphiopedilum

CYRILLA *Cyrillaceae* **I2LBM**

racemiflora (Virginia to Texas, West Indies, Mexico, E. South America), "Leatherwood" or "Titi"; handsome smooth shrub 1 m or more high, in warm climate occasionally as tree to 10 m tall, with red bark, oblanceolate leathery, glossy green leaves 4 to 12 cm long, deciduous in eastern No. America, turning orange and scarlet in autumn; evergreen in West Indies; it bears graceful, slender racemes of small white flowers in late summer, and loved by bees. *Warm-temperate to Tropical.* *p. 934*

CYRTANDRA *Gesneriaceae* **S3HFM**

schraderi ('Oomsis') (Papua); clamberer with semi-woody stems and long thin-leathery 15 cm ovate to oblanceolate leaves; axillary tubular-inflated flowers salmon-red tipped yellow. *p. 1234*

CYRTANTHUS *Amaryllidaceae* **I2LBMd**

herrei (So. Africa), a "Fire lily"; attractive bulbous plant with fleshy, vivid green, strap-shaped leaves; the swollen floral stalk with dense clusters of pendant tubular red flowers. *Subtropic.* *p. 111*

mackenii (Natal), "Ifafa lily"; bulbous herb with linear leaves 30 cm long, and umbels on 30 cm stalks with pure white fragrant flowers having a 5 cm long curved tube and 6 spreading lobes. *Subtropic.* *p. 112*

obliquus (Cape Prov., Natal), "Sore-eye flower"; evergreen bulbous plant with 4-12 leaves in two ranks, to 30 cm long, stalk with umbel of nodding trumpet flowers 8 cm long, yellow at base, flushed orange-red, tipped with bright green. *p. 112*

obrienii (So. Africa: Natal), "Red Ifafa lily" or "Fire-lily"; charming bulbous plant with narrow glossy green leaves 1 cm across, and to 30 cm long, appearing while plants are in bloom; umbels of flowers with curved tubes 5 cm long, bright scarlet; some variations also with pale or ivory flowers; spring-blooming. *p. 122*

ochroleucus (lutescens) (So. Africa); bulbous plant with arching, linear leaves; erect, pale-yellow, tubular flowers in umbels. *p. 112*

CYRTOMIUM *Polypodiaceae (Filices)* ***I1LNM**

caryotideum (Japan); possibly a variety of falcatum; pinnate fronds of drooping habit, fresh green not dark green, the numerous leaflets lobed at base, the margins toothed; arranged in thick, fleshy crown. *p. 1101*

falcatum (Japan, China, India, Celebes, Hawaii) the "Holly-fern"; with handsome pinnate fronds on brown scaly stalks, the leathery, shining dark green leaflets are ovate, slender pointed and very durable under adverse conditions. *Subtropic.* *p. 1101*

falcatum 'Rochefordianum', "Holly fern"; the variety mostly grown in greenhouses at present, its habit is more robust, the fronds broader and fuller, and the large leathery, glossy leaves are serrate and wavy at the margins. *p. 1101, 1103*

falcatum 'Rochefordianum compactum'; a horticultural form of dwarf, compact habit, and with shorter fronds, the leathery, lustrous deep green leaves of exceptional keeping quality and an ideal, tough fern as a pot plant. *p. 1104*

CYRTOPODIUM *Orchidaceae* **I2HFM**

andersonii (Brazil, W. Indies); bold terrestrial and on rocks, with long pseudobulbs and tall 1 m branching spikes of yellow flowers tinged with green, and rich yellow lip. (spring bl. but saw it in bloom near Rio, in September.) *Tropical.* *p. 1716*

punctatum (Florida, W. Indies to Brazil), "Cigar flower"; "Beeswarm", or "Cowhorn orchid"; noble 1 m terrestrial more floriferous than andersonii with branched racemes dense with flowers, greenish yellow, the basal halves thickly spotted with red-brown. (Feb.-May). (I) *p. 1695, 1716*

CYRTOPOGON: see Spiranthes (Cyclopogon)

CYRTORCHIS *Orchidaceae* **I3OFM**

arcuata (South Africa); handsome epiphyte with robust stem, thick-eathery leaves notched at apex, to 15 cm long; waxy, very fragrant flowers 4 cm across, pure white (spring-summer). *p. 1694*

arcuata variabilis (Kenya); vandaceous epiphyte with elongate leafy stems, blades in ranks, leathery, linear; fleshy flowers in axillary raceme, waxy, cream-white with linear petals and long greenish horn; spring. (I) *p. 1692*

hamata (West Africa); handsome epiphyte related to Angraecum; robust stems with leathery leaves notched at apex; pure white and fragrant flowers 8 cm across, with long green tail (winter). *p. 1691*

monteirae (Nigeria to Angola); curious epiphyte with arching stems to 60 cm tall, forming aerial roots and bearing obovate, leathery leaves with wavy margins; pendant inflorescence radiating from stem carrying small 4 cm fragrant, waxy brownish white flowers, with a long spur yellow at tip (spring). *p. 1694*

CYRTOSPERMA *Araceae* **S3HFM**

johnstonii (Alocasia) (Solomon Isl.); firm, sagittate leaves with long, widely spread basal lobes fresh green with crimson veins; spiny stem with dark purple zebra bands. *Tropical.* *p. 156, 181, 208*

lasioides (Trop. Asia); tropical rhizomatous herb with hastate leaves on spiny stems; the inflorescence with recurving, broad spathe and cylindric spadix densely covered with hermaphrodite, perfect flowers (stigma and anthers in same flower). *p. 209*

macrotum (Karkor Is., N.W. New Guinea coast); interesting aroid with flaring hastate, glossy green variable leaves on spiny, blackish, beige-marbled, wiry stalks, and spathe 38 cm long, purplish-brown striped green, enveloping the short green spadix, bearing perfect flowers with single ovule. *p. 183*

senegalense (Trop. West Africa); from swampy forest areas, tall rhizomatous plant with leaf-stalks to 2 m long, covered with small spines; green leaves oblong arrow-shaped 30-60 cm long; the spathe greenish-yellow outside, purplish-red inside and striped with yellow, 20-50 cm long at apex with a long slender, twisted point. *Humid-tropical.* *p. 209*

CYRTOSTACHYS *Palmae* **S3LFM**

lakka (Malaya, Borneo, Pacific Islands), "Sealing wax palm", known as "Maharaja palm" in the Philippines; beautiful feather palm, clustering with slender, glossy green trunks to 5 m high and 8 cm thick; very handsome with their 60 cm long scarlet red leaf bases sheathing the base of the crown of fronds; the leaves pinnate on scarlet petioles, the numerous leaflets dark green above, glaucous beneath; small 1 cm black fruit from red stalk. *Tropical.* *p. 1867*

renda (Sumatra), "Tall sealing wax palm"; clustering feather palm with slender trunks to 10 m high; pinnate fronds; linear leaflets gray beneath, the leaf bases and petioles a showy red. *Tropical.* *p. 1868*

CYTISUS *Leguminosae* **C2LBD**

battandierii (Algiers), deciduous, vigorous, silvery shrub, to 5 m high, with drooping branches; leaves large, 3-foliolate, leaflets soft, silvery-pubescent especially beneath, 5-9 cm long; flowers in cylindrical racemes, 8-12 cm long, bright yellow and fragrant. *p. 1379*

canariensis (Canary Isl.), "Florists' genista"; much branched shrub to 2 m, but trained into formal globes by shearing, and forced for spring blooming; trifoliate with small obovate silky leaflets and showy racemes of bright yellow, fragrant flowers. *p. 1374*

maderensis (Madeira); evergreen, half-hardy tree to 6 m high with stiff branches and silvery-pubescent young shoots; leaves trifoliate, leaflets oblong, silky-pubescent, to 1 cm long; fragrant, bright yellow flowers. *p. 1379*

x racemosus (canariensis x maderensis magnifoliosus), "Florists' genista"; a hybrid favored over canariensis because of its smaller, darker green leaflets, and shorter, more numerous racemes with flowers deep yellow, set closely on terminal racemes; longer-lasting blooms than canariensis. *Subtropic.* *p. 1374*

scoparius (W. Europe), "Scotch broom"; deciduous shrub to 2½ m high, with pubescent young shoots, small leaflets to 1 cm long; flowers axillary with bright, shining yellow corolla; May-June blooming; hardy in New York. *p. 1374*

DABOECIA *Ericaceae* **C2HBD**

cantabrica praegerae (Ireland: Connemara), a deep-rose flowered low growing form of the "Irish-heath"; evergreen heathlike little shrub with tiny dark green, shiny leaves, white-felty beneath; flowers with inflated corolla 1 cm long, in terminal racemes; summer. *p. 959*

DACRYDIUM *Podocarpaceae (Coniferae)* **C2LBD**

cupressinum (New Zealand), known as "Rimu" by the Maori, or "Red pine"; tall forest tree to 30 m, with cypress-like branchlets and overlapping scale-like leaves when mature; very interesting while juvenile when the branchlets are like Lycopodium and pendulous, the needles soft and awl-shaped. *Subtropic.* *p. 840, 849*

DACTYLOPSIS *Aizoaceae* **S3LBD**

digitata (Cape Prov.); extremely succulent plant forming stemless dense mats; cylindrical, blunt leaves 8-12 cm long, 2-3 cm thick, soft and gray; solitary white flowers; in habitat growing on the edge of salt pans; Jacobsen recommends the addition of salt to potting soil. *p. 59*

DAEDALACANTHUS: see Chamaeranthemum

DAEMONOROPS *Palmae* **S3LFM**

didymophyllus (Malaya, Sumatra); a climbing rattan palm with pinnate leaves to 5 m long, having about 30 pinnae arranged mostly in pairs, and terminating in a prickly tendril, nodding inflorescence, tiny broad ovoid fruit. *p. 1868*

hystrix (Malaya); climbing rattan-palm with pinnate fronds to 1½ m long, set with about 100 equidistant leaflets; leaf-sheaths inflated and prickly at mouth; inflorescence erect, small ovoid elliptic fruit. *p. 1868*

kunstleri (Malaya: Perak); upward-growing palm with stems to 1 m or more high; leaf-sheaths bear ascending spines near mouth; graceful pinnate leaves 1½ m long, with numerous narrow leaflets equidistant; erect inflorescence, with small spherical fruit. *p. 1868*

pseudosepal (Malaya); climbing rattan-palm to 5 m high, with elongate sheaths grooved and ridged lengthwise; pinnate leaves 1 m long with numerous equidistant pinnae; inflorescence short; small 18 mm globose fruit. *p. 1868*

DAHLIA *Compositae* **C2LB-FMd**

imperialis (Mexico), a "Tree-dahlia"; tree-like 2-6 m tall, with tuberous roots, few woody stalks mostly solid and 4-grooved; compound leaves lacy; flowers 10-15 cm across; florets white, tinged purple near base, disk yellow. *Subtropic.* *p. 807*

merckii (Mexico), the "Bedding dahlia"; low herbaceous tuberous bush 60-90 cm with finely cut leaves and daisy-like "single" blooms about 5 cm across, with broad lilac florets, much above foliage. *p. 806*

pinnata (variabilis) hybrid, the "Garden-dahlias", originally from Mexico, but now in about 14 groups, with thousands of named clones; herbaceous bush 1½-2 m tall, with tuberous roots, stout semi-woody stalks, turgid leaves 5-foliolate, fresh-green above, grayish beneath; showy flower heads in many horticultural forms, sizes and colors, originally purple, but now also in white, yellow, salmon, bronze, red, pink, violet-bluish, with diameters of flowers spreading from 25 cm for giants to 6 cm for miniatures. The main divisions are grouped as follows:

pinnata 'Cactus-flowered'; elegant, fully double flowers, with the margins of the straight floral rays almost completely turned back, nearly forming a pointed cone, and spreading to 15 cm wide. *p. 807*

pinnata 'Collarette'; open-centered heads, with one row of broad, flat floral rays, and in addition one or more rows of shorter petal-like florets, usually of a different color, forming a collar around the central disk. *Subtropic.* *p. 807*

pinnata 'Formal Decorative'; flower heads fully double, with margins of the usually broad florets only slightly or not at all turned back, the outer tending to recurve, and the inner slightly cupped. *p. 807*

pinnata 'Informal Decorative'; a selected cultivar with heads of ray flowers only; rays irregularly arranged, broad and twisted or pointed, margins usually turned under. *Subtropic.* *p. 807*

pinnata 'Mignon Single'; open centered flowers, showing yellow center disk, encircled by one row of petal-like ray florets; dwarf-growing in the 'Mignon' group. *p. 807*

pinnata 'Pompon'; attractive usually small, fully double flower heads round, ball-shaped or slightly flattened, the floral rays cupped or tubular and blunt, arranged spirally. *Subtropic.* *p. 807*

pinnata 'Semi-Cactus'; fully double flower heads with long pointed floral rays having margins turned back for less than half their length. *p. 807*

pinnata 'Unwin's Dwarf' ("Mignon"); dwarf growing strain suitable for growing as a compact pot plant, producing 6 cm and 8 cm double and semi-double blooms in colors red, salmon, yellow, and lavender; usually grown from seed but forming small tubers; blooming first year in cool climate. *Subtropic.* *p. 806, 807*

DALBERGIA *Leguminosae* **S3LBD**

tonkinensis (Vietnam) (cochinchinensis); evergreen tree to 25 m high; pinnate leaves 15-20 cm long; pale green above, glaucous beneath; flowers in loose axillary panicles up to 15 cm long, white; fruit 5-8 cm long. *p. 1380*

DALECHAMPIA *Euphorbiaceae* **S3LBD**

roezliana (Mexico); branched sub-shrub to 1 m with alternate 15 cm oblanceolate dark green leaves, and small fragrant, yellow flowers without petals in dense clusters, subtended by two rose-pink bracts and a fringe of waxy threads on top. *p. 1004, 1054*

DAMMAROPSIS *Moraceae* **S2-3LBD**

kingiana (New Guinea); extraordinarily interesting small branching tree about 3 to 5 m high which I collected in the Finisterre Mountains; very decorative with great leaves at first ovate, later much broader and 60 cm long, turgid, leathery, deeply corrugated, the margins undulate, deep glabrous green above, with red ribs when young, later changing to ivory, and pale beneath, petioles red; large pineapple-like brown fruit. *Tropical.* *p. 1569, 1579, 1585*

DAMNACANTHUS *Rubiaceae* **C3LBD**

macrophyllus giganteus (Eastern India to Japan); small, much-branched shrub with two spines at each node; elliptic leaves dark green to 4 cm long, recurved, and wavy at margins; small white flowers, followed by little 1 cm bright red berries; for cool location. According to Index Kewensis this name is referred to D. indicus. *p. 2017*

major (Japan); stiff, much-branched shrub 1 m high, with scurfy branches armed by needle-like spines; smooth elliptic 5 cm leaves; fragrant white funnel-form flowers 2 cm long, hanging beneath the shoots; small scarlet berries. Differs from D. indicus by its larger leaves and smaller spines. *p. 2012*

DAPHNE *Thymelaeaceae* **C-I2LFM**

blagayana (Austria: Styria); low evergreen to 30 cm with small obovate leaves and terminal clusters of fragrant, creamy-white flowers. *p. 2100*

cneorum (Spain, France, Germany to Balkans and Russia), the "Garland-flower", low evergreen shrub with trailing branches, small 2½ cm leaves shiny dark green and with sharp point, and fragrant carmine-rose flowers in clusters, in early spring. *p. 2100*

laureola (Azores, No. Africa, Sicily to S.E. Europe), "Spurgelaurel"; evergreen shrub to 1 m with ornamental lustrous green oblanceolate leaves 4-12 cm long; fragrant flowers with yellowish-green calyx, and blue-black berries. *p. 2100*

longilobata (Tibet, Yunnan); much branched evergreen shrub to 1½ m, the branches pubescent when young, green leaves narrowly oblanceolate 5-10 cm long; terminal inflorescence with flower tube pale green, the spreading lobes creamy-white; fruit red. *p. 2100*

mezereum (Europe to Caucasus, Asia Minor, Siberia); deciduous shrub with oblanceolate thin leaves 2½ to 8 cm long, vivid green, grayish beneath, usually appearing after bloom; the flower light carmine and very fragrant; scarlet fruit poisonous. *p. 2100*

odora (China, Japan), "Winter daphne"; ornamental evergreen shrub to 1 m high, with glossy dark green, leathery, 8 cm leaves; the flowers are creamy-white to purple and very fragrant, in dense terminal clusters, blooming Jan. to March. *Subtropic.* *p. 2091*

odora 'Marginata', "Variegated daphne"; attractive, slow-growing, compact bush having its glossy leaves prettily edged with ivory, and the waxy pink flowers radiating an intense sweet perfume; slower than odora. *Subtropic.* *p. 2091, 2101*

DARLINGTONIA *Sarraceniaceae (Carnivorous Plants)* **C3HNW**

californica (California, Oregon), "Cobra plant"; carnivorous bog plant with hollow, light green pitchers, equipped inside with downward pointed hairs entrapping insects; the top is hooded and has translucent windows, and a cobra-like, purple-spotted forked tongue; nodding flowers purple. *Subtropic.* *p. 774*

DASYLIRION *Liliaceae* **I2LBD**

acrotriche (Mexico), stiff tree-like desert plant with trunk 1 m or more, topped by a dense rosette of 1 m linear leaves only 4 cm wide, with fibrous tuft at tip, and sharp yellow spines; white flowers on panicle to 5 m high. *p. 1423, 1435*

glaucophyllum (E. Mexico); stem-forming dense formal rosette of hundreds of linear leathery leaves 1 m long and 2 cm wide, lightly convex and with prominent rib off-center; olive green with faint glaucescence, the margins closely set with small hookspines in both directions, tips usually straw-colored and splitting; inflorescence to 5 m high, with white flowers. *Tropical.* *p. 1434*

longissimum (Nolina longifolia in Hortus 3) (Mexico), "Mexican grass-tree" or "Junquillo"; stemless xerophyte with swollen base, to 3 m high, forming dense bundle of narrow-linear, stiffly erect olive green leaves without ribs, 1 m or more long; inflorescence a narrow cluster of small whitish flowers. *Arid-subtropic.* *p. 1435*

serratifolium (S.E. Mexico); dense rosette with stout stem, narrow wiry, grass-like, green leaves to 1 m long, 2-3 cm wide; margins set with vicious spines; apex divided and with feathery tufts of hairs; white flowers in dense clusters. *Tropical.* *p. 1435*

wheeleri (Arizona, Texas, Mexico), "Desert spoon"; dense rosette of narrow, flexuous, ribbed leaves to 1 m long and 2 cm wide, glaucous silvery, and with marginal spines tipped brown. *Arid-subtropic.* *p. 1435*

DATURA *Solanaceae* **I-S2LBM**

chlorantha (Peruvian Andes); free-blooming shrub with broad ovate, wavy leaves, and fragrant yellow, pendulous flowers; tubular calyx with 5 teeth, corolla funnel-shaped; August-October; prickly fruit. *p. 2071*

cornigera (Mexico); softly downy shrub to 3 m high, ovate leaves; creamy-white pendant flowers very fragrant at night, funnel-shaped, with five pointed lobes, and spurred calyx. *p. 2071*

metel florepleno (S.W. China), "Horn-of-plenty"; herbaceous bush with ovate, thin leaves downy when young; inflorescence erect, trumpet shaped, with 1 or more inner corollas, whitish to purple, to 20 cm long. *Subtropic.* *p. 2070, 2071*

meteloides (Texas to California, Mexico); perennial to 1 m cultivated as an annual, grayish-pubescent, with ovate leaves, and erect, 5-lobed, funnel-shaped flowers to 20 cm long, white tinged with violet, and fragrant; round fruit with long spines. *p. 2068, 2070, 2071*

stramonium (Trop. No. America), "Jimson-weed" or "Thorn-apple"; annual herb 1-1½ m with pointed, lobed green leaves; erect funnel-shaped flowers 10 cm long, white or violet; fruit very spiny. Poisonous. *p. 2071*

wrightii (inoxia in Hortus 3) (SW U.S., No. Mexico), "Indian apple" or "Horn-of-plenty"; large annual bush to 1½ m high, with gray-downy, ovate leaves; erect, sweet-scented flowers 15-20 cm long, the spreading, 5-pointed limb white, opening in the evening. Plant may cause skin inflammation. *p. 2070*

DATURA: see also Brugmansia

DAVALLIA *Polypodiaceae (Filices)* **·I-S1HNM**

bullata mariesii (Japan), "Ball fern"; long creeping, flexible, slender, light brown, hairy rhizomes with uniformly small, 4-pinnate, finely lacy yet tough fronds; I saw them in Japan trained into many shapes, such as balls, pillars, bells, animals, monkeys and dolls; deciduous in cool climates. Possibly D. mariesii. *p. 1102, 1103*

canariensis (Canary Islands, Spain, No. Africa), the "Hare's-foot fern"; sturdy epiphytic fern; the creeping rhizome covered with brown hair-like scales tipped with white, like a rabbit's foot; wiry stalks bear the leathery, light green fronds 20-50 cm long, finely cut in tripinnate fashion into broad ultimately toothed leaflets. A wonderful keeper in baskets. *p. 1104*

embolestegia (Philippines); large and showy fern from the mountains of Luzon near Baguio, with creeping rhizome covered with brown scales, the stalks glaucous, and fronds 4 times divided into fine, overlapping pinnae. Collected by David Barry of Los Angeles and Honolulu. *p. 1104*

fejeensis (Fiji Islands), "Rabbit's-foot fern"; a name referring to its brown woolly, creeping rhizomes, from which rise the graceful durable fronds on wiry stems, more finely cut than solida. *Humid-tropical.* *p. 1102, 1104*

fejeensis 'Plumosa' (Polynesia), a dainty, dwarf variety with fresh-green, more finely cut, 4-pinnatifid, plume-like, pendulous fronds of long-lasting character. *Humid-tropical.* *p. 1102*

griffithiana (India, So. China); epiphytic fern with creeping rhizomes, covered with glistening white scales; wiry fronds 3-4 pinnatifid into well spaced segments, with the ultimate leaflets deeply toothed; not deciduous. *Humid-tropical.* *p. 1102*

pentaphylla (Java, Polynesia), "Dwarf rabbit's foot"; a distinct dwarf growing species with black-haired creeping rhizomes bearing wiry fronds of two or three pairs of lateral wavy-toothed, linear, glossy green leaflets and a terminal one. *p. 1102*

solida (lucida) (Malaya, Queensland), "Rabbit's foot fern"; brown hairy rhizomes with broadly massive, stiff-leathery, 3-pinnate fronds to 60 cm high, the leaflets ovate-rhomboid and crenate. (S) *p. 1102*

trichomanioides (Malaya), D. "canariensis" of horticulture; "Squirrel's-foot fern"; small creeping rhizome covered with pale brown scale; wiry gray stalks bearing rather leathery fronds 15-22 cm long, 4 times pinnate, with leaflets overlapping, the final pinnae cut into strap-shaped segments. More durable than fejeensis, seldom fertile. *Humid-tropical.* *p. 1102*

DEAMIA *Cactaceae* **S3HFD**

testudo (So. Mexico to Colombia), "Tortoise cactus"; epiphytic climber with aerial roots and glaucous stems very variable in shape, triangular, flat like a tortoise, or to 8-ribbed; large white diurnal flowers, flushed copper outside. *Arid-tropical.* *p. 661, 665*

DEBREGEASIA *Urticaceae* **S3LBD**

longifolia (S. Asia); tree or shrub to 7 m high; leaves lanceolate, to 15 cm long, rough and dark green above, white-tomentose beneath; fruit orange or red, about 8 mm across, close along the length of branch. *p. 2108*

DECABELONE *Asclepiadaceae* **S3LBD**

meintjiesii (Tavaresia) (E. Transvaal); clustering succulent with cylindrical gray-green stems 8-10 cm high, the 6-12 ribs divided by sharp furrows, the angles with small bristle-teeth; large 5-lobed flowers cream inside with chestnut-brown crossmarkings, the lobes 4 cm long, the tube inside with long hairs. *p. 357*

DECAISNEA *Lardizabalaceae* **I2LBD**

fargesii (W. China); deciduous shrub with blue-glaucous branches, feathery leaves light green above, bluish beneath; 2½ cm pendulous flowers yellowish-green; blue, cylindrical, edible fruit from the inconspicuous female flowers. *p. 1361*

DECARYA *Didiereaceae* **S2LBD**

madagascariensis (S.W. Madagascar); tree with erect trunk, to 8 m high, spreading branches dividing into dense thickets of succulent zigzag twigs furnished with thorns to 8 cm long, and sparse, fleshy, tiny leaves. *p. 950*

DECKENIA *Palmae* **S3LFM**

nobilis (Seychelle Islands); huge and handsome spiny feather palm to 40 m tall; the trunk is erect and relatively slender, to 30 cm dia., losing its spines with age; pinnate leaves to 4 m long, with pointed leaflets hairy beneath, and spiny on stalk; the oblong purplish fruit 2 cm long. *p. 1854*

DEHERAINIA *Myrsinaceae* **S3LFD**

smaragdina (Mexico); shrub with hairy branches; 10 cm lanceolate toothed leaves smooth above, soft-hairy beneath; deep green wheel-shaped 5 cm flowers primrose-like, between the foliage. *p. 1602*

DELARBREA *Araliaceae* **S3LBM**

spectabilis (New Caledonia); tall tropical evergreen shrub with ash-gray stem and covered with dark brown warts; glossy grass-green, thin-leathery odd-pinnate leaves with oblique leaflets in 8-10 pairs and gracefully arched, each leaflet entire or 3-lobed; small flowers in large clusters, followed by globose berries. *p. 304*

DELONIX *Leguminosae* **S3LBM**

regia (Poinciana) (Madagascar), the "Flamboyant", "Royal poinciana" or "Mohur tree"; a regal flowering tree and one of the showiest; widely planted in the tropics; wide-spreading and to 15 m high; finely subdivided, ferney leaves often fall before blooming time; brilliant 8-10 cm flowers scarlet-red with broad cream lip marked red: followed by flat, woody black pods to 45 cm long. *Tropical.* *p. 1381*

DELOSPERMA *Aizoaceae* **I2LBD**

abyssinicum (Ethiopia, Eritrea); prostrate, freely branching succulent, with curving sub-cylindrical soft-fleshy leaves 4-6 cm long, appearing striped gray-green; flowers pink. *p. 59*

echinatum (Cape Prov.); small bush to 30 cm high, light brown stems repeatedly forked, small sausage-like succulent leaves sap-green set with white bristly tubercles; small flowers yellowish. *p. 66*

hirtum (So. Africa); mat-forming, creeping succulent with woody stem and channeled, linear-pointed, soft-fleshy leaves and daisy-like stalked flowers with narrow white petals. *p. 64*

sutherlandii (So. Africa: Transvaal, Natal) low succulent rosettes branching and hugging the ground; thin-fleshy lanceolate leaves grayish-green, somewhat keeled, to 8 cm long; showy rose-purple flowers 4-6 cm across, the ray-petals white at base, forming a contrasting eye. *p. 64*

DELPHINIUM *Ranunculaceae* **C2LBM**

ajacis (Switzerland to Taurus), "Larkspur"; erect branching annual to $1\frac{1}{2}$ m high, with lacily divided leaves and long, showy spikes of flowers, often double, with a prominent spur, and sepals in shades of blue, violet, pink to white. *Warm temperate.* *p. 1984*

'Ruysii' ('Pink Sensation'); hybrid of nudicaulis, elatum, cardinale, etc.; known also as the "Red larkspur"; 60 cm perennial with fibrous roots, divided leaves, and erect racemes with spurred, pink flowers; spring through summer. *p. 1985*

DENDROBIUM *Orchidaceae* **I-S3OFD**

acuminatum: see Epigeneium lyonii

aggregatum (Burma, Yunnan, Malaya); dwarf epiphyte with small 5 cm pseudobulbs bearing solitary leaves, the flat flowers golden yellow with orange center in arching sprays. (March-May). (S) *p. 1709*

atroviolaceum (New Guinea); club-shaped, furrowed 30 cm pseudobulbs with 2-3 leathery leaves, and racemes of 4-5 cm flowers with sepals and petals creamy-white spotted purplish-brown, and purple lip streaked white, green outside; winter-spring. (S) *p. 1708*

bellatulum (So. China to Vietnam); pretty, dwarf epiphyte with stout, black-haired pseudobulbs; 4 cm flowers white, lip orange with red in throat, fragrant and long-lasting (spring). *p. 1712*

bullenianum (topaziacum) (Philippines); long fleshy cane-like pseudobulbs to 40 cm high, with 5 cm leathery leaves; inflorescence dense with flowers along the stems, somewhat bell-shaped, 2 cm long, soft buttercup yellow marked with red lines; not opening fully (spring). *p. 1711*

canaliculatum (Queensland); pretty epiphyte with stout, ribbed pseudobulbs and persistent leaves; inflorescence to 30 cm tall, with 15-20 sweet-scented, yellowish white flowers 3 cm across, lip white with mauve disk (autumn). *p. 1714*

capituliflorum (New Guinea); stout, spindle-shaped pseudobulbs with leathery leaves, undersides purple; eventually deciduous; small flowers very numerous, 2 cm long, crowded in dense heads, delicate green and white. *p. 1711*

chrysanthum (Himalayas to Burma, China, Vietnam); pendant , stem-like, leafy pseudobulbs to 1 m or more long; flowers in two's or three's from nodes, 5 cm across, deep orange-yellow; fringed lip with maroon blotches; may bloom twice a year. *p. 1715*

chrysotoxum (Burma, Yunnan); strong epiphyte with cane-like pseudobulbs, producing from their leafy top arching racemes of golden yellow flowers with fringed lip having a deep orange throat. (March-July). Known in New Guinea as the "Fried egg orchid". (I) *p. 1707*

coelogyne (So. Burma); curious epiphyte with short, $2\frac{1}{2}$-5 cm pseudobulbs bearing 2 leathery leaves, and creeping on a long rhizome; large solitary flowers with sepals and petals yellowish green densely spotted with purple, lip dark purple (Oct.-Dec.). (S) *p. 1706*

d'albertisii, (Papua), a "Rabbit's-ear orchid"; pretty epiphyte with square, slender tapering stems set alternately with narrow, fleshy leaves, the axillary erect racemes of fragrant, spurred flowers with white sepals, the narrow greenish twisted petals standing erect resembling rabbit's ears, the lip marked purple. *Tropical.* *p. 1710*

dearei (Philippines); handsome epiphyte with erect stems 60-90 cm high and set with short leaves; racemes of large 8 cm flowers pure white, tinged lemon-green in center of lip; Dec. May, and July-August. (S) *p. 1708, 1713*

delacouri (Thailand); small epiphyte with swollen canes to 25 cm high; leaves partially deciduous; delicate 3 cm flowers buff-yellow, the lip deep yellow with red-brown lines and fringed with brown hairs (August). *p. 1715*

delicatum (Australia); epiphyte with pseudobulbs swollen at base, bearing several leaves; inflorescence with flowers 2 cm across, cream-colored tinged pink on outside, and spotted with brown (winter). *p. 1713*

densiflorum (Himalayas, Burma); beautiful epiphyte with tall, stout cane-like 4-sided pseudobulbs bearing 3-5 leathery leaves; the flowers golden yellow with velvety orange-yellow lip, in dense, pendant trusses, from near the top of either old or young growth. (March-May). *Tropical.* *p. 1705, 1707*

denudans (Himalayas); small epiphyte with cane-like, slender pseudobulbs 12-15 cm high; flowering during the leafless state on one-year old growth, in pendant racemes; sepals and petals pale yellow, striped red; lip striped red or pale yellowish-green; Aug-Oct. (I: subtropical to temperate). *p. 1708*

devonianum (Himalayas, Burma, Vietnam); lovely epiphyte with slender, pendulous pseudobulbs to 1 m long, with a few linear leaves which drop before bloom; axillary 5 cm flowers from nodes along the stem, cream-white tipped with rose, the fringed lip with two orange blotches; May-August. (S) *p. 1708*

distichum (Philippines); epiphyte without pseudobulbs; the flat and fleshy sickle-shaped leaves arranged in two ranks along stem, their bases overlapping; small 1 cm fleshy flowers in clusters at tip of stem, yellowish with conspicuous, red-brown stripes; March-May. (S) *p. 1710*

falconeri (Himalayas to Thailand); handsome species with pendant, branching reed-stems to 1 m long, with narrow, deciduous leaves; large solitary fragrant flowers 5-8 cm across, white, the petals and sepals tipped with rose-purple, lip with deep purple blotch flanked by two orange spots (summer). *p. 1711*

falcorostrum (Australia); showy epiphyte with slender pseudobulbs to 20 cm high, and leathery leaves; topped by terminal inflorescence with up to 20 fleshy, creamy white flowers having narrow sepals and 2 cm petals, lip marked yellow and striped crimson; free-flowering, spring on. *p. 1714*

farmeri (Himalaya, Burma); compact epiphyte with club-shaped, furrowed pseudobulbs tipped by leathery leaves; pendulous racemes of 5 cm flowers with sepals and petals white to pale rose, lip golden-yellow, tipped with rose; April-June. (S) *p. 1708*

fimbriatum (Himalayas, Burma); tall epiphyte with cane-like stems with numerous leaves topped by loose clusters of flowers, deep yellow with fringed lip rich orange and velvet-like; a large blood-red blotch at base of lip, in the variety oculatum. (March-April). *Tropical.* *p. 1706*

finisterrae (N. E. New Guinea); curious epiphyte 45 cm high, with weird flowers pale greenish, spotted and lined with black-brown, and covered outside with white translucent, beard-like scales (summer). *p. 1713*

formosum (Himalayas); epiphyte with stout erect pseudobulbs, thin leathery oblong leaves, and at the apex, several large fragrant long-lasting 10 cm flowers of good substance, snowy-white with orange throat. (late autumn). (I) *p. 1707*

formosum giganteum (Upper Burma); showy variety with shorter but stouter stems than the species, the fragrant flowers much larger, 12 or even 15 cm across, pure white with bright golden blotch in throat. (Spring). *Tropical* *p. 1712*

gracilicaule (Australia); slender cane-like pseudobulbs to 50 cm high, topped by several leaves, and short clusters of small variable 2 cm flowers curiously hooded, creamy-yellow, spotted with brown-red. *p. 1715*

griffithianum (Burma); beautiful epiphyte with cane-like pseudobulbs; leathery, persistent leaves; immense pendulous trusses of charming, perfect flowers 5 cm across, with sepals and petals golden yellow, and fringed orange lip (spring-flowering). *p. 1705*

hercoglossum, (Malaya); curious miniature epiphyte with spindle-like bulbs; small greenish flowers tinted orange-yellow, with red markings and tipped with crimson (autumn). *p. 1713*

heterocarpum (aureum) (Nepal, Assam, Ceylon, Java, Philippines); epiphyte with stout stems, deciduous leaves, and very fragrant 6-8 cm flowers in clusters, with cream or yellow sepals and petals, lip with golden, velvety disk, veined with crimson; October to March. (S) *p. 1708*

infundibulum (So. Burma); an epiphyte of great beauty with black-haired cylindric stems to 60 cm long and 2-4 showy flowers 8-10 cm across from the upper joints, snow-white with orange-yellow stain in the throat (May-Aug.). *Tropical.* *p. 1706*

infundibulum var. jamesianum (Burma); variety with pseudobulbs more stout; flowers white with cinnabar-red on the basal portion of the lip (spring). *p. 1712*

ionoglossum (New Guinea); big species with thin, swollen pseudobulbs to $1\frac{1}{2}$ m, leaves on upper parts; erect inflorescence, a dense raceme of some 20 lavender flowers 4 cm across, sepals twisted in a spiral; large purple lip streaked with pale lines. *p. 1714*

johnsoniae (macfarlanei) (New Guinea); noble epiphyte with erect cylindric, 2-3-leaved pseudobulbs bearing terminal racemes of large 10-12 cm flowers pure white except for 3-lobed lip marked purple; summer. *Tropical.* *p. 1710, 1715*

kingianum (Queensland, N.S. Wales); small epiphyte with 5-18 cm pseudobulbs bearing 2 to 5 leaves, and terminal clusters of $2\frac{1}{2}$ cm flowers whitish or rose streaked with purple, the 3-lobed lip with greenish crest; March-April. (C) *p. 1702, 1715*

linguiforme (N. S. Wales, Queensland), "Tongue orchid"; curious dwarf epiphyte with creeping rhizome, pseudobulbs almost absent, and thick-fleshy $2\frac{1}{2}$ cm leaves, furrowed and bean-like, olive-green, matted and hugging tree trunk or slab; small white flowers with narrow sepals and petals and short lip, with yellowish tips; season variable. (S) *p. 1710, 1714*

lituiflorum (Himalayas to Vietnam); clusters of slender, pendulous pseudobulbs to 90 cm; fragile, deciduous leaves; from the stem long-lived fragrant flowers, 5 cm across; sepals and petals rose purple with white translucent veins; center pale; lip purple with white veins and yellow band (spring). *p. 1712*

loddigesii (Yunnan, Hainan); small epiphyte with creeping rhizome, slender stems and axillary 4 cm flowers with sepals and petals rosy-purple, the fringed rounded lip orange, banded white and purple at tip; spring. (S) *p. 1708*

macrophyllum, (Philippines, Java, New Guinea); one of the finest of dendrobiums; very variable epiphyte with slender pseudobulbs becoming stout, to 30 cm tall; persistent leathery leaves glossy green; inflorescence erect with clusters of heavy-textured flowers to 5 cm across, and covered with blackish bristles; sepals and petals cream to greenish and spotted purple, the waxy lip yellow green veined purple (Spring). *p. 1705, 1712*

'Montrose' (ainsworthii x 'thwaitesiae'); gorgeous hybrid, with large bouquet of flowers rich yellow with deep brownish-black eye; almost as showy as 'thwaitesiae'. *p. 1712*

moschatum (Himalayas, Burma); epiphyte with tall, cane-like pseudobulbs, which can produce young plants at their tip; loose racemes of 8-10 cm flowers from the older wood, the petals pale to orange-yellow tinged with rose, pouch with black-purple blotches inside. (May-Aug.) (I) *p. 1709*

'New Guinea' (macrophyllum x atroviolaceum); a "different", compact hybrid with 3-4 broad leaves and an erect, short raceme of long-lasting long-stalked flowers with pointed greenish ochre-yellow sepals and petals, the cupped lip patterned with crimson over yellow, 5 cm dia. (early spring). *Tropical.* *p. 1706*

nobile (Himalayas, Assam, Yunnan); popular epiphyte with large fragrant 8 cm flowers produced in twos and threes from nodes of 2-yr. pseudobulbs, sepals and petals white, tipped rosy-pink, lip white with rosy tip and deep velvet-crimson throat. (Jan.-June). *Tropical.* *p. 1709*

nobile virginale (India); flowers pure white except for fringe of pale primrose on lip (winter). *p. 1705*

ovatum (India); epiphyte with cane-like, leafy stems later deciduous; erect inflorescence with raceme of 3 cm flowers greenish yellow with deep yellow eye (spring) (Bot. Garden Heidelberg). *p. 1704*

phalaenopsis (bigibbum var.) (Queensland, New Guinea, Timor); a most beautiful epiphyte with stiffly slender canes 60-90 cm tall, bearing leaves in 2 ranks, and long, arching chain-like sprays of large, neatly draped 8 cm flowers, the sepals pale magenta with reticulated darker nerves, petals rose, much larger; lip dark purplish-red; blooming variously, mainly in spring, sometimes also in fall to November. *Tropical.* *p. 1707*

phalaenopsis 'Pompadour'; (Louis Bleriot x schroederianum); an old French hybrid (Vacherot 1934), vigorous, compact grower with leafy stems, very popular for cut flower trade and shipping, in Bangkok, Thailand; long, striking sprays of bright magenta-red flowers 8 cm across; sepals and petals strong and thick; except for short resting period, flowering all year. *Tropical.* *p. 1711*

phalaenopsis schroederianum (New Guinea); beautiful variety of larger habit with stout cane-like pseudobulbs to 1 m tall, the flowers larger and variable, sepals and petals usually white, the lip deep violet, compactly arranged in a decorative pendulous raceme. (autumn). (S) (I) *p. 1707*

pierardii (Himalayas, Burma); epiphyte from steaming forests, with long cylindric, pendant stems, the flowers from the nodes, sepals and petals delicate pale rose, lip yellowish, veined with rose-purple (Feb.-May) *p. 1709*

primulinum (Himalayas, Burma); epiphyte with cylindrical fleshy stems, erect or pendulous, with flowers in 2 rows from nodes along the leafless pseudobulb, the large blooms with small sepals and petals pale rose, the shell-shaped lip primrose-yellow streaked red. (Feb.-May). *Tropical.* *p. 1709*

pulchellum (Himalayas, Burma, Vietnam); pretty epiphyte with tall pseudobulbs having purple lines running down the stem, and pendulous racemes of large 8-12 cm flowers pale yellow tinted with rose, and two purple blotches in throat; March-May. (S) *p. 1708*

sanderae (Philippines, Borneo); epiphyte with erect pseudobulbs topped by clusters of showy flowers of pure white, the throat shaded and striped with purple. (May-Aug.) (S) *p. 1709*

sanderae parviflorum (Philippines); long cane-stems, with short, lanceolate leaves set in close rank; flowers with long tube, glistening white with blackish-crimson lines in throat. *p. 1712*

secundum (Burma, Vietnam, Pacific Isl.); stout cylindric stems 60-90 cm high, the small somewhat tubular flowers shining rosy purple, with pointed orange-yellow lip, in dense one-sided stiff racemes from the top (winter). *Tropical.* *p. 1706*

senile (Burma, Thailand, Laos), "Cowslip orchid"; pseudobulbs spindle-shaped, covered with white hairs; persistent, leathery leaves; solitary or paired flowers from the upper nodes, waxy, long-lived, 5 cm across, bright yellow; lip darker and with green about disc (spring). *Tropical.* *p. 1714*

'Shokei' (ainsworthii x Perfection); slender nearly deciduous canes; handsome flowers 8 cm across, rosy-lavender with deep purple blotch surrounded by band of creamy-yellow on lip (1938). *p. 1713*

sophronitis (New Guinea); miniature epiphyte with tiny succulent, puckered leaves 2 cm long; waxy flowers 2 cm wide, beautiful peach pink, or flame red with orange-red lip outlined with brown; flowers last 5-6 months (July-December). *p. 1713*

speciosum (Queensland, New Guinea); robust epiphyte with swollen pseudobulbs, to 90 cm tall, topped by rigid, leathery leaves; large racemes with numerous fragrant flowers 8 cm across, not opening fully; sepals and petals linear, cream or yellow lip streaked with red (autumn, February in habitat). *p. 1714*

speciosum var. hillii (N. So. Wales, Queensland); stout stems with leathery leaves, and terminal inflorescence with numerous very fragrant flowers not opening wide, 5-8 cm when spread out; flowers cream yellow in the species, the lip spotted with purple; in the var. hillii creamy white, with segments more slender, and growth taller (autumn). *p. 1704*

superbum (Borneo, Celebes to Philippines); noble, deciduous epiphyte of pendulous habit, with cylindric stems to 1 m long, the 8-10 cm flowers appearing along them on each side, rose-purple with base of pubescent lip blood purple. *Tropical.* *p. 1706*

teretifolium (Queensland, New Guinea); epiphyte with creeping rhizome and slender, pendant stems; inflorescence usually from leaf bases, with fragrant flowers 3-8 cm across, narrowly linear sepals and petals cream-white or yellow, the lip marked with red. (summer). *p. 1715*

teretifolium fairfaxii (Australia); flowers white, the bases of sepals and of lip suffused reddish-brown or purple; fewer flowers than the species. *p. 1715*

tetragonum biganteum (New Guinea); slender stem expanding into a square pseudobulb topped by two elliptic leaves; small clusters of 6 cm flowers, the long-pointed sepals, and narrow and hair-like petals pale greenish-yellow spotted brown, the small lip white marked purple; winter. (S) *p. 1710*

x thwaitesiae (ainsworthii x wiganiae); cane-stem hybrid with large 10 cm flowers, one of the showiest of the genus; sepals and petals ranging from buttercup-yellow through gold and orange, and a deep brown-red disk on lip. *Tropical.* *p. 1710*

thyrsiflorum (Burma); showy epiphyte with the habit of densiflorum but stems are more round and taller, to 75 cm high, the flowers in longer pendant racemes, sepals and petals white, often flushed pink, the pubescent lip golden orange. (Feb.-May). *Tropical.* *p. 1707*

transparens (Himalayas, Burma); slender cane-like pseudobulbs to 45 cm, soft leaves to 10 cm, deciduous; from the pseudobulbs 4 cm flowers transparent purplish or pink with white at base, lip with blood-red blotch; delicately fragrant but not lasting well (spring). *p. 1714*

uncinatum; small clustering plant with small, angular pseudobulbs, leaves 5 cm high, purplish underside; flowers fan-shaped, lavender pink, 3 cm long; lip which lies tight against column, deep wine-purple with bright orange tip. *p. 1712*

undulatum (discolor) (No. Australia, New Guinea); robust species with swollen pseudobulbs to 1 m or more tall, leaves partially resistant; inflorescence terminal, gracefully arching, with numerous waxy, long-lived, honey-scented 5 cm flowers extremely variable in color, usually yellowish brown but sometimes pink with cream margins, sepals and petals crisped (spring). *p. 1714*

veratrifolium (New Guinea); robust epiphyte with elongate pseudobulbs and large clusters of spreading, stiff racemes of small flowers with white sepals and erect green-tipped petals looking like rabbit's ears, all marked with violet; Autumn. *Tropical.* *p. 1710*

victoriae-reginae (Philippines), "Queen Victoria's dendrobium"; beautiful species with fleshy canes bearing narrow leaves, soon deciduous; from the leafless stems the 3 cm flowers with spreading ovate segments white, tipped sky-blue and with dark blue lines (blooms most of year). *p. 1712, 1715*

DENDROCALAMUS *Gramineae* **S2LBW**

giganteus (Burma, Malaya), "Giant bamboo"; this tropical giant of the tribe, largest of all bamboos, grows to 35 m high with stems 25 cm or more in diameter, thin-walled, joints to 40 cm apart; later developing branches with large leaves to 50 cm long borne in graceful masses toward the top. The young emerging culms, growing at the rate of 45 cm a day, were an instrument of torture and death to prisoners of war in Ceylon, pushing through their bodies when they were tied down to the ground in a bamboo grove. In temperate climate for the large conservatory only. Widely planted in Southeast Asia and used for building, water-spouting or plant pots. *Tropical.* *p. 1305, 1313*

latiflorus (Sinocalamus) (Taiwan, Kwangtung, Vietnam), "Tim Chuk" or "Sweet bamboo"; handsome tropical and subtropical giant bamboo, with thick-walled culms to 20 m high and 12 to 20 cm in dia., and of a striking glossy, golden yellow coloring, forming clusters; the leaves rather large 15-25 cm long and 3-5 cm wide, rounded at base. Widely grown in Kwangtung for its excellent edible shoots. *p. 1314*

strictus (India, Java), the "Calcutta bamboo", also known as "Male bamboo" and "Stony bamboo" because of the hardness of its woody canes; a tropical clump type and very prolific when established, with glaucous green or bronzy culms to 20 m in our South, to 35 m high in the tropics, and 6 to 10 cm thick; leaves vary from 5 to 25 cm long and 2-4 cm wide, from branchlets formed as clusters from nodes 25 cm apart as well as at end of pendant branches. Used for the manufacture of split fishing rods. *Tropical.* *p. 1314*

DENDROCHILUM *Orchidaceae* **I-S3OFM**

abbreviatum (Java); small epiphyte with pseudobulbs 5 cm high, bearing solitary lance-shaped leaves; pendulous raceme of small 1 cm flowers in ranks, light green with lip brown in center; June-July. (S) *p. 1716*

cobbianum (Platyclinis) (Philippines), "Chain orchid"; graceful epiphyte with small, one-leaved pseudobulbs, producing from their apex a wiry stalk with gracefully pendant, dense, ribbon-like raceme of tiny, strongly and pleasantly spicy-fragrant straw-yellow flowers with orange lip. (April-Nov.) *Tropical.* *p. 1717*

filiforme (Philippines), "Golden chain orchid"; dainty little epiphyte with long pendulous, very slender, canary-yellow chains of tiny fragrant flowers. (March-July). (S) *p. 1717*

glumaceum (Platyclinis) (Philippines); small clustering epiphyte with lovely arching slender spikes of scented, 2-ranked flowers, sepals straw-white and greenish-yellow lip. *Tropical. p. 1717*

latifolium (Philippines); epiphyte of bolder habit than glumaceum, broader leathery leaves and taller, gracefully nodding racemes of creamy-white, 2-ranked flowers, with a reddish bract behind. (Feb.-July). (I) *p. 1717*

uncatum (Philippines); graceful, small epiphyte with tufted, slender conical pseudobulbs and linear leaves; the arching floral racemes short with numerous small pale green, pleasingly fragrant flowers with pointed sepals and petals. (Sept.-Jan., May-July). *Tropical. p. 1717*

DENDROPANAX *Araliaceae* **C2LBM**

chevalieri (Dendropanax arboreus; Gilibertia japonica) (Japan, Korea),"Tree aralia"; glabrous evergreen shrub with dark green, leathery, 3-lobed leaves with pale veins, variable becoming oval in later stage. *p. 307*

trifidus (Gilibertia) (Japan); small evergreen tree with gray-brown branches and thick green branchlets; shiny green, ovate leaves 7-12 cm long, 3-nerved, sometimes 2 or 3-lobed or 3 to 5-cleft; small yellow-green flowers in clusters, followed by black berries. *Warm-temperate. p. 314*

DENDROPHYLAX *Orchidaceae* **S3OFD**

lindenii (Polyrrhiza) (So. Florida, Cuba), the "Ghost orchid"; small, curious epiphyte with many prominent roots clustering along the bark of its host tree for over 1 m, leaves absent or fugitive, and singular white flower with petals and sepals lanceolate, the lip divided with the middle lobe spreading out like two spidery arms. *p. 1716*

varius (Cuba, Hispaniola); remarkable little epiphyte characterized by not possessing leaves, consisting of a tangle of grayish-green, chloroblast-bearing roots; from the center of the root cluster rises an inflorescence 25 cm long, bearing umbels of small 2 cm flowers pure white, with tiny spot of vivid yellow on the lip (spring). *p. 1704*

DENDROSICYOS *Cucurbitaceae* **S3LBD**

socotrana (Yemen: Socotra Isl.), "Cucumber-tree"; odd desert tree with conical swollen stem to 6 m tall, often 1 m dia., with white bark, and sparse pendant branches with scattered, lobed leaves 7 cm dia., rough with white bristles; axillary flowers, and hairy fruit. *Arid-tropical. p. 932*

DENNSTAEDTIA *Polypodiaceae (Filices)* **I3HFM**

adiantoides (West Indies); densely tufted and bushy fern with creeping rhizome; the fronds bipinnately divided into feathery plumes, 30-50 cm long, fresh green and of soft texture. *p. 1104*

cicutaria (Mexico, W. Indies, Brazil, Perú); robust tufting fern with stout, creeping rhizome, the massive fronds at first 30 cm, later 1 m or more long, borne on strong, hairy stalks; leaves bipinnately divided into feathery sprays, of a soft papery texture, light fresh green; the sori are covered by a cup-shaped shield. *p. 1104*

globulifera (Hispaniola, Cuba, Jamaica, Mexico, Venezuela); a cup-fern related to Dicksonia but having sori covered by little cups; large fern with tripinnate fronds, borne on hairy creeping rhizome. *p. 1108*

obtusifolia (Antilles to So. Brazil), submerged creeping stout rhizome, bearing erect, hairy stalks and 1-2 m deltoid, much divided, herbaceous fronds, thinly hairy. *p. 1108*

punctilobula (Nova Scotia to Georgia), a "Fragrant fern" or "Hay-scented fern"; hardy fern with hairy, creeping rhizome; bipinnate fronds to 1 m long, deeply cut, with pinnae coming to long slender points, and pleasantly fragrant. Often planted in the wild garden. *p. 1104*

DEPARIA *Polypodiaceae (Filices)* **S3HFM**

moorei in hort. (Tectaria moorei) (New Caledonia); handsome fern with showy fronds from short rhizome; long stalks bear the large matte green leaves, 30-50 cm long and 15-20 cm wide, bipinnately cut into broad segments, the margins lobed and frilled; small green sporangia occur along the edges of the leaves and on their upper surfaces. *p. 1105*

DERMATOBOTRYS *Scrophulariaceae* **S3LFD**

saundersii (So. Africa: Natal); curious small epiphytic shrub, with a long naked stem and brown, squarish branches; fleshy oblong leaves 5-15 cm long and coarsely toothed; curved-tubular flowers 5 cm long in whorls below the new foliage, the corolla red, and yellow inside. Although found on trees in Africa, it may be grown in pots. *p. 2049*

DERRIS *Leguminosae* **S3HBD**

indica (Trop. Asia), "Jewel vine"; scandent, woody plant with glossy-green, odd-pinnate foliage; small pale pink flowers. The tuberous root yields a resinous substance which is powdered and used to stupify fish in water; also a source of insecticide in the form of Rotenone. *Tropical. p. 1380*

DESFONTAINEA *Loganiaceae* **I-C2LBD**

spinosa (Chile, Perú); evergreen shrub to 3 m, with pale, shining branches; ovate, ilex-like 3-6 cm leaves glossy dark green with spiny margins; 3 cm flowers scarlet with yellow lobes. *p. 1517*

DESMONCUS *Palmae* **S3LFM**

horridus ("major" of hort.) (Trinidad, Guyana, Surinam), "Wait-awhile palm"; a horrible climbing palm, found in thickets along rivers in dense jungle on the Guiana coast, the dark green pinnate fronds very ornamental, but the axis with black spines and its whip-like tips set with pairs of vicious fish-hook spines which kept prisoners from escaping from Devil's Island. I can testify to some bloody slashes while exploring in this area. *Tropical. p. 1866, 1872*

isthmius (Panama, Venezuela); tall climbing palm with smooth, reed-like $2^1/_2$ cm stems, handsome pinnate fronds to $2^1/_2$ m long ending in sharp fish-hook like tips, the stalks black-spiny, and so is the spathe. *p. 1872*

"major" hort.: see horridus

polyacanthus (Brazil); a New World climbing palm resembling the rattan of Asia; lanceolate 15 cm leaflets well separated on spiny axis, and with a long sheath. *p. 1872*

DEUTEROCOHNIA *Bromeliaceae* **S2LBD**

longipetala (Dyckia) (Perú); dense rosette of spreading spiny leaves to 40 cm long; sessile flowers with yellow petals spotted green on tips. *p. 550*

meziana (So. Andes, Mato Grosso, Paraguay); xerophytic rosette with densely set, sharply recurved and tapering, flexible leaves light waxy green, with brown marginal spines in two directions; reverse with whitish scale; inflorescence a large 1 m panicle, to $2^1/_2$ m high, with red-orange petals. *p. 512, 549*

schreiteri (Argentina); elegant small xerophytic rosette of glossy gray, thick-fleshy recurved leaves with concave surface and with silvery scales beneath, the margins with pronounced spines; the inflorescence on tall, wiry, loosely branched stalks, with small yellow flowers. *p. 552*

DEUTZIA *Saxifragaceae* **C2LBMh**

gracilis (Japan), "Mayflower shrub" or "Slender deutzia"; attractive floriferous winter-hardy deciduous shrub of low habit, about 1 m high or sometimes more, with slender branches, wide-spreading or arching; lanceolate leaves with star-like hairs above, serrate at margins, to 6 cm long; masses of pure white 2 cm flowers in open simple or compound clusters; blooming outdoors in spring. *Warm temperate. p. 2041*

x lemoinei (gracilis x parviflora); best known of the taller deutzias, attractive floriferous hardy deciduous shrub to $2^1/_2$ m high, with elliptic lanceolate, serrate leaves to 10 cm long, and pure white 2 cm flowers in large clusters, in early summer; here belongs the favorite form 'Boule de Neige' (May-June). *p. 2039*

x rosea (gracilis x purpurascens); attractive flowering compact shrub with arching branches resembling gracilis, but the flowers soft rose and widely bell-shaped, in short clusters; ovate leaves toothed and slightly hairy. *p. 2039*

scabra (Japan, China); widely cultivated flowering shrub, especially in the double-flowered variety known as 'Pride of Rochester'; with arching branches, the shreddy bark reddish-brown; oval, hairy leaves deciduous; and large white flowers pinkish outside, the clusters spire-like and 8-12 cm long (June-July). *p. 2039*

x DIACATTLEYA *Orchidaceae* **S3OFD**

'Chastity' (Diacrium bicornutum x Cattleya granulosa); bigeneric plant to 50 cm with stout pseudobulbs topped by fleshy leaves, and heavy-textured, full-shaped fragrant 10 to 12 cm green flowers; blooming everytime a growth matures. *p. 1716*

'Fantasy', (Cattleya guatemalensis x Diacrium bicornutum); bigeneric bushy plant 30-35 cm high, with small leafy pseudobulbs topped by clusters of starry pink, 6 cm flowers; usually in spring. *p. 1716*

DIACRIUM *Orchidaceae* **S3OFD**

bicornutum (Epidendrum indivisum) (Tobago, Trinidad, Guayana, Brazil), "Virgin orchid"; handsome epiphyte with stout, hollow, furrowed pseudobulbs with 3-5 leathery leaves and long racemes of 5-20 pure white, fragrant flowers 5 cm across, with a few crimson spots on the lip and a yellow, fleshy crest (summer). (Caularthron) (S) *p. 1707*

DIANELLA *Liliaceae* **I2LFD**

caerulea (New South Wales), the "Blue flax-lily"; rhizomatous perennial about 60 cm high, with fibrous roots; long linear, sheathing, keeled, rough-edged leaves from the base and in two ranks along the erect stalk, bearing the inflorescence in branched panicles of blue flowers, with deep yellow anthers, followed by blue berries. *p. 1439*

longifolia (Tasmania); fibrous-rooted perennial with elongate leafy stems 60-90 cm; keeled sheaths with thin leaves dark green; clusters of greenish-yellow flowers, followed by light blue berries. *p. 1435*

tasmanica (Tasmania, Victoria, N. S. Wales), the "Tasman flax-lily"; with two-ranked, broadly sword-shaped leaves to 1 m long; turned down, spine-toothed margins; pale blue 2 cm flowers on tall branched stalks, followed by ornamental brilliant blue berries. *p. 1434*

DIANELLA: see also Dracaena

DIANTHERA *Acanthaceae* **S2LFM**

candicans (Jacobinia) (Mexico); straggling evergreen shrub with shining deep green lanceolate leaves, and axillary bilabiate flowers crimson-red, to

4 cm long, the lower lip divided into 3 segments. Described by Standley in Trees and Shrubs of Mexico as having corolla red, although the Latin species name candicans means "shining white". *p. 48*

DIANTHUS *Caryophyllaceae* **C2LBD**

barbatus (So. and S. Eastern Europe to So. Russia and East), "Sweet William" or "Bunch pink"; popular garden perennial better treated as a biennial; from some seed also annual; smooth herb 45-60 cm high with green flat and broader leaves than most Pinks; the sturdy stem with 3 cm flowers in large bracted heads, the spreading petals fringed and calyx bearded, in colors from white, pink, rose, red, purplish to bi-colored, blooming from June to August; winter-hardy. *Warm-temperate.* *p. 759*

caryophyllus (So. Europe to India), "Carnation"; tufted glaucous plant of stiff habit, with bluish linear leaves, the flowers showy, double, dentate, in many colors, and spicy-fragrant. Usually grown as biennial. *p. 758*

caryophyllus 'Apollo'; a diploid form of caryophyllus, typical of the "American Remontant carnation" commercially grown for cut flowers under glass, because of their perpetual, year round growing and flowering habit. 'Apollo' is a clear pink double flower with salmon sheen, and petals crenate, the inner ones incurved, and of good substance on stiff stem. *Warm-temperate.* *p. 758*

caryophyllus 'Cardinal Sim'; sport of Wm. Sim; a most vigorous and productive variety; fully double flower 9 cm dia., vivid scarlet red, with smooth edge, lightly fragrant. *p. 758*

caryophyllus 'Elegance'; a spray carnation; leading variety of the "Elegance carnation", a planned miniature with stiff, branching stalks each carrying 4 to 5 medium small, double flowers about 4 cm across, in this cultivar in white, flushed deep purple, and delightfully fragrant; advertised by Geo. Ball, West Chicago 1971, ideal as cut flowers for bouquets. *p. 759*

caryophyllus 'Juliet'; old-fashioned fragrant All America Selection 1975; a garden carnation to 30 cm high, normally biennial but grown as an annual, with silvery green foliage, and double flowers scarlet red, 6 cm across, and with old-fashioned fragrance; ideal as a border plant or for pots; fairly winter-hardy. *p. 759*

caryophyllus 'Mini Queen'; a special race of cut-flower carnations with tall, erect, wiry stems 30-50 cm long, each carrying several medium size 4-5 cm fully double, spicily fragrant flowers deep rose with white edges, the petals fringed; (photographed at the Scandinavian Flower Show, Malmoe, Sweden October 1970). *Warm-temperate.* *p. 758*

caryophyllus 'Pink Littlefield'; large flaring flower 9½ cm dia., with toothed petals carmine pink, on wiry stem. *p. 758*

caryophyllus 'Portrait'; high double flower 10 cm dia., clear rich rose pink with trace of white markings, fringed edge; wiry stem. *p. 758*

caryophyllus 'White Sim'; sport of 'Wm. Sim', high double flower 10 cm across pure white with creamy base and with lacy edge, spicy fragrant; stems wiry and slender. *p. 758*

chinensis heddewigii (China, Japan), "Rainbow pink"; blue-green tufted biennial; flowers in velvety colors and markings and petals much cut and frilled. *Warm temperate.* *p. 758*

deltoides (Great Britain to Japan), "Maiden pink" or "Meadow pink"; mat-forming, hardy perennial with green, linear leaves 2 cm long; floral stalks branched 10-30 cm high with single, pretty flowers 2 cm across, with toothed petals, in colors pink or red, or purple and white with red eye in hort. forms; may be grown as an annual. *p. 759*

hybrid 'Mitt's Pinks', a "Baby carnation"; a true miniature hybrid carnation (California 1962) derived from D. caryophyllus, plumarius, deltoides and latifolius; very cute as a diminutive flowering plant when grown in 6 cm pot, 20-25 cm high; dense little bush with narrow-linear, glaucous foliage and long-stemmed semi-double, fringed flowers 3 cm across, in several pretty colors, pink to blood-red with white eye, or red with pink border, blooming in spring. *p. 759*

DIAPHANANTHE *Orchidaceae* **S3OFM**

fragrantissima (Listrostachys) (Tanzania, Uganda, Angola); robust epiphyte with woody stem bearing 4-8 pairs of fleshy, sickle-shaped bilobed leaves 20-30 cm long; pendulous racemes of delicate fragile, almost transparent, greenish-white, spurred small 2 cm flowers, with fringed lip; mildly fragrant. *p. 1716*

DIASTEMA *Gesneriaceae* **S3HFM**

quinquevulnerum (Colombia, Venezuela); dwarf, hairy herb with creeping rhizome; ovate, rugose, serrate, bright green leaves; loose racemes of small, white, dainty, tubular flowers, the lobes each with a purple spot. *p. 1243*

vexans (Colombia); herbaceous gesneriad with hairy branching stems 10 cm high; ovate to lanceolate toothed hairy green leaves 8 cm in length on long petioles; stalked axillary white flowers with tube spotted purple-brown, and each spreading lobe has a purple brown spot at the base. *Tropical.* *p. 1243*

DICENTRA *Fumariaceae* **C2LFMhd**

cucullaria (Nova Scotia to Kansas); a perennial herb known as "Dutchman's breeches"; because of the small white flowers, tipped with yellow, appearing forked with their two diverging spurs, borne above the feathery basal leaves. *p. 1064*

spectabilis (Japan), "Bleeding heart"; perennial herb with divided leaves and arching stalks with pendulous, heartshaped, rosy flowers and protruding inner petals of white. *Temperate.* *p. 1064*

DICHAETANTHERA *Melastomataceae* **S2LBM**

crassinodes (Madagascar); tropical tree with robust branches having thickened nodes; small oblong, glabrous, sparsely bristly, 3-nerved, green leaves with cuneate base; flowers rosy or violaceous. *p. 1554*

DICHILOBOEA *Gesneriaceae* **S3LFW**

birmanica (Burma; China, Yunnan); erect herbaceous bush to 50 cm high, the woody stem covered by white or beige felt; the thick leaves well-spaced, deep green and quilted, to 12 cm long; inflorescence in axillary, elongate racemes of bracted, small white flowers, with corollas less than 1 cm long. *p. 1244*

DICHONDRA *Convolvulaceae* **I2LBM**

repens (West Indies); known as "Lawn-leaf"; used as a grass substitute in California; low herb creeping close to the ground and rooting, with close-matting stolons; small, rounded or kidney-shaped fresh green silky leaves to 2 cm across, tightly overlapping; the little flowers greenish-yellow; seeds freely. *p. 854*

DICHORISANDRA *Commelinaceae* **S3LFM**

reginae (Perú), "Queen's spiderwort"; stiffly erect, rather slow growing plant; the waxy, long pointed, dark green leaves banded and spotted on both sides with sparkling silver, the center metallic red-violet, and spilling over into deep purple beneath; flowers lavender. *Tropical.* *p. 779*

siebertii (Brazil); a bushy spreading plant which I first saw in Sao Paulo where it is used as a garden ornamental; the arching branches have ovate, glossy, metallic green leaves with two silvery length stripes; flowers blue. *Tropical.* *p. 783*

thyrsiflora (Brazil), "Blue ginger"; tall canes bearing rosettes of broad lance-shaped, glossy green leaves with purplish reverse, umbrella-like, topped by a huge raceme of brilliant, deep electric-blue flowers with yellow anthers. *Tropical.* *p. 779, 785*

thyrsiflora variegata; variety with the long green leaves having two silver bands down the length of the leaf, reddish midrib, and stem mottled purple. *p. 779*

warscewicziana (C. America); clustering plant with lance-shaped dark green leaves with purplish center and marked with silver bands when young, later growing into tall canes to 2 m high with leaves entirely green, and topped by a bold panicle of violet flowers marked white. *p. 5*, 784*

DICHORISANDRA: see also Campelia, Geogenanthus,

DICHROA *Saxifragaceae* **I2LBD**

febrifuga (Himalaya to China); attractive evergreen shrub 1-2 m; hydrangea-like, shoots and inflorescence downy; 10-20 cm leaves coarsely toothed; flowers white outside, bright blue inside. *p. 2048*

DICKSONIA *Dicksoniaceae (Filices)* **I2HFW**

antarctica (Australia, Tasmania), "Tasmanian treefern"; tree fern with woody trunk to 15 m high, covered with matted aerial rootlets, fronds to 2 m long, 3 pinnate, dark green with hard lanceolate toothed segments which are turned down at the margins, and a network of straw-colored veins. *Humid-subtropic.* *p. 1074, 1075, 1077*

fibrosa (New Zealand), "Golden treefern"; becoming tree-like, with trunk to 6 m tall, topped by a crown of handsome fronds bright glossy green, lighter and hairy beneath, 2-3 m long, bipinnate; trunk light brown. *Humid-tropical.* *p. 1073, 1074, 1075, 1076*

sellowiana (Brazil), "Brazilian tree fern"; arborescent trunk with elegant, glossy fresh green fronds 1-2 m long, bipinnately cut into feathery, linear segments. Photographed in the collection of Leningrad Botanic Garden, Soviet Union. *p. 1076*

squarrosa (New Zealand), "Westland treefern"; a medium-sized treefern to 6 m high, the slender black trunk clothed with leafbases, crown with fronds nearly horizontal, 2-3 pinnate, to 2½ m long, dull, dark green and stiff-leathery, and harsh to the touch; on black-brown stalks clothed when young by long brown, stiff hairs. *Humid-subtropic.* *p. 1073*

DICOMA *Compositae* **S3LBD**

argyrophylla (So. Africa; Natal), a "Toy sugarbush"; small perennial 30 cm high, the branches dense with narrow ovate leaves, thickly felted with white beneath; the flower heads are prickly and thistle-like, with silvery-white bracts; these may be cut as unusual and long-lasting material for a vase. *p. 827*

DICTAMNUS *Rutaceae* **I2LBD**

albus (fraxinella) (So. Europe to Palestine and China), "Dittany", "Gasplant", or "Burning bush"; aromatic perennial 60 to 90 cm or more high; the stems with pinnate leaves of 9 to 11 ovate, toothed leaflets, scented of lemon-peel; irregular flowers 4 cm across, the 5 petals white or rosy, with purplish lines and long curving stamens. The volatile oil exuding gas-like from the foliage and inflorescence during warm evenings is easily ignited by a match or extreme heat. By some authorities believed to be the bush "that burned with fire" of the Bible (Moldenke). *p. 2034*

DICTYOCARYUM *Palmae* **S3LFM**

globiferum (Colombia: Antioquia); tall feather palm from the Central Andes, to 35 m high, with straight, slender trunk and a crown of gracefully recurving pinnate fronds; the spherical fruit-kernels look like marbles. *p. 1852*

DICTYOSPERMA *Palmae* **S3LFM**

album (Mauritius), the "Princess-palm"; handsome feather-palm to 10 m, the slender, dark gray trunk with numerous vertical cracks, topped by a crown-shaft and the graceful pinnate fronds to 4 m long; the drooping leaflets shiny green with pale veins; the last undeveloped leaf always stands up in the center and unfolds from its binding as from a needle; fragrant reddish flowers at an early stage. *Tropical.* *p. 1878*

aureum (Réunion), "Yellow Princess palm", or "Hurricane palm", as they withstand high winds; straight, slender, dark gray trunk with swollen base; ring scars forming steps and many vertical cracks, to 8 m tall; long green crownshaft opens to a handsome crown of pinnate fronds 3 m long, with shiny dark green leaflets in one plane; the rachis twists 90 degrees so that leaflets parallel the trunk; reddish-yellow flowers and purplish fruit. *Tropical.* *p. 1873*

DICYRTA: see Achimenes

DIDIEREA *Didiereaceae* **S2LBD**

madagascariensis (S. W. Madagascar), "Madagascar cactus"; erect tree-like succulent 4-6 m high, in habitat with the appearance of a cactus-like euphorbia; thick gray stems set with short, thorn-like branches which at their ends produce one long spine and several shorter ones, and soft, succulent, narrow-cylindric green leaves. Attractive as young pot plant. *p. 949, 950*

mirabilis (Madagascar); cactus-like xerophytic tree to 4 m high with swollen trunk almost 60 cm thick, succulent and thorny branches, densely studded with clusters of long curving thorns in the center of which either sit bundles of linear leaves, or male or female flowers. *p. 950*

DIDYMAOTUS *Aizoaceae* **I2LBD**

lapidiformis (So. Africa: Karroo); small, extremely succulent plant with pairs of leaves joined at base, 2½ cm long, keeled on back, flat on top, rough, light grey-green to purplish; lateral flowers white with lavender center. *p. 77*

DIDYMOCARPUS *Gesneriaceae* **S3HFM**

humboldtianus (Sri Lanka); stemless herbaceous tropical plant with cordate, wrinkled leaves and hairy, the margins with rounded teeth; flowers pale lilac or light blue with yellow throat, in loose cluster, on fleshy stalk. *p. 1244*

kerrii (S. E. Himalayas); tropical herbaceous, fibrous-rooted, low, branching plant 15 to 18 cm high, with fleshy stems; pairs of slightly hairy, saintpaulia-like green leaves, crenate at margins; from the leaf axils arise branched clusters of small 2-3 cm dark purple flowers, the corolla a swelling tube with flaring lobes. *p. 1244*

mortonii ('crinitus') (Sikkim Himalaya); tropical herb with erect, fleshy stem and pairs of hairy, sharply-toothed leaves; axillary flowers a swelling white trumpet flaring into light blue lobes, on slender stalks. *p. 1243*

DIEFFENBACHIA *Araceae* **•S1LFD**

amoena (Colombia, Costa Rica); sturdy, thick-stemmed species with large, oblong-pointed, glabrous leaves, deep green and marked with cream-white bands and blotches along veins. *Tropical.* *p. 219, 223*

amoena 'Tropic Snow' (syn. 'Tropical Topaz' or 'Hi-Color'); beautiful Florida (Chaplin) mutation of very compact habit; showy leathery foliage glossy deep green highly variegated from center with cream and nile green. *Tropical.* *p. 215*

'Arvida': see 'Exotica'

aurantiaca (Costa Rica); stocky plant with broad-ovate leaves grass-green with indistinct mottling of nile green; channeled petioles; spathe orange. *p. 220*

x bausei (maculata x weirii); beautiful, pointed leaf delicate yellowish green with dark green and white spots and dark green at edge. *Tropical.* *p. 5*, 160A, 214, 217*

bowmannii (Colombia); some resemblance in markings to D. amoena, but the leaves are much broader, and the lateral markings of cream are less noticeable; reverse freely spotted white. The picture shown on page 219 may be D. macrophylla. *p. 219*

'Camilla'; outstanding Danish mutation of D. 'Exotica Perfection', similar to D. 'Marianne', of smallish, compact, sturdy habit and freely self-branching; highly colored ovate, slender-pointed leaves primarily creamy-yellow with lighter veins, bordered in rich green, 20 to 25 cm long. *p. 221*

chelsonii (Colombia); broad leaf deep, satiny green, midrib marked by gray band with feathering. *p. 217*

costata (Colombia; Perú); leathery, broad oval, unequal-sided leaf with sunken veins, dull metallic green with satiny sheen and occasional lighter marbling. *p. 218*

daguense (Colombia); thick-stemmed plant with heavy, leathery, pointed leaves; thick, elevated midrib, lateral veins depressed; rich shiny green. *p. 218*

delecta (Colombia); graceful species from the Choco with narrow lanceolate pendulous leaves, fleshy, dull, grass-green with irregular yellow area along midrib. *p. 220*

eburnea (Brazil); smallish oblong pointed, soft, green leaves with depressed veins and faintly spotted white; petioles striped white. *p. 220*

'Exotica' ('Arvida') (Costa Rica); attractive mutant, probably of hoffmannii, from the Rio Ysidro, quite compact and shapely; of slender, narrow habit; smallish ovate pointed, firm leaf, deep matte green and highly variegated cream-white, and of good texture. *p. 15*, 214, 218, 220*

'Exotica alba', photographed in Germany 1979; outstanding mutation of D. 'Exotica Perfection'; of smallish, compact habit and freely self-branching; of similar character as 'Camilla' (in Denmark) and 'Marianne' (in Germany); highly colored ovate slender-pointed leaves primarily creamy yellow with lighter veins, bordered in rich green, 20 to 25 cm long; freely self-branching for bushiness and ease of propagation. *Tropical.* *p. 221*

'Exotica Perfection'; a Florida selection of compact habit, the smallish leaves 15-20 cm long, broadly bordered with deep matte green and of leathery feel; highly variegated greenish ivory. Excellent keeper as a houseplant. *Tropical.* *p. 221*

fosteri (Costa Rica); dwarf species with small ovate-acuminate, deep green, leathery leaves with satiny sheen, closely set on slender cane. *p. 219*

fournieri (Colombia); upright, large, shiny leathery black-green leaves with white spots; slender and very elegant. *Tropical.* *p. 216*

"gigantea" hort., robust plant with thin-leathery, broad-ovate leaves smooth fresh green with irregular creamy-white blotches. *p. 222*

hoffmannii (Costa Rica, 3400 m); oblong pointed leaves deep, satiny green, marbled and spotted white as are petioles; midrib white. *p. 5*, 214, 218*

humilis (Perú: Upper Amazon); collected in Loreto, Perú 1960 and introduced by Bailey Hortorium, Ithaca, New York; a promising house plant of compact habit, the stems densely clothed by relatively small lanceolate leaves of sturdy texture 15-30 cm long and 4-6 cm wide, semi-glossy, bright medium green, and with prominent midrib; of good keeping quality and resembling Aglaonema. *p. 221*

imperialis (Perú); tall plant with large, leathery, dark green leaves, and silver-gray feathering along midrib, pale green and pale yellow blotching toward apex. *p. 219*

'Janet Weidner'; sport of D. maculata 'Superba' 1955; tall-growing plant similar to maculata but with large, more plentiful, chalk-white variegation and marbling. *p. 222*

jenmannii: see maculata jenmannii

lancifolia maculata; clustering rosette of compact habit, with firm-textured semi-glossy narrow, lanceolate leaves 20-30 cm long and 3-5 cm wide, dark green, spotted and blotched with greenish-white and ivory. Photographed under this name at Royal Botanic Gardens Sydney, Australia. See D. maculata angust. lancifolia.

leoniae (Colombia); attractive plant with satiny, somewhat reflexed, oblong leaves of firm texture, friendly green with dominant yellow variegation; faintly cream along midrib. *p. 214, 219*

leopoldii (Costa Rica); velvety, corrugated, emerald-green leaf with white midrib and pale band alongside it; brownish stem and petioles, spotted white. *p. 214, 215, 218*

longispatha (Panama); long-oblong, leathery leaves to 60 cm plain, glossy-green with sunken veins and thick midrib and stem, petioles winged; spathe 30 cm long. *p. 220*

maculata (picta) (Brazil), "Spotted dumbcane", in Latin America as "Cucaracha"; glossy, grass green, oval leaves with cordate base and ivory-white marbling and blotching; petioles dotted pale green; spathe greenish; found growing wild by the writer at the confluence of the Solimoes and Rio Negro in Amazonas. *Tropical.* *p. 19*, 214, 216*

maculata angustior (picta) (Brazil); robust, strong plant with narrow lanceolate, dark green, leathery leaves, with numerous sunken veins, and tapering toward base, on petioles winged ¾ up. *p. 215*

maculata angustior angustifolia (picta); elegant plant with narrow lanceolate leaves of almost leathery texture, glossy, grass-green, richly spotted with ivory-white; stem and winged petioles olive brown with lengthwise pink bands; spathe pale green. *p. 215, 216*

maculata angustior lancifolia (picta) (Brazil); sturdy erect plant with narrow lanceolate, leathery leaves dark green, sparsely variegated with scattered ivory-white spots and stripes. *p. 215*

maculata barraquiniana (picta) (Brazil); leaves oblong-pointed, bright green with bold, white midrib and occasional white spots; white leaf stalks. *p. 216*

maculata 'Gigantea' (picta) (Pará); large growing plant with broad, glossy, grass-green leaves with cordate base and depressed veins; midrib and petioles pale green, regularly and prominently mottled. *p. 220*

maculata jenmannii (Guyana); long-oblong leaves glossy, fresh green with distinct ivory bars in feather design. *Tropical.* *p. 214, 215, 216*

maculata magnifica (picta) (Venezuela); robust plant with broadly ovate-pointed, oblique, soft leaves, shiny-green, with depressed veins and occasional white blotches; glaucous beneath. *p. 220*

maculata memoria: see x memoria-corsii

maculata 'Pia'; robust cultivar of D. maculata 'Superba', with large green leaves rich in greenish-white to white, along the margins deep green. Grown in greenhouses in Germany and exhibited at the German National Flower Show in Cologne 1971. *p. 221*

maculata 'Rudolph Roehrs' (Roehrs cultivar, named by the author 1937), "Gold dieffenbachia"; a striking mutant having oblong pointed 25-30 cm leaves almost entirely yellow or chartreuse, with ivory-white blotches, and only the midrib and border dark green. Both beautiful and showy, and proven an excellent house plant. *p. 5*, 19*, 214, 215, 217*

maculata shuttleworthii (picta) (Colombia); long, lanceolate, deep green leaves with feathery, gray band along midrib and pea-green blotches on blade. *p. 219*

maculata 'Superba' (Roehrs 1950); very attractive, compact mutant of maculata, with thicker, more durable foliage dominated by a high degree of creamy-white variegation, over the glossy green leaf. *Tropical.* *p. 219*

maculata viridis (picta) (No. Brazil); free grower with deep green, glossy, oblong pointed leaves of thin texture and slightly cordate base; petioles fresh green; may be natural hybrid with seguina. *p. 216*

majestica (Colombia), sturdy plant with stiff, leathery, oblong obovate, slender-pointed leaves somber green with scattered bright yellowish blotches, and a feathery silver bar along the middle. *p. 222*

'Mary Weidner'; sport 1955 of D. maculata 'Superba'; very compact growing plant; petioles mottled ivory; leaves spotted cream. *p. 222*

meleagris (Ecuador); long-lanceolate leaf with acute, uneven base, leathery, deep green with white blotching surrounded by light green; long, deep green petioles streaked white. *p. 220*

x memoria-corsii (maculata x wallisii); broadly lanceolate leaves rather gray, with dark, gray-green veining, interrupted by solid green blotches and occasional ivory spots. *p. 214, 216*

oerstedii (Guatemala, Costa Rica); graceful plant; oblong-ovate, leathery, matte blackish-green leaves on slender petioles. *p. 219*

oerstedii variegata (Costa Rica); the slender, hard and smooth, dark-green leaf with a contrasting ivory-white midrib. *p. 214, 219*

parlatorei (Colombia); tall tropical foliage plant of robust habit, slowly forming stout stem, leaning with age and weight; long clasping petioles winged halfways, carry the leathery oblong 45 cm leaves, shiny deep green, with prominently broad, thick midrib, lightly channeled higher up. Photographed at Brooklyn Botanic Garden. *p. 221*

parlatorei marmorea (Colombia); long oblong, tough-leathery, dark lustrous leaves with fleshy midrib partially white; the blade blotched with silver, especially when young; strong, winged petioles. *p. 218*

picta: see maculata

pittieri (Costa Rica); long, satiny, emerald-green leaf with depressed veins, and marbled pale green or ivory; base of petioles surrounding stem. *p. 216*

reginae (Estado do Rio); oblong pointed leaves somewhat pendant, glabrous, pale pea-green on dark green and blotched cream-white; bluish-green beneath. *Tropical.* *p. 219*

rex (Colombia); beautiful plant from the Magdalena valley, very dark green, long ovate leaves with white blotches set in pale green, the white showing beneath; midrib marked white; stem green with brown veins. *p. 220*

'Sao Antonio' (S.E. Brazil); attractive novelty with broad, succulent leaves tapering to a point, rich green with yellow-green marbling near midrib, and freely spotted with white; the petioles white traced with green. *p. 222*

seguina (Puerto Rico, W. Indies), "Dumbcane"; robust species with long elliptic, dark green fleshy leaves, base acute, prominent midrib and depressed veins; pleasing green beneath; spathe green. *Tropical.* *p. 217*

seguina decora (Brazil); robust grower with glossy, firm leaves deep green, with faint, yellow-green marbling concentrated close to center and scattered, clear, white spots; petioles white. *p. 217*

seguina irrorata (Pará); oblong, pointed, rather thin leaf, predominantly yellow-green, with dark green blotching and edging; petioles whitish. *p. 218*

seguina lineata (marmorata) (Venezuela, Colombia); similar to the type but with petioles striated white. *p. 217*

seguina liturata (longispatha, wallisii) (Pará); large, leathery, dark green leaf with a rather broad, yellowish-green, ragged-margined stripe along the midrib. *p. 218*

seguina nobilis (bowmannii) (Venezuela); broad leaves pointed, medium green with some yellow-green blotching and marbling, showing through beneath; petiole white striped. *p. 216*

x splendens (leopoldii x maculata); velvet, bronze-green leaf with nile-green, and ivory spots and ivory midrib. *Tropical.* *p. 214, 218*

'Tropic Snow': see under amoena

'Tropical Topaz'; excellent indoor decorative plant of bold habit and good keeping quality under low light conditions; a compact cultivar of D. amoena with heavy-textured leaves highly variegated greenish-cream and ivory white over rich green. Several names are used for this or similar plant by different nurseries, but this may be the same as the patented D. 'Tropic Snow'. *p. 221*

velutina (Colombia); compact plant with satiny, firm, deep green leaves, rather oval, with yellow-green marbling; white-striped petioles. *p. 217*

wallisii (No. S. America); tall-growing, robust plant with oblique lanceolate leaves with long tapering apex, matte to semi-glossy grass-green, a broad feathery band of light gray to creamy-silver along midrib, on winged petioles. *Tropical.* *p. 215*

'Wilson's Delight'; handsome, bold plant; broad, fleshy leaves to 40 cm long, deep green with broad, cream-white midrib, the cream fanning out into the lateral veins. *Tropical.* *p. 221*

DIERAMA *Iridaceae* **I2LBMd**

pulcherrima (So. Africa: Cape to Transvaal), "East London harebell"; pretty, cormous herb about $1^1/_2$ m high, with basal long-linear, narrow, rigid leaves; blooming on branched, pendant spikes, the 3 cm funnel-shaped flowers bright purple or blood-red, in autumn. *Subtropic.* *p. 1334*

DIETES *Iridaceae* **C2LBDd**

bicolor (Moraea) (So. Africa: E. Cape), "Yellow wild iris"; tufts of evergreen, stiff and light green leaves growing to 60 cm and only 1 cm wide; the erect, branching floral stalk with most attractive flowers 5 cm across, with 3 inner petals clear lemon-yellow, and 3 round, flat petals blotched orange and maroon-black near base; summer blooming. *p. 1329*

grandiflora (So. Africa), "Large wild iris"; sword-shaped leaves in flat fan; big flowers with large white to pinkish petals and purple stripes in center. *Subtropic.* *p. 1329*

'Oakhurst hybrid' (Moraea) (vegeta, catenulata x bicolor); perennial taller and more robust than either parent, and willing grower; rhizomatous; iris-like, well rounded flowers, with spreading segments 6 cm across, creamy-white with lemon to orange and brown blotch, and violet to purple crests in the center, short-lived for one day, but producing continually; the flowering stems are perennial and will bloom for many years if not cut. *p. 1328*

prolongata hort. (Moraea iridioides prolongata) (So. Africa), the "White wild iris" of Africa; rhizomatous plant forming dense clusters of narrow, laxly drooping basal leaves, and stiff-erect stalks 50 to 80 cm high, bearing in succession the showy iris-like flowers, pure white except for a spoon-like design of mustard-yellow. *p. 1329*

vegeta (Moraea iridioides) (So. Africa: E. Cape, Natal), "African iris"; lovely, free-blooming rhizomatous, clustering plant with linear, dark green basal leaves arranged fan-like from creeping root stock; on long branching stalks the somewhat fleeting, iris-like flowers 5-8 cm across, white tinged with blue, and yellow on outer petals, the crest of style marked with blue; summer-blooming. Widely planted in California where it seems to be in bloom all year. *Subtropic.* *p. 1328, 1329*

vegeta catenulata (Moraea) (So. Africa), "African iris"; low growing plant with glaucous leaves arranged fan-like, flowers with flaring segments pure white with lavender style crests and yellow beard. *p. 1328*

DIETES: see also Moraea

DIGITALIS *Scrophulariaceae* **C2LFMd**

ambigua (grandiflora) (C. Europe, Balkans, So. Russia, W. Siberia), "Yellow foxglove"; hairy perennial with lanceolate toothed, veiny leaves, the nodding tubular 5 cm flowers pale ochre-yellow marked with brown inside. *p. 2054, 2060*

purpurea (W. Europe), "Foxglove"; biennial with wrinkled leaves in rosettes and on the erect $^1/_2$-1 m showy spike of dense, bell-shaped, bilabiate, nodding flowers, purple, varying to white, with dark purple spots, edged white inside, in summer. *Warm temperate.* *p. 2052, 2058*

DILLENIA *Dilleniaceae* **S2-3LFM**

indica (India to Java and Philippines), "Elephant apple"; handsome tree to 12 m high, usually evergreen but may lose foliage in dry season; very ornamental, large oblanceolate, thick leaves 30-40 cm long, bright light green above and strongly pinnately depressed-veined; rough beneath, and margins toothed; fragrant magnolia-like white flowers with golden stamens. Globose, acid fruit to 10 cm dia, edible when fresh; used in curries and jellies. *p. 951*

philippinensis (Philippines), "Simpoh"; handsome tropical spreading tree with ovate, shiny green leaves smaller than D. indica; the lateral ribs in quilted channels, and margins deeply toothed; the flowers with white petals, purplish stamens and styles; globose fruit also smaller, 5 cm in dia., and edible. *p. 951*

DIMORPHOTHECA *Compositae* **C2LBM**

aurantiaca (So. Africa: Namaqualand); perennial and shrubby but grown as a herbaceous annual; branches 22 cm high with linear leaves and solitary daisy-type flower heads with disk golden brown tipped with metallic blue, the florets bright orange. *p. 811*

chrysanthemifolia (Cape Prov.); shrubby perennial 60-90 cm high, with leafy branches bearing bluish, obovate, cut leaves, and solitary terminal blooms 8 cm across, with golden yellow florets, tan beneath, yellow disk; opening mid-day. *p. 811*

ecklonis (So. Africa), "Cape marigold"; shrubby perennial with narrow toothed leaves and large daisy-like flowers with ray-florets white above, purplish beneath, and blackish-blue disk, closing at night. *p. 809*

DIMORPHOTHECA: see also Osteospermum

DINTERANTHUS *Aizoaceae* **S2LBD**

inexpectatus (Southwest Africa), "Surprise split rock"; normally compact, stemless succulent with pairs of keeled gray leaves united halfway, translucent greenish dots; bright orange-yellow flower on a flat stalk. *p. 56*

pole-evansii (Cape Prov.); wrinkled rounded body with a fissure 1 cm deep, dove-gray; flowers with glistening golden-yellow petals. *p. 56*

puberulus (Cape Prov.), "Downy split rock"; cluster-forming succulent to 4 cm high, with 1-2 pairs of rounded leaves grayish-brown dotted dark green, with velvety feel; flowers golden yellow. *p. 56, 57*

punctatus (Cape Prov.); low, clustering succulent with pairs of thick leaves somewhat keeled beneath; bluish tinted pink and dotted; flowers inside yellow, outside reddish. *p. 56*

vanzijlii (Lithops) (Cape Prov.); a larger "Split-rock" with 1-3 pairs of leaves, pale buff with flat top marked purplish-brown; flowers orange-yellow. *p. 69*

wilmotianus (Cape Prov.), "Split rock"; tiny succulent like a round cleft stone 2 cm in dia., outside and top keeled, surface wrinkled, grayish, tinged with pink, and covered with violet dots; flowers golden-yellow. *p. 57*

DIONAEA *Droseraceae (Carnivorous Plants)* **C3H Sphag BW**

muscipula (Carolinas), "Venus fly trap"; carnivorous perennial rosette of damp mossy places, with leaves 3-12 cm long; in the upper part the two halves of a leaf are turned upward and equipped with long teeth which close traplike when entered by flies; the small 2 cm white flowers in clusters on tall stalks. *Warm temperate.* *p. 763, 765, 1952A*

DIOON *Cycadaceae* **S2LFD**

edule (Mexico), "Virgin's palm"; palm-like plant from the hot open country, closest to the fossil cycads, with stiff pinnate leaves 1-2 m long, and having spiny tips, the young petioles are covered with white wool; edible seeds borne in cones to 30 cm long. *Tropical.* *p. 935, 941, 943*

purpusii (So. Mexico); stout, short trunk, crowned with numerous stiff and ascending pinnate leaves 1 m or more, pinnae 5-10 cm long, sharp-pointed usually with 1-3 spinelike teeth on the upper margin; male cones 15-20 cm, ovate female cones 45 cm long, with woolly bract. *p. 936*

spinulosum (Mexico), "Giant dioon"; treefern-like plant from the rain forest, with tall trunks to 15 m high and slender, the spreading pinnate leaves to 2 m long in noble rosette, spiny teeth at margins. (M) *p. 941, 944*

DIOSCOREA *Dioscoreaceae* **S3LFMd**

amarantoides 'Eldorado' (Rio Negro, N. Brazil); herbaceous tropical twiner with the tuberous roots of yams; ornamental, cordate-pointed leaves coppery bronze with silvery areas along main veins, purplish reverse. *p. 953*

batatas (China, Korea, Japan, Philippines), "Chinese yam" or "Cinnamon vine"; fast-growing high climber with spiralling vines to 6 m long; the stems striped red and occasionally bearing small tubers; the broadly cordate, glossy green leaves are deeply furrowed along veins, and to 10 cm or more long; tiny greenish-white male flowers cinnamon-scented, in clusters from the leaf axils; cultivated in China and Eastern Asia for the club-shaped edible tubers, to 1 m long, and extracted from deep in the ground. Grown as ornamental both in the tropics, and in temperate zones where the growth is annual and the roots are winter-hardy. *p. 953*

bulbifera (Trop. Asia, Philippines), "Air-potato" or true "Yam"; twining plant without the large underground tuber of most yams, but forming aerial, axillary, angular gray-brown tubers to 30 cm long and edible; alternate leaves heartshaped, and small dioecious, greenish flowers. *Tropical.* *p. 952*

composita (Mexico), "Cortisone-root"; vigorous tropical twiner with wiry stem and handsome cordate, coppery-green leaves, the blade with depressed parallel veins and also quilted across; the large starchy tuber is processed to produce the healing drug cortisone. *p. 952*

discolor (Surinam), "Ornamental yam"; tall climbing plant with beautiful broad, heart-shaped leaves having long basal lobes, dark olive green marbled light green and silver-gray, veins carmine to silver, reverse purple. *p. 953*

dodecaneura (Brazil); leaves somewhat hastate, dark satiny green with brownish sheen, gray marbling along midrib and at lobes, purplish beneath. *p. 953*

elephantipes (Testudinaria) (Cape Prov., Natal, Transvaal), "Elephant's foot" or "Hottentot-bread"; curious-looking partially exposed tuber to 90 cm across, the bark divided into corrugated angled knobs and from which rises the annual vining stalk bearing heart- or kidney-shaped leaves and greenish-yellow flowers with dark spots. *Subtropic.* *p. 952, 953*

macrostachys (Testudinaria) (Mexico), the "Tortoise plant"; large, knobby woody, chocolate brown tuber 20 cm or more across, resting above the soil and looking like a horny turtle, its coat broken into numerous angled plates; sprouting slender, asparagus-like shoots becoming vine-like, 1 m or more high, with alternate leaves and small axillary greenish-yellow flowers; grown as a curiosity in greenhouse. *Arid-tropical.* *p. 952*

multicolor (Brazil); beautiful ornamental herbaceous climbing vine from large tuberous roots; the well-spaced handsome, heart-shaped, thin leaves 8-12 cm long, rich iridescent velvety green spotted and variegated with pale green especially near veins, purple beneath; small greenish-yellow flowers; needs winter rest, in cool greenhouse. *p. 952*

multicolor argyraea (Colombia), "Silver leaf yam"; attractive long oval pointed leaves of emerald green with the areas between veins silvery gray. *p. 953*

multicolor melanoleuca (Amazonas); large, cordate showy leaves, coppery when young, later evenly green with wide central band and lateral bands or spots of silver white; reverse purple. *p. 953*

DIOSMA *Rutaceae* **I2LBD**

reevesii (So. Africa), "Breath-of heaven"; evergreen heather-like shrub, with feathery, very small needle-like channeled leaves aromatically scented like pine-needles, and with little white flowers. *p. 2026*

DIOSPYROS *Ebenaceae* **S3LBM**

ebenum (India, Sri Lanka), "Ebony" or "Makassar ebony"; large evergreen tropical tree with smooth branchlets, elliptic, glossy green leaves 5 to 15 cm long; male flowers 3 to 15 together, female blossoms solitary, producing small 2 cm fruit. Wood is jet-black, sometimes streaked with yellow, very heavy and strong, the best ebony of commerce. *p. 955*

kaki (Japan, China), "Kaki" or "Japanese persimmon"; a well-known fruit tree of the Orient; bushy, deciduous tree 8 to 12 m high, with brownish branches, broad ovate leathery leaves 8-20 cm long and shining green above, pubescent beneath; 4 cm flowers yellowish-white; on female trees the depressed globose glowing red fruit 8 cm dia., with custard-like orange flesh; especially piquant and delicious when served frozen, with a taste like fruity sherbert. *Subtropic to Warm-temperate.* *p. 955*

DIPCADI *Liliaceae* **I2LBMd**

serotinum (Spain); bulbous plant 22 cm high, with linear, channeled leaves, long-stalked racemes of nodding tubular-bell-shaped brownish flowers, in June. *p. 1434*

DIPIDAX *Liliaceae* **I2LFMd**

triquetrum (So. Africa: Cape), "Star-of-the-marsh"; bulbous plant with radiating green leaves, rolled at base, half-round, grooved above; terminal spikes with starry white flowers flushed pink, two crimson nectaries at base of outer segments. *p. 1434*

DIPLACUS: see Mimulus

DIPLADENIA: see Mandevilla

DIPLAZIUM *Polypodiaceae (Filices)* **S3HNM**

esculentum (India to Polynesia), "Edible dwarf tree-fern"; lovely semi-dwarf tree-fern, with short trunk 30-60 cm long, the fronds 1-2 m pinnate or bi-pinnate, the segments notched or crenate, fresh green. *p. 1109*

lanceum: see Pyrrosia

plantaginifolium (Mexico and W. Indies south to Brazil); small tufted fern with leathery fronds on firm erect stalks, the blades narrow spear-shaped with undulated and toothed margins. *p. 1109*

proliferum (asperum) (Polynesia, Malaya, Trop. Africa), "Double-dot fern"; tufted fern with spreading pinnate fronds ½-1 m long, the leaflets 2½-5 cm broad, often bearing young plantlets in axils. *p. 1109*

sylvaticum (So. India, Java, Borneo); tropical fern closely related to Asplenium; forming a rosette from a central root stock, the pinnate fronds 30-60 cm long, somewhat spear-shaped, borne on firm brown stalks, scaly at the base; spreading leaflets of thin texture and fresh green. *p. 1100*

DIPLAZIUM: see also Pyrrosia

DIPLOTHEMIUM *Palmae* **I2LBM**

maritimum (Allagoptera arenaria) (S.E. Brazil); small feather palm forming colonies on sea-shore dunes from Bahia to the Restinga south of Rio; trunkless, with pinnate leaves arising directly from the ground, 1½ to 2½ m high, recurving, waxy dark green above, white-fuzzy beneath; inflorescence a spike with reddish spadix, the green fruit edible. *p. 1870*

DIPSACUS *Dipsaceae* **C2LBD**

laciniatus (C. and So. Europe to Siberia); biennial thistle-like prickly herb to 1 m, with much divided, lobed and jagged leaves bristly-hairy, and terminal, ovoid flower heads of stiff bracts, whitish flowers and reddish anthers. *p. 950*

DISA *Orchidaceae* **C3HFM**

stairsii (Kenya, Tanzania, Uganda, Zaire); terrestrial with underground tubers, forming a rosette; erect stem to 60 cm high, covered by sheathing leaves decreasing into bracts colored red; spike conical, dense with 2 cm flowers, deep rose-purple, the dorsal sepal cup-shaped forming a hood. A pretty flowering plant. *p. 1704*

uniflora (grandiflora) (So. Africa), "Pride of Table Mountain"; terrestrial rosette of shining, lanceolate leaves with tuberous rootstock, and producing an erect, leafy spike to 60 cm high with a lax cluster of showy flowers t cm across, the helmet-shaped dorsal sepal red outside, inside lighter, veined with crimson and shaded with yellow, the lower sepals vivid scarlet, lip small. (Jan.-April). *Subtropic.* *p. 1709*

DISCHIDIA *Asclepiadaceae* **S3LFD**

bengalense (India); epiphytic trailer, with twisting, wiry stems rooting at the joints; opposite narrow, fleshy two-edged, flattened leaves; small urn-shaped flowers. *Humid-tropical.* *p. 364*

cordifolia (Malaya); vigorous epiphytic tropical climber or trailer with long slender stems producing adventitious roots; distantly spaced medium-green narrow elliptic, fleshy leaves to 3 cm long. *p. 364*

imbricata (Malaysia), "Thruppence urn plant"; tropical epiphytic high-climbing vine with thin-wiry twining stems bearing opposite succulent, small rounded 2-3 cm leaves convex like an umbrella, and growing against their support shingle-like; small urn-shaped, hoya-like flowers. *p. 364*

minima: see Hoya engleriana

pectinoides (Philippines); epiphytic trailer with twining, rooting stems; some of the leaves ovate 18 mm long, others transformed into swollen sacs, mussel-like gray pitchers collecting rainwater or also ants; small carmine red flowers, urn-shaped, with fleshy lobes, in leaf axils. *p. 364*

platyphylla (Philippines); rambling vine with thin stems, opposite fleshy, gray-green leaves rounded or kidney-shaped, and pitcher-shaped, beige flowers 3-4 mm. dia. *Tropical.* *p. 364*

rafflesiana (Malaya, New Guinea), "Malayan urn vine"; epiphytic climber with oddly thick-fleshy oval leaves formed into pitchers; the mature, 8-10 cm, opposite leaves are pear-like, hollow, purplish inside, in habitat frequented by ants; yellowish flowers in umbels. *Tropical.* *p. 363*

rafflesiana nummularia (Queensland, Papua); succulent vine growing on small trees, starting out with small fleshy, round leaves less than 2½ cm dia., and called "Thruppence" in New Guinea; later forming large pear-like, hollow, angled bulbs glaucous-gray, harboring ants. *p. 363*

DISSOTIS *Melastomataceae* **S3LBM**

grandiflora (Sierra Leone, Senegambia); herbaceous plant 30-60 cm high with a woody, tuberous base, branches twiggy, 4-angled, bristly-hairy; lanceolate leaves few, 5-9 cm long, lightly hairy; purplish flowers 5-8 cm across. *p. 1552*

princeps (Tanzania to Transvaal); attractive, somewhat herbaceous shrub to 2 m tall, with 5-nerved hairy, puckered, ovate leaves; large violet-purple flowers; their hidden anthers attached to the filaments spring out to disperse their pollen when mature. *p. 1552*

DISTICTIS *Bignoniaceae* **I2-3LBD**

buccinatoria (Phaedranthus; Bignonia cherere) (Mexico), "Blood trumpet"; vine with showy flowers which I first saw, smothered with blooms, around the Union Buildings in Pretoria, South Africa; rough-leathery oval leaves and axillary clusters of large trumpet-shaped waxy flowers with flaring lobes, crimson-red with scarlet sheen, and yellow throat. *Subtropic.* *p. 498*

DITEPAPANTHUS *Balanophoraceae* **S3ONM**

malagasicus (Madagascar); a tropical parasite with brown stem without scales and oblong leaves; the inflorescence 5-10 cm high, in young stage covered by hexagonal, peltate scales of blackish color. *p. 352*

DIZYGOTHECA *Araliaceae* **S2LFM**

elegantissima (Aralia) (New Hebrides), "False aralia"; graceful shrub with palmately compound, leathery leaves, the threadlike, narrow segments metallic, red-brown and lobed; slender stem mottled cream. Forms a small tree to 8 m high, with leaflets much wider in maturity. *p. 305, 315, 318*

elegantissima 'Castor'; a compact growing, freely branching cultivar seen in Germany, with palmately compound leaves, the leathery leaflets broader than the species, purplish-green with ivory-white midrib. *Tropical.* *p. 304*

kerchoveana (Polynesia); small tropical evergreen tree with slender stem whitish with dark markings; digitately compound leaves, the 9-11 oblanceolate leaflets arranged in a circle, wavy on margins, deep glossy green except for pale midrib; reverse reddish; small flowers in umbels, followed by berry-like fruits. *p. 304*

veitchii (New Caledonia); slender shrub with leathery, palmately compound, dainty leaves dark, coppery green, the little segments long-elliptic and [illegible]ith pink ribs, the margins crisped. *p. 312*

[illegible]DECATHEON *Primulaceae* **C2LFM**

[illegible]adia (Manitoba to Pennsylvania and Texas), "Shooting-star"; small [illegible] herb with wavy-margined basal leaves, and nodding cyclamen-[illegible] with reflexed corolla lobes, rose with white base and long purple [illegible]erate. *p. 1966*

[illegible] *Sapindaceae* **I2LBD**

[illegible]a' (No. Mexico to So. America and West Indies), "Pur-[illegible]owing evergreen bush to 5 m high, dense with [illegible]hes; narrow willow-like obovate to lanceolate 10 [illegible]le in the cv. 'Purpurea', the color deepening in [illegible] short clusters. The straw-like pinkish, winged [illegible]y early settlers in Arizona. *p. 2038*

DOLICHOS *Leguminosae* **S3LBM**

lablab (Trop. Africa: Egypt), "Hyacinth-bean"; woody perennial climber with purple stems, usually grown as an annual; leaves of 3 ovate, purplish-green leaflets 8 to 15 cm long, and veined with purple; rosy-lilac 2 cm butterfly flowers in loose racemes, standing out from the foliage; followed by velvety, bean-like pods 6 cm long. *p. 1380*

DOLICHOTHELE *Cactaceae* **I2LBD**

baumii—described under Mammillaria

longimamma (C. Mexico), "Finger-mound"; interesting plant of globular shape to 10 cm high but consisting almost entirely of cylindrical knobs to 5 cm long, deep green and soft-fleshy, tipped with scattered soft pale spines; flowers yellow. *Arid-tropical.* *p. 708, 711*

sphaerica (Texas, Mexico); small depressed plant to 5 cm wide, with a thick root, the fleshy tubercles 1 cm long, pale green, tipped with pale, thin spines; showy flowers sulphur yellow. *p. 711*

DOMBEYA *Sterculiaceae* **S3LFD**

x cayeuxii (mastersii x wallichii), the "Mexican rose"; handsome shrub with bristly-hairy stems; broad cordate, dark green, netted, thin leaves 18 cm long, soft and rough-hairy; beautiful pendant 3 cm rosy pink flowers with light center, in dense round 9 cm clusters. *p. 2087*

rotundifolia (Transvaal), known in Africa as the "Wild pear"; deciduous tree to 8 m high, a gorgeous sight on the High Veld when trees are covered with small cream-white clustered flowers against the bare black branches; small round toothed leaves usually after bloom. *p. 2088, 2090*

viscosa (Madagascar), "Wedding flower"; small evergreen tree to 5 m, cordate leaves with serrate margins; flowers white, deep crimson at base, sweet scented. *p. 2090*

wallichii (E. Africa, Madagascar); evergreen tree to 10 m, with large 30 cm, lobed, herbaceous leaves matte-green, densely hairy beneath; showy bell-like flowers with flat, spreading petals salmon-rose to scarlet, in dense hanging heads. *Tropical.* *p. 2088*

DOODIA *Polypodiaceae (Filices)* **I3HFM**

caudata (Australia, New Zealand, New Caledonia); dwarf densely tufted fern on short, erect rhizomes with pinnate membranous fronds green to pale green, 12-30 cm long, slightly rough, borne on smooth stalks. *p. 1108*

maxima (New South Wales); clustering decorative fern with sword-shaped, pinnate leaves to 45 cm long, with many spreading linear segments each side to 8 cm long, fresh green and of firm texture. *p. 1105*

media (Australia, New Zealand); tufted fern with arching lancelike, pinnate fronds 30-45 cm long, of firm and stiff-leathery texture and rough to touch, dark green but when young rosy-red; the lower rachis with red bristly hair. *p. 1114*

DORITIS *Orchidaceae* **S3OFM**

pulcherrima (Phalaenopsis esmeralda) (Malaya, Vietnam, Thailand, Burma); phalaenopsis-like epiphyte with oblong, thick leaves to 20 cm long; often purplish beneath; racemes with flowers 3 cm dia., varying from amethyst-purple to nearly white, the 3-lobed lip deep purple often shading to orange; Oct.-Jan., July. (S) *p. 1716*

DOROTHEANTHUS *Aizoaceae* **I2LBD**

bellidiformis (Cleretum) (Cape Prov.), "Livingstone-daisy"; small annual herb branching from the root; short, fleshy obovate leaves, rough-puckered, to 8 cm long; masses of daisy-like flowers in colors red purple, salmon, straw-yellow, yellow, lavender, white or white with red tips, opening to the sun. *Arid-subtropic.* *p. 61*

gramineus (So. Africa: Cape Pen.), the "Tricolor mesembryanthemum" or "Buck-bay daisy"; colorful annual, spreading succulent forming clumps 20 cm across; opposite fleshy, fresh green cylindrical leaves 5-8 cm long, covered with crystalline blisters; the medium large 4 cm flowers normally bright carmine with dark center, but cultivated in South African gardens in many lustrous colors, in pink, rose, red, orange, yellow to white, sometimes with blue or red centers; the most beautiful of all annual Mesems, and blooming when the sun warms the sleeping buds. *p. 59*

DORSTENIA *Moraceae* **S3LFM**

argentata (Santa Catarina, Brazil); erect, small plant with a downy purple stem and lanceolate leaves to 12 cm long, dark green at margins while the main area, in the center, is metallic silver; the small male and female flowers crowded on a concave receptacle, margined with purple tubercles. *p. 1560*

barteri (Trop. West Africa: Guinea); herbaceous, hairy plant with creeping rootstock 60 cm high; elliptic green leaves to 18 cm long; the tiny monoecious flowers on the flat, round, grayish receptacle 2½-5 cm wide surrounded by a membranous margin and many unequal, pointed green rays. *p. 1560*

bornimiana (Ethiopia, S. Arabia, Kenya, Tanzania); plants with tuber; leaves similar to cyclamen 5-6 cm dia.; inflorescence oblong with long antennas. *p. 1561*

ceratosanthes (arifolia) (Brazil); leaves heart-arrow-shaped, undulate, crenate or lobed; receptacle green, fork-like. *p. 1561*

contrajerva (Mexico), "Torus-herb"; so named because of the curious green, flat receptacle (torus) with imbedded unisexual flowers open, and not enclosed as in figs; fleshy, rough-hairy, deeply lobed 20 cm leaves, deep green blotched with white, from creeping rhizome. *p. 1561*

crispa (Somalia, Kenya); curious succulent from dry regions; thick-fleshy stems 12 to 40 cm tall, with swollen base 4 cm thick; the branches pale brown and covered with tubercles and bearing leaf-scars; small, narrow obovate, turgid leaves 4-7 cm long, tinted coppery and with curly, dentate margins; receptacles are round stellate, 2 cm across, the margins with 6-10 spreading bracts. *p. 1561*

drakeana (Trop. America); bushy plant with long-stalked leaves shallowly or deeply lobed, and 12-20 cm long; inflorescence on round receptacle. *p. 1562*

elata (Brazil); shrubby plant with leathery shining green, elliptic leaves 12 to 18 cm long; inflorescence round-peltate, 3 cm across and vaguely 4-angled. *p. 1561*

foetida (So. Arabia); swollen succulent base, with elliptic, leathery leaves, 4 cm long, 5 cm wide; inflorescence star-like. *p. 1561*

gigas (Socotra); branching plant with thick succulent stems; foliage and inflorescence green. Inflorescence similar to figs but hundreds of flowers imbedded in an open, flat receptacle. *p. 1561*

hildebrandtii (Kenya); long succulent stem with small, narrow leaves; inflorescence star-like. *p. 1561*

indica (India, Sri Lanka); erect plant with fleshy elliptic leaves 6-8 cm long 2-3 cm wide; small receptacles. *p. 1561*

mannii (West Trop. Africa); erect plant 15-25 cm high, with flexuous stem swollen at nodes, densely hairy; obovate or elliptic dark green leaves, pale beneath; convex flower head 2½ cm dia., light purple, hairy on back, and fringed by numerous green bract arms. *p. 1560*

multiradiata (Trop. Africa); herbaceous plant with smooth, obovate, entire leaves, the flower-receptacle surrounded by about 30 pointed unequal bracts to 3 cm long, united at base. *p. 1560*

nervosa (Brazil); long branches with elliptic, corrugated leaves green irregularly variegated leaden-gray in area along the midrib; the stalked, concave flower head receptacle dark purple. *p. 1560*

turneraefolia (Trop. America); obovate, corrugated small hairy, green leaves sawed at margins; the irregularly rounded, green, concave receptacle holding the monoecious flowers. *p. 1560*

urceolata variegata (Brazil); interesting tropical herb with hard, long-lanceolate leaves having raised veins, the surface mottled light and yellow-green wth silvery band along center; the male and female flowers imbedded in a cupshaped yellowish-green receptacle. *p. 1560*

yambuyaensis (Zaire); erect, bristly herb with oblanceolate leaves to 15 cm long, shining green above, pale and dull beneath, and irregularly toothed; the green receptacle angularly rounded, almost 2½ cm across, the winged margins with rays to 10 cm long. *Tropical.* *p. 1560*

zanzibarica (Zanzibar); herb with erect stems alternate with toothed, corrugated green elliptic leaves and small flower heads pale gray-green surrounded by pale green rays. *p. 1560*

DORYANTHES *Amaryllidaceae* **I2LBD**

excelsa (New South Wales, Queensland), the "Globe spear-lily"; bold rosette of numerous succulent sword-shaped leaves to 2m long; and a leaning inflorescence to 4½ m long, the heavy head of 10 cm flowers with divided perianth segments crimson-red outside, pale inside, and with green bracts. *Subtropic.* *p. 130*

palmeri (Queensland), "Spear-lily"; large succulent rosette of broadly lanceolate spreading leaves to 2 m long and slightly ribbed; the giant inflorescence 3-5 m long, with the pyramidal spike dense with 6 cm funnel-shaped flowers scarlet-red, lighter in center, and with colored bracts. *p. 101*

DORYOPTERIS *Polypodiaceae (Filices)* **S3HNM**

ludens (India, Malaysia, Philippines); distinct species with wide-creeping rhizome bearing leathery fronds of two forms; the barren fronds on black stalks vary from triangular to hastate; the 10-15 cm fertile leaves on long 30 cm stalks are cut finger-like into 5 lanceolate lobes. *p. 1109*

palmata (West Indies to Perú and Brazil); small decorative species with thick-leathery, dark green fronds of two distinct forms: the 10 cm sterile leaves have 5 or more triangular lobes, the long-stalked fertile fronds of hand-shaped outline, deeply cut into narrow lobes. *p. 1108*

pedata (W. Indies to Argentina), "Hand fern"; an excellent dwarf fern with thin-leathery, bright green, palmate fronds 15 cm across, carried horizontally on black wiry stalks, the 3 main divisions having black veins, parted again into linear segments and pointed lobes which are edged by a line of sori. *p. 1108, 1109*

DOVYALIS *Flacourtiaceae* **I2LFD**

hebecarpa (Aberia gardneri) (Sri Lanka, India), "Ceylon-gooseberry"; decorative evergreen growing into a small dioecious tree to 6 m high; the alternate ovate, undulate, 10 cm papery leaves, glossy green with metallic sheen, and rosy midrib, grayish beneath; the thin wiry branches set with scattered 1 cm needle-like thorns; small greenish flowers, and 2½ cm purple, edible fruit. *Tropical.* *p. 1062*

DOXANTHA *Bignoniaceae* **I2LBM**

unguis-cati (West Indies to Argentina), "Cats-claw"; tropical woody vine high-climbing into trees, with opposite leaves each with a pair of leaflets separated by a tendril split into 3 claws; leaflets are thin, oval-pointed, to 8 cm long; funnel-form, allamanda-like lobed flowers rich yellow, to 10 cm wide, borne profusely in short clusters normally in spring, often also in autumn. *Tropical.* *p. 502*

DRACAENA *Liliaceae* ***S1LFW**

americana (Honduras to Panama); the only cultivated species native in America, a slender tree with swollen base resembling Yucca, trunk to 7 m high topped by a rosette of long, glossy-green, thin strapleaves clasping the stem; panicles of white flowers followed by orange fruit. *p. 1444*

arborea (North Guinea), "Tree dracaena"; tree-like, to 12 m with dense head of broad, swordshaped, evenly fresh-green, sessile, wavy leaves to 90 cm long, with sunken veins and prominently raised midrib. Roots of Dracaenas are orange-yellow (white in Cordyline). *p. 1437, 1438, 1442*

aurea (Hawaii); much branched native Hawaiian tree to 6 m high; long narrow, light green, recurving leaves without petioles, clustered at ends of slender branches. *Tropical.* *p. 1444*

cantleyi (Singapore); rosette of very ornamental, long-oblanceolate, leathery leaves, fresh grass-green liberally sprinkled with oblong blotches of chartreuse. *Tropical.* *p. 1442*

"Deeringii" hort. (Mexico); bold plant with thick stem and a crown of close-jointed, fresh green, leathery sword-shaped leaves 8 cm wide; resembling hookeriana. *p. 1435*

deremensis 'Bausei'; similar to warneckei but having the two white marginal bands brought close together in the middle of the leaf, with only a thin milky-green center stripe to separate them. The green species deremensis is from Trop. Africa. *Tropical.* *p. 1442*

deremensis 'Compacta', "Dwarf bouquet" or "Calypso Queen"; very compacted, dense rosette or bundle of thin-leathery lanceolate, corrugated dark green, shiny leaves; introduced from Puerto Rico and Florida 1973; very attractive as a pot plant. *Tropical.* *p. 1436*

deremensis 'Janet Craig'; green sport of warneckei, a rosette of freer, larger growing habit, similar to fragrans but more erect and stiff, with dark green, lustrous, wavy-margined leaves, corrugated lengthwise; of excellent keeping qualities. *Tropical.* *p. 1438, 1445*

deremensis 'J. A. Truffaut'; attractive French cultivar with broad spreading leaves; featuring the white center band of 'Longii' but the variegation is much broader, leaving only a narrow margin of dark green. *p. 1442*

deremensis 'Longii'; somewhat delicate variety having glossy-green, pointed leaves, corrugated lengthwise and abruptly pendant, and with clear white center band. *p. 5*, 1442*

deremensis 'Roehrs Gold' (1956); a handsome cultivar of warneckei, of shapely erect habit, with the broad center of the leaves creamy yellow, bordered by translucent white lines and edged by rich green borders. *p. 1442*

deremensis 'Souvenir de Aug. Schryver'; beautiful Belgian cultivar, first seen in Germany 1970; a symmetrical, wide-spreading rosette of soft-leathery, lanceolate leaves, deep glossy green in center with broad creamy-white margins. *Tropical.* *p. 1437*

deremensis 'Warneckei' (Trop. Africa), "Striped dracaena"; attractive house plant for dark locations; branching stout canes to 5 m high, covered with sessile, swordshaped, leathery leaves, fresh green streaked milky green in center, and bordered by a translucent white band on each side inside the narrow bright green edge, 25-40 cm long. *p. 5*, 1434, 1443*

dracaenoides (Trop. Africa); clustering plant with narrow, papery, light green leaves tapering in both directions, widest above the middle, and finely toothed, the narrowed basal end clasping; prominent yellow midrib beneath. *p. 1440*

draco (Canary Isl.); "Dragon tree"; forming large trees to 20 m, with monstrous trunks of 4½ m dia., decorative as young plants with crowded rosette of sessile, sword-shaped, thick fleshy leaves, smooth to glaucous green, translucent edges, outlined in red if in the sun; flowers greenish. Superstition believes that the dark red, resinous substance exuding from leaves and trunk is "dragon's blood". *Subtropic.* *p. 1439, 1444*

"ensifolia" hort.; sometimes found in horticulture as Dianella; erect plant to 2 m with fibrous roots but sprouting new canes from rhizomes, leaves long, narrow and straplike, wavy and with clasping base covering internodes, nice, glossy dark green. *p. 1444*

fragrans (Guinea, Nigeria, Ethiopia); tree-like, with cane to 6 m, sometimes branched, with broad, laxly recurved, oblanceolate, soft-leathery, sessile leaves 40-80 cm long, continually ascending into a shining green, showy rosette; fragrant yellowish flowers in clusters. *p. 1434, 1439, 1441*

fragrans 'Lindenii'; variety with the wide, limply pendant leaves having broad, often indistinct, greenish-yellow bands at margins, center green. *Tropical.* *p. 1441*

fragrans 'Massangeana', "Cornstalk plant"; an old-fashioned robust house plant with its rosette of rich green, laxly arching leaves broadly striped and banded light green and yellow down the center, 30 or more cm long and 10 cm wide. *Tropical.* *p. 1437, 1441, 1443*

fragrans 'Victoriae', "Painted dragon lily"; beautiful, slow-growing conservatory plant with gracefully pendant, wide, soft-leathery leaves green streaked silvery-gray in center, bordered by contrasting broad margins of cream to clear golden yellow. *Humid-tropical.* *p. 1408A, 1441*

'Gertrude Manda' (hookeriana x grandis), "Broad leather dracaena"; very decorative Manda hybrid intermediate between grandis and hookeriana and characterized by very thick leaves 10 cm or more wide, translucent margins; very durable. *p. 1445*

glomerata (Trop. Africa); slow-growing plant with slender stem bearing a rosette of horizontal leathery leaves broadly ovate and vertically corrugated, the surface deep green with faint crossbands of lighter green. *p. 1440*

godseffiana (Zaire, Guinea), "Gold-dust dracaena"; small shrubby plant with spreading, wiry stems bearing thin-leathery, elliptic leaves in pairs or whorls of three, glossy deep green, irregularly spotted yellow, maturing to white; greenish-yellow flowers followed by red berries. *p. 19*, 1440*

godseffiana 'Florida Beauty'; a striking seedling of kelleri, with the same characteristic thick-leathery leaf but almost entirely covered with creamy-white blotching. *Tropical.* *p. 1440*

godseffiana 'Friedman' ('Milky Way'); charming small branching plant; thin-wiry stems with pairs of elliptic, thin-leathery leaves to 10 cm long, glossy olive green, splotched and spotted cream, and a broad ivory band down center. *Tropical.* *p. 1437*

godseffiana 'Kelleri'; attractive horticultural form of good keeping quality, with long elliptic leaves thicker, and more liberally marbled and blotched with ivory-white. *p. 1440*

goldieana (So. Nigeria, 900 m), "Queen of dracaenas"; the most spectacular dracaena in cultivation, but requiring humid-warm conditions to thrive; I remember a branched specimen 3 m high in Pará, its slender canes furnished with leathery foliage from bottom to top; the ovate, glossy deep green, long-stalked leaves strikingly marked with crossbands of pale green, maturing to almost white. Flowers in a dense spiral head, fragrant white, opening at night. *Humid-tropical.* *p. 21*, 1408A, 1441, 1445*

hookeriana (rumphii) (Cape of Good Hope, Natal), "Leather dracaena"; heavy plant with woody trunk to 2 m high, occasionally branching, topped by a crowded rosette of spreading sword-shaped, very thick leathery leaves dark green and glossy, to 3-5 cm wide and with translucent edges; slow-growing; panicle of greenish flowers. *Subtropic.* *p. 1439, 1445*

hookeriana 'Latifolia'; tree-like variety with sword-shaped fleshy-leathery leaves narrowed at base and widening to 8 or 9 cm in the middle. *p. 1445*

hookeriana 'Rothiana'; horticultural form widely grown in the San Francisco area and a favorite because of its good keeping qualities; the thick, glossy dark green leaves 5-8 cm wide. *Sub-tropic.* *p. 1436, 1445*

kindtiana (Trop. Africa); interesting clustering plant with elliptic-pointed, deep green, leathery leaves having pronounced vertical furrows, the base narrowing into the long, channeled stalks. *p. 1442*

marginata (gracilis) (Madagascar), "Madagascar dragon tree"; a favored decorator; tree-like, with branching slender trunk, growing to 5 m high, each cane topped by a dense terminal rosette of thick-fleshy, narrow linear clasping leaves 40 cm long, rigidly spreading horizontally, shiny deep olive green prettily edged in red. The flexuous canes have the tendency to grow snaky and twisted, giving a branched specimen very artistic appearance. Slow and durable. *Tropical.* *p. 19*, 1438, 1443, 1444*

marginata 'Tricolor', "Rainbow tree"; magnificent cultivar found in Japan, developed in Puerto Rico and Florida (1973); multi-colored fountain of leaves striped cream between green and with rosy-red margins; bright light for most intense glow. *p. 1437*

x masseffiana (massangeana x godseffiana); interesting small Puerto Rican hybrid by Pennock, with oblanceolate, soft-leathery, persistent leaves in a rosette carried umbrella-like on a slender stalk, the surface dark glossy-green spotted with yellow. *p. 1440*

phrynioides (Fernando Po); attractive plant with short stem and long-stalked, leathery leaves resembling a maranta, ovate, to 20 cm long, and with parallel veining, dark glossy-green marked with yellow spots surrounded by a pale green circle. *p. 1442*

pubescens (Trop. West Africa); dense bush 2-3 m high, oval pointed thick-fleshy, light green leaves 15 x 30 cm, from slender, cane-like stem. *p. 1436*

reflexa (Madagascar, India); classified as Pleomele in Asia; for description see Pleomele. *p. 1436*

rothiana (Archipel des Comores); reported in Ill. Hort. 1896 as close to fragrans and deremensis but not like hookeriana 'Rothiana'; thin-leathery, glossy-green leaves more or less striped with white. *p. 1440*

sanderiana (Cameroons, Zaire), "Ribbon plant"; neat, very durable, little rosette, erect on slender cane until becoming too heavy, with narrow lanceolate, elegantly twisted leaves 10 to 20 cm long, deep green somewhat milky, and with broad marginal bands of white. *Tropical.* *p. 15*, 21*, 1441, 1443*

sanderiana 'Borinquensis'; a sport at Pennock's in Puerto Rico, of stiff, robust habit, having the variegation of its leaves more or less reversed, the center in milky green within two white stripes, while the broad margins are deep green. *p. 1441*

sanderiana 'Celes' (Pat.); handsome Puerto Rico mutation of stiffly erect habit; oblanceolate linear, leathery leaves 1-2 cm wide, dark green with white margins; for dishgardens. *Tropical.* *p. 1440*

sanderiana 'Margaret Berkery' (1958); attractive, robust Puerto Rico sport with bamboo-like stem, clasping leafbases, short 12 cm lanceolate, leathery deep green leaves contrasting against the broad cream-white center band; translucent margins. *Tropical.* *p. 1445*

sanderiana virescens; in this form the beautiful variegation is lacking leaving the small but tough plant entirely fresh olive-green, with occasional faint lines pale green. *p. 1441*

steudneri (Tropical East Africa); tree-like to 2-3 m, and branching into bushes; broad oblanceolate, thin-leathery green leaves; the inflorescence leaning, with red-brown flowers inside whitish; orange berries. *p. 1436*

surculosa punctulata (Sierra Leone); branching plant with whiplike, wiry stems distantly bearing pairs of whorls of long elliptic, olive-green, leathery leaves with indistinct yellow-green spots. *p. 1440*

thalioides (Pleomele) (Sri Lanka, Trop. Africa); for description see Pleomele. *p. 1436*

umbraculifera (Java, Mauritius); tree-like with slender single stem topped by crown of narrow strap-like leaves, pale and flat in center. *p. 1437, 1444*

DRACAENA: see also Pleomele, Dianella, Cordyline

DRACONTIOIDES *Araceae* **S3LFM**

desciscens (Brazil); tropical marsh-herb with long underground spongy rhizome; the hastate, arrow-shaped leaves 25 cm long, green with purple spots on 60 cm petioles; 10 cm spathe brownish violet outside with pale stripes, purple inside. *p. 213*

DRACONTIUM *Araceae* **S3LFMd**

asperum (N. Brazil, Venezuela: Orinoco); giant tuberous herb with short 10-15 cm leathery, hooded spathe brownish-green, violet inside; followed by a solitary much divided leaf, 90 cm across, 3-parted and cut again, on stalk, to 3 m high, mottled with green and brown or lilac. *Tropical.* *p. 208*

gigas (Nicaragua); a "Dragon plant" with tuber as large as a man's head, the spiny leaf stalk 3-4 m tall, shining metallic pale green and mottled brown; leaf blade umbrella-like to 3 m across, deep green above, pale beneath, deeply cut 3-partite, the lobes cut again bipinnately; the inflorescence on a 50 cm stalk, carrying an erect 60 cm spathe recoiled above middle and deep violet, brownish-red inside. *p. 213*

polyphyllum (Brazil: Pará and Amazonas); handsome tuberous plant with boldly erect terete petioles to more than 1 m tall, richly marbled with pale hieroglyphic markings, and carrying the wide-spreading umbrella of three-parted dissected leaves; near base the short inflorescence with curved, hooded brownish spathe. The large tubers are eaten by the Tupi Indians who cook or roast them for their meals. *p. 189*

DRACOPHILUS *Aizoaceae* **I2LBD**

dealbatus (Cape Prov., Namibia); low succulent, forming clusters, branches mostly 4-leaved; leaves flat above, keeled beneath, 3-4 cm long, light green; 3 cm pink flowers. *p. 60*

DRACOPHYLLUM *Epacridaceae* **I2HBD**

secundum (New So. Wales); evergreen shrub to 60 cm with 5-10 cm linear-lanceolate leaves, the bases clasping and hiding stem; flowers on slender cylindrical spikes, with 1 cm tubular white corolla. *p. 956*

traversii (New Zealand), "New Zealand grasstree"; handsome small tree found on South Island, of candelabrum-like habit, sparry very hard woody branches, and thick-leathery, stiff-recurving linear concave leaves deep bronzy, glossy green, with bases clasping and tips curling, in rosettes at branch-ends; the inflorescence in brownish terminal clusters. *Subtropic.* *p. 955, 956*

DRACULA: see Masdevallia

DRACUNCULUS *Araceae* **I2LBDd**

canariensis (Madeira, Canary Isl.); tuberous herb 40-70 cm high, with pedately divided leaf light green; the center segments 12-15 cm long, on 30-40 cm stalk spotted greenish-purple; narrow spathe 25-35 cm long, pale green to whitish; the yellow extension of spadix is like a mouse tail. *p. 213*

vulgaris (Arum dracunculus) (Mediterranean); tuberous herb with pedately dissected, bright green leaves with 13-15 segments; spathe tube purplish-white striped purple, the purple blade 30 cm long, deeper at margin; spadix tipped purple also; offensive odor in bloom. *p. 182, 187*

DRIMIOPSIS *Liliaceae* **S3LFM**

kirkii (Zanzibar); bulbous plant with lax, strapshaped, keeled, fleshy leaves narrowing toward base, pale blue-green with marbling of dark blotches; white flowers on short spike in July. *Tropical.* *p. 1460*

maculata (So. Africa); bulbous plant with globose bulb; fleshy, ovate leaves with cordate base, bright green blotched deep green; short stalk 20-30 cm, with spike of small flowers white at first, becoming greenish. *p. 1447*

saundersiae (South Africa: Transvaal); low bulbous plant with 2-4 broad-lanceolate, fleshy leaves grayish-green blotched with deep green; spike of greenish-white, small flowers. *Subtropic.* *p. 1434*

DRIMYS *Magnoliaceae* **S3LBM**
winteri (So. America), "Winters bark"; evergreen tree to 8 m, with aromatic bark, reddish branches; oblong leaves glaucous beneath; flowers 3 cm across, milk-white and fragrant of jasmine. *p. 1525*

DROSANTHEMUM *Aizoaceae* **I2LBD**
floribundum (Cape Prov.); cushion-forming succulent, creeping and freely branching, with 1 cm cylindrical light green leaves thickened toward apex; numerous 2 cm flowers pale pink. *p. 61*
speciosum (Cape Prov.); shrubby succulent with inclined branches, tiny 16 mm fleshy leaves curved upwards, semi-cylindrical blunt, fresh green, set with crystalline blisters; masses of beautiful daisy-like flowers glowing brownish to orange-red, greenish in center. *Subtropic.* *p. 61*

DROSERA *Droseraceae (Carnivorous Plants)* **I-C3HBW**
auriculata (Australia); curious insectivorous plant from the Sydney area, New South Wales; small leaf rosettes at base, from the center rise long wiry stems, along which are stalked tiny peltate leaves with two basal lobes, and glands each bearing a drop of mucilage which is extremely viscid and serves to entrap small insects. *p. 765*
binata (Australia), "Twin-leaved sundew"; small perennial 15 cm high, with long-stalked leaves deeply divided into two linear lobes with sensitive glandular hairs discharging sticky fluid to hold and digest insects. *p. 762, 765*
capensis (So. Africa); perennial 15 cm high with linear oblong, blunt leaves tapered toward base, and densely furnished with hairs giving off sticky sap attracting insects, whereupon the sensitive hairs curve inward acting as a trap until the fluid digests their body. *Subtropic.* *p. 765*
dichotoma (E. Australia, New Zealand); a subtropical "Sundew"; robust, stemless species to 45 cm high, with smooth, linear leaves simple or bi-forked, each division linear 5-15 cm long, 1½-2 cm wide, densely covered by red-brown gland-hairs, from their apex secretes the mucilous sap which entraps insects; strong floral stalks with numerous pure white flowers 3 cm across. *Subtropic.* *p. 765*
dichrosepala (Australia); small insectivorous rosette from shrubby root stock, forming clusters 2-3 cm high; with light green narrow leaves covered with hairs and stalked glands with suction cups secreting sticky glue; large white flowers on slender stalks 6-8 cm long. *p. 764*
filiformis (Atlantic N. America); "Sundew"; winter hardy, threadlike plant with linear green leaves equipped with fine red glandular hairs which curve inward to entrap insects to digest them. *p. 765*
rotundifolia (No. America, Europe, Asia), "Common sundew"; winter hardy small herb with flat hairy petioles and round hairy leaves to 4 cm long; small white flowers. *p. 765*
spathulata (Australia); small carnivorous flat rosette hugging the ground, and covered by tiny red-brown tentacles, each tipped with a droplet of perfumed, sticky liquid, attracting insects. *Subtropic.* *p. 765*
tracyi (Florida to Louisiana); insectivorous plant with tall, filiform-linear, yellow-green leaves, densely covered with mucilage glands secreting sticky juice to catch insects. *p. 764*

DROSOPHYLLUM *Droseraceae (Carnivorous Plants)* **C3LBD**
lusitanicum (Portugal, S. Spain, Morocco), "Dew leaf"; low shrubby carnivorous plant from gravelly locations, with linear leaves set with glands bearing a dewlike sticky drop by which insects are captured; flowers yellow. *p. 765*

DRYANDRA *Proteaceae* **I3LBD**
carduacea (Queensland), the "Honey pingle"; shrub 2-4 m high, with dark green narrow leaves to 8 cm long, deeply lobed into spine-tipped segments, white-downy beneath; honey-scented yellow flowers 2 cm across, in terminal heads. *p. 1976*
formosa (Western Australia), the "Showy dryandra"; evergreen shrub to 3 m high, with soft saw-tooth leaves; dense heads of golden-orange, silky flowers. *p. 1977*

DRYAS *Rosaceae* **C2LBM**
octopetala (Northern Latitudes); evergreen creeping plant shrubby at base, with elliptic 2 cm leaves; white-tomentose beneath; white 3 cm flowers; the feathery fruit on long stalk. *p. 2000*

DRYMOGLOSSUM *Polypodiaceae (Filices)* **I3OFM**
microphyllum (carnosum) (Himalaya, Nepal, Japan, China, Reunion), the "Bean-leaf fern"; wide-creeping, rooting, thread-like rhizome with small sterile waxy-glossy leaves 2-5 cm long, oval or elliptical, arranged shingle-like, the leathery fertile leaves linear-spoon-shaped 5-8 cm long. *p. 1106*

DRYMONIA *Gesneriaceae* **S3HFM**
macrophylla (Costa Rica, Guatemala); shrubby, to 15 cm high, with angular, purplish stems; fleshy, toothed, elliptic, grayish leaves and axillary, large, waxy, dipping, bell-shaped flowers creamy-white outside, beige-yellow in throat, and marked red-purple; calyx frilled. *p. 1243*
stenophylla (Costa Rica); shrubby plant with scandent branches bearing thickish, oblique-lanceolate leaves, and axillary 2½ cm trumpet-flowers with cream tube and pale yellow limb, the petals fringed. *p. 1244*

DRYMOPHLOEUS *Palmae* **S3LFM**
beguinii (Indonesia); pinnate-leaved palm to 5 m high, with hard slender 4 cm dark trunk, topped by a crownshaft and 1½ m dark glossy green leaves; the leaflets wedge-shaped and ruffled. *p. 1872*
olivaeformis (Indonesia; Amboina); small palm similar to beguinii but taller; the young plants have broad-ovate, entire leaves, irregularly toothed at margins; with age fronds are pinnate, the leaflets broadening toward apex and these ragged as if chewed off, the ones toward the tip usually united. *p. 1872*

DRYNARIA *Polypodiaceae (Filices)* **I-S3HFM**
fortunei (South China); found and photographed in Kwangtung, China, growing on rocks but also epiphytic; short fleshy rhizome, with leaves of two kinds, the shield-like sterile fronds 5-8 cm long, shielding the base, and the long fertile, deeply lobed fronds 30 to 80 cm tall, fresh green and of leathery texture, the triangular segments alternating along the rachis. *p. 1105*
quercifolia (Polypodium), (So. India, Queensland, Fiji), "Oakleaved fern"; growing on trees and rocks, with a thick, brown, woody rhizome, having stalkless brown, bluntly lobed barren fronds and long-stalked deeply pinnate rigid fertile fronds with brown veins, the pinnae cut to center. *Humid-tropical.* *p. 1107, 1150*
rigidula (Malaysia, Queensland, Fiji), "Feather polypodium"; epiphytic fern with thick creeping rhizome looking like a rabbit's foot covered with long brown hair-like scales, the fronds in two forms: the sterile ones stalkless to 22 cm long and merely lobed, the fertile fronds pinnate, leathery and rich green, on brown rachis first erect, later pendant, ½-1 m long. *p. 1106, 1107*
rigidula var. whitei (Queensland); very ornamental form growing into magnificent specimens, with firm, long pendant, pinnate dark green fronds having broad leaflets deeply lobed and cut and frilled, rattling like tinsel paper when stroked. *p. 1106*

DRYOPTERIS *Polypodiaceae (Filices)* **C-I3HNM**
atrata (hirtipes); probably more correctly Aspidium atratum (China, Japan, Malaya, India); tufted fern with scaly stalks bearing pinnate fronds 60-90 cm long, the leaflets bluntly lobed. *p. 1111*
crassirhizoma (Japan, Korea, Manchuria); from a short rhizome a handsome rosette of light green, gracefully arching bi-pinnate fronds 10-25 cm long, of soft texture, the ultimate pinnae finely cut into tiny linear lobes. Photographed at the Alpine Mountain garden near Nikko in Northern Honshu. Fronds deciduous in winter. *p. 1105*
decursive-pinnata (E. Asia); hardy rhizomatous fern with tufted, scaly stalks 10 cm long, herbaceous green fronds 30 cm or more long, bipinnately divided into tiny plumy segments. *p. 1105*
dentata (parasitica) (New Zealand, and widespread in subtropics and tropics), "Wood fern"; short creeping, erect rhizome bearing tufted pinnate fronds to 1 m long, both pinnatifid and entire, the segments smooth, hairy on veins, pale green, membranous and soft, and lobed only about half-way. *p. 1098*
eriocaulis (Brazil); attractive fern with lanceolate, once divided yellowish-green fronds up to 1 m long and 15 cm wide, with the leaflets deeply lobed, borne on stalks covered with a thick coat of golden hairs, on erect crown. *p. 1110*
erythrosora (China, Japan); tufted wood-fern with underground creeping stem, scaly stalks bearing 30-45 cm pinnate fronds of firm though papery texture, the leaflets lobed; the spore masses with bright red covers when young. *p. 1111*
extensa: see Thelypteris
filix-mas (England and throughout Europe; No. America from Greenland to So. America, Peru; Lapland to Japan; Himalayas to Malaysia; Azores to Africa), the "Male fern"; one of the commonest of ferns, densely tufted; crowns with scaly stalks bearing handsome bipinnate fronds ½-1 m long, the spear-shaped dark-green leaflets of papery texture, pale beneath, very variable; nearly evergreen, hardy. Has medicinal properties. *p. 1110*
filix-mas borreri (No. America, Europe), a "Male fern"; a compact-growing form with neatly arranged sturdy fronds of firm texture, deep green and with pinnae well spaced. *p. 1105*
filix-mas crispum cristatum, (Nephrodium) (Britain: Cornwall); beautiful variety with dark green, pinnate fronds to 1 m long, bending from the weight of their large, many times branched, and crispy terminal tuft or crest, the lobed leaflets also ending in smaller crests ringing the outline of the frond with a border of crispy crests. *p. 1111*
hexagonoptera (Québec to Florida and Texas, Lapland to Japan, Europe), "Broad beech-fern"; creeping rhizome bearing light green, soft and papery pinnate fronds 20-30 cm long, the leaflets deeply lobed and wavy, the lower ones deflexed, the underside weakly hairy. *p. 1108*
hirtipes (Nephrodium) (Himalayas, and Neilgherries, India); short fleshy stem topped by a rosette of gracefully arching, broad, steel-green fronds with wide, closely set pinnae toothed and undulate at margins, the stalks are conspicuously clothed with black scales. *p. 1126*
lepida (Lastrea, Nephrodium) (Polynesia), dainty "Shield-fern"; with herbaceous, simply pinnate, light green fronds to 38 cm long, gracefully arching on hairy stems, the well-spaced pinnae narrow-linear and cut into sickle-shaped lobes. *p. 1126, 1163*

ludoviciana (dentata) (Africa), "Wood fern"; naturalized in Florida; tall plant with creeping rhizome from which rise long, leathery, pinnate fronds, the glossy light green, lanceolate leaflets crenately lobed, on brown-scaly stalks. *p. 1106*

marginalis (spinulosa) (E. U. States); tufted fern with scaly stem and bipinnatifid fronds to 45 cm long, the segments cut to axis and with hairy teeth. *p. 1099*

megalodus (Florida, Cuba, Panama, Brazil, Perú); allied to tetragona (Polypodium); strong-growing, with erect stalks bearing pinnate fronds 30-90 cm long, the leaflets thin-papery, slightly hairy underneath, lightly lobed sickle-shaped. *p. 1111*

ovata (Himalayas: Sikkim, Bhutan); mountain-fern with creeping rhizome bearing pinnate fronds of firm, papery texture, 15-30 cm long on 20 cm wiry stalks, the leaflets finely lobed. *p. 1111*

parallelogramma (Nephrodium f. m. khasiana), (Himalaya, Tibet, So. China); tufted fern with scaly stalks and symmetrical pinnate fronds, the leaflets closely arranged, deeply cut into narrow lobes and somewhat revolute. *p. 1111*

punctata: see Hypolepis punctata

quadrangularis (Trop. America: Guayana); showy tufted wood-fern with suberect rhizome, gracefully arching pinnate fronds dark green and hairy on the surface, the broad leaflets symmetrically arranged and lobed two-thirds to the rib. *p. 1111*

reticulata (Mexico, Martinique, to Perú); tufted fern with stout stalks 30-90 cm long bearing simple pinnate fronds ½ -1 m long, the broad leaflets of firm texture, lightly undulate at margins. *p. 1110*

serra (Nephrodium) (West Indies, Cuba, Mexico to Venezuela); wide-creeping rhizome with wiry, glossy stalks bearing slender pinnate fronds 60-90 cm long; the leathery, light green narrow leaflets 1 cm wide, cut half down into sickle-shaped sharp-pointed lobes. *p. 1110*

sieboldii (Nephrodium), (Japan, China, Hong Kong); succulent prostrate stem covered with brown spear-shaped scales bears two kinds of simply pinnate leathery fronds; the glaucous-bluish leaflets on the short-stalked sterile fronds are undulated, the leaflets on fertile long-stalked fronds are more contracted and entirely covered with large spore-masses. *p. 1111*

spinulosa (No. America, Europe, So. Africa, Himalayas), the "Prickly shield-fern"; a tufted crown bearing scaly stalks and pale green, pinnate fronds 30-45 cm long; the broad, soft papery pinnae deeply lobed and tipped with sharp teeth. *p. 1110*

uliginosa; recently transferred to Thelypteris (Hortus 3) (Guam; naturalized in Florida); stout rootstock clothed with long brown scales, bearing 3-pinnate dark green fronds 1-2 m long, white hairy beneath. *p. 1110*

villosa (Ctenitis) (West Indies, Jamaica); stately terrestrial fern which may become 5½ m high, with thick trunk-like, hairy and scaly rhizome, the stout stalks hold large bipinnatifid fronds 1-2 m or more long, soft-herbaceous or papery in texture, pale green, and typically hairy above. *p. 1098*

DUCHESNEA *Rosaceae* **I2LBD**

indica (India), "Mock strawberry"; perennial herb with trailing branches rooting along the ground, bright green three-parted leaves; 2 cm yellow flowers followed by strawberry-like 2 cm red fruits of insipid taste; used as ground cover in California, and for hanging baskets. *Subtropic. p. 1997*

DUDLEYA *Crassulaceae* **I2LFD**

attenuata orcuttii (Stylophyllum) (Baja California); clustering rosettes of fleshy round, green leaves thickly covered with waxy bloom of silvery-white; flowers white, flushed pink. *p. 887*

brittonii (Mexico); low rosette of short stems, with few linear leaves, rounded at base, glaucous silver gray, and tipped red, later bluish; flowers whitish. *Arid-tropical. p. 872*

candida (California: Coronado Is.); clustering rosette with sharply pointed thick lanceolate leaves to 8 cm, beautifully covered with silvery-white glaucescence; flowers greenish-yellow. *p. 872*

densiflora (Stylophyllum) (California); glistening bluish-white very glaucous succulent from San Gabriel Canyon, Los Angeles, with numerous pencil-like nearly terete leaves to 10 cm long, forming dense clumps; flowers white or pinkish. *p. 872*

edulis (Calif.: San Diego; Baja California); curious succulent rosette of 10-20 linear cylindric, bluish pencil-like leaves to 15 cm long, with sharp point; flowers white. *p. 872*

farinosa (Coast of N. California); attractive rosette to 10 cm across; succulent, narrow-oblong, green or white-mealy leaves, and short-pointed; double, starry, pale yellow flowers. *Arid-subtropic. p. 874*

pulverulenta (Coast of So. California, Arizona, Baja California), "Chalk-lettuce"; large rosette to 60 cm across, with age forming trunk; the broad, fleshy leaves, powdery-white over green to 12 cm wide; small red flowers. *Subtropic. p. 888*

virens (coast of So. California), "Alabaster plant"; succulent, branching rosette with spreading strapshaped green leaves, 5 to 25 cm long, covered with white glaucescence, reddish toward tips; small yellowish flowers on tall leafy stalk. In hort. as Echeveria insularis. *Subtropic. p. 870, 872*

DURANTA *Verbenaceae* **I-S2LBD**

affinis (Trop. America); floriferous spreading shrub with broad, serrate leaves on thin woody branches; attractive pale purple flowers in long terminal racemes. *p. 2112*

lorentzii (Argentina); bushy shrub or small tree to 3 m, with 4-angled pendant branches; small ovate, leathery leaves finely crenate; short tubular flowers with flaring limb white, in terminal interrupted clusters toward ends of willowy branches; small juicy, orange fruit. *Subtropic. p. 2113*

repens (Florida, West Indies, Mexico, to Brazil), "Pigeon-berry"; small tree to 6 m, occasionally spiny and with drooping 4-angled branches; ovate 10 cm leaves; small flowers with cylindrical corolla and spreading limb lilac-blue, followed by orange-yellow berries. *Tropical. p. 2112, 2116*

repens 'Variegata', "Sky flower"; spreading willowy branches with thin-leathery, opposite leaves 8 cm long, glossy green and attractively bordered with creamy white; clusters of lilac flowers followed by the 6-10 mm yellow berries. *Subtropic. p. 2112*

stenostachya (Brazil); shrub with flexuous willowy 4-angled branches, opposite bright green, smooth, obovate leaves, 5-6 cm long, crenate to apex; with lilac flowers 1 cm across; yellow 1 cm berries. *p. 2112*

DURIO *Bombacaceae* **S3LBD**

testudinarum (Malaysia: Sabah, Malaya), the "Durian tanah"; fantastic tropical forest tree with more or less buttressed trunk at base of which are produced the numerous large globular fruit, hanging on short stalks directly from the trunk and elevated roots; the fruit is a thorny capsule 15-20 cm long with thick walls, splitting into five parts, enclosing the custard-like edible pulp; flowers red, with prominent stamens; leathery, lanceolate leaves covered with silvery scales underneath. *Tropical. p. 509*

zibethinus (Borneo, and widespread in Malaysia), the "Durian"; medium to large tropical evergreen tree to 25 m high, famous for its edible fruit; long ovate, shiny dark green, leathery leaves 10-16 cm long; white flowers with prominent stamens 5 cm long, are clustered in the branches; the green ovoid fruit becomes 20-30 cm long, with a spiny covering enclosing a creamy delicious, but unpleasant-smelling pulp, and is produced from the woody branches. Favorite aphrodisiac in S.E. Asia. *Tropical. p. 508*

DUVALIA *Asclepiadaceae* **S3LBD**

compacta (Cape Prov.); prostrate, branching succulent, dark green stems with big tubercles tipped with small teeth; flowers 2 cm across, chocolate-brown and with wide-spreading lobes 7 mm long. *p. 375*

modesta (So. Africa: Karroo); low succulent with angled stems 2-3 cm long, and with small teeth, the flowers with 5 long lobes, chocolate-brown, 2 cm or more across. *p. 374*

polita (Namibia to Mozambique); succulent with prostrate, dark green or brownish rooting stems, 6-8 cm long, 6-angled and with long teeth; 3 cm flowers brown-red with paler, hairy ring in center. *p. 374*

DYCKIA *Bromeliaceae* **•I1HFD**

altissima (Argentina); small, densely clustering star-like rosette with medium broad, slightly recurving thick leaves to 45 cm long light green and edged with prominent brown spines; gray pencil lines on rounded reverse; inflorescence a branched panicle with bright yellow flowers. *p. 549*

brevifolia (sulphurea) (So. Brazil), "Miniature agave"; dwarf clustering rosette of stiff succulent glossy green sharp-pointed leaves with silver lines beneath; inflorescence off center, a long stalk with bright orange flowers. *Tropical. p. 512, 549*

fosteriana (Paraná), "Silver and gold dyckia"; very ornamental small rosette in a dense whorl of stiff silvery-purple arched leaves with silver spines; inflorescence a spike of rich orange flowers. *Subtropic. p. 549, 551*

frigida (Pourretia) (Paraná); bold rosette with concave, recurving thick leaves to 1 m long, waxy fresh green with sharp brown-black marginal spines, reverse green tinged copper; the 30 cm inflorescence a branched spike with green base and orange-yellow flowers. *p. 549*

'Lad Cutak' (sulphurea x leptostachya); vigorous growing, stiff, ornamental rosette to 30 cm high, of spreading leaves bronzy green and concave above, green or grayish-scaly beneath, spiny at margins; tall erect, attractive inflorescence with orange flowers. *p. 550*

leptostachya (So. Brazil, Paraguay, Argentina); fleshy rosette of spiny channeled leaves tapering to an extended pendant tip, dark green with red-brown base; inflorescence of orange flowers from long stem appearing along-side of center. *p. 549, 551*

niederleinii (Argentina: Misiones); larger plant of loose habit, with long spreading, tapering leaves somewhat flexible, waxy green with hooked, brown-tipped marginal spines, underside with whitish pencil lines; inflorescence a long loose spike 1½-2 m high, with orange-yellow flowers. *p. 549*

rariflora (Minas Gerais); small clustering rosette with hard, recurving leaves to 15 cm long, narrow and slender, tapering to sharp point, green but covered with gray scales, margins with scattered soft black spines, underside rounded; inflorescence to 45 cm with orange flowers. *p. 549, 550*

remotiflora (So. Brazil, Uruguay, Argentina); small rosette with stiff lanceolate, strongly recurved leaves 22 cm long, sharply spiny; the inflorescence on tall mealy-white spike 1 m high, with orange-yellow flowers. *p. 550*

velascana (N.W. Argentina); succulent rosette forming dense clusters with narrowly triangular, recurving leaves 4 cm wide, grayish green and covered with gray scales, the margins with sharp spines; inflorescence on a stout stalk to 1 m high, topped by small, gray-pubescent clusters of sulphur-yellow flowers. *p. 552*

DYSCHORISTE *Acanthaceae* **S2LBD**

thunbergiflora (Kenya), known in Kikuyu as "Mushugushugu"; a shrub to 3 m high, with small 2½ cm obovate leaves, and axillary bracted flowers with 5 cm mauve and purple corolla. *p. 45*

DYSOPHYLLA *Labiatae* **I3HFW**

verticillata (Nepal); herbaceous plant of wet places, growing under water or surfaced; robust, grooved branches with linear-lanceolate 3 to 4 cm green leaves in whorls and with crenate margins, and having a strong peppermint-like fragrance; the inflorescence in spikes of small violet flowers. *p. 1351*

EARINA *Orchidaceae* **I3OFM**

mucronata (New Zealand); epiphytic herb with fleshy, fibrous roots, slender, leafy stems, narrow leathery leaves 10-15 cm long marked with whitish length-lines; small fragrant flowers in slender panicles, white with spotted lip; summer. (C) *p. 1730*

EBENOPSIS *Leguminosae* **S3LBM**

flexicaulis (S. Texas to Yucatán), "Texas ebony"; spiny tree to 15 m or shrub about 6 m high, twigs with spines bi-pinnate with 3 to 5 pairs of leaflets; small ½ cm fragrant yellow flowers with long stamens. *p. 1380*

ECBALLIUM *Cucurbitaceae* **I2LBD**

elaterium (Middle and E. Mediterranean), "Squirting cucumber"; annual rough-hairy trailer with triangular, grayish leaves 10 cm long, primrose yellow flowers, and prickly green, oblong rough-hairy fruit 5 cm long, squirting its seed when detached and ripe. The watery juice of the fruit yields a powerful purgative. *p. 929*

ECHEVERIA *Crassulaceae* ***I2LBD**

affinis (nigra) (Mexico), "Black echeveria"; distinctive rosette of fleshy dark green, waxy, pointed and keeled leaves 5 cm long turning almost completely black in full sun; cyme with scarlet-red flowers in winter. *p. 890*

x agavenbergii (agavoides x derenbergii); attractive German hybrid; very dense rosette of shingled obovate leaves, glaucous blue over green, keeled underneath and with purplish brown tips, forming a veritable pyramid. *p. 896*

agavoides (Urbinia) (San Luis Potosi), "Moulded wax"; solid starlike rosette with rigid fleshy leaves triangular pointed, glossy pale apple-green, margins frequently reddish, spinetipped; flowers reddish tipped yellow. *Tropical.* *p. 889, 2092*

agavoides cristata; curious crested form dense with narrow ovate pointed, thick-fleshy leaves arranged like a coxcomb, apple-green tipped red. *p. 876*

'Ballerina'; giant San Francisco hybrid rosette 45 cm across, with branching leafy stems carrying the inflorescence; glaucous leaves with waxy edges, the young foliage violet, and with very red border; flowers pink and glaucous, on pinkish-purple branches. *p. 899*

'Bradburyana' (prob. elegans hyb.); open rosette 8-10 cm across, with fleshy, oblanceolate leaves, light green, glaucous-waxy with pink tips; long-stalked flowers salmon-rose at base, yellow inside and at tips. This plant is mentioned in Hortus 3; photographed in collection of Harry Johnson, California 1964. *p. 898*

byrnesii (Mexico); broad, rather flat rosette resembling E. secunda, with obovate leaves 4-5 cm long and 2 cm wide, light green, often reddish, not glaucous. Possibly synonymous with E. secunda or a variety. *p. 897*

'Can-Can'; magnificent large California hybrid rosette 35 cm or more across, with thick-fleshy, stout leaves arranged in a perfect circle; glaucous copper-green to brown-violet when older; the margins are doubly crenulate, and the red edge is fringed and ruffled as a French pettycoat; flowers pink. *p. 899*

carnicolor (Mexico: Vera Cruz); stemless, flat rosette of broad oblanceolate fleshy leaves, pink amethyst-colored and glistening silvery, edge pale; flowers on long stems orange red. *p. 894*

x carnitricha (carnicolor x leucotricha); open rosette of fleshy, incurving spatulate or obovate smooth leaves 5 cm long; the stems elongated into the leafy inflorescence with orange-red flowers. *Tropical.* *p. 875*

chihuahuaensis (Mexico); large formal rosette densely composed of thick-fleshy obovate short-pointed keeled leaves, glaucous silvery flushed purplish-red toward apex. *Subtropic.* *p. 887*

coccinea (Mexico: Hidalgo); branching stems headed by loose rosettes of narrow, pliable, keelshaped leaves, gray-green turning reddish with age, and covered with fine white pubescence; flowers red. *p. 887*

x corderoyi (Urbinia) (San Luis Potosi); stemless, clustering rosettes of thick, broad and pointed leaves, glossy light green with red tips; flowers red tipped yellow; E. agavoides hybrid. *p. 895*

cotyledon (Dudleya) (Mexico); handsome large rosette 20 cm across, of spreading, curving, oblanceolate leaves, bluish glaucous over gray green; the flowers greenish-yellow with white mealy stripe down each petal. *p. 896*

crenulata (hoffmannii) (Morelos), "Scallop echeveria"; showy stem-forming large rosette with broad, obovate leaves to 30 cm long, and tapering to narrow petiole, pale green and glaucous bluish-gray, the margins undulate and red; flowers yellowish red. *Tropical.* *p. 893*

crenulata 'Roseo-grandis'; a very showy and decorative large rosette 25 cm diameter, with always rich green, waxy leaves beautifully undulated at the maroon-red margins; some light bluish glaucescence on young inside leaves. *Tropical.* *p. 890, 899*

crenulata 'Roseo-grandis Blue Giant'; beautiful large succulent rosette of formal appearance, with broad, rather flat, obovate leaves glaucous blue with red tips. *p. 899*

crenulata 'Roseo-grandis Buettner hybrid'; elegant rosette about 30 cm across, with broad leaves green with glaucous-blue covering, the lightly wavy edge red. *p. 899*

dactylifera (Mexico: Jalisco, Sinaloa, Durango); large, highly ornamental open rosette of broad ovate, flat, succulent leaves to 25 cm long, bronze over glaucous pale green and edged with red; the inflorescence to 1 m high in branched clusters, the flowers with tubular corolla glaucous pink, inside yellow with red dots along edges. *p. 898*

x dasyphylla (setosa x derenbergii); symmetrical large open rosette of many incurving, obovate fleshy leaves with short point, green and covered with short white hairs; flowers orange to brick-red. *p. 876*

derenbergii (Oaxaca), "Painted lady"; small, globe-shaped clustering rosettes of numerous thick leaves pale green, glaucous with waxy silvery blue bloom and tipped red; flowering freely on short stems, golden yellow with orange. *Tropical.* *p. 892, 894*

derenbergii x multicaulis; low, suckering rosette with short thick obovate leaves waxy deep green tinted purplish red at apex and underside. *p. 887*

'Derex' (E. derenbergii x expatriata); lovely little 5 cm rosette on short stem, sending out stalked ancillary branches, all topped with similar cute rosettes of gray-glaucous; apple-green thick leaves prettily tipped red; the stalked inflorescence with rosy-salmon flowers. Grown by Southern California nurseries for planting into dishgardens. *p. 896*

'Doris Taylor' (setosa x pulvinata), "Woolly rose"; tall robust rosette with glossy deep green, obovate leaves tipped red, and beautifully covered with white hair. *Tropical.* *p. 890*

elegans (Hidalgo), "Mexican snowball"; like small balls of ice opening into beautiful clustering rosette of spoonshaped leaves, 6-8 cm dia., waxy glaucous pale blue, with white translucent margins; flowers coral pink on pink stem. *Tropical.* *p. 892, 894, 897, 2092*

elegans 'Kesselringii', (Mexico); lovely globular, tight rosette 8-10 cm across, with glaucous-bluish incurving, succulent leaves, concave spoon-shaped above and rounded beneath; photographed at Gruga Botanical Gardens, Essen, Germany. *Subtropic.* *p. 886*

expatriata (Mexico), "Pearl echeveria"; short stems topped by a small rosette of thick, oblanceolate leaves, 3-4 cm across, rounded on both sides and pointed, glaucous gray; flowers pinkish yellow on horizontal stalks. *p. 892*

fulgens (Mexico); attractive stem-forming plant with cupped spatulate 10 cm leaves arranged in an open rosette, pale gray-green with silvery blue glaucescence, the rosy margins crisped; flowers yellow inside. *p. 893*

gibbiflora (So. Mexico); forming a heavy stem crowned with a large rosette of spoonshaped glaucous leaves 12-30 cm long, pale metallic green tinted pink and edged red; flowers red outside, yellow within. *p. 893*

gibbiflora 'Carunculata'; strange looking succulent I photographed in France, with erect stout stem, spoon-shaped leaves glaucous blue, tinted copper-purple, at crest with warty outgrowth and recurving *p. 889*

gibbiflora metallica (Mexico: Distrito Federal); handsome smooth rosette 30 cm or more across, with large spoonshaped leaves bronzy amethyst with metallic luster and glaucous purple, margins translucent. *p. 888, 892, 894*

gigantea (Mexico); loose, fleshy, large rosette of broad obovate spoon-shaped leaves, light green and glaucous gray, margins red; flowers salmon red. *p. 892*

x gilva (agavoides x elegans) (Mexico), "Waxy rosette"; shapely open rosette of pale green, broad obovate, spoon-like leaves, slightly silvery glaucous, with tip flushed orange red. *Tropical.* *p. 887*

glauca (Valley of Mexico), "Blue echeveria"; open rosette about 9 cm across, with numerous runners, leaves broad spatulate and almost round, pale glaucous blue-green tipped red; flowers on slender stems, reddish outside, yellow within. *p. 889, 894*

glauca pumila (Mexico); stemless, clustering, formal rosette of thin narrow obovate leaves, glaucous bluish-gray; flowers red with upper half yellow. *p. 19*, 895, 897*

x glauco-metallica (glauca x gibbiflora metallica), "Hen and chickens"; fairly large colorful rosette about 15 cm across with broad spatulate, flat leaves, olive-green covered with gray bloom and tinted amethyst toward edge; flowers dull orange-red. *p. 889*

'Haageana' (agavoides x pulchella?), "Fruit cups"; fleshy open rosette of obovate pointed, rather broad leaves keeled beneath, light green with a rough rugose white surface, tips slightly edged and flushed carmine. *p. 887*

harmsii (in hort. as Oliveranthus elegans) (Mexico), "Red echeveria"; soft hairy shrubby succulent, with fleshy leaves near ends of branches, obovate pointed 3 cm long, grass-green edged with red, in loose rosettes; beautiful flowers like lanterns, 1 to 3 to a spray, 10 to 20 cm long, with large red ovary turning back to show its yellow lining. *Subtropic.* *p. 898*

hirta (Mexico); semi-trailing thick stems with rosettes of fleshy, deep green, boat-shaped leaves, covered with white silky hairs; hairy flowers orange-red and yellow. *p. 897*

'Hoveyi variegata': see zahnii 'Hoveyi'

hyalina (Mexico: San Luis Potosi); handsome rosette of densely shingled, succulent leaves to 6 cm long, with sharp tip, delicate glaucous blue green in color, flushed with red and with translucent margin; tall inflor. of flesh-colored flowers. *Tropical.* *p. 886*

x imbricata (glauca x gibb. metallica); an old hybrid long grown in California gardens, clustering saucer-like rosettes of broad obovate, glaucous bluish-gray leaves tipped red, flowers dull orange-red. *p. 895*

insularis: see Dudleya virens

x kewensis; large open rosette about 10-12 cm across, of broad obovate leaves light olive green with silvery blue bloom, margins tinted pink and blunt apex tipped with red cusp; pinkish-red flowers tipped with yellow, on pink stems. *p. 889, 893*

leucotricha (Mexico: Puebla), "White-plush plant"; beautiful loose rosette with thick boat-shaped, oblanceolate leaves densely covered with glistening white hair, edged with brown hair toward apex; flowers cinnabar-red. *p. 891*

lindsayana (Mexico); beautiful stemless rosette rather flat, of obovate, thick-succulent leaves 5-9 cm long, keeled beneath, glaucous grayish green with red pointed tips; inflorescence on 50 cm stalks, with crimson rose flowers, yellow at tips and inside. Described by E. Walther, San Francisco 1959. *Tropical.* *p. 898*

linguaefolia (Mexico); stemforming rosette of thick-fleshy obovate leaves, spoonshaped, nearly round at base, deep green and glaucous, red apex; flowers cream-colored. *p. 895*

lozanii (Mexico: Jalisco); very attractive open spreading rosette with oblanceolate flat leaves turned upward, to 20 cm long, olive-green but entirely covered with silvery-blue glaucescence, the slender tips flushed and edged red; coppery flowers. *p. 887*

'Meridian' (crenulata hybrid); handsome, vigorous giant rosette 35-45 cm across, with thick-fleshy, fan-like glaucous green leaves crenulated and wavy toward apex, the double-curly leaf margins light red; flowers glaucous pink on long stalks; a show plant. On these giant forms propagation is usually made from floral stalks; or pinch out top, and suckers will form on stem. *p. 899*

montana (Mexico: Oaxaca); small thick-fleshy rosette 5 cm across, of short 2 cm obovate leaves olive-green, flushed red toward apex; tall inflorescence with yellow and red flowers. *p. 898*

multicaulis (Guerrero), "Copper rose"; stems branching, each with a small, loose rosette of waxy fresh-green spatulate leaves 3-4 cm long coppery toward apex and edged brown; flowers on branches red, yellowish inside. *p. 892*

'multicaulis x gibbiflora metallica'; a Hummel, California hybrid; open rosette of robust habit, with broad obovate leaves concave above, and rounded below; metallic green with coppery sheen and some glaucescence. *p. 898*

nodulosa (Oaxaca); little branched shrub with stem forming, to 60 cm high, topped by rosette of obovate spatulate leaves a delicate glaucous bluish-green with maroon marking down the center and around the margins; flowers straw-yellow, outside red. *p. 895*

nuda montana (Mexico: Oaxaca); succulent with obovate fleshy leaves slightly glaucous and edged red, in rosette and scattered along elongated stem, with raceme of flowers red below, yellow above. *p. 894*

orcuttii: see Dudleya

x orpetii; very attractive plant with fleshy orbicular leaves opalescent green with red edge arranged in compact rosette; apricot flowers on long stem. *p. 892*

pallida (Argentina), "Argentine echeveria"; spreading rosette of large obovate, spoon-shaped leaves pale green with edge lightly glaucous; bellshaped pink flowers. *Subtropic.* *p. 888, 892*

peacockii (desmetiana) (Mexico); lovely symmetrical, dense rosette of numerous cupped, oblanceolate fleshy leaves richly covered with silvery-blue glaucescence, edged and tipped with red; red flowers glaucous outside; a favorite for carpet-bedding in Europe. *Tropical.* *p. 886, 893*

peacockii var. subsessilis, according to Eric Walther; (subsessilis or desmetiana hort.) (Mexico: Tehuacan); beautiful rosette more compact than the species, with obovate leaves shorter, 4-5 cm long, covered with waxy bluish-white bloom, the margins and short-pointed tip red, and forming a tight round circle; numerous bright red flowers in one-sided tall clusters, freely blooming. *p. 889*

x perbella; nice dense rosette of thick, concave, obovate, waxy green leaves tinted copper and with contrasting reddish edge. *p. 891*

'Perle von Nuernberg' (potósina x gibbiflora metallica); large open rosette to 15 cm across, with broad, almost flat, obovate leaves deep bluish and glaucous, edged in red, with fine patina. *Tropical.* *p. 876*

pittieri (Guatemala); freely branched smooth subshrub 10 cm or more high; fleshy leaves in a loose rosette, fresh green with glaucous bluish reverse, the margins and tips red; flower in spikes, pale yellow, tipped red. *p. 896*

potosina, (Mexico: San Luis Potosi); charming blue-glaucous rosette, with broad leaves 4-6 cm long, and with purple tips; cup-shaped pink flowers. *Tropical.* *p. 886*

pubescens 'Tortuosa' (recurvata), (E. Mexico); tall branching stem to 60 cm high, tipped by loose succulent rosettes of oblique ovate foliage folded, twisted and recurved toward stem; velvety emerald green leaves covered with fine velour; flowers red with yellow tips. *p. 891*

pulchella (Mexico); attractive stemless rosette of numerous narrow spatulate, fleshy leaves 4-6 cm long, vivid green and densely covered with velvety white pubescence; long stalked, nodding, light red flowers. *p. 896*

'Pulvicox' (pulvinata x coccinea), "Red plush plant"; attractive hybrid forming red hairy stem with rosette of broad gray-green recurved leaves densely covered with white pubescence, turning reddish in strong light; flowers yellow and vermillion. *p. 887*

pulvinata (Oaxaca), "Chenille plant"; beautiful stemforming rosette of thick fleshy, broad obovate ashy-green, red edged leaves thickly covered with silver white felty hair, and forming a shaggy, rustcolor stem; spiked red flowers. *Tropical.* *p. 891, 895*

'Pulv-oliver' (pulvinata x harmsii), "Plush plant"; fine Oliveranthus hybrid with oblanceolate, broad medium-green leaves edged maroon only at apex, covered with glistening white velvety hairs; stem-forming; flowers orange and red. *Tropical.* *p. 64A, 890, 891*

purpusorum (Urbinia purpusii) (So. Mexico); charming regular rosette of nearly triangular pointed, keeled, fleshy leaves 4 cm long, gray green dotted and mottled with brown; flowers red outside, yellow inside and at tips. *p. 898, 923*

quitensis sprucei (Ecuador); a variety with narrow oblanceolate leaves rounded on both sides, fresh green and red toward apex, in dense rosette forming brown stem to 1 m high; flowers orange red. *p. 891*

rubromarginata (Mexico: Vera Cruz, Puebla); beautiful open rosette of fleshy obovate pointed leaves, hollow furrowed above, keeled beneath, to 12 cm long, gray glaucous with red margins; flowers pink. *p. 886*

runyonii (Mexico); clustering succulent rosette of numerous rather flat, obovate 8 cm leaves upcurving, very glaucous-blue; flowers pink. *Tropical.* *p. 896, 898*

runyonii x affinis; a Hummel hybrid; regular, open, bold rosette 20 cm dia., with closely set, spreading, obovate, short-pointed leaves, light green turning coppery toward apex. *p. 888*

x scaphophylla (Ech. agavoides x linguaefolia); massive, perfectly modeled rosette of fleshy, incurved leaves, pale green, glaucous silver, with sharp reddish cusp at tip; flowers pale cream to yellowish orange. *p. 889, 893*

secunda (So. America), "Blue hen-and-chickens"; small, saucer-shaped rosette of obovate leaves which stay narrow, always bluish-green, not metallic, apex with short tip red; flowers reddish. *p. 889*

semivestita (Mexico: Hidalgo); showy rosette to 30 cm across, of scattered, broad-obovate leaves 12-15 cm long, grooved down center, glaucous silvery blue with pink margins; flowers coral pink, yellow inside. *p. 886*

'Set-oliver' (setosa x harmsii), "Chenille plant"; a robust setosa x oliveranthus rosette of many close-set olive-green oblanceolate leaves white hairy beneath, flushed or edged maroon; flowers orange, yellow and red. *p. 19*, 888, 891, 895*

setosa (Mexico); stemless rosette of dense spatulate leaves dark green, red tipped, and nicely covered with glistening white hairs; striking, vivid vermilion, yellow-tipped flowers. *Tropical.* *p. 892*

shaviana (Mexico); beautiful rosette 7 to 10 cm across, spatulate, rather thin succulent leaves with upturned tips, glaucous-blue with bright red or white wavy edges; tall glaucous inflorescence with flowers pink outside, orange inside. *Tropical.* *p. 899*

simulans (gilva) (Northern Mexico), "True Mexican rose"; dense rosette of many comparatively narrow pointed, fleshy, concave leaves rather incurving in center, light green and lightly glaucescent, the upper half of leaf rich crimson red, particularly the short cusps; flowers reddish-yellow. *p. 887*

'Sonnenstrahl' (derenbergii major hybrid); very free-blooming, open succulent rosette with rather flat, obovate, grayish green leaves; in the center a veritable bouquet of an inflorescence dense with orange flowers. *p. 876*

'Spruce-oliver'; hybrid of sprucei x harmsii; smaller dense rosette of glossy fresh-green, narrow oblanceolate leaves, light green and rounded beneath, margins hairy and tips red; flowers orange and vermilion. *p. 891*

subrigida (C. Mexico); strikingly beautiful large rosette to 30 cm diameter, broad oblanceolate green leaves recurved or spreading, thickly covered with bluish-white glaucescence, the margins rosy-red; stem-forming sideways; flowers red. *p. 893*

subsessilis ("peacockii") (Mexico); beautiful compact rosette of broad leaves covered with waxy bluish-white bloom, margins and pointed tip red; numerous bright red flowers. *p. 889*

tolucensis (Mexico); open rosette of flat oblanceolate, very pointed leaves, glaucous blue-green; yellow flowers striped red outside. *p. 895*

turgida (Coahuila); stemless, freely clustering dense rosette of numerous spatulate leaves, grayish green tinged red, and glaucous and stiff upright; flowers rose. *p. 895*

x weingartii (purpusorum hyb.); dense rosette of thick fleshy, glossy olive green, flattened leaves with edge and tapering point reddish; flowers reddish-orange. *p. 891*

zahnii 'Hoveyi'; colorful large loose rosette of long spatulate, fleshy leaves, furrowed lengthwise and variegated in delicate blended stripes of soft pale bluish-green, mauve, pink and cream, and glaucous with waxy silvery bloom, apex raggedly crenulated; flowers pinkish orange. *p. 893*

ECHEVERIA: see also Dudleya

ECHIDNOPSIS *Asclepiadaceae* **S2LBD**

cereiformis (Ethiopia, Somalia, So. Arabia, Yemen); leafless snake-like succulent plant with cylindrical branches erect or becoming prostrate, the stout 8-angled stems dull dark green or brownish, divided into low tubercles with leaf scars but no spines; fleshy flowers bright yellow. *p. 356*

ECHINOCACTUS *Cactaceae* ***I-S2LBD**

grandis (So. Mexico: Tehuacán), "Giant Visnaga"; monstrous barrel cactus to 2 m tall and 1 m thick; with 30-50 ribs; 5-6 yellowish radial spines, and straight central spine to 5 cm long; yellow funnel-form flowers 5 cm long, and 5 cm woolly fruit. *Arid-tropical.* *p. 687*

grusonii (C. Mexico), "Golden barrel"; growing into a giant globe of 90 cm dia., light green, closely ribbed, covered with golden spines; yellow flowers imbedded around top, opening in sun. *Arid-tropical.* *p. 618, 687*

grusonii cristatus; a beautiful crested form shaped like a big, lively green coxcomb, with golden spines especially concentrated along the wavy apex. *p. 620*

horizonthalonius (Texas, Mexico), "Eagle claws"; broad globe, dome-shaped above ground, glaucous gray-green, usually 8 full ribs, heavy talon-like reddish spines; flowers pale rose. *p. 687*

ingens (Mexico); large barrel type, to 1½ m high, glaucous blue, woolly at top; few ribs as seedling, later densely ribbed, rigid straight brown spines; flowers yellow. *p. 687*

platensis (Echinocactus quehlianus) (So. Argentina: Cordoba); attractive small globe, depressed on top and half-hidden in the ground, 4-9 cm broad, bluish-green or bronze with 8-12 ribs divided into chin-like tubercles and with appressed spines; flowers 6 cm long, white with green and purplish. *p. 695*

ECHINOCEREUS *Cactaceae* **C-S2LBD**

albispinus (Oklahoma), "Lace cactus"; clusters of small green elongate-globular plants, their numerous ribs set with short white spines; large sweetly scented flowers with narrow petals dainty mauve-pink, throat old rose. *Subtropic.* *p. 666*

armatus (Mexico); slender cylindric, dark blue-green "Hedgehog" with 17 low ribs, covered with short white radials and brown central spine, and large bell-shaped rose pink flowers tipped mauve, with moss-green eye. *p. 672*

baileyi (Mountains of Oklahoma); shapely cylindric plant, 10 cm high, dark green, many-ribbed, densely set with thin straw-white spines tipped red, out of areoles with woolly tufts, flowers purple. *p. 667, 670*

berlandieri (Mexico); sprawling plant with dull green stems 10 cm long and 2 cm thick, freely branching, with 5 or 6 spiral ribs notched into warts and few brownish to white spines; free-blooming with wide-open rotate flowers of lively pink. *p. 670*

blanckii (So. Texas, Mexico), "Hedgehog"; branching plant with ascending or sprawling stems to 30 cm long and 3 cm thick, dark green, with 5-6 warty ribs set with glossy black central spines; beautiful purplish-pink flowers 9 cm long. *Subtropic.* *p. 672*

chihuahuaensis (Mexico); branching plant with spreading, slender cylindrical stems, about 9 ribbed and 2½ cm dia., with white radials and cinnamon central spine; small, beautiful funnel-shaped flowers deep red with orange glow. *p. 672*

chloranthus (W. Texas), "Brown-flowered pitaya"; globular, spiny cactus with bundles of white needle spines, small red-brown flowers. *p. 667, 672*

cinerascens (C. Mexico); erect or sprawling stems to 25 cm long and 5 cm thick, with 6-8 notched ribs, and covered with slender white needle-spines; blooming freely violet red. *p. 673*

conoideus (W. Texas, Mexico); mound-forming, globular to elongated stem grayish-green, 15-20 cm high, with 8-11 acute ribs, armed with needle-like radials and very long central spines yellowish-white; flowers fiery red. *p. 671*

dasyacanthus (W. Texas, Mexico), "Rainbow cactus"; small cylindric, hard and closely ribbed xerophyte densely stiff-spined in rainbow-like zones of straw-yellow, purple, tan, red-brown and amethyst, spines pointing out and downward; funnel-shaped flowers mostly yellow. *Arid-subtropic.* *p. *19, 618, 667, 668, 670, 674*

delaetii (Mexico: Coahuila); beautiful, clustering plant to 20 cm high, known as the "Lesser old man" because of the covering of long white curling hairs from the areoles, over the pale green stem; flowers pink. *p. 668*

ehrenbergii (Mexico); freely suckering plant of erect green stems 15 cm high and 3 cm thick, with 6 notched ribs and glassy-white needle-spines; flowers purplish to violet-red. *Tropical.* *p. 673*

engelmannii (No. Mexico, U.S.: California, Arizona, Nevada, Utah), "Hedgehog cactus"; cylindric column 10 to 45 cm high, and 4-6 cm thick with 10-13 warty ribs, branching from base and forming clumps, with long needle spines; funnel-shaped, day-blooming purple flowers to 10 cm long. Photo shown on p. 674 is of a plant carefully copied from nature and made of glass, in the collection of Harvard University. *Arid-subtropic.* *p. 674*

ferreirae (Mexico); clustering blue green plant with 12 ribbed stems 10-30 cm long, similar to fendleri but with longer brown central spines and bleached radials; outstanding flowers with incurved petals pinkish-mauve and a tangerine center. *p. 673*

fitchii (Texas); cylindric plant, or narrowed to top, slowly branching, dull green, with 12-14 ribs, covered with numerous yellowish spines; free-blooming with funnel-shaped violet-red flowers. *p. 671, 672*

gentryi (Mexico: Sonora); small clustering cereus with slender, angled columns to 15 cm long and 2½ cm thick, and with small spines; funnelform flowers to 8 cm long deep rose-pink inside and with red anthers, open mainly at night. *p. 674*

knippelianus (Mexico); interesting globular or oval plant 10-20 cm high, thick, branching, deep gray green, with 5-7 ribs separated by broad furrows, with small areoles and weak lemon-colored spines; flowers carmine-violet inside. *p. 668, 672*

longispinus (probably Mexico), a "Pitaya"; elongate plant, a variation of E. pectinatus, similar to baileyi but the cream spines appear longer and are red-tipped toward apex. *Tropical.* *p. 668*

melanocentrus (Mexico); cultivated in New Zealand, stiff cylindric dark green plant with 12-13 low ribs, flattened radial spines and brown central, topped by beautiful, wide-open flowers deep magenta with a deep red throat, and red filaments shading to yellow. *p. 668*

papillosus (West Texas), "Hedgehog cactus"; sprawling and branching green stems 3 cm thick with 6-10 ribs, notched into prominent warts; yellowish white to brown radials and one yellow central spine; flowers yellow, reddish at base. *Arid-subtropic.* *p. 667*

pectinatus var. rufispinus (Mexico); free-blooming plant with simple cylindric stem 10-15 cm high, with some 20 ribs thickly set with star-like radial spines normally white but in this form reddish; scented flowers lively pink with deeper midrib, petals shading through white to green at base. *p. 673*

pensilis (Mexico: Baja California); stems prostrate or hanging, 4 cm dia. with 8-10 notched ribs, spines yellow to reddish, 8 radials, 1 central; flowers bright red. *p. 667*

pentalophus (So. Texas, Mexico); cylindric branches sprawling and ascending to 12 cm long and 3 cm thick, green, with 4-6 warty ribs, and white areoles; pretty round flowers lilac or pink with reddish violet. *Arid-subtropic.* *p. 670, 671*

pentalophus monstrosus (E. Mexico); small plant lying flat with short branches upright, deep green 4-6 ribs in the type, with short white spines; reddish flower; the monstrose form developing multiple heads. *p. 670*

perbellus (Texas), a "Lace cactus"; colorful globe or short cylinder to 10 cm, closely ribbed, radial spines shaded from reddish to nearly white; flowers purple. *Arid-subtropic.* *p. 673*

pulchellus (Mexico); low inverted cone, branching from the base, bluish green to gray-green, with 11-13 low notched ribs, and small yellowish spines; flowers pink. *p. 673*

purpureus (Oklahoma), "Purple hedgehog"; cylindrical plant to 12 cm tall olive green with shallow ridges densely set with flattened, all-radial white spines tipped purple; flowers deep magenta-purple. *p. 668*

reichenbachii (Texas, Mexico), "Lace cactus"; small globe to 20 cm, close-ribbed, attractively covered by flat rosettes of stiff spines in a range of colors from white to red-brown; flowers iridescent light purple. *Arid-subtropic.* *p. 667, 668, 669*

rigidissimus (pectinatus) (Arizona, Sonora); attractive, short-cylindric plant 10-20 cm high, known as a "Rainbow cactus"; gray-green covered with small, stiff radial spines interlocking in older plants, alternate zones of cream, pink, reddish and brownish, the apex beautifully tinted purplish-red; purple flowers. Marshall-Bock suggests that this purple-flowered type should be listed a variety of E. dasyacanthus, and report a plant of dasyacanthus seen in New Mexico with a purplish flower from one side of the stem and a yellow flower opposite. *Arid-subtropic.* *p. 668, 670*

roetteri (Mexico, N. M., Texas); cylindrical plant to 15 cm high with 11-13 notched ribs dense with stiff, appressed straw-color radials, and straight, needle-like brown central spines; flowers violet-purple inside. *p. 668*

scheerii (Mexico); free-blooming, cylindrical plant to 25 cm high and 4 cm thick, erect or ascending, 7-9 tubercled ribs, dark glossy green with whitish spines; funnel-shaped, 12 cm flowers a beautiful pink. *p. 669*

sciurus (So. Baja California); low tufting plant with green stems 20 cm high and to 5 cm thick, 12-17 shallow, notched ribs covered with short bristle-like yellow spines; large and beautiful 12 cm flowers rosy violet. *Arid-tropical.* *p. 670*

stoloniferus (Mexico); low plant colony-forming by stolons, with cylindric stems 14-16 ribbed and lightly tubercled, dark spines becoming white; showy yellow flowers and red fruit. *p. 669*

triglochidiatus (W. Texas, New Mexico, Colorado), "Hedgehog cereus"; stems to 60 cm long, with 5-8 notched ribs in spirals, small reddish to fawn spines; the attractive scarlet flowers with yellow center. *p. 672*

viridiflorus (So. Dakota, Wyoming to Texas), "Green-flowered hedgehog"; small, nearly globular, rigid, dark green plant to 20 cm high, with 14 ribs, long stiff areoles and spines, in zones of white or brownish; flowers greenish. *Temperate.* *p. 671*

ECHINOCYSTIS *Cucurbitaceae* **I2HBM**

lobata (Canada; Idaho to Texas), "Mock-cucumber"; rapid-growing, tendril-climbing monoecious annual vine with angled stems and sharply 3 to 5-lobed leaves; small greenish-white flowers; small prickly, papery-puffy weak-spined pods, known as wild balsam-apple. *p. 932*

ECHINODORUS *Alismataceae* **I-S2-3HNW**

cordifolius (U.S., Mexico); stout water or swamp plant with tuberous root stock, heart-shaped leaves 10-20 cm long, with prominent parallel veins and with brownish translucent spots; flowers white with green sepals, on tall divided stalks as much as 1 m high. *p. 80*

palaefolius (Trop. America); tropical aquatic plant growing in shallow water, with fleshy petioles bearing very broad cordate, almost round leaves with ribs prominent; large branched inflorescence of white flowers. Photographed at Longwood Gardens. *p. 80*

tenellus (No. America: Mass. to Florida and Mexico; So. America: Colombia to Brazil), "Amazon-sword plant"; swamp and aquatic plant growing under water, spreading by creeping runners; 1-2 leaves oblanceolate, 1- or 3-nerved, green, seldom more than 20 cm high, but very variable according to growing conditions. Favored aquarium plant. *p. 80*

ECHINOFOSSULOCACTUS *Cactaceae* **S-I2LBD**

acroacanthus (Stenocactus) (Mexico), "Brain cactus"; solitary globular plant with 27 very acute ribs in narrow folds and irregularly wavy, looking like a green fossil, with recurved spines; flowers at the apex with broad petals white with a glowing purplish-red midrib. *p. 688*

coptonogonus (Mexico: San Luis Potosi); vicious looking, depressed globular plant to 10 cm high, glaucous olive green, with 10-14 undulate, sharp ribs, armed densely with clusters of gray, hard arching spines, central spine broad; flowers purple with white-margined segments. *p. 688*

crispatus (Mexico: Hidalgo); globe somewhat depressed at apex, 12 cm high with about 25 ribs narrowly compressed into sharp folds, somewhat wavy, with weaker spines; flowers central, white with purple stripes. *p. 688*

geminispinus (Mexico); shapely olive green globe with sharp wavy ridges set with white radials as well as a pair of long brown, awl-shaped, curving central spines; pretty white flowers with purple base. *p. 688*

hastatus (Mexico: Hidalgo); simple, depressed, light green globe, with 35 congested, steep wavy ridges set with curving spines and yellowish long and broad, upright, spear-like central spines through which the flowers must push; petals white with pink midrib. *p. 688*

heteracanthus (Mexico: Hidalgo); globular, light green plant, with 30-34 ribs nearly hidden by the closely set spines, the radials glassy white, fine central spines brownish; flowers purple with 3 rows of petals. *p. 688*

multicostatus (E. Mexico); globular plant 5-10 cm dia., with as many as 100 sharp ribs closely pressed together into wavy folds, bearing some very vicious yellowish spines; flowers white with a purple midrib on each petal. *p. 688*

zacatecasensis (Mexico: Zacatecas); depressed globe to 9 cm wide with pale green, 50-60 sharp ribs closely compressed into undulate folds, set with broad, hooked central spines and smaller radials; flowers white tipped lavender. *p. 688*

ECHINOMASTUS *Cactaceae* **S-I2LBD**

macdowellii (Thelocactus) (No. Mexico); small globular plant 8 cm high, with 20-25 ribs, white radials and long white needle spines; large flowers rose-pink. *Arid-subtropic.* *p. 687*

ECHINOPSIS *Cactaceae* **'I-S2LBD**

campylacantha (W. Argentina); globular plant becoming almost columnar, dark grayish green, with 12-14 straight, acute ribs, set with stiff gray brown spines; flowers outside brownish green, inner petals white flushed pink and perfumed. *p. 676*

hamatacantha (Argentina), "Lily cactus"; globular, flattened plant depressed at top, 15 cm thick, dark dull-green with some 15 notched ribs, straight and recurved spines; flowers white, night-blooming. *p. 666*

kermesina (So. America); a low, globular "Hedge hog" cactus coppery green with many pronounced ridges set with grayish to brown spines; long funnel-shaped flowers carmine rose with prominent yellow anthers and stigma; probably a dark-flowered form of E. multiplex. *p. 676*

leucantha (Argentina); oblong plant to 30 cm high, one of the few which grows old to cylindric shape, with 12-14 acute ribs, glaucous bluish-green, pale spines tipped black; flowers white tinged purple outside. *p. 676*

leucorhodantha (Argentina: Salta); globular to subcylindric dark green plant with about 20 acute ribs and gray to yellow spines; sweet-scented flowers brownish outside, white and pale pink inside. *p. 676*

mamillosa (ritteri) (Bolivia); small globes 10 cm dia., glossy green but densely spiny over the chin-like knobs; showy flower lily-like 8 cm across, white and flushed with rose at apex. *p. 675*

mirabilis (Setiechinopsis) (Argentina); cylindric plant to 15 cm high with some 11 notched ribs in spirals densely set with straw-colored needle spines; flowers white. *p. 676*

multiplex (S. Brazil), "Easter lily cactus"; small barrel to 15 cm high, forming clusters, dark green, close-ribbed, with sharp brown spines; long, erect funnelformed pink or rosy flowers to 25 cm long. *p. 675, 676*

multiplex cristata; this weird crested form is quite different from the regular type in its sprawling shape. *p. 620*

multiplex hybrida; according to Britton-Rose, a hybrid possibly with the white-flowering E. turbinata; a freely suckering, globular, "Lily-cactus" with fresh-green bodies many-ribbed and with small sharp spines, the large, showy funnel-form flowers 12-20 cm long, white inside, flushed pink to purplish outside, open in the morning; widely grown in California nurseries under this name for dishgarden planting. *Arid-subtropic.* *p. 675*

'Terracotta'; magnificent hybrid of the 'Paramount" group by Harry Johnson of California with numerous showy flowers from one plant, in a new shade of shell pink, with bronze orange outside. *p. 675*

tubiflora (zuccarinii) (So. Brazil, Argentina); globular stem, later cylindrical, to 60 cm high, dark green, sprouting along sides and at top, 11-12 acute ribs and light brown spines; long 20 cm funnel-form flowers with outer segments green tipped brown, inner petals white. *p. 666, 676*

uruguayensis (Uruguay); similar to E. tubiflora; subglobose, rather conical green body densely ribbed but with few spines, suckering from the base; flowers pinkish white. Photographed at Huntington Botanic Garden, San Marino, California. *p. 675*

'White Knight' (turbinata x 'Paramount'); free-blooming Harry Johnson of California hybrid with large pure white flowers. *p. 675*

ECHINOPSIS: see also Trichocereus

ECHITES *Apocynaceae* **S3LFD**

picturata (Trop. America); handsome vine with leathery narrow spear-shaped leaves dark green with gray veins and with red line down center. *p. 136*

rubrovenosa (Prestonia), (So. America: Rio Negro); tropical wiry climber with striking foliage on slender twining stems; the large elliptic emerald green leaves to 15 cm long, netted with red veins. The beautiful coloring of the leaves is brought out to perfection only under moist-warm conditions. *Tropical.* *p. 134*

ECHIUM *Boraginaceae* **I2LBD**

bourgaeanum (Canary Islands); bristly, shrubby biennial to 2½ m or more tall, with long, linear, silvery-hairy, drooping leaves on stout, leafy stem, with pyramidal inflorescence on showy spike with irregular trumpet-shaped rosy flowers. *p. 511*

fastuosum (No. Europe, Canary Isl.), "Pride of Madeira"; gray-hairy shrubby perennial ½ to 2 m high, with narrow lanceolate leaves covered with soft white hair, and deep blue, bell-shaped flowers with protruding red stamens, on one-sided spikelets formed in cylindrical inflorescence. *p. 511*

EDGEWORTHIA *Thymelaeaceae* **I2LFM**

papyrifera (Himalayas to China), "Paper-bush" or "Mitsumata"; strikingly beautiful deciduous shrub to 2 m high, seen in February bloom in gardens of Chekiang Prov. of Central China; the stocky branches tipped by dense clusters of vanilla-scented flowers, the corolla-like calyx tubes 3-4 cm long, silky outside and golden yellow inside and at flaring lobes; the subsequent lanceolate leaves 12 cm long. Used in So. Japan as a source of soft, tough paper. *Warm-temperate.* *p. 2098*

EDITHCOLEA *Asclepiadaceae* **S2LBD**

grandis (Somaliland, Kenya, Tanzania); succulent close to Caralluma but with larger 10 cm flowers, pale yellow, with red-brown spots on the 5 lobes, and ciliate margins; the 5-angled grayish-green stems to 30 cm, with hard, brown, thornlike teeth. *Arid-tropical.* *p. 357, 380*

EDRAIANTHUS *Campanulaceae* **I2LBD**
dinaricus (Yugoslavia: Dalmatia); low cushion-forming perennial herb; rosettes of narrow-linear leaves hairy on upper side; clusters of flowers with funnel-shaped violet-blue corolla. *p. 750*

EICHHORNIA *Pontederiaceae* **S3LFW**
azurea (Brazil), "Peacock hyacinth"; aquatic herb rooting in shallow water, and sending flexuous runners across its surface, with fleshy stalks not inflated, fresh green, waxy leaves rounded or obovate; terminal spikes of showy flowers, lilac-blue with purple center, the two lower petals fringed. *Humid-tropical.* *p. 1956*

crassipes (speciosa) (Trop. and Subtrop. America), "Water hyacinth"; small aquatic plant usually floating, with bluish, feathery roots, and runners forming clumps, the roundish, glossy green leaves in rosettes, on petioles much inflated at base causing them to stay afloat; clusters of large, lilac flowers with yellow center surrounded by blue blotch and purple stripes. *Humid-tropical.* *p. 1956, 1957*

heterosperma (Antilles, C. America, No. Brazil); tropical aquatic herb with floating or partially submerged leaves, long-stalked, broad obovate and glossy-green; flowers light purple. *p. 1957*

martiana (E. paniculata, Hortus 3) (So. America); aquatic plant rooting in soil, forming several soft, herbaceous branches to 40 cm high, long-stalked cordate, green leaves; two-lipped flowers in a compound spike, lower lip of 3 purple segments, upper 3 blue and smaller. This may be the same as E. paniculata. *p. 1957*

natans (Madagascar); a miniature aquatic herb; the submerged leaves linear 3-6 cm long, the floating leaves ovate with cordate base, on elongate petioles; solitary blue flowers. *p. 1957*

paniculata (Brazil); a different kind of tropical water hyacinth, with short, fleshy rhizomes; basal leaves cordate narrowed to a slender point, smooth and fresh green, the stem-leaves smaller; flowers 3 cm dia. with 3 rosy-lavender petals and 3 violet-colored, and marked with yellow. *p. 1957*

EKEBERGIA *Meliaceae* **I2LBD**
capensis (So. Africa to Ethiopia), "Dog plum" or "Cape ash"; large evergreen tree to 10 m, with shining, decorative pinnate leaves; small creamy-yellow flowers with orange-blossom scent, followed by 18 mm crimson berries. *p. 1551*

ELAEAGNUS *Elaeagnaceae* ***I1LFM**
pungens (Japan, China), the "Silver berry"; slow-growing brown-stemmed evergreen shrub of rather rigid, angular sprawling habit of growth, to 2-5 m high; leathery oval grayish green leaves with rusty-brown tinting, 3-8 cm long and with wavy edges and silvery beneath; the surface is covered with silvery scales reflecting sunlight which give the plant a special sparkle; white, fragrant flowers. *Warm temperate.* *p. 954*

pungens aureo-variegata (Japan, China); evergreen brown-stemmed shrub with leathery oval, wavy margined, green leaves painted yellow, young surface covered with silvery scales, silver beneath; white fragrant flowers. *p. 954*

ELAEIS *Palmae* **S3LF-BW**
guineensis (Trop. West and C. Africa), "African oil-palm"; feather-palm to 18 m or more tall, with ringed trunk crowned by graceful pinnate fronds to 5 m long, the ridged narrow leaflets green on both sides; male and female flowers in separate clusters on the same tree; the ovoid red to black 4 cm fruit in large clusters of 200-300; source of palm-oil. *Tropical.* *p. 1872, 1878*

ELAEOPHORBIA *Euphorbiaceae* **S2LFD**
drupifera (Guinea, Sierra Leone); succulent tree with roundish trunk obscurely angled, and large leathery, dark green, obovate leaves to 25 cm, a keeled midrib beneath; milk very poisonous. *p. 1028*

ELAPHOGLOSSUM *Polypodiaceae (Filices)* **S3HFM**
crinitum (Acrostichum) (West Indies, Mexico, C. America), "Elephant's-ear fern"; handsome fern, with creeping rhizome and simple leathery, rather succulent broadly oblong fronds to 60 cm long, on stalks with black silky scales. *p. 1113*

lingua (West Indies); wide-creeping rhizome bearing large leathery, ovate leaves 30-45 cm long, quickly narrowing toward base. *p. 1113*

longifolium (Acrostichum) (West Indies, Trop. America); tufted fern with creeping, scaly rhizome bearing long linear-lanceolate leaves of thick-leathery texture 30-45 cm long, glossy-green with prominent midrib; slightly undulated. *p. 1113*

pachycraspedon (Eastern Perú); tropical epiphytic fern with creeping rhizome, and long-stalked tongue-like leaves, hard-leathery and metallic glossy blue-green, 25 cm long and 5 cm wide, with bold midrib; underside dense-scaly when young; new growth hairy. *Humid-tropical.* *p. 1105*

pilosum (Acrostichum) (Mexico); small fern becoming crowded with narrow almost linear leathery leaves 15-20 cm long, the sterile fronds flexuous and bending back and forth, and covered on both sides with bright brown scales resembling a tuft of stellate hairs. *p. 1113*

ELATOSTEMA *Urticaceae* **S3LFM**
latifolium acaule (Thailand, Vietnam); beautiful ornamental foliage plant to 10 cm high; leaves 6-10 cm long, short-petioled, blade broad elliptic, somewhat unequal, green with silver blotches; young foliage with brownish net. *p. 2108*

sessile (Trop. Africa and Asia); herbaceous tropical plant to 30 cm high, with ornamental, rugose or quilted leaves ovate slender-pointed and serrate at margins, glossy green. *p. 2108*

ELEOCHARIS *Cyperaceae* **S3LBW**
dulcis (E. Asia, Pacific Islands), "Chinese Waterchestnut" or "Ma-Hai"; slender perennial rush-like plant allied to Scirpus, growing at edge of shallow water, with solid tuber or corm 5 cm thick, forming tufts of narrow, fresh-green leaves reduced to sheaths, the culms bearing at their tips the tiny flowers in spikelets. The tubers are much eaten by Chinese, and sold in their shops. *p. 948*

ELEPHANTORRHIZA *Leguminosae* **S2LBD**
burkei (Transvaal); shrub or small tree, with linear, leathery leaves, and ivory white flowers with long stamens along the twigs. *p. 1380*

ELEUTHEROPETALUM: see Chamaedorea

ELLEANTHUS *Orchidaceae* **I3HFM**
capitatus (West Indies, Mexico to Perú); terrestrial of the habit of Sobralia, with leafy, slender reed-stems 30 cm or more; thin but stiff leaves prominently length-ribbed ending in two short points; terminal heads of rose-purple flowers; April-June. *Tropical.* *p. 1729*

trilobatus (Panama); pretty terrestrial, close to Sobralia, with nerved, distant leaves and arching spike of tubular yellow flowers. (summer). (I) *p. 1717*

ELYTRARIA *Acanthaceae* **S3LFM**
caroliniensis (Trop. America); low herbaceous rosette with fresh green, broad ovate, quilted leaves; from the center the scaly, slender floral stalks 25 cm high, topped by tight clusters of small white flowers 1 cm across. *p. 45*

EMBOTHRIUM *Proteaceae* **S3LBD**
wickhamii (New Caledonia); magnificent evergreen shrub dense with long oval, leathery concave, waxy leaves, the inflorescence a striking flat brush of brilliant orange-red filaments tipped with yellow. I photographed this tropical bush, 2 m high, near Noumea. *Tropical.* *p. 1977*

EMMENOSPERMA *Rhamnaceae* **I2LBD**
alphitonioides (Australia); sparry evergreen shrub photographed at Taronga, near Sydney; stiff branches with long ovate, concave, leathery green leaves, and with terminal clusters of bright orange berries; very handsome. *Subtropic.* *p. 1991*

ENCEPHALARTOS *Cycadaceae* **I2LFD**
altensteinii (South Africa: E. Cape), "Prickly cycad"; stout trunk to 2 m high bearing crown of pinnate leaves 1-2 m long, the numerous leaflets thick, and with 3-5 spiny teeth on each margin, shining deep green; cylindrical male cones 30-40 cm long; female cones broadly oval to 45 cm tall. *p. 935, 942*

arenarius (So. Africa); handsome rosette of twisted leaves, glaucous blue with recurved apex, tips divided into spine-like sharp points, the margins of the rigid leaflets toothed. *Subtropic.* *p. 937*

caffer (Cape Prov.), "Kaffir bread"; a palm-like plant with stout trunk of about 1 m topped by crown of stiff pinnate leaves; the male cone often grows to 30 cm long. *p. 941*

hildebrandtii (Trop. E. Africa); splendid plant growing to 6 m high; pinnate leaves light green, somewhate rigid, to 3 m long, leaflets shorter near base, and are spiny along margin; the male cone to 60 cm long. *p. 941*

horridus (So. Africa), "Ferocious blue cycad"; wide spreading ornamental cycad with short stout trunk crowned by a cluster of stiff pinnate leaves, glaucous green, 60 cm long, leaflets oblique lanceolate and spinily lobed, male cone cylindric and stalked, 30 cm long, female cone broad ovoid 40 cm long. *Subtropic.* *p. 939*

kosiensis (So. Africa: Zululand); short trunk, bearing rosette of pinnate, vicious leaves about 1 m long; the broad leaflets 8-15 cm long formidably armed with large triangular teeth and spines; cones brilliant orange-red. *Subtropic.* *p. 944*

latifrons (horridus latifrons) (So. Africa: S.E. Cape); "Spiny kaffir bread"; stout, globular trunk to 2 m high, with recurved, vicious pinnate leaves 60-90 cm long, reflexed toward apex, the broad, thick leaflets overlapping and with coarse spine-tipped lobes; the cones brownish-yellow. *Subtropic.* *p. 942*

laurentianum (Trop. Africa: Uganda); palm-like tree with trunk to 10 m high and 75 cm thick; stiff, straight, pinnate leaves to more than 6 m long, the narrow-linear, leathery pinnae dark green, and with spine-tipped marginal teeth; cones red. *Tropical.* *p. 944*

lehmannii (So. Africa), "Blue-leaved cycad"; thick trunk to 1 m or more high, crowned by a mighty rosette of elegant, recurving fronds about 1 m long, the glaucous blue-green leaflets 16-18 cm long, with spiny tip and marginal spines. *Subtropic.* *p. 937*

transvenosus (South Africa: North Transvaal), the "Mujaji-palm"; forming tall, stout trunks crowned by stiff pinnate leaves; the glaucous dark green, leathery pinnae lightly hairy and curved back from the midrib. By special permission I was privileged to visit Mujaji village in the mountains of northern Transvaal, their habitat, where they are venerated as dedicated to the Rain Queen, with specimen, occasionally branched, 5 m tall; propagation from bulbils forming along trunk. *Subtropic.* *p. 939*

villosus (Natal); short trunk almost globular and woolly, leaves to 2 m long, erect in young growth, later outward; leaflets are green and spiny at edges; male cones are bright yellow 60 cm long. *p. 320A, 941*

woodii (So. Africa: Zululand); large cycad with massive trunk reaching 6 m tall, topped by a majestic crown of 50 or more gracefully arching fronds 2 m or more long, the dense linear leaflets are bright green and to 20 cm long, armed with a few spiny teeth; male cones slender cylindric to more than 1 m long. *p.943*

ENCYCLIA *Orchidaceae* **S3OFD**

oncidioides (Guyana, Brazil); according to latest research, this is merely a well-marked section of the variable genus Epidendrum; see both Epidendrum odoratissimum and oncidioides.

ENKIANTHUS *Ericaceae* **C2LBD**

campanulatus (Japan); deciduous shrub to 8 m with 4-angled whorled branches, red when young; serrate, elliptic leaves turning brilliant red in autumn; bell-shaped yellow flowers with red veins; fairly hardy. *p. 958*

perulatus (Japan), "White enkianthus"; much-branched deciduous shrub to 1½ m high, with smooth, reddish young shoots; oval, serrate leaves to 5 cm long; pendulous flowers in terminal clusters, urnshaped 1 cm white corolla with recurved lobes, blooming before foliage; fairly hardy. *p. 958*

ENSETE *Musaceae* **S2-3LF-BW**

maurelii (Musa) (Ethiopia), "Black banana"; symmetrical plant with the decorative habit of ventricosum; rosette of sturdy, broad, dark-complexioned leaves, deep green suffused with blackish-red above, with brown-purple midrib and margins, purplish-brown beneath. *Tropical.* *p. 1593, 1594*

ventricosum (Musa ensete) (Moist Central and E. Africa), "Abyssinian banana"; to 12 m, stout solitary pseudostems, not stoloniferous, conspicuously swollen at the base, bearing erect broad leaves to 6 m long in a cluster, banana-like, and dying after fruiting. Leaves bright green with red midrib and purple edge, on short red stalks. Erect inflorescence with dark red bracts and whitish flowers. Used as shapely centerpiece in summer beds. Have seen this at alt. 1,500 m on Mt. Kilimanjaro (Tanzania), and at 2,300 m in Kikuyu country of Kenya. *Subtropic.* *p. 1594, 1597, 1599*

ENTELEA *Tiliaceae* **I2LFD**

aborescens (New Zealand); handsome evergreen small tree to 6 m, the trunk with wood of the lightest weight, lighter than cork; large heart-shaped soft leaves to 25 cm long and with toothed margins; 2½ cm white, starry flowers with prominent patch of yellow stamens; bristly fruit. *p. 2099, 2102*

ENTEROLOBIUM *Leguminosae* **S3LBM**

cyclocarpum (Jamaica, Venezuela), "Ear tree"; huge, broad-headed tree to 20 m, with graceful bipinnate leaves; flowers in globose heads of greenish-white stamens; bearing black pods bent to form a circle shaped like monkey ears. *p. 1381*

EPACRIS *Epacridaceae* **C2HBD**

amaphilis (Australia); heath-like shrub with stiff, twisted branches, loosely set with small sharp-pointed, rigid leaves; toward apex with tight, globose clusters of charming bell-like white flowers. *p. 956*

x hybrida; an excellent example of the perfection and beauty which have been bred into modern pot Epacris, with large, showy flowers in white or red shades, for winter flowering, longer-lasting and tolerating more heat than Ericas. *p. 956*

impressa grandiflora (Australia, Tasmania); heathlike evergreen shrub to 1½ m, loosely branched, with small ovate leaves, long tubular flowers purplish-red and tipped greenish-yellow. *p. 956*

longiflora (New South Wales), "Australian fuchsia"; heath-like shrub 1 m or more, with downy shoots and closely-set, sharply pointed leaves 1-2 cm long; pendant slender tubular flowers 3-4 cm long, rosy crimson with white tips. *Subtropic.* *p. 955, 956*

pulchella (Queensland, N.S. Wales); small heath-like shrub with minutely downy erect branches, tiny 6 mm ovate leaves, and pink or white bell-flowers. *p. 956*

EPERUA *Leguminosae* **S3LBD**

jenmanii (Trinidad); evergreen tree with pinnate leaves of 3-4 pairs of leathery 15 cm leaflets; purple trumpet flowers in pairs 10 cm long; inside white with purple spots. *Tropical.* *p. 1381*

EPHEDRA *Gnetaceae* **S2LBD**

californica (So. California, W. Mexico); curious looking shrub of the Mohave and Sonoran deserts and west to San Diego, with pale glaucous green apparently leafless, jointed branches resembling equisetum; small leaf scales in three's; flowers inconspicuous but with cone-like reddish berries 15 mm long. *p. 1318*

x EPICATTLEYA *Orchidaceae* **I3OFD**

'Ecstasy' (Cattleya 'Rowena Prowe' x Epidendrum atropurpureum roseum); bigeneric hybrid with squarish flowers deep lavender, in outline resembling enlarged epidendrum blossoms. *p. 1729*

'Gaiety' (Epidendrum plicatum x Cattleya 'Rowena Prowe'); flowers 9 cm across, white and pale lavender, in spring; a bigeneric breeding fairly easily. *p. 1729*

orpetii (Cattleya amethystoglossa x Epid. obrienianum); pretty hybrid with leafy reed-stems, the small star-like, waxy flowers a bright scarlet-red, the lip frilled, several together on wiry stalks. (April and all year). (I) *p. 1717*

EPIDENDRUM *Orchidaceae* **I-S3OFD**

alatum (Guatemala); epiphyte having rounded pseudobulbs with 2 strap-like leaves and long straggling panicles of fragrant, long lasting 5 cm flowers, greenish-yellow shaded light brown, yellow lip striated rose-purple, on red-spotted wiry stem. (summer). (I) *p. 1719, 1727*

allemanii (Brazil); small epiphyte with ovoid, compressed pseudobulbs with dual leaves; fragrant 5 cm flowers lemon-white faintly flushed rose and tipped green, lip broadly heart-shaped (spring). *p. 1727*

altissimum (hodgeanum) (Bahamas); slender 8 cm pseudobulbs with 2-3 leathery leaves; branched inflorescence to 1 m tall, with waxy greenish-yellow 3 cm flowers flushed with brown, the lobed lip white; fragrant and long-lasting (winter). *Tropical.* *p. 1727*

aromaticum (Mexico, Guatemala); epiphyte with pearshaped pseudobulbs, with 1-3 linear rigid leaves; inflorescence a pendulous spray to 1 m long of numerous small dainty, powerfully and agreeably scented flowers, greenish-yellow with lip whitish, streaked red. (April-June). (I) *p. 1722*

atropurpureum (Mexico to Panama, W. Indies, Brazil), "Spice orchid"; handsome epiphyte with pear-shaped pseudobulbs bearing 2-3 long leaves, stout racemes of 5-8 cm flowers having sepals and petals chocolate with incurved green tips, often tinged with purple, large white lip with crimson center. Photo shown is cv 'Lionet'; the species usually is more white. (Dec.-June). *Tropical.* *p. 1721*

auritum (boothii) (Guatemala); small epiphyte with flat pseudobulbs densely clustering on creeping rhizomes, erect solitary narrow leaves and short stalks set with several small fragrant pale yellow, waxy flowers, blooming all year. (I) *p. 1720*

bahamensis (Bahamas); small terrestrial plant to 20 cm high; erect floral stalk with raceme of canary-yellow flowers tinged green, lip crisped and folded (summer). *p. 1724*

bicameratum (Mexico: Oaxaca); epiphyte to 40 cm high, with ovoid pseudobulbs bearing dual leathery leaves; floral stalk to 40 cm long with raceme of 15 to 20 very fragrant waxy flowers 3 cm across, chocolate-brown with lip buttercup yellow (spring). *p. 1727*

boothianum (So. Florida, West Indies, Honduras); small epiphyte with 2-leaved pseudobulbs, oblanceolate leaves to 18 cm long; few-flowered racemes with sepals and petals yellow spotted brown, lip yellow. *p. 1723*

boothii (Maxillaria), (Mexico, Cuba, Surinam); small epiphyte with creeping rhizome; short pseudobulbs with stiffly erect strap-like leaves; fragrant flowers between foliage, 3 cm across, greenish to yellowish white, lip bright yellow with white margin (spring). *p. 1724*

bracteatum (Encyclia) (Brazil); charming little epiphyte with small pseudobulbs and grass-like, leathery leaves; waxy flowers on thin-wiry basal stalks, greenish-yellow sepals and petals marked with brown, lip lemon-white flaring into purple. (summer). *p. 1725*

brassavolae (Guatemala); epiphyte with small pear-shaped, 2-leaved pseudobulbs, the waxy, spidery 10 cm flowers in erect clusters, narrow sepals and petals yellowish brown, the heart-shaped lip white, narrowing to a purple point; sweetscented in evening. (April-Sept.). (I) *p. 1722, 1728*

campylostalix (Costa Rica); epiphyte with compressed pseudobulbs bearing solitary, glaucous leaves; small flowers in erect racemes, the sepals and narrower petals 2 cm long, wine-red with yellow lines, white lip with red column. (S) *p. 1723, 1728*

candollei (Encyclia) (Mexico, Guatemala); epiphyte with clustered, ovoid pseudobulbs, 2-3 leathery leaves to 35 cm long, inflorescence to 60 cm tall, loosely-flowered; waxy flowers 3 cm across, pale green with brown markings, the lobed lip white with purple stripes. (summer). *p. 1718*

ciliare (W. Indies, C. America, Brazil); strong epiphyte with oblong, compressed pseudobulbs with 1-2 leathery leaves; the inflorescence an erect cluster of waxy, fragrant flowers with long linear, greenish-yellow sepals and petals and a lobed and fringed white lip spotted yellow. (Dec.-Jan., Sept.) *Tropical.* *p. 1719*

cinnabarinum (N.E. Brazil); slender leafy stems clambering to 3 m high, densely leafy with 4 cm foliage; erect inflorescence with clusters of flowers on long stalks, 4 cm across, orange red to scarlet fading to purplish crimson, creamy-yellow, feathered lip with red spots (spring on). *p. 1724*

circinatum (Costa Rica); uncommon species with broadly lanceolate leaves; the floral stalk to 35 cm long; greenish flowers with green lip, hooded by 3 cm caps (August-September). *p. 1724*

cochleatum (lancifolium) (W. Indies, C. America), "Cockle-shelled orchid"; epiphyte with pearshaped, usually 2-leaved pseudobulbs and erect cluster of curious upside-down flowers, the narrow greenish-white petals and sepals grouped together, the shell-shaped lip black-violet with yellow lines. (Nov.-Feb., and various). (I) *p. 1721*

condylochilum (Mexico to Panama and Venezuela); epiphyte with stalked, compressed pseudobulbs, 2-3-leaved; long-stalked inflorescence with 2 cm flowers not opening well, the sepals and petals greenish-yellow outside and brown inside, the column red (summer). *p. 1726*

conopseum (No. Carolina to Florida); the hardiest of epiphytic orchids of No. America; small epiphyte with slender 2-leaved pseudobulbs, and erect stalk with cluster of small greenish or lemon-yellow flowers with narrow sepals and petals flushed with copper, and a 3-lobed lip (July). (C) *p. 1722*

coriifolium (Mexico to Perú); variable species with stout stems to 40 cm high, forming clusters, leaves mostly toward apex; a zigzag inflorescence with green to purple bracts subtending the fleshy, long-lasting 3 cm flowers reddish-green to yellowish with darker lip (autumn). *p. 1727*

coronatum (moyobambae) (Guatemala, Costa Rica, Trinidad, Brazil, Colombia, Perú); epiphyte with erect, cane-like stems, bearing on top the inflorescence, an arching raceme of 5 cm flowers of varying colors, sepals and petals brownish green, whitish or yellow, the lip white. *p. 1702*

costatum (Mexico); small epiphyte to 20 cm high with leathery, lanceolate leaves; very curious pink flower suffused with green and marked rose (autumn). *p. 1718*

criniferum (Costa Rica, Panama, Perú); densely tufting epiphyte with narrow 10 cm leaves, and racemes with 3-7 flowers having narrow sepals and petals yellowish-green with cinnamon blotches and bars, and a hairy, white lip (autumn). *p. 1721*

cristatum (raniferum) (Mexico, Costa Rica, Trinidad, Guayana, Venezuela, Brazil, Bolivia, Perú); variable species both epiphytic and terrestrial, with erect leafy canestems to 1 m high; flowers 3-5 cm across, in pendant raceme, fleshy sepals and petals greenish-yellow spotted red-brown, 4-lobed lip white with greenish edges and red spots. (I) *p. 1702*

dichromum (Brazil: Bahia); handsome epiphyte with 2-3-leaved ovate pseudobulbs and stalks 60-90 cm high bearing bold clusters of 5 cm flowers with pure white sepals and petals, the 3-lobed lip rosy-crimson, yellow at base, and margined white (early summer). *Tropical.* *p. 1720, 1724*

difforme (Florida, West Indies, Mexico to Brazil); slender, fleshy stems with stem-clasping 5-8 cm leaves in two ranks; green 5 cm flowers with deeper green, divided lip; June-July. (I) *p. 1722*

diffusum (West Indies, Mexico to Colombia and Brazil); variable epiphyte from 8 to 45 cm high; leafy stems somewhat flattened, the foliage rigid flushed with purple; from the apex the branching racemes with small 1 cm flowers, translucent green sometimes turning red when dry (autumn). *p. 1726*

diguetii (Mexico); small terrestrial with pear like pseudobulbs, solitary strap-like, green leaves; flowers with greenish-yellow sepals and petals, the frilled, broad lip white, black violet in center (spring). *p. 1727*

endresii (Costa Rica); dwarf, pretty epiphyte with slender stems set with stiff 2½ cm leaves in two ranks; terminal racemes of 2½ cm waxy flowers white marked with lavender and orange on the lip. (I) *p. 1702*

erubescens (Oaxaca); desirable mountain epiphyte found at 2,950 m, the limit of orchids there; with spindle-shaped, 2-leaved pseudobulbs; the waxy flowers in large panicles, sepals and petals delicate mauve, the lip yellow at base. (winter). *Subtropic.* *p. 1721*

eximium (Mexico); small epiphyte 15-20 cm high, slender stems with glossy, bronze-green foliage; translucent yellowish-buff bell-flowers lacquered bronzy brown (spring). *p. 1727*

falcatum (Mexico); pendulous epiphyte with tiny cylindrical pseudobulb and a solitary thick, linear leaf, 1-2 spidery, waxy flowers, the narrow sepals and petals greenish-yellow, lip trilobed, side lobes wing-like, midlobe narrow, white with yellow throat. (June-Aug.) *Tropical.* *p. 1719, 1720*

faustum (Brazil); floriferous small epiphyte topped by long leaves; from the apex compact clusters of small creamy 5 cm flowers, having narrow sepals and petals, the pointed lip with yellow spot on column, and brown-purple stripes at base. *p. 1725*

floribundum (Brazil); epiphyte with reed-like stem, producing a graceful, pendant panicle of many small flowers, the sepals greenish, petals greenish-yellow, lip white, sometimes spotted red. (Oct.-Dec.). (S) *p. 1722*

x fragracarpum (fragrans x prismatocarpum); an old hybrid (1915) very pleasing and decorative, with swollen pseudobulbs bearing dual leaves and from the apex the attractive waxy flowers in clusters; sepals and petals deep cream, lip steaked with lavender. *p. 1725*

fragrans (W. Indies, C. America, Brazil); stocky epiphyte with compressed pseudobulbs with solitary leaf; the waxy, fragrant flowers in short clusters, sepals and petals creamy-white, narrow linear and curled, the heart-shaped pointed lip white, lined red-purple. (Feb.-Aug.) *Tropical.* *p. 1721, 1725*

ghiesbreghtianum (Mexico); delightful dwarf species with two-leaved pseudobulbs bearing the erect inflorescence of 1 to 2 fragrant blooms 4 cm across, of leather-like substance and long-lasting, sepals and petals gold-green overlaid with rich chocolate-brown, the huge lip chalk-white with some purple, and like a spreading skirt. (C) *p. 1723*

gracile (Bahamas); attractive species growing terrestrial or as an epiphyte; swollen pseudobulbs with long, leathery leaves; erect inflorescence to 1 m, with many scattered, fragrant flowers 4 cm dia., waxy sepals and petals green with purple-black markings, broad lip greenish yellow with dark red veins (autumn). *p. 1718*

ibaguense (radicans) (Perú, Colombia, Guatemala, Mexico), "Fiery reed orchid"; reed-type terrestrial with slender leafy stems to 1 m high, rooting from nodes, leaves very fleshy; small flowers on a long wiry stem in dense cluster, orange-scarlet or cinnabar-red, with yellow in fringed lip. *p. 1722*

ibaguense schomburgkia (Guyana, Brazil, Perú); slender stems with 2-ranked leaves, and large 15 cm terminal cluster of brilliant flowers orange to vermillion, lip yellow at base. *Tropical.* *p. 1720*

lancifolium (Mexico); epiphyte with flattened pseudobulbs each bearing two leaves at apex; erect floral stalks with numerous flowers 4 cm across, very fragrant, cream-colored with brownish tint and violet lines on lip (August). *p. 1725*

lanipes (Brazil, Venezuela, Perú); pretty species with leafy, slender reed-stems topped by a branching raceme of numerous little 1 cm yellowish flowers with narrow sepals, the ovaries and stemlets hairy, and with heliotrope fragrance (spring-summer). *Tropical.* *p. 1720*

latilabrum (Brazil); erect fleshy stems with light green leaves 2½-8 cm long; green 5 cm flowers, the front lobe of lip in two flaring wings; summer. (I) *p. 1723*

lemorea (Perú); handsome epiphyte found by Lee Moore on the upper Amazon; waxy, long-lasting flowers with dark brown sepals and petals, the lip white with red veins. *Tropical.* *p. 1718*

leucochilum (Venezuela, Colombia); handsome, robust cane-type species to 80 cm tall and covered with leaves; the inflorescence pendant with strongly fragrant 8 cm flowers; the sepals and petals narrowed, yellowish-green; the sepals changing to brown and the petals to yellow; the lip white. *p. 1725*

lindleyanum (Barkeria) (Mexico, Central America); handsome deciduous epiphyte with erect slender spindle-shaped, leafy stems 30 cm high, and racemes of rather large 5 cm flowers with sepals and petals rose, lip purple with white blotch in center; autumn. (I) *p. 1723*

lockhartioides (Costa Rica, Panama); epiphyte with drooping or scandent stems to 25 cm long, covered entirely by the flat and fleshy sickle-shaped leaves, arranged in 2 ranks and their bases overlapping; fleshy yellowish-green flowers in dense spike from the tip of the stem; Jan.-March. (I) *p. 1723*

mariae (So. Mexico); excellent little epiphyte; small pear-shaped pseudobulbs with 1-2 leaves, topped by clusters of several large waxy flowers with greenish yellow sepals and petals, and very broad, wavy white lip with green throat (summer). *Tropical.* *p. 1720*

mathewsii (Perú); miniature creeping epiphyte with small glistening fleshy, distichous green leaves often red-tinted, 5 cm high; watery-translucent flowers to 3 cm across, greenish tinged purple-brown, ciliate at margins, and with purple lip. *p. 1718*

medusae (Nanodes) (Ecuador); sinister looking epiphyte with densely tufted, branching pendant stems 10-30 cm long, without bulbs, and crowded with 2 ranked, glaucous green, fleshy leaves; the 5-8 cm flat, fleshy flowers from the axils of the terminal leaves, with narrow sepals and petals yellowish green tinged with brown, and very large round 5 cm lip deep maroon purple with green in center, and bordered with long fringes (May-June). (C) *p. 1721, 1726*

nemorale (Mexico); vigorous evergreen with ovate 2-leaved pseudobulbs, bearing a 1 m inflorescence of large 10 cm flowers, with sepals and petals lilac-rose, the tri-lobed lip white in center, with 3 short red lines and bordered with rose; April-July. (C) *p. 1723*

nocturnum (Mexico to Peru and Brazil); clustered stout, leafy stems to 90 cm tall; spidery-looking fragrant flowers to 10 cm across, the narrow thread-like sepals and petals greenish white, the 3-lobed lip white with bright yellow blotch on disc, blooming throughout the year. *p. 1726*

nutans (West Indies, Brazil); tall species with slender, leafy stems to 75 cm, arching inflorescence with charming 4 cm flowers, narrow sepals and petals soft green, the lip and column white and tinged with green; fragrant at night. *p. 1725*

x o'brienianum (evectum x radicans), "Butterfly orchid"; slender reed-stems with aerial roots and alternate leaves like in ibaguense, and extending into long stalks with showy clusters of brilliant carmine-red flowers, with bright yellow on the crested lip (spring-summer). *Tropical.* *p. 1722*

odoratissimum (Encyclia) (Brazil); inflorescence erect to 25 cm, sparsely branched; fragrant, firm greenish flowers with yellow lip veined red (summer). *p. 1730*

oncidioides (C. America to Brazil); stately epiphyte with spindle-shaped bulbs bearing 2-3 straplike leaves; arching inflorescence to 1 m long with many 4 cm flowers bronzy-yellow, lip marked red (June). *Tropical.* *p. 1720*

paniculatum (Bolivia, Perú, Ecuador, Colombia); a noble plant 1 m or more high, the dark green leaves arranged in two ranks along the stem, and on top a pendant inflorescence of nodding clusters with a profusion of lovely 2 cm rosy-lilac fragrant blossoms, the column tipped yellow (April). *p. 1720*

pentotis (C. America, Brazil); stiff epiphyte with long spindle-shaped pseudobulbs and 2 leaves, the large waxy, very fragrant flowers back to back in pairs on short stem, tapering fleshy sepals and petals greenish-white, lip white with purple (Mar.-July). *Tropical.* *p. 1719, 1724*

pfavii (Costa Rica); vigorous epiphyte with long leafy canes to 75 cm long, the leaves long elliptic; inflorescence arching, in dense racemes; flowers with tubes 4 cm long, petals strongly reflexed, deep old rose with white on lip. *p. 1726*

phoeniceum (Cuba), "Chocolate orchid"; handsome, large-flowered epiphyte with ovoid, 2-leaved pseudobulbs and on erect dense flowered panicle, sepals and petals chocolate-colored mottled green, lip rose marked crimson and yellow (Dec.-March) (I) *p. 1719*

polybulbon (West Indies, C. America); pretty, dwarf epiphyte to 8 cm high, with tiny pesudobulbs bearing two leaves, solitary 2 cm flowers brownish with yellow margins, pure white lip; winter. *p. 1723, 1725*

porpax (Mexico to Venezuela); small mat-forming epiphyte without pseudobulbs, dark green fleshy leaves less than 2½ cm long; solitary fleshy, comparatively large flowers conspicuous with their maroon lip, sepals and petals pale yellowish-green and almost translucent; July-September. (I) *p. 1723*

prismatocarpum (Costa Rica, Panama), "Rainbow orchid"; beautiful robust epiphyte with flask-shaped pseudobulbs bearing 2 leaves; and erect spike of brightly colored, waxy, long-lasting flowers, sulphur-yellow blotched maroon, lip marked rosy-red (May-June). *Tropical.* *p. 1664A, 1719*

pseudepidendrum (Costa Rica, Panama); excellent species with leafy, stem-like pseudobulbs to 1 m high; arching inflorescence with 8 cm flowers having narrow spoon-like green sepals and petals; and orange-red, fringed lip edged yellow. *Tropical.* *p. 1724*

pseudowallisii (Costa Rica); handsome epiphyte to 30 cm tall, without pseudobulbs, pencil-thin reed-stems with leaves toward apex; large 5 cm, long-lasting flowers bright orange-yellow with minute maroon spots inside and deeper orange in center, the lip fan-shaped and lobed (August). *p. 1726, 1741*

pygmaeum (Mexico to Perú and Brazil); small, pretty epiphyte with creeping rhizome, short 3-10 cm pseudobulbs rise at intervals, bearing two leaves; inflorescence short, with 3 cm flowers cream to greenish brown with purple veining, lip white and streaked with purple (summer). *p. 1728*

radicans: see ibaguense

radiatum (lancifolium) (Mexico); epiphyte with short spindle-shaped pseudobulbs and 2-3 stiff leaves; compact clusters of fleshy cream-white flowers, broad white lip with radiating purple lines (May-June). *p. 1719*

rhynchophorum (Mexico); stocky epiphyte with pseudobulbs bearing 2 stiff leaves, and short clusters of waxy, spidery flowers with narrow linear pale greenish petals and sepals, the lip is white with yellow throat, and trilobed, the side lobes wing-like, midlobe linear, (summer). (I) *p. 1719, 1728*

sceptrum (Venezuela, Colombia); compressed, two-leaved pseudobulbs; elegant floral spike to 60 cm long, with many long-stalked 2 cm flowers greenish-yellow carried well above the foliage, purple dots on white lip and on base of each petal (autumn). *p. 1728*

schlechterianum (Nanodes) (Mexico to Brazil, West Indies); dwarf branching trailer to 7 cm high, stems with alternate, distichous, or shingled, fleshy leaves; flowers 4 cm across, not opening fully, brownish or reddish green to pinkish, lip velvety green (summer). *p. 1726*

schumannianum (Costa Rica); epiphyte forming reed stems 60 cm or more, with small leaves and erect branched inflorescence of beautiful flowers, the rounded fleshy petals and sepals soft yellow, spotted red, with amethyst reverse, lip rose-pink and thickly spotted red. (spring). (I) *p. 1720*

serpens (Venezuela); low miniature epiphyte with short, thick-leathery leaves; waxy greenish flowers overlaid with brown-purple spots (autumn). *p. 1718*

skinneri (So. Mexico, Guatemala); clustered spindle-shaped stems to nearly 2 m tall, concealed by papery leaf sheaths; near the apex several fleshy leaves; long-stalked inflorescence with showy 5 cm flowers rosy-violet with white blotch on lip and deep purple at base (autumn). *p. 1726*

spondiadum (Jamaica, Costa Rica); epiphyte with spindle-shaped one-leaved pseudobulbs; from the apex the small inflorescence of 3-6 flowers each 4 cm across, sepals and petals greenish-yellow, brownish-purple toward tips, the lip brown with greenish-yellow edges (winter). *p. 1718*

stamfordianum (Honduras, Guatemala, Venezuela, Colombia); beautiful epiphyte with spindle-shaped pseudobulbs with 2-4 leaves, the inflorescence a lax panicle to 60 cm long from the base of the bulb, with fragrant 3 cm flowers yellow spotted bright red, lip fringed. (Feb.-May) *p. 1722, 1728*

tampense (Florida, Bahamas, Cuba); dwarf epiphyte with little, pear-shaped, clustering pseudobulbs topped by 1-2 linear leaves; several small, waxy 2½ cm flowers on wiry stalk, greenish-yellow tinged with brown, except for the white lip marked with purple. (April-July, Oct.-Dec). (I) *p. 1722*

vespa (variegatum) (Brazil); stout epiphyte with spindle-shaped 2-3-leaved pseudobulbs, and stiff spike of small waxy flowers, the sepals and petals greenish-yellow spotted red-brown, small white lip with purple center. (April-July). *Tropical.* *p. 1721*

vitellinum (Mexico, Guatemala); small epiphyte with ovoid pseudobulbs and 2 glaucous leaves, erect slender spike of waxy 4 cm flowers, sepals and petals nearly equal, bright cinnabar-red, the small lip bright yellow. (May-Oct.) (C-IM) *p. 1719*

wallisii (Panama, Colombia); striking orchid with clustered slender, leafy stems to 1 m high; arching inflorescence with many flowers 4 cm across, sepals and petals deep yellow spotted with maroon, broad white lip lobed and feathered with purple (autumn). *p. 1728*

EPIDRYOS *Rapateaceae* **S3LFM**

allenii (Panama); tropical herb with flattened light green leaves from flask-like base, arranged as in a fan; arching inflorescence with tiny pale flowers. *p. 1990*

EPIGAEA *Ericaceae* **C2HFM**

repens (Newfoundland to Florida), the "Trailing arbutus"; small evergreen creeper with woody, hairy, rooting stems, ovate 8 cm, deep green leathery leaves, and clusters of very fragrant, bell-shaped flowers with green sepals and flesh-colored corolla, in early spring. (h) *p. 958*

EPIGENEIUM *Orchidaceae* **S3OFW**

cymbidioides (Dendrobium) (Malaya, Sumatra, Java); small, pretty epiphyte 15-18 cm high with pseudobulbs bearing 2 leathery leaves; fleshy flowers 5 cm across, pale ochre yellow, white lip marked with red (spring). *p. 1731*

lyonii (Sarcopodium, Dendrobium) (Philippines); handsome small epiphyte from the mountains of Luzon, with angular pseudobulbs each with two leaves; pendant inflorescence with beautiful star-like flowers 8 cm across, crimson-red in center fading to a delicate pink near tips, and very fragrant. *Tropical.* *p. 1735, 1817*

x EPIGOA *Orchidaceae* **I3OFM**

'Olivine' (Domingoa hymenodes x Epidendrum mariae); small-growing bigeneric never over 15 cm high, with erect leaves of the epidendrum texture; wide-open 5 cm flowers in contrast to either parents, in two shades of chartreuse-green, lasting for several days; usually 3 to 4 on a thin arching stalk. (I) *p. 1729*

EPILOBIUM *Oenotheraceae* **C2LFM**

angustifolium (Chamaenerion), (No. temp. hemisphere), "Fireweed" or "French willow"; shrubby perennial to 2 m, with lanceolate, grass-green, 12 cm leaves; with undulate margins; 3 cm flowers rose to purple, or white in var. album. Seen at Rochford's Nurseries in England. *p. 1628*

EPIMEDIUM *Berberidaceae* **C2LFD**

x warleyense (alpinum x pinnatum colchicum); herb with creeping rhizome and annual stem; pinnate leaves; and dainty raceme of 2 cm flowers with outer sepals coppery-red, petals yellow with red-streaked spurs, in spring. *p. 496*

EPIPACTIS *Orchidaceae* **C3HBM**

gigantea (Western U.S. to No. Mexico); robust terrestrial with leafy stem, the clasping, broad ovate leaves with folds; elongate inflorescence with long leaf-like bracts; long-lasting flowers 5 cm dia., the sepals greenish to rose and red stripes, petals pink to rose, lip 3-lobed marked with purple, mid-lobe yellowish (June-August). *p. 1731*

latifolia (helleborine) (Europe, No. Asia); large terrestrial orchid with stout stem, to 1 m tall when in bloom; clasping, plicate (folded) leaves; floral stalk with flowers broadly bell-shaped 3 cm across, greenish flushed with purple, dark purple on lower half of lip (summer). *p. 1731*

palustris (No. Europe, Siberia); terrestrial orchid with leafy stem and terminal raceme of flowers reddish-white outside, reddish inside, lip white with yellow callus and red-striped lobes; summer. *p. 1730*

x EPIPHRONITIS *Orchidaceae* **C-I3OFD**

veitchii (Epid. radicans x Sophronitis grandiflora); attractive small bigeneric hybrid with reed-type stems with alternate leaves, topped by clusters of fiery red 2½ cm flowers with a golden yellow center on the lip (spring to fall). *Subtropic.* *p. 1717*

EPIPHYLLANTHUS *Cactaceae* **S2LFD**

obovatus (E. Brazil); branching cactus of the habit of Zygocactus but with flat joints resembling a miniature Opuntia, waxy green tinted purple in the sun, with areoles scattered over the surface set with tiny whitish spines; small zygomorphic flowers purplish rose. *p. 732, 735, 736*

EPIPHYLLOPSIS: see Rhipsalidopsis

EPIPHYLLUM *Cactaceae* **I2LFD-M**

ackermannii: see Nopalxochia

chrysocardium (Mexico: Chiapas), "Golden heart"; an interesting species growing at the base of trees, with bright green, flat stems cut into narrow segments like fishbones, and looking more like a fern; very large white flowers noted for their beautiful golden filaments; night-blooming, with unpleasant odor. *Tropical.* *p. 730, 731*

crenatum (Honduras, Guatemala); erect, densely branched epiphyte with cylindrical main stem, the branches stiff and thick, thin at margins, tender green or glaucous, thick midnerve, and deeply notched; flowers 10-20 cm across when open, very fragrant; outer petals greenish-yellow, inner petals white, day-flowering. *p. 730*

hybridum, "Orchid cactus" or "Pond-lily-cactus"; there are literally thousands of named "Orchid cacti", with large flowers of great beauty in iridescent colors from nearly blue through red, pink, yellowish to white. Recorded genera which were used in breeding were such epiphytes as Heliocereus, Nyctocereus, Hylocereus, Selenicereus. *p. 616*

hyb. 'Brilliant' (Phyllocactus); large growing plant with broad flattened, fresh green branches and very large bright red double flowers. *p. 730*

hyb. 'Elegantissimum', "Dwarf orchid cactus"; superb, dwarf basket type; large, perfect flower with broad petals bright crimson, the outer petals flushed scarlet, and green throat, on glossy green flattened branches. *p. 729*

hyb. 'Hermosissimus' (E. ackermannii x Nopalxochia); one of the brightest and best of "orchid" cactus, a vivid example of the bicolor type with deep crimson outer petals, while the inner petals and throat are a glowing electric violet painted orange through the center; free bloomer of vigorous growth. *Tropical.* *p. 730*

hyb. 'Hermosus', "Orchid cactus"; beautiful ackermannii cultivar with flat stems and large 15-18 cm showy tubular-trumpet flowers carmine to fuchsia-red, changing to rich purple in its center. *Tropical.* *p. 730*

hyb. 'Jubilee' ('Jubilaeum'); a beautiful orchid cactus by the old German cactus specialist firm of Haage in Erfurt; flowers with wide-spread, broad petals vivid orange with broad red bands down center. *p. 731*

hyb. 'Lilac Time' (Phyllocactus); an orchid cactus with angled main-stems and flat secondary branches, with large lilac to violet flowers, lighter in throat, to 20 cm across. *p. 731*

hyb. 'Merry Gardens Red'; compact growing orchid cactus very floriferous even as a small plant; large wide-open flowers crimson red, with petals lighter inside. *p. 731*

oxypetalum (latifrons) (Mexico to Brazil), "Queen of the night"; the best nightblooming cactus for the home, grows large, branches usually flat and thin, waxy green and deeply crenate; large fragrant white flowers, reddish outside. *Tropical.* *p. 618, 730*

pumilum (Guatemala); from tropical lowland forest, climbing or epiphytic, a small-flowered orchid cactus found by Thos. Mac Dougall and sent to the New York Botanical Garden; branches to 5 m long, the mainstems cylindric and often pendant, the branches flattened or 3-angled; small flowers with greenish tube and sepals, the white petals 4 cm long. *p. 731*

'White hybrid'; another large-flowered orchid cactus with lily-like flowers pure white; this to illustrate the wide range of colors that have been developed by hybridizers of this beautiful genus. *p. 731*

EPIPREMNOPSIS: see Amydrium

EPIPREMNUM *Araceae* **S3HFM**

aureum (Scindapsus aureus) (Solomon Islands, and South Pacific), "Devil's ivy", known commercially as "Pothos"; fleshy vine climbing tall by rootlets; juvenile leaves broad ovate, waxy, dark green with yellow variegation; mature leaves to 60 cm long, the blades becoming lobed or slashed; bisexual flowers on short spadix within the boat-shaped spathe. (Birdsey 1962: to Rhaphidophora; Bunting 1964: Scindapsus to Epipremnum). *p. 285, 286*

aureum 'Marble Queen', "Taro vine"; mutant with the green leaves richly variegated and streaked nearly pure white when grown in good light; resents chills and wetness. *p. 15*, 19*, 160A, 285, 294*

aureum 'Tricolor', "Devil's ivy pothos"; a colorful mutant having the succulent, ovate leaves highly variegated, marbled and spotted pale green, deep yellow and cream, on medium green. (D-M) *p. 285*

elegans (New Guinea); clambering epiphyte or tree-climber with thick, almost woody stems, and large pinnately lobed leaves to 1 m long, shining fresh green and leathery, borne on long angular, stiff petioles; spectacularly showy cone-like fruit 30 cm long, brilliant shiny orange-red. We collected this species in the lower Markham Valley Oomsis rain-forest. *p. 155*

falcifolium (Monsoon territory, Java); slender climber with narrow-lanceolate, glossy, green leaves on slender, winged petioles; spadix with sexes mixed as in Monstera. *p. 206*

pinnatum (Malaya through Java to New Guinea); prolific tropical climber with large, oblong leaves pinnately parted into regular segments, and tiny pinholes appearing as silvery dots along midrib. The juvenile leaves are entire, oblique-ovate. *Humid-tropical.* *p. 206, 223, 231*

EPIPREMNUM: see also Scindapsus

EPISCIA *Gesneriaceae* **S3HFM**

cupreata (Colombia), "Carpet plant"; tropical creeper, rooting at joints, with soft-hairy, oval, wrinkled leaves almost entirely a metallic copper, faintly marked silver; small solitary flowers with short corolla tube yellow-tinged below, the lobes orange-scarlet, and yellow with red spots inside. *Humid-tropical.* *p. 1247*

cupreata 'Acajou'; an exquisite hybrid of cupreata x variegata; leaves dark mahogany except for the contrasting network of veins and the central area of bright metallic silver-green; very excellent and a good keeper, more pubescent than 'Harlequin'. *Humid-tropical.* *p. 19*, 1246, 1248A, 1249*

cupreata 'Amazon'; an interesting variety with large, heavy textured, bristly-hairy, coarsely quilted, bronzy leaves occasionally spotted pink showing possible influence of Nautilocalyx; (this may be a distinct species). *p. 1248*

cupreata 'Chocolate Soldier', "Carpet plant"; a robust hybrid of cupreata x variegata having leaves of a dark chocolate color with a silver-gray center band. *p. 1246*

cupreata 'Emerald Queen'; a robust, heavy hybrid between cupreata and 'Variegata', with emerald-green leaves, at times turning coppery, and a glossy center band of silver spilling over into the lateral veins. *p. 1247*

cupreata 'Frosty', a silverleaf "Flame violet"; lustrous, robust growing cultivar with downy emerald-green leaves tinted copper at margins, the center area silvery white splashing over through the lateral veins. *Humid-tropical.* *p. 15*, 1247*

cupreata 'Harlequin'; sport of 'Variegata' (splendens) with waxy leaves very dark brown in the area along the margins, contrasting with the central pattern and veining of greenish silvery-white. Similar to 'Acajou' but more shiny. *p. 1246*

cupreata 'Metallica', "Kitty episcia"; variety with large quilted coppery leaves having a band of pale silvery green through the center, margined with metallic pink; similar to the cultivar 'Kitty'. *Humid-tropical.* *p. 1247, 1249*

cupreata 'Musaica' (Panama); seedling from the Canal Zone with coppery leaves attractively painted with an even network of silver veins. *p. 1248*

cupreata 'San Lorenzo' (Panama); compact variety with downy, coppery or chocolate-colored, broad-ovate leaves having a midrib of pinkish tint, light, but not silvery. *p. 1245*

cupreata 'Silver Sheen'; a most attractive branch mutant of cupreata with hairy, wrinkled foliage, most of the leaf and outer veins a bright silver-gray leaving only the marginal areas of coppery green. *p. 1247*

cupreata 'Sylvan Beauty'; a handsome leaf variant with smooth waxy gray-green leaves having a faint brown center vein and tinting of coppery olive in the margin areas. *p. 1247*

cupreata 'Tetra'; a branch mutant of 'Viridifolia', tetraploid with large waxy leaves of plain grass-green, lightly covered with hairs, and large orange-red flower with wavy lobes orange-yellow inside. Formerly cultivated as E. splendens. *p. 1248*

cupreata 'Tropical Topaz' (Panama Canal Zone), a mutant form of E. cupreata once known as "Canal Zone yellow", this clone is distinguished by having bright yellow flowers instead of scarlet as in cupreata viridifolia; plain pale green leaves with erect hairs instead of appressed. *p. 1248*

cupreata 'Variegata' (splendens) (Colombia); robust, pretty variety with large shiny leaves of dark green to coppery, decorated with bluish silver in the center and following along the lateral veins and veinlets in a network of silver; orange-red flowers. *p. 1247*

cupreata 'Viridifolia' (Colombia); natural variety with quilted leaves having hairs flattened against the shiny, fresh green surface. Flowers bright red. *p. 1246, 1249*

dianthiflora (C. Mexico), "Lace-flower vine"; small elliptic, pubescent, vivid to dark green, crenate leaves with purple midrib, in a miniature clustering rosette, sending out prolific rooting branches; free-blooming with glistening white, deeply fringed flowers, appearing singly in the leaf axils. *Humid-tropical.* *p. 1245, 1246*

'Ember Lace'; sport of 'Bronze Lace' (lilacina x cupreata), attractive cultivar which is as colorful as it is tough for culture in the home; dark bronzy brown quilted leaves splashed with large blotches of vivid rose-pink, brighter than 'Lady Lou'; flowers a lovely wild-rose pink. *p. 1246*

'Fire Ember', attractive rosette of oval, rugose and hairy, dark leaves almost black, with purplish-brown and grayish areas alongside green midrib, to 15 cm long by 8 cm wide; flowers clear rose-pink with yellow throat, 3 cm across. *p. 1250*

hirsuta (Trop. America); handsome low growing rosette with large wrinkled leaves deep green or brown-bronzy, the primary veins outlined with pale green; the tubular flowers with flaring lobes light lavender, the corolla 5 cm long. *p. 1250*

hirsuta 'Argentea'; a beautiful variation in the bronzy-green leaves, with the central area silvery green; flowers pale lilac. *p. 1250*

'Jasper'; small charming plant with rugose, puckered leaves dark metallic bronze, with grayish network of veins throughout. *p. 1250*

lilacina 'Cuprea' (Costa Rica); robust leaf variation from the Rio Reventazon with deep coppery velvet leaves only faintly marked with silver-green along center; free flowering lavender-blue with pale eye. *p. 1246*

lilacina 'Lilacina' (Costa Rica), "Blue-flowered teddy-bear"; a beautiful blue-flowered species also known as 'Fannie Haage' and 'Variegata'; pubescent creeper with dark coppery, rough-puckered 5-10 cm leaves decorated with a prominent fishbone pattern of silvery green; large flowers of lavender-blue; good grower but sensitive to cold; flowers 3 cm long. *p. 1247*

lilacina 'Panama' (chontalensis) (Panama); a variety with smaller, narrower, hairy leaves coppery-green and an inconspicuous silvery to light green midrib; shy bloomer with fringed light blue flowers. *p. 1246*

lilacina 'Viridis' (fendleriana) (Costa Rica); attractive variety having bright emerald-green leaves faintly traced with glistening silver from the midrib; foliage feels plushy; flowers light blue. *Humid-tropical.* *p. 1248*

lineata (Panama); tufted, fibrous-rooted plant with long oblanceolate leaves plain green above, grayish beneath, with reddish veins; tubular flowers, cream with red-purple spots on the expanded limb, low between foliage. *p. 1245*

melittifolia (Brazil; W. Indies: Dominica); sturdy upright grower with stout, angled stem to 30 cm high; large elliptic, glossy dark green 15 cm leaves with wrinkled surface and crenate margins, pale beneath; small axillary flowers toward apex, with down-curving tube carmine-purple, blooming more or less continuously but best in spring. *p. 1250*

'Moss-Agate' (1960); seedling with cupreata background; corrugated and puckered leaves blackish-green, and crimson-red flowers. *p. 1245*

punctata (Guatemala, Mexico); rank creeping, almost smooth species with leathery, ovate, crenate leaves green except for red-purple midrib, on lightly erect branches; tubular flowers solitary with spreading fringed lobes creamy-white and spotted purple into the throat. *Tropical.* *p. 1248*

reptans (fulgida, coccinea) (Brazil, Guyana, Surinam, Colombia), "Flame violet"; tropical pubescent creeper with broad ovate, quilted, brown-green leaves and bright silvery-green veins, margins crenate; flowers with long blood-red corolla tube with fringed edges and pink inside. *p. 1247*

reptans (fulgida) **'Lady Lou',** a handsome sport having its bronzy-green leaves with narrow silver veining beautifully variegated clear rose-pink and occasional white or gray; flowers red. *p. 19*, 1245, 1246, 1248A*

'Shimmer'; a lovely interspecific cupreata cultivar; a rosette of quilted leaves 8-10 cm long, exquisitely painted silvery green over chocolate brown in an iridescent moonglow effect; typical orange-red flowers. Originated by Dr. H. Moore 1960. *p. 1250*

x variabilis 'Filigree' (E. cupreata 'Viridifolia' x reptans); Cornell clone with well-marked, attractive foliage; the large 15 cm leaf-blades rather thick, flat, coppery to olive-green with pronounced veins of iridescent silver lined with green, sparsely hairy; reverse purplish; flowers clear red, in abundance. *p. 1245*

x wilsonii 'Catherinae'; robust grower with green leaves studded with silver flecks and feathered pale green veins. *p. 1245*

x wilsonii 'Pinkiscia' (cupreata x lilacina); lovely hybrid with leaves of thick texture, metallic chocolate-bronze with a touch of silver along the green veins, and covered with pink hair; flowers with broad rose-pink limb, and orange-yellow dotted rose inside the long tubes. *p. 1248, 1249*

EPISCIA: see also Nautilocalyx

EPITHELANTHA *Cactaceae* **I1LBD**

micromeris (Texas, N. Mexico), "Button-cactus"; tiny globes usually 1-2 cm dia., but may grow to over 5 cm; depressed on top; small tubercles in spirals almost entirely covered by flattened white spines; pinkish flowers. *Arid-subtropic.* *p. 705*

EQUISETUM *Equisetaceae* **I2LBW**

giganteum (So. America), the "Giant horsetail"; a remnant of ancient vegetation; rush-like tropical perennial with rhizomatous rootstock, at home in moist places; erect hollow jointed stems to 4 m high, without proper foliage, the leaves reduced to sheaths at the joints; the sterile branches are fresh green, set in whorls, and pendant from the joints. During the Carbon Age, the equisetums were forming gigantic forests, through millions of years turning into coal. Belonging to the fern-allies, they bear no flowers, but spores in a cone-like spike. *p. 954*

hyemale (No. America, Europe, Asia), "Horsetail", "Scouring rush" or "Dutch rush", names implying that its tough, wiry, rough stems are used for scrubbing. Furrowed, evergreen, jointed hollow stems to 1 m or more high, with scale-like pointed leaves, clustered at the joints in whorls. A fern-ally without flowers, but with cone-like spikes bearing spores. Equisetum represents a single living genus of a complex group that thrived during the Coal age more than 300 million years ago. As an indoor plant will grow immersed in water. *p. 954*

ERANTHEMUM *Acanthaceae* **S2LFM**

nervosum (pulchellum) (India), "Blue sage"; shrubby plant with rough, ovate, dark-green leaves and depressed veins; blue flowers from pointed bracts. (syn. Daedalacanthus). *Tropical.* *p. 47, 1952A*

wattii (N. India); herb close to E. nervosum but smaller; straggling with age; ovate, rugose leaves; tubular 5-lobed flowers in bracted spikes, deep rich purple. *p. 46*

ERANTHEMUM: see also Pseuderanthemum, Chamaeranthemum

ERANTHIS *Ranunculaceae* **C2HFMh**

cilicica (Greece, Syria); small herbaceous perennial about 15 cm high, with tuberous rootstock, basal rosette of palmately dissected bronzy leaves; solitary flowers with sepals petal-like, deep yellow, 4 cm across, in early spring. *p. 1989*

hyemalis (So. Europe), "Winter-aconite"; small perennial herb 10 to 15 cm high, basal leaves roundish and 7-parted, leaves on flower stem broad-linear; solitary 4 cm sessile flowers bright yellow, in very early spring. *p. 1989*

hyemalis 'Aurantiaca'; a horticultural cultivar with bright orange flowers; by Peterson, Copenhagen. *p. 1983*

x tubergenii 'Guinea Gold' (hyemalis x cilicica); showiest representative of the genus, with sweet-scented, large 5-6 cm sterile, long-lasting flowers deep yellow, on bronze stems and with bronze leaves. *p. 1989*

ERDISIA *Cactaceae* **I2LBD**

maxima (Cereus) (Andes of Cent. Perú); bushy plant about 1 m high with slender angular branches with 5 ribs bearing depressed areoles well furnished with white radials and 1 cream central spine; small but many-petalled red flowers, gold outside, and red stamens. *p. 648*

EREMURUS *Liliaceae* **C2LBM**

elwesii (Turkestan), "Desert candle"; stately perennial from the steppes of Central Asia, with narrow basal leaves and strong spike 2 m or more, with numerous stalked flowers having spreading segments, pink with deeper center stripe; May-blooming. *Warm temperate.* *p. 1446, 1460*

stenophyllus (bungei) (Iran), a "Desert candle"; with stately flowering stalk 1 m high, dense with 1 cm flowers with narrow, spreading segments bright golden-orange; rosette of firm linear leaves 30 cm long; thick fibrous roots. *p. 1446*

EREPSIA *Aizoaceae* **I2LBD**

inclaudens (Cape Prov.); woody perennial with succulent scimitar-shaped glossy green leaves, 2½ cm long with wide keel and translucent dots; flowers glistening purple with broad petals. *p. 64*

ERIA *Orchidaceae* **I3OFD**

cymbiformis (Borneo); attractive orchid 60 cm tall with stout pseudobulbs bearing sheathing, lanceolate, lax leaves; the dense inflorescence a pendant spike 8 cm long with cupped, pale yellow flowers. *p. 1733*

ferruginea (Himalayas); small epiphyte with cylindric pseudobulbs topped by 2-4 leathery leaves, the small flowers loosely in a lateral arching raceme, sepals olive-brown, the petals white flushed pink, lip white with pale purple throat. (March-May). (I) *p. 1717*

flava (Burma); epiphyte with compressed pseudobulbs with 3-5 fleshy leaves; inflorescence on erect hairy stalk with small 2 cm fragrant white-hairy flowers pale greenish with yellow tips; waxy forward curving lip pinkish, marked purplish-brown. *p. 1733*

javanica (India to Java and New Guinea); small ovoid pseudobulbs topped by dual leaves; floral stalk from near apex, 50-60 cm long, and hairy, the raceme with fragrant flowers facing in all directions, creamy-yellow with fine brown wool on backs of sepals, tip of lip margined violet. *p. 1733*

merrillii (Philippines); epiphyte with angular pseudobulbs grayish green, borne at intervals on the creeping rhizome, paired fleshy leaves; inflorescence from near apex, a raceme dense with starry white flowers, the center disc light yellow. *Tropical.* *p. 1733*

spicata (Himalayan Region to Vietnam), "Lily-of-the-valley orchid"; swollen pseudobulbs bearing 3-4 shiny, leathery leaves; the small inflorescence to 15 cm high, with nodding flowers very fragrant, 2 cm across, not opening fully, translucent waxy-white or straw-yellow, the lip golden-yellow at front. *Subtropic.* *p. 1733*

stricta (Burma to Vietnam); small clustering epiphyte with cylindric pseudobulbs and narrow, dual leaves; inflorescence with small ½ cm flowers all on one side; sepals white-hairy outside, the lip pale yellow. *p. 1733*

striolata hort. (javanica) (Monsoon Asia); creeping rhizome with egg-shaped pseudobulbs bearing two fleshy leaves; erect inflorescence to 60 cm long, with numerous small flowers 4 cm across, white to pale yellow with purple veins. *p. 1733*

ERICA *Ericaceae* **I-C2HBD**

amaphyllis (So. Africa: Cape Prov.); shrubby plant to 50 cm high, the small spiny needles appressed to near stems, toward apex a showy spire of tubular, inflated flowers 2 cm long with small crown, soft rosy-red. *p. 965*

australis (Spain, Portugal), "Spanish heath"; bushy shrub to 2½ m high, with hairy young shoots; the needles in fours, about 5 mm long; flowers in terminal clusters on previous year's twigs, corolla purplish-red 5 mm long, in late spring. *p. 964*

baccans (So. Africa), "Berry heath"; erect shrub 1-1½ m high, tiny linear bluish-green leaves; the globular bell-flowers, mostly in terminal fours, deep rose, the 6 mm corolla narrowed at throat; winter-spring. *Subtropic.* *p. 961*

bauera (bowieana) (So. Africa), "Bridal heath" or "Albertina heath"; charming flowering shrub to 1½ m high, with bluish-green leaves in fours, standing straight out; waxy flowers in leafy raceme, with tubular inflated corolla 2 cm long, translucent pink, in spring (August to October in So. Africa). *Subtropic.* *p. 965*

blanda (doliiformis) (So. Africa), "Red everblooming heather"; small shrub with tiny leaves and umbels of tubular, swelling to flask-like, purplish red flowers. *p. 961*

blenna (So. Africa), "Lantern heath" or "Orange heath"; dwarf heath 30 to 60 cm high; the needles dense and flaring outward; strikingly colored, waxy urn-shaped flowers inflated at base, to 18 mm long, glowing bright orange with green tips at the narrowed mouth. *p. 965*

buccinaeflora (Cape Prov.); handsome heath to 60 cm high, with smooth leaves 2 cm long; small tubular flowers 2 cm long, pure lemon yellow arranged along erect spikes, in spring. *p. 964*

caffra (Cape Prov. Natal), "Hedge-heath"; a dense shrub vigorously growing to 4 m tall, with green gray-pubescent leaves in three's; slightly puffed flowers 1 cm long, grayish-white or ivory. *p. 962*

canaliculata (So. Africa); erect heath 90-180 cm high, with densely hairy young shoots; the needles usually in three's, much recurved; profusely blooming with open bell-shaped flowers pale pink or white, 3 mm long, with protruding anthers; in spring. *p. 964*

carnea (Alps to Balkans), "Snow-heather"; tolerant to limestone, a low bush with prostrate branches, tiny leaves, and rosy-red flowers in short, one-sided racemes during early spring. *p. 963*

x cavendishiana (depressa x abietana hyb. 1842); striking color effect of the large tubular 2 cm flowers in lovely bright yellow; very compact bush with awl-shaped leaves; late blooming May into summer. *p. 967*

cerinthoides (So. Africa); a brilliant species with erect branches, leaves 4-6 in a whorl, ciliate; flowers in a close terminal cluster, the belled corolla $2\frac{1}{2}$-3 cm long, fiery crimson, blooming May-October. *p. 963*

chamissonis (So. Africa); small shrub to 75 cm with downy shoots, leaves in three's, very crowded; bell-shaped flowers fully open at mouth, rose-colored, 6 mm dia., in spring. *p. 962*

crinita (So. Africa: Cape); sparry shrub to 60 cm high, tiny scale-like, linear leaves 4 mm long, and tubular flowers arranged umbrella-like at ends of branches, dainty pink running into purple and edged by a small pink crown, throat dark purplish-red. *p. 961*

cruenta (So. Africa); shrub 60-90 cm high with tiny linear leaves in three's, pubescent when young; axillary tubular flowers toward ends of branches, $2\frac{1}{2}$ cm long, with small spreading lobes, cinnabar-red. *p. 965*

curviflora (So. Africa), the "Water heath"; striking species 50 to 150 cm high, with keeled needle-leaves in fours, the slender tubular flowers 3 cm long; curved corolla salmon-rose or red-orange, arranged along the erect branches as in a cylindrical spire. *p. 967*

forbesiana; a garden form at Schoenbrunn, Vienna, of short habit and large flask-shaped flowers 1 cm diameter, cherry-red with white crown. *p. 963*

gracilis (So. Africa), "Rose heath"; bushy shrub with small light green linear leaves, the side shoots loaded with terminal clusters of tiny globose rosy flowers (winter). *Subtropic.* *p. 961, 963*

hyemalis (So. Africa), "French heather"; spreading bush producing tall, tapering racemes of tubular rose-pink flowers 2-$2\frac{1}{2}$ cm long, and tipped with white, winter blooming. Possibly form of summer-fl. perspicua. *Subtropic.* *p. 961*

hyemalis 'Prof. Diels'; an excellent winter-flowering cultivar involving E. colorans x perspicua, with a multitude of long tubular flowers scarlet red with slate-blue undertone. *p. 963*

'Inspector Vorwerk' (1954); charming long-tubular hyemalis seedling cultivar of 'Roi Edouard' initiated by Director Vorwerk of the Botanical Garden, Berlin-Dahlem; parentage 'Wilmorei' x 'Cylindrica'; the tubular corolla purple with white crown, March-April blooming in Europe. *p. 967*

junonia (Cape Prov.); interesting low heath to 30 cm high, with short needle-leaves, and large, curious flask-shaped waxy flowers inflated at base, and with 4 spreading lobes like stars, 4 cm long, and a lovely rose. *p. 967*

longifolia (So. Africa), "Long-leaved heath"; bushy plant to 1 m high, found in coastal mountains of the Cape to 1600 m alt.; with usually long thin, rigid leaves, and a terminal spike of long tubular flowers with 4 lobes, in color varying from white to pink, salmon and purple. *p. 965*

mammosa (So. Africa); tall shrubby plant to 1 m, the little needle-like leaves in fours, or scattered; tubular flowers pendulous in a dense cluster, corolla 2 cm long, reddish-purple, blooming July to October (Autumn). *Subtropic.* *p. 963, 965*

mediterranea (purpurascens) (Portugal, N.W. Spain, S.W. France, Ireland); dense upright heath 1-3 m high, with tiny 1 cm needle-like leaves in four's; ovoid urn-shaped lavender pink flowers 5 mm long, with black anthers. *p. 964*

melanthera (So. Africa), "Christmas heather"; compact shrub with downy shoots and tiny linear leaves; the small globular flowers delicate pale rose with prominent black anthers, blooming in winter. *Subtropic.* *p. 961*

monsoniana (Cape Prov.); large heath, to 180 cm high, with spreading branches; needle-leaves 3-4 mm long arranged in opposite pairs; tubular inflated flowers greenish-white, 12 mm long, ending in a small white crown; in spring. *p. 964*

nana (So. Africa); a dwarf heath from the Cape region, where it scrambles along rocks on cliffs; 25 cm high, with tiny needles, and covered with conical flowers 3 mm long, greenish yellow at first, turning bright yellow, in spring. *p. 966*

'Osterglocken'; floriferous French heather of the hyemalis type, crosses of hyemalis 'Superba' x 'Hélene' (1939), literally covered with long-tubular dark-rose flowers, blooming March and April in European greenhouses. *p. 967*

'Ostergruss'; a good compact, spring-blooming hyemalis type French heather, greenhouse grown in pots for Easter sales in France and Germany; parentage hyemalis 'Superba' with the French 'Helene' (1939), long-tubular flowers purplish-rose, blooming into May. *p. 967*

pelviformis (viridipurpurea) (So. Africa); lovely small flowering heath similar to E. gracilis but blooming in spring instead of autumn; the small needle-leaves in whorls of four; the small fragrant bell flowers 4 mm long, rosy-pink. *p. 964*

persoluta alba (So. Africa); small, densely branched shrub with linear, three-angled, ciliate leaves in four's; tiny cup-shaped flowers rose-pink in the type, white in var. alba, in racemes at the end of lateral branches; March to May. *p. 962*

perspicua (Cape Prov.); lovely heath 60 cm or more high, with linear leaves in three's or four's; tubular flowers $2\frac{1}{2}$ cm long, slightly curved at tip, arranged in tall plumes, blush-white at mouth, deep rose toward base and showing dark anthers; summer-blooming. *p. 961*

'Pres. Carnot' (hyemalis hyb.); a colorful spring-blooming hybrid of the 'Wilmorei' type, with the numerous flowers crowded along the woody stem, the long corolla tubes deep pink tipped white. *p. 961*

quadrangularis (So. Africa), "Pink shower heath"; from the Cape mountains; very floriferous bush to 1 m or more high, the 4 mm leaves in fours and ciliate when young; small cup-shaped $\frac{1}{2}$ cm flowers white to rosy; in spring. *p. 966*

recurvata; beautiful winter-blooming heath 30-60 cm high, the branches dense with long, fresh green needles; flowers yellow with brown-red tips, and protruding red style. *p. 964*

regia (Cape Prov.), the "Royal heath"; striking heath of straggling habit 60-90 cm high but bearing lovely glossy sticky flowers with inflated tubular, waxy corolla 2 cm long, rich crimson-red; the small appressed needle-leaves fresh green. The photo shown on pg. 965 is probably E. regia var. variegata, their bicolored corolla crimson with white base, and popular in cultivation. *Subtropic.* *p. 965, 966*

speciosa (So. Africa); sparry heath 60-120 cm high, the short, plump needles close to stems; long tubular curved flowers to 3 cm long, and sticky, crimson red with yellow tips. *Subtropic.* *p. 966*

taxifolia (Cape Prov.); small shrub to 30 cm high, known as the "Double pink heath" because its small flowers appear to be double; the jar-shaped deep pink corolla, tipped red, is half concealed, like petticoats, by broad pink sepals; in clusters on the branchlets; linear leaves 3-sided. *p.961*

tricolor (So. Africa); sparry heath with small rigid, prickly needles; toward apex of branches the clustered inflated flowers with corolla green and white near base, pink in center and deep rose toward mouth. *p. 966*

umbellata (Spain, Portugal, Morocco); bushy heather 30-80 cm high, with tiny needles in three's; globose little 5 mm flowers rose pink salmon, red; in spring. *p. 964*

ventricosa (So. Africa), the "Wax heath"; stout bush to 2 m high, from the mountains near Stellenbosch; awl-shaped leaves arranged in fours; pretty spindle-shaped flowers 2 cm long, delicately shaded pink and white, shining as if glazed, in late spring. *p. 967*

verticillata (So. Africa); shrub to $1\frac{1}{2}$ m high with smooth linear leaves in dense whorls of 4 to 6; rosy tubular flowers almost $2\frac{1}{2}$ cm long, and showing brown stamens, forming dense leafy racemes. *p. 966*

vestita (So. Africa), "Wide-mouthed heath" or "Trembling heath", because its branches are completely covered with soft, needle-like leaves 2 cm long which tremble at the slightest breath of air, and giving the plant, to 1 m high, a feathery appearance; tubular flowers with wide mouth 2-3 cm long, deep crimson but varying to pink or white, in So. Africa's winter, May to September. *p. 965*

vestita incarnata (So. Africa); shrub to 60-90 cm high with leaves in sixes, flowers axillary, in whorls crowded at $2\frac{1}{2}$ - 5 cm below the end of the shoots, tubular corolla $2\frac{1}{2}$ cm long and downy but tapering, delicate salmon pink, tip light red; blooming winter-spring. *p. 963*

vestitale hort.; a bushy heath dense with plumy needles, and inflated tubular flowers red with green tips. Photographed by E. Hahn in Germany. *p. 966*

'Ville de Cherbourg' (mediterranea x persoluta); small, attractive French cultivar of sparry growth; about 30 cm high with linear 4 mm. leaves, and jug-like flowers ivory-white; suitable for pot-culture. *p. 962*

viridiflora (So. Africa); shrubby heath to 1 m high with spreading 1 cm needles; the nodding flowers unusual with tubular corolla green, 3-4 cm long, tapering to both ends. *p. 965*

walkeria (Cape Prov.), "Swellendam heath"; 30 to 50 cm high, with tiny soft leaves in fours; showy terminal clusters of flask-shaped, luminous flowers 12 mm long, opening to a starry face of 4 lobes, in colors from white to pink or rosy-red. *p. 966*

'Wilmorei', "Prince of Wales heather"; a grand old large-flowered hybrid well-known since 1835, probably of E. perspicua but with swollen tubes and more bushy; showy spikes with stiff linear leaves in threes, and tubular rosy flowers 4 cm long, prettily tipped with white; blooming winter to spring; very showy and with long-lasting flowers. *Subtropic.* *p. 962*

ERIOBOTRYA *Rosaceae* **I2LBM**
japonica (China), "Chinese loquat" or "Japan plum"; symmetrical evergreen tree with noble decorative thick foliage, 15-30 cm long obovate, glossy-green on the surface, strongly ribbed, and toothed, the underside and stalk rusty-woolly; fragrant white flowers, and pear-shaped yellow to orange edible fruit 3 to 8 cm long, of pleasant, sprightly flavor. *p. 1996, 1997*
japonica 'Gold Nugget'; medium-size evergreen tree with dark green leaves, and abundant large, pear-shaped orange fruit of very sweet flavor. *p. 2001*

ERIOCAULON *Eriocaulaceae* **S3LFM**
striatum (Madagascar, Mauritius, Réunion), a small "Pipewort"; perennial with white roots, forming a rosette of short grass-like, translucent channeled leaves; the inflorescence on long slender stalks topped by minute white flowers in button-like head; likes to grow along sandy shores of soft-water lakes; becoming taller when growing in water. *p. 1002*
trilobatum (Madagascar), a "Pipewort"; a swamp plant with creeping rootstock and tufting, narrow translucent, green, channeled leaves, to 10 cm long; the inflorescence on erect stalks, topped by a curious small head of minute white flowers, the males in the center, each with several stamens. *p. 1002*

ERIOGONUM *Polygonaceae* **I2LBD**
giganteum (California: Santa Catalina, San Clemente Is.), "St. Catherine's lace"; spreading shrub to 2 m, woody branches attractive with shreddy reddish bark, oval gray-green leaves and large clusters of white-woolly pink to rose flowers in profusion. *p. 1953*

ERIOPSIS *Orchidaceae* **S3OFW**
biloba (Perú, Guianas, Brazil); epiphyte with ovoid pseudobulbs bearing 2 leaves 40 cm long; inflorescence densely many-flowered, almost cylindrical; waxy, fragrant blooms 3 cm across, golden yellow with brown-red margins, lip deep yellow spotted with red (autumn). *Tropical.* *p. 1731*

ERIOSYCE *Cactaceae: Echinocactanae* **I2LBD**
ceratistes (Chile); large globular cactus, in habitat above Santiago de Chile; olive-green body to 50 cm dia. with 20 ribs, to 30 when older, divided into knobs of which each bears numerous curving, reddish to blackish spines 3 cm long, densely covering the surface; in a circle around the top appear the bell-shaped red flowers 3 to 4 cm long, and enveloped in a matting of white wool. *p. 694*

ERODIUM *Geraniaceae* **I2LBD**
chamaedryoides 'Roseum' (Majorca, Corsica), the "Alpine geranium"; a diminutive, spreading, perennial rosette 8 cm high with stout rootstock; tiny 1 cm ovate, lobed, hairy, green leaves and solitary 5-lobed flowers pink veined with deep rose; white in the species; goes dormant outdoors. *p. 1177*
pelargoniflorum (Asia Minor: Anatolia); shrubby, hairy perennial to 30 cm high, with heart-shaped, lightly lobed, green basal leaves, pubescent above; flowers white, two upper petals spotted brown-purple. *p. 1176*

ERVATAMIA: see Tabernaemontana

ERYCINA *Orchidaceae* **I3OFM**
echinata (Mexico); small epiphytic oncidium-like orchid, with ascending rhizome producing small 3 cm pseudobulbs at intervals, with solitary leaves; wiry stalks bear bird-like 2 cm flowers greenish-yellow or pinkish, the large lip golden yellow (spring). *Tropical.* *p. 1731*

ERYNGIUM *Umbelliferae* **C2LBDh**
alpinum (Europe: Maritime Alps to Balkans), "Alpine thistle"; handsome perennial 60 to 80 cm high, with rich green leaves lobed or palmately cut; the inflorescence with blue or white flowers in cone-like heads, subtended by ray-like silvery bracts. *Warm temperate.* *p. 2106*
bromeliifolium (Mexico); perennial rosette of fleshy olive green, channeled leaves edged by large thorny teeth; tall stalk to 2 m, with thistle-like inflorescence of bluish flowers. Photographed outdoors in the Botanic Garden, Strasbourg, France. *Subtropic.* *p. 2105*

ERYTHEA: see Brahea

ERYTHRINA *Leguminosae* **I-S2LBD**
abyssinica (Ethiopia, Kenya, Uganda), "Red hot poker tree" or "Kaffirboom"; deciduous tree to 12 m, with corky, yellow-brown bark with woody spines; the branchlets armed with strong recurved thorns; the leaves trifoliolate, leaflets ovate, and gray-hairy beneath; showy flowers with narrow lobes brilliant scarlet, in erect poker-like inflorescence. *Tropical.* *p. 1383*
acanthocarpa (So. Africa); a gorgeous shrub with leathery, trifoliate leaves and large, brilliantly showy flowers orange-red, tipped yellow and green. *p. 1383*
x bidwillii (crista-galli x herbacea), "Florida coral-bean"; handsome plant 1-2 m high, with leaves of 3 leaflets, and erect inflorescence of crimson-red curved flowers, blooming April to November. *Subtropic.* *p. 1382*
caffra (humeana) (E. Cape Prov., Natal), "Kaffirboom coral tree"; large spreading, deciduous tree to 25 m, trunk and branches with hooked thorns; pointed leaflets in three's; spade-shaped; tubular flowers more than 3 cm long, in a spreading spike, brilliant cinnabar-scarlet fading to purple; protruding stamens give a whiskery look. *Subtropic.* *p. 1382, 1383*
caffra 'Flavescens' (East London, So. Africa); flowers cream colored. *p. 1382*
coralloides (corallodendrum) (W. Indies), "Coral tree"; tree to 6 m, with woody stems prickly or unarmed; leaves of 3 broad leaflets; flowers with standard never opening, deep scarlet, in long racemes; appearing after leaves fall. *Tropical.* *p. 1382*
crista-galli (Brazil), "Coral tree"; small tree with trifoliate leaves on spiny petioles, and showy butterfly flowers deep scarlet-red, in dense racemes, usually produced before the leaves. *p. 768A, 1382, 1383*
falcata (So. Brazil); tropical tree with bright coral scarlet flowers; I will never forget the breathtaking sight of these leafless trees in red, blazing against the azure blue sky of the Organ mountains in the dry landscape of Minas Gerais in Brazil. *Tropical.* *p. 1383*
humeana (So. Africa), "Natal coral tree"; semi-evergreen shrub or tree; may grow to 10 m, but begins to bear its bright crimson-red blooms when 1 m high; flowers in long-stalked clusters at branch ends and inclined to be pendant or arching; foliage with 3 broad leaflets. *Subtropic.* *p. 1382, 1383*
indica (Ryukyu Islands, Western Pacific); compact shrub with woody, knobby stems; dense clusters of flowers deep crimson with pointed lip broadly spread open. *p. 1382*
indica picta (India, Malaya, Australia); a beautiful variegated-leaf form of E. indica; bushy tree with black spines, the large leaves with three broad leaflets fresh glossy-green, strikingly variegated cream to golden yellow along the primary veins; waxy flowers crimson red. *Tropical.* *p. 1363*
lysistemon (Transvaal, Zululand, Natal), "Kaffirboom"; spectacularly showy deciduous, thorny tree to 12 m with gray branches; leaves after bloom, the obovate leaflets arranged in three's; large tube-shaped, bright salmon-scarlet flowers, in large compact clusters reminding of a coxcomb. *Subtropic.* *p. 1363, 1383*
zeyheri (So. Africa), "Prickly Cardinal" or "Ploegbreker"; "ploegbreker" (plough-breaker) because of huge root going down 1 m into the ground, and not easy to dislodge; handsome shrub with large leaves with prickles, and stems to 60 cm, with large spikes of scarlet flowers. *p. 1382*

ERYTHROCHITON *Rubiaceae* **I-S3HFM**
brasiliensis (So. Brazil, Bolivia, Perú); small evergreen tree about 3 m, with long leathery lanceolate leaves; clusters of showy axillary flowers with large red calyx, and white, spreading corolla. *p. 2020*

ERYTHROCOCCA *Euphorbiaceae* **S2LBD**
fischeri (Kenya); evergreen tropical spiny shrub with woody branches and obovate or elliptic leaves 4 to 8 cm long, and with serrate margins; spines solitary at nodes; the small flowers yellowish, without petals, but stamens prominent. *p. 1004*

ERYTHRODES *Orchidaceae* **S3O-Sphag NM**
nobilis 'Argyraea', small terrestrial "Jewel orchid"; with fleshy creeping rhizome, clasping ovate leaves richly overlaid with silver, only margins and midrib showing dark green in this selected variety; small 1 cm white flowers with fringed lip, on tall spike. *p. 1730*
nobilis argyrocentrus (Physurus) (Brazil), "Silver orchid"; grown for its beautiful foliage; the clasping ovate leaves about 2½ to 5 cm long, light grayish-green or moss-green with a network of silver veins becoming more dense over the grayish center area, shimmering gray underneath; erect spike, with 1 cm waxy white flowers yellow at throat and marked purple; February. (S) *p. 1730*

ERYTHRONIUM *Liliaceae* **C2LFM**
americanum (Nova Scotia to Florida), "Trout-lily"; also known as "Dogtooth-violet"; bulbous herb with two lanceolate basal leaves, dotted and mottled with brown and white; solitary 5 cm flowers bright yellow with spreading, recurved segments. (h) *p. 1434*

ERYTHROPHYSA *Sapindaceae* **S3LBD**
transvaalensis (South Africa); attractive shrub or small tree 2-4 m high, with graceful pinnate leaves; irregular flowers not showy, but the inflated fruits are decorative, yellow green to red, with a shiny blackish seed inside, and used for necklaces. *p. 2038*

ERYTHRORHIPSALIS *Cactaceae* **S2HFM**
pilocarpa (Brazil: Rio, São Paulo), "Bristle-tufted twig-cactus"; attractive branched epiphytic cactus, at first erect, later pendant, thin cylindrical purplish-green stems, with joints clustered by whorls or alternate branches grooved, closely set with aeroles with whitish hair-like bristles; flowers white, fruit red. *p. 736, 741*

ERYTHROXYLUM *Erythroxylaceae* **I2LBM**
coca (Eastern Andes), "Cocaine plant"; densely leafy shrub to 4 m, obovate leathery leaves to 6 cm; small 1 cm yellowish flowers, followed by small reddish berries. Coca leaves mixed with lime are chewed daily by the Indians of the Andes for a powerful stimulant at high altitudes. *p. 1002*

ESCALLONIA *Saxifragaceae* **I2LBD**
organensis (So. Brazil: Organ Mts.); sturdy, ornamental evergreen, bushy shrub to 2 m with angled branchlets; obovate firm bronzy-green, toothed leaves to 8 cm long, often red-margined; small 1 cm fragrant, rosy flowers apple-blossom-like, in dense terminal clusters; autumn. *p. 2042*

ESCHSCHOLTZIA *Papaveraceae* **I-C2LBD**
californica (California, Oregon), "California poppy"; soft herb with gray-green, 3-pinnatifid leaves and large showy, poppy-like flowers, bright yellow with orange-red base, opening in the sun; widely naturalized in southern Chile where I noted them climbing even into the Andes. *p. 1920*

ESCOBARIA *Cactaceae* **I2LBD**
roseana (Mexico); small globular gray-green plant similar to Mammillaria but bearing its rosy flowers at the base of the young tubercles, and entirely covered with stiff golden-yellow needle spines; yellowish or pink flowers, fruit red. *p. 710*
shaferi (Mexico); small globe with spiralling tubercles hidden under bristle-like spine; flowers similar to Mammillaria, bronzy-pink. *p. 710*

ESCONTRIA *Cactaceae* **S2LBD**
chiotilla (S. Mexico), "Little star big-spine"; slender columns branching tree-like, sparry-branched to 6 m; seedlings stocky, bright green, 7-8 sharp ribs, light colored radial spines, central spines to 8 cm long, apparently dropping in old specimens; small 3 cm yellow flowers; edible purple fruit. *Arid-tropical.* *p. 642, 658*

ESPOSTOA *Cactaceae* ***I2LBD**
lanata (No. Perú, Ecuador), "Peruvian old man" or "Soroco"; from arid mountains at 1200 to 2250 metres; a small and very attractive column when young, with 20 to 30 ribs beautifully covered with cottony, snow-white hair; with age the trunk becoming thicker, to 20 cm dia., and branching with numerous wide-spreading arms, each to 15 cm dia., and to 5 m high; flowers whitish, 4-5 cm long, borne out of the cephalium wool on one side of the stem; the 3 to 4 cm carmine-red juicy fruit is sweet and eaten by the Indians. *Arid-subtropic.* *p. 19*, 620, 645, 656*

EUADENIA *Capparidaceae* **S3LFM**
eminens (West Trop. Africa); evergreen shrub with trifoliolate leathery, smooth leaves 40 cm long; inflorescence spidery in candelabra-like pendant clusters, the buff-yellow flowers with narrow petals 10 cm long, and green sepals. *p. 754*

EUCALYPTUS *Myrtaceae* **I2LBM**
caesia (Western Australia), the "Gungurru"; handsome small, graceful tree of weeping habit 5 to 7 m high; wood, leaves and seed pods beautifully coated with waxy, silvery white powder; gray-green lanceolate leaves contrast with the red stems; bark white and mottled, curling when older; dusty rose-pink flowers; seed capsules shaped like silver bells. *Subtropic.* *p. 1618*
cinerea (cephalophora) (N.S. Wales, Victoria), "Silver dollar tree"; small glaucous tree, with brown-red, willowy branches bearing pairs of sessile leaves rigid, stiff-leathery and silvery glaucous, rounded like a silver coin, to 8 cm across, in the juvenile stage; later when 2 m or more high the leaves become ovate to lanceolate, with yellow midrib; used by florists as cut branches; often preserved with glycerine. *Subtropic.* *p. 1613, 1618*
citriodora (Queensland), "Lemon-gum"; one of the most graceful of trees to 25 m, with smooth powder-white to pinkish trunk; branches pendant with long 8-20 cm sickle-shaped leaves, golden green and lemon-scented; white flowers in clusters. Older specimen are designer's trees, very picturesque with bare trunks. Oil has been distilled from leaves. *p. 1619*
erythrocorys (W. Australia), "Red-cap gum" or "Illyarie"; small tree 3 to 10 m high; smooth bark, peeling in thin flakes; thick, shiny green narrow sickle-shaped leaves 10-18 cm long; the inflorescence with bright scarlet caps which drop off to reveal yellow stamen flowers. *Subtropic.* *p. 1609*
falcata (Western Australia), "Silver mallet"; attractive tree to 10 m, with smooth, gray or silvery, mottled bark, gray-green, sickle-shaped leaves; pointed, conical buds on slender stalks, and fluted fruits. *p. 1619*
ficifolia (S.W. Australia), "Scarlet flowering gum"; slower growing, ornamental tree to 15 m high, with dark and furrowed bark, thick lanceolate green leaves with yellow midrib; well known for its showy masses of flowers with bright scarlet stamens and dark red anthers. *p. 1609, 1615, 1618*
globulus (Tasmania, Victoria), "Tasmanian blue gum"; a pretty plant when small, with shoots and clasping cordate leaves a glaucous blue, but rapidly growing into a gigantic tree to 100 m high, with leaves becoming long and dark green; much used for windbreaks in California; its foliage contains aromatic oil used for medicinal purposes.
Subtropic. *p. 1609, 1613, 1614, 1618, 1619*
globulus 'Compacta', the "Bushy blue gum"; a densely branched lower, more compact tree with grayish trunk; very glaucous-blue ovate leaves when young; with age leaves become 30 cm long, sickle-shaped, dark shining green. Flowers white. *Subtropic.* *p. 1613, 1619*
macrocarpa (Western Australia), "Mottlecah" or "Blue-bush"; curious sprawling shrub to 5 m; the stiff stems closely set with broad ovate, silvery blue, clasping leaves in ranks, 5-12 cm long and almost as broad; flat-topped fluffy flowers with filaments usually red or pink, directly from leaf axils. *Subtropic.* *p. 1618*
polyanthemos (Victoria, New So. Wales), "Red box" or "Silver dollar tree"; tree to 45 m high, with persistent bark, the slender, sparry, glaucous branches with distantly spaced attractive leathery leaves almost round, glaucous bluish gray and edged all around with purple.
Subtropic. *p. 1613, 1614, 1618*
rhodantha (W. Australia), "Rose Mallee"; ornamental sprawling shrub to 4 m, with horizontal branches densely set with clasping, sessile leaves in lovely glaucous-blue, 5-10 cm long and nearly round; showy inflorescence of long bright crimson-red stamens tipped yellow, looking like small brushes. *Subtropic.* *p. 1618*
salubris (Western Australia), the "Gimlet"; attractive tree to 15 m, with rich red-brown trunk and smooth with prominent spiralled flutings; branches are willowy, with shining dark green, narrow leaves. My photo shows a tree sheared for compactness in the streets of Perth. *Subtropic.* *p. 1621*
sideroxylon (Queensland to Victoria), "Red ironbark"; graceful medium-sized tree to 25 m, with furrowed, non-shedding, red to nearly black trunk; slim blue-green leaves turn bronze in winter; fluffy flowers light pink in pendulous clusters; seed capsules goblet-shaped. *p. 1618*
torquata (Western Australia), "Coral gum"; small aromatic tree to 4 m high, with willowy light brown stems, and blue-grayish-green leathery, lanceolate leaves; masses of flowers at an early age, in umbels, with vivid coral-red stamens, the base of calyx dilated into a ring. *Subtropic.* *p. 1613*

EUCHARIDIUM *Oenotheraceae* **I2LBD**
grandiflorum (Clarkia concinna) (California), "Red ribbons"; showy herbaceous annual to 60 cm, much branched with 4 cm elliptic leaves; flowers rose-pink to light purple with curious 3-lobed petals resembling parted little fans. *p. 1628*

EUCHARIS *Amaryllidaceae* **S3LFMd**
grandiflora (amazonica) (Andes of Colombia), "Amazon lily"; bulbous plant with broad, basal leaves narrowed into petioles; umbels of fragrant white flowers with spreading segments, 5 to 8 cm across. *p. 118, 131*
korsakoffii (Perú); a "Miniature Amazon lily", found near Moyobamba, Dept. San Martin; with globose 3 cm bulb, long-stalked fleshy glossy deep green, lance shaped leaves 15-18 cm long; the floral stalk to 28 cm with cluster of small, pure white, waxy flowers, the flaring segments 2 cm long. *Subtropic.* *p. 111*

EUCNIDE *Loasaceae* **I2LBD**
bartonioides (Texas, Mexico); herbaceous biennial 30 cm high, with flexuous, succulent stems, spreading on the ground; lobed leaves, with stinging hairs; flowers with 5 spreading petals bright yellow, opening in sunshine. *p. 1522*

x EUCODONOPSIS *Gesneriaceae* **S3HFM**
'Kuan Yin'; fascinating intergeneric hybrid between Achimenes longiflora and Smithiantha zebrina; in habit somewhat resembling Kohleria; with fleshy stems, and ovate dark green, smallish leaves with scalloped margins; large achimenes-like flowers with oblique limb, creamy-yellow streaked with purple, blooming late summer and autumn. *p. 1244*
picturata (Kohleria x eucodonopsis) (Achimenes or Eucodonia multiflora x Smithiantha zebrina); formerly known as Mandirola x Naegelia picturata; intergeneric hybrid in habit similar to Kohleria, with ovate leaves covered with purple hairs; tubular flowers deep rose with throat white and a touch of yellow. *p. 1254*

EUCOMIS *Liliaceae* **I2LBMd**
bicolor (Natal); robust herb with globose bulb, rosette of oblong plain green leaves crisped at margins; spotted stalk with dense pyramidal cluster 8-10 cm long of pale green flowers, petals with distinct purple edges. *p. 1447*
comosa (punctata) (So. Africa), the "Pineapple-flower"; interesting bulbous rosette with large attractive lanceolate dark green leaves to 30 cm long, mottled purple underneath; fragrant, star shaped flowers greenish white with purple center, 2 cm across, in cylindric raceme topped by a tufted crown of leafy bracts; July. *p. 1446*
humilis (Drakensberg, Cape Prov.); bulbous plant with a rosette of broad basal leaves, and a compact cylindrical spike of creamy-white star-shaped flowers. *p. 1447*
undulata (So. Africa), "Pineapple flower"; bulbous plant with broad, undulated bright green leaves to 8 cm wide, with tough margins and keeled beneath, thin and spreading, plain green; the inflorescence on cylindric stalk with dense head of bright green flowers crowned by a tuft of small leaves; August. *Subtropic.* *p. 1446, 1447*
zambeziaca (E. Trop. Africa); robust bulbous plant similar to comosa, with firm, lanceolate, channelled fleshy green leaves; from the center a dense cylindrical raceme of light green 2 cm flowers, on unspotted stalk. *p. 1447*

EUGENIA *Myrtaceae* **I-S2LBM**
myriophylla (Myrciaria); charming and shapely small evergreen bush densely branched, and with light glossy green, needle-like linear leaves 2 cm long. Seen at Fabricus, Leverkusen, Germany; originated in So. Brazil. *Subtropic.* *p. 1606*

myrtifolia in hort. (bot. Syzygium paniculatum) (New South Wales, Queensland), "Australian brush-cherry"; handsome evergreen shrub or small tree of dense habit, 6 to 15 m high; small thin-leathery elliptic leaves 4 to 8 cm long, vivid red when young, later shining bronzy green; small fluffy white stamen flowers 2 cm dia., followed by ovoid red, edible berries. Very ornamental trained or sheared into pyramid or other topiary forms. The fragrant fruit is used in jellies. See Syzygium paniculatum. **p. 1607**

uniflora (Brazil, Guayana), "Surinam cherry"; small glabrous tree to 8 m high, with glossy, ovate, 5 cm leaves, and fragrant white flowers; producing distinctive grooved, round fleshy fruit of deep crimson, edible and of spicy flavor. *Tropical.* *p. 1609*

EUGENIA: see also Syzygium

EULOPHIA *Orchidaceae* **S2HFD**

angolensis (Angola, Kenya, Tanzania, Transvaal); rhizomatous terrestrial with long, ribbed leaves to 45 cm; floral spike 1 m tall, with numerous long-lasting, nodding 5 cm flowers, sepals yellow suffused with red toward tips, petals yellow outside, gray inside, lip golden yellow (spring). *p. 1732*

cucullata (Kenya, Uganda, Tanzania, Zululand); handsome tuberous species; the flowering shoot appears before vegetative growth, to 75 cm high, carrying 5-10 bell-flowers each 5 cm dia., sepals olive-green to brown, petals and lip pink to vivid purple, throat lighter; tufted narrow leaves with ribbed surface, 30 cm long. *p. 1732*

hereroensis (S.W. Africa: Namibia); terrestrial species with long leaves, and straight-erect inflorescence of light red-brown flowers and yellow on lip. *p. 1732*

krebsii (Lissochilus) (Transvaal, Natal); terrestrial with small pseudobulbs, lanceolate, folded leaves, heavy-textured to 45 cm; inflorescence with 4 cm flowers, the reflexed sepals green blotched with brown, the broader petals bright yellow; 3-lobed lip golden yellow with short spur (winter). *p. 1732*

lurida (West Trop. Africa, Madagascar); cymbidium-like terrestrial with ovoid swollen pseudobulbs and 25 cm long plicate (folded) leaves and forming aerial roots; branched inflorescence on wiry stalks, bearing numerous small yellow-brown flowers. *p. 1732*

ovalis bainesii (complanata) (Transvaal); terrestrial orchid with lanceolate, folded leaves, and tall basal spike of ivory-white flowers. *p. 1732*

paiveana (Kenya to Southern Africa); xerophytic terrestrial with conical pseudobulbs bearing narrow lanceolate ribbed thin but tough leaves; basal tall, erect raceme 75 cm high, with flowers having green sepals marked brown, petals golden yellow, lip yellow with purplish veins and a brown spur. *Tropical.* *p. 1730*

paiveana borealis (Kenya, Tanzania, Uganda, Zaire); a variety smaller in its parts, with erect raceme of yellow flowers marked with purple, the folded lip bears a single horny keel of yellow. *p. 1730*

porphyroglossa (Lissochilus) (Kenya, Uganda, Zaire, Sudan), "Swamp orchid"; very large terrestrial, with indistinct pseudobulbs, sword-shaped plaited leaves to 75 cm long; the tall rigid erect raceme to 1¾ m high, with solid textured, 6 cm flowers with bronze-purple sepals, petals magenta outside, white within, lip yellow and purple, the spur bronze. *Tropical.* *p. 1730*

schimperiana (Arabia, Kenya, W. Africa); terrestrial with stout pseudobulbs, bearing 2 or 3 hard leaves folded along middle; floral stalk to 40 cm, with 3 cm flowers, sepals brownish green, petals green with lilac veins, lip white. *p. 1732*

speciosa (wakefieldii) (Mozambique, Transvaal); handsome terrestrial with flattened tubers, leaves narrowly lanceolate and fleshy, 25 cm long, present at time of bloom; floral stalk to 1½ m tall, with brilliantly colored flowers 5 cm across, sepals plain green, petals and lip bright yellow with red streaks at base of lip. *p. 1732*

streptopetala (Lissochilus) (So. Africa: Transvaal); terrestrial orchid with narrow 3-nerved leaves to 45 cm and floral stalk to nearly 1 m tall, with 3 cm flowers light to darker yellow, the reflexed sepals green with brown spots, petals golden yellow; lip yellow (spring). *p. 1732*

EULOPHIDIUM *Orchidaceae* **S3HFM**

ledienii (Trop. West Africa); terrestrial or epiphytic orchid with small pseudobulbs bearing solitary broad obovate 15 cm leathery leaf, green marbled greenish-white; erect raceme of 2½ cm flowers with brownish sepals, whitish petals, the lip cream flecked with red. *p. 1729*

mackenii (Natal); small pseudobulbs with solitary leathery, oblanceolate leaf, and basal erect raceme of light brown flowers with creamy lip veined purple. *p. 1729*

roseovariegatum (Madagascar), a "Foliage orchid"; the small dark rose leaves beautifully marbled dark green; insignificant whitish flowers marked red, on inflorescence 55 cm tall. *p. 1731*

trinioides (So. Africa: Natal); terrestrial species attractive as a "foliage orchid", with leaves marbled with white on dull green; the tall inflorescence with small yellow flowers. *p. 1731*

EULOPHIELLA *Orchidaceae* **S3OFW**

roempleriana (Madagascar); very large and robust epiphyte, in habitat found growing only on pandanus; pseudobulbous plant with creeping rhizome, 4 to 8 large plicate leaves 1 m long; bold basal inflorescence to 1½ m tall, with waxy, fragrant, long-lasting flowers 9 cm dia., broad sepals and petals rose-pink, lip rich violet-rose, white in throat, disc yellow (spring). *p. 1735*

x rolfei (roempleriana x elisabethae from Madagascar); lovely epiphyte, whose parents typically grow on pandanus trees; pseudobulbous plant with creeping rhizome, and long plicate foliage; basal flowers 8 to 10 cm across on stalk 30 cm or more, fragrant, with rose-carmine, waxy petals and sepals, and white lip. *Tropical.* *p. 1731*

EULYCHNIA *Cactaceae* **I2LBD**

floresii (Chile), "White fluff-post"; very pretty column, with age branching, to 3 m high, the branches 6-8 cm thick, olive green, with many close ribs, attractively and regularly dressed with large white-woolly tufts from the areoles, long brown-tipped central spines; funnel-shaped white or pinkish flowers. *Arid-subtropic.* *p. 647*

EUONYMUS *Celastraceae* **•C2LFM**

fortunei 'Marginatus' (China), "Winter creeper"; evergreen shrub trailing or climbing by rootlets; dense with small leathery, ovate leaves 2 to 6 cm long, glossy green with broad ivory-white border; small greenish white flowers; pale pink fruit. The variety coloratus has leaves turning deep purple in winter. *p. 759*

fortunei radicans 'Gracilis' (Japan, Korea), "Variegated creeping euonymus"; small evergreen shrub climbing by rootlets, small oval, serrate leaves gray green, variegated and edged white, tinted pink. (h) *p. 760*

fortunei 'Uncinata' (China); evergreen creeper with small oval leaves, gray green with pale gray veining, margins serrate. *p. 760*

japonica (Japan), "Japanese spindle tree"; dense evergreen shrub to 5 m high, with erect willowy branches closely set with opposite small leathery oval leaves 2½-6 cm long, obscurely toothed, glossy dark green; small greenish-white flowers. *p. 760*

japonica 'Albo-marginata' (So. Japan), "Japanese spindle-tree"; dense evergreen shrub to 5 m high, with erect willowy branches, closely set with opposite leathery glossy, small oval leaves 3-6 cm long, obscurely toothed, dark green in the species, and with small greenish-white flowers. This "Silver-leaf euonymus" has somewhat smaller, narrower leaves milky green bordered with a narrow white edge. *Warm temperate.* *p. 19*, 760*

japonica 'Argenteo-variegata' (Japan), known as "Silver Queen"; leaves oval, glossy fresh green with broad white marginal variegation. *Warm temperate.* *p. 760*

japonica aureo-variegata 'Yellow Queen'; the waxy green oval leaves are variegated and margined yellow toward edge. *p. 760*

japonica 'Medio-picta', "Goldheart euonymus"; waxy oval leaves fresh green at margin, golden yellow in the center and down the petiole and stem. *Warm temperate.* *p. 19*, 760*

japonica 'Microphylla' (pulchellus) (Japan); dense little, stiff erect shrub with closely arranged tiny, toothed leaves glossy deep green. p. 760

japonica 'Microphylla variegata', "Variegated box-leaf"; charming variety with a dense mass of tiny green leaves circled by a white border, 1 to 2 cm long. *p. 19*, 760*

EUPATORIUM *Compositae* **I-S2LBD**

araliaefolium (Mexico, Guatemala); shrub with leathery, long elliptic leaves, the flowers in terminal panicles of fluffy feathery white rays. *p. 817*

atrorubens (Mexico); herbaceous 75 cm bush with opposite large, ovate, toothed leaves to 30 cm long, covered with reddish hairs; heads of tubular flowers reddish with lilac shading, in clusters; in late summer. *p.817*

rugosum (New Brunswick to Florida and Louisiana), "White snake-root"; herbaceous subshrub to 1 m high, usually hairy, with ovate leaves to 18 cm long, coarsely toothed, the small disk-flowers white, in large terminal clusters. *p. 818*

sordidum (ianthinum) (Mexico), "Boneset"; shrubby plant with stems densely red-haired; corrugated leaves broad ovate, 10 cm long, with toothed margins; the clustered disk-flower heads violet and sweetly fragrant. *Subtropic.* *p. 818*

EUPHORBIA *Euphorbiaceae* **S-I2LBD**

abyssinica (Ethiopia, Eritrea), "Imperial Ethiopian euphorbia"; majestic plant, becoming a large tree; young succulent stems 8 angled, olive green marked milky and dark green, the undulate sharp notched ridges densely set with corky knobs and downward pointed pairs of light brown spines. *p. 1021*

alcicornis: see ramipressa

ambohipoesiensis (Madagascar); branching shrub 60-90 cm high, the stems irregularly angled and tubercled, with slender beige spines; narrow, dark green leaves 4-6 cm long, and small yellow-green flowers with yellow centers. *p. 1057*

angularis (So. Africa); tall shrub with branches constricted into joints to 20 cm long, with 3 broad horny-margined wings, blue-green. *p. 1028*

antiquorum (India); thorny, succulent shrub to 4 m, 4 to 5 angled stem, with branches 3-angled, constricted into joints, to 5 cm thick; the margins wavy-dentate and set with pairs of spines; small roundish leaves. *p. 1048*

aphylla (Canary Islands); low, spineless, succulent bush densely branched successively or in whorls; cylindrical jointed stems gray-green with roundish leaf scars, 6 mm thick; linear leaves. *p. 1050*

atropurpurea (Canary Islands: Tenerife); succulent shrub branching in ranks, with thickened fleshy stems 2 cm dia., becoming woody, with leaf scars, young branches densely leafy, with glaucous bluish narrow foliage 5-10 cm long; the inflorescence in clusters of flowers with deep maroon bracts. *Subtropic.* *p. 1057*

avasmontana (Namibia; Botswana; Cape Prov.); attractive succulent freely branching from base, forming large bushes 2 m high; 5-8 angled jointed stems curving upward 5-8 cm thick, yellow-green to bluish, angles lightly elevated and with horny edge set with sharp spine pairs. *p. 1048, 1056*

bergeri ("caput-medusae" hort., as in the California trade) (Cape Prov.); similar to E. caput-medusae, with short subglobose caudex, and numerous cylindrical, curved, green branches 8-22 cm long, covered with prominent tubercles. *p. 1021*

bevilanensis (Madagascar); shrubby succulent to 150 cm high, with smooth, brown, round branches 2½ cm dia., with distant spines; thick-fleshy leaves 3 cm long, rolled together to form a channel, the red flowers shaped like bells. *p. 1058*

bubalina (So. Africa); spineless succulent shrub to 1½ m with tubercled cylindric, green to gray branches 2 cm thick and soft and thin oblanceolate, light green leaves; the flowers on long stems with green bracts edged with red. *p. 1045*

bupleurifolia (So. Africa); thornless sphere becoming short cylindric 22 cm high and 8 cm thick, with spiralled brown scaly knobs, the 15 cm lanceolate light green leaves clustered at apex; stalked flowers with green bracts; from seed only. *p. 1030*

bupleurifolia x clava; attractive Manda hybrid, resembling a cycas; succulent stem set densely with spirals of purplish-brown, smooth knobs, and at the top a rosette of long linear obovate, fleshy yellow-green leaves. *p. 1049*

(bupleurifolia x clava) x heptagona; an interesting Manda hybrid, bushy and long slender cylindrical, light green branches densely covered with spiraling, high pointed knobs, and long linear obovate, glaucous leaves near tops. *p. 1026*

caducifolia (India); cylindrical stems with raised knobs set with small spines and deciduous leaves; tiny yellowish flowers. *p. 1033*

caerulescens (Cape Prov.); thorny shrub, branching underground and forming clusters of upright columns 5 cm thick, 4-6-angled, constricted to joints and with hollow sides, bluish green, margins toothed and horny. *Subtropic.* *p. 1021, 1036*

canariensis (Canary Islands), "Hercules club"; large cactus-like succulent branching from the base, to 10 m high; the stems 5, 4 or 6-angled, brownish fresh green, the sinuate angles set with black spine-pairs; small yellow flowers; poisonous. *Subtropic.* *p. 1019, 1034, 1048*

candelabrum (Sudan, Uganda); massive candelabra-like tree to 10 m high, at home in the Nile basin, with 4-angled yellowish green branches constricted to joints, the angles wavy-toothed and set with spines; commonly used as living fences. *Arid-tropical.* *p. 1035, 1036*

caput-medusae (So. Africa), "Medusa's head"; short globose stem with many snake-like gray-green branches densely knobbed and with tiny leaves at the growing tips. *Arid-subtropic.* *p. 1032*

caput-medusae minor (bergeri) (So. Africa); small succulent similar to caput-medusae but more slender, the short main stem forming a large number of radiating cylindric green branches spineless but with small deciduous leaves. *p. 1028*

cereiformis (So. Africa); thorny succulent to 1 m high with branching stems 5 cm thick, dark olive green with 9-15 steep ribs closely and deeply notched into pointed knobs either corky or with gray-brown short spines. *p. 1025*

clandestina (So. Africa); thornless succulent to 60 cm high, the stem cylindric club-shaped, covered shingle-like with wart-like knobs, the apex crowned with willow-like 6 cm linear channeled glaucous leaves edged purple, almost hiding the sessile green flowers; the gray-green knobs with milky streaks. *Arid-subtropic.* *p. 1045, 1048*

clava (Cape Prov.); spineless succulent with cylindrical stems to 1 m, branching with age, small tubercles spirally arranged; toward apex a crown of long linear 10-12 cm light green leaves, deciduous. *p. 1049*

cooperi (So. Africa); thorny tree to 5 m high, with round trunk and arching, upright branches divided into 4-6 angled joints, the angles winglike, green and marked with darker crossbands; poisonous. *Arid-subtropic.* *p. 1019, 1028, 1036, 1056*

cotinifolia (caracasana sanguinea hort.), (West Indies, Mexico to Venezuela and Perú), "Hierba mala"; ornamental, somewhat succulent shrub or small tree 1 to 6 m high; wiry purplish-red branches set with thin-fleshy ovate leaves 5-12 cm long, wine-red when young, metallic blue-green when mature, red veins and prominent midrib, and abounding in acrid, milky juice; whitish inflorescence. Used as fish-poison. *p.1033, 1047*

curvirama (East Africa); bold columnar succulent with thick, angled branches with dentate margins, forming clusters, later tree-like to 25 m high, developing thick trunk to 80 cm dia., the branches bearing at their tips numerous 3 to 4-angled fleshy, green branchlets, segmented and set with dual spines; small 1 cm leaves, soon falling. *p. 1059*

dawei (Uganda); interesting tree-like succulent peculiar to this lake area of Central Africa; slender trunk 5 to 6 m high topped by a flattened dense head of 3-angled green branches. *p. 1035*

decaryi (Southeast Madagascar); curious small succulent; the curving light brown stem to 12 cm long and covered with scales; fleshy elliptic leaves 3 to 7 cm long, arranged in rosettes toward stem tips, silver gray to green or reddish, the margins prettily wavy or frilled, underside silver gray; small greenish flowers with red border. *p. 1031*

decepta (Cape Prov.); low succulent 8 cm high, with globose stem grayish to olive green, topped by numerous brownish, spreading branches, spineless but with persistent remains of older leafstalks, the branches with spirally arranged tubercles; small deciduous leaves. *p. 1047*

deightonii (Sierra Leone); thick 3-angled, branching, dark green column, with the angles thin and winglike, furnished with heavy spines. *p. 1028*

dregeana (So. Africa, Namibia); curious large succulent with erect cactus-like columns but without spines, 1 to 2 m high and forming clusters; the main branches 3 to 5 cm thick, with convex leaf-scars, younger branches finely velvet whitish green; the inflorescence in terminal clusters at apex. *p. 1019*

duranii (Madagascar); thorny shrub 20-40 cm high, with slender, 8-angled, gray stems 2 cm dia., set with gray spines; fleshy, rich green, oval leaves 4-6 cm long, clustered near the top; the inflorescence greenish-yellow. *p. 1058*

echinus (So. Morocco); attractive dwarf succulent shrub to 30 cm high, much-branched with 6-7 ridged columns 5 cm thick, matte light green, shallowly furrowed and with dark line, the angles closely set with pairs of red to gray short spines. *p. 1031, 1059*

enopla (Cape Prov.); branching succulent shrub to 1 m high, with grass-green to bluish 6-8 angled stems, the low ridges warted and set with occasional reddish spines, the grooves distinctly sharp. *p. 1029*

esculenta (Cape Prov.); succulent plant with tuberous root continuing into the thick short trunk which is cone-shaped, to 20 cm thick, topped by a rosette of numerous cylindrical, spineless branches set with tubercles, matte-green to grayish. *p. 1032*

excelsa (Transvaal); spiny succulent tree to 12 m high, with slender trunk topped by a dense crown of usually 4-angled bluish branches, the angles with brown edge and set with spines. *p. 1035*

ferox (Cape Prov.); low succulent branched below ground, forming clumps; stems 9-12-angled, light green, 4 cm thick and set with spines. *p. 1050*

filiflora (Cape Prov., S.W. Africa); succulent 30 cm high forming a club-shaped, thick stem, branching toward top; spineless but with persisting leaf stalks, and covered with spiralled tubercles; linear leaves at tips of branches. *p. 1050*

fimbriata (Cape Prov.); branched plant with columns 4 cm thick, light green to brownish, 7-12 ribs divided into low knobs with white leaf-scars, and numerous woody old flower stalks from the cross furrows; the decorative flowers purplish-red with yellow stamens. *p. 1045*

'Flamingo' (lophogona x splendens), "Pink Florida Christ-thorn"; robust woody shrub with stout, angled branches densely set with thorns; long obovate leaves toward apex, topped by long-stalked clusters of flesh-pink bracted flowers. Probably only a coral-pink colorform of E. x keysii; an almost constant bloomer, especially all winter and spring, a great improvement over the regular "Crown of thorns". *p. 1043*

flanaganii (So. Africa: Cape Prov.), "Green crown"; low spineless dwarf succulent with short thick stem only 5 cm high, bearing a crown of 3 or 4 rows of slender, rich green branches, around the tubercled head; branches semi-erect, older ones spreading wide; tiny linear leaves deciduous. A pleasure for the collector. *p. 1059*

flanaganii cristata, "Crested green crown"; a cushion-like fasciation dense with multitudes of rich green little crests, fanning out from the short conical but invisible stem. A collector's plant photographed in San Diego, California. *p. 1059*

franckiana (So. Africa); bushy plant to 1 m high, branches 3-4-angled, constricted into joints, light green, later grayish, the margins toothed and set with dark spines. *p. 1031*

fulgens (jacquinaeflora) (Mexico), "Scarlet plume"; leafy shrub with slender thin-wiry branches gracefully arching, the small leaves narrow lanceolate, and the flowers in brilliant terminal sprays of small petal-like orange-scarlet bracts. *Tropical.* *p. 1039, 1056A*

fulgens 'Albatros'; a charming cultivar from Ten Aaar Holland, introduced in 1970, and displayed at Flower Shows in Hamburg and Cologne; the wiry, long arching branches with bluish green pendant, almost linear leaves; along the length of the branches with rows of starry flower bracts in pure white. *p. 1043*

x 'Giant Christ-thorn', "Giant California Christ-thorn"; a phenomenal flowering plant; the result of 25 years of hybridizing by Ed Hummel of Carlsbad, California, involving E. milii bojeri, breonii and lophogona; a swollen, stout grayish stem to 6 cm thick, with long brown thorns; toward the apex with bluish-green leathery leaves 20-25 cm long and, arranged as a giant bouquet, strong stalks bearing the clustered inflorescence with firm, large bracts 2 to 5 cm across, larger than a silver dollar, in glowing cerise pink with salmon sheen. Slow-growing. *Tropical.* *p. 1043*

globosa (Cape Prov.); dwarf spineless succulent with tuberous main-root, the branches constricted into globular joints, to 2½ cm dia., dark glossy green, later gray, and furrowed and tubercled; attractive green and white flowers, with fringed petals; on long branched stalks male, on short stalks bisexual. *p. 1045, 1047*

grandicornis (Natal to Kenya), "Cow horn euphorbia"; thorny branching succulent to 2 m, of interesting shape, the green to gray-green branches 3-angled, to 15 cm thick, irregularly constricted, angles winglike with horny margins. *Arid-tropical.* *p. 1019, 1021, 1031, 1056A*

grandicornis cristata, "Crested cowhorn"; formidable, crestate form a contorted body of angles and long spines in all directions; very slow to grow. *p. 1027*

grandidens (So. Africa), "Big-tooth euphorbia"; succulent tree to 12 m high, with 6-angled trunk and 3-4-angled branches in tiers, fresh green with silvery markings, the ridges toothed and set with brown spines. *p. 1027*

griseola (Transvaal, Botswana, Malawi, Mozambique); spiny-succulent shrub with short main trunk, freely branching from the base, forming dense clusters 50-75 cm high, stems 1-1½ cm thick, 4-to 6-angled, green with lighter markings in the furrows, the horny ribs set with spines. *p. 1058*

handiensis (Canary Islands); cactus-like plant branching from the base, to 1 m high, the columnar branches 8 cm thick, 8-12 angled, bright green, with white spine cushions and red spines on the ribs; tiny greenish flowers. *p. 1048*

heptagona (Cape Prov.); thorny succulent sparry branching shrub to 1 m high, 5-10 angled 4½ cm thick, grass-green turning silvery when old, with tiny linear leaves and light brown needle spines. *p. 1025*

hermentiana; the true species which I obtained at the Missouri Botanical Garden: robust sparry tree with thick branches deep green without pale markings, but prominent wing-like ridges fanning out toward margins, and set with pairs of short, strong brown spines and 6 mm deciduous leaves. *p. 1020*

heterophylla (Illinois to Perú), "Annual poinsettia", or "Mexican fire plant", noted annual with variable green leaves linear, ovate or even fiddle-shaped, the upper ones red at the base, bractlike, surrounding the little flowers. *Warm temperate.* *p. 1043, 1049*

heterophylla graminifolia (Montana to Florida, Central America), "Paint-leaf" or "Mexican fire plant"; also known as "Annual poinsettia"; annual or biennial branching herb to 1 m high, with bright green ovate or variable leaves in the species, linear in graminifolia, at the ends of branches; tiny flowers in terminal clusters, surrounded by bract-leaves scarlet at the base and blotched with white. *p. 1044*

horrida (Cape Prov.); clustering succulent with stems mostly low, the columns to 15 cm thick, with 8-14 sharp ridges with deep furrows, olive green with milky green horizontal bands, set mostly with groups of three red-brown flower stems turned to spines. *p. 1029*

horrida striata (So. Africa: Cape Prov.); interesting variety with gray columns deeply furrowed, the angles wavy, and regularly crosslined with white. *p. 1056*

hottentotae (So. Africa and Namibia); succulent shrub to 2 m; the primary branches slender 5-angled column 4½ cm diameter, with somewhat twisted ridges brown-corky, and set with pairs of brown spines, the shallow furrows light green with pale fish-bone design. *p. 1020*

inermis (Cape Prov.); low succulent with short, thick main stem, topped by rosette of series of circular, tubercled branches 2 cm thick and to 30 cm long; very small, deciduous leaves. *p. 1050*

infausta (meloformis) (Cape Prov.); cactus-like globose body 8-10 cm thick, later branching, with 8-10 deep ribs marked by leaf-scars and grooved, dull grayish green with lighter or reddish transverse bands; the little floral stalks dropping off or persistent. *p. 1056*

ingens (Natal, Transvaal, Mozambique, Zimbabwe), a giant "Candelabra tree" to 10 m high, stems to 5-angled, the leafless branches succulent, constricted into joints, dark green, 4-angled, winged and wavy. In habitat in the bush-veld of northern Transvaal, I noted that seedlings in their juvenile stage up to 1½ m are beautifully marked with silver. *p. 1022, 1033, 1034, 1035*

ingens monstrosa, "Totem pole"; interesting slender column, dark green with pale markings, the angles are dissolved and scrambled, the prominent teeth point in all directions and are set with brown spines. *p. 1022, 1023*

ingens x triangularis; Manda hybrid; erect branching stems glossy deep forest-green with 4 sharp wing-like angles regularly notched and set with short brown spines and brief oval leaves. *p. 1028*

x keysii (lophogona x milii), a "Giant crown of thorns", also known as "Flamingo"; resembling milii in habit but with branches much more stout, 15 cm long ovate fleshy leaves that turn coppery-red in the sun, and stalked clusters of large showy flowers rosy-carmine, or red in saline soil. *Tropical.* *p. 1044, 1056A*

lactea (India, Ceylon), "Dragon bone-tree"; cactus-like plant growing like a candelabra, the branches 3-4-angled, distantly but deeply scalloped and black-spined, dark green with greenish-white band down the center. Used in India medicinally, as a hot jam, for rheumatism. *Tropical.* *p 1020, 1026*

lactea 'Cristata', "Elkhorn"; an intricately monstrose form with fanshaped crested branches forming a snaky ridge or crowded cluster, attractively green marked silver-gray. *Tropical.* *p.19*, 1023, 1034, 1056A, 2092*

lathyrus (Tithymalus) (So. Europe), "Mole-plant"; annual or biennial to 1 m with blue-glaucous stiff erect branches, densely leafy when young, in two opposite ranks as in a cross, long linear leaves 8-10 cm long, the floral ones ovate; small flowers subtended by large green bracts. *p. 1050*

ledienii (Cape Prov.); sparry branching plant to 2 m high with slender, glossy fresh grass-green leafless branches 3-7-angled and prominently notched, the teeth set with needle-like dark brown spines. *p. 1028, 1058*

lemaireana (Zanzibar); unusual, strong succulent shrub to 5 m high, with branches constricted into joints with elongated 8 cm angled wings glaucous green with light green feathering, and irregular brown corky margins set with stiff spines. This could be the same as angularis. *p. 1022*

leucocephala, "Flor de Niño"; attractive shrub 2-3 m high, often seen from the West Indies to So. Mexico, Guatemala and Costa Rica, with pinkish stems bearing narrow oblanceolate, channeled leaves and a profusion of small yellow flowers literally obscured by masses of small, obovate white bracts 2-4 cm long. *Tropical.* *p. 1058*

leuconeura (fournieri) (Madagascar); similar to E. lophogona in appearance but differing in having sessile white flowers not stalked, without showy bracts; self-pollinating; with 4-5-angled club-like stem, and red-brown ridges sliced into hair-like fringes serving as modified spines, the rich-green, fleshy, ribbed leaves oblanceolate 12-15 cm long, petioles and midrib ruby-red underneath. *p. 1028, 1045*

lignosa (Namibia); curious succulent shrub to 50 cm high, with thick basal trunk, numerous twisted branches 1 cm thick, whitish gray to green, the tips spiny. *p. 1058*

lophantha hort.; branching succulent with angled stems set with small spines and leaf scars; the fleshy oblong leaves concave with sides turned up, glossy green and recurving; terminal clusters of reddish flower bracts. Photo taken by T. Everett of New York Bot. Garden. *p. 1057*

lophogona (Madagascar); branching shrub with clubshaped branches, angled with the ridges reddish and fuzzy-hairy, spatulate leaves with pale veins, stalked inflorescence with bracts light pink. *Tropical.* *p. 1049*

loricata (Cape Prov.); spiny, branching shrub to 1 m with fleshy cylindric branches, somewhat spirally tuberculate and with well developed leaves. *p. 1049*

mahafalensis (S.W. Madagascar); small tree with gray branches and pinkish spines; narrow green leaves 2-5 cm long; the flowers with yellow-green bracts, deep yellow in center. *p. 1057*

mammillaris (Cape Prov.); popularly known as the "Corncob cactus"; erect olive green cylindrical column to 4½ cm thick, 8-17 angled, the angles tubercled, looking like a corncob, occasionally set with 1 cm buff needle spines, and club-like lateral branches. *p. 1024, 1046*

mammillaris 'Variegata', "Indian corn cob"; a beautiful cultivar which I photographed in California at Los Angeles Plant Company, Vista; the notched columns are largely greenish-white marked fresh-green and tinted pink, with buff spines. The green species is from So. Africa. *p. 1024, 1056A*

'Manda's Cowhorn' (pseudocactus x grandicornis); a fasciated hybrid with deformed growths in a series of ascending fan-like crests, the largest and uppermost with long extended spine-tipped, horn-like tubercles, bright green with brown edging. *p. 1024*

'Manda's Zigzag' (grandicornis x pseudocactus) x pseudocactus, "Zigzag cactus"; erect 3-angled column growing more or less upright in zigzag fashion 3 cm thick, dark green prettily painted nile-green in herringbone pattern, the undulate edges corky gray-brown and set with pairs of sharp spines. *p. 1033*

marginata (variegata) (Plains of Minnesota, Dakota to Texas), "Snow-on-the-mountain" or "Ghost-weed"; hardy pubescent annual to 60 cm high; numerous branches with glaucous gray-green ovate to oval soft-fleshy leaves, 3-8 cm long with milky sap, the upper ones white-margined; inflorescence in umbels with showy bract-leaves 6-8 cm long, and having a striking, broad white border, and small white flowers in September; long lasting. *Warm temperate.* *p. 1039*

marlothii (Cape Prov.); dainty succulent with oval stem and slender spreading branches 40 cm long, warty and thornless but with thorn-like flower stalks. *p. 1046*

mauritanica (So. Africa); much branched spineless shrub to 1 m, with cylindrical green branches, and small, deciduous needle-like leaves. *p. 1028, 1036*

mauritanica cristata, interesting form with stem fasciated as a spread-out flat fan, dull grayish green, with tiny leaves attached along apex, and on occasional normal, pencil like stem. *p. 1023, 1059*

meloformis (So. Africa); low globe, to 15 cm dia., sometimes suckering from base, 8-10 deep ribs and recessed top, grayish green or grass green, transversely striped light green or red. *p. 1030, 1046*

milii (splendens) (W. Madagascar), "Crown of thorns"; xerophytic spiny shrub with slender scandent woody stems to 2 m long, the spreading branches about 1 cm dia., grooved and armed with spines; obovate 4 cm leaves dull green, deciduous,and soon falling if disturbed or too dry; flower bracts soft salmon-red with pale center. May be trained against trellis or wire frame; very cheerful when in bloom at Easter time; good house plant for warm location. From stem cuttings. *Tropical.* *p. 1049, 2092*

milii bojeri (W. Madagascar), "Dwarf crown of thorns"; bushy gray-spined plant with upright gray stem, freely branching, small persistent dark green leaves, and terminal clusters of large cardinal red rounded bracts. (*) *p. 1026, 1044, 1049*

milii breonii (Madagascar); fleshy, spiny shrub with stout circular, shallowly ribbed, thorny branches about 3 cm thick; bronzy, lanceolate leaves 10-15 cm long in terminal rosettes; the cup-flowers brilliant crimson-red. *Tropical.* *p. 1036, 1043*

milii hislopii (Madagascar); branching shrub with stout gray stem, furnished with heavy brown spines, later gray, the satiny bright green leaves are long and thin, the saucer-type bracts are large and soft salmon red with pale center. *Tropical.* *p. 1044, 1049*

milii var. imperatae (Madagascar), "Mini-Christ-thorn"; small, very bushy shrub to 50 cm high, with slender woody, brown stems not swollen at the base, the spines rather distant; leathery roundish or obovate leaves 1-2 cm long; the flower bracts red or yellow. *Tropical.* *p. 1043*

milii 'Koeniger's Aalbäumle'; a miniature Christ-thorn, grown in Europe as 'Aalbaumle', in Florida as 'Mini'; charming dwarf self-branching plant when grown in a 6 or 8 cm pot, from seed, 15 cm high, with rich green obovate leathery leaves, and fiery-red 1 cm bract-flowers; an ideal window-sill plant. According to J. Marnier-Lapostolle, this may be a seedling of E. milii var. imperatae. *p. 1043*

milii x lophogona; a Hummel hybrid taller and more stout than milii (splendens), with thick, erect stem and pale beige thorns, long and firm oblanceolate leaves; large and showy carmine-red, rounded bracts on glutinous stalks. *p. 1043*

milii lutea (Madagascar); robust plant with gray-brown stout stem with numerous tan spines, long fleshy leaves bluish-gray; banks of small cone-shaped lemon-yellow bracts edged red. *p. 1044*

milii prostrata, the type known in cultivation as "Crown of thorns"; xerophytic shrub with slender scandent stems to 1 m long and armed with spines; the leaves are dull green and soon falling if disturbed; flower bracts soft salmon-red with pale center. *p. 1044*

milii var. tananarivae (alba) (Madagascar); the sensational white-blooming Christ-thorn; similar in character to var. hislopii, spiny stem 2-3 cm thick, with few branches; narrow leaves 7-10 cm long, rounded at the tip; the inflorescence with stalked flower-like bracts creamy-white to pale yellow, edged in red. *p. 1043*

milii typica (W. Madagascar); the true collected species from Imerina province; stiff brown, grooved stem with tan spines, leaves gray green and long obovate; the inflorescence in banks of small, coneshaped rosy-red bracts. *p. 1044*

monteiroi (Angola to So. Africa); interesting plant with thickened tuberculated trunk from which arise the long flowering stems with narrow leaves, and tipped in summer by a pair of pointed green bracts spotted with maroon, and a tiny maroon red flower in the center, fringed with yellow hairs. *p. 1046, 1057*

morinii (So. Africa); stout, fleshy columns, 5-6 cm thick irregularly suckering and branching, nice green, with 7-11 acute ribs densely notched into little tubercles, set with occasional red-brown later gray spines. *p. 1022, 1025*

multiceps (Cape Prov.); spiny succulent to 60 cm high; base forming a cone with numerous crowded spreading branches becoming club-shaped above, with spirally arranged tubercles, smooth, deep green to grayish. *p. 1047*

myrsinites (So. Europe); branching succulent with prostrate then ascending yellow stems densely shingled with sessile ovate leaves bluish-glaucous, in whorls or spirals; umbels of yellow flowers. *Subtropic.* *p. 1033*

neglecta (Ethiopia); often called abyssinica, large succulent leafless tree with erect, 5-8 angled, columnar branches, dark grayish green, the angles wing-like and 5-8 cm deep, and with pairs of short spines on young growth. *p. 1031*

neohumbertii (Madagascar); small succulent column with 5 angles, densely set with thin brown spines, the fleshy moss-green obovate leaves 15-25 cm long, in a rosette on top; small dark reddish cupped flower bracts. *Arid-tropical.* *p. 1057*

neriifolia (South India), the "Oleander-leaved euphorbia"; succulent tree with branches in whorls, the stems weak, 5-angled and light green, later cylindric and gray and with weak spines, leathery-fleshy obovate light green glossy leaves to 12 cm long, deciduous in autumn; brick red flowers in the axils. *p. 1046*

neriifolia cristata (India: Deccan), "Crested oleander cactus"; monstrose form with dissolved ribs, succulent with normally 5-angled stems, light green, later gray, with short black spines, and obovate fleshy leaves, deciduous. *p. 1023*

neriifolia 'Variegata cristata', "Variegated oleander cactus"; weird fasciation with stems crested fan-like, grass-green with milk-white variegation, fleshy light green obovate leaves and short brown spines. *p. 1027*

nesemanii (Cape Prov.); spiny succulent with tuberous main root forming a cylindrical body branching into 6 to 14-angled, coppery-green columns; the high ridges twisted, and divided into tubercles set with persisting solitary leaf stalks. *p. 1047*

neutra (Brazil); big cactoid, bold fleshy column with 5-6 thick ridges, rich grass green and constricted into long joints, and set with pairs of short buff spines. *p. 1022*

nivulia (undulatifolia in hort.) (India); tree-like, with thick, fleshy 5-ribbed branches, the ribs with small black-brown spine-pairs; large fleshy green foliage to 18 cm long, with thin, wavy margins in older leaves; showy flowers (cyathia) brick-red. *p. 1048*

obesa (So. Africa), "Baseball plant"; beautiful small globes to 12 cm, in male and female plants, gray-green marked with reddish length and cross stripes, and rows of small knobs along ridges. *Subtropic.* *p. 1030*

obovallifolia (Ethiopia, Somalia, Kenya, Tanzania); tree with branching trunk, the green branches with 3, 4 and 5 wing-like angles which are undulate and wavy and irregularly constricted into segments, and set with small teeth; long 12 cm obovate leaves deciduous. *p. 1036*

ornithopus (Cape Province); unusual succulent and spineless little plant to 8 cm high; the turnip-shaped body produces many tuberculate, green finger-like growths, on the end of which are quaint flowers with whorls of white bracts each shaped like a bird's foot. *p. 1046*

pachypodioides (W. Madagascar); columnar succulent looking like a small Pachypodium, with erect stems 30-50 cm high; 4 cm and more thick, very fleshy and spiny, densely covered with old leaf scars arranged in spiralled rows; oblanceolate leaves 10-12 cm long during rains tufted at ends of stems; topped by an inflorescence of red flowers. *p. 1056*

pentagona (Cape Prov.); succulent to 3 m branching in whorls, acutely 5-6-angled, glossy fresh green later gray, pale line down each groove, and with solitary brown spines and yellowish leaf stalks. *p. 1048*

pfersdorffii; tiny branching succulent which is probably a growth-form of E. submammillaris, with smaller, slender, few-angled (5-6) branchlets, fresh green, with tubercles set with small brown soft spines. *p. 1029*

polyacantha (Ethiopia), "Fish bone cactus"; sparry branching plant to 1½ m, with 4-5 angled leafless stems grayish green, horny angles crenately toothed and spiny. *Subtropic.* *p. 1025, 1031*

polychroma (epithymoides) (E. and S.E. Europe); perennial herb 30-45 cm high forming a round bush, lightly hairy branches, with narrow oblong sessile, dark soft-hairy leaves; small flowers in terminal clusters surrounded by yellow-green bract-leaves. *p. 1050, 1052*

polygona (So. Africa); attractive columns to 1 m high, branching from base, dark green, densely and deeply furrowed, the ridges sharp and wavy, set with small spines. *p. 1029*

primulaefolia (Madagascar); from an almost cylindrical, tuber-like short trunk rise the short stems each supporting a rosette of obovate leaves, lying closely appressed and flattened to the ground. *p. 1058*

pseudocactus (Natal), "Yellow euphorbia"; thorny, succulent shrub with sparry branches usually 4-angled, bright green with yellowish fan-shaped markings, angles coarsely toothed. *p. 1031*

pseudocactus x ingens; pretty Manda hybrid with 5-angled stems and 4-angled branches, deep green with lighter green band down the furrows; knobbed irregular ridges gray-corky with short brown spines. *p. 1031*

pteroneura (Mexico); low succulent shrub with jointed branches 1 cm or pencil-thick, 5 to 6 angles, running down from leaf-bases; small 2½-5 cm ovate, deciduous leaves. *p. 1050, 1058*

pugniformis (Cape Prov.); dwarf succulent with brownish hemispherical body 8 cm thick and flat on top, with a crown of spineless rounded branches densely covered by tubercles; tiny deciduous linear leaves. *p. 1047*

pugniformis var. cristata; unusual form with the thick base exploding fan-like into a series of crests, studded with linear fleshy leaves. *p. 1048*

pulcherrima (So. Mexico), "Poinsettia" or "Flor de Noche Buena"; branching shrub to 3 m high, with woody trunk and milky juice, ovate leaves, deciduous when disturbed or resting, the terminal shoots forming dark red-velvet, lanceolate bract leaves, surrounding the tiny yellowish flowers during the short-day period of year. Buds will be initiated about Sept. 21-25 at latitude 40-45 deg. north, provided the night temperature is below 18°C. *Tropical.* *p. 1040*

pulcherrima alba; compact, willowy plant with grayish-green leaves having pale veins; floral bracts creamy-white. *p. 1056A*

pulcherrima 'Annette Hegg' (Norway 1964), "Christmas poinsettia"; durable variety of compact habit; freely branching; wiry stems; ovate leaves long lasting; blooms early; does well at temperate 16°C; develops broad, smooth bracts vivid medium red, even under low winter light intensity. *Tropical.* *p. 1037, 1040*

pulcherrima 'Annette Hegg Supreme'; introduced 1970, a bright red sport of 'Dark Red Hegg', with the most brilliant crimson-red color of the multiflower types, especially under artificial light; the bracts very substantial, and of larger size than 'Annette Hegg', forming stars with close-in center, according to my measuring in our green houses, of 40 cm across at Christmas time. *Tropical.* *p. 1037*

pulcherrima 'Barbara Ecke Supreme' (Ruth Ecke sport 1945); a tetraploid of superior quality, with the heavy stems of 'Mrs. Paul Ecke' but more freely branching, good fleshy, rich green leaves and broad flexible bracts of brighter, cardinal red to 40 cm. *p. 11*, 1039, 1041, 1042, 1056A*

pulcherrima 'Barbara Ecke Supreme x Indianapolis' (1958); sturdy Roehrs hybrid with flat wide bracts of 'Indianapolis'. *p. 1040*

pulcherrima 'Dark Red Hegg'; stronger grower than 'Annette Hegg', and of a deeper shading, dark cerise red; in culture requires little feeding to long remain in good condition which should be until Easter with good light. *p. 1038*

pulcherrima 'Ecke Pink': see under pulch. 'Rosea'

pulcherrima 'Eckespoint' (Paul Ecke 1967); strain of striking diploid hybrids of medium height, characterized by stocky growth, strong self-supporting stems, vigorous oakleaf foliage and a close-in circle of lush bracts lightly crinkled. The variety 'C-1 Red' has bracts intense scarlet-red with rosy sheen, and is ideal for Christmas bloom. Needs some warmth, feeding, and attention to moisture to best hold foliage. *Tropical.* *p. 1038, 1040*

pulcherrima 'Ecke's White' (E. pulch. alba cultivar), a "White poinsettia"; shapely, freely branching and late flowering seedling with bright green, ovate leaves, the flexible, wiry stems producing perfect close disks of creamy-white, membranous bracts; if kept cool, will hold both leaves and bracts from Christmas to Easter. *Tropical.* *p. 1041*

pulcherrima 'Elizabeth Ecke'; a very attractive sport of 'Barbara Ecke Supreme' introduced 1960, of shorter more compact growth habit and with wider bracts bright scarlet red, of heavy texture and good keeping quality. *p. 1038*

pulcherrima 'Henrietta Ecke', "Double poinsettia"; sported in 1927 in Hollywood, blooming early December, and with broader vermilion horizontal bracts and "double" crown. *Tropical.* *p. 1040, 1044*

pulcherrima 'Indianapolis Red' (1936); sport of 'Mrs. Paul Ecke', a very fine short, slower growing, symmetrical tetraploid, with shorter joints on robust stems and firm dark green, lobed rather persistent leaves, the wide and flat bracts intense scarlet red. *p. 1040*

pulcherrima 'Mikkel-Flare'; a variation 1970 with long-lasting foliage and bright red bracts somewhat shingled and undulate or ruffled at the margins. *p. 1038*

pulcherrima 'Mikkelpink'; a very excellent and lovely sport with clear rose-pink bracts, in a star 30 cm across. *p. 1038*

pulcherrima 'Mrs. Paul Ecke', a sport of 'Oakleaf' (1926); with shorter and heavier stems, not as freely branching, thicker leaves and wider fleshier bracts of blood red, brighter than 'Oakleaf'. *Tropical.* *p. 1042*

pulcherrima 'Oakleaf' (1918 seedling); vigorous growing tall and slender, freely branching seedling with oakleaf-type lobed leaves and somewhat long, narrow, stalked bracts of darkish red. *p. 1042, 1044*

pulcherrima 'Paul Mikkelsen' (1962); a Poinsettia seedling of 'Barbara Ecke Supreme' and 'Ecke's White'; a happy break-through in pot-grown poinsettias for Christmas; compact plant with strong root system, and sturdy, close-jointed, wiry stems leafy with smallish, durable foliage, and topped by an inflorescence with a circle of sturdy bright crimson bracts spreading 20 cm and up to 30 cm across from tip to tip; the small greenish flowers in center of the star. Keeping exceedingly well under adverse, even chilly conditions, and long holding its foliage. *p. 1037*

pulcherrima plenissima, "Double poinsettia"; wild in Mexico; large shrub with flexible branches and grayish-green leaves producing a striking inflorescence composed of a circle of vermilion red lanceolate bracts, as well as a bushy central head of smaller bracts, transformed from flowers; normally blooms in late winter. Needs high intensity tropical sun for best double crown. *Tropical.* *p. 1038, 1041*

pulcherrima plenissima 'Ecke's Flaming Sphere' (pat. 1951); a mutation of the double-bracted Poinsettia; very ornamental and different in having all the blood-red bracts ruffly and in a ball-like cluster with no horizontal bract-leaves; slow, sturdy growth. *Tropical.* *p. 1041*

pulcherrima 'Rosea', "Pink poinsettia"; sparry plant with pale green ovate leaves, green petioles and veins, and full, but smallish heads of fleshy, obovate bracts of delicate rose, with darker veining; flowering early. The cultivar 'St. Louis' is a sport of the pink poinsettia. 'Ecke Pink' is a clone of 'Rosea'. *Arid-tropical.* *p. 1041*

pulcherrima 'Ruth Ecke' ('Denmark') (1935); a dwarf, compact, freely branching sport of 'Oakleaf' originated in Denmark, with small leaves and smaller deep red bracts; similar to 'Oakleaf'. *p. 1040*

pulcherrima 'St. Louis'; an early selection about 1920 of the species pulcherrima and cultivated by Paul Ecke in Hollywood as 'Red Sport'; later in 1924 named 'St. Louis' by Louis Bourdet of Missouri, holding its foliage somewhat better than the imported species, and of a brighter crimson, with bracts elliptic or obovate with rather open center in the star; popular for its vigor in cultivation outdoors in gardens of the South. *p. 1038*

pulcherrima fol. variegata, the "Variegated-leaf poinsettia"; interesting variety with delicate, pale gray-green, lobed leaves variegated white along margins, flowering bracts carmine red. *Tropical.* *p. 1041*

pulvinata (So. Africa), "Cushion euphorbia"; low, clustering succulent with many even branches 5 cm or more high, mostly 7-ribbed and lightly notched, dark green, and set with numerous short wine-red, spine-like peduncles. *Subtropic.* *p. 1029, 1032*

punicea (West Indies: Jamaica, Cuba, Bahamas); tree-like to 9 m high, the branches with leaf-scars and with obovate, sharp-pointed leaves toward the ends, glaucous beneath; terminal clusters of flowers subtended by bright crimson-red bract-leaves 8 cm long. *Tropical.* *p. 1047, 1057*

quadrialata (Tanzania); symmetrical tree with straight, angled maintrunk, branching laterally more or less in whorls like a Christmas tree; the green branches 3-angled. *Tropical.* *p. 1034*

ramipressa (alcicornis hort.) (Madagascar); leafless succulent shrub to 3 m high, fleshy stems obscurely 5-angled, the narrow green branches flat and straplike, and scalloped at the margins. *p. 1027*

resinifera (Morocco); much-branched shrub with 4-angled erect stems, light gray green, the ridges slightly toothed; tiny brownish leaves. *p. 1029*

robecchii (Kenya); large tree looking like telegraph poles, as seen on the steppe in Tsavo National Park, in candelabra shape to 14 m high, the horizontal branches in distinct groups, 3-angled and twisted, 3 cm or more thick; leaves scale-like, the spines in pairs. *Arid-tropical.* *p. 1059*

roylena (India); stout columnar succulent, with age becoming arborescent 6 to 8 m high, with trunk 40-50 cm thick; the branches 5-angled 5-7 cm dia., fresh green; the ribs notched and slightly sinuate, and set with pairs of spines; thick-fleshy, obovate leaves deciduous. *p. 1056*

schimperi (So. Arabia: Aden); succulent bush to 2 m high, with numerous cylindric plain green pencil-like branches, with distant tiny, deciduous leaves but no spines; branched inflorescence at the end of tips. *p. 1046, 1050*

splendens: see milii

squarrosa (Cape Prov.); dwarf succulent with decumbent flat deep green branches, sometimes 3-5-angled 15 cm long, hugging the ground, the ridges toothed and set with pairs of short reddish spines. *p. 1029*

stellaespina (Cape Prov.); erect cylindrical cones 5-8 cm thick, branching at base and forming clumps, with 10-16 ribs notched into tubercles, sooty green; toward top with persisting petiole remnants set with triple spines; tiny deciduous leaves. *p. 1047*

stenoclada (Madagascar), "Silver thicket"; beautiful leafless but forbidding shrub 2 m or more high, densely bushy and flattened silvery gray limbs forking into vicious long-pointed spikes and thorns. *Tropical.* *p. 1033*

submammillaris (Cape Prov.); low clustering, spiny succulent, dense with short 5-8 angled cylindrical branches, the acute ridges toothed and set with 2½ cm long solitary spines and numerous thorn-like flowering stems shading from red to brown. *p. 1024*

susannae (Cape Prov.); small plant seemingly tufted but actually with a group of subterranean stems whose succulent bluish-green, club-like tops 2½-4 cm thick show above; toothed ridges with 8-16 rows of knobs, with small deciduous bristles. *p. 1029, 1030*

symmetrica (Cape Prov.); spineless dwarf succulent, a spherical globe similar to obesa but wider, mostly 6 cm high, usually with 8 broad ribs, gray green with transverse purple bands and narrow grooves across, tiny warts toward apex, and branched stalks with tiny flowers. *p. 1045*

tenuirama (Red Sea area); erect succulent shrub with 3-5 angled gently notched stems and branches, to 5 cm thick, grayish green with cross-marbling and bands of milky green, thin brown needle spines. *p. 1031*

tetragona (So. Africa); free growing thorny tree to 13 m high, trunk 6-7 angled, with numerous slender rich green branches usually 4-angled, nicely arranged in whorls. *p. 1031*

tirucalli (Uganda, Zaire, Zanzibar), "Milk bush"; forming tree to 10 m high, branches cylindrical and pencil-thick, glossy green and bursting with poisonous milk; narrow deciduous leaves. *Tropical.* *p. 1026, 1036, 1051*

triangularis (So. Africa); thorny, succulent tree to 15 m high, trunk 6-angled later round; sparry curving, slender branches 2-5 angled and notched, fresh-green to olive, the tubercles with short pairs of spines and tiny leaves. *p. 1028*

tridentata (Cape Prov.); succulent and spineless little plant, branches from the base to 15 cm long, cylindrical or tapering, with angled tubercles, tiny 6 mm leaves, soon falling; peduncles tipped with bracts at end of branches. *p. 1046*

trigona ("hermentiana") (Trop. West Africa: Gabon), "African milk tree"; attractive candelabra-form succulent usually winglike 3-angled, rich green and marbled pale green to white, ridges closely crenate and with deciduous, obovate leaves. (*S1) *p. 1020, 1026, 1056*

tuberculata (Cape Prov.); stout basal stem mostly buried in ground, producing from apex many leaning spineless branches, these circular, green and thickened to 4 cm toward tip, dense with pointed tubercles in spirals; linear 4 cm leaves deciduous, and with reddish margins. *p. 1032*

tuberosa (W. Cape Prov.); perennial, fleshy herb with large tuberous root, and short basal stem set with rosettes of concave-folded or undulate lanceolate, soft-leathery grayish 5 cm leaves; forming large globular capsules at first reddish, then greenish-gray. *Subtropic.* *p. 1032*

undulatifolia (India); similar to nivulia and neriifolia; stout stem more or less 5-angled with deep notches along the ribs, light green with gray markings, and short black spines; the large succulent, obovate leaves 6-10 cm long, crisped or undulate at margins; brown-red flowers (cyathia). *p. 1056*

valida (Cape Prov.); low hemispheric plant when young becoming more cylindric 12 cm thick and 30 cm high with 8 ribs; clustering; similar to meloformis but without beet-root; coppery green with light green transverse lines; numerous flowering stalks becoming woody, spine-like. *p. 1030*

vigueri (W. Madagascar); succulent shrub 30 cm to more than 1 m high, the dark green stem thickened and 2-3 cm dia., with 6 angles, set with light brown spines; large obovate leaves tufted at apex of branches 8-10 cm long, emerald green with whitish midrib, the petiole red; bract flowers scarlet. *Arid-tropical.* *p. 1057*

virosa (So. Africa); spiny succulent shrub to 2 m in clusters of heavy 4-5 angled branches constricted into joints, gray-green and hard, with horny gray ridges. *p. 1022, 1028*

x white-sloaniana (grandis x ingens); beautiful branching hybrid of robust habit with 3-4 high ridges, glaucous grayish green with elevated vein areas; decorated with brown knobs and short spines. *p. 1020*

woodii (So. Africa: Natal); spineless low succulent with a short obconical, underground stem 12-15 cm thick; sprouting with numerous slender branches arranged in two or more series surrounding a tubercled central area, branches light green, to 20 cm long, 1-2 cm thick, and tubercled with deciduous tiny leaves. *p. 1056*

wulfenii (Dalmatia); attractive hardy subshrub to 1½ m high, forming a clump with stems covered by long narrow 12 cm bluish-green leaves, and large terminal clusters of flowers surrounded by greenish-yellow bracts. *p. 1033, 1045*

xylophylloides (Madagascar); dense shrub with round trunk to 2 m high, green branches more or less in whorls, compressed and flattened or 2-angled and jointed, slightly toothed; minute leaves deciduous. *p. 1033*

EURYA *Theaceae* ***I1LFM**

japonica 'Variegata' (Japan, Korea); very neat evergreen bush of slow growth, the glossy, oblique-elliptic or obovate-pointed, leathery leaves remotely toothed, dark and milky-green, beautifully variegated creamy-white from the margin toward the center, 5 to 8 cm long, decoratively arranged and densely overlapping on willowy, spreading branches and woody stems; an excellent keeper. *Subtropic.* *p. 19*, 2091, 2095, 2101*

EURYALE *Nymphaeaceae* **S3LFW**

ferox (Tropical and Subtropical India to China and Japan); a widespread aquatic perennial with large circular floating bright glossy green leaves 1 to 2 m across, very spiny and with inflated bubbles, and spiny-ribbed beneath; small 5 cm flowers green outside, purplish red within, barely above the water and short-lived; the seeds are edible when roasted. Much at home in rice paddies in the Orient; stunning in the conservatory pool. *Humid-tropical.* *p. 1623*

EURYCHONE *Orchidaceae* **S3OFM**

rothschildiana (Africa: Uganda, Guinea Coast); nearly stemless epiphyte with two or three pairs of large clasping soft-leathery, shining metallic green, obovate leaves forked at apex, 12-15 cm long; clusters of 5 cm fragrant, bell-like flowers, greenish-white sepals and petals, frilled white lip blotched purplish-green in throat, and with a funnel-shaped spur. *p. 1657, 1730, 1733*

EURYCLES *Amaryllidaceae* **S3LBM**

amboinensis (sylvestris) (S.E. Asia, No. Australia); bulbous plant with roundish leaf 20-25 cm across, the blade with depressed parallel veining, connected by thin cross-nerves; amaryllis-like flowers with long tube and spreading lanceolate segments white, on stalk 30-45 cm long. *p. 122*

EURYOPS *Compositae* **I2LBD**

pectinatus (So. Africa), the "Resin bush"; shrubby, free blooming perennial with thick green leaves covered by white pubescence, pinnatifid and cut into narrow segments, strongly scented when bruised; daisy-like flowers with firm, pretty ray flowers sky blue, surrounding a yellow disk, 5 cm across; blooming nearly year-round. *Subtropic.* *p. 806*

EUTERPE *Palmae* **S3LFM**

edulis (Brazil), "Clustering Assai palm" or "Palmito" in the Mato Grosso; slender feather palm with graceful trunk to 30 m high, topped by prominent crown shaft and the crown of arching pinnate fronds 2 to 3 m long, dense with drooping, thin, plaited leaflets, on scaly rachis; small round fruit. Usually forming multistemmed clusters. A most delicate palm, with trunks containing pulp which is eaten in Paraná. *Tropical.* *p. 1871*

globosa (West Indies: Cuba, Puerto Rico, to Grenada), the "Mountain palm" or "Palma de Sierra" as it is known in the Luquillo mountain region of Puerto Rico; handsome palm to 12 m high, with ringed trunk bearing rather few, broad pinnate fronds to 2½ m. *Tropical.* *p. 1866, 1878*

EVODIANTHUS *Cyclanthaceae* **S3LFM**

funifer (Costa Rica to Brazil and Perú); palm-like climber hugging the tree, to 15 m high, with forked leaf-blade, 30-70 cm long, the two main divisions sometimes forked again, prominent parallel veining, on long 15 to 40 cm petioles. *p. 945*

EXACUM *Gentianaceae* **S3HFM**

affine (Socotra Is.), "Persian violet" or "Mexican violet"; bushy little herbaceous, free-flowering biennial with waxy, stalked, ovate leaves and tiny, wide open, bluish-lilac, star-like, fragrant flowers 1 cm across, with pretty eye of deep yellow stamen. *Tropical.* *p. 1168, 1170*

macranthum (Sri Lanka); showy biennial 30 to 50 cm high, the 4-angled branches with opposite small ovate, glossy green leaves, and terminal clusters of wide-open deep blue-purple flowers 5-6 cm across, with yellow at base of petals and yellow anthers. *p. 1168*

zeylanicum (Sri Lanka); tropical herbaceous plant grown as annual or biennial, 30 to 50 cm high, with 4-angled branches; ovate, slender-pointed 8 cm leaves; flowers a beautiful violet with obovate petals, 4 cm across. Photographed by J. Bogner, Munich Botanic Garden. *p. 1168*

EXCOECARIA *Euphorbiaceae* **S3LBM**

bicolor (Vietnam), "Picara"; smooth shrub with milky sap used as fish poison; shiny green, leathery leaves 12 cm long, and red beneath; small flowers in narrow spikes. *Tropical.* *p. 1004*

FAGUS *Fagaceae* **C-I2LBD**

sylvatica pendula (Europe to Caucasus), the "Weeping beech" or "European beech"; great ornamental deciduous tree to 30 or 40 m high, with smooth gray trunks and wide-spreading limbs, often horizontal, and pendulous branches with lustrous green, ovate leaves remotely toothed, 8-12 cm long, turning reddish in autumn; the female flowers producing triangular nuts with sharp edges, enclosed in a 4-lobed spiny husk. *p. 1062*

FARFUGIUM: see LIGULARIA

FASCICULARIA *Bromeliaceae* **I1HBD**

bicolor (Chile); dense rosette of stiff, gray-green spiny leaves turning red in center at blooming time; flowers pale blue. *p. 572*

pitcairniifolia (Chile); large clustering terrestrial rosettes of narrow, linear, spiny leaves light green above, gray underneath, 60 cm to 1 m long and 2 cm wide; the inflorescence deeply immersed in the center of the leaves, a dense cluster of blue-petaled flowers 4 cm long, the surrounding leaves turning red at blooming time. *p. 552, 559*

x FATSHEDERA *Araliaceae* **C-I2LBM**

lizei, "Ivy tree", "Miracle plant" or "Botanical wonder"; bigeneric hybrid between Fatsia japonica 'Moseri' and Hedera helix hibernica, the "Irish ivy". Evergreen shrub combining characters of both parents, growing erect over 2 m high if the woody stem has support; leathery leaves 5-lobed, similar to English ivy but larger, often 12-20 cm wide, dark lustrous green. Small light green flowers in dense clusters. *p. 307, 313, 317, 328*

lizei 'Variegata', "Variegated pagoda tree"; horticultural form with the fresh green leaves prettily variegated and edged cream-white. Prefers moist-temperate climate. *Subtropic.* *p. 307, 320A*

FATSIA *Araliaceae* ***C2LFM**

japonica (Aralia sieboldii) (Japan), "Japanese aralia"; evergreen shrub with leathery, palmately lobed leaves dark, shining green, the broad lobes pointed and toothed; tiny stamen flowers milky white, in terminal panicles. *Subtropic.* *p. 307, 313, 320, 323*

japonica 'Marginata'; grown by Oakhurst Gardens in California, a cultivar with large deeply lobed leaves grayish or milky green prettily edged in ivory-white. *p. 304*

japonica 'Moseri'; a robust French seedling of lower, more compact habit, and with more and larger, rich glossy green, deeply lobed, crenate leaves having yellow veins; pubescent beneath and on stem, turning woody. *Subtropic.* *p. 307, 320*

japonica variegata; a mutant having the palmately lobed, medium green leaves more or less edged or variegated cream-white, especially the leaf tips. *p. 307*

FAUCARIA *Aizoaceae* ***I2LBD**

acutipetala (Cape Prov.); small succulent with triangular leaves 4 cm long; 3-5 conical, bristle-tipped teeth at margins; large golden-yellow flowers. *p. 66*

albidens (Cape Prov.); thick-fleshy succulent rosette with 5-6 pairs of fresh green leaves 3 cm long, triangularly tapering, back surface boat-shaped, the edges with whitish teeth; 3-4 cm flowers golden yellow. *p. 60*

bosscheana (Cape Prov.); succulent with canoe-shaped leaves 3 cm long, shining green, the margins horny-white and dentate; flowers bright yellow. *p. 66*

duncanii (Cape Prov.); succulent with crowded, boat-shaped leaves 2½ cm long, gradually tapering; top flat, bottom keeled especially toward apex, green dotted red at apex, edges with recurved teeth. *p. 66*

felina (So. Africa: Karroo); attractive rather smooth succulent with grayish-green, keeled leaves covered with milk-gray dots, the edges with down-curved papery pink teeth; flowers yellow to orange. *p. 67*

longifolia (Cape Prov.); clustering succulent, with boat-shaped leaves 5 cm long, flat on top, with teeth at margins; flowers yellow. *p. 66*

speciosa (Cape Province), a "Tiger-jaw"; with keeled leaves having 5-6 teeth at margins, and 6 cm golden-yellow flowers, pale in center purple at edge. *p. 67*

tigrina (So. Africa: Cape Prov.), "Tiger jaws"; ferocious-looking small succulent with opposite, thick, keeled or boat-shaped, gray-green leaves 3-5 cm long, and marked with numerous white dots; margins armed with stout recurved teeth so that the leaf-pairs resemble a gaping jaw. Large golden yellow sessile flowers. *Arid-subtropic.* *p. 64A, 67, 2092*

tuberculosa (So. Africa: Cape Prov.), "Pebbled tiger jaws"; striking little succulent with wide-open jaws of dark green thick leaves about 2 cm long, upper side covered with white tubercles, the edges armed with stout teeth, underside keeled; 4 cm flowers yellow, opening in the afternoon. *Arid-subtropic.* *p. 63, 67*

FAUREA *Proteaceae* **S3LBD**

saligna (Transvaal), "Red Boekenhout"; tree 6-8 m high, with long narrow leaves; inflorescence like pale, pinkish-mauve, silky tassels 10 cm long, with scent of honey; a protected tree in South Africa. *p. 1974*

FEIJOA *Myrtaceae* **I2LBD**

sellowiana (So. Brazil, Paraguay, Uruguay, No. Argentina), "Pineapple guava"; small tree to 5 m high, dense with whitish-felted branches and small thick 6 cm oval, opposite leaves waxy dark green above and lightly rugose, midrib white, white to brown-tomentose beneath; flowers with fleshy petals white tomentose outside, purplish inside, and dark red stamen; green edible fruit tinged red, with pineapple-like flavor. *Subtropic.* *p. 1608, 1612, 1614*

FELICIA *Compositae* **I2LBM**

amelloides (Agathea coelestis) (So. Africa), "Blue daisy"; shrubby herb with opposite, obovate leaves and daisy-like flowers with sky-blue florets and yellow disk, on long stalks. *p. 813*

amelloides 'Astrid Thomas' (Agathea coelestis), a "Blue marguerite" of compact habit, a charming mutation of the So. African species, in the California nursery trade, with fresh green, thick leaves; the flowers with firm, broad ray florets a pretty sky-blue, surrounding the yellow center cushion. *Subtropic.* *p. 806*

amelloides 'Variegata', variegated-leaved "Blue daisy"; low spreading, shrubby plant with small green leaves prettily bordered with white; flowers sky blue with yellow center; an attractive ground cover in climates such as California. *Subtropic.* *p. 806*

echinata (So. Africa), "Prickly felicia"; small shrubby plant to 45 cm high, with erect branches, densely clothed by shingled little, 2 cm dark green leaves with sharp point; toward apex the clustered inflorescence of 3 cm flower heads bluish-mauve and yellow centers. *p. 806*

FENESTRARIA *Aizoaceae* **S2LBD**

aurantiaca (Cape Province), "Window plant"; clustering succulent with club-like gray-green glaucous leaves 6 cm tall, the pearly flat top whitish and with translucent windows; flowers golden yellow. *Arid-subtropic.* *p. 64A, 67*

podophyllum (So. Africa); attractive succulent clusters of tiny light gray, fleshy club-shaped bodies, having shiny translucent window on top; large white flowers with golden eye. The windows are like skylights, admitting the sunlight to filter down to reach the chlorophyll, especially when the plants are half-buried to their tops in sand or soil to escape the burning heat. *p. 60*

rhopalophylla (S.W. Africa), "Baby toes"; tufts of cylindrical, succulent leaves thicker above and bearing a translucent "window" at top; flowers white; wants dry, in sandy soil with lots of lime. *Arid-subtropic.* *p. 67, 2092*

FERNS: see FILICES in Pictorial Section

FERNSEEA *Bromeliaceae* **I2HFD**

itatiaiae (Brazil); epiphytic rosette of linear leaves; erect stem bearing loose heads of sessile, feathered flowers with red bracts and sepals and dark red petals. *p. 550*

x FEROBERGIA *Cactaceae* **S2LFD**

'Gil Tegelberg' (Leuchtenbergia principis x Ferocactus acanthodes); extraordinary bigeneric hybrid created by Gil Tegelberg, Lucerne Valley, California. Small elongate ribbed globe, the ribs strongly divided into pointed tubercles 10-12 cm long, without pronounced angles, dull green variegated with ivory-white, the tips with long radiating papery spines. *p. 703*

FEROCACTUS *Cactaceae* **I2LBD**

acanthodes (S. Nevada, California, Baja California), "Fire barrel"; globular plant glaucous green, becoming cylindric to 3 m tall, very spiny, ribs up to 27, the 12 cm long curving awl-shaped spines pinkish to red; flowers yellow to orange. *Arid-subtropic.* *p. 689, 695*

covillei (Mexico); globular to barrel type to 1½ m, dull green, 22-32 ribs, strong spines variable in color, red to white; flowers red, tipped yellow. *Arid-tropical.* *p. 689*

echidne (Mexico: Hidalgo); globular barrel to 25 cm high, sprouting around the base; pale green to grayish, with about 14 acute ribs, areoles with grayish wool, spines yellow to gray; flowers yellow. *p. 690*

latispinus (Mexico), "Fish-hook barrel"; depressed globe to 40 cm high, dull grayish-green, with many dented folds, the central spines very broad, curving and crimson-red; bellshaped flowers, 4 cm long, rose to purple. *Arid-tropical.* *p. 689*

melocactiformis (hystrix) (Mexico); globular, to 60 cm dia., bluish green, closely wavy-ribbed, curved spines yellow becoming brown; flowers bright yellow. *p. 702*

nobilis (Mexico); gray-green globe to 25 cm high with 10-14 notched ribs set with prominent, strong, flattened red-brown fishhook spines; flowers pink. *p. 689*

peninsulae (So. Baja California); globular when young becoming cylindric to 2½ m high; dark glaucous green, with 12-30 thick, notched ribs, the spines red, tipped yellow, one long central spine hooked at tip; flowers yellow. *p. 689*

pringlei (C. Mexico); one of the largest species; stem at first a bold globe, waxy olive green with 16-18 acute ribs somewhat irregular and notched, set with cluster of hard and sharp, curving red spines; growing into cylinders 3 m high, with yellow flowers red outside. *p. 689*

rectispinus (Baja California); knobby gray-green globe when young, becoming very large and cylindrical to 2 m high; 13-24 notched ribs, the knobs with woolly tufts and sets of strong spines, red at apex; flowers yellow. *p. 690*

robustus (Mexico: Puebla); globular plant to 20 cm thick, forming large clumps; with 8 thick ribs, dark glossy green, set with yellow radials and awl-like central spines; flowers yellow. *p. 689*

stainesii (E. pilosus) (Mexico); seedlings globose, later columns to 1½ m high, knobbed later ribbed, radial spines reduced to long white hairs, central spines purple fading yellow; flowers yellow. *p. 694*

wislizenii (Sonora, Texas, Arizona); robust globe when young, becoming cylindric to 2½ m high, matte grayish-green with 13-25 thick, notched ribs with woolly tufts and clusters of thin but hard curving spines crimson to gray; flowers yellow. *p. 689*

FERRARIA *Iridaceae* **I2LBMd**

undulata (So. Africa: S.W. Cape), "Spider flower" or "Orchid-iris"; cormous herb to 40 cm high, allied to Tigridia, with stiff flat bluish green leaves passing into ovate bracts; the branched leafy zigzag stalk bearing fascinating, curious, fragrant flowers 4-5 cm across, the 6 broad petals with crisped margins appearing orchid-like, basically green and cream but edged and spotted velvety brown, and with orange pollen; opening only for one day in spring; dormant late summer. *p. 1324, 1339*

FESTUCA *Gramineae* **I2LBD**

ovina glauca (No. Temp. Europe and Asia), "Blue fescue"; low tufted ornamental grass with thread-like, linear leaves rolled inward or circular, 15-20 cm long, silvery-blue-glaucous and almost wiry-stiff. *p. 1310*

FICUS *Moraceae* ***S1-2LFM**

afzelii (eriobotryoides) (Ghana, Nigeria, Zaire, Mozambique); large tree with foliage at ends of branches; stems bronzy with light brown hairs, closely-set long-oblanceolate leaves 40 cm long and 12 cm wide, dark olive green and smooth above, brown tomentose beneath; limply soft when young, stiff-leathery when mature. *p. 1574*

altissima (Assam to Malaya and Philippines), the "Lofty fig" or "Council tree"; magnificent banyan-tree with silvery gray bark and branches spreading to 20 m wide, dense with leathery, smooth oval or ovate leaves 10 to 20 cm long, and veins ivory to reddish; profuse with attractive axillary 2 cm fruit varying from yellow-orange to scarlet red. Widely planted in tropical North America as a shade tree, a marvel of beauty with its striking red fruit on slender branchlets. *Tropical.* *p. 1564*

aspera (parcellii) (South Pacific Islands), "Clown fig"; small shrub with sparry branches bearing large oblong, slender pointed leaves to 20 cm long, toothed, rough hairy, grass-green and milky-green, wildly variegated and marbled ivory white; even the pear-like fruits are variegated white. *Tropical.* *p. 1563, 1573, 2112A*

aurea (So. Florida), "Strangler fig"; epiphytic at first, growing into a tree 20 m high, leaves oblong, to 10 cm, and narrowed at both ends, but round-tipped, leathery, green, on buff branches; fruits orange. *p. 1573, 1585*

auriculata (roxburghii) (India), "Ornamental fig"; low, spreading tree to 6 m high, very showy for its large foliage on slender woody branches, the light brown petioles covered with white hairs; big papery, rounded and toothed, slightly glossy leaves to 40 cm long, their surface covered with a fine pubescence, and with depressed veins; when young an attractive mahogany-red. Big flat-globose figs are borne on the stems. Not a house plant as foliage easily catches red spider and drops. *Tropical.* *p. 1576*

australis: see rubiginosa

baileyana (macrophylla pubescens) (No. New South Wales, Queensland), the "Black fig"; often starting as an epiphyte; giant tree to 70 m high, with an enormous spread of roots and occasional aerial roots; younger growth pubescent; the leathery, long-elliptic, green leaves 10 to 22 cm long, reddish scurfy beneath, midvein almost white; small axillary oblong 2 cm fruits; food for cattle in Australia. Trees are partially deciduous leaving a litter of fallen leaves. *p. 1586*

battieri (Central America); small tree with branches having typically short-spaced internodes, narrow linear-lanceolate, leathery, long-pointed leaves to 25 cm long and 2-3 cm wide, resembling a small-leaved croton. *p. 1572*

benghalensis (India, Ceylon), "Banyan tree"; large tree, the top spreading by aerial roots which become secondary trunks; leathery leaves ovate or elliptic, to 20 cm long, dark green, with yellow-green veins, on pubescent stem; round red fruits. *Tropical.* *p. 1564*

benjamina (India, Malaya), the graceful "Weeping fig"; a beautiful tropical tree of dense growth, forming aerial roots, and with branches of somewhat pendant habit; the pendulous, shining deep green leaves long ovate, slender pointed 8-10 cm long; small round fruit blood-red when ripe. One of the most attractive tubbed decorators for tropical effect, preferring smallish containers, and rejoicing in warmth and good light, 40 fc. and up to 500 fc. (400 to 5000 lux), the more light the more leaves. Allow surface to become dry, then water. *Tropical.* *p. 1565, 1571, 1585*

benjamina 'Exotica' (Java, Bali), "Java fig"; especially graceful, weeping form with slender, arching branches, and smaller, rather narrow and pendulous glossy green, leathery, oblique 9-12 cm leaves, which are given special charm by the coquette twist of their slender tip; small red berries; thrip-proof. I have seen large trees of this variety quite common in Bali. Good indoor decorator tub plant but needs at least 50 fc (500 lux) of light; some leaves may drop at first when temperature changes, or a tree is moved to air-conditioning. *Tropical.* *p. 1565, 1567, 1571, 1574*

benjamina nuda (Philippines), "Small-leaved philippinense"; small-leaved variety planted in South Florida where it has grown into large banyan trees, and where it has become known as "philippinense"; the shiny leaves are inclined to be tufted toward the ends of zigzag branches 4-5 cm long, somewhat narrower than benjamina, more tapering toward base and slender pointed, and a distinct pair of basal veins run for some distance up the side margins before uniting with the most basal side-veins. The tiny figs are greenish-yellow whose basal bracts fall off early denuding the fruit. *p. 1570*

benjamina 'Variegata', "Variegated mini-rubber"; handsome cultivar grown in Florida and California; charming as bushy little tree, with slender brownish stem and small elliptic leaves 6-8 cm long, glossy light green, prettily margined and variegated with ivory-white. *Tropical.* *p. 1563*

brandegeei (Mexico); a curious xerophytic tree from Isla Ildefonso, Baja California, with beige trunk from a swollen base bottle-like; grayish green, leathery leaves, broad ovate with cordate base; young plants may be dwarfed by retarding growth and kept as bonsai. *Arid-tropical.* *p. 1584*

buxifolia (Zaire); fast-growing tree with willowy branches bearing on short petioles small leathery, wedge-shaped obcordate leaves, 6 cm long, the broad apex shallowly lobed. *p. 1572*

callosa (Java); large decorative tree with attractive foliage; willowy stem with leathery broad ovate leaves glossy dark green with contrasting pale midrib and somewhat sunken lateral ribs almost at right angles. *p. 1574*

cannonii (Artocarpus) (Tahiti); small tree to 4 m with sparry branches, short-stalked, broad-ovate leaves occasionally lobed, to more than 30 cm long, stiff-papery, corrugated and faintly hairy, bronzy tinted purple on the surface and underside fiery-red, stalks and midrib bright red. *p. 1568*

capensis (Cape Prov. to Ivory Coast and Sudan), "Cape fig"; wide spread cauliflorous tree to 12 m, with broad ovate, smooth, thin-leathery leaves to 22 cm long, larger than sycomorus, prominent pale ribs, margins coarsely serrate; small 2 cm edible green figs are dangling profusely on leafless stalks from the trunk and larger branches. *Tropical.* *p. 1584*

carica (Mediterranean region, Asia Minor), "Common fig"; broad, irregular, deciduous tree to 10 m high, much planted for its sweet, pear-shaped fruit; leaves thick, rough above, deeply 3-5-lobed and with palmate veining. *Subtropic.* *p. 1566, 1576*

cocculifolia (coccolobifolia) (Madagascar); large tropical tree in the plains of Western Madagascar, with oval leathery leaves 16 cm long and 10 cm wide, almost size of F. lyrata, matted light green and with prominent pale veins; the figs are 4.5 cm dia. and axillary. *p. 1586*

cotinifolia (Urostigma) (Mexico); tree with gray, young branches cinnamon-brown; leathery leaves elliptic to lanceolate, 20 cm long, with straw-yellow veins. *p. 1572*

cyathistipula (Trop. Africa); bushy tree with long-oblanceolate leathery, dark green leaves 10-25 cm long, suddenly tapering to a slender point at apex; globular fig 4 cm dia.; fruiting as a young plant. *p.1568,1584*

decora: see elastica 'Decora'

diversifolia (lutescens) (India, Malaya, Java), "Mistletoe fig"; woody shrub with small obovate, hard leaves 5 cm long, dark green with brown specks above, pale beneath; liberally bearing small yellowish fruit lined with gray. *Tropical.* *p. 1576, 1580*

dryepondtiana (Zaire), "Congo fig"; brown woody stem with stiff-oval, quilted wavy leaves metallic deep olive green, the underside red-purple. A very attractive colorful species. *Tropical.* *p. 320A, 1570, 1576*

dumosa (fulva) (Malaya, Burma, Java); dense bush with palmately lobed, leathery leaves with depressed veins, grass-green and with rugose surface. *p. 1573*

eburnea (India, Java), "Ivory-fig"; free-growing tree spreading wider than high, large 38 cm, oval leaves bright shining light green with ivory-white midrib and main veins; freely fruiting with cherry-like red figs. *p.1573*

edulis (New Caledonia); erect small shrub branching toward top; broad obovate smooth leaves, vivid light red when young, borne on short, brown-hairy petioles; fruit pea-size, green; yellowish when ripe, growing in dense clusters on the lower trunk. *p. 1572*

edworthii (Malaya); robust tree with large leathery, broad oval, smooth leaves 35 cm long and 20 cm wide, gray green with pale green veins, on brown branches. *p. 1586*

elastica (India, Malaya), "India rubber plant"; durable old houseplant, but grows into large trees to 30 m high, and rooting from the branches; young plants erect, with brown woody stem and thick-leathery oblong leaves glossy deep green, the young leaves enclosed in a rosy sheath; yielding latex-bearing milky sap. *Tropical.* *p. 1564, 1581*

elastica 'Belgica'; horticultural selection more closely jointed than decora, the deep waxy-green leaves corrugated and not as round, midrib cream to pink. *p. 1569*

elastica 'Decora', "Wideleaf rubber plant"; superb commercial seedling, originated about 1950, and introduced from Belgium; of bold habit, larger and much broader, heavier leaves, 25-35 cm long, deep glossy green, with prominent lateral depressed veins, at right angles to the ivory midrib which is red beneath, the sheath at the growing tips is red. *Tropical.* *p. 19*, 1564, 1565, 1567*

elastica 'Decora tricolor' (England); seen at Rochford Nurseries near London; beautiful as a decorative pot plant with broad, colorful gray-green leaves variegated cream, white and pink, with prominent red ribs. *p. 1584*

elastica 'Doescheri' (New Orleans 1925), "Variegated rubber plant"; outstanding variegated cultivar having a striking range of colors, from green with gray into white and cream-yellow, while midrib and leafstalks are pink; coloring is stable and not reverting to green. *Tropical.* *p. 1563*

elastica 'Rubra'; horticultural form distinguished by the maroon-red coloring of its young foliage and red midrib of the broad, short-pointed, oval leaves; not as large as decora and thinner, and not keeping quite as well. *p. 1576*

elastica 'Schryveriana' ('Schrijvereana'); robust Belgian cultivar (1959), of the broad-leaved 'Decora', with glossy, deep green leaves irregularly variegated gray-green in the center, light green, sea green and cream or light yellow toward the marginal area, the midrib cream, the petioles red. Known as 'Tricolor' in Australia. *Tropical.* *p. 1569*

elastica 'Variegata', the common "Rubber plant" in variegated form, the leathery leaves are usually variegated gray and edged in creamy-yellow, coloring variable. *Tropical.* *p. 1564*

eriobotryoides (afzelii) (Sierra Leone to Nigeria, Cameroun, Zaire); large spreading tree to 15 m high, starting as an epiphyte, with foliage at ends of branches, green leaves stiff, long-oblanceolate to 30 cm long, lighter colored underneath; young growth yellow-brown hairy; orange-brown figs 4 cm dia. *p. 1572*

exotica: see benjamina 'Exotica'

gibbosa (parasitica) (Indochina: Cambodia; Malaya, Ceylon); an epiphyte in young state, growing in the forks of trees, or as I have observed in Cambodia, on the stones of the ruins of Angkor, surrounding its host with strangling roots and becoming a large tree with spreading branches, bearing the smallish narrow elliptic, oblique leaves 4-15 cm long, often yellowish beneath; pear-shaped 8 cm figs reddish orange. *Tropical.* *p. 1579, 1582*

gillettii (Malaysia); ornamental tree richly bearing on its branches cauliflorous globular fruit similar to F. glomerata; hard-leathery leaves 22 x 8 cm. *p. 1568*

gilletii obovata (Zaire); big forest tree with long-stalked, obovate leaves 10-12 cm long, thin-leathery, rich green. *Tropical.* *p. 1582*

glomerata (racemosa) (India, Burma, Malaya, Australia); thick-topped tree known as the "Cluster fig" on account of the large clusters of edible reddish fruit borne on the sometimes large trunk and naked thickest branches; this production of flowers and fruit from trunks and branches is known as cauliflorous, a character also found on a few other species. The ovate leaves 10-18 cm long have a metallic luster. *p. 1567*

henneanana (superba) (Queensland, No. Australia); the "Cedar fig"; small tropical tree shortly deciduous, the branches forming aerial roots; thin-leathery, glossy green, 10-15 cm ovate leaves on twiggy branches; small axillary, 2 cm green figs flecked with white. *p. 1586*

hookeri (India); smooth tree to 12 m with dense covering of broad-elliptic leathery, green leaves 12-30 cm long, with wavy margins, pale beneath; small fruit like a strawberry, in a cup formed of the bracts. This species may be correctly F. mysorensis var. subrepanda. *p. 1572*

jacquinifolia (West Indies, Bahamas), "West Indian laurel fig"; small-leaved tree to 9 m high, forming thick trunk, close with oval or oblong, convex foliage 5-8 cm long, glossy-green with veins not prominent. *p. 1572, 1582*

krishnae (India, Pakistan); small tree sacred to Krishna, said to have folded its leaves into cups to collect drops of dew for the thirsty Hindu god;

leathery, irregularly cupped, deep green leaves with raised ivory ribs, finely pubescent inside, on grayish branches; possibly a form of benghalensis. *p. 1564*

lapathifolia (Mexico: Oaxaca, Yucatán); large tree, starting as an epiphyte, with vigorous willowy branches and elliptic to broad-oblong leaves to 25 cm long and pubescent, the upper surface thickly covered with white dots. *p. 1573*

lyrata (pandurata) (Trop. West Africa), "Fiddleleaf plant"; close headed tree to 12 m high, with large, thick-leathery leaves 30 to 60 cm long, fiddle-shaped, wide rounded apex, deep waxy green, quilted and wavy, with attractive yellow-green veins, on woody stem; fruits with white dots. *Tropical.* *p. 1564, 1565, 1568, 1581*

lyrata 'Phyllis Craig' (Craig 1956, Pat.); dwarf sport of lyrata, shorter and bushier than the parent, with nodes closely spaced, fairly uniform, very decorative fiddle-shaped leaves, glossy deep green contrasting against light veins. 20-38 cm long (against 25-60 cm in the type), with undulate margins. *p. 1569*

macrophylla (Queensland, New South Wales), the "Australian banyan" or "Moreton Bay fig"; large tree with ovate to broad oblong leathery leaves blunt at apex, to 25 cm long and 10 cm wide, cordate at base, glossy green with pronounced ivory veins, shiny light green underneath, netted. *Subtropic.* *p. 1569, 1573, 1578, 1580*

magnolioides (Malaya); large banyan, forming monstrous trunk and wide-spreading top; large leathery leaves magnolia-like, oval-elliptic, shining dark green above, reverse cinnamon-brown. *p. 1578*

"mexicana", in Florida hort. (Mexico); robust, densely branching decorative tree with wiry, erect branches; lanceolate leathery leaves 8-10 cm long; shiny deep green, tips lightly twisted; reverse green. *p. 1582*

microphylla hort., "Little-leaf fig"; rapid-growing, gray-barked evergreen tree with broad ovate to obovate, glossy, intense dark green, soft-leathery leaves 5-15 cm long, glossy green beneath. Grown as microphylla by California nurseries, but this may actually be F. rubiginosa or form. *p. 1569, 1570*

microphylla cv. 'Florida'; cult. in California nurseries; similar to microphylla, with grayish stem, foliage larger and richer green; reputed to be a better keeper with less leaf-drop. *p. 1582*

mysorensis (So. India, Burma); large tree with twigs tomentose becoming glabrous; large leathery, rich green, ovate leaves to 30 cm long, glossy under the loose pubescence, and with pale yellowish veins; fruit orange-red; tolerates some frost. *Tropical.* *p. 1576, 1583*

nekbudu (utilis) (Trop. Africa), "Zulu fig"; large forest tree, young growth pubescent; fresh green leathery leaves thick, oval to obovate, 15-40 cm long, rounded at both ends and with pretty, yellow ribs; small globular greenish to beige fruit 2 cm dia., covered with white felt, densely set toward apex of branches. Good examples of their shapely form are the old specimen in front of the Capitol in San Juan, Puerto Rico. *Tropical.* *p. 1564*

neriifolia (regularis) (Moluccas, Celebes); graceful tree with willow-like pendant branches and long, narrow-lanceolate, drooping leaves shiny green and resembling oleander. *p. 1571*

nitida (Malaya), "Indian laurel"; attractive, glabrous thick-topped banyan tree forming aerial roots and buttressed trunk in habitat; with erect branches and small, rubbery, elliptic leaves 10 cm long, waxy, nice green and very smooth; can be shaped into pyramids and standards resembling a true laurel. Good tub plant; also widely used as a containerized street tree in our Southwest. In the interior of buildings this sun-lover requires 50 fc. to 500 fc. (500 to 5000 lux); the more light, the more leaves it can hold. *Subtropic.* *p. 1571, 1577, 1583*

oblongata (So. Africa); big evergreen tree with large decorative oval stiff leaves 25 cm long and 12 cm wide, dark green with light green borders, straw-yellow veining, wavy at margins. *p. 1572*

palmeri (Baja California, Mexico); a magnificent xerophytic, desert-climate tree to 20 m tall, growing on rocky cliffs as a strangler fig; base swollen and bulbous; cordate 15 cm leaves soft-leathery grayish green with ivory ribs, velvety beneath; small yellowish figs. *Arid-tropical.* *p. 1584*

pandurata: see lyrata

'panduriformis': see wildemanniana

parcellii: see aspera

parietalis (India); shrub or tree with rusty-pubescent twigs and elliptic-oblong to obovate leathery leaves to 30 cm long, on stout, bristly petioles; small globose, orange fruit. *p. 1568*

petiolaris (Mexico), "Blue Mexican fig"; small tree to 1¾ m high, developing very wide, swollen base; attractive, heartshaped, leathery, wavy leaves with long pointed tip, metallic blue-green, with ivory pink to showy red veins and petioles. (syn. F. jaliscana). *p. 1573, 1584*

"Philippinense" hort.: see stricta and benjamina nuda

philippinensis (decaisneana) (Phillippines, Guam); true species, introduced by U.S.D.A. from Guam; climbing, woody, epiphytic shrub or small tree; dark green elliptic-lanceolate, shiny leathery leaves 8-20 cm long, with acuminate base; axillary ovoid fruit 5-8 cm. dia. *p. 1570*

platyphylla (Ghana); sparry tree with large stiff oval leaves dark green with creamy ribs and petioles. *p. 1573*

pretoriae (Transvaal), "Wonderboom"; big, spreading evergreen tree 12 m tall or more, the spreading branches bend down and take root developing into new trees; leathery lanceolate leaves 20 cm long; fruits orange-red. Grown in Holland from seed as an attractive pot plant. *p. 1562, 1582*

pseudopalma (Philippines), "Dracaena fig"; showy tree to 10 m high, with thin-leathery palm-like leaves 60-90 cm long, the stiffish foliage clustered near the top, acuminate and long-tapering toward the base, and coarsely notched, the surface somewhat glossy; dark green, ovoid figs 4 cm long. *Tropical.* *p. 1566, 1569*

pumila (repens, stipulata) (China, Japan, Australia), "Creeping fig"; freely branching creeper with small, obliquely cordate, dark green leaves less than 3 cm long, clinging to walls by roots like ivy and then flattened; fruiting branches erect, with stiff, much larger, oblong leaves to 10 cm long. *Subtropic.* *p. 1574, 1575, 1580, 1586*

pumila 'Gigas' (stipulata, repens), (South China through Malaysia), the "Climbing fig" or "Hug-me-tight-vine"; a polymorphic climber, wiry stems attaching themselves to trees or walls by the rubbery exudation from their cling-roots; small heart-shaped green leaves densely shingled; larger in this German cultivar than the normal 2-3 cm juvenile foliage. *p. 1586*

pumila minima; a slender, tiny-leaved form of the creeping stage, the dark green, quilted leaves less than 1 cm, and like little hearts; slow-growing. (3) *p. 1574*

pumila 'Quercifolia'; a German cultivar before 1939, with habit of growth like pumila, of the same low creeping or pendant character but differing by its little leaves being indented or lobed in oak-leaf pattern, dia. of leaf 15 x 10 mm. (F. quercifolia leaf 15 x 8 cm.). *p. 1575*

pumila 'Variegata'; cultivar with the small ovate leaves attractively variegated or marbled green and white or cream. *p. 1575*

quercifolia (Burma, Malaya), "Oakleaf ficus"; shrub with prostrate, stiff-hairy branches and elliptic or lobed leathery leaves 12-20 cm long, shaped like those of the common oak, deep green; produces small green figs. *p. 1574, 1575*

radicans (rostrata) (E. Indies), "Rooting fig"; coarse, robust, trailing species with rough-wiry stems and slender-pointed, small lanceolate, leathery leaves 5-10 cm long and quilted, glabrous above, rough beneath. *p. 1574*

radicans 'Variegata', "Variegated rooting fig"; attractive variegated creeper much grown under glass, with lanceolate, grayish green 5-8 cm leaves irregularly marked with creamy-white, the variegation beginning at the margin. *Tropical.* *p. 15*, 19*, 21*, 1574, 1575*

ramentacea (Philippines); seen at the Munich Botanic Garden; according to Condit a powerful epiphyte often eventually a tree, scandent shrub with heavy leathery, deep glossy green leaves with ivory midrib, and with fruit dark red to purplish. Possibly related to or synonym of F. radicans (Condit). *p. 1586*

religiosa (India), "Bo-tree"; sacred to Hindus and Buddhists, and under which Buddha received enlightenment; large glabrous tree to 30 m high, with gracefully pendant, thin, bluish-green leaves, heartshaped with tail-like drip-tip, ivory or pinkish veins, on slender branches; purple fruit. *Tropical.* *p. 1564, 1568, 1581*

repens: see pumila

retusa (So. China, Macao, Philippines), "Chinese banyan"; shapely tree with dense foliage, the branches first ascending but becoming pendulous, with small leathery 8-10 cm leaves broadly obovate and waxy; ideal for shaped standards as decorator trees growing in tubs. *Subtropic.* *p. 1567, 1571, 1577, 1579, 1581*

retusa nitida: see nitida

roxburghii: see auriculata

rubiginosa (australis) (New South Wales, Queensland), "Rusty fig"; broad tree, spreading by means of aerial roots like the banyan; small leathery 8-15 cm leaves oval or elliptic, rusty-pubescent beneath. *p. 1571, 1582*

rubiginosa fa. australis (New South Wales); evergreen tree with spreading willowy branches, in this form lacking the densely pubescent, rusty-downy character of the foliage; soft-leathery glossy dark green, oval to obovate leaves, with pale midrib, about 8 cm long in container-grown or smaller plants, to 20 cm long as trees in habitat under favorable moist conditions. *Subtropic.* *p. 1571, 1578*

rubiginosa 'Variegata'; a pretty miniature rubber plant with graceful branches and small, egg-shaped, deep green, leathery leaves richly marbled and edged yellowish-cream; tomentose during juvenile stage only. *p. 15*, 1563*

sarmentosa (Japan); evergreen creeper with thin-wiry root-forming and clinging stems set with tiny dark green ovate leaves usually lobed, very rugose 1 cm long; by their clinging aerial roots soon climbing and forming dense covers with their shingled foliage. *p. 1575*

saussureana (Brazil, Guyana); sparry tree with stems, young branches, and reverse of foliage cinnamon-brown; long obovate leaves to 30 cm long by 10 cm wide, with rough surface, dark-green with light green veins. *Tropical.* *p. 1569*

schlechteri (So. and Eastern Asia, New Caledonia); evergreen tree forming crown to 9 m dia.; willowy branches bearing leathery, oval-obovate leaves 6-8½ cm long, narrowed toward base, and resembling camellia; the leaves do not have hydathodes (water pores) scattered along the margins, as F. stricta has; figs are yellow. *p. 1570*

soldanella (So. Africa), "Rock wild fig"; growing on rocks in Kruger National Park, to 4 m high, with handsome, leathery leaves broad-heart-shaped, to 20 cm long, green with prominent pink or red veins. *p. 1584*

stipulata; a synonym for F. pumila, which see. The maturity stage with stiff-erect branches and larger, elliptic leaves to 10 cm long, produces the pear-like, brown-violet, hairy fruit 5 cm long. *p. 1568*

stricta (Guam); known in some So. Florida nurseries as "philippinense", but with generally smaller foliage; starting as a climbing woody epiphyte sending down aerial roots and developing into trees; triangular branches with broad-ovate leathery deep green, smooth leaves 15 cm or more long, equipped with water pores scattered along margins; fruits are axillary. *p. 1570, 1571, 1583*

sycomorus (Syria, Egypt, Sudan, south to the Transvaal), "Sycamore fig"; round headed, freely branching tree to 12 m high, partially deciduous. In Africa, one sees them often along rivers, very attractive with their pale fawn-yellowish trunk and shapely head; ovate, rugose leaves with hairy ribs, 8-10 cm long, soft when young, almost bluish-green; when mature with leathery "feel" but quickly desiccating, fresh green to deep olive, blunt apex; greenish flowers and small, abundant edible fruit produced from the trunk and branches. *Arid-tropical.* *p. 1569, 1574, 1578*

tikoua (China; Yunnan, Tibet, to Indonesia), "Waupahu fig"; scandent evergreen shrub, fast spreading with woody, flexible brown branches; leathery obovate, rough, wrinkled leaves to 12 cm long, shallowly toothed, matte dark green above, pale green beneath; small pear-shaped 1 cm brown to black figs are borne on prostrate branches; promising ground cover. *p. 1586*

triangularis (Trop. Africa); small evergreen ornamental tree with curious triangular, thick-fleshy, dark green leaves 5 cm long, the margins rolled down; masses of small 1 cm greenish beige berries are growing cauliflorous directly from the woody branches. *Tropical.* *p. 1582, 1584*

triangularis 'Variegata', "Sweetheart tree"; very handsome broadleaf evergreen bush with lax or pendant willowy branches; the thick-leathery, waxy, triangular, heart-shaped or obovate leaves 5 to 8 cm long and broad, beautifully variegated deep green to milky gray, from the margins in with contrasting creamy-white. *Tropical.* *p. 1571*

ulmaefolia (Philippines); tall tree-like shrub with rough, sparry branches, variable leaves ovate to oblanceolate 12-18 cm long, very rough on both surfaces, dentate or sometimes lobed; small purplish fruit. *p. 1570*

utilis: see nekbudu

villosa (barbata) (Malaya); epiphytic creeper with brown-velvety scandent branches forming a dense cover; ovate leathery, dark green leaves in two ranks, 8-10 cm long, on the margins and beneath brown-hairy; tiny 1 cm yellow fruit in clusters. *p. 1575*

vogelii (Sénégal, Nigeria, Zaire), "West African rubber tree"; widely distributed, conspicuous fig tree to 25 m, with leathery, broad ovate leaves to 25 cm long; showy with small red figs. The latex is the source of the "Lagos rubber", once widely used for caoutchouk elastic. *p. 1584*

wildemanniana (cyathistipula) (Trop. Africa); introduced by Vosters as 'panduriformis'; sturdy plant small enough to look good in a 10 cm pot; leaves are glossy dark forest green and very leathery oblique elliptic, and with their ivory midrib and lateral veins look very attractive. *p. 1573, 1582*

FITTONIA *Acanthaceae* **S3LFM**

verschaffeltii (Perú), "Mosaic plant"; a pretty tropical ground cover; low, creeping herb with hairy, rooting stems and colorful oval 8-10 cm leaves dark olive green and entirely covered with a network of deep-red veins. Although the leaves are somewhat papery they are fairly sturdy. Small yellow, green-bracted flowers. *Tropical.* *p. 43*

verschaffeltii 'Argyroneura' (Perú), "Nerve plant"; charming tropical herb, spreading and hugging the ground, with flat, papery, oval leaves vivid green and beautifully netted with white veins. Likes warmth and high humidity. *Tropical.* *p. 15*, 19*, 43*

verschaffeltii pearcei, "Snake-skin plant"; low creeper with larger, glaucous leaves light olive-green with rose-pink veins; thin-papery. *p. 43*

FLACOURTIA *Flacourtiaceae* **S2LBD**

indica (Trop. Asia, Madagascar), "Governor's plum" or "Ramontchi"; fruit-bearing shrub or tree to 8 m high; the branches with long slender spines and ovate, glossy green, toothed leaves to 8 cm long, partially deciduous; small yellowish flowers in leaf axils, followed by the globose maroon-red fleshy fruit to 2 cm diameter tipped with short radiating styles; the juicy, edible pulp surrounding several flattened stones. *p. 1064*

FLEMINGIA *Leguminosae* **S3LFM**

strobilifera (India, Malaya); shrub to 3 m; leaves simple, ovate, to 9 cm long, silky beneath; flowers purple, hidden by large bracts, in racemes to 15 cm long; pods to 1 cm long. *p. 1380*

FLICKINGERIA *Orchidaceae* **S3LFW**

comata (Desmotrichum) (Sumatra to Samoa); peculiar epiphyte or rock-dweller, with ascending, stem-like rhizome bearing subcylindric pseudobulbs together with lanceolate leaves; from the upper leaf axils the small fragrant, short-lived greenish white 2 cm flowers flushed with pink. *p. 1738*

FOCKEA *Asclepiadaceae* **I-S2LBD**

capensis (So. Africa); curious dioecious succulent with turnip-shaped root, forming with age, a tremendously thick, swollen caudex, from the apex of which rise thin woody, twining branches, with tiny opposite holly-shaped but fleshy, undulate leaves grayish green. *Arid-subtropic.* *p. 376*

crispa (Cape Prov.; Karroo); turnip-shaped, thick caudex which may grow to 3 m high in habitat, but largely buried in the ground; from the apex thin twigs with succulent, oval leaves glossy green with wavy margins, about 2½ cm long; small gray-green flower with brown spots. From my student days I remember the treasured plant grown in Schoenbrunn, Vienna, as a pot plant there since 1799, still alive. *p. 364, 376, 379*

FONTINALIS *Fontinalaceae* **S3LFW**

antipyretica (So. Europe, No. Africa, No. Asia), a "Sponge-moss"; aquatic plant from fresh-water rivers, with submersed stems densely set with small oval leaves in 3 ranks, fresh olive green, often fastened to rocks; suitable for aquarium planting. *p. 1064*

FORSYTHIA *Oleaceae* **C2LBD**

x intermedia 'Spring Glory' (suspensa x viridissima); both from China, deciduous shrub known as "Golden bells"; is amongst the earliest bloomers in the spring about April, but frequently forced as cut branches for late January, the showy clear yellow blossoms appearing before the leaves; flowers 4-parted into oblong, spreading corolla lobes 2 cm long, in successive clusters on long whip-like branches, leaves to 12 cm long, often trifoliolate. *p. 1627*

FORTUNELLA *Rutaceae* **I2LBM**

crassifolia (S.E. China), "Meiwa kumquat"; evergreen compact shrub with or without spines, leaves thick and trough-like, petioles narrowly winged; fruit slightly ovoid, to 4 cm dia., the attractive aromatic fruit are used for preserves, and the sweet rind may be eaten raw. *p. 2027*

hindsii (Hong Kong, Kwangtung), the "Dwarf kumquat"; ornamental, small spiny tree, with leathery green, oval-obovate leaves, and nearly round, small 1 cm orange-red fruit of 3-4 cells, almost without juice. *p. 2032*

margarita (Kwangtung), "Nagami kumquat"; small, vigorous, bushy citrus, often grown as a standard in tubs, with slender, erect, angled branches, long-pointed, shining dark green leaves, fragrant white flowers, and small, rather persistent, oblong, golden orange fruit of 2 cm dia., with finely-flavored pulp, produced prolifically in Oct.-Jan. and longer. The sweet fruit is used for preserves. *Subtropic.* *p. 2030, 2031*

FOSTERELLA *Bromeliaceae* **I2HFD**

penduliflora (Lindmania) (N.W. Argentina); terrestrial rosette of spreading linear-lanceolate soft leaves with smooth edges, satiny grayish green and a faint yellow-green stripe down the middle; tall 30 cm wiry stalk bearing branched inflorescence, bearing to one side small white flowers. *p. 550, 559, 560, 572*

FOTHERGILLA *Hamamelidaceae* **I2LFM**

major (U.S.: Georgia); deciduous shrub to 3 m high; coarsely-toothed witch hazel-like leaves to 10 cm long, glaucous and pubescent beneath; white, fragrant flowers without petals borne in dense terminal heads in which the stamens are the conspicuous part. *p. 1323*

FOUQUIERIA *Fouquieriaceae* **S2LBD**

formosa (So. Mexico); spiny shrub 2-3 m high, the woody branches with scattered fleshy oblong, deciduous leaves and spines topped by showy clusters of scarlet flowers with curved corolla tube. *p. 1064*

splendens (N. Mexico, Arizona, So. California), the "Ocotillo" of the desert;* a xerophytic shrub with many whip-like gray, furrowed basal stems, to 6 m; rigid spines bear clusters of small oval, deciduous leaves in their axils; and at the very tips of branches the brilliant-red flowers in showy racemes to 25 cm long. *Arid-subtropic.* *p. 1063, 1064*

FRAGARIA *Rosaceae* **C-I2LFM**

x ananassa (1766) (chiloensis x virginiana), the "Garden strawberry"; a herbaceous perennial with large white flowers, and big delicious red fruit, produced in spring. The late fruiting or everbearing varieties also include F. vesca blood, and these produce some berries from early spring to late fall. *p. 1994*

vesca 'Albo-marginata' (Europe), "Variegated wild strawberry"; low perennial herb with rooting runners, the attractive foliage with 3 green, toothed leaflets, silky beneath, irregularly margined white with some red on edge; the flowers white, and small, delicious red fruit. *p. 1994*

FRAILEA *Cactaceae* **S2LBD**

grahliana (Paraguay); globular stem 4 cm thick, freely sprouting around base, brownish green with 13 indistinct ribs cut into warts, yellowish radials; flowers pale yellow with red throat. *p. 694*

FRANCISCEA: see Brunfelsia

FRANCOA *Saxifragaceae* **C2LBM**

ramosa (Chile), "Maiden's-wreath"; stalked perennial to 1 m, with basal, lobed, crinkled leaves coarsely toothed, and showy, pubescent spikes of white 2½ cm flowers with 4 petals; used as cut flowers. *p. 2042*

FREESIA *Iridaceae* **C2LBDd**

x hybrida; large-flowered hybrid of such South African species as refracta and armstrongii; bulb-like corms with linear leaves, and very fragrant, firm, funnelform flowers on bent wiry spikes, creamy-white through orange to lilac-blue, 5-6 cm long. August blooming unless forced. *Subtropic.* *p. 1335*

x hybrida 'Fantasy'; large double-flowered creamy-yellow flowers with 2 or 3 rows of broad, round, waxy petals; of extra-ordinary keeping quality; listed in Synge, Collins Guide to Bulbs, London. *p. 1324*

FREMONTODENDRON *Sterculiaceae or Bombacaceae* **I2LBD**

californicum (Fremontia) (California), "Flannel-bush"; evergreen shrub or small tree to 3 m, dark green leathery roundish or lobed 3 cm leaves with felt-like covering beneath, lemon-yellow flowers of showy saucer-like calyx without petals, 3 cm wide, in late spring, making a gorgeous show of color in the mountains of southern and central California. *p. 2090*

mexicanum (Fremontia) (San Diego and Baja California), "Southern flannel bush"; evergreen shrub or small tree to 6 m, with spur-like branches bearing 5-lobed leaves, dark green above and covered with felt beneath, 4-8 cm long; flowers with showy orange-yellow calyx to 9 cm across, but without petals; black seeds. *Subtropic.* *p. 2088, 2090, 2093*

FREYCINETIA *Pandanaceae* **S3LFM**

arborea (Hawaii), "Climbing screw pine"; woody climber with brittle, rooting stems twining into treetops; every metre new branches will form, ending in tufts of narrow, spiny leaves tapering to a point, their center produces a curious, ornamental inflorescence of fleshy rosy-red bracts surrounding the purplish-red spadix. *Tropical.* *p. 1920*

elegantula (New Guinea); unusual climbing pandanus with short-ovate, shingled leathery leaves, ciliate-hairy at margins; the terminal inflorescence with globular spadix cradled inside broad triangular, whitish bracts. *p. 1919*

funicularis (insignis), (Indonesia: Java); a beautiful climbing screw-pine with long flexuous stems; sword-shaped leathery leaves glossy green with very few minute marginal spines; the terminal inflorescence very showy, with large triangular bright red bracts and cylindric yellow spadices in center. *Tropical.* *p. 1919*

javanica (Java), "Climbing pandanus"; slender climbing shrub with stems rooting onto the bark of trees, and pandanus-like branches with spirally arranged, narrow, glossy green, toothed leaves; in the mountains of Java whole trees are covered with this rambler, its pendant branches tipped by bright orange, bracted flowers, greenish outside, with green spadix. *p. 1920*

multiflora (Philippines), "Climbing pandanus"; climbing tropical shrub with slender rooting stems becoming pendant from trees; sessile leathery, black-green, linear lanceolate keeled leaves, and showy terminal inflorescence with glowing salmon-rose bracts; and with rosy spadix. *Tropical.* *p. 768A, 1920*

rigidifolia (Thailand, Malaya, Borneo); climbing dioecious screw-pine with leathery leaves to 25 cm long and 14 mm wide; at apex the attractive inflorescence with 6-8 cm red bracts, the cylindric spadix pale yellow. *Tropical.* *p. 1919*

walkeri (Sri Lanka); climbing screw-pine with rooting, flexuous stems, long-linear leathery leaves to 60 cm long and 2 cm wide; terminal inflorescence with dark green, cylindric spadices, and brown conical fruit on female plants. *p. 1919*

FRITHIA *Aizoaceae* **S2LBD**

pulchra (Transvaal), "Purple baby toes"; pretty, clustering rosette similar to Fenestraria, with club-like succulent gray leaves under 3 cm high, the flat top with translucent windows; large carmine-purple flowers with white center. *Subtropic.* *p. 67*

FRITILLARIA *Liliaceae* **C2LFDd**

acmopetala (Syria, Asia Minor); small bulbous plant with leafy stalks 30-45 cm high, linear leaves green; flowers usually solitary 3 cm long, outer segments green outside streaked brown-purple, yellowish and shining inside; inner petals brownish greenish within. *p. 1447*

dasyphylla; bulbous simple-stemmed herb 15 cm high; leafy stalk with fleshy foliage, and funnel flowers 2 cm long, purplish outside, yellow within, not checkered. *p. 1447*

imperialis (Iran, W. Himalaya), "Crown Imperial"; simple-stemmed stout, strong-smelling herb to 1 m, with scaly bulb, lanceolate leaves, with some in a terminal whorl above the nodding 5 cm flowers, with 6 veined segments purplish, terracotta or yellow, borne on a stiff-erect, purple-spotted stalk. *Subtropic.* *p. 1446*

meleagris (Britain, Norway, C. Europe to Caucasus), "Checkered-lily" or "Snake's head"; bulbous perennial to 45 cm high, with scattered linear to oblanceolate glaucous leaves along middle of stem; solitary bell-shaped 5-8 cm flowers, purple with white checkering, or white with green network of veins. *Warm temperate.* *p. 1446*

pallidiflora (So. Siberia; Altai); handsome bulbous perennial to 38 cm high, with stem bearing scattered oblong glaucous leaves and nodding cream-yellow 4 cm bell-flowers tinged green outside, dotted reddish inside, from the upper leaf-axils. *p. 1446*

FRULLANIA *Marchantiaceae* **C3LNW**

tamariscii (Alaska, Newfoundland, Iceland, and southward to No. Africa), an arctic "Liverwort"; mat-forming cryptogram (flower-less plant), a primitive plant between mosses and algae; leaf-like flat, scale-like plant body or thallus is green veined with purple (see Marchantia). *p. 1520*

FUCHSIA *Onagraceae* **C-I2LNM**

arborescens (Mexico, Guatemala, Costa Rica); small tree to 6 m or more high, with smooth, woody branches red when young; lanceolate, bright green leaves in three's, to 25 cm long; small 1 cm flowers in dense erect panicles resembling lilac bloom, pinkish-purple, followed by blue-black berries. *p.1636*

corymbiflora (Perú); shrubby plant to 2 m, with weak reddish stem needing support, as on rafters; long-ovate, downy leaves with rosy midrib; flowers deep red, in pendant clusters, with cylindrical tubes 8-10 cm long. *p. 1649*

denticulata (Perú, Bolivia); Andean shrub to 11 m high with erect, dark red branches; lanceolate, toothed red-ribbed leaves in three's; 4-5 cm flowers with wine-red tube, sepals red with green tips, petals carmine or tangerine, from the leaf axils. *p. 1636*

excorticata (New Zealand), called "Tree fuchsia", aptly descriptive, becoming a tree to 15 m high, with woody trunk to 60 cm thick, having loose, papery bark and brittle branches; thin dark green lanceolate leaves 5-12 cm long, silvery beneath; small waxy flowers with spreading calyx lobes first yellowish then deep dull red, the petals deep purple with blue stamens. *Subtropic.* *p. 1636*

fulgens (Mexico); robust shrub to 1 m high, with red branches and large, broadly ovate, green leaves, and numerous, brilliant, 8 cm flowers in nodding clusters, the long cylindrical tube vivid red with short, only slightly spreading lobes, greenish at tips, the short corolla scarlet-red, (summer). *p. 1639*

x hybrida (speciosa), a group name for most of our cultivated fuchsias, nick-named "Lady's eardrops"; and derived from such species as fulgens, magellanica and corymbiflora, having sturdier twigs, broader ovate leaves to 10 cm long, and large gay flowers, always pendant, with long showy stamens. Most fuchsias can be had in flower the year round, but most profusely during the season of warm long days from March to November, and they generally prefer a cool, moist climate. *Humid-subtropic.*

hyb. 'Autumnal'; a beautiful foliage fuchsia with bronze, orange, yellow and green leaves, and small single rosy-red flowers shaded pink. *p. 1638*

hyb. 'Black Prince'; popular slender, free-growing, commercial plant for early bloom, the strong shoots with pendulous, axillary and terminal, single flowers having red calyx lobes or sepals, and blue-purple, skirt-like petals. *p. 1639*

hyb. 'Blue Butterfly'; small white sepals, rose-purple to blue-purple corolla. *p. 1647*

hyb. 'Blue Waves'; double corolla with waved petals of deep violet, the outer ones splashed rose; tube flushed pink, the upturned sepals bright rose. *p. 1645*

hyb. 'Brigadoon'; huge flowers with double purple corolla, sepals flushed rose-red. *p. 1644*

hyb. 'Buttons & Bows'; small-leaved, bushy upright, ornamented with lots of cute round blossoms, double-white center and bright red sepals. *p. 1635*

hyb. 'Caledonia'; an almost hardy variety of lax habit and free blooming, small single flowers with long tube and sepals red-cerise, the corolla reddish-violet. *Subtropic.* *p. 1640*

hyb. 'Candlelight'; early blooming upright variety with attractive large flowers, having densely double fuchsia-purple corolla, with contrasting large sepals white outside, underside flushed pink. *p. 1646*

hyb. 'Carmel Blue'; striking variety with long single corolla beautiful blue, long greenish-white tube, and narrow outspread white sepals flushed pale blush on underside and tipped pale green. *p. 1637*

hyb. 'Cascade'; ideal basket plant with trailing branches, and single flowers with deep carmine-red petals and well recurving white sepals flushed carmine. *p. 1638, 1643*

hyb. 'Chickadee'; distinctive, profuse bloomer, with slender spreading spur-like sepals around a dainty orchid colored corolla. *p. 1647*

hyb. 'Countess of Aberdeen'; fetching plant with sturdy stem and large leaves with small, cute single flowers of waxy white to pink petals and blush sepals; compact growing and a most admirable small variety. *p. 1638*

hyb. 'Curtain Call'; color ranges from deep rose on center petals to crimson in outer ones; pale carmine tube and carmine sepals. *p. 1635*

hyb. 'Dark Eyes'; bushy basket plant with quantities of neat, double flowers, deep violet-blue and red; lush, shiny foliage. *p. 1635*

hyb. 'Dollar Princess'; an old floriferous pot and basket variety still in cultivation after 50 years, medium small but full plant and small, compact flowers 3 to 4 cm long, with densely double violet-purple corolla and carmine sepals. *p. 1642*

hyb. 'Dusky Rose'; late-flowering pendant type; large double flowers with fuchsia-purple corolla and red sepals, on short tube. *p. 1647*

hyb. 'Erecta Novelty'; upright plant with cute little flowers growing somewhat erect, the single globular corolla light lavender, and incurving sepals white with green tips. *p. 1640*

hyb. 'Fluorescent'; willowy grower with medium-small flowers, tube and broad sepals white faintly marked pink, semi-double corolla orchid. *p. 1647*

hyb. 'Flying Cloud'; a vigorous patented, charming semi-double white variety with corolla tinted a delicate pink, and with white sepals; more floriferous than 'Lace Petticoats'; a strong grower, for standards, or baskets also. *p. 1640*

hyb. 'Fort Bragg'; sport of 'Enchanted'; big fancy flowers in rosy-lavender with rose sepals; does not like heat but is heavy bloomer in shade, and makes a colorful basket. *p. 1635*

hyb. 'Frenchi'; gorgeous pendulous cultivar, large-flowered when in bloom; buds rose-shaped when opening, with fluffy double corolla silvery blue and pale rose, the recurving sepals silvery pink. *p. 1646*

hyb. 'Georgana' (1955); promising cultivar with huge flowers of good keeping quality, one of the largest introduced, with very double orchid-purple corolla, and rosy-red sepals; heavy bloomer and suitable for baskets. *p. 1640*

hyb. 'Golden Glow'; free-blooming, with single medium-sized flowers, with orange-red corolla, and linear spreading white sepals. *p. 1643, 1645*

hyb. 'Golden Marinka'; trailing variety easily branching, with green leaves variegated or edged with golden-yellow, later turning cream; single flowers deep red. *p. 1643*

hyb. 'Guinevere'; pink sport of 'Pink Delight', early-blooming single of pendant habit, the slender flowers with long pale pink corolla, the narrow sepals shaded darker pink. *p. 1647*

hyb. 'Harvest Moon' (1958); first hanging fuchsia with a flat white corolla, much like a hanging 'Citation'; single flaring white petals with red veins, tube and sepals rose-red. *p. 1640*

hyb. 'Jubilee'; spreading, heavy plant with light green foliage and large, double flowers, the corolla dark cerise, the tube and spreading calyx lobes waxy-white edged with deep rose. *p. 1639, 1645*

hyb. 'Lace Petticoats' (1952); intriguing large flowers with broad white recurving sepals and double white corolla with center petals serrated and fringed like lace with undertone of blush pink. *Subtropic.* *p. 1641*

hyb. 'Lilac 'n Rose'; trailing type very early blooming, with large double flowers, corolla rose to pale purple, the long narrow sepals pale pink to white. *p. 1646*

hyb. 'Little Beauty'; well-known commercial bedding and pot plant of dwarf habit, free-blooming; single flowers with red sepals and violet petals. *p. 1638*

hyb. 'Little Sister'; low-growing plant with small but tidy single flowers with orchid-pink stiff skirt of petals, and spreading pink sepals. *p. 1644*

hyb. 'Lord Byron'; an old, well-known, compact, garden hybrid with single flowers, calyx and sepals rich turkey-red, the widely open corolla deep blue-purple. *p. 1639*

hyb. 'Lucky Strike'; upright plant with double flowers, petals bluish-rose streaked with pink, and pale flesh-pink sepals. *p. 1642*

hyb. 'Mad. Corneliesen'; basket-type variety with small single, red and white flowers. *p. 1644*

hyb. 'Madame Dashu'; small flowered single with corolla coral pink, recurved sepals white. *p. 1644*

hyb. 'Mama Bleuss'; fine early-blooming trailing, patented cultivar, prolific with large double flowers, with puffed-up violet-blue corolla and broad rosy sepals. *p. 1646*

hyb. 'Marietta'; large double-flowering upright of good substance, tube and broad upturned sepals bright carmine, corolla dark magenta-red, maturing to clear cherry-red. *p. 1647*

hyb. 'Midge'; a little gem, early-blooming dwarf erect bush profuse with small double flowers having dainty pink corolla with sepals deeper rose. *p. 1646*

hyb. 'Midnight Sun'; of upright habit, with deep green foliage, and large double flowers; the outer petals of the corolla burgundy-purple, the longer inner petals fuchsia-red; spreading sepals pink outside, carmine underneath. *p. 1647*

hyb. 'Mrs. Marshall'; popular, upright grower with white sepals and single skirts of soft pink. *p. 1637*

hyb. 'Mrs. Rundle'; brightly colored, pendulous flowers pretty with long slender, flesh-colored calyx tube and spreading lobes, and a corolla of vivid orange. *p. 1639*

hyb. 'Mrs. Victor Reiter'; early blooming, good variety with lovely single flowers with slender white, spreading sepals and small carmine red corolla. *Subtropic.* *p. 1640*

hyb. 'My Dear'; free-growing and of upright habit, with medium-size double flowers, rosy-lavender corolla fading to pink, the tube and upturned sepals flushed white. *p. 1647*

hyb. 'Nightingale'; trailing plant with large double flowers; tube and sepals white flushed pink, the frilly corolla fuchsia-red, maturing to magenta and pink. *p. 1646*

hyb. 'Old Smoky'; large double corolla of a dusty smoky purplish rose, with flesh-colored sepals; suitable for baskets. *p. 1638*

hyb. 'Papoose'; of pendant habit, with very small flowers having purple petals and red sepals. *p. 1644*

hyb. 'Pepita' (1939); a miniature variety though vigorous, with small foliage and small single flowers with violet-blue corolla and rose-pink sepals. *p. 1642*

hyb. 'Peter Pan'; trailing plant with branches loaded down with medium-size single flowers having blue-purple corolla and rosy sepals. *p. 1645*

hyb. 'Pink Cloud'; free-blooming upright bush, suitable for espalier or pillar; large single flowers with short white tube, long pink sepals, and clear pink, flaring corolla. *Subtropic.* *p. 1647*

hyb. 'Pink Fairy'; self-branching upright grower with dark green foliage, and large double flowers with creamy-white tube, sepals dark pink and clear pink corolla petals. *p. 1645*

hyb. 'Pink Galore'; hanging plant type of restrained growth, with large flowers all soft pink, the tube and sepals a shade deeper than the corolla. *p. 1644*

hyb. 'Pink Jade'; low, bushy grower, and good pot plant; single corolla orchid-pink with deeper rose border, the upturned sepals pink and tipped green. *p. 1643, 1644*

hyb. 'Pin Wheel'; early bloomer of bushy upright habit, with large double flowers rather flat resembling a pin wheel; flaring corolla of folded petals violet, the waxy sepals rose-pink. *p. 1646*

hyb. 'Pride of Orion'; bushy plant with large double white petals against narrow bright red calyx lobes. *p. 1637*

hyb. 'Rollo'; floriferous variety with large white double corolla and shell pink falls, the flower measuring 8 cm long. Rollo, Duke of Normandy (860-930) was a 3 m giant, according to legend. *p. 1642*

hyb. 'Rufus'; vigorous upright variety said to grow to 5 m high, heat resistant and blooming all year; medium-small single flowers, self color, all bright turkey-red; a terrific bloomer. *p. 1642*

hyb. 'Shady Lane'; early bloomer of pendant habit, with large full-double flowers on long, strong stems, the flaring corolla with overlapping petals of lilac-blue splashed with pink, the sepals coral-pink tipped green. *p. 1646*

hyb. 'Sierra Blue'; graceful arching branches show off the nodding double flowers with blue-purple corolla, fading to soft lilac, wide-spreading sepals white, flushed with pink inside. *p. 1646*

hyb. 'Sleigh Bells'; excellent large all-white, single bell-shaped corolla and white recoiling sepals; of upright habit and with some resistance to heat. *p. 1642*

hyb. 'South Seas'; double trailer or upright; sepals pale pink; corolla rose pink. *p. 1635*

hyb. 'Springtime'; popular variety very useful for baskets, with large gay flowers with rosy sepals turned up, and flaring double white petals. *p. 1640*

hyb. 'Strawberry Sundae'; (1958); showy hybrid of the trailing type with small foliage, and flowers with a double bright strawberry-pink corolla, and white sepals tipped green. *p. 1640*

hyb. 'Streamliner' (1951); patented variety of the hanging type, with long flowers unfolding in a large semi-double corolla of glowing red-purple, and long wavy sepals rosy-red. *p. 1642*

hyb. 'Sunray'; an old dwarf variety of upright habit, with colorful foliage silvery light green with cream to yellow margins flushed cerise; small single flowers with fuchsia-red corolla and rosy-red sepals. *p. 1641*

hyb. 'Swanley Yellow'; an old English hybrid (1900), of the continuously-blooming honeysuckle type; pendant branches with single flowers having a long orange pink tube, pinkish white sepals and small orange-vermillion petals. *p. 1644*

hyb. 'Swingtime'; good trailer and early, free-blooming variety; large double flowers with milky-white corolla and shiny red, short, upturned sepals. *p. 1645*

hyb. 'Texas Longhorn'; difficult but showy plant; long red buds open to display a long white skirt with long red sepals spreading out 15 or 18 cm tip to tip. *p. 1635*

hyb. 'Thunderbird' (1957); very fine naturally cascading plant, profuse bloomer with very long tubes and gracefully twisted sepals flushed pink, and semi-double corolla cherry-red shaded orange; heat-resistant, late. *p. 1642*

hyb. 'Ting-a-Ling'; vigorous upright grower with large clusters of bell-like, all white flowers with flaring skirt-like single corolla. *p. 1643*

hyb. 'Voodoo' (1953); patented variety with large flowers having a very fluffed-up double corolla of deep violet and carmine red sepals; basket or upright. *p. 1642*

hyb. 'Waltztime'; natural trailer with good foliage, and willing bloomer in spite of hot weather; large double flowers; full-double corolla with folded petals of glowing pink, pale at margins, tube and sepals white tipped green. *p. 1646*

hyb. 'Whirlaway'; pendulous, patented cultivar with huge, semi-double, all white flowers, having long coiling sepals and slender corolla which shades to blush-white as the flower matures. *p. 1646*

hyb. 'White Bouquet'; early bloomer with double flowers ivory-white, the sepals are touched with pink, the full skirt of scalloped petals is of heavy texture, and displays the pretty pink pistil. *p. 1646*

hyb. 'Whitemost' (1942); strong grower with large single flowers, pure white corolla with sepals faintly pink; upright or basket use. *p. 1641*

hyb. 'Winston Churchill'; excellent commercial potplant of compact habit and a willing bloomer, with dark green leaves and large round flowers with salmon-red sepals, and deep purplish-blue, fully double petals, on stiff stem, (spring). *Subtropic.* *p. 1637, 1639*

magellanica (Perú, Chile, to Tierra del Fuego), known as the "Hardy fuchsia"; bushy, herbaceous plant growing into a shrub 2 m high, and with support on walls to 6 m, arching branches with small ovate leaves to 5 cm long, wavy-toothed at margins, and pendulous slender flowers with purplish-red calyx lobes longer than the purple-blue petals. *p. 1648*

magellanica gracilis (Mexico); slender, graceful variety with branches finely downy, small leaves and slender tubular nodding flowers with narrow scarlet calyx lobes and purple petals. *p. 1639*

magellanica gracilis variegata; pretty form with red-brown stems and petioles, small, variegated leaves pale milky-green edged with creamy-white, and long slender flowers. *p. 1639*

magellanica variegata, "Variegated hardy fuchsia"; a choice form having its small and narrow, ferny leaves variegated green, white and red. *p. 1638*

procumbens (New Zealand), "Trailing fuchsia"; creeping, branching plant with slender stems, roundish 2 cm leaves, forming mats; tiny erect, 2 cm flowers with calyx tube pale orange and reflexed purple calyx lobes, petals absent; followed by bright red small berries. Good basket plant. *Subtropic.* *p. 1649*

serratifolia (Chile, Perú); tall shrub with dark red branches and lanceolate, toothed leaves having a red midvein, slender flowers with calyx red at base becoming pink and the tips yellowish-green, the corolla scarlet red. *p. 1648*

splendens (Mexico, Guatemala); much branched shrub to 2 m, shiny 12 cm, corrugated leaves ovate-cordate, pale green, toothed; flowers drooping, rather short, about 3 cm long, crimson red, tipped green, base swollen, compressed above, and with prominent stamens. *p. 1649*

triphylla (West Indies: Haiti); bushy shrub to 60 cm high, with downy shoots, ovate to obovate, bronzy, toothed leaves to 8 cm long, purplish beneath; nodding 3 cm flowers in terminal racemes, the spreading tube cinnabar-red, the short corolla vivid coral-red. *Tropical.* *p. 1636*

triphylla 'Gartenmeister Bohnstedt', the "Honeysuckle fuchsia"; a pretty descendant of this little West Indian shrub, with dark metallic green, purple veined leaves, red-purple beneath, and lustrous, slender tubular flowers of salmon-rose with inner petals orange-scarlet, on purple stems, in terminal, nodding clusters, blooming during winter over a long period of time. (1906). *Humid-subtropic.* *p. 1639, 1641, 1643, 1952A*

triphylla 'Traudchen Bohnstedt' (1905); lovely, floriferous hanging variety with clusters of long tubular flowers of pale salmon pink with pointed tips white, and a short coral corolla inside. *p. 1640*

FUIRENA *Cyperaceae* **S3LBW**

simplex (South America); tropical aquatic or bog plant with reed-like stems, set along their length and at the top with long-linear, glossy dark green leaves, showing their paralleled veining. *Humid-tropical.* *p. 948*

FUNKIA: see Hosta

FURCRAEA *Amaryllidaceae* ***I2LFD**

bedinghausii (C. Mexico); large succulent, forming trunk to 1 m long, crowned by a rosette of 30-40 lance-shaped, bluish-gray, leathery-fleshy leaves to 1 m long and 8 cm wide, rough-margined and minutely dentate; inflorescence to 5 m high, with greenish flowers in loose panicle with drooping branches; bulblets are commonly borne on flower clusters. *p. 87, 98*

gigantea (foetida) (So. Brazil), "Giant false agave"; giant rosette of up to 50 fleshy, sword-shaped leaves 1-1½ m long, flat, shining green and with negligible spines; forming 1-1½ m stems; stalk 9-12 m high, bearing branched inflorescence with flowers milk-white inside, greenish outside. *p. 98*

gigantea 'Striata'; spectacularly showy, variegated, open rosette of broad, sword-shaped fleshy leaves 45-60 cm long, sharp-pointed and with occasional marginal spines; highly colored with stripes and broad bands of ivory and milky green over rich green. *Tropical.* *p. 98*

selloa marginata (Colombia), "Variegated false agave"; succulent rosette, forming trunk. Leaves sword-like, more than 1 m long, narrowed toward base, thin and flexible, glossy-green with broad cream margins, armed with vicious curved brown teeth. *Tropical.* *p. 64A, 98*

GAILLARDIA *Compositae* **C2LBD**

aristata (Minnesota to Brit. Columbia); the "Blanket flower"; flower garden hardy perennial 60-90 cm high, more or less rough-hairy, with narrow, gray-green foliage to 12 cm long; colorful flower heads 8-10 cm across, the ray florets red with yellow tips. The plants in cultivation are called G. 'Grandiflora', which may vary in colors, in warm shades of red and yellow with orange or maroon, from June until frost. *p. 806*

GALANTHUS *Amaryllidaceae* **C2HFMdh**

elwesii (Asia Minor), "Giant snowdrop"; spring-blooming bulb to 30 cm high, 2-3 basal narrow linear leaves 20 cm long, glaucous; solitary nodding, bell-like flowers 3 cm long, the 3 long, spreading outer segments white, the 3 short inner segments green at base and tips. *p. 113*

nivalis (France east to Caucasus), "Common snowdrop"; early spring-blooming bulb with 2-3 narrow basal leaves and solitary white 2 cm flowers, the short inner segments green on sinus. *Warm temperate.* *p. 113*

GALAX *Diapensiaceae* **C2HFM**

aphylla (urceolata) (Virginia to Alabama), the "Beetle-weed"; evergreen perennial herb with basal, tufted thin-leathery leaves to 12 cm across, heart-shaped to nearly round, waxy green with crenate red margins and prominent netted veins, on thin-wiry petioles; small white flowers. The leaves are widely used by florists. *p. 950*

GALEANDRA *Orchidaceae* **S3OFM**

baueri (Mexico, Central America to Guyana); semi-terrestrial with stem-like pseudobulbs which zigzag at leaf nodes, to 30 cm high, with numerous leaves, topped by a 25 cm long inflorescence of few 2 cm, fragrant yellow-brown flowers, the lip purple in front, white and purple in throat; long-lasting (summer). *p. 1734*

devoniana (Amazonas, Venezuela, Colombia, Guyana); slender epiphyte with erect leafy stems, with terminal racemes of 10 cm flowers with narrow sepals and petals brownish-purple margined yellow, the large white lip pencilled violet; autumn. (S) *p. 1736*

pubicentrum (Amazonian Perú); small epiphyte with clustered pseudobulbs and few leaves; bracted 15 cm inflorescence with long-lasting, fragrant flowers 4-5 cm long, tube greenish-yellow, sepals and petals tan or brownish green; lip white with pink area, and a large funnel-like spur (winter on). *p. 1734*

GALEGA *Leguminosae* **I2LBD**

officinalis (So. Europe, Asia Minor), "Goats rue"; bright green herbaceous perennial to 1 m, with pinnate leaves, and racemes of 1 cm purplish-blue pea-flowers similar to Wisterias, in summer. *p. 1383*

GALIUM *Rubiaceae* **C2LBD**

boreale (N. No. America: New England to Nebraska and west), "Northern bedstraw"; bushy, weak perennial herb with bright green whorled, lanceolate leaves 4 cm long, and very small, 4 parted wheel-shaped white flowers in panicles; hardy. *p. 2020*

verum (No. Eurasia), a "Yellow bedstraw"; bushy perennial with weak stems, whorls of 8 narrow-elliptic hairy leaves, and small yellow flowers in dense clusters; hardy. *p. 2020*

GALPHIMIA *Malpighiaceae* **S2LBM**

glauca (Thryallis) (Mexico to Panama), "Gold shower thryallis"; handsome bush of open habit, 1 to 1½ m high, with scandent branches, opposite thin-leathery oblong bluish glaucous leaves to 5 cm long, and small 2 cm yellow flowers in showy, elongate clusters. Very floriferous evergreen for the warm greenhouse or conservatory. *Tropical.* *p. 1518, 1521*

GALPINIA *Lythraceae* **S3LFM**

transvaalica (Transvaal); evergreen shrub with opposite, narrow lanceolate leaves, the branches after blooming, terminating in showy clusters of red berries. *p. 1523*

GALTONIA *Liliaceae* **C-I2LBDd**

candicans (So. Africa), "Giant summer hyacinth"; beautiful bulbous plant to 1 m high, with flat, linear leaves and showy white fragrant flowers, nodding like little bells in tall, loose clusters; summer. *Subtropic.* *p. 1446, 1447, 1452*

GARCINIA *Guttiferae* **S2LBM**

mangostana (Malaya), the "Mangosteen"; important tropical fruit tree 6 to 10 m; in Peradeniya, Sri Lanka are magnificent specimens to 30 m high; the opposite, dark green and leathery elliptic foliage is 15 to 25 cm long; purple or yellow-red male flowers with fleshy petals are 4 cm across; the brilliant purplish-crimson fruit, measuring 6 to 8 cm dia., with rind and edible segments like an orange, yellow juice and with large flat seeds; at the base with 4 persistent sepals. The white delicious pulp has a flavor between a grape and peach. Fruit usually ripens in Peradeniya in July or August, but differs according to season. *Tropical.* *p. 1319*

tinctoria (morella) (India, Malaya, Thailand); the "Indian camboge"; tropical evergreen tree with long lanceolate, leathery, glossy green leaves 10-15 cm long; yellowish flowers, the males axillary, the female flowers larger; the fruit resembling a cherry in size, slightly 4-lobed; the resinous juice of the tree yeilds a well-known pigment for artists paints and a purgative in medicine. *p. 1319*

xanthochymus (India), the "Camboge tree"; tall tropical evergreen shrub or tree to 12 m high, with handsome dark green leathery lanceolate leaves 25-45 cm long; small 2 cm white flowers in summer, followed by lemon-yellow, pointed fruit 6 cm long, the thick rind containing pith-like flesh and one large seed. The slightly acid fruit yields cathartic. *p. 1319*

GARDENIA *Rubiaceae* **S2HBM**

jasminoides 'Belmont' (Plant Patent No. 93), the "Opera-gardenia"; also commerically grown as 'Hadley', a mutation (1926) of the horticultural variety 'Grandiflora'; the leading variety for cut-flower production under glass; well-branching bushy shrub with large magnolia-like leaves 10-15 cm long, producing in succession large double, pleasantly fragrant velvet white flowers, 10-12 cm across, turning to deep ivory with age; the petals are of thick texture; primarily in bloom during late winter and spring to June; the cut blooms are usually 'tailored' by wiring and taping them through a rosette of leaves stapled together onto a paper collar, for wear as a corsage. *p. 2013*

jasminoides 'Fortuniana' (syn. florida) (So. China), "Cape jasmine"; robust shrub with strong woody branches rather sparry, large, shining dark green, leathery, quilted leaves, and big 10 cm, fragrant, waxy-white flowers of heavy substance, turning creamy-yellow with age, spring and summer; the yellow fruit is eaten in China. *Tropical.* *p. 2013*

jasminoides 'Mystery'; known in horticulture as 'Grandiflora', the old "Southern gardenia"; evergreen shrub with large 8-10 cm dark green, glossy, quilted foliage; waxy-white semi-double or double flowers 8 cm dia., very fragrant, used for corsages. Not as profuse in flowering as 'Fortuniana', but with larger blooms. *p. 2012*

jasminoides 'Veitchii', "Jasmine rose" or "Everblooming gardenia"; double-flowering form of the Chinese species, of compact, bushy habit, dense with smaller, shining green leaves, and while the sweetly fragrant, pure-white flowers average only 8 cm in dia., they are extra double and willing to bloom from January to May; often laden with buds and flowers. *Tropical.* *p. 2013, 2015, 2016, 2112A*

radicans florepleno (Japan), "Miniature gardenia"; dwarf, shrubby plant with spreading, rooting branches, narrow, 5-8 cm pointed leaves and small, solitary, irregularly double, white flowers, very fragrant. *Subtropic.* *p. 2012, 2013*

spatulifolia (Trop. Southern Africa), the "Transvaal gardenia"; evergreen tree to 6 m, smooth branches with spatulate leaves 3-8 cm long; tubular-flaring flowers to 10 cm across, pale yellow becoming deep yellow, with 6-9 lobes. *p. 2012*

taitensis (Society Islands: Tahiti), the charming "Symbol flower" or "Tiare tahiti"; considered the most beautiful flower of the islands; evergreen bush some 2 m high, with dark and glossy obovate 10 cm foliage with creamy midrib; the fleshy salver form waxy flowers with 6-8 linear petals arranged like a pin-wheel, 4-5 cm across, snow-white, incomparably scented, blooming in the evening and lasting several days; Tahitians put a blossom behind the ear after bathing, collecting it in the bud. *Tropical.* *p. 2012*

thunbergia (So. Africa: Natal); robust bush with woody branches, leathery, glossy green, broad-elliptic 10-15 cm leaves; large 8-14 cm long-tubed, waxy-white single flowers of 8-9 petals overlapping shingle-like, very fragrant. *Subtropic.* *p. 2012, 2013*

GASTERANTHUS *Gesneriaceae* **I3HFM**

atratus (Besleria) (W. Ecuador); compact cloud forest terrestrial of rather succulent habit, with fleshy stems and deeply bullate or puckered, unequal-sided ovate, thick leaves 12 to 17 cm long, the surface deep green and waxy, overlaid with metallic black patina, the margins crenate, and underside red-dish purple; flowers tubular with long spur, to 7 cm long, lemon-yellow and marked with maroon stripes. *p. 1241*

x GASTERHAWORTHIA *Liliaceae* ***I2LBD**

'Royal Highness' (Gasteria verrucosa x Haworthia margaritifera); attractive California bi-generic hybrid, small shapely, easy-growing rosette with short tapering, stiff leaves concave on top, dark green and densely covered with white warts. *p. 1453*

GASTERIA *Liliaceae* ***I2LFD**

armstrongii (So. Africa: Cape), "Wart plant"; low, depressed, slow-growing plant forming offshoots; in youth usually two-ranked, but later forming spiralled rosette; thick-succulent, stiffly recurving leaves 3 cm or more broad, dark green with whitish warts and spiny tip, toward base very concave, to 6 cm long. *Subtropic.* *p. 1449*

batesiana (So. Africa: Zululand); star-like succulent rosette with broad triangular olive green leaves keeled beneath, rough by large deep green dots and smaller silver tubercles. *Arid-subtropic.* *p. 1448*

caespitosa (Cape Prov.), "Pencil leaf"; small succulent with slender, recurving leaves in 2 ranks and freely suckering, with confluent light green markings, and horny margin. *p. 1449*

croucheri (So. Africa); large stiff rosette of 60 cm dia., with stiff, succulent, channeled leaves tapering to a point, off-center keels beneath, dark green with light green blotches; flask-like flowers green with salmon base in semi-pendant racemes. *p. 1450*

echinata hort.; bold rosette of triangular, deeply concave fleshy leaves gradually tapering to a sharp point, and set with minute prickles, deep blackish green with pale green striplets throughout. *p. 1448*

glabra major (South Cape); stemless succulent, forming suckers, fat, fleshy leaves in spiralled rosette, concave and green with white spots, margins horny. *p. 1452*

'Hybrida', "Ox-tongue" or "Bowtie-plant"; representative of the numerous unnamed hybrids in California nurseries, with thick, tongue-shaped leaves spirally arranged, dark green turning purplish, and with large greenish-white tubercles; of free growing habit. *p. 1449*

laetipunctata (So. Cape Prov.); nice spiral rosette with long-tapering, triangular fleshy leaves 10-12 cm long, furrowed above, obliquely keeled beneath, dark green with numerous white tubercles. *p. 1448*

liliputana (Cape Province), a miniature "Ox-tongue"; attractive, suckering miniature, smallest of the genus, with first two-ranked, later spirally arranged, thick, short-stubby, keeled leaves dark green and glossy, mottled nile-green. *Arid-subtropic.* *p. 1449*

lingua (disticha) (Cape Prov.); attractive two-ranked succulent with tongue-like leaves to 25 cm long and 5 cm wide, flat on top and with sharp edges, dark green with round white spots in crossbands; unbranched inflorescence 1 m high, with scarlet flowers. *p. 1450*

maculata (Cape of Good Hope); sturdy succulent with tongue-shaped leaves arranged in two ranks, thick-fleshy, rounded below, dark green with white blotches slightly raised and rough horny edges; flowers scarlet. *p. 1449*

obtusifolia (So. Africa); compact two-ranked, stemless succulent with broad, stubby leaves dark green mottled greenish white, and with a rough surface. *p. 1449*

stayneri (Cape of Good Hope); succulent with opposite, recurved, concave, tongue-shaped leaves tipped with fine point, fresh green, tinted copper, thickly covered with light green warts. *p. 1449*

transvaalensis (Transvaal); spiralling rosette with fleshy, tongue-shaped leaves arranged in ranks, dark green and smooth, 10-12 cm long, and toothed toward the white-horny apex, spotted pale green. *p. 1448*

trigona (Cape Prov.); spiralling, suckering rosette with fleshy tongue-shaped leaves more or less opposite, slightly curving inwards, 15-20 cm long, fresh-green with white spots in loose bands, margins horny-tubercled. *p. 1448*

verrucosa (So. Africa), a "Warty aloe"; attractive succulent suckering from the base, with 2-ranked, fleshy, concave leaves pointed at tip, dull deep green and covered with raised white warts; clusters of small rosy flowers 2 cm long on tall stalks to 50 cm high. *Arid-subtropic.* *p. 1449, 2092*

GASTROCHILUS *Orchidaceae* **S3OFM**

calceolaris (Burma to Java); small epiphyte with few, folded leaves to 18 cm long; inflorescence very short with few flowers 2 cm dia., sepals and petals greenish or yellowish with purplish spots, the sac of the lip yellow outside, white with orange inside (autumn). *p. 1734*

dasypogon (Saccolabium calceolare) (Himalayas); small epiphyte with stout leafy stem and axillary brown flowers, the white lip with orange blotch and tiny purple spots. (S) *p. 1736*

x GASTROLEA *Liliaceae* ***I2LBD**

beguinii (Aloe in hort.) (Aloe aristata x Gasteria sp.), "Pearl aloe"; dense rosette of rather narrow, leathery, short-pointed, keeled leaves dark green marked with pale warty dots, and warty teeth at margins. *Arid-subtropic.* *p. 1396*

rebutii (Aloe variegata x Gasteria); attractive rosette with thick-fleshy, pointed 14 cm leaves spirally arranged, dull green with numerous spots in transverse bands; horny margins. *p. 1452*

smaragdina (Aloe variegata x Gasteria candicans); suckering bigeneric succulent with slender, long linear fleshy leaves spreading more or less opposite inclining to spiral 20 cm or more long, flat. *p. 1448*

'Spotted Beauty' (Gasteria x Aloe); a California hybrid combining the rosette-shape of Aloe with the hard nature of Gasteria in an attractive, trim miniature; deep green leaves, tinged bronze, are covered with white tubercles and have translucent spines on keel and margins. *p. 19*, 1449*

GAULTHERIA *Ericaceae* **I2LFM**

shallon (W. No. America: Alaska to California), "Salal" or "Lemon leaf", a "Florist's greens"; low evergreen shrub to 1 m high in sun, in shade to 3 m, densely spreading and forming thickets, as in the Redwood forest along the Pacific coast; the decorative foliage oval, 8-10 cm long, leathery bright green and with depressed ribs; white or pinkish bell-like flowers on reddish stalks; edible black fruits resembling large huckleberries, but are bland in flavor. *p. 968*

GAUSSIA *Palmae* **S3LFM**

princeps (Cuba); slender feather-palm to 15 m high, with tapering trunk thickened toward base and partially exposed woody roots; few arching pinnate dark green leaves 2 m long, closely crowded with rigid leaflets; small fruit purple to red. *p. 1878*

GAZANIA *Compositae* **I2LBD**

krebsiana (So. Africa); attractive perennial with long spatulate, lobed leaves, and large, solitary daisy-like orange or red flowers, with the base-part of the broad florets blackish-brown forming a dark inner circle, and opening to a warming sun. *p. 808*

pavonia (So. Africa); low herbaceous perennial with lanceolate leaves white woolly beneath; short daisy-like flowers orange-terra cotta with basal blackish spot ringed white in beautiful peacock pattern. A midday flower open from 11 to 2 on warm afternoons. *p. 808*

pavonia var. hirtella (So. Africa); low plant with small pinnate leaves, silver gray beneath; large daisy-like flowers deep orange, with white and brown peacock design at the base of each floret, forming a ring around center. *Subtropic.* *p. 808*

rigens 'Gold Nuggets'; beautiful hybrid involving G. rigens and others; with small foliage, forming clumps; short-stalked large, showy daisy-like flowers 5 to 8 cm across, rich yellow with black at base of each ray; a dazzling color display during peak of bloom in late spring and early summer, in mild climate. *Subtropic.* *p. 806*

rigens hybrida, small perennial dense with narrow obovate leaves white-woolly beneath, the pretty flower heads golden yellow in the So. African species, brown-black in center; hybrids in various colors red, cream, orange, buff, with pretty markings. *Subtropic.* *p. 808*

splendens; possibly a hybrid; free-blooming, tall-growing to 45 cm; narrow-spoon-shaped leaves silky-white beneath; large heads of orange ray-flowers each black at base with a white spot, forming a pretty ring around the dark disk. *p. 808*

splendens florepleno; curious form with outer florets folded and in more than one circle, also long-linear rays appear out of the center disk. *p. 808*

splendens variegata; a variegated-leaf form; the dense narrow-oblanceolate foliage prettily edged in creamy-white; flowers orange with dark ring around cushion. *p. 808*

GEISSORHIZA *Iridaceae* **I2LBD**

rochensis (Cape Prov.), "Wine-cups"; a very pretty small cormous herb 15-22 cm high, with long-linear, ribbed, basal leaves; wiry stalks bear several wide cup-like flowers 3 cm across, the outer area satiny violet-blue, the base crimson, both colors separated by a thin white line. *Subtropic.* *p. 1336*

GEITONOPLESIUM *Liliaceae* **I3LFM**

cymosum (E. Australia); woody perennial, climbing by twining, with linear 8 cm leaves, and small 1 cm purplish-green drooping flowers in loose terminal clusters. *p. 1478*

GELSEMIUM *Loganiaceae* **I2LFM**

sempervirens (Virginia to Florida, Texas and Central America), "Carolina yellow jessamine" or "False jasmine"; sparry evergreen shrub with scandent or clambering brown branches reaching to 6 m; leathery glossy-green ovate-lanceolate, opposite leaves 4 to 10 cm long; small flaring trumpet flowers 3 cm dia., yellow and sweetly fragrant like a tea rose blooming from December into summer and later. *Warm temperate.* *p. 1517*

GENISTA of florists: see Cytisus

GENLISEA *Lentibulariaceae (Carnivorous Pl.)* **S3LFW**

repens (Brazil); tiny insectivorous plant from Sao Paulo, growing submersed in shallow water, from a rhizome without roots, but blooms above water; has two kinds of leaves, true foliage leaves usually spoon-shaped, and dangling trap leaves which are hollow and partially inflated for 1 cm, like a lobster trap, furnished with glandular hair secreting sticky mucilage, and insects entering cannot get out and are digested. *p. 766*

GENTIANA *Gentianaceae* **C2LBM**

acaulis (Europe: Alps and Pyrenées), "Blue gentian"; very pretty low, tufted perennial to 10 cm high with narrow elliptic leaves and solitary 5 cm, funnel shaped flowers deep blue, in spring. *Temperate.* *p. 1168, 1169*

andrewsii (Eastern No. America), the "Closed gentian"; hardy perennial to 60 cm high, with opposite ovate leaves, the stems topped by clusters of purplish-blue flowers with white on lobes, nearly or quite closed, 4 cm long. *p. 1169*

asclepiadea (So. Europe; Caucasus); perennial with arching leafy 60 cm stems, light green ovate leaves, and solitary, bell-shaped 4 cm flowers dark blue with pale stripes, and spotted purple inside. *p. 1169*

forwoodii (No. America: Pacific Northwest); leafy perennial 20-30 cm high, rarely branched; thick oblong 2-4 cm leaves, narrowed at tip, at apex of stem the tubular flowers 3-4 cm long, deep blue streaked with green; similar to G. affinis. *p. 1169*

lutea (Pyrenees, Alps, Balkans, Asia Minor), "Yellow gentian"; leafy perennial 1-1½ m tall, ovate leaves blue-green; 2½ cm flowers in whorls on erect stalks, yellow, veined or spotted. *Temperate.* *p. 1169*

saponaria (Ontario to Florida and Louisiana); erect perennial to 75 cm high with leafy stems and oblong foliage; topped by clusters of club-shaped blue flowers in Aug.-Sept. *p. 1168*

'Sino-ornata hybrid' (x sinora); cultivar of sino-ornata (Yunnan, Tibet), vigorous prostrate perennial with ascending leafy stems, bearing large trumpet-like 6 cm flowers silvery-blue striped green, inside green and spotted blue; autumn. *p. 1168, 1169*

tibetica (Himalayas); robust mountain perennial 60 cm high, from a basal rosette of fleshy, broad lanceolate leaves to 30 cm long, the stem-leaves forming a tube round the stem, the uppermost enclosing the inflorescence; the numerous flowers at apex greenish white and tubular-funnel-shaped. *p. 1169*

GEOFFROEA *Leguminosae* **S3LBM**

inermis (Panama); spreading tree with large pinnate leaves on arching branches, terminated by racemes of waxy small flowers, lilac-pink with purple center. Seen along the streets in Balboa. *Tropical.* *p. 1384*

GEOGENANTHUS *Commelinaceae* **S1HFM**

ciliatus (Siderasis 'Blackie' hort.) (Perú); handsome tuberous plant with succulent, rounded, quilted leaves 10-12 cm across, waxy blackish purple with red veins, even darker beneath. *p. 785*

undatus (Perú), "Seersucker plant"; compact, low growing suckering plant with stiff-fleshy broad ovate, quilted leaves dark metallic green with parallel bands of pale gray; wine-red beneath. *Tropical.* *p. 768A, 780, 782*

GERANIUM *Geraniaceae* **I-C2LBD**

anemonifolium (canariense) (Canary Islands), "Storksbill"; true geranium; perennial with a thick root stock and large, glossy green, palmately 5-parted leaves, the lobes finely dissected; flowers rosy-purple, and long-beaked fruits. *p. 1177*

grandiflorum (Sikkim); branching perennial 30 cm high, with roundish long-stalked leaves deeply 5-lobed and toothed; the 4 cm flowers characteristic with 5 equal petals and 10 stamens, lilac with purple veins. *Subtropic.* *p. 1177*

napuligerum (China, Korea); tufted perennial to 38 cm with short rhizome, slender leaning stems with rounded deeply lobed bright green leaves and 5-lobed rosy-lilac flowers 2½ cm across. *p. 1177*

subcaulescens (cinereum) (Pyrenées); small almost stemless perennial with hairy, glaucous deeply lobed leaves, and 2½ cm flowers bright rose with darker veins. *p. 1177*

traversii elegans (Chatham Isl., New Zealand); gray pubescent perennial with stout stems and round 7-parted leaves of beautiful silvery color, the lobes wedge-shaped and 3-parted; flowers pink. *p. 1177*

GERANIUM: see also Pelargonium

GERBERA *Compositae* **I2LBD**

jamesonii (Transvaal), "African daisy"; herbaceous tufted perennial with pinnately lobed leaves very woolly beneath; long-lasting flowers daisy-like with slender, usually orange-flame colored florets, but also in shades from brick-red to yellow and white. *Subtropic.* *p. 809*

jamesonii florepleno, "Double Transvaal daisy"; cultivars with large flowers of perfect symmetry fully double, the inner disk developed out with a burst of linear rays shorter than the outer ring, in a range of colors from yellow to red. *p. 809*

viridifolia (South Africa); tufted perennial with crown of rootstock silky; obovate leaves, and long-stalked daisy-like flowers variable in colors ranging from white to pink above, pink, purplish or brown beneath. *p. 809*

GESNERIA *Gesneriaceae* **S3HFM**

christii (Dominican Republic); rough-hairy, herbaceous tropical plant with tuberous rhizome; the oblong, rugose leaves shiny deep green; inflated oblique tubular flowers crimson red with blackish tips, and covered with silky hair; photograph on pg. 1244 by Ruth Katzenberger. *p. 1244*

cuneifolia (Pentarhaphia reticulata) (Cuba, Puerto Rico, Hispaniola), "Firecracker"; low-growing rosette of leathery, glossy grass-green, long wedge-shaped leaves with toothed margins; and tubular somewhat bottle-shaped flowers burning red, yellow inside, borne singly on short stalks. *Humid-tropical.* *p. 1251, 1252*

ventricosa (Antilles); tuberous tropical plant with fleshy ovate, rich dark green leaves; from fleshy stems the slender-stalked curved tubular flowers orange red, the corolla 3 cm long, with stamens long protruding. *p. 1244, 1257*

verrucosa (Pentarhaphia) (Cuba); evergreen subshrub with waxy, obovate leaves, crenate and lightly lobed especially near apex, olive green above, pale beneath; tubular salmon-red, 2-3 cm solitary flowers with five small lobes on thin stalks. *p. 1258*

GESNERIA: see also Sinningia

GIBASIS *Commelinaceae* **S2LFD**

geniculata (Jamaica); in hort. trade as Tradescantia multiflora, the "Tahitian bridal veil"; small free-branching creeper with string-like stem, narrow shining olive-green 2½ to 5 cm leaves purplish beneath; tiny white flowers. *Tropical.* *p. 782, 787*

GIBBAEUM *Aizoaceae* **S2LBD**

album (Cape Prov.); light-gray clusters of split fleshy ovoid leaves to 4 cm long, with keeled apex, densely set with minute white hairs; the young bodies appear through the widening cleft; flowers white. *p. 68*

dispar (Cape Prov.); cluster-forming growth of 2 unequal succulent oval leaves somewhat keeled, gray-green with velvety touch; flowers lilac-pink. *p. 68*

fissoides (nelii) (Cape Prov.); cluster-forming succulent with long, finger-like leaves in uneven pairs, more flat inside, rounded outside, gray-green to reddish; red or violet flowers 4 cm. *p. 68*

heathii (Cape Prov.); large whitish-green obovoid, ball-like body to 4½ cm high, the pressed-together leaves only separated by a small cleft; splitting from side and doubling with age; flowers white turning pink. *p. 68*

petrense (So. Africa: Cape Prov.), "Flowering quartz" or "Shark's heads"; minute, nearly stemless succulent with fleshy roots, forming clumps; growths with 1 or 2 pairs of modified fat leaves, united at base and only 1 cm long, whitish gray-green, flat on top, keeled below; small reddish flowers. As in Lithops, water must be withheld when growth is completed and the plant rests. *Arid-subtropic.* *p. 79*

GILIA *Polemoniaceae* **I2LBD**

androsacea (California); attractive annual branching herb with erect stems to 40 cm high, with leaves palmately divided into thread-like segments; flowers 3 cm long, in various colors white, yellow, pink or violet, summer-blooming. *p. 1950*

californica (Leptodactylon) (California), "Prickly-phlox"; low spreading shrub to 1 m high, crowded with leaves divided into rigid linear lobes, 1 cm long; flowers rosy lilac 4 cm across. *p. 1950*

dianthoides (So. California, Baja California), "Ground-pink"; small tufted annual with hairy, linear, thread-like 2½ cm leaves, toothed or fringed lilac flowers with 5 spreading corolla lobes. *p. 1951*

rubra (So. Carolina to Florida and Texas), "Standing-cypress"; biennial to 2 m high, dense with leaves divided needle-like, numerous trumpet-shaped scarlet flowers, 4 cm long, yellow dotted with red inside. *p. 1950*

GILIBERTIA: see Dendropanax

GINKGO *Ginkgoaceae* **I2LBDh**

biloba (China), the "Maidenhair-tree"; deciduous resinous tree to 40 m high; perhaps the most ancient existing flowering plant, sole survivor of an extinct race of the carbon age. Woody trunk with gray, corky bark, and broad fan-like leathery grayish green leaves with parallel veining; flowers without petals in catkins, male and female on separate trees; grown in pots as dwarfed bonsai in Japan. The kernels or ginkgo nuts are much eaten in the Orient. *Temperate.* *p. 1317*

GLADIOLUS *Iridaceae* **I2LBDd**

alatus (So. Africa); small cormous species to 30 cm with rigid linear leaves, and zigzag spike with tubular-flaring carmine-red and pink flowers having very unequal segments, the lower smaller ones yellow-green and pink. *p. 1334*

dracocephalus (So. Africa); erect plant with leaves to 45 cm long, the floral stalk to 60 cm, with few flowers yellowish-green and spotted purple, the tube much curved and to 5 cm long, the upper segments hooded. *p. 1330*

x hortulanus 'Valeria', "Garden gladiolus", "Florists glads" or "Painted lady"; large soft salmon-red flowers similar to 'Halley', in shape of spreading, curved funnels on stiff spike, with sword-shaped leaves, produced on bulb-like corm; descendant of numerous So. African species. *p. 1327*

orchidiflorus (So. Africa); curious little cormous plant 30 to 50 cm high, with 3 to 4 linear leaves; stiff stems with 4-6 small, scented greenish-yellow and white flowers, with upper petal strongly curved or hooded reminding of a snake, the side petals with wine-purple central stripe and red angles on lower petals; spring blooming. *p. 1330*

palustris (Italy, Balkans); perennial plant with base of stem swollen into a corm; ribbed leaves, and slender, stiff stalk to 45 cm, bearing trumpet-shaped purplish-red flowers with curved tube, facing to one side. *p. 1334*

segetum (Mediterranean Reg.), the "Corn-flag"; slender plant 40-50 cm high, with 2-4 leaves 30 cm long, flowers on zigzag stalks, in loose clusters, funnel-shaped with flaring segments bright purplish rose, 4 cm across face, inside with white central line outlined in violet. *p. 1330*

symetranthus (So. Africa); unusual species with slender awl-shaped leaves, and thin-wiry stalks bearing at apex small pale yellow flowers almost bell-shaped with petals nearly even and rounded at tips, on the outside with a reddish line. *p. 1330*

tristis (Natal); cormous plant 60 cm high, with 3 terete, ribbed leaves; fragrant curved tubular trumpet flowers yellowish-white with purplish on the keels, in a loose, strongly one-sided spike; summer. *p. 1334, 1338*

GLAZIOVA *Bignoniaceae* **S3LFD**

bauhinioides (Brazil); tropical climber with clinging roots on the slender stems, the small oval 6 cm leaves arranged in whorls of four; plant photographed at Botanic Garden Heidelberg. *p. 496*

GLAZIOVA Mart. (Palm.): see SYAGRUS

GLECHOMA *Labiatae* **C-I2LFMh**

hederacea, better known as Nepeta hederacea, (Europe, Asia); naturalized in North America, "Gill-over-the-ground"; small, lively creeper useful as ground cover or for baskets, the hairy, kidney-shaped leaves light green, crenate at the margins, 2-4 cm across, and rooting at the nodes; small light blue flowers. *Temperate.* *p. 1349*

hederacea variegata (Nepeta), "Variegated ground-ivy"; very attractive small mat-forming herbaceous spreader, with thin, string-like creeping or pendulous stems, opposite little rounded leaves milky green, with scalloped margins, and more or less variegated toward outer edge. An ideal and charming basket plant. *Warm-temperate.* *p. 1353*

tuberosa (Nepeta) (Spain), "Cat-mint"; soft herb with shrubby base, and hairy, angled stems, the cordate ovate, wrinkled grayish green, pungent leaves 3 cm long, crenate at margins and covered with white down; tiny 5 mm lavender flowers marked purple, in bracted spikes. Of minty scent, cats like leaves and blossoms, especially when dried, as a stimulant, also used as tea to soothe the nerves. *p. 1341*

GLEICHENIA *Gleicheniaceae (Filices)* **I3HF-BM**

bifida (West Indies: Dominica); handsome low tropical fern with creeping rhizome; on thin wiry stalks the soft green fronds divided into biforked sections, each with long pinnate leaves extending almost like lacy ribbons, the pinnae lightly undulate and with pale tips. *p. 1079*

linearis (dichotoma) (Malaya to Borneo), "Savannah fern"; thicket-forming tropical fern with long creeping rhizome; leathery leaves on zigzag rachis, repeatedly 2 or 3 branched, ultimate branches bearing a pair of forked pinnae. *Humid-tropical.* *p. 1082*

rupestris (New South Wales, Queensland); large creeper, wide-spreading, with fronds ½-2 m long, on wiry purplish stalks; the pinnately lobed leaflets smooth and leathery, bluish beneath, the margins recurved. *p. 1082*

GLIRICIDIA *Leguminosae* **S3LBD**

sepium (Central America, Colombia), "Madre de cacao"; ornamental tropical tree to 9 m, with pinnate leaves; clusters of flowers pinkish-lilac with white in profusion before the leaves; pods to 12 cm long; a favorite shade tree for coffee and cacao plantations. *Tropical.* *p. 1384*

GLOBBA *Zingiberaceae* **S3LFM**

atrosanguinea (Borneo); rhizomatous herb with slender, arching stems to 1 m high, shiny dark green sessile leaves, and inflorescence with scarlet-red bracts and yellow corolla. *p. 2134, 2137*

bulbifera (India: Eastern Himalaya, Malabar); perennial herb with fleshy rhizomes and leafy stems to 25 cm high, stem-clasping leaves broad lanceolate, soft-hairy beneath; erect or arching inflorescence with waxy flowers, the corolla and lip yellow; along the lower floral stalk many breeder bulblets cradled in boat-shaped bracts. *p. 2134*

schomburgkii (Thailand, Vietnam); stiff erect leafy stalks to 45 cm high, bearing nodding inflorescence with light green bracts and yellow flowers, the divided lip yellow with red spots. *p. 2137*

winitii (Thailand); perennial herb to 1 m high, with slender rhizome and fibrous roots; large lanceolate leaves, the base sheathing the stem, and hairy underneath; flowers in a loose, drooping terminal panicle to 15 cm long, with rose-purple bracts, and corolla yellow with a curved tube; autumn. *Tropical.* *p. 2130, 2135, 2137*

GLOMEROPITCAIRNIA *Bromeliaceae* **S3HBM**

penduliflora (Guadeloupe, Dominica, Martinique); the giant of Antilles bromeliads; epiphytic leaf-rosette to 2 m tall and 2-2½ m in dia., the leaves covered with scurfy scales, later smooth, reddish toward apex; the branched inflorescence to 3 m or more tall, red throughout, with erect leathery floral bracts, the dark red sepals covering the small yellow petals; the species is monocarpic, or dies after flowering and setting seed. *p. 579*

GLORIOSA *Liliaceae* **S2-3LBMd**

carsonii (Central Africa); tuberous climber with shiny wiry stems set with clasping 10-12 cm thin leaves ending in a grasping tendril; magnificent flowers with broad recurving 6 cm segments wine-purple, edged with lemon-yellow especially toward base. *Tropical.* *p. 1451*

'Greeneae' hort.; canary-yellow, smooth, straight petals, lightly tinted copper. *Tropical.* *p. 1451*

rothschildiana (Kenya, Uganda), "Glory lily"; a climbing "lily" with tuberous roots, the fresh-green, lanceolate leaves prolonged into tendrils; striking flowers with broad, recurved petals crimson-scarlet, golden-yellow toward base; blooms early spring on, but can be flowered anytime. I remember this growing north of Mombasa, clambering over coastal jungle. *Tropical.* *p. 1408A, 1450, 1451, 1452*

simplex (virescens, plantii, greenei) (No. Uganda, Mozambique, Zaire, Fernando Po), a dwarf "Glory lily"; with broader petals, not crisped, and which I first saw in Surinam where, in the shade of trees, it is a clear yellow, while in sunlight, the petals turn orange; summer-blooming. *Tropical.* *p. 1451, 1452*

superba (India, Ceylon), "Crisped glory lily"; tall vining herb blooming late summer to fall only, flowers are smaller, with narrow but crisped petals, to 8 cm long, first green, then yellow, changing to orange red; at its best into autumn. *Tropical.* *p. 1451*

superba lutea; showy variety with crisped petals entirely yellow, blooming from late summer into fall. *p. 1450*

verschurii (East Africa); tuberous vine rather compact-growing to 2 m, leaves broader than rothschildiana, shorter pedicels; 9 cm flowers with broad, reflexed segments of substantial texture, deep vivid crimson, yellow at base and margins. *Tropical.* *p. 1451*

virescens hort. (Surinam), "Yellow glory-lily"; herbaceous climber from tuberous roots; fresh glossy green leaves prolonged into tendrils; flowers with smooth petals clear yellow. *p. 1452*

GLOSSOCALYX *Monimiaceae* **S3LBM**

longicuspis (Gabon, Equatorial Africa); small tree with sparry branches, long lanceolate, leathery leaves, and tiny white, tailed flowers from the base of leaves. *p. 1523*

GLOTTIPHYLLUM *Aizoaceae* **I2LBD**

fragrans (Cape Prov.); low succulent with fleshy, twisted, tongue-shaped leaves flat on top, keeled beneath, 6-8 cm long; flowers 8-10 cm across, shining golden yellow and sweetly scented. *Arid-subtropic.* *p. 65*

latum (Cape Prov.); clustering succulent with large soft-fleshy, glossy bright green leaves, to 15 cm long; pairs of uneven length, flat above, rounded beneath and curved like a sickle; bright yellow flowers 5 cm across. *p. 65*

linguiforme (So. Africa), "Green tongue leaf"; small, branching succulent with tongue-shaped, soft-fleshy leaves, glossy green; flowers yellow. *p. 64*

oligocarpum (Cape Prov.); succulent with creeping branches, growths 4-leaved, keeled leaves arranged in two rows, of unequal length, to 5 cm, whitish-olive green or chalky-white, set with prominent dots; flowers yellow. *p. 66*

platycarpum (Cape Prov.); very succulent perennial, with tongue-shaped, glaucous leaves in uneven pairs; 5 cm flowers yellow. *p. 66*

regium (Cape Prov.); robust succulent forming clumps; each growth with 1-2 pairs of leaves, very soft-fleshy, glossy vivid green, concave on top, rounded under-side, 3-10 cm long and recurving; golden yellow flowers 4 cm acoss with orange anthers. *p. 65*

surrectum (Cape Prov., to Karroo); densely clustering succulent, branching, pairs of tapering or awl-shaped leaves; fl. yellow. *p. 66*

x GLOXINERA: see SINNINGIA

GLOXINIA *Gesneriaceae* **S3HFMd**

perennis (maculata) (Colombia, Brazil, Perú), "Canterbury bells"; fleshy, spotted stem to 45 cm high, on scaly rhizome but no tuber, bearing large downy, bell-shaped fragrant flowers 4-5 cm long, purplish blue with darker throat; basal leaves heartshaped, crenate, waxy above and reddish beneath. *Tropical.* *p. 1251*

sylvatica 'Redbird' (Seemannia); a distinguished cultivar of this species, from Tropical America; by Prof. R. Lee of Cornell University, Ithaca, New York; tall growing with square gray stem; dark green, shiny ovate leaves; the inflated tubular flowers orange red, inside yellow with brown-red spots; flowers in one axil only at each leaf pair. *p. 1276*

GLOXINIA: see also Sinningia

GLYCOSMIS *Rutaceae* **S3LFM**

pentaphylla (India, Malaya, Philippines); small ornamental spineless evergreen bush with pinnate leathery leaves, 5-7 long-elliptic leaflets but occasionally less, 15 cm long; small white, fragrant flowers from leaf axils, and small 1 cm translucent pinkish berries. *p. 2033*

GLYCYRRHIZA *Leguminosae* **I2LBM**

glabra (C. Europe, Spain, Mediterranean), "Licorice" or "Sweet-wood"; perennial with sweet, woody rootstock inside yellow and which furnishes licorice; erect stem to 1½ m high with vivid-green pinnate leaves, small pale blue pea flowers in axillary raceme. *p. 1378*

GNAPHALIUM: see Helichrysum

GNIDIA *Thymelaeaceae* **I-S3LFD**

denudata (South Africa); floriferous evergreen shrub 1-4 m high, with densely hairy shoots, small oval 2 cm opposite leaves; flowers in terminal clusters, with yellow hairy calyx 2 cm long, and tiny petals in spring. G tomentosa is similar, but with alternate leaves. *p. 2098*

GODETIA: see under Clarkia

GOETHEA *Malvaceae* **S3LFM**

cauliflora (Brazil); evergreen shrub 45 cm high; erect woody stems with large decorative oval leaves; flowers minute but their waxy calyx showy with 4-6 segments yellowish and scarlet-red, developing from leafless stems or old wood. *p. 1532*

strictiflora (Brazil); small shrub with long-ovate, crenate leaves tinted red; the inflorescence axillary or directly out of woody stems, with bracts 2 cm long and beautifully glowing crimson, longer than the white petals. *p. 1532*

GOMESA *Orchidaceae* **I3OFM**

crispa (Brazil), a "Little man orchid"; floriferous epiphyte with 2-leaved pseudobulbs, arching inflorescence; small 2 cm, fragrant yellow-green, waxy, crisped flowers, into summer. (I) *p. 1692, 1734, 1736*

planifolia (Brazil), "Little man orchid"; small epiphyte with 2-leaved pseudobulbs and gracefully pendant spray of small waxy, sweetly fragrant greenish-yellow flowers. (spring-summer). (I) *p. 1737*

scandens (glaziovii) (Brazil); dwarf epiphyte with little, compressed, single-leaved pseudobulbs, borne at intervals on a stout ascending rhizome; arching spikes with many small fragrant yellowish-white flowers, the lip with greenish keels (spring). (C) *p. 1737*

sessilis (Brazil); attractive epiphyte with clustered pseudobulbs and dual leaves; the arching inflorescence to 30 cm long, with numerous nearly stalkless small 2 cm flowers yellow-green, lip white with orange markings (spring). *p. 1734*

GOMPHRENA *Amaranthaceae* **I2LBD**

globosa (India), "Globe amaranth"; erect annual branching herb with elliptic leaves ciliate at edge, and strawy clover-like flower heads which if cut just before maturity are "everlasting", retaining their color, usually white, to purple, for a long time. *Tropical.* *p. 82*

GONATANTHUS *Araceae* **I3LFM**

sarmentosus pumilus (Sikkim); small, tuberous plant of the Himalayas with peltate, waxy, green leaves, some marked brown; thickened veins and gray-marked stem; plants I dug out of rock crevices in the Himalayas, kept bare root for weeks without wilting. *p. 208*

GONATOPUS *Araceae* **S3LFM**

boivinii (Trop. E. Africa: Zanzibar); from a flattish tuber 15 cm dia. rises the solitary, robust leaf, several times divided and distantly pinnate, the ovate or elliptic leaflets 10 cm long and quilted, on 75 cm stalk marbled with blackish brown; the inflorescence on 30 cm spotted stem, with lanceolate spathe yellow-green outside marbled with brown, spadix yellowish white. *Tropical.* *p. 224*

marattioides (Microculcas) (Tanzania); curious tropical aroid with long creeping rhizome; pinnate leaf 10-12 cm long, the leaflets very narrow and channeled down center; spadix near base thick and cone-like, and ovate, deflexed spathe. *p. 227*

petiolulatus (E. Africa: Tanzania); tuberous tropical aroid with dissected leaf 40-80 cm long, the leaflets concave, and waxy green; the inflorescence with spadix having upper flowers with rudimentary ovaries, the lower without staminodes or anthers; the spathe 15-20 cm long, outside light green, inside whitish green. *p. 224*

rhizomatosus (Transvaal, Natal, Mozambique); very curious rhizomatous aroid with leaves dividing into several dissected branches, the leaflets glossy green, lanceolate and slender pointed; inflorescence on 10 cm stalk with 6-7 cm greenish-yellow spathe closely wrapped around spadix, slit open on one side and coming to an awl-shaped point. *Subtropic.* *p. 224*

GONGORA *Orchidaceae* **S-I3OND**

armeniaca (Nicaragua); epiphyte with small oval pseudobulbs and long elliptic, light green leaves; flowering raceme lax and pendulous, with salmon-yellow sepals spotted red, tiny petals, and a fleshy, inflated, yellow lip; fragrant. (June-Sept.). (S) *p. 1735, 1737*

atropurpurea (Venezuela, Guyana, Amazonas), "Punch and Judy orchid" because of their curious blooms; epiphyte with ribbed pseudobulbs bearing two large pleated leaves; inflorescence pendant, to 70 cm long, with numerous strongly scented, intricately shaped flowers 4 cm long, yellowish and lacquered deep brown-red (summer). *p. 1734*

galeata (Mexico), "Punch and Judy orchid"; curious epiphyte with small, clustered pseudobulbs bearing 2 plaited leaves; graceful, pendulous raceme of strongly scented, small flowers on arching stalks, sepals and petals brownish-yellow, the upper sepal hooded, lip wine-red. (May-Sept.) (I) *p. 1737*

quinquenervis (maculata) (Brazil); epiphyte; bulbs and 2-ribbed leaves both pale green; nodding flowers yellowish-white spotted with dull wine-red, in pendulous raceme. *Tropical.* *p. 1736*

quinquenervis tricolor (Perú); epiphyte, thickly ribbed, 2-leaved pseudobulbs, and pendulous racemes of small, scattered flowers, the sepals rich bright yellow blotched brown; petioles pale yellow lightly spotted, the tip of lip stained with cinnamon, the base white and with 2 horns. (spring, and various). (I) *p. 1737*

truncata (Mexico); clustering, leafy species with small, grooved pseudobulbs; extraordinary inflorescence pendulous, to 70 cm long, with many fragrant 4 cm flowers on arching stalks, whitish and freckled with brownish-red, the curved lip clear yellow (summer). *p. 1734*

GOODENIA *Goodeniaceae* **I2LBD**

ovata (Southeastern Australia); attractive slightly sticky shrub to 1 m or more high, ovate, toothed leaves 3 to 5 cm long; small yellow pansy-like flowers 2 cm across, bright lemon-yellow with brown lines in throat, and scattered through the bush. *p. 1318*

GOODYERA *Orchidaceae* **C-I3HNM**

hispida (Himalayas); beautiful small terrestrial with creeping then ascending stem to 15 cm high, clothed with lanceolate, hairy, dark green leaves edged in red, overlaid with a network of white veins, rosy toward margins; small flowers brownish, in terminal spike. (I) *p. 1736*

procera (India, Malaysia, So. China); erect growing terrestrial to 1 m, with light green lanceolate leaves, the narrowed bases clasping; spike with dense head of tiny white 1 cm hooded flowers. *p. 1734*

pubescens (E. North America); the "Rattlesnake orchid"; charming dwarf terrestrial with a tuft of ovate dark velvety green, 8 cm leaves marked with a network of silvery-white veins; sticky-hairy flowering stalk with small greenish-white flowers; summer. (C) *p. 1736*

GORGONIDIUM *Araceae* **S3LFM**

mirabile (Bolivia); interesting aroid with depressed globular bulb-like corm, giving rise to a short-stalked boat-shaped spathe brownish purple lined with white, 20 cm long, with purple spadix sheltered inside; after blooming the robust 2 or 3 times dissected leaf, the green leaflets crisped at margins, on stalk with pale spotting. *p. 224*

GOSSYPIUM *Malvaceae* **S2LBD**

herbaceum (Arabia, Asia Minor), "Levant-cotton"; annual, little-branched herb to 1 m, with thin-leathery, palmately 5-7-lobed leaves, and showy yellow flowers with purple center; capsular fruits or "bolls" whose seeds bear fleece or lint, furnishing cotton. *Tropical.* *p. 1528*

hirsutum (C. America), the "Upland cotton"; usually annual subshrub $\frac{1}{2}$ - $1\frac{1}{2}$ m high, much branched with hairy, reddish stems, 3-lobed, tomentose leaves; flowers white or pale yellow soon turning purplish-pink; the surrounding bracts fringed; seeds with greenish-white fuzz or lint, a source of cotton. *p. 1528*

GOVENIA *Orchidaceae* **S3OFM**

utriculata (Mexico, C. America to Argentina, W. Indies); terrestrial with subterranean tuber-like pseudobulbs from fibrous rhizome; 1 or 2 large plicate, stalked leathery leaves to 40 cm; wiry stalk supports a many-flowered inflorescence, to 1 m long; hooded flowers 4 cm across, creamy-white tinged with purple, spotted and striped brown within, lip marked red (autumn). *Subtropic.* *p. 1738*

GRAMMANGIS *Orchidaceae* **S3OFM**

ellisii (Madagascar); handsome, robust epiphytic orchid, with large spindle-shaped angled pseudobulbs, carrying 3-4 leathery, oblong leaves to 60 cm long, glossy dark green; the arching inflorescence arises with new growth, to 1 m long, in many-flowered racemes; blooms are heavily fragrant, waxy and long-lasting, to 8 cm across, the sepals yellow barred with brown, petals whitish with rose apex, the lip striped with red. *p. 1746*

GRAMMATOPHYLLUM *Orchidaceae* **S3OFM**

measuresianum (Philippines); strong-growing handsome epiphyte with clustered, ovoid pseudobulbs with several oblanceolate leaves to 60 cm; long erect or arching inflorescence that may extend $2\frac{1}{2}$ m; raceme with up to 50 waxy flowers 5 cm across, sepals and petals wavy, creamy yellow spotted and tipped blackish-red, lip yellowish with brown veins (summer). *p. 1738*

papuanum (New Guinea); handsome giant epiphytic orchid with tall stem 1-2 m long, set with leaves in two ranks; showy racemes of 8-12 cm waxy-firm, rounded flowers, brightly colored lemon-yellow and spotted purplish-brown. (S) *p. 1736*

scriptum grandiflorum (measuresianum) (Moluccas); attractive epiphyte of relative small size in the genus, with stem-like ribbed pseudobulb some 60 cm high bearing strap-shaped leathery leaves, and basal raceme 60-90 cm long with many 8 cm waxy flowers, the spreading oblong sepals and petals canary yellow blotched all over with brown, the lip marked brown and gold (summer). (S) *p. 1737*

speciosum (Java, Malaya, Vietnam), magnificent epiphyte, meriting the title of "Queen of orchids"; with stout stems $1\frac{1}{2}$-3 m long, bearing numerous 2-ranked strap leaves, and basal floral stalks to $1\frac{1}{2}$ m long with as many as 100 showy flowers 8-15 cm across, the undulated sepals and petals rich yellow, blotched with reddish-brown (winter). *Tropical.* *p. 1737, 1738*

GRAPHORKIS *Orchidaceae* **S3OFW**

lurida (Trop. West Africa); clustering epiphyte resembling a small cymbidium; small pseudobulbs with pleated, deciduous leaves 30 cm long, and with aerial roots; wiry, branched raceme with many small $1\frac{1}{2}$ cm flowers brownish-purple, lobed lip white with yellow midlobe (winter). *p. 1734*

GRAPTOPETALUM *Crassulaceae* **I2LBD**

amethystinum x Echeveria flammea: see PACHYPHYTUM

filiferum (Mexico: Chihuahua); attractive stemless rosette 5-6 cm across, with 75-100 spatulate fleshy leaves, densely shingled and recurving downward, forming a symmetric mound, convex and shining green to silver-gray, with wing-like white margins and ending in a brown bristle; branched floral stalk with flower spotted red inside, white outside. *p. 913*

paraguayense, also known by its synonym Sedum weinbergii (Mexico), "Ghost plant" or "Mother-of-pearl plant"; branching succulent loose rosette forming thick stem and fleshy, broad 5-8 cm leaves flat and somewhat recurved on surface, keeled beneath, amethyst-gray with silvery bloom; flowers white. The foliage has a subtle opalescent blending of colors, but the leaves are brittle and drop easily when handled. *p. 914, 922*

GRAPTOPHYLLUM *Acanthaceae* **S1LBM**

pictum (hortense) (South East Asia), "Caricature plant"; dense evergreen shrub to $2\frac{1}{2}$ m high, with leathery elliptic leaves 10-15 cm long, deep green variegated creamy-white along central area; crimson red flowers. *Tropical.* *p. 46*

x GRAPTOSEDUM *Crassulaceae* **I2LBD**

'Peach-glow', (Graptopetalum x Sedum); charming succulent hybrid, forming clusters, photographed at Indian Rock Nursery in Vista, California 1963; perfect rosette of obovate pointed, concave, thick leaves symmetrically arranged to form a rounded nest 8-10 cm across; light green, waxy leaves overlaid with a shimmering beige and peachy glow, the apex edged in rose. *p. 914*

GRAVISIA: see Aechmea

GREENOVIA *Crassulaceae* **I2LBD**

aurea (Sempervivum) (Canary Islands); beautiful cushion-forming succulent shrub, in habitat growing to altitudes of 1700 m; cup-shaped rosettes to 40 cm across, of thin, erect, obovate leaves waxy blue-green, and with narrow white margin; flowers golden yellow with spreading linear petals, in showy terminal clusters. *Subtropic.* *p. 913*

dodrantalis (Canary Islands); small 5 cm rosette of fleshy, spoon-shaped leaves vivid blue-green with waxy surface, flat open when in growth, urn-shaped when resting; clusters of yellow flowers on elongated leafy growth. *p. 888*

GREIGIA *Bromeliaceae* **I2HBD**

sphacelata (Chile); terrestrial rosette to 1 m, spreading soft-leathery glossy-green leaves, spiny-margined; flowers rose, in heads with spiny bracts. *Subtropic.* *p. 512.*

GREVILLEA *Proteaceae* **I2LBD**

alpina (Australia: Victoria); bushy shrub to 1 m with felty shoots crowded with dark green narrow $2\frac{1}{2}$ cm silky-hairy leaves, small, pretty 1 cm flowers red at the swollen base, yellow upward, with protruding style. *p. 1969, 1974*

asplenifolia (New So. Wales); tall shrub to 5 m; linear, saw-edged leaves 10-25 cm long, silky beneath; red flowers arranged like a tooth-brush on the underside of axillary spikes. *Subtropic.* *p. 1969*

banksii (Queensland), "Scarlet grevillea"; small tree $4\frac{1}{2}$-6 m high, hairy branches with pinnate leaves to 25 cm long, segments linear and white-silky beneath; bright coral red flowers downy outside, in dense, one-sided clusters. *Tropical.* *p. 1969*

bipinnatifida (W. Australia); shrub to $1\frac{1}{2}$ m with branches appressed-hairy, stiff leaves bipinnately lobed and spine-tipped, twisted in all directions, often obscuring the handsome heads of vivid scarlet, curiously snail-shaped blooms. *p. 1969*

crithmifolia (Western Australia); shrub to 2 m high; leaves $2\frac{1}{2}$ cm long, much divided into needles; terminal clusters of densely packed white flowers. *p. 1974*

juniperina (sulphurea) (New So. Wales); small shrub to 2 m, densely set with needle-like leaves to $2\frac{1}{2}$ cm long, silky beneath; silky flowers pale yellow tinted red, with long protruding style. *p. 1969*

lavandulacea (So. Australia to Queensland); compact shrub with downy branches and flowers in terminal clusters, rich rose, with lobes much recurved, and protruding style. *p. 1969*

'Noellii'; low and compact evergreen hybrid with beautiful rose-red and white blooms in spring; needle-like green foliage (Monrovia Nursery, Calif.). *p. 1974*

punicea (New South Wales), "Red spider-flower"; woody shrub to $1\frac{1}{2}$ m high; narrow-elliptic 3 cm leaves covered with fine silky hairs flat on the surface; inflorescence 6 cm across, with long curving styles deep red. *p. 1974*

robusta (Queensland, New S. Wales), "Silk oak"; daintily lacy, ornamental plant while small, but growing into a mighty tree 45 m high; silvery downy shoots with fern-like, green leaves, 2-pinnate into finely lobed segments silky-haired, giving them a grayish appearance; flowers golden yellow in one-sided racemes to 10 cm long. *Subtropic.* *p. 1968, 1969, 1974*

rosmarinifolia (New Caledonia); woody shrub 2 m high, with needle-shaped foliage and curled red flowers. *p. 1974*

thelemanniana (W. Australia), "Orange spider-flower"; showy shrub with bipinnate silky, bluish leaves divided into linear segments; flowers with rosy-red tube and yellowish-green recurved lobes, and long, curving $2\frac{1}{2}$ cm red style. *Subtropic.* *p. 1969*

vestita (W. Australia); large spreading bush $2\frac{1}{2}$ m high, with arching branches, the wedge-shaped leaves divide into 3 sharp points at apex; axillary clusters of small white flowers. *p. 1969*

wilsonii (Western Australia), "Fire wheel"; an erect shrub 1-$1\frac{1}{2}$ m high, densely branched, with fern-like, 2-3 pinnately divided foliage into linear light green segments, rigid and sharply pointed; the odd red and yellow flowers in loose racemes, with showy styles and bright red perianth in fluffy heads.

GREWIA *Tiliaceae* **I3LBD**

caffra (So. Africa), "Lavender star-flower"; spreading evergreen shrub to 2-3 m high, dense with small oval waxy, moss-green leaves with finely crenate margins, 6-8 cm long; charming starry flowers soft lavender pink with prominent yellow stamens in center, 4 cm across; larger and more perfectly shaped flowers than the similar G. occidentalis. *Subtropic.* *p. 2098*

hexamita (Transvaal); spreading bush of the Veld 2-3 m high, with roundish, glossy green, thick leaves, and starry yellow flowers with reflexed petals and prominent stamen bundles. *p. 2098*

GREYIA *Melianthaceae* **I2LBD**

radlkoferi (Transvaal), "Mountain bottle brush"; bushy shrub to 12 m; with big, fleshy-herbaceous, downy, bronzed foliage, deeply toothed; terminal erect raceme of glossy scarlet red, cup-shaped flowers. *p. 1549*

sutherlandii (Natal, Transvaal), "Mountain bottle-brush"; small tree with deciduous, broad, deeply toothed, smooth leaves to 8 cm; inflorescence brush-like, bright scarlet, with conspicuous purplish-red filaments. *Subtropic.* *p. 1549, 1550*

GRIFFINIA *Amaryllidaceae* **S3LFDd**

hyacinthina (Brazil); bulbous plant with stalked, thick, ovate-oblong dark green leaves to 20 cm long, with netted veining; lily-like lilac flowers 8 cm across, the broad upper segments directed upward, blue at top, white toward base, in stalked umbels. *p. 130*

GRISELINIA *Cornaceae* **I2LBD**

lucida (New Zealand) "Shining broadleaf" or "Kapok"; handsome evergreen shrub or tree to 10 m often epiphytic, forming aerial roots; leathery-fleshy, shining green oblong or broad-ovate leaves 10-20 cm long, oblique at base; minute dioecious flowers in axillary clusters. *p. 855*

lucida 'Variegata' (New Zealand); lovely ornamental, dense bush or tree to 8 m, often epiphytic and forming aerial roots; the oblique oval thick-leathery leaves normally glossy green, 6-10 cm long; in this cultivar variegated or edged in ivory white; minute male flowers with purplish-green petals. *Subtropic.* *p. 855*

GROBYA *Orchidaceae* **S3OFW**

amherstiae (Brazil); unusual epiphytic orchid of the humid rainforest; pseudobulbs with narrow foliage, and arching raceme of complex waxy flowers with brownish-yellow sepals and reddish petals with darker spots. *p. 1738*

GRUSONIA *Cactaceae* **S1-2LBD**

hamiltonii (Opuntia hamiltoniae) (Mexico: Baja California); cylindrical joints similar to Opuntia but longitudinally ribbed; slender light green columns with rounded ridges, and lightly marked elevations, the areoles set wtih long lemon-yellow tufts of glochids that rub off easily; in the California nursery trade. *p. 624*

GUADUA *Gramineae* **S3LBD**

angustifolia (Panama, Jamaica, Colombia, Venezuela, Brazil to Argentina); a giant non-hardy timber bamboo with culms to 20 m or even 30 m tall, and 10-20 cm thick, widely arched above; the internodes hollow with wood 2 cm or more thick, higher up the branches usually thorny, leaves oblong lanceolate 16 up to 20 cm long. Used much for timber in South America, also by opening large culms out flat in place of sawn boards of wood. Locally cut into sections to use instead of flower pots. *Tropical.* *p. 1301*

GUAIACUM *Zygophyllaceae* **S2LBD**

officinale (West Indies, N. So. America), "Lignum-vitae tree"; to 10 m high, with trunk of very hard, heavy, greenish-brown, resinous wood; glossy pinnate leaves with 5 cm leaflets in 2 to 3 pairs; small blue flowers at ends of twigs. *p. 2126*

GUILLAUMINIA *Liliaceae* **S3LBD**

albiflora (Aloe) (So. Madagascar); unusual succulent with linear leaves spirally arranged, these 15 cm long, channelled on top, rough with white tubercles, olive green with grayish spots, finely toothed; flowers white marked olive. *p. 1459*

GUNNERA *Haloragidaceae* **C2LBW**

chilensis (scabra) (Chile, Ecuador, Colombia), "Chilean rhubarb"; large perennial herb with creeping rhizome and dark green hard, puckered leaves to 1½ m diameter, palmately and deeply cut into pointed and toothed lobes, on reddish stalks with fleshy green spines; the inflorescence spikes with branches short and thick, while they are long in manicata. *p. 1320, 1321*

hamiltonii (New Zealand); low perennial creeper 3 cm high, with tufts of dark olive or grayish green, serrated leaves of leathery texture, 2-3 cm long, and forming cushions; small greenish flowers in clusters 6 cm high, followed by small 3 mm red berries. *p. 1321*

manicata (So. Brazil), "Prickly rhubarb"; the largest species with huge leaves to 2 m across, palmately lobed, more kidney-shaped than chilensis; hard, rough puckered, light green with buff veining, on thick light brown stalks with thorn-like prickly hairs. *Subtropic.* *p. 1320*

GURANIA *Cucurbitaceae* **S3LFM**

malacophylla (Upper Amazon); tall tendril climber with usually 3-lobed, hairy leaves; male flowers reddish, in long-stalked clusters; the female flowers later, axillary. *Tropical.* *p. 932*

GUSSONAEA *Orchidaceae* **S3OFW**

exilis (Microcoelia) (Madagascar); leafless orchid growing epiphytic, a curiosity for its absence of leaves when mature; from a short central stem the fleshy roots carrying chloroplast assuming the function of the missing leaves, spreading in all directions and clinging to trees; the short inflorescence of small whitish flowers rises from the center. *p. 1738*

guyoniana (Microcoelia) (Eritrea to Angola), a "Leafless orchid"; remarkable genus growing epiphytic, with a tiny central stem from which radiate thick-fleshy or woody gray roots, and containing the chlorophyll normally in green leaves; short inflorescence 5-8 cm long with tiny 5 mm bell-shaped flowers pure white, the lip with long curving spur. *p. 1763*

physophora (Microcoelia) (Madagascar, Zanzibar); remarkable leafless epiphyte from Tsarantanana forest; an interesting orchid reduced to a cluster of fleshy, grayish-green, flattened roots 1 cm wide, clinging to the trunks of trees; small white flowers rising from a tiny central stem, the lip with a long spur. *Tropical.* *p. 1735, 1763*

GUZMANIA *Bromeliaceae* **S1HFM**

berteroniana (Puerto Rico), "Flaming torch"; formal rosette of wine-red or sometimes fresh green, thin leathery leaves with showy inflorescence in form of a tight cylindrical head of scarlet bracts with yellow flowers. *Tropical.* *p. 512, 512A, 555*

berteroniana 'Rubra', a habitat form with highly colored foliage deep coppery red. *p. 575*

crateriflora: see sanguinea

cryptantha (Colombia, Venezuela, Guyana); rosette with laxly drooping, strap-shaped leaves to 60 cm long, often reddish, densely flat-scaly; inflorescence on erect bracted stalk with scurfy-scaly floral bracts and long yellow petals. *p. 558*

dissitiflora (Costa Rica, Panama, Colombia); shapely rosette with recurving linear leaves 30 to 90 cm long, light green with fine length-stripes, the base brownish, dotted scaly beneath; erect inflorescence with bright red scape-bracts and floral bracts, and tubular flowers with white petals. *Tropical.* *p. 554, 560*

'Fantasia'; beautiful hybrid, photographed in the Palmengarten Frankfurt, Germany; rosette of narrow, soft-leathery, glossy green leaves laxly pendant; showy inflorescence with branched heads of yellow flowers as in a bouquet, subtended by coppery red bracts. *Tropical.* *p. 557*

fuerstenbergiana (Andes of Ecuador); pretty rosette with channeled leaves 30 cm long, medium green distinctly lined maroon toward base and over back; inflorescence in a simple short, cylindrical, dense spike with bright red bracts and whitish flowers. *p. 555*

globosa (Colombia); grass-like rosette, usually epiphytic, with numerous narrow-linear, smooth green leaves 60 cm long, brown at base; inflorescence with long red scape bracts and many-flowered head filled with jelly; transparent yellow floral bracts and green sepals with red base, and white petals. *p. 559*

gloriosa (Colombia, Ecuador); rosette of broad leathery leaves to 60 cm long, green with bright red tip, the base covered with fine brown scales; stout erect, leafy stalk with red floral bracts and yellow flowers. *p. 553*

insignis (Colombia); rosette of leaves 60 cm long and 5 cm wide, reddish underneath; showy branched inflorescence with light amaranth-red floral bracts and lemon-yellow flowers, on leafy stalk. Dr. L.B. Smith (Smithsonian) refers this to Tillandsia insignis. *Tropical.* *p. 554, 557*

x intermedia (lingulata var. cardinalis x splendens); attractive, medium-sized rosette with characteristics of both parents; soft relaxed leaves light olive green changing to reddish at base, reverse wine-red; the stout, leafy floral stalk topped by a star-like rosette of peach-colored, recurving bracts flushed with red, and small white flowers in the center of the nest. *p. 556*

lindenii (Northeastern Perú), "Large snake vase"; showy large rosette of glossy-leathery leaves beautifully mottled moss-green with jagged ivory or pinkish cross-bands, made up of parallel lines across the leaf; these lines show brownish beneath. Inflorescence with numerous white flowers. *Tropical.* *p. 557, 561*

lingulata (C. America to Guayana, Pará, Mato Grosso, Ecuador, Bolivia); striking epiphytical rosette from the rainforest, with smooth metallic green leaves, forming a showy, raised head of leathery, brilliant fiery-red bracts, with a contrasting center of hooded, waxy orange-red inner floral bracts tipped yellow to white, and with white flowers. *Tropical.* *p. 512, 554, 556*

lingulata 'Broadview'; magnificent clone of a plant collected in Ecuador, with its bold inflorescence of recurving, long, vivid scarlet red, glossy-leathery bracts spreading to 16 cm dia., the center with short waxy incurved red bracts tipped yellow, and white flowers; the scape-leaves typically red at base. *p. 512A, 553*

lingulata cardinalis; striking plant with slender metallic purplish leaves, spineless; inflorescence a raised cup of cardinal-red bract-leaves with cream-white flowers. *p. 555*

lingulata minor, "Orange star"; small, clustering rosette of strap-like, thin-leathery, yellowish green leaves, with maroon pencil lines starting at base and diminishing toward tip; long floral bracts bright orange-red, and small white flowers. *Tropical.* *p. 554, 555*

lingulata minor flammea (Colombia); similar to type except the inner red bract leaves of the inflorescence are white-tipped. *p. 555, 558*

lingulata minor flammea 'Striata'; small rosette 17 cm high, of strap-shaped arching leaves light green striped and banded lengthwise with pinkish cream, the base with brown-red lines; inflorescence with salmon-rose bract-leaves also banded with creamy salmon, the flowers white. *p. 560, 572*

x lingulzahnii (lingulata x zahnii); a beautiful combination by Geo. de Meyer of Ghent; formal rosette of broad, glossy leaves light green suffused with red, soft-leathery and reflexed; the stout inflorescence with a dense head of creamy flowers subtended by triangular orange-red leathery bracts. *p. 556*

x magnifica (lingulata cardinalis x minor); a magnificent epiphyte when the inflorescence develops its stalked star-like, raised 15 cm head of brilliant scarlet, leathery bracts lasting from November to April, flowers white; soft leaves green with reddish lines. *Tropical.* *p. 553, 555*

monostachia (tricolor) (W. Indies, C. America, to Brazil), "Striped torch"; formal rosette of thin-leathery bayonet shaped yellow-green leaves; inflorescence a stiff spike with bracts salmon-red striped brown, and white flowers. *Tropical.* *p. 555, 558*

mucronata (Venezuela); compact epiphytic rosette with green leaves 30-40 cm long and 5-6 cm wide, the margins with brown; short cone-like inflorescence to 10 cm long, with shingled green bracts margined yellow or brown, and displaying the yellow-green bell-shaped flowers 8 cm long. *p. 560*

musaica (Colombia), "Mosaic vase"; showy rosette to 60 cm or more across, of broad pea-green leaves marked with crossbands consisting of multiple wavy lines dark green to red-brown; underneath purplish with lines much darker; flower spike with red-lined bract leaves, the head with orange-red bracts, and golden flowers tipped white. *p. 19*, 512, 512A, 553, 555, 558*

'Naranja' ('Hummel's Memoir' x lingulata 'Major'), a lovely hybrid rosette with shiny, fresh green recurving leaves, from the center a raised nest of scarlet-red bracts, the inner bracts tipped yellow, and white flowers. *p. 560*

nicaraguensis (So. Mexico, C. America, Panama); epiphytic rosette of tropical forests at about 1000 m; linear, smooth green leaves, the underside with thin red pencil lines lengthwise, to 25 cm long and 2 cm wide; inflorescence a cone of red bracts with yellow flowers 6 cm long. *p. 556*

sanguinea (crateriflora) (C. America, Trinidad, Colombia, Ecuador); stout, compact, rather flat rosette with broad, thick leaves 30 cm long, scaly at base, the inner leaves ruby-red from the middle up to the apex, the lower part yellow and chartreuse at flowering time; the flowers a slender yellow tube with spreading white lobes, in a center cup. *Tropical.* *p. 556, 558*

strobilantha (Ecuador, No. Perú); epiphytic or terrestrial rosette with strap-shaped green leaves 35-45 cm long and 2-3 cm wide; the inflorescence on a tall stalk, a cone of reddish bracts with yellowish-white flowers. *p. 556*

vittata (Colombia, Brazil), "Snake vase"; attractive epiphyte with stiff-leathery, narrow leaves 4 cm wide arranged more or less erect and partially funnelshaped, about 60 cm long, glossy dark green beautifully cross-banded with small silvery scales; the inflorescence an erect spike with insignificant bracts and white flowers. *p. 554*

zahnii (Colombia, Panama); very ornamental plant with strap-like, papery, olive green leaves pencil-striped maroon-red, the center tinted pink to coppery red; strong branched inflorescence with pink to yellow bracts and white flowers. *Tropical.* *p. 512, 554, 555, 557*

GYMNADENIA *Orchidaceae* **C2HFM**

conoptera (conopsea) (No. Europe to Arctic Lapland, No. Siberia, No. Japan), "Purple orchid"; tuberous terrestrial orchid with linear, keeled leaves, the inflorescence an erect 30-45 cm spike of numerous small fragrant, purple or carmine-rose flowers, the upper sepals and petals hooded, lip 3-lobed and with a slender spur; May-June. (h) *p. 1739*

GYMNOCALYCIUM *Cactaceae* ***C2LBD**

bodenbenderianum (Argentina: Cordoba), a "Chin-cactus"; so named because of its characteristic knobs featuring a chin below the aeroles; rather flat and disk-like globe to 8 cm dia., gray green or brownish, with 11-14 tubercled, broad ribs, spines curved back; flowers pink with brown stripe; free-blooming. *p. 692*

bruchii (Argentina), "Chin cactus"; depressed little globe, bearing many offshoots, shallowly ribbed, and with curved bristle-like white spines; pinkish flowers; will grow faster and bloom earlier if grafted. *Arid-subtropic.* *p. 692*

damsii (Paraguay), a "Chin cactus"; small globular cactus, flattened on top, with 10-12 wide, tubercled ribs, spines white tipped brown; flowers white, outer segments green tipped red. *Arid-subtropic.* *p. 692*

denudatum (So. Brazil to Argentina), "Spider cactus"; broad globe to 15 cm dia., deep green, with 5-8 very broad, notched ribs, spidery, curved yellowish spines; flowers white or pale rose. *Arid-subtropic.* *p. 691*

gibbosum (Argentina, Patagonia); globular to cylindrical cactus to 20 cm high, dark bluish green, with 12-19 notched ribs, pale brown spines; flowers white to reddish. *p. 692*

gibbosum gerardii; variety densely covered with long, needle-like, stiff yellowish spines on the prominent cone-like knobs; flowers pinkish to red outside. *p. 695*

kurtzianum (Argentina: Cordoba); depressed globe to 15 cm across, olive green, with 10-18 ribs cut into high knobs tipped by hard buff, recurved spines; flowers white and reddish base. *p. 693*

lafaldensis (Argentina: Cordoba); small globular plant, to 4 cm dia., clump-forming, dark green, with 12 low ribs divided into roundish knobs, bristle-like white spines; flowers violet pink; (may be the same as G. bruchii). *p. 692*

leeanum (Argentina, Uruguay), "Yellow chin-cactus"; small depressed globe, glaucous green, with 11-14 indistinct ribs, covered with slender spines; large flowers yellow, the outer perianth segments purplish. *p. 691*

mihanovichii (Paraguay), "Plain chin cactus"; grayish green, depressed little globe to 6 cm thick, with 8 triangular, notched ribs and banded with maroon, straw-colored spines; free-flowering chartreuse. *p. 618, 691*

mihanovichii friedrichii (Uruguay, Argentina), "Rose plaid cactus"; little depressed globe, coppery green with triangular ribs, banded cream and yellow spines; flowers when young, pink. *Arid-subtropic.* *p. 19*, 691*

mihanovichii friedrichii 'Gold Crown'; small depressed globe with 8 ribs and thin spines, 3 to 6 cm dia., in this colorful chlorophyll-poor mutant a beautiful, glowing gold-orange tinted with red; usually grafted on Selenicereus pteranthus as shown on pg. 695; mostly grown in Japan and exported. *p. 695*

mihanovichii friedrichii 'Rubra'; the novel "Red cap", "Oriental moon", "Hibotan"; strikingly colorful red (or yellow) small globe; variant with chlorophyll-poor body; for better growth and survival usually grafted on night-blooming Hylocereus undatus, or Selenicereus. *Arid-subtropic.* *p. 691*

multiflorum (So. Brazil to Argentina); globe to 10 cm high, glaucous bluish green, 10-15 ribs with narrow furrows, cut into prominent knobs with a chin below, thick radials radiating comb-like; flowers pinkish. *p. 693*

platense (Argentina); small depressed globe, partly hidden in ground, to 8 cm dia., bluish-green or purple, 8-12 notched ribs with a prominent chin below the areoles and few spines "("Chin cactus"); flowers bluish-green outside, white inside. *p. 693*

quehlianum (Argentina); depressed globe resembling a bishop's cap, 15 cm dia. and 4½ cm high, 8-13 ribs with rounded tubercles dark olive, horny recurved radials; flowers white with red center. *p. 693*

saglione (Argentina: Tucumán); broad depressed globe, to 30 cm dia., when young the top surface velvety grayish green, wrinkled into an attractive design, later with 13-32 ribs with large low tubercles with curved spines; flowers pinkish. *Arid-subtropic.* *p. 691, 693*

schickendantzii (N. W. Argentina); broadly globular and flattened, to 10 cm dia., mostly with 7-16 ribs, cut into broad 5-sided warts, spines slightly flattened; flowers pinkish. *p. 691*

venturianum (Uruguay: Montevideo); globe lightly depressed, 5 cm thick, pale bluish green, with 9 broad rounded ribs cut into knobs with chins below; yellow radials; flowers bright carmine. *Arid-subtropic.* *p. 693*

GYMNOSTACHYS *Araceae* **S2LBM**

anceps (Queensland); tuberous rooted plant with grass-like, long-linear, rigid leaves prominently veined; white flowers not showy. *p. 207, 294*

GYMNOSTACHYUM *Acanthaceae* **S3LBM**

ceylanicum (Cryptophragmium), (Sri Lanka); small tropical ornamental with downy stems spreading horizontally; dark green oval leaves with rib and veins banded white, white-felted beneath; 30 cm spikes of small white flowers tipped green and yellow, and white anthers. *p. 45*

GYNURA *Compositae* **S2LBM**

aurantiaca (Java), the popular "Velvet plant"; a beautiful tropical herbaceous plant with stout stems and fleshy, broad-ovate, serrate 12 cm leaves densely velvety with violet or purple hairs and deeper purple veins; orange disk-flowers. *Tropical.* *p. 817*

bicolor (Moluccas), "Oakleaved velvet plant"; tropical branching foliage plant with heavy, fleshy, slightly clammy leaves, 12-15 cm long, deeply and irregularly lobed on sides, metallic green with purple cast and short-hairy on top, midrib light purple and glossy, rich purple beneath; terminal flower heads with orange florets. *Tropical.* *p. 823*

x sarmentosa (aurantiaca x bicolor), "Purple passion vine"; twiner with reddish stem, lanceolate leaves with wavy-toothed or shallowly lobed margins, and covered by purple hairs; wine-red beneath; small orange flower heads in clusters at ends of branches. In Europe (Hay-Synge Blumenbuch 1973) as G. procumbens (Lour.) Merr. *Tropical.* *p. 823*

GYPSOPHILA *Caryophyllaceae* **C2LBD**

elegans (Caucasus), "Baby's breath"; annual with forking stems and narrow leaves, numerous small white or rosy flowers; good bouquet-plant. *p. 758*

GYROCARPUS *Hernandiaceae* **S3LBD**
americanus (jaquinii) (Rhodesia or Zimbabwe); deciduous tree 6 m or more high with trunk to 30 cm dia., smooth gray bark bleached white on sunny side; broad 3-lobed pubescent leaves 8-12 cm long; the inflorescence a dense cluster of small greenish yellow flowers, followed by pendulous ovoid, velvety brownish fruit 5-8 cm long, with long 5-14 cm spatulate reddish wings dangling in the breezes; found near Victoria Falls and along the Zambezi River. *p. 1323*

HAAGEOCEREUS *Cactaceae* **I2LBD**
bicolor (So. America); light green column with some 14 dense ribs with areoles thickly clothed with cream-colored woolly tufts, hair-fine radials and set of weak needle spines tipped brown. *p. 644*
chosicensis (Perú); "Foxtail"; fresh-green column with as many as 21 low ridges completely hidden by the masses of bristle-like golden-yellow spines; night blooming with rosy-red flowers. *p. 644*

HABENARIA *Orchidaceae* **C-I2LFMd**
antennifera (Transvaal), "Fringe orchid"; a terrestrial or ground orchid of the Veld; tuberous roots produce an annual shoot bearing broad ovate, clasping leaves and the densely flowered erect inflorescence about 50 cm high; the very complicated flowers 6-8 cm long, greenish-white. After blooming and forming seed capsules the growth wilts, and plant remains dormant to the next season. *p. 1741*
bifolia (Platanthera) (Europe, No. Africa, No. Asia); tuberous-rooted terrestrial orchid, with a pair of elliptic basal-leaves, and leafy stems 30 cm high; fragrant white flowers with linear lip and long spur. *p. 1740*
blephariglottis (Canada to Mississippi), "White-fringed orchid"; terrestrial 75 cm high with 20 cm leaves; clusters of pure white flowers with lip beautifully fringed, and with long slender spur on tall stalks; summer. *p. 1740*
bracteata (No. America, Europe, No. Asia), "Satyr orchid"; small terrestrial with 15 cm leaves, and erect spikes with long leafy bracts next to the small green flowers; May-August. *p. 1740*
flava (Nova Scotia to Florida), a terrestrial "Rein orchis"; from tuberous roots rise leafy spikes to 60 cm high, the dense racemes with yellow-green, the lip with tubercle near base (summer). *p. 1743*
hookeri (Nova Scotia to Iowa); small terrestrial to 38 cm with 2 large rounded or oval leaves, and yellowish green spurred flowers in erect spike. *p. 1740*
keiskei (Japan); small plant with 1 to 3 lanceolate leaves 4 cm long; lax raceme of pretty flowers with large 1 cm lip having 3 spreading lobes pale pink or white with two rows of red-purple dots; small cupped, mauve sepals and petals. *p. 1739*
kraenzliniana (Transvaal); a tuberous "ground orchid" from shady hills, forming annual growth with a pair of broad leaves at the base, reduced to narrow scales along the stalk, bearing an inflorescence of spidery white flowers, each with dangling long greenish strings; goes dormant after blooming. *p. 1741*
lacera (Newfoundland to Minnesota and Mississippi), "Green fringed orchid";. to 75 cm high, with 20 cm leaves, and dense, erect racemes of yellowish-green flowers, having a tri-lobed lip deeply fringed, and long spur. *p. 1740*
nivea (Platanthera) (N.J. to Florida, Texas); terrestrial with stout roots, basal leaves becoming smaller along the erect spike, to 50 cm tall; dense raceme of very fragrant, 1 cm flowers pure white and with long spur (summer). *p. 1741*
psycodes (Newfoundland to Minnesota and Georgia), "Small purple-fringed orchid"; bulbous orchid to 1 m high; stem-clasping lance-shaped leaves to 25 cm; erect many-flowered racemes of fragrant rosy, spurred flowers with tri-lobed fringed lip. *p. 1740*
psycodes grandiflora (Newfoundland to Tennessee), "Large purple fringed orchid"; showy terrestrial about 75 cm high, with 22 cm leaves 10 cm wide, tuberous roots and erect racemes of fragrant rose to purple flowers with trilobed fringed lip (July-Aug) (C) *p. 1740*
radiata (Japan), the pretty "Egret flower"; terrestrial orchid with tuberous roots, with slender, erect leafy stems to 60 cm high, topped by solitary or clustered small green sepals and white petals, and a 2½ cm wide white lip with side lobes fringed and the long green spur, appearing like a bird in flight (July-Aug.). (C) *p. 1740*
rhodocheila (So. China); terrestrial orchid with narrow lanceolate leaves, and erect raceme to 38 cm high, of flowers with green sepals united hood-like, and large lip bright salmon-red. *p. 1740*
tridactylites (Canary Islands); a sub-tropical ground orchid with tuberous roots and leafy spike; the rather appressed flowers soft nile green tinged with yellow, and yellow on lip. *p. 1741*

HABERLEA *Gesneriaceae* **C2HFD**
ferdinandi-coburgii (Bulgaria); tufted perennial rosette with spatulate, leathery leaves in a rosette, deeply toothed, and umbels of tubular, 5-lobed, nodding, lilac flowers with broad upper lip, spotted yellow and violet in throat. *p. 1252*

HABRANTHUS *Amaryllidaceae* **I2LBDd**
andersonii texanus (Texas, probably introduced from Argentina); bulbous herb with narrow linear leaves, 10 cm long, rounded beneath, lightly channelled above; solitary flowers bell-shaped, golden yellow inside, coppery striped with purple outside; summer-blooming. *p. 120*
brachyandrus (So. Brazil); lovely bulbous plant with long narrow, channeled, recurved leaves and a 30 cm stalk carrying a solitary, funnel-form flower orchid-pink, with deep crimson throat. *p. 113*
robustus (Argentina); bulbous herb with linear channeled, glaucous leaves, the trumpet-like 8 cm flowers usually solitary, purplish-rose, becoming white, and preceding foliage. *p. 113, 114*

HADRODEMAS *Commelinaceae* **S2LFD**
warscewiczianum (Tripogandra), (Guatemala); very thick-fleshy rosette with stout stem, resembling a small Dracaena or Agave; the clasping leaves broad, long pointed, to 30 cm long, pale green, ciliate at edge and recurved; clusters of small pale purple flowers on long stalk. *Tropical.* *p. 780, 784*

HAEMANTHUS *Amaryllidaceae* **I2LBMd**
albiflos (So. Africa), "White paint brush"; bulbous plant to 30 cm high, fleshy, wide evergreen leaves with ciliate margins, the inflorescence of white flowers in heads 5 cm across. *Subtropic.* *p. 114, 115*
amarylloides (So. Africa); showy bulbous plant 24 cm high, with large umbels dense with starry flowers white to pink, the flowers with linear segments; late summer-blooming. *p. 121*
carneus (pubescens) (So. Africa); bulbous plant with 2 broad basal softly-hairy leaves 15 cm long, developing after bloom; small pink flowers 1 cm long in a dense globose umbel, on stalk mottled purple; summer. *p. 114*
coccineus (So. Africa), the "Blood lily"; producing annually two wide tongue-shaped leaves fully developed after flowering; inflorescence 25 cm high in dense head of blood-red flowers with orange anthers, followed by purple berries. *p. 114, 115*
katherinae (Natal), "Blood flower"; robust bulbous plant branching from offsets, the soft-fleshy fresh green sword-shaped leaves with channeled midrib running into channeled petiole, separate solid stalk bearing umbrella-shaped head of star-like flowers with salmon petals and long red stamens. *p. 115*
katherinae 'King Albert' (katherinae x puniceus), "Blood lily"; beautiful hybrid of So. African species, a robust bulbous plant with broad scarlet red flowers having long, thread-like stamens in globular heads, 12-18 cm in dia., on a separate thick stalk. *Subtropic.* *p. 115*
multiflorus (Trop. Africa), "Salmon blood lily"; bulbous plant with leaves on short spotted petioles; the showy inflorescence, separate from foliage, forming a perfect ball with up to 100 flowers, 8-12 cm across, coral pink to red, crimson at base of narrow petals with long extended stamens tipped yellow. *Subtropic.* *p. 115*
multiflorus x katherinae; like katherinae, flowering when in leaf, the foliage smooth rich green with ivory white midrib and brown spots at base, the flowers coral-pink with crimson center, tipped by yellow stamens. *p. 115*
natalensis (So. Africa: Natal), "Natal paintbrush"; bulb bearing 7-9 glossy green, strong-nerved lanceolate leaves; dense globose head of pale green 3 cm flowers, showing orange-salmon styles. *Subtropic.* *p. 114, 115*
pole-evansii (Zimbabwe); tropical bulbous plant with broad basal leaves; solid floral stalk with dense umbel of starry red flowers; for summer and autumn bloom. *p. 111*
puniceus (So. Africa), "Pink paintbrush"; bulbous plant with many wavy leaves on reddish stems; the summer flowers in dense 10cm heads pale red to white and not too showy, but they are followed by a nestful of scarlet berries. *Subtropic.* *p. 115*

HAEMARIA *Orchidaceae* **S3HNM**
discolor dawsoniana (Anoectochilus) (Malaya), "Jewel orchid"; vigorous terrestrial with creeping, branching rootstock and fleshy, ovate, gorgeous leaves of blackish red-green velvet with a network of coppery-red veins, wine-red beneath, 5-8 cm long; small, waxy-white flowers, with yellow center, in terminal raceme, (Oct.-Feb.). *Tropical.* *p. 1739, 1749*
discolor dawsoniana nigricans, the "Black jewel orchid"; a terrestrial with velvety leaves of singular beauty, 8 cm long, blackish forest green with thin white midrib, purple beneath; small waxy white fragrant flowers 2 cm across, of stiff spike 30 cm tall (autumn). *p. 1741*

HAKEA *Proteaceae* **I2LBD**
baxteri (W. Australia); thick, fan-shaped silvery leaves, sharply toothed along apex; small brown flowers and large fruit. *p. 1976*
cristata (Western Australia); woody shrub 2½ m high, with small yellow flowers among the attractive oval, toothed gray leaves. *p. 1976*
laurina (W. Australia), "Sea urchin"; handsome, vigorous evergreen shrub to 8 m, with parallel-veined, narrow-elliptic foliage to 15 cm long, and edged in red; crimson flowers in sessile globose clusters, with long golden yellow styles, like a pincushion. *p. 1971*
suaveolens (W. Australia); conifer-like shrub to 5 m, with slender, yellow-brown, silky-downy branches, and stiff, pinnate foliage, the light green segments round, needle-like, 2½-5 cm long, and spine-tipped; fragrant white small flowers in dense racemes. *p. 1971*

victoriae (Western Australia), "Royal hakea"; magnificent, colorful sparry tree 3-4 m high, with broad, rigid leaves 5 to 10 cm across, densely shingled, and with sharp spines along margins, light glossy green beautifully veined and variegated with yellow and into red, the base golden yellow and looking like big flowers; pinkish blooms among the foliage. *p. 1976*

HAMAMELIS *Hamamelidaceae* **C2LBD**
japonica (China, Japan), "Witch-hazel"; deciduous shrub reaching 10 m with broad-ovate, toothed 10 cm leaves, unequal at base, and stellate-hairy when young; flowers yellow in roundish heads on the leafless branches, slightly scented, the 4 petals linear, and reddish bracts; in January-March. (h) *p. 1320*

HAMATOCACTUS *Cactaceae* **I2LBD**
hamatocanthus (Ferocactus) (S. Texas, Mexico); solitary globe, later cylindrical to 60 cm high; ribs notched, radials white, central spine reddish and hooked; flowers yellow. *p. 690*

setispinus (No. Mexico, So. Texas), "Strawberry cactus"; globose plant to 15 cm high, with 13 thick ribs arranged spirally, grayish matte green, the areoles with tufts of white wool; radials gray-brown, the long central spines with fish hook; flowers yellow with red throat. *p. 640A, 690, 703*

uncinatus (Ferocactus) (Texas: Big Bend, to C. Mexico); globular or ovoid plant to 20 cm high, dark blue-green, glaucous, with 9-13 thick, notched ribs, furnished with long hooked spines, red at first, and zoned; flowers reddish brown. *p. 689*

HAMELIA *Rubiaceae* **S2LFM**
erecta (Florida to Brazil), the "Scarlet-bush"; evergreen gray-pubescent shrub to 8 m with 15 cm ovate leaves, and tubular 5-lobed 2 cm flowers orange or scarlet-red. *p. 2015*

HAPALINE *Araceae* **S3LFM**
brownii (Malaysia); attractive small tuberous aroid with waxy, heart-shaped leaves green lightly spotted with white, 7-9 cm long, 6 cm wide; ovate spathe cream on slender stalk. *Tropical.* *p. 224*

HARDENBERGIA *Leguminosae* **I2LBD**
monophylla (Queensland to Tasmania), "Coral-pea"; climbing evergreen shrub growing over low bushes, with ovate or linear dark green leaves 5-12 cm long, profuse with violet or rose pea flowers with a yellow basal spot, in axillary racemes. *p. 1387*

violacea (Australia, Tasmania), "Purple coral pea"; evergreen twining shrub found wild growing over low bushes. Leaves simple, cordate-ovate 4-12 cm long; axillary clusters of small flowers, often in pairs, purple with yellow basal spot, notched at the top. *Subtropic.* *p. 1384*

HARPAGOPHYTUM *Pedaliaceae* **I2LBD**
peglerae (Africa: Transvaal), a "Grapple plant" of the Veld; procumbent, hairy perennial herb with lobed leaves; pretty, tubular flaring dark pink trumpet flowers, but not so well liked for its fruit, beset with woody, grapple-like hooks 3 cm long, pointed and barbed, and troublesome to the feet and jaws of animals. *p. 1922*

HARPEPHYLLUM *Anacardiaceae* **I2LBD**
caffrum (So. Africa: E. Cape, Natal, Transvaal), "Kaffir-plum"; attractive evergreen tree to 12 m with pinnate, glossy deep green leathery leaves, the leaflets lanceolate, slightly curved, to 6 cm long, and wavy-margined; small white or greenish flowers in clusters; the female tree bears edible plum-like fruit. *p. 132*

HARPULLIA *Sapindaceae* **I2LBD**
arborea (Philippines), "Puas"; tropical tree with thin, green pinnate foliage; green-petaled flowers; the fruit in coppery red capsules 4 cm dia., with large black seeds inside. *Tropical.* *p. 2038*

HARRISIA *Cactaceae* **I2LBD**
bonplandii (Brazil, Paraguay, Argentina); night blooming cactus erect at first, later arching or clambering, stems 5-8 cm thick and strongly 4-5 angled, velvety dark green, with a few gray spines; white flowers closing soon after sunrise. *Subtropic.* *p. 660*

bonplandii brevispina; variety with long spines absent; flowers large and showy, to 25 cm long, the outer petals brownish-green, the inner ones white, blooming at night. *p. 660*

fragrans (Louisiana, Florida); clambering night-bloomer, with ridged stems with grayish spines; flowers white or pinkish and fragrant. *p. 660*

guelichii (Eriocereus) (Argentina); night-blooming, long and straggling stems 5½ cm thick, pale green, 3-4-angled, spines reddish passing to gray; large flowers greenish outside, white within; fast growing and free-flowering. *p. 660*

martinii (Argentina); nightblooming, much branched, clambering vine, 4-5-angled, with needle-like pale spines; large white flowers tinged with red. *p. 643, 660*

tortuosa (Argentina), "Red-tipped dogtail"; nightblooming with slender arching stems bright green, round with indistinct ribs and knobby, awl-like spines; white funnelform flowers. Large round, red fruit. *p. 643, 660*

HARTWEGIA *Orchidaceae* **S3OFM**
purpurea (Nageliella) (Florida, Mexico, Guatemala, to Nicaragua); attractive little species with stem-like pseudobulbs and mottled fleshy foliage, green marked with reddish spots; inflorescence to 30 cm high, with 1½ cm flowers purplish-red, the lip with sac-like base (summer). *p. 1742*

HATIORA *Cactaceae* **S2HFM**
bambusioides (Brazil: Guanabara); epiphytic spineless cactus with stems becoming 2 m long and stouter than salicornioides; joints club-shaped, 4 mm dia.; flowers yellow-orange, star-like, without tube, opening in sunlight. *p. 738, 745*

cylindrica (Brazil: Guanabara); branching epiphyte forming dense masses, with pale green cylindric joints 2½ cm long, becoming red-spotted; flowers with reddish sepals and orange-yellow petals. *p. 738*

herminiae: described under RHIPSALIS

salicornioides (S.E. Brazil), "Drunkard's dream"; so called in Brazil because of the bottle-shaped branchlets of this epiphytic tree dweller; the stems constricted into joints each 3 cm long; plant much branched, green or purplish; salmon flowers tipped yellow. *Tropical. p. 618, 737, 738, 740, 746*

HAUYA *Onagraceae* **S2LBD**
elegans (Mexico: Hidalgo); evergreen shrub to 12 m tall; ovate leaves to 6 cm long, grayish beneath; flowers 12 cm long with pink petals. *p. 1649*

HAWORTHIA *Liliaceae* ***I1LFD**
arachnoidea (So. Africa); small, dense rosette formed by a multitude of tiny, succulent leaves, the inner ones incurved, light green, the upper third translucent, transversed by dark lines, the margins and keels set with long translucent teeth. *p. 1457*

armstrongii (Cape Prov.); suckering erect rosette densely spirally leafy; blackish-green sharply pointed and obliquely keeled, succulent, recurving leaves with pale tubercles. *p. 1458*

atro-fusca (Cape Prov.); small rosette with tough-fleshy leaves erect when young but bent back at tip, the swollen surface with numerous reddish warts and red lines, keeled beneath. *p. 1454*

attenuata clariperla (Cape Prov.); striking, dense rosette of perhaps 50 hard-fleshy, short tricornered leaves dark glossy green, closely covered with large white tubercles, faint ridging beneath. *p. 1453*

batesiana (Cape Prov.); low rosette to 5 cm dia., suckering from the base and forming cushions, dense with short, plump, grayish-green leaves 2½ cm long, keeled at base and rounded on the surface, flattened at the apex; darker lines down both sides. *p. 1456*

bilineata (Cape Prov.); compact rosette forming colonies; triangular leaves 3-5 cm long, above with length lines and bristly tip. *p. 1459*

blackbeardiana (Cape Prov.); small incurving dense rosette grayish pale green with gray lines, and ciliate at margins, transparent in the upper third and tipped by a long bristle. *p. 1456*

browniana (Cape Prov.); stiff rosette with leaves spirally arranged, leaves quickly tapering, 5-8 cm long, gray-green almost glossy, white tubercles in cross-lines. *p. 1456*

chloracantha (Cape Prov.); small 8 cm rosette with short, rigid, tapering leaves 4 cm long, grayish or dark green to purplish, flat on top, 3 angled beneath and set with ivory teeth. *p. 1456*

coarctata (Cape Prov.), "Cowhorn haworthia"; elongated rosette to 20 cm high, making basal offsets, leaves in a close spiral, incurved, short and wide, keeled, dark green with a few greenish white tubercles. *p. 1453*

cooperi (So. Africa), "Window haworthia"; rosette similar to pilifera, having longer, fleshy, boat-shaped leaves purplish-brown, with translucent ciliate edges and window-like, translucent point. *Subtropic.* *p. 1457*

cordifolia (trigona hort.) (So. Africa); small succulent with extended stem, forming basal off-shoots; short-triangular leaves in 3 shingled rows, sharp-tipped, dark green, often rough. *p. 1459*

cuspidata (Cape of Good Hope), "Star window plant"; small, stocky, tufting, 6 cm rosette with short, fat, wedge-shaped and keeled leaves, pale grayish green, with abruptly shortened tip having transparent window marked with green lines. *p. 1453*

cymbiformis (Cape Prov.), "Window boats"; robust, stemless, suckering rosette of thick, broad-obovate, pointed leaves, hollowed above, keeled beneath, smooth pale grayish green, with darker green veins running into the translucent tip. (S) *p. 1453*

dielsiana (Cape Prov.); low rosette of numerous very short, thick leaves, toward the apex suddenly pointed, green to reddish on the surface with translucent lines, keeled beneath. Possibly form of obtusa. *p. 1454*

emelyae (So. Africa); tiny stemless rosette with fleshy, broad leaves, matte surface, with tip obliquely flattened to a triangle somewhat translucent, with numerous green warts and lines. *p. 1455*

fasciata (So. Africa), "Zebra haworthia"; very attractive commercial, small erect rosette 5-8 cm across, forming offsets, of slender tapering somewhat incurved leaves dark green, with large white warts in neat connected cross bands. *Subtropic.* *p. 1453, 1459, 2092*

glauca (Orange Free State); elongate, ascending rosette close with bluish green leaves flat on top, keeled beneath, and lined dark green. *p. 1456*

gracilis (Cape Prov.); small rosette of short 4 cm succulent leaves bluish-green, the margins set with pale teeth, and the apex with bristle. *p. 1456*

greenii (Cape Prov.); elongate rosette becoming 20 cm high, with short incurving leaves deep olive green to brownish and covered with whitish tubercles. *p. 1458*

herbacea (atrovirens) (Cape Prov.); tufting little rosettes with numerous, flexible, spreading, lanceolate leaves, dark green, translucent and spotted toward tip, the margins and keel beneath set with translucent teeth. *p. 1457*

herrei depauperata (Cape Prov.); small, loose column forming clusters, with spirally arranged, erect, slender, gray-green leaves lightly glaucous, keeled beneath and lined with small tubercles. *p. 1458*

incurvula (Cape Prov.); soft-fleshy small rosette with numerous ovate, blunt-pointed leaves watery green, on the smooth upper surface glassy-translucent, lined dark green; rounded beneath. *p. 1455*

lateganae (Cape Prov.); open rosette with succulent-stiff, quickly tapering smooth olive green leaves 6 cm long, reddish toward base. *p. 1456*

limifolia (Swaziland), "Fairy washboard"; exquisite small rosette 8-10 cm across; leaves triangular pointed, the upper surface concave, dark green-brown, on both sides with 15-20 transverse ridges. *p. 1456, 1459*

limifolia keithii (So. Africa: Swaziland); interesting rosette to 12 cm across, with sharply pointed, sickle-shaped almost spirally turned leaves, hollowed on top, coppery green with pale green elevated cross-ridges of warts. *p. 1455*

margaritifera (So. Africa: Cape Prov. to Karroo), "Pearl plant"; stemless rosette freely suckering, to 15 cm dia.; leaves at first bent inward, later spreading, to 8 cm long, thick and firm-fleshy, upper surface flat, lower keeled toward apex, blackish-green, on both sides with prominent creamy tubercles. *p. 19*, 1458, 1459*

"Margaritifera" hort.; widely cultivated as a durable dishgarden plant; low suckering rosette of numerous spreading, slender-tapering leaves, matte deep green with evenly scattered pearl-white tubercles; small white bilabiate flowers in racemes. *Subtropic.* *p. 1453*

margaritifera maxima (Cape Prov.); form with broader and heavier dull green leaves; few warts above, underneath with large, milk-white, and very prominent isolated puckers. *p. 1457*

mirabilis (So. Africa); small succulent with spirally arranged triangular leaves, light olive green, the upper half bent back to a horizontal plane which is translucent and marked with pale green lines, toothed at edges. *p. 1457*

nigra var. schmidtiana (Cape Prov.); knobby rosette with elongate stem, the small 2½ cm triangular leaves arranged in 3 twisted series, the upper surface concave, blackish-green, with thick, brownish tubercles, margins horny-banded. *p. 1458*

obtusa pilifera (So. Africa); attractive "Window plant"; a small tufting, 4 cm rosette, with fleshy, light green, obovate leaves, rounded on both sides, suddenly pointed to fine bristle, the upper third transparent like water, marked with dark lines. *p. 1454*

papillosa (Cape Prov.), "Pearly dots"; beautiful, robust rosette with erect, lanceolate leaves rich deep green, adorned with rows of greenish-white raised, often hollow warts, rounded beneath. *p. 1408A, 1457*

paradoxa (So. Africa); small flat rosette hugging the ground, with thick dark green leaves suddenly pointed and with windows at the triangular apex, divided by vertical lines, and tipped with pale bristles. *p. 1454*

planifolia (So. Africa); robust rosette freely suckering, rather watery, fleshy, matte pale gray-green, with obovate, flattened leaves and somewhat transparent apex, keeled beneath. *p. 1454*

pygmaea (Cape Prov.); small, 5 cm rosette of few leaves with upper third suddenly as if cut off into a tricornered level, almost transparent dark green, transversed by pale lines, keeled beneath. *p. 1454*

radula (Cape Prov.); small clustering rosette with spreading dark green leaves tapering to a slender tip, covered with minute white tubercles, edge rough and red, reverse often keeled. *p. 1454*

reinwardtii (So. Africa), "Wart plant"; attractive, slender, elongate, with stem to 15 cm high, making basal offsets, slender lanceolate leaves in a close spiral, keeled beneath, with cross rows of white tubercles. *p. 1455*

reinwardtii chalwinii (So. Africa); columnar rosette to 20 cm high, with squat, short, thick leaves arranged in a tight spiral, keeled beneath and with white tubercles in longitudinal rows. *p. 1455*

reinwardtii kaffirdriftensis (Cape Prov.); shorter form, clustering from the base, with leaves close and incurved especially at the tips, dark green with pure white, round warts in lengthwise rows, those on the margins small and translucent. *p. 1455*

reticulata (Cape Prov.); numerous crowded succulent fresh green leaves inflated, and rounded both top and bottom, thicker toward the apex and nearly transparent, with a bristle at tip, the margins horny dentate. *p. 1458*

retusa (Cape Province), "Star cactus"; stemless rosette forming clusters, with fat and stubby deltoid pale green leaves to 4 cm long, the upper half recurved with a smooth triangular face almost translucent and with pale lines. *Subtropic.* *p. 1455*

retusa 'Zebra'; low rosette with triangular fleshy leaves olive green, keel-like beneath; the apex flattened and with translucent window, and transversed by prominent pale green lines. *p. 1456*

rugosa (So. Africa); spirally arranged rosette of numerous spreading leaves, 3-angled, lanceolate, long pointed into a 3-cornered apex, dark green and few warts; occasional larger warts somewhat translucent. *p. 1454*

ryderiana (So. Africa); small stemless rosette with matte brownish or bluish-green leaves, spreading, with triangular apex, flat on top, with lines of transparent spots, keeled beneath, the margins set with pale teeth, and transparent bristle tip. *p. 1455*

schuldtiana (Cape Prov.); small clustering rosette 4 cm dia., with fat triangular leaves bluish green to brownish, recurving and ending in a sharp point, margins and keel set with whitish teeth. *p. 1456*

setata (Cape Prov.); stemless formal, succulent rosette 5 cm dia., dense with triangular, deep green leaves, margins and keels with white bristles, and a long transparent one at apex. *p. 1458*

skinneri (So. Africa); erect, sturdy elongate rosette, deep gray-green, triangular leaves 3 cm long, with numerous tubercles, these white at margins. *p. 1459*

subfasciata (Cape Prov.), "Little zebra plant"; shapely rosette with erect spreading, tapering leaves longer than fasciata, and crossbanded with regular, thinner rows of translucent white tubercles, lightly keeled beneath. *p. 1457, 1459*

tenera (minima) (So. Africa); tiny grayish, dense rosette of incurving flexible leaves slender pointed with translucent stripes toward the bristle-tipped apex, and with ciliate margins. *p. 1457*

tessellata (So. and Southwest Africa); pretty, star-like rosette of few but thick leaves, tricornered tapering to sharp tip, stiff, recurved, dark translucent green with network of pale green lines, reverse rough and often reddish. *p. 1454*

triebneriana (Cape Province: Karroo); small stemless star-like rosette to 6 cm with thick green leaves almost flat on top, translucent toward tips which are reflexed, covered with small pale warts and edged with whitish teeth. *p. 1453*

truncata (Cape Prov.), "Clipped window plant"; most unusual "Window plant" with succulent leaves oval in cross-section, arranged in 2 ranks, dark green-brownish and rough-warty, apex of each leaf flat as if cut off, and translucent. *Subtropic.* *p. 1457*

turgida (Cape Prov.); small rosette with short fleshy keeled leaves, glossy pale green, at the tip recurved and translucent and marked with green lines. *p. 1453, 1456, 1459*

viscosa (Cape Prov.); attractive elongate rosette to 20 cm high, the rigid, short, recurving leaves overlapping and arranged in 3 ranks, dull green and rough, surface concave. *p. 1456*

viscosa torquata (So. Africa); columnar succulent to 20 cm high, branching from base, with thick-fleshy, yellowish-green leaves spirally arranged shingle-like in 3 ranks, recurved, keeled beneath and warty. *p. 1458*

HEBE *Scrophulariaceae* **I-C2LBD**

'Alicia Amherst' (veitchii); a speciosa hybrid also listed as Veronica; shrubby, bushy plant 30-50 cm high with shiny ovate leaves, and slender cylindric axillary racemes of deep royal purple flowers. *p. 2055*

x andersonii (Veronica) (salicifolia x speciosa); evergreen shrub symmetrically branching and shapely when small, but growing to 2 m high, with soft-fleshy, small obovate, opposite leaves 8-10 cm long; and axillary spikes 8-12 cm long of densely packed flowers bluish-violet fading to lilac and white, especially toward the base of the raceme; Aug.-Sept. *p. 2053, 2057*

x andersonii 'Snowflake' (E. Hahn, Germany); vigorous branching bush with long-elliptic, glossy green leaves, and axillary, long and slender cylindric spikes of white flowers. *p. 2057*

x andersonii 'Variegata'; very pretty ornamental, evergreen bush with its cross-ranked glossy-green leaves broadly margined with creamy-white. *p. 2054*

anomala (New Zealand), an "Evergreen veronica"; dense bushy shrub to 40 cm high, leaves 2 cm long, keeled and shiny; white or pale pink flowers in short spikes; similar to buxifolia; ideal as a hedge plant in mild climate. *p. 2055*

armstrongii (Veronica) (New Zealand); evergreen shrub to 1 m high, often branching fan-like, slender shoots in the adult state densely clothed with appressed, overlapping tiny 1 mm roundish leaves, white flowers in terminal clusters. *p. 2055*

buxifolia 'Variegata' (Veronica) (New Zealand); dense evergreen bush resembling euonymus, with small, soft, 2 cm obovate leaves, opposite and overlapping, dark, waxy green with gray, variegated cream-white from the margin inward; small white flowers in closely packed spikes. *p. 2053*

colensoi (Veronica) (New Zealand); evergreen shrub 30-50 cm high, the stems crowded with narrow-oblong 2-4 cm leaves, glaucous beneath; small white or lavender-blue 1 cm flowers in dense racemes. *p. 2056*

'Cranleighensis'; hybrid shrub with sparry branches, narrow lanceolate leaves, and dense cylindrical inflorescence of small flowers light pink when first open, fading to white, so that the spike is two-toned, pink above and white below. *p. 2053*

cupressoides (New Zealand: Otago); evergreen shrub 1-2 m high of dense rounded habit resembling a dwarf cypress; leaves scale-like, densely appressed to the stem in maturity stage; flowers pale purple with conspicuous red anthers. *p. 2056*

dieffenbachii (New Zealand: Chatham Isl.); spreading evergreen shrub 1-1½ m high, dense with narrow oblong, 5-10 cm leathery leaves with bases clasping stems; small 1 cm flowers purplish-lilac with blue anthers, in dense 10 cm clusters. *p. 2056*

diosmaefolia (New Zealand); evergreen shrub to 1½ m or more, dense with small 2½ cm linear leaves; white to pale lavender flowers in terminal clusters. *p. 2054*

elliptica (Veronica decussata), (Tierra del Fuego, Falkland Isl., Chile, New Zealand); much branched evergreen shrub or a tree to 6 m high, with opposite, soft leathery and quilted, obovate leaves. and pyramidal racemes dense with rich red-purple, fragrant flowers feathery with their prominent stamens. *p. 2053, 2057*

epacridea (New Zealand: Marlborough); prostrate half-hardy shrub with overlapping tiny leathery 1 cm obovate leaves, each pair united at the base; 2 cm white flowers densely packed in terminal clusters. *p. 2056*

x imperialis (speciosa x salicifolia); luxuriant bushy evergreen with shiny green to reddish oval leaves in opposite ranks; large cylindrical heads of magenta purple flowers in summer. Resembles H. speciosa. *p. 2055*

lyallii (New Zealand: South Island); low sub-shrub dense with soft-leathery 1 cm leaves; flowers white with lilac veins, and with prominent blue anthers; found in the beautiful, moist-cool virgin area around Milford Sound, in Fiordland Prov. of New Zealand. *p. 2055*

salicifolia (New Zealand), "Evergreen veronica"; evergreen shrub to 3 m with shining, lanceolate leaves 15 cm long, and variable flowers densely packed in cylindrical racemes, lilac-tinged white to bluish-purple. *p. 2054*

speciosa (Veronica) (New Zealand), "Showy veronica"; robust, evergreen shrub with spreading, angled branches dense with opposite, thick, oblong leaves glossy dark green and downy on the midrib above, 5-8 cm long; the small purple-crimson flowers in dense axillary racemes opposite near tips of branches, summer blooming. *Subtropic.* *p. 2053*

speciosa 'Variegata'; attractive, bushy plant with glossy green oval leaves prettily variegated with creamy white toward margins. *p. 2055*

subalpina (New Zealand: Fiordland); densely branched shrub, with stout branchlets, small 3 cm leathery, pale green leaves, and white flowers in elongate clusters. *p. 2056*

vernicosa (New Zealand: South Island); dense evergreen shrub 30-80 cm high, with spreading branches, small lustrous green 15 mm leaves crowded near tips of shoots; tiny 1 cm white flowers in 3-5 cm racemes. *p. 2056*

HEBE: see also VERONICA

HEBENSTRETIA *Scrophulariaceae* **I2LFD**

dentata (So. Africa); subshrub 30-50 cm high, with woody stems densely clothed by needle-like leaves to 4 cm long, the margins rolled under, at apex a terminal feathery 15 cm spike of yellow or white flowers with orange-red blotch on limb; summer-blooming. *p. 2057*

HECHTIA *Bromeliaceae* **S-I1HBD**

argentea (Mexico), "Vicious hechtia"; attractive terrestrial rosette of stiff dagger-shaped, dark glossy green leaves 30 cm or more long, with prominent sawtooth spines; gray pencil lines beneath; tall inflorescence with orange flowers. *Subtropic.* *p. 551, 559, 562*

ghiesbreghtii (Mexico: San Luis Potosi); symmetrical rosette of stiff, recurving leaves to 20 cm long, densely covered with silvery scales, top concave and marked red-brown, the margins with prominent thorns; inflorescence 25 cm long, greenish-white. *p. 559*

glomerata (Mexico); dangerous low rosette of fleshy, glossy green recurved leaves, on occasion turning entirely red, and with silvery-white reverse, to 40 cm long, and armed with vicious spines; sending out creeping off shoots; flower petals white. *Subtropic.* *p. 512, 551*

marnier-lapostollei (Mexico); relatively small plant with thick-fleshy, slender, recurving leaves, smooth and lustrous, brownish at base, pale scurfy toward apex, to 12 cm long, spiny at margins; inflorescence laxly branched, with ovate floral bracts and white flowers. *p. 562*

podantha (tehuacana) (Central and So. Mexico); stout terrestrial rosette 1-2 m high, in habitat found growing on lime stone near Tehuacan, also south to Oaxaca; the rigid leaves to 4 cm wide at base, margins armed with brown teeth; under intensive sunlight the leaves are blotched red and yellow. *Tropical.* *p. 559*

rosea (Mexico: Oaxaca); succulent rosette with concave leaves to 50 cm long, brownish gray-scaly and becoming red in strong sunlight, and with spiny margins; erect reddish floral stalk to 70 cm high with lax, branching inflorescence of numerous tiny flowers with rosy-red petals. *p. 562*

schottii (Mexico); armed rosette of stiff, recurving, narrow leaves dull lacquered green above, beneath with prominent white striation lengthwise, the margins with formidable pale green spines; flowers white. *p. 559*

stenopetala in hort.; correct name may be ghiesbreghtii (So. Mexico); handsome but viciously spiny rosette to 30 cm across, found growing in the lava rock of the Pedregal region near Mexico City; stiff, concave leaves light green and heavily splashed with blood-red when growing in sunny exposure; the margins with strong hook thorns; flowers white, in cylindric inflorescence. From the base of the mother plant, long runners form to produce new plantlets. *Tropical.* *p. 562*

texensis (Texas); large rosette growing on limestone bluffs on the Big Bend of the Rio Grande in southwest Texas; stiff-succulent, narrow linear leaves 40-80 cm long and to 4 cm wide, shiny gray-green above, white-scurfy beneath and arching downward, the margins serrate with vicious spines; the inflorescence to 1 m high branched with spikelets of white flowers. *p. 562*

tillandsioides (Bakerantha) (So. Mexico); tillandsia-like rosette with narrow, channeled, tapering leaves recurving and loosely curling in different directions, surface waxy green, rough margins, and whitish scales on rounded underside; the inflorescence very open and finely divided, rough cylindric in outline. *p. 551*

HEDERA *Araliaceae* **•C-I2LBM**

canariensis (Azores, Canaries, Morocco), "Algerian ivy"; robust creeper, or climbing by roots; burgundy-red twigs and petioles with glossy, fresh green, leathery leaves broadly ovate and quite flat, even recurved, shallowly lobed and usually with slender main lobe; covered with grayish-white scales. *Subtropic.* *p. 322, 332*

canariensis var. azoricus; handsome large green leaf of leathery texture, 5 to 7-lobed, 12-15 cm wide, 8-10 cm long from sinus. *p. 336*

canariensis 'Gloire de Marengo'; long cultivated in Europe under this name, this is probably identical with H. canariensis 'Variegata' or one of its color forms. The relatively large leaves are usually 3-lobed, green in the center changing to milky-gray, then white or cream to yellowish in irregularly variegated areas, mostly along the margins; stems and petioles red. *Subtropic.* *p. 342*

canariensis 'Golden Leaf'; large leaves broad and leathery, lightly lobed and slightly undulate, 8 to 20 cm long, grayish green variegated with greenish-yellow to deep golden yellow in middle; photographed in New Zealand. *p. 342*

canariensis 'Margino-maculata', "Canary Island ivy"; differs from 'Variegata' by its creamy yellow variegation speckled and marbled with green, running over into fresh green and dark green areas; stems and petioles red. (I) *p. 325*

canariensis 'Oxheart'; large deep green heavy-bodied leaf, 3-lobed, 12-14 cm long and 10-12 cm wide, on long petiole. *p. 336*

canariensis 'Variegata' (maderensis), known as 'Gloire de Marengo' and "Hagenburger's" commercially, very colorful with the thin-leathery leaves in the center fresh-green to slate-green, joined by a zone of blue or gray-green, and marginal variegation of creamy white, 6-12 cm long. *Subtropic.* *p. 15*, 19*, 325, 331, 343*

canariensis 'Variegata Ghost tree'; so called because of the ghostly trembling of the pendant foliage in a breeze; arborescent form of the Algerian ivy with ovate, hard leaves with cream variegation on light green or gray; fruit black; very tough. (I) *p. 322, 343*

colchica aurea, the "Golden Persian ivy", high-climbing, with broad leathery leaves lightly lobed 8-20 cm long; in this form with leaves in greenish-yellow to deep gold. *p. 335*

colchica dentata (Caucasus, Iran); the tall-growing "Persian ivy" with pea-green twigs and large, lustrous leaves broadly ovate, lightly lobed; covered with about 20 rayed scales. *p. 326, 327*

colchica dentata 'Sulphur Heart'; large leathery leaf lightly indented, 9-10 cm long, 10-12 cm wide, yellow-green. *p. 336*

colchica 'Dentato-variegata' (Caucasus, Iran), "Variegated Persian ivy"; twigs pea-green with large, leathery, green leaves broadly ovate to 25 cm long, lightly lobed and remotely toothed, with dense, scaly pubescence, and broad cream-white margin. *Warm temperate.* *p. 322, 327*

helix (Europe, Asia, N. Africa), "English ivy"; root climbing vine with juvenile leaves 5-lobed, glossy forest green, with creamy veins, to 6 cm, and somewhat cupped; this species has 4-12 stellate hairs covering the foliage, mostly underneath, seen through a magnifying lens; in the arborescent stage leaves are unlobed, the fruit black. *Temperate.* *p. 305, 324, 327, 339, 341*

helix 'Abundance'; slow trailer, and bushy, with broad and large 10 cm 4-5 to 7-lobed variable leaves dark green with pale veins, some are wavy in the sinus, some have 2-pointed apex. *Temperate.* *p. 334*

helix 'Adam'; photographed at Rochford's Nurseries near London, England; a vigorous freely branching ivy with small, rather dainty, distinctly 5-lobed leaves 3 cm long, fresh green with white edges. *p. 343*

helix 'Albany', "Albany ivy"; selfbranching from strongly flattened (fasciated) twigs with leaves sharply 5-lobed, to 9 cm long, rich green to purplish green with pale veins; purplish beneath. *p. 329*

helix 'Anchor'; interesting clone from a garden wall in Washington, D.C.; self-branching with graceful anchor-shaped leaves large in outline but deeply cut into 5 narrow, lanceolate segments, 6 to 9 cm long and spreading almost as wide; lustrous green; the typical leaves on the short branches rather than the leaders. *p. 337*

helix 'Arrow', "Arrow-ivy"; a sturdy California cultivar with leathery foliage, in variety from densely shingled small leaves 3 cm long, barely lobed or with 3 lobes, each rather ovate and overlapping, to large leaves 3-to 5-lobed and 5-6 cm wide, dark green, smooth to shiny with pale network of veins. *p. 338, 339*

helix 'Aureo-variegata', a mutant which I noticed at Weber's in California, with the typical cupped, dark green leaf of the "English ivy" richly variegated creamy-yellow. *p. 325*

helix baltica (Latvia), "Baltic ivy"; clinging vine similar to English ivy but the leathery foliage not so large and more cut, whitish veins; very hardy. *Temperate.* *p. 324*

helix 'Big Deal'; the "Geranium ivy" because of the 5 cm rounded and puckered leaves, margin turned down and crimped, leathery, dark green; on reddish stem; slow. *p. 334*

helix 'Bulgaria'; a tough variety found growing in a dry hot region of Bulgaria where it has proven very resistant and requiring little moisture, and therefore thought ideal for comparable locations in our Midwest; similar to English ivy, deep green, thin-leathery, 5-lobed leaves with pale veins. *p. 328*

helix 'Bunch'; slow non-trailing, compact grower crowded with leathery deeply 5-lobed deep green leaves. *p. 334*

helix 'Caenwoodiana'; classic small-leaved ivy; pronounced 3-lobed, dark green leaves with raised ivory veins. *p. 329, 332*

helix 'California Fan'; wiry stems with broad, leathery green 7-lobed, pleated leaves medium-large, lobes ovate and the sinuses wavy; branchlets starting in axils of main stems. *p. 332*

helix 'California Gold'; mutant of 'Weber's California' with rather rounded leaves light green marbled with yellow especially in younger leaves; stays selfbranching and bushy. *p. 322, 331*

helix 'Carolina Crinkle' (syn. 'New Ripples'); very handsome ivy from Oregon; leaf blades variously crinkled and deeply cut into lacy segments, shiny light green, broader than long, 8-10 cm wide, and 6-8 cm from base to tip; prominent parallel veins; resembles 'Fleur'. *p. 337*

helix 'Cathedral Wall'; rather formal leaf triangular shield-shaped, angular cordate to 3-lobed, 4-7 cm long, with blunt tip, light moss-green and with prominent veins; from the Washington Cathedral, D. C. *p. 337*

helix 'Cavendishii'; medium-large leaves to 6 cm of pentagon shape, with gray-green center and broad, cream-white margin especially near the base. *p. 322*

helix 'Chicago' ('Typ Schaefer'); small "Emerald ivy" of classical leaf shape, much grown in Europe for its elegantly 3- to 5-lobed, medium green, intermediate-size leaves of good texture, measuring 5 cm long and 4 cm wide; of willing, fast-growing habit and good keeping quality; like 'Pittsburgh', but more short-jointed, slower growing and somewhat self-branching, the slightly larger leaves, brighter green and with raised light veins. *p. 339*

helix 'Chicago variegata'; small leaves with irregular variegation giving blotched or marbled effect over whole leaf with more cream than green, some leaves altogether green, others only margined with white; plant photographed in New Zealand, and popular in Australia and Europe as an indoor house plant. *p. 340, 342*

helix 'Chrysanna'; thick-leathery leaves ovate or almost triangular, lightly 3-lobed but side lobes small; dark green. *p. 334*

helix 'Conglomerata', "Japanese ivy"; slow growing shrubby, contorted stems closely crowded with small undulate leaves dark green and stiff, with green veins. *p. 326, 333*

helix 'Conglomerata minima'; tiny-leaved form of the "Japanese ivy"; the thick-leathery, roundish, wavy leaves closely set on stout meandering branches; very slow-growing. *p. 333, 337*

helix 'Crenata'; handsome green leaves 5-7 cm wide and 4-5 cm long, crenate with 5-7 ovate lobes, the sinuses between overlapping. *p. 337*

helix cristata 'Curlilocks'; sport with young growths sprouting from every axil of the crested leaves resulting in densely bushy vines. *Temperate.* *p. 305, 324, 327, 335, 341*

helix 'Cuspidata minor'; straggly creeper with wiry, rooting stems, sparsely set with small triangular 3-lobed, leathery leaves 3-5 cm long, dark gray green with whitish veins, on red petioles and branches. *p. 340*

helix 'Deltoidea'; dark green leaves leathery with pale veins, cordate to shield-shaped, somewhat like 'Scutifolia' but longer and narrower leaves, and lobes of mature size leaves overlap at base; from Laurenson of New Zealand. *p. 340*

helix 'Denticulata'; robust growing vine with medium-small, roundish, thick leaves, somewhat cupped, 5-lobed, with basal lobes full-round. *p. 324, 329*

helix 'Diamant'; low miniature, photographed at the German National Show in Hamburg 1973; graceful, flexuous branches set evenly with several 1½-2½ cm leaves, obscurely 3-lobed and all about equal size, with milky-green center and creamy-white variegation and edging. *p. 342*

helix 'Digitata' (palmata); an old, freely vining variety, small, dark, leathery leaves shaped like a fan, the whitish veins also palmate, and usually with 5, almost equal, toothlike lobes. *p. 326, 329, 337*

helix 'Digitata plathii'; a form with young branchlets appearing along the long vines; small leaves 5-lobed, roundish, dark green with whitish veins, on reddish petioles. *p. 322*

helix 'Discolor' (marmorata minor), "Marmorata ivy"; robust, old-time variety with wiry twigs and the small, scattered, leathery leaves deep green mottled or spotted with white. *p. 325, 331*

helix 'Emerald Gem'; prolific grower with spreading vines, thin-leathery 5-lobed leaves cordate at base, and fresh green. *p. 333, 337*

helix 'Emerald Jewel'; vigorous variety with long-spreading slender vines set with glossy-green, small, trilobed leaves, the center lobe slender-pointed and longer than side lobes. *p. 338*

helix 'Erecta' (conglomerata erecta) (Japan); similar to conglomerata but the stout twigs grow more erect, the leaves are more broadly triangular pointed and not undulate, dark green with whitish veins, and rigidly arranged opposite each other. *p. 326*

helix 'Fan' (crenata), "Fan ivy"; vining variety with attractive broad, lightly 5-7-lobed leaves rich to dark green, palmately veined pale green, the lobes wavy or pleated at sinus, and fairly even. *p. 329*

helix 'Fanette' (Manda); attractive viner of selfbranching habit, with decorative green leaves broadly fan-shaped, deeply 7-fingered and undulate in sinus, palmate pale veins. *p. 327*

helix 'Fantasy'; small-leaved variegated ivy from the Merry Gardens collection, Camden, Maine; lightly 3-lobed leaves 4 cm long, fresh green mottled with yellow. *p. 337*

helix 'Ferney'; small-leaved climber of the ramosa complex, with twigs very leafy and self-branching from leaf axils; leaves 3-4 cm long, 5-lobed with midlobe prominent, dark green with whitish veins; of fern-like appearance. *p. 337*

helix 'Fleur'; elegant clone with shiny, deeply 5-lobed medium-large leaves lightly crinkled and somewhat wavy. *p. 333*

helix 'Fleur de Lis'; freely branching with slender shoots, variously shaped small leaves from lightly 5-lobed to deeply divided with three large and two small ovate lobes. *p. 333*

helix 'Fluffy Ruffles'; unusual ivy with scattered roundish leaves very much undulate and crested at the margins; quite selfbranching. *p. 328*

helix 'Four Square'; attractive rambler with long runners, non-branching; big leaves 6 to 10 cm wide, 4-8 cm long, shallowly 3-lobed, very dark green with strong veins; from an old Columbia, S.C. garden. *p. 337*

helix 'Freed's Miniature'; tiny-leaved rambler from W. Freeland's collection, Columbia, So. Carolina; shield-shaped little leaves 2 to 4 cm long, 3-lobed, light green with prominent veins; resembles H. h. 'Minima'. *p. 337*

helix 'Garland'; compact, bushy variety with medium-large leaves mostly shallow to deeply trilobed, lightly corrugated and pleated, causing the sinuses to become wavy. *p. 332*

helix 'Glacier'; good vining growth combined with nicely variegated, small, triangular, leathery leaves of several shades of green down to gray, with white marginal areas and pink edge, 3 to 5 cm long. *p. 325*

helix 'Glacier var. Edward jr.'; a selected clone by Hummel with gray-green leaves distinctly spear-shaped and edged white; good basket plant. *p. 328*

helix 'Gladiator'; found in the Deep South; leaf blades large and shield-shaped, to 8 cm wide and 8-10 cm long, shallowly 3-lobed, medium green; attractive when draped over a tree branch and allowed to fall in a curtain of pendulous branches. *p. 336*

helix 'Glymii'; creeper hugging the surface with horizontal, wiry, green branches making aerial rootlets; the small, medium green, ovate cordate leaves spoonlike cupped. *p. 324*

helix 'Golddust'; trilobed leaves varying in width and shape; variegated and mottled green and yellow, especially on new growth. *p. 325, 332*

helix 'Goldheart'; "d'Oro di Bogliosco"; a small leaved ivy from Italy with slender vines and neat, pointed, 3-5-lobed, leathery, green leaves with the middle golden yellow and cream, on reddish stems. *p. 322, 331*

helix gracilis; a small-leaved ivy of spindly growth with long internodes and sparry twigs, in cultivation represented by the "ramosa complex" of improved cultivars with vernacular names such as H. h. 'Pittsburgh', which is bushier, having shorter internodes, and leaves lighter green, but otherwise of similar size, texture and outline; gracilis has 3- to 5-lobed thinnish leaves 2½ cm long to 4 cm wide, dull dark to yellowish-green turning bronzy, with grayish-white veins, the large one raised, stellate hairs often 8-rayed; twigs and petioles reddish. *p. 337*

helix 'Green feather'; a graceful, decorative plant with a feathery look; the narrow laciniate, 3-5-lobed leaves 2-4 cm long, with side-lobes, spoonlike; of compact neat growth habit, with dense-leaved green twigs pointing in all directions; resembling 'Meagheri' but with smooth, satiny leaves generally larger and more fresh green, more decorative and graceful. *p. 338*

helix 'Green Ripples'; simple bold leaves large and small, bright green and dark, often deformed and frilly but produced in abundance, and clothing the stem in a pleasing way. *p. 324, 335*

helix 'Green Spear'; free growing form with willowy foliage of spear-shaped, medium green leaves with light green veins, long pointed and laciniate. *p. 326, 334*

helix 'Hahn's nana'; a New Zealand cultivar, of very low growth habit; the medium green leaves rounded in outline, 4-5 cm across, divided into 5 broad lobes with some overlapping, or wavy in the sinus between segments; the veins prominent light green. Leaf form similar to 'Weber's Californian'. *p. 339*

helix 'Hahn's Selfbranching'; a bushy variant of "Pittsburgh ivy", branching near the growing tip making a close mat of stems and leaves; constant reselection necessary to maintain selfbranching character. *p. 324*

helix 'Hahn's Variegated'; probably the best grower of the small albinos; long vines with silver-gray, leathery leaves and narrow white edge turning reddish. *p. 19*, 325*

helix 'Harald', "White and green ivy" or "Improved Chicago variegata"; a medium small-leaved yet robust, variegated clone favored in Europe because its 4 to 7 cm, 3 to 5-shallowly lobed leaves, somewhat rounded, are mostly green but not gray in the center, broadly margined creamy white; also quite durable as a house ivy. *Warm temperate.* *p. 342, 343*

helix 'Heise-Denmark'; like 'Silver King' but leaves are larger, thin, and of faster growth, more green in winter; in the spring the foliage becomes highly variegated cream around the gray and green center. *p. 325*

helix 'Helvetica'; shield-like, deep matte-green leaves, cordate to 3-lobed, with contrasting white veins, on strong, stiff, woody vines. *p. 329*

helix 'Herold'; pretty, bushy plant with small to medium-sized rather rounded leaves shallowly lobed, 4 to 7 cm long, light green variegated white along margins. This is probably the same as the European clone 'Harald'. *p. 337*

helix hibernica (Ireland); the "Irish ivy" is the largest of the helix varieties, growing more dense and vigorous than the "English ivy" with roundish leaves to 12 cm across, bright green with pale green veining. *p. 323, 326*

helix hibernica 'Variegata'; creeping vine with firm broad leaves similar to English ivy, shallowly 3-5-lobed, dark green with irregular cream-white variegation and mottling; veins milk-white. *Temperate.* *p. 327*

helix 'Improved Chicago variegata', or "Golden Chicago ivy"; nice, regularly 3 to 5- lobed variegated golden yellow small leaves, with basal lobes not prominent; vigorous growth on strong stems. *p. 342*

helix 'Itsy-bits' ('Itsy-bitsy'); charming small ivy of compact graceful habit with each branch distinctly curving, and dense with shingled deep green leaves with white veins, first ovate, later leaves narrowly 3-lobed, 1½-2½ cm long; in the axils of larger leaves are found nesting a cluster of tiny birdsfoot leaves as if bursting with itsy-bitsy foliage. *p. 339*

helix 'Ivalace'; vining plant with self-branching characteristics resulting in close growth, the 5-lobed, dark green, leathery leaves with upcurled margins creating a lacy appearance. *p. 326, 339*

helix 'Jubilee'; tiniest of the variegated leaf forms, self-branching; the little snubnosed leaves friendly light green, gray and white, and quite irregular. *Warm temperate.* *p. 325, 328*

helix 'Lady Kay'; attractive very bushy cultivar freely branched and dense with small leaves mostly trilobed, the midlobe usually long-pointed like a dagger. *p. 330*

helix 'Lancelot'; strong vining 'Glacier' mutant with dominant, spear-shaped center lobe gracefully curved, irregular white marginal variegation around green and gray leaf. *p. 322*

helix 'Little Diamond'; small-leaved, self-branching variegated ivy with very small leaves almost without lobes, when young appearing lance-shaped, 2½ cm long and 2 cm wide, dark gray-green with ivory margins; in time becoming 3-lobed, 4 cm long but very slowly. *p. 342*

helix 'Little Fingers'; grown in Australia; a miniature form of 'Sagittaefolia'; light green leaves 3 cm long cut into 3 spread-out, narrow segments looking like little fingers of a hand; of prostrate densely bushy habit and can be mistaken for a fern. *p. 340*

helix 'Liz'; compact grower with stiffish red stems and waxy tri-lobed leaves smaller than 'Glacier' or 'Schaefer', somewhat irregular, silver gray with creamy-white edging and variegation; European cultivar photographed in Duesseldorf, Germany. *p. 342*

helix 'Lobato-major'; from New Zealand, with large, dark green leaves to 8 cm long, 5-lobed, the midlobe very broad at base and pointed; petioles and stems bright red. *p. 340*

helix 'Long Point'; from the collection of W. Freeland of Columbia, So. Carolina; leaves 3-lobed to strongly star-shaped 5-lobed leaves, the midlobe the longest, 7-8 cm long and wide. *p. 336*

helix 'Lutzii'; sport of 'Adam'; self-branching ivy with small 3 to 5-lobed, roundish green leaves attractively spotted and mottled more or less pale green or pale yellow in mosaic patterns on red petioles and stems (Wisley Show, England, 1971). *p. 340*

helix 'Maculata'; may be a slow-growing, variegated form of the Irish ivy; the leaves are roundish, shallowly 5-lobed, rather flat and fleshy, and the yellow-green mixed with dark green beautifully variegated white or cream. *Temperate.* *p. 15*, 325*

helix 'Manda's Cresfed'; attractive plant with star-shaped, jade-green leaves with rosy edge, the long lobes fluted and undulate, on straight, upright, reddish stalks. *Warm temperate.* *p. 19*, 324, 335, 341*

helix 'Manda's Fringette'; long-vining plant with a "streamlined" draping effect, wiry stem, firm green leaves slender fan-shaped with 5 tapering lobes, pale veins; self-branching. *p. 327*

helix 'Manda's Monstrose'; mutation of 'Pittsburgh', stiff, somewhat erect-growing plant with leathery 3-5-lobed leaves, the branch tips densely fasciated like a flattened fan. *p. 328*

helix 'Manda's Star'; freely vining, flexible stems with large 5-fingered thin leaves nicely draped; dark green with light veins. *p. 19*, 327*

helix 'Maple Queen'; very satisfactory variety indoors; although branching freely, its habit is even and constrained, the small, leathery leaves are fresh to dark green with pale veins; the keeping quality excellent. *p. 324*

helix 'Marginata', "Silver garland ivy"; an old, variegated-leaf variety with small, leathery, 3-5-lobed leaves which will grow progressively larger, green with gray, and margined white, edge turning reddish. *p. 325*

helix marmorata: see helix 'Discolor'

helix 'Meagheri'; a sport from Fred Danker's greenhouses in Albany, New York before 1940; sometimes called 'Greenfeather' and so listed in Exotica Series 3; its leaves are genarally more tiny, 1 to 2 cm long, narrowly 3-5 lobed with long terminal segments and narrow lateral lobes, the tiny basal lobes are hardly discernable; color is deep green with lighter veins; slow, stiffish grower reluctant to branch. *p. 326*

helix 'Merion Beauty' (procumbens); dense little plant with weak twigs weighted down by little auxiliary shoots breaking out of all axils, the small leaves of varied shape. *p. 324, 330*

helix 'Minima'; form with flexuous twigs, green petioles and small, 3-5-lobed, thin leathery leaves, somewhat undulate, base cordate. *Temperate.* *p. 324*

helix 'Minor': see h. 'Walthamensis'

helix 'Mount Vernon'; a selection from the home of Gen. George Washington at Mount Vernon, Virginia; resembles 'Scutifolia' but lobes more angular; blade pronounced 3-lobed with 2 smaller lobes at cordate base, midlobe longest; some leaves nearly star-shaped, 5 to 8 cm wide and long, medium green with prominent veins. *p. 336*

helix 'My Heart'; true, heartshaped leaves only rarely lobed, medium size and leathery, deep, waxy green. *p. 334*

helix 'Nagud'; sport of deltoides, found in Columbia, So. Carolina garden; small shield-formed leaves or sometimes 3-lobed, of leathery texture, 4 cm long, and 3-4 cm wide, basal lobes overlapping, and with prominent veins. *p. 336*

helix 'Needle-ivy' ('Manda's Needlepoint'); very graceful bushy, self-branching cultivar full of small 2 cm leaves with 3 very slender, needle-narrow lobes; some of the older leaves develop to 5 lobes; ideal as a small house plant. *p. 339*

helix 'Needlepoint'; dwarf plant self-branching from leaf axils, with twigs upright when young, the tiny elongate leaves usually slender 3-lobed, arranged in ranks and facing one side. *p. 328, 334, 339*

helix 'Nielson'; charming plant similar to both 'Pittsburgh' and 'Chicago' but leaves smaller and much closer together, darker green than 'Chicago', self-branching in great profusion; originally from California. *p. 340*

helix 'Palmata'; broad fan-like leaves with 5 lobes cut into apex, of leathery texture, dark green, 5-6 cm long and 5-8 cm wide with prominent veins. *p. 336, 338*

helix 'Parsley crested' (cristata); long vining variety called "Parsley ivy" because the small, leathery, medium green, 5-lobed, roundish leaves are minutely frilled and crimped on margins. *p. 324*

helix 'Patricia'; sport of 'Pittsburgh', an excellent Philadelphia cultivar; dense self-branching ivy with medium-sized leathery leaves to 3-6 cm wide and long, usually remotely 5-lobed, and prettily curled in at sinuses. A good keeper and favorite in a 13 cm pot, with its neatly draped reddish branches. Better keeper indoors than the "Pittsburgh ivy". *p. 341*

helix 'Pedata', the "Birdsfoot ivy" with dainty leaves cut into narrow lobes, apple-green becoming much darker with contrasting whitish veins; long vining. *p. 322, 326, 334, 335*

helix 'Pedata variegata'; the "Variegated birdsfoot" with long strands of narrow, 3-lobed leaves grayish green and broad, cream edging. *p. 325*

helix 'Permanent Wave'; beautiful crested-leaf ivy from Augusta, Georgia; light green leaf blades 6-8 cm long and 9 cm wide, 3-5-lobed with deep sinuses and strongly crested; resembles 'Manda's Crested' but more robust. *p. 336*

helix 'Pin Oak'; weak, selfbranching creeper with thin-leathery leaves gracefully cut into narrow curving lobes, on reddish stem. *p. 326, 330*

helix 'Pittsburgh'; strong vining, bushy plant with leaves smaller than the English ivy, more long pointed, not as black-green, venation less pronounced, and green. One of the cultivars of the "ramosa complex", probably a bud-sport of H. h. gracilis but less spindly; quite hardy. *p. 324, 327*

helix 'Pixie', "Pixie miniature"; fine miniature variety of very compact, almost stunted growth, with densely shingled small, very variable leathery leaves deeply trilobed to more shallowly 5 to 7-lobed. *p. 338, 339*

helix 'Poetica' (chrysocarpa) (Italy, Greece, Asia Minor); yellow fruited variety, with flowers greenish and adult leaves unlobed; in juvenile stage twigs green and with aerial rootlets, leaves broadly 5-lobed with prominent palmate veins. *p. 323, 326, 332*

helix 'Preston Tiny'; found in the garden of Preston House in Columbia, S. C., one of the finest a century ago; small leaved, 3 to 5 cm long and wide, on wiry, flexible stem, 3 to 5-lobed, with light veins, on white petioles. *p. 336*

helix 'Purpurea'; small, mainly 3-lobed, leathery leaves bronzy-purple mottled with dull green; in autumn and winter almost black, contrasting with the white ribs; photographed in New Zealand. *p. 340*

helix 'Rheder's Gold'; lovely cultivar with shallowly 3-lobed leaf primarily red-gold all the time, not like 'Russell Gold' or 'Buttercup' where only the new growth is gold; from W. Freeland collection, Columbia, S.C. 1972. *p. 336*

helix 'Ripples'; pendant branches heavily loaded with medium-large roundish foliage irregularly lobed, the margins more or less curled or crested. *Temperate.* *p. 335*

helix 'Rubaiyat'; from the Brooklyn Botanic Garden collection; leaf blades shallowly 3-lobed and shallow cordate base, to 7 cm long and 8 cm wide; veins green above, purplish between veins in cold weather. *p. 336*

helix 'Sagittaefolia' (taurica) (Turkey), "Taurian ivy"; flat growing variety with narrow-sagittate, small leaves, very heavy, deep grayish green with whitish vining, on spreading, purplish vines. *p. 324, 334*

helix 'Sagittaefolia variegata' (New Zealand); slow growing vine with medium-sized leaves 4-6 cm long, mostly 3-lobed into narrow segments, the midlobe long and curved downwards; dark grayish green with cream-white variegation mainly along margins. *p. 340*

helix 'Scutifolia' (cordata), "Heartleaf ivy"; small, heartshaped leaves, thick leathery and a deep, matte green with pale veining, on reddish petioles and wiry vines. *p. 324*

helix 'Shamrock'; wiry plant with red stems and tiny, bright to rich green, leathery leaves having 3 lobes more or less of same size, side lobes folded forward alongside the center segment. *p. 326, 330*

helix 'Shannon'; freely trailing small-leaved ivy with leaves of the birds-foot type, mostly 3-lobed deeply cut into narrow segments, dark green; very dense and bushy. *p. 338*

helix 'Silver Emblem'; wiry grower lightly selfbranching, with leathery, medium-small, pointed leaves bright green and gray-green with narrow cream border. *p. 325, 331*

helix 'Silver King', "Small variegated ivy"; tiny, selfbranching variety with leaves smaller than Glacier, weaker and softer, pointed, closely set and nicely arranged, light green to gray with white edge; slow and particular. *p. 325*

helix 'Smithii'; medium size, star-like, 5-lobed, thin-leathery leaves, medium to dark green, with lobes somewhat fluted and tips curving downward. *p. 324*

helix 'Spinoza' ('Spinozia'); curious small ivy with the look of a dwarfed bonsai tree; upright, knobby branches dense with glossy, leathery leaves with a fresh green look; the small leaves 1-3 cm long, from oval or barely lobed to fan-shaped and 3-lobed, with midlobe to 2 cm, the pronounced veins are light green. *p. 338*

helix 'Star'; shapely selfbranching, bushy variety, leaves 5-pointed, star-shaped with slender finger-like lobes. *Temperate.* *p. 329*

helix 'Star dust'; charming small-leaved clone, free-growing with long flexuous, rooting branches and ideal for trellis-training or hanging baskets; the little 3 cm leaves 3 to 5-lobed and almost star-like, grayish-green with creamy-white edging. *p. 342*

helix 'Sylvanian'; densely clothed twigs with leaves overlapping each other shingle-like and selfbranching, pointed blade leathery, unequally lobed, forest green. *p. 324*

helix taurica: see helix 'Sagittaefolia'

helix 'Teena'; a reversion from 'Gold Heart'; small-leaved ranging from 2 to 5 cm long and wide, shield-shaped, shallowly 3-lobed. *p. 336*

helix 'Telecurl'; vigorous, bushy, red-stemmed plant with interesting 5-7-lobed leaves, the main lobe deeply cut to base and recessed, the adjoining lateral lobes overlapping or ruffled. *p. 329, 330*

helix 'Tribairn'; also known as 'The Three Children'; a delightful small-leaved rambler with woody stems, the leaves 1 to 3½ cm long, trilobed deeply cut into narrow linear segments. *p. 337*

helix 'Triloba'; dwarf variety with small dark, purplish-green leaves with light veins, lightly trilobed but the leaf as a whole is narrow and oblong pointed. *p. 329, 333*

helix 'Triton'; very curious leaf, narrow palmate 7-9 cm long and 3-4 cm wide, leathery deep green deeply cut into slender, pointed segments, with prominent veins running fan-like; from the collection of W. Freeland, Columbia, So. Carolina. *p. 337*

helix 'Trustee'; robust plant with cordate to 3-lobed deep green leaves with prominent veins, found in Savannah, Georgia, at the old Trustee's Garden, the first Experiment Station in Colonial America. *p. 336*

helix '238th Street'; this maturity stage ivy produces, in addition to flowering twigs, stiff, viny, green shoots with unlobed, waxy green leaves, spreading horizontally, and which stay green in winter; flower greenish-cream, fruit green to black. First seen in the Bronx, New York City. *Warm temperate.* *p. 323, 326*

helix 'Typ Schaefer'; charming small-leaved and bushy plant with 3-4 cm 3-lobed leaves milky green with margins clearly outlined in white, the midlobe long and pointed; a cultivar popular in Holland and Germany for indoor culture; photographed in Aalsmeer, Holland. *p. 338*

helix 'Variegated Californian'; a sport originated from the durable small-leaved indoor variety 'Weber's Californian', with sections of leaves variegated white. *p. 328*

helix 'Walthamensis' (minor), the "Baby ivy"; because it is the smallest variant of the typical English ivy group; leaves tiny, deep green and leathery, veins whitish. *p. 324, 330*

helix 'Weber's Californian'; a really satisfactory indoor plant of bushy habit, medium green, 5-lobed leaves with light green veins, notched deeply and wavy in the sinus, lobes rounded off, reddish stem. *p. 326*

helix 'Weber's Fan'; perhaps a fasciated form of crenata, its broad rounded leaves with 5-8 small, rounded lobes and undulate margin, and light green palmate veining. *p. 326*

helix 'Williamsiana'; shapely and vigorous variety with 3-5 small, lobed leaves, the long tips curled downward while edges of leaves are wavy; greenish ivory border around apple-green or gray-green center. *Warm temperate.* *p. 325, 331*

helix 'Yalta'; robust cultivar found by Dr. J. Creech in the wooded hills above Yalta in The Crimea, Russia; remotely 3-lobed leaves to 8 cm long and 7 cm wide with cordate base, dark dull green with light green veins. *p. 336*

nepalensis chinensis (Himalayas); climbing vine with scaly stems, somewhat tender; dark green leaves 3 to 5-lobed on sterile, juvenile stems, and unlobed, cordate on flowering branches, 4-7 cm long; fruit yellow. *p. 336*

HEDYCHIUM *Zingiberaceae* **I-S2LFW**

coccineum (Himalaya, Burma, Ceylon), "Scarlet ginger-lily"; robust perennial herb with suckering rootstock and leafy stems to 2 m high, long, stiff leaves to 50 cm long, smooth green above, bluish beneath; the scarlet red flowers with long corolla tube and pink filament, dense on a stout spike. *Tropical.* *p. 2133*

coronarium (Himalayas into China), "Butterfly lily"; also known as "Garland flower", this "White ginger" is most popular in Hawaii and used for leis because of the sweet perfume of its broad-petaled, pure white flowers, showing a yellow heart on their lip, and appearing from behind a green, waxen bulb of scale-like bracts in terminal clusters, on robust, leafy canes to 2 m long, the leaves silvery-haired beneath. *Subtropic.* *p. 2133*

densiflorum (E. Himalayas); long lanceolate, smooth leathery green leaves along cane-like arching stems 45 cm high, terminated by ascending inflorescence, a dense cylindrical bracted spike 15 cm long, tangerine-orange or deep coral colored, and with coral-red stamens without anthers. *p. 2137*

flavum (Indian Himalaya), "Yellow ginger"; luxuriant green herb with leafy canes to 1½ m high; long, glabrous, slender pointed leaves almost 60 cm long and sheathing, alternate along the stem in 2 rows, bearing on its summit a head of shingled green bracts from which appears a broad cluster of heavily perfumed flowers, yellow with orange patch and with cream stamens; threaded into leis in Hawaii. *Tropical.* *p. 2133*

gardnerianum (No.India), "Kahili ginger"; beautiful, desirable species growing in the Himalayas to 2500 m, of stiff habit, canes to 1½ m high, leaves to 45 cm and powdery-white beneath when young; the delightfully fragrant flowers in elongate, open terminal spikes to 45 cm long, and from a cylindrical cone of green bracts appear the yellow flowers having long, conspicuous, bright red filaments. *Tropical.* *p. 2112A, 2131, 2134*

greenei (Alpinia) (Bhutan); beautiful ginger with stout leafy canes ½-2 m high, dense with heavy leaves to 25 cm long and a dense terminal head of large, fiery orange-red flowers with dark-red lip and red filament. *p. 2133*

x kewense (coccineum var. angustifolium x gardnerianum); handsome plant to 2½ m high; stout canes alternately set with long lanceolate leathery leaves terminated by erect cylindrical spike of orange flowers with long protruding stamens. *p. 2130*

thyrsiforme (India), a "Ginger lily"; robust tropical perennial with fleshy rootstock, and leafy stem to 2 m high; fleshy lanceolate leaves to 35 cm long; the inflorescence at apex a dense spike with white flowers, the corolla tube 3 cm and with long protruding filaments. *p. 2135*

HEDYSCEPE *Palmae* **S2LFM**

canterburyana (Kentia) (South Pacific: Lord Howe Is.), "Umbrella palm"; handsome erect palm to 12 m tall, with ringed trunk and a crown of pinnate 2 m fronds recurving downwards umbrella-like, the leaflets sword-shaped, leathery, green; purple fruit egg-shaped 4 cm long. Young plants look almost exactly like a Howeia, but are of slower growth. *p. 1886*

HEIMERLIODENDRON *Nyctaginaceae* **I1LFM**

brunonianum (Pisonia) (Queensland, N.S.W.), "Bird-catcher tree" or "Para Para"; branching evergreen tree to 20 m, with soft, light-colored wood; leathery, glossy green oval leaves to 25 cm long; small greenish flowers; the narrow, angular fruit is covered with a dark viscid gum, which traps small birds. *p.. 1615, 1621*

brunonianum 'Variegatum' (Pisonia) (New Zealand), "Bird-catcher-tree"; showy sport of the "Para-Para" tree 6 to 15 m high and native from Tahiti and Marquesas to New Zealand and Australia, with oblong foliage to 40 cm long, having very sticky ribs, on short, robust petioles, and slightly angled stem; the glossy leaves are marbled in two shades of green, edged with warm cream to almost white; unfolding young growth has a tinge of red at edge and midrib; clusters of inconspicuous greenish flowers. The seed pods are covered with a sweet gum which attracts birds. *p. 320A, 1620, 1621*

HELCIA *Orchidaceae* **C3OFM**

sanguinolenta (Ecuador); dwarf, pretty epiphyte with ovate pseudobulbs with solitary leathery leaf; individual showy 6 cm flowers from the base, the oblong sepals and petals yellowish and barred with brown, the lip white, veined with crimson (winter or early spring). (C) *p. 1739*

HELENIUM *Compositae* **I2LBD**

bigelovii (California), "Sneezeweed"; perennial to 1 m, with unbranched stems forming a clump; lanceolate leaves sparsely hairy; disk cushion brownish, ray flowers yellow. *Subtropic.* *p. 811*

HELIAMPHORA *Sarraceniaceae* **I3H Sphag BW**

heterodoxa (heteradextra) (Venezuela); from Mt. Divroa; from a rhizome, full, slender funnel-shaped light green leaves with apex ending in a small spoon-shaped cap; a passive death-trap to insects, the tube holding sweet-tasting but deadly fluid, which can be reached only after passing one-way hairs, blocking any attempt to flee out to freedom. *p. 774*

minor (Venezuela); from Mt. Auyan-Tepui at 2200 metres alt.; insectivorous clustering rosette of short, funnel-shaped pitchers, constricted in the middle, 10-12 cm long, with large rounded spoon; the hairs inside directed down and with many nectar glands to trap insects; flowers white, later greenish; enjoys full sun similar to nutans but sturdier. *p. 774*

nutans (Guyana); "Sun pitcher"; carnivorous rosette from the moist Roraima savannah, with funnel-shaped pitchers hairy inside, forming an insect trap of the pitfall type; leaves are red-veined; the delicate nodding flowers white. *Humid-subtropic.* *p. 774*

HELIANTHUS *Compositae* **I2LBM**

annuus (Western United States), the "Common sunflower"; coarse stiff-hairy annual with stout straight stalk to 5 m tall, rarely branched, and leafy with large ovate, rough hairy, toothed foliage to 30 cm long, and topped by tilted, immense heads sunlike to 50 cm across in cultivation, large disk of yellow tubular rays and blackish bracts, the large outer ring of florets orange-yellow. The white seed is used as food, as birdfeed, and furnishes oil. Wild on the prairies the flowers are only 8-15 cm across. *p. 806*

annuus fl. pl. 'Sungold', the "Double sunflower" or "Cut-and come-again"; annual; a dwarf form 1-1½ m high with golden yellow chryanthemum-like fully double flowers about 10 cm across, the rays very dense and largely serrated at tips; makes a good cut flower. *p. 803*

HELICHRYSUM *Compositae* **C2LBM**

bracteatum (Australia), "Strawflower"; annual herb with narrow leaves and stalks of solitary flower disks enclosed by strawlike colored bracts, 3-4 cm across, in shades from white through yellow to red, and suitable for drying. *Subtropic.* *p. 805*

milfordiae (So. Africa: Natal, Basutoland); cushion-forming perennial rosettes of oblong 1 cm leaves; attractive solitary daisy-like white flowers 3 cm across, the surrounding bracts tipped crimson. *p. 818*

orientale (S. E. Europe, Asia Minor), an "Everlasting", hardy perennial subshrub with woody base and erect, leafy flowering shoots, 15-40 cm high, leaves gray-hairy 3-8 cm long; papery 1-2 cm flower heads lemon yellow with orange center in terminal clusters; late summer-blooming. *p. 818*

petiolatum (Gnaphalium lanatum) (So. Africa), an "Immortelle"; shrubby perennial with woolly stems and vine-like shoots; oval white-woolly leaves; flower heads with yellow disk flowers and cream-white bracts. *p. 818*

scutellifolium (Australia); hairy shrub to 3 m or more, with scale-like thick leaves 2 mm long; yellow disk flowers in small heads with pale brown bracts. *p. 818*

stoechas (So. Europe), "Goldilocks"; perennial subshrub with woody root stock sending up erect slender stems 30-50 cm tall, and covered with silvery down, the linear leaves 2-5 cm long, dark green above, silvery-white underneath; yellow flower heads crowded into terminal clusters 3-5 cm across. *p. 818*

HELICODICEROS *Araceae* **I2HFMd**

muscivorus (Corsica, Sardinia), "Twist-arum"; curious tuberous herb to 45 cm with stalk specked purple; leaves palmately cut, the lobes spirally rolled around the ribs; the thick spathe in a bent, spotted tube flaring wide, purplish-brown white-hairy inside, 40 cm long, with unpleasant odor. *p. 183*

HELICONIA *Musaceae* **S2-3LFM**

acuminata 'Espiritu Santo' (Venezuela); clustering tropical plant 2-3 m tall, with dull green, leathery, lanceolate 50 cm leaves on long, slender petioles; erect inflorescence on wiry stalks of 2-ranked slender bracts orange shading to yellow at edge, 12 cm long; the small flowers orange yellow. Grown in Florida. *Tropical.* *p. 1589*

angustifolia (brasiliensis) (Brazil); striking perennial herb with stout stalks about 1 m high, bearing 60 cm long leathery leaves; erect inflorescence between foliage, boat-shaped orange-red bracts becoming darker as they mature, from their axils rise the creamy-white flowers; the seeds first orange later blue. *p. 1590*

aurantiaca (So. Mexico); reed-like stems 75 cm high, bearing oblong, smooth-leathery leaves, topped by a showy, erect inflorescence with lower bracts orange tipped green, the upper bracts yellowish-red, flowers greenish-red stalked red. *Tropical.* *p. 1590, 1591, 1592*

bihai (W. Indies, Brazil, New Caledonia, Samoa), "Wild plantain" or "Firebird"; large perennial herb to 5 m high, long-stalked, oblong, smooth-textured, pointed, green leaves having a pale midrib and raised lateral veins; greenish-yellow flowers clustered in the axils of large, stiff boat-shaped, crimson-red, flattened bracts with pointed tip, and arranged in two ranks, on erect inflorescence. *Tropical.* *p. 1588*

caribaea (West Indies: Martinique), "Wild plantain"; huge perennial with large leaves 90 cm or more long and rounded at base resembling bananas but arranged in two ranks, the striking inflorescence is carried erect between the foliage, being a series of large, fleshy boat-shaped, pointed, stiff bracts holding water, and compacted shingle-like on two alternate series, waxy golden-yellow with keel and tip greenish. *Tropical.* *p. 1587, 1590, 1592*

caribaea var. purpurea; of similar habit as the species but the alternate, rigid, clasping spathes crimson red with a touch of yellow at the upper edges. *Tropical.* *p. 1588*

choconiana (Guatemala); clustering plant to 1 m high, the reedlike stems with linear oblong, thin-leathery leaves topped by the sessile inflorescence of orange-scarlet bracts and cream-yellow flowers tipped buff. (2) *p. 1588*

collinsiana (pendula in Hortus) (Guatemala); robust tropical perennial with lush growth to 3 m tall, big banana-like foliage dull green, on thick petioles; the striking inflorescence pendant below the leaves, with spreading bracts crimson-red and covered with waxy powder, yellowish toward tips; cream flowers. *Tropical.* *p. 1592*

distans (Trop. America); long-stalked, clustering plant with fresh green foliage; slender bracts lemon-yellow at base, crimson on top and to apex. *Tropical.* *p. 1592*

elongata (Puerto Rico, C. America), known in the Caribbean as "Wild banana"; sturdy banana-like leaves on stiff petioles; inflorescence pendant, with broad triangular, boat-shaped bracts, yellow with red in center and green on upper edge. Photographed at New York Coliseum Flower Show labeled H. hybrida from Puerto Rico. *p. 1592*

hirsuta (Venezuela); graceful plant 1½ to 2 m high; smallish lanceolate leaves well separated; the sparse inflorescence erect on wiry, straight stalks, with slender red bracts about 12 cm long, reduced down to 6 cm in the upper ones; the spreading flowers vivid orange-colored. *p. 1590*

humilis (Trinidad, Brazil), "Lobster's claw"; related to H. bihai, but with leaves shiny green, and smaller, salmon-red, boat-shaped bracts changing into green toward tip, and ridge of greenish-yellow; flowers yellowish white. *Tropical.* *p. 1587, 1590*

illustris 'Aureo-striata' (South Pacific cv.); striking foliage plant with broad, recurving leaves 30-60 cm long, shining fresh-green with contrasting ivory-yellow and pink midrib, and closely parallel lateral ivory veins showing on both surfaces; sheathing petioles pinkish striped or mottled green. *Tropical.* *p. 1591, 1592*

illustris 'Edwardus Rex'; richly colored, robust plant with large showy leaves of an intense, deep red with coppery sheen, more so underneath, and especially the veins and stalks. *p. 1591*

illustris 'Rubra', as grown at Hummel's, Carlsbad, California; colorful tropical plant with large 40 cm, pointed leaves first green with red midrib, turning brown-red; glossy wine-red beneath; petiole salmon-red mottled with black. *Tropical.* *p. 1592*

illustris rubricaulis; has beautiful foliage light green with midrib and the dense lateral veins clear rose pink, on clasping petioles vermillion red, and red underneath; rather delicate. *Tropical.* *p. 1591, 1592*

jacquinii (Fiji), "Lobster's claw"; large banana-like plant; tall, stout stalks with broad leaves, bearing between the foliage the erect, showy inflorescence of alternating, boat-shaped slender pointed leathery bracts salmon shaded to crimson, the upper edge and tips green. *Tropical.* *p. 1590*

latispatha (Cent. America, No. S. America); showy plant with green broad-oblong leaves 1 m long and 30 cm wide, and an erect flexuous inflorescence with well separated boat-shaped bracts 15 cm long, orange yellow at the base near axis, lacquer red toward slender-pointed tip; flowers greenish. Occasional forms with colors reversed, or entirely red and entirely yellow. *Tropical.* *p. 1588, 1590, 1591*

mariae (C. America: Venezuela, Colombia), the "Beefsteak heliconia"; big plant to 5 m tall, with hanging inflorescence 25 to 80 cm long, having overlapping scarlet-red bracts with pink flowers. *Tropical.* *p. 1592*

metallica (Colombia); slender perennial to 3 m high, with long red stalks and banana-like, oblong leaves shimmering, velvety, emerald green and pearl-white midrib, purplish-red beneath; waxy inflorescence erect, rosy-red flowers with pale green tips, in green, widely separated, boat-shaped bracts. *p. 1590, 1591*

platystachys (Guatemala, Colombia); large banana-like plant with big leaves green on both sides; pendant inflorescence with folded bracts widely separated on snaky, brown hairy axis; the tapering bracts to 18 cm long, vivid green edged with greenish-yellow. *Tropical.* *p.1587*

psittacorum (coast of Guyana; Brazil), "Parrot flower"; tufted perennial with long-stemmed, narrow lanceolate, leathery, rich green leaves and a stalked inflorescence of shining orange, long-pointed bracts tipped red, and greenish-yellow flowers with black spots near apex. *Tropical.* *p. 1588*

rostrata (Perú), "Hanging lobster-claws"; beautiful tropical herb 1 to 3 m high, with banana-like, leathery, green leaves; magnificent pendant inflorescence of alternating bracts, each 6-10 cm long, scarlet red tipped with cream to yellow. *Tropical.* *p. 1589*

spectabilis (South Pacific: Melanesia); showy clustering plant with large, succulent, pointed leaves bronzy-green having a brown-red midrib, wine-red beneath, on winged, deep red petioles; the several overlapping reddish bracts are deeply boatshaped in a short-stalked inflorescence not higher than the foliage. *Tropical.* *p. 1591*

velutina (Trop. America); compact plant with beautiful, satiny, grass-green, pointed, short leaves and prominent pale midrib, lateral veins raised and very dense, shining green beneath; petioles and stem green. *p. 1591*

HELIOCEREUS *Cactaceae* **S2LFM**

speciosus (Central Mexico), the "Sun cactus" because of its large and showy, day-flowering, bright scarlet flowers with a lovely steel-blue sheen; 4-angled or flattened stems erect or clambering, freely branching; the spines all alike. *Tropical.* *p. 653*

HELIOTROPIUM *Boraginaceae* **I2LFM**

arborescens (Perú), "Heliotrope"; fleshy herb with small ovate wrinkled leaves and large clusters of small purple flowers very fragrant like vanilla. *Tropical.* *p. 510*

arborescens album, "White cherry pie", variety with dense clusters of the tiny 3 mm sweetly-scented flowers in pure white. *p. 510*

HELLEBORUS *Ranunculaceae* **C2LFMd**

foetidus (W. and So. Europe); winter green subshrub to 60 cm high, with leafy stems; the leathery foliage dark shining green, cut birdfoot-like into 7-10 narrow, toothed segments; nodding, cup-shaped flowers green, the petal-like inner sepals marked red-brown, the tubular nectaries funnel-shaped; fairly hardy. *p. 1984*

lividus (corsicus) (Corsica); evergreen, rather woody perennial with glaucous 45 cm stems; bluish-green, thick-leathery 3-parted leaves borne near bottom of plant; nodding 5 cm cup-shaped flowers yellowish-green, in profuse clusters; early spring. *p. 1983, 1984*

niger (Europe: Alps, Italy, Balkans), the "Christmas-rose"; known since the 16th century; a wintergreen herb with palmately divided leathery, olive green leaves; solitary waxy flowers white or purplish, with green petals, 4 to 6 cm across. *Temperate.* *p. 1824A, 1989*

orientalis atrorubens ('Atropurpureus') (W. Asia: Black Sea area, Armenia), the "Lenten-rose"; with basal leaves palmately divided, green above, pale beneath; leafless, branched stalk striped reddish, with several 5 cm flowers dark purple outside, greenish-purple inside. *p. 1989*

orientalis x niger; a Lemoine hybrid combining the "Lenten-rose" (orientalis) and the "Christmas rose" (niger); with palmate leaves, and flowers with petal-like sepals, chartreuse-green and purple. *p. 1984*

viridis (Ireland to Yugoslavia); hardy perennial with deciduous palmate leaves of 7-11 green leaflets; stalk with 5-6 cup-shaped nodding flowers bright green, the petal-like sepals wide, and yellow-green nectaries, (February). *p. 1984*

HELMINTHOSTACHYS *Ophioglossaceae (Filices)* **S3HFM**

zeylanica (Himalayas to Queensland); curious fern with thick succulent, creeping rhizomes, fronds with palmate-pinnate barren segments, often in 3 main divisions, stalked and again forked, the ultimate divisions linear, to 10 cm long; the fertile spike arising from base of barren segments bearing crested clusters of sporangia. *p. 1080*

HELXINE *Urticaceae* **I3-2HFM**

soleirolii (Corsica, Sardinia), popularly known as "Baby's tears", also as "Mind-your-own-business", "Irish moss", "Corsican curse" and "Japanese moss"; low moss-like creeping herb hugging the ground and forming dense mats or cushions as ground cover or over pots in subtropical plantings; tiny roundish lush-green leaves 6 mm or less across on threadlike intertwining branches, with minute greenish flowers in leaf-axils. *Subtropic.* *p. 2104, 2110*

soleirolii 'Aurea'; cultivar with most of its tiny leaves all colored ivory to deep yellow, forming moss-like cushions. *p. 2110*

soleirolii 'Marginata', a variegated form of "Baby's tears"; the tiny 5 mm circular leaves fresh glossy green with creamy margins around the edge. *p. 2108*

HEMEROCALLIS *Liliaceae* **C2LFMh**

fulva 'Mikado'; one of the numerous day-lilies of Chinese ancestry; perennial herb with spreading rhizomes forming clumps with basal leaves and showy wide-funnel-shaped flowers with spreading petals, coppery-red with dark markings on branched stalks. *p. 1460*

lilio-asphodelus (flava) (Siberia to Japan), "Tall yellow day-lily"; vigorous perennial herb with spreading rhizomes; linear basal leaves 60 cm long and weak, arching, branched stalks 60-90 cm high with lily-like lemon-yellow, fragrant flowers spreading 9 cm; May to July. *p. 1460*

HEMIGRAPHIS *Acanthaceae* **S3LNM**

colorata (Java), "Red ivy"; prostrate tropical herb with stringy, rooting branches and opposite, broad-cordate, puckered and toothed leaves 6 to 10 cm long, shimmering silvery violet, underneath red-purple; terminal heads of small white flowers between large bracts. *Tropical.* *p. 48*

'Exotica', (New Guinea), "Purple waffle plant"; trailing plant of robust habit, with flexible pubescent reddish branches, opposite oval to ovate 8 cm leaves irregularly depressed-puckered, metallic purplish-green surface, margins crenate, reverse wine-red. A showy species we found in N.E. New Guinea. *Tropical.* *p. 48*

repanda (Malaysia); prostrate tropical herbaceous plant spreading by rooting stems, the red branches with narrow linear crenate leaves 6 cm long, satiny purplish green, and red beneath; small white 15 mm flowers in cone-like spikes; good in hanging baskets. *Tropical.* *p. 48*

HEMIONITIS *Polypodiaceae (Filices)* **I2HFM**

arifolia (So. India, Bengal, Ceylon, Burma, Philippines); dwarf fern with thin-leathery, hastate fronds to 8 cm, smooth above, tomentose beneath, the barren leaves generally cordate and on short stalks; the fertile fronds on long 30 cm glossy brown stalks, fibrous toward base. *p. 1114*

palmata (W. Indies, Mexico, So. America), "Strawberry-fern"; small tropical fern with palmate pubescent fronds to 15 cm long and wide, with 5 triangular divisions; the fertile leaves stiff and long-stalked, the sterile ones on short stalks. *p. 1114*

HEMIONITIS of hort.: see also Tectaria.

HEPATICA *Ranunculaceae* **C2LFM**

americana (Nova Scotia to Manitoba, and Florida), "Liver-leaf"; low perennial herb to 15 cm; leaves with 3 rounded lobes on shaggy-hairy petioles; solitary 2 cm flowers with petal-like sepals lavender-blue passing into white; blooming before new leaves. (h) *p. 1989*

HEPPIELLA *Gesneriaceae* **S3LFM**

corymbosa (Jamaica); tropical species of stiff shrubby habit with rough-hairy, rugose, ovate-pointed leaves shining green; curved tubular flowers with flaring, frilled lobes creamy-white with bronzy maroon tint. *p. 1257*

HEPTAPLEURUM

stelzerianum: see Schefflera venulosa erythrostachys

HEREROA *Aizoaceae* **I2LBD**

granulata (Cape Prov.); soft-fleshy succulent with 5 cm triangular leaves lightly keeled and connate (united) at base, light green, roughened with darker tubercles, 4-6 cm long; flowers yellow. *p. 65, 79*

muirii (Cape Prov.: Karroo); distinctive cluster forming smooth succulent rosette to 7 cm high, with spreading, soft-fleshy, boat-shaped, semicylindrical, silver-gray leaves rough above and keeled, 5 cm long; yellow flowers, on leafy stalk. *Arid-subtropic.* *p. 65*

HERITIERA *Sterculiaceae* **S2LBD**

fischeri (macrophylla) (E. Indies), "Glass-tree" or "Looking glass tree"; handsome tropical evergreen tree with large oblong, quilted leaves 25 cm or more long, shining yellow green above, opaque silvery beneath, reflecting the sun like so many mirrors; reddish when young; small greenish flowers in clusters. Photographed as H. fischeri at the Botanic Garden in Leningrad. *Tropical.* *p. 2087*

HERMANNIA *Sterculiaceae* **I2LBD**

candicans (So. Africa); subshrub to 1 m high, with downy shoots; oblong 2 to 4 cm leaves wrinkled at margins, green above, gray with soft down underneath; nodding bell-shaped 1 cm yellow flowers near apex. *p. 2090*

grandiflora (Namibia, So. Africa); a xerophytic shrub of the Karroo desert, small obovate, soft verbena-like leaves sharply toothed; in spring the plant is literally covered with pretty red flowers, the flaring petals making a great show. *p. 2090*

plicata (So. Africa); evergreen shrub 1-1½ m high, with small oval, hard-leathery corrugated, rough leaves 2½ cm long, green on surface, reverse gray-green, margins toothed; tiny nodding bell-flowers with petals propeller-like twisted, ochre-yellow. *p. 2088*

HERMODACTYLUS *Iridaceae* **I2LBMd(Su)**
tuberosus (So. France to Greece), "Snake's-head iris"; tuberous plant close to Iris, 30 cm high with 2-3 four-angled glaucous leaves; solitary flowers black-purple, inner segments green, 5 cm long; April-May. *p. 1326, 1335*

HERNANDIA *Hernandiaceae* **S2LBM**
ovigera (peltata) (Queensland, Trop. Asia, Trop. Africa), "Sea cups"; handsome evergreen tree to 12 m, with broadly ovate peltate decorative leaves to 20 cm long, leathery-glossy olive to dark green; small greenish-yellow flowers. *Tropical.* *p. 1320*

HERTIA *Compositae* **I2LBD**
cheirifolia (Algeria, Tunisia); low, somewhat succulent sub-shrub to 50 cm high, fleshy gray-green branches with obovate, blue-glaucous leaves 10 cm long and 2 cm wide; the pretty daisy-like flower heads with yellow ray florets. *p. 818*

HESPERALOE *Liliaceae* **I2LBD**
parviflora (Texas to Mexico), "Western aloe" or "Red yucca"; evergreen yucca-like cluster-forming rosette of hard, recurving, channeled leaves to 1 m long, and 2½ cm wide, linear, thick and leathery, bright green lined with gray, and white coiling threads hanging from the corky margin; branched slender stalks to 2 m long, with racemes of small, nodding, waxy, bell-like 2½ cm flowers salmon-red outside, yellow inside. *p. 1452*

HESPERANTHA *Iridaceae* **I2LBDd**
bauri (Transvaal); cormous herb with 3 grass-like ribbed basal leaves to 30 cm long; tubular 3 cm flowers flaring star-like, bright rose-red and fragrant, opening to the sun. *p. 1337*
stanfordiae (So. Africa), "Evening flower"; cormous plant to 40 cm with sickle-shaped basal leaves, and erect stalks of bright yellow flowers with flaring lobes. *p. 1332, 1337*

HESPERIS *Cruciferae* **C2LBM**
matronalis florepleno (So. Europe, east to Siberia), "Double dames-violet"; branched perennial partially hairy, with lanceolate, toothed 10 cm leaves, and 1 cm double flowers lilac to purple, fragrant in evening. *p. 927*

HESSEA *Amaryllidaceae* **I2LBD**
zeyheri (Cape Prov.); tender bulbous plant with narrow leaves and long-stalked clusters of starry pink flowers having narrow linear segments; normally summer-blooming. *p. 121*

HETERANTHERA *Pontederiaceae* **I2LFW**
dubia (graminea) (U.S.A., Mexico, Cuba), "Water star-grass"; aquatic plant with stems submerged in water, or floating on the water surface, or creeping on wet ground; linear green leaves 6-12 cm long; spidery yellow flowers carried above the water. *Humid-subtropic.* *p. 1958*
reniformis (Trop. and Subtrop. America); aquatic plant with long-stemmed kidney-shaped small leaves, rich green with yellow base; carried above the water; sparse flowers, white or pale blue. *p. 1958*
zosterifolia (syn. osteniana) (So. Brazil, Paraguay, Uruguay, Bolivia, Argentina); aquatic plant with stems both submerged or floating, or creeping on boggy ground; fresh-green linear leaves 2-4 cm long; starry blue flowers on terminal stalks. *Humid-subtropic.* *p. 1958*

HETEROARIDARUM *Araceae* **S3LFM**
annae (Sarawak, Borneo); small ornamental aroid of moist-tropical locations; from a very short stem with cord-like roots rise vaginate petioles, having long free sheath, bearing narrow, long elliptic, deep green leathery leaves to 25 cm long, arranged in two ranks, midrib very strong and lateral veins parallel; the handsome inflorescence with fluted, creamy-white spathe green at base, and club-shaped yellowish spadix. *p. 290*

HETEROCENTRON *Melastomataceae* **I2LBD**
roseum (Lasiandra) (Mexico), "Pearl flower", small evergreen shrub to 50 cm, with 4-angled branches; opposite elliptic 5 cm leaves, and clusters of bright rose flowers of 4 spreading petals. *Tropical.* *p. 1557*

HETEROMELES *Rosaceae* **I2LBD**
arbutifolia (Photinia) (California, Baja California), "Toyon" or "California holly"; also known as "Christmas-berry"; evergreen drought-resistant shrub or multiple trunk tree of the Sierra Nevada foothills, 3 to 8 m high, with leathery, recurved, shining leaves to 10 cm long; small white 1 cm flowers, followed by masses of bright red, long persistent berries through winter; a striking ornamental. *Subtropic.* *p. 1999*

HETEROPSIS *Araceae* **S3HFM**
jenmanii (Guyana); shrubby tropical forest climber of unusual non-aroid appearance; the thin-wiry stems with internodes 3-6 cm apart carry alternate thin-leathery, elliptic leaves 7-12 cm long, 2-4 cm wide, and shining green; cream-colored spathe soon falling; spadix with perfect flowers, followed by 1½ cm berries. *p. 189*

HETEROPTERYS *Malpighiaceae* **S3LFM**
chrysophylla (Brazil); twining climber, branches clothed with dense appressed rusty hairs; opposite oval, leathery leaves, smooth above, and with golden-brown downy hair underneath; small axillary flowers orange, becoming reddish. *p. 1525*

HETEROSPATHE *Palmae* **S3LFM**
elata (Philippines, Amboina); slender feather-palm with ringed trunk to 13 m, arching pinnate fronds about 5 m long, with numerous deep green gracefully hanging, slender pointed leaflets. *p. 1878*

HETEROTOMA *Campanulaceae* **I3LFM**
lobelioides (Mexico, C. America), "Bird-plant"; branching herb with hairy stems woody at base, lanceolate, toothed leaves, and terminal clusters of 5 cm flowers with corolla and 2 sepals forming a spur, the red corolla tube split to back, the 3-lobed limb golden yellow. *p. 750*

HEUCHERA *Saxifragaceae* **C2LBM**
sanguinea (Arizona, Mexico), "Coral bells"; attractive herbaceous perennial with a tuft of rounded, lobed leaves with silver markings; slender stalks bear airy racemes of small bell-shaped flowers, bright rose-red; winter-hardy. Seen in the Swiss Alps as a potted plant. *Subtropic.* *p. 2048*

HEVEA *Euphorbiaceae* **S3LBM**
brasiliensis (Amazonas), "Para rubber"; tropical tree, growing to 18 m, with milky juice containing latex which when coagulated becomes rubber; large palmate leaves of 3 stalked, quilted, papery segments bluish beneath; flowers greenish-white. *Tropical.* *p. 1052, 1053, 1054*

HEXISEA *Orchidaceae* **I3OFM**
bidentata (Costa Rica, Panama, Colombia); epiphyte with small spindle-shaped two-leaved pseudobulbs set above each other like a jointed stem; small bright scarlet flowers with linear petals and sepals, arising from the nodes. (April-June). (I) *p. 1709*

HEYWOODIELLA *Compositae* **S3LFD**
oligocephala (Canary Islands); small rosette of glossy green, narrow lanceolate leaves with saw-toothed margins; from the center the stalked, solitary flowers double with several rows of yellow florets. *p. 822*

HIBBERTIA *Dilleniaceae* **I2LFM**
cuneiformis (Candollea) (Western Australia); evergreen shrub to 3 m high, with leathery oblong leaves 2-4 cm long, toothed at margins; showy, rich yellow, solitary flowers 4 cm, among the crowded upper foliage. *p.951*
dentata (Australia: Victoria, N.S.W. Queensland), "Twining Guinea-flower"; handsome twining or trailing woody vine with slender red stems; deep coppery green, oblong velvety leaves 6-8 cm long, veined with chocolate brown, the margins serrate with teeth turned down; pretty flowers golden yellow, 4 cm across with red-purple calyx, and numerous stamens. *p. 951*
volubilis (Queensland, N.S. Wales), "Snake vine"; twining shrub with obovate leaves glabrous above, silky-hairy beneath; flowers rich yellow, unpleasantly scented. *p. 951*

HIBISCUS *Malvaceae* **I-S2LBM**
arnottianus (Kauai, Hawaii), the native "Kokio-Keokeo"; dense bush with dull green thin-leathery ovate leaves, flowers white with protruding style carmine-red. *Tropical.* *p. 1531*
eedtveldtianus (India); shrubby herb with wiry stems; thorny petioles with bristly trilobed leaves crenate at margins, olive green with brownish veins; flowers deep wine-red with blackish-red veining, 7 cm dia. *p. 1531*
huegelii (Australia), "Blue hibiscus"; erect, tomentose shrub with small, deeply 3 to 5-lobed, dark green, coarse-hairy leaves, and numerous small, single, rosy-purple flowers with spreading petals. *Subtropic.* *p. 1526*
malacospermus (Transvaal); dwarf, spreading perennial with linear leaves sharply serrate at margins; pretty flowers 8 cm dia., in varying colors yellow or purple, and with maroon eye, in the same colony of plants. *p. 1531*
moscheutos 'New Blood-red' (Eastern U.S.), "Swamp rose-mallow"; perennial herb to 2½ m; with ovate leaves, white-woolly beneath; enormous blooms up to 20 cm dia., bright crimson red in this garden hybrid; the species has pink or rosy flowers. *p. 1531*
moscheutos 'Southern Belle'; a "Rose-mallow"; garden hybrid to 80 cm high, serrate leaves, white-downy beneath; flowers crimson-red or rose with red center; blooms extremely large, to 20 cm or more across.
Warm temperate. *p. 1531*
mutabilis (South China), "Confederate rose" or "Cotton-rose"; fast-growing shrubby bush becoming tree-like where planted in the tropics and subtropics; green stems becoming woody, the large 3 to 5-lobed leaves 10-20 cm wide, dull green and rough pubescent; toward branch ends the showy axillary flowers 10-12 cm across, opening white or rose in the morning with crimson center and a divided maroon column; by evening the flower becomes deep red. In colder areas the plant is deciduous. *Subtropic.* *p. 1531*
rosa-sinensis (Trop. Asia), "Chinese hibiscus"; magnificent flowering shrub of vigorous habit, to 3 m high; glossy green, serrate leaves, and mostly very large 5-petaled flowers from white to yellow and red to magenta. Hibiscus are among the most showy flowers of the tropics, especially the Chinese hibiscus, which is the state flower of Hawaii where some 5000 varieties are known. Raw flowers are eaten there to aid digestion. In Tahiti, a flower worn over the right ear shows that one is looking for a mate.

Blossoms of most varieties remain open for one day only, unfolding early in the morning and dying after closing near sunset, but in good sunlight are almost everblooming, especially if given liberal watering and nourishment. Much used as flowering shrubs and hedges in tropical gardens. Chinese hibiscus are also wonderful container plants for pots or tubs indoors, or on the summer patio, preferring some rest, and cutting back in winter; need lots of food and water when growing, to support adequate foliage and prodigious bloom. *Tropical.*

rosa-sinensis 'Agnes Goult'; fast vigorous grower with very attractive, large single flowers bright rose pink, heavily veined with rose, and with crimson-red throat. *p. 1530*

rosa-sinensis 'California Gold'; shapely bush of robust habit, with fresh-green, broad ovate leaves, and medium large, firm, single flowers golden yellow, with crimson-red center, blooming with the sun. Very popular in California gardens. *Subtropic.* *p. 1530*

rosa-sinensis 'Cherie'; bushy Danish hybrid (Nielsen 1960), of compact habit, with flowers in champagne color or light beige. *p. 1533*

rosa-sinensis 'Cooperi' (E. Indies), "Checkered hibiscus"; ornamental shrub mainly grown for its colorful foliage, the narrow lanceolate leaves are metallic green and brightly variegated and marbled with dark olive, white, pink and crimson; small scarlet flowers. *Tropical.* *p. 1526, 1527*

rosa-sinensis 'Lady Hamilton'; Swedish cultivar (Hamilton-Haelsingborg 1960), then a breakthrough to showy tri-colored flowers apricot, vivid red and dark crimson. *p. 1533*

rosa-sinensis 'Lateritia'; an excellent cultivar of compact, bushy habit, with dark green, lobed leaves; charming 10 cm flowers bright orange yellow with blackish-red eye in center; a favorite pot plant for window sills in Germany. *Tropical.* *p. 1531*

rosa-sinensis 'Lateritia variegata'; a Danish cultivar with leaves different, being irregularly lobed, the lobes pointed, predominantly variegated with milky-white; flowers golden-yellow. *p. 1528*

rosa-sinensis 'Matensis', "Snowflake hibiscus"; probably a clone or colorform of H. rosa-sin. Cooperi; vigorously branching shrub with willowy reddish stems dense with rough ovate, toothed leaves grayish-green, variegated mainly toward margins with creamy-white; single 8 cm flowers carmine-red with crimson veins and center. *Tropical.* *p. 1530*

rosa-sinensis plenus (India to China), "Double Rose of China"; magnificent robust flowering bush of somewhat sparry habit, with fresh green foliage and large showy blooms, 10-15 cm across, typically carmine-rose with dark center, but with flowers fully double; in bloom whenever the sunlight is intense enough, best during the warm summer season but also in winter. Other cultivars are in shades of yellow to deep red. *p. 1527*

rosa-sinensis 'Regius maximus' (E. Indies to China), "Flower-of-a-day", "Chinese hibiscus" or "Rose of China"; vigorous, free-flowering, spreading, tropical shrub with large ovate, toothed leaves deep glossy-green, and large showy 12 cm single flowers with recurved wavy petals glowing deep scarlet and a blackish center; staminal column red with golden anthers. *p. 1527*

rosa-sinensis 'Scarlet', also known as 'Brilliant'; a cultivar very floriferous with single, medium-large flowers in blazing scarlet-crimson, blooming with the sun from early spring into late fall and through the winter if kept light and warm; its strong habit with its glossy foliage, lends itself to training into attractive tree-like semi-standards. *Tropical.* *p. 1529*

rosa-sinensis 'Silver Streak'; vigorous cultivar with ovate, toothed leaves similar to cooperi but without the autumn hues of cooperi; has some pure white variegation along with green and bright pink in its colorful foliage; flowers red. *p. 1530*

rosa-sinensis 'Snow Queen'; bushy cultivar with variegated foliage; the toothed leaves broad ovate with tapering base, marbled and mottled green, gray-green and white; smallish single flowers rose pink. *p. 1530*

rosa-sinensis 'Toreador'; vigorous, erect grower with pubescent, serrate leaves; free-blooming with single 12-15 cm flowers maize-yellow, in the center a contrasting, definite eye of ruby-red with striking effect. *p. 1824A*

rosa-sinensis 'White Wings'; large flowers with linear, spreading petals 9 cm long, freely separated to base, white with contrasting feathery crimson base, and long red staminal column. Willing grower of spreading habit, and profuse with blooms. *Tropical.* *p. 1530*

schizopetalus (Trop. E. Africa), "Japanese lantern"; glabrous shrub with slender drooping branches, and smooth, ovate-elliptic, toothed leaves; the showy orange-red flowers hanging from slender stalks, petals deeply slit and recurved, and a long projecting, pendulous staminal column. *p. 1527*

schizopetalus x rosa-sinensis; a cultivar at Fairchild's subsequently named 'Dainty La France'; erect, whippy branches, and small, lobed ovate leaves; large single flowers tending to hang, bright rose with darker veining, the rounded petals prettily lobed and frilled. *p. 1530*

syriacus albus (Althaea alba) (China, Japan), "Rose of Sharon"; shrub to 4 m high with lush-green, rhomboid-ovate or 3-lobed leaves, crenate toward apex; 8 cm widely bell-shaped, axillary, glistening white flowers with prominent ivory staminal column, in late summer. (C) *p. 1526*

syriacus amplissimus; an interesting form of the "Rose of Sharon" with double flowers of purple-pink with carmine center. *p. 1526*

syriacus coelestis; a form of "Shrub-althaea" with flaring bell-like single flowers in a shade of delicate mauve-blue with darker eye. *p. 1526*

tiliaceus (Trop. Asia and Polynesia); crooked shrub or much branched tree to 4 m or more, with large cordate, matte-green leaves, white hairy beneath; 8 cm flowers open lemon-yellow with or without brown-red base inside, later in the day they change to orange and by night to red. In Polynesia, the fiber of its inner bark is used for ropes or tapa cloth. *Tropical.* *p. 1531*

trionum (So. Europe, W. and C. Asia, E. and So. Africa), "Flower-of-an-hour"; bushy annual with leaves deeply divided into coarsely toothed lobes; cupped 8 cm flowers sulphur-yellow or white with velvety purple center. *Subtropic.* *p. 1531*

HILLEBRANDIA *Begoniaceae* **S3HFM**

sandwicensis (Hawaii); tall branched, succulent herb to 1 m, clothed with long reddish hairs, differing from Begonia in the ovary being free in the upper part and bearing petaloid organs in the female flowers. Tuberous-rooted; leaves to 20 cm obliquely rounded; showy flowers with 5 petals, white tinged rose. *p. 392*

HIMANTOGLOSSUM: see Barlia

HIPPEASTRUM *Amaryllidaceae* **I-S2LBMd**

tropical American bulbous plants popularly known as "Amaryllis" and classified as Hippeastrum in Hortus 3; differing from the true Amaryllis in having hollow flower stalks and the presence of scales between the filaments in the flower. The Amaryllis belladonna, on the other hand, is African, with solid stalks and without scales between the stamens. With their striking, lily-like trumpets, amaryllis are amongst the showiest of all bulbous flowers, which appear in long-stalked clusters before or with their basal, strap-shaped leaves usually after the bulbs have been given a long rest in autumn or into winter.

ackermanii (Brazil, Paraguay); tall floral stalk with flowers 15 cm long, light crimson, green at base inside, outside deep pink above, light green and with whitish markings along center. Possibly a natural hybrid near aulicum. *p. 104*

advenum (Chile); free-flowering species, blooming before leaves appear; linear, glaucous green leaves 30 cm long; flowers 5 cm long, dark crimson, pale green at bases, and narrow white stripe up from along segments; these are narrow-elliptic and not wide-spreading; stamens curved upwards, with yellow anthers. *p. 104*

bifidum (Argentina, Uruguay); from 4 cm bulb two or three linear leaves slightly glaucous, 30 cm long, appearing after flower fades; hollow 30 cm stalk carrying 2 to 6 bright red or orange-red flowers with greenish markings on outside, and yellow with red stripes in throat, only 5 cm long and 5 cm across. *p. 103*

evansiae (Bolivia); lovely amaryllis, from 4 cm bulb the hollow 25 cm stalk with vivid yellow-green flowers; darker inside, the tips flushed orange, 5 cm long. *p. 103*

'Leopoldii hybrid' (Amaryllis), a Dutch "Amaryllis"; the leopoldii hybrids are considered the finest class of fancy flowering amaryllis in pots, the result of breeding H. leopoldii from Perú with reginae and other species; large flat, open-faced flowers generally 20 cm but even to 30 cm across, with roundish, overlapping segments, and short tubes. Hybrid clones come in a wide range of colors, from deep glowing red, clear scarlet, orange-red, light rose, and white with stripes or finally, all white. *Tropical.*

leopoldii hyb. 'Claret', a crimson "Dutch amaryllis" by Warmenhoven, Holland; fancy flowering cultivar for growing in pots; large open-faced flowers crimson on wine-red with blackish-red lines, 20 cm and more in dia. Such clones are propagated vegetatively. *p. 103*

leopoldii hyb. 'Giant White'; typical of the high perfection of breeding, with large 20 cm, full-round flowers glistening white and faintly green in the throat; thick petals of good lasting quality. *p. 105*

leopoldii hyb. 'Scarlet Admiral'; superb Dutch clone with large flat rounded flowers 18 cm dia. or more, glossy deep scarlet; the flowers appearing before leaves unless long established in pots before forcing. *p. 103*

pratense (Habranthus) (Chile); linear, laxly pendant leaves 25 cm long; flowers with tube very short, bright scarlet feathered yellow at base, the segments 6 cm long; somewhat winter-hardy. *p. 103*

procerum (Worsleya rayneri) (Brazil), "Blue amaryllis"; bulb with neck to 30 cm long, from which extend the drooping leaves; lilac blue flowers with pointed segments to 15 cm long. *Tropical.* *p. 104, 105*

psittacinum (Brazil), "Parrot amaryllis"; bulb with long neck, 6-8 strap leaves with the flowers, the trumpet-shaped blooms green and scarlet striped, with spreading 12 cm segments rather narrow. *p. 105*

puniceum (H. equestre) (West Indies and Mexico to Brazil), popularly known as the "American belladonna" or "Barbados lily"; a smaller-flowered amaryllis with bulb having brown scales and short neck, narrow strap-shaped, pointed waxy green leaves 2 to 3 cm wide, and long round stalk bearing 2 or more obliquely trumpet-shaped flowers of 12 cm dia. and 10 cm long, salmon-red, with center creamy-whitish with greenish bands, an oblique feathery corona in base; stamens when straight larger than stigma; an old-fashioned flowering houseplant almost continuously in bloom. *Tropical.* *p. 103*

reticulatum striatifolium, "Stripe-leaf amaryllis"; an interesting variety of this bulbous Brazilian plant because of its strapshaped dark green leaves having a prominent ivory-white midrib; the lily-like flowers are rose-pink lined with darker rose. *Tropical.* *p. 105, 129*

rutilum (Venezuela, Brazil); attractive flowering plant with clustering bulbs 5-8 cm thick, 6-8 strap-shaped leaves 25 cm long; flowers bright crimson, keeled green halfway, and with red filaments; the segments 8-12 cm long, on hollow stalk 30 cm long. *p. 103*

rutilum crocatum; attractive variety with flowers saffron or buttercup yellow, the segments wavy. *p. 103*

striatum fulgidum (So. Brazil), the "Everblooming amaryllis"; vigorous bulbous plant with broad obovate, fleshy green leaves 4-5 cm wide; in time forming bushy clumps from lateral bulbs; the trumpet-like blooms clustered on stout stalk, salmon rose with yellow center and base, the flowers 10 cm long, with 3-parted slender tube without corona inside. Recurrent blooming, and an ideal flowering house plant. *p. 103*

vittatum (Peruvian Andes), "Striped amaryllis"; large bulb producing trumpet-shaped flowers white with purple stripes; fairly broad, pointed petals; stalks hollow; strap-shaped leaves appearing with or after flowers. *p. 105*

'Vittatum hybrid', commercial "Amaryllis", developed from species of the Peruvian Andes; large bulb producing spectacular trumpet-shaped flowers to 15 cm across, several on a hollow stalk, most often scarlet red with white; strap-shaped leaves appearing with or after bloom, in late winter; parentage includes H. leopoldii, reginae, aulicum, solandriflorum, reticulatum. *Tropical.* *p. 105, 129*

HIPPEASTRUM: see also Amaryllis

HIPPOBROMA *Lobeliaceae* **S3LFM**

longiflora (Indonesia); low growing, pretty plant seen around temples and kampongs in Bali; soft-fleshy lanceolate, dark green leaves with toothed margins and pale midrib; white flowers with spreading petals and long slender tube. *Tropical.* *p. 1514*

HIPPOPHAE *Elaeagnaceae* **C2LBD**

rhamnoides (Europe; Caucasus, Iran, Siberia), "Sea-buck-thorn"; spiny shrub, very hardy, to 10 m high, covered with silvery scales; narrow willow-like, thin-leathery leaves; inconspicuous yellow flowers, and masses of bright orange-yellow 1 cm fruit, staying on all winter. *Temperate.* *p. 954*

HIPPURIS *Haloragidaceae* **I3LFW**

vulgaris (No. America, No. and C. Europe, No. Asia, Patagonia), "Mare's-tail"; perennial species suggestive of a horse-tail or a slender needle-tree, but aquatic or as marsh plant; the trailing stems to 1 m long when floating or rooting in the mud, erect and unbranched above water; the linear leaves in whorls, 1-2 cm long, Tolerates water temperature down to 10°C. *p. 1322*

HOFFMANNIA *Rubiaceae* **S3HFM**

'Fantasia' (ghiesbreghtii x roezlii); Wilson cultivar of vigorous habit, shorter than ghiesbreghtii, with obovate, quilted leaves dark coppery olive green shimmering satiny, with lighter veins, reverse bronzy-red, on elongate, 4-angled fleshy stem. *p. 2015*

species 'Fantastic' (So. Costa Rica); attractive tropical foliage plant with somewhat fleshy, very corrugated, lanceolate leaves 10 cm long and 4 cm wide, metallic green, gray-green beneath, the young leaves red on fleshy brown, 4-angled stems. Introduced by Bob Wilson, Miami. *p. 2017*

ghiesbreghtii (Higginsia) (Mexico), "Tall taffeta plant"; erect, herbaceous ornamental with 4-cornered, winged, green stems to 1 m tall, the long lanceolate leaves soft and shimmering-velvety, bronzy to moss-green, quilted between the silvery green and pink ribs, rosy-red beneath; small, tubular flowers yellow with red spot. *Tropical.* *p. 21*, 2014*

ghiesbreghtii 'Variegata', "Variegated taffeta plant"; delicate form with its long perfoliate leaves variegated and mottled on the quilted surface with cream and pink over milky-green and bronze; red beneath. *p. 2014*

refulgens (Chiapas), "Quilted taffeta plant"; beautiful, low, herbaceous plant with the short-jointed, red stem hidden by the broadly obovate, heavily quilted leaves almost fleshy, iridescent-velvety coppery-purple, shading to greenish, with bluish or light green ribs and red-hairy, red margin; wine-red beneath; flowers pale red. *Humid-tropical.* *p. 2014*

refulgens 'Vittata'; a beautiful form with the satiny, quilted leaves very coppery-olive on the ridges between contrasting, silvery-gray, sunken veins, the margin silver, set with silvery hairs, reverse wine-red. *p. 2014, 2015*

roezlii (Mexico), "Quilted taffeta plant"; ornamental plant possibly a variety of H. refulgens, with 4-angled stem and roundish ovate leaves 10-20 cm long, scanty-hairy, wine-red in the center, puckered all over and with a satiny lustre caused by the reflected light playing on the shades of green and rose-purple on the surface; underside purple; small, dark red flowers. *p. 2014, 2017*

HOHENBERGIA *Bromeliaceae* **S1HFD**

augusta (So. Brazil); large rosette growing on rocks in coastal forest at low elevation, broad green leaves with dark green mottling to 120 cm long, 8-12 cm wide, gray-scaly mainly underneath, the margins spiny and spine-tipped; robust, branched inflorescence with whitish flowers and green bracts. *p. 562*

ridleyi (Brazil: Pernambuco); epiphytic rosette with spiny strap-shaped, concave, bronzy golden green leaves, and tall, branched inflorescence with elongate, white-woolly spikes with short entire, purplish floral bracts, and small flowers with lobed sepals and vivid blue petals. *p. 559*

stellata (Brazil, Venezuela); loose rosette of green leathery leaves, finely toothed; inflorescence a long leaning spike with alternate clusters of red bracts with purple flowers. *Tropical.* *p. 513, 530, 575*

HOHERIA *Malvaceae* **I2LFM**

populnea (New Zealand), "Lacebark"; evergreen small tree graceful as a birch to 10 m, with downy branches; bright green, leathery ovate leaves with crenate margins, flowers pure white borne profusely in axillary clusters. *p. 1532*

populnea 'Argentea' (New Zealand), "Variegated lace-bark"; evergreen small tree, forming trunk covered with tough, lacy, perforated inner bark, willowy deep brown branches, and alternate, ovate, rugose 12 cm leaves with irregularly double sawed margins, matte, rich deep green beautifully variegated creamy-white toward edge; white, starry axillary flowers in profusion. *Subtropic.* *p. 1528*

HOLARRHENA *Apocynaceae* **S3LBD**

antidysenterica (Wrightia) (Trop. Asia), the "Easter tree"; tropical evergreen shrub with cord-like branches, and opposite, oval leaves; charming tubular pure white flowers with 5 spreading, ovate petals, 4 cm across, in center a small white corona; blooming over a long period. *p. 138*

HOLMSKIOLDIA *Verbenaceae* **S2LBM**

sanguinea (Himalayas), "Chinese-hat-plant"; subtropical, straggling shrub attaining 10 m, with slender-pointed ovate leaves to 10 cm long, and curious flowers having scarlet tubular corolla 2 cm long, and a spreading bell-shaped, orange calyx. Widely grown for its odd and beautiful blossoms. *Subtropic.* *p. 2119*

sanguinea 'Aurea', "Mandarin-hat plant"; originally from subtropic Himalaya and Malaysian region, now widely planted or naturalized in Tropical America; handsome evergreen wide-ranging rambler with wiry branches and opposite broad green leaves; toward the end the showy racemes of flowers with both hat-like calyx and tubular corolla vivid orange yellow, blooming all summer or longer. *Tropical.* *p. 2113*

HOLOCHLAMYS *Araceae* **S3HFM**

beccarii (Melanesia); attractive ornamental plant to 60 cm high; from the fleshy base rise sheathing petioles carrying glossy green, oblanceolate leaves 30-60 cm long and recurving at an angle, the surface corrugated with depressed lateral veins, and bold ivory midrib; the furled greenish-white spathe on short stalk. *p. 153*

guineensis (New Guinea); tropical creeping aroid 45-60 cm high, with plain green, maranta-like leaves, 26-32 cm long, the blade long-stalked, 18-25 cm, lanceolate and with depressed lateral veins and prominent midrib; oblong, 5 cm spathe, and spadix 5 cm long. *p. 224*

x HOMALOCASIA *Araceae* **S3HFM**

miamiensis (Homalomena rubescens x Alocasia korthalsii); bigeneric, Mauro hybrid with broad, sagittate, satiny leaves light green, with depressed veins. According to J. Bogner of Munich Botanic Garden, such a bigeneric cross is probably not possible and should be referred to Homalomena lindenii. *p. 225*

HOMALOCLADIUM *Polygonaceae* **S2LBM**

platycladum (Muehlenbeckia) (Solomon Isl.), "Ribbon bush", or "Tapeworm plant"; odd curiosity plant with perfectly flat, jointed, fresh-green stems and small, lanceolate leaves; leafless in the blooming stage, with small greenish flowers at alternate joints; in the tropics making round canes to 4 m long. *Tropical.* *p. 1954*

HOMALOMENA *Araceae* ***S1HFM**

crinipes (wendlandii) (Costa Rica); hastate leaf dark green with pale center vein and reddish margins, glabrous; pale beneath. *p. 225*

humilis (Java); dwarf tropical plant with shiny, dark green, narrow lanceolate leaves in rosette; depressed veins. *p. 225*

lindenii (in hort. as Alocasia) (New Guinea); very ornamental, stocky plant with broad cordate leaves of thin-papery texture, to 25 cm long, glossy green with pronounced yellowish-white midrib and lateral veins, carried on white petioles. *p. 153, 157*

paucinervia (Borneo: Sarawak); small clustering tropical plant, with dark green, narrow linear-lanceolate, leathery leaves 5 to 10 cm long, on short petioles, and having depressed midrib; miniature inflorescence with short 1-2 cm stalk carrying a small green spathe 1-1½ cm long. *p. 148*

picturata (Colombia); small, pretty herb with cordate-ovate dark green leaves variegated silvery-white along each side of midrib, on sheathing slender petioles; spathe green, spadix white. Photographed under this name in Florida, but is probably synonymous with Schismatoglottis emarginata. *Tropical.* *p. 225*

pygmaea (Malaysia: Java, Sumatra, Borneo, Celebes, Philippines); small, clustering herb with short rootstock, leaves elliptic-lanceolate, dark green, reverse purplish, 5-10 cm long, with undulate margins, on short, partly vaginate petioles; oblong spathe yellowish green. The var. purpurescens has purple spathe. *Humid-tropical.* *p. 280*

rubescens (Sikkim to Java); durable plant with heartshaped leaves, reddish green with red-brown edge and sunken veins; the slender, brown-red petioles on thick stem. (L) *p. 225*

siesmeyeriana (Malaya); tropical foliage plant with oblong cordate leaves; waxy green with midrib, veins and margins tinged red beneath, on wine-red petioles; spathe red-purple outside, white inside, on red stalk. *p. 226*

sulcata (Borneo); dwarf plant with long, heartshaped, metallic coppery green leaves on slender brown petioles in rosette. *Humid-tropical.* *p. 225*

sulcata 'Argentea'; attractive cultivar, with its oblong-cordate, corrugated, coppery-green leaves beautifully painted with silver in two broad bands midway between central rib and margins. *p. 226*

wallisii (Curmeria) (Colombia), "Silver shield"; low, compact, leathery plant with broad, oval, reflexed leaves 12-18 cm long, dark olive-green and beautifully blotched with yellowish-silver, translucent-silvery edge. *Tropical.* *p. 15*, 225*

wallisii 'Mauro'; compact, low-growing ornamental with satiny, leathery deep green leaves predominantly marbled and blotched with gray to light chartreuse-green, in this fine seedling clone. *p. 225*

HOMERIA *Iridaceae* I2LBM

collina ochroleuca (So. Africa: Cape Prov.), "Cape tulip"; pretty cormous herb 45 cm high, and allied to Moraea, with usually one linear basal leaf longer than the leafy flowering stalk; clusters of conspicuous yellow flowers 4 cm long, with orange markings, bell-shaped at first, then opening nearly flat into 6 separate segments spreading 6-8 cm across but closing on dull days. The type species collina has vivid red blooms with yellow center. Flowering in South Africa from August to October; in the Northern hemisphere in early summer. *p. 1330*

glauca (So. Africa); attractive species with coated corm and linear leaves basal and along the stalk; the flowers bell-shaped at first, opening wide in the afternoon with spreading petals clear pale yellow, closing again in the absence of sun-shine. *p. 1330*

lilacina (So. Africa), "Lilac shower"; small, dainty summer-flowering plant with 3 basal leaves narrowly linear, to 30 cm long; masses of starry lilac flowers veined with purple, and yellow-speckled purple blotch, the long lobes spreading wide and nearly flat, 8 cm across, clustered at the top of slender stalks 24 cm high; they open in mid-afternoon and remain open until dusk. *p. 1330, 1339*

HOMOGLOSSUM *Iridaceae* I2LBD

salteri (So. Africa), in habitat known as "Flames" or "Red Afrikaner"; slender cormous plant, with few linear or awl-shaped leaves; the stalks with tubular-flaring flowers with slender pointed segments, vivid flame-red with yellow in the throat and dark anthers, measuring 5 cm across, blooming autumn-winter; dormant during summer. *p. 1330*

HOODIA *Asclepiadaceae* I2LBD

bainii (Cape Prov., Namibia); cactus-like succulent with grayish, many-ribbed columns, the angles armed with numerous spiny teeth spirally arranged; flowers 6-7 cm across, bell-shaped, slightly 5-lobed, dull-yellow turning reddish when fading. *p. 374*

dregei (So. Africa: Karroo); succulent with thick, cactus-like stems 4 cm or more dia. 20-24-angled, with conical tubercles bearing a stiff bristle; flowers 3½ cm across light brown and thickly covered with white hairs. *p. 374*

gordonii (So. Africa); succulent with thick, cylindrical, angled stems covered with warty teeth; cupshaped flowers yellowish-brown. *p. 376, 377*

macrantha (Namibia); large-flowered succulent forming clumps with cactus-like columns 80 cm high and to 8 cm thick, with many grooves cut into numerous tubercles; the big blooms to 20 cm across, the lobes purplish, more yellowish along nerves and covered with purple hairs; inside tube orange-yellow; the largest flowered of all Hoodias, summer-blooming. *p. 374*

parviflora (Angola); succulent columns branching from the base, 30-60 cm high, 5-6 cm thick, pale gray-green, many-angled, divided by transverse grooves and with sharp spines; flowers round, saucer or cup-shaped, 8 cm across, at first greenish yellow outside, darker inside and with violet hairs. *p. 374*

rosea (So. Africa, Botswana), "African hat plant"; clustering cactus-like succulent to 30 cm high with leafless circular grayish-green stems branching from the base, ribs about 14, dense with tubercles armed with pale brown spines; the spectacular flowers have a saucer-shaped flat corolla 8 cm across, rosy to cinnamon and covered with thin hairs. Keep dry and warm in winter. *Arid-subtropic.* *p. 374*

HORRIDOCACTUS *Cactaceae: Echinocactanae* I2LBD

tuberisulcata (Neoporteria in Hortus 3), (Chile, near Santiago); low globular, dark green to bluish cactus to 20 cm thick, with 14 to 20 tubercled ribs; on the knobs the areoles sunken and with felt-like hairs, and giving rise to bundles of 4-5 strong, brown to gray central spines 2½ cm long, surrounded by shorter radials; funnel-like yellowish flowers 4 cm across, brownish outside. *p. 690*

HOSTA *Liliaceae* C2LFMh

crispula (Japan) (syn. H. fortunei var. marginato-alba, H. coerulea); elegant plant densely tufted, slow growing but forming large groups; elliptic long-pointed leaves with 7-9 veins, matte green above, bordered white, and undulate; glossy beneath; lavender flowers, on long lax stalk. *Warm temperate.* *p. 1462*

decorata (Japan: Honshu); clustering plantain-lily with oval green leaves 15-20 cm long, 4-5 pairs of lateral veins, on winged petioles; dark lilac to violet flowers with striped segments, on stalks exceeding foliage. *p. 1462*

decorata 'Marginata'; form with 20 cm oval green leaves bordered white; the drooping lilac flowers on scape to 60 cm high. *p. 1462*

decorata 'Minor'; known popularly, and particularly in Sweden as 'Thomas Hogg'; a small-leaved cultivar with leaves almost spoon-shaped, green with a narrow white border. *p. 1462*

fortunei (Japan), the "Tall-cluster plantain-lily"; broad leaves about 20 cm long, cordate at base, dark green to bluish green slightly glaucous, with 10-12 nerves either side of midrib, grayish beneath; funnel-shaped flowers white flushed lavender, 4 cm long, the scapes much taller than foliage, to 60 cm. *p. 1461*

fortunei 'Albo-marginata' (Funkia) (Japan), "Plantain lily"; handsome, herbaceous perennial with thick roots, forming large clumps of pointed heartshaped, light green leaves with sunken veins, bordered in white; flowers pale lilac. *p. 1461*

fortunei 'Gigantea'; a form with larger, longer-petioled dark green leaves to 42 cm long, underside grayish; rather bigger pale lavender flowers but standing less high above the foliage. *p. 1461*

glauca (Japan); long-stalked cordate or ovate leaves to 30 cm long, glaucous or blue-green; funnel-shaped 5 cm flowers pale lilac, in racemes scarcely taller than foliage. *p. 1461*

lancifolia (Japan); narrow, tapering lanceolate green leaves 12 cm long, with 3 to 4 nerves either side of midrib, on long slender petioles; funnel-shaped flowers pale lavender, with spreading segments, on 60 cm stalks. *p. 1462*

lancifolia 'Albo-marginata'; elegant variety with slender, trim green leaves with narrow white border. *p. 1462*

minor 'Alba' (coerulea) (Japan, China, Siberia); dainty rosette of narrow lanceolate green leaves 2½ to 3 cm wide, papery-thin, with prominent parallel veining, on long slender petioles. *p. 1462*

plantaginea (Japan, China), "Fragrant plantain-lily"; bold plant with large ovate-cordate green leaves 25 cm long, 7-9 veins either side of midrib, stalk with incurved wings; large white, 10 cm trumpet-like, ascending fragrant flowers in short racemes, but above foliage. *p. 1461*

sieboldiana (Japan), the "Seersucker-plantain-lily"; giant roundish to ovate 25-40 cm leaves with many deeply depressed veins, deep green on surface, glaucous-blue beneath; nodding flowers white tinged lilac, in cluster above foliage. *Warm temperate.* *p. 1461*

sieboldiana 'Variegata'; large heart-shaped leaves with numerous depressed ribs deep green variegated with white toward margins; glaucous beneath. *p. 1461*

subcordata (plantaginea) (China, Japan); thought the most beauiful species as a flowering plant, with its large white blooms; shapely plant with medium-large corrugated, fresh-green leaves papery-thin, shining on both sides especially beneath, in shape roundish with cordate base 15 cm long. *p. 1461*

tardiflora (lancifolia var., syn. sparsa) (Japan); close to lancifolia; low-growing dwarf variety, forming mounds 15-30 cm high, with almost leathery, lanceolate long pointed, dark green leaves; flowers pale purple with darker veins, late-blooming. *p. 1462*

undulata 'Medio-picta' (Japan), "Waxy-leaved funkia"; stout clustering herb with ovate basal leaves 15 cm long, narrowed toward base, sharp-pointed and curved, margins undulate, largely variegated cream in the center areas; pale lavender flowers on stalk 45 cm high. *p. 1461*

ventricosa (E. Asia); bushy plant with broad ovate-cordate green leaves 22 cm long; tall many-flowered raceme on stiff stem to 1 m long, with expanded tubular corolla dark lavender specked white inside; in May. *p. 1462*

HOTTARUM *Araceae* S3HFM

lucens (Sarawak, Borneo); small tropical waterside rhizomatous herb forming basal crown and clustering; the wiry, short green petiole 4-6 cm long, bearing very narrow-elliptic 10 to 15 cm leaves, the blade concave with prominent midrib, and shining green; the inflorescence with spathe furled, constricted and green in lower part, upper portion whitish to cream and dark tip. *p. 189*

HOULLETIA *Orchidaceae* S3OFW

lansbergii (Guatemala to Venezuela and Brazil); attractive species with small pseudobulbs carrying a 30 cm solitary, rigid ribbed leaf; pendulous inflorescence of fleshy, fragrant, waxy flowers 4 cm long, sepals orange with red spots, the smaller petals similar but darker, lip white with red stripes and purple warts (autumn). *Tropical.* *p. 1741*

wallisii (Colombia); remarkable epiphyte allied to Stanhopea; flask-shaped pseudobulbs with solitary leathery, plaited leaves; the pendant floral spike from base of plant, with large fleshy 4 cm globose flowers inverted, golden yellow richly tiger-banded and blotched chocolate brown; yellow lip spotted crimson and with horns (summer). *p. 1741*

HOUSTONIA *Rubiaceae* **C2LFM**

serpyllifolia (Pennsylvania to Georgia), "Creeping bluets"; bushy perennial with creeping stems to 25 cm, tiny 12 mm round leaves, and solitary funnel-shaped, 4-lobed 1 cm flowers deep blue. (h) *p. 2020*

HOUTTUYNIA *Saururaceae* **C-I2LFM**

cordata (Himalaya to Japan); swamp perennial 30 to 90 cm; creeping rootstock; 6-10 cm leaves red beneath; small flowers with 4 white bracts. *p. 2038*

HOVEA *Leguminosae* **I2LBD**

trisperma (Western Australia); small shrub to 60 cm with leathery 8 cm leaves nearly linear, pubescent beneath; axillary pea-flowers intense violet. *p. 1386*

HOWEIA (HOWEA) *Palmae* **•I1LFM**

belmoreana (Kentia) (Lord Howe Island), "Sentry palm"; handsome feather palm to 8 m, with pinnate leaves erect and then arching downward, the segments crowded, narrower than forsteriana, first upward then gracefully pendant and slender-pointed, on reddish stalks; fruit yellow green. *Subtropic.* *p. 1875, 1877*

forsteriana (Kentia) (Lord Howe Isl., near Australia), "Paradise palm"; elegant, sturdy decorator, widely used by florists because of its good keeping qualities; graceful pinnate fronds growing successively larger on slender stalks, the well-spaced, waxy deep green pinnae leathery and durable; with age forming a robust trunk 20 m high; yellow-green, olive-shaped fruit, in heavy clusters, in successive 4-strand racemes; the seed requiring about 4 years to ripen after first flowering. *p. 19*, 1870, 1877, 1878, 1900*

HOYA *Asclepiadaceae* **•I-S2LBD**

australis (Queensland), "Porcelain flower"; robust vine with broad oval, pointed leaves, thick, waxy, green with occasional silver spots, fuzzy beneath; dainty pink, waxy flowers with red crown, fragrant. *Tropical.* *p. 366, 371*

bandaensis (Java, Moluccas); robust climber with large, oval-pointed, fleshy leaves dark green and glossy; blooms greenish-white with scarlet centers. *Tropical.* *p. 366*

bella (paxtonii) (India), "Miniature wax plant"; dwarf, shrubby plant with flexuous branches first upright, later drooping, the small, thick leaves ovate, deep green; flowers waxy-white with purple center. *Tropical.* *p. 365, 373*

carnosa (Queensland, So. China), called "Wax plant" because of the waxy, wheel-shaped, fragrant, pinkish-white flowers with a red, star-shaped crown in pendant umbels; root climbing vines with elliptic fleshy-waxy leaves. *Subtropic.* *p. 368*

carnosa 'Argentea picta', ('Silver Princess'); leaves painted milky silver, variegated white to rosy-red toward margin. *p. 367*

carnosa 'Compacta' ('Hummel's Compacta'), "Hindu rope plant" or "Honey plant"; contorted cultivar of Hummel's H. carnosa 'Exotica' in California, a tortuous wax vine densely compacted with folded and cupped foliage oddly twisted, the 4 to 5 cm leaves glossy green with occasional silver spots, grayish beneath; the waxy flowers in a dense cluster, old ivory tinted pink petals and starry crown, on brown base. Slow-growing and ideal for training on trellis for near the window. *Tropical.* *p. 367, 371*

carnosa 'Compacta Regalis', "Variegated Hindu rope"; curiously interesting Florida plant, slow-growing and rather erect for a long time, dense with waxy, thick leaves, twisted and crinkled, green and prettily bordered with ivory to rosy margins. *Subtropic.* *p. 370*

carnosa 'Exotica' (marmorata); mutant with the waxy leaves in two shades of green, variegated, yellow and pinkish cream. *p. 367*

carnosa 'Krimson Queen'; listed under its patented name, H. carnosa 'Tricolor', which see.

carnosa 'Krinkle Kurl' (Hummel); monstrose, with very green leaves folded and then recoiled; flowers white. *p. 367*

carnosa 'Rubra', "Krimson princess"; brilliantly colored Florida vining cultivar of H. carnosa with younger leaves rosy crimson over ivory center, the margins rich olive green; developed and patented by Cobia's of Winter Garden, Florida. *Subtropic.* *p. 370*

carnosa 'Tricolor', "Krimson queen"; (Pat. Cobia, Florida); foliage beautifully coppery with salmon-rose while young, green edged ivory when mature; blooms pink. *Tropical.* *p. 367*

carnosa 'Variegata', "Variegated wax plant"; ornamental variety with the fresh green to bluish leaves broadly bordered creamy-white and even pink; more variegated than 'Marginata'. *Tropical p. 19*, 365, 367, 1952A*

cinnamomifolia (Java); "Cinnamon wax plant"; olive green leaves with silvery veins, bronzy while young; yellowish flowers with purple corona. *p. 367*

coronaria (Java); long vining climber with waxy, oval, fresh-green leaves with margins recurved, hairy beneath; waxy flowers pale yellow with 5 red spots at base of crown. *Tropical.* *p. 368*

darwinii (Philippines); clambering vine with thin-wiry stems, and distant internodes bearing oblong-ovate recurved leaves; stunning cupped 3 cm flowers rose with purple center. Occasionally with pouched leaves as in Dischidia. *Tropical.* *p. 365, 369, 371*

engleriana (Thailand); originally in trade as Dischidia minima; orbicular dull green foliage 15 mm dia.; pink flowers covered with silky scales, center crimson. *p. 366*

gigas (New Guinea); one of the many Hoyas we collected on government expedition in the Finisterre Mountains; a beautiful liane with 4-6 cm waxy flowers reddish brown with light tips. *Tropical.* *p. 369*

globulosa (Sikkim, Himalayas); slender vine with thick oval-pointed, spoon-like, lightly hairy leaves, and round clusters of cream colored waxy flowers, the corona marked brown-red at base. *Subtropic.* *p. 368*

'Hummel's Dapple Grey' (purpureo-fusca x australis); handsome Hummel hybrid with its large 12 cm elliptic waxy green leaves densely sprinkled and marbled with silver gray; flowers deep purplish rose with crimson corona, similar to purpureofusca; tolerates cooler temperatures. *p. 371*

imperialis (Borneo), "Honey plant"; tall climber with silky stems and elliptic shiny leaves lightly downy, margins wavy; flowers with cream corona in reddish-brown, waxy flowers to 7 cm across. *Tropical.* *p. 366, 373*

kerrii (obovata hort.) (Thailand, Vietnam, Fiji), "Sweetheart hoya"; robust twiner; curious, thick succulent, leathery leaves in form of an inverted heart; small flowers cream-white, corona lobes rose-purple. *Tropical.* *p. 370, 373*

keysii (Queensland), close-jointed creeper with thick stem and pale, gray-green, obovate, thick leaves covered with gray felt; starry flowers in large clusters all-white. *p. 367, 370*

lacunosa (Malaysia); tall twiner with thin, rooting stems; long-elliptic leaves; velvety, fragrant flowers greenish yellow. *p. 371*

latifolia (Malaya); broad thick-fleshy ovate, glossy deep green leaves with pale parallel veining on purplish petioles; sap milky; young growth coppery; small 1 cm flowers soft yellow. *p. 366*

longifolia shepherdii (angustifolia) (Sikkim); wiry climber with fleshy, long linear leaves channeled above and roundish beneath; small waxy-white flowers, crown white with carmine. *p. 368, 371, 373*

macrophylla (Java); slow creeper with large, fleshy, ovate quilted, coppery leaves and pale veins; flowers white. *p. 366*

micrantha (Burma); small leathery, pointed leaves; clusters of straw-white flowers covered with velvet. *p. 366*

motoskei (Indonesia), "Spotted hoya"; climber with waxy, broad elliptic leaves irregularly spotted silver, thinner than australis; waxy, star-like prolific blooms, pinkish cream with maroon center. *p. 368*

multiflora (Malacca in Malaya), "Shooting stars"; stout, smooth climber with elliptic, leathery leaves 8 cm long; magnificent inflorescence a dense cluster of starry straw-colored flowers tipped brown; silky inside. *p. 373*

'New Guinea White' (Papua); large glossy oblong leaves and clusters with up to 15 large waxy, cupped 3 to 5 cm flowers pure white. *p. 368, 370*

pallida (parasitica) (India, China); twining plant of the habit of H. carnosa but weaker, with fleshy, elliptic 4 cm leaves, smaller and more pale green; tiny flowers 1 cm dia., pale yellow with pinkish crown, covered with silky hairs and very fragrant, in clusters hanging, facing down. *p. 366, 370*

polyneura (Himalayan Reg.), "Fishtail hoya"; broad ovate, opposite glossy green leaves with darker veins, 6-8 cm long; waxy flowers like white stars, corona bronzy red. *Subtropic.* *p. 366*

purpureo-fusca (Java); tropical vining species with broad-ovate, fleshy, dark green leaves with short point and prominent and parallel veins; large globular clusters of flowers ashy-brown, the corona rich purplish-brown. This name has been wrongly given to the Hoya known as 'Silver Pink', but according to a plate from the French 'Serre Chaude', this is a different plant. *p. 371*

rubida (New Guinea); a beautiful climber which we collected in the wild Finisterre Mountains; fleshy glossy green, 10 cm obovate leaves; stunning 3 cm flowers lacquered maroon, with red corona. *Tropical.* *p. 369*

sikkimensis (Himalaya); dwarf plant with flexible, pendant branches set with small fresh green, pointed leaves; clusters of white-waxy starlike flowers, pink crown with purple tips. *Subtropic.* *p. 368*

'Silver Pink'; attractive vining plant found in Queensland and introduced from Hawaii as 'Silver Pink', with leathery long ovate leaves to 11 cm long, distinguished by raised pinkish-silver blotching over the waxy green, supported on red petioles; waxy flowers rusty-red and hairy, with white, starry corona and with purple stems, in large axillary umbels. *p. 365, 371*

'Verna Jeanette'; pretty variation of H. carnosa marginata with leaf blades covered as if with silver, some dark green mottling showing through; margins creamy-white; young leaf edges tinted pink. *p. 370*

HUERNIA *Asclepiadaceae* **•I-S2LFD**

keniensis (Kenya); small succulent from the west slopes of Mt. Kenya and Mt. Elgon, with mostly prostrate green or reddish stems with furrowed sides and tiny leaves; bell-shaped warty flowers reddish purple outside, inside deep purple. *p. 377*

kirkii (Zimbabwe); prostrate succulent 3-5 cm high, with sharply 5-angled stems armed with conical teeth; flowers 4-5 cm across, with saucer-shaped limb and 5 pointed lobes, deep yellow with crimson spots. *p. 375*

macrocarpa cerasina (Ethiopia, Sudan), a "Dragon flower"; small leafless succulent with olive-green, 5-angled and toothed stems to 10 cm high, star-like flowers near base velvety blackish-red with wart-like elevations; reverse gray-brown. *Arid-tropical.* *p. 377*

macrocarpa penzigii (Ethiopia, Eritrea); clustering succulent with 5-angled olive green stems about 9 cm long, with numerous fleshy teeth; the bell-like flowers with pointed lobes and nodding, 2 cm across, outside pale yellow with reddish veins, the warted inside dark maroon. *p. 375, 377*

oculata (Namibia); attractive succulent with numerous 5-angled stems forming clusters, 8-12 cm high, the angles sinuate into pointed knobs with spine-like fleshy teeth; the flowers 3 cm across, with 10 larger and smaller pointed lobes, blackish purple, sharply contrasting to the white base of the tube. *p. 375*

pendula (East Cape Prov.); long succulent, green to grayish-green stems 50 to 90 cm long, cylindrical or slightly 4-angled, branches spreading at right angles; small bell-shaped flowers 1½-2 cm across, deep maroon-red and with triangular lobes. *p. 375*

penzigii (Ethiopia, Sudan); little, succulent, 5-angled stems with fleshy teeth, small, blackish purple, pimpled flowers; now considered form of macrocarpa, which see.

pillansii (Cape Province), "Cockle burs"; fleshy, little columns with spiral rows of soft, maroon spines; densely clustering and creeping; the small flowers yellow, spotted crimson. (W) *p. 377, 2092*

schneideriana (Malawi, Mozambique); light-green succulent stems to 20 cm long, 5-7 angled, sparsely toothed; 2½ cm flowers bell-shaped, outside brownish, inside velvety black. *p. 377*

thuretii (Cape Prov.); succulent tufted gray-green stems 3-5 cm high, sharply 5-angled, the angles with acute teeth; flowers bell-shaped with spreading lobes 2 cm across; yellow with blood-red spots and lines. *p. 375*

transvaalensis (Transvaal); prostrate leafless succulent with angled glossy green stems 4-6 cm long, with prominent sharp-pointed tubercles; the cup-shaped flowers 4-5 cm across, rather round, yellow with red-brown markings. *p. 375*

zebrina (So. Africa), "Owl eyes" or "Zebra flower"; thick clusters of little, fleshy, angled stems, to 8 cm high, marked reddish, with spreading teeth; small, yellow flowers with purple bands, 5 cm across. *p. 64A, 377*

HUERNIOPSIS *Asclepiadaceae* **I-S1LBD**

decipiens (Namibia, Cape Prov.); low succulent with knobby stems 3-7 cm long and armed with teeth, gray-green and tinted with purple; bell-shaped flowers 3 cm across, with triangular lobes, outside greenish, inside purple with yellow spots; with unpleasant odor in the evening. *p. 375*

HUMATA *Polypodiaceae (Filices)* **I3HFM**

tyermannii (Central China), "Bears-foot-fern"; related to Davallia, with creeping light brown rhizome covered with silvery-white scales and looking like a rabbit's foot; brown, channeled petiole bears sturdy dark green, leathery, tripinnate 15 cm frond, always with spores; slow growing. *Humid-subtropic.* *p. 1112, 1114*

HUMBERTINA: see Arophyton

HUMEA *Compositae* **I2LBD**

elegans (Australia); biennial herb to 2 m with stem-clasping lanceolate wrinkled, sweet-scented leaves 25 cm long; minute red disk-flowers in graceful grass-like drooping panicles. *p. 813, 816*

HUMULUS *Moraceae* **I2LBM**

lupulus (Eurasia), "European hops"; vigorous rough-stemmed, tall-climbing woody perennial with 3 to 5-lobed, rough leaves coarsely toothed; flowers greenish-yellow, the males small in loose clusters; the female plants bearing their flowers in imbricated green cones or "hops" which are stripped and used in brewing. *p. 1562*

HUNNEMANNIA *Papaveraceae* **I2LBD**

fumariaefolia (Mexico), "Mexican tulip-poppy"; erect perennial 60-90 cm high, woody at base, grown as annual; glaucous 3-parted leaves 5-10 cm, with linear segments, and long-stalked yellow flowers 5-8 cm across, of four concave petals. *Subtropic.* *p. 1923*

HUNTLEYA *Orchidaceae* **S3OFM**

burtii (Costa Rica); pretty epiphyte without pseudobulbs, but fans of broad green leaves to 35 cm long, solitary star flowers 8-10 cm across, sepals and petals white, yellow at base, toward apex marked with red-brown, petals have red blotch at base, lip white with darker veins. *p. 1742*

meleagris (Brazil); epiphyte without pseudobulbs; bluish-green leaves, to 40 cm long, arranged fan-like, in 2 ranks, the solitary 8 cm flowers on long stalks, with sepals and petals whitish at base, passing into yellow, heavily flushed and marked red-brown; fringed lip cordate, white, with front yellowish-brown. (June-July). *Humid-tropical.* *p. 1739*

HURA *Euphorbiaceae* **S2LBD**

crepitans (West Indies, Costa Rica, So. America), "Sandbox-tree", or "Monkey-dinner-bell"; great tree to 30 m; the trunk and branches spiny, with poisonous milky juice; large hairy, poplar-like ovate, toothed leaves to 60 cm long; small red flowers without petals; the hard-shelled, ribbed 8 cm fruit bursts with loud noise when ripe, ejecting its seed. *p. 1054, 1061*

HYACINTHUS *Liliaceae* **C2LBWhd**

'Anne Marie'; a Dutch garden hyacinth, derived from H. orientalis, a species native from Greece to Iraq; bulbous plant with glossy green, fleshy, strap-shaped leaves and producing showy spikes of fragrant, waxy, delicate soft, clear pink flowers, heads smallish, but fine for earliest forcing. *p. 1463*

'Blue Giant'; big heads of large porcelain blue bells, washed with violet. *Subtropic.* *p. 1463*

'Blue Jacket'; large heads of single dark blue flowers, with small purple stripe; excellent for Spring forcing. *Subtropic.* *p. 1463*

'Carnegie' (orientalis cv.); an excellent late-blooming Dutch hyacinth of robust, compact habit with large and full heavy heads of pure white, waxy flowers; a favorite for flowering in pots especially if Easter is late, while the ivory-white 'L'Innocence' is recommended for an early Easter. *p. 1463*

'City of Harlem'; a "Garden hyacinth" with dense, compact heads of single-flowered pure lemon-yellow bells, for late blooming; an unusual color. *p. 1464*

'Delft Blue', a "Dutch hyacinth"; excellent for Easter flowering in pans; large 3-4 yr. bulbs will produce a full spike of bright porcelain-blue flowers of rich fragrance. *Subtropic.* *p. 1464*

'Edelweiss'; large, heavy heads, easily bending from their weight, on long stalks; pure white; early. *p. 1463*

'Lady Derby'; medium-sized head of single flowers of vivid rose pink, for midseason blooming. *p. 1464*

'L'Innocence', a popular "Dutch hyacinth", and a willing forcer with large spikes of pure white waxy flowers with slender spreading segments, grows rather tall, needing staking if the season is late; bulbs for forcing should be 3 years old at least. *p. 1464*

'Ostara' (orientalis cv.); robust Dutch garden hyacinth with large, heavy spikes of medium sized, 3 cm porcelain-blue or violet-purple waxy flowers on pale center, suitable for both early and Easter flowering in pots; an improvement of the old favorite, pale blue 'Bismarck'. *Subtropic.* *p. 1463*

'Pink Pearl'; an excellent, vivid pink hyacinth, often with two spikes per bulb; the trumpet-shaped flowers are more loosely set, the stout stalks are brittle as in all hyacinths, and leaves are linear. *Subtropic.* *p. 1464*

tabriziana (Iran); interesting bulbous plant with long erect linear leaves concave on surface; flowers in small cluster with short pale lavender to white petals. *p. 1463*

HYDNOPHYTUM *Rubiaceae* **S3OFM**

formicarum (Malaya), a curious "Ant plant"; epiphytic shrub, with large tuberous base 10-12 cm dia., without spines, and inhabited by stinging ants which excavate the tuber; several branches with opposite fleshy, oval leaves and small sessile, axillary white flowers, and red berries. *p. 2014*

HYDNORA *Hydnoraceae* **I3OFD**

esculenta (South Africa), "Jackal-food"; a most remarkable parasite living on roots of casuarina, acacia or euphorbia; the curious leathery flowers reach the surface only when they open; their warty stem is 2-3 m distant from the host root where it is attached; the fleshy petals are brown-red outside and pinkish within; later an underground globular fruit develops which is eagerly eaten by baboons and jackals. *p. 1318*

HYDRANGEA *Saxifragaceae* **C-I2LBWd**

arborescens (New York to Louisiana); shrub 10-25 cm high, with bright green ovate leaves 10-20 cm long, and small fertile flowers dull white, in rounded terminal clusters to 15 cm across; few sterile blooms. *p. 2042*

aspera (syn. sargentiana) (Himalayas, China); shrub to 2 m or more, of stiff habit, with downy branches; slender-pointed 10-22 cm, toothed leaves with harsh surface, gray-downy underneath; 3-4 cm sterile flowers with 4-6 blue or white petals. *Warm temperate.* *p. 2042*

bretschneideri (No. China); shrub to 3m of spreading habit, oblong-ovate 12 cm leaves pubescent beneath; numerous sterile 3 cm flowers with 3 or 4 sepals white becoming purplish; the fertile flowers dull white, in 15 cm clusters. *p. 2042*

macrophylla 'Alpengluehn' (1950); robust freely branching plant of even habit and easily budding with firm, shining fresh-green, deeply dentate leaves and medium heads of crimson-rose flowers of good substance, greenish in opening. *Warm temperate.* *p. 2044*

macrophylla 'Ave Maria'; German cultivar of shapely compact habit, smallish, dark leaves, and tight globular heads of numerous small, greenish-white flowers 3 cm across; early-blooming. *p. 2044*

macrophylla 'Chaperon Rouge' (Red Ridinghood), also known as 'Chapeau Rouge' (Red Cap), "French hortensia"; suberb French (Mouillere 1951) cultivar of compact habit, with smallish dark green foliage on stiff-erect stem, which bears a large firm, rounded head dense with flowers in vivid, pure rosy-crimson to clear carmine, depending on degree of temperature and pH of soil; ideal pot plant, medium-early. *p. 2043*

macrophylla (hortensis) **'Enziandom'** (1949); excellent, free-branching, tallish potplant for early forcing, with dark green, glossy leaves and large, dense heads of flowers, by nature vivid red but by the use of aluminum sulphate in an acid soil, of pH5 or below, easily coloring a beautiful, deep gentian-blue. *Warm temperate.* *p. 2045*

macrophylla 'Flamboyant';vigorous grower with smallish leaves on good stems supporting the large heads of carmine 5 cm ruffled flowers, a shade darker than Merveille. *Warm temperate.* *p. 2044*

macrophylla fl. pl. 'Tosca'; unusual cultivar with large round showy heads of rosy flowers 5 cm dia., and lobed at margins, with additional sepals of varying size arranged to form double blooms. *p. 2046*

macrophylla 'Kuhnert' (1926) (Gartendirektor Kuhnert), "Snowball"; an old freely branching variety easily becoming tall, with small toothed foliage and medium size flower-heads normally rose, but mostly grown as a good blue; not as showy as 'Enziandom', but a ready forcer and good keeper, responding willingly to aluminum treatment with a clear sky-blue and cream center, to corn-flower blue. *Warm-temperate.* *p. 2045*

macrophylla 'Maculata' (variegata); colorful form long cultivated; the dark green leaves variegated irregularly white to ivory; flowers white, in both sterile and fertile flowered cyme. *p. 2046*

macrophylla 'Mariesii'; old variety used for otdoor planting, of robust habit, with broad leaves, and flat flower clusters with numerous insignificant fertile flowers, the marginal, pink sterile flowers very large 5-8 cm across. *p 2046*

macrophylla 'Mein Liebling'; German cultivar, a very willing grower with broad, shiny leaves and good round heads of flat rose-pink flowers 5 cm across; somewhat soft; medium-early. *p. 2043*

macrophylla 'Merveille' (1927), "French hortensia"; robust, vigorous, midseason variety of excellent keeping qualities, with stout stem not requiring staking, firm foliage and large heads of big round, carmine rose flowers of good texture; lend themselves also to coloring into blue or lilac; the showy calyces hold well after forcing. *Warm temperate.* *p. 11*, 2043, 2044*

macrophylla 'Otaksa'; formerly well-known old "Hortensia", in cultivation for about 100 years, one of the first to be tried for pot forcing but later used for planting outdoors; a hybrid Japanese clone of Thunberg's original H. macrophylla, forming the foundation for the modern race of pot-flowered hydrangeas. 'Otaksa' is of dwarfer habit than the type species, yet vigorous, with obovate, short-pointed leaves rather thick and smooth, the rounded heads of blooms partly with insignificant fertile flowers, partly showy sterile ones with obovate, entire petals, pink or blue. However, it flowers only on 2nd year wood, and only if buds were not hurt by cold. *Warm temperate.* *p. 2046*

macrophylla 'Rosabelle' (1928); a good variety where extremely large "Snowballs" are desired, of robust growth with rigid, thick stems and tough, dull green, smooth leaves becoming rather tall, supporting fewer but giant heads of carmine-rose flowers 20-25 cm across, the individual showy sepals large and not crenate; late season and Mother's Day; normally extremely durable but does not keep well if forced early. *p. 2045*

macrophylla 'Sensation' (bi-color); inflorescence rose-pink with white margins; first bi-colored Hortensia in horticultural trade. *p. 2041*

macrophylla 'Soeur Therese' (1945); willing grower and early forcer, freely branching, with strong stems and dark foliage which sets off beautifully the noble flower heads of pure white, a great improvement over E. Mouillere: *Warm temperate.* *p. 2044*

macrophylla 'Strafford' (1937) (Mad. Cayeux) favorite commercial, well-proportioned variety with strong erect stem, small, dark green foliage, and medium-large, firm heads of clear rosy-red flowers—actually the enlarged calyx lobes, which are first pale yellow-green, then colored; mid season, free to bud, but flowers have a tendency to drop after forcing. *Warm temperate.* *p. 2045*

macrophylla 'Todi', "German hortensia", of short habit, with rather weak stem carrying a heavy head of individually large, dark pink flowers with entire sepals; aluminum sulphate treatment results in purple flowers; inclined to blindness on the numerous branches. *Warm temperate.* *p. 2044*

macrophylla tricolor 'Lace caps'; originally from the coasts of Japan and China, this deciduous shrub has large, fleshy, ovate, serrated leaves variegated deep green and sea-green with margins of ivory-white, and a large clustered inflorescence, with small pink to blue sterile flowers surrounded by the showy white, enlarged calyx lobes looking like petals. *p. 2044*

macrophylla 'Variegata'; a variegated form of the "Big leaf hydrangea", with broad leaves silvery green and edged with creamy white; fairly hardy but deciduous outside in cold climate of the temperate zones; inflorescence in terminal panicles, some of the marginal sterile flowers with large petal-like sepals, colored blue in acid soil with available aluminum, pink in sweet soil with calcium. *Warm temperate.* *p. 2048*

paniculata grandiflora (China, Japan); the commonest hardy hydrangea in cultivation; tree-like shrub 2½-8 m high, with elliptic leaves pubescent beneath; the small fertile flowers yellowish, the larger showy outside, sterile flowers white changing to purplish, in panicles to 38 cm long, in large masses for midsummer bloom. *p. 2044*

petiolaris (Japan); tall deciduous clamberer clinging by aerial roots, and reaching to 20 m or more, but can be kept as a straggly bush; the woody stems with peeling bark, ovate 10 cm leaves and nearly circular open clusters with marginal white 2½ to 4½ cm sterile flowers, the few small fertile flowers dull white, on very long pedicels. (h) *p. 2043*

quercifolia (Georgia to Florida and Mississippi), "Oakleaf hydrangea"; shrub to 2 m, with stout brown-woolly branches, deeply 3-7 lobed 20 cm leaves, dull green above, pale downy underneath; pyramidal 30 cm panicles of white sterile 2-3 cm flowers turning purplish, and small fertile ones; fairly hardy. *Warm temperate.* *p. 2044, 2046*

sargentiana (China); tall, sparry shrub 2-3 m with stout, ribbed branches covered by bristly hairs; ovate leaves to 25 cm long, dull green above, pale, bristly beneath; inflorescence almost flat, with 3 cm white sterile marginal flowers, small fertile flowers rosy-lavender. *p. 2046*

serrata (thunbergii) (Japan, Korea); hardy shrub to 1½ m with slender shoots, small pubescent leaves to 10 cm; flat inflorescence 6 cm dia. blue, pink or white. *p. 2048*

serrata acuminata (Japan, Korea); deciduous shrub to 1½ m with slender erect branches, slenderly pointed ovate thin, dull-green 10 cm leaves; numerous 6 cm small clusters with the 2 cm sterile flowers usually blue. *p. 2046*

xanthoneura var. wilsonii (W. China); woody shrub 2 to 5 m high, of loose habit, leaves in pairs or threes 8-15 cm long, whitish hairs beneath; inflorescence to 15 cm dia., white becoming pink. *p. 2048*

HYDRIASTELE *Palmae* **S3LFM**

wendlandiana (Queensland); tall unarmed feather palm with slender trunk 12 m high, and few arching pinnate fronds 3 m long, the leathery dark green leaflets irregularly arranged and stiff erect, some narrow-linear, others broad or united and prominently ribbed especially toward apex with the tips cut off raggedly; purplish-brown small fruit. *p. 1872*

HYDROCLEYS *Butomaceae (Alismataceae)* **S3LF-water**

commersonii (Brazil, Venezuela), "Water-keg"; aquatic herb forming runners; the floating, basal 5-8 cm leathery oval leaves with spongy midrib to make them float, on long stalks; solitary yellow flowers. *p. 615*

nymphoides (C. America to Argentina), "Water poppy"; perennial water plant with floating leaves, broadly heart-shaped or almost round, leathery-pulpy, and glossy green; everywhere in the leaves and stalks are airy tissues that causes them to float; beautiful flowers shining yellow with red center, 4-5 cm wide. *Humid-tropical.* *p. 80*

HYDROCOTYLE *Umbelliferae* **I3LFW**

rotundifolia (Trop. Asia, Africa), "Water-pennywort"; creeping herb forming ground cover, with slender rooting branches and small 6 mm-2½ cm round, shining leaves lightly lobed, cordate and cup-like depressed; very small white axillary flowers. *p. 2102*

umbellata (So. Europe, and warm climate elsewhere), "Marsh pennywort"; a dwarf waterside plant with fleshy leaves similar to Tropaeolum, peltate rounded 5 cm dia., clusters of tiny white flowers to 35 cm high in shallow water 30 cm deep. *p. 2106*

HYDROSME: see AMORPHOPHALLUS

HYDROSTACHYS *Hydrostachyaceae* **S3LFW**

pinnatifolia (Madagascar, E. Africa); aquatic plant with floating foliage in running water, with long ferney leaves; greenish spikes with tiny flowers. *Humid-tropical.* *p. 1958*

HYDROTRICHE *Scrophulariaceae* **S3HFW**

hottoniifolia (Madagascar); tropical underwater aquatic; light green forked leaf blades in whorls at intervals along a threadlike stem; inflorescence above the water level, the flowers white with yellow spot. (S) *p. 2050*

HYDROTRIDA *Scrophulariaceae* **I2LFW**

caroliniana (Bacopa in Hortus 3) (New Jersey to Florida and Louisiana); semi-aquatic perennial living in wet bogs, with stoloniferous stems creeping or ascending to 50 cm, with few branches; small ovate, parallel-veined fleshy leaves with ciliate margins; small 1 cm blue flowers in leaf axils. Can be grown in 3 cm of water in greenhouse or aquarium; quite attractive. *p. 2050*

HYGROPHILA *Acanthaceae* **S3LFD**

auriculata (West Trop. Africa); stout erect herb of wet places, ½ to 2 m high, with 4-angled usually bristly stem; long fresh green obovate leaves with pale midrib; bluish or purple flowers 3 cm long, in dense whorls with about 6 strong spines. *p. 47*

gigas (Malaysia), a "Water-friend"; tropical aquatic growing in pot with soil surface just below water level; erect slender stems with narrow ovate leaves, and showy flowers 4 cm long, pale lavender with crossbands of brown on lower lip; throat hairy inside. *p. 47*

stricta (Malaysia); tropical aquatic plant growing in shallow water, with numerous erect, square, reddish stems to 50 cm tall, and softly hairy; long-petioled, broad ovate leaves 10 cm long, grayish green and soft-pubescent; flowers violet blue with bilabiate corolla 2 cm long, in axillary clusters. *p. 49*

HYLOCEREUS *Cactaceae* **S2-3HBM**
lemairei (Trinidad, Tobago); beautiful night-blooming climber with triangular dark green stems rooting on one side; very large and odorous flowers 25 cm long with outer linear segments greenish yellow tipped bronze, the broad inner perianth segments white suffused pink. *Tropical.* *p. 664*

undatus, known in horticulture as Cereus triangularis (Brazil), "Honolulu queen"; one of the largest night-blooming cereus; epiphytic, deep green 3-angled clamberer of 5 cm dia.; white flowers nearly 30 cm long, blooming one night. Edible red fruit. Used as understock for grafting of Gymnocalycium, Rhipsalis or Zygocactus, for better root system. *p. 618, 663, 665*

HYMENOCALLIS *Amaryllidaceae* **I-S2LBd**
americana (littoralis) (Trop. America), "Crown beauty"; bulbous plant with basal, strapshaped leaves 75 cm long x 6 cm wide; the inflorescence in umbels on top of solid stalk; white flowers with 10 cm tube and long linear segments, in the center a cupped, toothed crown formed by united stamens; in summer. *p. 116, 117*

caribaea (Lesser Antilles); tropical summer-flowering "Spider lily" with globose bulb, a dozen leaves in several ranks, narrowing at base, and solid scape bearing an umbel of elegant fragrant white flowers with toothed crown and long linear segments, green outside at base. This may be H. pedalis from South America, naturalized in Florida and the West Indies. *Tropical.* *p. 116, 117*

expansa (Trop. America); tropical bulbous plant with long, glossy-green strap-shaped leaves, grooved down center; spidery flowers pale green, more or less tri-cornered, with long narrow linear segments; November-blooming. *p. 117*

'Festalis' (calathina x elisena longipetala from Perú); beautiful flowers with large white central crown recurved and frilled at margins, the narrow-linear outer petals cream-white. *p. 116*

harrisiana (Mexico), "Mexican spider lily"; bulbous plant with sessile, oblanceolate leaves to 30 cm long; few-flowered inflorescence in clusters on erect stalk, the flowers with slender, greenish tube 10 cm long, the narrow-linear segments shorter and whitish; well-formed corona with green stamens. *Tropical.* *p. 106*

horsmannii (Mexico); low tropical bulbous plant with short, broad leaves to 30 cm long; short floral stalk with white flowers, 10-12 tubes expanding into narrow linear segments 6-8 cm long, in the center the wheel-shaped corona, extending into long stamens; summer-blooming. *p. 117*

littoralis (Polynesia: Marquesas; So. America); a "Spider lily" which I photographed on the South Pacific Island of Nuku Hiva; tropical bulbous plant with broad leaves, and very spidery, pure white, waxy flowers, with 8-10 cm tube and long, thread-like segments, in the center a wavy-edged cup or corona. *Tropical.* *p. 117*

littoralis 'Variegata' (Trop. So. America); white-scaly bulb with attractive variegated foliage, the long-oblanceolate fleshy leaves to 45 cm long, glossy green striped lengthwise pale green or cream, with broad marginal bands of cream; white flowers with extra long tube 17-20 cm long, narrow segments and deep corona. (The plant shown in Exotica 3 and 4 may be a variety of H. pedalis). *p. 130*

narcissiflora (Ismene calathina) (Andes of Perú, Bolivia), "Peruvian daffodil"; bulbous plant with strap-shaped leaves; umbels of large, fragrant, white flowers, crown funnel-shaped, lobes fringed. *Subtropic.* *p. 116, 117*

speciosa (W. Indies), "Winter spice"; evergreen flowering plant with big bulb; the thick-fleshy, dark green oblanceolate leaves on tapering, channeled petioles; from the center rises a flattened, glaucous stalk crowned by a cluster of fragrant, spidery pure white flowers with long greenish tube and linear segments 5 cm long, a distinctive inner cup bearing the long anthers. *Tropical.* *p. 116*

HYMENOCYCLUS *Aizoaceae* **I2LBD**
crocea (Cape Prov.); mat-forming succulent, dense with leaves $2\frac{1}{2}$-$4\frac{1}{2}$ cm long, pale green with mealy wax covering, 3-angled with blunt tip; 3 cm flowers golden yellow within, reddish on reverse. *p. 62*

latipetalus (Cape Prov.), "Carmine ice plant"; creeping woody perennial with succulent keeled leaves to 3 cm long, glaucous blue to reddish; buds purplish-red opening into daisy-like flowers of orange-red. *Subtropic.* *p. 64*

HYMENOGYNE *Aizoaceae* **I2LBD**
glabra (So. Africa: Cape); succulent annual with weak prostrate branches, smooth, green, spoon-shaped lanceolate, fleshy stalked leaves, and shiny straw-yellow flowers. *p. 77*

HYMENOPHYLLUM *Hymenophyllaceae (Filices)* **I3HNM**
demissum (now Sphaerociomium) (New Zealand, Philippines, Malaya), "Filmy-fern"; small very delicate, moisture-loving fern growing on the bark of trees or rocks where they are almost constantly saturated with dripping moisture; shallow-rooted thin black rhizome, with pendant, delicately membranous fronds pale green and practically translucent, $2\frac{1}{2}$-22 cm long, usually bipinnate not much more than a skeleton, but often 3 to 4-pinnate. Occurs in a number of forms. *p. 1113*

HYMENOSPORUM *Pittosporaceae* **I2LBD**
flavum (Queensland, New South Wales), "Sweetshade"; graceful evergreen shrub or tree to 15 m high, of open habit, with shining light green, leathery leaves 8-15 cm long; clusters of honey-scented bright yellow flowers 3 cm wide, blooming spring into summer. *Subtropic.* *p. 1950*

HYOPHORBE: see Mascarena

HYOSCYAMUS *Solanaceae* **I2LBD**
aureus (Crete), "Golden henbane"; spreading semi-woody, white-woolly plant dense with short, serrate leaves; tubular trumpet-like flowers $2\frac{1}{2}$ cm long, creamy-white with throat striped purple, the larger, expanded lip yellow. Plant photographed in Heraklion, growing out of an ancient stone wall, the branches hanging downward. *Subtropic.* *p. 2067*

HYPENANTHE *Melastomataceae* **S3HFM**
venosa (Medinilla) (Moluccas); small, finely hairy, epiphytic shrub with graceful, ovate, brownish leaves with velvety sheen, and contrasting pale green ribs, underside purple; flesh-colored flowers in small cymes. *p. 1556*

HYPERICUM *Hypericaceae* **I2LBD**
aegypticum (Mediterranean Reg.); attractive evergreen shrub, crowded with glaucous gray-green, small $\frac{1}{2}$ cm leaves; the flowers with spreading yellow lobes 1 cm across, terminating short shoots, blooming in summer. *p. 1319*

leschenaultii (Malaya); ornamental shrub 2-3 m high usually evergreen but deciduous in colder climate; obovate leathery leaves 4-6 cm long, glaucous beneath; large cupped, clear yellow flowers with concave petals, to 8 cm across, displaying the numerous stamens. *Tropical.* *p. 1319*

patulum henryi (Japan), "St. John's-wort"; evergreen spreading shrub to 1 m or more high, with 2-edged, purplish branches, stiff-leathery oblong leaves to 6 cm, glaucous beneath; the showy flowers bright golden yellow, with long silky stamens; extra large in the variety henryi to 6 cm across; photographed in Leucadia, California. *Warm temperate.* *p. 1319*

revolutum (leucoptychodes) (Africa: E. Africa, Transvaal, S. Arabia, Cameroons, Mauritius), the "Forest primrose" as known in Africa, from mountain forests; ornamental flowering shrub to 3 m high, dense with small needle-like leaves, showy golden yellow flowers 5 cm across, showing a tuft of prominent stamens. The foliage has glands which release the pleasant scent of roasting coffee. *p. 1319*

HYPHAENE *Palmae* **S-I2LBD**
coriacea (Kenya); interesting fan palm with slender, twisting trunks forking dichotomously several times, resulting from the equal growth of an axillary bud; palmate glaucous green leaves on yellow petioles, armed with black teeth; pear-shaped fruit 8 cm long, eaten by elephants. Photo of young plant taken in Mazeras, Kenya. *p. 1884*

crinita (South Africa: Transvaal; Zimbabwe, Mozambique); the "Elala palm"; stiff-erect fan-palm, and where I have seen it along the Limpopo usually not branched; trunk clothed with old leaf-bases, the palmate leaves bright green deeply divided into segments; pear-shaped fruit. *p. 1878*

shatan (Madagascar); robust fan palm from dry habitats; the straight trunk with old leaf-scars, topped by a rounded crown of rigid palmate fronds, the stiff reddish petioles armed with strong teeth, and extending for some distance into the leaf itself, which is known as costa-palmate; the female trees bear pendant clusters of attractive, large red fruit 5-7 cm long, with edible fleshy interior. *p. 1885*

thebaica (Upper Egypt, Sudan, Yemen, Kenya, Tanzania), "Dhoum palm" or "Gingerbread palm"; botanical wonder with its repeatedly forked habit, to 15 m high; the slender trunk and branches smooth like a cordyline, each branch end tipped by a rosette of smallish, stiff, green fan-leaves, the blade 60-75 cm long, deeply cut to the middle, on spiny petiole. The orange edible fruit tastes like gingerbread. Although palms normally are not hosts to epiphytic orchids, I have often seen Ansellias growing in the forks of their branches in East Africa. *Tropical.* *p. 1879, 1881*

ventricosa (Zimbabwe, Zaire), "Gingerbread palm"; tall, slender fan-palm 10 m high, usually growing with a single trunk, frequent along the Zambesi river, their deep roots reaching for moisture, their trunks somewhat bulging above the middle, the deeply cut, smallish, palmate, blue-green fronds, on long stalks, forming a large cluster reaching for the burning sun. *Tropical.* *p. 1879*

HYPOCALYMMA *Myrtaceae* **I2LBD**
robustum (Western Australia); smooth, evergreen shrub to 1 m with stiff $2\frac{1}{2}$ cm linear leaves having thick midrib; axillary tiny flowers with 5 petals rich pink and numerous stamens, forming long leafy spikes; spring. *p. 1613*

HYPOCHOERIS *Compositae* **C2LBM**
uniflora (So. to S.E. Europe), "Cat's ear"; small alpine perennial found throughout the Alps to the Carpathians, low rosettes of oblanceolate hairy leaves with toothed margins; the globular flower heads of narrow strap-shaped florets, 3 cm across. *p. 822*

HYPOCYRTA: see Alloplectus, Nematanthus

HYPOESTES *Acanthaceae* **I-S2HFM**
aristata (So. Africa), "Ribbon bush"; perennial herb of erect habit to 1 m high, with downy ovate leaves 8 cm long, entire; downy 3 cm tubular flowers rose-purple with short lobes striped and spotted purple or white. *Subtropic.* *p. 48*

sanguinolenta (rotundifolia, phyllostachya) (Madagascar), "Freckleface"; herb with soft, downy, small leaves green with rosy-red marking, 4-6 cm long; flowers lilac. *Tropical.* *p. 49*

sanguinolenta 'Splash'; cultivar with large, moss-green leaves lavishly splashed with clear rose. *p. 49*

verticillaris (So. Africa); leggy semi-shrubby, hairy plant with slender erect stems; ovate green leaves, and toward apex the cylindrical inflorescence 10 cm long, of lavender-rose flowers with white blotch, the upper reflexed petal spotted magenta; calyx brown. *p. 48*

HYPOLEPIS *Polypodiaceae (Filices)* **I3HNM**
punctata (helenensis) (Dryopteris), (Japan, Trop. Asia, Australia, Polynesia, Hawaii, St. Héléna, Africa, Trop. America to Chile), "Poor man's cibotium"; from thick, hairy, spreading rhizome, purplish stalks bear bipinnate, triangular fronds to 1 m long, soft and papery in texture, friendly light green. Needs much attention in watering when in container, or the firm-looking but actually only turgid fronds will suffer and collapse if not watered regularly. *p. 1108, 1112*

HYPOPTERIGIUM *Musci* **C3HNM**
filiculaeforme (New Zealand), the "Umbrella-moss"; robust in habit, gregariously covering the forest floor or over rocks in damp places, the attractive bright green fronds are pinnatisect into linear segments, 3-6 cm. wide; pendulous capsule 2 mm. long, pale brown, ovoid or oblong. *p. 1548*

HYPOXIS *Amaryllidaceae or Hypoxidaceae* **I2LBD**
hemerocallidea (So. Africa: Natal), "Natal star-grass"; clustering, grass-like plant from fleshy roots, with narrow-linear spreading leaves to 30 cm long, thinly hairy above, more so beneath; star-shaped yellow flowers 5 cm across, closing in cloudy weather, or in darkness. The genus Hypoxis is with Amaryllidaceae in Hortus 2; separated as a Tribe under Hypoxidaceae in Hortus 3. *p. 100*

hygrometrica (Australia), "Golden weather glass"; pretty little bulbous plant to 15 cm high, with narrow, grass-like channeled leaves to 25 cm long and somewhat soft-hairy; the starry 6-parted flowers golden yellow, 2½ cm across, singly or in clusters; the petals closing in cloudy weather or when dark; spring-blooming. *Subtropic.* *p. 121*

nitida (Transvaal), "Yellow star-grass"; small cormous herb to 25 cm, with concave leaves, and pretty, starry, yellow flowers 4 cm across. *p. 1463*

stellata (Spiloxene capensis) (So. Africa), "White star-grass"; cormous herb with basal, keeled, grass-like 30 cm leaves; the small star-like flowers white inside, green-keeled outside, on few-flowered stalks. *p. 131*

IBERIS *Cruciferae* **C2LBM**
amara (W. Europe), "Candytuft"; erect branching annual with thickish, oblanceolate leaves and large white, fragrant flowers on racemes that lengthen with age. *p. 927*

IBERVILLEA *Cucurbitaceae* **I-S3LBD**
lindheimeri (Maximowiczia ammocodon) (Texas to California and Sonora), "Balsam gourd" or "Hierba de Vibora"; dioecious vine forming thickened tuber-like rootstock extending above ground; the stems thin and flexuous growing to 3 m long, bearing unbranched tendrils and dissected, small green leaves 3 to 5 cm long, the segments deeply lobed and toothed; small 1 cm flowers yellow and striped with green; red 3 cm berries. *p. 951*

tenuisecta (Arizona, Texas; Mexico), "Deer apple" strange xerophyte with thick tuber-like, hard, gray stem 30 cm dia., and of irregular shape, forming fibrous roots during growing period; from the top grow several thin, leafy, annual climbing stems to more than 1 m long; thick leaves rounded in outline, deeply 3-lobed bluish-green to 10 cm across; opposite each leaf a spiralled tendril; small yellow flowers, and spherical red fruit 2-3 cm long. *p. 933*

IBICELLA *Martyniaceae* **I2LBM**
lutea (syn. Proboscidea lutea) (Martynia) (Argentina); coarsely bushy, sticky pubescent herb to 50 cm, with clammy rounded leaves to 30 cm dia.; flowers in compact clusters, greenish yellow outside, deeper yellow to orange inside and with occasional red dots; long-horned spiny fruit. *p.1547*

IBOZA *Labiatae* **C2LBD**
riparia (Moschosma) (So. Africa), "Misty plume bush"; stout, musk-scented perennial subshrub to 1½ m, with 4-angled stems, broad ovate, toothed leaves, and numerous small flowers creamy-white with dark anthers in erect, plumy panicles. *Subtropic.* *p. 1353*

IDRIA *Fouquieriaceae* **S2LBD**
columnaris (Mexico,Arizona), "Boojum tree"; bizarre desert tree with soft swollen, often hollow trunk to 15 m high, tapering to apex, spreading spiny branches and obovate, deciduous leaves 2 cm long; small yellow flowers in long panicles. *Arid-subtropic.* *p. 1063*

IGUANURA *Palmae* **S3LFM**
geonemaeformis (Malaysia); short palm growing in clusters, slender stem to 1 m, the 60 cm leaves entire with prominent pinnate ribs, wedge-shaped, rarely pinnately divided, large lobes, with red downy midrib. *p. 1882*

ILEX *Aquifoliaceae* **C-I2LBM**
x altaclarensis (aquifolium x perado); evergreen shrub with purplish bark; hybrid resembling the English holly but the stiff-leathery, 11 cm elliptic leaves are larger, thinner, and flatter at the margin which has more numerous and more regular spiny teeth, and slightly glossy. *p. 146*

x altaclarensis 'Jas. G. Esson', hybrid of the "English holly"; aquifolium x perado from the Canaries, a favorite, thrifty evergreen with waxy-glossy leaves and less spiny; distinguished on female plants by large clusters of bright red berries, bigger than aquifolium; rapid grower. (Ch) *p. 147*

aquifolium (Europe, No. Africa, W. Asia), "English holly"; evergreen tree to 12 m or more; alternate leathery, ovate leaves shining, and with coarse spiny teeth along wavy margins; small unisexual flowers whitish, followed by scarlet-red berries on female trees. *Warm temperate.* *p. 146, 147*

aquifolium 'Albo-marginata'; attractive horticultural form with black-green waxy leaves having ivory margins, silvery in places, especially on the underside. *p. 146, 147*

aquifolium 'Cookii'; attractive form with leathery broad-ovate leaves rather flat, and with weak spines, center very dark green blotched greenish-yellow, along the margins a band of lighter yellow. *p. 146*

aquifolium flavescens; variety with the green, spiny leaves variegated with yellow, especially in the center area, or all yellow. *p. 146*

cassine (SE. U.S.), "Dahoon"; obovate, entire leaves, usually not spiny; berries red. *p. 147*

cornuta (Eastern China), "Chinese holly" or "Horned holly"; evergreen shrub of dense bushy growth, to 3 m high; recurved shining green, leathery leaves 8-10 cm long, nearly rectangular with pronounced spines at the 4 corners and at the tip of each leaf; large bright red, long-lasting berries. The cv. 'Dazzler' is of more compact habit. *Warm-temperate.* *p. 147*

cornuta 'Burfordii', a globose form of the "Chinese holly"; with shining leaves, few spines, and scarlet berries. (C-1) *p. 147*

crenata (Japan), "Japanese holly"; stiff evergreen to 6 m, with smooth, dark green, oval leaves 6 cm long, sharply pointed and sparsely toothed; small black berries. *Warm temperate.* *p. 147*

opaca (Massachusetts to Florida and Texas), "American holly"; evergreen, spreading tree to 15 m, with stiff, elliptic or obovate leaves dull green above, yellowish beneath, to 9 cm long, and with large spiny teeth; small red fruit, usually solitary. *Temperate.* *p. 146*

paraguariensis (So. Brazil, Paraguay), "Yerba-de-Maté"; small evergreen tree with oblong, wavy-toothed, leathery leaves, 10-15 cm long; forked clusters of small greenish-white flowers in leaf axils; berries red; the dried, powdered leaves contain caffeine and produce the South American favorite, "Maté" or "Paraguay tea", with somewhat bitter taste reminding of quinine, but giving a stimulating effect. *Subtropic.* *p. 147*

pernyi (China); evergreen sparry shrub to 6 m with willowy branches dense with closely ranked, small 5 cm quadrangular-ovate leaves glossy black green, with 1 to 3 spines on each side and a larger terminal one; berries red, in clusters. *p. 146*

vomitoria (Virginia to Florida and Texas), "Yaupon"; monoecious evergreen to 8 m with obovate, shiny green, leathery leaves 4 cm long, slightly toothed; small scarlet berries, in clusters. *p. 146*

ILLICIUM *Magnoliaceae* **C2LBM**
anisatum (Japan, Taiwan), "Star anise"; shrub or small tree; wood and leaves very aromatically fragrant; leaves 5-10 cm long; flowers with numerous linear petals, pale greenish-yellow, without fragrance. *p. 1525*

IMPATIENS *Balsaminaceae* **•I2HBM**
auricoma (Kenya); very attractive herbaceous plant with fleshy red stems and petioles, light green oblanceolate leaves to 12 cm long and finely crenate; waxy flowers bright orange with brown lines in throat 3 cm across. *p. 389*

balfouri (W. Himalayas: Kashmir); fleshy branched herb with succulent stems, lanceolate, toothed, smooth leaves 8-12 cm long, and flowers with deep pink lower lip, pale pink upper lip, and with yellow spots in throat and lower lip, on long stalks. *p. 386*

balsamina (India to China), "Garden balsam"; annual herb 45-60 cm tall, with succulent knotty stem and soft-fleshy, often reddish branches and lanceolate leaves; charming double camellia-type 5 cm flowers in the leaf-axils, white to red, borne close to succulent stem; leaves lanceolate. *p. 385*

balsamina 'Beijo do Frade'; a beautiful cultivar from Brazil, with reddish, succulent stems and fleshy, fresh-green obovate, 10 cm leaves toothed at margins; the showy, waxy flowers crimson-rose with bold white blotching. *Tropical.* *p. 386*

campanularia (So. India); herbaceous tropical species with fleshy stem 60-90 cm tall; broad-ovate satiny leaves with marked depressed veins, and serrate margins; the long-stalked flowers 2 cm across with short spur, white with red spots in throat and on lower petals. *p. 389*

cardiophylla (Chumphon, Thailand); succulent species with glossy green, fleshy, broad ovate leaves obscurely crenate at margins; the tubular flowers with spreading limb pale lavender-pink. *p. 388*

flaccida (India, Sri Lanka); smooth herbaceous annual with red stems, 15-45 cm high; shining dark green, ovate leaves 5-12 cm long; flowers pale lilac-rose with crimson center and long slender spur. *p. 389*

glanduligera (roylei) (India); tall herbaceous plant with reddish succulent stem, large ribbed leaves on long petioles; flowers in clusters, toward top of stem, inside pink and outside red and with short spur. *Tropical. p. 389*

hawkeri (New Guinea, Sunda Isl.); herbaceous species with branching, purple stem to 50 cm high; dark green, quilted leaves with red midrib, 10-12 cm long and finely toothed; showy flower scarlet-red with white eye, but variable, 4 cm across and with red spur. *Tropical. p. 389*

hawkeri 'Exotica' (New Guinea); beautiful discovery from the Central Highlands; densely branching bush with succulent, channeled red stalk and showy stalked long ovate or obovate, waxy leaves, ciliate 8-10 cm long, dark green to bronzy in the outer area, cream to golden yellow in the center, the bold midrib and petiole crimson-red; large flowers carmine-rose with white throat. Collected during my Finisterre expedition 1960. *p. 320A, 387*

kilimanjari (Tanzania), a "Snapweed"; spreading creeper which I collected in the rainforest zone at about 2,100 m on Mt. Kilimanjaro, creeping over fallen, rotting trees and rocks; watery-brittle round stems, with small shiny, fresh-green, crenate leaves with sharp-tipped apex, and beautiful waxy, fiery-scarlet flowers ending in a thick curling yellow spur tipped with green. *Subtropic. p. 387*

linearifolia (New Guinea); a colorful, variable species which I collected (1960) in the mountains surrounding the mysterious Chimbu Valley in the Central Highlands; herbaceous, rather succulent, erect branching plant with long elliptic, almost linear, ciliate, smooth leaves, usually with yellow center and dark green outer area, the midrib wine-red; rosy flowers with long spur. *Tropical. p. 387*

marianae (Assam); herbaceous, creeping, light green, hairy stems with thin, oval crenate leaves 5-8 cm long, dark green with silver bands between the veins; light purple flowers having long spur. *Tropical. p. 385*

mirabilis (Sumatra); curious in habit, with soft-fleshy thick, tapering trunk to 120 cm high and to 20 cm dia. in habitat; with succulent branches and fleshy leaves to 30 cm long and toothed at margins; flowers 4 cm long with strongly recurved spur, pale pink with yellow in throat. *p. 388*

'New Guinea hybrid'; magnificent ornamental herbaceous plants, the results of much hybridization of several New Guinea species such as hawkeri and linearifolia, collected between 1960 and 1970, and further crossed with species from Java and Celebes likewise having 32 chromosomes; the best selections are commercially segregated into several series and many named cultivars, all forming spreading bushes 25 to 40 cm high, with each succulent branch topped by a beautiful rosette of frequently corrugated ovate leaves 8-15 cm long, in a riot of color and variegation, usually creamy-yellow along center with green, serrate margins and red to milky-white ribs; showy spurred flowers 3-7 cm across, in shades from crimson to scarlet, red, orange, salmon, pink, chartreuse, purple or blush white. Ideal for shade gardens, as summer annual or as house or basket plants in winter. *p. 387*

niamniamensis (Fernando Po); branching herb with fleshy, brittle stems having woody base, long crenate, ovate, smooth, soft leaves 8-12 cm long, dark green above, underside reddish-brown, the margins ciliate; flowers in the axils of the upper leaves, contrasty with ivory to greenish yellow hood, and blood-red lips, pure white at mouth; anthers yellow. *p. 386*

oliveri (Trop. E. Africa), "Giant touch-me-not"; large growing, fleshy herb with long, oblanceolate, succulent leaves olive-green with prominent, pale midrib, edged with coarse bristles; large spurred flowers a delicate lilac-pink. *Tropical. p. 385*

platypetala aurantiaca (Celebes); fleshy herb with fresh-green, ovate, corrugated leaves and pink midrib; spurred flowers orange-yellow with crimson eye; very attractive. *Tropical. p. 385*

platypetala 'Tangerine'; lovely cultivar offered by Park Seed, Greenwood, So. Carolina; herbaceous plant 35 cm high, prolific with large single flowers bright tangerine with red eye, very showy. Probably a form of I. platypetala aurantiaca from Celebes. *Tropical. p. 386*

'Princess Sakura'; a distinctive tall "Balsam" 75-90 cm high, perfect for background planting; dark red, succulent stems with serrate green foliage; in the upper part, the large deep pink flowers produce bright color all summer. *p. 386*

pseudoviola (Kenya); sub-shrubby semi-trailer from Mt. Kenya; small ovate, fleshy leaves with spiny margins, 2 cm long; flowers white tinged with rose, and with rosy-violet stripe down center of each of the 4 lower petals. *p. 389*

psychadelphoides (Mozambique); herbaceous, branching plant with fleshy red stems, and ovate, pebbled green leaves serrate at margins; the pinkish flowers with long slender spur. *p. 388*

repens (Ceylon), "Creeping impatiens"; small trailer with creeping fleshy red branches and alternate small round or kidney-shaped, ciliate leaves 2 cm wide, waxy deep green, purplish beneath, on long red petioles; golden yellow hooded flowers with brownish net-like striping, and curved spur. *Tropical. p. 386, 387, 388*

roylei (India); fleshy herbaceous plant grown as an annual, with stout, succulent stems 2 m and more high; opposite, ovate leaves 10 cm long, sharply toothed; flowers dark purple in small clusters in upper leaf axils, with sac-like lip and short spur. *p. 386*

schlechteri (New Guinea); handsome species with narrow ovate, quilted leaves rich deep crimson, and with finely serrate margins; spurred flowers deep scarlet 4 cm across. *p. 389*

sultanii: see walleriana

tinctoria (Ethiopia); robust species with succulent stems $1^1/_2$ m tall, the leaves narrow lanceolate and quilted; flowers in axillary long-stalked clusters white with purple stripes and spots, 4 cm across and each with long slender spur. *p. 389*

tuberosa (Madagascar); fleshy cane-stem with characteristic thickened base to 40 cm dia.; erect brown stem 40-60 cm tall, with soft ovate waxy, grass-green serrate leaves 10-15 cm long, underside amaranth-red; flowers rosy-red, 3 cm across. *Tropical. p. 388*

'Uganda Red' (Uganda); dense herbaceous bush with waxy, corrugated small ovate green leaves, against which contrast the vivid, bright crimson flowers characterized by two large front lobes. *Tropical. p. 387*

walleriana (sultanii; wallerana in Hortus 3) (Zanzibar), "Patient Lucy"; in continuous bloom, the carmine flowers 3-4 cm dia., and with an upturned spur; long, tapering, fresh-green, waxy, crenate leaves on watery-succulent stem. *Tropical. p. 385*

walleriana flore pleno; collected in Mauritius; tall, vigorous grower 60-75 cm tall, with deep green leaves serrate at margins; double flowers bright crimson red. *p. 386*

walleriana holstii (Trop. E. Africa), "Busy Lizzie"; watery-succulent herb with fleshy stem striped red, and small, coppery, ovate leaves; flowers fiery vermillion-scarlet with spurs pointing downward. *Tropical. p. 385*

walleriana holstii 'Orange Baby'; dwarf form of our well-known "Busy Lizzie"; with creeping succulent branches and only about 15 cm high, leaves are small, and flowers deep orange; good pot plant for Mother's Day. *p. 387*

walleriana 'Variegata' (sultanii 'Variegata'), "Variegated patient Lucy"; long, tapering leaves gray-green, irregularly bordered white; flowers carmine-red. *Tropical. p. 385, 388*

INCARVILLEA *Bignoniaceae* **C2LBD**

delavayi (W. China, Yunnan, Tibet), "Hardy gloxinia"; herbaceous perennial to 50 cm high, with fleshy pinnate leaves, the 15 or more crenate leaflets alternately arranged; curious two-lipped, tubular flowers bright rose-red with yellow throat and spreading segments, 4 to 6 cm long. *p. 504*

INDIGOFERA *Leguminosae* **I2LBD**

incarnata (decora) (Japan, China), "Indigo"; deciduous shrub, with attractive pinnate leaves of 3-6 pairs of leaflets 6 cm long; inflorescence wisteria-like in pendant racemes of rose-pink flowers with pale standard, showy. Since early Egyptian times, used in the manufacture of permanent blue-colored Indigo dye by extracting it from the herbage. *Warm temperate. p. 1385, 1386*

INGA *Leguminosae* **S2LBD**

edulis (C. and So. America), "St. John's bread"; tropical tree to 15 m, with broad crown and gray bark; pinnate leaves glossy dark green, the leaflets separated by winged axis; flowers with long white stamens and brown hairy corolla; long 4-angled pods contain edible, sweet white pulp, and split open when ripe. *Tropical. p. 1384*

INGA: see also Calliandra

IOCHROMA *Solanaceae* **I2LBD**

coccineum (Peru); robust shrub with downy shoots; and soft herbaceous green, flaccid leaves 8-12 cm long; clusters of pendant lovely, tubular bell-shaped flowers carmine-red, 5 cm long, near apex of branches. *Tropical. p. 2067*

lanceolatum (Ecuador, Colombia); handsome tropical pubescent shrub 1-2 m high, with woolly lanceolate leaves to 15 cm long; the attractive trumpet-shaped tubular 4 cm flowers deep blue varying to purplish and with pale tips, in dense clusters near apex. *p. 2067*

tubulosum (Lysiloma) (Colombia); tropical downy shrub to 2 m high, with soft herbaceous thinly pubescent, long-elliptic grayish green leaves 12 cm long, pendulous tubular flowers 4 cm long purplish blue, inside the flaring, toothed mouth pale lavender. *p. 2067*

warscewiczii (Trop. America); handsome spreading shrub with pubescent shoots, and large herbaceous, ovate leaves with depressed ribs; from the apex a cluster of charming pendant flowers 5 cm long with balloon-like calyx and lavender-blue tubular corolla striped dark blue, photographed at Royal Botanic Garden, Sydney. *Tropical. p. 2067*

IONOPSIS *Orchidaceae* **I3OFM**

utricularioides (Cent. America to Brazil), a "Violet orchid"; small, tufted, pretty epiphyte with rigid, keeled leaves and racemes of flowers white flushed rose, and marked purple at base of large hairy, 2-lobed lip (spring). (I) *p. 1739, 1742*

IONOXALIS *Oxalidaceae* **I2LBMd**

nelsonii (Mexico); stemless bulbous plant with strong petioles bearing leaves with 4-5 large segments, notched at the apex, and marked with a clear cross zone of purple; the flowers, in umbels, on long stalks, purplish-rose with yellow base. *p. 1845*

IONOXALIS: see also OXALIS

IPHEION *Amaryllidaceae* **C2LBMd**

uniflorum (Brodiaea, Leucocoryne) (Argentina), "Spring-star-flower"; small cormous herb with onion-like odor, grass-like leaves, and solitary, starshaped flowers with spreading petals white tinged with blue, opening in bright weather. *p. 119*

uniflorum caeruleum (Brodiaea); pretty variety 15-20 cm high, with starry 2½ cm porcelain-blue flowers; spring and summer blooming. Can be grown in pots. *p. 119*

IPOMOEA *Convolvulaceae* **S2LBM**

batatas (prob. Trop. America), "Sweet Potato vine"; in the Southern U.S., commonly called "Yam"; an economic as well as a hanging basket plant, trailing perennial with deeply rooted yellow-brown tuberous roots, the long vines are stem-rooting, with milky juice, the variable leaves ovate, angular or digitately lobed; tubular flowers spreading widely, pinkish lavender; the tubers are often grown in water, provided they have not been previously cured. A food plant of great economical importance in the tropics; the tubers when cooked or baked become mealy, similar to potatoes, but are more sweet in taste with white or yellow flesh. *p.851,852*

batatas 'Blackie', "Black-leaf sweet potato"; an ornamental variety grown for its decorative effect, as the whole plant, vines and foliage is in shades of blackish red; stems are purplish brown, and the deeply lobed leaves at first greenish with blackish veins, later almost all black-purple, and wine-red beneath; an easy vine for the warm window. *p. 852*

crassicaulis (fistulosa) (Brazil); large straggling herbaceous plant, becoming woody, climbing when finding support, the stems with milky juice; leaves heart-shaped to 15 cm long, soft hairy beneath; funnel-shaped pinkish flowers with ruffled margins, 6 cm across, singly or in pairs. *p. 853*

horsfalliae (W. Indies), "Morning glory", or "Princess vine"; twining winter-flowering perennial with palmately lobed leaves, the showy, 6 cm waxy-glossy, bell-shaped flowers deep rich rose or red. *Tropical.* *p. 853*

learii (acuminata in Hortus 3), (Trop. America), "Blue dawn-flower"; perennial twiner with ovate entire or lobed leaves to 20 cm long; trumpet-shaped flowers to 12 cm across, with white tube and sky-blue limb, turning purple and pink. *Tropical.* *p. 852*

leptophylla (South Dakota to New Mexico), "Bush Moon-flower" or "Bush morning-glory"; charming perennial clamberer 60 cm to more than 1 m high, with large tuberous roots, and triangular-ovate leaves 5-10 cm across, lavender pink deepening to rosy-purple in throat. *p. 852*

nil (hederacea) (Old World Tropics), "Imperial Japanese morning-glory"; floriferous hairy perennial; rank tendril-climbing vine, with yellow-green, 3-lobed leaves 10-15 cm wide; showy axillary, funnel-form flowers about 10 cm wide, blue purple or rose. Can be grown as a bushy pot plant for the cool, sunny window as in Japan, where plants are pinched back every second or third leaf to prevent climbing, resulting in large blooms all summer and fall; blooms open in morning and fade afternoon. *p. 852*

palmata (W. Africa: Guinea coast); deciduous twiner with white tubercular stem and tuberous root; leaves palmately divided into linear lobes; funnel-form flowers with 5-angled limb white with purple center. *p. 852*

paniculata (digitata) (Tropics of both hemispheres); wide-spread tropical tuberous-rooted Morning-glory vine with 17 cm leaves divided into 5 to 7 narrow lobes; numerous 8 cm broadly bell-shaped flowers lilac or pink, with thick sepals. *p. 852*

purpurea (Pharbitis) (Trop. America), "Common morning-glory"; widely naturalized; annual twiner with 12 cm cordate-ovate leaves and large funnel-shaped flowers deep purple with pale tube, opening from early morning until about 10 a.m.; garden forms in white, pink, carmine blue, striped, or double. *Tropical.* *p. 853*

transvaalensis (Trop. Africa; Zimbabwe, No. Tranvaal); a "One-day flower" with large tuberous rootstock, producing annual stems to 1 m long with hairy cordate leaves, and funnel-shaped rose-pink flowers with spreading limb and red throat, 4 cm across. *p. 852*

tricolor (rubro-coerulea) (Trop. America); annual climber with cordate leaves and large, purplish blue, disk-shaped flowers, to 10 cm dia. The cultivar 'Heavenly Blue' has flowers dark-sky blue. *Tropical.* *p. 853*

tuberosa (transferred to Merremia in Hortus 3) (India), "Wood-rose" or "Ceylon morning-glory"; perennial viner with 20 cm leaves digitately parted into 5-7 narrow lobes; funnel-form yellow flowers; the globular fruit ultimately a woody pod, when ripe opens and which with its persistent large, rounded leathery sepals form the "Wooden" rose some 8-10 cm across; used for decoration, especially in Hawaii. *Tropical.* *p. 851, 852*

welwitschii (Namibia); slender, graceful vining perennial plant with wire-like stems and compound leaves palmately cut to bare ribs; large and showy funnel-flowers in rosy-pink with darker eye. *p. 853*

IPSEA *Orchidaceae* **S3OFM**

speciosa (South India, Sri Lanka), "Daffodil orchid"; handsome terrestrial, with onion-like pseudobulbs topped by narrow ribbed leaves to 30 cm long; erect slender spike to 60 cm, usually with a solitary fragrant, waxy flower 8 cm across, golden yellow and long-lived (winter). *p. 1742*

IRESINE *Amaranthaceae* **I2LBM**

herbstii (Achyranthes verschaffeltii) (So. Brazil), a "Beefsteak plant"; bushy tropical herb with waxy 2 to 6 cm leaves almost round, and notched at tip; glowing purplish-red and traced with light red veins. The ornate foliage coloring is brought out best in good sunlight. A bedding or border plant where red is required. Small woolly flowers not showy. *Tropical.* *p. 84*

herbstii 'Acuminata' (versicolor), "Painted bloodleaf"; a variety with ovate, sharply-pointed leaves deep red with veins a showy, light carmine, also the stem. *Tropical.* *p. 83*

herbstii 'Aureo-reticulata', "Chicken gizzard"; rounded leaf with notched apex, fresh green with yellow veins; stem and petioles red. *Tropical.* *p. 83*

lindenii (Ecuador); "Bloodleaf"; slender herb with leaves narrow and sharp-pointed, deep blood-red. *p. 84*

lindenii formosa (reticulata), the "Yellow blood-leaf"; very attractive, colorful form with broader, pointed 5-8 cm leaves yellow with light green area between veins; stems and petioles red. Charming for carpet bedding and as a window plant. *Tropical.* *p. 15*, 84*

IRIARTEA (SOCRATEA) *Palmae* **S3LBM**

exorrhiza (Brazil); graceful fan palm with ringed, straight, slender trunk blotched with gray; long crown-shaft supporting a handsome crown of pinnate fronds, with glossy-green leaflets sickle-shaped and irregularly notched or serrate along one side and at tips. Referred to SOCRATEA by Dr. H. E. Moore. *p. 1883*

IRIS *Iridaceae* **C2LBWd**

antilibanotica (Lebanon); species to 30 cm or more high, with sickle-shaped gray-green leaves 2 cm wide, the floral stalk with solitary flower, the reflexed outer segments or falls deep brown-purple with black signal patch, beard yellow, and purple standards 9 cm long; May-blooming. *p. 1326*

bucharica (Turkestan); robust bulbous species to 35 cm high; the flowers with creamy-white standards and 5 cm pendant outer segments or falls; these falls with golden yellow blotch and yellow central ridge; leaves lanceolate, glaucous on underside. *p. 1326*

douglasiana (California, Oregon); rhizomatous plant with evergreen leaves equalling or surpassing stems; flowers variable, lilac purple to cream, outer segments oblanceolate, inner standards clawed; beardless. *p. 1327*

x germanica (probably Mediterranean); of mysterious hybrid origin, now as a class of "Common bearded iris"; rhizomatous, with flat glaucous leaves to 45 cm long; tall stems 60-90 cm, forked, with fragrant flowers, the outer segments bright purple, the claw white with brownish veins; beard yellow, the erect inner segments deep lilac; May. *p. 1326, 1327*

x germanica var. florentina variegata; albino form of germanica, of slender habit, with white flowers showing traces of blue on the "falls" or outer, pendant segments. In addition, the leaves in this variety have a broad white band along the inner edge. *p. 1325*

graeberiana (Turkestan); graceful species (30 cm) with leafy succulent zigzag stalks bearing most distinct, light cobalt blue flowers; late April blooming. *p. 1325*

graminea (C. and So. Europe, to Caucasus); rhizomatous species with two edged stem, its narrow 30-90 cm grass-like leaves often surpassing the 1-2 fragrant flowers, with pendant segments creamy-white veined purple, the erect standards more purple. *p. 1325*

histrio (Asia Minor, Turkey, Syria, Lebanon), "Syrian iris"; dwarf bulbous iris only 15-20 cm high, the linear leaves 4-angled, deeply grooved on each face and to 30 cm long, usually appearing before the flowers; a short stalk bearing the solitary large, 8 cm blossom, in early February in habitat, the outer segments or "falls" violet blue with yellow line in center bordered with creamy white and spotted with blue, the standards lilac. *p. 1326*

innominata (Oregon); sturdy, rhizomatous plant (75 cm), with dark green, grassy, tufted leaves and showy white with deep yellow flowers streaked purple on "falls" or reflexed outer petals; the standards lighter yellow. *p. 1325*

kaempferi (No. China, Japan), the "Japanese iris"; rhizomatous species, 60 cm high, leaves with marked midrib; flowers purple with yellow, and various; falls 8 cm long. *p. 1327*

pallida 'Argentea' (South Tyrol), "Variegated orris"; attractive fan of flat leaves light or milky green edged in cream; flowers lavender-blue with brown, beard white, tipped yellow. *Temperate.* *p. 1326, 1327*

reticulata (Russia, Caucasus, Iran); enchanting dwarf iris, a favorite early-blooming plant typical for this species for its reticulated or netted bulb, with leaves linear and slightly ribbed or rounded almost rush-like, 20-25 cm long; and a single, scented flower raised on a long tube, deep violet, veined and spotted with orange, the erect standard petals 6 cm long. *p. 1326*

sisyrinchium (Gynandriris) (Portugal, Mediterranean to C. Asia); small cormous plant with few narrow leaves; with small fragrant, bright lilac-blue flowers with golden markings, the outer segments, or falls 4 cm long and with a white patch, on short stems to 20 cm long; in So. Europe blooming in spring and summer in succession, but lasting only one day. This species is now properly referred to Gynandriris as a monotypic genus, growing from a corm, rather than a bulb as typical in iris. *p. 1326*

susiana (Asia Minor, Iran), "Mourning iris" or "Palestine iris"; rhizomatous plant with linear leaves, stem 30-45 cm high with large solitary flowers, basically gray, tinged with lilac, and overlaid with brown-black veins and velvety purple-black patches, and a brownish beard. *p. 1327*

tectorum (China); rhizomatous plant 30 cm high, with thin, pale green, sword-shaped leaves, and wiry stalks with 2-3 flowers bright lilac or blue-purple, spotted segments quite horizontal, crest cut and white-violet; May-June. *p. 1327*

tenax (Pacific Coast: W. Oregon and Washington); rhizomatous species with 30 cm stems bearing bract-like leaves and flowers gray to wine-purple with yellow ridge; the linear tough-fibrous basal leaves longer than the inflorescence. *p. 1325*

'Wedgwood', "Forcing iris"; bulbous hybrid of the No. African I. tingitana and the "Spanish iris", xiphium; sword-like leaves and stiff spike with striking violet-blue flowers, the outer segments or "falls" lavender and marked with yellow; much grown under glass. *Subtropic.* *p. 1327*

xyphium hybrid, known as "Dutch iris"; large-flowered bulbous hybrid group 45-60 cm high, a class resulting from breeding in Holland of the "Spanish iris"; I. xyphium (from Spain, Portugal, No. Africa), and known for their brilliant colors with strong contrasts, and numerous flowers, in purple, blue, bronze, yellow, white. Dutch Iris have larger flowers, and flower 2 weeks earlier (June) than the Spanish, and lend themselves to cool forcing. *p. 1325*

xyphium var. hollandica 'Golden Harvest', a "Dutch iris"; golden yellow early-blooming tuberous hybrid from xiphium, tingitana, and other Mediterranean species, with narrow, channeled leaves and heavy single flowered stems 45-60 cm high, with showy flowers, and orchid-like; late May. *p. 1327*

ISMENE: see Hymenocallis

ISOCHILUS *Orchidaceae* **S3OFW**

linearis (Mexico, Cuba, Argentina); curious orchid forming clumps to 75 cm high, of thin, grass-like arching stems clothed by alternating narrow-linear leaves; small 1 cm flowers toward the apex commonly rosy-magenta, with darker lip, blooming over long period. *Subtropic.* *p. 1742*

ISOLEPIS: see Scirpus

ISOLOMA: see Kohleria

ISOPLEXIS *Scrophulariaceae* **I2LBD**

canariensis (Calianassa) (Canary Islands); from the heath region; a stiff-bushy evergreen related to Digitalis with shining thick, lanceolate leaves downy beneath; erect 45 cm spike-like raceme dense with curved tubular 5-lobed bilabiate flowers orange-yellow. *p. 2051*

sceptrum (Canary Islands, Madeira); shrubby plant to 2 m high, close to Digitalis, its stiff stalk with thick, shining leaves 15 cm long, lance-shaped and sharply toothed; tubular flowers with long upper lip, yellow with darker veins, closely packed in an erect raceme 12 cm long; not 2-lipped as in canariensis. *p. 2057*

ISOTOMA *Lobeliaceae* **I2HFM**

axillaris (Australia); perennial 30 cm high with pinnatifid, toothed leaves; flowers with long green tube and starry, spreading blue petals. *p. 1514*

longiflora (West Indies); perennial herb with oblanceolate coarsely indented, toothed, hairy leaves, and white flowers with slender tube and spreading linear segments; in summer. Prob. Hippobroma. *p. 1513*

petraea (Australia); branching perennial 30 cm high, with leaves serrate at margins; 3 cm flowers white, tinged pink, with yellow eye. *p. 1514*

ITEA *Saxifragaceae* **I2LFD**

ilicifolia (W. China); evergreen shrub (4 m) with 5-12 cm ovate, spiny-toothed leaves like holly but thinner, dark glossy green; tiny greenish-white flowers in arching and pendulous racemes foxtail-like, to 38 cm long. *p.2042*

IXIA *Iridaceae* **I2LBDd**

'Bridesmaid'; one of the many spring-blooming horticultural hybrids that have been developed for 150 years, of unknown parentage, but possibly involving I. maculata and columellaris; cormous plant with about 6 grass-like leaves in two ranks, and fragrant, bright-colored flowers at first cup-shaped, opening with the sun, a little wider on succeeding days until wide open and starlike. 'Bridesmaid' has white flowers with red eye; free-flowering. *p. 1337*

maculata (So. Africa); slender cormous plant to 60 cm high with grass-like leaves conspicuously ribbed; attractive, brilliantly colored flowers normally yellow, but varying to white marked with red or purple, on wiry stems; spring blooming. *p. 1332, 1338*

'Rose Queen', popular hybrid with starry flowers uniform soft pink. *p. 1337*

scariosa (incarnata) (So. Africa); cormous species (45 cm) with short, sword-shaped leaves and numerous flowers flesh-colored or lilac and with yellow anthers; usually 4 to 6 blooms on wiry stems. *p. 1337*

viridiflora (So. Africa), the lovely "Green ixia"; tall, late-blooming species growing to 60 cm with linear leaves and erect spikes of starry flowers of delicate texture, light turquoise-green with blackish eye, yellow anthers on black filaments, measuring 3 cm across, and opening with the sun; looking almost artificial. *p. 1337*

IXIOLIRION *Amaryllidaceae* **I2LBDd**

tataricum (montanum) (So. Russia, C. Asia), "Tartar lily" or "Siberian lily"; attractive small lily-like plant from the Steppe of Southern Russia to Afghanistan with ovoid bulb 3 cm dia.; 3 to 8 broadly linear, mostly basal, persistent leaves, and clusters of long-lasting 4-5 cm lilac flowers with spreading segments; filaments, style and stigma violet, the anthers white, on wiry, leafy stalks 30-45 cm long; blooming spring to June, and becoming dormant in autumn. *p. 101, 121, 1337*

IXORA *Rubiaceae* **S2-3LBM**

borbonica (bot. Enterospermum); a beautiful tropical foliage plant somewhat resembling a croton, from the Indian Ocean Isle of Réunion; branching shrub with stiff-leathery narrow-lanceolate leaves about 25 cm long, in bluish or mossy-green, mottled with pale green; the midvein a bold salmon-red; small whitish flowers. With age, leaves are longer and less colorful. *Tropical.* *p. 2019*

chinensis (So. China, Malaya); small evergreen shrub with rich green, firm, obovate leaves 10 cm long; waxy tubular flowers with spreading lobes light orange-red, varying to yellow and white, in dense clusters. *p. 2015*

chinensis 'Rosea' (Bengal), "Pink flower of the woods"; natural variety of taller habit, to 1 m high, with dark shining green leaves; the flowers a lovely soft, clear pink, becoming darker with age, in large corymbs. *p. 2015*

coccinea (East Indies), "Flame of the woods"; evergreen, tropical, flowering shrub to 1 m, with sparry branches; opposite, sessile, short leathery leaves, and clusters of dark scarlet, tubular flowers with spreading lobes. *Tropical.* *p. 2013*

coccinea 'Morsei'; flowers almost 5 cm long, with pointed lobes bright orange, sometimes shaded red, in large corymbs. *p. 2015*

duffii (Caroline Is., Micronesia); an old favorite, grown as a potted plant in greenhouses since 1878; and listed by Roehrs in 1907 catalog; tropical evergreen shrub with slender elliptic leaves 10-12 cm long, on thin-wiry branches, and topped by a full cluster of small but numerous flowers deep red. There seems to be a discrepancy: Hortus Second lists duffii as synonym of macrothyrsa but the latter is a much larger species, with leaves 30 cm long, and flowers more bold. Valid as duffii in Hortus 3. *p. 2019*

javanica (Java), "Jungle geranium"; showy flowering shrub with forking, willowy, red branches; opposite, long slender-pointed, smooth, leathery leaves; and large, terminal clusters of waxy, soft salmon-red flowers having long thin tubes and expanded lobes, blooming in summer. *Tropical.* *p. 1824A, 2013, 2018*

x kewensis alba; handsome English hybrid with elliptic thin-leathery leaves glossy yellowish green 15-30 cm long; at branch tips compact clusters 8 cm across, of pure white flowers; I. x kewensis has flowers orange scarlet. *p. 2018*

macrothyrsa 'Super King'; probably hybrid of I. coccinea var. fraseri x macrothyrsa (duffii); vigorous free-blooming, very showy evergreen shrub with stout, cane-like branches with large leathery leaves, bearing 15 cm ball-shaped clusters of brilliant orange-scarlet flowers tinted cinnamon, 1-3 cm across. *Tropical.* *p. 2015*

odorata (Madagascar); tropical evergreen shrub to 1 m high, dense with leathery green lanceolate leaves to 30 cm long; terminal clusters of ray-like slender tubular flowers 8-10 cm long, pinkish with red base, very fragrant. *Tropical.* *p. 2019*

'Orange King' (coccinea 'Fraseri' x macrothyrsa), "West Indian jasmine"; compact plant with dark green leathery leaves, the slender branches each carrying a showy, full cluster of many small, but beautifully orange-scarlet flowers; grown in Holland as an excellent small potted plant. *p. 2019*

parviflora (India); tropical evergreen shrub with dark green, obovate leaves 8-15 cm long; tiny flowers white or pale green, tinged pink in short clusters 6 cm across; not showy. *p. 2018*

x 'Williamsii' ('Kirsten') (coccinea x chinensis); vigorous plant, very floriferous forming large clusters reddish salmon or orange scarlet; parent of numerous hybrids; requires less heat; listed in Roehrs catalogs since 1907. Similar to I. 'Kirsten', a coccinea x macrothyrsa (duffii) hybrid. *p. 2018*

JABOROSA *Solanaceae* **I2LBD**

integrifolia (Argentina); herbaceous perennial with creeping stems to 22 cm high, with large oval dark green leaves serrate at margins; bell-shaped greenish-white flowers with spreading lobes; in spring. *p. 2076*

JACARANDA *Bignoniaceae* **S2-3LBD**

acutifolia (mimosifolia, ovalifolia) (Brazil), "Mimosa-leaved ebony"; shrub or small tree 3-10 m high, with lacy, bright green, bipinnate foliage to 45 cm long, lightly downy; blue-violet flowers 4 cm long, with silky, inflated tubular corolla, in long panicles. *p. 500, 502*

chelonia (Paraguay, Argentina), "Blue jacaranda"; deciduous or semi-evergreen hardwooded flowering tree, in their homelands growing to 30 m high, but in cultivation coming into bloom when only 1 m high; the highly ornamental foliage is bipinnate, feather-like; after leaves drop into winter, new foliage may form quickly, or remain bare until flowering time in spring; the large inflated bell-shaped flowers are purplish-blue, 4-5 cm long, in showy terminal clusters 30 cm long; a glorious sight when in full bloom. *p. 501*

JACOBINIA *Acanthaceae* **S2-3LFM**

carnea (Justicia magnifica) (Brazil), "Flamingo plant"; upright plant with ovate, grayish-green, satiny leaves, reddish stem and terminal head of arched clear rose, 5 cm flowers. *Tropical.* *p. 49*

ghiesbreghtiana (Mexico); bushy subshrub to 1½ m high, with leathery leaves ovate-lanceolate, smooth bright green; slender tubular orange-red bi-lobed flowers 3-4 cm long, in loose terminal clusters. *p. 50*

ghiesbreghtiana var. coccinea; a bushy variety with ovate, green leaves; flowers with slender tubular corollas vivid scarlet red. *p. 50*

pauciflora (Libonia floribunda) (Brazil); downy shrub to 60 cm high, with small 2 cm elliptic leaves on round stems and numerous nodding 3 cm solitary tubular flowers with short lips, scarlet tipped with yellow. *p. 50*

x penrhosiensis (ghiesbreghtiana x pauciflora); shrubby plant similar to pauciflora but more sparry, with larger narrow-elliptic leaves, and bilabiate-tubular flowers 3 cm long, vivid crimson-red, lightly ringed with yellow, in winter. *p. 50*

pohliana (Justicia) (Brazil); showy tropical flowering shrub to 1½ m high, with large 20 cm lanceolate quilted leaves glossy purplish green; flowers in terminal cluster, the curving corolla bright carmine -rose. *p. 50*

suberecta (Justicia) (Uruguay); spreading low, herbaceous, pubescent plant with small ovate, velvety 6 cm green leaves; downy 2-lobed flowers 3 cm long, reddish-orange, in small clusters. *p. 50*

velutina (Brazil), "Brazilian plume"; somewhat shrubby plant with long, olive-green leaves, soft hairy on both sides. The beautiful inflorescence a dense, fountain-like terminal head of arched rosy-pink blooms; from early summer. *Tropical.* *p. 49, 1952A*

JACQUINIA *Theophrastaceae (Myrsinaceae)* **S3LBD**

armillaris arborea (W. Indies), "Bracelet-wood"; attractive small evergreen shrub or tree to 3 m or more, with thick-leathery, grayish green obovate leaves; terminal clusters of fragrant white inconspicuous flowers, followed by handsome, glossy bright orange-red berries. *Tropical.* *p. 1601*

pungens (Mexico), "Cudjoe wood"; evergreen shrub with leathery, long-elliptic leaves; small scarlet red cup flowers opening star-like, in clusters; small orange fruit. *Tropical.* *p. 1601*

ruscifolia (Cuba: Havana); evergreen shrub to 3 m; spine-tipped rigid leaves glossy green 5 cm long; small red flowers; orange-scarlet berries. *p. 1601*

JAMESONIA *Polypodiaceae (Filices)* **I3HFM**

canescens (Venezuela); an odd fern of the Andean paramos, with black, woody creeping rhizome, the stalked fronds quite remarkable, being tall and slender 30-40 cm high but less than 1 cm wide, pinnate with tiny roundish segments and covered with yellowish brown woolly hair hiding the hoary pinnae. *p. 1112*

JASARUM *Araceae* **S3HNW**

steyermarkii (Venezuela: Eduardo Bolivar); tropical aquatic herb with erect rhizome 10-12 cm long; 30-45 cm petiole carries the long-linear, corrugated, dark green leaf blade 20-33 cm long and 2 cm wide. Known only from this locality in Venezuela; photo by J. Bogner, Munich Botanic Garden. *p. 207*

JASMINUM *Oleaceae* **S-I-C2LMB**

angulare (capense) (So. Africa), "East London jasmine"; twining shrub to 6 m, with angled stems, leathery trifoliolate leaves, and sweetly scented white flowers, for many months of the year. *p. 1630*

grandiflorum (Kashmir, Himalayas), "Poets jasmine", also known as "Spanish jasmine"; straggling tender bush with slender, angled branches, opposite, pinnate leaves of usually 7 small leaflets, and showy white, fragrant flowers, reddish beneath, commonly in clusters; June-October blooming. *Subtropic.* *p. 1631, 1633*

humile revolutum (Himalaya, Afghanistan), "Italian jasmine"; shrub of spreading habit, with strong, angled branches, alternate, dark green, pinnate leaves with 3 to 7 thick leaflets revolute at the edges; fragrant, lemon-yellow 1 cm flowers in axillary and terminal clusters from June to September. *Subtropic.* *p. 1631*

ilicifolium hort.: see nitidum

mesnyi (primulinum) (China), "Primrose jasmine"; free-flowering, evergreen, rambling shrub up to 5 m if trained, with 4-angled, glabrous branches, opposite trifoliate leaves with small, lanceolate shining green leaflets and showy, single or semi-double, solitary yellow flowers with darker center, to 4 cm across, in spring. *Warm temperate.* *p. 1631*

multiflorum (China, India), "Angel-hair jasmine"; popular, wide-spread tropical jasmine, prized for centuries in the Orient, especially India; vigorous, freely spreading, downy shrub; cordate, dull green leaves hairy beneath; pure white, star-like, sweetly scented flowers, borne in clusters at the ends and along the often drooping branches. *Subtropic.* *p. 1630*

nitidum (So. Pacific: Admiralty Isl.); known in Florida hort. as J. ilicifolium, in California hort. as magnificum; the "Angelwing jasmine"; semi-vining small evergreen shrub with shiny dark green leaves ovate with tapering tip, 6 cm long; large 4 cm windmill-like, glistening white flowers with lanceolate petals, purplish in bud, and sweetly fragrant. *Tropical.* *p. 1630, 1632*

nudiflorum (No. China); twiggy, nearly erect shrub with 4-angled stiff branchlets bearing small opposite, deep glossy green foliage of 3 little ciliate leaflets, deciduous; solitary, yellow, axillary flowers; late winter and early spring bloomer. (C) *p. 1631*

odoratissimum hort. (Madeira, Canary Islands); erect evergreen shrub with pinnate, glossy green leaves to 10 cm long; flowers white, 3 cm across, with spreading lobes purplish outside, more or less fragrant. Photo by T. Everett (N.Y. Bot. Garden) shown on pg. 1630 is plant as known in hort.; description of J. odoratissimum from Madeira in Baileya 13, Dec. 1965 does not agree, having simple leaves and yellow flowers with narrow petals. *p. 1630*

officinale (floribundum) (Nile region, Africa), "Free-flowering jessamine"; rambling bush with 7-9 pinnate leaves and white, fragrant flowers having broader lobes only half as long as the tube, in axillary and terminal clusters. (S) *p. 1631*

parkeri (Himalaya of N.W. India); small prostrate shrub to only 35 cm high; stems green with tiny pinnate 3 cm leaves of usually 5 leaflets; relatively large solitary flowers 1½ cm wide, clear yellow; forming low mounds and suitable for rock gardens. Also grown in California. *p. 1630*

polyanthum (Yunnan), "Pink jasmine"; freely blooming, shrubby plant rapidly climbing, and reaching up to 6 m with red, glabrous branches having small pinnate leaves of 5-7 lanceolate leaflets; early in the year it produces masses of deliciously scented flowers white inside and rosy outside. (I) *p. 1630, 1632*

primulinum: see mesnyi

rex (Southwest Thailand), "King jasmine"; glabrous climber with young branches green, round and wiry; simple, rigidly hard opposite leaves broad-ovate, dark green, 10-20 cm long; large pure white, salver-shaped flowers without scent, 5 cm or more across, during winter, usually in 2-3 flowered clusters. Very showy in bloom. *Tropical.* *p. 1631, 1824A*

sambac (Arabia, India), "Arabian jasmine"; woody shrub clambering to 2 m high, with firm, broad elliptic, dark green leaves, opposite or in threes, to 8 cm long; 3 cm flowers in clusters, gardenia-white but turning purple as they fade, and very fragrant, blooming from early spring to late fall. *p. 1631*

sambac 'Grand Duke of Tuscany' (trifoliatum), "Gardenia jasmine"; a button-flowered form from Italy with large, 3-4 cm tightly double, gardenia-white blooms that won't drop off, of a penetrating sweet fragrance; waxy, quilted, oval leaves in whorls, on stiff pubescent stems; flowers more fully double than 'Maid of Orleans' and slower growing. *Tropical.* *p. 1631*

sambac 'Maid of Orleans', "Arabian jasmine"; woody evergreen shrub of sparry habit and slow growth, with broad ovate, deep green leaves, and waxy-white, semi-double, somewhat cupped 2-3 cm flowers, and intensely fragrant. *Tropical.* *p. 1633*

simplicifolium (South Sea Islands), "Little star jasmine"; rambling evergreen shrub, with leaves privet-like, ovate, 5 cm or less long, dark green and glossy; the sweetly fragrant, tiny star-shaped flowers white, 1½ cm across, with narrow-linear petals, in terminal clusters very free-blooming. Attractive as a little flowering pot plant. *Tropical.* *p. 1630*

volubile (simplicifolium hort.) (Australia), "Wax-jasmine"; attractive scandent shrub or climber, with dark green, glossy broad-ovate, 5 cm leaves; tiny 1 cm star-like waxy-white flowers with small calyx lobes, and sweetly fragrant. *p. 1630*

volubile variegatum; evergreen shrub with thin, willowy branches; the opposite leaves shiny bright green, 5 cm long, variegated greenish-yellow and cream in center. *p. 1635*

JATROPHA *Euphorbiaceae* **S3LBM**

curcas (Trop. America), "Barbados-nut"; tree to 5 m bearing seeds which are used for their oil; leaves lightly 3-5-lobed, resembling ivy; small yellowish-green flowers. *p. 1051, 1060*

hastata (Cuba), "Peregrina"; small shrub with oblong-obovate leaves constricted below into fiddle-shaped, and with tapering apex; showy scarlet flowers. *p. 1051*

integerrima (Cuba), "Peregrina"; evergreen shrub to 1 m, with milky sap, more or less 3-lobed leathery, glossy green leaves, and clusters of red flowers. *Tropical.* *p. 1049, 1052, 1056A*

multifida (Mexico to Brazil), "Coral plant"; growing tree-like, with milky juice; leaves nearly circular in outline but deeply parted, the narrow segments pinnately lobed; flowers scarlet. Seen as a street tree in Nigeria, West Africa. *Tropical.* *p. 1051, 1055*

nudicaulis (Ecuador); tropical shrub with thick stems and milky juice, the branches twisted and knobby with leaf scars; foliage palmately lobed and bipinnately cut into narrow segments; pretty inflorescence in long-stalked clusters of starry flowers with 5 petals deep pink. *p. 1060*

pandurifolia (West Indies); evergreen shrub to 1 m or more high, with variable ovate or obovate, somewhat fiddle-shaped leaves with an occasional tooth here or there, and small scarlet flowers in branched clusters. *Tropical.* *p. 1052*

peltata (North Perú); ornamental evergreen shrub to 2 m high, with club-like stems; attractive leaves peltate and rounded in outline, 25 cm across, light green with yellow veins, lightly lobed and with ciliate margins; clusters of brick-red flowers. *p. 1060*

podagrica (West Indies, C. America, Colombia); succulent shrub with short trunk thickened at base, to 60 cm high, knobby branches, and peltate, 3 to 5-lobed, dark green leathery leaves, to 25 cm across; fleshy inflorescence of small scarlet-red or coral flowers in long, red-stalked clusters. *Tropical.* *p. 1051, 1060*

JOVELLANA *Scropulariaceae* **C2LFM**

sinclairi (Calceolaria) (New Zealand); erect, slender subshrub, with hairy branches, ovate 8 cm soft, coarsely toothed leaves, green and downy above, smooth beneath; small cup-shaped, two-lobed flowers whitish spotted with purple, in terminal clusters. *p. 2054*

JUANULLOA *Solanaceae* **S3HFM**

aurantiaca (Perú), known as "Guacamaya" in Mexico; evergreen shrub 1-2 m high, growing epiphytic in habitat; branches covered with felt; oval-pointed leathery matte dark green leaves 5-12 cm long; axillary pendant tubular flowers toward ends of branches, orange corolla in large, fleshy, angled calyx, in forked racemes. *Tropical.* *p. 2071, 2080*

JUBAEA *Palmae* **I3LFD**

chilensis (spectabilis) (Chile), "Syrup-palm"; or "Chilean wine-palm"; massive feather-palm with trunk usually swollen and to 1 m thick and 12-24 m high, crowned by spreading pinnate fronds 2-4 m long; the numerous green pinnae in pairs, standing out in different directions, and split at apex; the short thick petioles covered with brown fibers at base. The sap of the trunk yields syrup. *Subtropic.* *p. 1870, 1878, 1883, 1884*

JUGLANS *Juglandaceae* **C2LBD**

cinerea (Eastern Canada, to Arkansas), "Butternut"; deciduous tree 20 m or more, with round, downy branches, and odd-pinnate leaves 25-50 cm long, the ovate leaflets finely toothed; small male, staminate flowers in long drooping catkins; pointed sticky-pubescent fruit 5-10 cm long with thick-shelled fruit and sweet, oily kernel. (h) *p. 1340*

nigra (Massachusetts to Texas), "Black walnut"; great tree reaching 45 m with thick trunk; pinnate leaves 30-60 cm long and toothed; tiny male flowers in hanging catkins, the female ones in small erect clusters; petals absent; the hairy 5 cm black fruit nearly round, containing the hard-shelled, wrinkled, edible nut. (h) *p. 1340*

JUMELLEA *Orchidaceae* **S3OFM**

papangensis (Angraecum) (Madagascar); rare epiphyte with elongate, slender leafy stem; flowers pure white, long-spurred, deliciously fragrant, about 8 cm across. *p. 1742*

sagittata (Angraecum); basket plant; clustering, small flattened pseudobulbs each with several folded, strapshaped dark green leaves; white flowers between foliage and having long spurs. *p. 1742*

JUNIPERUS *Cupressaceae (Coniferae)* **C2LBM**

barbadensis (Bermuda, Barbados); tender evergreen tree with branchlets spreading in all directions, needles spiny-pointed and overlapping, pale bluish-green. Junipers form small fleshy cones resembling berries. *p. 839*

chinensis (China, Mongolia, Japan), "Chinese juniper"; erect pyramidal evergreen tree to 20 m high, or sometimes dense with short branches, and leaves of two kinds on the same tree; juvenile in three's, awl-shaped, glaucous above; adult type scale-like in four's, in opposite pairs; glaucous brown, fleshy, berry-like fruit; winter-hardy. Subject in Japan for training into dwarfed bonsai, growing in shallow containers. *p. 844*

chinensis 'Sargentii' (Japan); procumbent variety, used for bonsai culture in Japan, with whorled, scale-like leaves, or linear with white bands below. *Temperate.* *p. 839*

chinensis 'Torulosa' ('Kaizuka'), (Japan), "Hollywood juniper", "Twisted juniper", or "Dragon Chinese juniper"; very artistic irregular growing juniper to 5 m high, branching with an appealing twisted effect; the tiny imbricated scaly leaves rich green on brown stem, the cordlike branchlets somewhat flattened and contorted; cones berry-like 5-7 mm dia., at first blue-glaucous, dark brown later. Fairly winter-hardy. Very decorative as container plant. *Temperate.* *p. 844*

horizontalis (Nova Scotia to Brit. Columbia, Northern U.S.), "Creeping juniper"; popular prostrate evergreen with long rooting branches to 40 cm high, the short flat branches with awl-shaped needles while young, later scale-like and shingled, bluish green; blue-glaucous cones to 1 cm dia. There are many named cultivars differing in habit and leaf color. *p. 842*

sabina 'Tamariscifolia' (So. Europe), "Tamarix juniper"; low spreading evergreen to 50 cm high but 2 m wide, with branches arching out from the center carrying the upward-facing branchlets, with short awl-shaped bluish green needles, scale like near the top; fruit brownish glaucous blue; fairly hardy in colder climate; a favorite for ground cover. *Temperate.* *p. 842*

scopulorum (Brit. Columbia to Colorado and Texas), "Western red cedar"; evergreen tree with stout, spreading branches, leaves coarsely scale-like and glaucous when young, later yellowish green. (h) *p. 839*

scopulorum chandleri, "Chandler's silver juniper"; a beautiful silvery form of the Rocky Mountain red cedar, dense with outward arching, scaly branchlets and of compact, pyramidal habit. *p. 844*

virginiana burkii (Maine to Florida), "Red-cedar"; columnar form of this evergreen tree, with steel-blue short scale-type needles on upright branches. (h) *p. 839*

JURINEA *Compositae* **C2LBD**

species Wats, (Asia Minor); interesting xerophytic subshrub, gray-hairy; notched foliage to 20 cm, on hairy petioles; globe-shaped inflorescence 5 cm dia., filled with small straw-yellow flowers between the long filaments. *Arid-subtropic.* *p. 822*

JUSSIAEA *Onagraceae* **I2LBM**

longifolia (Brazil), "Primrose willow"; erect herbaceous plant to 60 cm with linear-lanceolate leaves; large yellow flowers; usually grown as an annual. *p. 1649*

JUSTICIA *Acanthaceae* **S3HFM**

extensa (Zaire); shrubby plant with small, ovate, fresh-green leaves marked with silver. *p. 49*

flava (C. Sudan: Blue Nile); herbaceous plant sometimes tall-growing, and variable in appearance; leaves elliptic or lanceolate, and the lemon-yellow flowers with large tri-lobed lip in erect slender terminal racemes. *p50*

JUSTICIA: see also Jacobinia, Pachystachys

KAEMPFERIA *Zingiberaceae* **I-S2LFMd**

angustifolia (India, Malaya); low tropical rhizomatous herb with aromatic tubers, small rosette of narrow oblanceolate green leaves; small flowers pale rose-purple with deep purple center. *p. 2140*

atrovirens (Borneo); clustering rhizomatous plant with showy oval or ovate satiny leaves to 15 cm long, dark green, zones with pale grayish green, purplish beneath; flowers with slender corolla tube white, and violet lip spotted yellow. *p. 2136*

brachystemon (East Africa), "Dwarf ginger lily"; tropical clustering plant with tuberous roots, forming rosettes of light green, elliptic leaves 10-12 cm long; pretty flowers from base light blue with white eye, 5 cm across. *Tropical.* *p. 2138*

decora (Mozambique), "Dwarf ginger lily"; a fine, showy ginger growing along the road from Beira to Salisbury; tuberous plant with large leathery, lanceolate leaves glossy dark green, the underside grayish, depressed veins nearly parallel; the channeled petioles lined deep green and clasping; a separate basal stalk bears a raceme of large 8 cm bright canary-yellow funnel-shaped flowers, sweetly fragrant. *p. 2136, 2138*

elegans (Burma); tropical rhizomatous low herb of erect habit, the corrugated broad obovate, fleshy leaves light green of shimmering satin, grayish on back; roundish flowers light purple, white at very tip of tube only. *p. 2139*

ethelae (So. Africa: Natal); floriferous perennial with thick tuberous root, leafy stem to 75 cm high after flowering; lanceolate sessile leaves 10-16 cm long; large solitary flowers from base, with long 5 cm tube, the lobes rose-purple with a yellow blotch; spring-blooming. When leaves turn yellow, plant should have a rest. *p. 2140*

galanga (India); rhizomatous, stemless herb with aromatic, edible tubers and opposite, horizontally spreading, fleshy, roundish, to oblique-ovate leaves shiny green; flowers with two violet bands on lip. *p. 2138, 2139*

gilbertii (So. Burma), "Variegated ginger-lily"; stemless fleshy-rooted herb with tufted, oblong-lanceolate soft-fleshy leaves grass-green, the marginal areas prettily variegated with milky-white, and gray beneath; the flowers on separate stalks with white corolla and long white lip with violet stripes, in summer. *p. 2136, 2139*

grandiflora (Kenya); erect herb with tuberous rhizome bearing a rosette of stalked, shining fresh green, unequal sided, lanceolate leaves with depressed veins, and light blue flowers, appearing before the foliage. *p. 2136, 2140*

involucrata (Sikkim, Assam, Upper Burma); ornamental clustering plant producing offsets freely, long stalked with broad oval, light green leaves prominently ribbed, and pretty whitish flowers marked lilac, in summer. *p. 2136*

masonii (elegans) (Trop. Asia); similar to pulchra, fleshy leaves more upright, blackish coppery with silvery-green; flowers light purple with white eye. *p. 2136, 2138*

pandurata (India, Java), "Aromatic ginger"; from tuberous aromatic rhizome a stemless rosette of ovate-oblong leaves to 25 cm long, smooth green above and downy on midrib beneath; flowers in a stalked spike with white corolla tube 5 cm long and with lobes rose; lip white with rosy-red dots and stripes. Grown in India for its ginger-like rhizome. *p. 2138*

'Pobeda' (K. decora x kirkii elatior); similar to decora but with spikes bearing white flowers; a yellow eye framed by lavender bars; aromatic tuberous plant with large leathery, lanceolate leaves rich green. (Korsakoff, Florida 1969). *Tropical.* *p. 2138*

pulchra (E. Tropical Asia: Burma), "Pretty resurrection lily"; attractive tropical rhizomatous herb with broad, corrugated leaves flat to the ground, a gray band in peacock design over the bronze blade; large 4 cm light purple flowers with broad petals and narrow translucent lip, white eye in center. *Tropical.* *p. 2139*

roscoeana (pulchra) (Burma), "Peacock plant"; stemless plant with fleshy rhizome and wide, fleshy leaves spreading horizontally, beautiful like shining bronzy-chocolate taffeta, iridescently veined and zoned pale green like a peacock tail, purplish and shining gray beneath; fleeting flowers pale purple with white eye, appearing day after day in summer. *p. 2136*

rotunda (Himalaya, India, Sri Lanka), "Resurrection lily"; cultivated in Java and elsewhere in the Orient for its edible tubers and fleshy leaves with deep green feather in center; purple and hairy beneath; white fl. with lilac lip, a "Tropical crocus". *p. 2136*

KALANCHOE *Crassulaceae* ***I2LBD**

ballyi (Kenya, Tanzania); erect succulent with leafy stems, clambering to more than 1 m; the fleshy gray green leaves opposite, oblong spatulate, to 20 cm long, and fuzzy; large clusters of yellow to coral-red flowers. *p.908*

beauverdii (scandens) (Madagascar); climbing plant with very slender, wire-like stems 2 to 3 m long; opposite reddish-brown, narrow leaves 5-8 cm long and to 1½ cm wide, curved reflexed; at leaf tips are adventitious buds giving rise to young plantlets; lax inflorescence with blackish violet, spotted flowers. When I first received this plant it was labeled "Hoya", which it resembles. *p. 908*

beharensis (S. Madagascar), "Elephant ear" or "Napoleon's hat"; woody succulent shrub to 3 m high, with large, broadly arrowshaped, lobed leaves, rich green, but densely rusty-haired above, silver-haired beneath and on leaf stalks; flowers yellowish, violet inside. *p. 901, 907*

beharensis viridis; a variety of the "Felt-bush" which I photographed in Kenya, of robust habit, the knotted branches with thick-fleshy, tough, triangular leaves 20-30 cm long, brown-hairy only while young, later gray-felty over green. *p. 902*

blossfeldiana (globulifera coccinea) (Madagascar), "Flaming Katy"; compact branching plant with small obovate, glossy-green leaves, topped during the short-day season of the year with clusters of bright scarlet red flowers. *Tropical.* *p. 900*

blossfeldiana 'Tom Thumb', a dwarf and very compact "Christmas kalanchoe"; with bronzy foliage, and covering itself during late winter with masses of bright red flower clusters. To encourage budset, place the plant outside for the summer. If flowers are wanted earlier than usual, daylight should be restricted to between 9 or 10 hours during July and August by covering the plant with black paper or a box; for Christmas flowering short-day treatment from early September until buds show. *Subtropic.* *p. 900*

blossfeldiana 'Vivid'; an excellent Dauernheim sport of 'Tom Thumb', of solid habit, with large, succulent, dark green leaves and firm full clusters of good-sized orange-red flowers. (F-B) *p. 900*

blossfeldiana 'Vulcan'; excellent, compact pot plant with waxy fresh-green leaves and a red crenate edge, covered during the short-day winter months with clusters of vivid red flowers; foliage more green and not bronzy as in 'Tom Thumb'. *p. 903*

"crenata" hort.: see mortagei

daigremontiana (Bryophyllum) (Madagascar), "Devil's backbone"; easy-growing robust, erect plant with fleshy, long tricornered brownish-green leaves nicely arched and producing plantlets from the serrate margins, reverse gray flecked purple; flowers gray-violet. *Tropical.* *p. 904, 2092*

'daigremontiana x tubiflora', the "Good-Luck plant"; hybrid with pinkish-brown narrow leaves, channeled on surface, keeled beneath, and spotted and lined purple; plantlets appearing on the toothed margin where they drop off forming masses of young on the ground. *p. 19*, 901, 903*

dyeri (Kenya); in the trade as dawii; large cup-shaped succulent with broad-obovate leaves soft-fleshy, crenate toward apex, light green bluish glaucous with veins faintly pink and margins pink. *p. 902*

'Engleri'; branching succulent to 30 cm high, in the California trade; with wiry stems closely set with light green leaves, margins sharply dentate faintly suggestive of Ilex, and edged in red. See K. serrata. *p. 902*

eriophylla (Madagascar); pretty succulent bush with slender tomentose stems, and thick-fleshy, ovate, sessile soft leaves clasping at base, green, shaded coppery purple mainly at margins, densely covered with long white wool, especially the young growth, and with brown spots toward the apex along edge. *p. 905*

farinacea (Socotra Is.); compact almost compressed succulent with short, mealy-white stem; the thick obovoid, flat or slightly concave leaves 2-3 cm long, pale green and covered with waxy silvery powder, the margins pink; inflorescence a sessile cluster of yellow tubular flowers with red lobes. *p. 910*

fedtschenkoi (Madagascar), "Purple scallops"; bushy succulent with wiry branches erect or creeping, small fleshy leaves notched at apex, metallic green and delicately glaucous amethyst, edged purple; flowers brownish rose. *p. 901, 910*

fedtschenkoi 'Giant'; as known in the California nursery trade; large leafed robust plant similar to the type but much larger—possibly a species but probably a tetraploid; strong stems with heavy leaves to 9 cm long deeply scalloped and bluish-glaucous to purplish, the margins orange-red. Possibly K. waldheimii. *p. 907*

fedtschenkoi 'Marginata', "Aurora Borealis plant"; an attractive sport which I first photographed in Mr. Orpet's garden in Santa Barbara; the pale bluish gray leaves beautifully margined creamy-white flushed with pink. *Tropical.* *p. 64A, 907, 909*

fedtschenkoi 'Rosy Dawn'; exquisite variegated cultivar with fleshy obovate leaves 5 cm long, and with crenate margins, in pastel coloring of cream streaking through the center, pinkish on midrib and edge, glaucous green along sides. *Subtropic.* *p. 910*

'Fernleaf' (beharensis x (possibly) tomentosa), "Fernleaf felt bush"; a moderate-sized attractive California hybrid; fleshy succulent entirely covered with short stiff hairs, with features of the giant K. beharensis but much smaller and more graceful; the thick, triangular lobed leaves doubly dentate, gray-felty with brown edge. *p. 911*

figuereidoi; creeping succulent with erect stems to 20 cm; obovate smooth leaves crowded, 3-5 cm long, crenate toward tip, pale blue-green with purple spots; flowers pale green with the lobes tipped rose. *p. 906*

flammea (Somaliland), succulent plant with few branches, the grayish-green leaves ovate and toothed; inflorescence on rather long, branching stalks with clusters of large scarlet flowers, yellow outside. *p. 900*

flammea 'Yellow'; vigorous succulent with coppery tinted leaves, and a tendency to grow to 45 cm tall like K. flammea, but with canary-yellow flowers. Possibly a hybrid. *p. 900*

gastonis-bonnieri (Madagascar), "Life plant"; loose, fleshy plant with large, lanceolate leaves, pale to coppery green with darker spots, glaucous white, especially young growth, brownish margins as if stitched and toothed; forms young plantlets on foliage. Flowers with corolla tube pale pink. *Arid-tropical.* *p. 904, 909*

grandiflora (E. Africa, India); erect succulent with sessile, obovate toothed leaves to 5 cm long, covered with bluish waxy coating flushed with purple; clusters of yellow flowers. *p. 906*

'Grandiflora hybrid'; a striking, compact-growing cultivar with large clusters of 2 cm flame-scarlet blooms, of a type that won't close overnight as the blossfeldiana varieties tend to do. A number of good hybrids have been created involving blood of K. grandiflora, blossfeldiana, flammea and others. The plant illustrated on pg. 914 is of a small cutting; normally larger and grown under the name 'Surprise' in U.S., but appears identical with the late blooming Swiss 'Grob's Triomphe du Chef', a large-flowered stocky succulent plant of vigorous habit, with shiny rich green, crenate leaves, and long-lasting leathery blooms; normally spring-blooming, but winter-flowering can be induced by short-day treatment. *p. 914*

grayii; branching succulent with large broadly obovate or rounded fleshy leaves, with sides prominently and irregularly crenate, light green and covered with gray bloom. *p. 907*

x kewensis (teretifolia x flammea), "Spindle kalanchoe"; succulent stem with fleshy, grayish-green to coppery, long boatshaped tapering leaves with an occasional fleshy tooth. *p. 904, 908*

laciniata (glaucescens) (Africa, India, Java, China, Brazil); free-growing, variable succulent with erect stem to 1 m, oblong or lanceolate leaves, the upper ones lobed, or pinnatisect; flowers yellow, orange, pink, or red, to 1 cm dia. *p. 905, 911*

lanceolata (Eritrea, E. Africa, Zaire, Angola); hairy succulent, with basal rosette of elliptic olive green leaves, and leafy stems to 35 cm high, the inflorescence in globose cluster of pink flowers. *p. 908*

longiflora (somaliensis in the trade) (Natal); robust leafy succulent with 4-angled stem and stalked oval leaves scalloped toward apex, pale gray-green turning coppery, and edged orange; light orange flowers with spicy fragrance. *p. 904*

longiflora var. coccinea; a variety in which the fleshy, scalloped 6 cm leaves turn into glowing, brilliant crimson during winter; small flowers yellow, on long stalk. *p. 906*

manginii (Madagascar); succulent shrubs with wiry branches loosely set with small 2½ cm thick-fleshy obovate leaves waxy olive green, and terminal pendant flask-like flowers orange red with green calyx. *p. 900, 902*

marmorata (Ethiopia), "Pen-wiper"; stout plant with fleshy, broad obovate leaves pinkish to bluish green, dusted glaucous blue and blotched purple on both sides, margins scalloped; flowers white. *p. 19*, 901, 903, 906*

marnieriana (S. W. Madagascar); subshrubby succulent creeping at the base, later ascending, with thin woody stems to 30 cm long, forming stiff aerial roots; toward upper branches with pairs of rounded leaves 3 cm long, bluish green with red edge and spotted with violet; during the natural short days (winter) with numerous adventitious buds along the margins; large pink flowers on 12 cm stalk. *p. 908*

maughanii (E. Africa); more or less trailing succulent with obovate glossy green leaves, 3-4 cm long; the nodding, tubular-inflated flowers 2½ cm long, deep coral pink outside, inside yellow with coral stripes. *p. 910*

millotii (Madagascar); branching succulent with gray-green spatulate leaves densely covered with short white felt, and arranged crosswise, the upper margins daintily notched; inflorescence paniculate, green tubular corolla with rosy segments. *p. 904*

mortagei (Madagascar); known in the trade as K. crenata, tall branching succulent to 1 m high, attractive with opposite, lanceolate fleshy leaves friendly waxy green, with red doubly crenate margins; stems, petioles and bold midrib thickly covered with white bloom; flowers red. *p. 901, 907*

nyikae (East Africa), "Shovel kalanchoe"; erect succulent with opposite peltate leaves 5 cm long, bluish with red edge; very curious with the basal end turned up, and looking shovel-like with a long handle; stout terminal inflorescence with yellow green flowers tipped rose. *p. 910*

'Oakleaf', "Oakleaf felt-bush", fascinating large tomentose succulent, a bud sport of K. beharensis and resembling it in habit but the gray-felted thick giant 30 cm leaves deeply lobed and laciniately cut. Very attractive sun-plant but requiring elbow-room. *p. 911*

'Orange Triumph' ('S' Gravenmoer's Glorie'), (Grob 1957); a Swiss grandiflora hybrid, very robust, stocky succulent plant 22-30 cm high, with thick ovate, shiny deep green, 6 cm leaves deeply double-serrate and with faint red edge; the showy 2 cm flowers in long-stalked clusters a rosy coral or orange-red, remaining open at night. Normally spring-blooming, it can be timed for Christmas by reducing day length to less than 12 hours beginning in September. *p. 914*

orgyalis (Madagascar); stocky branching succulent with oblong spatulate leaves green to brownish but entirely covered with beautiful silvery tan to metallic bronze felt matting; flowers yellow. *p. 904, 911*

paniculata (So. Africa); shrubby succulent with spoon-shaped obovate, sessile leaves irregularly crenate at margins, waxy gray with pinkish edge. *Arid-subtropic.* *p. 902*

peteri (Tanzania); smooth plant with woody stems to 50 cm high, opposite thin-succulent, oval, bluish leaves, tip rounded and with a few crenate lobes; large inflorescence, with pendant inflated tubes pale yellow. *p. 910*

petitiana (Ethiopia); handsome succulent with erect fleshy stems, the paired ovate leaves bluish green with margins turned up and serrately lobed; branched inflorescence with inflated tubular yellow flowers. *p. 911*

pinnata (Bryophyllum) (India, and other trop. regions), "Air plant"; also known as "Miracle-leaf" or "Curtain plant", because young plantlets are produced from the leaves, even if broken off, and pinned to window curtains; the fleshy foliage 5 to 20 cm long, greyish green and tinged with red, at first undivided oval oblong and notched, in later stages divided into 3 to 5 scalloped leaflets; nodding greenish flowers tinted purple. *Arid-tropical.* *p. 901, 903, 905*

prolifera (Bryophyllum) (C. Madagascar); fleshy succulent to 1 m or more tall, with stalked entire or pinnate leaves; the oblong leaflets 3-5 cm long, glossy green and crenate at margins; sometimes with adventitious buds; tubular yellow flowers; numerous plantlets develop in the inflorescence. *p. 911*

pubescens (aliciae) (Madagascar); succulent, hairy perennial with stems to 1 m, the oval leaves toothed; flowers red-orange, lined red-brown. *p. 902*

pubescens var. alexiana (Madagascar); hairy succulent with opposite fleshy leaves lobed and crenate at margins; the tubular flowers yellowish-red, with 5 red lines in the lobes. *p. 911*

pumila (C. Madagascar), "Dwarf purple kalanchoe"; bushy plant with closely-set obovate leaves notched on upper margin, purplish brown and covered with white bloom; pitcher-shaped red-violet flowers. *p. 904, 906*

quartiniana (Ethiopia, Malawi); succulent perennial to 75 cm with stout stems; smooth broad-elliptic, toothed, glaucous leaves 10-20 cm long; 5 cm white flowers in terminal clusters. *p. 902, 905*

rhombopilosa (Madagascar); beautiful small succulent with branching silvery stems mottled brown; rhombic olive green to coppery brown, fan-like leaves 2 cm long, largely covered with silvery-white scurf, the outer margin beige with acute points; tall inflorescence with small yellow-green flowers lined with red. Falling leaves root easily and soon develop plantlets. *p. 908, 910*

'Roseleaf' (beharensis x pilosa); an attractive Hummel hybrid with stocky stem, triangular, thick, spatulate-pointed, toothed leaves symmetrically arranged as in a cross, with brown felt above, and silver felt beneath; teeth brown. *Tropical.* *p. 904, 911*

'Rotgluth'; good flowering plant from Switzerland, translated 'Red glow', a Grob grandiflora hybrid that comes true from seed; the heavy and broad, rich green leaves crenate at margins; of compact habit and only 25-30 cm above pot; large flat-topped clusters of fiery scarlet 2 cm flowers which stay open at night, unlike K. blossfeldiana. Normally late winter-blooming, this variety may be timed for Christmas by short-day treatment. *p. 914*

rotundifolia (flammea) (So. Africa); branching succulent with slender stems, roundish gray-green, obovate leaves 4 cm long, occasionally lobed, obtuse at apex; small flowers vermillon-red, in large clusters. *p. 906*

scapigera (Trop. Africa: Angola); stout succulent to 40 cm high, dense with ovoid, flat and thick grayish green leaves 2-3 cm long, covered with waxy powder; sessile cluster of tubular red flowers. *p. 910*

schizophylla (C. Madagascar); branching perennial climber with woody base; wiry stems 6 to 8 m long; pinnatisect leaves 8-10 cm long, with narrow segments partially recurved; the branched inflorescence with violet flowers. *p. 908*

serrata ('Engleri' in Calif. hort.), (C. Madagascar); shrubby, smooth succulent with creeping branches, later erect 30 cm or more high, with oval or obovate, bluish-green leaves 4 to 6 cm long, the margins toothed; becoming narrow-elliptic up along the flowering stem, lightly dusted white, and with a few reddish spots; tubular red-orange flowers 3 cm long. *p. 902*

somaliensis: see longiflora

suarezensis (No. Madagascar); shrub to 60 cm high with gray-green leaves 12-15 cm long, irregularly dentate and bearing adventitious buds near apex. *p. 907, 909*

synsepala (C. Madagascar), "Cup kalanchoe"; attractive short-stemmed succulent with cupped, broad oval, fleshy leaves, pale green with purple band inside of marginal teeth; flowers white or light pink. Unique for its sending out young plants on runners from the leaf axils, and also forming plantlets on roots. *Tropical.* *p. 901, 909*

teretifolia (kewensis) (India, Arabia, Madagascar); succulent with shrubby base, stem to 1 m high, corky with age; thick cylindrical gray-green leaves, to 35 and 40 cm long, occasionally forked at tips; light yellow flowers jasmine-like. *p. 908*

tetraphylla (C. Madagascar); broad-leaved succulent related to synsepala but always with 4 or more leaves; these 12-15 cm long, soft-hairy, and lightly toothed; the inflorescence on stout stalks, with showy clusters of bell-shaped rosy flowers. *p. 910*

thyrsiflora (in hort. as "Vertical leaf") (Cape Prov., Transvaal); stem-forming succulent with almost oval leaves flat on the surface, rounded beneath and arranged diagonally, light green with silvery hoary covering, apex flushed red; flowers yellow. *Subtropic.* *p. 907*

tomentosa (pilosa) (C. Madagascar), "Panda plant"; strikingly beautiful succulent with erect branching stem and soft fleshy spoon-shaped leaves entirely clothed in dense white felt, apex dentate and the teeth marked brown; whitish flowers with light brown stripes. *Arid-tropical.* *p. 15*, 19*, 64A, 901, 905, 2092*

tubiflora (verticillata) (Bryophyllum) (Madagascar), "Chandelier plant"; slender erect succulent with pinkish-brown stem with many almost cylindric, pinkish leaves blotched purplish, young plants forming at tips; flowers red. *Arid-tropical.* *p. 901*

uniflora (Kitchingia) (Madagascar); epiphytic creeper, rooting at joints, with small fleshy, obovate, bright green leaves and pitcher-shaped red flowers. *p. 900*

velutina (kirkii) (Angola, Zaire, Malawi, Tanzania, Zanzibar); hairy succulent with fleshy rootstock, creeping branches; the lower leaves ovate and crenate 10 cm long, upper leaves narrower; flowers yellow to salmon. *p. 902*

waldheimii (Madagascar), "Ghost plant"; shrubby, branching succulent, with fleshy, obovate, bluish glaucous leaves notched toward apex, 10 cm long; nodding orange or salmon-pink flowers. *p. 902*

'Yellow Darling' (blossfeldiana x schumacheri), "White kalanchoe"; compact, short bushy plant with waxy light green crenate leaves topped by dense clusters of creamy-white flowers with lemon-yellow center. *p. 900*

KALMIA *Ericaceae* **C2HFM**

angustifolia (E. No. America), "Sheep-laurel"; erect evergreen to 1 m high, of thin, open habit; leathery, fresh green, 6 cm lanceolate leaves usually opposite; small 1 cm saucer-shaped flowers purplish-rose, in axillary clusters, along terminal part of previous season's growth. *p. 959*

latifolia (E. No. America), "Mountain-laurel" or "Calico bush"; thicket-forming evergreen shrub to 3 m or more high, with leathery elliptic, glossy green leaves and large terminal clusters of beautiful pink saucer-shaped flowers marked with purple. *Temperate.* *p. 959*

KALMIOPSIS *Ericaceae* **C2HBM**

leachiana (Oregon); small evergreen shrub 25-40 cm high, dense with woody stems and small leathery, deep green elliptic leaves 1 cm long and somewhat cupped; little rose-colored flowers with red-fleshy calyx; blooming March to May. *p. 959*

KALOPANAX *Araliaceae* **C2LBD**

pictus maximowiczii (Japan, Kuriles, Korea, China); deciduous tree to 25 m high, with thick grayish branches and stout spines; thin-leathery, smooth, dark green leaves palmately lobed, 15-30 cm across, more deeply cut in the variety than in the species; the margins finely serrate and brown pubescent beneath; small whitish flowers in umbels, followed by blue-black berries. *p. 314*

KEFERSTEINIA *Orchidaceae* **I3OFM**

tolimensis (So. Ecuador at 2400 m); lovely little epiphyte with tufted, narrow lanceolate leaves and short-stalked basal 3 cm flowers very pretty, yellowish-green densely covered with small purple spots, broad, fringed whitish lip marked yellow and spotted maroon, darker in center (various—Jan. or June). (I) *p. 1737*

KELSEYA *Rosaceae* **C2LBM**
uniflora (Montana, Wyoming); curious semi-prostrate subshrub 5-8 cm high, forming cushions, from the Rocky Mountains; with overlapping gray-green leathery 3 mm leaves; small white 6 mm flowers. *p. 2000*

KENNEDIA *Leguminosae* **I2LBD**
rubicunda (Australia: Victoria, N.S.W., Queensland), "Coral pea"; strong growing bean-like twiner, the young growth covered with silky brown fur; variable palmate-trifoliate leaves, the leaflets ovate, 5-8 cm long; red pea-shaped, pendulous axillary flowers in pairs, a long standard, or upstanding petal, reflexed upward. *Subtropic.* *p. 1387*

KENTIA: see Howeia, Ptychosperma

KENTIOPSIS *Palmae* **S3LBD**
macrocarpa (Chambeyronia in Hortus 3) (New Caledonia), "Lucian palm"; handsome feather palm with slender trunk to 20 m; open crown with graceful pinnate fronds that may be from 1 to 2 or 3 m long; dark green leaflets prominently ribbed, on yellow petiole, the young unfolding leaves blood-red. Photographed under this name at Botanical Garden Rio de Janeiro, but this may be same as Chambeyronia macrocarpa. *p. 1884*
olivaeformis (New Caledonia); lofty feather palm, with elegant pinnate fronds, gracefully recurving, the broad leaflets glossy green and leathery. *Tropical.* *p. 1884*

KERRIA *Rosaceae* **C2LBM**
japonica 'Aureo-variegata' (China, Japan), "Japanese rose"; ornamental shrub, distinguished by dense, green branches with small ovate, doubly-toothed, shining bright green, thin leaves variegated yellow inward from the margins, the solitary flowers golden yellow. *p. 1995*

KIGELIA *Bignoniaceae* **S2LBD**
pinnata (Trop. Africa: Sudan, Uganda, Kenya, Zimbabwe, Transvaal, Mozambique), "Sausage-tree"; spreading tree to 15 m, with pinnate leaves, and pendant racemes of large, showy flowers with curved tubular-flaring corolla orange-yellow at base, the 6 cm corrugated lobes blood-red; on reverse striped yellow; a curiosity mainly because of the cylindric pale brownish-gray fruit 30-45 cm long, hanging on a cord often to 1 metre long; the Kikuyu make beer with this fruit, adding sugar water and honey. *p. 497, 500, 502*

KIRENGESHOMA *Saxifragaceae* **C2LBM**
palmata (Japan); herbaceous perennial to 1 m, with thin, roundish-cordate, palmately lobed, hairy, toothed leaves to 17 cm long on purple stems; trumpet-shaped, nodding flowers yellow, 10 cm long. *p. 2047*

KITCHINGIA: see KALANCHOE

KLEINIA: see Senecio

KLUGIA *Gesneriaceae* **S3HFM**
notoniana (India: Deccan; Ceylon); herbaceous gesneriad rather succulent to 45 cm, with fleshy stem, leaves oblique ovate to 20 cm long, green above, pale beneath, and numerous nodding tubular two-lipped 2-3 cm flowers gentian-blue with sulphur-yellow throat, the upper lip white; in one-sided raceme. *p. 1254*
zeylanicum (Sri Lanka, Eastern India); branching herbaceous plant of rangy habit, 30-50 cm high, with fleshy stems; alternate oblique leaves to 25 cm long, soft green above, pale beneath; from near the apex a one-sided raceme of numerous, nodding, 2½ cm flowers, the tubular corolla with 2 unequal lips, the short upper lobe white, the broad lower lip rich violet with yellow spot at base, blooming from spring to fall. *p. 1257*

KNIPHOFIA *Liliaceae* **C2LBMd**
multiflora (So. Africa); stout perennial herb with thick roots; strap shaped lax leaves 2 m long, 8 cm wide; small white flowers in dense spikes 2½ m high. *p. 1463*
rufa (Natal), a smaller "Poker plant"; forming perennial clumps of linear leaves 1 cm wide, and 45 cm spikes topped by racemes of drooping flowers, the lower ones primrose yellow, the upper ones tinged red; June to Fall. *p. 1460*
uvaria (Tritoma) (So. Africa), "Torch lily"; stout perennial herb with thick roots, clumps of long grass-like basal leaves, and a showy poker-like 1 m spike of nodding tubular flowers, the upper ones scarlet-red, and lower ones yellow. *Subtropic.* *p. 1460*
zuluandiae (So. Africa); fairly newly discovered species with linear leaves, which sends up stout 1½ m stalks surrounded by masses of orange flame-colored flowers, in mid-winter. *p. 1460*

KOCHIA *Chenopodiaceae* **I2LBD**
scoparia trichophylla (S. E. Europe, Temperate Asia), "Summer cypress", or "Fire bush"; densely branched, ornamental annual with its formal globe or columnar shape resembling cupressus; ½ to 1 m high; subshrub with numerous narrow, partly almost threadlike leaves 5 cm long, fresh green, the type remaining green; this form becoming purplish-red in autumn; tiny green flowers. *p. 777*

KOELLIKERIA *Gesneriaceae* **S3HFM**
erinoides (Venezuela, Colombia), "Dwarf bellflower"; dwarf, delicate, herbaceous, clustering plant having scaly rhizomes; downy, quilted, elliptic leaves velvety green spotted silver, and numerous sprays of tiny, 2-lipped flowers flushed purplish-red, with white lip and throat, blotched yellow and lined red. *p. 1252*

x KOELLIKOHLERIA *Gesneriaceae* **S3HFMd**
rosea (Koellikeria erinoides x Kohleria spicata); small bigeneric herbaceous hybrid to 30 cm high, from scaly white rhizomes to 3 cm long; plant covered completely with translucent hairs; short stem with ovate leaves 4-5 cm wide and dark green, lower surface reddish; margins crenate; the inflorescence in loose racemes with small flowers red outside and white inside, 1½ cm long. *p. 1257*

KOELREUTERIA *Sapindaceae* **I2LBD**
paniculata (China, Korea, Japan), "Golden raintree"; deciduous tree 3-12 m with pinnate leaves, the thin ovate leaflets coarsely toothed and notched, and showy panicles to 45 cm long, of irregular yellow flowers in summer. *p. 2034*

KOHLERIA *Gesneriaceae* **S3HFMd**
allenii (Trop. America); stout stems with large tomentose, lanceolate leaves, and hairy flowers with long inflated red tube, and small spreading lobes yellow with red spots. *p. 1254*
amabilis (Colombia); low growing species with weak stems and scaly rhizomes; small friendly green, hairy, scalloped leaves with red-brown pattern along veins; free-blooming with small bright pink tubular flowers, 3 cm long, dotted carmine-red on limb; good for hanging baskets. *Tropical.* *p. 1252, 1254, 1255*
'Amabilis hybrid' (Isoloma ceciliae); plant of compact habit with lanceolate hairy leaves bronze along veins; tubular rosy-red flowers, red inside marked creamy-yellow. *p. 1255*
bogotensis (Isoloma pictum) (Colombia); erect tropical herb with velvety dark green to brownish-tinged, ovate leaves, pale along the veins, not bordered with reddish hairs; nodding 3-4 cm flowers red above shading to yellow at the swollen lower side of tube, the lower lobes yellow marked deep crimson. *Tropical.* *p. 1255*
'Bogotensis hybrid', a "Tree gloxinia"; plant prostrate when older, the white-hairy leaves are more slender, bronzy-green and lacking pale veins; corolla tube crimson-red changing to white beneath, throat and limb white spotted and lined with red. *Tropical.* *p. 1248A, 1255*
digitaliflora (Isoloma) (Colombia), "Foxglove kohleria"; erect, hairy herbaceous plant with large ovate leaves, and big bell-shaped flowers bulging in lower part, the tube rosy-lavender with white hairs, white beneath, the showy lobes greenish with purple spots. *p. 1253*
eriantha (Isoloma hirsutum) (Colombia); erect, soft-hairy species from scaly rhizome, with deep green, ovate, toothed leaves having a conspicuous border of reddish hairs; orange-red corolla tubes 4 cm long, widening toward the throat which is pale yellow and marked blood red. *Tropical.* *p. 1255*
eriantha 'Columbia'; vigorous erect plant with stems and leaves softly hairy; flowers 4 cm long, warm tangerine red, the upper two corolla lobes red, the lower three yellow and freely marked with red spots. *p. 1253*
'Eriantha hybrid' (Isoloma hirsutum multiflorum); robust plant more floriferous than the species and with more prominently inflated orange-red corolla tube and large, spreading limb, throat and lower lobes yellow and all marked red. *Tropical.* *p. 1255*
hirsuta (Venezuela, Trinidad); hairy plant resembling K. eriantha in habit but with shorter corolla tube, more slender, and with short lobes, red outside, with pale throat. *p. 1254, 1255*
lanata (Trop. America), the "Woolly kohleria"; with stem and crenate, ovate leaves covered with pale hairs, and the tubular flowers with spotted, spreading lobes are like a soft mass of yellow fuzz. *p. 1254*
lindeniana (Tydaea) (Ecuador); erect bushy, pretty plant with beautiful velvety, ovate leaves vivid green changing to copper toward the crenate margin, and a pattern of silvery veins; small white bell-shaped flowers with purple throat; blooming late fall. *p. 1255*
x luciana (Mexican hybrid); tall tropical shrub to 150 cm high, with stout, hairy stem; quilted ovate leaves crenate at margins and with soft ciliate hairs; inflated tubular flowers 5 cm long, outside carmine-rose, the flaring lobes and inside tube lemon yellow with purple spots and stripes. *p. 1253*
'Sciadotydaea' (Sciadocalyx x Tydaea sections of Kohleria); a larger growing upright hybrid of stout habit with ovate, white-downy, green leaves and large flowers with hairy purplish-red tube and spreading limb, the lower lobes greenish-yellow dotted and lined with violet-purple. *p. 1252, 1255*
spicata (Mexico to Northern So. America); distinctive species with erect red-hairy stems which may reach 1 m and more; elliptic, thickish, toothed leaves 5-15 cm dark green and covered with pale hair like velvet, reddish hairs beneath; the hairy, bright flowers borne in a terminal inflorescence, orange-red, the tube inflated in lower part, the 3 lower lobes marked with pale yellow. *p. 1254*
strigosa hort., bot. elegans; (Mexico to Panama); densely and softly pale-hairy branching stems reach 50 to 75 cm and more; elliptic-ovate softly hairy leaves to 15 cm long, dark green above, and reddish beneath, with crenate margins; 4 cm flowers orange-red outside, yellow inside, the lobes yellow and flecked with red, on red stalks. *p. 1253*

tubiflora (Colombia), "Painted kohleria"; robust, tall-growing, hairy plant with large ovate, toothed, unmarked corrugated leaves, and slender cylindrical swollen 2½ cm flowers orange-yellow with yellow faces or lobes neatly dotted red. *p. 1254*

KOPSIA *Apocynaceae* **S2LBM**

fruticosa (India, Malaysia to Philippines), the red-eyed "Shrub vinca"; large tropical evergreen shrub, with opposite elliptic-lanceolate, somewhat leathery leaves 10 to 20 cm long; the vinca-like flowers in clusters, white with crimson center, 5 cm across, blooming in late spring. *p. 138*

ornata (Indonesia: Ceram); attractive flowering shrub widely distributed in the tropics; large leathery, oblong-lanceolate, glossy green leaves; exquisite wheel-shaped flowers blush-white with purple center. *p. 138*

KOPSIA of hort: see Ochrosia

KORTHALSIA *Palmae* **S2LFM**

laciniosa (Burma, Indonesia); climbing, hook-bearing rattan palm to 15 m, cane-like stems 1 cm thick, with pinnate leaves to 1 m, the rachis prolonged into a whip-like part bearing sharp thorny claws; the leaflets broadened toward apex and irregularly cut off. *p. 1882*

LABURNUM *Leguminosae* **C2LBM**

x watereri (alpinum x anagyroides); "Golden chain"; small ornamental deciduous tree from So. Europe, with trifoliate leaves and long pendulous, very showy, 40 cm racemes of rich yellow flowers. *p. 1384, 1386*

LACHENALIA *Liliaceae* **C2LBM(d:su)**

aloides (tricolor) (So. Africa), "Tricolor Cape cowslip"; dainty hyacinth-like bulbous plant to 30 cm high, with two broad linear lanceolate spreading, fleshy leaves dark green and spotted purple; bright, colorful nodding waxy tubular flowers 2½ cm long, the outer segments yellow tipped green, inner ones scarlet-red at tip, much exceeding the outer, on erect fleshy stalk; spring blooming. *Subtropic.* *p. 1464, 1465*

aloides var. aurea; attractive variety with a spike of plain, golden-yellow tubular flowers, the stalk purplish-brown, the leaves fresh green. *p. 1466*

aloides var luteola; waxy tubular flowers yellow, tipped light green; buds red. *p. 1465*

aloides var. nelsonii; compact plant with leaves spotted purple; purplish stalk bearing the nodding orange-yellow flowers. *p. 1465*

aloides var. quadricolor; variety with flowers red at base, greenish-yellow in middle, the outer segments tipped with green and the inner ones with red-purple. *p. 1466*

bachmannii (So. Africa), "White Cape cowslip"; small bulbous herb to 20 cm high, with thick linear, channeled, recurving basal leaves, and short 6 mm bell-shaped flowers with white segments keeled red, in short spikes; spring. *p. 1466*

contaminata (So. Africa); bulbous plant 22-30 cm high, with 6-10 slender channeled leaves becoming terete toward the apex; the small 6 mm flowers in dense racemes, inner segments tipped greenish brown and outer ones often flushed red. *p. 1466*

glaucina (So. Africa); small cool-house spring-flowering plant 15-30 cm high, with strapshaped leaves 2½ cm wide, often spotted, clasping the base of the flowering stalk, with its 2 cm erect white flowers more or less tinged yellow or red. *p. 1464*

glaucina pallida (So. Africa), yellow form of the "Opal lachenalia"; attractive plant 30 cm high, with fleshy leaves; sturdy erect stalk with yellowish-green 2 cm flowers which turn red as they fade. *p. 1465*

lilacina (So. Africa), "Lavender Cape cowslip"; small bulbous plant 10-12 cm high, with sickle-shaped 10 cm basal leaves spotted with purple, and red-brown-mottled stalk with numerous lavender flowers, their outer segments with blue base. *p. 1466*

liliflora (So. Africa); unusual species with cylindrical white flowers 2 cm long, their segments spreading and anthers protruding; basal lanceolate, sickle-shaped leaves with blistered surface. *p. 1466*

mutabilis (So. Africa), "Fairy lachenalia"; dainty plant allied to L. orchioides, but with longer inflorescence, flowers more loosely arranged, at first sky-blue, inner segments later yellowish-green becoming crimson with age, 2 cm long. *p. 1465*

orchioides (mutabilis) (So. Africa); small bulbous, variable plant to 25 cm high, with lanceolate dark green leaves often spotted, and with horny edge; small fragrant, waxy, rounded flowers whitish tinged with red or blue, closely set on the spotted stalk. *p. 1464, 1465*

x pearsonii (L. pendula x tricolor var. nelsonii); New Zealand cultivar, a tall, early-blooming plant with tubular flowers brilliant yellow edged with red, on 45 cm stalks, in mid winter. *p. 1466*

pendula (bulbifera) (Cape Prov.); robust species with broad, succulent leaves, and stout 15 cm stalks with nodding, tubular flowers 3 cm long, deep crimson with yellow, the inner tube which peeps out at tip is green with patches of mauve; winter-blooming. *p. 1466*

purpureo-caerulea (So. Africa), "Purple Cape cowslip"; bulbous plant to 30 cm; with lanceolate, blistered leaves, small 6 mm bell-shaped flowers purplish-blue with protruding stamens. *p. 1466*

rosea (So. Africa), "Rosy Cape cowslip"; small plant to 15 cm high, with solitary broad leaf spotted inside; slender spike of delicate soft pink flowers, varying to maroon. *p. 1465*

rubida (So. Africa); showy species 22 cm high, lanceolate leaves lightly spotted; tubular flowers crimson, on heavily spotted stalk. *p. 1465*

violacea (So. Africa); sturdy, colorful species with long flower-spike to 18 cm, crowded with flowers, these small and rounded, 2 cm long; outside bluish-green, inner segments tipped brilliant purple; stem long and slender and leaves narrow. *p. 1465*

LAELIA *Orchidaceae* **C-I3OFD**

albida (Mexico, Guatemala); small epiphyte; the pseudobulbs with 2 narrow leaves, and wiry stalk bearing a cluster of 5 cm fragrant flowers, delicate lemon-white often tinged with rose, lip pink or white streaked in center with yellow lines. (Nov.-Jan.) *Tropical.* *p. 1748*

albida sulphurea; flowers pale sulphur yellow, tinged light mauve each side of midlobe of lip, with dark purple marks at base. *p. 1743*

anceps (Mexico), known in horticulture as "Amalia"; handsome epiphyte with egg-shaped, angled pseudobulbs to 12 cm high, usually single-leaved, topped by long wiry stems to 1 m high, bearing small clusters of slender, variable 8-10 cm flowers, sepals mostly lilac-rose, the petals slightly darker, lip purplish crimson with yellow throat. (Nov.-Feb.) *p. 1749*

anceps alba (Mexico); very attractive variety with flowers pure white except for shade of yellow in throat. *Subtropic.* *p. 1743*

anceps williamsiana (Mexico); variety with large, pure white flowers, throat orange yellow, lined with crimson. *p. 1743*

autumnalis (Mexico); epiphyte with ribbed, tapering pseudobulbs, and 2-3 leathery, bright green leaves; tall spikes with several fragrant 10 cm flowers, vivid rose becoming pale at base, the lip purple on white base, (Nov.-Jan.). (I) *p. 1745, 1746*

cinnabarina (Brazil); charming epiphyte of compact habit with cylindric tapered 12-25 cm pseudobulbs and usually single-leaved; flower stalks 30-60 cm high, with clusters of 5-8 cm flowers bright orange-red, lasting 6 weeks (March-May, Nov.). *Tropical.* *p. 1749*

crispa (Brazil); epiphyte with tall club-shaped pseudobulbs and solitary leaf; the exquisite, fragrant 10-15 cm flowers in clusters, the narrow, undulate sepals and petals white, the crisped lip purple edged in white, and yellow throat, (July-Aug.). (I) *p. 1747*

dormaniana (Cattleya) (Brazil); epiphyte with thin round stems to 40 cm high and with 2-3 short leaves, spikes with 2-4 attractive, 8 cm flowers, having narrow sepals and petals olive-brown with darker veins, the side lobes of lip rose veined purple, front lobe bright crimson-purple, (autumn). (I) *p. 1746*

x finckeniana (Mexico); supposed natural hybrid of L. anceps x albida;two-leaved pseudobulbs; floral stalks with 4-5 flowers each 10 cm across, creamy white flushed with lavender, lip with yellow blotch and purple veinings. (I) *p. 1745, 1748*

flava (Brazil); small epiphyte with clustered, thin, 1-leaved pseudobulbs, and a slender truss of small golden yellow flowers, 6 cm across, with narrow petals and sepals, and crisped lip, (Jan.-June). *Tropical.* *p. 1746*

furfuracea (Mexico); small epiphyte with pear-shaped pseudobulbs bearing narrow leaves; large 12 cm, pretty flowers orchid-pink with darker lip, fragrant and long-lasting (autumn). *p. 1743*

gouldiana (Mexico); attractive epiphyte with rounded, tapered pseudobulbs with 2 leathery leaves; the dainty 10 cm flowers clustered on slender stalks, sepals and petals light purple and darker crimson at the tips, lip trilobed, deep crimson with yellow throat, (Dec.-Jan.). *p. 1747*

grandis (Brazil: Bahia); beautiful epiphyte distinctive for the color of its large 10-18 cm flowers, sepals and petals coppery-brown, the lip white flushed purple, darker in throat; furrowed stems with solitary leaf (May-July). *Tropical.* *p. 1748*

x harpophylla (Brazil); handsome epiphyte with 1-leaved terete stems to 45 cm high, and topped by a cluster of showy 5-8 cm flowers with lanceolate sepals and petals brilliant orange vermillion and the trilobed lip margined with white. *Tropical.* *p. 1746*

jongheana (Brazil); oval pseudobulbs with 1 or 2 fleshy leaves, 10-12 cm flowers rose-purple, the trilobed lip dark rose-purple with yellow center, its margins crisped (March-April). *p. 1748*

lindleyana (x Brassocattleya) (Brazil); small, vigorous epiphyte, with slender stems bearing 1-2 stiff, linear leaves, inflorescence shorter than leaves, large, waxy, star-shaped flowers blush-white, lip marked with rose-purple, (July). (I) *p. 1746*

lundii (regnellii) (Brazil); small pseudobulbs usually two-leaved; 4-5 cm flowers lilac-rose, with narrow sepals and petals, the lip trilobed; summer. *Tropical.* *p. 1748*

perrinii (Brazil); charming epiphyte with clusters of pseudobulbs topped by solitary leaves; big 12 cm flowers with sepals and petals rose, front of lip deep crimson-purple, throat lemon-yellow (winter). *p. 1745*

pumila (Brazil); variable dwarf epiphyte with small, one-leaved pseudobulbs from a creeping rhizome; single, short-stalked, relatively large, flat flowers usually orchid-lavender, with broad petals and maroon-purple lip, yellow in the throat. *Subtropic.* *p. 1746*

purpurata (Brazil); grand, robust epiphyte with tall, clubshaped pseudobulbs 30 cm or more, and a long, dark green, solitary leaf; the elegant flowers in clusters and fragrant, 12 cm or more across, the narrow sepals and slender petals glistening white, sometimes flushed pink, large lip crimson-purple, with pale yellow throat striped crimson. *Tropical.* *p. 1747*

purpurata alba (Brazil); natural variety with pure white sepals and petals, the lip white also and veined with pale rose; early summer. (I) *p. 1748*

rubescens (acuminata) (Mexico); dwarf epiphyte with oval, flattened pseudobulbs with solitary leaf; a wiry stem to 45 cm tall bearing a small cluster of 5 cm lilac-mauve flowers, lip lemon-white with purple throat, and fragrant. (Sept.-March). *Tropical.* *p. 1746*

rupestris (Brazil); dwarf epiphyte of sturdy habit, with cylindrical pseudobulbs and usually solitary leaves; the flowers 4 cm across, lavender pink with purplish lip yellow in throat (autumn). *p. 1743*

speciosa (majalis) (Mexico); epiphyte with one or two 20 cm leaves topping the pseudobulbs; short-stalked, big, fragrant flowers 15 cm across, sepals and petals rosy-lilac, lip white flushed or streaked with purple toward margin, rather heavy-textured and long-lived (spring). *p. 1745*

superbiens (Schomburgkia) (Mexico, Guatemala); strong epiphyte with spindle-shaped pseudobulbs to 30 cm high and 2 leaves; the inflorescence, in tall spikes 1-2 m high, topped by a cluster of large fragrant flowers with linear sepals and petals, rose-mauve, lip purple with golden throat, (Dec.-Feb.). (I) *p. 1747*

tenebrosa (Bahia to Rio); similar to grandis; showy flower to 16 cm, usually brownish-yellow; lip rosy with purple; fragrant. *p. 1745, 1746*

x LAELIOCATTLEYA *Orchidaceae* **I3OFD**

bella (C. labiata x L. purpurata) (1884); fine hybrid resembling in habit a cattleya; large flowers with sepals and broader petals pale lilac and the lip with broad, wavy lobe of warm purple, with two zones of yellow in throat (Jan.-Feb.). *Tropical.* *p. 1684, 1745*

canhamiana alba (L. purpurata x C. mossiae reineckeana); excellent intergeneric hybrid of robust habit, free blooming with clusters of large elegant flowers, sepals and petals ivory or pure white, with deep violet-purple frilled lip edged white, and a golden throat, (Feb.-June). *Tropical.* *p. 1664A, 1747*

elegans (Brazil) (Cattleya guttata leopoldii x Laelia purpurata); handsome hybrid with fleshy flowers, narrow sepals and undulate petals rose, the trilobed lip pale rose, the midlobe purple-crimson; on stout pseudobulbs. (I) *p. 1748*

'Golden Girl'; a sturdy as well as charming bigeneric hybrid with broad petals flame-red, and darker red, fringed lip (shown in color by Rebecca Northen). *p. 1650*

hassallii alba 'Majestica' (L.C. Britannia x C. warscewiczii); charming bigeneric hybrid with glistening white sepals and broad wavy petals, and bright purplish-violet lip, yellow in the throat and frilled (spring). *p. 1747*

'Queen Mary' (L. C. Lustre x C. peetersii); very large flower in a lovely shade of rose-pink, and an expanded, frilled lip beautifully lined and veined with crimson, and golden yellow along both sides. (I) *p. 1747*

LAGENANDRA *Araceae* **S3LFW**

bogneri (Sri Lanka); interesting small tropical waterside plant with creeping rhizome; fleshy petioles extend into elliptic-ovate, dark green leaves 6-10 cm long, the margins undulate; long-stalked inflorescence featuring an extended rolled-in spathe 8-13 cm long with slender tail, light green or yellowish. *p. 189*

erosa (Sri Lanka); a rare aquatic species found along a tropical river in Palewater Forest; heavy root-stock giving rise to thin, membranous leaves 15-30 cm long, 7-10 cm wide, crisped along the margins; the spathe with inflated base and lanceolate limb 15-22 cm long, striped with white and purple. *p. 226*

koenigii (Sri Lanka); tropical aquatic plant from Singaraja; robust rootstock carries dark green ribbon-like leaves slender at each end, 40-50 cm long, 1-1½ cm wide; small spathe smooth outside, pale green and red-purple. *Humid-tropical.* *p. 226*

meeboldii (India: Mysore, Malabar); tropical bogplant for shallow water, not submerged; creeping rootstock, with broad ovate, fleshy leaves 7-10 cm long, dark green and sometimes spotted with silver, or entirely reddish; spathe cupped below, ending in a long 8 cm tail, wine-red inside, outside greenish to reddish. *p. 226*

ovata (Cryptocoryne) (W. India, Sri Lanka); large tropical waterside plant with thick, creeping rootstock, bearing rosette of lanceolate, fleshy leaves matte grass green, nearly 1 m long with stalk; spathe short and thick-fleshy covered with coarse purplish-red scales. *Humid-tropical.* *p. 226*

thwaitesii (Sri Lanka, Bengal); tropical aquatic plant for shallow water or moist ground, not submerged; strong rootstock with rosette of rather irregular, narrow lanceolate leaves 10-25 cm long, with undulate margin, silvery at high humidity, the central rib very prominent; spathe 5-10 cm long, inflated base and twisted on upper limb, inside purple, outside velvety greenish purple. *p. 226*

LAGENARIA *Cucurbitaceae* **I2LBD**

siceraria (vulgaris) (Trop. Africa to Asia), "White flowered gourd" or "Bottle gourd"; proliferous, quick-growing tropical annual, musky-scented vine with sticky-hairy stem, climbing by forked tendrils, to 10 m or more; broad kidney-shaped downy leaves 15-30 cm wide; showy white, male and female night-blooming flowers 5-10 cm wide, separate but on same plant, usually withering by midday; pendulous fruit very variable 8 cm to 2 m long, hard-shelled. This bottle-shape and other varieties and forms, when ripened and after forming a hard shell, have long been used in Africa and Polynesia as receptacles for food and water; much cultivated in tropical countries with various shapes of fruit; harvested when vines are dry. *p. 931, 934*

siceraria edulis; pendulous, cylindrical edible green fruit 20-30 cm long, and used for cooking, picked before becoming ripe and hard-shelled. *p. 930*

siceraria gourda, a "Ladle gourd" or "Bottle-gourd"; light green, oblong fruit 30 cm long, inflated at base and constricted along center; used for making ladle-spoons, or flasks. *p. 931*

siceraria longissima, a "Snake gourd"; pendulous cylindrical, club-shaped fruit to 1 m long, green and mottled with gray; grown for ornament. *p. 930*

siceraria maxima; a "Gourd" of flattened globular shape, green with pale green bands and marbling down the sides. *p. 930*

siceraria pererima; a "Calabash gourd", with pear-shaped green fruit, the hard shell used in Paraguay and Uruguay as a vessel for drinking mate. *p. 930*

siceraria 'Siphon', "Bottle gourd"; green, flask-shaped pendant fruit grown for ornament, or to make bottles, ladles or spoons. *p. 930*

LAGERSTROEMIA *Lythraceae* **S-C2LBM**

indica (Japan, Korea, China), the "Crape myrtle"; handsome flowering tree to 10 m high, foliage falling annually, the elliptic leaves 2 to 6 cm long; at branch tips the gorgeous clusters of frilled, though scentless flowers pink or purple and resembling crepe-paper, blooming profusely all summer, and fall from August to October; best in hottest or sunniest season. In older trees the bark flakes off to reveal a smooth pinkish inner bark. *Subtropic.* *p. 1522*

indica 'Petite Snow'; large snowball-clusters of flowers glistening white. *p. 1522*

speciosa (India to Australia), "Rose of India" or "Queen's crape myrtle"; in Hawaii as the "Giant crape myrtle"; a beautiful flowering tree to 20 m high; thin-leathery ovate leaves 25 cm long, and clusters of large, very showy flowers with frilled petals, to 8 cm across; colors usually mauve to purple, but in Tahiti have seen trees with flowers in gorgeous clear rose. *Tropical.* *p. 1523*

LAGUNARIA *Malvaceae* **I2LBD**

patersonii (New South Wales, Queensland), the "Pyramid-tree"; of symmetrical pyramid shape, evergreen, 6-15 m high; the young growth scurfy; thick, ovate 10 cm leaves white-scaly beneath; 6 cm axillary, bell-shaped flowers rosy-pink, with 5 recurved petals. *Subtropic.* *p. 1528*

LAMBERTIA *Proteaceae* **I2LBD**

formosa (New So. Wales), "Honey-flower"; evergreen shrub to 2½ m with 2½-5 cm rigid, linear, spine-tipped leaves; bright red tubular, 4-lobed flowers surrounded by colored yellow bracts, in terminal clusters; peculiar horned woody seed pods gave rise to the name "Mountain devil." *p. 1971*

LAMIUM *Labiatae* **C2LFMh**

galeobdolon 'Variegatum' (Québec, C. and E. Europe, to Urals), "Yellow archangel"; rampant creeper with square thread-like, rooting stems covered with appressed pale hairs; nettle-like, opposite, crenate leaves 3-5 cm long, deep green and rugose, prettily zoned and painted with silver; two-lipped yellow flowers, the lower lip marked red. *p. 1347*

maculatum (No. Europe, Russia, Iran); perennial herb with erect square rooting reddish stems, opposite, small 5 cm ovate leaves with crenate margins, rugose and short-hairy matte-green with broad silver band down the middle; small hooded, axillary flowers carmine-red. *p. 1347*

purpureum (Temperate Eurasia); annual herb with reclining stems, ovate, rough, hairy, toothed leaves, and purple-red bilabiate axillary flowers toward ends of branches. *p. 1347*

LAMPRANTHUS *Aizoaceae* **I2LBD**

aureus (Mesembryanthemum) (Cape Prov.), "Orange ice plant"; succulent creeper with brown-barked branches, leaves shortly connate, sides convex, 5 cm or more long, narrowing to a point, fresh-green, with transparent dots; large 5 cm flowers deep, shining orange with yellow center. Naturalized in So. California. *Subtropic.* *p. 61*

comptonii (S. W. Cape Prov.); shrubby, spreading succulent, with stems 15-25 cm high; fleshy green, boat-shaped leaves united at the base, curving sickle-like, 4 cm long; 3 cm flowers pale pink or white, center rosy-purple. *p. 62*

conspicuus (Cape Prov.); succulent shrub with stout, creeping branches, fleshy, 3-angled linear, incurved leaves crowded at ends of branches to 8 cm long, green, often dotted and with red point at end; 5 cm daisy-like flowers purple-red, with cream centers. *p. 77*

emarginatus (So. Africa), "Ice-plant"; branched, succulent plant with woody stem and linear, gray, 3-angled leaves; flowers purplish-red. *p. 64*

floribundum (Cape Prov.), "Rosy ice-plant"; dense ground-hugging creeping succulent with brownish, white-hairy stems, and sausage-like green 4 cm leaves with peach icing; flowers purplish rose, 2½ cm across. *p. 62*

glaucus (Cape Prov.), "Yellow ice-plant"; shrubby succulent with leaves somewhat 3-cornered, blunt, grayish green to blue-glaucous 1-2 cm long; 3 cm flowers glistening bright yellow; popular in California for ground-cover. *p. 62*

lunatus (Cape Prov.); erect succulent shrublet with slender branches; leaves in the short branches curved and 3-angled 1-2 cm long, covered with waxy gray powder; 2½ cm rosy flowers in clusters. *p. 62*

multiradiatus (roseus) (So. Africa); branching, shrubby succulent with keeled, linear, gray-green leaves and daisy-like, pale rose flowers. *p. 64*

productus (Cape Prov.: Karroo), "Purple ice-plant"; freely branching, shrubby succulent, with bluish to coppery, long linear leaves 3-4 cm long; the large 3 cm flowers glistening purple with long rays; popular for planting on steep banks in California. *Arid-subtropic.* *p. 62*

roseus (Cape Prov.: Table Mountain), "Pink ice plant"; spreading succulent, with compressed 3-angled, linear leaves 3 cm long, covered with translucent spots, and large soft pink flowers becoming deeper toward center, and with yellow in center. *Arid-subtropic.* *p. 77*

spectabilis (Mesembryanthemum spectabile) (So. Africa: Cape Prov.), "Red ice plant"; somewhat woody perennial, branching with long prostrate reddish flowering stems; succulent keeled leaves 2-5 cm long, glaucous gray olive; the 4-5 cm flowers gleaming in brilliant color, normally purplish, and with longer leaves. The color forms in the California trade as L. spectabilis are probably hybrids such as the pictured "Red ice plant" in shining crimson; other colors available are pink or rose. Beautiful flowering plants in spring and summer. *Arid-subtropic.* *p. 62*

tricolor (Transvaal), "Copper ice plant"; low creeper with small linear, succulent, glaucous leaves; masses of brilliantly colored daisy-like heads of ray-flowers brick-red to crimson toward apex, with whitish button in center. *Arid-subtropic.* *p. 61*

LANDOLPHIA *Apocynaceae* **I2LBD**

capensis (So. Africa: Transvaal), "Wild apricot"; small shrub with rambling, intertwining stems filled with latex, climbing or rambling to 5 m high; flowers white tinged with red, and sweetly fragrant with jasmine-like perfume; edible orange 4 cm fruit with sweetish pulp. *p. 138*

LANGSDORFFIA *Balanophoraceae* **S3OFW**

malagasica (Madagascar); tropical parasite with glossy green, quilted leaves; the inflorescence 3-6 cm dia. with brownish scales and yellow flowers. *p. 352*

LANIUM *Orchidaceae* **S3OFM**

berkeleyi (Brazil); graceful dwarf epiphyte with pseudobulbs at intervals along the creeping rhizome, leaves in 2's and 3's; terminal erect inflorescence on wiry stem to 15 cm high, with numerous scattered, waxy 2 cm flowers greenish-yellow tinged with copper, sparsely spotted with red (autumn). *p. 1743*

LANKESTERIA *Acanthaceae* **S3LFM**

barteri (West Trop. Africa); tall evergreen herbaceous plant, with opposite ovate-oblong leaves to 20 cm long, white beneath; flowers yellow with orange eye, 2 cm across, in cone-like, green bracted spikes. *p. 49*

LANTANA *Venbenaceae* **C-I2LBD**

camara ('Red-orange') (West Indies), "Shrub verbena" or "Yellow sage"; small hairy shrub with thin-woody, angled branches sometimes prickly, with ovate, toothed, rough-bristly leaves; very floriferous with stiff-erect, small but showy heads of verbena-like flowers, changeable, usually opening pink or yellow, becoming red or orange, and several color combinations may be found on the same plant; summer blooming. *p. 2119*

camara nivea (E. Indies); attractive variety with flowers white, the outer ones becoming bluish, in round clusters, June-October, and earlier in pots. *p. 2119*

montevidensis (Uruguay), "Trailing lantana"; small, downy, spreading shrub with weak, vine-like, pendant branches, used as a ground cover or in baskets; small ovate, rough leaves, a profuse bloomer winter and summer, with pretty 3 cm heads of rosy-lilac flowers. *Subtropic.* *p. 2119*

'Red-orange': see camara

LAPAGERIA *Liliaceae* **C3HNM**

rosea (Chile), "Chile bells"; showy vine with alternate ovate, leathery leaves, and many large 8 cm pendulous axillary bell-shaped flowers, rich rosy crimson, spotted white inside; summer blooming. *Subtropic.* *p. 1467*

rosea var. albiflora (Chile), "White Chile bells"; a variety beautiful in contrast, with the hanging waxy flowers pure milky-white; the long-elliptic leathery leaves grayish green with wavy margins. *Subtropic.* *p. 1467*

LAPEIROUSIA *Iridaceae* **C2LBDd**

grandiflora (Zimbabwe, Mozambique); cormous plant, with leathery leaves and carmine-red tubular flowers with spreading segments 5 cm across, twice the size of laxa. *p. 1336*

laxa (cruenta) (Anomatheca) (Transvaal), "Woodland painted petals"; miniature cormous plant with flat narrow basal leaves, the small flowers on a one-sided wiry raceme, long tubes with spreading lobes bright orange-red with blood-red border; summer blooming. *Subtropic.* *p. 1336, 1338*

LARDIZABALA *Lardizabalaceae* **I2LBM**

biternata (Chile); handsome tall climber, leaves of 3 leaflets dark green, glossy, leathery; flowers purple; male 2 cm wide, in drooping racemes; female about 2½ cm wide, solitary; fruit sausage-shaped, sweet, pulpy, edible, about 6 cm long, dark purple. *p. 1361*

LARIX *Pinaceae (Coniferae)* **C2LBM**

leptolepis (Japan), "Japanese larch"; deciduous coniferous tree with linear needle-like leaves arranged spirally on the young shoots and clustered on the short spurs, light or bluish green; can be grown in pots and trained into miniature bonsai. *p. 840*

LASIA *Araceae* **S3LFM**

spinosa (Malaysia); tropical swamp plant having thick stem with long, spiny leafstalk and variable, matte, green leaf with spines beneath, arrowshape, later with lateral lobes; recurved spathe brown. *p. 226, 285*

LASIANDRA *Melastomataceae* **I2LFM**

macrantha hort. (Tibouchina semidecandra) (So. Brazil), the "Princess flower"; hairy shrub to 8 m high, with brittle, hairy, quadrangular stems, and green oval-pointed, densely hairy leaves to 10 cm long; lovely velvety flowers 5-7 cm across, with 5 large spreading petals brilliant purple to violet, and purplish stamens. See Tibouchina semidecandra. *p. 1557*

LASIANDRA: see also Heterocentron

LASTHENIA *Compositae* **I2LBD**

glabrata (No. California), "Yellow-rayed lasthenia"; semi-succulent annual 15 to 50 cm high, with fleshy, linear leaves 3-10 cm long; the inflorescence long-stalked with yellow ray florets and disk flowers 2-3 cm across. *p. 820*

LASTREA: see Dryopteris

LATANIA *Palmae* **S3LFM**

loddigesii (Mauritius); handsome fan palm 15 m tall, with rough, slender trunk, bearing a large crown of numerous palmate, rigid blue-gray leaves to 1 m across, the deeply cut segments fuzzy beneath, the petioles and leaf veins colored orange. *p. 1882, 1884*

lontaroides (borbonica, commersonii) (Mauritius), "Red latan"; robust, rapid-growing fan palm to 16 m, with gray trunk swollen at base, bearing a large crown of numerous handsome thick leaves palmate fan-shaped, gray-green, and deeply cut, 2-2½ m across; the segments edged with tiny sawteeth, veins and margins tinged with red, fuzzy beneath; the stalks colored orange, thorny when young, the rachis extending into the leaf for 45 cm or more. Highly ornamental. Loves warmth and moisture with good drainage. *Tropical.* *p. 1882, 1883*

verschaffeltii (Mascarene Isl.), "Yellow latan palm"; robust fan palm more than 15 m high, with rough trunk, palmate fronds light green, white tomentose beneath, with thin yet rigid segments, long-pointed; petiole yellow. *Tropical.* *p. 1882*

LATANIA: see also LIVISTONA

LATHYRUS *Leguminosae* **C2LBM**

odoratus (Sicily), "Sweet pea"; annual, tendril-climbing herb with brittle, winged stems, paired oval leaves, and large, sweetly fragrant, butterfly-like 4 cm flowers originally purple, but now hybridized into many delicate pastel tints. *Subtropic.* *p. 1386*

odoratus 'Late Spencer'; a race of large-flowering, fragrant sweet-peas, developed in England beginning in 1904, with the standard (top) petal ruffled or wavy; this type is most commonly used for garden planting, but also flower in the greenhouse for spring if sown in September; in all colors except yellow, from white through rose to purple and blue. *p. 1386*

LAURENTIA: see Isotoma

LAURUS *Lauraceae* **•C2LBM**

nobilis (Asia Minor, naturalized in So. Europe), "Sweet bay", or true "Laurel"; evergreen, pyramidal aromatic tree, very leafy, with elliptic, stiff thin-leathery 8 cm leaves dark green and lightly crimped, and small, inconspicuous greenish-yellow flowers; much grown in tubs and clipped into formal shapes, mainly in Belgium. The leaves are used in cooking and seasoning. *Subtropic.* *p. 1359, 1360*

LAVANDULA *Labiatae* **I2LBD**

canariensis (Canary Islands); aromatic herb with erect branches, opposite, dissected, fragrant leaves, and long-stalked spikes with tubular bilabiate flowers, the upper two lobes blue with deep blue spots, the lower 3 petals violet. *p. 1354*

officinalis (spica) (Mediterranean reg.), "English lavender"; aromatic subshrub with square stems with narrow linear leaves white tomentose when young; spikes of fragrant purple-blue flowers in late summer. Use: medicinal, in perfumes, soaps, sachets; moth prevention. *p. 1349*

stoechas (So. France), "French lavender"; gray-tomentose tender perennial shrub with gray green linear leaves and spikes of dark purple flowers. Use: flowering tips for perfumes, scented sachets; young tips for flavoring in jellies and beverages. *p. 1348, 1350*

LAVATERA *Malvaceae* **I2LBD**

bicolor (So. France), "Tree-mallow"; shrubby plant to over 1 m high, covered with gray hairs; leaves lobed maple-like; wide open flowers white or rose with purple veins from deep purple base, about 4 cm across. *p. 1532*

maritima (Malvastrum) (So. Europe); shrub to 60 cm high; angled hairy leaves with crenate margins; showy, axillary flowers white with purple lines toward base of petals. *p. 1532*

trimestris (Mediterranean), "Tree-mallow"; rough-hairy annual herb 1-2 m high, with lower leaves nearly round, upper ones angled or trilobed and toothed; showy axillary, solitary saucer-like flowers 6-10 cm across, rosy with darker veins. *Subtropic.* *p. 1528*

LECANOPTERIS *Polypodiaceae (Filices)* **I3HFM**

carnosa (Malaysia: Perak, Sumatra, Java to Philippines); curious small epiphytic fern with fleshy, hollow rhizome inhabited by ants, bearing fronds 30 cm long on swollen knobs, the thin-leathery leaves pinnately lobed, growing at altitudes from 1000 to 1800 metres on large trees. *p. 1083*

LECYTHIS *Lecythidaceae* **S3LBM**

zabucajo (Guyana), "Paradise nut" or "Sapucaya nut"; known in commerce as paradise or cream nuts, are about 8 cm long and are better tasting and more delicious than the better known Brazil nut; small tree with 18 cm leaves, white flowers. *p. 1361*

LEDENBERGIA: see Trichostigma

LEEA *Vitaceae* **S3LFM**

amabilis (Borneo); beautiful little tree with alternate long leaves each set with several pairs of lanceolate, bronzy-velvet, toothed leaflets, red while young, with clear white stripes along the nerves, strikingly contrasting with the red midrib. *p. 2126*

coccinea (Burma); willowy shrub with long, 3-pinnate leaves of scattered, lanceolate, glossy green leaflets, with margins wavy or recurved and dentate; the small flowers in a large, flat-topped cluster, scarlet red in bud, the spreading corolla lobes pink; starts flowering when small. *p. 2126*

roehrsiana (sambucina) (New Guinea); showy small tree introduced by Sander 1899, with erect stem and large, elegant, pinnate or 3-pinnate leaves to 1 m long, the ribbed leaflets are bronze-green with red veins, wavy-margined and toothed. *p. 2126*

rubra (India, Burma, Malaya); evergreen shrubby herb with dark bronzy, pinnate foliage, and clusters of flowers opposite the leaves, brick-red; when open the petals are pink inside, red outside; the fruit a small berry. *Tropical.* *p. 2124*

LEIOPHYLLUM *Ericaceae* **C2HBM**

buxifolium (U.S.: New Jersey to Florida), the "Sand-myrtle", low evergreen shrub to 20 cm with tiny 2 cm glossy leathery leaves, and small flowers of 5 spreading petals, with white corolla tipped pink, in terminal clusters. *p. 960*

LEMAIREOCEREUS *Cactaceae* **·I2LBD**

aragonii (Costa Rica); the only columnar cactus in Costa Rica, to 6 m; dark green with glaucous bands at intervals of growth; 6-8 high rounded ribs, short spines; flowers white. *p. 652*

beneckei (C. Mexico), "Silver tip" or "Chalk candle"; slender cylindrical column to 3 m, usually unbranched, heavily coated with waxy powder, ribs 5-9 very knobby, few spines; flowers rose to white. *p. 620, 640, 652*

chende (Heliobravoa) (Mexico); branching tree type of sparry habit, to 6 m, slender column, glaucous green, 7-9 fleshy ribs, yellow spines turning gray; small rose flowers. *p. 654*

chichipe (Mexico); treelike to 5 m, much branched, trunk to 1 m, stout columns, 9-12 ribs, gray spines; small yellowish-green flowers. *p. 640, 649*

dumortieri (Central Mexico); lush green column with 5-6 acute ribs, set with fine cream needle spines, becoming tree-like to 15 m high; funnel-shaped flowers white inside. *p. 618, 652*

hollianus (Puebla); slender column 5 cm thick, freely branching from the base, grayish green, with 8-10 angular ribs, areoles with hairlike white radials and thin red-brown needle spines; flowers white. *p. 652*

humilis (Colombia); Britton-Rose: Lemaireocereus, Backeberg: Armatocereus; weak-stemmed, forming thickets, dark green, 1 to 4 m long, 4 cm dia., with 3 or 4 ribs, more or less interrupted, white-felted areoles and small cluster spines; flowers greenish-white, 6 cm long. *p. 658*

longispinus (Guatemala); erect, rather stout column light green, the young growth glaucous, 6 ribbed and set with stiff gray spines to 8 cm long. *p. 644*

marginatus (Pachycereus) (Central and So. Mexico), "Organ-pipe cactus"; beautiful column cactus tree-like, or branching from base, to 8 m tall; slender, smooth green stems to 12 cm thick, with 5-7 ribs and gray spines; bell-tubular flowers 5 cm long, red outside, greenish-white inside; globular orange fruit 4 cm dia, with reddish flesh and black seed. Often planted in Mexican villages as a natural fence. *Arid-tropical.* *p. 640, 652, 657*

marginatus gemmatus (Pachycereus); smaller than the type, areoles white with few spines. *p. 654*

martinezii (Mexico: Sinaloa); trunk-forming tree to 5 m high, emerald green column with 9 high but somewhat rounded ridges, the scattered areoles set with black-brown tufts and almost black spines. *p. 652*

pruinosus (Mexico); column, becoming tall, dark green but attractively glaucous-gray when young, with 4-5-6 high ribs and few blackish spines; small white flowers tinged pink. *p. 640*

stellatus (So. Mexico), in the trade as "treleasei"; pretty, slender columns to 3 m high, branching, pale bluish-green, 8-12 ribs, short white spined; flowers red, borne at the apex; edible fruit known in Mexico as "Joconostle". *Arid-tropical.* *p. 616, 640, 652*

thurberi (Arizona, Mexico), "Arizona organ pipe"; forbidding-looking columns with 12-17 acute ribs, dark green to grayish, the dense areoles with black cushions and clusters of stiff spines gray to black; branching from the base and becoming 6 m high; dayblooming, purplish flowers with white margin. *Arid-subtropic.* *p. 652, 658*

treleasei (Mexico); stout column to 6 m, scarcely branched, closely ribbed and covered with short yellow spines; flowers pinkish. *p. 653, 657*

weberi (Sierra Madre of Oaxaca and Puebla, Mexico), "Candelabra cactus"; magnificent much branched tree to 10 m high, columns glaucous dark green, 10-ribbed, set with short and sharp gray to black spines; flowers white and brown hairs, to 10 cm long; orange-red fruit 8 cm long and edible. Backeberg refers this to Pachycereus, which see. *p. 640*

LEMNA *Lemnaceae* **I2-3(water)B-FW**

minor (Temperate and Subtropical No. Hemisphere), "Duckweed"; small floating perennial aquatic herb without stems, and consisting of one minute frond or thallus to 6mm long and one unbranched root; they cohere by their edges in two's and three's, and new fronds will grow out of the edge of old ones; in autumn they fall to the bottom of a pool and rise in the spring. *Subtropic.* *p. 1362*

perpusilla (Eastern U.S.), aquatic "Duckweed"; small floating green leaf-like, rounded bodies, with tiny flowers consisting of only a stamen or a pistil; on the surface of ponds or aquaria. *p. 1362*

trisulca (World-wide, even Lapland), the "Star duckweed"; three-furrowed duckweed, an underwater species; lanceolate structures, bright green, 2-10 mm long, occurring in colonies; central root on the underside. *p. 1362*

LENOPHYLLUM *Crassulaceae* **I2LBD**

guttatum (Sedum) (Mexico: Saltillo; Texas, So. California), "Basin-leaf"; pretty, suckering succulent with thick stem, and obovate spatulate 4 cm leaves, olive green-gray and scurfy, and covered with fine dots and stripes of black-brown, the margins folded upward to form a concave trough; an elongate leafy stalk topped by light yellow flowers with thick sepals. *p. 913*

LEOCHILUS *Orchidaceae* **S3OFM**

'Mexican species' (Mexico); tiny epiphyte, waxy flowers with cupping petals and lip, coppery bronze over cream (A. Hawkes). *p. 1743*

LEONOTIS *Labiatae* **C-I2LBM**

leonorus (So. Africa), "Lion's ear"; tall perennial with light green, soft pubescent, crenate, elliptic leaves; the 2-lipped, orange-red, downy flowers in dense showy whorls, during winter. *Subtropic.* *p. 1353*

LEONTICE *Berberidaceae* **I2LBD**

leontopetalum (Greece to Iraq); herbaceous plant with tuberous rhizome, 30-45 cm high; pinnatisect fleshy leaves, the glaucous-green segments to 4 cm long; stalked inflorescence with elongate raceme of yellow flowers with showy sepals and golden anthers, in spring. *p. 495*

LEONTOPODIUM *Compositae* **C2LBD**

alpinum (Alps, Pyrenées, Himalaya), "Edelweiss"; low tufted woolly perennial herb which I found even in Central Asia in view of Mt. Everest, the star-shaped floral bracts very pronounced silvery-white at high altitudes. *Temperate.* *p. 805, 819, 827*

LEPANTHES *Orchidaceae* **S3OFW**

pulchella (Jamaica); small cluster-forming epiphyte with slender secondary stems supporting a single 2 cm leaf at apex; from the base the flower spikes with minute blossoms less than 1 cm across, complex and colorful but short-lived, greenish-yellow and crimson-red (all year). *Tropical.* *p. 1744*

wagneri (Venezuela); tiny plant with slender stems bearing leathery almost circular leaves and tiny 5 mm flowers with translucent greenish sepals, the petals and lip pinkish and old gold, with crimson-red in center. *p. 1744, 1750*

LEPANTHOPSIS *Orchidaceae* **S3OFM**

astrophora (Pleurothallis) (Venezuela); miniature epiphyte without pseudobulbs; 2 cm leaves on long petioles; raceme of minute, starry 5 mm flowers whitish and crimson, almost black, on erect hair-like zigzag spikes. *p. 1744*

LEPIDOZAMIA peroffskyana: see Macrozamia

LEPISMIUM *Cactaceae* **S2HFM**

cruciforme (Pfeiffera) (E. Brazil), "Tree-and-rock cactus"; branching cactus with angled stem 2-2½ cm thick, waxy green tinted purple, the areoles sunken in margins set with tufts of white hair-spines; small white flowers tipped pink; fruit red. *Tropical.* *p. 738, 741, 746, 747*

cruciforme var. anceps; variety with more elongate fruit than the species, reaching dia. of 10 mm; the stem edged in red. *p. 746*

cruciforme var. cavernosum (E. Brazil); sparingly branched creeping epiphyte, j ints flat or 3-angled, narrowed to a round stem at the base, deeply notched; areoles with a tuft of wool and gray bristles; flowers at areoles on the sides, with 9 petals, bell-shaped, outer petals greenish, inner petals white; fruit purple. *p. 746*

cruciforme myosurus (Brazil, Argentina, Paraguay); rhipsalis-like epiphyte with flattened, pendant stems, coarsely crenate at margins, 2-3 cm wide, green with wine-purple margins and prominent tufts of white hairs in indentations, from which emerge the small 2 cm flowers with white petals tinged pink, opening in the morning and closing at night. *p. 739*

megalanthum (Rhipsalis) (Brazil); slender cylindrical, branching dull green stems spotted purple, erect at first, later pendant, 8-10 mm thick, covered when young with thick white silk; large keeled flowers 4 cm wide, yellowish-white; fruit white or pink. *p. 738*

neves-armondii (Rhipsalis) (Brazil: Rio); stout cylindrical, branching, pendant stems 8-10 mm thick, deep green, with whitish spreading flowers, and small (10 mm) globular red fruit. *p. 738*

puniceo-discus (Rhipsalis) (Brazil); pencil-like pale green, freely rooting stems, branches in terminal whorls; flowers white, and variably colored fruit, from red and vermillion, passing with age through rose toward orange-yellow. *p. 738, 739*

trigonum (Rhipsalis) (Brazil: São Paulo); branching epiphyte with aerial roots; pendant slender, glossy-green stems 1 m or more, compressed 3-angled, changing position at each zigzag joint; flowers white; small flattened rosy fruit. *p. 738*

tucumanense (Rhipsalis) (Argentina: Tucuman); epiphyte much branched, the stems usually pendant, when young nearly cylindrical, bright green with red spot at areoles, later angled or furrowed and yellowish-green; flowers pink; flattish fruit white tinged red. *p. 738*

LEPTOCHILUS *Polypodiaceae (Filices)* **I-S3HFM**

cantoniensis (Kwangtung, China); pretty fern with creeping rhizome covered by black scales, the leaves on 5-8 cm green stalks; sterile, barren fronds 5-8 cm long, broad ovate, green and firm-textured, undulate and with rounded lobes all around the sides, the narrow fertile fronds 8 cm long and only 1 cm wide. *p. 1112*

zeylanicus (So. Asia, Mauritius, Borneo); small tufted fern with creeping rhizomes; two types of fronds, the sterile ones lobed, oak-like, the small fertile leaves on slender, hairy stalks and 3-lobed leaflets. *p. 1113*

LEPTOCHITON *Amaryllidaceae* **I2LBMd**

quitoensis (Pamianthe) (Ecuador); bulbous plant with glabrous, linear leaves 30 cm long, and solitary flower with a green tube and long-linear white segments, the large corona broadly funnel-shaped and serrate at edge. *p. 118*

LEPTOPTERIS *Osmundaceae (Filices)* **I3HNM**

barbara (Todea) (New Zealand, Australia, Tasmania, So. Africa), "Crape-fern"; handsome dark green fern of rather primitive nature, without breathing spores (stomata), and its sporangia all ripen at once; lacily cut bipinnate, very delicate fronds 1 m long, on strong 30 cm square stalks. *p. 1082*

superba (New Zealand), the "Prince of Wales plume"; considered the most beautiful fern in New Zealand; we found this species hiding in wet calcareous sink holes deep in dense mountain forest near Nelson on South Island; from a stout rhizome rise shimmering deep green, plume-like tripinnate fronds from 45 cm to 1 m long, on woolly-hairy stalks; thin and membranous leaflets steeped in moisture and densely arranged and overlapping feather-like. Orchid growers have used the fibrous roots as potting medium, although it takes hundreds of years to form a large caudex. *p. 1082*

LEPTOSPERMUM *Myrtaceae* **I2LBD**

scoparium (Australia, New Zealand), "Manuka" or Tea-tree"; an attractive flowering shrub which may grow to 6 m high, the young growth silky, dense with tiny rigid sharp pointed leaves under 1 cm, dotted with fragrant oil glands; and numerous small white or rosy axillary flowers amongst the foliage, in summer. *Sub-tropic.* *p. 1613, 1614*

scoparium 'Ruby Glow', "New Zealand tea tree"; excellent cultivar of compact habit, with age growing to 2 m or more; tiny dark needle-like foliage, and semi-double, crimson red flowers with dark center, 2 cm across, in great profusion. *Subtropic.* *p. 1605, 1608*

LEPTOTES *Orchidaceae* **I3OFD**

bicolor (Brazil, Paraguay); small epiphyte with short stems on creeping rhizome and a solitary round, channeled leaf; the fragrant flowers with narrow white sepals and petals, lip trilobed and white, purple in center, (Jan.-March). (I) *p. 1749*

bicolor alba (Paraguay); epiphyte with stem-like pseudobulbs and fleshy terete, grayish leaves grooved on one side; short inflorescence from base, with fragrant, waxy long-lasting 5 cm flowers pure white in the variety, with magenta rose lip in the species. *p. 1744*

unicolor (Brazil); miniature epiphyte of tufted habit, with a single 10 cm fleshy leaf tinged or flecked with purple; short inflorescence with nodding, fragrant 4 cm flowers vivid rosy-violet (winter). *p. 1744*

LESCHENAULTIA *Goodeniaceae* **I2LBD**

laricina (Western Australia); ornamental, much branched shrub 30-50 cm high, with heath-like crowded, grayish green needle-like leaves 1 cm long; in the upper leaf axils the 3 cm flowers with split tube and oblique corolla with spreading lobes, in a variety of colors from white or lilac to rich red with yellow base. *Subtropic.* *p. 1318*

LEUCADENDRON *Proteaceae* **C-I2LBW**

adscendens (So. Africa: Cape Prov.), "Geelbos"; low-growing shrub with thin, woody branches and long narrow leaves, attractively bright yellow near the small floral cones. *p. 1976*

argenteum (So. Africa), "Silvertree"; beautiful, eye-catching tree to 10 m high, the branches dense with clasping, pointed leaves to 15 cm long, thickly covered with silvery pubescence which glistens like shining silver in the sun; globular flower heads yellow. *Subtropic.* *p. 1968, 1971*

daphnoides (So. Africa: Cape Prov.); handsome compact shrub to 1 m high, of delicate appearance; narrow leaves becoming quite red around the flower head; the globular terminal inflorescence like a ball of golden-yellow stamens on male plants, surrounded by chrome-yellow bract leaves. *p. 1976*

discolor (Cape Prov.), "Flame gold-tips"; striking, erect evergreen shrub, with narrow, gray-hairy leaves, and blooming at the tips of each branch; the flowers with obovate golden-yellow bracts tinged with red, in bright mahogany-red, cone-shaped inflorescence in the male plant, on the female plant the bracts are flushed with green. *p. 1970*

grandiflorum (Cape Prov.); spreading shrub 1 m high, with willow-like smooth leaves 8-20 cm long, edged in red; the inflorescence fist-size, egg-shaped artichoke-like; the female cone is reddish, ending in silvery-white tips, and the bract-leaves flushed deep rose. *p. 1971*

salignum (So. Africa: Cape Prov.), "Narrow gold-tips"; large bushy shrub to 2 m with narrow leaves 8-10 cm long, turning bright yellow at tips when coming into bloom; the inflorescence like a golden cone in a basket of tongue-like yellow bracts. *p. 1971*

stokoei (So. Africa: Caledon); dense smooth shrub with woody branches, obovate, leathery leaves 5-10 cm long; the male (2½ cm) inflorescence surrounded by sticky brown bracts. *p. 1971*

venosum (So. Africa); slow-growing small shrub to 1 m with smooth, lanceolate leaves 9 cm long; the male and female plants are both quite colorful with their rust-red and green bracts, the staminate heads 2½ cm across. *p. 1970*

LEUCAENA *Leguminosae* **S3-2LBD**

glauca (Tropical America, naturalized elsewhere in tropics), "Wild tamarind"; tree to 9 m with brown stems; leaves 2-pinnate; leaflets in 10 to 20 pairs, glaucous beneath; flowers lemon-yellow in globose, fluffy heads about 3 cm across, stamens 3 times as long as petals. *Tropical.* *p. 1385*

LEUCHTENBERGIA *Cactaceae* **I-S1LFD**

principis (Mexico), the "Prism cactus" or "Agave cactus"; to 20 cm high, a very different type of small cactus with a parsnip-like root and the elongated tubercles looking like triangular fleshy grayish-green leaves as in Agave but with the tips cut off and bearing grayish wool and angular papery spines; fragrant yellow flowers near the center, borne at the tip of new tubercles. *Arid-tropical.* *p. 694, 702*

LEUCOCORYNE *Amaryllidaceae* **C2LBMd**

ixioides (odorata) (Chile), "Glory-of-the-sun"; originally in the Liliaceae family but now included with the Amaryllidaceae; small bulbous plant, with many linear basal leaves, and stalks 30-45 cm bearing umbels of lavender fragrant flowers with 1 cm tube and flaring lobes pale blue to light purple. *p. 1467*

LEUCOCORYNE: see also Brodiaea

LEUCOJUM *Amaryllidaceae* **C2LB-FMd**

aestivum (Europe, No. Africa), "Giant snowflake" or "Summer snowflake"; small, bulbous plant with basal leaves; nodding, bell-shaped, white flowers tipped green, the 6 segments of even length; in late spring. *p. 113*

LEUCOPHYLLUM *Scrophulariaceae* **I2LBD**

texanum (Texas: Rio Grande Valley); evergreen, loose-growing gray shrub 1-3 m with small obovate 2½ cm leaves silvery white-woolly beneath; axillary bell-shaped 5-lobed 2½ cm flowers with violet -purple corolla. *p. 2054*

LEUCOSIDEA *Rosaceae* **I2LFM**

sericea (So. Africa); shrub or small tree, found along streams in Transkei or Natal usually at over 1200 m with deeply lobed foliage; the flowers in compact, candle-like axillary racemes. *p. 2000*

LEUCOSPERMUM *Proteaceae* **I2LBD**

bolusii (Paranomus reflexus) (Cape Prov.), "Pincushion-plant"; large shrub to 2 m with gray-downy brown branches; 9 cm oblanceolate hard-leathery, clasping leaves toothed or notched at apex; light orange flowers crowded together, and with protruding, ray-like colored styles, in terminal pincushion heads. *p. 1970, 1976*

buxifolium (S. W. Cape); sparry shrub to 1½ m high, with grayish, shingled small leaves entirely covering the branches; small white 2 cm flower heads in groups of three. *p. 1978*

candicans (So. Africa: Cape Prov.), "Yellow pincushion"; neat bushy shrub to 1½ m high; broad oval dove gray leaves becoming narrower toward the apex, topped by small yellow flower heads grouped into flat-topped tufts, with a scent of honey. *p. 1978*

catherinae (Cape Prov.), the "Catherine wheel"; handsome shrub with stiff, gray, lanceolate leaves edged red, and terminal head of flowers with spreading flesh-colored filaments reddish near tips. *Subtropic. p. 1978*

conocarpum (Cape Prov.), "Cripple-wood"; showy shrub with gnarled wood, crowded broad leaves, and golden yellow flowering cone. *p. 1972*

ellipticum (spathulatum) (S. W. Cape); neat spreading bush with broad green leaves; dome-shaped inflorescence 10 cm across, with long glossy orange incurving styles in pincushion heads. *p. 1976*

lineare (So. Africa); low bush with scattered linear, thin leaves 8-10 cm long; flowers yellow and red in rounded head 10 cm across, and with long incurving styles. *p. 1970, 1978*

nutans (So. Africa: S.W. Cape), "Nodding pincushion"; beautiful bush about 1 m high, of low spreading shape, dense with small 8 cm tough-leathery, concave, gray green sessile leaves, and a showy, symmetrical inflorescence, the flowers curled tightly in the center like a pincushion, 10 cm across, with long curving, waxy styles varying in color from yellow to orange, or pinkish; the heads sometimes nodding to one side, and lasting for about one month. *Subtropic. p. 1972, 1978*

prostratum (So. Africa), "Creeping pincushion"; low creeping shrub with densely matting, long wiry branches set with needle-like leaves, and masses of small round heads of ball-like flowers looking like strawberries, 4-5 cm across, from lemon to deep orange and red as they mature, resulting in a variety of colors at one time. *Subtropic. p. 1970*

reflexum (So. Africa), the "Rocket-pincushion"; strikingly beautiful gray-downy shrub which can become 4 m high; the branches densely and regularly set with small obovate silvery leaves 6 cm long and becoming shorter toward the brilliant terminal head of salmon tubular flowers with yellow base, exceeded by the showy 8 cm long, thread-like glossy scarlet styles and stigmas, which become reflexed and look like a rocket with red streamers. *Sub-tropic. p. 1970, 1978*

tottum (Cape Prov.), "Fire-wheel pincushion"; round-shaped woody shrub to 2 m high, literally covered with flower heads, of 8-10 cm dia., with reddish-orange stigmas arranged like a pincushion with dark heads; small dark green leaves arranged regularly around the stem. *p. 1978*

LEUCOTHOE *Ericaceae* **C2LFM**

catesbaei (fontanesiana) (Eastern U.S.: Virginia to Georgia), "Sweet bells"; evergreen shrub to 2 m with glossy dark green, leathery lanceolate leaves, the young branches red; small cylindrical 6 mm white flowers in crowded clusters; fairly hardy. *p. 960*

catesbaei 'Girard's Rainbow'; colorful cultivar with its shining deep green leaves striped and blotched with pink and spotted white; the young leaves are red-brown. *p. 960*

LEWISIA *Portulacaceae* **C2LBD**

brachycalyx (Utah, N. Mex., Arizona, California); fleshy perennial herb with thick, sturdy roots, basal oblanceolate 8 cm leaves in a rosette glaucous green; solitary 3 cm flowers pure silky white, in May. *p. 1961*

cotyledon (No. California, So. Oregon); beautiful rosette with thick, starchy roots, and spatulate fleshy, green 8 cm leaves; lovely flowers of white petals veined rosy-red and spreading wide to 3 cm across, in late spring. Often difficult, needing excellent drainage. *p. 1962*

howellii (Western U.S.: Oregon); perennial herb with oblong persistent leaves in a rosette, and handsome deep rose flowers of spreading sepals and petals in clusters on stalks to 15 cm high. *p. 1952, 1960*

rediviva (Western U.S.), "Bitter-root"; perennial herb with fleshy rootstock; linear, fleshy leaves 3 cm long, deciduous after blooming, large solitary flowers rose or white with red veins, 3 cm long, on 5 cm stalks. *p. 1962*

LEYCESTERIA *Caprifoliaceae* **I2LBD**

formosa (Himalayas), "Himalaya-honeysuckle"; to 2 m, with glaucous hollow branches, ovate leaves 5-18 cm long, grayish-downy beneath; the tubular 5-lobed 2 cm purplish flowers from between showy purple bracts, in drooping spikes. *p. 755*

LIBERTIA *Iridaceae* **I2LBM**

formosa (Chile); perennial herb with fibrous roots, the numerous rigid, flat, blue-green leaves arranged fan-like; white flowers with spreading segments, clustered in axils of sheathing bracts, on erect stalks; May-blooming. *p. 1330, 1331*

grandiflora (New Zealand); perennial herb with short creeping rhizome and fibrous roots; numerous linear leaves crowded at base of stem, 2-ranked and rigid; tall stems to 1 m with 2½ cm flowers clustered in axils toward top, white, the outer segments greenish; summer. *p. 1335*

LICANIA *Chrysobalanaceae* **S3LBD**

tomentosa (No. Brazil), the "Oiti"; large tropical tree which I photographed in Bahia, with thin-leathery ovate, glaucous green leaves 8 cm long, the flowers deep maroon and yellowish; the ovoid fruit 5-6 cm long, with leathery yellow skin covering a large hard seed, containing about 30% of oil and burning readily when ignited; locally strung on sticks for illuminating; oil is used for candles, soap and grease. *Tropical. p. 761, 2037*

LICUALA *Palmae* **S3LFM**

grandis (New Britain Isl. near New Guinea), "Ruffled fan palm"; very attractive small fan palm with slim solitary 3 m trunk, topped by plaited bright green leaves almost round, lobed and toothed along the continuous margin, on slender, thorny petioles; glossy crimson fruit. *p. 1875, 1880, 1887*

muelleri (Australia); beautiful fan palm of compact habit, slow growing; remarkable for the near perfect circle of its glossy-green fronds approximately 60 cm in dia., the wheel-shaped blade divides itself into numerous sectional folded fans, their apex lobed with each fold, and notched. *Subtropic. p. 1883*

paludosa (amplifrons) (Malaya, Borneo, Sumatra, Vietnam); a gregarious palm with stems as thick as an arm and to 6 m high; the large peltate rounded, stiff leaf is divided into up to 48 ribbed segments, squared off at the apex and dentate; petioles toothed; 1 m branched inflorescence, and small round fruit. *p. 1880*

peltata (India: Bengal); clustering fan palm with slender trunks to 5 m, leaves orbicular appearing as if peltate, 120-150 cm across divided into wedge-shaped, ribbed segments. *Tropical. p. 1876*

spinosa (Malaya to Java), "Spiny licuala palm"; clustering fan-leaf, densely suckering palm forming compact tufts with a mass of foliage from top to bottom, with age to 4 m tall; glossy-green leaves parted to the center into plaited segments ending abruptly in a toothed apex as if cut off, the rigid petioles armed with curved black thorns; fruit lustrous red. *Tropical. p. 1876, 1880, 1887, 1906*

LIGULARIA *Compositae* **C-I2LFM**

tussilaginea 'Argentea' (kaempferi) (China, Korea, Japan); attractive, perennial herb, with creeping rootstock, the solitary cordate-orbicular toothed leaves rising from rhizomatous basal rosette, glaucous fresh to grayish-green, variegated cream or white especially at margin. *p. 817*

tussilaginea 'Aureo-maculata' (L. kaempferi or Farfugium japonicum) (Japan), "Leopard plant"; with large rounded, green, smooth leaves blotched yellow and cream, 10 to 15 cm long; light yellow daisy-like flowers. *Subtropic. p. 816, 817, 823*

tussilaginea 'Crispata'; rhizomatous perennial with crested basal leaves glossy green and covered on both sides with grayish tomentum that rubs off, the margins gracefully frilled and coarsely toothed; flowers yellow rayed. *p. 817*

LIGUSTRUM *Oleaceae* ***C-I1-2LBD**

japonicum (Japan, Korea), the "Japanese privet"; fast growing evergreen bush to 3 or even 6 m high, with leathery, rich dark glossy green ovate, short-pointed leaves 4-10 cm long, on minutely downy twigs; small white flowers in terminal clusters, and black berries. *p. 1629, 1632, 1634, 1635*

japonicum 'Compactum'; dense evergreen, compact-growing California cultivar with thick, waxy dark green 5 cm leaves somewhat undulate; with some shearing grows into a very decorative pyramid for use as container plant in cooler indoor areas. *p. 1634*

japonicum variegatum; leaves variegated and edged with white. *p. 1634*

lucidum (China, Korea, Japan), the "Glossy privet" of the South, or "White-wax tree" in China, planted widely in the southern states; dense leafy evergreen shrub to 10 m high, with glossy, dark green, thick-leathery, ovate leaves 8-15 cm long, on flexible, glabrous branches; white flowers in long panicles followed by black berries. *Subtropic. p. 1629*

lucidum 'Erectum'; a form in Florida nurseries of pyramidal habit with willowy branches growing very erect and upward and the thick-waxy, deep green acuminate leaves arranged more or less in symmetrical ranks. *p. 1629*

lucidum 'Texanum', the "Wax-leaf privet"; a cultivar of compact habit, with glossy, thick-leathery dark green, ovate-acuminate leaves 6-9 cm long, somewhat wavy; ideally suited to shaping by trimming, and an enduring decorator under unfavorable conditions. *Subtropic. p. 1629*

lucidum 'Texanum variegatum', the 'Variegated waxleaf"; an attractive cultivar of vigorous habit and very picturesque having rich deep green foliage margined with gold around each leaf. *p. 1629*

ovalifolium (Japan), widely known as the "California privet"; densely branching half-evergreen shrub of erect habit to 4 m high, and much used for hedging including planter boxes for the sidewalk restaurants of New York, where it is quite hardy; the willowy, fast growing shoots are either evergreen, or if the leaves fall off during cold winters, quickly cover themselves anew with oval, rich green smooth leaves 3-7 cm long; summer blooming, if not trimmed back, with erect panicles of white flowers, followed by shining black berries. *Temperate. p. 1629*

sinense 'Variegatum', (China), "Chinese silver privet"; shapely variegated bush; the green species in China to 4 m high and deciduous; densely branched with thin twiggy, woody stems, the small ovate leaves 1 to 2 cm long and faintly dentate, to 8 cm long in older plants, milky green with white borders irregularly outlined; pubescent on midrib beneath; fragrant whitish flowers. Not very winter hardy. *Warm temperate.* *p. 1634*

vulgare buxifolium (Mediterranean Reg.), a semi-deciduous form of the "Common privet"; shrub with fresh green, small ovate thin-leathery leaves 3 cm long; the species very vigorous, with straight, willowy shoots to 5 m tall, leaves 4-6 cm; deciduous in cold climate; white flowers in erect clusters, heavily scented, followed by 1 cm black fruit. *p. 1634*

LILAEOPSIS *Umbelliferae* **I2LFM**

novae-zelandiae (New Zealand); small rhizomatous creeping herb with stems rooting at nodes; the leaf-like phyllodes (petioles) to 12 cm long and spoon-shaped or spatulate; small white flowers. *p. 2106*

LILIUM *Liliaceae* **C-I2LF-BDd**

auratum (Japan), "Goldband-lily"; tall erect, leafy stalk from a scaly bulb, to 2 m, with flaring, fragrant trumpet-flowers 25 cm across, white spotted with crimson, each segment with a central yellow stripe. *p. 1468*

auratum var. pictum (Japan), "Goldband-lily"; large-flowered lily to 2 m tall, fragrant blooms to 30 cm across, white densely spotted with crimson, each segment with yellow central stripe and tipped with crimson. *p. 1472*

auratum var. rubrum, "Red Goldband lily"; to 2 m; flowers white spotted with crimson, each segment with broad red central band, to 30 cm across, fragrant, horizontal or drooping. *p. 1472*

canadense (Nova Scotia to Alabama), "Meadow lily"; widespread, erect, $\frac{1}{2}$-1$\frac{1}{2}$ m tall; beautiful bell-shaped flowers orange-yellow to red, spotted purplish-brown, 8 cm across, pendant. *p. 1472*

candidum (Turkey), "Madonna lily"; lovely bulbous plant 1 m high, with numerous leaves becoming successively shorter, the trumpet-shaped flowers delicately fragrant, pure waxy white, the upper ones erect, the lower drooping, June blooming. Much used in churches and cemeteries. *p. 1470*

dauricum (Siberia), "Candlestick-lily"; about 1 m high, with erect flowers to 12 cm wide, the spreading elliptic segments orange-red spotted with purplish-black. *Temperate.* *p. 1468*

elegans (Japan); possibly hybrid between concolor and dauricum; showy erect-flowered lilies of Japanese gardens, about 60 cm high, the stem dense with leaves, the waxy flowers with spreading lobes 15 cm across, orange-red with darker black-purple spots. *p. 1468*

'Empress of India' (auratum x speciosum) (Jan de Graaff 1950); a giant lily hybrid from Oregon; tall stem dense with leaves crowned by clusters of big 30 cm wide open flowers pink with crimson center and dark red spots. *p. 1471*

'Enchantment'; Midcentury hybrid (umbellatum x tigrinum), with stocky, leafy stem, topped by bouquet of erect flowers with spreading segments, 15 cm across, orange-red with brown spots and prominent blackish stamens. *p. 1472*

'Harlequin' (cernuum x davidii) (Harlequin hybrids by Jan de Graaff, Oregon); varying in colors and pastel shades, pink, yellowish, crimson; with red or black spots; good garden subjects. *p. 1471*

'Harmony' (tigrinum hybrid); a "Mid-century lily", one of the finest, early-flowering in rich orange, the wide-spread blooms 12 cm across and spotted with brown; numerous flowers and buds on a stiff-erect leafy stem about 50 cm high or more; normally blooming in June. One of the best for forcing in pots; may be planted in the garden after flowering, but leave all the foliage possible to help mature the new bulb. *Warm temperate.* *p. 1472*

'Imperial Crimson', an "Empress hybrid lily"; fantastic strain of magnificent, vigorous lilies raised by Oregon Bulb Farms, involving blood of L. auratum, speciosum, japonicum and rubellum; tall, leafy, wiry stalks 1$\frac{1}{2}$-2 m high carrying giant, rather flat, firm flowers 20 cm across, the petals gently curling back, basically white but toward the middle changing to pink with red spotting, the center of each segment intense crimson; blooming in August. *Warm temperate.* *p. 1471*

longiflorum 'Ace'; Oregon cultivar of the "Croft Easter lily" complex; prolific bloomer of rather short, compact habit, dark shining green foliage on stem about 45 cm above pot, toward the apex of which appear buds and flowers one above the other, unlike Croft which are all in one cluster; the firm-textured white trumpets are generally shorter (12-14 cm long) and force well from a slow start. *Warm temperate.* *p. 1468*

longiflorum 'Croft', leading "Easter lily", superior commercial pot plant because of its large and elegant, firm-textured, white, trumpet-shaped flowers 12-16 cm long, carried horizontally on stiff, medium-tall, green stems, densely furnished with glossy-green leaves; developed in the Pacific Northwest from a hybrid of the Japanese L. 'Giganteum' x 'Erabu'. *Warm temperate.* *p. 11*, 1469*

longiflorum 'Estate'; a clone of the American Easter-lilies from seed raised by Dr. Griffiths of the U.S. Dept. of Agriculture Experiment station Bellingham, Washington 1928, which also produced the well-known 'Croft-lily'; 'Estate' is taller and later than 'Croft', with the pure white flowers wider open, strong stems bearing 4 to 8 large blooms. *p. 1472*

longiflorum eximium (harrisii), the "Bermuda Easter-lily"; largely cultivated on Bermuda Isl., is a stronger grower than the type, sometimes 1 m high with 15-20 larger white flowers 15-20 cm long, but somewhat herbaceous, and with recurving segment tips. Broader foliage, joints further apart on green stems, than giganteum. *p. 1469*

longiflorum eximium 'Creole'; clone of the "Bermuda lily"; and grown in Louisiana, of fairly tall habit and free-blooming; the large white trumpets are softer than 'Croft', the broad petals have a watery margin and have a tendency to split after temperature extremes in forcing. *p. 1468*

longiflorum eximium 'Georgia Belle'; free-flowering clone of 'Creole', a harrisii lily, and grown in Georgia; of tall habit $\frac{1}{2}$ to 1 m with firm, pure white trumpet-flowers shorter than Croft but opening wide and producing numerous blooms from small bulbs, but will grow quite tall in localities with little sunshine while being forced under glass. *p. 1468*

longiflorum eximium 'Jesuit'; a cultivar grown early in World War II (1942) in the lower Mississippi-delta of Louisiana, a very tall lily growing 1 m above the soil, with green stem straight like a candle and densely set with fresh green leaves like eximium (harrisii), bearing to 9 white trumpet flowers to 15 cm long, of good substance. *p. 1468*

longiflorum formosum 'Erabu' (So. Japan); robust, free flowering, cool-growing, bulbous plant with tallish, black stem, broad, scattered leaves, very floriferous with numerous large white, though somewhat herbaceous, flowers, scattered along the upper portion of the stem; early flowering. *p. 1468, 1469*

longiflorum giganteum (Japan), "White trumpet-lily"; native and cultivated in Southern Japan; of medium height, usually brownish stiff erect stem dense with medium-short glossy green leaves, and topped by an elegant cluster of medium-large firm flowers about 12 cm long, pure waxy white and fragrant in the evening; blooming normally in July; suitable for early forcing if given at least 4 weeks storage at 1°C. *p. 1469*

longiflorum 'Giganteum green stem'; a variant of the Japanese Easter lily with stout green instead of the more common black stem, slightly taller and with slender white trumpet flowers. *p. 1468*

monadelphum (Caucasus, Iran), "Caucasian lily"; bold species with golden yellow flowers sometimes tinged or spotted purple, 12 cm dia., segments reflexed; very early. *p. 1472*

nobilissimum (Ryukyu Islands, Okinawa); interesting little lily with pure white, erect flowers. *p. 1471*

x parkmannii (auratum x speciosum); glorious old hybrid (1869), long wiry stems with wide-spreading starry flowers 25 cm across, ruby-red with white edges and dark red spots. *p. 1471*

x parkmannii 'Jillian Wallace', (speciosum x auratum); dramatic, large-flowered hybrid lily from Australia, opening flat, with broad segments 10-15 cm long, ruby-red edged with rose, pronounced green nectaries, on leafy stem 1-2 m high. *p. 1468*

'Prosperity'; compact plant 50 cm high, slender stalk with papery foliage, 12 cm flowers with firm segments, lemon yellow with brown spots. *p. 1472*

pumilum (China), "Coral lily"; to 50 cm high, with wiry stem, numerous linear leaves; fragrant nodding flowers, 5 cm dia., waxy scarlet, with reflexed segments. *Warm temperate.* *p. 1408A*

regale (Szechwan), "Regal lily"; bulbous plant with wiry, purplish stem to 2 m high, covered with numerous, short, narrow leaves and topped by a cluster of fragrant, trumpet-shaped, white flowers with recurved tips, pale purple outside and with yellow throat. (h) *p. 1469, 1470*

speciosum (Japan), the "Japanese lily"; well-known, attractive species with scaly bulb and wiry stem to 1 m high with scattered rather broad, lanceolate leaves, bearing 3-10 stalked fragrant flowers 10-12 cm across, with reflexed petals, white tinted rose, and spotted with purplish-red. *p. 1468*

speciosum rubrum (Japan); wiry purplish stem $\frac{1}{3}$-1 m high, with scattered, lanceolate leaves and nodding flowers with reflexed petals having wavy margins, rose-pink flushed carmine and with purple spots; August-September. (h) *p. 1470*

superbum (E. Canada to Missouri), "American Turk's-cap"; superb lily, 1 to 2$\frac{1}{2}$ m tall; stem carries 15-20 orange-scarlet flowers spotted purplish-brown, 10 cm across; segments strongly reflexed. *p. 1472*

testaceum, the "Nankeen lily"; believed to be a hybrid between candidum and chalcedonicum; tall-growing to 2 m high with scattered linear leaves and bearing to 12 cupped, fragrant flowers 8 cm across and with reflexed segments, light apricot (nankeen yellow) flushed with pink. *p. 1468*

tigrinum (China), "Tiger lily"; hardy, stem-rooting bulbous plant 1 m or more high; strongly recurved Turk's cap flowers bright orange-red, spotted purple-black, and prominent anthers with red pollen. *p. 1470*

tigrinum splendens, a variety of "tiger lily"; with glossy leaves and larger flowers salmon-red with large glossy black spots, more numerous to 25 on a strong, leafy stem. *p. 1470*

x umbellatum, "Candle-stick lily"; an old Japanese croceum hybrid, rarely over 60 cm high, very pleasing, with showy, upright, large cup-shaped flowers of glowing scarlet, or similar shades, and dense, broad-linear leaves. (h) *p. 1470*

'Valencia' (umbellatum x tigrinum); typical of the showy group of mid-century hybrids with 1 m stems topped by open clusters of large, outward facing flowers, the firm textured petals are a glowing soft gold with bronze midribs and tiny maroon dots; June flowering. *p. 1470*

LIMNANTHES *Limnanthaceae* **C2LBM**

douglasii (California, Oregon), "Meadow-foam"; small sprawling annual herb with lacy pinnatifid yellowish-green leaves; a profusion of fragrant 2½ cm flowers with 5 spreading petals white or pinkish with yellow base, in early spring. *p. 1515*

LIMNOBIUM *Hydrocharitaceae* **S3LFW**

stoloniferum (laevigatum) (Mexico, West Indies, to Brazil); perennial floating aquatic plant, with long trailing runners forming rosettes of dark green oval, spongy leaves 2-2½ cm long; flowers greenish-white, arranged in three's. Photographed in the tropical pool in Botanic Garden Munich. *Humid-tropical.* *p. 1322*

LIMONIUM *Plumbaginaceae* **C2LBD**

sinuatum (Mediterranean reg.), "Statice", or "Sea-lavender"; biennial or perennial with tufted, lobed leaves, and panicles of numerous, small, clustered flowers with blue calyx and yellowish-white corolla, on winged branches; used as an "everlasting" when cut. *Subtropic.* *p. 1949*

sinuatum atrocoeruleum; perennial to 60 cm high, with leathery, wavy, lyrate basal leaves, and winged, angular stalks bearing large panicle of minute dark blue flowers. *p. 1949*

LINARIA *Scrophulariaceae* **C2LBM**

maroccana (Morocco), "Toadflax"; very pretty annual, with slender, branching stems bearing narrow-pointed leaves and long, dense spikes of bright violet-purple flowers, each with a long, pointed spur and a yellow blotch on the lower lip. *p. 2058*

LINARIA: see also CYMBALARIA

LINDERA *Lauraceae* **C2LFM**

benzoin (Ontario to Texas), "Spice bush"; aromatic deciduous shrub, leaves entire, obovate, 5-12 cm long; flowers greenish-yellow, small, opening during March and April in dense clusters; fruit oblong, 1 cm long, red. *p. 1359*

LINDHEIMERIA *Compositae* **I2LBD**

texana (West Texas); erect, rough-hairy branched annual 30-60 cm high, with toothed, spoon-shaped basal leaves, and stem-leaves lanceolate, the 4 to 5 ray-flowers golden yellow to cream, to 3 cm across. *p. 811*

LINOSPADIX *Palmae* **I3LFM**

minor (Bacularia) (Queensland); attractive, delicate small fan palm forming clusters, slender, cane-like trunks ½-1½ m high, the pinnate leaves with only a few broad leaflets on short petiole; leaves in older specimen may become 1 m long, with 12-14 leaflets; long inflorescence with 2 cm fruit. *p. 1886*

monostachya (New South Wales; Queensland), the "Walking stick palm"; clustering small palm (2 3 m) with cane-like smooth green stem less than 3 cm thick, partly covered by remnants of leaf-petioles; few pinnate fronds to 90 cm long, the leaflets dark green and variable in width. *p. 1880*

LINUM *Linaceae* **C-I2LBD**

grandiflorum (North Africa), "Flowering flax"; floriferous, densely branching erect annual herb to 75 cm tall; thin leafy stems with alternate linear, grass-green foliage, toward apex with masses of showy 5-petaled flowers 3 cm across, glowing red with dark center, opening to the sun. *Tropical.* *p. 1517*

hypericifolium (Caucasus), "Mallow-flowered flax"; biennial with erect branches, oval 5-nerved leaves in pairs; showy flowers a pretty rose, strongly veined. *p. 1517*

perenne (Europe), "Perennial flax"; upright perennial with linear leaves, lower part of stem usually leafless, the cupped, shortlived flowers deep, chicory-blue, during summer. *p. 1515*

LIPARIA *Leguminosae* **I2LBD**

spherica (So. Africa), "Mountain dahlia"; striking very leafy shrub of stiff habit, to 2½ m; leaves crowded and overlapping, 4-5 cm long; flowers in showy terminal heads to 10 cm wide, subtended by numerous bracts in a confused mass, bright yellow or orange. *Subtropic.* *p. 1385*

LIPARIS *Orchidaceae* **C2HFW**

atropurpurea (Sri Lanka); clustering plant with small cylindrical pseudobulbs topped by light green, succulent, plaited leaves to 12 cm long, the erect inflorescence to 40 cm tall with many small 2 cm flowers dark red-purple with tan lip (summer). *p. 1744*

elata (Florida, C. America to Peru), "Twayblade"; terrestrial herb with large pleated leaves to 30 cm, encircling the erect 60 cm floral stalk; loose head of 2 cm flowers reddish or greenish-white streaked with purple (summer). *p. 1744*

loeselii (N. America, Europe, Asia); northern hardy terrestrial 15-25 cm high with a pair of elliptical leaves and 3-angled stalk with raceme of small 1 cm flowers yellowish-green or pale yellow (May-Aug.). (C) *p. 1749*

longipes (viridiflora) (India, Malaya, Vietnam, Philippines); terrestrial with elongate pseudobulbs thickened at base, bearing 2 leaves to 20 cm long; very small greenish-cream flowers dense on erect raceme; summer. (I) *p. 1749*

neglecta (Kenya, Uganda, Tanzania, Zimbabwe, Transvaal); small terrestrial orchid 15-20 cm high, with crowded pseudobulbs each carrying two leaf-pairs, the leaves broad-elliptic, light-green; the erect inflorescence with small 1 cm flowers pale green, fading into ochre. (I) *p. 1749*

LIPPIA: see Aloysia

LIQUIDAMBAR *Hamamelidaceae* **I2LBD**

styraciflua (Connecticut to Florida and Mexico), "American Sweet gum"; attractive tree, deciduous in colder climate, to 20 m or more high, with furrowed bark and corky wings on twigs, the leaves maple-like and deeply cut into 5-7 lobes, 8 to 15 cm wide, deep glossy green, but turning purple, yellow or deep red in autumn; flowers inconspicuous, but the dangling spiny fruits add ornament in winter. *Warm temperate.* *p. 1323*

LIRIODENDRON *Magnoliaceae* **C2LBMh**

tulipifera (Mass. to Florida and Mississippi), the noble "Tulip-tree"; becoming 60 m high, with curious lobed, almost square deciduous leaves to 12 cm each way, and bell-shaped flowers to 10 cm across, greenish yellow with orange at base, very fragrant. *Warm temperate.* *p. 1524*

LIRIOPE *Liliaceae* **C-I2FMh**

exiliflora (E. Asia), "Lily-turf"; rhizomatous clump-forming plant with leathery, dark green linear leaves to 30 cm long and 1 cm wide; inflorescence carried well above foliage, with showy violet flowers in spike-like clusters; followed by numerous small, berry-like black fruit. *p. 1474*

gigantea (grandiflora in Calif. hort.); big plant for fountain-like effect; linear leaves to 1 m long, 1½ cm wide, thick-leathery, glossy dark green, underside striated; spreading by underground stems; flowers purplish-violet and white in clusters on slender stalk; used for decoration in California (Giridlian 1963). *p. 1474*

graminifolia (Japan, China); rhizomatous perennial with green, grass-like linear leaves to 40 cm long and ½-1 cm wide, tapering to slender point; flowers cup-shaped, light violet, almost white (photographed 1963 at Giridlian's Arcadia, Calif.). *p. 1474*

muscari (Japan, China), the "Big blue lily-turf"; deep green, leathery leaves to 45 cm long and 1 cm wide, from a clump of roots and tubers, the erect deep violet flowers in closely packed heads mostly not exceeding foliage; fruit black. *p. 1473*

muscari 'Variegata' (exiliflora?) (Japan, China), "Variegated lily-turf"; tufting, grass-like perennial with firm linear leaves to 45 cm long, rich green with yellow margins and bands; the little lilac flowers carried erect on purple spikes. *p. 1473*

platyphylla (China, Japan); robust, clustering plant with long linear, thin-leathery leaves, and tall cylindrical inflorescence of pale purple flowers. *Warm temperate.* *p. 1474*

LISIANTHUS *Gentianaceae* **I2LBM**

nigrescens (Eustoma) (U.S.: Nebraska to Texas), the "Black gentian"; annual or biennial erect herb 30-60 cm high, with opposite glaucous, ovate leaves on slender, wiry branches, topped by clusters of tubular-flaring lavender-purple flowers 4 cm long, blooming during summertime. A lovely bloomer for the window-sill or outdoor planter. *p. 1170*

LISSOCHILUS *Orchidaceae* **S3OFD**

hebdingianus (Madagascar); handsome terrestrial with pleated leaves and tall erect floral stem bearing a raceme of curious flowers red-brown and white. *p. 1745*

LITCHI *Sapindaceae* **I2LBD**

chinensis (Nephelium litchi) (So. China), the "Lychee nut"; round-topped evergreen fruiting tree, 6 to 12 m high, with spreading branches; leaves compound with 2-4 pairs of shiny leathery, ovate leaflets 8-16 cm long; small flowers with greenish-white sepals, no petals, followed by the round, juicy red fruit, enclosed in brittle warty shell, 2 to 3 cm in dia., according to variety, in pendant clusters, looking like strawberries hanging from the end of the twigs. Opened with fingernails, the firm, whitish pulp is exposed, delicious to the taste and mildly acid. The dried fruit called "Litchi nut" and with sweeter taste, is eaten like a raisin. Very popular in China. *Subtropic.* *p. 2033, 2037*

LITHOCAULON: see Pseudolithos

LITHOPS *Aizoaceae* **I2LBD**

alpina (Southwest Africa); circular body 1 cm high and broad, straw-colored, the glossy top with grayish fields and darker, light-brownish dots and markings; flowers yellow. *p. 73*

aucampiae (Transvaal); cluster-forming large split bodies only 1 cm high but flat tops 5 cm wide, light brown with coffee-brown reticulation; flowers yellow. *p. 73*

aurantiaca (Southwest Africa); clustering oval bodies deeply cleft, gray-brown, the top nearly flat and light yellow-brown, marked with coffee-brown reticulation; flowers orange-yellow. *p. 73*

bella (So. Africa), "Pretty stoneface"; small succulent plant with two thick leaves united, except for fissure across top and resembling pebbles which they mimic; brownish yellow with darker markings; flowers white. *Arid-subtropic.* *p. 64A, 69, 71, 72, 2092*

bromfieldii (Cape Prov.); cluster-forming split body almost round, red-brownish at sides, the flattened top strewn with gray translucent windows, and a network of brown and purple; flowers yellow. *Arid-subtropic.* *p. 71*

chrysocephala (Cape Prov.); conical body 10-15 mm wide, usually two together, pale gray; cleft surface rugose, greenish-gray to brown window with yellowish islands and chocolate markings toward scalloped edge; flowers white. *p. 72*

comptonii (Cape Prov.); cluster-forming pebble-plants with a large cleft, amethyst with brownish markings; flowers deep yellow. *p. 69*

deboeri (So. Africa); oval body with gaping cleft disclosing pale lavender blisters, body gray-blue to chocolate-brown with dark-blue or brown windows; flowers white. *p. 71*

dinteri (Southwest Africa); club-like cleft body to 2½ cm high, with purplish-gray sides; apex of lobes with a large transparent grayish-green window and a few red to purplish islands; flowers yellow. *p. 71*

divergens (Cape Prov.); small succulent split body with green sides, and large gray-green translucent windows on rounded tops, the leaves separating toward apex; flowers yellow *p. 72*

dorotheae (Cape Prov.); beautiful cleft stone 2½ cm high, pale dove-gray, the deep green translucent top windows are deep gray with blood-red reticulated tracings; flowers yellow. *p. 72*

elevata (Namibia); bodies heart-shaped when seen from the side, 2 cm high, pale fawn-colored with net-design of gray on gaping cleft surface; flowers white. *p. 72*

erniana (Namibia); cluster forming succulent 2 cm wide, smooth-bodied split-rock divided into two unequal halves, reddish-grey, the surface with scattered brownish lines or dots, few opaque windows. Flowers white. *p. 72*

fossulifera (So. Africa); divided gray-brown oval body constricted where cleft opens, surface somewhat rounded, largely gray-ochre with few, thinly connected brown markings. *p. 71*

framesii (Cape Prov.); cluster-forming lightly rounded cleft body pinkish dove-gray, 5 cm high, the lightly rounded surface a large gray window with few beige islands; flowers white, anthers yellow. *p. 71*

fulleri (Cape Prov.); attractive, tuft-forming gray or brownish bodies to 2½ cm high with deep cleft; top light gray with gray-brown islands and a row of purple spots around edges; flowers white. *p. 73*

fulviceps (Southwest Africa); mostly single bodies 3 cm high, sides gray with reddish tint, top ochre with raised translucent dark dome-like dots with rusty red lines; flowers yellow, whitish beneath. *Arid-tropical.* *p. 70, 75*

gracilidelineata (S. W. Africa); single-headed, dainty species 2 cm dia., with shallow cleft, of various coloring according to minerals in surrounding habitat, from almost white, to red; shallow cleft, opaque surface whitish tinted pinkish to orange, depressed brown lines. Flowers yellow. *p. 72*

gulielmii (Namibia); small 2 cm bodies with gaping cleft, sides light gray with dark gray band around edges, top wrinkled with sunken purplish lines and little windows; flowers yellow. *p. 70*

helmutii (Cape Prov.); greenish-gray deeply split body to 2½ cm wide, top obliquely rounded, with large translucent gray-green windows and light gray markings; flowers deep yellow and fragrant. *p. 71*

insularis (Cape Prov.); mouse-gray cleft body with rugose surface having raised dark windows, and blood-red markings and little white dots on raised ridges; flowers yellow. *p. 71*

jacobseniana (ursulae) (Namibia); attractive cleft oval body, clustering; violet-gray-yellow, top pinkish beige marked by light brown; flowers white. Now referred to L. karasmontana mickbergensis. *p. 70*

julii-pallida (Namibia); small conical body with split, slightly convex top, 2 cm across, the fissure running right across, deep pearl-gray, the margin of the fissure always with 4 brown dots each side, connected by brown lines; sides flushed reddish; flowers white. *p. 70*

julii-reticulata (Namibia); tufted stone-face with club-like growths 2½ cm high, with deep fissure, pearl-gray and shimmering opalescent, the top with a pronounced network in dark brown. *p. 69, 71*

karasmontana (Namibia), "Mountain pebble"; turf-forming , club-shaped cleft body almost circular, pearl-gray, with wrinkled top brownish-ochre and obscure dark markings; flowers white with yellow anthers. *p. 70*

kuibisensis (Namibia); almost cylindric cleft growths in clumps, 3 cm high, gray-brown, with red-brown depressed network of markings; flowers deep yellow. Now to L. schwantesii. *p. 70*

lericheana (S. W. Africa: Great Namaland); mat-forming, with circular, flat tops 3 cm across, shallow cleft, reddish to bluish to ochre-yellow, with translucent window spots; flower sweetly fragrant like heliotrope; otherwise similar to bella. *p. 70*

lesliei (Transvaal, Cape); split growths to 6 cm high, rust brown, top flat with network of deep gray, and islands of light brown; flowers bright yellow, pinkish on back. *Arid-subtropic.* *p. 71, 74*

lineata (Namibia); unevenly split oval, light violet-gray body with nearly cream-colored rounded surface and a few light brown markings; flowers yellow. *p. 70*

marmorata (Cape Prov.), "Big marble plant"; pale buff body 2 cm thick, with top surface slightly convex, with bold marble design of contrasting translucent brown; prominent fissure; scented flowers white. *p. 71, 73*

marthae (Namibia); cleft growths 2½ cm high and broad, top slightly convex, grayish-yellow or pale brown, with translucent dots and often reddish lines; yellow flowers. *p. 69*

mennellii (Cape Prov.); small species 16 mm wide, lightly cleft, with grayish-buff opaque top; blackish-brown depressed lines resembling Hebrew script; flowers golden yellow. *p. 72*

mickbergensis (Namibia); tufting, club-like bodies 2 cm high, obliquely split, reddish-gray, top greenish brown with yellow-brown grooves, brownish zone along cleft; flowers white. *p. 72, 73*

olivacea (Cape Prov.); clusters of cleft bodies to 2 cm high, dark olive to brownish, top with lighter, matte, spotted windows; flowers yellow. *p. 69*

opalina (Namibia); constricted oval cleft body 3 cm high, milk-blue, with beige surface and having amethyst tint like an opal; flowers white. *p. 70, 74*

optica rubra (S. W. Africa); cluster-forming succulent 3 cm high, rather rare; with amethyst-colored body; when splitting showing young growth in greenish-gray, the surface gray dotted with fawn; flowers white with pink tips. *p. 72*

otzeniana (So. Africa: Bushmanland); attractive living-stone 2-3 cm wide with smooth light gray body, the split apex rounded, the large darker gray semi-transparent window area showing a few pale blotches along cleft; flowers deep yellow. *p. 72*

peersii (Cape Province); pretty, cleft oval, 4 cm high, with grayish sides, the lightly rounded surface brownish with many dark green translucent dots; flower golden yellow. *p. 71*

pseudotruncatella (S.W. Africa); tufted split-rocks, pale brownish-gray with network of brown lines; however, color of body changes according to soil color—brown over yellowish to chalky gray-white; flowers yellow. *Arid-tropical.* *p. 69, 72*

pseudotruncatella mundtii (Namibia); lightly cleft full oval body gray-brown, the flat top reddish marked with greenish network; flowers orange tipped red. *p. 71*

pseudotruncatella pulmonuncula (Namibia); mostly single bodies almost round, a variety of pseudotruncatella but more reddish-gray, with red-brown tracings on top and greenish window islands; flowers yellow. *p. 70, 71*

rugosa (Namibia); clustering conical body 1 cm dia., reddish-gray to mouse-gray, deeply split, with convex, wrinkled surface showing network of gray to brown window-lines and transparent dots. Flowers yellow. *p. 72*

salicola (Oranje Free State); oval cleft body of beautiful silver-gray 2½ cm high, the top a large translucent gray-green window, set with little gray islands; flowers white. *p. 70*

schwantesii (Namibia); tufted oval growth to 4 cm high, reddish-gray, evenly split surface beige marked with outer buff zone and purple tracings; the old leaves sometimes last 2 years; yellow flowers. *p. 70*

summitatum (Namibia); club-like growths 2½ cm high with cleft clear across, grayish beige, more light brown on top, and with subdued grayish-purple blotching; flowers white. *p. 70*

terricolor (Cape Prov.); small "Living stone" 2 cm high; top oval, 3 cm long, grayish, dotted with red-brown; flowers yellow. *p. 69, 70*

triebneri (var. of schwantesii) (Namibia); split oval 2 cm high with beige gray sides and light brown surface marked with little translucent windows and reddish spots and lines; 4 cm flowers yellow. *p. 70*

turbiniformis (So. Africa: Cape Prov.), "Flat-top mimicry plant"; elegant round, split body to 4 cm high and broad, the sides gray, the top brownish and wrinkled, with dark brown branched grooves between the pebbly surface. The succeeding pair of leaves splits open the older body. Large 4 cm yellow flowers. *Arid-subtropic.* *p. 73*

turbiniformis 'Monstrosus'; curious crestate form with the succulent body elongated sideways fan-like and with two fissures instead of one across the pebbly brown top. *p. 74*

umdausensis (Cape Prov.); pretty deeply cleft body of light gray, the rounded surface covered by a translucent window with gray islands; fl. white. Now classified L. marmorata: which see.

vallis-mariae (Namibia: Bastardland); clump-forming "Cleft stone" becoming large, to 5 cm dia., with deep fissure, beige gray to milk-colored; surface wrinkled with minute brown depressions, being opaque windows; looks like limestone with weathered surface; flowers yellow. *p. 70*

vanzijlii: see Dinteranthus

venteri (Cape Prov.); elegant oval body lightly cleft, nice gray, the surface gray-brown overlaid with a window area design of dark gray green. *p. 71*

viridis (So. Africa); small cleft species dominantly grayish-green with convex translucent greenish top without islands. *p. 72*

werneri (Namibia); tiny cleft body less than 1 cm high and probably the smallest of Lithops; grayish brown with a rounded surface yellowish-beige and thin tracings of translucent greenish windows; flowers clear yellow. *p. 71*

LITHOSPERMUM *Boraginaceae* **C2LBM**
diffusum (Lithodora) (So. Europe); low-growing, prostrate or creeping rough-hairy evergreen subshrub 2 cm high, forming broad matting; hairy stems with small oblong 1 cm dark green leaves; small 1 cm funnel-shaped flowers deep gentian blue striped with purple, in bracted clusters, blooming spring and summer. *p. 510*

LITTONIA *Liliaceae* **S2-3LBMd**
modesta (So. Africa), "Climbing lily"; tuberous herb with climbing, flexuous leafy stem similar to Gloriosa, to 2 m; bright shining green leaves ending in a tendril, and axillary bell-shaped flowers rich orange, 3 cm long. *p. 1467*

LIVISTONA *Palmae* **I-S2-3LFW**
australis (Queensland, New South Wales, Victoria), "Australian cabbage palm"; with slender, ringed trunk to 25 m or more, when younger covered with brown leaf bases and brown fiber; dense crown of soft-leathery palmate fronds rounded in outline, 1-1½ m across, divided to middle into narrow glossy green segments with yellow central nerve, and without threads between; the petiole with stout curved spines; the rib extends to 10 cm into base of leaf. *Subtropic.* *p. 1880, 1884, 1885*
chinensis (South China), the formerly widely grown "Latania borbonica" of horticulture, "Chinese fan palm"; spectacular, large fan palm with thick trunk that may grow to 10 m high, but extending in spread sideways to a diameter of 8 m, with gigantic, glossy, fresh green, plaited leaves more broad than long, to 2 m wide, cut halfway into many narrow, one-ribbed segments which are split again, the tips will hang like a fringe; petioles armed with small spines when the palms are young, usually disappear later; fruit metallic blue. Long popular in Europe and America in parlors, hotels and winter gardens before the advent of Howeias. Satisfied with medium-warm conditions but requiring lots of water and big space. *Subtropic.* *p. 1861, 1880*
decipiens (Australia); handsome fan palm of medium size, with slender trunk, partially persistent leaf bases; loose crown of palmate leaves to more than 1 m across, glaucous beneath; center rib curves downward, the segments deeply cut to the base with tips freely pendulous; round 2 cm fruit. *Subtropic.* *p. 1888*
mariae (Australia); a bronze fan palm of the semi-arid interior of Australia; trunks to 12 m high, with leaf bases persistent for several years; the crown of palmate fronds is of an open habit; leaf blades 1-2 m long and deeply cut; when young, leaves and spiny petioles are bronzy red, later glaucous. *Tropical.* *p. 1884*
muelleri (North Queensland); fine symmetrical fan palm of compact habit; the specimen I have seen in habitat, growing under the roof of the light Melaleuca forest, on the tropical York Peninsula, were rarely over 3 m high; large crown of trim palmate fronds, cut about halfway into narrow, leathery glossy green segments, carried on rough petioles. *p. 1881*
rotundifolia (Malaya, Indonesia), "Round-leaf livistona"; fan palm 15 m or more high, brown trunk topped by a dense crown of palmate fronds ½-1½ m across, with broad lobes cut only 1/3 to base when young, and arranged almost in a circle, slightly notched at tip, glossy green on both sides, on thorny red stalks. *p. 1880, 1887*
saribus (cochinchinensis) (Cambodia, Vietnam, Malaya, Java, Philippines), a "Sugar palm"; noble fan palm with straight, slender trunk to 25 m tall, raising the dense globular rosette of palmate fronds well above canopy of the tropical rain forest; the ribbed, deeply segmented leaves to 1½ m long, on brown-red petioles with vicious thorns; small 1 cm blue fruit, in large clusters. *Tropical.* *p. 1881, 1887*

LOASA *Loasaceae* **C2LBMh**
hibiscifolia (Caiophora) (Argentina); twining herb with thin stems, trifoliate, wrinkled leaves, and curious pendant flowers; foliage has stinging properties. *p. 1523*

LOBELIA *Campanulaceae or Lobeliaceae* **I2HF-BM**
cardinalis (New Brunswick to Florida and Texas), "Cardinal flower"; hardy erect, stiffish perennial 30-100 cm or more high, with oblong lanceolate leaves 8-12 cm long, coarsely toothed, flowers bright scarlet 14 cm long in one-sided leafy raceme; late summer. The genus Lobelia is listed in Hortus under Lobeliaceae; in Royal Hort. and Zander with Campanulaceae. *p. 751*
erinus 'Crystal Palace'; an old horticultural variety of the So. African species; low, bushy annual much used for bedding; 'Crystal Palace' is very dwarf, about 10 cm high, densely branched with thread-like stalks, tiny obovate toothed leaves green in the shade, turning deep purplish bronze in sun, and topped by a profusion of small but bright rich deep blue flowers. *p. 1513*
erinus 'Emperor William'; low, bushy herb with fresh-green foliage, and vivid blue flowers, 10-15 cm high, and growing into a perfect globe. *p. 1513*
erinus 'Waverly Blue'; an English cultivar; pretty bedding lobelia of low, dense habit, with large sky-blue flowers. *p. 1514*
gibberoa (Central Africa, Uganda, Kenya), the "Giant lobelia"; interesting mainly because this species reaches almost tree-like dimensions, to 10 m high, in a genus that consists mostly of species of small habit; the Giant lobelia, really an out-grown herb, grows at higher altitudes, like tall candles, with erect solitary, hollow stalks, dense with oblanceolate, soft leaves to 60 cm long at base, becoming shorter toward top; long spike-like inflorescence of tiny greenish-white flowers. *Tropical.* *p. 1513, 1514*
laxiflora (Mexico); tall perennial herb to 1½ m with thinly hairy branches, lanceolate, toothed leaves, and nodding 3 cm red and yellow cylindric flowers with protruding stamens. *p. 1513*
linnaeoides (New Zealand: Canterbury); small creeping perennial with thick, rounded, toothed leaves purple beneath, on thin-wiry, rooting stems; flowers white, purplish beneath, 1-2 cm long, the 2 lower lobes egg-shaped, the upper one narrower and pointed; summer-blooming. *p. 751*
siphilitica (Maine to Louisiana), the "Great lobelia"; hardy perennial 50-75 cm high, with oval to lanceolate, toothed leaves; erect racemes dense with bluish purple flowers 2-3 cm long, in autumn. *p. 751*
tenella (Dobrowskya) (So. Africa); charming herbaceous perennial only 8-10 cm high, with prostrate branches, and suitable as a basket plant; a profusion of small 1 cm flowers resembling a violet, with 5 tapering petals, pale lavender tinted deep purple, on slender stalks with small ovate, serrated leaves. *p. 1513*
tupa (Chile); perennial 2-2½ m high, with erect leafy, thick stem; oblong, toothed leaves white downy and wrinkled; large downy 5 cm flowers blood-red, the corolla-lobes united at tips, in terminal spike-like raceme. *p. 1513*
vedraiensis hort. (So. Africa); tall-growing with floral stalks to 50 cm high, set with pyramids of brilliant violet flowers; foliage green. *p. 1514*

LOBIVIA *Cactaceae* **•I2LBD**
aurea (Argentina: Cordoba), "Golden lily cactus"; lovely globular to cylindrical small plant similar to Echinopsis, dark green, to 10 cm high, with 14-15 acute ribs, spines yellowish brown; short funnel-form flowers freely borne, glossy lemon-yellow. *Arid-subtropic.* *p. 666, 678*
backebergii (Bolivia); from the Puna near La Paz, at 3600 m altitude, small pale green globe 5 cm dia., with some 15 notched ribs arranged spirally, radial spines brown to gray; flowers carmine with bluish sheen. *p. 677*
binghamiana (S.E. Perú), "Cob-cactus"; small depressed globe, to 10 cm dia., pale green with white dots, about 22 wavy ribs with orange radial spines; flowers purplish-red. *Arid-subtropic.* *p. 677, 679*
bruchii (Argentina: Tucumán); simple plant at first cylindric, becoming fairly large and globular with age, to 30 cm thick; up to 50 notched ribs or more and apex depressed, dark green, densely set with straw-colored spines and radials; small flowers deep red. *Arid-subtropic.* *p. 618, 679*
corbula (Perú); small globe with depressed apex, and forming clusters, from the shores of Lake Titicaca at above 4100 m altitude; green with 12-18 acute notched ribs, spines horny yellow; night-blooming with outer petals scarlet, inner salmon. *p. 677*
cylindrica (Argentina: Cordoba); small, deep green cylindrical plant 12 cm high with 11 ribs, bristling with whitish radials and brown needle spines; the large 5 cm flowers pale canary yellow outside, the inside petals deeper orange-yellow and spreading outward like a star. *Arid-subtropic.* *p. 678*
famatimensis (No. Argentina); small oval or elongated body to 15 cm high, with some 20 notched ribs somewhat spiral, and many yellowish short spines; flowering freely varying from yellowish to deep red. *Arid-subtropic.* *p. 677*
formosa (Soehrensia, Echinopsis) (No. Argentina); solitary globe becoming elongate to 60 cm high, with 15-22 or more ribs slightly notched, pale grayish green; long spines reddish when young, 11-13 radials, and 6-8 central needle-like spines with dark tip; funnel-shaped flowers with inner petals glossy golden yellow. *p. 678*
hertrichiana (S. E. Perú); attractive globular plant to 10 cm thick, clustering, with 11 acute ribs deeply notched above the woolly areoles, glossy light green, spreading spines yellowish; flowers rather large, fiery scarlet. *p. 681*
huascha (Trichocereus, Helianthocereus) (W. Argentina); cylindrical erect stem 30-90 cm high and 5-8 cm thick, branching from the base, light green with 12-18 ribs, whitish areoles, and numerous needle spines yellow to brown; large yellow flowers with brownish hairs. *Arid-subtropic.* *p. 678*
huascha rubriflora (W. Argentina); variety with tall clustering columns more slender, yellowish green, with 12 ribs and shorter spines; prolific bloomer with red flowers. *Arid-subtropic.* *p. 678*
jajoiana (Argentina: Salta); small globular plant tender green, from the Andes at 2700 m, acute ribs deeply notched into sharp-edged tubercles, with pinkish-white radial spines; flowers dark wine-red tinged blue in throat. *p. 677*
leucomalla (Argentina); solitary or clustered small species with oval stem to 3 cm high, 24 ribs and long whitish spines; flowers borne freely, beautiful yellow. *p. 678*
longispina (No. Argentina); stem globular to cylindric to 25 cm high with usually 24-30 tubercled ribs, the brown to gray central spines 8 cm long; flowers white. *p. 678*
peclardiana (Andes of So. America); lovely globular dark green plant with tubercled ribs and recurving colorful spines red, pink, brown and cream; free-blooming with wide-open orchid pink flowers showing golden stamens. *p. 678*

pentlandii (Andes of Bolivia); globular plant to 15 cm wide, branching into large clumps, glaucous green, with 12-15 prominent ribs, spreading brownish spines; flowers rose-colored inside; the round green fruit with the flavor of pineapple. *p. 677*

pseudocachensis (No. Argentina); from Salta at 2500 m elev.; globular small green plant 3 cm high and 4 to 6 cm thick, with turnip-like root and appressed yellowish spines, forming clusters; funnel flowers 6 cm long, vivid dark red. *Arid-subtropic. p. 674*

rossii (Bolivia); small globe with apex not depressed, 13-18 ribs notched into hatchet-shaped tubercles, set with woolly areoles and spreading spines first reddish-brown, then straw-color; beautiful funnel-shaped beet-red flowers. *p. 677*

LOBIVIOPSIS *Cactaceae* **I2LBD**

'Orange Glory' (Lobivia x Echinopsis); very free-blooming bigeneric raised by Harry Johnson in California; small globular plant with flowers in a new color direction of shimmering vivid orange. *p. 674*

'Stars and Stripes'; another Harry Johnson bigeneric hybrid with conical ribbed globes very profuse in day-blooming, large funnel-flowers with glistening petals in two colors, carmine-red and pinkish-white. *p. 674*

LOBOSTEMON *Boraginaceae* **I2LBD**

trichtomus (So. Africa); shrubby plant related to Echium, with branches dense with sessile, hairy leaves, topped by clusters of light blue cup-shaped flowers 2-3 cm across, in spring and summer. *p. 511*

LOBULARIA *Cruciferae* **I2LBM**

maritima (Mediterranean), "Sweet alyssum"; a much branched little plant grown as an annual, with linear leaves, and many small pure white, very fragrant flowers blooming a long time. Very popular in summer garden beds. *Subtropic. p. 927*

maritima florepleno, "Double sweet alyssum"; with rather persistent spreading branches and cute little double flowers, white, fragrant; very trailing, a greenhouse perennial used for cut flowers. *p. 927*

LOCKHARTIA *Orchidaceae* **S3OFM**

acuta (Trinidad); small epiphyte with stem densely clothed with little shingled leaves folded flat, and axillary stalked, tiny flowers lemon yellow marked with red (summer). *Tropical. p. 1752*

lunifera (Brazil), "Braided orchid"; curious epiphyte having erect stems clothed with triangular leaves folded flat, out of which appear the tiny, golden yellow, long-lasting flowers with red-spotted lip. (Jan.-Aug.) *Tropical. p. 1752*

pallida (acuta) (Trinidad, Panama, Colombia); interesting epiphyte with ribbon-like arching flattened slender stems to 60 cm long, entirely covered by imbricated triangular leaves 2 cm long; small soft yellow flowers 1 cm across (summer) (see acuta). *p. 1750*

robusta (Guatemala); epiphyte with 30 cm stem, flattened densely shingled pointed leaves 3 cm long; small lateral, nodding bracted flowers, the oval sepals and petals yellow, the lobed lip yellow spotted red; July-August. *p. 1752*

LODOICEA *Palmae* **S3LFM**

maldivica (seychellarum) (Seychelles Isl. in the Indian Ocean), the "Coco-de-Mer"; slow-growing solitary fan palm to 30 m high, and trunk 30 cm dia., the large palmate fronds in dense crown on 4 m petioles, the deep glossy green blade 6 m long, cut 1/3 into segments whose ends are drooping; the female trees bear the famous "double coconuts", immense dark brown, woody fruits weighing to 20 kg., 45 cm long, taking 6 years to mature, the nut inside two-lobed or "double". *Tropical. p. 1882, 1888*

LOMARIA: see Blechnum

LONCHOCARPUS *Leguminosae* **S2LBD**

sericeus (domingensis) (Sénegal, Trop. America); small tree with leaves of 7-13 dark green leaflets conspicuously veined; pinkish or purplish flowers in slender racemes. *Tropical. p. 1384*

violaceus (Trinidad, Tobago), "Lance-pod"; small tree with pinnate, fresh green foliage, racemes of rose-purplish flowers. *Tropical. p. 1384*

LONICERA *Caprifoliaceae* **I2LFM**

x brownii (hirsuta x sempervirens), "Scarlet trumpet honeysuckle"; beautiful winter-hardy deciduous twiner; thin-woody stems with broad-ovate leaves downy and glaucous beneath; striking clusters of glowing red, slender tubular flowers 4 cm long with mouth somewhat 2-lipped; evergreen in warmer climate. *p. 756*

fragrantissima (China); semi-evergreen bushy shrub 2-3 m high, with spreading branches; ovate leaves 3-6 cm long, bluish green beneath; evergreen in mild climate; flowers 2 cm across, creamy-white, and very fragrant in axillary pairs, appearing usually before the foliage in early spring, where deciduous. *p. 756*

hildebrandtiana (Burma, Thailand, So. China), "Giant honeysuckle"; evergreen climber, the woody stem reaching 18-24 m; ovate 15 cm leaves, and axillary, fragrant, creamy-white flowers deepening to orange-red, the corolla 10-15 cm long with 2-lipped limb. *Subtropic. p. 756*

japonica; twiner with hollow stems growing to 10 m; the bilabiate fragrant flowers 3 cm long, pure white changing to yellow. The species japonica (Japan, Korea, China) has white flowers tinged purple. *p. 756*

japonica 'Aureo-reticulata' (brachypoda), "Japanese honeysuckle"; evergreen twiner with wiry stems and small ovate leaves veined and netted bright yellow; fragrant flowers white, tinged purple. *p. 757*

maackii (Manchuria, Korea); deciduous wide-spreading shrub to 5 m with ovate 8 cm downy leaves, and fragrant bilabiate white flowers fading to yellowish, the corolla 2 cm long, in pairs. *p. 756*

sempervirens (Connecticut to Florida and Texas), "Trumpet honeysuckle"; twining woody vine, with ovate leaves to 8 cm long, glaucous beneath; pretty, tubular flowers orange-scarlet, yellow inside, 4-6 cm long, in whorls at ends of branches in summer; scarlet fruit; evergreen in warmer climate. *Warm temperate. p. 756*

LOPEZIA *Onagraceae* **I2LBM**

coronata (Mexico), "Crown-of-jewels"; herbaceous annual to 45 cm,densely branched, the thin stems with small ovate leaves, and a profusion of attractive little flowers rose or lilac, the two side petals red at base. *p. 1648*

lineata (coccinea) (Mexico), "Mosquito-flower"; shrubby plant 30-90 cm, with hairy stems and serrate ovate leaves, the small winged red flowers with 5 petals, the 2 upper ones bent away from center disclosing an apparent drop of honey, actually a glossy piece of hard tissue which deceives flies. *Tropical. p. 1648, 1649*

LOPHANTHERA *Malpighiaceae* **S2LBM**

lactescens (Brazil: Amazon); small slender flowering tree rising like an elongated cone, with opposite papery, clasping leaves 20-30 cm long; the inflorescence in long, pendulous, cylindrical clusters dense with small salmon-yellow flowers, to 50 cm long. *p. 1518, 1525*

LOPHOCEREUS *Cactaceae* **I2LBD**

gatesii (Baja California); columnar plant olive green with some 10 marked ridges, the raised areoles set closely, with ash-gray woolly tufts and dense with groups of gray to black-brown needle spines. *p. 642*

schottii (Sonora, Arizona, Baja California), "Totem pole"; moss-green column 8 cm thick, with 5-9 acute ribs, the areoles set with small clusters of white wool, and short black spines; night-flowering red. The monstrose form L. mieckleyanus grows more slender, with irregular smooth ribs. *Arid-subtropic. p. 642*

schottii 'Monstrosus,' "Monstrose totem"; very peculiar yet attractive form consisting of a short column entirely composed of large, smooth knobs or remnants of ribs with spineless areoles, waxy moss-green. *Arid-subtropic. p. 646*

LOPHOPHORA *Cactaceae* **I2LBD**

echinata diffusa (So. Texas, Mexico); a form of the Aztec Peyote, a god to which the Indians ascribed magic powers; soft-succulent, depressed globular bodies to 12 cm dia., with beet-like roots and forming clusters; bluish-green and with the tubercles confluent around the top; the white flowers from the white-woolly areoles in center, 2½ cm across; fruit pink. *P. 704*

williamsii (So. Texas, Mexico), the famous "Mescal" or "Peyote" of the ancient Mexicans, because of its powerful exhilarating and narcotic properties; small depressed globe to 8 cm dia., freely sprouting laterally, bluish-green, 5-13 low and wide ribs, tubercles white tufted; flowers pink to white. Venerated as a god by certain Indians in Mexico, at sacrifices or religious rites. *Arid-subtropic. p. 694*

LORANTHUS *Loranthaceae* **S2 (on host tree) BD**

sansibarensis (Kenya, Tanzania, Zanzibar), the "Matchstick vine"; a parasitic straggler, which I have often encountered throwing a fiery splash over the colorless bush of the East African savannah; clambering shrub with oval 10 cm leaves, and axillary flowers 4 cm long with tubular corollas greenish at base, changing to orange-red and tipped black, and deep yellow stamen, the long slender tubes resembling a matchstick. The berry germinates on the host tree, and the roots appropriate its sap. *p. 1521*

LOROPETALUM *Hamamelidaceae* **I2LBM**

chinense (China); free-blooming, ever-green shrub to 3 m high or more, the twiggy branches brown with starry down; the oval leaves 4 to 6 cm long; flowers white with strap-shaped petals 2-3 cm long, March-April blooming. The white petals and evergreen leaves distinguish this from Hamamelis. *p. 1323*

LOTUS *Leguminosae* **I2LBD**

berthelotii (peliorhynchus) (Cape Verde, Canary Isl.), "Winged pea"; silvery-haired shrub spreading along the ground with straggling branches, having pinnate, grayish foliage of thread-like leaflets, and butterfly-type scarlet flowers. *Subtropic. p. 1386*

corniculatus (Europe, No. Asia, naturalized in No. America), "Birds-foot tree-foil"; perennial to 60 cm often procumbent, foliage with 3 leaflets, and small 2 cm flowers bright yellow fading to orange, the standard striped red. *p. 1386*

LOUREA: see Christia

LUCKHOFFIA *Asclepiadaceae* **I2LBD**

beukmanii (West Cape Prov.); curious succulent with angled, gray-green stem deeply cut into knobs in cross-sections to look like a creeping chain, to 75 cm long; star-like, puckered flowers 6 cm across, brown and spotted with yellow. *p. 375*

LUCULIA *Rubiaceae* **I2LFM**

grandifolia (tsetensis) (Bhutan Himalayas); dense ornamental shrub to 6 m, with red stems; deep green ovate, corrugated leaves with reddish midrib 30-40 cm long, and showy clusters of tubular waxy, fragrant flowers with spreading limb pure white. *Subtropical.* *p. 2020*

gratissima (Himalayas, to Yunnan); tree or shrub to 5½ m with reddish-downy branches, ovate leaves 10-20 cm, very fragrant tubular flowers soft rosy-pink, 4 cm across the limb; in rounded clusters. *p. 2020*

LUDOVIA *Cyclanthaceae* **S3LFM**

lancaefolia (crenifolia) (French Guiana); attractive small palm-like plant related to Carludovica, with thick rooting stem; leaves in two ranks, thick and rigid, sheathing at base, lanceolate, to 50 cm long, deep green and plaited like a feather, with rounded teeth near tip; pale yellow flowers in spirals near base, with 3-5 spathes in 2 ranks. *p. 945*

LUDWIGIA *Onagraceae* **S3LFW**

helminthorrhiza (Trop. So. America), "False loosestrife"; an aquatic oxygenating plant growing largely submerged; branching stems with broad glossy green leaves 3-5 cm long; in the axils above the water the small white flowers. *p. 1649*

mulertii (natans) (Trop. So. America), "Swamp-spoon"; small bog or aquatic perennial with opposite spoon-shaped leaves glossy green above and crimson beneath, on slender stems rooting at nodes; solitary inconspicuous, yellow flowers in leaf axils. Does well as an aerator, submerged in aquarium but likes to break the surface. *p. 1649*

LUEHEA *Tiliaceae* **S2LBD**

divaricata (Paraguay); handsome tree 3-6 m high with elliptic, irregularly toothed leaves, grayish beneath; showy white flowers with 5 petals that change to rose, in pendant racemes. *p. 2102*

LUFFA *Cucurbitaceae* **S3LBM**

cylindrica (Eastern hemisphere Tropics), the odd "Vegetable sponge", "Dishcloth gourd" or "Sauna sponge", is produced by a fast growing tropical climber of the cucumber family; 4-angled stems pull themselves up by coiling tendrils, the rough-hairy herbaceous angled or lobed green leaves cucumber-like, 10-15 cm wide; separate male and female 8 cm flowers golden yellow; when pollinized the pistillate flowers produce the swollen cylindric fruit to 60 cm long, which may be eaten when young, but the ripe yellow fruit contains the sponge-like fiber that is washed and dried, and marketed for scrubbing, stimulating massage and skin care. *Tropical.* *p. 930, 931*

x LUISANDA *Orchidaceae* **S3OFM**

'Uniwai' (Luisia teretifolia x Vanda 'Miss A. Joaquim'); bigeneric hybrid of vandaceous habit, with attractive fleshy, lavender-pink flowers 4 cm across, the petals darker pink, the lip basically creamy marked with purple. *p. 1787*

LUISIA *Orchidaceae* **S3OFW**

teretifolia (India to Monsoon Asia and New Caledonia), "Bee orchid"; remarkable epiphyte with slender, thin stems to 1 m long, set with pencil-like cylindric leaves; small heavy-textured 2 cm flowers nesting against the stem, yellowish green overlaid with bronze, the lip velvety brown-red (autumn). *Tropical.* *p. 1743*

LUNARIA *Cruciferae* **C2LFD**

biennis (annua) (Europe: Sweden, etc.), a biennial variously known as "Silver dollar"; "Honesty", "Moonwort" or "Satin flower"; to 1 m high, with toothed ovate leaves, erect stems with violet to white flowers followed by moon-shaped seed pods opening to papery satiny, translucent disks which are cut and used for lasting winter bouquets. *p. 926, 927*

LUPINUS *Leguminosae* **C2LBM**

'Russell's hybrids'; strikingly handsome herbaceous perennials, the result of hybridizing L. polyphyllus (Wash. to Calif.) with the tree-lupine arboreus; this strain has massive spikes of pea-like flowers in many colors: pink, salmon, red, white, yellow, violet; leaves digitately compound. *Warm temperate.* *p. 1386*

LYCASTE *Orchidaceae* **C-I3OFD**

aromatica (Mexico); dwarf epiphyte with oval pseudobulbs having 1-2 dark green, elliptic leaves; flower stalks clustered , each with a solitary, fragrant, waxy blossom, to 15 cm high, sepals greenish-orange, petals golden-yellow, the concave lip golden-yellow dotted red. (April-Oct.). *Tropical.* *p. 1751*

candida (Costa Rica, Panama); floriferous epiphyte with 2-leaved pseudobulbs, the plicate foliage eventually deciduous; wiry stalks bearing fragrant 5 cm flowers, sepals pale green, petals white, lip white, tinted with yellow and dotted red-brown (spring). *Subtropic.* *p. 1750*

crinita (Mexico); charming small epiphyte with clusters of ovoid, compressed pseudobulbs, topped by two pleated, deciduous leaves; fragrant waxy flowers to 8 cm across, yellow to orange (summer). *p. 1750*

cruenta (Guatemala); epiphyte with 2-3-leaved pseudobulbs and small 5 cm, long-lasting, individually stalked flowers, sepals greenish-yellow, petals deep golden-yellow, lip orange-yellow with blood-red throat, (March-April, and longer). *Tropical.* *p. 1751*

deppei (So. Mexico); epiphyte with compressed pseudobulbs bearing 3-4 plaited leaves, and solitary, waxy, 10 cm flowers, the sepals greenish-yellow, spotted with red, petals ivory-white, lip white with golden crest and spotted with red, (June-Sept.). (C-I) *p. 1751*

dowiana (Costa Rica); epiphyte with ovoid pseudobulbs topped by 2-3 folded, oblanceolate leaves and deciduous; fragrant waxy flowers 10 cm across, on pendant stalks, sepals brownish green, petals yellowish white at tip, lip lemon-yellow; near macrophylla but smaller. *p. 1750*

gigantea (Colombia, Ecuador); robust species with large pseudobulbs and leaves to 75 cm high; large flowers with greenish-yellow sepals and petals inclined forward, the toothed lip orange, center purplish-brown, the whole flower appearing like a laughing face, (spring). (C-I) *p. 1751*

macrophylla (Perú); robust epiphyte with large, ribbed pseudobulbs and plaited, 60 cm leaves; 10 cm flowers on solitary stalks olive-green, inside red-brown, petals white with red tips, lip white and dotted red, (Nov.-Jan.) (I) *p. 1751, 1752*

micheliana (crinita) (Mexico); small epiphyte species with fragrant, waxy flowers yellow or orange-yellow (see L. crinita). *p. 1750*

schilleriana (Colombia, C. America); epiphyte with pseudobulbs topped by 2 or 3 large plaited leaves; short-stalked, waxy, fragrant 8 cm flowers with sepals pale olive green suffused with brown; the petals creamy white, lip white in front and yellow inside, with brown dots and lines (spring). *p. 1750*

virginalis (skinneri) (Mexico, Guatemala, Honduras); handsome profusely flowering epiphyte with large pseudobulbs, each with 2-3 broad, plaited leaves to 60 cm long; large, waxy, solitary flowers to 15 cm across, rose-pink, shaded carmine-rose in the center, lip whitish, thickly spotted with rose and crimson, (Nov.-May). *Subtropic.* *p. 1751*

virginalis alba (skinneri alba) (Guatemala), "White Nun orchid", national flower of Guatemala; beautiful form with large waxy flowers pure white, crest of lip light yellow. (Winter). *Subtropic.* *p. 1751*

xytriophora (Ecuador, Costa Rica); epiphyte with small compressed pseudobulbs usually bearing a plaited leaf 30-38 cm long; the flowers 8 cm wide, sepals greenish-brown, petals yellow-green at base, white at tip, lip white spotted red, and with yellow in center. (I) *p. 1752*

LYCIUM *Solanaceae* **C2LBD**

ruthenicum (So. Russia to Iran), "Box-thorn"; spiny shrub with sessile glaucous green 3 cm leaves, dense with small axillary 2 cm lavender flowers; black berry-like fruit. *p. 2067*

LYCOPERSICON *Solanaceae* **S2-3LBM**

lycopersicum (esculentum) cerasiforme, the "Cherry-tomato"; in cultivation since the 16th century, and before by the Incas of western South America, their native home; fleshy herb with strong-smelling, pinnately compound, hairy foliage, small yellow flowers, and long clusters of globular red or yellow fruit 2-3 cm in dia., during the hot season, and used for ornament or in the kitchen; closely related to the potato, Solanum tuberosum, and I have proved for myself this relationship by successfully grafting tomatoes on potatoes, a combination known as 'Potomato'. *p. 2083*

lycopersicum 'Tiny Tim'; an edible miniature tomato, the little round scarlet fruit 1½-2 cm dia., in axillary clusters; the cute little decorative plant is of dwarf habit, about 30 cm high, and suitable for pot culture. *Tropical.* *p. 2075, 2081*

lycopersicum 'Yellow Pear'; an ornamental pear-shaped tomato, of exceedingly mild and pleasing flavor, 4½ - 5 cm long, borne prolifically in clusters. *p. 2081*

LYCOPODIUM *Lycopodiaceae* **C-S3H-OFM-W**

cernuum (Pantropic), tropical "Ground-pine"; evergreen herb with scale-like leaves; stems 20-80 cm high, much-forked; leaves bright light green, form conspicuous cones. *p. 1520*

gnidioides, a tropical "Clubmoss"; pendant branches with fresh green, imbricated needle-like leaves; needs high humidity. *p. 1520*

nummularifolius (Indonesia); epiphytic tropical clubmoss, with pendulous, branched ribbons 30-80 cm long; the 7-8 mm leaves oval and light green, set densely in two ranks along flexuous rachis. *p. 1521*

obscurum (Newfoundland to Alaska, South to Alabama), "Ground pine", also known as "Princess pine"; evergreen moss-like herb, allied to the ferns; main stem creeping horizontally, sending up aerial branches 10-25 cm high, like miniature pine-trees, the branches covered by dark green scale-like leaves and topped by club-shaped spikes producing spores. Bound together into little Christmas trees and sold by florists as "Mystery plant". The small flowers in the photo are dyed "Immortelle" flowers. *p. 1520*

phlegmaria (Queensland, and Tropics of Eastern hemisphere), "Queensland tassel-fern"; handsome tropical epiphyte, slender, wiry stems first erect then pendant, the pale rope-like, forking branches set closely with stiff-leathery, needle-like, glossy green ovate leaves 1 cm long in spirals or whorls, light green beneath, the fertile tasseled fronds thin, like catkins. *Humid-tropical.* *p. 1521*

remoganense (Osaka, Japan); epiphytic club moss with rope-like pendant, branching stems, densely set with linear, stiff, needle-like, fresh-green leaves. *p. 1520*

squarrosum (Polynesia, Trop. Queensland), the "Rock tassel" or "God's-strings"; a difficult epiphyte often found growing on rocks, branched flexuous yellow-green, arching stems set with grass-green narrow ovate needle-hard, sessile leaves like a spruce tree. (S) *p. 1521*

taxifolium (Florida, West Indies, C. America); a Western hemisphere tropical epiphytic club-moss, with slender rope-like, forking branches eventually pendant, thickly clothed with bright green, pointed leaves 1 cm long; the ends of pendant branches are swollen, holding the sporangia at the base of leaves. (S) *p. 1521*

tetrastichum (New Guinea); epiphytic plant with thin pendulous branches covered with shingled scale-like leaves, dark green; at apex forming cone-like spikes containing spores. *p. 1520*

LYCORIS *Amaryllidaceae* **I2LBDd**

aurea (China), "Golden spider-lily"; a pretty, bulbous plant about 30 cm high, with narrow, strap-shaped bluish leaves which appear in spring, ripen, then die down before bloom stalk develops; clusters of spidery-looking bright yellow flowers 8 cm long, with narrow, undulate segments; late summer. *p. 121*

radiata (China, Japan), "Red spider lily"; formerly sold as Nerine sarniensis or N. japonica; bulbous plant 45 cm high, good grower with linear basal leaves with silver band along middle, and disappearing before the flowers which are borne in an umbel, the recurved and crisped petals bright scarlet-red and edged with gold, the long stamens curving upward; late fall-blooming and hardy. *Warm temperate.* *p. 118*

squamigera (Japan), "Magic lily" or "Resurrection lily"; bulbous herb with leaves 2½ cm wide, the fragrant flowers in umbels, petals separated and a pretty lilac-pink, yellow in base, the long stamens turned up; hardy. *Warm temperate.* *p. 118*

LYGODIUM *Schizaeaceae (Filices)* **I3LFM**

japonicum (Japan to Himalayas to No. Australia), "Climbing fern"; with twining, thread-like stems bearing pretty, pleasing green, pinnate, papery leaflets, the sterile pinnae with lobed segments (pinnules); the fertile pinnae narrow, 3-times divided. *Humid-subtropic.* *p. 1083, 1084*

microphyllum (scandens) (So. China, Himalayas, Queensland, Malayas, N. Guinea); twining vine-like fern with pinnate leaflets, the sterile lanceolate segments unlobed and bluish-green; larger, broader pinnules than japonicum; fertile pinnae only 2-times divided. *p. 1084*

volubile (Trop. America: Cuba, Brazil); somewhat close-growing, dense and bushy with fronds, their stalk on rachis slowly elongating and forming the vine, set with thin-leathery bright green leaflets pinnate into narrow segments, pinnae 20-30 cm long. *p. 1084*

LYONIA *Ericaceae* **S3LFM**

foliosa (Thailand); attractive tropical shrub with broad-oval, quilted leaves to 5 cm long; pendant cup-shaped flowers pure white with narrow tan margins on petals, in terminal racemes. *p. 968*

LYSICHITON *Araceae* **C2HFWd**

americanum (sometimes spelled Lysichitum), "Skunk cabbage"; swamp herb of the temperate zone; oblong leaves from thick rootstocks; spathe boat-shaped, pale yellow; ill-scented. *p. 222, 225*

camtschatcense (Japan, Kuriles, Sakhalin); robust marsh plant with stout erect white rhizome, soft-fleshy oblong-ovate leaves 40-80 cm long, fresh green, in rosette; showy white spathe 8-12 cm long, and cylindric spadix; fruit a green, 2-seeded berry. *p. 227*

LYSIMACHIA *Primulaceae* **C-I2LBM**

clethroides (China, Japan), "Loose-strife"; erect, little branched herbaceous perennial to 1 m, with ovate, hairy leaves 8-15 cm; small 1 cm bell-shaped white flowers with spreading petals, dense in slender pyramidal spikes, in late summer. *Warm temperate.* *p. 1966*

nummularia (C. Europe and Britain, nat. in E. No. America), "Creeping Jennie" or "Creeping Charlie", "Moneywort"; prostrate perennial creeper, with herbaceous dull light green, rounded leaves to 2½ cm long, in pairs along a thread-like, squarish, pink stem, forming rootlets opposite the axils; flowers bright yellow 2 cm across, winter-hardy. *Warm temperate.* *p. 1965*

punctata (S.E. Europe, Asia Minor), "Garden loose-strife"; erect perennial hairy herb, branches in three's, 30-60 cm high, with ovate leaves, and starry yellow flowers in axillary whorls. *Subtropic.* *p. 1966*

quadrifolia (New Brunswick to Georgia), "Loose-strife"; summer-blooming herbaceous perennial to 1 m high, with erect stalk bearing ovate leaves in whorls of 4 or 5; toward the top the axillary flowers, yellow with dark streaks. *p. 1962*

LYSIONOTUS *Gesneriaceae* **I3LFM**

serratus (Himalayas: India); small shrubby plant to 30 cm with dark green, waxy, elliptic leaves with pale veins, and light green, shiny reverse, margins lightly crenate; bracted funnel-shaped, bilabiate flowers, inflated in the middle, pale lilac with deeper veins 4 cm long, in drooping clusters. *p. 1258*

LYTOCARYUM *Palmae* **I3LFM**

hoehnei (Syagrus) (São Paulo, Brazil); beautiful and rare feather palm of small stature, somewhat resembling Syagrus weddelliana; the handsome pinnate fronds with about 60 pairs of regularly spaced linear leaflets narrowing to a pointed tip, bright green above and white tomentose beneath, the rachis and main ribs a contrasting pale pink or cream; long-stalked spadix; fruit coat splits into 3 parts exposing the seed, which to do so is most unusual in palms. *p. 1894*

MACADAMIA *Proteaceae* **I2LBD**

ternifolia (Queensland), "Small-fruited queensland-nut"; ornamental evergreen tree to 5 m high and wide, the new growth pink to red; narrow oblanceolate, leathery leaves in whorls of mostly three, to 15 cm long, serrate at margins; small cream to pinkish very fragrant flowers, in catkins to 12 cm long; pubescent fruit opening while still on tree, exposing bitter, inedible small 1 cm nuts. *p. 1973*

tetraphylla (Queensland, New South Wales), "Queensland nut" or "Macadamia nut"; evergreen tree to 15 m, with stiff, dark branches, sessile leaves in whorls mostly of 4, finely serrate in the juvenile stage; older leaves narrow, oblanceolate, stiff-leathery, 10-30 cm long; flowers pinkish; the hard-shelled fruit in pendant clusters, each 2-3 cm dia., and holding edible sweet nuts. *Subtropic.* *p. 1977*

MACARANGA *Euphorbiaceae* **S1LBM**

grandifolia (Guatemala), "Coral tree"; growing into a big tree, with rosettes of large peltate pointed, leathery leaves prominently veined, to 60 cm across; small petal-less flowers. *Tropical.* *p. 1054, 1060*

MACHAEROCEREUS *Cactaceae* **S2LBD**

eruca (Baja California), the "Creeping devil"; a ferocious creeper; prostrate stems to 10 cm thick and 3 m long, dark green with coppery tint, many-ribbed, ribs low and very spiny, with white central spine flattened, dagger-like and directed downward; dayblooming, creamy flowers. *Arid-tropical.* *p. 653*

MACKAYA *Acanthaceae* **I2LBD**

bella (Asystasia) (So. Africa); attractive erect shrub to 2 m, with ovate, slender-pointed, toothed leaves 12 cm long; 5 cm flowers bell-shaped with spreading segments, lilac, pencilled in throat. *Subtropic.* *p. 55*

MACLEANIA *Ericaceae* **I2HBM**

coccinea (Perú, Chile); smooth evergreen tropical shrub with pendant branches to 2 m high and wide; oval, hard-leathery leaves 6 cm long; the inflorescence pendant in terminal racemes, dense with tubular flowers 3 cm long, the corolla constricted toward mouth, scarlet red. *p. 968*

glabra (Psammisia) (Central America); tropical evergreen shrub with pendant, smooth branches, with thin-leathery, rich green oval, 5 cm leaves pitted with black; the beautiful tubular flowers 3 cm long, old rose-pink, edged with white at spreading limb, thick and waxy on stout stalks. *p. 968*

insignis (Mountains of Veracruz to Guatemala); scandent shrub with tuberous base; the slender branches dense with glossy 5 cm leaves, reddish when young; charming waxy, tubular flowers bright scarlet with apricot tips, 4 cm long. Photos on pg. 968 collected by J. Bogner of Munich Bot. Garden, as M. salapa; compare M. insignis in Tropica, p. 394. *p. 968*

MACODES *Orchidaceae* **S3HNM**

petola (Anoectochilus) (Java, Borneo), "Gold-net orchid"; small, handsome terrestrial growing in caves, with broad ovate 8 cm leaves a beautiful velvety olive-green and a contrasting network of shimmering gold bronze; small flowers on long spike, brown with white tips; should be removed to conserve the strength of the plant, (Jan.-Feb.) (S) *p. 1754*

sanderianus (New Guinea); pretty terrestrial with fleshy stem densely clothed by broad ovate, soft-leathery leaves to 10 cm long, velvety satin-green, beautifully veined lengthwise with pale green, and reticulated with lines of copper-red and gold, and thin white edging. *p. 1754*

MACRADENIA *Orchidaceae* **S3OFD**

multiflora (paraensis in hort.) (Brazil); small epiphyte with pear-shaped pseudobulbs and solitary 15 cm leaf; small flowers in pendant raceme, the lanceolate petals and sepals red-brown edged buff, lip white marked purple (winter). (S) *p. 1761*

MACROPIPER *Piperaceae* **I1LFM**

excelsum (New Zealand, Tahiti), "Lofty pepper"; small tree growing to 6 m high, having aromatic, cordate rounded, leathery 12 cm leaves, olive-green with prominent pale veins and undulate margin, pale gray beneath; flowers very small. *p. 1944, 1946*

excelsum psittacorum (New Zealand: Poor Knight Isl.), "Lofty pepper"; small aromatic tree to 6 m high; cordate leathery, glossy green 12-15 cm leaves with pale veining, larger than the species; small flowers in spikes, and with edible yellow fruit. *Tropical.* *p. 1945*

MACROZAMIA *Cycadaceae* **I2LFM**

peroffskyana (Bot. Lepidozamia) (Queensland), a "Palmfern"; with trunk to 6 m high, having arched pinnate leaves to 60 cm long, leaflets sickle-shaped; male cones 15 cm; female cones 40 cm long. *p. 941*

riedlei (Western Australia), "Zamia palm"; the only cycad in S.W. Australia; palm-like crown of fronds from thick, partially underground trunk 1 to 4 m high; the bluish green pinnate leaves 1 m or more long; rigid, well-spaced leaflets without distinct midvein and with needle-tips; nestling at base the large cone-like flowers, the male cones 25 cm wide. *p. 937*

spiralis: see Ceratozamia

tridentata (Queensland, New So. Wales); small palm-like cycad to 1 m or more high, forming a short trunk which is pulled underground in deep rich soil; the dark green fronds finely pinnate, 60 cm to more than 1 m long, the narrow lanceolate leaflets 15-30 cm long, together forming a compact, symmetrical crown. *p. 938*

MAESA *Myrsinaceae* **I2LBM**

argentea (Himalayas); subtropical shrub with branches densely hairy when young; elliptic, membranous, toothed leaves 10-20 cm long, dull green above; many-flowered clusters usually from leaf axils of small ½ cm white blossoms; small whitish berry-like fruit. *p. 1603*

MAGNOLIA *Magnoliaceae* **C-I2LBM**

campbellii (Sikkim); deciduous tree 10 to 30 m high, with elliptic-oblong leaves to 30 cm long, glaucous beneath; 15-25 cm cup-shaped fragrant flowers before the leaves, pink outside deep rose inside, in February-March. *p. 1524*

grandiflora (Carolina to Florida and Texas), the "Southern magnolia"; noble evergreen pyramidal tree to 30 m high, with decorative thick-leathery, rich-green ovate oblong leaves to 20 cm long with shining surface and rusty tomentose beneath; large and beautiful 20 cm cup-shaped flowers creamy white and fragrant; rust-brown cone-like fruit. *Warm temperate.* *p. 1524, 1525*

x soulangeana, (hybrid of M. denudata x liliflora) both from China, the "Saucer magnolia" is common in cultivation and one of the showiest spring-flowering small trees; obovate deciduous leaves and solitary 15 cm flowers white, tinged purplish rose outside, blooming ahead of foliage; (hardy). *Temperate.* *p. 1524*

stellata (halliana) (Japan), "Star magnolia"; deciduous, much branched shrub to 8 m high; dull green obovate 12 cm leaves; fragrant white flowers with narrow petals, spreading 8 cm across, later reflexed, and appearing before the foliage in early spring; red fruit; fairly hardy. *p. 1524*

virginiana (Massachusetts to Texas), "Sweet-bay"; large deciduous shrub, or tree to 20 m with smooth branches and hairy buds, half evergreen in the subtropics, with elliptic 12 cm leaves glaucous-gray beneath; 8 cm very fragrant flowers with the foliage, the cupping fleshy petals creamy-white, in May-June; hardy. *p. 1524*

MAHERNIA *Sterculiaceae* **I2HBM**

verticillata (So. Africa), "Honey-bells"; rambling bush with fern-like, lacy foliage, and small 2 cm nodding, golden, bell-shaped flowers, very fragrant like lily-of-the-valley, in winter and spring; used for hanging baskets. *p. 2088, 2091*

MAHONIA *Berberidaceae* **I2LBM**

aquifolium (Brit. Columbia, Oregon to No. California), "Barberry", "Oregon grape" or "Holly mahonia"; handsome hardy evergreen thornless shrub to 1 m or more, with flexible stems and pinnate leaves with spiny-toothed, leathery leaflets 8 cm or more long, glossy dark green, the young foliage a pretty bronzy-red; lemon-yellow flowers in dense clusters, followed by blue-black, edible berries with glaucous bloom. Very durable, hardy in So. New England. *Warm temperate.* *p. 495*

beallei (China), "Leatherleaf mahonia"; distinctive evergreen shrub with stout, erect woody stems, to 4 m high, carrying horizontal leaves 25 cm long, with 7-15 thick-leathery, broad leaflets as much as 12 cm long, bluish-green with yellow at base; underneath, glaucous green veins, the margins with a few large teeth, on red petioles; fragrant yellow flowers in spike-like clusters followed by powdery blue berries; fairly winter-hardy. *p. 495*

lomariifolia (China: Yunnan), "Chinese holly grape"; evergreen shrub with erect woody, bamboo-like stem with rosette of long pinnate leaves, the hard leathery, holly-like, undulate 9 cm leaflets olive green with lighter veins, with pointed spiny lobes, set in pairs on long wiry axis to 30 cm long; berries blue. *p. 495, 496*

repens (Berberis) (Brit. Columbia, No. California, East to Rocky Mountains), "Creeping mahonia"; small spreading evergreen creeping by underground stolons or stems, 30 cm or more high, dull bluish-green leaves have 3-7 spine-toothed leaflets, turning bronze in winter; yellow flowers in 8 cm clusters followed by dark blue, powdery berries. *Warm temperate.* *p. 495*

MAJORANA *Labiatae* **I2LBD**

hortensis (Europe), "Sweet marjoram"; bushy, half-hardy perennial, sweet-scented, with furry gray-green foliage; white flowers with green bracts. Use: leaves used for flavoring in cooking vegetables, stews, beef, chicken, sausage. *p. 1348, 1349*

MALACOCARPUS: see Wigginsia

MALAXIS *Orchidaceae* **S3HFM**

calophylla (Microstylis) (Malaya), "Plaited jewel orchid"; handsome terrestrial with ornamental foliage on fleshy base; the oblique ovate leaves plaited or grooved, 10-15 cm long, greenish-brown in center, pale grayish green in outer area, dark spotted, the margin undulate, reddish beneath; small yellowish flowers, with spreading sepals and narrower petals, on erect stalk. *p. 1754*

lowii (Microstylis) (Borneo); beautiful little terrestrial, with short, fleshy, leafy stem, the ovate leaves dark coppery-brown with pale gray band down center, the margins crisped; flowers purple, the ears of the lip yellowish. *p. 1754*

ocreata (Mexico); small terrestrial 18 cm tall with 2 glossy green leaves; inflorescence a spike of numerous tiny green flowers, with purple lip. *p. 1763*

soulei (Texas, Arizona, Mexico to Panama); terrestrial 20 cm high, small pseudobulbs topped by solitary, sheathing leaf glossy green and expanded above the middle, spike of many tiny 4 mm green flowers with green lip (summer). *p. 1763*

spicata (Virginia to Bahamas and West Indies); terrestrial with small fleshy pseudobulbs covered by leaf-sheaths, paired broad leaves keeled beneath; the erect floral spike to 35 cm tall, the inverted small flowers 1 cm long, sepals and petals green, lip yellow to vermilion (autumn). *p. 1763*

MALEPHORA: see Hymenocyclus

MALESHERBIA *Passifloraceae* **I2LBM**

linearifolia (Gynopleura) (Chile); hairy herb to 45 cm high, with wiry greenish purple stems and foliage gray green; narrow leaves 4 cm long; showy 3 cm flowers in terminal cluster, rosy lavender sepals and petals pale blue, the tube with green stripes. *p. 1927*

MALLOTUS *Euphorbiaceae* **C2LBM**

japonicus (China, Japan); semi-hardy, ornamental shrub or small tree 3 to 4 m high, ornamental, deciduous in colder climates, with pith in the scurfy shoots; large palmately lobed or cut, quilted reddish leaves 20 cm or more long; small inconspicuous flowers in terminal clusters; followed by the prickly capsule fruits. *p. 1061*

MALPIGHIA *Malpighiaceae* **·I2LBD**

coccigera (W. Indies), "Miniature holly"; bushy evergreen shrub, densely covered with tiny, 2 cm holly-like, stiff leaves glossy dark green with coarse spiny teeth; small pink flowers, and red fruit. Also known as "Singapore-holly". *p. 1518*

glabra (So. Texas to So. America), "Barbados cherry", known in Puerto Rico and Mexico as "Acerola"; shrub or small tree to 4 m, with shining green ovate, leathery 8 cm leaves; pretty flowers carmine-rose with fimbriate petals, 1 cm across, followed by small 1 cm cherry-like edible fruit, of acid flavor and high in Vitamin C (Ascorbic acid), and ranking as its richest known natural source. Can be made into high-vitamin jelly or fruit juice. *Subtropic.* *p. 1518, 1525*

MALUS *Rosaceae* **C2LBMhd**

x atrosanguinea (halliana x sieboldii) (China); handsome, floriferous "Crab-apple"; a small tree with purplish twigs and ovate, deciduous, glossy leaves finely serrate, covered in spring with masses of rosy carmine flowers with narrow petals, not fading to white, followed by small, yellow and dark red apples. *p. 1995*

baccata (Siberia, China), "Siberian crab apple"; tree with hard branchlets, and small ovate leaves, 2 cm white flowers; miniature 2 cm wax-like fruit yellow or red; trained into dwarfed bonsai trees in Japan. *p. 1998*

floribunda 'Scheideckeri', beautiful "Flowering crab-apple"; of pyramidal habit, with ovate leaves and large, semi-double, 3 cm flowers of delicate rose-pink to pale tinged pink, borne with great profusion in large clusters during May, followed by small 2 cm yellow to reddish tart fruit, used for jellies. *Temperate.* *p. 1995*

prunifolia (N. E. Asia including Japan), an ornamental "Crab-apple"; small tree with deciduous ovate leaves; flowers white 3 cm dia., attractive pendulous little 2 cm apples yellow with red cheeks. *p. 1997*

pumila, (Europe and W. Asia),"Common apple"; round-headed deciduous tree to 12 m high, with oval, leathery leaves 5-10 cm long, and flowers white or light pink, 3-5 cm across, appearing with first foliage, and followed by its large depressed globular edible fruit, with firm, tart-sweet flesh. *Temperate.* *p. 1992*

pumila paradisiaca (Europe, W. Asia), the "Paradise apple"; deciduous, winter-hardy tree with ovate thin-leathery leaves, obtusely serrate; flowers usually appearing with first foliage, white or light rose, 2 cm across; the edible, tart-tasting, delicious fruit usually globular, 5-8 cm dia., in greenish-yellow; this variety ideal as a dwarf tree, or for training on espaliers. *p. 1998*

MALVASTRUM *Malvaceae* **I2LBM**

x hypomadarum (So. Africa), "False mallow"; (capense x scabrosum); much branched, hairy, shrub to 3 m high; branches slender, with 3-lobed, toothed leaves; flowers in spike-like racemes white flushed pink with deep purple streaks in center, 3-4 cm across. *p. 1532*

MALVAVISCUS *Malvaceae* **I-S2LBM**

arboreus (Mexico), "Wax mallow"; evergreen shrub 3 to 4½ m high, broadly ovate, crenate 3-lobed leaves to 12 cm long; rough above and soft-downy beneath; 3 cm flowers usually solitary in leaf axils, rich crimson red but petals do not open; long-protruding style. *Tropical.* *p. 1533*

arboreus mexicanus, "Turk's cap"; tall tropical shrub more or less hairy, with narrow ovate, toothed leaves, narrower than the species; flowers hibiscus-like 3 cm long, with scarlet corolla, but which do not open, and with protruding staminal column. *Tropical.* *p. 1533*

penduliflorus (conzatii) (Mexico), "Turk's-cap"; herbaceous shrub with large ovate, doubly crenate, hibiscus-like leaves, very showy with pendulous, narrowly folded, bell-like flowers of brilliant red. *p. 1527*

MAMMEA *Guttiferae* **S2LBD**

americana (West Indies, So. America), the "Mammee apple"; handsome tropical tree 10 to 20 m high, with a broad crown of shiny leathery, oval leaves 10-20 cm long; fragrant white 2 cm male and female flowers; in spring the large globose, russet-brown fruit 8 to 20 cm dia., with rough, bitter skin and orange, apricot-flavored pulp surrounding 1 to 4 round seeds; the pleasantly sweet flesh is eaten raw or cooked; the juice also makes a refreshing drink. *Tropical.* *p. 1319*

MAMMILLARIA or MAMILLARIA *Cactaceae* **•I (C to bl.) 2LBD**

affinis (polythele) (Hidalgo); globular to cylindric body, dark bluish-green; prominent tubercles in symmetrical spirals, and with showy, amethyst-brown spines; reddish flowers near top. *p. 710, 715, 721*

albescens (Mexico); globose, clustering plant 9 cm high, with long tubercles set with long, spidery white radials; flowers white. *p. 716*

albicoma (Mexico: Tamaulipas); small globe to 5 cm, with small warts dense with pure white, hair-like radials, glossy and soft, few central spines, axils with white wool; profuse white flowers. *p. 716*

albilanata (Mexico: Guerréro); elongate plant 15 cm high dense with little grayish tubercles with tiny light brown tufts and grayish-white radials, and light brown, short spines; flowers deep carmine. *Arid-tropical.* *p. 712*

aljibensis (Mexico); attractive little globe, the dark green dense knobs evenly covered with spreading white radials, and a pair of short needle spines pinkish cream tipped purple, the apex of the plant tinted purple; small flowers in a circle purplish carmine with a silky sheen. *p. 715, 718*

applanata (Texas); flattened dark green globe with conical tubercles, the new areoles woolly, 10-18 spreading, brown radials, and solitary central brown spine; 2½ cm flowers creamy-white with green midrib. *p. 713*

armillata (Baja California); cylindric plant becoming 30 cm high, angular knobs bluish to gray green set with white radials tipped black, and long hooked brown needle spines; flowers greenish or pink. *p. 717*

auriareolis (Mexico: Querétaro); flattened globes 8 cm dia., and branching; bluish green tubercles, with milky sap, axils with white wool and bristles, radials glossy white, stiff central spines tipped red; fruit bright carmine. *p. 718*

aurihamata (Mexico), "Yellow-hook cushion"; pretty little globe with shining tubercles with white, silky hairy radials and yellow to brown central spines; yellow flowers. *p. 714, 716*

baumii; correctly Dolichothele (Mexico); elongate, 8 cm high, green with soft tubercles each tipped with over 30 soft, white radials and white central needle spines; flowers yellow inside. *p. 716*

baxteriana (Baja California); elongate globe to 10 cm dia., olive green with high nipples densely armed with long cream needle spines tipped black; flowers yellow marked red. *p. 715*

blossfeldiana (Mexico: Baja California); small globular plant somewhat elongate 4 to 5 cm thick, medium green; the short knobs with whitish radials and a central black hook-spine; flowers carmine-red. *Arid-subtropic.* *p. 708*

bocasana (Mexico), "Powder puff"; like a bursting cotton boll, the little, mound-forming globes covered with snow-white silky hair as well as brown fish-hook spines, to 5 cm thick; 2 cm flowers cream-white. *Arid-tropical.* *p. 618, 640A, 713, 714, 717*

bocasana 'Ed Hummel', known as "Hummel's powder puff"; a California seedling, makes many offsets quickly forming a tall pyramidal cluster; the individual little globes, dense with green tubercles, are clothed all over with silky white hair and half-hidden wiry brown fishhook spines. *p. 717*

"bogotensis"; said to come from Mexico, with large tubercles topped by recurving spines. *p. 711*

bombycina (Mexico); globular, becoming cylindric with age to 20 cm high, fresh green, the top silky white-haired and well-furnished with beautiful brown-red hook spines; flowers clear red. *p. 718, 720*

bravoae (Mexico: Guanajuato); small globe 6 cm high, glossy bright green, tubercles arranged in dense spirals, almost hidden by spines and wool, radials white, stiff centrals; flowers pink. *p. 707, 718*

cadereytense (Mexico); clubshaped little plant with close, neatly arranged tubercles covered by white hair-like radials and chalky-white central spines tipped red-brown. *p. 715*

camptotricha (Mexico), "Birdsnest"; small clustering globes to 5 cm, fresh green, with extended nipples and long yellow bristle-like spines often twisted; flowers white, greenish outside, hidden in axils. *p. 717*

candida (C. Mexico), "Snowball cactus"; an exquisite little globe closely tubercled and covered with a multitude of pure white radial spines; clustering flowers rose-colored. *Arid-tropical.* *p. 712, 714, 718*

caput-medusae (sempervivi tetracantha) (Cent. Mexico); depressed globe 6 cm high, with multiples of bluish green, slender nipples, woolly axils, white, bristle-like radials rarely persistent, short white central spines spreading cross-wise; flowers flesh-colored. *p. 718*

carnea (C. and S. Mexico); small cylindric plant 9 cm high, with spirals of 4-angled tubercles woolly in axils, the areoles without bristles and few spines; flowers salmon pink. *p. 717*

celsiana (So. Mexico), "Showy pincushion"; attractive small deep green globe becoming cylindric and forming clusters with age, tubercles neatly arranged and white-woolly in axils, radials white, central spines pale yellow; flowers red. *Arid-tropical.* *p. 618, 714, 715, 723*

chionocephala (Mexico: Coahuila); symmetrical, globular plant slowly becoming branched, 8 cm dia., dark green but the milky tubercles nearly hidden by bristly straw-white radials and short central spines tipped black; flowers rose. *Arid-subtropic.* *p. 718*

collinsii 'Chiapas variety' (Mexico); olive green globe with prominent pointed knobs tipped with cream radials and straight, sharp needle spines, the depressions with lemon-colored wool. *p. 715*

collinsii 'Oaxaca variety' (Mexico); attractive globe from Salina Cruz, olive green with prominent pointed knobs tipped by small white radials, central spines tipped brown; white-woolly top. *p. 715*

columbiana (bogotensis) (Colombia), "South American pincushion"; solitary, small clubshaped gray-green plant 10-25 cm high with dense nipples set with 20-30 white radials and reddish-brown central spines with dark tip; flowers deep pink with yellow throat. *p. 715*

compressa (C. Mexico), "Mother of hundreds"; small globes, pale bluish green, in clumps; knobs short, axils woolly; white spines; flowers pinkish, 2 cm long. *Arid-tropical.* *p. 717*

compressa rubispina, variety differing from the species in having spines red, when new. *p. 717*

confusa (Mexico: Oaxaca), "Variable pincushion"; elongate globe close to pyrrhocephala, 5 cm thick, depressed center with white wool, pyramidal green tubercles set with curving spines; flowers greenish-straw-colored, midline of petals pink. *p. 717*

crassispina; properly a form of rhodantha, with thick yellowish-brown central spines. *p. 718*

crucigera (Mexico); very pretty obconical light green body looking like an upside-down egg, branching from the base and forming clusters; the many tubercles furnished with small radials and one or two short, stout reddish to yellow central spines; small 1 cm carmine flowers in a ring. *p. 708*

denudata (Texas, Coahuila); small globe of 4 cm dia., low tubercles, the areoles with 50-60 short spines, the small flowers with white petals having reddish center line. *p. 728*

"dolichocentra" in hort., "Ruby dumpling"; similar to tetracantha; bluish green; spines white; small 8 mm flowers rosy-red. May be var. of kewensis. *Arid-tropical.* *p. 719*

durispina (Cent. Mexico); globose or short cylindric to 30 cm high, dark green, with high pointed knobs, awl-shaped gray spines radiating and star-like; flowers carmine. *p. 721*

echinaria (gracilis) (Mexico), "Needle-fingers"; short cylindric plant forming clusters, similar to elongata but having glossy central spines with the golden yellow radials; flowers yellow with salmon outer petals. *p. 714, 723*

elegans (Central Mexico); lovely elongate globe 5 cm dia., glaucous green, densely tubercled and covered with fine white bristle-like radials and contrasting brown needle-like central spines; flowers carmine-red, followed by a ring of red fruit 2 cm long. *Arid-subtropic.* *p. 719*

elongata (Mexico), "Golden stars"; small, clustering cylinders to 3 cm thick, light green, tubercles in spirals and covered with yellow, interlacing radial spines; flowers white. *Arid-tropical.* *p. 708, 714, 727*

elongata 'Cristata'; beautifully crested form with many snaking ridges, growing larger with age, handsomely covered with golden-yellow spines. For best survival and growth, crests are usually grafted on column cactus. *p. 707*

elongata minima, "Lace cactus"; diminutive form with slender stems in dense clusters and covered with golden radials and wanting central spines. *p. 727*

erectohamata (Mexico: San Luis Potosi); little 6 cm globes easily clustering, glossy light green densely covered with bristly white spines, few centrals dark red; flowers pure white. *p. 716*

fragilis (gracilis var.) (Mexico), "Thimble cactus"; little oblong stem branching toward top, to 8 cm high, bright green, knobs with white radial spines; flowers cream, pinkish outside. *Arid-tropical.* *p. 716, 727*

fuscata (Mexico); olive green globe, later cylindric to 30 cm high, dense with tubercles thickly covered with radials white to yellowish, central spines yellow; a form of rhodantha. *p. 715*

geminispina (bicolor) (C. Mexico), "Whitey"; small clubshaped plant becoming cylindric and clustering, glaucous, with prominent knobs topped by white radials and needle-like white, black-tipped central spines; flowers red. *Arid-tropical.* *p. 19*, 707, 714, 722, 723*

geminispina nivea (Mexico); a beautiful form densely furnished with very long 5 cm needle spines glistening pure white tinted pink and tipped red, curving out and downward. *Arid-tropical.* *p. 727*

gigantea (Mexico: Guanajuato); depressed globe 10 cm high and 15 cm wide, dark green, with white wool on top as well as in axils; numerous high tubercles close together set with awl-shaped spines white to black; flowers greenish-yellow. *p. 718*

hahniana (Mexico), "Old lady cactus"; attractive little globe, rich green with long and curly snowy-white hair-like bristles and red-tipped spines; flowers violet-red. *Arid-tropical.* *p. 620, 712, 714, 723, 728*

hahniana var. haseltonii; large elongate olive green globe covered with white hair and white hair-like radials, flexible needle spines white tipped brown; flowers red in late autumn. *p. 723*

hemisphaerica (No. Mexico, Texas); flattened globe to 12 cm dia., tubercles elongated, dark green, woolly at top; yellowish radials needle-like, one straight brown central spine; flowers cream-white. *p. 710, 721*

hidalgensis (Mexico: Hidalgo); pretty, cylindrical plant to 30 cm high, dark green and rounded at top, woolly and with reddish spines; large tubercles conical, with floccose white wool in axils, few grayish spines; small carmine flowers. *Arid-tropical.* *p. 721*

johnstonii (Mexico); attractive globe to 20 cm high, apex depressed, prominent, elongate tubercles topped by stiff white radials and stouter central spines; flowers white, fruit carmine-red. *p. 719*

johnstonii sancarlensis (Sonora); an attractive globe to 20 cm high, with flattened apex and elongate tubercles, whitish radials, more numerous in this form, and stout central spines; flowers white. *p. 716*

karwinskiana (Mexico: Oaxaca); small dark bluish green globe flat at top, 8 cm high, the high angular tubercles emitting a milky juice when wounded, short white spines tipped red-black; flowers cream, reddish outside. *p. 719*

kelleriana (Mexico: Querétaro); elongate globe to 12 cm high, dense with cylindric conic grayish olive tubercles, spines black purplish becoming pale; white wool in the axils near the apex; flowers magenta, fruit scarlet. *p. 720*

kewensis (Mexico: Hidalgo); elongate globe 4 cm dia., deep green, with peaked knobs tipped by clusters of short, hard, purplish radials paler at base, the upper axils filled with white wool; flowers reddish purple. *p. 722*

klissingiana (Mexico: Tamaulipas); beautiful globular plant to 15 cm high, glossy green, entirely covered with interlaced white spines, the axils very woolly; small flowers in a ring around center, lively pink. *p. 720*

kunzeana (Mexico); small globes 10 cm high, freely clustering, glossy green, the axils with long curly bristles, thin white radial spines and needle-like or hooked central spines yellow to brown; flowers yellowish white. *p. 720*

lanata (No. Mexico); beautiful small, short cylindric plant entirely covered by wide-spreading white radials as well as white wool in the axils and at the top; small magenta red flowers. *p. 720*

lewisiana (Baja California); a variation of M. brandegeei; flattened deep green globe with closely set high nipples, each tipped by long gray radials and a curving black-brown central spine; flowers yellow. *p. 725*

longicoma (Mexico: San Luis Potosi); small globe 5 cm wide, tubercles dense with hair-like and silky whitish radials, the central spines brown, some with hooks; flowers white suffused with rose. *Arid-tropical.* *p. 716*

macracantha (Mexico: San Luis Potosi); dark green globe with large oval, 4-angled knobs with few white radials but stiff yellowish brown central spines like needles, white-woolly in axils; flowers carmine red. *p. 725*

magnimamma (centricirrha) (C. Mexico), "Mexican pincushion"; clustering globe, to 10 cm, dark green and milky, with large conic tubercles topped with 3-5 recurved horn-colored spines; cream flowers. *p. 721*

martinezii (So. Mexico); small cylindric plant close to albilanata, entirely covered with pale-brown spines tipped brown, longer than albilanata, as well as dense straw-white radials; rosy flowers. *p. 722*

mazatlanensis (Mexico: Sinaloa); cylindrical plant 4 cm thick and freely branching, grayish green, axils woolly and spiny, the bristly radials white spreading flat like stars, golden brown central spines, one with a hook; flowers carmine-rose. *p. 725*

melanocentra (No. Mexico); globe to 9 cm thick and glaucous green, pointed tubercles pyramidal set with needle-like, spreading spines pale yellow to black; flowers pinkish red. *p. 716*

microhelia (Mexico: Querétaro) "Little suns"; short cylindric plant 15 cm high, with short tubercles tipped by regularly radiating, bristle-like but stiff spines white to yellow, and 1-2 blackish red central spines toward apex, increasing in number in older plants; small silky flowers canary yellow to whitish. *p. 723*

microheliopsis (Mexico: Queretaro); cylindric, smaller plant than microhelia, 6 cm high, dark green, neatly furnished with regular radiating, almost white radials, and 6-8 flesh to brown central spines; flowers pale violet, sometimes tinged with pink. *p. 720*

multiceps (N. E. Mexico), "Grape cactus"; possibly a variety of prolifera; small globes 2 cm thick and clustering, dark green covered by white hair-like radials and needle-like yellow central spines; flowers salmon. *p. 721*

mystax (C. America); globose as seedling, later short cylindric, flat-topped, dull green prominent high knobs with white spines; flowers dark red. *p. 725*

nejapensis (Mexico: Oaxaca); beautiful elongate clustering globe to 15 cm high, with fresh green, prominent nipples tipped with white-woolly tufts, and sets of stout glistening white spines, red-brown at the extreme tip, the axils also filled with white wool especially near apex; yellow flowers shaded with red-purple. *Arid-tropical.* *p. 723*

nejapensis cristata; a normally clustering plant of several olive green, white-spined globes uniting to form a fasciated crest covered with white areoles and shaped like a wide-grinning mouth, earning to this plant the apt name "Smiling Jack"; photographed in the collection of Crestview Nursery, Carlsbad, California. *p. 707*

neophaeacantha (Mexico); depressed globe with pronounced nipples set regularly with "dusky" spines radiating outward; very lovely with a complete ring of pink blossoms which hold their petals wide to the sun and shine like satin. *p. 720*

nivosa (West Indies); globular to cylindric plant to 17 cm wide, clustering; tubercles milky, and white-woolly in axils, very spiny with long golden to brown needles; flowers cream. *p. 620, 720*

ocotillensis (Mexico: Queretaro); small globular plant 6 cm high, dark green, with milky sap, the broad, high knobs tipped by white woolly tufts and white radials, also 1-2 red-black central spines; cream flowers. *p. 725*

ortiz-rubiona (Mexico); small clustering globes densely covered with white spines, and white woolly areoles; flowers rosy-yellow. *p. 719*

pacifica (Baja California); depressed globe to 15 cm dia., olive green tinted copper, with elongated tubercles set with long thin white radials and yellow central spines tipped maroon; flowers yellowish green. *p. 719*

parkinsonii (C. Mexico), "Owl's eyes"; branching and clustering little cylinder to 8 cm thick, glaucous green, tubercles neatly arranged and topped by white radials and prominent central spine; flowers yellowish. *p. 719*

parkinsonii brevispina; small depressed globe 8 cm across, forming cushions, covered with white and reddish spines only 1/2 cm long. *p. 708*

parkinsonii cristata; a clustered old plant partially becoming deformed into fasciations and developing crests shaped like a down-turned mouth, accented by the straw-colored spines, giving rise to the name "Sadsack" in this particular plant 25 cm across; photographed at Crestview Nursery, Carlsbad, California. *Arid-tropical.* *p. 707*

parkinsonii tegelliana; a beautiful form richly furnished with snow-white wool, bristle-like white radials and long white needle spines. *p. 620*

pettersonii (Mexico: Guanajuato); broad globe to 12 cm thick, later short cylindric; glaucous green, with plump, 4-sided knobs, axils with white wool and bristly, very spiny with whitish radials tipped dark, the centrals fawn to brown; flowers reddish brown to magenta inside. *p. 724*

phaeacantha (Mexico); quick growing globose plant dark green with close tubercles topped by bristly white radials and awl-shaped black spines; dark red flowers. *p. 719*

plumosa (No. Mexico), "Feather cactus"; remarkable clustering little globes on which the snowy-white spines have lost their normal identity and have become soft and feathery completely covering the plant; flowers white. *p. 722*

potosina (Mexico); elongate globe with closely-set knobs which are milky if bruised, covered with white hair-like radials and topped by long reddish yellow spines; flowers yellowish white. *p. 723*

pottsii (Coryphantha) (W. Texas, Chihuahua); densely spiny, cylindric plant to 12 cm high; numerous interlaced, slender white radials, and stouter central spines curving up, and tipped red-brown; small light purple flowers. *Arid-subtropic.* *p. 710, 722*

pringlei (Mexico); small globular or short cylindric, solitary plant, dull green, tubercles with woolly and bristly axils, yellow spines; flowers deep red. *p. 727*

prolifera (pusilla) (N. E. Mexico, Texas, Cuba, Santo Domingo); freely clustering colonies of globose or short-cylindric plants 6 cm thick, dark green with soft tubercles, the axils with long hairs, white hair-like radials and needle-like centrals; small yellowish flowers; fruit coral-red. *p. 708, 724*

pseudocrucigera (Mexico: Querétaro); flattened globe 5 cm wide, olive gray-green knobs dense with fine white horizontal radials and short stout chalky-white central spines tipped black; flowers pink. *p. 724*

pygmaea (Mexico); clustering small cylindric plant, 2$\frac{1}{2}$ cm dia., with round tubercles, white radials and golden yellow shining central spines; flowers cream, tinged red outside. *p. 720*

pyrrhocephala (Mexico: Oaxaca, Hidalgo); globular to cylindric plant 8 cm thick, with prominent grayish green pyramidal tubercles tipped by white and black spines; the apex furnished with white wool; flowers in a ring around the top, glossy carmine red. *p. 726*

recurva (magnimamma recurva) (Mexico); attractive thick globe with pyramidal knobs dark brownish green with 4 short radials and one curved short thick central spine honey yellow. *p. 724*

rekoi (Mexico: Oaxaca); slender cylindric stem to 12 cm long and 5 cm thick, clustering and spreading, pale green and very spiny, the spines white to brown; flowers carmine-red. *p. 721*

rhodantha (Mexico), "Rainbow pincushion"; seedlings globose, later cylindric to 30 cm, dull green, with round tubercles, radials white and central spines reddish-brown; rose-colored flowers. *p. 723*

ritteriana quadricentralis (Mexico); low globe with sunken apex, dark gray with angular knobs tipped with fine white radials and four, not 1-2, pale to purplish, black-tipped central spines; flowers greenish white inside. *p. 722*

saetigera (Mexico); small cylinder, solitary; top white-woolly; pointed knobs, short white radial spines; flowers white striped rose pink. *p. 726*

schiedeana (Mexico: Hidalgo); globe 5½ cm wide and clustering, dark green, tubercles bristly in axils, numerous short white radials and short sharp central spines; flowers white. *p. 724*

seitziana (Mexico: Ixmiquilpan); attractive globe becoming cylindrical to 25 cm high, prominent large pointed, conical knobs glaucous green, tipped by a few whitish spines, the centrals tipped black; flowers rose. *Arid-tropical.* *p. 719*

sempervivi (Cent. Mexico), a "Strawberry cactus"; the true species is an attractive globular plant dense with long angular nipples tipped by very short, hard spines, the axils toward apex filled with wool; flowers carmine rose. *Arid-tropical.* *p. 725*

shurliana (Mexico); small globe deep green with nipples densely covered by regular starlike circles of straw-white radials and tipped by a long maroon fishhook spine. *p. 726*

solisioides (Mexico: Puebla); small globe somewhat squarish, to 4 cm dia., largely buried in the ground as a turnip-like root in habitat, the upper part barely 1 cm above ground; small conical tubercles studded with small white spine-clusters; pale yellow flowers 2½ cm across. *p. 708*

spinosissima (Cent. Mexico); cylindric plant to 30 cm high, dark green, densely covered with spines, the radials bristly, central spines thicker, from white to reddish brown; flowers purplish. *p. 721*

tegelbergiana (Mexico: Chiapas); beautiful, perfect little globe dense with small dark green tubercles, completely clothed with interlacing, thin white radials and stouter central spines tipped black-brown; the axils toward apex filled with white wool; flowers rosy-pink. *Arid-tropical.* *p. 726*

tenampensis (Mexico); small fresh-green globe 5 cm thick, dense with pointed knobs containing milky juice, and topped by short dark spines and white bristles; flowers purplish-red. *p. 722*

tetracantha (dolichocentra) (Mexico: Hidalgo); attractive globe, becoming cylindric, to 8 cm dia., glaucous green, white-woolly at the top; with high angled knobs, set crosswise with 4-5 yellowish, stiff central spines; small flowers carmine-red. *p. 726*

tetracantha galeottii (Mexico), "Ruby dumpling"; attractive variety with conic tubercles lighter green, axils naked, long central spines yellowish and recurved and flexuous, radial spines usually none except for short bristles. *p. 726*

tetrancistra (phellosperma), (S. W. United States, Mexico); small globe becoming cylindric, to 30 cm and clustering; needle-like radials and center spines, large funnel-shaped rosy flowers. *p. 714*

tolimensis (Mexico: Querétaro); broad globe to 10 cm across, gray to yellowish green and forming suckers, divided into numerous rounded tubercles carrying long and slender, spreading white spines to 5-6 cm long, the areoles with white wool, and with red flowers. *p. 707*

tolimensis longispina (Mexico: Querétaro); flattened globe to 10 cm wide, dark green, with dense knobs tipped with grayish radial spines and sets of vicious angular gray central spines curved downward and to 6 cm long; the areoles white-woolly at apex; flowers reddish. *p. 725*

trichacantha (Mexico); globular plant 5 cm wide, bluish-green, pronounced nipples tipped with radiating long white radials and reddish central spines, one hooked; flowers yellowish edged pink. *p. 724*

vagaspina (Mexico: Querétaro), low globular plant with high angular nipples set with short stiff radials and curving long straw-white central spines; axils toward apex filled with white wool; flowers light pink. *p. 722*

vaupelii (Coryphantha) (Mexico), "Vaupel's pincushion"; small solitary globe closely tubercled and covered with yellowish radials and long shiny central spines; flowers yellow. *p. 725*

vaupelii cristata, "Silver brain"; fantastic fasciations of coiled and wavy crests growing into a large and tight symmetrical globe; fine brown spines silvery at crest over the fresh green body; small 2 cm pink flowers. *p. 713*

viereckii (Mexico: Tamaulipas); globose plant 4 cm thick, becoming cylindric to 10 cm high, occasionally clustering; green softish tubercles tipped by many white radials star-like, and few central spines; flowers lemon yellow. *p. 724*

werdermannii (Mexico); large cylindrical plant dense with grayish green tubercles, each tipped with fine white hair and short, thin blackish spines; toward apex the axils are filled with white wool; probably a form of hahniana, less hairy, and winter-blooming, while hahniana blooms in summer. *p. 712*

wildii (Mexico: Hidalgo), "Fish-hook pincushion"; cylindric plant to 8 cm thick; dark green tubercles thickly set with bristle-like white radials and honey-colored central spines, rosy hairs in axils; numerous white flowers. *Arid-tropical.* *p. 726*

winteriae (No. Mexico); depressed globe to 10 cm wide, with large dark green 4-angled fleshy knobs, the axils with white wool, grayish radials some short, others long needle-like and tipped brown; flowers sulphur-yellow. *p. 726*

woodsii (Mexico: Guanajuato); flattened globe 8 cm wide, with sunken white-woolly apex, olive green knobs set with sparse white hair-like radials and long, gray needle spines with black tip; flowers dark pink. *p. 722*

zeilmanniana (Mexico: Guanajuato), "Strawberry cactus"; choice small globe 7 cm high, glossy green, with high cylindrical knobs covered by long white interlaced, soft radials, and reddish central spines, one hooked; flowers bright violet-purple. *Arid-tropical.* *p. 726*

MANDEVILLA *Apocynaceae* **I2-S3LFD**

x amabilis 'Alice du Pont' (Dipladenia), (formerly 'Splendens hybrid'); grown by Longwood Gardens (Baileya March 1962), a hybrid apparently derived from M. splendens, glabra, and superba. Woody climber growing to perhaps 10 m long; leaves opposite, dark green, rugose, lustrous, oblong-elliptic, 8-20 cm long; inflorescence a raceme from alternate leaf axils, each with to 20 blossoms; flowers funnel-shaped 6-10 cm dia., dawn pink with darker throat, turning dark rose. *Tropical.* *p. 138*

x amoena (Dipladenia) (amabilis x splendens); climbing shrub with oblong, rugose leaves 10-20 cm long, funnel-shaped 9 cm rose-pink flowers with deep rose eye, throat yellow. *p. 137, 1824A*

boliviensis (Bolivia), "White dipladenia"; free-blooming shrubby climber with slender branches; shining green oblong, slender pointed 5-8 cm leaves; and 5 cm funnel-form flowers white, with orange-yellow throat, in axillary racemes. *Subtropic.* *p. 137, 138*

x rosacea; old free-blooming splendens hybrid with oblong leaves and showy, soft rosy-pink flowers flushed and bordered deeper rose, throat yellow with bright rose ring at mouth. *p. 137*

sanderi 'Rosea' (Dipladenia), "Brazilian jasmine"; a cultivar of the Brazilian rose-flowered species; woody vine, wiry stems with milky sap; small leathery 3-5 cm ovate leaves glossy green, bronzy beneath; the 6-8 cm flowers salmon pink with pure yellow throat, blooming all year even as smaller plant. *Tropical.* *p. 137*

splendens (Dipladenia) (S.E. Brazil); woody twiner with stems finely hairy, and with milky sap; opposite, thin-textured leaves broadly elliptic, to 20 cm long; clusters of showy flowers 8-10 cm across, in a lovely rose-pink. *Tropical.* *p. 137*

suaveolens (laxa) (Argentina, Bolivia), the "Chilean jasmine"; woody vine with opposite, thin-leathery, ovate-cordate leaves 8-15 cm long, bright green and smooth, purplish to grayish beneath, on brownish wiry twining stems covered by rough warts; pure white funnel-shaped flowers 5 cm across and deliciously fragrant, in racemes of 6-8 or more, in summer. *Subtropic.* *p. 138*

MANDRAGORA *Solanaceae* **I2LFD**

officinarum (So. Europe), "Devil's apples", or "Mandrake"; herbaceous perennial steeped in superstition, with thick spindle-shaped tuberous roots often divided into two leg-like parts; the large wavy, ovate leaves to 30 cm long grow from the tips of the roots; bell-shaped, yellowish or purplish flowers cradled in the foliage, followed by the juicy berries. Mandrake root contains the alkaloid hyoscyamine. *Subtropic.* *p. 2072*

MANDULEA *Leguminosae* **I2LBM**

sericea (Transvaal); shrub or small tree to 3 m high; pinnate silvery foliage, and wing-like flowers lilac to purple. *p. 1384*

MANETTIA *Rubiaceae* **I2-3LFM**

inflata (bicolor) (Paraguay, Uruguay), "Firecracker plant"; twining herb with threadlike stems, thin-fleshy, green, ovate leaves and attractive solitary, 2 cm, tubular, waxy flowers from the axils, flask-like and vivid yellow, the lower part of the tube densely covered with bright scarlet bristles, giving the appearance of a red corolla tipped yellow. *Subtropic.* *p. 2014, 2112A*

MANFREDA *Amaryllidaceae* **I2LFM**

brachystachys (Mexico, Guatemala); bulbous herb with fleshy, concave, basal leaves to 35 cm long and 4 cm wide; the tubular night-blooming flowers green, 5 cm long, with long-protruding stamens, in long-stalked inflorescence to 2 m tall. *p. 122*

maculosa (Agave pubescens) (Mexico: Chiapas, Morelos); ornamental rosette of thin, soft-fleshy, sword-shaped concave leaves to 30 cm long, glaucous blue with large chocolate blotches; margins smooth; the inflorescence on long stalks to 1 m or more, with small pinkish-white flowers, opening at night. *Tropical.* *p. 122*

MANGIFERA *Anacardiaceae* **S2LBM**

indica (No. India, Burma, Malaya), the "Mango" tree; with large, spreading, evergreen crown, 18-30 m high, and grown for its delicious fruit all over the tropics; leathery, lanceolate leaves to 40 cm long; small pinkish flowers in terminal panicles, followed by large, variably yellow to reddish sweet-fleshy fruit averaging 12 cm or more long, containing the large adhering stone. *Tropical.* *p. 132*

MANGONIA *Araceae* **S3LFM**

uruguaya (Felipponiella) (Uruguay); subtropical tuberous aroid with vivid green lobed leaves on 20 cm petioles, vaginate below; the front lobe 15 cm long and 7½ cm wide, back lobes 20-50 cm long; the inflorescence appearing before the leaves with spathe slender boat-shaped, 8-16 cm long, pale rose and with spike-like spadix to 15 cm long. *p. 227*

MANIHOT *Euphorbiaceae* **S3HFM**

esculenta (Brazil: Goias), "Tapioca" or "Manioc"; evergreen bush with milky juice and long tuberous roots; leaves deeply parted into 3-7 lobes; flowers without petals. The sturdy, tuberous, edible roots yield tapioca, cassava and starch. The poison in the roots is destroyed by cooking. A most important root-crop in tropical cultivation. *Tropical.* *p. 1004*

esculenta 'Variegata' (Brazil), "Cassava" or "Variegated tapioca plant"; widely grown in tropical regions for the starchy tubers which yield tapioca; digitate, fresh green leaves in this form are beautifully variegated yellow along veins. *Tropical.* *p. 1051*

MANILKARA *Sapotaceae* **S3LBM**

zapota (Achras) (Trop. America), the "Sapodilla" or "Chicle"; tropical evergreen tree with milky juice, the source of chicle gum; leathery, long-elliptic shining green leaves 12 cm long, set in a circle; small white flowers; edible round fruit 5 to 8 cm dia., rough, brown with yellow brown translucent flesh, sweet and edible. *p. 2036*

MAPANIA *Cyperaceae* **S3LFW**

mannii (West Tropical Africa); perennial with woody rhizome, from bogs of waterside moist places; leaves clustered and united at apex of long leafless stalks to 1 m high, the many-flowered spikelets with lilac-colored stigma and yellow stamens. *p. 948*

MARANTA *Marantaceae* **S3LFM**

arundinacea (Mexico to So. America), "Arrow-root"; decorative perennial herb; the erect, slender branches to 2 m or more high, from starchy roots, with green, lanceolate basal and stem-leaves sheathing at base, to 30 cm long and 10 cm wide; small white flowers in unevenly branched clusters. White starch is extracted from the roots, a valuable food in West Indies, Africa, Monsoon Asia and East Indies. *p. 1541*

arundinacea 'Variegata' ('Phrynium micholitzii'), (Mexico to S. America), "Variegated arrow-root"; erect herb to 1 m high, with starchy roots and forking, zigzag branches; in this variegated form having the narrow lance-shaped, light green, papery leaves prettily variegated or margined with white; variegation passing through the leaf, showing underneath. *p. 1541*

bicolor (Brazil, Guyana); low plant with tuber-bearing roots; the oval leaves, to 15 cm long, usually horizontal, glossy, with broad, gray, feathered center, adjoining which is a zone of dark green, then grayish-green to margin, purple beneath; flowers white, lined violet. *p. 1543*

leuconeura erythroneura (Brazil: Estado do Rio), the beautiful "Red-veined prayer plant" from the Organ Mts. near Petropolis; a low-growing herbaceous plant, the foliage more or less horizontal with the ground; 10 to 12 cm leaves obovate, on short winged petioles, patterned with a herringbone design of carmine-red veins over light yellow-green to dark velvety olive green, jagged silvery green along center; reddish beneath except green along center; flowers whitish with purple eye. *p. 1545, 1546*

leuconeura kerchoveana (Brazil), "Prayer plant"; low-growing plant with 15 cm oval leaves mostly hugging the ground, and folding upward in the evening; the surface is vivid to pale-grayish green, more pronounced along the midrib and feathering along the veins, with a row of chocolate, later dark green, blotches on either side; blotched red beneath; small flowers white, striped purple, in a raceme. *p. 5*, 19*, 1543, 1544*

leuconeura kerchoveana 'Manda's Emerald'; attractive cultivar of the common "Prayer plant" with leaves basically a clear, friendly chartreuse to emerald, with the typical chocolate blotches turning moss-green with age. *p. 1540*

leuconeura 'Massangeana', (Brazil); low strikingly beautiful plant having satiny bluish-green leaves, with feathery centerband of silver in thin stripes of pink, later silver, extending out toward the margin, after first passing a broad zone of reddish brown; red-purple beneath.
Tropical. *p. 15*, 19*, 1536A, 1543*

"repens" hort.; a low plant grown in England, very close to M. leuconeura kerchoveana, but with branches more spreading, leaves smaller, 5-8 cm long, contrasting with the 12 cm leaves of the species, and of the same coloring green with chocolate blotches. *p. 1544*

MARANTA: see also Calathea, Ctenanthe

MARATTIA *Marattiaceae (Filices)* **S-I3LFM**

attenuata (Queensland, New Caledonia); handsome tropical fern with thick, fleshy crown, the fronds dark green and glossy, to 1 m long, tripinnate with broad ovate leaflets deeply toothed and undulate, the stems nearly black. *p. 1079*

excavata (Costa Rica, Guatemala); a heavy fern considered very ancient, with great green spreading tripinnate fronds, the fleshy leaflets more or less sickle-shaped and serrate bearing on the underside the characteristically fused together sporangia along the edge. The fronds reach a length of 1-2½ m. *p. 1081*

fraxinea (Angola to Zimbabwe, So. Africa, India, Sri Lanka, Philippines, Queensland, New Zealand, Polynesia), the "King fern"; noble giant with massive starchy rhizome, short-stalked bipinnate fronds to 5 m long, the thick-leathery, fine-toothed leaflets dark glossy green. In favored tropical rainforest this fern will luxuriate with fronds 9 m long and 5 m wide. *p. 1081*

salicina (New Zealand, to Tahiti, Samoa, north to Hong Kong), the "Para" or "Horseshoe fern"; large tropical fern with starchy rootstock, and bipinnately divided dark green fronds, the leaflets leathery and smooth, on yellow axis and brown stalks; a good indoor plant in tubs in younger specimen. This species named according to Chas. Harrison of Palmerston North, and H.B. Doobie, N.Z. Ferns; the plant known as M. fraxinea may be the same species. *Humid-subtropic.* *p. 1079*

sinclairi (New Zealand), a "King fern"; photographed near Auckland on North Island, with elegant, giant leathery fronds glossy green, measuring 2 to 3 m or sometimes even 10 m long, dense with long pinnae frilled at margins; underneath with little boat-shaped sori. *p. 1079*

smithii (Polynesia, Fiji, New Guinea); large bipinnate fronds with oblong leathery pinnae narrowed toward base, on smooth axis. Fronds to 4 m long. *p. 1081*

MARCGRAVIA *Marcgraviaceae* ***S1HFM**

paradoxa (Puerto Rico), "Bejuco de palma"; epiphytic climber of the rainforest, forming two stages; the stem-rooting juvenile, with small ovate leaves appressed to the tree bark; later the maturity stage with larger leathery, long-elliptic 12 cm leaves on woody, pendant stems, and forming curious green and red club-like inflorescence in circular clusters. The name is often confused with an aroid, Monstera dubia in the juvenile stage of shingled leaves. *p. 1547*

picta (Brazil to C. America); epiphytic forest creeper with small alternate ovate leaves marked gray-green, to 2½ cm long in the juvenile stage; becoming much larger in the maturity or fruiting stage. *p. 1547*

rectiflora (Cuba, Hispaniola, Puerto Rico), "Shingle plant"; climbing epiphytic shrub; the sterile shoots with small 2 cm leaves clinging shingle-like to tree bark; the mature, freely pendant fruiting branches with 12 cm lanceolate, leathery leaves, tipped by greenish inflorescence, followed by globular fruit capsules. *Tropical.* *p. 1524*

sintenisii (Cordillera of Puerto Rico); creeper on tree trunks, quite common on Cerro Gordo, the stem-rooting branches with small roundish leaves in 2 ranks, adhering to bark; the mature flowering branches drooping away, with larger, thicker, lanceolate leaves; pendulous terminal inflorescence in form of a dense candelabrum, suspending the attractive, hoodlike, red-tinged bracts. *p. 1524*

umbellata (Antilles to Brazil), a "Shingle plant" of the tropical forest; epiphytic climber with small oval, thin two-ranked leaves in the juvenile stage, stem-rooting and growing flat and overlapping up a tree trunk; later with fruiting stage the branches hang free, with larger ovate, leathery leaves, and pendant inflorescence a cluster of berry-like green flowers and appended by red-colored sac-like nectaries. *p. 1547*

MARCGRAVIA: see also Monstera, Rhaphidophora

MARCHANTIA *Marchantiaceae* **I-C3LNW**

calcarea (Philippines Bontoc Prov.); in habitat along the rice terraces of the Igorots; a tropical liverwort (or liver-plant) of the frond-like class, with the flat, scale-like plant body (thallus) similar to the prothallium of a fern, tight to the surface of the soil, or on rocks; thallus dark green, 4-5 cm long, 3-4 mm wide, short branching, the margins hairy; receptacle or raised cup (capitulum) of the male or fertilizing "flower" (antheridium) with 5-9 entire lobes irregularly arranged, in the female or fruit-bearing "flower" (archegonium) with 5-9 lobes arranged in a perfect circle. *p. 1548*

geminata (Java, Sumatra); tropical liverwort found in the Tjibodas mountains of Java at 1600 m; evergreen mat-forming creeper attached tight to the ground, with branching, fleshy-firm, flat thallus 3-5 cm long and 2.5-7 mm wide, glossy dark green or slightly glaucous with faint dark median line, and toothed margins; the male cups with 4-10 linear lobes, the graceful female fruiting heads with rays reflexed and directed downward. Like all Marchantia, this species has a light-form with strongly swollen frond often colored purplish; and a shade-form with broader, flat fronds more vivid green. *p. 1548*

polymorpha (E. United States), a "Liverwort"; interesting plant looking like a prehistoric creation, botanically between the mosses and the algae, useful for colonizing in rockgardens, also in conservatories and moist dishgardens; leaf-like flat scale-like plant body or thallus is 10-12 cm long and 2½ cm wide; the fruiting body on female plants looks like a tiny umbrella. *Warm temperate.* *p. 1548*

stenolepida (Philippines: Baguio, Benguet Prov., also Bontoc Prov., Luzon); a flowerless plant (cryptogam) called liverwort because the epidermic cells resemble the shape of the liver; these plants bear no flower but have organs by which fruit is produced, the male antheridia and female archegonia. M. stenolepida is very variable, the grayish-green frond (thallus) 3-5 mm wide, frequently branches; older plain green thalli produce single-axis dark green thalli with broad, black median line, and prominent breathing spores, the margins with tiny teeth; the masculine receptacle has 5-6 linear lobes. *p. 1548*

MARIANTHUS *Pittosporaceae* **I2LBD**

pictus (Western Australia), "Bell climber"; lovely woody scrambler with narrow-linear leathery foliage; flowers with spreading petals lemon-yellow striped and spotted purple. A genus dedicated to the Virgin Mary. *p. 1950*

ringens (Western Australia), "Red bell climber"; twining sub-shrub with slender branches; lanceolate leaves scattered, 5-10 cm long; charming tubular flowers yellow at base, and spreading red limb 2 cm across. *p. 1950*

MARICA: see NEOMARICA

MARNIERA *Cactaceae* **S3LBD**

chrysocardium (Epiphyllum) (Costa Rica; So. Mexico: Chiapas); handsome epiphyte, with flattened branches deeply cut leaflike to strong midrib, to 30 cm wide; the large flowers 30 cm on long tube, outside pinkish, inner petals white, night blooming. *Tropical.* *p. 661*

MARRUBIUM *Labiatae* **I2LBD**

candidissimum (So. Europe), "Horehound"; aromatic, white-woolly low woody perennial, with small ovate pebbled leaves with crenate margins, and spikes of whitish flowers. Used for tea and candy, and medicinally for coughs and colds. *p. 1349*

MARSDENIA *Asclepiadaceae* **S3LFM**

quadrialata (Madagascar); tropical vining plant related to Stephanotis, with opposite cordate leaves having wide sinus; creamy white small flowers with urn-shaped corolla and with 5-parted calyx. *p. 372*

MARSILEA *Marsileaceae (Filices)* **I-S3L (in water) FW**

drummondii (W. Australia), "Water-clover"; aquatic perennial tufted herb with creeping rhizome rooting at nodes, and floating 4-parted clover-like leaves 8 cm dia., the fan-like leaflets covered with whitish hairs, and with wavy margins, on long slender stalks; the bean-like spore cases or fruiting bodies at the base of leaf stalks. *Subtropic.* *p. 1078*

fimbriata (West Africa: Ghana, Guinea), a tropical "Waterclover" with petioles 15-30 cm long, the fan-like leaflets about 3 cm long, smooth above, stiff-hairy beneath, outer edge entire; spore case globose, solitary and hairy. *p. 1078*

quadrifolia (North Temperate Zone: Europe, No. India, Japan, E. U.S.), "Clover fern"; hardy, wide-creeping aquatic with long runners, thin petioles 8-15 cm long, bearing the floating 4-parted leaves, the deltoid smooth leaflets to 2 cm long, the outer edge rounded. *p. 1078*

MARTINEZIA: see Aiphanes

MARTYNIA *Martyniaceae* **S3LFM**

annua (Timor, Moluccas), "Elephant's trunk"; according to Hortus widely distributed from Mexico, W. Indies, India to Malaysia; hairy, herbaceous plant which I found in Timor, and identified by Dr. Burtt-Edinburgh; angled, heavily ribbed green leaves, with attractive tubular flowers white, the 5 flaring segments with lip blotched purple. *p. 1547*

lutea in European literature; Hortus refers this to Ibicella, which see.

MASCARENA *Palmae* **S3LFM**

lagenicaulis (Hyophorbe amaricaulis) (Mascarene Isl.), "Bottle palm"; grotesque, solitary palm to about 4 m high, the trunk very fat and bulging at base and quickly tapering upward, like a flask, topped by few heavy pinnate, arching fronds, 1-2 m long, the leaflets erect and rigid, yellowish green, the bases forming a prominent crown-shaft. *Tropical.* *p. 1889, 1890*

revaughanii (Mauritius); another "Bottle palm", remarkable for its massive trunk thickly swollen from the 50 cm dia. base, becoming gradually smaller and forming an elongated neck; pinnate leaves few but beautifully arching on brown-red petiole, almost 2 m long, the red-edged leathery leaflets 45 cm long; black fruit 2 cm dia. *Tropical.* *p. 1886, 1889*

verschaffeltii (Hyophorbe) (Mauritius), "Spindle palm"; thick-growing erect palm to 9 m, the trunk conspicuously ringed and bulging toward the upper part where the flowers appear; from the long crown-shaft extends a dense crown of arching pinnate fronds to 2½ m long, with golden yellow axis, the yellow-green leaflets both erect and hanging; small black fruit. *p. 1886, 1890*

MASDEVALLIA *Orchidaceae* **I-C3OFM**

attenuata (Costa Rica, Panama); miniature epiphyte 8 cm high, clustering obovate leathery leaves, waxy bell-shaped flowers creamy white, 3 cm long, with purple lines extending into 3 long tails. *p. 1758*

bella (Colombia); weird epiphyte from 2600 m elevation, with tufted, oblanceolate leaves to 22 cm long; with long drooping stalks suspending large, triangular flowers pale yellow spotted with brownish-crimson, ending in long red-brown tails; oscillating, white, shell-like lip (autumn-June). (C) *p. 1753, 1759*

carderi (Colombia); epiphyte with clustered, glossy, spatulate leaves to 12 cm long; odd flowers to 4 cm long, reminding of a bat, pale lemon richly warted with brown-purple, at each apex extending into long blackish tails and with ciliate margins; tiny cupped, pinkish lip. *p. 1756*

chimaera (bot. Dracula) (Colombia); beautiful, very variable orchid of tufted habit with short-stalked leaves 12-25 cm long, and basal stalks with clusters of large flowers, brownish-yellow spotted with brownish-purple, the petals and lip small but the united 4 cm sepals large and showy and prolonged into reddish tails to 10 cm long; spring and summer. *p. 1759*

chontalensis (Costa Rica); miniature epiphyte from the cool Chiriqui highlands; flowers translucent white with pinkish horns (summer). *p. 1758*

civilis (Perú); interesting plant with clustered stems bearing a deep green solitary fleshy leaf 15 cm long; short-stalked flowers flaring, formed by sepals which extend into stiff, greenish-yellow recurving tails, greenish-yellow outside, inside deep purple at base, and with offensive odor; spring-summer. (C) *p. 1759*

davisii (Perú); leathery oblanceolate leaves glossy green to 20 cm long; curious, heavy-textured, fragrant flowers to 5 cm across the sepals, these yellow with orange marks at base; the lateral sepals united, running into horns, the dorsal sepal extended into a slender tail; brownish lip (spring). *p. 1758*

deorsa (Colombia); epiphyte with pendant oblanceolate glaucous green leaves to 30 cm long, on reedy stems; flowers old gold or bronze, the segments running into long tails, marked with brown, small waxy lip purple and frilled. *p. 1757*

x 'Doris' (racemosa x triangularis); striking flowers flame-colored to mandarin-red with brownish sheen; clustered plant to 12 cm high, with broad leathery leaves (cool-growing). *p. 1756*

ecordata (Costa Rica); small epiphyte to 12 cm high from the cool Chiriqui highlands; pretty flowers translucent white with purple lines in charming design, tips old gold (summer). *p. 1755*

elephanticeps (Colombia); unusual species clustering with narrow spatulate leaves; from the base the pendulous bell-shaped flowers 8 cm long, yellowish outside, reddish purple inside; tails yellow (spring). *p. 1763*

ephippium (Colombia, Ecuador); epiphyte with clustered leaves narrow lanceolate 15 cm long, narrowed into a channelled petiole; stout triangular floral stalks to 30 cm long, bearing 2 to 3 large flowers, in all 20 cm long, heavy-textured, upper sepal small, the two lateral sepals forming large cup chestnut brown, greenish-yellow flexuous tails to 10 cm long. *p. 1755*

erythrochaete (Colombia); small epiphyte from cool Andean highlands, clustering leaves to 20 cm long; handsome flowers 10 cm across, white tinged with yellow and spotted with red-purple; long 5 cm black-brown tails; white lip shaded with pink (summer). *p. 1756, 1757*

floribunda (Mexico to Costa Rica); miniature epiphyte forming small clusters, with glossy green stalked leaves but no pseudobulbs 8-10 cm long, the numerous small yellow flowers on wiry stalks nearly bell-shaped and covered with tiny purple spots, about 3 cm long, slender recurved tails reddish, lip white with red-brown blotch (summer). *p. 1755*

grandiflora (Ecuador); small rosette dense with narrow oblanceolate leaves, the numerous spidery flowers pale lemon-yellow, extending into long curving spurs. *p. 1755*

horrida (Costa Rica); small, tufted plant with narrow linear leaves 5 cm long; greenish and bristly hairy inside, flowers cupshaped, with 3 short, fleshy, droopy yellow tails, maroon-red inside. *p. 1754*

houtteana (Colombia); bushy species with linear, folded leaves to 16 cm long; small blossoms canary-yellow dotted with purple, and white hairy; small white lip; these flowers 2 cm across plus the long brownish-red tails (summer). *p. 1756*

infracta (Brazil, Perú); small tufted epiphyte with spatulate leaves but without pseudobulbs; the flowers of fantastic shape, the prominent sepals extending into long tails, upper sepal whitish shaded yellow, lower sepals violet-purple inside and tails yellow, (May-July). *Humid-subtropic.* *p. 1753*

infracta purpurea (Brazil, Peru); small, interesting plants 12-17 cm high, from the Organ Mountains, with petioled, obovate, leathery leaves, and slender stalks bearing solitary, campanulate flowers with long-spreading yellowish-green tails, inside of sepals silky maroon purple and yellow base (spring-summer). (C) *p. 1753*

laucheana (attenuata) (Perú); cool-loving miniature epiphyte 8 cm high; clustering plant with oblanceolate, leathery leaves, and no pseudobulbs, small spidery creamy-white flowers between foliage, the long tails, extensions of the sepals, dusted with cinnamon (autumn). *p. 1758*

leontoglossa (Colombia, Venezuela); small epiphyte with clustered fleshy, spatulate leaves to 16 cm long; arching short floral stalks bearing solitary flowers 4 cm long, outside greenish, inside rose-red, densely red-spotted, and with long tails (summer). *p. 1756*

liliputana, (Brazil); miniature terrestrial with folded leaves; 2 cm flowers greenish, boldly overlaid with blackish tubercles, small lip blackish-red (spring) (cool). *p. 1756*

x measuresiana (tovarensis x amabilis); small plant with tufts of obovate leaves and flowers with the lateral sepals partly united, the perianth white with nerves and margin lilac, and tails purplish-brown near the base, paler and greener toward the tips. *Humid-subtropic.* *p. 1753*

militaris (ignea) (Colombia); clustering species with rigid leaves to 10 cm long, stalked at base; handsome inflorescence, a long stalk 35 cm tall with solitary flowers 6 cm across, bright cinnabar-red, the dorsal sepal prolonged into linear tail (summer). *Subtropic.* *p. 1759, 1763*

pandurilabia (Perú, Ecuador); small epiphyte 8-20 cm high, from the Andes at 3000 m altitude, with obovate leathery leaves 6 cm long; flower forming a shallow cup, greenish-yellow speckled brown outside, deep-yellow spotted red inside, the 3 red-brown tails 2½ cm long. (C) *p. 1759*

paranense (Ecuador); miniature epiphyte from the cool Andes, 3 cm high with leathery long oval leaves; flowers brownish-green with dark red-brown spots, and black-crimson lip (spring). *p. 1755*

platycentra (Ecuador); small epiphyte with attractive flowers light brown with chocolate stripes and ivory-white tails (autumn). *p. 1755*

reichenbachiana (Costa Rica); free-flowering species densely tufted with spatulate leaves; angular stalk with flowers with tube crimson above, the reflexed upper sepal greenish yellow, the lower sepals greenish-white, and 2½-5 cm green tails; summer. (C) *p. 1759*

schroederiana (Colombia, Perú); handsome clustered small epiphyte with erect oblanceolate leaves to 15 cm long; slender stalks bearing 2-4 flowers in succession, the curious blooms 6 cm long, dorsal sepal blackish crimson, connate lateral sepals bright red on top, white on lower half, the tails all translucent yellow, lip pink (winter-spring). *p. 1755*

simula (C. America, Colombia, Ecuador); diminutive species; bushy plant with rich green, linear channeled 8 cm leaves; flowers hooded 2 cm near base, sepals and petals greenish yellow marked with chocolate, tongue-shaped lip wine-purple (summer). *p. 1756*

stroebelii (Andean region); cool-loving miniature epiphyte with pretty, tubular flowers hairy inside, pale lemon alternating with deep yellow, long recurved yellow tails (autumn). *p. 1758*

tovarensis (Colombia, Venezuela); small epiphyte with spatulate, leathery 15 cm leaves and pure white waxy, basal flowers with short tube and prominent veins, the lateral sepals partly connected and with tails, the dorsal erect and with long spur to 4 cm long (November to January blooming). (C) *p. 1753, 1754*

triaristella (Nicaragua, Costa Rica, Colombia); miniature epiphyte from cool regions, forming tufts; slender awl-shaped leaves grooved inside, floral stalks with 1 or 2 flowers 2 cm long and looking insect-like, red-brown with yellow tails (summer). *p. 1763*

veitchiana (Perú); a most beautiful species with densely tufted leathery, dark green leaves linear oblong and shining, and a wiry stalk bearing 1 or 2 showy, bright orange-scarlet flowers to 15 cm long, the dorsal sepal with long tail, the tailed lateral sepals partly grown together, closely studded with purple hairs (May-July). *Humid-subtropic.* *p. 1759*

veitchiana 'Grandiflora'; striking cultivar with flowers of exceptional size, to 20 cm long, opening widely and long-lived, brilliant cinnabar-red with an iridescent bluish sheen, the upper sepal narrowing into long tail. *p. 1753*

wagenerana (Venezuela); tiny tufted epiphyte with spatulate leaves 5 cm long; basal flower 6 cm long, waxy translucent white, sprinkled with red dots, the lip extending into long curving yellowish green tails (late spring). *p. 1758*

weberbaueri (Perú, Ecuador); small terrestrial from cool Andean region, with waxy flowers on stout stem, creamy-white with yellow horn, and spotted purple; small white lip (summer). *p. 1758*

MATRICARIA: see Chrysanthemum parthenium

MATTHIOLA *Cruciferae* **C2LBD**

incana, "Stocks" or "Gilliflower"; well-known for their spicy-sweet fragrance, by origin a semi-shrubby plant, usually grown as a biennial and lately as annual (10-14 weeks); at home around the Mediterranean from the Canary Islands to Asia Minor; cool-temperature plant highly developed, with brittle stems and grayish pubescent leaves; clusters of mostly double, quite fragrant flowers 3 cm wide, in many pastel or vivid colors from rose, apricot and red to blue, violet, lavender, even canary-yellow and white. Normally blooming from April to fall in cool climate. *Warm temperate.*

incana 'Annua' (So. Europe), "Annual stocks"; grown as an annual, blooming in 10 weeks from seed. *Subtropic.* *p. 926*

incana 'Column'; a commercial class of late-blooming non-branching "Stocks" with tall columns of large fragrant, double flowers about 5 cm dia., on sturdy 1 m stalks; horticultural colors are from white to tints of pink to red, lavender, blue and purple. These forms were developed from the Mediterranean species incana, a biennial with oblanceolate, grayish pubescent leaves and 2½ cm purple flowers, 30-60 cm high, in erect terminal raceme. *p. 927*

incana 'Imperial'; commercial group of early-flowering branching stocks 60-75 cm tall, also known as "Giants of California" or "Bismarck". Fragrant flowers with a high percentage of doubles in colors white, pink, ivory, lavender, red or purple. *p. 927*

vallesiaca (E. Mediterranean Reg.); interesting perennial with long linear, gray-hairy leaves in basal rosette; from the center the stalked inflorescence of purplish flowers with flaring petals; blooming in May. *p. 926*

MAURANDYA: see Asarina

MAURITIA *Palmae* **S3LBM**

flexuosa (Brazil: Amazonas); tall fan palm of the floodlands of the Amazon, with smooth trunks to 40 m high, and 50 cm dia., sometimes swollen; large crown of palmate deep green leaves of rigid texture to 3 m across, drooping at tips; oblong fruit 8 cm long, covered with reddish scales, in heavy clusters. *p. 1886*

MAXILLARIA *Orchidaceae* **I-C3OFM**

brunnea (Colombia); pretty epiphyte, having peculiar, onion-like circular pseudobulbs each with solitary, stalked leaf; floral stalks from base and covered with brown scales; waxy flowers 4 cm across, chestnut brown outside, yellow and brown inside (June). *p. 1760*

coccinea (Jamaica); small epiphyte with little, 1-leaved, clustered pseudobulbs, and short stalks with solitary flowers, freely produced, the sepals and petals pointed and spreading, bright scarlet-red. (Feb.-July). (I) *p. 1762*

densa (Ornithidium) (Mexico to Honduras); epiphyte with small, compressed, single-leaved pseudobulbs; flowers borne in dense clusters on 3 cm stalks, sepals and petals creamy-white, often tinted with rose or green, lip white with red center, (Dec.-Sept). *Tropical.* *p. 1762*

elatior (Costa Rica, Honduras, Guatemala, Mexico); large epiphytic or terrestrial plant consisting of an elongated leafy rhizome that gives rise to axillary inflorescences and a few scattered pseudobulbs, to 45 cm tall; fleshy flowers reddish-yellow to deep brick-red, blackish wine-red in center. (I) *p. 1762*

grandiflora (Ecuador); clustering, compressed pseudobulbs with solitary leaves; inflorescence on stout stalk, the heavy-textured flowers fragrant, 10 cm across, sepals and petals cream-white, with petals reflexed and tinged with red outside, lip orange-yellow, striped or painted wine-purple inside (late spring). *p. 1760*

juergensii (So. Brazil: Rio Grande do Sul); small clump-forming, bushy species from cooler Brazil, with small ovoid pseudobulbs and linear, grooved leaves, and tulip-like, waxy bell-flowers lacquered brown-red, marked with yellow inside. *p. 1760*

lepidota (Colombia, Ecuador); very exotic-looking species with ovoid pseudobulbs and solitary handsome leaves with pale blotches on darker blade; the nodding flowers spidery, 12 cm long when spread out, long-lasting, the sepals tail-like, yellow at broader base, to brown at apex, the shorter petals yellow; the yellow lip spotted black-purple (early summer). *p. 1760*

luteo-alba (Colombia, Venezuela); epiphyte with small, clustering, compressed pseudobulbs bearing solitary, stalked leaves; large fragrant flowers on individual stalks, sepals and petals yellow, shaded brown, creamy-white at base, lip white streaked purple, (April-June). (I) *p. 1761*

ochroleuca (Rio de Janeiro); epiphyte with compressed, 1-leaved pseudobulbs, and short-stalked yellowish-white, scented flowers with narrow sepals and petals and a bright orange-yellow lip, (summer). (C) *p. 1761*

picta (Brazil); epiphyte with ovoid pseudobulbs, each with 1 or 2 thick, strapshaped leaves; the individual fragrant flowers yellow streaked and dotted purple and chocolate inside, petals incurved, lip white spotted purple. (Oct.-Aug.). *Tropical.* *p. 1761*

porphyrostele (Brazil); small species with densely clustered 3 cm pseudobulbs each bearing 2 leaves, and flowers 3 cm wide, yellow with purple median stripe on petals, and purple streaks on side lobes of lip; February. (C) *p. 1759*

reichenheimii (Costa Rica); short-stemmed leathery, mottled leaves to 25 cm long; wiry stalks bear bizarre lemon-yellow flowers 6 cm across, with sepals and petals very narrow, the lip lightly twisted; August-September. *p. 1762*

rufescens (Cuba to Jamaica, Guatemala to Perú); clustered ovoid pseudobulbs with robust, solitary leaf to 20 cm long, short inflorescence of fragrant flowers 3 cm across, the sepals pinkish-brown, petals pale yellow, the yellow lip spotted dark red (winter). *Tropical.* *p. 1760*

sanderiana (Ecuador, Perú); considered the finest of the genus, an epiphyte with clustered, compressed pseudobulbs with 30 cm solitary leaf, and large, fleshy flowers 12-15 cm across, sepals and petals white blotched with blood-red at base, lip maroon near base, pale yellow toward apex (May-July, Oct.-Dec.). (C) *p. 1761*

sanguinea (Cent. America); small epiphyte with 2½ cm pseudobulbs and grass-like leaves tufted one after another on elongate ascending rhizomes, and basal, solitary flowers, the sepals brown tipped with yellow, petals yellow spotted with red crimson, lip purple with white apex (spring). (C) *p. 1761*

seidelii (Brazil); small compressed pseudobulbs with narrow-linear, grooved leaves, and between the foliage the waxy flowers cream with yellow lip. *p. 1760*

sophronitis (Ornithidium) (Venezuela); floriferous low epiphyte with glossy green leaves, solitary on small, angled pseudobulbs, waxy 2 cm orange-scarlet flowers, the small lip yellow inside (summer). *p. 1776*

tenuifolia (Mexico); small clustering epiphyte; flattened pseudobulbs at intervals on ascending rhizomes, topped by solitary, linear leaves almost hiding the small, individually stalked, strongly scented flowers, sepals and petals dark rusty-red, lip spotted blood-red on yellow base, (Dec.-June). *Tropical.* *p. 1761*

triloris in hort. (luteo-alba) (Colombia); bushy species with flat pseudobulbs and solitary leaves; fragrant flowers 10 cm across, greenish at base, toward apex cinnamon-brown; whitish lip marked black-purple. *p. 1760*

variabilis (Mexico, C. America, to Panama); pretty species terrestrial on rocks or epiphytic on trees; densely clustering little 4 cm pseudobulbs bearing solitary leaves; small variable flowers with sepals and petals bronzy-yellow, the lip wine-red with yellow blotch at apex; free-blooming year-round. (C) *p. 1762*

MAXIMILIANEA: see Cochlospermum

MAYACA *Mayacaceae* **S3LFW**

fluviatilis (So. U.S. to So. Brazil); small swamp or aquatic herb; plants above water moss-like, 5 cm high; leaves linear, thin light green; flowers rose; submerged plants 30-50 cm long, leaves very thin and longer; flowers only on emergent growth. *p. 1520*

sellowiana (Brazil); tropical bog plant with slender, creeping stems clothed along their length with small needle-like pointed leaves; flowers solitary on slender stems, three petalled, the petals pink with a white edge, anthers yellow. *p. 1520*

MAZUS *Scrophulariaceae* **I2LBM**

reptans (Himalayas), "Wart flower"; tiny mat-forming herb to 5 cm high, rooting at nodes, with toothed obovate 3 cm leaves, and purplish-blue bilabiate flowers, the lower lip spotted white, yellow and purple. *Subtropic.* *p. 2059*

MEDEOLA: see Asparagus

MEDINILLA *Melastomataceae* **S3HFM**

ericarum (Madagascar); interesting tropical evergreen shrub to 1 m high, with woody branches bearing sessile oval, leathery leaves prominently veined; the curious inflorescence in dense clusters of rose-pink flowers arising directly from the stems at leaf junctures. *p. 1557*

ledifolia; small evergreen shrub with procumbent branches, small opposite, ovate, slender pointed leaves; the inflorescence in terminal racemes of pinkish flowers. *p. 1557*

magnifica (Philippines, Java), "Rose grape"; gorgeous evergreen shrub to 2 m high, with angled woody branches and large, opposite, sessile, thick-leathery leaves to 30 cm long and with ivory midrib; striking inflorescence in a pendulous panicle to 30 cm long, of carmine-red flowers with purple anthers and great showy pink bracts. *Tropical.* *p. 1553, 1556, 2112A*

scortechinii (Perak in Malaya, to Java); low-growing, shrubby epiphyte which I first found in the mountains of Java, with pendant warty, wiry branches; the paired, smooth leathery, ovate leaves 10 to 15 cm long, and featuring an attractive pink midrib; the inflorescence in small clusters of pink-tipped flowers and waxy bright coral red bracts. *Tropical.* *p. 1552, 1556*

sedifolia (Madagascar); small trailing, stem-rooting vine with dark green, fleshy, orbicular leaves about 2 cm long; pink flowers solitary in leaf axils; photo shows them in bud. *p. 1557*

MEDINILLA: see also Hypenanthe

MEDIOCALCAR *Orchidaceae* **S-I3LFW**

species (New Guinea); epiphyte with fleshy pseudobulbs formed at intervals from the apex of the older ones, each topped by succulent grayish leaves, and forming aerial roots; tiny buff-yellow flowers bell-like with welded sepals and sac-like lip; from the tropical cloud forest. *p. 1763*

MEGACLINIUM *Orchidaceae* **S3OFM**

falcatum (Bulbophyllum) (West Africa: Sierra Leone); curious dwarf epiphyte with 4-angled pseudobulbs and 2 leaves; the small flowers borne on both sides of a peculiar flattened brownish axis extending from the stalk, yellow and brownish-red above, green beneath (April-June). (S) *p. 1767*

purpureorhachis (Bulbophyllum) (Zaire), the "Cobra orchid"; a sinister-looking, fantastic epiphyte from inner Africa, with clustered pseudobulbs and paired, rigid leaves to 15 cm long; the curious inflorescence 30 cm long, stalk a singular flattened green axis, densely spotted and overlaid with deep red, the tiny 1 cm deep brown flowers, borne in a single row on the flat sides; blooming August into winter. Snake-like in appearance, this is a striking curiosity plant in collections. *Tropical.* *p. 1757*

MEGAKEPASMA *Acanthaceae* **S3LBD**

erythrochlamys (Adhatoda cydoniifolia) (Venezuela), "Brazilian red-cloak" or "Red justicia"; showy tropical shrub to 3 m high, with appressed reddish hairs; stout stems with broad ovate leaves 12 to 30 cm long, dark green with pink midrib; inflorescence with conspicuous crimson bracts and two-lipped white flowers. *Tropical.* *p. 47*

MEIRACYLLIUM *Orchidaceae* **I-C3OFM**

gemma (wendlandii) (Mexico, Guatemala, El Salvador); small epiphyte with elongate rhizome; broad oval, fleshy leaves 5 cm long; pretty flowers 3 cm across pink flushed purple, the pointed lip rosy, with purple lines, and yellow at base (spring). *p. 1764*

trinasutum (Mexico); small, pretty epiphyte with creeping rhizome, little pseudobulbs, and a solitary, oval leaf; inflorescence short, flowers creamy-white changing to purple toward tips and on the concave lip, (summer). *Subtropic.* *p. 1753*

MELALEUCA *Myrtaceae* **I-S2LBD**

filifolia (Western Australia); shrub to $1\frac{1}{2}$ m high, the branches with long linear, needle-like leaves 3-5 cm; inflorescence clusters mauve pink with long stamens. *p. 1610*

genistifolia (Australia),"Bottle-brush"; tall shrub or tree to 12 m, with narrow almost linear, flat, stiff, sharp-pointed leaves to about 3 cm long, and showy spikes of white flowers with protruding bundles of stamens, resembling a bottle-brush. *Arid-subtropic.* *p. 1612*

huegelii (Western Australia), "Chenille honey-myrtle"; spreading shrub 2 m high with spiral foliage, the tiny 6 mm ovate, sharp-pointed leaves overlapping; the creamy-white flowers with protruding stamen-clusters densely packed in cylindrical spikes. *p. 1612*

hypericifolia (New South Wales); evergreen shrub to 6 m with rather narrow, attractive, firm 3 cm leaves in 4 ranks; showy orange-red bottle brushes in dense spikes. *p. 1610*

leucadendron (Australia, New Caledonia, Malaya), "Paper bark"; slender tree to 10 m, its undulate trunk with papery white bark, peeling off in broad strips; lanceolate 10 cm rigid bluish-green leaves, softly downy when young, with prominent veining, and bearing masses of honey-laden cream bottlebrush-like flowers, the stamens variable whitish, greenish-yellow, pink, or purple. *p. 1610, 1615*

quinquenervia (Australia), "Cajeput tree"; (usually sold as leucadendra); evergreen tree with thorny green trunk to 12 m; pendulous branches with narrow, stiff, pale green leaves 5-10 cm long, the young foliage covered with silky pubescence; fluffy flowers lemon-white, occasionally purple, with bundles of long stamens in short spikes. *Subtropic.* *p. 1605*

radula (W. Australia); evergreen shrub to 3 m; slender branches with opposite, linear leaves 1 to 5 cm long, grooved above, boat-like; axillary flowers lilac-purple, pink or white, with prominent stamen bundles in pairs, opposite on stems. *p. 1610*

MELAMPODIUM *Compositae* **I2LBD**

paludosum (Louisiana, to So. America); annual, branching herb 45 cm high with rugose, ovate 8 cm leaves, and 5 cm star-like lemon-yellow flowers with a raised orange to brownish center disk. *p. 810*

MELASPHAERULA *Iridaceae* **I2LFM**

graminea (ramosa) (Cape Prov.), "Fairy-bells"; cormous, branching straggling plant to 1 m with long linear freesia-like basal leaves having a violet mid-rib; tremulous branchlets bear small scented 1 cm flowers greenish-white, with 6 pointed bracts of purple, long-lasting, in spring. *p. 1334*

MELASTOMA *Melastomataceae* **S3LFM**

decemfidum (sanguineum) (Sunda Islands); tropical shrub 1-2 m; with ovate-pointed, shining green leaves, and with 5 depressed parallel veins, ribs beneath and stalk red; large purplish-pink flowers. *p. 1557*

malabathricum (India), the "Indian rhododendron" or "Malabar melastome"; spreading shrub to 2 m, with 4-angled branches, and narrow, bristle-hairy leaves, flowers 3 to 7 cm across, pink to purple. *p. 1557*

MELIA *Meliaceae* **I2LBD**

azedarach (No. India, China), "Pride of India", "Bead-tree", "China berry", "Indian lilac"; spreading, partially deciduous tree to 20m, naturalized in Europe and America; handsome bipinnate foliage with feathery, toothed leaflets; clusters of fragrant, 2cm pale lavender flowers with purple stripes, followed by bright yellow but poisonous berries usually during a brief leafless stage. *Sub-tropic.* *p. 1551*

azedarach floribunda (India), "Umbrella tree"; bushy form, very free-blooming as shrub 2 m tall; flowers in terminal clusters, fragrant, with 4 or 5 petals white or pale lilac, with violet stamens. *p. 1551*

MELIANTHUS *Melianthaceae* **S2LBD**

comosus (So. Africa), "Honey-flower"; semi-woody, strong-scented shrub to $1\frac{1}{2}$ m, with handsome pinnate foliage to 15 cm long, the leaflets toothed and white-tomentose beneath; flowers in axillary clusters orange-yellow to brick red inside, green at base. *p. 1549*

major (South Africa), "Honey bush"; evergreen semi-woody shrub with widely creeping roots and herb-like stems erect to 3 m high or sprawling, with striking pinnate foliage 20-30 cm long, the deeply serrate, soft-fleshy leaflets in pairs, glaucous green above, grayish beneath; strong-scented when bruised. Reddish-brown 3 cm flowers in dense racemes secreting honey. *Subtropic.* *p. 1549*

MELISSA *Labiatae* **C2LBD**
officinalis (Europe, Asia), "Lemon balm"; aromatic herbaceous perennial, with ovate toothed leaves fragrant of lemon when bruised; light yellow 2-lipped flowers in July. Use: leaves in tea, fruit drinks, salads, stews. *p. 1349*

MELOCACTUS *Cactaceae* **S2LBD**
bahiensis (Brazil: Bahia), a "Turk's-cap"; globose body dark green with deep ribs and clusters of straw-colored stiff spines; the white woolly cap (cephalium) full of cinnamon bristles; flowers pink but hidden; seed pods pink. *p. 705*
communis (Cactus melocactus) (West Indies; Jamaica), "Turk's head" or "Turk's-cap cactus"; short-cylindric body to 30 cm and occasionally to 1 m high, glaucous green, with 10 to 14 and 20 acute ribs, clusters of awl-shaped, sharp spines to 4 cm long, red at first, later yellow or brown; the body topped by a cylindric cap of massed wool and bristles (cephalium) 20 cm high, developed from the central areoles, and from which appear, year after year, the small pink flowers tipped red. When the cephalium begins to form, the plant ceases to grow in size. *p. 705*
intortus (Cactus inaguensis) (West Indies), known as "Turk's cap" in reference to the tall, cylindric cephalium on top of mature plants, its white woolly head setting off the red bristles making it look like a Turk's cap. Barrel-shaped plant to 1 m tall, with 14-20 ribs and yellow or brown stout spines; small pink flowers 2 cm long; 2-3 cm red fruit. *Arid-tropical. p. 705*
matanzanus (Cuba), "Melon-cactus"; small domeshaped plant, deep green, 8-9 rounded ribs, yellowish clusters of recurved spines, "Turk's cap" of white wool and red bristles; flowers rose-pink. *Arid-tropical. p. 705*
maxonii (Guatemala); depressed little globe, to 15 cm high, fresh green, with notched ribs, and strong recurved yellow to reddish radial spines; flowers rose. *p. 618, 705*
melocactoides (violaceus) (S. E. Brazil); small conical, light green body 9 cm high and 15 cm wide, with 10 broad ribs, recurved, awl-shaped all-radial spines whitish; low, white cephalium with brown bristles; flowers pink, fruit pale pink. *p. 705*
neryi (Brazil: Amazonas); attractive small depressed globe 10-12 cm high, dark green with gray marbling, 10 acute ribs edged with clusters of mostly curving spines; at apex a low cushion-like cephalium on mature plants, white with red bristles; pale pink flowers 2 cm long, from top; fruit carmine-red. *Tropical. p. 705*
townsendii (peruvianus) (Perú); little globe, often clustered, with 12-13 ribs, brown, recurved radial spines; flowers pinkish; the raised head with brown bristles and white wool. *p. 705*

MENADENIUM *Orchidaceae* **S3OFW**
labiosum (Venezuela, Guianas, No. Brazil); small epiphyte with flat pseudobulbs bearing two broad herbaceous leaves 25 cm long and with prominent veins; handsome large, 10 cm fragrant flowers heavy-textured, greenish-yellow tinged with copper, the large lip white with purple lines (spring). *Tropical. p. 1764*

MENDONCELLA *Orchidaceae* **S3OFW**
grandiflora (Mexico to Panama and Colombia); epiphyte with prominent pseudobulbs and paired folded leaves to 35 cm long; inflorescence from base with showy, fragrant, waxy flowers to 9 cm across, pointed sepals and petals yellowish green with purplish-brown stripes, lip white with red streaks. *Tropical. p. 1764*

MENTHA *Labiatae* **C2LBD**
citrata (Europe), "Orange-mint"; perennial with bronzy green, smooth, egg-shaped leaves; purple flowers in upper axils on short spikes. Use: to flavor lamb, fish, sauces, applesauce, beverages, jelly, teas. *p. 1348*
piperita (Europe), "Peppermint"; perennial with spreading root stocks and numerous branches with dark green toothed leaves and reddish stems, with pungent or pepper like oil; flowers purple. Use: leaves for tea and flavoring liqueurs; oil in menthol. *p. 1348*
requienii (Corsica), "Corsican mint"; small creeping and spreading herb used for ground cover, with very tiny round, stalked, bright green leaves strongly peppermint-scented; flowers pale purple. *p. 1348*
rotundifolia (Europe), "Woolly apple-mint" or "Round-leaved mint"; hardy, pubescent perennial from a running rootstock; erect slender stems 50-80 cm high; opposite ovate, wrinkled leaves to 5 cm long, opposite and sessile on the stalk; small purple flowers in branched, dense spikes 5 to 10 cm long; apple-scented, sometimes used as substitute for peppermint or spearmint. Naturalized in North America. *p. 1358*
rotundifolia 'Variegata' (Europe), "Pineapple mint"; perennial with soft-woolly oval leaves variegated light green and white; purple flowers. Use: to flavor fruit drinks, juleps, iced beverages, teas, jellies, soups and meats. *p. 1348*
spicata (Europe), "Spearmint"; hardy perennial by leafy stolons, with smooth light green leaves, and purple flowers in dense terminal spikes. Use: leaves to flavor cold drinks and tea, chewing gum, jelly. *p.1348, 1349*

MENYANTHES *Gentianaceae* **C2HFWh**
trifoliata (Temp. No. hemisphere), "Bog-bean"; perennial fleshy herb with creeping root stocks, olive-green trifoliolate leaves and small 1 cm white flowers with recurved petals and beard-like purplish stamens; bog-plant. *p. 1170*

MERENDERA *Liliaceae* **I2LFMd**
bulbocodium (Spain, Portugal); small cormous plant bearing 1 or 2 fragrant flowers with 6 linear clawed perianth segments free to base, rosy-lilac, with yellow anthers, in autumn; three sickle-shaped, channeled, linear leaves 8-10 cm long, appearing after flowers. *p. 1467*

MERREMIA tuberosa: see Ipomoea tuberosa

MERYTA *Araliaceae* **I2LBM**
lanceolata (South Pacific Isl.); small evergreen, dioecious (separate male and female) trees, usually non-branched, dense with long-oblanceolate, leathery leaves to 1 m long, the margins undulate and with thick midrib. *p. 314*
sinclairii (New Zealand), "Puka tree"; small evergreen tree with oblong, entire, leathery leaves crowded at ends of branches; blade glossy-green with irregular margin, pale, prominent veins, up to 50 cm long; petioles striped brown. *Subtropic. p. 320, 321*

MESEMBRYANTHEMUM: most species formerly listed under this genus are now referred to segregate genera in the Aizoaceae family, such as Lampranthus, Aptenia, etc.; see Aizoaceae in the Pictorial section for the new generic divisions.

MESEMBRYANTHEMUM *Aizoaceae* **I2LBD**
caulescens (Oscularia) (Cape Prov.); creeping succulent with reddish branches; numerous short shoots from the axils, light gray, waxy powdered leaves 2 cm long, armed with several small reddish teeth; scented pink flowers 12 mm across. *p. 62*
crystallinum (Cryophytum) (So. Africa, S.W. Africa; carried off to the shores of California), the California "Ice plant"; annual branching succulent with soft-fleshy stems creeping close to ground; spatulate soft-fleshy leaves 2-5 cm long, grayish green, thickly covered with crystal-clear bubbles filled with watery fluid and looking like ice-crystals; the starry flowers 1-3 cm across, translucent white tinted lavender. *Subtropic. p. 79*
deltoides (Oscularia) (Cape Prov.); dense ground cover of branching reddish stems with 10-15 mm triangular light gray leaves covered with waxy blue powder; small 12 mm pale purple or pink flowers; very free-blooming. This is probably the same plant as Oscularia deltoides, which see. *p. 62*

MESOSPINIDIUM *Orchidaceae* **S3OFM**
warscewiczii (Brazil); small epiphyte with flattened pseudobulbs bearing an oblanceolate leaf and arching panicles of small flowers with lateral sepals united, and spoon-shaped, concave lip. *p. 1752*

MESSERSCHMIDTIA *Boraginaceae* **S3LBD**
argentea (So. Pacific Islands to Indian Ocean coral isles), "Tree heliotrope"; large shrub or small umbrella-shaped tree to 6 m high, at home on tropical shores; with deeply furrowed bark; thick ovate, fresh green leaves 15-20 cm long, covered with silky hairs, and densely clustered at ends of branches; small white flowers in silky clusters of coiled spikes; the fruit resembles small pointed brown peas. *Tropical. p. 511*

METASEQUOIA *Taxodiaceae (Coniferae)* **C2LBM**
glyptostroboides (Central China: Hupeh), "Dawn redwood"; this "Fossil-age conifer" has been found growing to 30 m high, by Chinese botanists near Chungking (1941) after having been thought extinct; handsome, monoecious, moisture loving tree with reddish bark, symmetric branches and soft textured, deciduous light green needles, two-ranked on horizontal plane; small, nearly globular brown cones, 2 cm dia. *Temperate to subtropic. p. 838, 850*

METROSIDEROS *Myrtaceae* **I2LBD**
excelsus (tomentosus), (New Zealand), "Pohotukawa" or "New Zealand Christmas-tree"; handsome tree 10 to 20 m, with spreading branches; oval-pointed, leathery shining green leaves 5-10 cm long, the flowers in terminal clusters of showy brilliant scarlet stamens, exceeding the small petals; blooming at Christmas time during December-January (in N.Z.). *p. 1610, 1612*
robustus (New Zealand), the "Rata" or "North Island rata"; tall evergreen tree to 30 m, but often grown as shrub which will flower young when 2 m high; leathery oblong leaves to 4 cm long; flowers with prominent stamen bundles dark crimson red, in dense terminal heads; commonly germinates as an epiphyte in the forks of trees, sending down aerial roots and ultimately form the trunk. *p. 1610*
scandens (perforatus) (New Zealand); evergreen woody climber reaching the top of high trees; with rounded 1 cm leaves leathery and shining green; appressed hairy beneath; flowers white with dense clustered stamens in terminal leafy clusters. *p. 1610*
tomentosus: see excelsus

METROSIDEROS: see also Callistemon

METROXYLON *Palmae* **S3LBD**
sagus (Indonesia, Philippines, Malaya), "Spineless sago palm" of commerce; tall growing monocarpic feather palm to 12 m high, with smooth trunk becoming 40 cm thick; the pinnate fronds erect and gracefully arch-

ing, to 6 m long, the numerous leaflets glossy green; dull yellow 5 cm fruit; flowering only once, with tall branching inflorescence at apex, then leaves fall and tree dies. The trunks contain the edible flour-like sago, extracted from the pith-like center, and the staple food for millions of people in the Far East. Similar to M. rumphii, but sagus does not have spines on the flower stalk. *p. 1891*

vitiense (Fiji); a handsome feather palm, with long, stiff-erect pinnate fronds on sturdy petioles with dense, glossy green pinnae; cultivated in Fiji for its sago, extracted from the pith of the trunk just before flowering; the 8 cm fruit yields hard ivory-nuts; leaves are used for roofing. *p. 1891*

MEZOBROMELIA *Bromeliaceae* **I3LFM**

lyman-smithii (Ecuador); big epiphyte found in Andean cloud-forest at 2000 m in Cotopaxi Prov., by Prof. W. Rauh of Heidelberg in 1973; large rosette closely related to Guzmania, with many leaves to 60 cm long and 13 cm wide, green with purple spots and smooth; the red floral stalk with inflorescence to 3 m high, laxly branched with pendant spikes to 10 cm long with red axis, the shingled floral bracts carmine-red at base and yellow at tips, the flower-petals pale yellow 3½ - 4½ cm long. *p. 589*

MICHELIA *Magnoliaceae* **I2LBD**

figo (Magnolia fuscata) (South China), "Banana shrub"; evergreen shrub to 3 m high, with velvety brown-hairy twigs and buds; the thick, broad-oval leaves 5 to 10 cm long and shiny green; waxy flowers strongly banana-scented, 3 cm across, with petals creamy-yellow and edged with purple. Very popular in China because of their fragrance, the flowers are also used to perfume hair oil and tea. *p. 1523*

MICONIA *Melastomataceae* **S3HFM**

calvescens (magnifica) (Mexico), "Velvet-tree"; tropical foliage plant with woody stem and beautiful, long ovate, thin leaves to 75 cm long, velvety green with the sunken primary ribs ivory, and a network of pale green secondary veins; reddish purple beneath. Flowers insignificant. A show piece for the humid greenhouse. *Tropical.* *p. 1553, 1558*

hookeriana (Cyanophyllum) (E. Perú); handsome tropical shrub with large opposite 3-nerved, elliptic leaves to 30 cm long, with a rugose and wrinkled, velvety surface, deep olive green with broad silvery band following the midrib and branching laterally; the underside hairy and bluish-gray; flowers pale red-brown. *p. 1553*

magnifica in hort.: see calvescens

ovata (Brazil); woody shrub with large, decorative, leathery, green leaves having depressed pale veins, tawny pubescent beneath; flowers white, and coral-colored, berry-like fruits. *p. 1558*

pulverulenta (Perú); much branched bushy shrub, brown stems and handsome large elliptic, recurving 3-nerved leaves to 30 cm long, very velvety green and reticulately wrinkled, silvery along midrib, the underside bluish-gray and hairy; tiny rusty white flowers in erect raceme. *p. 1556*

MICROCOELIA: see Gussonaea

MICROCOELUM *Palmae* **S3-2LBD**

insigne (Brazil); small feather palm with short, thin trunk without crownshaft; the crown with long, gracefully recurving pinnate fronds, the glossy green leaflets 22 cm long and 2 cm wide, silvery underneath. *p. 1896*

MICROCYCAS *Cycadaceae* **S2-3LFD**

calocoma (Cuba); tropical cycad, forming tall stout trunk usually covered with bases of petioles; dense crown of slightly pubescent, pinnate leaves 1 m long with about 80 pairs of leathery long-linear leaflets, the margins recurved. *p. 944*

MICRODRACOIDES *Cyperaceae* **S3LFW**

squamosus (Trop. Africa); large shrubby tropical bog plant to 1 m high, with long-linear, grass-like leaves, crowded towards tips of branches, and closely sheathing the bifurcate branched stem. *p. 948*

MICROLEPIA *Polypodiaceae (Filices)* **I3HFM**

cristata (Assam); tropical fern with slender green rhizomes, freely sprouting with soft, hairy, bipinnate fronds on white-hairy stalks to 75 cm long, the pinnae light green and hairy. *p. 1148*

hirta (pilulosa; speluncae var. hirta), (So. India, Ceylon, Malaysia, Polynesia), grown in Europe as "speluncae" hort.; strong growing variable fern with creeping rhizomes, bushy when small but developing handsome fronds 1-2 m long, 2 or 3 times pinnate, the ultimate segments deeply lobed, and toothed, rich green almost glossy, matte-green beneath, on brown-purple stalk. *p. 1148*

platyphylla (India to Japan); tall fern with creeping rhizomes, thin wiry stalks supporting soft 3-pinnate fronds 1-1½ m high, with broad bluish green segments deeply lobed and toothed, and covered with short white hairs. *p. 1148*

pyramidata (strigosa var. cristata, Davallia marginalis) (Himalayas, China); robust, bushy plant from rhizomes, with fronds 45-60 cm high, somewhat thin-leathery, the glossy, dark olive-green pinnae lobed or deeply cut, and the ends of fronds usually divided and forked. *p. 1156*

setosa (Hawaii); endemic fern 1 m high, with lacy, ovate, slightly hairy fronds 60-90 cm long, and borne on slender 30 cm stalks which rise from underground stems. The leaves are 3 times divided, ultimately into 4-sided, notched segments. *p. 1114*

speluncae (Davallia polypodioides) (East Indies, Polynesia), "Grotto lace fern"; prolific grower with strong stalks and herbaceous, soft and papery, pale green fronds 1-2 m high and covered with sparse white hair, 3-4 pinnate, the lower pinnae 15-30 cm long, and with toothed lobes. *p. 1114*

"speluncae" hort.: see hirta

strigosa (Japan, China, Trop. Asia, Polynesia); robust fern with stout creeping rhizome bearing wiry brown stalks and lacy bipinnate fronds 30-90 cm long, the oblique pinnae dentate, olive-green, thin but hard and somewhat glossy. *Humid-subtropic.* *p. 1148*

MICROSORIUM *Polypodiaceae (Filices)* **•S-I1-3HFM**

pteropus (Polypodium) (Trop. Asia); rhizomatous epiphyte forming dense clusters of simple, long lanceolate leaves, glossy green and very much quilted and with depressed ribs, the older blades bullate and tubercled. *p. 1112*

steerei (Polypodium) (Taiwan); clustering small fern with creeping rhizome, long strap-shaped, waxy-smooth, rich-green leaves of leathery texture. *p. 1112*

MICROSORIUM: see also Polypodium

MICROSTYLIS *Orchidaceae* **S3OFW**

discolor (Malaxis) (Sri Lanka); lovely terrestrial attractive for its foliage; plaited leaves deep metallic reddish purple edged and variegated with green and crisped at margins; thin floral stalks with clusters of minute yellow flowers, changing to orange. *p. 1763*

MIKANIA *Compositae* **S2-3LFM**

apiifolia (Brazil); evergreen climber, with palmately dissected softly hairy leaves, each of the 5 leaflets lobed again, softly hairy; their underside, and the stems, dull purple. *p. 823*

hemispherica (São Paulo); twining tropical herb having opposite arrowshaped to hastate leaves with toothed margins, beautifully satiny green with silvery veining, purplish beneath; flowers flesh-colored. *Tropical.* *p. 813*

scandens (Maine to Florida and So. America); twining herb with long internodes on slender purplish stem, opposite leaves hastate-heartshaped, ivy-like, thin, bronzy olive green with brownish veins, purplish beneath. *p. 813, 814*

ternata (Brazil), "Plush vine" or "Purple haze vine"; a most attractive and promising, rapid-growing trailer with brown stems, covered with lighter, felt-like hairs; opposite small herbaceous, palmately compound leaves 4 cm long, consisting of 5 lobed leaflets dark coppery green, purple beneath, densely covered all over with whitish hairs. Very graceful and eye-catching. *p. 823*

MILA *Cactaceae* **I-S2LBD**

caespitosa (Perú: Lima); cylindric stems to 15 cm high branching into small clusters, with about 10 ribs almost hidden by the needle-like yellowish spines; wheel-shaped yellow flowers. *p. 694*

MILLINGTONIA *Bignoniaceae* **S2-3LBD**

hortensis (Burma), "Indian cork tree"; graceful tropical evergreen tree to 25 m high, with deeply cracked, spongy, cork-like bark; leaves opposite, unequally pinnate, with elliptic, crenate leaflets 3-5 cm long; long tubular, waxy flowers 8-10 cm long, pinkish-white, night-blooming and deliciously fragrant, in great profusion during the early hot months. The bark produces an inferior grade of cork. *Tropical.* *p. 502*

x MILPASIA (x MILTONPASIA) *Orchidaceae* **I3OFM**

'Gold Star' (Miltonia flavescens x Aspasia principissa); bigeneric hybrid with flattened pseudobulbs bearing strap-like leaves; stalk 30 cm long bears a cluster of 5 or 6 deep yellow flowers like a golden star; winter. *p. 1752*

'Spectacular' (Miltonia spectabilis x Aspasia principissa); bigeneric forming large flat pseudobulbs, the young growth producing a wiry stalk with 8 cm flowers almost round, greenish lavender with purplish-red markings; February-April. *p. 1752*

x MILTASSIA *Orchidaceae* **I3OFM**

'Cartagena' (Miltonia x Brassia); handsome bigeneric hybrid with large inflorescence of spidery, waxy white flowers spotted purple. (Moir-Honolulu). *Subtropic.* *p. 1764*

'Flower Drum' (Miltonia warscewiczii x Brassia verrucosa); handsome bigeneric hybrid with compressed pseudobulbs and usually single leaves to 25 cm long; inflorescence with 8 cm flowers yellow heavily blotched with chocolate. *p. 1757*

MILTONIA *Orchidaceae* **C-I3ONM**

x bluntii (Brazil); reported to be a natural hybrid between M. spectabilis x clowesii; in habit like M. spectabilis; beautiful, fragrant, heavy-textured 8 cm flowers with sepals and petals greenish-white and painted with large purple blotches; lip pinkish-white (autumn). *p. 1764*

candida (Brazil); beautiful epiphyte with flattened, pear-shaped, 2-leaved pseudobulbs; large, waxy, 8 cm flowers in loose, erect clusters, sepals and petals chestnut-brown tipped and barred with yellow, lip white tinged rose near base (Aug.-Nov.) *Tropical.* *p. 1766*

candida 'Grandiflora'; differs from the typical species in having flowers twice as large, sepals and petals almost completely brown except for yellow tips, the lip white. *Tropical.* *p. 1762*

clowesii (Brazil); showy epiphyte, ovate pseudobulbs with 2-3 sword-shaped light green leaves and long racemes of 5-8 cm flowers chocolate-brown barred with yellow, lip with violet base and white in front; August-October. (I) *p. 1768*

endresii (Central America); lovely epiphyte with small flattened pseudobulbs and ranked lanceolate leaves; erect stalk with cluster of 6 cm cream-white flat flowers, each segment with a rosy blotch at base, crest of lip bright yellow; spring. (S) *p. 1768*

flavescens (Brazil, Paraguay); creeping rhizome with compressed pseudobulb and 2 pale green strapleaves to 35 cm long, wiry stem with loose inflorescence of 6-8 cm flowers with linear greenish yellow sepals and petals, and pointed white lip with cinnamon brown spots (summer). (I) *p. 1766*

x gattonensis (bleuana x charlesworthii), a "Pansy orchid"; large white flowers with yellow mask in front of the blackish base, (spring). (I) *p. 1765*

x hyeana (bleuana x vexillaria), "Pansy orchid"; nice colorful hybrid pink with deep blackish-crimson petals and white mask in center, (spring and fall). *Tropical.* *p. 1765*

'Ketha' (Greta x Lycaena), a lovely "Pansy-orchid"; with sepals and small lateral petals deep rose edged white, the large lobed lip white veined with red-purple. (I) *p. 1765*

laevis (Mexico, Guatemala); handsome epiphyte with compressed pseudobulbs topped by 2-3 strap-shaped leaves to 45 cm long; branched erect inflorescence to more than 1 m tall, with numerous waxy 6 cm flowers yellow blotched with red-brown, lip white and purplish in front (summer). *p. 1764*

'Liberté' (Parnasse x Piccadilly); lovely hybrid with purplish-red flower edged in white, center design and crest orange with yellow to white tracings; season in spring, but blooming usually again in autumn. *p. 1765*

'Marietta Armacost' (charlesworthii x 'Reine Elisabeth'); showy hybrid and easy grower, large blood-crimson flowers, lip pale carmine with white zone across it, center dark scarlet and yellow, (spring and fall). (I-C) *p. 1765*

phalaenopsis (Miltoniopsis) (Colombia), "Pansy face"; small epiphyte with clustered, 1-leaved pseudobulbs, and a spray of white flowers, blotched and streaked purple-crimson on the large, lobed lip, with yellow base, (April-Aug.). (I) *p. 1766*

regnellii (Brazil); epiphyte with flat pseudobulbs having 2 long leaves and a tall, stiff inflorescence with 3-5 flat flowers, each 5-8 cm across, sepals and petals white, flushed pink, lip rose veined with red-purple, crest yellow, (Aug.-Oct.). (I) *p. 1766*

roezlii (Colombia); showy epiphyte with flattened pseudobulbs bearing a single narrow leaf; stalks loosely 2-6-flowered, each about 10 cm across, sepals pure white, petals with wine-purple eye, large, flat white lip with yellow eye; fragrant, (March-July). (I) *p. 1765*

roezlii alba (Colombia), "Pansy orchid"; large handsome flowers wholly white except for the yellow shading at the base of lip; autumn. *p. 1768*

schroederiana (Costa Rica); bold epiphyte with ovoid pseudobulbs and fresh green fleshy, obovate leaves to 25 cm long; fragrant, waxy flowers chestnut brown, marked and tipped with yellow, large lip purplish rose at base, white in front (summer). *p. 1764*

spectabilis (Brazil); handsome epiphyte with flattened pseudobulbs bearing 2 thin, strapshaped leaves and showy large solitary flowers 8-10 cm across, the narrow petals and sepals pure white, large rosy lip with dark purple center and vein; blooming from spring to summer and into fall. This variable species has many color forms from white to deep purple. A spectacle when larger plants may bloom with dozens of flowers at the same time, lasting 6 weeks in beauty if kept cool and free from damp. The cv. 'Warneri' has petals and sepals richly blotched with purple. *p. 1764, 1766*

spectabilis moreliana (Brazil); has larger flowers with deep rich purple sepals and petals and rosy lip streaked and shaded violet-rose. (I) *p. 1766*

'Storm' (Mokadem x Piccadilly); small plant with light green, strap-shaped leaves, and lovely large flowers spreading 9 cm, dark blood-red with velvety texture and a yellow brown face outlined in white, blooming in spring and again in autumn. *Tropical.* *p. 1765*

vexillaria (Ecuador, Colombia); beautiful floriferous epiphyte with 1-2-leaved pseudobulbs, surrounded at base by 6-8 two-ranked leaves; each inflorescence carrying 3-9 large, flat, lilac-rose flowers, petals shaded deep rose, the lip marked with rosy purple, center yellow, (May-July). (I-C) *p. 1766*

vexillaria 'Volunteer'; very floriferous form, with flowers lavender pink veined purple, and a distinct pattern with a white eye stained in the center with deep yellow (May). *Tropical.* *p. 1767*

warscewiczii (Colombia, Perú); epiphyte with flattened, dark green pseudobulbs bearing a solitary leaf; inflorescence in erect raceme with 3 cm flowers, the narrow sepals and petals red-brown tipped yellow, undulate at edge, lip rose-purple with white margin and brown blotch above middle, (Dec.-March). (I) *p. 1766*

x MILTONIDIUM *Orchidaceae* **I3OFD**

'Aristocrat' (Miltonia schroederiana x Oncid. leucochilum); clustering plant with flattened pseudobulbs and strap-shaped leaves; inflorescence in loose arching racemes of small waxy flowers with narrow sepals and petals basically yellow but almost completely overlaid with deep maroon, the lip white with purple base (autumn). *Tropical.* *p. 1765*

'Lustre' (Oncidium powellii x Miltonia warscewiczii var. weltonii); a bigeneric in growth similar to miltonia, with inflorescence an arching spray carrying up to 50 or 60 small yellow and brown flowers with a very definite broad smooth labellum below the crest, resulting in a compact flower. *p. 1762*

MIMETES *Proteaceae* **I2LBD**

hottentotica (Cape Peninsula); shrub to 2½ m high; branches hidden with overlapping leaves, entirely covered with soft silvery pubescence; flower cones white with yellow bracts and colorful projecting orange styles. *p. 1975*

MIMOSA *Leguminosae* **S2-3LFM**

pudica (Brazil; naturalized in tropics), "Sensitive plant"; short-lived, spiny perennial; remarkable because of the ability of its pinnate leaves to go to sleep at the slightest touch, causing the leaflets to close and the petiole to fall; the flowers resemble little purplish puffs. An ubiquitous weed throughout the tropics, and it is thought that its mechanism is actuated by heat. I have seen it not only in Brazil, but in the West Indies where it is called "Mori-Vivi"; through Africa, and in Viet Nam where it is known as the "Shame plant". *Tropical.* *p. 1387*

spegazzinii (Argentina), a "Sensitive shrub"; small shrub; leaves pinnate, prickly at base; flowers rose-purple, with purple filaments; in 4 cm globose heads; prickly pods. The many leaflets fold along their axis when touched. *p. 1385*

MIMULUS *Scrophulariaceae* **I2LBD**

aurantiacus (Diplacus glutinosus) (Oregon, California), "Monkey flower"; branching shrub with narrow, leathery leaves toothed and turned down at the margins and sticky to the touch, pubescent beneath; the showy orange-salmon flowers 3 cm long, having notched, spreading lobes giving the effect of a monkey-face. *Subtropic.* *p. 2053, 2059*

guttatus (luteus) (Alaska to Mexico), "Monkey flower"; smooth perennial herbaceous plant to 45 cm high, leaves nearly oval with small marginal teeth, to 15 cm long; pretty two-lipped yellow flowers, 4 cm across, with two red marks at mouth; summer-blooming. *p. 2050*

lewisii (British Columbia to California and Utah); clammy-hairy herbaceous perennial to 75 cm with sessile, ovate 8 cm toothed leaves; bilabiate 5 cm flowers pink or rosy-red with spreading lobes. *p. 2059*

moschatus (Montana to California), "Musk-plant"; spreading, sticky-hairy perennial with musky odor, sessile ovate leaves and pale yellow flowers dotted and splashed brown, 2 cm long. *p. 2059*

MIMUSOPS *Sapotaceae* **S2LBD**

commersonii (Madagascar), a "Spanish cherry"; dense evergreen tropical tree with milky sap, handsome obovate, leathery, glossy green leaves with yellow midribs; axillary small fragrant white flowers, followed by long-stalked pendant globular greenish to yellow fruit 3 cm dia., with yellow, edible pulp of mild flavor. *Tropical.* *p. 2036*

roxburghiana (India), "Pagoda tree" or "Kanapalei"; tropical fruit tree with short, oval, leathery leaves; small, fragrant, white flowers, and globular, orange colored fruit 4 cm dia. with groove on one side; dry, mealy, yellow sweet edible flesh. *p. 2036*

MIRABILIS *Nyctaginaceae* **C2LBM**

jalapa (Perú), "Four-o'clock"; deep-rooted, bushy, tuberous perennial herb but usually grown as an annual; with smooth, ovate leaves and large fragrant flowers opening in late afternoon, closing in morning, in shades of red, yellow and white, often striped, blooming profusely in late summer. *Subtropic.* *p. 1616*

MISCANTHUS *Gramineae* **I2LBM**

sinensis 'Variegatus' (China, Japan), "Eulalia" or "Zebra grass"; very pretty ornamental perennial landscape grass, forming leafy clumps, 1 to 3 m tall, the linear leaves to 1 m long and 2 cm wide, green with broad ivory-white margins and a prominent pale central line; the flowers in beautiful feathery terminal plumes that may reach up to 3 m tall. *p. 1316*

MITCHELLA *Rubiaceae* **C3HFMh**

repens (E. No. America), "Partridge berry"; low evergreen creeper with thin, rooting stems to 30 cm long; tiny 2 cm oval, shining dark green leathery leaves often with white lines; twin white flowers with 4 spreading lobes, and fiery-red 1 cm berries characterized by having two navels. *Warm temperate.* *p. 2020, 2024*

MOLUCCELLA *Labiatae* **C2LBM**

laevis (Syria), "Bells of Ireland"; old-fashioned herbaceous annual interesting because its 60 cm stalks are closely set with whorls of the oversized, light-green, bell-shaped calyx in which nestle the little pinkish, bilabiate, fragrant flowers. *Subtropic.* *p. 1347, 1352*

MOMORDICA *Cucurbitaceae* **S3LFM**

balsamina (Trop. So. Africa to Tanzania), "Balsam apple"; vigorous climber with herbaceous tendril-bearing stems arising annually from a perennial rootstock; the shining green, thin leaves 3-10 cm across, are deeply lobed and toothed; flowers yellow spotted brown; followed on female flowers by the globular 8 cm orange-yellow warted fruit, which splits open when ripe, becoming very ornamental. *p. 929*

MONADENIUM *Euphorbiaceae* **I2LBD**

coccineum (Tanzania: Masai Dist.); semi-scandent or erect fleshy plant occasionally branched, with 5-angled green stem 1/3-1 m tall, 5-8 cm fleshy obovate leaves with keeled midrib and serrate margin; pretty, bright scarlet flowers, the lower petals green. *Tropical.* *p. 1052*

echinulatum (Tanzania); fleshy herb 30-60 cm high, with cylindric, prickly stem; 2½-12 cm elliptic leaves, and with soft prickles beneath, the midrib sharply keeled; flowers with bract-cup pale green or pinkish, with dark network and white margin and with soft teeth outside. *p. 1052*

guentherii (Kenya, Tanzania); small succulent 15-20 cm high, the knobby column with branches becoming rampant, to 90 cm long, densely set with long tubercles; linear, sickle-shaped leaves folded along the middle, 1 to 4 cm long, crowded in rosettes near apex; small axillary inflorescence with bract-cups greenish white and purple mottling. *p. 1060*

lugardae (Transvaal, Natal), "Green desert rose"; spineless succulent with bright green plump stem marked with raised rhombic fields, and deciduous, fleshy, deep green, obovate leaves; flowers insignificant, pale green. *p. 1052, 1053*

magnificum (Tanzania); succulent shrub to 1½ m high, with stem to 4 cm thick, and branches 1 to 2 cm dia., sharply angled and set with reddish-brown spine-clusters; fleshy, obovate leaves normally reflexed and with keeled midrib; the clustered inflorescence with bright scarlet bract cups. *p. 1060*

ritchiei (Kenya); succulent plant with tuberous root, branching with several erect or trailing stems, to 40 cm long, cylindrical to 2½ cm thick and ridged into shingle-like knobs; tiny dark green, ovate leaves; bract-cups white veined with pink. *p. 1060*

MONANTHES *Crassulaceae* **I2LBD**

brachycaulon (Aichryson divaricatum) (Canary Islands); shrubby succulent with branching stems bearing at their ends rosettes of nearly flat spatulate, fleshy leaves; the inflorescence cob-webby, with small whitish flowers. *p. 874*

polyphylla (Canary Isl.); dainty, cushion-forming, small succulent rosettes to 2 cm dia., with prostrate stems, dense with little light green, club-shaped leaves , and small reddish flowers. *p. 874*

MONILARIA *Aizoaceae* **I2LBD**

moniliformis (Cape Prov.), "String of pearls"; low branching succulent forming clumps; with thick knotted stems jointed like a necklace; leaves when growing, dark green and soft; when resting the united leaves form a roundish body. *p. 66*

MONODORA *Annonaceae* **S3LBM**

grandiflora (West Trop. Africa), "African orchid nutmeg"; tropical tree to 6 m high with oblong, glossy-green leaves purplish beneath, and pendulous orchid-like yellow flowers spotted red, the crisped outer petals 8-10 cm long, strikingly beautiful, blooming early in summer. *Tropical.* *p. 134*

tenuifolia (Trop. Africa), the "African nutmeg"; medium-sized shrub or tree to 12 m high, one of the prettiest of flowering trees; with narrow oblong leaves, and strangely beautiful flowers about 10 cm across, resembling orchids, with 3-pointed crinkly white sepals, and 6 united white and yellow petals with crimson spots, appearing from the underside of the twigs. *Tropical.* *p. 133*

MONOLENA *Melastomataceae* **I2LFM**

primulaeflora (Bertolonia) (Colombia); exquisite plant of the rainforest, with thick rhizome; brownish pubescent petioles carry the ornate, fleshy leaves, cordate in outline, glossy deep green and with sunken veins, 10-15 cm long, purple beneath; the charming baby-pink flowers 2 cm across, in a bouquet. *Subtropic.* *p. 1556*

MONOPHYLLAEA *Gesneriaceae* **S3HFM**

horsfieldii (Sumatra); very unique glabrous herb bearing at the apex of a succulent stalk a single giant heartshaped sessile leaf of thick texture, with clusters of tiny, bilabiate flowers appearing from its base. *p. 1241*

MONSONIA *Geraniaceae* **S3LBD**

biflora (Transvaal); annual flowering herb of the veld, with creeping roots and fleshy red stems, and set with small ovate leaves; pale pink showy flowers with 5 broad spreading petals, followed by the long-beaked fruits typical of the family, and scattering its seed. *p. 1175*

MONSTERA *Araceae* ***S1LFM**

acuminata (Guatemala); called the "Shingle plant" because the hard juvenile, oval leaves cling close to trees; later becoming pointed, unequal-sided and perforated. (3) *p. 230, 235*

deliciosa (Philodendron pertusum) (So. Mexico, Guatemala), "Ceriman"; stout, woody-stemmed, close-jointed tree-climber forming long hanging, cord-like aerial roots, with large, thick, leathery leaves, glossy green, to 1 m, pinnately cut and perforated with oblong holes; bisexual spadix and boat-shaped, white spathe; cone-like, edible fruit with pineapple aroma; also known as "Mexican bread-fruit". The long-jointed, rapid-climbing juvenile stage with smaller, less perforated leaves is known as Philodendron pertusum. *p. 160A, 229, 231, 232, 233, 234, 255*

deliciosa borsigiana (Cordoba, Mexico); vining type with smaller, glossy leaves with pinnate lobes widely and evenly separated, few, if any holes; the leafstalk is wrinkled where it joins the leaf. *Tropical.* *p. 231*

deliciosa 'Variegata' (Philodendron pertusum variegatum); "Variegated philodendron"; a mutant with irregular variegation where parts of the leaf may be entirely green, and other sections marbled cream to greenish-yellow, or entirely cream; new growth may be found to revert back to green. (3) *p. 230, 253*

dilacerata (Costa Rica); climber with hard-leathery, dark green leaves, in juvenile stage oblique-cordate, on short, winged petioles; toward maturity the leaves are more elongate and deeply slashed from margin to midrib. *p. 230, 235*

dubia (Mexico, C. America); long leaves pinnatisect in mature stage; the round, juvenile leaves have been mistaken for Marcgravia paradoxa. *p. 232*

epipremnoides (Costa Rica); interesting large climbing aroid with leaves somewhat resembling Epipremnum; thick, slowly elongating stem close-jointed, with long ovate leaves 60 cm long, on petioles winged two-thirds up from leaf axils; the deep green blades deeply and widely perforated to a rounded sinus, the lobes with square tip; along the midrib a dual row of small or large oval holes; the spadix club-like, shielded by ivory, boat-shaped spathe. Photographed at Longwood Gardens, Pennsylvania 1976. *Tropical.* *p. 229*

fendleri (Trinidad); leaves dark green, ovate, unequal-sided, widely pinnate-parted, with tips of segments twisted upward. *p. 230*

friedrichsthalii (valid name: adansonii) (Costa Rica); prolific climber with medium-size ovate, oblique, fresh green leaves, with many, mostly oval, perforations evenly distributed between veins; wavy margins; normally will not develop holes unless climbing up. *Tropical.* *p. 229, 232*

karstenianum (C. America); unequal-sided, ovate, corrugated leaf mottled light and dark green; on winged and channeled petiole. *p. 230*

karwinskyi (Mexico: Cordoba); climber with thick, waxy leaves, unequal-sided and twisted, with some oblong perforations, veins depressed, light green, on stout winged petioles. *p. 231*

leichtlinii: see obliqua expilata

"nechodomii" hort.; climbing plant, oblong pointed leaves pinnately parted, with tiny pinholes in rows along midrib; found in Puerto Rico but this is almost certainly the Asiatic Epipremnum pinnatum, brought to the island long ago by some ship-captain, (see Epipremnum). (3) *p. 231*

obliqua (Alto Amazonas); tall climber, having curious elliptic leaves with tapering apex, developing large, irregular, rather oval holes in older stage. *Tropical.* *p. 232*

obliqua expilata (leichtlinii), "Window-leaf"; a form of obliqua; the perforated leaves of this interesting "laceleaf" are not much more than an ovate skeleton of veins, with very little green left of the blade. The leaves become 60 cm large, the holes in the blade are usually arranged in double rows. *Tropical.* *p. 230, 232*

perforoides (Costa Rica); mountain species with medium-sized, hard, grayish-green, broad leaves, pinnately lobed and with large holes, prominent veins pale green; petioles edged in black. *p. 231*

pertusa (Panama, Guyana); lush climber with soft-textured, unequal-sided leaves perforated and pinnatisect; a poor keeper, from tropical lowland forests. *Tropical.* *p. 229, 231*

pertusa jacquinii; climber with oblique-ovate leaves dark green and undulate with depressed ribs and large oval perforations; petiole channeled; spadix greenish, spathe white outside. *p. 232*

peruviana (Perú); rather graceful tree-climber with leathery ovate, deep green, glossy leaves with sunken veins, widely cut and perforated. (3) *p. 230, 278*

pittieri (Costa Rica); climber with small ovate, slender pointed, unequal-sided, papery leaves, with occasional large holes, fresh-green with satin sheen. *p. 231*

punctulata (Mexico); quickly growing vine with fresh-green, long pointed leaves, unequal-sided, with irregular oval holes, becoming increasingly perforated and lobed in subsequent leaves; petioles lightly winged. *p. 231*

siltepacana (Mexico); tree-climber with rather large, broad ovate leaves with cordate base and pointed apex, the blade is irregularly perforated with many oblong holes; large club-like spadix. *p. 235*

standleyana (in horticulture as "guttiferyum"), (Costa Rica); close-jointed climber, with thick leathery, dark green, small oval leaves, with depressed veins, on broadly winged petioles when young; broader and more smooth in maturity. The venation curves upwards, suggesting Pothos. *p. 230*

MONTANOA *Compositae* **S2LBD**

grandiflora (Honduras); warm-climate flowering shrub with opposite foliage, the broad, rough-textured leaves deeply palmately lobed; charming double flowers with ray florets creamy white, and shaped like wide-open roses. *Tropical.* *p. 822*

MONTBRETIA: see Tritonia

MONTEZUMA *Malvaceae* **S2LBM**

speciosissima (Thespesia grandiflora) (Puerto Rico), "Hibiscus tree"; showy evergreen tree to 15 m; slender woody branches with heavy cordate, leathery leaves to 25 cm long, glossy green; large 15 cm waxy flowers, glossy crimson red, heavily veined, and with protruding style. *Tropical.* *p. 1533*

MONTRICHARDIA *Araceae* **S3LBW**

arborescens (Guyana); tree-like aroid, growing by the side of tropical rivers, with glossy-leathery, broad sagittate leaves 20-30 cm long, deep green with pale veins, on slender canes. *Humid-tropical.* *p. 227*

linifera (Brazil); tropical tree-like herb growing in wet places and along rivers; robust, fleshy stems 1 to 4 m high, with leathery, waxy green, hastate arrow-shaped leaves 20 cm long; spathe oblong, slender-pointed, 20 cm long, green outside, inside white. *p. 227, 281*

MONVILLEA *Cactaceae* **I2LFM**

cavendishii (Brazil, Paraguay, Argentina); nightblooming cactus with half erect slender 2½ cm stem branching at base, 9-10 ribbed, and needle-like spines; flowers white, pinkish outside. *p. 618, 660*

diffusa (Ecuador); night-blooming cactus with half erect, long slender, snaky, deep green stems 2 cm thick with 8-9 shallow ribs, and set closely with white radials and yellow needle spines tipped maroon; flowers white. *p. 643*

MORAEA *Iridaceae* **I2LBD**

edulis (South Africa); iris-like cormous herb forming 3 to 7 leaves; slender tall stem with solitary long wiry leaf, and fragrant 5 cm lilac flowers with yellow basal patches, remaining open 4 to 6 hours only. *p. 1328*

glaucopsis (tricuspidata), (So. Africa: Cape Prov.), "Peacock iris"; stem to 60 cm sometimes branching, with solitary, narrow-linear leaf, and short-lived white flowers with flaring outer segments having bluish-black blotch at base. *p. 1328, 1329*

iridioides: see Dietes vegeta

pavonia (So. Africa), "Peacock iris"; charming cormous plant with hairy, linear leaves and slender stalks with colorful flowers blue in base, zoned by orange-red, and edged yellow, short-lived but a succession appears; June-blooming. (Pictured in Exotica I).

pavonia var. villosa (So. Africa); flowers bright purple, with bluish-black peacock-zoning at base of outer segments, and with hairy claws; another form is white with blue base. *p. 1328*

polystachya (So. Africa); iris-like plant with black corm, 3-4 strongly ribbed leaves, and 1 m stalks with fleeting flowers lilac, the base of each petal with a yellow blotch, and flowering one after another in lax cluster. *p. 1325, 1329*

ramosa (So. Africa); leafy-stemmed herb to 1 m high, zigzag stem with narrow-linear leaves; cluster of numerous bright yellow 5 cm flowers. *p. 1328*

spathacea (Cape of Good Hope); perennial of the hillsides, with narrow leaves and iris-like but short-lived flowers with spreading yellow petals, claw with purple lines; fragrant; March. Moraea is the African representative of Iris. *p. 1328, 1329*

MORAEA: see also DIETES

MORINA *Dipsaceae* **I2LFD**

longifolia (Nepal), "Whorl-flower"; thistle-like perennial to 1 m with furrowed stem and pinnatifid, spiny-toothed leaves about 30 cm long; the tubular flowers in crowded whorls in upper leaf-axils, at first white, turning delicate pink and finally crimson, and subtended by spiny-toothed bracts. *p. 950*

MORINDA *Rubiaceae* **S3LFM**

citrifolia 'Variegata'; striking variegated-leaf form of the green species (S. E. Asia, Australia, Pacific Isl.); a small tree with large leathery, ovate leaves to 25 cm long, with prominent curving side veins, shining green contrasting with creamy-white mainly along the lateral veins; funnel-shaped white flowers. I photographed this variegated form in Fiji. *p. 2021*

MORMODES *Orchidaceae* **S-I3OFD**

atropurpureum (Colombia); small epiphyte with short pseudobulbs, lanceolate leaves, and stalk with raceme of deep purple 5 cm flowers, the 3-lobed lip smooth and with fleshy midlobe; December. (S) *p. 1768*

buccinator (Venezuela, Mexico); attractive epiphyte with stout pseudobulbs topped by membranous, plaited leaves to 30 cm long; lateral raceme, loosely flowered, with sepals and petals pale red-brown sprinkled with crimson dots; trumpet-shaped, fleshy, yellow lip, (Feb.-April). (I) *p. 1768*

colossus (Cent. America); large epiphyte with tapering 15-30 cm pseudobulbs and plaited leaves; the stalk 60 cm or more, with 12-15 cm flowers of narrow-lanceolate sepals and petals, their basal part pink with darker veins, yellow toward the tips, the lip bright yellow dotted with red, incurved and pointed (summer). (I) *p. 1767*

hookeri (Panama); stout pseudobulbs with 15-22 cm leaves, and clusters of 5 cm flowers having sepals and petals dark reddish-brown, the velvety lip deep crimson, covered with short hairs; January. (S) *p. 1768*

igneum (Cent. America), robust, handsome epiphyte 45-60 cm high, with long stout pseudobulbs carrying several plaited leaves; fleshy flower stems from the body of the pseudobulb, with sepals and petals reddish-brown, the contorted lip orange, clawed at base (winter). (S) *p. 1767*

lineatum (Guatemala); showy epiphyte with plaited leaves on strong pseudobulbs; lightly arching raceme of very fragrant flowers, sepals and petals tongue-shaped, outside greenish, inside yellow with purple stripes, lip yellowish with red dots, (Jan.-March). *Tropical.* *p. 1768*

skinneri (Costa Rica); epiphyte with thick, cylindrical pseudobulbs bearing folded leaves; the attractive flowers in many-flowered raceme produced during the leafless resting period, whitish and more or less spotted or flushed purplish-red, the lip covered with long white hairs; March-April. (S) *p. 1768*

variabilis (Ecuador); cylindrical pseudobulbs with lanceolate, ribbed leaves; blooming at beginning or end of resting period; the flowers strongly spicy fragrant, sepals and petals pink often flushed olive green, lip bright rose; March-April or September-October. (S) *p. 1770*

MORUS *Moraceae* **C2LBMhd**

nigra (West Asia), "Black mulberry"; large shrub or tree to 10 m high, with rough, dull-green broad-ovate 20 cm leaves, crenate at margins; flowers in drooping catkins; luscious edible red to black berries somewhat hidden on underside of branches. Has the largest and juiciest fruit of the mulberries. *Warm temperate.* *p. 1562*

rubra (Mass. to Florida and Texas), "Red mulberry"; deciduous tree to 20 m high with ovate leaves, sometimes lobed, downy beneath, used to feed silkworms; the sweet, dark purple fruit resembles a blackberry. *p.1576*

MUCUNA *Leguminosae* **S2-3LFM**

bennettii (New Guinea), "New Guinea creeper"; striking vine with glossy green, compound leaves on woody, twining stems, and long axillary pendant racemes of sickle-shaped, claw-like, waxy, fiery scarlet flowers; probably the most showy of all tropical climbers. *Tropical.* *p. 1388*

novo-guineensis (Papua), "D'Albertis-creeper"; magnificent woody twiner with leaves of 3 smooth leaflets; claw-like orange-scarlet flowers in large clusters. *p. 1385*

MUEHLENBECKIA *Polygonaceae* **°I-2-3LB-FM**

complexa (New Zealand), "Wire vine" or "Maidenhair-vine"; twining, threadlike, purplish-brown, wiry stems furnished with scattered, tiny round, fresh-green 1-2 cm leaves; flowers greenish-white, in small spikes; a graceful basket plant. *Subtropic.* *p. 1954*

MUEHLENBECKIA: see also Homalocladium

MUIRIA *Aizoaceae* **I2LBD**

hortenseae (So. Africa: Karroo); tiny succulent with growths consisting of two completely united leaves, ovoid to globose, 2½ cm high, light green, with velvety hairs, the fissure barely visible until pinkish-white inflorescence forces its way through. Water once a year. *p. 74*

MURRAYA *Rutaceae* **°I2LFM**

alata (India, Malaya, Vietnam); evergreen shrub 1 m high, with hard-leathery, glossy green leaves similar to camellias; flowers with 5 wide-spreading, recurving petals, jasmine-like, pure white and strongly fragrant; blooming and fruiting all year, the red fruit and flowers both at all times. *p. 2034*

exotica (India, Ceylon to Australia), "Orange jessamine"; handsome ornamental, evergreen shrub dense with glossy-green, odd-pinnate leaves and sweetly fragrant, bell-shaped, white flowers in clusters, succeeded by small, vivid-red berries; blooms several times a year. *p. 2025, 2026*

koenigii (India), "Curry-leaf" or "Karapindra"; evergreen shrub with pinnate leaves, usually hairy, pungently aromatic; starry small flowers whitish-yellow, in terminal clusters; the leaves are an ingredient of curries. *p. 2025*

paniculata (India), "Satinwood" and "Cosmetic bark tree"; related to M. exotica but more tree-like with strong and durable light yellow wood, and bark which is the source of a cosmetic; pinnate leaves of 3-9 obovate, glossy green leaflets, 6 cm long; the large strongly scented 5-petaled white blooms in few-flowered clusters, and worn in the hair for their beauty and fragrance by the women of the East Indies. *Tropical.* *p. 2026, 2034*

MUSA *Musaceae* **S2-3LF-BW**

basjoo (Southern Japan: Liu-Chiu archipelago), "Japanese fiber-banana"; cluster-forming to 4 m or more, slender reddish pseudo-stem bearing shining thin leaves to 3 m long, bright green on both sides; arching inflorescence with yellowish flowers under reddish bracts; followed by bunches of 30 to 60 curved fruits, 8 cm long. Grown for its fiber in Japan. *Subtropic.* *p. 1598, 1599*

coccinea (Vietnam: Cochin), "Flowering banana"; showy flowering plant to 1½ m high and stoloniferous, with green pseudo-stems topped by spirally arranged, long-stalked, bright green leaves and erect flowering head with flaming fiery-red bracts yellow at tips and yellow flowers. Small fruit orange-yellow 5 cm long, and with white flesh. *p. 1593, 1594*

Fehi (troglodytarum) (No. New Guinea), "Cooking banana"; tree-like, stoloniferous plant to 7 m high; stem cylindrical, formed of sheathing leaf-petioles, with violet sap; broad shining green leaves 2 m long, 60 cm wide, often windblown into shreds; inflorescence erect, the flowers hidden under colored bracts; small, angled fruit in large erect clusters, orange, 12-15 cm long, and eaten only after cooking. *Tropical.* *p. 1593, 1597*

ensete: see ENSETE ventricosum

maurelii: see ENSETE

nana (cavendishii) (So. China), "Dwarf banana"; also known as "Dwarf Jamaica"; shapely stoloniferous plant of compact habit, to 2-3 m high, with short stem and dense rosette of oblong, glaucous green, leathery leaves with satiny sheen, blotched with red when young, on short stout petioles; produces edible, deliciously fragrant yellow, 12 cm fruit; stands more cold than most bananas; good tub plant. Probably a form of M. acuminata. *p. 1595, 1596*

nana 'Costa Rican' (C. America), an "Eating banana"; forming larger, more slender trees from underground rhizome; with broad leaves, and producing pendant clusters of golden-yellow edible fruit 15 cm long, with sweet and fragrant pulp; one bunch may carry 200 to 300 banana fruits. *p. 1593*

nepalensis (Himalayas); medium high, graceful species with conical trunk becoming thick, topped by a rosette of arching gray-green leaves with red midrib; fairly 'hardy', having seen it endure the winters in the lower Himalayas at 2300 m. (I) *p. 1594*

x paradisiaca (x sapientum; acuminata x balbisiana) (India, Ceylon), "Common banana"; tree-like herb to 7 m high, with spirally arranged green leaves with reddish midrib, becoming frayed or broken by the wind, forming a slender trunk by their sheathing bases; flowers yellow, bracts violet, and the well known, yellow, edible fruit, about 20 cm long; after fruiting the stem dies but is replaced by new suckers. *Tropical.* *p. 1595, 1596*

x paradisiaca 'Koae'; probably an Hawaiian bud mutation triploid of some Maoli banana of the Pacific; this most beautiful variegated-leaf banana is named after the Koae bird with "hair prematurely graying"; the leaves are striped or banded white and very light green on dark green, laterally; the midrib, petiole and trunk alternating white and green, even the immature fruit is variegated, but ripens to yellow, is short and roundish, with yellow flesh. *Tropical.* *p. 1600*

x paradisiaca 'Vittata', "Variegated banana"; beautiful plant with the light green leaves variegated milky green and white, the midrib white and edges red; loves shade and warmth. Short and roundish fruit ripens yellow, and is generally cooked to eat. *Tropical.* *p. 320A, 1596*

rosacea (ornata) (Chittagong Hills of India); slender, attractive species reaching only to 2 m, freely suckering, reddish stem with oblong, rich blue-green leaves marked with occasional wine-red, and red midrib, purplish-red beneath; flowers yellow; stays small. *p. 1594*

sumatrana (Sumatra), "Blood banana"; desirable plant to 2½ m high, not as tall as zebrina, leaves shorter and to 40 cm wide, on short petioles, deep grayish green blotched with dark wine-red, and red beneath as well, but losing this coloring with age; more tolerant to winter chills. *p. 1594*

textilis (Philippines), "Manila hemp"; stoloniferous plant to 6 m high, furnishing fiber for rope; oblong, bright green leaves, glaucous beneath, occasionally blotched brown, on 30 cm petioles; bracts purplish-red; small yellow fruit not edible. *p. 1594*

velutina (Assam); dwarf species to 2 m or more high, slender, with pinkish in stem, petioles and into midrib, leaves 1 m long and 30 cm wide; erect inflorescence with red bracts, pale yellow flowers and small, red velvety fruit. *Tropical.* *p. 1594, 1598*

zebrina (Java), "Blood banana"; known in horticulture as sumatrana; slender plant to 4 m high with tall pseudo-trunk bearing rather delicate long-stalked leaves, satiny bluish green richly variegated with blackish blood-red, the channeled midrib brown-red, underside reddish-wine; maintaining its coloring with age but sensitive to cold. *Tropical.* *p. 1594, 1596*

MUSA: see also Ensete

MUSCARI *Liliaceae* **C2LBWhd**

armeniacum (Turkey), "Grape hyacinth"; May-blooming bulbous plant to 20 cm high, suitable for forcing in pots, with narrow, channeled basal leaves, and delicate spires of nodding, urn-shaped flowers azure-blue, tipped white. *Subtropic.* *p. 1464*

botryoides album (So. Europe), "Pearls of Spain" or "Starch hyacinth"; charming hardy bulbous flowering herb to 25 cm, soft-fleshy linear, glaucous leaves; the erect stalks with pretty spike-like racemes of tiny fragrant, pure white flowers. *p. 1475*

comosum monstrosum (plumosum) (So. Europe), "Feather hyacinth"; unusual looking bulbous plant to 30 cm, with lax leaves, and all sterile flowers, violet blue to reddish purple, cut into fine shreds. *p. 1475*

racemosum (Europe and Asia Minor), a "Grape-hyacinth"; small bulbous spring-blooming plant to 20 cm high, with stiff, fleshy, linear leaves, and small fragrant dark blue flowers. *p. 1475*

MUSSAENDA *Rubiaceae* **S3LFM**

arcuata (Mauritius, Trop. Africa); evergreen shrub to 2½ m high, obovate-elliptic, fleshy leaves to 12 cm long; the inflorescence a lax cluster of star-shaped yellow flowers with brown eye, but usually lacking the enlarged calyx or colored bracts found in other species. *p. 2018*

erythrophylla (Zaire), "Ashanti blood"; beautiful spreading shrub or rambler with roundish ovate, bright green, silky-hairy, soft leaves, and tiny 1 cm creamy-white flowers with cushion of blood-red felt in center, each having appended one large, odd, ovate 10 cm showy sepal of rich vermilion-scarlet with parallel dark veining, which cover the bush almost entirely by their masses. *Tropical.* *p. 2011, 2021*

erythrophylla 'Queen Sirikit', (Singapore); a beautiful tropical cultivar with arching branches, broad ovate, glossy-green corrugated leaves, the elongate inflorescence a veritable spray of colored pseudo-leaves, or broad oval bracts rosy-crimson shading to delicate cream. *p. 2023*

incana (Himalayas); branching shrub with slender wiry shoots bearing opposite ovate, grayish, corrugated leaves, and inflorescence with small starry yellow flowers and an enlarged ovate-slender-pointed, showy white sepal. This may be M. frondosa, from Malaysia and Polynesia. *p. 2021*

luteola (flava) (Trop. Africa), "Yellow Buddha's lamp"; erect shrub 1½-2 m high, with lanceolate leaves hairy beneath; small star-like tubular flowers bright yellow with orange center, and a broad ovate, enlarged, creamy-white sepal. *p. 2021*

philippica (Philippines, New Guinea); shrub with large ovate, soft-hairy or satiny leaves red-veined beneath, and terminal clusters of small star-like deep yellow flowers, subtended by one large ovate, pure white petaloid bract, actually a calyx-lobe expanded into a large sepal. *Tropical.* *p. 2021*

philippica 'Aurorae' (Philippines: Luzon); an outstanding variety which I have seen offered at the flower market in Manila, as "Dona Aurora"; a bushy shrub with large corrugated, green, downy 8-15 cm leaves, each twig bearing a showy, pubescent inflorescence of small golden yellow flowers, surrounded by a circle of gleaming white, pendant, obovate enlarged sepals, almost the year round; this variety differs in having all the calyx lobes developed into 5 petal-like white bracts, not just a single one as in the species. *Tropical.* *p. 2021*

roxburghii (Himalayan Reg.); evergreen tropical bush with ovate to obovate herbaceous, fresh green quilted leaves; the inflorescence with tubular yellowish flowers, subtended by stalked white bracts. *p. 2018*

MUTISIA *Compositae* **I3LBM**

clematis (Colombia, Ecuador); pubescent climbing evergreen vine with pinnate leaves, the midrib extended into a tendril; nodding, woolly flower heads bright orange-scarlet with 9-10 bright red spreading rays. *p. 828*

coccinea (Brazil); shrub with alternate leaves and solitary terminal heads of disk-flowers, and a few recurved crimson-red ray flowers. *p. 828*

decurrens (Chile); climbing shrub with narrow-oblong leaves 8-12 cm long, dark green above and glaucous beneath, with long, branched tendril; solitary flower heads 10-12 cm across, with linear florets brilliant orange or vermilion. *p. 823*

oligodon (Chile); woody climber with straggling stem, the young shoots ribbed and woolly; oblong leaves stem-clasping 3-4 cm long, and coarsely toothed, shining green above, woolly beneath and with terminal tendril; flower heads with 6-12 broad florets satiny pink. *p. 823*

MYOPORUM *Myoporaceae* **I2LFM**

'Carsonii'; robust evergreen shrub with willowy branches and alternate, leathery, glossy deep green, long-elliptic leaves; small white bell-shaped flowers, in axillary clusters amongst foliage, in early summer. Chance seedling listed by California nurseries. *p. 1600, 1601*

laetum (New Zealand), the "Ngaio" or "Mouse-hole tree"; vigorous evergreen tree or shrub of exceptionally fast growth to 10 m high and 6 m spread, forming a dense, billowing mass of dark green; older growth stiff-woody, young shoots flexible, with narrow elliptic 8-10 cm soft-leathery, glossy leaves with translucent oil glands; clusters of 1 cm flowers white with purple markings; small purplish fruits. Favours the seashores in New Zealand and is very salt-resistant. *Subtropic.* *p. 1601*

sandwicense (Hawaii), the "Naio" or "Bastard sandalwood"; small evergreen tree at home on volcanic slopes in Hawaii up to 3000 m; wood is scented like sandalwood; dark gray, grooved bark and hard, yellow green wood; rather thick, smooth or hairy leaves to 15 cm long, with translucent dots; small pink or white flowers, white berried fruit. *p. 1601*

MYOSOTIS *Boraginaceae* **C2LFW**

sylvatica (Europe, N. Asia), "Forget-me-not"; small tufted herb with oblong leaves, and racemes bearing the appealing little skyblue flowers with yellow eye, and 1 cm across. Often listed as alpestris. *Temperate.* *p. 510*

sylvatica 'Compacta'; a dwarf "Forget-me-not" of dense and bushy, compact habit about 15cm high, with deep sky-blue flowers. *p. 510*

MYRIALEPIS *Palmae* **S3LFM**

scortechinii (Malaya: Perak); climbing, spiny palm with pinnate fronds, the slender, cane-like stems set with clusters of whorls of long spines, the leaflets arranged very sparsely and irregularly along rachis. *p. 1890*

MYRICA *Myriacaceae* **C-I2LBD**

pensylvanica (Nova Scotia to Florida and Alabama), "Bayberry"; handsome shrub $\frac{1}{2}$-$2\frac{1}{2}$ m high, conspicuous in winter when covered with its waxy grayish white fruits which stay on the branches until spring; the branches pubescent, with dark green obovate leaves 5-10 cm long, resinous dotted beneath; the flowers in catkins. *p. 1548, 1601*

MYRIOCARPA *Urticaceae* **S3LFM**

stipitata (Boehmeria argentea) (Mexico); ornamental tropical tree to 9 m high, with large and showy, bluish-green, quilted leaves to 30 cm long, shading to silver toward the crenate-toothed margin, quilted and bristly on the surface, veined red-brown beneath; flowers without petals in long catkins. *p. 2114*

MYRIOPHYLLUM *Haloragidaceae* **I3HFW**

brasiliense (Brazil, Argentina, Uruguay, Chile); vigorous aquatic underwater or marsh plant with stems to $1\frac{1}{2}$ m long, rarely branched, the bright green leaves are in whorls, 3-5 cm long divided into linear, 1 cm segments; stems and leaves above water are stiff and succulent bluish green; flowers with 4 white or rosy petals. *p. 1322*

hippurioides, (Washington, Oregon, Florida, Mexico), the "Water-milfoil"; aquarium or marsh plant, suitable for heated aquaria; branching stem to 1 m long, with yellow-green leaves in whorls 3-5 cm long, divided into 6-10 segments on each side of a rib. In strong light stems and leaves turn a beautiful wine-red, and very popular among aquarists and growers, and sold as "red" species from Florida. *p. 1322*

proserpinacoides (Chile, Uruguay), "Parrot's feather"; aquatic herb used for oxygenating the water; normally rising about 15 cm above the surface, with whorled feathery leaves on shoots from a creeping rhizome-like stem in mud on the bottom of pond or aquarium. *p. 1320, 1322*

MYRISTICA *Myristicaceae* **S3LFM**

fragrans (Indonesia: Moluccas), the "Nutmeg tree"; evergreen, dioecious, 10-18 m high, with willowy green branches, and leathery, yellowish olive green ovate, aromatic leaves 5-12 cm long, bluish beneath; axillary pale yellow flowers; the yellow pear-like fleshy 5 cm fruit opens by two valves and showing red pulp—the spice—which surrounds a brown, hard-shelled seed; the kernel of the seed is nutmeg, borne on female trees. *Tropical.* *p. 1600, 1603*

MYRMECODIA *Rubiaceae* **S3SphagFM**

armata (tuberosa) (Malaya), "Antplant"; curious epiphytic tropical shrub with a prickly, tuberous rhizome with thick-fleshy branches; heavy leathery, obovate stalked leaves clustered near tips; small white flowers with urn-shaped 4-lobed corolla; the hollow tuberous base is commonly inhabited by ants. *p. 2023*

platyrea (New Guinea); remarkable epiphytic subshrub with prickly tuberous rhizome which serve stinging ants as nests in hollow chambers inside the inflated tuberous stem, to 20 cm dia.; the short 4-angled, fleshy branches with crowded obovate, fleshy leaves and small white, sessile, tubular flowers. *p. 2014*

MYRSINE *Myrsinaceae* **·I2LBM**

africana (So. Africa, Arabia, to C. China), "African boxwood"; shrubby bush resembling boxwood but more graceful, to 1 m, with angled, downy, red shoots, dense with small rounded, shiny dark green, 1 cm leaves finely serrate; tiny pale brown axillary flowers and purplish-blue berries. *Subtropic.* *p. 1602, 1604*

MYRTILLOCACTUS *Cactaceae* **·I2LBD**

cochal (Baja California); attractive branching columnar plant with club-shaped branches intensely glaucous bluish, with 6-8 ribs and shallow furrows between, strong gray central spine on black areole; small flowers tinged purple, and edible red fruit. *p. 643*

geometrizans (S. Mexico), "Blue myrtle" or "Blueberry cactus"; branching tree type to 4 m high; smooth, slender columns six-ribbed, 8 to 10 cm dia., glaucous powder-blue; with practically no spines; small diurnal flowers greenish-white; berry-like, edible blue fruit. *Arid-tropical.* *p. 638*

schenckii (Mexico); dark green branching column to 10 cm thick with 7-8 angular ribs, the areoles not woolly, and set with clusters of short thin spines; flowers lemon yellow, brown outside. *p. 638*

MYRTUS *Myrtaceae* **·I-C2LBD**

communis (Mediterranean reg.), "Greek myrtle"; evergreen shrub to 4 m high, loosely leafy with leathery, rather broad-ovate, 5 cm leaves, dark lustrous green, spicy when bruised; fragrant white flowers with numerous stamens, and purple-black berries. *Subtropic.* *p. 1609, 1614, 1615*

communis boetica, "Citrus myrtle"; very attractive variety of the classic myrtle, with smooth, dark green, 3 cm boat shaped ovate leaves with sharp tip, very fragrant, dense and symmetrical on erect branches forming a compact, decorative bush. *p. 1614, 1615*

communis 'Compacta', "Compact myrtle" or "Dwarf myrtle"; slow-growing, small, compact form with densely set small black-green leaves, 2-3 cm long, and which may be trimmed and sheared into various topiary or Bonsai forms; also for low edgings indoors or the patio. *Subtropic.* *p. 1605*

communis 'Microphylla', "Dwarf myrtle"; the compact form grown by European plantsmen in pots and sheared into little globes and used for weddings; densely leafy shrub with brown twigs and small, needle-like, shining black-green leaves, and white flowers of aromatic fragrance. *p. 1609*

communis romana, "Roman myrtle"; handsome dense evergreen shrub, as seen in the plantings of the San Diego Zoo, (Calif.); the leathery shiny dark green leaves are so wide as to be nearly round, 3 cm long and 2 cm wide; the inflorescence in large heads of white flowers with prominent long stamens. *p. 1615*

communis 'Variegata', "Variegated myrtle"; small evergreen shrub with leathery, pointed, green leaves attractively variegated or margined with creamy-white. *Subtropic.* *p. 1609*

obcordata purpurea (New Zealand); dense evergreen shrub to 5 m high, with thin-wiry brownish branches; small leathery, opposite 1 cm leaves, roundish with notched tips, glossy green in the species; edged with purple and with purple veins in purpurea, gray beneath; small 1 cm dull white flowers; red or violet berries. *p. 1615*

MYSTACIDIUM *Orchidaceae* **S3OND**

capense (Southeastern Africa and Madagascar); miniature epiphyte almost stemless, with few leathery leaves to 8 cm long; starry fragrant flowers to 4 cm across, of waxy texture, glistening pure white and with awl-shaped spur (summer). *p. 1769*

distichum (Angraecum) (Sierra Leone, W. Africa); neat little epiphyte, with stem covered by two ranks of 1 cm fleshy, bright green, folded over, sickle-shaped leaves, with small, white, upside-down, spurred flowers from the axils of the foliage, (July-Oct.). (S) *p. 1761*

MYSTACIDIUM: see also Angraecum

NAEGELIA: see Smithiantha

NAJAS *Najadaceae* **S3LFW**

madagascariensis (Madagascar), "Bushy pondweed" or "Nixkraut"; aquatic herb of tropical waters to 4 m deep, freely branching, with linear, ribbon-like leaves; suitable for aquaria. *p. 1608*

NANANTHUS *Aizoaceae* **I2LBD**

aloides (Cape Prov.); small succulent with crowded keeled, pointed leaves, dark green with white warts; daisy-like yellow flowers. *p. 68*

malherbei (Cape Prov.), "Miniature blue fan"; small 4 cm branching rosette, with flat, bluish-gray fan-like, spatulate leaves attractively decorated at the apex with a row of ivory warts; stalked, biscuit-colored flowers. *p. 68*

villetii (So. Africa); little, pretty succulent rosette with bluish-green spatulate leaves, densely white-warty; pale yellow flowers nestling amongst leaves, blooming in the afternoon. *p. 68*

NANDINA *Berberidaceae* **I-C2LFM**

domestica (China, Japan), "Heavenly bamboo"; attractive shrub usually low, but to $2\frac{1}{2}$ m, slender cane-like stems with 2 to 3-pinnate leaves, the ultimate leaflets narrow; turning red in fall; small white flowers in large panicles, followed by bright red berries; fairly hardy. *p. 496*

domestica longifolia 'Ito'; a curious form of "Heavenly bamboo", the woody stems with apparent leafless branches, the foliage reduced to ribs only, in red or green; photographed at Ono's Nursery, Honolulu. *Warm temperate.* *p. 495*

NANODES *Orchidaceae* **S3OBW**

medusae (Epidendrum) (Ecuador); small, erect plant of vandaceous habit, with broad leaves in 2 ranks; terminal flowers with fleshy sepals and petals dull green tinged with purple, 5 cm across, and with broad fringed lip blackish velvety red, greenish in throat. *p. 1769*

NARCISSUS *Amaryllidaceae* **C2LF-BMhd**

'Actaea' (Poeticus type); large flat, pure white petals, with yellow eye, broadly margined scarlet; derived from N. poeticus, the "Poet's narcissus", from France to Greece. *Warm temperate.* *p. 126*

asturiensis ('Minimus') (Spain, Portugal); perfect miniature of a large trumpet daffodil but only 5-10 cm high; flower deep yellow, shaded green, the mouth of the 1 cm long trumpet wavy; early blooming; leaves glaucous. *p. 124*

bulbocodium (So. France to Morocco), "Petticoat daffodil"; distinct variable small species with slender, almost threadlike leaves to 38 cm long, exceeding the blooms; solitary flowers bright yellow, the tubular funnel-shaped crown to $2\frac{1}{2}$ cm long, on stalk 10-20 cm high. The popular variety **conspicuus** grows only 10-15 cm high, with deep yellow flowers (Div. 10). *p. 124, 128*

cyclamineus 'February Gold', a hybrid of N. cyclamineus from Portugal with a "Trumpet" type blossom; compact "Pot narcissus" about 25 cm high, with narrow linear leaves, and smallish but numerous flowers having lemon yellow perianth segments spreading 5 cm across, and orange yellow trumpet, crenate at mouth. Normally early blooming, this pretty hybrid is ideal for pots from Valentine to Easter. *Warm temperate.* *p. 125*

cyclamineus 'February Silver'; a cultivar with silvery-white trumpet with reflexed perianth segments; result of breeding of cyclamineus (Portugal) with a Trumpet narcissus; height 30 cm; early March on (Div. 6). *p. 124*

'Empress of Ireland' (Div. 1: Trumpet); broad pure white flower with ruffled white trumpet 5 cm wide. *p. 127*

'Estelle de Mol'; an orchid-daffodil developed by Dr. DeMol through changing the chromosome count in Giant Trumpet types by the use of ultraviolet rays; heavy-textured, long-lasting flowers to 10 cm across, with broad-petaled pure white perianths, intermingled with an expanded 5 cm orange-yellow flattened ruffled cup. *p. 130*

'Flower Record' (Large Cupped type); creamy white, flaring outer petals, wide open golden-yellow crown edged bright red; long stemmed. *p. 126, 127*

'Forum' (pseudo-narcissus) (Div. 1); stocky daffodil 30 cm high, shorter than 'Gold Medal'; large golden yellow flowers 10 cm across, similar in shape to 'King Alfred'. *p. 125*

'Geranium' (tazetta: Divis. 8); large white petals, cup deep orange-red; medium late. *p. 126, 127*

'Gold Medal' (pseudo-narcissus); a true, short pot daffodil; outstanding large-flowered trumpet variety almost exactly like 'King Alfred' except that it is more stocky and shapely in pots for spring; the large 9 cm flowers clear yellow with richer colored trumpet, carried on solid stalks 30 cm high, 2 to 3 to a bulb; late blooming. *Warm temperate.* *p. 125*

'Golden Harvest' (Yellow Trumpet type); a giant, uniform deep golden all-yellow flower, earlier than 'King Alfred'. *p. 126, 127*

'Golden Phoenix' (Double daffodil); the golden yellow variety of this fully double 'Phoenix' group with multified petals. *p. 126*

'John Evelijn' (Div. 2: Large-cupped); large flower with outer perianth round and flat and of great substance, the large expanded ruffled cup soft apricot-orange. *p. 127*

juncifolius (So. France, Spain, Portugal); known as a miniature "Rush-leaved daffodil"; about 10 cm high, with narrow leaves, and small rich yellow flowers, to 2½ cm wide, with a flattish darker yellow, ruffled little crown (Div. 10). *p. 130*

'King Alfred' (Div. 1: Trumpet type), "Lent lily"; spring-flowering, bulbous plant with basal leaves; large, solitary, golden-yellow, trumpet flowers; very substantial, with strong stem, an outstanding florists forcing and pot "daffodil"; probably the best-known cultivar derived from the W. European species N. pseudo-narcissus. *p. 126, 127*

'Laurens Koster' (tazetta x poeticus) (poetaz type); two or more larger flowers than tazetta and more pleasantly fragrant; perianth white, cup orange; free flowering. *p. 126*

'March Sunshine' (Div. 6: cyclamineus hyb.); a small plant 25 cm high, free-flowering, with perianth butter-yellow and an orange-yellow cup 2/3 the length of the perianth segments; early. *p. 128*

moschatus (Spain, Portugal); flowers rather small, nodding, scented, with narrow tube shaded yellow outside, the sulphur-white twisted segments drooping over corona, on 25-35 cm stalk, and with glaucous leaves. *p. 130*

'Mount Hood' (White Trumpet type); large pure ivory-white outer petals, creamy-white trumpet. *p. 126*

'Mrs. R. O. Backhouse' (Large Cupped type); petals, or perianth, creamy-white, small trumpet-shaped cup of pale apricot, passing to pink. *p. 126*

'Music Hall' (Bicolor Trumpet type); petals creamy white with pleasingly contrasting, large golden-yellow trumpet; medium early. *p. 126*

obvallaris (Europe); hardy bulbous plant with flat, glaucous leaves and medium-size scented flowers, with the tube broad and short, 1 cm long, tinged green, the spreading segments deep golden yellow, the broad, 6-lobed corona of same color. *p. 128*

odorus 'Orange Queen' (Div. 7: Jonquils), a miniature daffodil to 30 cm tall, derived from odorus (Mediterranean, east to Yugoslavia); clustering, slender, narrow channeled leaves, and numerous stalks bearing 2-3 pretty, small 4 cm flowers with 6 segments and small cup, rich orange-yellow and very fragrant. Free flowering and very striking. *Temperate.* *p. 124*

x poetaz (tazetta x poeticus ornatus) (Div. 8); similar to tazetta, the "Paper-white" but the white flowers larger and more pleasantly fragrant, and with a short yellow cup, 2 to 6 on each stalk. *p. 128*

x poetaz 'Early Perfection' (Div. 8); excellent "Cluster narcissus", with the larger blooms of the Poet's narcissus and the several flowers on each stalk characteristic of tazetta; large white, rounded perianth segments and a shallow cup egg-yellow, in its pleasantly scented, long-lasting blossoms on strong stems. *p. 125*

poeticus (Spain, through the Alps, to Greece), "Poet's narcissus"; clustering bulbous plant 25-45 cm high, with narrow gray-bluish leaves and two-edged stalks with solitary, very fragrant flowers glistening white tinted yellow at base, the flat corona with a crisped red edge; spring. *p. 123*

poeticus 'Red Rim' (Div. 9); vigorous, distinct cultivar, the flowers with large white perianth or outer, flat segments, and a small center cup with yellow eye shading to green, and a broad red rim; midseason. *p. 127*

poeticus 'Snow King' (Div. 9); a pleasing "Pheasant's eye narcissus" having flowers with glistening white perianth with broad oval overlapping segments and a cup with an extra wide edge of red, and yellow center. *p. 127*

'Rembrandt' (Div. 1: Trumpet); flowers with large trumpet, uniform deep golden yellow, identical in color to King Alfred but the blooms are larger and of better shape. *p. 124*

'Rococo' (Div. 2: Large-cupped); flowers with rounded, overlapping perianth segments apricot-colored; the large expanded, frilled cup orange. *p. 127*

rupicola (Spain, Portugal) (Div. 10); small flowered species 20-25 cm high, with very slender leaves nearly round; solitary flowers 2 cm across, bright yellow; early spring blooming. *p. 125*

tazetta canaligulatus (Canary Is.), a "Polyanthus narcissus"; sweet-scented, miniature with bunches of 2½ cm flowers; perianth white, small yellow cup. *p. 128*

tazetta var. orientalis (China), "Chinese sacred lily" or "Joss-flower"; a sweet little miniature of the "bunch-flowered" class, to 30 cm high, with flat, strap-shaped, bluish-green foliage; stiff stalks carry clusters of small, white flowers 3 cm across, with short yellow corona cup, and daintily fragrant. During a stay in Shanghai, I have seen this "Polyanthus" narcissus happily blooming on window-sills during February, growing in glazed bowls filled with water and pebbles. *Subtropic.* *p. 125*

tazetta papyraceus (Canary Is.), "Paperwhites"; small white, fragrant flowers; tube short, several together on each stem. *p. 125, 126*

'Texas', "Double daffodil"; large double flower; outer and inside petals bright yellow, orange-red petals through the center. (Divis. 4). *p. 126*

triandrus albus (Spain, Portugal) (Div. 10), "Angel's tears daffodil"; leaves narrow and rush-like, with stalks bearing clusters of to 6 nodding flowers creamy-white, the narrow perianth segments reflexed, and cup-shaped corona. *p. 124*

triandrus aurantiacus (Div. 10); pretty variety with nodding little flowers deep yellow. *p. 128*

triandrus 'Horn of Plenty' (Div. 5); triandrus hybrid 30 cm high, with beautiful large flowers glistening snow-white; free blooming and long-lasting, usually 3 flowers to a stem; late. *p. 125*

watieri (Morocco, Turkey) (Div. 10); charming little narcissus 15 cm high; pure white flowers solitary with segments 2 cm across, above erect slender, channeled, glaucous leaves; in spring. *p. 125*

'W. P. Milner' (Trumpet miniature); an old but useful dwarf cultivar 20 cm high, similar to moschatus, with creamy-white flowers having large, expanded trumpet serrated at apex; free-blooming and early. *p. 128*

NASTURTIUM *Cruciferae* **C2LFW**

officinale (Europe, W. Asia), "Watercress"; naturalized in streams in No. America; hardy perennial with much branched stem, sometimes short and creeping or floating in shallow water, in marshes, or sometimes along the shore as bushes; with small pinnate leaves of 3-9 ovate leaflets; pungent tiny white flowers; used for salads. *p. 928*

NASTURTIUM of hort: see Tropaeolum

NAUTILOCALYX *Gesneriaceae* **S3HFM**

bullatus (Episcia tessellata) (Amazonian Perú); erect plant with large much-wrinkled, bronzy leaves stiffly-hairy above, wine-red beneath, and small pale yellow, hairy tubular flowers from leaf axils usually in clusters. *p. 1256*

forgetii (Perú), "Peruvian foliage plant"; ornamental foliage plant with erect, stout stems and opposite, large glossy, wavy-margined, fleshy leaves bright green with a distinctive red pattern about the veins above and underneath; the hairy flowers pale yellow with reddish calyx lobes spotted green. *p. 1256*

lynchii (Alloplectus) (Colombia), "Black alloplectus"; erect, stout, fibrous-rooted, succulent plant with bronze to blackish-red, shiny, elliptic crenate leaves; flowers in axillary clusters, creamy with purplish hair, not showy. *Tropical.* *p. 1256*

NAVIA *Bromeliaceae* **S3LBD**

nubicola (So. Venezuela: Amazonas Ter.); quaint terrestrial often growing on rocks to 1200 m elevation; flat, starlike, symmetric rosette with narrow, pointed leaves, the margins undulate, to 38 cm long and 16 mm wide, smooth above with pale median stripe and red toward base, underside with gray scales; the inflorescence nesting, globose with silver-scaly bracts and white flowers. *p. 560*

splendens (Venezuela, Guyana); small xerophytic, flat rosette living on rocks, and forming stems to 20 cm long; leaves to 37 cm long, strap-shaped with crisped margins and small spines; the inflorescence a barely stalked rounded nest-like head with white-scaly red bracts and yellowish flowers. *p. 560*

NEANTHE: see Chamaedorea

NELUMBO *Nymphaeaceae* **S-I2LBWd**

nucifera (Nelumbium nelumbo) (Trop. East Asia to N.E. Australia), "East Indian lotus"; large, aquatic, stemless plant symbolic of perpetual life in Buddhism; long, milky, prickly petioles bear shield-like leaves above the water, 30-50 cm across and more; and bold stalks with large, delicate pink flowers of a haunting fragrance; the petals soon fall leaving the prominent, flat-topped receptacle bearing edible seed. *Tropical.* *p. 1622, 1624*

nucifera 'Alba plena', "Shiroman"; a beautiful, large, double-flowered Japanese form, at first cream with greenish tinge, becoming pure white, and delightfully fragrant. *Tropical.* *p. 1624*

nucifera var. **'Rosea'** (nucifera), the "Lotus"; big aquatic plant growing from tuberous, wide-spreading rhizome, with shield-like leaves to 60 cm dia.; on bold stalks the beautiful, fragrant flowers to 25 cm dia.; in this variety a beautiful rose. *p. 1622*

NEMATANTHUS *Gesneriaceae* **S3HFM**

fissus (Hypocyrta selloana), (Brazil); fibrous-rooted, robust plant with fleshy, oblong, deep green, hairy leaves with reddish midrib, purplish beneath; axillary, deep red, downy, long cylindric flowers with ventricose throat. *Humid-tropical.* *p. 1252*

fluminensis (Brazil), "Thread-flower"; epiphytic climbing stems, with opposite, satiny green elliptic leaves of fleshy texture, blotched red underneath; from the axils long thread-like stalks with 5 cm flowers suspended like small orange-red dangling pouches; winter-blooming. *p. 1257*

longipes (Brazil); sometimes grown as Columnea splendens, but the flowers of this genus are distinctly different, hanging from long slender stalks; the green calyx lobes are long slender stalks; the green calyx lobes are long-pointed and covered with hair; the brilliant scarlet corolla, also covered with white hairs is about 5 cm long, oblique funnel-shaped and saccate but flattened on both sides; slender woody, pendant branches with opposite waxy green, elliptic leaves. *p. 1258*

perianthomegus (Hypocyrta, Orobanche) (Brazil); attractive plant with scandent stems, set distantly with pairs of fleshy ovate leaves, glossy green wth ciliate margins; several pubescent flowers from leaf axils, 3 cm long and with balloon-shaped corolla, lemon-yellow with maroon lines; subtended by large shrimp-pink bracts. *p. 1257*

strigillosus (Hypocyrta) (Brazil), "Pouch flower"; pendant branches with pairs of lanceolate dark green leaves, with bristly hairs; solitary flowers in leaf axils, with coppery calyx and crimson red and yellow hairy corolla swollen like a pouch. *p. 1254*

wettsteinii (Hypocyrta) (Brazil); handsome plant with lax stems, and glossy green elliptic 2 cm long leaves, with depressed midrib, and looking as if polished; the oddly-shaped, pouch-like 3 cm flowers solitary from leaf axils, tangerine orange with small yellow mouth. *p. 1257*

NEMESIA *Scrophulariaceae* **I2LBM**

strumosa (So. Africa), "Cape jewels"; floriferous, densely branching annual with opposite, sessile, linear, dentate leaves, and erect racemes of attractive, bilabiate flowers, with a pouch at base and bearded throat, borne in great profusion from June to Dec., in white, yellow, rose, orange, crimson, with spotted throat. *Subtropic.* *p. 2058*

strumosa 'Blue Gem'; a dwarf hybrid suitable for pots, about 20 cm high, bushy, with lanceolate leaves 5 cm long, and a profusion of pretty, sky-blue flowers, reminding of Forget-me-nots; summer. *p. 2054*

strumosa 'Suttonii', ('Grandiflora') "Cape jewels"; charming annual herbaceous plant to 50 cm high, with opposite 8 cm lanceolate leaves, and terminal clusters of attractive irregularly shaped flowers, a broad lip in front and a pouch at base; in all colors — yellow, orange, scarlet, carmine, rose or white, even bi-colored, blooming June to September. The 'Suttonii' strain has much larger flowers 3-4 cm across. *p. 2060*

NEMOPHILA *Hydrophyllaceae* **I2LBD**

maculata (California), "Five-spot"; small soft, fragile annual herb with hairy branches, to 30 cm high, small lobed foliage, and 3 cm flowers white with purple spot at each of the 5 lobes; for spring and summer blooming. *p. 1318*

NEOBENTHAMIA *Orchidaceae* **S3OFM**

gracilis (E. Africa: Zanzibar); tall branching terrestrial to 1½ m high, with numerous 2-ranked linear 20 cm leaves and long-stalked, dense terminal clusters of white flowers, the lip spotted rose alongside a yellow center stripe (Jan.-April, Sept.). *Tropical.* *p. 1770*

NEOBESSEYA *Cactaceae* **Ssu-Cwi2LBD**

missouriensis (Dakota, Montana, Kansas, Oklahoma); globular cactus of the Great Plains, clustering with age, glaucous green with cylindrical knobs, the areoles and axils with white wool, gray needle spines; flowers outside reddish, inside yellow. *Temperate.* *p. 727*

NEOBUXBAUMIA: see Cephalocereus

NEOCARDENASIA *Cactaceae* **I2LBD**

herzogiana (Trichocereus) (Bolivia); stout column to 10 m high, branching above; 6 to 7 deep ribs, bluish-green; the areoles set with straw-brown tufts, radials and needle spines brown; flowers rose-pink 6-7 cm long, the elongate tube stiff-bristly. *p. 638*

NEOCHILENIA *Cactaceae: Echinocactanae* **I2LBD**

setosiflora (Neoporteria) (Coast of Central Chile); small semi-globular cactus 4 to 6 cm dia., somewhat elongating with age, dark gray-green; 13-17 ribs divided into prominent chin-like knobs; the areoles lightly white-felted and with needle-like yellowish spines; characteristic are the wide-open funnel-flowers 4-6 cm across, pale yellow occasionally tinted purple, and white-woolly. Separated from Neoporteria which has typically light red flowers with inner petals forming a close cup. *p. 690*

NEOCHILENIA: see also Neoporteria

NEOCOGNIAUXIA *Orchidaceae* **S3OFW**

monophylla (Jamaica); charming epiphyte, with slender stems bearing solitary leaf; inflorescence arching, with spectacular flowers bright orange-scarlet, 2-5 cm across (autumn). *Tropical.* *p. 1769*

NEODYPSIS *Palmae* **S3LFM**

decaryi (So. Madagascar); peculiar feather palm 6-10 m high, with distinctive 3-sided appearance of its trunk caused by the bulging leaf bases attached in 3 ranks; the ascending pinnate fronds to 2½ m long, continue this 3-sided effect; leaflets gray-green and erect, the lower ones pendulous. *Tropical.* *p. 1882, 1889*

lastelliana (Madagascar); very beautiful, elegant feather palm, the trunk with red crown shaft as of corduroy, the rigidly erect, long pinnate fronds with stiffish, rich green leaflets at right angles from the rachis; rare in cultivation. *Tropical.* *p. 1897*

NEOFINETIA *Orchidaceae* **S3OFW**

falcata (Angraecum falcatum) (Japan, Korea); lovely miniature epiphyte 8-15 cm high, with leathery linear light green, keeled leaves arranged in 2 ranks; freely blooming with clusters of pure white, waxy flowers 3 cm across, having a slender spur 5 cm long, and blooming in summer; intensely fragrant, mostly at night. *Subtropic.* *p. 1658, 1769*

falcata 'Variegata' (Angraecum); variegated-leaf form, the arched leathery linear leaves green with yellow margins; flowers white. *p. 1658*

NEOFINETIA: see also Angraecum

NEOGLAZIOVIA *Bromeliaceae* **S2HBM**

variegata (So. Brazil); tall reedlike tubular plant with narrow, clasping, rigid erect leaves to 1 m long brownish purple with brown spines, and silvery-white cross-bands; inflorescence an erect raceme with violet flowers. Fiber from leaves used for weaving. *p. 563*

NEOGOMESIA *Cactaceae* **I-S2LBD**

agavioides (Mexico: Tamaulipas); small curious succulent with turnip-like base, and very long, leaf-like, rugose tubercles, at first dark green, later grayish, about 8 cm across; the woolly areoles are set back some distance from the tips; the bell-shaped pink flowers from the woolly axils, to 5 cm long but lasting only one day; fruit pink to purple. Found near Tula at 1200 m. *p. 704*

NEOMARICA *Iridaceae* ***I2LFW**

bicolor (Brazil), "Toad-cup lily"; vigorous tropical iris-like plant with perennial rootstock, the broad, fresh-green leaves arranged like fans; from their sheathing base rise stout stalks bearing at an angle the attractive, if fleeting flowers lavender blue, the center segments yellow with brown cross-lines, their tips marked with blue. *Subtropic.* *p. 1333*

caerulea (So. Brazil), "Twelve apostles"; beautiful iris-like plant with large flowers having outer petals bright sky-blue, the center petals pale and marked with yellow and brown; unforgettable sight when I first saw such a field of blue on the Serra do Mar above Santos in Sao Paulo state. Flowers carried on clear stem not clasped by leaves, as on northiana. *Subtropic.* *p. 1331*

gracilis (Mexico to Brazil), "Apostle plant"; swordlike leaves from short rhizome, stalks with iris-like but short-lived successive flowers, outer petals white, small inner petals recurved and blue, base marked brown. *Tropical.* *p. 1331, 1952A*

"longifolia" hort.: see Trimeza caribaea

northiana ('Marica') (Brazil), "Walking iris"; perennial herb with flat, glossy green leaves arranged like fans with a leaf-like spike bearing fragrant flowers, followed by young plants from the same point, bending down and rooting; white outer petals marked brown at base, recurved inner segments tipped violet with base striped brown and yellow. Popularly known as "Twelve apostles" because twelve leaves are said to form before one turns brown. *p. 1331*

x NEOMEA *Bromeliaceae* **S1HFM**

marnieri (Neoregelia carolinae var. carolinae x Aechmea chantinii); handsome bigeneric hybrid by Mulford Foster, very vigorous rosette with broad leaves not barred like in chantinii but the center leaves turn deep rose to bright crimson at beginning of flowering time; the small flowers with violet petals are surrounded by orange bracts. *p. 572*

'Popcorn' (Neoregelia spectabilis x carolinae and Aechmea miniata); handsome Hummel bigeneric hybrid photographed at his Carlsbad, California greenhouses 1964; very spready, open rosette to 75 cm across; flexible leaves lacquered coppery olive green 5-6 cm wide, the margins with small spines, the apex tipped with red, deep wine-red underneath; nested flowers violet. *p. 560*

NEOMOOREA *Orchidaceae* **S3OFW**

irrorata (Panama, Colombia); stately orchid, epiphytic or terrestrial with robust pseudobulbs bearing 2 broad folded leaves to 80 cm long, erect inflorescence 50 cm high with waxy, fragrant flowers 6 cm across, the sepals and petals red-brown, white at base; lip yellow marked with brown (spring). *p. 1769*

NEOMORTONIA nummularia: see Alloplectus

x NEOPHYTUM *Bromeliaceae* **S1HFM**

lymanii (Neoregelia bahiana x Orthophytum navioides); bigeneric cross by M. Foster, rosette of narrow glossy, stiff leaves rather plain until blooming time when the inner leaves surrounding the inflorescence turn a beautiful crimson-red; flowers with white petals. *p. 572*

NEOPORTERIA *Cactaceae* **I2LBD**

atrispina (Chile); dark green globe or cylindric, with tuberous roots, ribs of confluent, spiraled tubercles which later become straight ribs, set with numerous bristly, black spines; small rosy flowers. *p. 696*

heteracantha (Chile), "Unkempt boy"; flattened globe dark in color, with about 19 ribs, close areoles set with bristly radials and long gray central spines to 5 cm; small carmine flowers. *p. 696*

nidus (No. Chile), "Birdsnest cactus"; solitary stem at first globular, later almost cylindrical to 12 cm thick, entirely surrounded with long curved grayish spines, 16-18 ribs, the areoles set with wool; funnel-shaped reddish flowers on apex. *Arid-tropical.* *p. 620, 703*

nigrihorrida (Chile); flattened globose, dark gray green, 16-18 ribs closely set with interwoven radials and thick and heavy, silvery central spines; carmine flowers 4 cm long. *Arid-tropical.* *p. 696*

senilis (gerocephala) (Chile); small globe later elongate, to 4-6 cm dia., with raised tubercles and entirely covered with long, recurving and interwoven soft white spines; similar to N. nidus but with larger pinkish, funnelform flowers 5 cm long. *p. 695*

subgibbosa (Chilenia) (Chile: Valparaiso); globular to barrel, to 12 cm high, densely rusty-spiny at the top, light green with 15-20 rows of prominent knobs; flowers bright pink. *p. 696*

NEORAIMONDIA *Cactaceae* **S2LBD**

macrostibas (W. Perú); remarkable columnar cactus to 4 m high, branching near base, the stems very stout, 30 cm thick, with few ribs with brown-felted areoles, spines to 25 cm long; flowers greenish-white. *p. 644*

NEOREGELIA *Bromeliaceae* **•S1HFM**

ampullacea (Brazil: Espirito Santo and Guanabara); small tubular rosette 12 cm high found growing on rocks along the coast of Brazil; hard, channeled and recurving leaves to 12 cm long, glossy olive green with irregular brown-purple cross-bands or spots, purple teeth at margins; clustered at base of vase the white flowers tipped with purple, lasting one day only; plant sends out long stolons, branching freely, and ideal in a hanging pot. *p. 571*

bahiana viridis (S. E. Brazil); tubular rosette with stiff, glossy pea-green leaves, inner leaves red on the upper side, very slow growing; inflorescence deep in center, the flowers white with blue-tipped petals. The form viridis has leaves wholly green. *p. 568*

carcharodon (S.E. Brazil); large spreading rosette with stiff green to gray leaves spotted purplish-maroon above, and blotched and banded beneath, purplish spines and red tips; flowers white tipped lavender. *p. 565*

carolinae (Brazil); spreading rosette of strapshaped leaves 30 cm long and 4 cm wide, metallic copper over green, toothed margins; inflorescence formed by brilliant lacquer orange-red bract leaves surrounding the flowers with violet-purple petals edged white, deep in center. *Tropical.* *p. 512A, 563, 567*

carolinae 'Marechalii', "Blushing bromeliad"; dwarf variety with flattened metallic leaves; at flowering time the inner leaves are brilliant rosy-crimson, remaining so for six months or more, flowers lilac. *Tropical.* *p. 564, 567*

carolinae 'Marechalii tricolor'; magnificent rosette with the broad leaves of marechalii but in varying tints of color, from olive green to cream and warm salmon, the central leaves a brilliant lacquered rosy crimson at flowering time, surrounding the nest of lilac flowers; photographed 1960 in a Cairns, Queensland collection. *p. 570*

carolinae 'Marechalii Volckaert's Favorit'; beautiful Belgian cultivar, a showy flattened rosette of broad leaves deep forest green, the margins a contrasting creamy yellow, center cup lacquer red; the nested inflorescence with violet flowers; photographed in Frankfurt Botanic Garden, Germany 1971. *p. 570*

carolinae 'Meyendorffii' (Karatas); broad rosette of flat olive green leaves with coppery tinting; at flowering time the inner leaves turn a dark maroon; flowers lilac deep in center. *Tropical.* *p. 564*

carolinae 'Tricolor' (Brazil), "Striped blushing bromeliad"; very attractive variety with the glossy green leaves having ivory-white lengthwise bands becoming rose-tinted in good light; at flowering time they become shorter and carmine-red; flowers violet-purple edged white. *Tropical.* *p. 513, 563, 564*

'Cathryn Wilson', handsome carolinae hybrid by Mulford Foster of Orlando, Florida; formal rosette 50 cm across, leaves 8 cm wide, broader than carolinae, and with fine spines at margins, intense burgundy-red with some green spots; bluish flowers in center cushion. *p. 571*

concentrica (Nidul. acanthocrater) (Rio de Janeiro); stiff, fresh green rosette with purple blotches and black spines; when in flower the center leaves are purplish-carmine with blackish tips, blue flowers deep in center. *p. 565, 566*

'Concentrica hybrid': see N. x decora

concentrica 'Morobe'; showy Belgian cultivar with blackish-green leaves, the underside purplish red with bluish cast, the inner cup vivid crimson. *p.571*

concentrica 'Plutonis'; an interesting cultivar found in Ghent, Belgium; low rosette of broad, light green leaves, contrasting vividly with the blood-red leaves around the center cup, the margins finely toothed; flowers pale lavender. *Tropical.* *p. 570*

concentrica 'Souvenir de Charles Delbaeke'; Belgian cultivar by Spa in Ghent 1945, with smooth edged green leaves without spines at margins, the inner bract leaves carmine-red. *p. 571*

cruenta (Brazil: Guanabara); stout rosette with broad leaves about 30 cm long and 8 cm wide, brownish-green with blood-red blotch at spine-tipped apex, the margins spiny also; flowers blue surrounded by bluish bracts, deep in center of plant, which turns rosy at blooming time. *p. 570*

cyanea (Brazil: Minas Gerais); open rosette of broad leathery leaves with spiny margins, gray green above, paler beneath; flower violet in a small head in the center of reduced leaves. *p. 570*

x decora (concentrica x princeps); open rosette with light green, thin-leathery, waxy leaves with darker spots, edged with small, closely set brownish spines, reverse same glossy green; rosy bracts. *p. 563*

farinosa (Espirito Santo, Rio), called "Crimson cup", because at flowering time the short inner leaves and bases of others turn a vivid crimson in advance of the small purple flowers; outer leaves deep olive to purplish. *Tropical.* *p. 564*

fosteriana (Rio de Janeiro); dense rosette of broad coppery leaves with grass-green blotching, center and tips burgundy-red, gray lines on purple beneath; pale blue flowers deep in center. *p. 558*

johannis (Brazil); open rosette with fluted base, shiny, broad, dark green,, thin-leathery leaves partially covered with grayish scales, the apex rounded and twisted; the center violet-lavender at flowering time. *p. 563*

johannis rubra; imported by Flandria, Belgium and grown as 'Species 1885'; noteworthy because of its terrific bright color of lavender-purple over olive-green in good light; rosette of broad, thin-leathery leaves with black spines, and silvery scales outside. *p. 563*

x 'Mar-Con' (marmorata x concentrica), "Marbled fingernail"; beautiful bold rosette 45 cm across, the broad leaves leathery, and 10 cm wide, glossy light fresh green overlaid with red-purple design leaving a pattern of apple green blotches; tips typically wine-red; margins with scattered red-brown teeth; inflorescence very slightly raised in center, flowers lavender. *Tropical.* *p. 571*

marmorata (Brazil: São Paulo, Paraná), "Marble plant"; bold rosette of thick-leathery broad leaves to 30 cm long, 8 cm wide, glossy yellowish-green to grass-green heavily blotched and marbled with blood-red, the margins spiny; the inner center brownish-red; numerous white flowers. *Tropical.* *p. 565*

'Marmorata hybrid' (spectabilis x marmorata), "Marbled fingernail plant"; bold rosette with light olive-green stiff leaves blotched maroon and with red tips; lavender tinted flower deep in center cup. *p. 567*

melanodonta (Brazil: Espirito Santo); known in Europe as 'Richter's Red bract', from its bright colored inflorescence with light blue petals; the flaring rosette of broad, thin-leathery leaves waxy fresh-green with prominent black fingernail apex and coal-black base. *p. 563*

mooreana (Amazonian Perú), "Ossifragi vase"; introduced as 'Ossifragi' by Lee Moore from near Iquitos; a very distinctive tubular epiphytic rosette 20-25 cm high of numerous leathery, glossy, grass-green to deep green leaves, tapering to a slender point, in collected plants the tips markedly recoiling, in cultivated plants less so, the rosette more open and leaves arching, and with pale lines lengthwise, the margins armed with long black spines; deep in center the almost hidden head of white 3-petalled flowers. *p. 569*

ossifragi: see mooreana

pineliana (formerly in the trade as princeps) (Brazil); rosette with constricted, narrow strap-shaped, coppery green leaves covered on both sides with gray scales, bases broadening into a cup which at time of bloom is carmine-red, the stalked flowers pale blue. *p. 566*

sarmentosa (Brazil: Espirito Santo, Guanabara, São Paulo); slender rosette of linear concave, plain green leathery leaves rounded at apex and with short point, the margins sparsely spiny, 30 cm long, 3 cm wide; few flowers blue, subtended by red bracts. *p. 565*

sarmentosa chlorosticta (Rio de Janeiro); small rosette with bright-green leaves painted maroon in such a way that the green shows as circular blotches; silver spotted or with a touch of silver beneath; sharp tips red; pale lavender flowers. *Tropical.* *p. 564, 565*

spectabilis (Brazil), called "Fingernail plant" because of the red tips of the metallic olive green leaves; gray crossbands beneath; blue flowers in low cushion. *Tropical.* *p. 513, 563, 564, 567*

tristis (Espirito Santo, Rio), "Miniature marble plant"; dwarf rosette of few leaves, deep olive to grayish green and mottled purplish maroon; gray-banded beneath and red-tipped; pale lavender flowers. *p. 564*

tristis x marmorata; tough rosette of good lasting quality, broad leaves green largely overlaid with deep purple marbling, tips blackish purple, and gray-scaly beneath; flowers deep in center cushion, azure-blue edged white. *p. 567*

zonata (Espirito Santo); shapely rosette of hard-fleshy broad leaves olive green and heavily marbled and banded wine-red on both sides; flowers deep in center cushion, pale blue. *p. 565*

NEOTTIA *Orchidaceae* **C3HFM**

nidus avis (Forests of Europe); terrestrial orchid in habitat living on dead organic matter; brown leaves sheathing the brown stem, dense terminal spike of brown flowers with 2-lobed lip; May-June. Interlacing fibrous roots, the young plants forming under ground from the ends of roots; when mature they produce the flowering stem, and in turn die. *p. 1770*

NEPENTHES *Nepenthaceae (Carnivorous Pl.)* **S3(O,H,Sphagnum)FW**

These tropical "Pitcher plants" are climbers of the open country as well as the jungle trees, in temperatures around 24°C (75°F) with high humidity. The prolonged midrib of the leathery leaf acts as a clinging tendril from which develops the hollow pitcher with thickened rim, and a lid to keep out the rain. Insects are attracted inside where they drown in pepsin liquid which digests them. The greenish flowers are not conspicuous, and male and female are on separate plants. A few species are non-climbing. *Humid-tropical.*

ampullaria (Malaya to New Guinea); contrary to others, this species grows mostly on the ground, and I have collected it in wet savannahs in Malaya where the little rounded green pitchers grow in matted clusters hidden by moss or clay. *Humid-tropical.* *p. 768*

x atrosanguinea (distillatoria x sedenii); slender pitchers rich maroon over greenish yellow, wings fringed; willing grower. *p. 21*, 770, 771*

x balfouriana (mixta x mastersiana); long slender pitchers yellow-green with few red-brown spots toward the margin; large fringed wings. *p. 768*

x boissiense (gracilis x superba); a very vigorous Lecoufle hybrid with succulent-green obovate leaves to 30 cm long and closely set, the numerous pitchers first urn-shaped then further on, large funnel-shaped 15 cm long, very colorful with yellow-green cylinder striped wine-red with ciliate wings, the rolled-back ribbed rim shiny nile green marked ruby; spotted purple inside. *p. 769, 771*

x chelsonii (hookeriana x dominii); flask-shaped pitchers yellow-green and marbled with purple; ciliate wings. *p. 770*

x chelsonii excelsa; large flaskshaped pitchers, so pale as to be almost white, heavily painted reddish purple. *p. 770*

x coccinea (distillatoria x mirabilis); a very satisfactory old hybrid (1882), with gracefully pendulous flask-shaped pitchers pale yellowish green, richly splashed with red-brown, the ring around the top lined with maroon, and with ciliate wings in back; inside bluish with red spots. We have found this plant very willing to produce its colorful pitchers, more so on young branches. *Humid-tropical.* *p. 772*

'Courtii' (psittacina x purpurea); a durable old hybrid, advertised by Roehrs Exotic Nurseries since 1911, and growing for years at our greenhouses in New Jersey; have always found this of easiest culture, tolerating lower than the most humid-warm conditions; firm leathery leaves, and pitchers mostly green with maroon marbling toward apex, and fringed wings. *Humid-tropical.* *p. 763, 773*

x dicksoniana (rafflesiana x veitchii); robust hybrid with large cylindrical pitchers, light green densely speckled with bright crimson, broad rosy rim marked crimson. *p. 770, 771*

'Dir. G. T. Moore' (chelsonii x dominii); Missouri Botanical Garden hybrid 1943; a red pitcher type with subcylindric flasks 12 cm long, 5 cm wide, purplish-red with green marmorations; pitcher wings prominent, rim purple-lined; leaves to 45 cm long and 6 cm wide. *p. 772*

x dominii (gracilis x rafflesiana); robust, easy-growing plant with dark green, leathery leaves and firm, deep green pitchers slightly spotted; wings fringed. *p. 768*

x goettingensis (mixta x dicksoniana); robust hybrid with large mugshaped to cylindrical pitchers light green with maroon-red markings, broad, ciliate wings. *p. 769*

gracilis (Malaya, Borneo); slender climber with thinly flask-shaped pitchers, pale green with small purple spots. *p. 769*

'Henry Shaw' (chelsonii x dominii); large mugshaped pitchers of good solid substance which keep over a long period; light green with wine-red spots; small wings. *p. 768*

hookeriana (Borneo); large pale-green pitchers marked with purple, to 15 cm long and 6 cm across, the wings broad and doubly fringed. *p. 772*

x intermedia (rafflesiana x gracilis); leathery leaves tapering to both ends; 15 cm pitchers green with purplish-red spots, and with broad wings fringed. *p. 769*

'Lieut. R. B. Pring'; strong-growing chelsonii hybrid with large pear-shaped pitchers reddish-purple at first, showing green marmorations with age, prominent wings with purple hairs. *p. 768*

madagascariensis (Madagascar); tropical pitcher plant growing in low jungle and rambling over Gleichenia ferns, the glossy green leaves with prolonged midrib acting as a tendril from which develops a yellow-green pitcher carried upright like a funnel, with open lip, and looking like a cobra ready to strike. *p. 772*

x mastersiana (sanguinea x distillatoria); long pitchers cylindrical flaring, claret-red with green, and purple spots, red rim. *Humid-tropical.* *p. 768*

maxima (Celebes, Borneo, N. Guinea); slender, high-climbing species with colorful pitchers; the lower ones flask-shaped, the upper ones funnelshaped, pale green and heavily marbled wine-red. *p. 770, 771*

mirabilis (Papua, Queensland); sturdy species which we found growing terrestrially in heavy pebbly red clay in light forest on the highlands of Papua, in company of Cycads and Dischidias; short plants with beet-like roots, the leafy stems bearing at their tips on prolonged wiry threads the pretty yellowish green constricted pitchers covered by rusty-red lids; the small flowers brown-red and white, in erect racemes. *Humid-subtropic.* *p. 767, 772*

x mixta (maxima x northiana), a "Pitcher plant"; large funnelshaped pitchers to 30 cm long, yellow-green occasionally marked crimson, increasingly toward the ribbed rim. *Humid-tropical.* *p. 767, 769*

x mixta superba (maxima x northiana); a color selection of this hybrid listed in the Julius Roehrs catalog 1911, with its large pitchers mostly crimson red with some green mottling. *p. 773*

x morganiae (hookeriana x phyllamphora); compact plant with mugshaped pitchers pale green with dark purple markings, blood-red in adult stage; flared fringed wings. *p. 768*

papuana (New Guinea); epiphytic clamberer which we collected in the rain forest on the steep slopes of the Finisterre Range in N. E. New Guinea; slender yellowish green pitchers with mouth and lid marked blood-red; large racemes of small brown-red flowers. *p. 767*

pervillei (Seychelles: Mahé); tropical clambering pitcher plant growing in high places, strong woody stems with long oblanceolate leaves, the inflorescence axillary with racemes of small greenish flowers; the photo on p. 772 shows female flowers in full bloom; pitchers are carried erect and look like small inflated pipes with lid, yellow with purple spotted top. *p. 772*

rafflesiana (Sumatra to Borneo); straggling climber on low trees of the open savannah; the lower pitchers are urnshaped, the upper large funnelform, greenish-yellow marked purplish-brown; I have collected pitchers of giant size as long as 25 cm or more, in Johore state, Malaya. *Humid-tropical.* *p. 762, 768*

x ratcliffiana (hookeriana x mirabilis); an old English hybrid (1882), with pitchers 12 to 15 cm long, 5 cm wide, flask-shaped, green, spotted with red and with variegated lid, and ciliate wings. *p. 773*

sanguinea (Malaya); small to large flaskshaped to cylindrical pitchers deep red to reddish green and broad rim. *p. 769, 772*

'St. Louis' (chelsonii x dominii); pitchers pearshaped, dark blood-red when young, lighter in age, sparsely green mottled; prominent mottled wings. *p. 768*

stenophylla (Borneo); handsome pitcher plant photographed in the collection of Osaka University, Kosobe, Japan; pitchers flask-like, 15 to 18 cm long, and 3-4 cm wide, bronzy-green with red markings, narrow rim and small lid, from long, strap-shaped leaves. *Humid-tropical.* *p. 767*

'Superba'; vigorous epiphyte with long soft-leathery, deep green leaves, and variable pitchers 15 cm or more long, some urn-shaped, later funnel-shaped, yellow-green blotched with wine-red, the glossy ribbed rim with wine-red and crimson, inside spotted red, the lid striped red, the fringe in back with red hairs. This may be a hybrid. *p. 773, 1952A*

ventricosa (Philippines); curious pitchers constricted in the middle, pale green, suffused pink toward the base, crimson rim; without wings. *p. 769*

x williamsii (sedenii x hookeriana); medium-size flaskshaped pitchers in carmine-red marked yellow-green, and red rim. *p. 770*

NEPETA: see Glechoma

NEPHELAPHYLLUM *Orchidaceae* **S3LFW**

cordifolium (Monsoon Asia); terrestrial with pearshaped pseudobulbs and broad fleshy foliage, overlaid with silver: erect raceme of green and pinkish flowers. *p. 1769*

NEPHELIUM *Sapindaceae* **S3LBD**

lappaceum (Malaysia), "Rambutan" or "Hairy litchi"; large evergreen tropical fruit tree to 12 m high, similar to litchi, with leaves compound of 5-7 pairs of oblong leaflets each 10 cm long, shining dark green; small pubescent flowers with cleft calyx, but without petals, in axillary panicles or from branch tips; the fruit in clusters of ten or twelve, are oval, 5 cm long, crimson red and covered with soft fleshy spines; the outer covering is thin-leathery, easily torn off, exposing the white, juicy flesh; the flavor is somewhat acid like a grape; very popular in Malaya and Vietnam. *p. 2037*

NEPHELIUM: see also Litchi

NEPHRODIUM: see Dryopteris

NEPHROLEPIS *Polypodiaceae (Filices)* ***I2LFM**

acuminata (Malaya); short rootstock sending out stoloniferous runners, tufted simply pinnate fronds becoming 30-90 cm long, scaly toward base, narrow when young, later much broader, fresh green. *p. 1122*

biserrata (acuta) (Cuba to Perú, Polynesia, Queensland, So. China, So. India, Trop. Africa), "Bold sword fern"; tufted fern with spreading rhizome, large fresh-green pendant pinnate fronds ½-1 m long, the pinnae somewhat leathery and lightly notched, the upper basal side eared. *p. 1123, 1127*

biserrata furcans (Cuba to Brazil, Africa, Hong Kong to Queensland), "Fishtail fern", massive fern with long arching pinnate fronds, the segments widely spaced, broad, leathery yellow-green, and forked toward their tips. *Humid-tropical.* *p. 1118*

cordifolia (tuberosa), (Jamaica, Chile), the "Erect sword fern"; clustering fern bearing tubers on the roots; the dark green pinnate fronds are 60 cm long and slender and of narrow linear form, the short pinnae bearing many sori; blackish stalks with hair-like scales. *p. 1118*

cordifolia 'Plumosa' (tesselata) (Japan to New Zealand), "Dwarf whitmanii"; tufted plant with long stiff, dark green, rather narrow fronds, bearing spores, on wiry blackish stalks, the pinnae more or less crenate or pinnately lobed and lacy toward their tips, the runners forming tubers. *p. 1118, 1122, 1123*

duffii (New Zealand, Polynesia), "Pigmy sword fern"; densely crowded, compact fern with brown downy scales at base, the erect wiry stalks sometimes forked, and closely set with tiny rounded, toothed, leathery 1-2 cm leaflets. *Humid-subtropic.* *p. 1121*

ensifolia (E. Indies); strong growing with long pendant pinnate fronds to 1 m long on wiry stalks, the pinnae are thin-leathery, bright green and simple and tapering to a slender, drooping point. *p. 1118*

exaltata (Florida to Brazil, Africa, So. Asia, Australia), "Sword-fern"; tufted plant with simply pinnate, rather stiff, fresh green fronds which can continue to grow in length almost indefinitely, and bearing sori beneath; the rootstock sending out threadlike runners which produce buds, giving rise to new plants. *p. 1118*

exaltata 'Amerpohlii'; a form of 'Smithii', and a good type, has long, fresh green tripinnate fronds but others revert back to bipinnate and simply pinnate. *p. 1121*

exaltata 'Anna Foster'; form of 'Barrowsii', low, spreading plant with broad, finely bipinnate fronds becoming pendant, the pinnules well spaced on lateral axis. *p. 1116*

exaltata 'Barrowsii' (1905); cultivar of 'Piersonii', elegant plant with long fronds 60 cm or more, with bipinnate leaves and reversions to pinnate, the pinnae wavy. *p. 1121*

exaltata 'Bostoniensis', the "Boston fern", a variety found in Boston in 1894, and an old time house plant; rich green fronds simple pinnate larger and wider than the basic species, to 1 m long; the leaflets not lobed and nearly flat, more graceful and pendant; entirely without fertile spores; therefore propagation by division or runners. Still a favorite for decoration, appreciating good light, 25 fc. (250 lux) minimum, or better 100 fc. (1000 lux), but not burning sun; not too warm, and all the atmospheric moisture possible. Air too dry favors white scale, brown scale, white fly and mealy bugs. Active growth is fairly fast from May to October. Tolerates air conditioning but dislikes cold drafts of air. *Tropical.* *p. 1117*

exaltata 'Bostoniensis compacta', "Dwarf Boston fern"; long used as a house plant, of more compact habit, the wide simply pinnate fronds fresh green and spreading; freely clustering and usually not over 30 cm high. Propagated successfully by meristem tissue culture. *Tropical.* *p. 1115*

exaltata 'Brooklyn'; a sporeling of the famous Brooklyn Botanic Garden collection; elegant plant of vigorous habit, with more or less stiff, erect leaves on wiry rachis; the bipinnate fronds freely dissected with pinnae recurving and presenting a neat regular appearance. *p. 1123*

exaltata 'Childsii'; a very dwarf and slow growing variety with short, waxy green, monstrose fronds, the short pinnae closely set along stalk and overlapping, curled under or crisped. *p. 1121*

exaltata 'Colorado'; plant becoming large, with strong, stiff erect, bipinnate fronds on good axis, the pinnae crenate and rather flat and symmetrical. *p. 1116*

exaltata 'Dreyeri'; spreading plant with simple pinnate, light green fronds, evenly wide and long like ribbons, the pinnae flat and lightly convex. *p. 1119*

exaltata 'Elegantissima' (1904); sport of 'Piersonii', a good "lacefern" with firm 2-3-pinnate leaves 45-50 cm long and 15-20 cm broad, almost completely divided into acuminate, overlapping pinnules, these entire or deeply pinnatifid into linear segments. *p. 1116, 1118*

exaltata 'Falcata'; mutation of 'Scottii', pinnate fronds like 'Scottii' except that the ends of pinnae are 1 or 2-forked. *p. 1122*

exaltata 'Fluffy Ruffles', "Dwarf feather fern"; a dwarf variety with rather stiff upright fronds under 30 cm long, closely drawn together, rich dark green and almost leathery, yet finely and densely bipinnate with congested pinnae; close to the older ex. 'Muscosa'. *p. 1117, 1123*

exaltata 'Giatrasii' (1909); sport of bostoniensis, bushy, similar to 'Scottii' but more graceful with leaves flexible on wiry petioles. *p. 1120*

exaltata 'Gretnae'; spreading plant with leathery pinnate fronds 1 m long or more, looking like evenly narrow, long ribbons, the pinnae simple and smooth but each is either square at tip or forked. *p. 1116*

exaltata 'Hillii', "Crisped feather fern"; an excellent, strong growing variety with sturdy, fresh-green pinnate fronds, the broad pinnae closely set and overlapping and wavy or deeply lobed and crisped. *p. 1118*

exaltata 'Maasii'; a vigorous European pot plant of low, shapely habit with decorative, fresh green, broad, pinnate, horizontal fronds and long wavy leaflets rather firm. *p. 1117*

exaltata 'Magnifica'; form of 'Whitmanii', a free grower of open habit, with light green tripinnate, lacy fronds 28 cm long, with small ovate segments. *p. 1120*

exaltata 'M. P. Mills'; slow growing cultivar of 'Scottii', with twice-pinnate leathery leaves, characterized by extreme hardiness and by frequent reversion to the 1-pinnate type. *p. 1121, 1122*

exaltata 'Muscosa' (1911); cultivar of 'Superbissima', practically its dwarf form, but symmetrical; true type fronds are tri-pinnate, 15-20 cm long, very firm and dense, with the pinnae set at an angle and closely overlapping. *p. 1121*

exaltata 'Neubertii'; a German cultivar similar to 'Smithii'; soft feathery fern of loose habit with short, tripinnate fronds loosely set with crenate pinnae, and becoming pendant. *p. 1119*

exaltata 'New York' (1913); sport of 'Giatrasii', shorter than bostoniensis, a strong shapely plant with broad, fresh waxy-green pinnate fronds of good texture, the long pinnae attractively wavy. *p. 1119*

exaltata 'Norwoodii' (1915), a compact "Lace fern"; a sport of 'Metropoli', a cultivar similar to 'Whitmanii', elegant commercial form of short habit with broad, tripinnate leaves to 45 cm long, the fresh-green, dense pinnae set in even ranks behind each other, on wiry brown axis. *Humid-tropical.* *p. 1115*

exaltata 'Ostrich Plume'; apparently similar to 'Fluffy Ruffles'; a Pacific coast cultivar; feather-fern of larger habit, with lacy, rather erect bipinnate to tripinnate fronds not as finely cut as whitmanii but stiffer; some of the fronds reverting back to simply pinnate like the Boston fern. *p. 1122*

exaltata 'Piersonii' (1902); the first of the bipinnate forms and forerunner of other cultivars, tall growing with the habit of bostoniensis, the strong, elegant leaves over 1 m long, unevenly divided, some 1-pinnate, others 2-pinnate, some partly pinnate and bipinnate. *p. 1121*

exaltata 'Randolphii'; stiff plant with long fronds of good strong texture, wide with substantial, simple pinnae long and wavy. *p. 1119*

exaltata 'Rooseveltii'; sport of bostoniensis; large, handsome "Boston-fern" with broad pinnate fronds, having pinnae beautifully waved and usually eared; similar to 'Harrisii' in undulation but not quite so large a form. *p. 1117*

exaltata 'Rooseveltii plumosa', "Tall feather fern"; the tallest form of the feathered type, with the longest 1 m fronds arching or pendant, the long, wavy pinnae lobed or monstrose at their tips; ideal for large baskets. *p. 1118*

exaltata 'Scholzelii' (1908); sport of 'Scottii', erect compact variety with leaves 38 cm long and 10-12 cm broad, simply bipinnate, the pinnae somewhat recurved as in 'Scottii', the ultimate segments entire or crenulate. *p. 1121, 1122*

exaltata 'Scholzelii tripinnata'; a lacy form with broader, tripinnate leaves, erect or spreading, the pinnae fairly dense and recurved. *p. 1122*

exaltata 'Scottii'; sport of bostoniensis, forming a compact dense cluster of leaves with good lasting qualities; fronds spreading, recurved, the pinnae close, rolled back convex from the margin and recurved on strong stalks. *p. 1119, 1122*

exaltata 'Smithii'; sport of 'Amerpohlii', a real "lacefern", with leaves usually less than 30 cm long, quadripinnate, or divided 4 times into very small, close segments, the pinnae are so crowded that the leaves are dense and easily rot from careless watering. *p. 1120*

exaltata 'Splendida'; fine, strong plant with large fronds usually bipinnate, over 1 m long, the pinnae spaced loosely but becoming densely crested toward forked apex. *p. 1120*

exaltata 'Superbissima' (1908); sport of 'Elegantissima', interesting type with large firm, almost leathery, bipinnate fronds 25-38 cm long, with pinnae irregularly twisted on snaky axis sometimes twisted back; often grows 1-pinnate leaves. *p. 1116*

exaltata 'Teddy Junior'; sport of 'Rooseveltii', strong-growing cultivar of compact habit, with dark green fronds simply pinnate, the segments broader than 'Scottii', wavy and ruffled. *p. 1122*

exaltata 'Trevillian' (1935); commercial cultivar of 'Elegantissima', fronds very lacy but more erect and sturdy in habit than 'Whitmanii', the deep rich green pinnae more dense, thick and overlapping; an extremely lacy form has ruffling so accentuated that a single leaf appears to be just a green ball, and reported to become proliferous, bearing vegetative buds on the stem which serve to produce new, but plain pinnate plants. *p. 1120*

exaltata 'Verona', "Dwarf lace-fern"; a dwarf 3-pinnate variety of Boston fern with delicate, small, very finely lacy fronds of drooping habit, the tips unfolding from pearly buds; one of the best of the lace type for house conditions. *Humid-tropical.* *p. 1115, 1118*

exaltata 'Victori'; a bushy erect, stubby and rather tough cultivar found by Victor's, with both fertile and sterile fronds on wiry black stems, dense with pinnae nicely wavy and frilled. *p. 1119*

exaltata 'Viridissima'; a reversion of 'Superbissima', stiff plant with rigid erect dark green pinnate fronds 25-38 cm long, the almost leathery leaves resembling a sword fern but smaller and narrower; the close pinnae curly and twisted. *p. 1116*

exaltata 'Wagneri'; dwarf sport of 'Scottii', with dark green, rigid pinnate fronds having segments very close, wavy and somewhat recurved; resembles 'Viridissima' but more regular. *p. 1122*

exaltata 'Whitmanii', a sport of 'Barrowsii', old fashioned "Lace-fern"; of open habit, the broad, light green fronds are relatively short and arching, or pendant when older, the segments deeply and evenly cut and not bunched; tripinnate, with small segments, leaves up to 45 cm long. *Humid-tropical.* *p. 1115, 1118, 1123*

exaltata 'Wicheri'; large, rambling fern with leaves to 1 m long, irregularly bipinnate-pinnatifid on wiry stems, the pinnae crested toward apex, and leaf tips forked. *p. 1120*

hirsutula (India, China, Polynesia, Tropical America); handsome robust sword fern with thin-wiry rhizome from which at intervals form the crowns which give rise to straight erect fronds 40-50 cm tall, the densely rusty-downy rachis with long lateral pinnae, toothed at margins and gracefully curved, and also covered with brown hairs. *p. 1123*

hirsutula cv 'Weston'; a magnificent cultivar with stiff pinnate fronds, some 50 cm long, the thick midrib, or rachis, flat and rusty-hairy on top; the pinnae fresh green and overlapping, and in this form charmingly frilled and twisted. From the fern collection of Brooklyn Botanic Garden, New York. *p. 1123*

pendula (Pantropic); cultivated in England since 1841; according to Carl Christensen in 1906 a var. of N. cordifolia; Johnson, 1917, a form of N. exaltata; commanding attention because of its extraordinary pendulous fronds which may become 2 to 3 m or more long; growing epiphytic on trees or rocks; a stoloniferous base gives rise to odd-pinnate, sturdy leaves, the sickle-shaped leaflets glossy green and 4-6 cm long, on brown-fuzzy thread-like rachis, eventually bending over and growing downward like long green ribbons. *p. 1123*

philippinensis (Philippines); a lovely species of small dimensions and compact, upright habit, with narrow pinnate fronds, stalk brown, leaflets set close and deflexed, dark green, leathery, and finely toothed. *p. 1121*

radicans (volubilis) (E. Himalayas to Vietnam, Malaysia, New Guinea); dark green, stiff, pinnate fronds carried on wide-climbing, wire-like rhizome; the sori separated, distant, from margins. *p. 1122*

NEPHTHYTIS *Araceae* **S3HNM**

afzelii (Liberia, Sierra Leone); African herb with creeping rhizome bearing sagittate, papery leaf to 35 cm long, sinus acute; green spathe not dotted. *Tropical.* *p. 278*

gravenreuthii (Cameroon); broadly halberd-shaped, yellow-green leaf with dark veining and wide, open sinus on slender petiole; spathe dotted, spadix white with green dots; fruit orange. *Tropical.* *p. 278, 286*

'Green Gold': see Syngonium podophyllum xanthophilum.

hallaei (Equatorial Africa: Gabon); low tropical plant 8-10 cm high, with fleshy green broad, nearly triangular leaves on grooved, stout petiole, the fleshy, hooded spathe green, the spadix when ripening with orange berries. Originally described by J. Bogner as a Callopsis, he later referred this to Nephthytis, as published in AROIDEANA July 1980. *p. 209*

liberica: hort. name for Syngonium podophyllum.

poissonii (Cameroun); dwells in swampy forest, with rhizomes 3 cm thick, petioles 60 cm long, bearing sagittate, arrow-shaped, triangular leaves 30 cm long, rich green; the elliptic spathe green finely spotted brown. *p. 162*

NEPHTHYTIS: see also Rhektophyllum, Syngonium

NEPTUNIA *Leguminosae* **S3HFW**

oleracea (Tropics of Southeast Asia and elsewhere), "Water-mimosa"; aquatic plant with long floating or anchored roots, branching stems with dark green bipinnate leaves, lightly sensitive to touch; yellow flower heads. *Tropical.* *p. 1385*

plena (flava) (Trop. America, Trop. Asia); creeping or floating aquatic perennial with shrubby, long pendant branches forming water roots; touch-sensitive, bi-pinnate leaves with 2 to 4 pairs of grass-green leaflets; the underwater stems are thickened and white-spongy, full of air cells, enabling them to float; flowers bright yellow. *p. 1385, 1387*

NERINE *Amaryllidaceae* **C2LBDd**

bowdenii (So. Africa), a "Spider lily"; bulbous plant 45 cm high, with glossy green linear basal leaves rather thick; large umbels of beautiful soft pink flowers with a darker line on each segment, recurved at apex; blooming before foliage. *Subtropic.* *p. 119*

curvifolia (So. Africa); bulbous plant 45 cm high, with long linear green glaucous leaves depressed in middle; flowers bright glittering scarlet, with straight stamens, many in a convex umbel; blooming in summer; not frost-hardy. *p. 119*

curvifolia fothergillii, "Curve-leaf Guernsey lily"; bulbous So. African plant with linear, glaucous leaves, and showy umbel of numerous 6 cm flowers, soft salmon-red to crimson, with straight stamens. *p. 119*

filifolia (E. Cape, Swaziland, Transvaal), "Grass-leaved nerine"; delightful, free-blooming plant with 6-10 grass-like leaves forming tufts, more or less evergreen; the leaning 25 cm high stalk carries 8 to 10 rosy flowers 3 cm across, with narrow segments, deepening in color. *p. 119*

flexuosa (So. Africa); robust species to 1 m with bright green, broad linear leaves; the flowers pale pink in large umbels, the margins of the segments crisped. *p. 119*

masonorum (So. Africa), "Dwarf pink Guernsey lily"; an exquisite small evergreen species, with grass-like leaves, and floral stalk hardly more than 15 cm high and bearing a small cluster of pale pink flowers with crisped, thread-like segments. Somewhat hardy in sheltered locations in warm-temperate zones, but very pretty in pots in the cool winter garden. *Subtropic.* *p. 121*

sarniensis (So. Africa); sometimes in hort. as Lycoris radiata, the "Guernsey lily"; bulbous herb with strap-shaped basal leaves and funnel-form, crimson flowers with green, crisped segments, and protruding stamens not as long as in L. radiata, appearing in long-stalked clusters before the foliage; numerous hybrids have been developed, in various colors from white and pink to red. *Subtropic.* *p. 119*

NERINE: see also Lycoris

NERIUM *Apocynaceae* ***I2LBM**

oleander (Mediterranean), "Common oleander" or "Rose bay"; evergreen shrub from 2-6 m high, often used in tubs, with willowy branches set with pairs or whorls of linear-lanceolate, leathery leaves, and flowers in terminal cymes, rosy-red to crimson. All parts are poisonous if eaten. *Subtropic.* *p. 140*

oleander 'Album', "Sister Agnes oleander"; large flowered cultivar with white flowers; favored by So. California nurseries because the single varieties have a way of "cleaning" themselves, or "shed" their faded blooms. *Subtropic.* *p. 140*

oleander 'Atropurpureum'; cultivar with large single carmine-red blooms; stretched and enlarged to size shown in photograph by spraying with dilute gibberallic acid while still in bud. *p. 140*

oleander 'Carneum florepleno', known in the trade as 'Mrs. Roeding', somewhat weaker in growth and with a slightly weeping habit; the long branches loaded with double salmon-pink blossoms, having a tendency to "hang on". *Subtropic.* *p. 140*

oleander 'Variegatum'; form with narrow, gray-green leaves edged creamy white; flowers carmine rose. *Subtropic.* *p. 140*

oleander 'Variegatum plenum', ornamental form with dark green leaves attractively edged with cream; the large double flowers 4-5 cm across, carmine-pink, with deep rose center. *Subtropic.* *p. 143*

NERTERA *Rubiaceae* **C2LFM**

granadensis (depressa) (Andes, to Cape Horn, New Zealand, Tasmania), "Coral-bead plant"; mat-forming, creeping ground cover with tiny, broad-oval, leathery, opposite leaves and inconspicuous, greenish flowers in June, followed by the attractive, pea-size, translucent, orange-red berries. I have collected this species along cold Milford Sound, in the Fiordland of New Zealand growing on dripping rocks, frozen stiff in winter—as well as in the mountains of New Guinea at 2,100 m under rippling water, in company of sphagnum moss. *p. 2010, 2112A*

NERVILEA *Orchidaceae* **S3OFW**

acuminata hort. (aragoana) (Monsoon Asia); curious terrestrial with round tubers; solitary, stalked, heart-shaped green leaves with undulate margins; inflorescence after leaf has withered, flowers 5 cm long, the sepals and petals light green, 3-lobed lip white with purple veins. *p. 1769*

renschiana (Madagascar); beautiful terrestrial orchid growing from subterranean tuber, and sprouting a solitary fleshy, stalked broad-ovate leaf to 25 cm long; straight wiry stems will carry handsome flowers with spreading sepals and petals greenish yellow, and a lip with network of purple veining; the inflorescence appearing before the foliage. *p. 1760*

NICODEMIA *Loganiaceae* ***S2LBM**

diversifolia (Madagascar), "Indoor oak"; free growing bush with woody stems and thin-leathery quilted leaves with lobed and undulate margins, looking remarkably like an oak-leaf, the surface has an iridescent, metallic-blue sheen, with bronzy petioles. *p. 1518*

NICOLAIA *Zingiberaceae* **S2-3LBM**

elatior, long known in horticulture as Phaeomeria magnifica (Amomum) (Indonesia), the magnificent "Torch ginger"; gigantic herb forming clumps of robust, leafy, arching canes to 6 m high, with alternate, pointed leaves to 60 cm long in 2 ranks; the striking inflorescence of large, torch-like heads of brilliant red, formed of innumerable waxen bracts, on separate leafless stems 2 m high or more, subtended by red basal bracts, margined white, forming a nest for the red cone, brightened by yellow-margined lips of the small red flowers. *Tropical.* *p. 320A, 2131*

NICOTIANA *Solanaceae* **I2LBM**

alata grandiflora (affinis) (Brazil, Uruguay, Paraguay), "Jasmine tobacco"; tender herbaceous perennial with tall, sticky-hairy stalks set with large, pubescent, ovate, soft leaves, terminated by loose racemes of long, trumpet-shaped flowers white within, yellowish outside, closing in cloudy weather, and with a sugar-sweet perfume at night. *p. 2076*

glauca (Argentina, Bolivia, Paraguay), "Tree-tobacco"; erect, glaucous shrub, tree-like, to 6 m high, with ovate, long-petioled bluish leaves 12-45 cm long; tubular, salverform flowers in loose clusters, open during daytime, first greenish, later yellow. *p. 2076*

x sanderae (alata x forgetiana), "Flowering tobacco"; herbaceous hybrid annual with clammy-hairy spoon-shaped pointed lower leaves to 30 cm long and undulate; the fragrant, showy flowers salverform with greenish-yellow tube tinted with rose to 8 cm long, the face carmine rose, at the end of branches 60-90 cm high. *p. 2076*

sylvestris (Argentina); perennial grown as annual, 1½ m high, with wrinkled oblong or lyre-shaped leaves to 30 cm long, sessile or clasping; drooping salver form white, fragrant flowers 9 cm long. *p. 2076*

tabacum (West Indies, South Pacific),"Common tobacco"; herbaceous clammy-hairy plant growing to 1½ m high, closely furnished with huge, membranous, pale green leaves, and used in the manufacture of tobacco; loose terminal clusters of rosy, funnelshaped, fragrant flowers, open during daytime. *Tropical.* *p. 2067, 2076, 2077*

tabacum macrophylla 'Variegata'; a large-leaved tobacco-plant 2½ m high cultivated under the name 'Connecticut Shade'; with its large membranous 38 cm leaves irregularly variegated creamy-white with green; pinkish-white flowers. *p. 2076*

tabacum 'Variegata'; an ornamental variegated leaved tobacco-plant with leaves 30 cm long, prettily margined and variegated with milky-white. *p. 2076*

NIDULARIUM *Bromeliaceae* ***S1HFM**

"amazonicum": see N. innocentii var. innocentii

billbergioides (So. Brazil); rosette of dark metallic leaves with fine toothed edge; inflorescence a raised head on stalk, the stiff bracts are dark burnt-red and flowers white. *Subtropic.* *p. 513, 568*

billbergioides 'Flavum' (citrinum) (So. Brazil); rosette of thin-leathery, lance-shaped coppery-green leaves, finely toothed; inflorescence a small raised center cup of yellow bracts with white flowers. *p. 564, 568*

x chantrieri (fulgens x innocentii); a pretty plant with stiff lustrous green leaves with pronounced dark mottling and tipped red; tinted pink beneath; center cup fiery-red, with white flowers. *p. 566*

'Cloro-marechalii'; open rosette of soft-spined coppery-green leaves; at blooming time the center cup is magenta-red and flowers white. *p. 568*

'Francois Spae' (innocentii viridis x fulgens); a large plant entirely green and very striking at time of bloom when the center cup turns a brilliant orange-red. *p. 566, 568*

fulgens (S.E. Brazil), "Blushing cup"; showy rosette with numerous flattened shiny leaves pea green with dark mottling and conspicuous spines; inflorescence cup in center bright crimson tipped nile-green, flowers blue. *Tropical.* *p. 513, 566, 569*

innocentii var. innocentii (Brazil: Espirito Santo to Santa Catarina), "Black Amazonian birdsnest"; in the trade as Nid. "amazonicum"; showy rosette metallic purple to almost black, with finely toothed margins, glossy beneath; inflorescence a short cup of rusty-red bracts with white flowers. *Tropical.* *p. 567, 573*

innocentii 'Lineatum'; striking large rosette of broad leaves lined lengthwise with green and white bands and stripes, the inner cup of leaves glowing crimson as the blooming season approaches. *Tropical.* *p. 513, 568, 571, 573*

innocentii var. nana, "Miniature birdsnest"; small rosette of broad, thin-leathery leaves, matte olive-green, finely toothed, underside glossy purple; at flowering time, an inner nest of short leaves turns orange-red; flowers white. *Tropical.* *p. 564, 569, 573*

innocentii var. paxianum (Brazil); open rosette with broad, lanceolate leaves to 1 m long, dilated at base; like soft parchment, waxy grass-green and edged with small green spines, reverse shining green; inflorescence on a 30 cm stalk with striking purplish bract leaves, the floral bracts bright red with blue flowers. *p. 568*

innocentii striatum (Brazil), stocky rosette of broad light green recurved leaves striped lengthwise with yellow-ivory; finely toothed margins; white flowers deep in carmine-tipped center cup. Looking like Dracaena 'Massangeana' but sturdier. *Tropical.* *p. 513. 567, 573*

innocentii viridis; flattened rosette with broad pea green to fresh green, somewhat mottled leaves and with marginal teeth; the shorter leaves surrounding the center are tipped carmine-red at flowering time. *p. 567*

'Maureanum'; a Belgian plant, possibly 'Morrenianum' (innocentii x ferdinandi-coburgii); bold rosette of broad olive green leaves suffused with purple, glossy purple beneath; center cup burnt-rose toward tips, and white flowers. *p. 566, 567*

procerum (So. Brazil); large robust plant in symmetrical rosette, broad leathery, waxy light green foliage tinged copper, edged regularly with small teeth; flowers vermilion, in a contracted panicle among the beautiful red bract leaves. *p. 568, 573*

purpureum (S. E. Brazil); flaring rosette with broad metallic green, rather soft leaves, suffused with purple, glossy maroon beneath; at flowering time forming a rusty-red center cup with green to rosy flowers. *p. 566*

regelioides (S.E. Brazil); compact rosette of rich-green leathery leaves mottled dark green; inflorescence a cup of rusty-red bracts and red flowers. *Subtropic.* *p. 563, 566, 568*

'Souvenir Casmir Morobe' (rutilans x marechalii); a promising, large Belgian hybrid rosette with broad leaves bright green and faintly mottled with darker green, the inner circle of leaves a vivid red. *p. 570*

terminale (Brazil: Estado do Rio); rosette of numerous sword-shaped leaves to 1 m long and 5-6 cm wide, rich green above, pale beneath and often blotched, the margins armed with small brown teeth; the raised inflorescence carried on a stalk to 50 cm long, topped by a cup of broad-ovate bracts, rose-colored to purple and toothed along edges; flowers pale blue. *Tropical.* *p. 556*

NIDULARIUM: see also Wittrockia

NIEREMBERGIA *Solanaceae* **C2LFM**

caerulea (hippomanica var.) (Argentina), "Cup flower"; lovely small herbaceous plant freely spreading with thin erect, hairy stems and spatulate leaves; bearing numerous wide bell-shaped flowers 2 cm dia., lavender blue with violet lines and yellow eye. *Subtropic.* *p. 2066, 2074*

NIGELLA *Ranunculaceae* **I2LFD**

damascena (So. Europe), "Love-in-a-mist" or "Devil-in-the-bush"; annual ornamental herb to 45 cm, with leaves pinnately cut into thread-like segments; showy flowers 3 cm dia., white or light blue, with prominent green pistils united at base. *Subtropic.* *p. 1983*

NIVENIA *Iridaceae* **I2LBD**

corymbosa (So. Africa); evergreen shrubby plant to more than 1 m high, with narrow, stiff, glaucous green leaves arranged in a flattened fan; the many branches, becoming woody, are also covered with fans, from which emerge the clustered flowers, 2 cm across, a long tube opening into 6 spreading petals deep blue, blooming summer into autumn. *p. 1339*

NOLINA *Liliaceae* **S-I2LBD**

bigelovii (Dasylirion) (California, Arizona, Sonora), "Bear grass"; stiff linear leaves in large numbers arranged in a symmetrical rosette, their margins shredding away in brown fibers; with striking tall plumy panicles of uncounted whitish-green minute flowers standing far above the leaves 2-3 m high. *Arid-subtropic.* *p. 1477*

parryi (So. California, Mexico); bold rosette to 2 m, seen in the Mohave Desert, stiff linear leaves in dense crown, 1 m long, 2 cm wide; flowering stalk with small whitish flowers. *p. 1505*

NOLINA: see also Beaucarnea

NOPALEA *Cactaceae* ***S2LBD**

brittonii (Trop. America); of sprawling habit, the trunk usually flattened, the spineless joints 60-90 cm long, the areoles more distant than in cochenillifera; flowers only half-open, stamens protruding. *p. 630*

cochenillifera (Opuntia) (Puerto Rico, South America), "Cochineal plant"; tree-like, to 5 m, with long fleshy, flattened joints usually spineless, glossy dark green; rosy flowers. Host to mealybug furnishing cochineal dye. *Arid-tropical.* *p. 618, 627, 632*

dejecta (So. Mexico to Nicaragua); straggling plant to 2 m high, spiny trunk with narrow joints green to grayish-green with white glochids; flowers red, and deep red fruit. *p. 629*

NOPALXOCHIA *Cactaceae* **I2HFD**

ackermannii (Epiphyllum) (Mexico: Chiapas, Oaxaca 2000-2700 m); a species "Orchid cactus"; in habitat mostly epiphytic, with flattened green branches, sometimes 3-angled, the angles notched (crenate); large and showy funnelform flowers glowing red 10 cm or more across; good flowering plant. *Subtropic.* *p. 640A, 729*

ackermannii 'Fire Glory'; a beautiful hybrid cultivar with large 10 cm flowers soft rosy-red not as deeply scarlet as the species, on angled green stems. *p. 731*

phyllanthoides (Mexico); an old, free-flowering house plant widely grown under the name "Deutsche Kaiserin" (German Empress); an epiphyte from Puebla state at 1700 m; densely bushy with flattened, pendant, crenate branches bearing a profusion of day-flowering, carmine-rose flowers of medium size 5 cm across, and with pale tips and short tube; a lovely basket plant. Responds well to feeding. *Subtropic.* *p. 729, 732*

NORANTEA *Marcgraviaceae* **S3LFM**

brasiliensis (Brazil); handsome tropical evergreen scandent shrub with leathery, obovate leaves; the singular reddish inflorescence at first with colored bracts covering the small flowers, and forming vessels holding nectar; later developing small berry-like blackish fruit. *Tropical.* *p. 1522*

guianensis (Guyana), "Red popcorn"; beautiful tropical clambering shrub, climbing by roots from the red branches, with oval, leathery foliage 12 cm long, and a striking inflorescence of long spikes of large, hollow or hooded, fleshy rosy-scarlet bracts, the small sessile flowers violet. The nectar-bearing bladders, open at top, attract small birds for cross-pollination. *Tropical.* *p. 1547*

tepuiensis (Venezuela); small shrub with leathery leaves obovate-oblong, 8-15 cm long; inflorescence to 50 cm long, bearing many small flowers with red, spoon-like hollow appendages, or honey-leaves; the flowers sessile at the base of the nectar-bearing honey-leaves. *p. 1547*

NORMANBYA *Palmae* **S3LFM**

normanbyi (Queensland), the "Black palm"; tall-growing, slender feather palm with trunk 20 m tall almost black, crowned by arching pinnate fronds to 4 m long and without petioles, the long dark green leaflets in clusters, whitish beneath, and cut off and jagged at apex. *p. 1890*

NORONHIA *Oleaceae* **S-I3LBD**

emarginata (Malagasy Rep.), "Madagascar olive"; tropical evergreen tree, with paired, leathery 15 cm leaves dark green with cream midvein; clusters of fragrant yellow flowers from leaf axils, with thick, 4-parted corolla; purplish fruit 3 cm dia., with sweet-tasting edible pulp, enclosing a large seed. *Tropical.* *p. 1634*

NOTHOLAENA *Polypodiaceae (Filices)* **I3HFM**

marantae (So. Europe to Ethiopia and Himalayas); tufted fern with horizontal rhizome covered with silky scales, the stalks purplish-black bearing leathery bipinnate fronds to 30 cm long, scaly beneath. *p. 1127*

NOTHOLIRION *Liliaceae* **I2LBM**

thomsonianum (Afghanistan to Himalayas); bulbous plant forming bulbils at base of bulb; long basal leaves becoming shorter on the stem; floral stalk to 1 m, with long raceme of funnel-shaped fragrant flowers 5 cm long, rose pink. *p. 1475*

NOTHOPANAX *Araliaceae* **•C-1LBM**

arboreus (Neopanax in Hortus 3) (New Zealand); known as "Five fingers"; evergreen tree with palmately compound leaves, the stalked segments leathery, dark green with coarsely serrate margins, pale center veins, and brownish petioles and stem. *p. 306, 316*

davidii (China); smooth evergreen tree 3-12 m high, with lanceolate simple, leathery, green leaves, or compound with 2 or 3 leaflets, to 15 cm long, 3-veined; small greenish-white flowers in panicles of numerous clusters. *p. 316*

laetus (Neopanax in Hortus 3) (New Zealand); willowy shrub to 3 m high, with slender, smooth branches and fine leathery leaves palmately compound usually of 5 broad elliptic leaflets; very attractive with purplish-red petioles and midribs; robust, tough, and vigorous. *p. 316, 318*

scutellarius (Java), "Saucer-panax"; large shrub with smooth branches bearing large thick-leathery, deep green oval leaves cupped or saucer-like with crenate or wavy margins, simple or compound with 2 to 5 leaflets 5-12 cm in dia., occasionally variegated yellow or white; numerous small flowers in panicles. *p. 320*

NOTHOPANAX: see also Polyscias

NOTHOSCORDUM *Liliaceae* **C2LBD**

bivalve (Virginia to Florida, Texas; Mexico), "False garlic"; small allium-like plant with onion-like bulb, linear basal leaves to 30 cm long and small yellowish flowers 1 cm long, in umbels. *p. 1467*

inodorum (fragrans) (Bermuda, So. U.S.), "False garlic"; bulbous herb with flat linear basal leaves to 45 cm; fragrant flowers white, lined with pink, in clusters on tall stalks; allium-like but without the onion odor. *p. 1475*

NOTOCACTUS *Cactaceae* **I2LBD**

apricus (Uruguay), "Ball cactus"; tiny, clustering globe to 5 cm thick, dark green densely covered with reddish, interlocking bristly spines; flowers yellow. *Arid-subtropic.* *p. 698, 700*

concinnus (So. Brazil, Uruguay); glossy green, depressed globe 6 cm high, with about 18 ribs notched into warts, recessed white woolly areoles and fine yellow spines; flowers red outside, satiny canary yellow inside. *Arid-subtropic.* *p. 698, 700*

graessneri (So. Brazil); small, fresh green globe 5 cm high and 10 cm across, with about 60 indistinct ribs usually in spirals, densely set with hair-like lemon-yellow spines; flowers greenish yellow. *p. 700*

haselbergii (So. Brazil), "White-web ball"; lovely small globe to 8 cm, occasionally sprouting from the base; with about 30 low ribs, covered with soft glossy, silvery-white spines pale yellow at the top; flowers orange red to crimson. *Arid-tropical.* *p. 698, 699, 700*

leninghausii (So. Brazil), "Golden ball"; attractive, smallish clustering, cylindrical column, to 1 m high and 10 cm thick, close-ribbed, covered with soft golden hair; flowers yellow at top. Beautiful, and of easy growth. *Arid-subtropic.* *p. 618, 620, 698, 699, 703*

leninghausii 'Cristata'; beautiful fasciation in form of a spread fan, especially when grafted on a columnar cereus as shown in photo pg. 695; entirely covered with soft golden hair as well as some white wool in the recesses of the folds and between the numerous ribs. *p. 695*

mammulosus (Brazil to Argentina), "Lemon ball"; simple plant nearly globose, to 8 cm thick, shining green, with 18-25 high ribs, and yellowish to reddish spines from recesses on the knobs; fragrant yellow flowers to 4 cm long, appearing at an early stage. *Arid-subtropic.* *p. 698, 699, 700*

ottonis (Brazil, Argentina), "Ball cactus"; small globe to 5 cm, glossy green, 10 broad ribs, short needle-like spines rising from notches; free flowering bright yellow. *Arid-subtropic.* *p. 698, 700*

ottonis tenuispina; in the trade as spiralis; a form having its broad ribs arranged in a spiral, as well as the spidery radial spines. *p. 698*

pampeanus (Uruguay, Argentina); small globe or somewhat cylindrical, to 10 cm, 21 straight ribs, dark green, sharp straw-colored spines; yellow flowers. *p. 697*

rubriflorus (Argentina); attractive, bright green globe with 21 acute ribs spirally arranged, thin spines, the central spines red, crown and areoles with white wool; a prolific bloomer each year with a complete circle of ruby red flowers, 6-8 cm across, with orange stamens. *p. 697*

rutilans (Argentina), "Pink ball cactus"; dark green globe with 25 rows of long knobs, the recessed areoles with straw-white radials and straight brownish central spines; flowers bright pink with yellow throat, shimmering like silk. *Arid-subtropic.* *p. 697*

schumannianus (Paraguay, No. Argentina); fresh green globe growing to 30 cm across, with about 30 acute ridges, compressed when young, set with long, thin, yellowish spines; flowers citron-yellow. *p. 697*

scopa (Brazil, Paraguay), "Silver ball"; globular to cylindrical, 45 cm high, closely ribbed and nearly covered with short, soft-hairy white radials and long brown needle-spines; flowers silky canary-yellow deeper in center. *Arid-subtropic.* *p. 697, 698, 700*

scopa 'Cristata', "Spiralled silver ball"; a strangely beautiful fasciated form taking on the shape of a coiled snake, entirely covered with glistening, pure-white hair. *Arid-subtropic.* *p. 699*

scopa ruberrimus; attractive variety with central spines crimson red. *p. 697*

submammulosus (Uruguay, Argentina), "Lemon ball"; small shining green globe 8 cm high with 13-25 rows of knobs, the recessed areoles with straw-yellow radials and very long brown-gray central spines; free-blooming flowers yellow, darker in throat. *p. 697*

NOTONIA: see Senecio

NOTYLIA *Orchidaceae* **S3OFM**

bungerothii (Mexico); small epiphyte with stout pseudobulbs bearing leathery leaves to 22 cm long; the inflorescence in pendant spikes to 25 cm long; tiny 1 cm flowers creamy-yellow with minute orange spots on lateral sepals. *p. 1771*

lyrata (Brazil); epiphyte with small clustered pseudobulbs bearing rigid leaves; pendant raceme of small, light yellow flowers. *p. 1771*

sagittifera (Brazil); small epiphyte having little pseudobulbs bearing solitary 8 cm leaves; from the base an arching inflorescence 8 cm long with numerous tiny 1 cm, fragrant flowers white tinged green. *p. 1771*

xyphophorus (N. E. Ecuador); small epiphyte with sheathing leaves arranged fan-like; the inflorescence pendulous, with clusters of feathery flowers purplish-lilac, not fragrant (April-June). (S) *p. 1770*

NUPHAR *Nymphaeaceae* **I2LBW**

luteum (Europe, Temp. Asia), "European pond lily"; aquatic plant with stout rootstock creeping in the mud; large rounded leaves, some submerged, others floating or standing erect above the water, to 30 cm across; small yellow flowers slightly above the water or floating. *p. 1622*

NYCTOCEREUS *Cactaceae* **•I2LBD**

serpentinus (Mexico), a "Queen of the night" or "Snake cactus"; slender erect or clambering night-bloomer; cylindric many-ribbed stems, to 5 cm thick, deep green; woolly areoles and white to brownish spines; large white, sweet-scented funnel-form nocturnal flowers to 25 cm long; edible red fruit. *Tropical.* *p. 618, 653*

serpentinus cristatus, the "Crestate snake cactus"; broadly fasciated, the body fresh green, even glossy, with shallow ridges set with thin cream-white spines, yellow when older. *p. 653*

NYMANIA *Aitoniaceae* **S3LBD**

capensis (Aitonia) (So. Africa: Karroo, Namibia), "Chinese lanterns"; large woody evergreen shrub 2 m high, valued for its balloon-like, rose-pink papery seed pods, with folds down their length looking like paper lanterns; about 4 cm in dia., following the deep rose, 3 cm bell-flowers in bloom for a long time, with 4 overlapping petals and protruding anthers; the gnarled branches are covered with tufts of narrow leathery leaves. *p. 352*

NYMPHAEA *Nymphaeaceae* **I-S2-3LBWd**

caerulea (Egypt to C. Africa), "Blue lotus of Egypt"; tender, free blooming water lily, with large leathery, floating leaves glossy dark green, and light blue, faintly scented flowers with numerous narrow petals, borne well above the water. *Humid-tropical.* *p. 1625*

capensis zanzibariensis (E. and So. Africa, Madagascar), the "Cape blue water-lily"; forming perfect floating carpets of leaves, with sinuate margins, 40 cm across; large bright blue, fragrant flowers, with yellow filaments and bluish anthers, to 30 cm across, larger than the species. *p. 1623*

'Col. Lindbergh'; large, day-blooming, zanzibariensis hybrid with floating leaves attractively marbled and blotched red-brown, the flowers are carried well above the water and azure-blue with a yellow base; tropical. *p. 1625*

colorata (Trop. Africa: Dar-es-Salaam); lovely pygmy tropical day-bloomer; from erect rhizome the vigorous, abundant foliage dark green, 25 cm dia.; light-blue broad-petalled 10 cm flowers with darker center; develops clusters of tiny tubers; good for tub culture. *Tropical.* *p. 1623*

x daubeniana, a tropical viviparous "Pygmy water lily"; for confined spaces, very free blooming with small, fragrant, light blue flowers carried well above the water; young plants develop at the junction of petiole and leaf; possibly a hybrid of micrantha and caerulea. *Humid-tropical.* *p. 1623, 1624, 1625, 2112A*

flava (mexicana) (Mexico, Florida), "Yellow water-lily"; fairly hardy aquatic plant with tuber-like rootstock, spreading by runners or suckers; floating leaves roundish with shallow crenations, 10-20 cm long, blotched brown above, crimson-brown with blackish spots beneath; flowers bright yellow, 10 cm across, standing 12 cm above the water; open before noon. *p. 1620*

gigantea (New Guinea, Queensland), "Giant water-lily" or "Australian waterlily"; big leathery, glossy green leaves 50 cm dia.; flowers light blue with broad petals, tipped dark blue and with yellow center, 15-30 cm across; day-blooming for 7 days, and remaining open from the fourth day; very fragrant. *Tropical.* *p. 1626*

'Gladstoniana' (hardy) (alba x odorata); large-flowered hardy day bloomer, with gleaming white, waxy flowers 15-20 cm across, the centers with golden yellow stamens; foliage dark green. *p. 1626*

'Gloriosa'; hardy variety with glorious red flowers, perfect in form and rather double, with a delightful fragrance reminiscent of apple blossoms; floating on the water. *p. 1624*

'Golden West'; floriferous tropical, day-blooming water lily in autumn shades of yellow and pink, with lovely red-mottled foliage. *p. 1624*

'H. A. Haarstick'; tropical night-blooming water-lily brilliant red, somewhat shy in blooming; the flowers carried well above the dark coppery foliage. *p. 1624*

x helvola ('Pygmaea helvola'), a "Pygmy water-lily"; probably the smallest in cultivation, a hybrid of tetragona, originally from Japan, Siberia, also Idaho and Ontario; with white flowers, but the variety helvola has small yellow flowers 5 cm across, afternoon blooming; 8-10 cm leaves floating, blotched with brown; the rootstock bears detachable tuber-like branches; hardy. *p. 1620*

leucantha (Tanzania); tropical night bloomer; robust aquatic with fleshy floating leaves, and big, pure white flowers raised above the water. *p. 1622*

Lotus (Egypt to West Africa), "White Lotus of Egypt"; illustrated from Bot. Mag. 1804; a tender water lily of history and legend; tropical night bloomer; from fleshy rootstock the orbicular, toothed floating leaves 30-50 cm across; large 12-25 cm flowers without scent, fleshy petals white or tinged pink, open for 4 successive nights, into morning. *p. 1622*

'Margaret Mary'; a day-blooming pygmy water lily; miniature day-blooming tropical water-lily that blooms indoors under either natural or artificial light; small enough for an aquarium. Flowers held above surface of the water, star shaped, 4 cm dia. with petals bright light blue and golden-yellow stamens; the floating pads 8 cm dia. deep green. Viviparous, producing young floating plantlets. *p. 1622*

x marliacea 'Chromatella' (mexicana x alba); free-blooming, hardy water lily with floating leaves, much blotched with brown, rising above the water when crowded; flowers bright yellow with concave petals and yellow stamens. *Humid-subtropic.* *p. 1625*

x marliacea rosea (alba x odorata rosea); one of the best hardy day bloomers, glossy green, floating leaves; profuse with large substantial deep pink flowers, fragrant and most pleasing. *p. 1626*

micrantha (West Africa); a strange tropical daybloomer, with relatively small foliage; flowers the first season almost perfectly white, with bluish tinge the second, and definitely blue-white the third, 15 cm across; and with yellow anthers on blue filaments. Produces young plants viviparously. *Tropical.* *p. 1622*

x odorata 'Sulphurea' (mexicana x odorata); hardy; an old hybrid, with floating green leaves blotched with brown; flowers light yellow borne slightly above the water, open during the morning; without runners. (C-I) *p. 1625*

'Pink Pearl'; tropical day-bloomer; medium sized, silvery pink flowers with yellow stamens surrounded by a ring of pink anthers; free-blooming. *p. 1626*

'St. Louis'; tropical night-bloomer, the first yellow hybrid of importance (Pring, St. Louis); clear yellow flowers 15-18 cm dia., pleasantly fragrant, and with deeper yellow stamens; foliage green, mottled bronze. *p. 1623*

'Sumptuosa'; hardy water-lily with large and fragrant flowers rosy pink deepening toward the center, and lightly spotted carmine, quite double. *p. 1624*

'Sunrise'; hardy day-bloomer, opening early in the day; very large flowers bright yellow, very free-blooming when once established. *p. 1626*

tuberosa 'Postlingsberg', the "Magnolia water lily"; an Austrian cultivar of the tuberosa at home in N.E. United States; a giant of all Nymphaeas, day-blooming until afternoon; noble flowers pure white, especially large to 30 cm dia., semi-double and with yellow center; leaves to 45 cm; valuable as a cut flower. *p. 1626*

'White Missouri'; spectacular tropical night-bloomer, large, beautiful white flowers with broad petals, above attractive leaves tinted red. *p. 1624*

NYPA *Palmae* **S3HF-BW**

fruticans (Philippines, Malaya, India, to Australia), "Nypa" or "Nipa palm"; low, shrubby palm usually growing with base more or less submerged in brackish water; trunk-like rootstock forming colonies with age, the pinnate fronds erect-recurving and rigid, 3-9 m tall, the leaflets 1-1½ m long, folded, and shiny bright green, grayish beneath; large compound fruit near base, to 30 cm dia., and consisting of a clump of carpels, each enclosing a seed kernel. The immature seeds are eaten fresh or are made into sweetmeat. The juice from the flower spathes produces an alcoholic brew, or sugary syrup. *Humid-tropical.* *p. 1890, 1897, 1899*

NYPHEA *Gesneriaceae* **S3HFM**

oblonga (Mexico), a "Snowwort" from Chiapas and collected by Thos. MacDougall in 1961 (Gloxinian Nov. 1970); attractive herbaceous species with scaly rhizomes, growing to 30 cm high, with fleshy red stem and several pairs of 10 cm, rugose leaves with depressed red veins and toothed margins; flowers with white corolla 4 cm across, carried on slender red stalks. *p. 1257*

OBREGONIA *Cactaceae* **I1LBD**

denegrii (Mexico), "Artichoke cactus"; low, interesting cactus with thick tap root, occasionally sprouting into groups; globular, flat on top, grayish to dark green, 8-12 cm across, with leaf-like tubercles spirally arranged, stiff and angled, without spines except at tips; white 4 cm flowers. *p. 702*

OCHAGAVIA *Bromeliaceae* **I2HBD**

carnea, in the trade as lindleyana (Rhodostachys, Fascicularia) (Chile, Perú); small free-suckering terrestrial rosette with many linear recurved succulent channeled leaves dark green, spiny-toothed; gray scurfy lines underneath; inflorescence a short-stemmed tight head of pink bracts nestling in the center and covered with mealy-white dust; flowers pinkish-lavender. *p. 513, 551, 575*

lindleyana (Chile); small succulent rosette, in habitat growing terrestrially or on rocks on dry mountain slopes; linear recurving, spiny leaves to 50 cm long and 2½ cm wide, shiny green above and with grayish-mealy lines underneath; the hemispherical inflorescence nesting in the center with white-woolly bracts and rose-pink flowers 5 cm long, in dense cluster. This species may be the same as O. carnea. *Arid-subtropic.* *p. 574*

OCHNA *Ochnaceae* **I-S2LBD**

atropurpurea (So. Africa), a "Mickey Mouse plant"; ornamental small shrub to 2 m high, with leathery ovate leaves sharply toothed; flowers yellow with dark purple calyx, when in fruit displaying shining black seed cases. *p. 1628*

kirkii (Trop. S.E. Africa), "Mickey-mouse plant"; evergreen smooth shrub with leathery oblong, finely toothed 5-8 cm leaves on woody branches; flowers bright yellow, the 5 petals soon falling, the glossy calyx lobes turning a glowing red and later the red to shining black fruit, this peculiar inflorescence looking like a fairy-tale Mickey Mouse. *Tropical.* *p. 1628*

pulchra (Angola to Transvaal), the "Lekkerbreek" of the Boers of the Veld because of its brittle wood; small tree with distinctive white bark, partially deciduous; with leathery ovate leaves, in spring in shades of green, bronze and red; sweet scented yellow flowers soon lose their petals but green sepals enlarge and turn bright red; protruding from these the small black fruits. *p. 1628*

serrulata (multiflora hort.) (Natal), "Birdseye bush"; woody shrub to 1½m high with hard leathery, narrow-elliptic leaves to 12 cm long, serrate glossy green at the margins; the flower corolla yellow but quickly falling, the sepals at first greenish then turning bright red and persistent; interesting black berry-like fruit seated on a red receptacle. *Subtropic.* *p. 1627*

OCHROSIA *Apocynaceae* **S3LFM**
elliptica (Kopsia arborea) (New Caledonia); evergreen tree to 6 m, with milky juice; smooth, green, obovate feathery leaves to 15 cm long; fragrant ivory-white, small flowers followed by scarlet red angled fruit 5 cm long; salt-resistant plant. *Tropical.* *p. 139*

OCIMUM *Labiatae* **I2LBM**
basilicum (Trop. Asia, Africa, Pacific Isl.), "Sweet basil"; pretty, aromatic annual with light green, broad leaves, and small white flowers. Use: the scented leaves for culinary seasoning of fish, meats, game, salads, stews. *p. 1347*

OCTOMERIA *Orchidaceae* **C3OFM**
alboviolacea (Venezuela); small epiphyte with clustered stems and narrow, solitary leaves; cupped flowers axillary, translucent white and tinged with purple, chocolate in center (spring). *p. 1771*
tunicola (Brazil); small epiphyte with grass-like tufts of leaves, without pseudobulbs, and small straw-yellow flowers clustered in the axils of the leaves, freely produced, and with trilobed lip (summer). (C) *p. 1770*

ODONTADENIA *Apocynaceae* **S3LBM**
speciosa (grandiflora), (Costa Rica, Trinidad, Guyana, Brazil); tropical woody vine closely related to Mandevilla, with leathery dark green oblong leaves 15 cm long; and bearing large showy clusters of bright yellow funnel-shaped flowers tinged with orange, 8 cm across, and delicately scented. *p. 144*

x ODONTIODA *Orchidaceae* **C3OFM**
'Charlette' (Odontioda 'Marie Antoinette' x Oda. charlesworthii); charming bigeneric Odontoglossum-Cochlioda hybrid with waxy flowers rich crimson-red and with undulate margins; yellow at base of lip; column white with lavender stripes. *p. 1773*
'Dolcoath' ('Castalia' x 'Cheer'); a showy spray of rounded, brown-red, waxy flowers marked and edged in white especially the lip, and a yellow center; typical of the bigeneric hybrids between Odontoglossum and Cochlioda, which while resulting in smaller flowers, are better lasting and more colorful, introducing scarlet shades (May-June). (C) *p. 1770*
'Gloriosa' (Oda. 'Coronation' x Odontoglossum amabile); interesting bigeneric with large waxy flowers to 8 cm across, brown tinged rosy-violet and with undulate margins, lip rose with yellow patch and bearded, column crimson (winter). *p. 1776*
'Lola' (Argia x Sapphira); beautiful Odontoglossum-Cochlioda hybrid with arching stalk carrying star-like, waxy flowers of dark scarlet marked and edged with white, and a yellow center, (May-June). (C) *p. 1770*
'Wey' ('Laurette' x 'Cheer'); striking English bigeneric hybrid (Odontoglossum x Cochlioda) with showy, waxy flowers vivid rusty-red, 6 cm across, and of excellent keeping quality (Stuart-Low 1953). *p. 1773*

x ODONTOCIDIUM *Orchidaceae* **S3OFW**
'Surprise' (Odontoglossum pulchellum x Oncidium macranthum); exquisite small bigeneric orchid with waxy flowers white, shaded with a blush of pink. *Humid-tropical.* *p. 1773*

ODONTOGLOSSUM *Orchidaceae* **C-I3ONM**
'Alispum' (Alorcus x crispum); typical of many of the hybrids originated so successfully in England 50 years ago, featuring beautiful, large, rounded, 8-10 cm flowers with white base, blotched, barred or spotted brown, mauve, purple or crimson, and with crisped margins, (bl. various). *p. 1775*
bictoniense (Guatemala); attractive epiphyte with pseudobulbs surrounded by leaf-bearing sheaths; inflorescence in erect raceme to 75 cm tall, with 4 cm flowers, sepals and petals yellow-green blotched with brown, lip heart-shaped, shaded violet with yellow keels, (Aug.-Jan.). *p. 1774*
cariniferum (Costa Rica); tall-growing, free-blooming epiphyte, with two-leaved pseudo-bulbs 8 cm high, and large branched stalks 60 cm long, with 5 cm flowers, the sepals and petals chestnut brown bordered greenish-yellow, greenish and keeled on back, lip yellow, with violet claw; autumn. (C) *p.1777*
cervantesii roseum (So. Mexico, Guatemala); pretty, dwarf epiphyte with clustered pseudobulbs bearing a solitary petioled leaf; clusters of 4-6 cm roundish flowers pale rose with interrupted concentric circles of crimson (Oct.-May). *Humid-subtropic.* *p. 1772*
chiriquense (coronarium) (Costa Rica, Panama to Perú); straggly epiphyte with compressed pseudobulbs and solitary short, broad leaves; inflorescence on long wiry stem, waxy flowers 6 cm across, with brown sepals and petals, the prettily frilled margins yellow; small lip lemon yellow (spring). *p. 1773*
cirrhosum (Ecuador, Colombia); dainty epiphyte with ovoid pseudobulbs and straplike leaves; elegant 10 cm flowers in arching raceme, the narrow crisped sepals and petals white, irregularly blotched purple, the small pointed lip yellow in center and lined purple. *p. 1773*
citrosmum (pendulum) (Mexico); epiphyte with compressed pseudobulbs bearing 2 strap-shaped leaves; pendulous racemes of large 5 cm, fragrant, white flowers sometimes flesh-tinted, lip rose with yellow, red-spotted crest (May). *Humid-subtropic.* *p. 1777*
citrosmum album (Mexico); flowers pure white, except for the yellow crest on the lip; early summer. *p. 1774*
constrictum (Venezuela); pretty epiphyte with compressed, ribbed pseudobulbs carrying two dark green leaves 30 cm long, and slender stalk with 3 cm scented flowers, sepals and petals bright yellow blotched with reddish-brown, the fiddle-shaped lip white with two rosy blotches; late winter. (C) *p. 1777*
convallarioides (Mexico, Costa Rica); epiphyte with clustered, flattened, two-leaved pseudobulbs, the leaves hard and leathery, over 30 cm long; bell-shaped white nodding blossoms, in many-flowered raceme from the base of the pseudobulb; April-May. (C) *p. 1772*
cordatum (Mexico, Guatemala); beautiful, free-blooming epiphyte, with flatly oval pseudobulbs and a short leaf; erect stalk with large, star-shaped, 8 cm flowers, sepals sepia-brown marked with yellow, petals and pointed lip lemon-yellow spotted brown, (Jan.-April, July). (C) *p. 1774*
crispum (Colombia); very handsome epiphyte with stout, 2-leaved pseudobulbs, and arching racemes of daintily crisped, waxy star-shaped 9 cm flowers of pure white, the lip yellow at base and blotched reddish toward front; variable, (Feb.-April). *Humid-subtropic.* *p. 1664A, 1775*
cristatum (Perú, Ecuador); compact-growing epiphyte with shining green, conical pseudobulbs 5 cm high, narrow lanceolate leaves, and wiry stalk with several 6 cm flowers, the sepals and petals honey-yellow blotched with brown, crested lip pale yellow blotched and spotted brown; spring. (C) *p. 1772*
'Elise' (triumphans x 'Ascaria'); an exquisite, colorful flower, yellow flushed orange toward the margins and irregularly splotched red-brown; the blooms are firm and on a close spray; flattened pseudobulbs with 2-3 leathery leaves. *Humid-subtropic.* *p. 1775*
grande (Guatemala, Mexico), "Tiger orchid"; very beautiful epiphyte of compact habit, an easy grower, with thick, 2-leaved pseudobulbs, and erect, 30 cm stalks with large 12-15 cm flowers, sepals yellow barred with brown, petals half reddish-brown, tips yellow, lip cream spotted with brown, (Aug.-March). *Humid-tropical.* *p. 1775*
insleayi (Mexico); noble epiphyte with 2-leaved compressed pseudobulbs, and an erect stalk with 5-10 cm flowers with oblong sepals and petals greenish-yellow transversely banded with chestnut red, the spoon-shaped lip bright yellow with a border of crimson spots (Aug.-Sept., Dec.-Jan.). *Humid-subtropic.* *p. 1772*
krameri (Costa Rica); dwarf epiphyte with broad, pale green pseudobulbs topped by a solitary leaf; short, erect stalks with 2-5 fragrant, 3-5 cm, waxy flowers, freely produced, sepals and petals rose shading to white, lip purplish banded with white and red at base, (Aug.-Sept.). *Humid-tropical.* *p. 1774*
laeve (Guatemala, Mexico); free-growing epiphyte with compressed 2-leaved pseudobulbs and slightly branched racemes 5-8 cm long, with about 5 cm fragrant flowers having narrow sepals and petals cinnamon-brown banded yellow, lip deflexed, violet with white apex, and with a broad claw parallel with column (spring). (C) *p. 1774*
laeve reichenheimii (Mexico); attractive variety; epiphyte with compressed 2-leaved pseudobulbs and slightly branched racemes of 5 cm fragrant flowers, with narrow sepals and petals yellowish green barred with purplish-brown, lip light purple without claw; willing bloomer (spring). *Humid-subtropic.* *p. 1772*
luteo-purpureum (Colombia); robust epiphyte with conical, 2-leaved pseudobulbs, and arching raceme of star-like, 8-10 cm waxy flowers, creamy-yellow, heavily overlaid or blotched with chestnut-brown, lip fringed, (March-Aug.). (C) *p. 1774*
maculatum (Mexico); epiphyte with short, thick, 1-leaved pseudobulbs, closely crowded; inflorescence in spike of 5-9 flowers 5-8 cm across, the keeled, pointed sepals brown, broad petals and lip yellow spotted with brown, (Jan.-May). (C) *p. 1772*
oerstedii (Costa Rica); pretty, dwarf epiphyte with roundish, 2-edged pseudobulbs in dense masses, each with a single, small, stalked leaf; short stems with 2-5 scented, waxy-white flowers and a yellow, orange-spotted crest, (Feb.-May). (I) *p. 1774*
pendulum (citrosmum) (Mexico); lovely epiphyte with two-leaved pseudobulbs, leaves to 30 cm long; inflorescence pendulous with numerous fragrant, waxy flowers 5 cm across, white flushed with rose-pink, with wavy margins, bright yellow blotch at base of lip (autumn). *p. 1773*
pulchellum (Guatemala), "Lily-of-the-valley orchid"; dainty epiphyte with dark green pseudobulbs topped by 2-3 grass-like leaves, and clustering; erect racemes with small waxy, sweetly fragrant 2-3 cm flowers of crystalline white with yellow crest, (Dec.-May). *p. 1773, 1774*
rossii (Mexico, Guatemala); pretty epiphyte of dwarf habit, with 1-leaved pseudobulbs, delicate though wiry inflorescence with star-like, 5-8 cm flowers, linear sepals white, barred with brown, crisped petals, and lip white with yellow crest, (Feb.-April). *Humid-subtropic.* *p. 1774*
schlieperianum (Costa Rica, Panama); showy epiphyte similar to grande, with smaller, waxy flowers, 3 to 6 on erect stalk, sepals and petals yellow, barred with brown, lip pale sulphur-yellow marked brown and crimson, (May-July). (C-I) *p. 1772*
triumphans (Colombia); magnificent epiphyte with large compressed pseudobulbs to 10 cm high, 30-38 cm dark green leaves, and 45-90 cm arching racemes with numerous large 10-12 cm variable flowers, sepals

and petals golden yellow, barred and blotched with brownish-crimson; the pretty lip white at base, marked cinnamon-brown in front, bordered with white or pale yellow; spring. (C) *p. 1772*

uroskinneri (Guatemala); strong-growing epiphyte with creeping rhizome, compressed 1-2 leaved pseudobulbs spotted purple, and basal raceme 60-90 cm long with 5-8 cm flowers with sepals and petals greenish-yellow mottled reddish-brown, the rosy lip mottled with white (Mar.-April, July-Aug.). (C) *p. 1772*

warscewiczii weltonii (C. America); handsome epiphyte with flat green pseudobulbs each with solitary leaf; floral stalk 20 cm long, with several glossy flowers 6 cm across, yellow and overlaid with chocolate brown, wavy at margins, large lip old rose tinted pink and spotted yellow. *p. 1773*

ODONTONEMA *Acanthaceae* **S2LFM**

callistachyum (Mexico, C. America); tall hairy shrub with 4-angled stems, ovate wrinkled leaves to 30 cm long; the tubular 3 cm red flowers with deflexed lower lip, on erect stalks in branched racemes. *p. 55*

schomburgkianum (Colombia); shrubby plant to 2 m, with long-elliptic leaves 8-20 cm long, the 4 cm tubular red flowers in pendulous racemes. *p. 55*

strictum (C. America); handsome shrub 1 m high, with stiff erect stems and slender-pointed leaves shiny rich green; terminal inflorescence of waxy crimson-red flowers 1 cm long, and very attractive. *Tropical.* *p. 48*

strictum variegatum (Thyrsacanthus) (Honduras); willowy bush with 4-sided stems, opposite leathery leaves long elliptic, bluish or grayish green irregularly variegated white along outside; small 2½ cm tubular scarlet-red flowers with spreading lobes on terminal raceme. *p. 47*

x ODONTONIA *Orchidaceae* **I3OFM**

'Vesta' (Odontonia Dora x Miltonia W. Pitt); a lovely hybrid with loose racemes of colorful flowers, sepals flushed mauve with white tips, petals rosy-purple with maroon spots, and having a wide lip; an intergeneric hybrid developed for culture in warmer climates, (spring). (I) *p. 1770*

ODONTOSPERMUM: see Asteriscus

OENOTHERA *Onagraceae* **C2LBD**

caespitosa (Western U.S.), "Evening primrose"; short-lived perennial herb with woody root; pubescent, narrow oblong leaves, sinuate and lobed at margins; fragrant white flowers aging pink, 5-8 cm across, and opening in the evening. *p. 1649*

tetragona fraseri (glauca) (Eastern U.S.) "Sundrops"; charming day-blooming perennial freely branching, 40 to 60 cm high; pubescent reddish stems with bluish-green, narrow-lanceolate leaves and toothed at margins; bright golden-yellow cupped flowers 3-5 cm across, during summer, opening from colorful red buds. Very similar or related to Oe. fruticosa. *p. 1648*

OLDENBURGIA *Compositae* **I2LBD**

arbuscula (So. Africa: Cape Mountains); beautiful evergreen shrub to 2½ m, with spreading branches densely clothed with striking, big leathery, convex, oblanceolate leaves to 45 cm long, thickly covered with snow-white felt, with age shining dark green; fluffy clusters of purple and white flowers. *Subtropic.* *p. 829*

OLEA *Oleaceae* **•C-I2LBD**

europaea (E. Mediterranean reg.),"Olive tree"; small, sparry, evergreen tree with stiff-leathery, narrow lanceolate leaves gray-green above, silvery scurfy beneath; flowers yellowish-white and fragrant; oblong 3 to 4 cm fruit green turning shining black when ripe, used for its valuable oil. *p. 1627, 1633*

europaea 'Manzanillo'; a Spanish cultivar, evergreen tree with rounded head and distinctive gray-green foliage, bearing choice edible fruit. Excellent decorative tree and grown in standard form in California nurseries. *p. 1632*

OLEA: see also Osmanthus

OLEANDER: see Nerium

OLEARIA *Compositae* **C2LBM**

avicennifolia (New Zealand); evergreen tree to 6 m with grooved branches, very hard, leathery 5-10 cm oval leaves white tomentose beneath; the small flower heads with 1-3 creamy-white ray florets, and 2 disk florets, in large clusters. *p. 822*

oleifolia (New Zealand); evergreen shrub 1½-3 m high; erect downy branches with leathery, lanceolate leaves 5-8 cm long, white-downy beneath; numerous white flower-heads with 4-8 rays, in broad clusters. *p. 822*

nummularifolia (New Zealand); woody shrub 1 to 3 m high, of dense growth, with sticky shoots closely set with rounded thick, shining leaves 1 cm long, topped by small flowerheads with yellowish florets. *p. 822*

stellulata (New So. Wales); shrub to 1½ m with oblong or lanceolate leaves to 8 cm with toothed margins, white tomentose beneath; heads of white ray flowers and yellow disks, in leafy clusters. *p. 810*

OLIVERANTHUS: see Echeveria harmsii

OLMEDIELLA *Flacourtiaceae* **I2LBD**

betschleriana (Guatemala), "Guatemala holly" or "Manzanote"; ornamental evergreen, dioecious small tree from 6 to 8 m high, dense with alternate stiff-leathery, dark green, long-elliptic leaves 10 to 15 cm long, spiny-toothed at margins, somewhat like English holly (Ilex); inconspicuous flowers with numerous stamens but without petals; female trees produce hard-shelled, flattened orange-sized fruit to 8 cm dia., but inedible. *Subtropic.* *p. 1064, 2107*

OLYRA *Gramineae* **S2LFM**

latifolia (Trop. Africa: Kenya, Uganda, Zaire, also E. Indies, Trop. America); a bamboo-like grass with underground running stolons sending up thin-wiry, cane-like yellowish stems from ½-2 m tall, set with alternate lanceolate thin-leathery, deep green leaves. When I found this species in the Ituri forest, in Pygmy country near the Mountains of the Moon in Central Africa, I had considered this to be the true Bamburanta which it closely resembles. *Tropical.* *p. 1310*

OMPHALEA *Euphorbiaceae* **I-S2LBD**

triandra (West Indies), "Pig-nut"; spreading tree to 4 m high, with obovate, leathery leaves; the flowers without petals, but 3 anthers; pendant, furrowed yellow fruit 4 cm dia., fleshy outside, 4-celled, containing nuts, these edible after removing the poisonous embryo. Juice extracted from this species turns black and is used for ink and glue. *Tropical.* *p. 1060*

ONCIDIUM *Orchidaceae* **I-S-C3OFD**

"alatum" in hort.; robust plant with large, flat pseudobulbs bearing pair of strap-like leaves 45 cm long; arching spray extending 1½-2 m with 4 cm waxy flowers, brown petals and sepals, wavy-edged and tipped yellow; bright yellow lip. (Roehrs collection). *Tropical.* *p. 1779*

altissimum (W. Indies); lofty epiphyte, with rapidly clustering pseudobulbs bearing 1-2 strap-like leaves, forming gigantic clusters and flower stems to 3 m long, with well-spaced sparry, lateral branchlets bearing several small, waxy flowers, sepals and petals narrow-pointed, greenish-brown with greenish yellow edge, lip lemon-yellow (April-Sept.) (I) *p. 1783*

ampliatum (C. America, Trinidad, Colombia); epiphyte, with wrinkled, brown-mottled pseudobulbs bearing broad, leathery leaves 20-30 cm long; the arching stalks ½-1 m long with 3 cm flowers, the small sepals yellow blotched red-brown; petals yellow, white beneath; the spreading lip canary-yellow. *p. 1786*

ampliatum majus (Costa Rica, Guatemala); stiff epiphyte with 1 or 2-leaved pseudobulbs mottled brown, and a stout raceme to 1 m long, of 5 cm bright yellow flowers blotched with red-brown, and marked with white beneath, (Dec.-June). *Tropical.* *p. 1784*

ansiferum (Costa Rica, Panama); epiphyte with flat pseudobulbs, bearing two thin-leathery leaves 30 cm long; large panicle often with more than 100 flowers having sepals and petals yellow with brown spots, their tips yellow; lip fiddle-shaped, bright yellow; callus with 9-10 prong-like teeth, pale yellow with brown spots and surrounded by chocolate brown area; wings of column spreading sideways; September-November. (I) *p. 1786*

aurisasinorum (Honduras); epiphyte with small pseudobulbs bearing a solitary fleshy, bluish-green, slightly folded leaf 15-20 cm long; 2½ cm flowers faintly fragrant, with sepals and petals greenish-white, the lip shiny milky-white. *p. 1786*

baueri (W. Indies, Guyana, Brazil); robust epiphyte with 1 or 2-leaved pseudobulbs and a long inflorescence to 2½ m high, branching from the very base, the small yellowish-green, waxy flowers spotted with red-brown, lip yellow with white crest, (May-Sept.). (I) *p. 1784*

carthaginense (C. America, W. Indies); epiphyte with much-reduced pseudobulbs bearing a fleshy, broad and keeled, leathery leaf; inflorescence in a loosely-branched stem to 1½ m long, of small, creamy-white, crisped flowers spotted rose, (summer). (I) *p. 1780, 1785*

cavendishianum (Guatemala, Mexico); showy species with broad, rich green leaves lacking pseudobulbs, and panicled inflorescence 60-90 cm high with fragrant 4 cm flowers with crisped yellow segments, the clawed sepals and petals spotted red (Oct.-May). (I) *p. 1785*

cebolleta (Mexico, W. Indies, Brazil, Paraguay); known since 1800, but not the best; free-blooming with arching branched inflorescence 45-75 cm long, of 3-4 cm flowers yellow spotted red-brown, lip canary yellow; small pseudobulbs with solitary 30 cm cylindrical leaf (Jan.-May). *p. 1779,1780*

cheirophorum (Colombia), "Colombia buttercup"; compact, pretty epiphyte with small, compressed, 1-leaved pseudobulbs, and slender, arching panicles of numerous, small, bright yellow, sweetscented flowers. (Oct.-Dec.) *Subtropic.* *p. 1780*

concolor (Brazil); lovely little epiphyte with 2 or 3-leaved flattened pseudobulb and cluster of large flowers 4-5 cm across, lemon-yellow and large yellow lip (Oct.-May). *Subtropic.* *p. 1780*

crispum (Brazil); splendid epiphyte from the Organ mountains, with 2-3-leaved, compressed pseudobulbs; the panicled inflorescence ½-1 m high, with large, crisped flowers to 8 cm, chestnut-brown with center of golden yellow, (May-Nov.). *Subtropic.* *p. 1783*

cucullatum macrochilum (olivaceum) (Colombia); pretty epiphyte with ovate pseudobulbs bearing leaves 15 cm long, branched floral stalk to 60 cm, with 3 cm waxy flowers; narrow sepals and petals yellow and blackish crimson, the broad lip light rose and richly spotted purple (spring). *p. 1778*

'Doctor Schragen' (O. lanceanum x splendidum); magnificent primary hybrid with large waxy 6 cm flowers, crisped sepals and petals brilliant chestnut brown tipped with chartreuse, large lip yellow with ruby flush on upper portion (autumn-winter). *p. 1776*

excavatum (Perú, Ecuador); attractive epiphyte with stout, compressed, 1-leaved pseudobulbs, and many-flowered inflorescence to 1 m long, the 4 cm flowers yellow, barred with red except the broad lip, (Oct.-March). *Tropical.* *p. 1784*

falcipetalum (Venezuela); pseudobulbs with leaves 22-45 cm long, the inflorescence a scrambling flexuose panicle often 6 m long; large 8 cm flowers curiously lobed, the sepals brown with yellow margins, the small wavy petals yellow spotted brown, the narrow lip purplish-brown; autumn. (C) *p. 1785*

flexuosum (Brazil, Paraguay), "Dancing doll orchid"; beautiful little epiphyte with 1-2-leaved pseudobulbs, and dainty, thin-wiry sprays of small "dancing doll"-like golden yellow flowers with center marked deep red, (Oct.-Aug.). *Tropical.* *p. 1781*

forbesii (Brazil); handsome epiphyte with compressed pseudobulbs and solitary leaf; many-flowered panicles of waxy, showy 5-6 cm blooms with crisped petals rich chestnut brown and broken golden borders (Mar.-April, Oct.-Nov.). *Subtropic.* *p. 1781*

gardneri (Brazil); handsome epiphyte with 2-leaved pseudobulbs and many-flowered inflorescence to 1 m long, flowers about 5 cm across, sepals rich brown barred with yellow,petals chestnut brown edged yellow, lip bright yellow with red-brown spots along margin, (Aug.-Dec.). (C) *p. 1784, 1785*

ghiesbrechtianum (Mexico); miniature epiphyte with small waxy flowers, sepals and petals white striped with crimson, large lip light yellow, deeper in center (spring). *p. 1778*

globuliferum (Costa Rica to Venezuela and Perú); climbing epiphyte with creeping, wiry, scandent rhizomes, at intervals forming small bulblet-like, compressed, leafy pseudobulbs with aerial roots; short-stalked flowers 3 cm long, bright yellow barred with red-brown, the large lip yellow. (Summer). *Tropical.* *p. 1779*

x haematochilum (Trinidad); handsome natural hybrid of O. lanceanum x luridum, with red-spotted leaves springing direct from the crown, panicles 30-60 cm or more with 5 cm flowers with sepals and petals greenish-yellow blotched with brown, lip crimson with yellow margin mottled with red (autumn). (S) *p. 1781*

hastatum (Mexico, Guatemala); resembling Odontoglossum, with loose inflorescence to 1½ m long, 3 cm star-like flowers with slender pointed sepals and petals yellowish-green barred with brown, lip with side lobes whitish, and red midlobe tipped with green; compressed pseudobulbs with 1-2 leaves (spring). (I) *p. 1782*

'Helen Brown' (triquetrum x variegatum); floriferous, charming miniature orchid forming dense clumps; lanceolate folded, recurving leaves; short inflorescence with dense clusters of flowers orange-brown and white, lasting over 6 months and looking like an old-fashioned bouquet (Moir-Honolulu). *p. 1779*

isthmi (Costa Rica, Panama); epiphyte with elliptical, sharp-edged, 2-leaved pseudobulbs, the leaves 45 cm long; 2½ cm flowers sweetly fragrant, in long panicle; sepals and petals golden-yellow with brown cross-bars; lip with long and narrow isthmus between front lobe and side lobes, yellow with brown cross-bar in front of callus; June-August. *p. 1785*

'Java' (flexuosum x varicosum rogersii); very free-blooming epiphytic hybrid with flowers larger than either parent, bright yellow marked red on petals and sepals, on graceful arching panicles, flowering almost continuously. (I) *p. 1783*

jonesianum (Paraguay); pretty species with small, clustered pseudobulbs bearing a solitary pendant leaf; pendulous raceme of large 8 cm flowers, sepals and petals white shaded with yellow and spotted brown, the broad lip white sparsely spotted red in front of crest; autumn. (S) *p. 1785, 1786*

kramerianum (Ecuador, Colombia); beautiful epiphyte with small round pseudobulbs bearing a solitary leaf; flower stalks to 75 cm long and round, with several very curious, highly colored flowers in succession, the long narrow dorsal sepal and petals chocolate-brown, lateral sepals broad, orange-red mottled with yellow, lip lemon-yellow bordered red-brown, (March-May, Nov.-Dec.). *Tropical.* *p. 1664A, 1783*

lamelligerum (Ecuador); handsome epiphyte with 15 cm long, 2-leaved pseudobulbs, and flexuous stalk 1½-3 m long with short branches bearing flowers 8 cm high, the upper sepal broad, light brown and margined with yellow, lower sepals curving, light brown, the crisped petals light yellow, brown at base, the narrow lip light yellow, stained with purple; summer. (C) *p. 1785*

lanceanum (Trinidad, Guyana), "Leopard orchid"; strikingly beautiful epiphyte with minute pseudobulbs, broad and thick, brown-spotted, solitary leaves and erect spikes with large, vanilla-scented flowers, the fleshy sepals and petals yellow shaded green, blotched with chocolate-brown, the large lip violet at base, rose in front, (May-Aug.). *p. 1781*

lankesteri (ansiferum) (Guatemala, Nicaragua, Costa Rica, Panama); epiphyte with compressed thin pseudobulbs, broad, usually solitary leaves to 35 cm, arching inflorescence to 1½ m long, with numerous small waxy crisped 3 cm flowers, brown with yellow tips, the fiddle-shaped lip bright yellow (autumn). *p. 1778*

leucochilum (Mexico to Honduras); bold epiphyte with compressed pseudobulbs bearing 2 strap-like leaves, and arched inflorescence to 2½ m high, with waxy 4 cm flowers, sepals and petals lemon-yellow, barred and spotted dark brown, lip white with purple center, (March-Nov.). (C-I) *p. 1781*

limminghei (Brazil, Venezuela); miniature epiphyte of creeping habit, with small leathery leaves prettily painted with purple; relatively large 3 cm flowers yellow, tinted with copper and marked with red-brown, the yellow lip dotted bright red (summer). *p. 1778*

luridum (Florida, W. Indies, Cent. America, So. America); bulbless epiphyte with leathery keeled leaves 30-60 cm long often spotted brown, and slender panicle sometimes 2½-3 m long, with 3 cm flowers, larger than carthaginense, yellowish green with nearly confluent reddish brown blotches (summer). (S) *p. 1782*

macranthum (Colombia, Ecuador, Perú); large epiphyte with 2-leaved pseudobulbs and scandent inflorescence to 3 m long, the waxy , crisped flowers large, to 10 cm across,sepals brown-yellow, petals golden yellow, the pointed lip yellow edged with wine-red, (May-July). (C) *p. 1784*

maculatum (Mexico, Guatemala, Honduras); clustered pseudobulbs with paired leaves to 25 cm long; the inflorescence to 35 cm, dense with glossy 5 cm flowers greenish-yellow heavily blotched blackish maroon, lip greenish white, the crest streaked with red (spring). *p. 1778*

meirax (Brazil, Venezuela); interesting small epiphyte with compressed pseudobulbs and solitary leaves 5-6 cm long; flowers yellowish green spotted with maroon, cordate lip yellow and marked with purple. *p. 1778*

microchilum (Guatemala); small compressed pseudobulbs with solitary leaf 20-30 cm high; branched stalks bearing 2½ cm roundish flowers, sepals and petals brown marked with yellow, lip with small front lobe, the side lobes white with purple; summer. (I) *p. 1777*

onustum (Ecuador); xerophytic epiphyte with crowded conical, 3-cornered pseudobulbs marbled with black, with fleshy, solitary keeled leaf only 5-8 cm long; arching raceme with flowers having tiny sepals and larger petals clear lemon-yellow, also the large lip; autumn. (S) *p. 1777*

ornithorhynchum (Mexico to Salvador); small epiphyte with twin leaves on small pseudobulbs, prolific with dainty, arching sprays of small, very fragrant flowers of soft rosy-lilac, with darker shading on lip and a yellow crest, (Aug.-Dec.). *Tropical.* *p. 1783*

ornithorhynchum majus (Central America); robust plant with arching inflorescence 60 cm long, dense with fragrant, long-lived rosy-lavender flowers 2 cm across, the petals undulate; purple lip with yellow crest. *p. 1778*

panamense (Panama); large pseudobulbs with 2 or 3 leaves, which are to 75 cm long and 6 cm wide; the inflorescence in a large panicle to more than 3 m long and with several hundred flowers; sepals and petals undulate, greenish-yellow with brown cross-bands, lip bright yellow. *p. 1786*

papilio (Trinidad, Venezuela, Brazil, Perú), "Butterfly orchid"; epiphyte with small pseudobulbs bearing a single leaf mottled purplish-brown; the large, unusual flowers developing successively on flat stalks to 1 m long, dorsal sepal and petals long linear, reddish-brown marked with yellow, lateral sepals oblong, brown barred with yellow, lip yellow with brown border. *Tropical.* *p. 1783*

pardinum (Ecuador); similar to a large Oncidium crispum but with many-flowered inflorescence to 1 m long, undulate flowers of medium size, bright yellow marked brown; compressed pseudobulbs with 2-3 leaves (Dec.-Jan.). *Tropical.* *p. 1782*

phalaenopsis (Ecuador); beautiful epiphyte of slender habit with small furrowed pseudobulbs with two strap-like deep green leaves, the stalk bearing 5-6 large flowers 5 cm high, the sepals creamy-white mottled with purple, petals creamy and barred with purple, the broad bilobed lip creamy-white, spotted at base with crimson; spring. (C) *p. 1777*

phymatochilum (Mexico); pretty species with compressed pseudobulbs bearing one oblanceolate leaf; the distinctive flowers 5 cm across, with sepals and petals pale yellow spotted with brown, the lateral sepals lengthened out into a long tail; the white lip spotted red at base; April-June. (I) *p. 1785*

picturatum (Venezuela); creeping epiphyte with furrowed pseudobulbs and lanceolate leaves, and sending out a very long, snaky inflorescence to 5 m long, with branchlets carrying numerous small brown flowers with yellow tips; front lobe of lip bright golden yellow, marked at the base chestnut brown (summer). *p. 1782*

planipes hort.; small compact plant with linear leaves on compressed pseudobulbs; short inflorescence with small waxy flowers brown edged deep yellow green, the broad lip bright yellow. *p. 1779*

powellii (Panama); fairly big epiphyte with compressed, 1-leaved pseudobulbs and flexuous sprays of crisped flowers, the narrow sepals and petals chocolate-brown tipped with greenish yellow, (Dec.-Jan.). (S) *p. 1783, 1785*

pubes (Brazil); long slender, compressed pseudobulbs bearing 2 rigid, obovate leaves to 12 cm; long flexuous, wiry stem to 60 cm long, bearing an inflorescence alternately branched in 2 ranks, of numerous small 2 cm flowers, red-brown barred and spotted with yellow (summer). *p. 1779*

pulchellum (West Indies, Jamaica); dwarf plant without pseudobulbs, folded leaves 8-15 cm high; slender, branched stalk with small white flowers flushed with rose, the lip with a yellow spot in front of crest; summer. (S) *p. 1777*

pulvinatum (Brazil, Paraguay, Argentina); free-blooming, compact epiphyte with small, compressed, 1-leaved pseudobulbs, with long flexuous, loosely branched inflorescence of small waxy, brown-red flowers edged yellow, the lip golden-yellow spotted red, (June-Dec.). (I) *p. 1783, 1786*

pumilum (Paraguay, Brazil); small clustering epiphyte with folded, rigid, stubby 10 cm leaves from creeping rhizome; horizontal inflorescence dense with numerous small 5 mm, crisped, deep yellow flowers, spotted with red (summer). *p. 1779*

pusillum (Cent. America); miniature epiphyte 8 cm high with small fleshy leaves arranged fan-like; 8 cm flowers pale yellow with petals marked purple and lip with claw (summer). (I) *p. 1782*

sarcodes (Brazil); vigorous epiphyte having dark green, tapering pseudobulbs with 2-3 shining green leaves; inflorescence to 2 m long, with short branches of large 5 cm flowers, sepals and petals chestnut-brown bordered yellow, lip bright yellow with red-brown spots, (April-July). *Tropical.* *p. 1778, 1780*

sphacelatum (Mexico to Honduras), "Golden shower"; prolific epiphyte with elongate, flattened pseudobulbs of 2-3 leaves; the branched, loose inflorescence to 1½ m long, with many small, yellow flowers, marked with brown, 2 to 3 cm across. (Feb.-Sept.). *Tropical.* *p. 1777, 1784*

sphegiferum (Brazil); small one-leaved pseudobulbs, and branched stalks to 1 m long bearing numerous 2½ cm orange-yellow flowers, all segments red-brown at base; summer. (I) *p. 1777*

splendidum (Guatemala); handsome stout epiphyte with short pseudobulbs bearing a single stiff-fleshy, mahogany leaf, and erect, 1 m spike with large substantial flowers, 5 cm across, small sepals and petals yellow barred with brown, the large lip golden yellow, (Dec.-Feb.). *Tropical.* *p. 1784*

stipitatum (Panama); pendant epiphyte with small pseudobulbs and cylindrical leaves; inflorescence drooping and may carry 200 small yellow flowers marked red-brown on petals and sepals, (early winter to March). (S) *p. 1783*

suscephalum (Brazil); epiphyte with long panicles of showy flowers with wavy yellow sepals and flaring petals, dark reddish-brown with yellow cross-bars; lip with large, bright yellow side-lobes, the small front lobe yellow with large, pale brown spots (winter). (I) *p. 1782*

tetrapetalum (W. Indies); epiphyte with short, fleshy, folded leaves in tufts but without pseudobulbs; erect spikes with 2½ cm flowers, sepals and petals chestnut-red barred with yellow, lip white with a red blotch, (summer). (S) *p. 1780*

tigrinum (Mexico); free-blooming, attractive epiphyte with flat, stout pseudobulbs bearing 2 or 3 lanceolate leathery leaves, and from the base a panicle of numerous showy, fragrant flowers, sepals and petals yellow barred with brown, the spreading lip bright clear yellow; autumn-winter. (C) *p. 1786*

triquetrum (Jamaica); very pretty miniature known since 1793, without pseudobulbs, having 10-12 cm leaves in tufts, and clusters of 2½ cm flowers with greenish sepals, petals rose bordered with white, deeply stained and spotted dark crimson (autumn) (S) *p. 1781*

uniflorum (Brazil); small epiphyte of bushy habit; the short inflorescence with 1 or 2 waxy flowers, sepals and petals greenish-yellow shaded brown, lip bright yellow (April to December). *p. 1782*

uniflorum longipes (Brazil); small epiphyte with 1 to 2-leaved pseudobulbs; erect inflorescence with 3 to 5 glossy flowers, red-brown tipped yellow, lip canary-yellow (Spring). *p. 1780*

varicosum rogersii (Brazil); very showy epiphyte with 2-3 -leaved pseudobulbs, small by comparison with the long, branching sprays of numerous, large, 5 cm delicate, bright yellow flowers, sepals and petals small, barred red-brown, and a large golden lip, (Sept.-July). (I) *p. 1781*

variegatum (W. Indies); miniature, free-blooming epiphyte without pseudobulbs, leaves folded, and short but full sprays of small white or pink, crisped flowers, richly stained and blotched cinnamon-red, and a yellow center, (spring and various). (S) *p. 1781*

wentworthianum (Guatemala); robust epiphyte with 1-2-leaved pseudobulbs; heavy arching flower-stalks to 2 m or more long, with lateral clusters of small, long-lasting, lemon-yellow flowers boldly blotched with red-brown, (April-July). *Tropical.* *p. 1780*

ONCOSPERMA *Palmae* **S3LFM**

tigillarum (Malaya to Sumatra, Java and Philippines), "Nibong palm"; very ornamental forming extensive, many-stemmed clumps, the slender spiny trunks to 20 m or more, topped by crowns of graceful feathery fronds 6 m long, on spiny petioles, the leaflets acutely pendant; inflorescence bright yellow; dark purple fruit; grows primarily along the coast. *p. 1893*

ONOCLEA *Polypodiaceae (Filices)* **C2LFMh**

sensibilis (Newfoundland to Louisiana, Siberia, Japan), called "Sensitive fern" because the herbaceous barren fronds are sensitive to cold or if cut, and fold their leaflets face to face; handsome sterile fronds of glaucous pale green pinnae with undulate, lobed margins; underground creeping rhizome; hardy. *Temperate.* *p. 1112*

sensibilis var. obtusilobata (Pennsylvania); an abnormal form in which the leaflets of barren fronds become again pinnatifid and contracted. *p. 1157*

ONOSERIS *Compositae* **I-S2LBD**

isotypus (So. Mexico, Guatemala to Venezuela); showy tropical shrub 1-1½ m high, with yellow felted stem, long-petioled leaves broadly hastate 20-40 cm long, waxy-lobed and toothed, light green above, underside snow-white hairy; from the apex a wiry stalk bearing a loose cluster of slender red flowers. *p. 821*

ONOSMA *Boraginaceae* **C-I2LBD**

echioides (So. Europe, W. Asia); hairy, much branched sub-shrub to 30 cm high, with silvery-gray obovate or linear leaves, and nodding tubular pale yellow flowers. *p. 510*

giganteum (Israel, Syria, Turkey); hairy biennial with inflorescence spirally uncoiling, densely covered with light hairs; creamy-yellow tubular flowers. *p. 511*

ONYCHIUM *Polypodiaceae (Filices)* **C-I3HNM**

japonicum (Japan, China, Sikkim); short creeping rhizome bearing dainty, waxy green fronds, lacily divided into very small segments, the ultimate leaflets with sharply pointed lobes. *p. 1126*

OOPHYTUM *Aizoaceae* **I2LBD**

oviforme (Cape Prov.); tiny, clustering, pointed egg-shaped succulent 2 cm high, with small fissure on top, glossy deep green, slightly rough; small flowers white in center, pink toward the outside. *p. 77*

OPHIOGLOSSUM *Ophioglossaceae (Filices)* **S3HFM**

"bulgatum" (E. Australia), "Ribbon fern"; interesting epiphyte with long narrow grass-like bluish dark green pendulous fronds 60-90 cm long, hanging like ribbons from baskets or trees. *Humid-subtropic.* *p. 1080*

grande (Queensland), "Queensland ribbon-fern"; epiphytic fern with long, pendant, ribbon-like, narrow-linear fronds thin-leathery, deep green, spiralled and wavy, to 60 cm long. *p. 1080*

pendulum (Polynesia, Queensland, Philippines, Ceylon, Madagascar), a curious epiphytic "Ribbon fern"; with fleshy roots and ribbon-like pendulous, fleshy grass-green sterile fronds from 1 to 4 m long, sometimes forking; the small, slender fertile frond, to 15 cm long, rises from the middle of the barren blade. *Humid-tropical.* *p. 1080*

reticulata (Tropical Africa and America, Samoa), "Adder's tongue"; curious small species without tuberous root stock; the broad heart-shaped, concave sterile leaves 5-8 cm long, are attached about the middle of a slender stalk, while the narrow fertile fronds extend on upwards into a narrow flattened spike with 2 rows of sporangia. *p. 1124*

OPHIOPOGON *Liliaceae* ***I2-3LFM**

intermedius 'Argenteo-marginatus' (China); lovely tufted plant with leathery, narrow linear leaves 6 mm wide, deep green with pure white edging, and gracefully recurving; flowers white or lilac; mat-forming. *p. 1473*

jaburan (Japan), "White lily-turf"; evergreen sod-forming tufting perennial, with cord-like roots, long, grass-like but thick-leathery, dark green leaves, and pure white, drooping flowers on flattened stalk. *p. 1473*

jaburan 'Variegatus', "Variegated mondo grass"; attractive form which I have collected in Java, with long linear, symmetrically arranged leaves friendly milky-green, striped and edged in white; the drooping little, waxy-white flower bells on erect raceme. The species O. jaburan, or "White lily-turf" is from Japan, an evergreen clump-forming perennial with cord-like roots, and dark green, thick-leathery recurving leaves 30-60 cm long and 1 cm wide. *Subtropic.* *p. 1473*

japonicus (Japan, Korea), "Snake's beard"; low tufts of narrow linear, grass-like, but leathery, blackish-green leaves gracefully arching, with long underground stolons and the roots tuber-bearing; small, pale lilac flowers. *p. 1473*

japonicus 'Kyoto Dwarf' (Japan); "Snake's-beard"; lawn-forming stemless perennial with long underground stolons with tufted, recurving leaves only 4 cm high, dark-green; small pale lilac flowers. Seen planted at old Imperial Palace in Kyoto, dating from 780 A.D. *p. 1474*

japonicus 'Minor' (China, Japan), "Mondo grass"; a very dwarf, compact form dense with blackish-green, leathery leaves 5 to 8 cm long. *p.1474*

planiscapus nigrescens, in hort. as "arabicus" (So. Japan), the "Black dragon"; small grass-like clustering plant 10-15 cm or more high, with narrow-linear, leathery, curving leaves 4-6 mm wide, arranged in opposite ranks, at first bright green and glossy, later almost black; lavender flowers followed by black berries. Very attractive as a somber ground-cover. *Subtropic.* *p. 1473*

OPHIOPOGON: see also Liriope

OPHRYS *Orchidaceae* **I-C2HFM**

fusca (South Europe), "Bee orchid"; handsome terrestrial orchid to 30 cm tall, from rhizomatous tuber; with leaves at base and along the floral stalk; flowers 2 cm across, yellow-green and hairy, the lip covered with velvety brown hairs and two small, yellow-edged, mirror-like areas, in all resembling bees or flies. *Subtropic.* *p. 1771*

lutea minor (Greece: Delos); terrestrial rosette of dagger-shaped fleshy foliage, miniature, cupped, waxy flowers 15 mm dia., yellow with black eye; found growing amongst the ruins of the ancient temple of Apollo on Delos (Spring). *p. 1771*

muscifera (C. Europe, So. Europe), "Fly orchid"; terrestrial orchid to 50 cm high, the rhizome forming small tuber with short, clasping, almost linear leaves, and erect stalk bearing scattered flowers resembling a fly; with green sepals, linear red petals, and 4-lobed lip with pale blue spot in middle; without spur. *p. 1787*

speculum (So. Europe, to Greece), "Mirror of Venus"; miniature terrestrial 10-25 cm high, with tuberous rhizome producing a leafy stalk with remarkable 3 cm flowers, sepals pale green outside and light brown within, the shorter petals violet-brown, brown fringed lip with disk a steel-blue glassy mirror edged in gold and margined maroon. (spring). *p. 1771*

OPHTHALMOPHYLLUM *Aizoaceae* **I-S2LBD**

lydiae (Cape Prov.); succulent with small obconical body 2½ cm high, compressed at sides and cleft on top, olive-green, covered with tiny puckers, top translucent; flowers white with pink petal tips. *p. 74*

schlechteri (Cape Prov.); stemless dwarf succulent with cylindric body 1 cm high and cleft at top, matte-green to reddish, all over set with tiny pale dots; flowers white. *p. 74*

verrucosum (Cape Prov.); attractive, cylindric soft-fleshy bodies 3 cm high split toward top and with flattened apex, red-brown, points of lobes warty and with many translucent dots; flowers shimmering white. *p. 74*

OPITHANDRA *Gesneriaceae* **C2HFD**

primuloides (Japan); evergreen rosette with broad rounded or pointed dark green leaves to 6 cm long, pale hairy and coarsely toothed, on long, hairy petioles; lilac flowers with curved white tube and spreading lobes. *p. 1242*

OPLISMENUS *Gramineae* **I-S2-3LF-BM**

hirtellus 'Variegatus' (Panicum variegatum) (W. Indies), "Basket grass"; weak, creeping grass, rooting at nodes, with flowering culms generally erect; the rather broad, lanceolate, thin leaves daintily striped white and pink, 4-6 cm long. *Tropical.* *p. 1310*

OPLOPANAX *Araliaceae* **C2LBMh**

horridus (Alaska to California), "Devil's-club"; deciduous shrub to 4 m high, with alternate rounded, palmately lobed, bright green leaves to 25 cm across, toothed margins, and prickly on both sides; greenish white flowers in terminal clusters, and fleshy scarlet fruit. *p. 316*

x OPSISANDA *Orchidaceae* **S3OFW**

'May Kawanashi' (Vandopsis lissochiloides x Vanda 'Tatzeri') ; large bigeneric hybrid of Hawaii; dense raceme of lacquered flowers painted coppery red and with darker spots, the small lip cream inside. *p. 1776*

OPUNTIA *Cactaceae* ***I-S1-2LBD**

aciculata (Texas); spreading pad-cactus to 1 m; the lower branches reclining; obovate flat joints to 20 cm long, dark green or glaucous, with large, closely-set areoles with several slender spines and numerous golden-brown glochid tufts; 10 cm deep yellow flowers, and pear-shaped, purple fruit. *p. 632*

alcahes (Baja California); branched bush with warty, cylindric stems to 5 cm thick, very pale green, dense with long spines covered with white sheaths; flower yellowish-green with brown outside. *p. 626*

basilaris (S.W. United States, Mexico), "Beaver tail"; growing in clumps, broadly obovate fleshy pads a bluish coppery color, almost spineless; large purple flowers 5 to 8 cm across, variable to rose or yellow. *p. 622, 631*

bigelovii, a typical "Cholla cactus"; characteristic of the stony deserts from New Mexico to Southern California; erect trunks to 1 m high with short light green branches to 5 cm thick, densely set with glistening cream spines; purple flowers 4 cm across, and yellow fruit. *Arid-subtropic.* *p. 629*

brasiliensis (Brazil, Argentina, Bolivia), "Tropical tree-opuntia"; tree-like, to 4 m high; trunk and branches cylindrical, the terminal joints flat and leaf-like, glossy fresh green, with few spines; pale yellow flowers. A good and attractive house plant because of its tropical origin, resembling a miniature tree even as a young plant. *Subtropic.* *p. 622*

'Burbank's Spineless': see ficus-indica

caribaea (Santo Domingo, Venezuela); densely branched plant with slender tubercled joints 1 cm thick and long stiff spines; yellow flowers and red fruit. *p. 627*

chlorotica (Sonora, California, Nevada, New Mexico), "Flapjack cactus"; tall branching bush to 2½ m high, with large flat pads almost round 12-30 cm long, light bluish green, very spiny with long white or brownish needle spines and yellow glochids; yellow flowers 7 cm across, and pear-shaped yellow fruit. *p. 633*

clavarioides (Austrocylindropuntia) (Chile), "Sea coral"; a very interesting and curious plant known because of its shape and color as "Black fingers", "Nigger hand", or "Fairy castles"; low straggling plant with cylindrical grayish-brown joints but usually growing fan-shaped or in other fasciated forms, covered with short white, hair-like spines; rarely flowering, pale greenish-brown. *Arid-subtropic.* *p. 621, 623*

compressa (humifusa) (Ontario, Mass. to Alabama, Missouri); low and spreading succulent with grass-green pads, almost smooth, oblong to 12 cm long, with few spines; yellow flowers 5-8 cm across. *Temperate.* *p. 633*

cylindrica (Ecuador, Perú), "Emerald idol"; branching plant to 4 m; succulent cylindrical dark green joints regularly notched, deciduous short leaves, short white spines often wanting; flowers scarlet. *p. 622, 624, 628*

cylindrica cristata; curious crested form with the normal dark green cylindric stems contorted and coiled and fused together with a snake-like crest along apex. *p. 634*

dillenii (S.E. U.S., W. Indies, N.E. Venezuela), "Tuna"; either low spreading, or tall branched, the long fleshy, flat joints bright green when young, glaucous bluish later, and heavy orange-yellow spines; flowers yellow and edible red fruit. *Subtropic.* *p. 630, 631*

elata (Brazil, Paraguay), "Orange tuna"; erect bush to 1 m with fat obovate, waxy-smooth pads rich green with brown purple blotches around areole; occasional straw-colored to gray needle spines; 5 cm flowers orange-yellow. *Subtropic.* *p. 631*

elata elongata (Paraguay), "Green wax cactus"; very attractive with more elongate, smooth, fat but flattened joints, 20 cm or more long, nearly spineless, rich nile green to dark olive, and purplish brown below each areole, and with satiny, waxy surface; pretty flowers with 2 layers of petals rich orange. *Subtropic.* *p. 616, 625, 640A*

elatior (Panama to Venezuela); tree-like, to 4 m high, with long-oval or obovate fleshy joints 10-40 cm long, rather thin, glossy green, with occasional long straw-colored spines; the ovaries more slender and longer than vulgaris; numerous flowers sprouting prolifically, reddish outside, whitish inside; pear-shaped red fruit. *p. 630*

engelmannii (Texas, Ariz., Mexico); wide-spreading bush with pale green joints to 30 cm almost round, thick 5 cm spines white with reddish base; large yellow flowers. *p. 631*

erectoclada (Argentina), "Dominoes"; small clusters of trapeziform flat pads to 5 cm long, covered with sharp brown spines, the ventral edge of young pads always facing parent; flowers yellow. *p. 626*

erinacea (Calif., Ariz., Utah, Nev.), "Bear-cactus"; low clump with oblong, thick, flattened joints covered with spines to 5 cm long, white or white tipped brown; flowers pink or yellow. *p. 622*

erinacea ursina (California), the famous "Grizzly bear" of hidden reaches of the Mohave desert; forms low clumps with oblong, thick, grayish green flattened joints 10 to 15 cm long, densely covered with glistening white, thread-like spines usually 10 to 15 cm long, and I have seen them in the Mohave as long as 25 cm. Flowers may be red or yellow. *p. 623, 626, 633*

exaltata (Ecuador, Perú, Bolivia); branching, 2-4 m high, with stems or joints cylindrical, grayish green and with brownish needle-spines; large reddish flowers; similar to subulata. *p. 634*

falcata (Consolea) (Haiti), a "Tree opuntia"; tree-like, with stout, straight, spiny brown trunk when older, and a heavy crown of thick-fleshy, oblong flat joints sickle-shaped, 20-30 cm long and 8 cm wide, glossy rich green, with raised knobs especially on margins, nearly spineless; flowers red turning orange. *p. 623, 632*

ficus-indica (Trop. America: prob. Mexico), the "Indian fig"; a flat jointed cactus that may grow bushy, or with woody stems to 3 m or more high; widely spread into warm-climate countries and cultivated for its pear-shaped juicy, orange-red fruit 6-8 cm long, which is peeled and the pulp eaten raw or cooked for its flavor and food value, from Mexico to Spain and Southern Italy and Eastward. The oblongish flat joints are green or glaucous bluish from 30 cm to almost 60 cm long, in some forms spineless but with irritating yellow bristles; the flowers are yellow to 10 cm across. These are monstrous plants, but durable with sculptured and exotic decorative effect. *Arid-tropical.* *p. 633*

ficus-indica 'Burbank's Spineless', "Spineless Indian fig"; a lightly glaucous bluish-green, tree-like form to 4 m, with long flattened joints almost 60 cm long, with yellow flowers and edible orange fruits. A cultivar selected by Luther Burbank for its almost total absence of spines. *Arid-subtropic.* *p. 19*, 621, 625*

fragilis (Wisconsin to Brit. Columbia and south to Texas and Arizona), "Pigmy tuna"; low spreading plant not over 5 cm high, with fresh green, roundish or cylindrical joints very fragile, dropping off easily; small white areoles and brownish spines; pale yellow flowers. Also found as far north as Cache Creek, Alberta. *Temperate.* *p. 627*

fulgida mamillata 'Monstrosa' (mamillata in hort.) (Arizona, Mexico), "Boxing glove"; succulent knobby joints to 5 cm thick growing irregular and forming monstrose crests toward tips; sharp yellowish spines; flowers pink. *Arid-subtropic.* *p. 622, 624, 634*

galapageia (Galápagos Islands); a jointed succulent becoming tree-like with stems 45 cm thick and 2 m long; the elongate pads dark green to bluish green, to 40 cm long, covered with golden brownish needle spines; small 2½ cm yellow flowers and small fruit. Photographed at Marnier-Lapostolle in France. *p. 634*

gosseliniana (Sonora, Baja California); the "Flapjack cactus"; very attractive with round, smooth, glaucous pads to 20 cm often purplish along margin, and with prominent tufts of yellow glochids; flowers yellow and fruit red. *p. 626*

hamiltoniae: see Grusonia

imbricata (arborescens); (Colorado to Mexico), "Chain-link cactus"; tree-like to 3 m; slender, woody joints 8 to 20 cm long, strongly tubercled, small deciduous leaves, stiff brown spines, sheathed; flowers purple. *p. 622*

leptocaulis (frutescens) (S.W. United States, Mexico), "Tesajo"; brushlike, to 2 m, pencil-thin branched joints, dull green and woody, slender spines and small deciduous leaves; flowers yellowish 1 to 2 cm across. *Arid-subtropic.* *p. 622, 628*

leucotricha (Mexico), "White-hair-tree-cactus"; tree-like and branching, to 4 m, the flat oblong joints pubescent and covered with long white bristles; flowers yellow. *p. 628, 631*

linguiformis (So. Texas); bushy freely-branching cactus, to 1 m, with flat joints elongated, to 50 cm long, broad at base, tapering upward, rich green; brown areoles with yellow glochids and 2-4 slender yellow spines; yellow flowers, and purplish fruit. *Arid-subtropic.* *p. 632*

linguiformis 'Maverick', "Maverick cactus"; very attractive California mutation, a flat joint forming monstrose branches, the fleshy pad rich green, with multitudes of bulb-like and finger-like growths sticking out from the areoles, and tipped by beige bristles and glochids; resembling a miniature pyramidal tree. *Arid-subtropic.* *p. 632*

littoralis (So. California coast), a "Prickly pear"; with rounded or oblong fresh-green pads to 15 cm long, covered by numerous long white to yellow spines; large 12 cm golden yellow flowers, and red, juicy fruit. *p. 629*

macrarthra (U.S.: So. Carolina); low spreading cactus with prostrate branches with dull light green, oblong pads 10-25 cm long, brownish areoles distant, with pale brown glochids; nearly spineless, the few thick spines straw-colored zoned with red; pear-shaped red fruit. *p. 630*

macrocentra (Mexico; Texas, Arizona); branching pad-cactus with oblong or rounded joints 10-20 cm dia., often bluish or purplish; the areoles grayish with brown glochids, and 1-2 spines nearly black at base; yellow flower, and purple fruit. The plant shown in Exotica 3 may be O. azurea. *p. 630*

mamillata in hort.—see fulgida mamillata 'Monstrosa'

microdasys (No. Mexico); called "Bunny ears" because of the young pads appearing ear-like at the apex of the older ones; plant low with rounded and flat, fleshy joints satiny green and set with neat rows of yellow to light brown tufts of barbed bristles which rub off easily and are painful to the skin; flowers yellow. *p. 19*, 626, 628*

microdasys 'Albata', "Angelwings" or "Angora bunny-ears"; freely clustering baby opuntia with miniature pads or "wings", and covered with snow-white hair-like glochids. *Arid-subtropic.* *p. 626*

microdasys 'Albispina' (albescens), "Polka dots"; vigorous normal large type succulent pads with areoles having soft white glochids (tufted barbed hairs) prominently arranged in neat rows; flowers pale yellow, 3-5 cm across. *Arid-subtropic.* *p. 626*

microdasys 'Aurispina'; sport of albispina with neat satiny green pads densely covered with golden-yellow glochids; in the California nursery trade grown for planting in dishgardens. *p. 633*

microdasys 'Lutea', "Honey mike"; a horticultural form with pale honey-colored, soft hair tufts which are safer to the touch than microdasys. *p. 626*

monacantha: see vulgaris

orbiculata (crinifera) (New Mexico); spreading or arborescent to 2 m or more, stem-forming, with flat, nearly round pads to 15 cm or more dia., pale bluish-green with grayish areoles and long straw-colored needle spines; large yellow flowers reddish at base; base of plant with white wool. *p. 634*

pachypus (Tephrocactus) (Perú); candelabralike plant to 1 m, cylindric branches marked with spiralled tubercles and tiny deciduous leaves, awlshaped yellow spines; inconspicuous scarlet flowers. *p. 620, 624*

platyacantha deflexispina (S. Chile, Patagonia); low, spreading plant, with prostrate branches, the joint spherical or oval 2½-6 cm long, olive green or brownish, almost smooth or with low warts; large yellowish areoles; 5-7 spines, the lower ones whitish, flat and papery; all spines reflexed in this variety; yellow flowers. *p. 628*

puberula 'Cristata'; a crested form of the Mexican species, normally with broadly oval joints 7-12 cm long, yellowish-green and covered with velvety pubescence, and with prominent tufts of yellow glochids; few if any yellow spines; greenish-yellow flowers 4 cm across. *p. 634*

quimilo (No. Argentina); much branched spreading pad-cactus to 5 m high, with obovate, flat fleshy joints to 50 cm long and 25 cm wide, smooth, grayish green or glaucous; long white spines to 15 cm long; red flowers, and greenish yellow fruit. *p. 628*

rafinesquei (New Mexico, Missouri, Kansas, Tennessee); low, prostrate cactus with flat oval; elongated joints, 8-12 cm long; areoles distant, with brown glochids, a few spines only at the margins, white tipped dark; numerous flowers sulphur-yellow with red base. Possibly Op. compressa (Gleason). *p. 628*

ramosissima (Cylindropuntia) (Southwestern U.S.; Mexico, Sonora, B. Calif.), a "Pencil cactus"; photographed in the Mohave Desert, California; growing into a densely branched bush of slender, cylindric, rigid, angled stems 2 to 4 cm thick, bluish green to gray, and with long reddish spines; flowers greenish-yellow, 4 cm across. *Arid-subtropic.* *p. 634*

rufida (microdasys rufida) (Texas, No. Mexico), "Cinnamon-cactus"; bushy plant to 2 m high, eventually forming trunk; fleshy pads velvety grayish-green covered with tufts of short brown bristles (glochids), which rub off easily and cause itching under the skin; 5 cm yellow flowers. Will rot if too wet. *Arid-subtropic.* *p. 622, 626*

salmiana (So. Brazil to No. Argentina); much branched plant some 1 m high, with long cylindric, smooth branches 1 cm thick, deep glaucous green, and with small yellowish spines; flowers yellowish, the fruit deep red. *p. 629*

santa-rita (violacea var.) (Arizona, Texas), "Blue blade" or "Dollar cactus"; thick bush to 1½ m high, with round joints to 20 cm long, often broader than long, bluish green marked with purple; glochids brown and occasional brown spines; deep yellow flowers. *p. 625, 629*

schickendantzii (N. Argentina), "Lion's tongue"; shrub-like and much branched, elongate, warted, flattened, rather thin and narrow joints to 20 cm long, fresh green with reddish spines; yellow flowers 4 to 5 cm across. *Arid-subtropic.* *p. 622, 631, 632*

stenopetala (C. Mexico); bushy, semi-prostrate plant with obovate joints 10-20 cm long, first reddish passing to grayish, with brown areoles and red-brown spines; flowers orange red, 4 cm broad; scarlet ovoid fruit. *p. 633*

streptacantha (Mexico), "Tuna cardona"; economically important in Mexican markets because of the sweet pulp of its red fruit used for sweets and alcoholic drink; tree to 5 m with dark green flat joints to 30 cm long; flowers yellow. *p. 626*

stricta (inermis) (Cuba, Florida to S. Texas); naturalized in Chile, So. France and W. Australia; spreading semi-prostrate bush with obovate, flattened joints to 15 cm long, green or grayish green, with few spines; flowers yellow, and red pear-shaped fruit. *Arid-subtropic.* *p. 629*

strobiliformis (Tephrocactus) (Argentina), "Spruce cones"; branching succulent with blue-gray, oval or conical joints with prominent tubercles appearing on circular folds and resembling a pine cone; flowers yellow. *p. 624*

subulata (Chile, Argentina), "Eve's-pin cactus"; tree-like and branching, to 4 m, smooth cylindrical, bright green, with persistent, long fleshy needle-like leaves, spines few; flowers orange or greenish yellow. *p. 624, 627*

subulata cristata; mutation with some of the green branches forming fan-like crests at ends, the fleshy needle-like leaves crowded. *p. 628*

tesajo (Baja California); low straggling bush with slender pencil-like joints to 8 cm long and 6 mm thick, light glaucous green, almost smooth; white areoles with brown glochids; a grayish needle spine, 2 brown radials; sulphur-yellow flowers tipped red. *p. 628*

tetracantha (So. Arizona); low branched bush to 1½ m, slender cylindrical, purplish-green joints with elongate knobs, deciduous leaves and needle-spines; flowers greenish purple. *p. 622*

tomentosa (velutina) (Mexico), "Velvet opuntia"; tree-like, to 4 m; very thick-fleshy long joints velvety green, with few pale spines; flowers yellow; velvety carmine-red fruit along apex. *p. 625, 631*

traceyi (Mississippi, Georgia, Florida); much branched plant to 20 cm high with flat oblong, pale green joints, nearly cylindrical when young, set with long gray needle spines; pure yellow flowers. *p. 627*

tuna (West Indies to Jamaica); growing to 1 m high, with light green flat joints rounded to obovate and 15 cm long, brownish around the areoles, and pale yellow spines; flowers yellow tinged with red, and red fruit. *p. 627*

tunicata (C. Mexico as well as Ecuador to Chile); a beautiful and sun-loving species to 60 cm high, branched in whorls, tuberculate joints globular or oblong cylindric, glaucous green, entirely covered with white-sheathed vicious barbed spines; flowers yellow. *p. 627, 630*

turpinii (glomerata) (Tephrocactus) (Argentina), "Paperspine cactus"; low spreading clumps, joints globular or ovoid, smooth, dull grayish brown, curious long spines flat and papery; flowers cream-colored. *p. 624, 627*

verschaffeltii (Northern Bolivia); clustering plant with cylindrical stems branching with little fingers of tubercled joints, light dull-green, the knobs supporting small fleshy, deciduous leaves, slightly woolly areoles and occasional straw-colored needle-spines; deep red or orange flowers very beautiful. *Arid-subtropic.* *p. 624, 630*

vestita (teres) (Tephrocactus) (Bolivia), "Cotton pole"; clump-forming with erect branched stem, cylindrical joints, fragile, covered with long white hairs, and small deciduous leaves; deep red flowers. *p. 624, 629*

vestita cristata; mutation with joints contorted into fan-like crests, dense with white hairs. *p. 630*

vilis (Mexico), "Little tree-cactus"; branching plant with short cylindrical joints, pale green and covered with whitish sharp spines; brilliant purple flower. *p. 622, 627*

vulgaris (monacantha) (So. Brazil to Argentina), "Irish mittens"; treelike to 2½ m, flattened fleshy, glossy green joints almost spineless; flowers yellow; the unripened fruit will root and grow forming little ears, and offered as "Eared buds". *Subtropic.* *p. 618, 622, 630, 631*

vulgaris 'Variegata', "Joseph's coat"; variegated form with the long smooth joints beautifully patterned green and white; large yellow flowers 8 cm across. *Subtropic.* *p. 623, 631, 632*

OPUNTIA: see also Nopalea, Grusonia

ORBIGNYA *Palmae* **S3LFM**

cohune (Attalea), (Mexico to Costa Rica), "Cohune palm"; large feather palm with trunk 6 m long and to 60 cm thick, the characteristically erect pinnate fronds to 9 m long, with glossy-green stalk and folded, leathery leaflets; abundant egg-shaped brown fruit to 8 cm long, in large clusters with nuts furnishing cohune oil. *Tropical.* *p. 1890*

ORCHIDANTHA *Musaceae* ***S1HFM**

maxillarioides (Malaya), "Orchid flower"; perennial herb with tufted foliage of the feel of aspidistra and with flowers resembling orchids; lanceolate leathery leaves on wiry petiole, light moss-green with some mottling, depressed midrib; flowers with violet calyx and green lip variegated purple. *Tropical.* *p. 1588, 1598*

meleagris (Lowia) (Malaya); a handsome tropical foliage plant; dense, tufted growth of long-petioled pointed-elliptic leaves, the largest with an 18 cm petiole and blade 20 cm long; plant resembles a dwarf Aspidistra, but the texture of the leaves is less leathery, and bright green; the waxy flowers greenish-white and purple. *p. 1598*

ORCHIS *Orchidaceae* **C-I2HFM**

elata (Algeria); terrestrial with green leaves, and inflorescence stalks sometimes more than 60 cm long, bearing a dense cylindrical spike of violet-purple flowers. *p. 1787*

militaris (Europe); tuberous terrestrial at home in moist meadows, with broad lanceolate leaves, and 30-60 cm stem with spike of many flowers, sepals purple, together with petals forming a helmet, the pale rose, 4-lobed lip spotted purple; spring. *p. 1787*

papilionacea (Portugal, Algeria, Greece, Turkey); "Pink butterfly orchid"; tuberous terrestrial forming a rosette of broad, dark green fleshy leaves 8-10 cm long, from the center a spike with pale purple flowers 3 cm long, the lip veined with crimson, the petals forming a hood; photographed amongst ancient ruins on Rhodes, Greece. *Subtropic.* *p. 1771*

sambucina (C. and So. Europe); tuberous terrestrial with herbaceous, leafy stem to 22 cm high, leaves linear blotched with purple; spike compact with 2 cm cream-colored flowers, the lip bright yellow with red hairs on disc (spring). *p. 1771*

spectabilis (New Brunswick to Georgia and Missouri), the "Showy woodland orchis"; hardy terrestrial with tuberous roots, with two obovate, shining leaves and 4-angled spike to 30 cm high, with 2-7 flowers 2½ cm long, sepals and petals purple and united in a hood, ovate white lip (May-June). *p. 1787*

ORECTANTHE *Xyridaceae* **S3LBM**

sceptrum (Venezuela); stiff rosette on short stem, with numerous dagger-shaped leaves 10-30 cm long, 2 to 4½ cm wide, glaucous with red-brown margins; long-stalked inflorescence 30-120 cm high, with terminal head of yellow flowers becoming reddish brown, and subtended by lanceolate bracts. *p. 2127*

OREOCEREUS (BORZICACTUS in Hortus 3) *Cactaceae* **I-C2LBD**

celsianus (Andes of Bolivia, Perú, Chile), "Old man of the Andes"; growing in clumps, creeping when young, later upright to 1 m, areoles with long white hairs and long thin red spines; dark red flowers 10 cm long. *Subtropic.* *p. 649*

doelzianus (Andes of Perú); beautiful clustering mountain species with club-shaped stems to 1 m high, olive green to grayish green with 9-10 ribs, the areoles with silky hairs and reddish needle spines; the red flowers rise from a tuft of grayish wool at apex. *p. 649*

fossulatus (Andes of Bolivia and Perú), a "Mountain cereus" of medium height, branching from the base; the grass green columns with 8-14 ribs, the areoles with fawn tufts of wool as well as long silky-white hair, the straight spines straw-colored; flowers red. *p. 649*

fossulatus rubispinus; column clothed in silky white hair like the type but the straight needle spines are deep red-brown. *p. 649*

maximus (So. Bolivia); stout column, becoming 3 m high; light green with 8 shallow ribs, colorful spines, and entirely covered with snow-white hair; the areoles clothed with tufts of light brown wool. *p. 649*

ritteri (hendriksenianus var. densilanatus, Backeberg) (So. Perú); beautiful, snowy column to 10cm dia., forming colonies, to 1m high; green body, with 10 ribs, hidden by long silky, silvery hairs; short yellowish needle spines; red flowers 7cm long. *p. 649, 656*

trollii (Bolivia, Perú); columns to 12 cm thick, branching from base, light green, 10-25 ribs becoming indistinct with age, covered with long, cream-colored silky hairs, and reddish needle spines; flowers rose. *p. 649*

OREODOXA: see Roystonea

OREOPANAX *Araliaceae* **I2LBD**

capitatus, also known as nymphaeifolius (Mexico, C. America, West Indies); small evergreen tree having glossy-green, broad ovate, leathery leaves very variable, juvenile stage having peltate base, adult obtuse or cordate, on slender stalks. *Subtropic.* *p. 306, 314, 318*

dactylifolius (Mexico); slender erect evergreen shrub 4 to 6 m or more high; thick leathery leaves 25-45 cm across, cut into 5-7 lobes, dark glossy green, beneath brown-felted as are the branches; the inflorescence in elongate racemes with minute flowers. Attractive with the young growth covered by golden brown felt. *p. 314*

peltatus (salvinii) (Mexico), "Mountain aralia"; evergreen tree with thin-leathery, palmately lobed leaves, the lobes fresh green with pale veins and toothed or lobed again; rough beneath; stalks with loose hairs. *p. 306*

platanifolius (Aralia); (Andes of Perú); tree-like evergreen with cane-like stem, bearing near apex a rosette-like cluster of glossy-green, leathery leaves, brownish-hairy beneath, cut into 3 to 7 pointed lobes on long, thin-wiry petioles; the small white flowers hairy outside, in clusters. *p. 314*

sanderianus (Guatemala); evergreen tree dense with variable leaves, ovate when young, 3-lobed when older, glossy green; on flowering branches heart-shaped; small primitive flowers in globose heads. *p. 314*

xalapensis (Mexico, C. America); evergreen shrub with palmately compound, thin-leathery leaves, the segments obovate, light green and corrugated, serrate, on brown petioles. *Tropical.* *p. 306*

ORIGANUM *Labiatae* **I2LBD**

dictamnus (Greece), "Crete dittany" or "Hop marjoram"; tender perennial to 30 cm; small woolly gray round leaves on trailing stems; rosy blooms with large bracts in hop-like heads. Use: aromatic and tonic, flowers for tea, medicinal for toothache. *p. 1348*

pulchellum (S. E. Europe, Asia Minor), the "Showy marjoram"; small subshrub with woody base 30 to 50 cm high, with gray hairy, ascending stems; small opposite ovate, sessile leaves; toward tips the showy rose-pink flowers, in nodding head-like spikes; both a decorative blooming plant, and also economic uses in seasonings, such as for pizza and other Italian dishes. *p. 1358*

ORNITHIDIUM: see Maxillaria

ORNITHOCEPHALUS *Orchidaceae* **I3ONM**

bicornis (Panama), "Mealybug orchid"; miniature epiphyte 5-6 cm high with bright green leaves spreading and overlapping fan-like; small greenish flowers with white petals and waxy greenish lip (winter and various). *p. 1788*

cochleariformis (Panama); remarkable epiphyte, with a short, stiff-fleshy leaf on short pseudobulbs, arranged as in a fan; short racemes of small flowers, sepals and petals translucent white, lip deep green with white tip, (Feb.-March). (I) *p. 1788*

dolabratus (Ecuador); small epiphyte, with pseudobulbs usually growing more or less downward; the fleshy, sickle-shaped leaves arranged in an open fan; comparatively large fragrant, clear white flowers, with pointed lip, along an ascending raceme rising from the axils of the leaves; September. *p. 1787*

grandiflorus (Brazil); epiphyte with small pseudobulbs sheathed by broad 15 cm fleshy leaves; arching inflorescence with clusters of waxy white, cupped 2 cm flowers; roundish, crisped lip green inside, outlined in darker green (summer). *p. 1776*

inflexus (tonduzii) (Mexico to Honduras and Panama), "Bird's head orchid"; floriferous small epiphyte with green leaves sickle-shaped and arranged as in a fan, to 10 cm long; inflorescence arching, dense with small 1 cm flowers whitish green, and lip with darker green; known as "Bird's head" because of the unique shape of the tiny blossoms (winter). *p. 1776*

ORNITHOCHILUS *Orchidaceae* **S3OFM**

fuscus (Burma, Nepal, So. China); attractive small epiphyte with short stem, leathery leaves 8-22 cm long, and pendulous raceme of 1 cm flowers, sepals and petals yellow streaked with red, petals linear, the spurred lip with a dark red fringed, lobed lip; May-August. (S) *p. 1788*

ORNITHOGALUM *Liliaceae* **I-C2LBDd**

arabicum (Mediterranean), "Star of Bethlehem"; bulbous plant with pale green, linear, thick basal leaves 30-45 cm long and 2½ cm wide; stalk 30-60 cm high with a cluster of 2½ cm fragrant, white flowers, with black pistil; in summer. *p. 1476*

caudatum (So. Africa), "False sea-onion"; an old-fashioned window-sill plant, with ovate, green bulb to over 10 cm thick, usually showing above the soil, 5-6 basal strap leaves and a stalked raceme 45-90 cm long with 50-100 small white flowers with petals having a green median stripe. The filament is wide at base (narrow in Urginea); the narrow channeled leaves 4 cm wide, and form a tube at base. Also known as "Healing onion", or "Meerzwiebel", crushed leaves are tied over cuts and bruises; also used as cooked syrup with rock-candy, against colds. *Subtropic.* *p. 1476*

nutans (Europe, S. W. Asia); bulbous plant to 60 cm, with flaccid, strap-shaped basal leaves 1 cm wide; 2½ cm flowers white inside, green with white margins outside. *p. 1475*

saundersiae (So. Africa), the "Giant chincherinchee"; tall-growing 1-2 m high; broad, sword-shaped basal leaves to 60 cm long; 2½ cm flowers grouped in a flat-topped cluster on long erect stalk, each bloom with 6 spreading, creamy petals and prominent black center. *Subtropic. p. 1476*

splendens (Cape Prov.); showy bulbous plant to 40 cm; glaucous sword-shaped basal leaves; clusters of cup-shaped 2½ cm flowers satiny vermilion. *p. 1475*

stapfii (Namibia); small bulbous herb with strap-shaped leaves, and compact raceme of starry yellowish green flowers. *p. 1475*

thyrsoides (So. Africa), "Chincherinchee" or "Wonder flower"; spring blooming, tender bulb with fleshy lanceolate leaves and strong 60 cm racemes with numerous long-lasting flowers with segments spreading 3 cm across, white with buff eye. *Subtropic. p. 1475, 1476, 1477*

umbellatum (Mediterranean), "Summer snowflake"; small spring-blooming bulb with grass-like leaves and 15 cm stems with clusters of numerous star-like flowers satiny-white inside, green striped white outside. *Subtropic. p. 1477*

ORNITHOPHORA *Orchidaceae* **S3OFM**

radicans (Stigmatostalix) (Mexico, Guatemala, Brazil); miniature epiphyte not over 10 cm with pearshaped, ribbed pseudobulbs on creeping rhizome, and straplike leaves; inflorescence in arching raceme of tiny greenish-white flowers with reflexed segments, contrasting dark brown column, and broad lip with mauve margins and spotted purple, lobed in back, (Sept.). *p. 1776, 1788*

OROBANCHE *Orobanchaceae* **C-I2HsphagBM**

uniflora (No. America); parasitic herb attached by suckers to the roots of such as Aster, Sedum, Solidago etc., and growing up alongside the stems of their host; annual with yellowish scales and spikes with white to violet trumpet flowers 2 cm long. *p. 1842*

ORONTIUM *Araceae* **C2HFWh**

aquaticum (Atlantic No. America), "Golden club"; aquatic perennial growing in ponds or along streams, with fleshy rootstocks and leaf-stalks 25-50 cm long, the parallel-veined, oblong, dark green leaves floating or ascending, 15-30 cm long; long bright yellow, club-like spadix, and small inconspicuous spathe, on white 60 cm stalks. *Warm temperate. p. 222*

OROSTACHYS *Crassulaceae* **C2LBD**

chanetii (Sedum) (China: Kansu); small clustering rosette 3 cm diameter, of light green somewhat glaucous, fleshy oblanceolate leaves, the brownish apex tipped by a soft, translucent bristle; flowers white, outside red. *p. 916*

iwarenge (Japan): found growing on roofs along the Inland Sea; starting as a flat rosette 4 to 18 cm across, and forming suckers from base, soon extending upward like a pyramid, with densely shingled, waxy glaucous leaves becoming smaller, and ending in a spire-like spike to 40 cm tall, with white flowers subtended by pointed bracts. *p. 913*

iwarenge fa. 'Fuji'; variegated cultivar from Japan; beautiful succulent rosette 12-15 cm across; persistent through winter; obovate leaves milky green with broad cream bands along sides; later pushing up a tall spike to 35 cm high with small white flowers. *Warm temperate. p. 913*

malacophyllus (E. Siberia to So. Korea and Japan); winter-hardy succulent rosette forming suckers; flat, obovate, fresh green or glaucous leaves 1 to 10 cm long; from the center a spire 10-35 cm tall, dense with white flowers, showing prominent white stamens. *p. 913*

spinosus (Siberia, Manchuria, Mongolia, Tibet); hardy, clustering succulent gray-green rosette similar to sempervivum; dense with shingled obovate wedge-shaped leaves with a soft white spiny tip; cylindric inflorescence 30 cm high, with star-shaped yellow flowers. *p. 876*

OROTHAMNUS *Proteaceae* **I2LBM**

zeyheri (So. Africa: Hottentots Holland Mts.); evergreen erect shrub 2-3 m high, densely clothed with overlapping concave, dark green, leathery, triangular 3-5 cm leaves edged with soft white hairs; 2½-6cm terminal, nodding flower heads, with waxy petal-like green to rosy bracts shaggy outside, and lemon-yellow perianth segments. *p. 1970*

OROYA *Cactaceae* **I2LBD**

peruviana (neoperuviana) (C. Perú); attractive small globe to 15 cm dia., from the Andes at 3,800 m; depressed on top, dark green, with 12-23 low rounded ribs, slightly notched into tubercles, these with yellowish areoles, and 2-5 brown central spines if present; pale pink flowers yellow at base, and red at tip; reddish fruit. *p. 702*

ORPHIUM *Gentianaceae* **I2LBD**

frutescens (So. Africa), "Sticky flower"; shrubby perennial to 60 cm, with narrow-linear, leathery, light green leaves, and showy, shining rosy, star-like flowers 4 cm dia. *Subtropic. p. 1170*

ORTHOPHYTUM *Bromeliaceae* **S2HFD**

foliosum (Brazil); growing on rocks in Espirito Santo; large succulent species with reddish-green leaves 50-60 cm long, 4-5 cm wide, dull green, underneath gray-scaly in ribs, the margins with brown spines; the inflorescence on elongate leafy stems, with green triangular bracts and white flowers. *p. 574*

fosterianum (Brazil); named after Mulford Foster, who discovered this species in Espirito Santo at 750 m elevation; curious succulent with short, fleshy, fresh-green leaves spiny at margins; the inflorescence on a leafy stalk and arching, to 50 cm long, carrying both the white flowers and young-forming plantlets toward apex. *p. 574*

maracasense (Brazil: Bahia); star-like rosette with thick-fleshy tapering leaves 30 cm long, coppery to amethyst red, edged with prominent reversed spines, green tipped brown, the reverse pencil-grooved and thickly covered by mealy scales; erect inflorescence with spreading bracts and white flowers. *Tropical. p. 513, 575*

navioides (Brazil: Bahia); dense rosette with narrow glossy-green flexible 30 cm leaves tinged copper, edged with small sharp spines, glossy beneath; leaves flattening back at flowering time to bare inflorescence sunk in center; the foliage turns brilliant red at blooming season; flowers white in tight cluster of petals. *p. 575*

rubrum (Brazil: Bahia); relatively large, loose rosette of spreading narrow, concave flexible, recurving leaves to 60 cm long, light green with red edges and spines, reverse with pale, faint lines; inflorescence a long stalk with spreading red spikes and white flowers. *p. 574, 575*

saxicola (Brazil); xerophytic, rock-dwelling rosette, dense with concave, soft-leathery 30 cm coppery green leaves lightly covered with silvery scales, more so underneath; margins set with hook-spines; stalked, bracted bronzy inflorescence, and with white sepals. *p. 575*

vagans (Brazil: Espirito Santo); semi-succulent trailing plant rambling over rocks forming large mats; rosettes of narrow metallic-green, thorny leaves, toward apex these becoming floral bracts brilliantly colored from orange to red, and forming a colorful red head with green and white flowers. *Tropical. p. 561, 574*

ORTHOTHYLAX *Philydraceae* **I3LFM**

glaberrimus (Pacific Isl.); tufted herbaceous perennial (1 m) with folded, sword-shaped, dull-green leathery leaves, and leafy stalk with branched panicle of small creamy-white flowers with orange-red center. *p. 1923*

ORYCHOPHRAGMUS *Cruciferae* **I2LBM**

violaceus (China); herbaceous rosette of broad, pale green leaves, cordate or sometimes lobed or lyre-shaped and clasping stem; the flowers to 3 cm across, lavender blue, in terminal clusters; an attractive blooming plant grown as annual or biennial, like stocks. *p. 926*

ORYZA *Gramineae* **I2HBW**

clandestina, "Wild rice". I photographed this plant in the aquatic greenhouse of Nymphenburg Botanic Gardens in Munich where it is listed as from the North Temperate zone, growing in shallow water. However, Oryza are primarily tropical from Asia or Africa, as is the true rice, Oryza sativa; the temperate climate wild rice is Zizania aquatica which provided grain for American Indians. The handsome grass shown is perennial and clustering with slender canes about 1 m high, with narrow, matte rich green leaves, very ornamental at the edge of ponds. Its valid name may be Leersia oryzoides, the "Cut grass". *Tropical. p. 1315*

OSBECKIA *Melastomataceae* **S3LFM**

crinita (N. W. Himalaya to China); handsome shrubby plant ½-2½ m high, with 4-angled reddish branchlets; ovate membranous, 5-nerved leaves to 15 cm, ciliate at margins; flowers of 4 lilac-rose petals attractive with yellow stamens and anthers. *p. 1556*

OSCULARIA *Aizoaceae* **I2LBD**

deltoides (Mesembryanthemum) (So. Africa), "Pink fig marigold"; shrubby succulent with short, triangular, keeled, blue-gray leaves, 6 to 10 cm long, toothed; flowers pink. *p. 76*

OSMANTHUS *Oleaceae* ***C-I2LBM**

armatus (China), "Chinese osmanthus"; attractive and shapely evergreen shrub with holly-like narrow-elliptic, leathery, glossy green leaves having ivory midrib, 16 cm long, the margins with spines, slow-growing and with stiff reddish branches; tiny white, fragrant flowers. *Warm temperate. p. 1634*

delavayi (Siphonosmanthus) (Yunnan); broadly spreading shrub to 2 m high, with arching, downy branches, small elliptic, leathery leaves sharply toothed at margins, dark glossy green; small tubular, pure white, fragrant flowers in axillary and terminal clusters. *p. 1627*

fragrans (Olea) (Himalayas, China, So. Japan), "Sweet olive"; small tree to 10 m high, with wiry twigs and holly-shaped, stiff-leathery, olive-green leaves to 10 cm long, finely toothed at margins; the small white flowers in clusters, strongly and deliciously fragrant. *Subtropic. p. 1627*

heterophyllus 'Gulftide', (ilicifolius); attractive, neat-appearing evergreen of very compact growth, the upright branches with small high-glossy dark green, holly-like 4 cm leaves, the margins twisted and with pointed spine-tipped lobes. *p. 1634*

heterophyllus 'Variegatus' (ilicifolius var.), "False holly"; extremely attractive, slow-growing, dense evergreen shrub resembling variegated holly but a better keeper; the spiny, glossy-leathery leaves somewhat smaller, 4 to 6 cm long, fresh green to bluish-gray-green, edged and variegated creamy-white, tinted pink when young; should be grafted on privet for best growth. The green-leaved species is from Japan and Taiwan. *p. 15*, 1627*

OSMARONIA *Rosaceae* **I2LBM**

cerasiformis (British Columbia to California), the "Osoberry"; deciduous shrub to 5 m high, with oblong leaves to 10 cm long; flowers dioecious, greenish-white and fragrant, in pendant racemes; female plants with bluish-black berries. *p. 2000*

OSMUNDA *Osmundaceae (Filices)* **C2HFWh**

cinnamomea (E. No. America, Mexico to Brazil, E. Asia), "Cinnamon-fern"; coarse but attractive deep fibrous rooted fern with large crowns of 1½ m fronds, the fertile fronds 2-pinnate and becoming brown as spores mature; its fibrous roots are used as a growing medium for orchids in pots or baskets. *Humid-subtropic to Temperate. p. 1081*

claytoniana (E. No. America, Himalaya, China), "Interrupted fern"; decorative fern forming crown of pale green, pinnate fronds 30-60 cm long, from massive root stock; the pinnae deeply lobed and papery; the fertile fronds quite erect and distinct in having the spore-bearing, very much contracted leaflets about halfway up the stalk, exceeded above by more, normally flat, barren pinnae. *p. 1081*

regalis (No. America, Europe, Siberia, Japan, China, India, So. Africa, etc.), "Royal fern", also known as "Flowering fern"; rootstock with blackish-brown fibrous roots developing a spongy clump of great thickness; the bipinnate, fresh-green, papery fronds ½ to 2 m long on firm, naked stalks. The leaves bearing spores have their fertile portion in the upper part of the frond transformed into brown panicles full of spores, resembling an inflorescence of "flowers" borne above the foliage. *p. 1081*

OSTEOMELES *Rosaceae* **I2LBD**

schweriniae (W. China); graceful semi-evergreen shrub 2-3 m high with slender branches, downy pinnate leaves, and white 1 cm flowers of 5 petals, in small clusters. *p. 1993*

OSTEOSPERMUM *Compositae* **I2LBD**

fruticosum (Dimorphotheca) (So. Africa: Cape, Natal), "Trailing African daisy" or "Burgundy mound"; semi-shrubby plant spreading rapidly by trailing, rooting branches; small fleshy leaves with several points; large ray-flowers to 5 cm across, lilac above, fading nearly white by second day, deeper purple beneath, and dark purple center cushion; excellent ground cover for sunny, mild climate. *Subtropic. p. 804*

OSTROWSKIA *Campanulaceae* **I2LBD**

magnifica (Turkestan), "Giant bellflower"; striking herbaceous perennial to 1½ m, with tuberous roots, the foliage in distant whorls of 4 or 5 ovate, toothed leaves to 15 cm long, and 10 cm pale lilac, bell-shaped flowers suffused with white in terminal raceme. *p. 751*

OTHONNA *Compositae* **I2LBD**

capensis (crassifolia) (So. Africa: Cape Prov.), "Ragwort vine"; succulent stem-rooting creeper with slender trailing branches to 1 m long; fleshy, spindle-shaped, glossy-green 3 cm leaves scattered or in clusters, hanging as if on strings; small daisy-like yellow flowers, opening in sun. Excellent for hanging pots or baskets. *p. 831*

euphorbioides (Namibia); small succulent shrub 10 cm high, with spoon-shaped leaves 2½ cm long, light green covered with white waxy powder, arranged in tufts at the ends of branches, and with long white spines between; yellowish flower heads. *p. 832*

herrei (So. Africa: Namaqualand); curious succulent with short, thickened stem, and knotty from the persistent leaf bases; soft-fleshy leaves 5 cm long, irregularly obovate and undulate, bluish glaucous, at the ends of branches; deciduous when resting; small yellow flowers. *p. 829*

OTOCHILUS *Orchidaceae* **I3OFM**

fusca (Nepal, Burma); epiphyte with 5 cm pseudobulbs produced one above the other, and bearing 2 narrow leaves; sweetly scented whitish flowers in dusky, pendulous raceme, from the young growth. *p. 1787*

OTTELIA *Hydrocharitaceae* **S3LFW**

alismoides (Tropical Asia, Australia, Egypt, So. Italy); an aquatic plant with two kinds of foliage, the submersed young leaves are narrow and ribbon-like, the older ones which develop later are stalked, with a light green, rounded or ovate blade 5 to 17 cm long, the borders are lifted and show above water; the long-stalked flowers are lifted above the surface and have 3 white or greenish petals. In aquarium need warm 25° to 28° C. *p. 1322*

OTTOSONDERIA *Aizoaceae* **I2LBD**

farinosa (So. Africa); succulent shrub with opposite, small fleshy, club-shaped leaves slightly notched at apex, glossy-green with covering of white powder; pinkish flowers on elongated floral branches. *p. 77*

OURATEA *Ochnaceae* **S2LBM**

ilicifolia (West Indies); evergreen shrub with hard-leathery, ovate-pointed leaves lightly indented at margins, and weakly spiny; flowers orange, with greenish-yellow bracts; the roots with medicinal properties. *p. 1648*

olivaeformis (Gomphia) (Brazil), "Button flower"; evergreen tree to 5 m, with leathery lanceolate 12 cm leaves shining dark green and with toothed margins; flowers rich yellow in dense, much branched terminal clusters. *p. 1628*

OURISIA *Scrophulariaceae* **C2LFM**

coccinea (Chile); small rosette to 30 cm with creeping rhizome, of dentately lobed oval leaves close to soil, and a stalk bearing a panicle of trumpet-shaped, scarlet, nodding flowers 4 cm long, with cream, protruding anthers. *p. 2051*

OUVIRANDRA: see Aponogeton

OXALIS *Oxalidaceae* **C-I2LBD**

acetosella (No. Europe), the "European wood-sorrel"; stemless perennial 8 cm high with creeping root, producing long-stalked leaves 2 cm dia. with 3 obcordate, slightly hairy leaflets; 2 cm flowers with oval petals white with rosy veins; half the size of O. oregana. *p. 1844*

adenophylla (Chile); hardy stemless perennial 10-15 cm high, from a roundish, bulb-like base; long-stalked leaves in basal rosette, with 12-22 obcordate leaflets 1 cm long, glaucous grayish-green; 2½ cm flowers lilac pink with deeper veins and orange throat and with blackish-red spots at base of each of 5 petals; solitary or in umbels. *p. 1846, 1848*

bowiei (purpurea) (So. Africa), "Giant pink clover"; stemless plant with thickened roots and scaly bulbs, the fleshy, long-stalked leaves with 3 large, obcordate, waxy, light green segments; strong flower stalks to 30 cm long, topped by a cluster of giant, rosy-carmine flowers, during summer and fall. (d) *p. 1844, 1845*

braziliensis (Brazil); bulbous plant without stem, 8-15 cm high, with stalked bright green basal leaves having 3 bluntly obcordate leaflets 1 cm long and wide; flowers 2½ cm dia., bright rosy-red with darker veins, and yellow in throat; in winter and spring. One of the "Shamrocks" sold by florists. *Tropical. p. 1847*

carnosa (Chile, Perú); rhizomatous plant with erect, thick stem, topped by small shining light green succulent leaves with obcordate leaflets on long petioles, becoming pendant, the underside glistening like with dew; yellow flowers in spring. *p. 1843, 1846*

cernua: see pes-caprae.

crassipes: see O. rubra

deppei (esculenta; Ionoxalis) (So. Mexico), "Lucky clover"; bulbous plant with edible tuber, large leaves having 4 truncate segments (cut off straight at the apex) 4 cm long, and crossed by a purplish-brown zone; flowers rosy-red with yellow base. Attractive pot plant for winter bloom. *Tropical. p. 1845, 1847*

dispar (Guyana); branching, hairy subshrub with stout stem sparse with leaves; 3 lanceolate leaflets prominent with depressed veins; golden yellow flowers 1 cm long, on axillary stalks. *p. 1848*

enneaphylla (Patagonia, Falkland Is.); herbaceous plant from horizontal rhizome with thick, fleshy scales; leaves with 9 to 20 obcordate leaflets, in two series or whorled, gray-green and pubescent, on 8 cm stalks; large white, or pale rose, fragrant flowers about 3 cm across. *p. 1842*

flava (So. Africa); bulbous plant with long fleshy petioles and succulent leaves digitate with 5-12 long narrow to oblong fingers, and large flowers with a full, deep-yellow corolla. *p. 1843, 1846*

fruticosa (rusciformis hort.) (Perú: Rio de Lomas); small tropical shrub with narrow-elliptic, glaucous-green leaves, and small yellow flowers in axillary clusters. *p. 1842, 1848*

gigantea (Chile); erect shrub becoming tree-like, 2 to 4 m high, with curious growth resembling columnar cactus; tiny green trifoliate, clover-like leaves with obcordate 1 cm leaflets; small 2 cm yellow flowers. *p. 1842*

hedysaroides rubra (Colombia, Venez., Ecuador), "Firefern"; beautiful plant with erect, shrubby, wiry stem and thin, fern-like foliage of glowing, satiny wine-red, each petiole with 3 stalked ovate leaflets which are sensitive to the touch; many, little, bright yellow flowers in attractive contrast to the showy leaves. Subshrub to 1 m tall. *Tropical. p. 1844, 1846*

herrerae (Perú), "Succulent oxalis"; succulent, fibrous rooted species known in the trade as O. "henrei", more diminutive than O. peduncularis; densely branched woody stem with swollen keeled glaucous petioles topped by 3 tiny lightly notched fleshy leaflets; clusters of small yellow flowers on long stalks; suitable for hanging pots. *p. 1844, 1846*

hirta (So. Africa); winter-blooming plant with branching leafy pubescent stem from a large brown bulb, at first erect but becoming procumbent; with feathery foliage of 3 small spatulate leaflets nearly sessile, alternate and scattered; axillary flowers deep rose with yellow tube, and silky sepals. *Subtropic. p. 1844*

incarnata (Southwest Africa); tufting perennial with long ascending or procumbent vine-like stems forming at intervals rosettes of long thin stalked leaves; the 3 heart-shaped leaflets light-green and deeply notched, forming small bulbs at the base of the rosettes; winter-flowering with whitish 1 cm flowers tinged lavender-pink, yellow in tube; dormant in our Northern hemisphere summer. *p. 1843*

lasiandra (Ionoxalis) (Mexico); large, stemless plant with scaly bulbs and long-stalked, fleshy leaves pendant by their weight, having 5 to 11 wedge-shaped leaflets, going to "sleep" in darkness; slender stalks with umbels of rosy-carmine flowers opening over a period of 6 weeks. *Subtropic.* *p. 1845*

martiana 'Aureo-reticulata' (corymbosa var.) (Trop. America); attractive ornamental "Sour-clover", with scaly bulb producing numerous prostrate and ascending stalks, bearing large herbaceous leaves to 8 cm across, the 3 leaflets obcordate, fresh to deep green, beautifully veined and reticulated with yellow; long-stemmed flowers carmine-rose with red lines from white throat; goes "to sleep" at night. *Tropical.* *p. 768A, 1847*

melanosticta (So. Africa); attractive, low, bushy plant, dense foliage on green petioles, with 3 hard leaf-segments covered with soft gray hair glistening like silver in the sun; fall-blooming with yellow flowers. *p. 1845, 1847, 1848*

oregana (Washington to California); a "Woodsorrel" sometimes sold as "Irish Shamrock"; 8-20 cm high; from creeping roots rise stalks with large bright green, hairy leaves; the 3 obcordate leaflets 2½-5 cm wide; flowers white or rose veined with purple, yellowish at base; hardy. *p. 1847*

ortgiesii (Andes of Perú), "Tree oxalis"; attractive perennial to 50 cm tall, with leafy succulent stem, and olive-green to brown-red leaves of 3 segments, fish-tailed at apex, maroon beneath; small yellow flowers opening in the sun. *Subtropic.* *p. 1845*

paucartambensis (So. America: Perú); bushy, branching plant with fleshy, trifoliate leaves, the leaflets with fold in center and notched at apex; long-stalked clusters of large yellowish flowers. *p. 1842*

peduncularis (Ecuador); erect plant with thick fleshy stem and long swelling petioles in rosettes, bearing waxy leaves with 3 small fresh-green segments; dense clusters of showy, orange-yellow flowers on long stalks, in continuous bloom. *p. 1844*

pes-caprae (cernua) (So. Africa), "Bermuda buttercup"; perennial with thickened roots and deep scaly bulbs, with many basal, long-stalked leaves of 3 obcordate leaflets hairy beneath; nodding bell-shaped bright yellow flowers 2½-4 cm across, in spring; a weed in Bermuda and Florida and other mild districts. *Subtropic.* *p. 1843*

pes-caprae florepleno, the "Double Bermuda buttercup"; with bright yellow double flowers in early spring; suitable for hanging baskets; bulbs dormant in summer. *p. 1844*

purpurea (variabilis) (Cape Prov.), known in the cultivated form 'Grand Duchess'; a low, spreading bulbous perennial with succulent, fresh green foliage of 6-8 cm across, of three ciliate leaflets not notched, on rosy-red stalks pubescent with soft white hair, barely topped by large and showy, pretty flowers to 5 cm dia., bright rose with yellow base, winter-blooming in the sun. *Subtropic.* *p. 1843*

regnellii (So. America); in horticulture sometimes as "rubra alba", shapely, freeblooming perennial with tuberculate rhizome and grass-green leaves with 3 deltoid, thin, finely ciliate segments, the apex as if cut off almost straight across, and with slender white flowers. *p. 1845*

rubra (crassipes or "rosea") (Brazil); old-fashioned, free-blooming perennial often used for hanging baskets, with thick erect stalk, long hairy petioles and 3 coppery green obcordate hairy leaflets; clusters of rosy flowers with red veins, opening to the sun. *p. 1843*

rubra alba; free-blooming tuberous, wide-spreading, white-flowered variety, the clusters of long-stalked small white blossoms borne well above the green foliage. *p. 1846*

rusciformis hort.; small, bushy shrub with wiry stems, dense with long linear-lanceolate leaves, from the leaf axils the pretty yellow flowers; bot. fruticosa, which see.

siliquosa hort.; branching succulent bush, with fleshy, red stems, 3-foliate leaves dull deep brown-red, purple beneath; 2 cm flowers rich yellow, with maroon-brown lines from center (bot. vulcanicola, which see). *p. 1842, 1848*

succulentum (Chile); creeping succulent with small light green, fleshy leaves in threes on flexuous stalks; the stems reddish. Seen at Royal Botanic Gardens, Sydney. *Subtropic.* *p. 1842*

variabilis: see purpurea.

vulcanicola (siliquosa) (Costa Rica to Panama); mat-forming creeper with red stalks, the foliage with 3 reddish obovate or obcordate leaflets, and golden yellow flowers. *Tropical.* *p. 1842, 1848*

OXALIS: see also Ionoxalis, Trifolium

OXERA *Verbenaceae* **S3LFM**

pulchella (New Caledonia); climbing shrub with opposite oblong leathery leaves to 12 cm long, and trumpet-shaped 4-lobed white flowers 5 cm in length, with conspicuous calyx and long protruding stamens. *p. 2116*

OXYANTHUS *Rubiaceae* **I2LBD**

natalensis (Posoqueria) (So. Africa: Natal); very ornamental shrub with elliptic, satiny green, leathery leaves to 20 cm long, undulate like those of a coffee tree; inflorescence axillary, in clusters of creamy white, intensely fragrant flowers, the corolla with slender tube 6 cm long, the stigma protruding and petals recurved or twisted. *p. 2024*

OXYPETALUM *Asclepiadaceae* **I3LFM**

caeruleum (Argentina); twining subshrub with heart-shaped oblong, hairy leaves; attractive 2½ cm flowers with 5 linear blue lobes, with darker blue, fleshy corona, in axillary clusters. *p. 373*

OXYTROPIS *Leguminosae* **C2LBD**

lambertii (U.S. : Minnesota to Montana); perennial, silky-pubescent herb to 45 cm high; pinnate leaves, and raceme of pea-like small flowers bluish-purple; hardy. *p. 1392*

PACHIRA *Bombacaceae* **S2LBM**

aquatica (So. America), the "Guinea chestnut" or "Oje"; large tropical tree with palmately compound leaves of 5-7 leathery-oblong leaflets 8-20 cm long; large flowers with narrow pinkish petals 10-15 cm long, which drop off and expose numerous long white stamens; the large green or brown woody ovoid five-valved fruit is 10-30 cm long, containing rounded seeds, without floss; these can be eaten raw or roasted. Known in Hawaii as the "Malabar chestnut". *Tropical.* *p. 508*

insignis (West Indies); tropical evergreen tree to 20 m, with digitately compound leaves of 5-7 leathery obovate leaflets; axillary flowers with spreading petals light red to purple, brownish-downy outside, disclosing masses of white anthers and red style. *p. 508*

PACHYCARPUS *Asclepiadaceae* **I2LBM**

schinzianus (Transvaal); spring-blooming herb of the High Veld, 30-45 cm high, with clusters of pale rose 4 cm flowers having a corona of 5 incurving, purple inner lobes, carried high above the undulate leaves. *p. 372*

PACHYCEREUS *Cactaceae* **I2LBD**

chrysomallus (Puebla, Oaxaca); heavy branched tree to 15 m high, columns 12-15 ribbed and glaucous green; the top of flowering stems densely clothed in long white to yellowish brown hair; flowers cream. *p. 642*

marginatus: see Lemaireocereus

marginatus gemmatus: see Lemaireocereus

pecten-aboriginum (Chihuahua, Sonora, Baja California), the "Hair-brush cactus"; waxy-green column growing into a branched tree 8 m high and arms 25-45 cm thick; 10-12 acute ribs, spines gray to fawn, 1-2 large central spines tipped black toward apex, the upper areoles with tufts of some white wool; day-flowers red outside, white inside, 10 cm long; woolly 8 cm fruit. *p. 642*

pringlei (Mexico: Sonora, Baja California), "Mexican giant"; one of the most massive cacti, stout branching tree to 11 m high and 1 m thick at base, the olive green columns to 40 cm dia., with 10-16 prominent but rounded ribs, closely studded by large oval areoles with short white or grayish wool especially toward apex, numerous ash-gray radials and 1-3 long central spines at first reddish, afterwards gray; bell-shaped flowers 10 cm long, greenish-red outside, white inside. *Arid-tropical.* *p. 618, 637, 642, 653*

weberi (Lemaireocereus) (Mexico: Puebla, Oaxaca), "Candelabra cactus"; tree-like, 10 m or more high, branching from 1 m trunk into many parallel columns like a chandelier, glaucous bluish green 10 cm thick, with 8-10 prominent ribs, yellow radial spines and gray central spine 5-7 cm long; white flowers 10 cm long; large round 7 cm fruit. Also listed under Lemaireocereus as in Hortus 3, but Backeberg refers this to Pachycereus. *p. 656*

PACHYCEREUS: see also Lemaireocereus

PACHYPHYTUM *Crassulaceae* ***I2LBD**

amethystinum x Echeveria flammea; flat, stem-forming bigeneric rosette of few broad-elliptic, rather flat leaves, glaucous gray with amethyst sheen and rosy margins. Properly x Pachyveria. *p. 922*

bergerianum (x Pachyveria); cultivated in Germany; a handsome compact succulent with thick, obovate leaves bluish glaucous, with pink margins and tips. *p. 912*

'Blue Haze'; a robust, stemforming brevifolium hybrid with thick-fleshy, oblanceolate leaves jade green covered with a haze of glaucous blue, apex red; flowers yellow tinged pink, enclosed in bracts. Possibly a Pachyveria. *p. 19*, 915*

bracteosum (Mexico), "Moonstones"; branching succulent with stout stem to 30 cm high; rosette of obovate swollen club-shaped leaves 5-10 cm long, gray-glaucous with rosy tint; 20-30 cm stalk with red flowers. *Arid-tropical.* *p. 874, 922*

brevifolium (Mexico), "Sticky moonstones"; branched stems which are sticky, and scattered blunt thick-fleshy leaves blue diffused with red, and covered with waxy bloom; bell-shaped flowers dark red. *p. 915*

compactum (Mexico: Hidalgo), "Thick plant"; small compact plant with thick cylindrical leaves somewhat angled and keeled at pointed apex, green suffused with brown and silvery glaucous; flowers reddish. *p. 912, 915, 2092*

'Cornelius Hybrid', "Moon stones"; robust succulent rosette of large, heavy leaves bluish-gray, often tinged with pink, and tipped red; flower petals red. *p. 915*

oviferum (San Luis Potosi), "Pearly moonstones"; fine colored succulent reminiscent of "Moon stones", the swollen, long egg-shaped leaves are beautifully glaucous in delicate silver-white, iridescent and shading to pink and amethyst, 3 to 5 cm long; bellshaped red flowers. *p. 915, 922*

PACHYPODIUM *Apocynaceae* **S2LBD**

bispinosum (So. Africa); succulent with massive base and green stem; slender leafy branches with grayish spines in pairs; small fleshy leaves dull green and hairy above; showy tubular flowers, white to purplish inside, soft pink outside of tube, the petals old-rose, 3 cm across. *p. 143*

brevicaule (Madagascar); stone-like, branched, swollen caudex to 60 cm across, with sessile elliptic 2½ cm leaves on short elevations, and a few spines; showy yellow flowers. *p. 142*

geayi (S. W. Madagascar); handsome succulent becoming tree-like 8-10 m high; as a young pot plant attractive as a small gray column dense with grayish spines and with pink ribs; crowded toward the apex narrow strap-like purplish-green leaves 20 cm long, 5 to 10 mm wide and gracefully recurving. *p. 143*

horomboense (Madagascar); rock-dwelling small succulent with a caudex that may weigh 4½-18 kg.; short branches densely armed with spines, oval leaves 2-6 cm long; cup-shaped yellow flowers, on long stalks. *p. 142*

lamerei (Madagascar: Fort Dauphin), "Madagascar palm" or "Club-foot"; weird succulent, a thick, spiny gray column 1-3 m high and scarcely branched; at the base spindle-shaped, the pinkish spines 3 cm long; toward the top the spirally arranged strap-like leathery 20 cm leaves, dark shining green with white midrib; small funnel-shaped white flowers. A member of the queer vegetation prevailing in Southern Madagascar. *Arid-tropical. p. 143*

lealii (So. Africa); arborescent succulent with club-shaped trunk with numerous erect branches; small narrow leaves between stout spines; white flowers at ends of branches. *p. 142*

namaquanum (So. Africa: Cape Prov., Namibia), called "Ghostman" by the Hottentots; stout succulent column to 1½ m or more high, armed with 5 cm spines as protection against animals; in winter when growing, a tuft of leaves forms at apex, 10-12 cm long and 5-6 cm wide; flowers from the leaf axils velvety and reddish, striped yellow inside. The stems are leaning toward the sun. *Arid-tropical. p. 143*

rosulatum (Madagascar); short and thick succulent caudex branching into cylindrical arms dense with stout spines, and topped by a rosette of narrow oblanceolate leaves, and long-stalked sulphur-yellow flowers. *p. 142*

rutenbergianum (Madagascar coast); tree-like succulent with trunk 3-5 m high and 30-45 cm thick at base, tapering toward apex; spiny branches with deciduous, lanceolate leaves, and white flowers. *p. 142*

windsori (baronii var. windsori) (So. Madagascar); dwarf succulent shrub with thick, globose trunk to 8 cm dia., with a few thick, rough-skinned, cylindrical branches, with tiny spines; pairs of leathery obovate leaves to 6 cm long, shining surface and felted reverse; 5 cm red flowers between the foliage. *p. 142*

PACHYSANDRA *Buxaceae* **C2LFMh**

stylosa glaberrima; low evergreen plant with compound leaves, the leaflets waxy green and obovate, shallowly toothed toward apex, and spreading by underground stolons, forming clusters. Photo by T. Everett, N. Y. Bot. Garden. *p. 614*

terminalis (Japan), "Japanese spurge"; low evergreen perennial herb spreading by means of creeping rootstocks, with fleshy obovate leaves grouped whorl-like, coarsely toothed toward apex and 3-8 cm long; terminal spikes of greenish-white flowers. *Warm-temperate. p. 614*

terminalis 'Variegata', has its soft-leathery evergreen leaves bordered and variegated ivory white. *Warm temperate. p. 614*

PACHYSTACHYS *Acanthaceae* **S3LFM**

coccinea (Jacobinia) (Trinidad, So. America), "Cardinal's guard"; herbaceous shrub 1-2 m high, with elliptic, rugose leaves to 20 cm; scarlet flowers in terminal heads, the calyx with 5 linear segments, 5 cm corolla two-lipped and reflexed. *Tropical. p. 49*

lutea (Perú), "Lollypops"; introduced in Europe as Beloperone "Super Goldy"; semi-woody plant 25 cm or more high with lanceolate, depressed-veined herbaceous, matte dark green leaves; contrasting with a striking, erect inflorescence of hops-like, shingled, orange-yellow bracts, bursting with creamy-white flowers in late summer. *Tropical. p. 49*

PACHYSTACHYS: see also Jacobinia, Justicia

PACHYSTIGMA *Rubiaceae* **I2LBD**

thamnus (Transvaal); woody plant with prostrate branches, leathery ovate, concave leaves toward apex; small clusters of yellow-green flowers. Plant poisonous to the cattle on the Veld. *p. 2018*

x PACHYVERIA *Crassulaceae* **·I2LBD**

clavata cristata (Pachyphytum bracteosum x Echeveria x rosea); many-clustered miniature rosettes on a monstrose stem, the short fleshy leaves are glaucous silvery blue and very crowded. (F) *p. 915*

'Curtis'; bigeneric hybrid known in California horticulture as "White cloud"; nice, compact rosette of bluish-green, narrowish obovate, boat-shaped leaves covered with silvery bloom, tips red. *p. 915*

'E. O. Orpet' (Pach. bracteosum x Ech. flammea), "Large jewel plant"; large, loose rosette of long obovate, spoonshaped, thick leaves covered by silvery-gray bloom shading to coppery rose toward apex; flower petals reddish. *p. 889*

haagei, "Jewel plant"; compact star-like hard rosette of short fleshy, boat-shaped leaves flat on top, bluish green dipped in purplish red toward apex and bluish glaucous; flowers yellow and orange red. Possibly P. glauca. *Subtropic. p. 915, 917*

muelleri (Pachyphytum oviferum x Echeveria derenbergii); stiff rosette 10 cm across, of oblanceolate thick, incurving leaves 5 cm long, blue green and with white-waxy coating; cultivated in Germany. *p. 912*

nigra (Pachyphytum sp. x Echeveria multicaulis or metallica); handsome Hummel-California cultivar known as "Black Magic"; low, flat rosette 12 cm across, of obovate-pointed, concave leaves 4 cm long, waxy green but turning black-purple in strong sun. *Arid-subtropic. p. 912*

orpetii (Pachyphytum bracteosum x Echeveria flammea); ornamental, large, open stem-forming rosette 20 cm across, freely branching from base, with long obovate spoon-shaped, concave leaves blue-glaucous, with amethyst tinge; flesh-colored flowers in long-stalked, leafy raceme. Can be propagated from leaves. *p. 912*

pfitzeri (Pachyphytum oviferum x Echeveria elegans); attractive open rosette freely sprouting ancillary baby rosettes; leaves obovate spoon-like with concave surface, 6 cm long, pale and nearly white glaucous like translucent alabaster; long-stalked flowers orange red. *p. 912*

scheideckeri (P. bracteosum x E. secunda), "Powdered jewel plant"; short-stemmed, clustering rosette of fleshy, narrow spoonshaped leaves softly colored glaucous bluish-gray, flushed with pink and with reddish tips; bright red flowers tipped with yellow. *p. 915*

scheideckeri cristata, "Jewelled crown"; a form of the hybrid P. bracteosum x Ech. secunda, on monstrose crested stem bearing dense clusters of short ovate leaves covered with white bloom. *p. 894*

PAEONIA *Ranunculaceae* **C2LB-FMh**

lactiflora (albiflora sinensis) (China), the "Chinese garden peony"; hardy perennial with roots a collection of narrow tubers; herbaceous leaves, twice compound; stems to 1 m high; large fragrant flowers, 10-12 cm across, typically white. *Temperate. p. 1992*

lactiflora 'Festiva' (Siberia, China, Japan), "Double-flowered peony" or "Chinese peony"; outstandingly beautiful hardy perennial herb to 1 m high, with spindle-shaped dahlia-like tuberous roots; large ornamental, herbaceous, compound leaves, and magnificent rose-type fragrant flowers to 15 cm across, with double incurved white petals with pink sheen; blooming normally in our gardens in late May or early June. *Temperate. p. 1992*

'Sophie' (lactiflora hybrid); shapely perennial with tuberous rootstock and herbaceous compound leaves, solitary double flowers 18 cm dia., soft crimson; needs winter chilling to bloom well. *p. 1983*

suffruticosa (Moutan) (W. China, Tibet, Bhutan); the beautiful "Chinese tree-peony"; highly developed and admired in China for centuries; woody shrub, branching and becoming 2 m tall, with bipinnate leaves; showy flowers 12 cm across, red to white; usually grafted. *p. 1992*

tenuifolia (Rumania to Caucasus); perennial herb with creeping rootstock and leafy stem 30-60 cm high, dark green fern-like leaves lobed 3-pinnately into linear segments; deep crimson, cup-like flowers 8-10 cm across. *p. 1992*

PAGIANTHA *Apocynaceae* **S3LBD**

dichotoma (So. India, Sri-Lanka, So. China), "Forbidden fruit of India"; large evergreen shrub dense with shiny green, leathery, ovate leaves to 20 cm long; very exotic with waxy white flowers 4 cm across, their 5 long linear petals curved sickle-shaped windmill-like, twisted and with margins turned under, and very sweetly fragrant. *Tropical. p. 136*

PALISOTA *Commelinaceae* **S3LFM**

barteri (Fernando Po); dark green rosette with spreading, stalked elliptic glossy leaves having parallel veins, and edged with hairs; flowers purplish, near base, followed by a dense cluster of showy orange-red, pointed berries. *Tropical. p. 783, 784*

mannii (West Equatorial Africa); fleshy perennial from the Cameroon Mountains at 750 m; with heavy root stock forming short trunks; large robust, glossy green, spear-shaped leaves 30 cm long, 6-12 cm wide, on channeled petioles; striking clusters of scarlet red, pointed fruit. *p. 787*

pynaertii (Trop. Africa); ornamental perennial herb with oblanceolate leaves 60-90 cm long, gray-pubescent with greenish-yellow along the middle and reddish hairs along margins; white flowers, in dense cylindric panicle. *p. 784*

pynaertii 'Elizabethae' (W. Equatorial Africa); ornamental leafy rosette becoming large; the thin-leathery oblanceolate, stalked foliage 20-50 cm long and spreading; glossy rich green surface, with feathered pale green or cream center-band, and reddish hairs along margins; in the center a dense cone of small white flowers, followed by attractive purplish berries. *Tropical. p. 783, 784*

PALIURUS *Rhamnaceae* **C2LBDh**

spina-christi (So. Europe to No. China), "Christ-thorn" or "Jerusalem-thorn"; large shrub or tree to 6 m, branches armed with twin spines, and ovate, 3-veined leaves 3 cm long, finely toothed, alternate in 2 ranks; small greenish yellow flowers; 2 cm fruit brownish yellow; cultivated more for religious interest than as ornamental. *Warm temperate.* *p. 1990*

PAMIANTHE *Amaryllidaceae* **S3LFM**

peruviana (Perú), "Peruvian daffodil"; bulbous plant with basal linear leaves 30 cm long, and having rounded keel; angled stalk bearing several scented, showy flowers with deep green 10 cm tube, 8 cm bell-shaped, white corona, the spreading white, inner segments with yellowish-green median stripe; February-March. *p. 114*

PAMIANTHE: see also Leptochiton

PANAX: see Nothopanax, Polyscias, Pseudopanax

PANCRATIUM *Amaryllidaceae* **S3LBMd**

illyricum (Corsica, Sardinia, Malta, So. Italy); bulbous plant 35 cm high, with broad basal strongly veined, deciduous leaves to 5 cm wide; solid floral stalk 25 cm or more long, topped by clusters of fragrant flowers with green tube and spreading white segments 4 cm long, in center a toothed crown or cup formed by the stamens united at base; spring to summer; somewhat hardy. *p. 120*

maritimum (Spain to Syria); showy, bulbous plant; 5-7 cm bulb with dense reddish skins; the basal evergreen, persistent, linear leaves gray green, to 75 cm long; white, fragrant flowers with tube 8 cm long and linear segments 4 cm long, and with large crown inside; summer-blooming. *p. 120*

PANDANUS *Pandanaceae* ***S1LFD**

baptistii (New Britain Isl. near New Guinea), "Blue screw-pine"; very decorative, symmetrical plant with stiff channeled leaves spirally arranged, gracefully arching, and tapering to a long point, blue-green with several yellow center stripes, without thorns at the margins. *Tropical.* *p. 1918*

heterocarpus (Mascarene Isl., east of Madagascar); branching tree to 6 m with numerous stilt-roots and branches; the clasping, soft-leathery rich green leaves in spirals, purple marginal teeth. *p. 1918*

kirkii (Tanzania, Zanzibar), the "Mkadi screwpine"; branching tree with stiltroots common along the sandy shore of the Indian Ocean just above high water, forming dense clusters to 10 m high; flexible leaves 1 m long, dark green and spiny at margins and midrib; male flowers white and sweetly scented; fruits cone-like and pendant, orange-colored 20 cm long. Photographed near Dar-es-Salaam. *p. 1919*

leram (Sri Lanka), "Nicobar bread-fruit"; large tree dividing into numerous twisting branches and supported by stilt-roots; topped by long pendant bluish-green, prickly leaves arranged in spirals; notable for its large ovoid fruits made up of many wedge-shaped 12 cm drupes (ripened ovary) containing sugar and starch, and nut-like seeds. *Tropical.* *p. 1917*

odoratissimus (Hawaii, Polynesia to New Hebrides, Queensland, Monsoon Asia), the "Hala screw-pine" or "Walking tree"; forming groves, but favoring the seashores; picturesque tree branching into twisted woody and flexuous, ringed stems to 6 m high, and with straight, supporting aerial roots as if standing on stilts; the thin-leathery, pliable sword-shaped leaves arranged spirally are grayish green 1 m or more long, and prickly at margins; flowers on male trees fragrant; brownish 20 cm fruit looks like a pineapple, consisting of nut-like, edible seeds. *Tropical.* *p. 1917*

pacificus (South Pacific Isl.); stout, compact plant with broad stubby leaves 8 to 10 cm wide, abruptly narrowed to a tail-like tip, plain fresh green and glossy, with light green, marginal spines, the center deeply channeled. *p. 1918*

pristis (Madagascar); clustering rosette 2 to 4 m high, dark green glossy leathery foliage with prominent pale spines, the leaves spreading out horizontally and recurving beyond the middle; beginning to flower when 1 m high. *Tropical.* *p. 1919*

pygmaeus (graminifolius) (Madagascar, Mauritius); low spreading shrub to 60 cm high, sending out from the base numerous horizontal, stilt-rooting branches with long narrow-linear, rich glossy green leaves spirally along the stem, the margins and keels with whitish spines, glaucous beneath. *p. 1918*

sanderi (Moluccas, Polynesia); a handsome, very ornamental screwpine with short green stem, but suckering freely with great spiralling rosettes of magnificent long leaves, glossy green largely variegated with ivory-white to yellow, green band toward finely spiny margins, with age breaking above the middle and laxly pendant. *Tropical.* *p. 1917*

sanderi 'Roehrsianus' (Timor, Solomon Isl.); robust, beautiful rosette with long leathery 1 m sword-like leaves often pendant beyond the middle, friendly green and shining, transversed lengthwise with stripes and bands of light golden yellow, the young growth golden orange, margins finely spiny; tufting with suckers. *Tropical.* *p. 1918*

stellatus (Madagascar); climbing pandanus with flexuous slender stem, with narrow-linear, channeled leaves to 35 cm long and 1 cm wide, the margins and midrib very spiny; at apex a fuzzy spadix enveloped within pale bracts. *p. 1919*

tectorius (Southern trop. Asia to Polynesia), a "Pandanus palm"; widely cultivated for its economic values, especially the pendulous clusters of edible seed; slender, branching, 6 m tree with flexuous trunk supported by brace-roots, light green fibrous leaves pendant above the middle, with white spines. *Tropical.* *p. 1920*

utilis (Madagascar), a useful as well as ornamental "Screw pine"; spiral rosette of long curving, strap-like, thick-leathery leaves to 2 m long and 10 cm wide, keeled beneath, deep olive-green with showy red spines; with age becoming a branching tree to 18 m high, with stilt-like brace roots; the leaves are used for making hats and baskets. *p. 1917, 1918, 1920*

veitchii (Polynesia), "Variegated screwpine"; shapely and attractive house plant; rosette of thin-leathery, recurving leaves to 8 cm wide, narrowing to a long point, shining light to deep green lined and broadly margined with creamy-white, the edges and keel beneath with small spines; with age developing stilt-like, thick aerial roots. *p. 1918*

veitchii 'Compactus' ("nelsonii"); a very desirable form of compact habit, the leaves dense and more rigid, and the white variegation comes always clear, unlike veitchii; the green is deep green, contrasting sharply with a white that is real white; easily sprouting suckers. *p. 1918*

PANDOREA *Bignoniaceae* **I2-3HBD**

jasminoides (Bignonia) (New So. Wales, Queensland), "Bower plant" or "Bower of beauty"; tall flowering climber with compound leaves feather-fashion, of 5 to 9 glossy green elliptic leaflets 3-5 cm long; the Tecoma-like trumpet flowers 5 cm long, opening to 5 crepy lobes; pinkish-white streaked with pink or red inside of throat. *Subtropic.* *p. 502*

PANICUM variegatum: see Oplismenus

PAPAVER *Papaveraceae* **C-I2LBD**

alpinum (Europe: Alps, Carpathians); tufted perennial with glaucous, finely divided basal leaves, and bristly-hairy stalks 10 to 25 cm long with solitary white flowers. *p. 1923*

orientale (Mediterranean to Iran), "Oriental poppy"; a showy perennial with milky-colored juice and white-hairy sparsely leafy stem to 1 m high, the thick, green leaves pinnately dissected and toothed, and large 10-15 cm flowers scarlet with black spot in the base, followed by an ornamental glaucous capsule; summer-blooming. *Warm-temperate.* *p. 1920*

PAPHINIA *Orchidaceae* **S3OFW**

cristata (Colombia to Guianas); small epiphyte; clustered pseudobulbs with 2-3 fleshy, pleated leaves 15 cm long; pendant inflorescence of strange flowers to 10 cm dia., spreading petals and sepals pale yellow tigered and banded brown-maroon, the clawed lip chocolate-purple with tuft of white hair at apex (autumn). *Tropical.* *p. 1807*

PAPHIOPEDILUM *Orchidaceae* **I-S3 (H or O) NM**

'Albion' (Astarte x niveum); chaste hybrid with leaves lightly mottled gray, and demure, waxy-white flower thinly dotted with red and green disk in center (spring and fall). *Tropical.* *p. 1792*

x aureum 'Surprise' (spicerianum x nitens); a good old, free-blooming "Lady slipper"; tufted with faintly mottled green strap-leaves; medium size, pure yellow, waxy flowers with overtones of buff, the upper part of the dorsal white, (spring). (I) *p. 1792*

bellatulum (Burma, Thailand); dwarf terrestrial with fleshy dark green leaves mottled with pale green, purple beneath; solitary 5-8 cm waxy flowers on very short stalk, shell-shaped, creamy-white, covered with raised spots and blotches of purple-maroon, (April-Sept.). *Tropical.* *p. 1790, 1792*

bullenianum (Cypripedium) (Borneo, Malaya); showy terrestrial with 15 cm leaves blue-green painted with light gray; floral stalk to 30 cm, with waxy slipper flowers 8 cm across, the dorsal sepal light green with dark stripe, petals greenish with brown warts, pouch purplish-red (summer). *p. 1795*

callosum (Thailand, Vietnam); colorful species with leaves tesselated bright green on deep green, and large 9-10 cm flowers with greenish petals deflexed and strap-like, purple at tip and with several black warts, the dorsal white lined with purple and green veins, and a brown-purple pouch. *Tropical.* *p. 1794*

callosum splendens (Thailand, Vietnam); strong terrestrial with light and dark bluish-green marbled leaves, and 1 or 2 large flowers on a stem, dorsal white striped with green and crimson, the ciliate petals greenish and mahogany, pouch brown-purple, (March-July). (S) *p. 1791*

chamberlainianum (Sumatra); strap-like, green basal leaves, and stalk with raceme to 60 cm long, of 3-5 flowers 8-12 cm across; sepals greenish marked with purplish-brown, twisted and wavy petals greenish marked with brown dots in lines; pouch green at base shading to rose and covered with purplish dots; all year. (S) *p. 1793*

concolor (Burma, Thailand, Vietnam); dainty, dwarf terrestrial with gray-mottled leaves and 5-8 cm waxy flowers on short stalk, pale yellow densely covered with tiny violet dots, (Aug.-Sept.). (S) *p. 1790*

curtisii (Sumatra); tessellated foliage, and solitary, bold flowers with greenish dorsal sepal margined white and veined with green, large 10 cm purplish-brown pouch; the rosy, ciliate petals veined green and spotted with purple; April-September. (S) *p. 1793*

dayanum (Cypripedium) (Borneo); attractive leaves pale green mottled with dark green; waxy flower 10-12 cm dia., dorsal white with green and black-purple lines, petals flushed purplish brown and with blackish spots, fringed with black hairs, pouch a lacquered blackish-brown (spring). *Tropical.* p. 1796

delenatii (Vietnam: Tonkin); neat species with gray-tessellated leaves, and 22-30 cm stalks bearing 1 or 2 flowers, the small dorsal and the broad petals satiny-white flushed rose, the round pouch deep rose on white ground. p. 1793

exul (Thailand); distinct species with stout green leaves to 25 cm long, and 8 cm flowers with dorsal green edged with white, and brown-spotted petals yellow-green with dark spots at base, lip brownish-yellow (Feb.-July). *Tropical.* p. 1790

fairrieanum (Himalayas, Bhutan, Assam); dwarf terrestrial with pale green leaves and uniquely pretty flowers; dorsal white, greenish at base and with purple lines, petals similar, sickle-shaped, pouch green flushed red and veined with purple, (July-Jan.). *Tropical.* p. 1664A, 1790

x gaudianum (curtisii x harrisianum); beautiful hybrid with green leaves and erect stalks often bearing 2 great big flowers, the dorsal red with dark stripes, the pendant pale petals ciliate and covered with reddish warts, and a waxy, deep mahogany-red, over-size pouch, (late spring and summer). (I) p. 1794

godefroyae (Vietnam, Thailand); attractive terrestrial growing on rocks, with dark green leaves checkered with gray above, reddish beneath; the rounded, 8 cm flowers satiny white spotted with red-purple, one or two on a short stalk, (June-Aug). (S) p. 1790

godefroyae var. leucochilum; hooded flowers creamy-yellow with markings of red-brown, lip without spots. p. 1796

x harrisianum 'C.S. Ball'; distinct form with large 6-8 cm, sinister, very dark vibrant deep wine red, waxy flower having dorsal greenish yellow and white striped with red; leaves mottled light and dark green (summer). *Tropical.* p. 1792

x harrisianum superbum (villosum x barbatum); excellent dark hybrid with leaves mottled light green on dark, and large flower lacquered deep red marked with green, dorsal with purplish-red veining into the white apex, stem and petals hairy, (spring-summer). (I) p. 1791

hirsutissimum (Assam); terrestrial with strapshaped leaves faintly marbled, and large, ciliate flowers on hairy stalks, dorsal densely spotted black-purple and dotted brown, pouch green, stained brown-purple, (March-May). (S) p. 1794

hookerae (Borneo); low rosette of marbled leaves to 15 cm; slender stalk with solitary flower 10 cm dia.; dorsal sepal creamy white flushed with green, and purplish nerves, petals green with blackish spots and purple edge, the helmet-like lip brownish purple flushed with green (spring). p. 1796

insigne (Cypripedium) (Nepal, Assam), terrestrial "Lady slipper"; growing on rocks in the Himalayas at 2000 m; small plant with green leaves, soon forming tufts; the flowers waxy, 10 cm across, dorsal yellow-green with purple spots at base, white at apex, petals yellowish-green veined with brown, slipper reddish-brown, (Oct.-March). *Subtropic.* p. 1791, 1793

insigne 'Harefield Hall' (Assam); perhaps the best of many named forms; exceptionally large, waxy flowers, with dorsal yellowish, margined white, and heavily blotched with chocolate, (winter). *Subtropic.* p. 1791

insigne punctatissimum (Himalayas); bushy terrestrial of glossy green leaves 20-30 cm long and 2-3 cm wide; waxy slipper flowers 10-12 cm dia., the large wide green dorsal sepal covered with brown spots, side petals and glossy pouch-like lip suffused with brown. p. 1795

insigne 'Sanderae' (Assam); desirable form with flowers of a beautiful primrose-yellow, except the upper part of the dorsal which is pure white, (winter). *Subtropic.* p. 1791

insigne 'Striatifolium'; a rare leaf variation cultivated in Japan and imported into California by Giridlian: the dark green leaves are distinctly banded and striped with cream. (I) p. 1792

lawrenceanum (No. Borneo); robust terrestrial with long leaves brightly mottled pale green, and bold flowers, dorsal white with shining purple stripes, greenish at base, the horizontal petals greenish, shaded purple and black-warted, lip brown-purple, (April-Aug.). *Tropical.* p. 1790

x leeanum (Assam); natural hybrid of insigne x spicerianum, willing grower and free bloomer with green leaves and waxy flowers, dorsal white with purple spots and greenish base, crisped petals yellow-green veined with brown, slipper brownish-red, (winter-spring). (C-I) p. 1791

x leeanum clinkaberryanum; well-known, free-flowering, distinctive form having generally larger flowers, with more dark area of greenish-brown on the large, much flattened-out white dorsal, (spring). (I) p. 1792

x leyburnense magnificum (Charlesworthii x Haywood); stocky hybrid with broad foliage and beautiful, large flowers on hairy stalks, the dorsal wine-red shading to pink, apex white, pouch and petals coppery olive, with wine-red veining, (autumn). (I) p. 1791

lowii (No. Borneo); beautiful epiphyte on trees or limestone rocks, with straplike, light green leaves and stalks to 1 m, with 2 to 6 hairy flowers, dorsal greenish with purple stripes, the narrow, obovate petals greenish yellow blotched brown and purple-tipped; pouch coppery green with purple lines, (Feb.-July). *Tropical.* p. 1793, 1794

x maudiae (Cypripedium) (callosum x lawrenceanum); beautiful and highly desirable hybrid with marbled leaves yellow-green and bluish-gray; the usually single flowers with a white dorsal striped with green, the slender petals greenish closely lined with green, pouch yellowish-green, (April-Aug.). *Tropical.* p. 1789, 1790

x nitens (villosum x insigne); old, free-blooming, robust-hybrid with large green leaves and large flowers, dorsal green with white margin and elevated lacquer-blotches of brown, petals and slipper yellow-green with lacquered mahogany veining, (Dec.-Feb.). (I) p. 1791

niveum (Malaya); lovely dwarf species, with close-set oblong 15 cm leaves purple beneath and dark green above, tesselated with lighter oblong spots; the 6-9 cm flowers are satiny white inside, minutely speckled with dots of red-purple. *Tropical.* p. 1790

'Olivia' (niveum x tonsum); dainty hybrid with leaves mottled yellowish green on dark green, and purple underside; hairy stalk with waxy flower white flushed pink and regularly lined and dotted with purple (winter). *Tropical.* p. 1792

philippinense (Philippines); terrestrial species with leathery, glossy green leaves to 30 cm long; floral stalks to 50 cm high, bearing 3-5 striking flowers, with dorsal sepal white, striped with brown purple, the long thread-like red-purple petals pendulous and twisted, 15 cm or more long; lip tawny marked with brown. *Humid-tropical.* p. 1796

praestans (New Guinea); beautiful species; with green leaves to 30 cm; a purple stalk carries several interesting flowers; the dorsal sepal whitish streaked with purple; the petals linear and twisted, 12 cm long, yellow green with brown veins and black warts; lip yellow. *Tropical.* p. 1796

rothschildianum (Papua, Borneo); remarkable terrestrial, strong growing, with leathery green leaves and racemes with 2-5 flowers having long pointed petals yellowish green, spotted red-purple, dorsal yellowish, striped with dark purple, pouch red-brown, with yellow at the opening, (Jan.-Aug.). *Tropical.* p. 1789

spicerianum (Assam); fine species with lurid green leaves and 6 cm flowers with crisped petals yellow-green with a crimson line, the pouch red-brown and the wide dorsal snow-white with green base and a purple stripe from base to apex (Nov.-Dec.). (I) p. 1794

sukhakulii (Thailand); checkered leaves gray-green and pale green; flowers with dorsal sepal pale green and dark lines, petals blotched blackish purple, the glossy pouch with purple veins. *Tropical.* p. 1796

venustum (Himalayas, Nepal); compact terrestrial with bluish-green leaves mottled light green; solitary flowers with dorsal white, striped with green, petals greenish with darker lines and purple tips and warts, pouch yellow-green tinged rose and veined with green, (Nov.-March). (I) p. 1791

villosum (So. Burma); large terrestrial with light green strap-leaves to 45 cm long; large flowers, nearly 12-15 cm across and very glossy, dorsal green with white border and lined purplish-brown, petals yellowish-brown and purple midline, pouch brownish-yellow (Oct.-Mar.). p. 1790

PARANOMUS bolusii: see Leucospermum

PARATROPIA *Araliaceae* **I3LFD**

rotundifolia (Trop. Asia, Trop. Australia); willowy tree with slender branches bearing leathery palmate leaves of about 5 oval, long-stalked glossy-green leaflets. p. 316

PARKINSONIA *Leguminosae* **S2LBD**

aculeata (Trop. America to Cape Verde Is.), "Jerusalem thorn" or "Mexican palo verde"; small spiny ornamental tree, with narrow bipinnate, fern-like foliage; small yellow flowers sweet-scented, in loose racemes; 12 cm pods constricted between the seeds. *Subtropic.* p. 1385

PARMENTIERA *Bignoniaceae* **S2LBM**

edulis (Mexico, Guatemala), "Guajilote tree"; tropical tree of dense, thorny growth to 10 m high, with ovate leaves; large, funnelform flowers greenish-yellow; oblong, grooved greenish-yellow fruit 10-15 cm long, edible but of poor quality. *Tropical.* p. 498, 499

PARMENTIERA: see also Crescentia

PARODIA *Cactaceae* ***I2LBD**

aureispina (N. Argentina), "Tom Thumb"; tiny 3 cm bluish-green globe with spiralled ribs, and covered with bright yellow spines; golden flowers at an early stage. *Arid-subtropic.* p. 618, 701

chrysacanthion (Argentina); small cylindric plant to 8 cm high, pale green, with 24-30 tubercled, spiral ribs, set with numerous bristle-like, glossy lemon-yellow spines; flowers golden yellow. p. 695, 700

maassii (Bolivia), "Tom Thumb cactus"; small globe, yellowish green, with 13 spiraled prominent ribs, with white radial and hooked central spines on knobs; flowers orange-red. p. 701

microsperma (Argentina); globose to short cylindric to 20 cm high, dark gray-green, with spiral rows of tubercles set with woolly white areoles, glassy-white radials and some brownish hook spines; flowers outside red, inner petals orange yellow. p. 700

microsperma cristata (Echinocactus); a crestate fasciation with the globes fused into a continuous arch of tubercles and each covered by a cluster of small white spines; such highly contorted forms are best grafted on a columnar cactus for support and better growth. p. 695

mutabilis (Argentina: Salta); small globe to 9 cm, glaucous to olive green, with tubercles densely set with bristly white radials, and a hooked orange spine; white-woolly at apex; flowers golden yellow. *p. 701*

mutabilis ferruginea; variety with central spines rusty red, the beautiful golden yellow flowers with red eye, and lasting for several days. *p. 701*

sanguiniflora (Argentina: Salta), "Red Tom Thumb"; solitary little soft green globes woolly on top, with spiralled tubercles set with bristly white radials and brownish central spines, one hooked; numerous flowers a silky blood red. *Arid-subtropic.* *p. 701*

sanguiniflora violacea, "Crimson Tom Thumb"; a color form with the silky flowers reddish-violet. *p. 701*

PARROTIA *Hamamelidaceae* **C2LBD**

persica (No. Iran, Caucasus); deciduous tree to 5 m with 10 cm oval leaves coarsely toothed above middle, green but turning to brilliant autumn colors; flowering before foliage; dense clusters of flowers without petals surrounded by brown-hairy bracts, and protruding, pendant stamens with red anthers. *p. 1320*

PARTHENOCISSUS *Vitaceae* **C-I2LB-FM**

henryana (Ampelopsis) (China); ornamental, vigorous, tall climber with young branchlets 4-angled, the divided tendrils clinging by adhesive tips, grape-like leaves of 5 slender, oblanceolate, thin-fleshy leaflets, toothed above middle, dull olive-green with broad silver band following midrib and feathering into lateral veins, reddish beneath. Sometimes known as "Cissus gongyloides". (F) *p. 2121*

himalayana (Himalayas, China); vigorous climber, with red, smooth vines, tendrils with sticky tips, and foliage with 3 stalked, ovate, toothed leaflets 5-12 cm long, olive green and smooth above, and with depressed veins; underneath reddish, and downy on the midrib; flowers yellow-green. *p. 2124*

quinquefolia (Ampelopsis, Vitis) (U.S.: New England to Florida and Texas), "Virginia creeper", or "American ivy"; vigorous climber with smooth stems having tendrils with 5-12 branches; sticky-tipped; large palmate foliage with usually 5 coarsely toothed dull green leaflets 4-15 cm long, glaucous beneath, turning crimson-red in autumn; small blue-black berries; frost-hardy. *Temperate to Subtropic.* *p. 2122*

quinquefolia vitacea (P. inserta) (E. Canada to Texas), a "Virginia creeper" known in California greenhouses as 'Cissus sicyoides', and grown there on treefern poles, an attractive decorative plant, with lustrous deep green, palmately compound leaves, the 5 leaflets lanceolate and deeply toothed, vines climbing by tendrils without disks; fruit bluish-black. (h) *p.2120*

tricuspidata (Vitis veitchii) (Japan, China), "Boston-ivy" or "Japanese ivy"; popular, quick-growing deciduous climber attaching itself to walls and houses by their sticky-tipped tendrils; densely shingled, variable smallish foliage, mostly broadly ovate irregularly lobed and toothed, or trifoliolate, 5-12 cm wide; when adult occasional large leaves are produced 15-25 cm across; the shining green color changes to autumn shades of crimson; small blue berries. *Warm temperate.* *p. 2122, 2123*

tricuspidata 'Lowii'; attractive variety dense with 5 to 7-lobed leaves, often forked and resembling a butterfly, each wing with about 3 main lobes; the bronzy green changing to red in autumn. *Warm temperate.* *p. 2122*

x PASCHIA *Gesneriaceae* **S3HFM**

hybrida; alleged to be a bigeneric hybrid of Sinningia speciosa x Kohleria eriantha; known in the hort. trade also as "Gloxiloma" or "Sinningoloma"; originiated by Federico Pasch in Guatemala in 1953; both supposed parents have 13 chromosomes, but this parentage is doubted by P. Arnold and others who suggest that this may possibly be a hybrid between S. speciosa and regina, and re-crossed. Resembling gloxinia but with oblique flowers facing sideways (zygomorphic); the large frilled corolla a glowing purplish red; foliage silvery-hued typical of Kohleria eriantha. *p. 1276*

hybrida 'Guatemala'; a bigeneric hybrid clone (Sinningia x Kohleria) from seed Mr. Pasch gave me in Guatemala City and was sown and grown in a 12 cm pot at Roehrs greenhouses in New Jersey; handsome plant with velvety fresh green foliage 12 cm long; the flowers oblique dipping bells 5 cm long, velvety crimson with black-red in throat. *p. 1253*

hybrida 'Holtkamp' (Sinningia x Kohleria); this hybrid strain is grown by Holtkamp greenhouses in Germany, from seed originally received from R. Blossfeld - Luebeck; magnificent show plant with bronzy velvety foliage with pale veins; and large oblique flowers soft velvety crimson marked dark red in pale throat. *p. 1253*

PASITHEA *Liliaceae* **I2LBM**

caerulea (Chile); bulbous herb with distichous narrow-linear grass-like leaves; floral stalk branched with blue flowers 2½ cm across the spreading segments. *p. 1494*

PASSERINA *Thymelaeaceae* **I2HBD**

filiformis (So. Africa); evergreen, heath-like shrub with tiny, 3-angled leaves appressed to twigs; small 2 cm cream to reddish flowers in terminal clusters. *p. 2100*

PASSIFLORA *Passifloraceae* **I-S2-3LBM**

x alato-caerulea (pfordtii) (alata x caerulea), "Showy passion flower"; free-blooming hybrid well-known because of its large and showy, fragrant, axillary, 10 cm flowers with sepals white, petals pink, and a fringed crown purple, white and blue; with trilobed leaves. *Tropical.* *p. 1925, 2112A*

amethystina (Brazil); luxuriant climber with very slender stem, smooth leaves deeply 3-lobed, 10 cm wide; flowers 7 cm across, lapis-lazuli blue, corona rays deep purple. *Tropical.* *p. 1929*

antioquiensis (Colombia), "Banana passion fruit"; tendril-climber with slender stems, leaves either lanceolate and unlobed, or deeply 3-lobed with long slender-pointed segments; beautiful flowers rich rosy-red to 12 cm across, with long tube, small violet corona; fruit edible. *Tropical.* *p. 1928*

aurantia (mixta) (New Guinea to New Hebrides); vigorous climber with glossy green, deeply 3-lobed leaves; lovely starry flowers with rosy, convex petals, and blood-red corona; photographed in the rainforest in the mountains of S.E. Papua. *Tropical.* *p. 1929*

bryonioides (Mexico); slender vine with rounded leaves lightly 3-5-lobed; small 3 cm flowers white with violet ring around corona in center; 2½ cm green fruit ripens to black-purple. *p. 1926*

caerulea (Brazil), a showy "Blue passion flower"; religious symbol to early missionaries who saw in its greenish-white petals the 10 apostles at the crucifixion, in the blue, white and purple rays of the corona the crown of thorns, in the 5 anthers the wounds, the 3 stigmas the nails; cords and whips in the coiling tendrils of the vine, and in 5-lobed leaves the cruel hands of the persecutors. The 6-10 cm flowers keep best floating on water. *Tropical.* *p. 1925, 1929*

x caeruleo-racemosa (caerulea x racemosa); vigorous climber with glossy green leaves deeply 3 or 5-lobed; attractive 8 cm flowers with rosy-purple sepals and petals, the corona purple with white at ends of each filament, stamens and anthers pale green, the stigma pink. *p. 1924*

capsularis (W. Trop. America); climber with 3 to 5-angled stem, two-lobed leaves, downy beneath; 2½-5 cm flowers greenish-white or yellow-green, pale yellow spreading corona. *Tropical.* *p. 1924, 1928*

cinnabarina (Australia); slender climber with 12 cm 3-lobed foliage; scarlet 6 cm flowers star-like with 5 long sepals, the petals shorter, the corona yellow; green, aromatic fruit. *Tropical.* *p. 1926*

coccinea (Trop. So. America), a "Red passion flower"; climbing with grooved purplish downy stems, leaves 8-15 cm long, ovate and coarsely crenate; free-blooming with flowers of medium size, with glowing scarlet petals, red sepals yellowish outside, the crown filaments deep purple, pink to white base; ovoid yellow or orange fruit 5 cm dia., and edible. *Tropical.* *p. 1927, 1930*

x colvillei (caerulea x incarnata); charming tendril climber with deeply 3-5-lobed or digitately compound leaves; flowers to 10 cm across, white petals, corona blue at tips, wine-colored in center, white between; fruits orange. *p. 1928*

coriacea (So. Mexico to Perú), "Bat-leaf vine"; vigorous climber with red stems, interesting mainly because of its hard to being brittle, transversely oblong-peltate leaves, more broad than long like a butterfly, blue-green blotched with silver-gray; small 2½ cm flowers in clusters, with pale green petals, a yellow ray-crown, and purplish-chocolate base. *Tropical.* *p. 1924*

edulis (Brazil), the "Purple granadilla"; sturdy climber with angular stems, large 15 cm leaves deeply lobed, with wavy edges; 6 cm white flowers, its corona white banded with purple, mostly summer-blooming; the 8 cm aromatic, edible fruit thickly purple-dotted and quite ornamental; widely grown in warm climates for its delicious flavor in beverages, fruit salads, sherbets, also jam and marmalade; fruiting in spring and fall. *Tropical.* *p. 1926, 1927*

x exoniensis (antioquiensis x mollissima); climber with downy stems and leaves, 3-lobed almost to base, green, 10 cm long; flowers 10-12 cm across, with long purple tube, sepals and petals rose-pink, small whitish corona. *p. 1928*

holosericea (Central America); tall-climbing, densely downy, with smooth leaves lightly lobed to 8 cm wide; fragrant flowers 4 cm across, in axillary double clusters, the sepals white or lemon-yellow, petals white spotted with red, corona rays deep yellow with purple base; several flowers at each node. *Tropical.* *p. 1929*

'Imperatrice Eugenie' (alata x caerulea); famous hybrid; tendril-climbing, with deeply 3-lobed rich green leaves; flowers 50% larger than caerulea, measuring 10-16 cm across; white sepals, rosy-purple petals, ray-crown purple and white. *Tropical.* *p. 1928*

incarnata (Virginia to Florida and Texas); "Wild passion flower"; tall climber with 3-lobed leaves and axillary 5 cm flowers, the sepals pale lavender with a horn-like point, petals white, corona with purplish filaments; yellow, egg-shaped fruit. *p. 1924, 1925, 1928*

maculifolia (Venezuela), "Blotched-leaf passion vine"; attractive climber with lightly hairy, wiry stem and curious, nearly triangular leaves, having three brief lobes at the cut-off apex, the quilted surface green, irregularly spotted and marbled with yellow; the underside purple and glandular-hairy; small creamy-white flowers. Also known as maculosa and organensis. *Tropical.* *p. 1930*

maliformis (Trop. America), (naturalized on Tonga, South Pacific); strong tendril-climber to 6 m; ovate green leaves 15 cm long; fragrant flowers to 10 cm across, sepals green, petals greenish-white spotted purple, rays of corona white and violet; edible 5 cm yellow fruit within hard green capsule. Juice with grape-like flavor. *Tropical.* *p. 1928*

manicata (ignea) (Colombia, Ecuador, Perú); strong climber, with angled stems, finely downy; leathery, 3-lobed, toothed leaves to 10 cm wide; flowers 10 cm across, vivid scarlet with tiny blue crown; fruit yellowish-green. *p. 1928*

mollissima (Tacsonia); according to Hortus, from the Andes of S. America; but on expedition in the New Guinea highlands, I found this species at the remote Chimbu Pass, beyond Goroka; rambling tropical tendril climber, with deeply 3-lobed leaves, and flowers 8 cm across on long tube, a lovely pink with pale center; pendant oblong 8 cm fruit yellow, insipid taste when eaten. *p. 1927, 1929*

platyfolia (El Salvador); robust climber with deeply lobed leaves; flowers with sepals and petals white and purple, filaments barred dark purple; produces delicate orange-colored, large fruit. *p. 1929*

quadrangularis (Trop. America), "Giant granadilla"; robust climber with winged stems and oval leaves, much grown in the tropics for its edible fruit, which is oblong, 12-25 cm long, yellowish green and pulpy; 8-12 cm fragrant flowers with oval, white sepals, reddish petals, and crown with 5 rows of white and purple rays. *Tropical.* *p. 1925, 1927, 1930*

racemosa (princeps) (Brazil), a "Red passion-vine"; climbing by tendrils, with deeply 3-lobed or occasionally ovate leaves; 10 cm flowers in pendulous racemes, the narrow petals rosy-crimson and spreading, the fringed crown with outer rays purple tipped white, the short inner rays red. *Tropical.* *p. 1927, 1930*

rubra (West Indies); climbing 3 to 5 m high; stems softly downy; 2-lobed or sometimes 3-lobed 5-12 cm quilted leaves purplish beneath; flowers 5 cm across, sepals and smaller petals light carmine rose, outer rays of corona reddish-purple; 2 cm red fruit. *Tropical.* *p. 1927*

subpeltata (Mexico to Venezuela); smooth climber with 3-lobed leaves 5-10 cm across; 5 cm flowers with sepals green outside, white inside, and with green horn, narrower petals; filaments of corona white; egg-shaped fruit green ripening yellowish. *p. 1924*

tetraden (Amazonas); rambling vine with coarse leaves and large 12 cm flowers of blazing scarlet-red; I remember seeing it growing in the red soil, favoring sunny clearings in the primeval forest, on the upper Amazon. *p. 1924*

trifasciata (Venezuela, Brazil, Perú), "Three-banded passion vine"; ornamental climber with wiry stems and broad, beautifully colored, lightly 3-lobed leaves, satiny olive to deep bronze-green with 3 broad, pink to silvery-green zones along the purple veins, and purple beneath; small, fragrant, yellowish flowers 3 to 4 cm across; globose $2^1/_2$ cm fruit. *Tropical.* *p. 1926, 1930*

violacea (Brazil, Paraguay, Bolivia), "Purple passion flower"; tall climber with trifoliate leaves, the segments occasionally lobed again, gray-green beneath; fragrant 10 cm, pretty flowers pendant from long stalks, sepals pinkish-lilac, petals violet, crown with violet and white rays. *Tropical.* *p. 1924, 1926, 1929*

vitifolia (Tacsonia) (Nicaragua to Perú), "Crimson passion flower"; climber with rusty-downy stems and grape-like leaves, coarsely toothed; showy, 10-15 cm flowers orange-scarlet to blood-red, with bristle-tipped sepals, outer rays of corona bright red, the shorter, inner ones pale red; shy bloomer. *Tropical.* *p. 1924*

PATERSONIA *Iridaceae* **I2LB-FM**

longiscarpa (Eastern Australia); perennial herb with short rhizome, the rigid, linear leaves arranged in a fan, 15-50 cm long; the floral stalks with flowers 3 cm across, the tube velvety and the 3 spreading petals purple with yellow stamens and cream stigma; the blooms emerging one at a time from two leafy, brown bracts, and lasting only a few daylight hours. *p. 1339*

PATRINIA *Valerianaceae* **C2LBM**

triloba (Japan); hardy perennial to 40 cm, hairy at nodes and on stalks; leaves heart-shaped, palmately 3-5-lobed to entire, lower ones coarsely serrate; flowers golden-yellow, in branched clusters to 10 cm across. *p. 2107*

PAULLINIA *Sapindaceae* **S3LFM**

thalictrifolia (Brazil); tendril-bearing climbing shrub, with leaves fern-like, tripinnate, light green, 10-20 cm long, bronzy when young; small flowers pinkish; grown as a greenhouse foliage plant. *p. 2038*

PAULOWNIA *Scrophulariaceae (Bignoniaceae in Hortus 3)* **C2LBD**

imperialis (tomentosa) (China); hairy tree to 15 m with broad ovate leaves to 30 cm long, entire or 3-lobed; tubular flowers 5 cm long, with spreading lobes, pale violet spotted dark inside in showy panicles. *p. 2059*

tomentosa (China), "Empress tree"; deciduous, hairy tree 12-20 m tall, resembling Catalpa, with horizontal branches; light green, cordate leaves 12-30 cm long; flowers before leaves, forming upright clusters of trumpet-shaped, fragrant flowers of lilac blue with dark spots and yellow stripes inside, 5 cm long. *Warm temperate.* *p. 502*

PAUROTIS *Palmae* **S2LBW**

wrightii (Acoelorrhaphe in Hortus 3) (So. Florida, West Indies, C. America), "Everglades palm"; cluster palm at home in the Everglades swamps, with slender trunks to 12 m, covered by red-brown matting and bases of leaf stalks; palmate nearly round leaves 60-90 cm dia., divided more than halfway toward center, with stiff segments light green above, silvery beneath, and split at apex; young plants have entire leaves not divided. *Tropical.* *p. 1889, 1894*

PAVETTA *Rubiaceae* **I3LFM**

caffra (So. Africa); small evergreen shrub to 1 m with smooth obovate leaves, and white tubular flowers with spreading lobes and long-protruding style, in clusters. *p. 2022*

indica (Sri Lanka), "Pawatta"; small tropical shrub 1 m high, with long lanceolate stalked leaves; flowers in clusters, similar to Ixora but with lobes twisted and with protruding styles; corolla white and sweetly fragrant. The foliage has little warts inhabited by bacterial colonies. *p. 2017*

PAVONIA *Malvaceae* **S3LFM**

intermedia (Brazil); possibly a form of multiflora, very variable; shrubby plant with spear-shaped glossy, rich green leaves, rough beneath, and with smooth or barely toothed margins, 15-20 cm long; inflorescence with small purple flowers and showy crimson red bracts, unfolding into flaring narrow filaments and revealing pink style and purple stamens. *Tropical.* *p. 1533*

intermedia 'Kermesina'; a commercial form of compact habit, the inflorescence with scarlet petals, and feathery carmine-red bracts. Charming winter bloomer. *Tropical.* *p. 1533*

intermedia rosea hort. (Brazil); evergreen shrub with lanceolate, lightly toothed leaves, and rosy flowers in terminal clusters, with long stamens and bluish anthers. Foliage variable, margins smooth or barely toothed. *p. 1528*

multiflora (wiotii) (Brazil); robust tropical shrub with lanceolate, toothed, slender-pointed leaves and unusual flowers in terminal clusters, with many hairy, narrow red bracts in whorls below calyx, the calyx purplish, and purple corolla rolled together; September. *Tropical.* *p. 1526*

PEDDIEA *Thymelaeaceae* **I2LBD**

africana (Cape Prov. to E. Transvaal); evergreen branching shrub to 4 m high; elliptic, thin-leathery 8 cm leaves shining dark green; inflorescence in umbels of 12-16 pale green, slightly scented, tubular flowers. *p. 2101*

PEDILANTHUS *Euphorbiaceae* **S2-3LFM**

bracteatus (Mexico); succulent bush with smooth stems, fleshy oblong leaves 8-10 cm long, occasionally notched at tips and rounded at base; the inflorescence with large crimson lacquered bracts subtending the greenish flowers. *Subtropic.* *p. 1061*

smallii (Brazil); similar to tithymaloides variegatus; stout stem with sparse foliage, gray-green leaves edged and variegated white, margins turned upward or crested, in boatshape. *p. 1053*

tithymaloides cucullatus (C. America), "Devil's backbone"; erect, blackish-green, zigzag, fleshy stems with 2 rows of alternate, lanceolate leaves somewhat convex, pale green tinged red, dark green along midrib. *p. 1053*

tithymaloides nanus (Venezuela); dwarf branching plant with erect glossy stems closely set with two rows of small lanceolate, leathery black-green leaves which leave pale scars when dropping off. *p. 1053*

tithymaloides 'Variegatus' (W. Indies), "Zigzag plant"; branching succulent bush with milky juice, gray green, fleshy stems bent with each waxy, pale green, ovate leaf, highly variegated white, and tinged carmine-red; flowers red. *Tropical.* *p. 1053, 1061, 2092*

PEIXOTOA *Malpighiaceae* **S3LFM**

glabra (Brazil); shrubby climbing plant with wiry stems, at intervals with round clusters of frilled yellow flowers. *p. 1525*

PELAGODOXA *Palmae* **S3LBD**

henryana (Marquesas, French Polynesia), "Vahana palm"; unusual feather palm with brown trunk to 8 m tall and 20 cm thick, without crown-shaft; spectacular leaves 3 m long, pinnately veined but undivided except for apex and notched margins, vivid green above, silvery underneath; 10 cm fruit. *Tropical.* *p. 1897, 1899*

PELARGONIUM *Geraniaceae* ***C-I2LBD**

abrotanifolium (Cape Prov.), aromatic "Southernwood" or "Hazelnut scented"; shrub with erect wiry branches and tiny, lacy white hairy leaves divided into narrow linear lobes; the long-spurred white flowers flushed pink, upper petals with a red spot. *p. 1174, 1182, 1188*

acerifolium foliis variegatis; variegated-leaved form of the Maple-leaved geranium with its deeply lobed foliage edged with creamy-white; shrub to 1 m with leaves having 3-5 angular lobes, hairy above, about 8 cm across; flowers purple with dark streaks. *p. 1178*

acetosum (So. Africa); shrubby plant of climbing habit with slender stems and waxy, cupped fan-shaped, silver green leaves shallowly lobed at apex; the curiously spidery flowers have rosy-salmon, narrow-linear petals. *p. 1172, 1173, 1186*

acraeum (So. Africa: Transvaal, Cape Prov.); small species with weak stems and variable leaves, green and more or less hairy; the flowers of good texture, with petals light rose marked with red lines. *p. 1175*

'Alliance' (hortorum x peltatum); a beautiful, semi-trailing geranium, with thick arching or lax stems; gray, zoned leaves with variable lobing; long-stemmed clusters of double flowers lilac-white marked rose. *p. 1211*

x ardens (fulgidum x lobatum), "Glowing storksbill"; short knobby stems with few stubby branches and large hairy, lobed leaves to 20 cm, deciduous; flowers garnet-red with lighter edge and dark spots on upper petals. Goes dormant in summer; blooms winter-spring. *p. 1173, 1186*

bicolor (So. Africa); scented like green almonds; leaves ovate in outline but pinnately lobed, the lobes toothed toward the tips, softly hairy; reddish-purple flowers with dark velvety spot in center and light margins. *p. 1188*

x blandfordianum (graveolens x echinatum); musk-scented; slender, spindly stems, rambling rather tall, with attractive bluish gray-green leaves, softly white-hairy, deeply divided into narrower segments than graveolens; small white flowers veined purple and spotted red on upper petals. *p. 1172, 1186, 1188*

'Brilliant': see 'California Brilliant'

'California Brilliant'; sometimes known as 'Brilliant'; hybrid showing influence of x domesticum and fulgidum, of bushy growth, with bright green, round leaves, shallowly lobed and sharply toothed, with scent of real musty woods; single cherry-red flowers pale in center. *p. 1172,1181,1188*

capitatum (Cape Prov.),"Rose-scented storksbill"; a shrubby plant with rambling stems and light green, shallowly three-lobed, ruffled, soft hairy leaves emitting a minty-rose fragrance; small lavender blooms. *p. 1188*

capitatum 'Attar of Roses'; strongly rose-scented; sprawling, shorter plant with leaves deeper lobed than the species, with slightly hairy surface; flowers orchid-pink with upper petals conspicuously veined purple. *p. 1188, 1189*

'Capri'; mildly-scented domesticum hybrid of bushy habit, with grayish-green variable leaves heartshaped or three-lobed, quilted surface and with prominent teeth; brilliantly scarlet flowers. *p. 1188*

carnosum (So. Africa); weird-looking succulent forming thick, twisted trunks, dense with soft and downy, lobed and cut leaves; umbels of tiny creamy-rose flowers. *p. 1179*

citriodorum: the old popular name for what is now known as 'Prince of Orange', which see.

citriodorum 'Variegatum' ('Prince of Orange' var.); attractive, robust plant with fleshy leaves scented of orange-peel, the deeply lobed leaves silvery green and prettily bordered with white. *p. 1176*

x citrosum (citriodorum); lemon-scented, crispum derivative; small 2½ cm rounded leaves, irregularly shallow-lobed and sharply toothed; pale rose flowers feathered red on upper petals. *p. 1188*

'Clorinda' (cordifolium hybrid); Eucalyptus-scented; habit close to domesticum but longer blooming, with large trilobed and toothed leaves, the flower clusters showy and with large rose-pink flowers marked dark carmine-red. *p. 1172, 1184, 1188*

'Concolor Lace' ("Schottesham's pet", "Filbert"); hazelnut-scented; compact, free-blooming plant with small, light green, softly hairy, ruffled leaves deeply lobed and toothed; bright scarlet flowers. *p.1172,1187,1188*

cotyledonis (So. Africa); woody plant with corky stem; small reniform or kidney-shaped, thick and corrugated leaves; small white flowers. *p. 1176*

crispum (So. Africa); mildly lemon-scented; shrub with rigidly erect branches, reddish petioles, and tiny round, crinkled, satiny green leaves, lobed and crisped, often held close to stem; used in finger bowls, or hung in closets; small lavender flowers. *p. 1172, 1188*

crispum minor; very small-leaved form of 'Lemon crispum', with crinkled leaves hugging the stem; usually branches well and grows bushy. *p. 1172, 1181*

crispum variegatum, known as "Gooseberry geranium"; mildly lemon-scented, with small crisped leaves variegated green with specks of cream, like a gooseberry-bush; flowers lavender. *p. 1186, 1188*

crithmifolium (Namibia); "Succulent geranium" with stout glabrous fleshy stem and lacy bipinnate succulent leaves, grayish green, clustered at end of branches and deciduous; umbels of small white flowers with a red spot on each narrow petal. *p. 1178, 1179, 1184A*

dasycaulon (So. Africa), "Succulent geranium"; bushy succulent shrub, forming a globose plant with numerous fleshy branches; leaves deeply pinnatifid and lobed; flowers with narrow petals, whitish with deep red spot in throat, in umbels. *p. 1173, 1176, 1179, 1192*

denticulatum (So. Africa), "Pine geranium"; pine-scented; branching, shrubby, sticky plant with dark green leaves cut down almost to the bare pinnate ribs, lobes toothed; small pinkish flowers marked crimson. *p.1172,1189*

denticulatum filicifolium, "Fernleaf geranium"; pungent-scented, reminiscent of pine; green leaf blades very finely cut and reduced to bare ribs, very lacy in appearance and delicately fern-like. *p. 1189*

x divaricatum (fulgidum derivative); absinthe-scented bushy plant with finely cut, feathery gray-green leaves; rosy blooms. *p. 1173, 1182*

x domesticum; "Martha Washington geranium" or "Regal geranium"; complex hybrids involving P. grandiflorum and other species; soft-hairy brittle stems, to 50 cm or more high; toothed leaves 5-8 cm across; large showy flowers 3-6 cm, in clusters in colors white, pink, red, purple, the two upper petals with dark blotches and veins. *Subtropic.*

x domesticum 'African Belle' (Belle of Africa); meritorious vigorous variety of the swarthy group, with large flowers 8 cm or more, all petals very dark red overlaid with black velvet bloom, and pencilled pink around the edges, center of flower pink with red veins. *p. 1172, 1173, 1216*

x domesticum 'Azalea'; free blooming "Lady Washington geranium" with clusters of large rosy-red flowers, the showy upper petals darker and each with a velvety black-purple eye. *p. 1216*

x domesticum 'Baby Snooks'; a pansy-type cultivar, early and free-blooming, with small flowers pale orchid pink, the top petals veined and with red-black blotch, the margins carmine. *p. 1173, 1214*

x domesticum 'Bimbo'; of low habit, flowers carmine-red with dark blotch on upper petals; early. *p. 1222*

x domesticum 'Burgundy'; flowers with wavy petals richly painted with black-maroon and crimson. *p. 1173*

x domesticum 'Carlton's Pansy'; a small-flowered vigorous pansy type with blooms slightly larger than 'Mad. Layal', and more white on lower petals. *p. 1173, 1214*

x domesticum 'Carmine Queen'; compact, low grower close with flowers bright rose-red with dark lines or blotches on all petals; free-blooming. *p. 1222*

x domesticum 'Chicago Market', "Martha Washington geranium"; bushy plant with an abundance of lavender blooms early in spring. *p. 1173, 1220*

x domesticum 'Chickadee' (Little Rascal); blooms in great profusion over long period; small-flowered pansy-type; lower petals lavender with violet eye, upper petals with deep violet blotch. *p. 1214*

x domesticum 'Chorus Girl'; shapely plant with ruffled flowers bright lavender, almost covered with vivid orange-salmon blotch, leaving a lavender throat and narrow edging. *p. 1223*

x domesticum 'Circus Day'; a premium cultivar with big heads of very large flowers rosy pink, the upper petals deep pink with velvety brown-black blotch flushed with salmon. *Subtropic.* *p. 1215*

x domesticum 'Congo'; crimson-maroon with rose edging and black lines in center. *p. 1173*

x domesticum 'Cover Girl'; strong, bushy plant, with ruffled flowers light pink, shading to white center, and with crimson blotch on upper petals; long-lasting bloom. *p. 1223*

x domesticum 'Dubonnet'; low growing, with beautiful flowers of an unusual bluish wine-red color. *p. 1173, 1223*

x domesticum 'Earliana'; of the dwarf "Pansy" type, bushy plant with 2½ cm leaves and small flowers orchid, the upper petals largely maroon shading through rose to the white margins. *p. 1172, 1173, 1216*

x domesticum 'Easter Greeting'; popular early and long-blooming variety; rosy-carmine flowers 6 cm across, each petal with a long black blotch. *Subtropic.* *p. 1217*

x domesticum 'Edith North'; good, free-blooming vigorous pot plant, with trusses of flowers well above the foliage; salmon pink, shaded deeper on upper petals and with blotches dark brown. *p. 1215, 1219*

x domesticum 'Empress of Russia'; beautiful variety of shapely habit, with all petals dark wine-red to blackish, edged nearly white. *p. 1173, 1218*

x domesticum 'Fire Dancer'; brilliant cultivar with plain green leaves setting off the vivid crimson of the well-rounded flowers; dark maroon blotch in center, and a narrow white edge all around. *Subtropic.* *p. 1221*

x domesticum 'Gay Nineties'; good commercial cultivar with large 6 cm frilled flowers white with crimson eye. *Subtropic.* *p. 1223*

x domesticum 'Grand Slam'; excellent, free-blooming premium variety of bushy habit, and with handsome umbels of large, good-holding flowers flame-red, with wavy margins, the top petals with velvety red-brown eye. *Subtropic.* *p. 1172, 1217, 1220*

x domesticum 'Grossmama Fischer'; favorite salmon pot plant of compact habit, early blooming with large wavy flowers of clear rich salmon, marked brown-black. *Subtropic.* *p. 1219*

x domesticum 'Haile Selassie'; flowers pinkish lavender, paling toward the margins, and a velvety brown-red blotch on each petal. *p. 1172, 1215*

x domesticum 'Happy Days'; low, bushy plant; salmon-pink flowers with blackish maroon blotch on upper petals. *p. 1173*

x domesticum 'Holiday'; distinctive cultivar of good branching habit, and free-blooming with large ruffled flowers white, with bold crimson blotch on top petals. *p. 1173, 1220*

x domesticum 'Jessica May'; good, early-flowering plant with light salmon-red blooms with wavy petals and blackish center. *p. 1221*

x domesticum 'Jessie Jarrett'; flowers of an exceptional shade of dark violet rose to purple with black maroon blotch on all petals. *p. 1219*

x domesticum 'Josephine'; compact plant of constant, free-blooming habit, the white flowers with rosy-pink blotches. *p. 1173, 1223*

x domesticum 'Kate Bornemann'; smallish ruffled flowers with lower petals white with pink tinge, upper petals pink tinted salmon, veined and blotched crimson. *p. 1172*

x domesticum 'La Paloma'; good early bloomer with large pure white flowers having a faint flush of pale mauve in center. *p. 1173, 1220*

x domesticum 'Lavender Queen'; popular, long-blooming variety with large flower clusters lavender blotched black-purple on all petals. *Subtropic.* *p. 1219*

x domesticum 'Little Rascal' (Chickadee); bushy, small-flowered pansy-type; flower petals light violet-crimson, upper petals blotched dark purple. *p. 1173, 1214*

x domesticum 'MacKay No. 2'; well-shaped commercial plant with flowers dark salmon-pink, and crimson blotches in center. *p. 1221*

x domesticum 'MacKay No. 12'; strong growing variety with pansy-like flowers lavender rose with white center, and purplish crimson upper petals. *p. 1219*

x domesticum 'Mackensen'; good, bushy plant with showy rose-pink flowers, each petal boldly lined with deep purple, forming a star. *p. 1222*

x domesticum 'Mad. Layal', "Pansy geranium"; compact, bushy French hybrid with small waxy, toothed leaves and cute, small, pansy-like flowers, the upper petals violet with white margin, lower petals white, tinted and veined rose. *p. 1172, 1173, 1183*

x domesticum 'Marie Vogel' (grandiflorum hyb.), "Lady Washington pelargonium"; popular, free-blooming variety with large, showy flowers 6 cm dia., rich salmon-rose, having crimson blotches on upper petals; toothed, glabrous leaves on hairy, brown-woody stems. *Subtropic. p. 1217*

x domesticum 'Mary-Elizabeth'; large old free-blooming variety with flowers watermelon pink to salmon-rose, lighter and veined at throat. *p. 1219*

x domesticum 'Mrs. F. Bachler'; deep rose-red with salmon sheen daubed red in middle of lower petals, the upper ones with black-purple blotches. *p. 1219, 1221*

x domesticum 'Mrs. Mary Bard'; compact grower and early bloomer, with medium-size flowers pure white, striped purple at base of petals. *Subtropic.* *p. 1184A, 1223*

x domesticum 'Neuheit C. Faiss' (Andenken an Carl Faiss); distinctive hybrid with flowers silvery bluish orchid like heliotrope, with long velvety violet-black blotch on each petal and with violet veins at base. *p. 1172, 1173, 1216*

x domesticum 'O'Homer Bryan'; free-blooming rosy orange-red blotched with brown. *p. 1172, 1216*

x domesticum 'Pansy'; "Pansy geranium"; pretty hybrid with 'Mrs. Layal' but with flowers 3 times as large; the lower petals white with purple lines, the two upper petals almost entirely violet-purple edged white. *Subtropic.* *p. 1219*

x domesticum 'Pink Conspicuous'; fine large ruffled flowers light pink, with dark blotch on upper petals. *p. 1172*

x domesticum 'Pink Fascination'; prolific bloomer of bushy habit, flowers very light pink, with crimson markings. *p. 1222*

x domesticum 'Pink Vogel'; upright grower with large flowers of rose-pink lower petals and deeper rose upper petals decorated with a black-crimson eye; free-blooming, over a long period. *p. 1215*

x domesticum 'P. M. Menzies' (Prime Minister Menzies); fiery red-orange blooms with maroon markings on a medium-sized, free-flowering plant. *p. 1221*

x domesticum 'Rouge'; compact plant with large ruffled flowers 6 cm across, deep cardinal red, slightly lighter around lower petals, and with large black eyes and dark lines. *p. 1223*

x domesticum 'Ruthie Eleanore'; old favorite, very prolific, with medium-sized, ruffled bright pink flowers, having dark crimson center. *p. 1218*

x domesticum 'Salmon Splendor'; bushy plant with striking, deep salmon flowers, with dark markings and blotch; early-blooming. *p. 1222*

x domesticum 'Salmon Springtime'; bright salmon-rose with light edge and white throat; excellent early-blooming. *p. 1220*

x domesticum 'Senorita'; gay orange-salmon flowers with dark crimson on upper petals; good bloomer throughout season. *p. 1218*

x domesticum 'Solano'; nice, bushy variety with flowers coral pink, feathered with dark maroon; free-blooming in season. *p. 1219*

x domesticum 'South American Bronze'; unusual color form with flowers bronzy-red, or brown and maroon, with dark center and pale orchid border. *p. 1218*

x domesticum 'Springtime'; lovely, long-blooming variety with white flowers 6 cm across, prettily edged bright rose, and dainty, ruffled white margin. *Subtropic.* *p. 1172, 1184A, 1217*

x domesticum 'Sunset Magazine'; strong, bushy-growing cultivar with extra large flowers, with lower petals pale pink, the upper petals nearly covered with dark crimson. *p. 1221*

x domesticum 'Swabian Maid'; old commercial variety, the medium-sized 5cm flowers carmine-rose, with darker upper petals and blackish-crimson blotches. *Subtropic.* *p. 1223*

x domesticum 'Topper'; strong-growing plant with good clear pink flowers, marked with crimson. *p. 1222*

x domesticum 'Vera Watts'; early, free-blooming variety with large circular, flat flowers of light salmon pink, all petals prominently veined crimson, the two upper ones blotched deep crimson-red. *p. 1216*

x domesticum 'Waltztime'; large ruffled flowers appearing double, bright lavender-pink with dark blotch on upper petals. *p. 1218*

x domesticum 'Wedding Gown'; robust all-white cultivar with large ruffled flowers glistening white, without markings of any kind; long-blooming. *p. 1223*

x domesticum 'Wolfgang Goethe'; distinctive cultivar, prolific with striking ruffled flowers dark rose-red, with bold black blotch on all petals. *p. 1173, 1218*

echinatum (Cape Prov.), "Sweetheart geranium", a "Cactus geranium"; succulent stem with hooked, soft, thorn-like stubbles, and gray-green, lobed leaves, white hairy beneath; single white flowers marked maroon in the shape of a heart. Deciduous when resting. *Arid-subtropic.* *p. 1172, 1176, 1184A, 1185*

ferulaceum (So. Africa); succulent shrub to 60 cm high, with thick-fleshy stem swollen at nodes, the oblong leaves pinnatifid to pinnatisect, hairy on both sides; white flowers with narrow petals, the upper ones spotted rose. *p. 1174, 1180*

'Fingered Flowers'; same as 'Formosa', which see.

'Formosa', or **'Fingered Flowers';** of compact habit, and with curious small leaves palmately 5-lobed and crenate at apex; clusters of small flowers with 10 or more petals in flaming salmon except for the pale-colored notched and pointed tips. *p. 1172, 1173, 1183, 1186*

x fragrans (exstipulatum x odoratissimum), "Nutmeg geranium"; of branching, bushy and spreading habit, with small rounded, lobed and ruffled but variable, grayish leaves, soft hairy, on wiry petioles; small white flowers marked purple. *p. 1172, 1185, 1188, 1189*

x fragrans 'Snowy Nutmeg'; lovely cultivar of low habit, with the small leaves mainly grayish in the center, and cream-white in a broad outer area. *p. 1180*

x fragrans 'Variegatum', "Variegated nutmeg-geranium"; low, compact plant with small rounded green leaves irregularly variegated with white and strongly scented of nutmeg. *p. 1178*

fulgidum (So. Africa: Cape Prov.); shrubby plant with beautiful plush-like pinnately lobed grayish leaves covered with soft silky silvery hairs, and long-spurred flowers bright fiery scarlet, streaked with nearly black in upper petals. *p. 1173, 1184*

gibbosum (So. Africa), "Knotted geranium"; curious plant with shrubby climbing stem much swollen at the distant joints; grey-green, pinnately lobed, ruffled leaves; small, evening-scented, greenish-yellow flowers. *p. 1173, 1179, 1185*

x glaucifolium (gibbosum x lobatum), the "Black-flowered geranium"; with large glaucous leaves pinnately lobed and ruffled; long-petioled flowers striking dark maroon edged with gold, and sweetly fragrant in the evening. *p. 1172, 1173, 1181, 1183*

glutinosum (So. Africa), also called "Pheasant's-foot"; pungent-scented, large hairy leaves sticky to the touch, dark along ribs, deeply 5-7 lobed, and toothed; short-spurred flowers orchid pink blotched with crimson on upper petals. *p. 1172, 1182*

grandiflorum (So. Africa); a species responsible for the form and size of the modern 'domesticum' group; shrubby plant with small toothed, lobed leaves and relatively large pale purplish flowers with purple stripes on upper petals. *Subtropic.* *p. 1190*

graveolens (Cape Prov.), old fashioned "Rose geranium"; the rose-scented leaves of which are used in cookery, sachet, and for making perfume; bushy plant with deeply lobed leaves 3 to 6 cm across, appearing gray-green because of their covering of soft white hair; small blooms lavender pink marked purple. *Subtropic.* *p. 1172, 1174, 1185, 1188, 1189*

graveolens 'Camphor Rose'; similar to the species but generally coarser, with larger leaves and bristly-hairy, and scent is of camphor rather than rose; flowers rose-pink. *p. 1188*

graveolens 'Grey Lady Plymouth'; rose-scented, vigorous plant with spreading branches and regularly lobed and toothed gray-green, soft white hairy leaves with a narrow white line around the edges. *p. 1172, 1180, 1184, 1188*

graveolens 'Lady Plymouth', "Variegated rose geranium"; a lower growing and less vigorous mutant of graveolens, with lobed leaves quite small and deformed looking but more white variegation and less green than 'Grey Lady Plymouth'. *p. 1184, 1188*

graveolens 'Minor', "Littleleaf rose"; similar to the species but smaller in all its parts, with rough hairy, deeply lobed, small leaves; flowers deeper in color, the narrow petals lavender rose with crimson markings. *p. 1189*

graveolens 'Variegatum', "Mint-scented rose"; an elegant plant having the largest leaf of all variegated rose-geraniums, pale grayish green, deeply lobed and prettily edged in white; however, in place of the rose fragrance it has a strong odor of mint. *p. 1172, 1180, 1188, 1190*

grossularioides (So. Africa), "Gooseberry geranium"; coconut-scented, small rounded, glossy leaves with closely toothed, scalloped margin, resembling those of a gooseberry; trailing on slender, wiry stems; small rosy-red flowers; fairly hardy. *p. 1182*

x hortorum (So. African origin), "Zonal geranium"; as grown by commercial nurseries today, these are of complex hybrid origin, largely derived from P. zonale and inquinans, familiar as potplants, in window boxes or in garden beds. Succulent stems 30-50 cm high with rounded or kidney-shaped leaves 6-10 cm across, often colorfully zoned or variegated; the flowers varying from 3-5 cm across, in showy clusters, with petals nearly equal, in many vivid colors, primarily scarlet red, purple, soft pink or salmon, pure white, or bicolor, also double-flowered and miniatures; in many fancy-named cultivars. *Subtropic.*

x hortorum 'Alcyone'; attractive dwarf with rich green almost zoneless leaves and large single flowers orange-salmon with narrow petals. *p. 1172, 1173, 1206*

x hortorum 'Aldebaran'; a Carlton dwarf, with brilliant, single rose-pink flowers and small dark green leaves with dark zone. *p. 1172*

x hortorum 'All Aglow'; old variety medium-tall, free-blooming with large semi-double flowers very dark red with small white center. *p. 1197*

x hortorum 'Alpha'; colored-leaf geranium of small, bushy habit, with thin, hard stems; smallish, shiny yellow-green leaves with narrow rust-red zone; attractive single scarlet flowers in great profusion. *p. 1172, 1204, 1210*

x hortorum 'Alphonse Ricard' (Bruant 1894); a popular commercial "French" type geranium, with large semi-double scarlet flowers. *p. 1195*

x hortorum 'Altair'; semi-dwarf with lovely double flowers salmon-orange; dark green foliage. *p. 1172, 1173*

x hortorum 'Antares'; miniature geranium with dark foliage and large, single flowers in dark burning scarlet. *p. 1172, 1173, 1184A, 1206*

x hortorum 'Appleblossom' (Mme. Jaulin); French type, habit small and bushy, large heads of cupped appleblossom flowers, semi-double, delicate soft pink, almost white at margins. *p. 1195*

x hortorum 'Appleblossom Rosebud', "Rosebud geranium"; compact and bushy plant with dense clusters of beautiful double white flowers edged pink, and resembling miniature roses. *p. 1172, 1173, 1211*

x hortorum 'Arcturus'; semi-dwarf, bushy plant, and free blooming with bright scarlet, double flowers. *p. 1172, 1173, 1210*

x hortorum 'Attraction'; vigorous, bushy plant with slightly silvered, bright green leaves, with ivory border narrower and paler than 'Flowers of Spring'; small single, scarlet flowers. *p. 1172, 1204*

x hortorum 'Autumn'; large double flowers soft orange-apricot, with white center. *p. 1197*

x hortorum 'Bantam'; bushy dwarf, with dark leaves, and large double, reddish-salmon or rosy flowers. *p. 1173*

x hortorum 'Beckwith's Pride'; a silver-leaved French type with variable foliage, from solid green to all-white, but usually streaked and segmented with ivory-white, and with faint brown zone; the flowers semi-double, scarlet, of fair size. *p. 1172*

x hortorum 'Better Times'; commercial cultivar with large semi-double flowers salmon-scarlet fading lighter, and with crimson lines; low growing, compact plant with medium green foliage. *Subtropic.* *p. 1196*

x hortorum 'Bismarck' (Prince Bismarck); a fancy-leaved geranium, lobed gold leaf with wide rust-red ring, and single salmon flowers. *p. 1172*

x hortorum 'Black Diamond'; a revert from 'Mrs. Cox', medium-large variety with neat foliage velvety green and very broad zone of blue grape purple suffusing older leaves, wine-red beneath; single salmon flowers. *p. 1172, 1202*

x hortorum 'Black Knight'; Dutch semi-dwarf, with dark green, well-zoned foliage, and orange-scarlet single flowers. *p. 1173*

x hortorum 'Black Lace'; unusual cultivar of low habit, and ruffled flowers deep maroon-red, almost pure black; free-blooming. *p. 1220*

x hortorum 'Black Vesuvius'; very dwarf plant with dark olive-green small leaves zoned blackish brown, and relatively large orange-scarlet, single flowers. One of the oldest dwarfs. *p. 1173, 1206*

x hortorum 'Bronze Beauty'; favorite slow-growing plant with large round golden-green leaves with a narrow red-brown zone and scalloped margins; single light salmon flowers. The 'Bronze Beauty' grown in the West, also known as Bronze Beauty No. 1. *p. 1172, 1204*

x hortorum 'Bronze Beauty No. 2'; more delicate with foliage a lighter golden tone and a striking wide red-bronze zone; single vermilion flowers. This is 'Bronze Beauty' as grown in the East. *p. 1172*

x hortorum 'Brooks Barnes'; dwarf, slow-growing geranium with very dark leaves, and large single flowers a lovely soft salmon pink. *p. 1172, 1173, 1206*

x hortorum 'Brownie'; dwarf variety, with new leaves golden brown, and chocolate zone; scarlet single bloom. *p. 1173, 1209*

x hortorum 'Bumble Bee'; dwarf, with large rounded, single, deep crimson red flowers, and small foliage distinctly zoned. *p. 1173*

x hortorum 'California Appleblossom', or 'Appleblossom single'; eye-catching geranium with large single flowers fiery cherry-red and contrasting to white in center. *Subtropic.* *p. 1195*

x hortorum 'Caligula'; dwarf variety, with small leaves prettily zoned dark brown; double flowers clear crimson-red. *p. 1173*

x hortorum 'Capella'; miniature geranium with plain foliage and a head of double flowers with narrow petals which tend to curl up, pale pink, flushed and striped with red. *p. 1173, 1206*

x hortorum 'Carefree Coral' (Panamerican Seed Co. 1974); with bright coral-salmon flowers, one of several outstanding color-forms of a new race of garden geraniums; these F[1] hybrids or heterosis seed strain of single and double garden geraniums are grown directly from seed and are available also in shades of pink and red, also bicolors and white; the flower heads can measure 10 cm across, and its dark green foliage is prettily zoned. *p. 1191*

x hortorum 'Carefree Deep Salmon'; All-American selection 1974 as an outstanding color form of the new F[1] hybrid strain of single and double geranium by Pan-American Seed Co., grown directly from seed. Geraniums from seed do not bloom as early as those propagated from cuttings but begin to come into flower in June-July and are at their best from August to October. For early bloom seed has to be started warm 21-24°C. in January. *p. 1213*

x hortorum 'Carlton's Velma'; attractive cultivar with tricolored foliage, similar to 'Mrs. H. Cox', but of stronger growth, with larger leaves. *p. 1202*

x hortorum 'Carmel'; outstanding, strong-growing variety with single white flowers and rosy-red edging to each petal. *p. 1194*

x hortorum 'Cinderella'; very pretty, small white flowers with pink edge. *p. 1194*

x hortorum 'Cloth of Gold'; fine, unzoned yellow-green foliage, with single bright pink flowers. *p. 1172*

x hortorum 'Damon's Gold'; fancy variety with large gold leaves zoned with a faint brown ring; single salmon pink flowers. *p. 1172*

x hortorum 'Dancer'; semi-dwarf of robust habit, dark-zoned foliage, and large single, orange-salmon blooms. *p. 1173*

x hortorum 'Dark Beauty'; free-blooming plant of trailing habit, with dark bronze scalloped leaves and single salmon flowers. *p. 1172*

x hortorum 'Dark Red Irene'; vigorous commercial plant profuse with large semi-double, rich red flowers similar in color to 'Radio Red', more resistant to shattering than regular 'Irene'. *p. 1196*

x hortorum 'Daybreak'; beautiful large round heads of semi-double flowers, fine rose-pink of good substance. *p. 1196*

x hortorum 'DeWitt's Dwarf'; dwarf plant with very dark leaves, and single flowers carmine-red. *p. 1173*

x hortorum 'Distinction'; old variety of small, spreading habit, with smooth, roundish leaves light green with a clean-cut brown-black circle just inside the toothed and crinkled margin; small single, cherry-red flowers. *p. 1172, 1204*

x hortorum 'Doc'; distinctive semi-dwarf similar to 'Scarlett O'Hara', with light green leaves; a good bloomer with large single, bright scarlet flowers. *p. 1173, 1206*

x hortorum 'Dr. Margaret Sturgis'; beautiful large-flowered single, mottled and striped rosy-pink in outer areas with large white center. *p. 1195*

x hortorum 'Dopey': see 'Rober's Dopey'

x hortorum 'Double New Life'; known also as 'Flag of Denmark', or 'Stars and Stripes', compact grower, free-blooming with double flowers, the narrow petals striped alternately scarlet red and white. *p. 1172*

x hortorum 'Dwarf Gold Leaf'; a golden-leaved variety of compact habit, with yellow to yellow-green leaves without zone; small single flowers brilliant scarlet. *p. 1172*

x hortorum 'Emma Hossler'; good semi-dwarf, bushy plant, free-blooming, double light pink. *p. 1173, 1210*

x hortorum 'Epsilon'; semi-dwarf with large full, single blush pink blooms with bright pink phlox eye; very light pea green foliage. *p. 1172, 1173*

x hortorum 'Etna Tillson'; dwarf with dark-zoned foliage, and single rosy-pink flowers. *p. 1173*

x hortorum 'Fairy Land'; striking little miniature, with small, dark gray-green leaves margined ivory, and edged in winter with pink or red, zoned with splashes of rosy-red; small single scarlet flowers. *p½ 1173*

x hortorum 'Fairy Princess'; semi-dwarf, with large single blooms of bright salmon; green foliage with dark zone. *p. 1173, 1208*

x hortorum 'Fairy Tales', free-blooming miniature, with large single ruffled flowers white with lavender pink tint, deepest in center. *p. 1172, 1173*

x hortorum 'Festival'; low growing, bushy plant, with prettily zoned leaves, and large round heads of double, rich salmon flowers, on long stalks; very free-blooming. *p. 1197*

x hortorum 'Fiat Queen', mutant of 'Fiat'; compact plant with large double, salmon-coral blooms, the margins of each petal notched; same color and good constant blooming habit as 'Fiat'. *p. 1197*

x hortorum 'Firefly'; rugged dwarf with brownish-green foliage; free-blooming with double orange-red flowers, having wavy petals. *p. 1173*

x hortorum 'Fleurette'; semi-dwarf; compact, strong-growing, with small dark green leaves; free-blooming with double orange-salmon flowers. *p. 1173, 1208*

x hortorum 'Flowers of Spring' (Mary Ann); shapely plant with slender stems and leaves glistening bright green with a wide, irregular white border; single vermilion flowers. *p. 1172, 1202*

x hortorum 'Fortune'; medium size, free-blooming, bushy plant, with long-stalked, large clusters of double white flowers, variably margined and flecked with pink. *p. 1198*

x hortorum 'Freak of Nature'; an old English (1800) fancy-leaf form of compact habit, with smallish leaves, ivory-white bordered with bright green, and ruffled at the edges; stems, leafstalks and flower stalks creamy-white; sparsely flowering with small single red blooms. *p. 1205*

x hortorum 'Fringette Pink'; sport of 'Pink Fiat' but with deformed flowers; unusual geranium, robust plant with zoned leaves and large semi-double salmon pink flowers with notched and fringed petals. *p. 1173, 1211*

x hortorum 'Fringette Red'; large semi-double notched and fringed blooms in red. Sport of 'Red Fiat'. *p. 1172*

x hortorum 'Galaxie' (Iowa State University) (Pink Cloud x Dark Red Irene) x (Pink Cloud x Cardinal); a new geranium raised by Iowa State University 1966; an eye-stopping scarlet-rose in extra large flower heads on stiff stems that resist damage in wind and rain; some individual florets measure over 5 cm across; its habit of growth is bushy and compact, with distinct zoning in the leaves. *p. 1191*

x hortorum 'Gallant'; vigorous grower of compact habit, and very free-blooming, good double salmon-red, of the Ricard type. *p. 1197*

x hortorum 'Genie Irene'; attractive, vigorous cultivar very free-blooming, large semi-double flowers an unusual clear pink. *p. 1196*

x hortorum 'Glacier'; medium-tall plant, good spring and summer bloomer; good double pure white, over plain green foliage. *p. 1197*

x hortorum 'Gleam'; bushy, free-blooming geranium; soft orange-salmon double flowers in small but numerous heads over the plain green foliage. *p. 1197*

x hortorum 'Goblin'; semi-dwarf with large double flowers bright red; dark green foliage. *p. 1172, 1173*

x hortorum 'Golden Oriole'; dwarf, free-blooming plant with golden scalloped leaves zoned with a red ring, single flowers salmon-pink. *p. 1172, 1204, 1205*

x hortorum 'Gypsy Gem'; a dwarf variety with small dark leaves; stout stalks with tight clusters of double-flowers, cerise red. *p. 1173, 1213*

x hortorum 'Happy Thought', "Butterfly geranium"; old English mutant (1877) of vigorous medium-large habit, with attractive, gaily colored leaves bright green painted cream-yellow in center, in shape of a butterfly, and zoned with splashes of brown; single 3-4 cm flowers glowing carmine-red, scarlet on upper petals, in clusters 8 cm across. *p. 1172, 1202, 1204, 1205*

x hortorum 'Hills of Snow'; small plant with slender stems and thin-textured leaves silver gray-green with narrow white edge; small double pink flowers. *p. 1172*

x hortorum 'Honeymoon'; bushy, slow growing, free-blooming variety, with large single flowers apricot-salmon, fading to lighter tint at margins. *p. 1198*

x hortorum 'Imp'; very dwarf, slow-growing, never more than a few centimeters high, small black-green leaves with black zone; single salmon flowers. *p. 1172, 1173*

x hortorum 'Improved Ricard'; excellent commercial cultivar, freely branching, of shapely habit, foliage only lightly zoned; and with good heads of large semi-double flowers light brick-red or orange-scarlet. *Subtropic.* *p. 1184A, 1196*

x hortorum 'Inspiration'; French type cultivar fairly small but free-blooming, the beautiful buds opening to large semi-double flowers in cream flushed with light salmon. *p. 1199*

x hortorum 'Irene'; good commercial, bushy plant with fine, zoned foliage, and free-blooming with semi double red flowers close to American Beauty cerise. Introduced 1942 and progeny of many excellent named varieties. *Subtropic.* *p. 1191, 1196, 1199*

x hortorum 'Jean Oberle'; also known as 'Double Apple blossom'; compact, bushy plant with plain green leaves faintly zoned; the large double blooms pale pink, changing to white toward margins; free blooming. *p. 1196*

x hortorum 'Jubilee'; sturdy plant with green-gold leaves having the widest and darkest brown to purple zone; small single, salmon-pink blooms. *p. 1172, 1204*

x hortorum 'Jupiter'; good dwarf variety with dark foliage, and rosy-red double flowers. *p. 1173*

x hortorum 'Kiffa'; a Carlton dwarf to 15 cm with unzoned leaves and of bushy habit; double flowers with curled petals pink and white. *p. 1172, 1173*

x hortorum 'Kleiner Liebling' (Little Darling); semi-dwarf, dainty plant 5-15 cm high with small $2\frac{1}{2}$ cm leaves plain fresh green; free-blooming with small bright rose pink single flowers. *p. 1172, 1173, 1210*

x hortorum 'Lady Cullum'; tricolor geranium of small bushy habit, leaves green edged with creamy yellow and the zone splashed with red but not as bright as 'Mrs. Pollock'; single flowers dull-red. *p. 1172*

x hortorum 'Lady Luck'; compact, bushy plant with cream-white stems, and fancy foliage with light green-gold center; dark red double flowers. *p. 1199*

x hortorum 'Layton's White' ('Appleblossom Pink' deriv.); excellent commerical seedling of heavy, sturdy growth, and a continuous prolific bloomer with heads larger than 'Mme. Buchner', and enduring double flowers very white. *p. 1195*

x hortorum 'Light-pink Bird's Egg'; a new cultivar of this old geranium type originated in France about 1900, free-blooming with lovely clear light pink single flowers heavily speckled with darker spots. *p. 1194*

x hortorum 'Little Trot'; known as 'Mme. Salleron Upright', with similar thin leaves, glistening green, irregularly and more deeply cream-edged leaf, and producing small, single pink blooms. *p. 1172*

x hortorum 'Luster'; good winter-flowering, medium-small geranium with large round, single flowers salmon-coral flushed violet. *p. 1194*

x hortorum 'Lyric'; dwarf cultivar of compact habit with dark-zoned foliage, and large semi-double flowers lavender pink with white center, freely produced in good-size heads. *p. 1213*

x hortorum 'Madame Salleron', "Carpet-bed geranium"; a unique, old French hybrid which I remember my father using in fancy carpet bedding; small plant sprouting multiple short branches from the base, with little papery, crenate leaves glistening gray-green with white border on long, thin petioles; rarely blooming, with small salmon-red flowers. *Subtropic.* *p. 1202*

x hortorum 'Magenta Rosebud'; also known as 'Rosette' or 'Crimson Rosebud'; medium tall plant with plain green leaves; very double blooms in tight clusters, of typical rosebud form, magenta or crimson-purple. *p. 1172*

x hortorum 'Marquis de Montmart'; very fine geranium of compact habit, and a bouquet of several stiff erect stalks with clusters of double flowers in an unusual shade of cerise-purple; listed by Merry Gardens, Camden, Maine. *p. 1213*

x hortorum 'Mars'; very dwarf, a miniature only 15 cm high, with dark green leaves heavily zoned; double flowers deep crimson-red, darker than 'Meteor'. *p. 1206*

x hortorum 'Maxime Kovalevski' ('Santa Barbara', 'Diablo'); medium size plant with big heads of large single flowers in clear bright orange. *p. 1195*

x hortorum 'Maximilian'; small tricolored plant introduced from Mexico, with lobed, bright green leaves outlined by a yellow border, the brown zone splashed with crimson and scarlet; distinctive because of its double orange-salmon flowers. (I-S) *p. 1202*

x hortorum 'Merope'; dwarf, stocky geranium with blackish-green foliage and semi-double dark scarlet blooms. *p. 1172, 1173, 1207*

x hortorum 'Meteor miniature'; bushy plant to 15 cm tall, with dark, black zoned, scalloped leaves and fully double, blood red flowers. (I-S) *p. 1173, 1206*

x hortorum 'Minx'; miniature with double purple-crimson flowers; dark green foliage. *p. 1172, 1173*

x hortorum 'Mischief'; miniature with dark foliage and double blooms with dark salmon red curled and twisted petals. *p. 1172, 1173*

x hortorum 'Miss Burdett Coutts'; a compact old tricolor with beautiful, firm, rounded leaves differing from others by its silvery hue, the leaf center is grayish-green, margins ivory-white, and the circular zoning deep blood-red splashed with rose-pink; single scarlet flowers. English hybrid 1860. *Tropical.* *p. 1172, 1184A, 1203*

x hortorum 'Missouri'; low, bushy, free-blooming plant, with foliage prettily zoned with brown; large double flowers salmon-red, similar to Red Fiat, but darker and more compact. *p. 1199*

x hortorum 'Mme. Fournier' (Scarlet Pimpernel); old dwarf, with very dark leaves, and small single scarlet flowers; very prolific. *p. 1173*

x hortorum 'Monmouth Red', (Moreau 1958); an excellent mutation from 'Moreau's Ricard'; of compact habit, very vigorous and free-blooming; smaller bright green foliage zoned gray-green; strong stems of handsome trusses of semi-double flowers bright vermilion scarlet, of good keeping quality. *p. 1195*

x hortorum 'Moonbeam'; showy semi-dwarf with robust, dark-zoned foliage, and single, full-rounded, salmon-pink flowers. *p. 1173*

x hortorum 'More Mischief'; attractive sport of the semi-dwarf 'Mischief' (orange-scarlet), a "cactus-flowered" geranium with blackish-green foliage and light coral-pink flowers veined deep salmon, the narrow petals rolled and twisted. *p. 1173*

x hortorum 'Morning star'; a "Raggedy-Ann", or "cactus-flowered" geranium, with plain green foliage and double, shrimp-pink or soft pink flowers. *p. 1173*

x hortorum 'Mountain of Snow'; low, bushy, spreading plant with thin leaves shimmering silver-green with broad white margins; small single flowers scarlet. *p. 1172, 1202*

x hortorum 'Mr. Everaarts'; free-blooming semi-dwarf, with pretty dark-green, zoned foliage; double dark pink flowers. *p. 1173, 1210*

x hortorum 'Mr. Wren'; a very striking variety with single, bright red flowers edged in white, but not very freely produced, on strong plants. *Subtropic.* *p. 1172, 1173, 1184A, 1201*

x hortorum 'Mrs. Henry Cox'; medium-size plant with tricolored foliage, grayish green center, followed by a rosy-red zone bordered in creamy yellow; salmon flowers. *Subtropic.* *p. 1172, 1184A, 1203*

x hortorum 'Mrs. Parker'; an excellent old free-blooming English variety of compact habit with shimmering green, rather thin, quilted leaves beautifully bordered in white; small semi-double, soft pink flowers. *Subtropic.* *p. 1172, 1203*

x hortorum 'Mrs. Pollock'; bushy plant having tricolor leaves with yellow margin, red and crimson break from the broad brown zone; single scarlet flowers. Famous fancy-leaved England 1858. *Subtropic.* *p. 1172*

x hortorum 'Mrs. Pollock double'; "Double tricolor"; popular tricolor leaf medium green to milky in center with dark red and orange splashed irregular zone, the scalloped margin creamy-yellow; semi-double and double flowers vermilion-red. *p. 1172, 1184A, 1202*

x hortorum 'Mrs. Pollock No. 137'; tricolor, a more robust and less colorful form, with single red flowers. *p. 1172, 1204*

x hortorum 'Mrs. Strang'; beautiful multicolored foliage silvery-green zoned with black-maroon and red, edged with gold and canary-yellow. *Subtropic.* *p. 1176*

x hortorum 'Multicolor'; compact plant, free-blooming with large single flowers pale pink, gradually changing to old rose. *p. 1200*

x hortorum 'Natalie Webster'; excellent Arndt hybrid of low, compact habit, fancy foliage with dark zoning; free-blooming, with single flowers bright salmon with white eye, the petals very rounded. *p. 1200*

x hortorum 'New Life' (England 1877); old-time but still a real lively collector's plant, of compact habit freely producing single flowers with round petals coral-red, flecked and striped white. Also known as 'Peppermint-stick'. *p. 1172, 1173, 1193*

x hortorum 'New Porter'; fascinating cultivar of exceptionally prolific growth habit forming large well-shaped plants in containers, covered with large clusters 12-15 cm across of single flowers vivid scarlet red; photographed in Vista, California 1973. *p. 1213*

x hortorum 'Night and Day'; bushy semi-dwarf with small dark green leaves and lovely large single flowers light pink shading to white; free-blooming. *p. 1173, 1207*

x hortorum 'Noel'; strong, bushy plant with double white flowers, odd with narrow, rolled and twisted petals typical of "poinsettia" or "cactus" flowered geraniums. *p. 1172, 1173, 1201*

x hortorum 'North Star'; semi-dwarf, of strong, bushy habit, the single flowers white, with pink veins radiating from center. *p. 1209*

x hortorum 'Old Rose'; of moderate growth habit; beautiful semi-double, soft rose, large flowers, with white center. *p. 1198*

x hortorum 'Olivia Kuser'; excellent, vigorous, free-blooming seedling with large single flowers pure white, the petals rounded and overlapping. *p. 1195*

x hortorum (zonale) 'Olympic Red' (Ricard x Radio Red); popular commercial geranium of early-blooming, free-flowering and branching habit; beautifully zoned leaves and large heads of semi-double, fiery red flowers each 3-4 cm across. *Subtropic.* *p. 1193*

x hortorum 'Orange Galore'; dwarf variety with orange-salmon, double flowers, with twisted petals. *p. 1173*

x hortorum 'Pastel'; medium size, bushy, fancy-leaved type, with silvery-green foliage irregularly bordered ivory, widely zoned with coral pink splashed purplish-brown; single flowers salmon-pink. *p. 1205*

x hortorum 'Patricia Andrea'; introduced and patented from Holbrook, Mass.; Gold Certificate New York Flower Show 1967; highly recommended commercial geranium of vigorous, free-branching habit, with deep green, waxy foliage, and large trusses 10-15 cm across, consisting of 40-60 firm cupped florets carmine-rose with pink shadings; early and continuous bloomer. *p. 1213*

x hortorum 'Peace'; dwarf, with foliage almost black, and full, salmon-pink, single flowers with darker flush in center. *p. 1173*

x hortorum 'Penny Irene'; excellent bloomer, with large heads of semi-double, dark pink flowers. *Subtropic.* *p. 1196*

x hortorum 'Perky'; semi-dwarf, bushy, compact plant to 25 cm with dark olive leaves, and large single flowers clear red with distinct white center; free-blooming. *p. 1172, 1173*

x hortorum 'Phlox New Life'; sport of 'New Life'; compact, free-blooming plant with single white flowers occasionally flushed pink, with soft coral eye. *p. 1173*

x hortorum 'Pigmy'; distinctive miniature about 15 cm high, self-branching, with 2 cm rather light green scalloped leaves; free-blooming with flat double flowers vivid red. *p. 1173, 1208, 1210*

x hortorum 'Pink Barney' (syn. Mad. Barney); bushy old French, strong-growing variety, with plain green foliage; very free-blooming, with small double flowers bright rose-pink, showing pale center. *p. 1199*

x hortorum 'Pink Cloud'; low, compact variety, free-blooming, with double light pink flowers, in full heads well above attractive foliage. *p. 1198*

x hortorum 'Pink Happy Thought'; not as vigorous as 'Happy Thought', with colorful leaves creamy yellow in center in shape of a butterfly, dark zoned and bordered green, and pink single flowers. *p. 1172, 1204*

x hortorum 'Pink Poinsettia'; a "Cactus-flowered geranium" of bushy habit and with twisted narrow petals orchid-pink. *p. 1172, 1173*

x hortorum 'Pink Rosebud'; compact plant with very double flowers that resemble miniature roses, rose pink with silver pink on underside. *p. 1172, 1173*

x hortorum 'Pixie'; favorite dwarf with dark leaves, and large, single, soft salmon-pink flowers. *p. 1173*

x hortorum 'Poinsettia'; a so-called "Cactus-flowered geranium" with flower clusters rather dense and globular; blooms double with narrow, rolled and twisted petals, bright scarlet. *p. 1172, 1173*

x hortorum 'Polaris'; dwarf plant with dark foliage, compact, with single white blooms tinted pink on margins. *p. 1172, 1173, 1207*

x hortorum 'Pride'; semi-dwarf, robust plant, with very large single, salmon blooms; free-blooming; stronger and larger growing type than 'Pixie'. *p. 1173, 1210*

x hortorum 'Princess Fiat'; mutant of 'Fiat', large double flowers with notched petals soft shrimp pink shading to an almost white picotee edge. *p. 1195*

x hortorum 'Prince Valiant'; showy, semi-dwarf, with dark foliage; single, vivid purple-crimson flowers flushed orange; good grower and free-blooming. *p. 1173, 1209*

x hortorum 'Puff'; a dainty, double "cactus-flowered" geranium with very narrow, rolled and twisted white double petals. *p. 1173*

x hortorum 'Radio Red'; tall grower with slender stems, light green foliage, and with a profusion of medium-sized double flowers intense clear crimson. *Subtropic.* *p. 1196*

x hortorum 'Red Brooks Barnes'; miniature, improved 'Black Vesuvius', orange-scarlet, single flowers; blackish foliage. *p. 1172, 1173*

x hortorum 'Red Comet'; miniature, with butterfly zoned foliage and single flowers with bright red narrow petals with white eye. *p. 1172, 1173*

x hortorum 'Red Fiat'; rich red sport of the salmon-pink 'Fiat'; constant bloomer with semi-double flowers, on self-branching plant with pubescent foliage. *Subtropic.* *p. 1196*

x hortorum 'Red Riding Hood'; practically a semi-dwarf version of 'Radio Red', very profuse with brilliant red double flowers. *p. 1173*

x hortorum 'Red Rosebud'; best-blooming rosebud type with bright scarlet flowers. *p. 1172, 1173*

x hortorum 'Red Spider'; semi-dwarf, free-blooming variety, with single scarlet flowers having narrow, rolled petals. *p. 1172, 1173, 1201*

x hortorum 'Red Streak'; dwarf plant forming woody base and short succulent stem with small zoned foliage; large heads of spidery red single flowers with narrow obovate petals. Listed by Merry Gardens, Camden, Maine 1972. *p. 1213*

x hortorum 'Reverie'; compact plant with numerous long-stemmed, round heads of double orchid-pink flowers, with some white in center. *p. 1198*

x hortorum 'Rober's Cerise'; dwarf, with dark, small foliage, and large round, single flowers a pretty lavender-pink with darker eye. *p. 1173*

x hortorum 'Rober's Dopey'; miniature plant with leaves dark green, the lovely single flowers rose-pink shading to white in the center like phlox. *p. 1172, 1173, 1207*

x hortorum 'Rober's Dwarf Red'; strong-growing semi-dwarf, with dark red double blooms. *p. 1173*

x hortorum 'Rober's Lavender'; semi-dwarf type, strong plant with dark green foliage, and large single lavender-pink blooms. *p. 1173, 1208*

x hortorum 'Rober's Sneezy'; bushy, free-blooming semi-dwarf with dark green, zoned leaves, and single to semi-double flowers scarlet shading to white. *p. 1173, 1206*

x hortorum 'Rober's White with Pink Eye'; semi-dwarf; large single blooms salmon-pink in center, fading to pale pink in outer area. *p. 1173*

x hortorum 'Robin Hood'; semi-dwarf, with prettily zoned foliage, and long-stemmed fiery-red double flowers. *p. 1173, 1209*

x hortorum 'Rocket'; dwarf with dark foliage, and deep velvety vermilion, double flowers, with purple cast. *p. 1173*

x hortorum 'Rosette' ('Double Poinsettia'); double "cactus" or "poinsettia"-flowered type of slender habit; shining crimson flowers with twisted narrow petals. *p. 1173*

x hortorum 'Rosy Dawn'; bushy dwarf remaining small even in age; blackish-brown, lightly zoned foliage; very double flowers with twisted petals a lovely shade of salmon orange-red. *p. 1172, 1173, 1210*

x hortorum 'Royal Fiat'; a lovely improvement over 'Fiat' (California 1919); large carnation-like $4^1/_2$ cm semi-double flowers of good substance, light clear pink with darker, rosy lines, remarkable for their sharply notched petals; small green foliage with darker zoning. This fringed beauty from California with its bushy habit is a charming window plant. *p. 1191*

x hortorum 'Ruffles'; very dwarf miniature, slow-growing but free-blooming at all seasons, with dark olive to blackish green leaves dark-zoned; flowers semi-double salmon with some ruffled petals. *p. 1172, 1173*

x hortorum 'Salmon Comet'; free blooming miniature with narrow-petaled, single, salmon flowers, and tiny leaves marked with a pretty dark ring. *p. 1172, 1173, 1206*

x hortorum 'Salmon Supreme'; distinctive commercial variety of the French type, more vigorous than 'Poitevine' and a freer bloomer but of the same fine, large semi-double flowers of clear light salmon pink. *p. 1193*

x hortorum 'S. A. Nutt'; old-fashioned Ohio commercial cultivar (1886), of compact habit, the dark foliage with bronzy zones, and free-blooming with numerous medium-sized clusters of smallish, double flowers in deep velvety crimson-red. *p. 1199*

x hortorum 'Saturn'; miniature with pretty, dark-ringed foliage, and bright red double flowers. *p. 1172, 1173, 1210*

x hortorum 'Scarlett O'Hara'; semi-dwarf variety with large bright red single flowers. *p. 1172, 1201*

x hortorum 'Sheratan'; semi-dwarf bushy little plant to 15 cm high; green foliage with medium dark zone, and double flowers rosy-carmine. *p. 1173*

x hortorum 'Shirley Summers'; freely blooming, bushy plant with attractive, medium large, double rose-pink flowers having irregular white margins and a white center. Sport of 'Pink Barney'. *p. 1193*

x hortorum 'Silver Ruby'; vigorous, fancy-leaved variety with gray-green foliage edged in white; double, dark red blooms. *p. 1172, 1205*

x hortorum 'Silver S. A. Nutt'; attractive, rather slow-growing plant, with silvery green leaves bordered and variegated with ivory white; double, velvety red flowers similar to 'S. A. Nutt'. *p. 1205*

x hortorum 'Silver Star'; "cactus-flowered" type of compact habit; single white flowers with petals appearing broader than in 'Puff', because they are less rolled. *p. 1173*

x hortorum 'Single New Life'; see 'New Life'.

x hortorum 'Sirius'; dwarf, free-blooming variety, with starry single salmon-pink flowers, shading to white in center. *p. 1173, 1208*

x hortorum 'Skelly's Pride'; charming cultivar with interesting flowers resembling carnations, the petals soft apricot and fringed along margins, in showy heads. Photographed at Merry Gardens, Camden, Maine; listed also by Logee's Greenhouses, Danielson, Connecticut. *p. 1213*

x hortorum 'Skies of Italy', "Mapleleaf tricolor geranium"; small plant of tricolored, maple-like leaves with pointed lobes, carried on slender petioles, green with creamy marginal variegation, and a brown zone tinted with orange-red and crimson; single scarlet-red flowers. *Subtropic. p. 1204*

x hortorum 'Small Fortune'; dwarf type; bushy plant with small, dark olive-green foliage, and large double white flowers, edged and flecked with pink. *p. 1173, 1208*

x hortorum 'Sneezy': see 'Rober's Sneezy'

x hortorum 'Snow White'; free-blooming semi-dwarf of Rober's 'Snow White and the 7 Dwarfs' series, with plain olive green leaves and extra large pure white, single flowers. *p. 1172, 1173, 1201*

x hortorum 'Southern Cross'; odd geranium of fair size, producing double coral-red flowers with narrow, rolled and twisted petals characteristic of the "Poinsettia geraniums". *p. 1172, 1173, 1211*

x hortorum 'Souvenir de Mirande' (Harriet Ann); bushy plant in constant bloom, with rosy-red single flowers, shading to white in center; apple-blossom type. *p. 1200*

x hortorum 'Sparkle'; semi-dwarf type, with dark foliage, prolific with semi-double, cheerful bright red flowers. *p. 1173, 1209*

x hortorum 'Sprite'; very miniature type with small silvery green and white foliage tinted pink; single flowers salmon-coral. *p. 1172, 1173*

x hortorum 'Tangerine'; miniature geranium, with small foliage, and large single flowers salmon tinted with orange; free-blooming. *p. 1173, 1209*

x hortorum 'Tempter'; bushy, semi-dwarf, with dark foliage, and large single purplish-crimson flowers. *p. 1173, 1209*

x hortorum 'Tiny Tim' (Pink or Red form); miniature geranium, with very small foliage prettily zoned with brown; either light pink or red single flowers; can be grown for years in same pot, and lends itself to bonsai training. *p. 1173, 1209*

x hortorum 'Trinket'; slow-growing dwarf variety, with small foliage, and large semi-double apricot-salmon flowers. *p. 1172, 1173, 1200*

x hortorum 'Tu-Tone'; shapely dwarf variety, dense with leaves, and semi-double pale pink flowers with white streaks. *p. 1173, 1209*

x hortorum 'Tweedle Dee'; semi-dwarf with small succulent scalloped leaves and single flowers with narrow salmon petals. *p. 1172, 1173, 1200*

x hortorum 'Tweedle Dum'; semi-dwarf with succulent foliage and single flowers with narrow petals darker salmon. *p. 1172, 1173*

x hortorum 'Twinkle'; semi-dwarf, spreading plant with dark leaves, and double coral-rose flowers of medium size, in clusters close to the foliage. *p. 1172, 1173, 1208*

x hortorum 'Variegated Kleiner Liebling'; small attractive slow-growing plant, with smallish, crinkled, grayish-green leaves with white borders; single rosy flowers. *p. 1173, 1205*

x hortorum 'Venus'; excellent miniature, bushy plant, with dark green foliage; double light flesh pink flowers. *p. 1172, 1173, 1210*

x hortorum 'Verona' (Pink Cloth of Gold); tall-growing, fancy-leaved variety with pure gold foliage and single light pink flowers. *p. 1172, 1201*

x hortorum 'White Bird's Egg' (Mrs. J. J. Knight); beautiful old type geranium, low growing and slow, with single flowers sometimes white, sometimes blush pink stippled with rosy-red dots. *p. 1194*

x hortorum 'White Magic'; large-flowered white geranium, with beautifully formed blossoms in graceful clusters, semi-double pure white; of bushy habit, and free-blooming. *p. 1198*

x hortorum 'White Wonder'; good commercial, free-blooming geranium with fairly large heads of double pure white flowers and attractive reddish anthers; an Eastern cultivar. An older, Western variety of the same name is said to have single flowers. *p. 1194*

x hortorum 'Wicked Lady'; low, bushy free-blooming hybrid, with pretty, dark-zoned foliage, and strikingly beautiful, large single flowers glowing purple, blended with violet and orange. *p. 1200*

x hortorum 'Wilhelm Langguth'; spreading plant of low habit, with attractive, glistening grayish green leaves bordered in white; double, cherry-red flowers. *p. 1172, 1203*

inquinans (South Africa); spreading species with hairy, brown branches and plain green velvety, fleshy 7-lobed leaves, toothed at margins; profuse with stalked clusters of vivid brownish-red single flowers, with petals almost $2\frac{1}{2}$ cm long. *Subtropic. p. 1178*

x jatrophaefolium (denticulatum x quercifolium); pungent-scented, with smooth, sticky, deeply cut leaves of few narrow lobes, the margins with sharp, finely serrate teeth; small light pink flowers with darker markings. *p. 1189*

'Jeanne' (cultivar of hortorum and peltatum); known also as 'Sweet William' or 'Carnation'; habit like a small garden geranium but with leaves intermediate in form; blooming with clusters of small single salmon pink flowers with notched petals like Dianthus. *p. 1172, 1173, 1211*

'Joy Lucille' (graveolens x tomentosum); musty peppermint scented; big vigorous grower of rangy habit, large green, white hairy, velvety leaves lobed like a grape leaf; flowers pink with red markings. *p. 1188*

juttae (Namibia); a curious low succulent shrub with short, tuberously thickened stem to 10 cm high, with brown skin, and a few short branches, bearing at their ends the long-stalked light green, downy, dissected leaves. *p. 1190*

x kewense; an English hortorum hybrid with thin, smallish green leaves lightly zoned; the 4 cm single flowers in large heads, 10-12 cm across, bright crimson, the two upper petals even more brilliant red than the 3 lower. *p. 1174*

'Kleiner Liebling variegated'; see x hort. 'Variegated Kleiner Liebling'.

'Lady Mary'; crispum derivative, mildly lemon-scented, similar to P. x citrosum in habit, the small lobed leaves more hairy, and the flowers larger and more brightly colored showy pink, the upper petals feathered and blotched. *p. 1172, 1187*

x limoneum, "Lemon geranium"; a pretty crispum hybrid and considered the true lemon-scented geranium used in old English finger bowls; small, three-lobed leaves crenate at apex, on longer wiry petioles than crispum; flowers small crimson-rose. *p. 1172, 1182, 1188*

'Little Gem', (graveolens hybrid); pungent-scented; pretty flowering plant with hairy leaves more lobed than graveolens, crenately toothed margins; blooms lavender pink with two purple lines on upper petals. *p. 1187, 1188*

'Lumière du Midi' (peltato-zonale hyb.), a "Strassbourg geranium"; a new French hybrid strain, photographed in Germany 1974, has become very popular in window boxes and outdoor containers for its prolific habit of bloom, even in dark and cool central European climate; single crimson-red flowers in smaller clusters, but literally covering the plants with masses of color, without requiring great care. *p. 1192*

luridum (So. Africa: Transvaal); interesting species with leaves in various forms; as seedling the foliage is rounded and only shallowly lobed, as the plant matures the foliage is progressively more dissected until in final form the leaves are divided into filiform, linear segments; large cluster of white to salmon flowers. *p. 1174*

'M. Ninon' (scabrum), "Apricot geranium"; apricot-scented; bushy, branched plant with strong stems with coarse leaves deeply lobed, the lobes divided again and overlapping, with margins toothed and curled; bright pink flowers with carmine spot and purple veins on upper petals. *p. 1188, 1189*

moniliforme (So. Africa: Cape Prov.); interesting species with fleshy leaves, and profusely blooming with salmon pink flowers having two broad upper petals blotched with crimson, the 3 lower, smaller ones plain pink. *p. 1175, 1176*

x moreanum (ignescens x dianthiflorum); attractive hybrid, much seen in South Africa, with brilliant brick-red single flowers; the upper, larger petals with dark velvety spot in center, free-blooming; the shrubby branches dense with deeply lobed, hairy, aromatic green leaves, the segments pleated. *p. 1178*

'Mrs. Kingsley'; a mildly-scented, bushy plant of fulgidum parentage, with rounded, light green leaves densely hairy, broad lobes folding into quilted ruffles and margins coarsely toothed; cherry-red flowers. *p. 1172, 1184, 1188*

'Mrs. Taylor'; graveolens type, free-blooming; not free-branching, with deeply lobed, smooth green leaves, the margins coarsely toothed, with a faint scent of musty fruit; pretty red flowers with upper petals marked deep purple. *p. 1172, 1189*

myrrhifolium (coriandrifolium) (So. Africa); prostrate, trailing branches with dark green ferny, bipinnate leaves, and lavender-pink blooms with darker rose markings. *p. 1173, 1181*

x nervosum, "Lime geranium"; lime-scented; an old English hybrid (1820), of bushy growth, with small rounded, green leaves with sharply toothed margins, and lightly ruffled; showy clusters of lavender flowers. *p. 1186, 1188, 1190*

odoratissimum (Cape Prov.), "Apple geranium"; low-growing sprawling plant with trailing stems and rounded, ruffled silky moss-green leaves, apple-scented; small white flowers with short spur, upper petals spotted red. *p. 1174, 1188, 1190*

'Old Spice' ('Logeei') (fragrans x odoratissimum); strong apple and nutmeg fragrance; low-growing, spreading plant with small grayish green leaves variously lobed and nicely ruffled; fluffy, white flowers. *p. 1188*

peltatum (Eastern South Africa), called the "Ivy geranium", because of the ivy-like, pointed 5-lobed leaves which are fresh green, waxy and rather succulent, 5-8 cm across, on trailing, zigzag branches; flowers normally single and rose-carmine, but now highly hybridized into many types and colors with single or double flowers, in rounded clusters, in white, pink, rose, red and lavender; the 2 upper petals usually blotched or striped. Ivy geraniums are ideally suited for hanging baskets, window boxes, patio containers or as ground cover. *Subtropic.* *p. 1212*

peltatum 'Album' (South Africa); an ivy-geranium with waxy, lobed leaves, producing clusters of white flowers with purple markings in throat. *p. 1174*

peltatum 'Duke of Edinburgh' (Mme. Margot); popular ivy-geranium with light silvery-green foliage mottled yellow and edged cream-white, or some leaves all-white; the small single flowers are salmon pink. *p. 1212*

peltatum 'Galilee'; old cultivar with clusters of double flowers a soft pink. *Subtropical.* *p. 1184A*

peltatum 'Gay Baby'; a miniature ivy-leaf geranium forming a compact head of small waxy leaves entirely covered by double flowers a soft pink. *p. 1213*

peltatum 'L'Elegante', an old French variety known as "Sunset ivy"; with beautiful waxy gray-green leaves edged in white, later adding a pink tinting or red border; small single white flowers with lavender tints, and darker markings in throat. *Subtropic.* *p. 1212*

peltatum 'Leopard'; a compact growing variety with rather short stems and relatively large, semi-double flowers orchid pink, veined and spotted cerise-red. *p. 1212*

peltatum 'Mexican Beauty'; dark sport of 'Comtesse de Grey', free-trailing; handsome ivy-geranium with semi-double flowers intense velvet-red; one of the finest colors in this group. *p. 1212*

peltatum 'New Dawn'; fine bushy variety, free trailing with lively green waxy leaves, and full clusters of double flowers vivid rose-cerise. *p. 1214*

peltatum 'Santa Paula'; fine ivy-geranuim, well branching, with medium green leaves, and double lavender flowers. *p. 1214*

peltatum 'Variegatum', "Variegated ivy geranium"; charming variety with silvery-green waxy foliage, having margins beautifully bordered with creamy-white. *Subtropic.* *p. 1174*

'Pretty Polly'; pungent-scented like almond, with 5-lobed leaves resembling P. domesticum; lovely lavender-pink, medium-sized flowers, with upper petals brushed and blotched with maroon. *p. 1214*

'Prince of Orange', "Orange geranium"; scent of orange-peel; a bushy branching plant with 5 cm light green leaves, broader than crispum and not as crisped, three-lobed, and dentate at the margins; white flowers tinged pink, upper petals veined purple; (syn. P. citriodorum). *p. 1172, 1186, 1188, 1190*

'Prince Rupert'; lemon-scented; branched and densely erect plant with small, crinkly, parsley-like, lobed leaves larger than crispum, shorter petioles; orchid flowers, the upper petals veined purple. *p. 1188, 1190*

'Prince Rupert variegated', also known as "French lace"; lemon-scented; habit of P. crispum but bushier and more prolific, the small lobed and crisped leaves are light green and prettily edged in white. *Subtropic.* *p. 1172, 1182, 1184A, 1188, 1190*

'Pungent Peppermint' (denticulatum x tomentosum); handsome plant with good minty scent, small but long, 5-lobed, downy leaves, and tiny white flowers with upper petals marked carmine. Also known as 'Mopsy'. *p. 1172*

quercifolium, "Oak-leaved geranium"; low, free-blooming plant with hard-textured leaves, deeply pinnate and with extra lobes, of medium size, veined purple; small flowers rosy-lavender with purple markings on upper petals. *Subtropic.* *p. 1172, 1190*

quercifolium 'Fair Ellen', "Oakleaf geranium"; upright plant with medium size oak-leaf having dark zoning; flowers bright magenta-pink with purple spot in upper petals; free flowering and the best true oakleaf variety. *p. 1172, 1189*

quercifolium giganteum 'Giant Oak'; musty oak-scented; deep green, sticky leaves twice as large as the species, usually 5-lobed, with cordate base; old leaves will turn red and yellow; smaller flowers bright rose with small dark spots, but somewhat shy to bloom. *p. 1172, 1189*

quercifolium 'Haviland', "Oakleaved geranium"; pungent-scented, shrubby plant with oak-shaped, rough-quilted leaves having 3-angled lobes on each side, deep green with pretty brown pinnate zone along midrib; deep orchid flowers. *p. 1189*

quercifolium 'Skelton's Unique'; sprawling variety with ruffled leaves, less deeply lobed, light green with brownish center, slightly tomentose; freely flowering lavender pink; good for hanging baskets. *p. 1189*

quercifolium 'Village Hill Oak'; bushy habit of growth, sticky, and pleasantly pungent-scented, leaves deeply lobed with rounded tips; lavender-pink blooms in dense clusters. *p. 1184, 1189*

radens (radula) (Cape of Good Hope), "Crowfoot geranium"; shrubby, free-blooming plant with musty-scented, feathery but coarse, twice pinnately lobed leaves, the upper surface covered with short, rasping hairs, and margins rolled under; flowers lavender-pink marked purple. *p. 1172, 1189*

radens 'Dr. Livingstone' ('Skeleton Rose'); similar to radens, but slightly taller and bushy, with deeply cut and lobed leaves; not a free bloomer but has a lovely lemon scent. *p. 1172, 1189*

radula (radens) (Cape Prov.); a balsam-scented rose-geranium; gray-green shrub to 1 m with 4-8 cm rough-hairy leaves deeply palmately lobed and pinnatisect into linear segments; flowers rose with purple markings in center. *p. 1178*

ranunculophyllum (So. Africa: Cape Prov.); herbaceous perennial with succulent stem and rounded, hairy leaves resembling ranunculus; showy single flowers with pale rose obovate petals, in large globular clusters. *p. 1174*

'Red-flowered Rose' (graveolens deriv.); faintly rose-scented, of shorter habit than graveolens, with deeply-lobed leaves; the cerise flowers bigger, with upper petals darker with black-red spot. *p. 1187*

reniforme (So. Africa); wiry stems with slender flowering branches, the kidney-shaped gray leaves densely white-hairy beneath; flowers pink-magenta, the upper petals spotted with black. *p. 1172, 1173, 1175*

'Rober's Lemon Rose' (graveolens x tomentosum); strongly spicy rose-scented, and distilled in California for its volatile oil for perfume, also used in cooking; shrubby plant with irregular leaves of several simple lobes, dark green and white tomentose; flowers pink marked crimson. *p. 1188, 1190*

'Rollison's Unique'; an old Irish variety, upright, somewhat climbing, with few branches; coarse, rounded, light green, hairy, ruffled leaves, roundly lobed and toothed; showy flowers cherry-red marked purple. *p. 1188*

'Roundleaf Rose' (capitatum x quercifolium); branching plant with lax stems, and large rounded, light green, hairy leaves lightly lobed and frilled, of a delightful minty-rose fragrance; small lavender flowers. *p. 1188*

x rutaceum (gibbosum x multiradiatum); stems swollen as in gibbosum but with larger, hairy leaves deeply divided, the more numerous segments pinnately cut and toothed; tall inflorescence with dark maroon flowers edged with greenish yellow. *p. 1173, 1182*

salmoneum (So. Africa); similar to P. zonale, with stems to nearly 1 m high, but the few 5 cm lightly lobed leaves scarcely zoned, somewhat glaucous, fleshy and soft-hairy; flowers with narrow petals salmon-pink, lined with red on the upper ones. *p. 1172, 1173, 1181*

scabrum, see 'M. Ninon'

scandens (So. Africa); lax plant with slender, flexuous stems and glossy-green leaves slightly zoned and shallowly lobed and toothed; long-spurred flowers pale lavender, the upper petals dark-veined. *p. 1172, 1173, 1185*

x scarboroviae ('Count of Scarborough'); strawberry-scented, branched plant with small rigid, glossy dark green 3-lobed leaves, margins toothed and crisped; attractive long-spurred, bright pink flowers feathered in red on upper petals. *p. 1172, 1184*

'Scarlet Unique'; an old English herbaceous fulgidum hybrid, lax with few branches, with large grayish-green leaves heartshaped in outline, roundly lobed and coarsely toothed, silky white-hairy and ruffled; showy scarlet blooms, the upper petals feathered deep purple. *p. 1181, 1188*

'Shrubland Pet' (fulgidum, capitatum, and quercifolium); a colorful, free-flowering hybrid with pretty rosy-crimson blooms marked with purple; the glossy leaves slightly tomentose on lax, spreading branches. Also known as 'Shrubland Rose'. *p. 1172, 1184*

'Snowflake'; distinguished rose-scented capitatum hybrid, also known as 'Roundleaf Rose variegated', with large rounded, hairy and frilled, light green leaves streaked with white. *p. 1172, 1187, 1188*

x stapletonii (echinatum and reniforme); succulent stems with stubby "thorns" or stipules, similar to echinatum, but with smaller soft velvety, gray-green lobed leaves, deciduous, white hairy beneath; flowers cerise or rose, the upper two petals white at base, all spotted red. *p. 1172, 1173, 1185*

'Sweet William' ('Mad. Thibault') (peltatum x hortorum); old hybrid with lightly pubescent, waxy leaves and small single flowers delicately pink, with white in throat and at the margins of the notched petals. *p. 1172, 1173, 1211*

tetragonum (Cape Province), the "Square-stalked cranesbill"; a peculiar, succulent plant of scandent habit and a quadrangular or triangular stem with small rubbery leaves and 4-petaled rose and white flowers with a long spur. *p. 1172, 1173, 1178*

tomentosum (Cape of Good Hope), "Peppermint-geranium"; strongly scented species of sprawling habit, with large, soft velvety, emerald green leaves, triangular-heartshaped, shallowly lobed, with a felt-like covering of white hairs; small, fluffy white flowers. *p. 1175, 1180, 1188, 1189*

tomentosum 'Variegatum'; attractive cultivar with the velvety, emerald-green leaves edged with creamy-white; of compact habit. *p. 1180*

'Torento', "Ginger geranium"; sweetly ginger-scented; similar to nervosum, of bushy habit, with larger, light green, rounded leaves evenly dentate at margin; fair-sized rosy-lavender flowers with darker markings on upper petals. *p. 1172, 1187, 1188, 1189*

triste (So. Africa); tuberous-rooted species with short, thick-fleshy, hairy stem, the large leaves to 30 cm long, 3 times pinnately divided and very feathery; the inflorescence in long-stalked clusters of brownish flowers with yellow margins, fragrant at night. *p. 1178*

'Ville de Paris' (peltato-zonale hyb.), "Strassbourg geranium"; color form of this new French hybrid race, introduced about 1965; profusely blooming ivy-leaf type geranium with thin-leathery leaves, and 3-4 cm single flowers with narrow-linear or obovate petals glowing carmine-rose with blood red stripes, in small clusters but forming a blanket of color with cascades to 1 m long, during summertime, even in sun-poor regions such as Northern Europe, where it has become immensely popular in window boxes and outdoor urns. *Subtropic.* *p. 1192*

violarium (So. Africa), "Viola geranium"; odd species with low spreading branches; long-stalked powdery-gray ovate, toothed leaves; and pansy-faced flowers, with lower petals white, the two upper petals ruby red with dark blotch. Nice in baskets and hanging pots, blooming in spring and summer. *Subtropic.* *p. 1175, 1192*

vitifolium (So. Africa), the "Grapeleaf geranium"; shrubby, shaggy plant with branched leafy stem, large, harshly hairy leaves light green, rough and lobed like grape; small rosy flowers with purple veins in upper petals. *p. 1183*

PELATANTHERIA *Orchidaceae* **S3OFW**

ctenoglossa (Thailand); miniature epiphyte with elongate, clambering stems with alternating 2-ranked fleshy leaves of vandaceous character; the inflorescence in short axillary racemes of small waxy flowers creamy-white, the petals with pink stripes, the lip rosy-purple with beard at apex. *p. 1807*

PELECYPHORA *Cactaceae* **S2LBD**

aselliformis (Mexico: San Luis Potosi), "Hatchet cactus"; globular to cylindric plant to 5 cm thick, with grayish green tubercles strongly flattened sidewise and in spirals, the minute spines arranged comblike and not prickly; flowers purple. *Arid-tropical.* *p. 728*

PELEXIA *Orchidaceae* **I3HFM**

maculata (Spiranthes) (W. Indies); terrestrial; like foliage plant, with fleshy, metallic bronzy green leaves spotted white, running into a channeled petiole, reverse purplish; erect purple flower spikes with small greenish flowers tipped with pink, lip whitish, (April-May). (I) *p. 1788*

PELIOSANTHES *Liliaceae* **I2LFM**

graminea (India); grass-like perennial herb with short rhizome, forming tufts; long-stalked linear-lanceolate, recurved leaves, 2½ cm wide; inflorescence in spikes of bell-shaped flowers with spreading segments, said to be greenish. *p. 1474*

speciosa (Malaysia); perennial foliage plant with broad, green, lanceolate, corrugated leaves carried on long petioles; from near base slender racemes entirely set with small greenish flowers. *p. 1474*

PELLAEA *Polypodiaceae (Filices)* **I3LHNM**

atropurpurea (No. America: Canada to Mexico); spreading fern inhabiting rocks; pinnate or bipinnate fronds 10-30 cm long, the leathery, linear, reddish pinnae, lightly glaucous, set opposite at right angles to the black-brown, tomentose stalks; hardy. *p. 1125*

calomelanos (So. Africa: Natal); charming small semi-tropical fern with fibrous roots; from the crown rise tufts of polished blackish, wiry stalks to 30 cm bearing pinnately or bipinnately broad angular leaflets 2 cm dia., with cordate base, of thin-leathery texture and glaucous blue on both sides; spores are borne in a line along the margin of the pinnae. Photo on pg. 1124 is of a juvenile plant. *p. 1124*

cordata (Mexico, Perú); erect, wiry, straw-colored stem with fronds to 30 cm long consisting of thin-leathery, medium-green, heartshaped leaflets arranged bi-pinnately and shortly stalked, the young leaves metallic red. *p. 1125*

falcata (India to Australia, New Zealand); attractive low-growing fern with wide-creeping rhizome, short pubescent stalks and long-linear pinnate fronds 15-45 cm long, leathery dark green. *p. 1124, 1125*

ovata (flexuosa) (Mexico to Perú); thin-wiry zigzag stems with bipinnate fronds, the pinnae and pinnules (leaflets) at right angles to rachis; the leaflets cordate, nearly round. *p. 1126*

rotundifolia (New Zealand), "Button fern"; small rockloving fern with creeping rhizome and pubescent stems, fronds nearly uniform, and staying near ground; simply pinnate, evenly spaced leaflets, round when young, later oblong, dark green and waxy leathery. *Humid-subtropic.* *p. 1125, 1126*

viridis (West Indies); "Green cliff-brake"; tufted fern with bipinnate fronds 45 to 60 cm long, on shining black stalks, the pinnae at base with numerous segments, decreasing upwards. Formerly in the trade as P. "hastata". *p. 1125, 1126*

viridis macrophylla, better known in horticulture as Pteris adiantoides; variety with bipinnate fronds to 45 cm high, having thin-leathery leaflets much larger and broader than in the species, although less in number on each pinna, and resembling Holly-fern, but leaves are not as leathery. Used in small fern-dishes as a "Table-fern". From S.E. Africa. *Humid-subtropic.* *p. 1125, 1126*

PELLIONIA *Urticaceae* **S3LFM**

sp. 'Argentea'; ground-hugging creeper with fleshy, oblique cordate leaves to 4½ cm long, chartreuse to pea-green, whitish-green beneath, the margins crenate and crisped, ribs faintly pink; on rosy petioles and stems. *p. 2110*

daveauana (South Vietnam, Malaya, Burma), "Trailing watermelon begonia"; depressed herbaceous creeper with succulent, pinkish stems and 2-ranked, flattened, alternate, thin-fleshy leaves oval when small, lanceolate-pointed, and 2-5 cm long in older plants, brown-purple to blackish with pale green to gray center area, base oblique. *Tropical. p. 2119*

pulchra (Vietnam: Cochin), "Satin pellionia"; attractive fleshy creeper hugging its support or pendant from a basket, with pinkish stems and stipules, obliquely oval leaves light green to grayish, entirely covered with a network of blackish or brownish veins, pale purple beneath on gray. *Tropical.* *p. 2119*

PELTANDRA *Araceae* **I2HFWdh**

virginica (Maine to Florida and Missouri), "Arrow arum"; hardy aquatic perennial herb with thick fibrous roots and large bright green, firm arrow-shaped leaves 15 to 75 cm long, on long sheathing petioles; undulate, fleshy, greenish-white spathe to 20 cm long; the spadix with female flowers in lower third; male, staminate flowers on upper two-thirds. *p. 227*

PELTIPHYLLUM *Saxifragaceae* **C2LBM**

peltatum (Oregon, California), "Umbrella plant"; perennial herb similar to Saxifraga; stout rhizome, with 30-60 cm hairy petioles supporting large roundish peltate, lobed leaves with toothed margins, often 30 cm across; the flowers on erect hairy stalks appearing before the leaves, with numerous pinkish or white flowers, in April. *p. 2040*

PELTOSTIGMA *Rutaceae* **S3LBM**

ptelioides (Jamaica); low, fragrant evergreen tree with green shoots, trifoliolate leaves, dark glossy green and somewhat wrinkled; saucer-shaped creamy-white flowers 3 cm across, with yellow anthers, sweetly scented. *p. 2025*

PENNISETUM *Gramineae* **I2LBD**

setaceum 'Cupreum' (ruppelii) (Ethiopia), "Fountain grass"; handsome perennial tall grass with bamboo-like canes, forming tufts to 1 m or more high, long lanceolate arching leaves 20 to 30 cm long, of thin-leathery texture and veins prominent length-wise, very ornamental in blackish red coloring; at the apex the arching spikes of bristly, coppery, purplish floral plumes during summer. Photographed in Leningrad Botanic Garden. *p. 1315*

PENSTEMON *Scrophulariaceae* **C2LBMh**

diffusus (serrulatus) (British Columbia to Oregon); herbaceous, downy perennial to 50 cm high, opposite, ovate, thick leaves with toothed margins; two-lipped tubular purple flowers 2 cm long in dense clusters on a leafy stalk. *p. 2060*

x gloxinioides, "Garden penstemon"; hybrid of Mexican P. hartwegii; strong herbaceous perennial with lance-shaped leaves and dense spikes of large, gloxinia-like, bell flowers to 5cm across, in many brilliant colors, blooming late summer to autumn. *Temperate.* *p. 2052, 2060*

x gloxinioides 'Fire King'; brilliant red trumpets carried in a raceme along slender stalk, the throat white. *p. 2060*

PENTAPHRAGMA *Pentaphragmataceae* **S3HFM**

philippinense (Philippines, Malaysia); attractive tropical herbaceous plant with stout stem, petioles channeled along top, and running into fleshy, ovate leaves 15 to 20 cm long and 12-15 cm wide, much puckered and corrugated, silky bright green and ciliate along margins, the underside white-pubescent; inflorescence axillary near base in pretty clusters, 5 cm flowers with spreading sepals creamy-white and unequal, and smaller pale yellow petals in center. *p. 1953*

PENTAPTERYGIUM *Ericaceae* **S3HFM**

serpens (E. Himalayas, Khasias); epiphytic shrub 60-90cm high, from a tuberous rootstock, with slender pendant stems, small lanceolate 2cm leathery leaves, and tubular nodding flowers bright red with darker markings. *Subtropic.* *p. 958*

PENTARHAPHIA: see Gesneria

PENTAS *Rubiaceae* **I-S2LBM**

lanceolata (Trop. Africa, Arabia), "Egyptian star-cluster"; herbaceous flowering plant with woody base, downy branches and soft or limp, ovate, bright green, hairy leaves, with sunken veins; the tubular flowers in showy clusters, hairy in the throat, purplish rose. *Tropical.* *p. 2016, 2022*

lanceolata coccinea; a scraggly shrub which I have often seen in Kenya brightening the bush with its bright crimson flowers. *p. 2011*

zanzibarensis (E. Trop. Africa); rather loose-growing shrubby plant with 4 cm heads of small pale lilac flowers, slightly fragrant, on long woolly stalks bearing whorls of narrow ovate pubescent leaves. *p. 2017*

PEPEROMIA *Piperaceae* ***S1LFD**

acuminata (Mexico); fleshy, scandent stems with narrow ovate, waxy grass-green leaves larger than glabella and having slender curved tip; double red rings at internodes from which develop the young branchlets. *p. 1936*

alata (prob. Trop. America); branching, bushy plant in bloom 35 cm high; thick hairy stems reddish, densely clothed with whorls of small elliptic 2 cm dark green leaves, thick and fleshy except those nearer inflorescence, which are larger, thinner, and not hairy beneath; the floral spikes green with tiny cream flowers. *p. 1942*

angulata (Venezuela, Brazil); nice little creeper with thread-like, reddish vines bearing pairs of small oval, deep green leaves with yellowish parallel veins. *p. 1932, 1941*

arifolia grandis (Brazil); similar to sandersii but with much larger foliage, on the same red petioles marked green, with short stem; peltate leaves very concave, marked silver-gray between the pale veins, gray-green beneath. *p. 1931*

arifolia litoralis (São Paulo); compact rosette with hard, flat, cordate leaves dark green with lustrous silver bands between the primary veins, looking like a shining shield. *Tropical.* *p. 1931*

asperculata (Hawaii); low succulent with thick, ovate leaves, the concave surface with translucent window, keeled beneath. *p. 1944*

'Astrid' or **'Princess Astrid':** see orba

bicolor (Ecuador), "Silver velvet peperomia" or "Inca princess"; beautiful plant with red-brown stem covered with white hair, and broadly oval, velvety leaves olive to gray metal-green, with broad silver center band as well as parallel silver stripes and edge, rosy-red underneath. *p. 1931*

blanda (Venezuela to Bolivia); shapely branching plant covered with short pubescence, the pinkish-brown, erect stems with opposite, broad-oval or obovate leaves, nice vivid-green with contrasting parallel light green veins. *p. 1934*

calvicaulis (Costa Rica); scandent, light olive-green stem with large elliptic or oval-pointed, lightly pubescent leaves, light green above, pale beneath. *p. 1936*

camptotricha (pulchella in hort.) (So. Mexico); succulent plant with white-felted stems; thick-fleshy, small oval or nearly round, green 2 cm leaves, longer in upper growth, opposite or sometimes whorled, densely hairy on both surfaces, and reddish beneath; slender floral spikes. *p. 1932*

campylotropa (Mexico); small tuberous, branching plant with tiny 1½-3½cm orbicular-peltate leaves glossy green and cupped; erect spikes of greenish, insignificant flowers; in the collection Botanic Garden, Munich, Germany. *Tropical.* *p. 1939, 1942*

caperata (Brazil), "Emerald Ripple"; sturdy, very useful little species with short, branching stem developing dense clusters of roundish, heart-shaped or peltate leaves deeply corrugated and quilted like a washboard, waxy forest-green, the valleys tinted chocolate, the ridges often grayish, reverse pale green, the pink petioles striped red; the slender flowering catkins greenish-white. *Tropical.* *p. 19*, 1933, 1939*

caperata 'Crespa' (So. Brazil); a sturdy little plant which I obtained in São Paulo under this name; almost stemless with stiff, thick-fleshy, rounded and quilted leaves shining green to olive, chocolate in the center area, and pale beneath, on stout pink petioles. *p. 1935*

caperata 'Little Fantasy' (Brazil); cute form more dwarf than 'Emerald Ripple', with smaller, peltate-pointed leaves glossy deep-green, some brown in the deep folds and grayish on ridges, gray-green beneath; stalks marked red; very durable and remaining dwarf. *p. 1933*

caperata 'Tricolor', "Tricolor ripple"; (Roehrs 1957), a beautiful, variegated sport of sturdy habit, with corrugated leaves milky-green, broadly margined with creamy-white, red around the base and spreading out into the veins, on red petioles. *p. 1933*

caperata 'Variegata', "Variegated ripple"; attractive variety with the little succulent, quilted leaves waxy deep green and broadly margined with white, on pink petioles. *Tropical.* *p. 768A, 1938*

cerea (in hort. as 'Dr. Goodspeed') (Perú), introduced in California; succulent little bush to 45 cm high; stem red of numerous stripes, set dense with fat little ovate, 2½cm leaves in whorls of three, matte olive green; the underside keeled and brown-purple. *Tropical.* *p. 1938*

clusiifolia (West Indies), "Red-edged peperomia"; stocky, slow-growing plant with thick-fleshy, rather oblanceolate, concave leaves, 8-15 cm long, metallic olive-green with broad, red-purple margin, light green beneath except for the purple midrib. *Tropical.* *p. 1934, 1941*

clusiifolia 'Variegata'; attractive sport with elongate, stiff thick-fleshy, concave leaves, pale green variegated with creamy-yellow inward from the margin, and edged with red. *p. 1935*

columella (No. Perú: Amazonas); decorative dwarf species highly succulent, to 15 cm high, freely branching with round fleshy stems, densely shingled with 7 mm thick club-like leaves having flat window at apex. *p. 1940*

columnaris (Perú); succulent creeper with small fat bodies of leaves, the flat surface with translucent windows. *Tropical.* *p. 1940*

"cordata" (Brazil); showy, large plant from São Paulo, of uncertain standing; glossy green, quilted leaves broad cordate with overlapping basal lobes and slender pointed apex. *p. 1937*

crassifolia (Trop. Africa), "Leather peperomia"; stiffly erect, fleshy green stem with alternate, rhombic or obovate, succulent leaves 8 cm long, waxy grass-green with pale midrib, light green beneath. *p. 1934*

cubensis (rotundifolia) (West Indies); known as 'rotundifolia' or "Yerba Linda" from Puerto Rico, this little succulent has soft, waxy, friendly fresh-green broad ovate leaves with depressed parallel veins, on reddish stems. *Tropical.* *p. 1936*

cubensis 'Variegata' (rotundifolia variegata); graceful branching little plant with pink to red stem dense with broad ovate, almost round leaves, milky green, prettily margined and variegated creamy white. *p. 1936*

cuspidilimba (Perú); attractive trailer with flexible wiry stems, narrow elliptic, pointed leaves moss-green with pale parallel veining, and red underside, set in whorls at intervals on branches. *Tropical.* *p. 1941*

deppeana (Mexico); attractive low, spreading creeper with wire-like, flexible green branches marked with red; small obovate, almost circular, matte-green leaves; short 2 cm white catkins looking like little candles. *p. 1944*

dolabriformis (Perú), "Prayer peperomia"; curious plant with fleshy spatulate leaves folded together, showing the pale green underside, glued tight with a translucent layer and appearing like a swollen sickle. *p. 1935*

"elongata" (Venezuela); robust succulent plant with large elliptic or obovate thick-fleshy leaves deep glossy green with pale midrib, and the minute flowers in long slender catkins. *p. 1938*

fosteri (Brazil), "Vining peperomia"; very attractive creeper with thick foliage in whorls or 2 or 3 along the slender red stems, rooting at nodes, the small, short elliptic leaves forest-green with light green parallel veins. Discovered by Mulford Foster growing as an epiphyte. *p. 1932*

fraseri: see resedaeflora

galioides (Colombia); small branching plant with succulent light green stems with a dot of red at joints and glands beneath; the waxy fresh green needle-like leaves 2½cm long in whorls of 4-5, depressed along center. *Tropical.* *p. 1937*

gardneriana (Brazil); loose rosette with pink to red stem and long petioles almost colorless, bearing peltate-pointed, waxy, quilted leaves with ribbed surface glossy light green, the edges undulate, pale beneath. *p. 1934*

glabella (Cent. America), "Wax privet peperomia"; branching plant smaller than acuminata, with slender, flexible, red stems and little, 4 cm broadly elliptic leaves, waxy fresh-green, and tapered at the base. *p. 1936*

glabella 'Variegata', "Variegated wax privet"; dainty, freely branching plant with slender rosy-red stems and small elliptic leaves, tapered toward base, light green or milky green, broadly bordered or variegated creamy-white, to 4 cm long. Very attractive basket plant. *Tropical.* *p. 1933*

grandifolia (Guyana); succulent, fleshy plant with very large and thick ovate leaves, somewhat cupped, deep glossy-green with pale midrib. *p. 1943*

griseo-argentea (Brazil), known in Brazil and introduced in Europe as hederaefolia, "Ivy peperomia"; very attractive, bushy rosette with long pink petioles bearing round cordate, shield-like, thin, quilted leaves painted with glossy silver, while the sunken veins are purplish olive; long, erect, greenish-white catkins. Somewhat difficult in cultivation. *Tropical.* *p. 5*, 1935*

griseo-argentea 'Blackie'; small rosette with thin cordate and peltate waxy leaves of metallic olive-green to blackish coppery with grayish reverse, on red-spotted petioles; Hummel in California found this form as a branch sport on P. hederaefolia. *p. 1935*

griseo-argentea 'Nigra' (Brazil); compact rosette of peltate cupped leaves and much ridged and quilted, glossy black-olive with pale gray reverse, the pinkish petioles marked red; long greenish catkins. *p. 1934*

hederaefolia: see griseo-argentea

hirta (Cuba); freely-branching, rambling plant, pubescent pale green branches and small obovate-pointed, limply soft green leaves, covered with grayish pubescence with a satiny sheen, pale beneath. *p. 1935*

hoffmanii (C. America); low succulent creeper hugging the ground, with reddish stems and tiny 1cm obovate waxy leaves dull olive green set in whorls of 4 along branches; collection Brooklyn Botanic Garden. *Tropical.* *p. 1940*

sp. "Horace Anderson" (So. Mexico); sleek, branching plant with glossy, willowy stem lightly spotted red; leaves in two's or three's, short obovate pointed, parallel-veined, glossy fresh green, pale beneath, 6 cm long. In the California trade. *p. 1938*

humilis (Florida Keys); branching species with obovate succulent, soft pubescent leaves silvery green; an attractive hanging basket subject for shady corners (Fairchild Trop. Garden, Miami). *p. 1944*

incana (Brazil), "Felted pepperface"; amazing little plant that should be rated as a succulent; I have found it growing on granite rocks between cacti and bromeliads on the Restinga in South-east Brazil; stiff green, hard stem with broadly heart-shaped stiff-fleshy, gray leaves entirely covered with white felt. *Arid-tropical.* *p. 1935*

japonica (Okinawa); dwarf, densely branching species with small rounded leaves, waxy light green and flat on top, almost white and rounded boat-like beneath, on pale petioles; flowers in green catkins. *p. 1943*

krahnii (prob. Trop. America); low succulent creeper of very slow growth; the hair-like stems with tiny green, round and fat 5 mm leaves. *p. 1940*

longispicata (Central America); luxuriant little creeper with succulent zigzag branches and shining green broad ovate leaves coming to a sharp point. *p. 1941*

maculosa (Santo Domingo), "Radiator plant"; ornamental, fleshy species with long pendant, narrow-lanceolate leaves to 16cm long, waxy bluish gray-green, with silvery-green to ivory ribs; petioles prettily spotted red-purple; inflorescence of tiny flowers in spikes to 30cm long. *p. 1943*

"madisonii" hort. (resedaeflora cuprea) (Perú); scandent rather succulent species with fleshy branches, ovate-cordate 5 cm furrowed leaves with a rough surface burnished gold with crimson spots along vein areas, white underneath; slender green inflorescence. *p. 1942*

magnoliaefolia (West Indies), "Desert privet"; robust species with large, fleshy obovate-elliptic leaves 10-12cm long, glossy fresh-green with depressed veins, on brownish stem; stalk of flower spike not hairy. *Tropical.* *p. 1943*

margaretifera (Juan Fernandez, Chile), "Chilean pepper face"; spreading bush with glossy green elliptic leaves on erect stems; collection Brooklyn Botanic Garden. *Subtropic.* *p. 1941*

marmorata 'Silver Heart' (So. Brazil); attractive plant with thin, heart-shaped leaves rich green to bluish, tapering to a long point, with basal lobes overlapping, the ridges prettily painted with silver-gray between the sunken, grass-green veins; gray-green beneath; pink stalks striped red; long, white catkins. *p. 1931, 1939*

"masonii" (Perú); rosette with cordate, corrugated leaves rosy-coppery-red with red spots and darker, depressed parallel veins. *p. 1942*

meridensis (Mexico); small erect rosette 15 cm high with tiny waxy 2-3 cm leaves almost circular and deeply quilted, glossy rich green, on reddish petioles and stems, light green beneath; the inflorescence an erect spike 10 cm long, with minute creamy flowers. *p. 1939*

metallica (Perú); attractive little plant with erect, dark reddish stem and narrow, waxy leaves of copper with metallic lustre and a silver green band down the middle; silver beneath with bright red veins. *p. 1933*

moninii (Réunion, Ind. Ocean); small-leaved, upright, branching plant with slightly felty, red stem and petioles with small, hard, opposite, rhombic leaves, moss-green and pubescent above, reddish beneath. *p. 1936*

nivalis (Perú); attractive, low clustering plant, each branch a little upright rosette of small, keelshaped, almost folded, aromatic leaves, the inner surface green, outer side buff-colored. *p. 1943*

nummulariaefolia (Jamaica); small creeper or trailer with hair-like stems, set with alternate tiny rotund leaves 1 cm dia., moss-gray with silver markings; in collection University Botanic Garden, Cologne, Germany. *p. 1940*

"nummularifolia" (Trop. America); succulent plant with scandent slender stems red at junctions, alternate elliptic leaves 3 cm long, waxy green and with tapering apex, pale beneath; tiny flowers on small catkins. In the California trade. *p. 1938*

obtusifolia (Venezuela), "Pepper face" or "Baby rubber plant"; long cultivated as a good dishgarden plant; succulent stem with reclining base and short petioles both striped maroon-brown, and waxy-green, fleshy obovate or spatulate, 5-8cm, concave leaves, obtuse or notched at apex, pale green beneath; growing to 30cm high; stalk of flower spike minutely hairy, topped by slender, greenish-white flower spikes, resembling catkins. *p. 1943*

obtusifolia 'Alba'; an albino form cultivated by Manda, with the younger growth having leaves entirely creamy-yellow, of remarkable lasting quality, on cream stem and petioles, both marked prettily with bright red. *p. 5*, 1934*

obtusifolia 'Albo-marginata'; small-leaved cultivar with thick-fleshy, small obovate leaves variegated with cream from the margins in, suffusing the pale green surface with a milky hue. *p. 1937*

obtusifolia 'Gold Tip' (Hummel); sturdy California cultivar with waxy oblique leaves deep green, variegated and marbled creamy-yellow particularly so toward apex. *p. 1937*

obtusifolia 'Lougenii'; a miniature version of obtusifolia with the small leaves variegated green with cream. *p. 1934*

obtusifolia 'Minima' (Manda); shapely miniature cultivar dense with small obovate, glossy dark green leaves 4-5 cm long; light green beneath. *p. 1937*

obtusifolia 'Variegata', "Variegated peperomia"; beautiful, small, succulent plant with pale stems blotched bright red; alternate, rounded or obovate-elliptic, waxy leaves, light green variegated with milky-green, and from the margin inward, a broad area of creamy-white. *Tropical.* *p. 21*, 1933, 1941*

orba; 'Princess Astrid' in hort.; introduced to U.S. from Sweden; stem dotted red and white pubescent, with numerous, waxy, light green, ovate leaves spoon-like on short stiff petioles, showing their true shape when few-branched, but if crowded, leaves stay small and densely clustered, pixie-like. *p. 1935*

orba 'Pixie'; diminutive form known as "Teardrop"; this plant is just a cushion of miniature branches and tiny ovate, succulent leaves grass-green; when divided each branch will grow into the larger leaved individual known as P. 'Astrid'. *p. 1937*

ornata (So. Venezuela); lovely, succulent species with short stout stem supporting a cluster of symmetrical, elliptic, fleshy leaves on stiff red stalks, silky-green above with lengthwise light veins, paler beneath with conspicuous, parallel, purplish-red ribs. *p. 1933*

peltifolia (Venezuela, Brazil); succulent plant with thick peltate, somewhat cupped leaves having lightly sunken ribs, metallic bluish-green faintly marked with silver between the veins, red petioles marked with white striplets. *p. 1931*

pereskiaefolia (Brazil, Venezuela), "Leaf-cactus peperomia"; branching plant resembling Pereskia, with red stems first ascending then creeping, the small elliptic or obovate leaves succulent and waxy, dull green with pale veins. *p. 1936, 1939*

perrottetiana (Mauritius); sprawling and spreading plant with oval green, rather succulent leaves; and with stalked purplish catkins. *p. 1939*

persicifolia; creeping species with long, wire-thin, flexible stems set at intervals with generally 3 long-elliptic dark green, fleshy leaves transversed by silvery gray parallel veins; long slender catkins; in collection Botanic Garden, Copenhagen. *p. 1939*

polybotrya (pericatii) (Colombia), "Coin-leaf peperomia"; succulent plant with erect, fleshy, green stem and stiff reddish petioles, the thick, shining, waxy, smooth, peltate-pointed, shield-like leaves of vivid green with fine purple edge, gray-green beneath; branched white catkins. *Tropical.* *p. 5*, 1931, 1939*

prostrata (Colombia); beautiful, though tiny, little creeper with minute, circular, 1 cm, waxy leaves brown to bluish-gray etched with filigree of silver on the surface, rounded and pale beneath; on thin, red, thread-like vines. *p. 1932, 1937*

pruinosifolia (Perú); creeping low succulent with small, thick, elliptic leaves folded as in an oyster shell, with green translucent windows along upper fold. *p. 1940*

pulchella (verticillata in hort.) (Jamaica), "Whorled peperomia"; small erect plant with fleshy stem closely set with whorls of fleshy, dull-green, 3 cm oval leaflets covered with white pubescence and showing some faint lighter veining, in short petioles. *p. 1934*

puteolata (Perú), "Parallel peperomia"; gorgeous hanging plant with angled stems and slender, lanceolate, leathery leaves 10cm long, waxy dark green with 5 contrasting, yellowish, sub-translucent, parallel veins depressed on the surface and raised on the light green reverse. *Tropical.* *p. 1933, 1941*

quadrangularis (Costa Rica); low creeping plant with wiry green vines set with opposite, small round-oval, convex, green leaves, transversed by yellowish veins, pale beneath. *p. 1932*

'Queremal' (Colombia); scandent stem on creeping rhizome, with broad, almost round subcordate rough-bristly leaves emerald-green, with prominent veins, and gray underneath. *p. 1938*

rauhii (prob. Trop. America); succulent with stiff-erect, fleshy stems, dense with thick ovate 4cm leaves keeled beneath, placed all around the smooth velvety olive green stem. *Tropical.* *p. 1942*

resedaeflora (fraseri) (Ecuador, Colombia), "Mignonette peperomia"; a "flowering" plant with small, quilted, round-cordate, begonia-like leaves, dull-green and finely white-pubescent as it frosted, red-ribbed beneath; the inflorescence on tall red stems with whorls of 3-4 leaves topped by fluffy white flower spikes resembling mignonette. *p. 1935, 1938*

rosifolia (So. Brazil); small rosette known as "Pinkie" because of the pink overtones over coppery glossy leaves, these broadly peltate, of thin-brittle texture, 4-5 cm across. *p. 1942*

rotundifolia (nummularifolia) (Puerto Rico to Jamaica); low rambling creeper covering the ground, the thread-like, green vines rooting at nodes, with alternate, tiny 1 cm, very round and fat, waxy leaves evenly pale green; much seen in the Luquillo rain forest, Puerto Rico. (I-S) *p. 1932, 1940*

rubella (Orizaba, Mexico), "Yerba Linda"; branched little bush with thin, upright, hairy, crimson stems densely set with whorls of tiny obovate leaves, olive-green marked with a silver network; vivid crimson beneath. *p. 1932*

sandersii (argyreia) (Brazil), "Watermelon peperomia"; attractive rosette, almost stemless, with deep-red petioles bearing fleshy, broad peltate-pointed, concave leaves 8 to 10 cm across, glossy fresh-green to bluish, painted with showy bands of silver radiating from their upper center, pale beneath; minute flowers in long, whitish catkins. *Tropical.* *p. 1931*

sarcophylla (pseudovariegata) (Ecuador, Colombia); heavy plant with large, broadly lanceolate, thick-fleshy, pendant, 20 cm leaves of shining forest-green, ivory-green ribs and a band of gray alongside them, on thick petioles heavily blotched red; long brown catkins. *p. 1943*

scandens (Perú), "Philodendron peperomia"; scandent creeper with fleshy, reddish stem and petioles, the waxy fresh-green, small heartshaped leaves resembling a philodendron, and well spaced, with long internodes. *Tropical.* *p. 1936*

scandens 'Variegata'; colorful, scandent, semi-erect, fleshy creeper with small cordate leaves gracefully slender-pointed, light green to milky-green, irregularly bordered with creamy-white, on red petioles and reddish stems. Somewhat rank in growth, but useful for baskets. *Tropical.* *p. 1933*

serpens (Trop. America); small rambling creeper with rounded 2 cm waxy leaves polished copper with network of light green, and wavy margins on angled pink stems. *p. 1942*

spathulifolia (South Florida); native creeping plant with oblanceolate, fleshy leaves glossy dark green, similar to obtusifolia in appearance except for longer and narrower foliage; distributed, 1969, by Fairchild Trop. Garden, Miami. *p. 1942*

subpeltata (Java); heavy plant with stout, red-spotted petioles and thick, shield-like, cordate leaves to 30 cm long, the glossy surface deep green with gray sheen, and a pale green midrib, covered underneath with fine pubescence; long, elegant flower spike. *p. 1934*

tithymaloides (Santo Domingo), "Pepper face"; robust species with branching stems, with alternate, fleshy, 12 cm leaves broadly rhombic or elliptic with tapering base and pointed apex, glossy dark green with paler veins, light green beneath, the petioles keeled beneath; greenish catkins. *p. 1943, 1944*

trinervis (Bolivia, Perú, Venezuela); rank little creeper with soft-fleshy, red branches and alternate, small, succulent leaves ovate-slender pointed and a glossy rich-green, prominently showing 3 depressed parallel veins. *p. 1932, 1936*

trinervula (Venezuela: Roraima); trailing plant with small succulent green, ovate or broad-elliptic leaves 2½ cm long, slightly pubescent; the flowers in long slender catkins. *p. 1938*

urocarpa (Paraguay to Colombia); rambling plant with succulent, green, scandent branches and medium size, fleshy, green, pubescent, cordate leaves having the parallel veins in gentle furrows, silvery-white beneath. *p. 1932, 1937*

velutina (Ecuador), "Velvet peperomia"; dainty, branching, red-stemmed plant with small ovate, velvet-pubescent, deep bronzy green leaves marked with narrow, pale green midrib and parallel veins, red underneath. (3) *p. 1931*

verschaffeltii (Alto Amazonas), "Sweetheart peperomia"; a beautiful shapely plant which I rediscovered on the upper Amazon; a short-stemmed rosette of fleshy, oval-heartshaped leaves 10 cm long, similar to marmorata but basal lobes not overlapping, and alternate on short branching stem, the waxy surface is bluish-green with broad silver bands between the recessed yellowish veins, on petioles red with dots, (Ill. Hort. 1869). *Tropical.* *p. 15*, 1931, 1937*

verticillata (Jamaica, Cuba); white-hairy plant with erect, red stems and small obovate, green leaves, arranged by tiers in whorls of 4-6, the young leaves thin with pale veins, older leaves thick and boatshaped with round bottom which is pale green tinted red; tiny greenish catkins. *p. 1942*

viridis (Mexico); vigorous erect plant with succulent green stem, green petioles and thick, ovate leaves of vivid green. *p. 1943*

PERESKIA *Cactaceae* **S2LFD**

aculeata (Venezuela to Mexico), "Barbados gooseberry" or "Lemon vine"; leafy shrub with flexible, woody stems not jointed, straggling and climbing; waxy green, ovate leaves 8 cm long, the areoles with needle-like spines; lemon-scented flowers creamy yellow to pinkish, 3 to 4 cm across; small 2 cm yellow edible fruit resembling goose-berries, agreeable to eat fresh, or made into preserves. Widely used in the West Indies. *Tropical.* *p. 618, 622, 708*

aculeata godseffiana; colorful sport with broader leaves a pretty yellow-green, tinted copper and salmon red, rosy-red beneath. *p. 622*

bleo (Rhodocactus) (Panama, Colombia), "Wax rose"; a tree-like primitive cactus with leaves, to 6 m high; the young branches red; thin oblanceolate leaves to 20 cm long, black needle spines; rosy flowers. *Tropical.* *p. 622*

grandifolia (grandiflora in hort.) (Brazil), a "Rose cactus"; a shrub or tree to 4 m with very spiny trunk, the elliptic fleshy waxy, rich green leaves to 15 cm long; flowers like wild roses rose-pink, 3-4 cm across, in terminal clusters. *Tropical.* *p. 616, 640A*

moorei (Brazil); branched shrub to 1 m; thick and fleshy obovate leaves 8 cm long; prominent blackish needle spines; flowers purplish red. *p. 622*

sacharosa (Paraguay, Argentina); erect shrub to 6 m high, with obovate to oblanceolate, smooth dark green, fleshy leaves 8-12 cm long, keeled underneath; large areoles with numerous straight spines to 5 cm; beautiful rose-like flowers about 8 cm across, rose-pink fading to whitish in center and with yellow stamens, in terminal clusters; silky white hairs beneath sepals; fruit roundish, 4 cm long. *p. 621*

PERILLA *Labiatae* **I2LBM**

frutescens crispa (India, China, Japan); ornamental annual coleus-like herb to 1 m with 4-angled stem, and with colored foliage; ovate toothed, bullate leaves 5-10 cm long, a showy purplish-brown or bronzy; small white flowers. *p. 1347*

PERIPLOCA *Asclepiadaceae* **I2LBD**

graeca (So. Europe, Asia Minor), a "Silk vine"; deciduous hardy, woody scandent shrub with wiry branches climbing 6-12 m high; ovate leaves 10 cm long, shining dark green; the small 2 cm flowers in clusters, greenish outside, brownish within and with spreading lobes and covered with short hairs; typical milkweed fruits with small winged seeds. *p. 372*

sepium (China); tall hardy vine with pairs of ovate leaves, thin, leathery, 5 cm long; tiny 1 cm flowers lemon yellow, purplish brown inside covered with silky gray hairs. *p. 372*

PERISTERIA *Orchidaceae* **I-S2HFM**

elata (Costa Rica, Panama, Colombia), "Dove orchid", or "Holy Ghost orchid", national flower of Panama; vigorous, handsome epiphyte also growing terrestrial, with ovoid pseudobulbs bearing 3-5 plaited leaves to 1 m long; inflorescence tall, erect, to 1½ m high, with fleshy, waxy-white, very fragrant, 6 cm flowers, almost globose, the column with its wings resembling a dove, (Aug.-Oct.). *Tropical.* *p. 1797*

guttata (Guyana: Demerara); curious species with conical pseudobulbs bearing 2-3 plaited leaves 30-38 cm long; flowers from the base yellow and red, spotted purple, with sepals and petals cup-shaped; lip tipped purple; September. *p. 1788, 1807*

pendula (Panama to Guyana); remarkable epiphyte with robust pseudobulbs, carrying elliptic, plaited leaves to 35 cm long, deciduous before flowering; the inflorescence a short, pendant raceme of hooded flowers 5 cm dia., lemon-white and heavily spotted with blackish red (winter). *Tropical.* *p. 1807*

PERISTROPHE *Acanthaceae* **I-S3LFM**

hyssopifolia 'Aureo-variegata' (angustifolia var.) (Java), "Marble-leaf"; colorful, spreading herb, with small lanceolate fresh-green leaves to 8 cm long, variegated yellow in center; small rosy flowers. *Tropical.* *p. 52*

speciosa (India); shrubby plant with gray stems, to 1 m long; elliptic, grooved leaves glossy dark green to 12 cm long; twisted tubular flowers with corolla deeply split, purple with crimson blotch. *p. 55*

PERNETTYA *Ericaceae* **C2HBM**

mucronata 'Alba' (Magellan region to Chile); bushy little evergreen shrub with woody branches densely set with small stiff 1 cm ovate leaves lightly toothed, glossy dark green, and tipped by a sharp translucent spine; numerous tiny urn-shaped nodding white or pinkish flowers, followed on female plants by stalked small white berries, depressed globose to 1 cm wide, persistent through the winter. *p. 960*

mucronata 'Rosea'; has pink fruits. *p. 960*

mucronata 'Rubra', produces brilliant red berries. *p. 960*

PERSEA *Lauraceae* **I-S2LBM**

americana (W. Indies, Guatemala and Mexico), the "Avocado" tree; also called "Alligator pear"; a round-headed tropical and subtropical tree 6 to 10 m high or more, spreading wide with large leathery, elliptic or oval 10-20 cm leaves, glaucous beneath; and small 6 mm greenish flowers, forming in winter. The Avocado tree grows fast in well-drained soil containing humus, beginning to bear when 4 to 8 years old, the large fleshy apple or pear-shaped edible fruit, for which it is usually cultivated, is about 10 cm across with green or purplish skin, its flesh is buttery and of high nutritional value rich in vitamins and containing 7 to 23% fat; it is served in salads. *Subtropic.* *p. 1359*

americana 'Fuerte', "Pear avocado"; a pear-shaped avocado, belonging to the 'Mexican race' which includes the hardiest types (Persea drymifolia x americana); fruit 10 cm long, dull green; flesh cream yellow of buttery texture and with rich flavor; season Jan.-August in California. *p. 1359*

PESCATOREA *Orchidaceae* **I30FM**

cerina (Costa Rica); pretty epiphyte from Volcano Chiriqui at 2,300 m, with tufted leaves tapering to the base, the short-stalked, solitary 8 cm flowers fragrant and showy, the waxy sepals and petals lemon-yellow, the convex lip bright yellow with red-brown ridges in throat, (June-Dec.). *Tropical.* *p. 1807, 1811*

PETALIDIUM *Acanthaceae* **S3LFM**

coccineum (Trop. Africa); tropical shrub with arching branches, and ovate, downy leaves; solitary red flowers in axils of upper leaves, with large hooded bracts. *p. 48*

PETIVERIA *Phytolaccaceae* **S3LBM**

alliacea (Mexico to Brazil), "Guinea-henweed"; tropical slender herb, shrubby at base, with forking branches, and with strong garlic odor; alternate ovate leaves to 10 cm long; the small pink or white flowers along thin, arching floral stalks. *p. 1922*

PETREA *Verbenaceae* **I-S3LFM**
volubilis (racemosa) (Mexico to Panama), "Purple wreath"; one of the most beautiful of tender twiners, climbing perhaps 10 m high, with woody or wiry stems, ovate to long lanceolate brittle-hard, rough leaves to 20 cm long, and showy racemes of lovely, star-like flowers of long, lilac-blue sepals and small violet corolla; primarily in March-April. *Tropical.* *p. 320A, 2114, 2116*

PETROCOSMEA *Gesneriaceae* **I3HFM**
kerrii (Thailand, Vietnam), "Hidden violets"; low, flattened rosette from the jungle floor, with long-pointed, cordate, quilted leaves rather thick and fleshy, velvety green, attractively covered with white hairs, on brown petioles and with crenate margins; small violet-like flowers with upper petals cream-yellow, lower petals white, several to a short stalk usually hidden between or under the arching foliage. *p. 1258*
parryorum (Assam); softly hairy perennial with a small corm, the cordate fleshy, wrinkled leaves in a rosette, 6 to 10 cm long, with toothed margins; white-hairy stalks carry clusters of oblique bell-shaped, small violet flowers. *p. 1253*

PETRONYMPHE *Amaryllidaceae* **S3LFM**
decora (Mexico); tuberous plant with shoe-string-like narrow, succulent, channeled leaves 60 cm long and 6 mm wide; long-stalked inflorescence of tubular flowers in pendulous umbels, the 6 cm corolla pale creamy-yellow with green length-stripes to tip of corolla lobes. *p. 131*

PETROPHYTUM *Rosaceae* **C2LBM**
caespitosum (Spiraea) (South Dakota to California); prostrate evergreen hardy shrub forming mats to 1 m across; small silky 2 cm leaves; small white flowers in dense spikes. *p. 2000*

PETROSELINUM *Umbelliferae* **C-I2LFM**
crispum (Europe, W. Asia), "Parsley"; hardy biennial herb with much divided, rich green, curly leaves; small greenish-yellow flowers. Use: for flavoring in cooking and for garnish. *p. 2104, 2106*

PETTERIA *Leguminosae* **C2LBD**
ramentacea (Yugoslavia); deciduous shrub 1-2 m with leaves of 3 leaflets; fragrant yellow flowers 2 cm long, in dense, erect racemes. *p. 1388*

PETUNIA *Solanaceae* **C-I2LBD**
x hybrida 'California Giant'; herbaceous plant, whose ancestry goes back to the So. American species violacea and nyctaginiflora; with small oval leaves, dwarfed by giant single flowers ruffled toward the margin, 10-15 cm across, in shades from white, rose, orchid, purple, combined with showy centers in contrasting colors or designs; desirable potplant for Mother's Day. *p. 2079*
x hybrida 'Celestial Rose'; dwarf herbaceous, floriferous plant of bushy habit, with small, light green, downy leaves, single flowers carmine-rose with pale eye. *Tropical.* *p. 2079*
x hybrida fl. pl. 'Caprice'; compact plant with clear carmine-rose flowers densely double with frilled petals pale beneath, early flowering; a named variety of the Panamerican strain, which also comes in white, lavender, purple, or variegated forms, all of which make superb potplants. *p. 2079*
x hybrida fl. pl. 'Sonata'; favorite commercial pot variety for large fully-double, pure white flowers, beautifully fringed and crisped at margins; should be pinched to encourage bushy growth; Panamerican strain. *p. 2079*
x hybrida grandiflora 'Bingo'; huge bicolor flowers up to 12 cm across, richly variegated wine-red and white in shape of a star; part of the blooms are only 8 cm in dia., but are equally colorful; of compact habit. *p. 2080*
x hybrida grandiflora 'Calypso'; vigorous F1 or heterosis hybrid with an amazing number of fringed flowers 8-9 cm across, in bright colors carmine-red with white in various patterns often star-like. *p. 2080*
x hybrida grandiflora 'Crusader'; large single flowers gaily striped or banded starlike with bright carmine rose on white base with nicely frilled white edge. *Tropical.* *p. 2079*
x hybrida grandiflora 'Elk's Pride', "Blue balcony petunia"; so reminiscent of the deep blue single balcony petunias in the Swiss and Bavarian Alpine villages, but of more erect and shorter habit; still a favorite rich velvety deepest violet shade, though some strains become tall and lanky. *p. 2079*
x hybrida grandiflora 'Maytime'; excellent F1 hybrid of dense, vigorous habit, covering itself with large ruffled flowers soft salmon-pink with darker veining. *p. 2080*
x hybrida grandiflora 'Pink Magic'; F-1 or first generation hybrid, a favorite bedding and pot plant of uniform, dwarf, bushy habit, loaded with numerous medium sized single, smooth flowers of bright carmine-rose with darker veining and small white eye; larger than 'Celestial Rose'. *p. 2079*
x hybrida grandiflora 'Popcorn'; good pot variety because of its shorter, bushy habit, yet with large white, single blooms with quilted surface and ruffled margins. *Tropical.* *p. 2079*
x hybrida multiflora 'Glitters'; an All-America winner for 1957; floriferous F-1 hybrid of the smaller single flowered, bushy multiflora strain ideal for bedding and pots, a striking combination of a salmon-red star alternating with white. *Tropical.* *p. 2079*
x hybrida multiflora 'Satellite'; lovely free-blooming F1 hybrid with brilliant bright rose flowers with a perfect white star; excellent bedding or pot plant. *Tropical.* *p. 2080*

PFEIFFERA *Cactaceae* **S2HFM**
ianthothele (ianothele in Hortus 3) (No. Argentina), "Tree-and-rock cactus"; epiphytic or terrestrial cactus with erect or pendant light olive green stems 30 to 60 cm long, usually 3 or 4-ribbed and about 2 cm dia., the ribs undulate and set with needle-spines at areoles; small day-blooming flowers 2 cm long, creamy-white inside to pinkish outside; berry-like globose red fruit. *Tropical.* *p. 746*

PHAEDRANASSA *Amaryllidaceae* **S3LFMd**
carmiolii (Costa Rica), "Queen lily"; bulbous plant with 1 to 3 stalked oblanceolate, fleshy leaves to 38 cm long, appearing at blooming time, and showy nodding, curved tubular 5 cm flowers crimson at base, greenish toward segmented apex, and with protruding stamens, clustered on 60 cm stalk. *p. 131*
chloracra (Perú); bulbous plant with fleshy lanceolate leaves and rosy-pink tubular flowers tipped green. *p. 131*

PHAEDRANTHUS: see Distictis

PHAENOSPERMA *Gramineae* **C2LBM**
globosum (China, Korea, Japan), "Taki-Kibi"; perennial ornamental grass from short rhizome, with thin bamboo-like canes to more than 1 m high; narrow linear dark green leaves 30-50 cm long with margins finely serrate; arching stalks with pendulous cylindrical spikes of numerous small green flowers. *p. 1315*

PHAEOMERIA magnifica: see Nicolaia elatior

x PHAIOCALANTHE *Orchidaceae* **I3HFMd**
'Stanny' (Phaius grandifolius x Calanthe 'Baron Schroeder'); bigeneric terrestrial resembling Phaius with onion-like flattened bulb and 3 long, corrugated leaves, and an erect inflorescence similar to Phaius but smaller, the colors vary according to clones but normally with long white sepals, creamy pink petals, and a showy lip overlaid with maroon (January). (I) *p. 1797*

PHAIUS *Orchidaceae* **I2HFD**
maculatus (No. India); handsome species stronger than flavus, with large pseudobulbs and plaited leaves to 60 cm long, dark green and spotted with yellow; inflorescence to 90 cm long with raceme of yellow flowers to 8 cm the fleshy lip orange-brown at apex and wavy (spring-summer). (I) *p. 1797*
tankervilleae (grandifolius) (No. India, So. China, Malaysia to No. Australia), "Nun's orchid"; charming, robust terrestrial from grassy savannahs, with plaited leaves on stout pseudobulbs, and erect spikes to 1 m high with spreading, fleshy flowers, sepals and petals light brown, silvery white behind, lip rose with darker throat. (Feb.-April). *Tropical.* *p. 1797, 1803*
wallichii (Sikkim Himalayas, Khasia); grand terrestrial, stronger than grandifolius, with furrowed leaves, and flowers having buff-brown sepals and petals, white in back, the large lip orange-yellow at base and beneath, wine-red in middle and white at outer fringes, on tall spike, (March-May). (I) *p. 1797*

PHALAENOPSIS *Orchidaceae* **S3ONM**
amabilis (Malaya, Sunda Isl.), "Moth orchid"; exquisite epiphyte without pseudobulbs; fleshy, light green, deflexed leaves, and a pendant spray of flowers to 6 cm across, glistening snowy-white, except for its yellow crest spotted with red, (Oct.-Jan.). *Tropical.* *p. 1664A, 1801*
amabilis var. formosana (Taiwan); a charming variety with pendant inflorescence of large pure white flowers with rather slender obovate sepals; photographed at Sun-Moon Lake near Taichung. *p. 1799, 1800*
amabilis 'Summit Snow'; Lager hybrid of 'Doris' x 'Confirmation', with pure white flowers of exceptional size and good substance, branching raceme bearing as many as 30-50 flowers of 10-12 cm dia. in continuation from Nov. to March and longer. (S) *p. 1801*
buyssoniana (Doritis pulcherrima) (Cochin, Vietnam); epiphyte with obovate leaves resembling Esmeralda but stronger, flowers having sepals rose and petals crimson-purple, lip crimson-purple shaded with scarlet and ochre-yellow, (summer). (S) *p. 1801*
cornu-cervi (Burma, Malaya); pretty, bulbless species, with bright glossy green leaves 15-25 cm long, and ascending stalk with 5 cm flowers, having petals and sepals yellowish-green spotted with red-brown, the clawed lip whitish. (S) *p. 1800*
'Doris' ('Elizabethae' x 'Katherine Siegwart'); a tetraploid of excellent keeping quality; magnificent sprays of heavy-textured flowers 10-12 cm across, glistening white; derived from P. amabilis and rimestadiana parentage (Duke Gardens). *Tropical.* *p. 1798*
'Esmeralda' (Doritis pulcherrima) (Trop. Monsoon Asia to Vietnam and Sumatra); rosette of short, fleshy broad ovate leaves with furrowed center; stocky brown stalks carry small 2 cm rose-pink flowers, small rosy lips with purple stripes, the side lobes cinnamon brown. (see Doritis). *p. 1799*
gigantea (Borneo); striking epiphyte with broad, recurving leaves that in habitat become 75 cm long; pendant inflorescence dense with waxy,

fragrant flowers 5 cm across, broad sepals and petals white or creamy, thickly spotted with dark violet-brown, orange on lip, with purple spots. *p. 1799*

'Golden Chief' (mannii x 'Chieftain'); free-blooming hybrid with large flowers of good substance, the obovate sepals and petals lemon-yellow flushed with pink toward center. *p. 1798*

'Hellé' (Marmouset x Adonis); excellent French hybrid with schilleriana and sanderiana blood; flowers of perfect shape, and very fine deep rose flushed pink toward the edges, and maroon spots in the center (early spring). *Tropical.* *p. 1801*

x intermedia (rosea x Aphrodite) (Philippines); natural hybrid with pale green leaves, and moderate size white flowers, the trilobed lip spotted with red at base, the lobes purple; winter. (S) *p. 1800*

kunstleri (Malaya: Perak); attractive flowers to 5 cm with narrow sepals and petals yellow with brown in center, the lip pale yellow, midlobe streaked brown; May. (S) *p. 1800*

lueddemanniana (Philippines); compact epiphyte with pale green, fleshy leaves, and short racemes with thick, waxy flowers whitish and beautifully marked with cinnamon-brown and bars of amethyst; stalks often bearing offshoots, (May-June and various). *Tropical.* *p. 1801*

lueddemanniana alba; lovely waxy flowers 4 cm across, creamy-white with subdued cross bars of brownish spots; foliage pale green. *p. 1798*

mannii (Assam); epiphyte with long green leaves spotted and shaded with violet; 4-6 small flowers loosely on each arching stem, the spreading sepals and petals tongue-shaped, golden yellow, barred with cinnamon-brown, lip white, anchor-shaped, (April-Aug.). (S) *p. 1801*

parishii lobbii (Burma); a lovely little epiphyte with thick fleshy roots, two-ranked deep green leathery leaves 5-10 cm long, and short racemes of small 2½ cm flowers with sepals and petals white, and white lip with two brown bands (summer). (S) *p. 1801*

'Rosy Pam' ('Pink Pamela' x rosea); arching inflorescence dense with substantial, long-lasting flowers a lovely shade of rosy-pink. *p. 1799*

x rothschildiana (schilleriana x amabilis); old James Veitch hybrid with leaves dark green mottled with silvery gray; well-rounded, dainty flowers in large sprays, with white petals, the sepals pale sulphur, tinted with rosy-pink, the lobed lip spotted with purple. *Tropical.* *p. 1800*

sanderiana 'Burgeffii'; magnificent Burgeff breakthrough into red: exceptionally large 9 cm flowers deep carmine-rose, the white antennae from base of lip coppery red in center; bronzy-green leaves with faint, darker markings; spring. (S) *p. 1800*

sanderiana 'Wuerzburg Self'; new development in red by Dr. Burgeff; floriferous plant with olive green leaves, and 6-8 cm flowers deep rose with darker markings; spring. (S) *p. 1800*

schilleriana (Philippines), "Rosy moth orchid"; beautiful epiphyte with flat roots and long, flat, tongue-like leaves transversely blotched with silvery gray, purplish-red beneath; arching, branched inflorescence with delicate, 5-8 cm flowers of dainty rose in varying tints, (Feb.-May). *Tropical.* *p. 1798, 1801*

'Star of Rio'; Burgeff hybrid of P. 'Aphrodite' (tetraploid) x lueddemanniana (diploid); flower petals waxy-white, lightly dotted purplish, lip marked brown-red; April-May. *p. 1800*

stuartiana (Philippines, Fiji); epiphyte with oblong fleshy leaves dark green and mottled with silver gray; inflorescence arching and may extend 90 cm; flowers to 5 cm across, three upper segments pure white, other two and constricted lip cream with red spots, yellow at center (spring). *p. 1798*

sumatrana purpurata (Indonesia); small epiphyte with flowers 5 cm wide, petals yellowish-white, sepals purplish, the fleshy lip white with purple streaks; fleshy, bright green leaves 15 cm long. *p. 1798*

violacea (Sumatra, Borneo); spreading, shiny green, fleshy leaves 20 cm long; stout inflorescence with flowers 5-8 cm long, yellowish green with white at base, bright rosy-violet in center of lip (spring). *p. 1798*

PHALANGIUM: see Chlorophytum

PHALERIA *Thymelaeaceae* **S2LBD**

capitata (Java); a small tree with beautiful waxy-white flowers, sweet-scented like daphne, blooming in clusters directly from trunk or heavy branches. This is an example of tropical cauliflory where flower buds form deep within the tissues of the tree and then burst out through the bark. *p. 2099*

PHANERA *Leguminosae* **S3LFM**

kockiana (syn. Bauhinia) (Borneo: Sarawak); woody tropical climber, becoming large and bushy; ovate leaves 6 to 10 cm long, not bifid, waxy light green, and prominently showing three parallel main veins; beautiful flowers with wide-spread petals scalloped at margins, 3½ - 4 cm across, and vivid orange to brilliant scarlet. *p. 1388*

williamsii, a "Chain liane" of the jungles of New Guinea; leguminous tree climber with hairy, tendril-bearing branches and small, cleft leaves; with age the stems become woody and chain-like. *p. 1389*

PHANEROPHLEBIA *Polypodiaceae (Filices)* **S3HFM**

macrosora (Aspidium juglandifolium) (Costa Rica); tropical tufting fern with fronds resembling Pteris; on slender wiry rachis the simple pinnate fronds, with broad ovate leaflets glossy green and of thin-leathery texture, the margins undulate and lightly toothed. *p. 1124*

PHASEOLUS *Leguminosae* **I2LBM**

caracalla (Vigna in Hortus 3) (Trop. So. America), "Snail-flower"; perennial twiner with leaves usually of 3 leaflets, and light purple, fragrant flowers tinted yellow, to 5 cm long and with contorted standard, the keel and wings spirally coiled like a snail shell. Also known as "Corkscrew flower". *Tropical.* *p. 1388, 1390*

coccineus (Trop. So. America), "Scarlet runner bean"; an ornamental bean; deep green leaves, and bright scarlet flowers held well above the foliage, blooming over a long period and followed by the 20 cm beanpods; when ripe the 2½ cm seed is mauve-pink spotted and striped with black. *Tropical.* *p. 1388*

PHILADELPHUS *Saxifragaceae* **C2LB-FD**

x virginalis (lemoinei x nivalis), "Mock orange"; showy floriferous, deciduous shrub with curved branches, the brown bark peeling; leaves ovate to 8 cm long, pubescent beneath; double white blooms in 3-7 flowered clusters; late spring. *Temperate.* *p. 2047*

PHILLYREA *Oleaceae* **C2LBD**

angustifolia (So. Europe, No. Africa); attractive evergreen shrub to 3 m, with dense foliage on arching branches, smooth, dark green linear-lanceolate leaves 6-8 cm long; small inconspicuous 1 cm flowers dull white and fragrant; blue-black berries. *p. 1634*

PHILODENDRON *Araceae* ***S1LFM**

acutatum (Brazil to Venezuela); thick-stemmed, semi-selfheader with long sagittate, thin but firm, glossy leaves, basal lobes triangular; glabrous beneath; wiry, channeled petioles. *p. 264*

adamantinum (Paraguay); resembling selloum but the large, bipinnate leaves are densely lobed and the side lobules are long and slender; the basal lobes overlap, closing the sinus. (I-S 2) *p. 243*

alatum: see latilobum

x allenii (bipinnatifidum x eichleri); self-header with large, leathery, glossy-green leaves pinnately lobed, the segments broad and widely spaced, the basal lobes broadly fanned. *p. 250*

andreanum; juvenile form of P. melanochrysum, which see.

'Angra dos Reis' (Brazil); slowly creeping, stocky rosette with leathery, broad-sagittate, green leaves so glossy that they appear to be lacquered; the fleshy leafstalks blotched red. *p. 250*

angustialatum (Perú); climber with oblong-obovate leaves, becoming broader toward apex with maturity, and base truncate; petioles vaginate at base. *p. 261*

angustisectum (Colombia), "Peinetas"; climber with leathery, rich green, hastate leaves pinnately parted, the segments narrow pointed, basal lobes divided again. *p. 258*

anisotomum (Mexico, Guatemala); creeping or climbing by rooting nodes; leaves somewhat leathery, trilobed but with center lobe broadly lanceolate, the basal lobes much smaller and gracefully curved. *p. 260*

applanatum (Brazil: Amazonas); robust tree-climber with close-jointed stem; the petioles flattened in upper part, with margins winged; waxy green leaves hastate and deeply divided into ovate lobes to 15 cm long; inflorescence with green 6 cm spathe and cylindric spadix. *p. 276*

asperatum (Bahia); slowly climbing on thick stem, leaves broadly cordate, dull green, to 45 cm long, deeply corrugated by numerous sunken veins; petioles covered with dense, warty scales. (3) *p. 260, 274*

auriculatum (biauriculatum) (Costa Rica, Honduras); compact rosette with oblong leaves dark green with pale, broad midrib, carried stiffly upright on long, swollen, mottled petioles sheathed at base. *p. 261, 262*

auriculatum x imbe; compact growing hybrid with stout petioles bearing erect all-green, long-cordate, leathery glossy leaves to 38 cm long, lighter beneath, and with pale veins. *p. 268*

auyantepuiense (Venezuela); climbing on slender stems forming aerial roots; the fleshy leaves hastate, arrow-shaped to 30 cm long and 13-16 cm wide, with pale midrib, on 30 cm petioles; spathe 12 cm and spadix 10 cm long. *p. 207*

bahiense (So. Brazil); climber with oblong-pointed leaves metallic green, sunken veins, on winged petioles. *p. 265*

'Ballenger's Exotica' (speciosum x eichleri); California hybrid (1962) of two of the largest of arborescent species; with age forming tremendous leaves 1 to 1½ m long, glossy rich green and of good substance, hastate in outline and deeply lobed and serrate, close to P. eichleri, but tender to frost. *p. 277*

x barryi (selloum x bipinnatifidum); decorative selfheader with the full head and attractive glossy leaves of bipinnatifidum but with broader segments and a more vigorous growth. (I-S 1-2 F-B) *p. 237*

'Beleza do Acre' (Territorio do Acre, W. Brazil); beautiful climber with showy leaves broadly sagittate and 1 m long, the glossy surface somewhat quilted, margin undulate, and pale, contrasting ribs. (3) *p. 249*

bipennifolium (Hortus 3): see panduraeforme

bipinnatifidum (Rio to Mato Grosso); stout tree with a formal head of upright, waxy green, stiff leaves to 1 m long, bipinnate with 10-12 segments each side of prominent midrib, the lobes are narrow, and lobed again, with long lobe at apex; spathe chestnut-brown; pale yellow berries; tender. *Tropical.* *p. 235, 243, 276*

bipinnatifidum 'Seaside' (So. Brazil); robust tree philodendron with large, leathery leaves deeply cut, the lobes undulate and frilly, salt resistant. (I-S 2F-B) *p. 239, 243*

x borinquensis (melinonii x warscewiczii); semi-selfheader with large, cordate undulate leaves shallowly lobed, mossgreen, with reddish veins beneath, on long, rounded petioles. *p. 258*

brasiliense (Minas Gerais); arborescent plant with large cordate, waxy, friendly green, quilted leaves; sinus open; long, fleshy petioles marked with pale stripes. *p. 263*

'Brazilian Arrow'; elegant rosette slowly arborescent, becoming tree-like; long slender petioles with large arrow-shaped, hastate leaves 60 cm or more long, elegantly lobed, deep shining green and of firm, durable texture, with light green veins. Delicate-looking but most hardy to - 5°C; (Ballenger-California). *p. 240*

brenesii (Costa Rica); stem-rooting climber with fairly large and showy oblong-cordate leaves waxy, rich green; midrib light green to ivory; round petioles shielded by purple-blotched sheaths. *p. 269*

'Burgundy'; fine commercial hybrid involving P. hastatum, erubescens, species No. 2, wendlandii, and imbe; compact grower slowly climbing, with arrow-shaped leathery leaves about 30 cm long, deep green with reddish cast, on wine-red stem and winged petioles, base cordate or hastate; ribs beneath, and the young growth, burgundy red; thicker, tougher leaf than mandaianum. *p. 268, 270*

burle-marxii (Amazonas); a new climbing species from the upper Amazon, distinguished by the long, narrow, swordshaped, leathery leaves carried alternately at right angles to the stem on stout winged petioles. *p. 251*

'Burle-Marx's Fantasy' (Brazil); beautiful species introduced by Bob Wilson—Florida; slowly climbing, with elegant foliage symmetrically shingled, leaves on winged petioles ovate-oblong with cordate base and slender twisted tip, waxy light olive-green overlaid with blackish forest-green mosaic network of veins, the margins translucent, underside pale gray-green tinted purple. *p. 255*

calophyllum (Guyana; Brazil), creeper with stem growing below ground, tufted leaves 60-90 cm long, elliptic, shining above and with depressed veins; fleshy leafstalks. *p. 272*

cannifolium (Guyana), "Flask philodendron"; epiphyte with slowly creeping stem bearing leathery, lanceolate leaves with tapering leaf base, swollen leafstalks are channeled. *Tropical.* *p. 271*

caracasense (Venezuela); climber with smallish, cordate, leathery, smooth, deep olive-green leaves with pale midrib; light green beneath; on wiry petioles marked red. *p. 263*

"Choco" (Colombia, Panama); attractive climber of compact habit, with thick, leathery leaves about 35 cm long, deep, clear velvety green with silvery veins. *p. 252*

coerulescens (Colombia, Venezuela, Panama); tall climber with long ovate, straight leaves with cordate base, dull grayish-green, midrib pinkish, reverse grayish-blue. (3) *p. 269*

"colombianum" (Colombia); attractive, compact climber from Villavicencio with large and heavy-textured, heartshaped leaves a deep, glossy green. *Tropical.* *p. 272*

corcovadense (Rio de Janeiro); small arborescent species growing on the granite of the Corcovado and in the sand of the Restinga near Rio, with tough, leathery, arrow-shaped leaves closely grouped in shapely rosette; seed black, not cream. *Tropical.* *p. 247*

cordatum (So. Brazil); climbing trees and rocks on the Corcovado, with 45 cm leaves, elongate-cordate, harder and more glossy than scandens, which is the so-called "cordatum" of florists. *p. 259*

cordatum of florists: see scandens oxycardium

corrugosum (Guyana); creeper with closely set foliage, the ovate leaves deep green and corrugated by the numerous sunken veins; short petioles winged, rough, and red near top. *p. 269*

x corsinianum (lucidum x coriaceum, Florence 1888), "Bronze shield"; Italian historical hybrid; slow creeper with large, broadly cordate, coppery green, quilted leaves having sinuate edge, the veins light green, and purplish-red beneath. *Tropical.* *p. 273*

crassinervium (Brazil); creeping in sand near lagoons south of Rio; with long, fleshy, strapshaped, glossy, olive green leaves, edged red, and a thick midrib flecked with reddish spots; spathe whitish. *p. 246, 273*

crassum (Brazil); thick-stemmed, slow creeper forming upright rosette of large shiny, heavy cordate leaves, plum green, veins depressed; petioles winged. *p. 273*

crenulatum (Brazil); selfheading plant with interesting leathery, broad, pinnately cut leaf, the narrow segments with curly margin and the basal lobes like staghorns. *p. 240, 242*

cruentum (Ecuador, Perú); upright growing creeper with waxy green, oblong-pointed leaves with cordate base and depressed veins; back of leaf a beautiful wine-red, hence the name "Red-leaf"; petioles winged. *p. 264*

curvilobum (Brazil); climber with corrugated, olive-green leaves with lighter primary veins, the basal lobes rounded and folding outward; lighter green beneath. *p. 262*

cymbispathum (Brazil); 'Foster species No. 1'; according to Barroso; a shapely selfheader forming trunk, the leathery, cupped leaves at first ovate-sagittate and undulate, later becoming lobed but not as deeply cut as bipinnatifidum, arranged more tightly, compact and formal; spathe boatshaped and purplish. (I-S2F-B) *p. 241, 243, 249*

decurrens (No. Brazil); slowly creeping, loose rosette of straplike, oblanceolate, stiff-leathery leaves somewhat recurved; midrib prominent. *p. 248, 271*

deflexum (Perú); creeper with robust, thin-leathery, halberd-shaped to trilobed, waxy, rich-green leaves on long, round, succulent, fleshy stalks. *p. 272*

devansayeanum (Andine Perú); slow creeper with broad, heart-shaped leaves, young growth red, the older leaves large and leathery, with pale midrib; elevated, pale lines on petioles; fibrous base. *p. 269*

discolor (Costa Rica); slender climber with small, heartshaped leaves tapering to point, young leaves shimmering, velvety bronze, older leaves grayish-green velvet, with pale veins; reverse red. *p. 259*

distantilobum (Amazonas); an unusual climber which I found growing in the light forest up the Rio Negro from Manaus. The glossy leaves are pinnately parted with the pointed segments narrowed toward base; spathe whitish-green. *Tropical.* *p. 247, 248*

dolosum (Bahia to Amazonas); stem climber with ovate-cordate, triangular, fresh green, glossy leaves, later sagittate to 45 cm long, and having many depressed veins, and sinuate margins. *p. 249, 265*

domesticum (hastatum hort.) (Brazil), "Elephant's ear"; lush fresh green arrow-shaped leaves, later hastate and undulate; pale veins raised and ascending; gorgeous inflorescence with tubular, pale green spathe, red inside. *Tropical.* *p. 160A, 255, 256*

domesticum 'Variegatum'; a striking mutant with the fleshy, light to dark green leaves irregularly variegated and splashed nile-green, yellow and cream white. *Tropical.* *p. 253*

(domesticum x imbe) x wendlandii; slow climber with stout petioles, and lush, leathery glossy dark green leaves oblique oblanceolate and irregularly wavy. *p. 267*

"dubia", or better "dubium", is the name under which the juvenile stage of P. radiatum is cultivated (which see).

duisbergii (Colombia); rosette of very stiff, deep glossy-green leaves deeply cut like a skeleton, the long, narrow segments tapering and distantly spaced, the basal lobes staghorn-like; pale raised veins; juvenile leaves oakleaf-shaped. Valid name: P. fendleri. *p. 244*

'Edmundo Barroso' (Rio, Espirito Santo); slowly creeping on rocks, with erect ovate-oblong leathery leaves having prominent midrib and stiff, winged petioles. *p. 248*

eichleri (Minas Geraes, Alto da Serra), "King of tree philodendrons", with magnificent, pendant leaves to 2½ m long, sagittate, metallic glossy and with scalloped edges; spathe rosy-red, hooding a white spadix. *Tropical.* *p. 238, 242, 250*

eichleri x undulatum; good hybrid combining the lush green of P. eichleri with the good texture of P. undulatum. Leaves are over 1 m long, on stiff, blush-pink petioles; compact plant holding lower leaves well. *p.239*

elaphoglossoides (Brazil: Alto Amazonas, Perú: Loreto); beautiful rosette with foliage arranged in birdsnest form; short-stalked leaves oblanceolate and leathery, 25-35 cm long and 9 cm wide, with blade corrugated by deeply recessed veins; cupped white spathe, and spadix with female flowers at base, males in cylindric upper part (id. by Dr. G. S. Bunting). *p. 277*

elegans (Trop. So. America); high climber sending out aerial roots freely from internodes; large leaves thin-leathery, deep green, deeply pinnatifid with the finger-like segments barely more than ribs; very distinctive and ornamental. *Tropical.* *p. 19*, 264*

elongatum (Rio de Janeiro); climbing on trees or shady granite rocks on Monte Tijuca, with thin-leathery, elongate-hastate leaves 30 cm long, rounded basal lobes, on long, fleshy stalks; spathe yellowish-white. *p. 251*

'Emerald King'; new hybrid developed and patented by R. McColley of Bamboo Nurseries of Florida; huge, spade-shaped medium green leaves similar to 'Emerald Duke' but with leaves more pointed, 30 cm or more long; can be trained against a pole; more resistant to disease than P. domesticum (hastatum); recommended for home or office (photo Feb. 1976). *Tropical.* *p. 266*

'Emerald Queen'; an F1 hybrid of two unidentified species, of good keeping quality, and disease resistant to "shot-gun" fungus and bacterial rot; deep green, vigorous plant with short petioles and close internodes; hastate, medium sized, shiny leaves; an excellent totem pole subject because foliage stays about same size in new growth; cold resistant. *Tropical.* *p. 268*

erubescens (Colombia), "Blushing philodendron"; clamberer rooting at every joint, with arrow shaped, 25 cm waxy leaves bronzy green edged red, wine red beneath; petioles green with red, occasionally winged. *p. 256*

'Espirito Santo' (Brazil), the juvenile form of williamsii, which see. ***258***

x evansii (selloum x speciosum); semi-selfheading, showy plant with large sagittate, dark green glossy leaves like elephant's ears, to 1 m long or more; the blade undulate, margins lightly lobed and wavy; young growth pinkish beneath. One of the most beautiful of all arborescent philodendrons; tolerant of both hot climate and chilly nights. *Tropical to Subtropic.* *p. 241, 274*

eximium (Rio de Janeiro); stem at first climbing, with leathery, broadly cordate, fresh-green leaves, becoming corrugated and undulate, to 30 cm long, and developing prominent basal lobes; spathe green outside, pale inside. *p. 249, 263*

fenzlii (Mexico, Costa Rica); climber with aerial roots at internodes; thin-leathery, trilobed leaves shiny, fresh-green; segments broad and not divided to base; spathe green outside, pale yellow and striped inside. *p. 251, 260*

ficutissimum (Trop. America); elegant climber with dense foliage and freely sending out aerial roots; waxy-green, leathery, oblong-cordate leaves with prominent veins. *p. 272*

'Florida' (laciniatum x squamiferum); attractive hybrid with slender climbing stem having very little hairy fuzz, the petioles slender, round and rough-warty, the soft-leathery, deep green leaves usually cut into 5 pointed main-lobes; pale midrib, ribs depressed and brown-red on reverse. *Tropical. p. 254*

'Florida compacta' (quercifolium x squamiferum); an excellent hybrid needing no support as it is non-vining, or only very slowly creeping; the tough petioles are round, and marked purplish-red, the interestingly lobed leaves are thick-leathery, deep waxy-green with veins barely recessed. *Tropical.* *p. 254, 266*

'Florida variegata'; striking mutation with its deep green leaves irregularly variegated with creamy-white. *p. 274*

x fosterianum (bipinnatifidum x Foster species No. 1); similar to bipinnatifidum but leaves not so deeply cut; petioles shorter; glossy green, hard texture, lobes tapering and occasionally lobed again. (I-S F-B) *p. 243*

Foster's species No. 1: see P. cymbispathum

fragrans (So. Brazil); slow creeper with heavy, broad, cordate leaves having full round basal lobes, glossy green with primary veins sunken; stocky, triangular petioles from fibrous base. *Tropical.* *p. 250*

fragrantissimum (valid name grandipes) (Guayana, Venezuela), short-stemmed species growing on rocks, or epiphytic in forests; large leaves broad sagittate, glossy green and corrugated by its many depressed veins; slender petioles in fibrous base caused by decaying leaves. (3) *p. 250*

fraternum (Venezuela); lanky climber with slender stem and long petioles winged at base; large cordate leaves corrugated with numerous veins, to 30 cm long; narrow purplish spathe. *p. 270*

frits-wentii (C. America); sturdy, slow vining species with thick, heart-shaped leaves, waxy-glossy grass-green, vaginate petioles halfway up the stalk; small cylindric spathe encloses the spadix. *Tropical.* *p. 276, 277*

'German selloum'; raised in Florida from German seed, this cultivar is of more graceful habit, with finely cut and wavy leaf segments. *p. 240*

giganteum (Puerto Rico to Trinidad), "Giant philodendron"; a giant with climbing trunk and beautifully lacquered leaves to 1 m long, ovate in outline, with cordate base, pale veins and undulate margins, on closely bunched, fleshy petioles. *Tropical.* *p. 236, 245, 265*

giganteum x imbe; climber with lush spear-shaped leaves glossy green and with pale veins, erect or pendant, occasionally tinted with gold along lateral ribs, and more than 30 cm long; the reverse reddish; long slender petioles. *Tropical.* *p. 267, 268*

giganteum x 'wend-imbe'; large, very slowly climbing hybrid, with close internodes, and large sagittate, leathery leaves 1 m long, bright glossy green with lighter veins, the margins undulate; new growth pinkish. *p. 267*

"glaucophyllum" (Brazil); slowly scandent species with showy, leathery, heartshaped leaves wider than long, the surface waxy but deeply ribbed, glaucous underneath. *p. 260*

glaziovii (So. Brazil: Guanabara); tall climber from the forest at the foot of the Corcovado, and on Monte Gavea; deep green, lanceolate leathery leaves 30-45 cm long with pale midrib; the axillary inflorescence with spathe crimson inside the pale yellowish-green tube. *p. 280*

gloriosum (Colombia), "Satin leaf"; slow surface creeper with heart-shaped, stiff, satiny leaves a beautiful silver-green and contrasting pinkish to white veins, margin reddish; slender petioles with pale stripes. *p. 257*

gloriosum 'Terciopelo Redondo' (Choco); slow creeper with thick, heart-shaped, velvety leaves moss-green and a beautiful pale green veining; glaucous pinkish-gray beneath. (3) *p. 258*

goeldii (syn. Thaumatophyllum spruceanum) (Brazil: Alto Amazonas); rare and most curious tropical aroid with scandent, fleshy stem from rambling roots, bearing large pedate leaves, 10 or more oblanceolate segments without marginal vein, arranged in a semi-circle along a long basal axis, on petioles 50-60 cm long; thick spathe and cylindric spadix. *p. 294, 295*

'Golden erubescens'; rampant climber with slender round stems; variant with solid golden yellow arrow-shaped leaves, the new growth and underside of leaves pinkish. *Tropical.* *p. 252*

'Goldiana'; a beautiful Florida clone selected by Bamboo Nurseries from seedlings of imbe with wendlandii and x mandaianum; compact grower with deep green long-ovate leaves flecked throughout with deep yellow, the underside red; short petioles; the developing leaves are bright gold. *Tropical.* *p. 280*

"grandiflorum" (Trop. America); climber with broadly cordate, membranous leaves deeply furrowed by sunken veins. *p. 262*

grandifolium (Venezuela, Guayana); tree climbing species with 60 cm long, sagittate leaves, somewhat leathery, undulate and with wavy margins; spathe yellow-green with inside purplish. *p. 242, 261*

grazielae, in hort. as "fibrillosum" (Brazil, Ecuador); small, shallow, cordate, broad leaves with cuspidate apex, thick waxy, dark green; petioles winged; similar to pittieri but smaller. *p. 273, 275*

guttiferum (Paraná, Perú, Costa Rica), "Leathery-leaf philodendron"; slow climber with stiff-leathery, elliptic oblong leaves on short, vaginate petioles. *p. 261*

hastatum: see domesticum

hastifolium (Bahia); heavy textured climber with deep green, durable, broad-cordate leaves to 45 cm when mature, hastate when young. *p. 264*

hederaceum: pre-Linnaean name for scandens, which see.

hoffmannii (Guatemala to Panama); climber with thick, short cordate leaves, long basal lobes and wider toward apex, deep green with prominent center vein, glaucous beneath; on long, stiff, flattened petioles. *p. 263*

houlletianum (Guyana); slow climber with rounded, light green, lobed leaves, in mature stage bipinnately parted to 60 cm long, on long fleshy petioles. *p. 264*

ilsemannii (Brazil); may be a variegated form of sagittifolium; spectacular climber with leathery, sagittate leaves almost entirely white or cream with gray and dark green marbling; petioles vaginate at base. *p. 15*, 253*

imbe (Pernambuco to São Paulo); "Imbe" is the Brazilian Indian's name for most climbing philodendron. The species has leaves oblong sagittate, parchment-like and with veins nearly at right angles, some reddish beneath, to 35 cm long and 18 cm wide; petioles marked red. *Tropical. p. 256, 263*

imbe x domesticum (hastatum); shapely hybrid of durable texture, with thick-leathery, long, arrow-shaped leaves. *p. 266, 268*

imbe 'Variegatum' (Guanabara); waxy sagittate leaves with pointed basal lobes, and irregularly variegated; one side of leaf may be dark green with cream marbling, the other side cream with nile green and dark green spots. *Tropical.* *p. 253*

"imperialis" (speciosum?) (Brazil); spectacular species with scandent trunk bearing sagittate leaves to 2 m long, silvery in juvenile stage, later dark green, very much corrugated and margins wavy; bold fresh-green veins. Photographed in Golden Gate Conservatory, San Francisco. *p. 237, 242*

insigne (Guianas to Eastern Colombia); self-heading rosette with short stem; erect leaf-blades oblanceolate, to 1 m long and 20 cm wide, of thick-leathery texture, waxy-green and with prominent midrib, on 12 cm petioles; the cupped spathe greenish outside, blood-red inside. *p. 235*

'Jungle Gardens' ('São Paulo' x selloum); excellent hybrid, with age forming trunks and becoming tree-like; large, fresh green, very shiny leaves pinnately cut, the segments irregularly lobed and slightly frilled. (Ballenger, California hybrid 1962). *p. 240*

'Jungle Gardens Variegated'; a variegated cultivar with parts of the leaf milk-white to creamy yellow contrasting with the waxy green. *p. 240*

karstenianum (Oaxaca), "Mexican philodendron"; climbing species known as 'Mex', with brittle-glazed stem, oblong cordate, thin-leathery leaves, fresh green, on reddish petioles, some round, some vaginate; the 20 cm leaves always stay about the same size. *Tropical.* *p. 246, 261, 275*

krebsii (Puerto Rico, Virgin Is.); tall forest climber with cordate oblong, 20 cm leaves, leathery, shiny deep green; winged petioles. *p. 269*

lacerum (Cuba, Haiti, Jamaica); stem climber with juvenile leaves ovate, entire and with undulate margin; later leaves crenately lobed and mature leaves deeply incised, glossy-green with light green veins, to 75 cm long; tubular spathe reddish outside, blade yellow-green. *p. 244, 245, 273*

lacerum crestifolium (Jamaica); juvenile leaves heartshaped, glossy-green, with lobed margins, in successive leaves more cut and fingered, beautifully wavy-crested. *p. 244*

laciniatum (Perú); climber with oddly-shaped, leathery leaves having five distinct lobes, and with elevated pale green center markings. *p. 254, 258*

laciniatum palmatisectum (Brazil to Surinam); spready clamberer with shiny, olive-green leaves with occasional light green markings, three-parted, the lobes again cut into broad pointed lobes; veins depressed; rough petioles. *p. 264*

latilobum ('alatum') (Perú); tree climber with sturdy, ovate triangular leaves trilobed, with two deep indentations to form broad wings; stiff, round petioles. *p. 248, 260*

lehmannii (Colombia); creeper with woody stem, thick leaves oblong-elliptic, cheerful green, pale beneath; long petioles flat on top. *p. 259*

ligulatum (Costa Rica); slender climber with shiny, oblong-obovate leaves broadening toward apex; flattened petioles without wings. *p. 261*

lindenii: see verrucosum

lingulatum (Puerto Rico to Martinique); high tree climber with ovate, rich green, corrugated leaves; petiole with wings, and flattened near base of leaf. *p. 261*

linnaei (Surinam); slowly creeping and scandent stems with close joints, forming a crown; the thick-leathery leaves long oblanceolate 50-60 cm long, waxy green above, tinged bronze; reddish underside, and with thick midrib; spathe inflated below, constricted in the middle, and with white hood. *Tropical.* *p. 276, 277*

loefgrenii (São Paulo); slowly creeping plant, growing down rocks, with stiff-leathery, lanceolate leaves having pale midrib, carried on slender fleshy stalks. *p. 271*

longilaminatum (Bahia); creeper with very long and narrow, glossy-green, stiff, upright leaves with prominent midrib and red edge; long, fleshy petioles somewhat marbled. *p. 264*

longistilum (Brazil); resembling a self-heading wendlandii but sends out creeping runners; glossy-green, leathery, oblanceolate leaves with bold midrib and distinctive wine-red back, on abbreviated stalks. *Tropical.* *p. 250, 262, 268*

lundii (C. Brazil); tree with ultimate leaves tripinnatifid, leathery lobes overlapping; fresh green and with wavy edge; wide sinus; spathe green like selloum, and orange berries; highly frost-resistant. (1-2 F-B) *p. 242*

lundii var. 'São Paulo' (São Paulo); better than the type; cupped, and the richer green is less likely to yellow in sun. This may be a natural hybrid of lundii with selloum. (I-S 2 F-B) *p. 236*

'Lynette' (wendlandii x elaphoglossoides), "Quilted birdsnest"; very attractive rosette in form of a birdsnest; the leathery, fresh-green leaves with showy, ribbed depressions. *Tropical.* *p. 19*, 265*

x magnificum (selloum x eichleri); a selfheader with the long, waxy leaf of eichleri but more deeply cut, with the lobes widely spaced. *Tropical.* *p. 236*

'Majesty'; new Florida hybrid of rather compact habit, with large spear-shaped glossy leaves 20-25 cm long, deep coppery-green with wine-red underside and red petioles and stocky stems; good table plant with several cuttings per pot. Bred and patented by R. Mc Colley of Orlando. *p. 266*

mamei (Ecuador), "Quilted silver-leaf"; slow creeper with large arrow-shaped, waxy, cordate-ovate, quilted leaves grass-green to grayish green marbled with silvery areas; flattened petioles green suffused pink, with horny edges, smooth and with whitish length-stripes, rounded at bottom of petiole. *Tropical.* *p. 269, 275*

x mandaianum (domesticum x erubescens), "Red leaf philodendron"; the best clone of this hybrid, selected by Manda for darkest red coloring, both the glossy, arrowshaped leaves and the stems being deep wine to metallic purplish-red; the first philodendron hybrid in the United States, 1936. *Tropical.* *p. 266*

martianum (Brazil); epiphytic clusters of waxy green, ovate leaves with pale, inflated stalks growing on procumbent stem; differing from cannifolium, according to Burle-Marx and Blossfeld, by the boatshaped, merely flattened stalks, and a leaf with obtuse or cordate base, and red edge. *Tropical.* *p. 271*

x mcneilianum (F. species no. 1 x selloum); self-heading plant with large leaves almost triangular, deeply lobed and wavy; basal lobes staghorn-like; "cold" resistant. *p. 241*

melanochrysum, known in juvenile stage as **andreanum,** (Colombia, Costa Rica), "Black gold" or "Velour philodendron"; beautiful climber from the moist coastal forests, with oblong-sagittate, iridescent, velvety leaves 20 to 70 cm long, nearly black-olive and shimmering with copper, and bordered by translucent margins, the veins ivory-white. *Humid-tropical.* *p. 257, 273*

melinonii (Guyana), "Red birdsnest"; shapely rosette of ovate, large fresh green leaves with pale veins, and distinguished by channeled, swollen, red leafstalks. One can see these spots of red a far distance, high on 45 m forest trees, when traveling in a dugout canoe deep in the interior of Surinam. *Tropical.* *p. 241, 245, 261*

mello-barretoanum (Acre, N.W. Brazil); majestic tree forming a stout trunk, with a crown of large, broadly hastate leaves deeply cut, and the pointed segments lobed again and overlapping; wide basal sinus; has robust thorns on the trunk between leaf scars. *Tropical.* *p. 241, 242, 244*

mexicanum (Cordoba), robust climber with fleshy, elongate-hastate leaves, shiny, rich green, the basal lobes appearing like ears and turned outward. *p. 262*

micans (Dominica, Tobago), "Velvet-leaf vine"; leggy vine with small, heartshaped leaves glittering silky bronze above, reddish beneath; very susceptible to cold. This may be merely the juvenile form of Ph. scandens oxycardium. (3H) *p. 259*

microstictum (pittieri) (Costa Rica); slow climber with broad heart-shaped, thick, glossy, apple-green leaves, attached to round petioles at edge of shallow sinus, giving a pleasing appearance. *p. 255, 273*

miduhoi (Mexico; Guatemala); slender climber known to florists as 'Silver Sheen'; leaves heartshaped, generally larger than oxycardium but silvery-gray satin with gray veins. *p. 259, 263*

minarum (Minas Gerais); self-heading arborescent species of smaller proportions, with trunk bearing a head of good green, solid but lobed hastate leaves 45-60 cm long. *p. 238*

'Minas Gerais' (Minas Gerais); miniature selfheader growing on trees, with massed head of leathery leaves perfectly arrow-shaped, the margins curly, on slender petioles. *p. 247*

'Miniature selloum'; a dwarf form with short, stout petioles, and leaves reduced in size but of thicker texture and more sturdy than the parent. *p. 240*

montanum (Colombia); tall tree climber from the moist coastal forests, heartshaped leaves with pronounced basal lobes, waxy green above, glaucous gray-green beneath. *p. 265*

myrmecophilum (Amazonas); robust climber from the tall forests between the Rio Negro and Colombia; large, arrow-shaped, glossy-green leaves with numerous depressed veins, on mottled, swollen petioles. *p. 248, 265*

'New Yorker'; slow climber with aerial roots along stem; similar to P. youngii, but more compact and with more natural gloss, and more red; joints close, petioles spotted blood-red, leaves sagittate, rusty-red in younger foliage,dark green with pale veins when older, leathery glossy, somewhat cupped. *p. 270*

nobile (Venezuela, Guyana); birdsnest-like rosette of thick-leathery leaves broadly oblanceolate, with bold midrib, on thick, slowly creeping stem. *Tropical.* *p. 271*

ochrostemon (Rio to Mato Grosso); branching climber with more or less broadly ovate oblique leaves dark green and corrugated, later perforated. *p. 269*

ornatum (Rio, Espirito Santo, Bahia); climber of the mountain forests with fresh-green, leathery leaves broad ovate-cordate, long basal lobes and many depressed veins; spathe ovate with tubular base. *p. 249*

"orthophyllum"; climber introduced in Germany, and resembling erubescens; cordate, pointed leaves lacquered green, underneath brown-red as are petioles and new stems. *p. 272*

oxycardium: see scandens

panduraeforme (bipennifolium) (So. Brazil), "Fiddle-leaf"; climber with unusual leaves shaped like a violin, the basal lobes extended, central lobes narrowed toward middle, of leathery texture, dull olive green. Very decorative trained to poles. *Tropical.* *p. 255, 273*

pedatum (Ter. Amapa, Brazil; Guayana); epiphytic on trees, or climbing on rocks; broad leathery leaves usually cut into 5 broad lobes, center segment largest; spathe greenish. *p. 246*

x pennockii (melinonii x giganteum); rosette of fleshy, broadly cordate, pointed leaves, light green, with sunken veins, on flattened petioles. *p. 266*

"pertusum" (So. Mexico), "Split-leaf philodendron"; the fast-climbing juvenile stage of Monstera deliciosa; the smallest leaves are roundish entire, later growth will be more pinnatisect and forming occasional perforations. *Tropical.* *p. 231, 233, 255*

"pertusum variegatum": see Monstera deliciosa 'Variegata' *p. 253*

pilatonense (Ecuador, Colombia); creeper with large, round-cordate, thin-leathery leaves iridescent satiny, pale emerald green, with depressed pinkish veins; reddish beneath; red petioles thickly covered with long, pale green hairs. *p. 272*

pinnatifidum (Venezuela, Amazonas); selfheader growing tree-like, with leathery leaves pinnately parted, the lobes well apart with wide sinus, metallic green, veins sunken; the channeled petioles spotted red. *p. 243*

pinnatifidum 'British Guiana'; resembles pinnatifidum; the elegantly pinnate leaves are smooth and have a satiny luster; purple spots on petioles from a fibrous base. *p. 240*

pinnatilobum (Brazil: Alto Amazonas); handsome tree-climber with elegant pinnate leaves on round, red-spotted petioles, the pinnae narrow lanceolate and concave, from a winged central axis, waxy green and leathery; the tubular-inflated spathe pale green. Photograph by J. Bogner, Munich, but I have also collected this species on the Rio Negro near Manaos. *p. 276*

pinnatilobum 'Fernleaf', "Fernleaf philodendron"; graceful tropical climber with leathery leaves cut much finer into narrow-linear segments than the species or distantilobum. Originally listed by Florida nurseries as "Fernleaf". *p. 276*

pittieri: see microstictum

poeppigii (Alto Amazonas); semi-selfheading tree-dweller with cupped, heartshaped leaves on long, stiff petioles with edges rolled up; base fibrous. *Tropical.* *p. 247*

polytomum (Vera Cruz); almost stemless, with large, glossy leaves rounded in outline, and pinnately cut, lobes pointed, and occasionally lobed again. *p. 244*

pseudoradiatum (Mexico: Chiapas); slow climber with large 60 cm attractive, sagittate leaves glossy green with prominently contrasting pale ribs and undulate margins; on cylindrical petioles; tubular spathe green outside, brilliant purple inside. *Tropical.* *p. 267*

pulchellum (Costa Rica); weakly scandent species creeping downwards, with cordate oblong or fiddle-shaped leaves, quite papery, grass-green with satin sheen, on thin wiry petioles. *p. 265*

pulchrum (Amazonas); a new species from the upper Amazon, forming a shapely rosette of stiffly upright, leathery, ovate leaves, waxy green with pale, red-spotted ribs, on firm stalks. *p. 251*

quercifolium (Brazil); climber with olive-green, lacy leaves widely spread, deeply laciniate with narrow pointed segments widely separated; smooth round petiole marked purple. *p. 264*

'Queremal' (Colombia); decorative rosette with stiff, upright, long, heart-shaped leaves beautifully lacquered. *p. 247*

radiatum (dubium) (So. Mexico, Guatemala); lush climber with broad, rich green leaves deeply lobed; in the smaller and less incised juvenile stage known commercially as P. 'dubia'. *p. 244*

'Red Duchess'; patented new hybrid bred by Bob Mc Colley of Orlando, Florida, to withstand the rigors of office environment; dark glossy green, heart-shaped leaves with reddish underside, 20-25 cm long, and with red petioles and slowly climbing stem, for training along a supporting pole. (Photographed Feb. 1976). *Tropical.* *p. 266*

'Red Emerald'; robust Florida erubescens hybrid with long ruby-red, round petioles, and long-cordate leaves 30-40 cm long, dark glossy green with ribs red on reverse; smooth stems also wine-red. *Tropical.* *p. 276*

regelianum (So. America); selfheading type forming stout caudex; the foliage on long slender petioles; large hastate leaves with prominent basal lobes, and prettily sinuate and lobed at margins. *p. 270*

renauxii (Brazil: Santa Catarina); pretty and decorative slow climber with strong creeping stems 2½-5 cm thick; stiff petioles hold the concave, soft-leathery, lanceolate, sickle-shaped leaves 30-35 cm long, with base generally cordate, and blunt apex, brilliant dark green with pale midrib and with translucent edge and densely nerved; spathe white inside. *p. 270*

rothschuhianum (Mexico, Nicaragua); climber with dull-green, papery leaves hastate-trilobed, the lobes broadly ovate, numerous sunken veins; long, terete petioles. *p. 262*

rubens (Trinidad, Venezuela); thick-stemmed rosette of broad, sagittate ovate leaves, dark green and leathery, pale beneath; rough petiole with raised lines toward top; spathe red inside. *p. 258*

x rubescens; probably a clone selected from the many varied erubescens x hastatum hybrids; arrow-shaped leaves metallic bronze-green with veins red beneath; petioles with and without wings and striped red. *p. 262*

rubrocinctum (Colombia); rare climber with delicate, long cordate leaves, satiny, coppery-brown with light green veins, red reverse. (3) *p.258*

"rubrum"; probably an erubescens hybrid; with larger leaves, waxy, deep reddish-green, heartshaped, pointed; veins coppery to white, reddish beneath; petioles striped red, with wings on juvenile leaves only. *p. 256*

ruizii (Perú); large, elongated, crinkled leaves dull green with the numerous veins depressed; very changeable from cordate to sagittate with overlapping basal lobes. *p. 263, 269*

sagittatum (So. Mexico); climber with large, leathery, sagittate oblong leaves with sunken veins almost at right angle to midrib, reverse glossy; petioles not winged. *p. 256*

sagittifolium (So. Mexico); climber with arrow to halberd-shaped foliage, the basal lobes in advanced leaves widely spread, the blade wavy, veins depressed. *Tropical.* *p. 256*

sanguineum (Mexico); climber with thick, elongate sagittate leaves, dark green with prominent light midrib, lower surface red on young leaves, green on older ones; petioles sparingly spotted red. *p. 250, 256*

'Santa Leopoldina' (Espirito Santo); an important species having the most beautiful leaf I have seen in Brazil; it is slowly climbing, the stems and petioles are red, with elegant, long sagittate, leathery leaves 1 m long, glossy dark green with ivory ribs and red margins; spadix enveloped in a reddish spathe. *Tropical.* *p. 248, 257*

saxicolum (Brazil); growing on rocks in Bahia and forming short trunks; the leathery leaves are twice pinnately cleft and triangular, base sagittate. *p. 238, 242*

scandens cuspidatum (Puerto Rico); slender, stem-rooting tree climber with thin, glossy, dark green, small cordate leaves, the tip slender pointed; internodes brownish; shorter lobes than scandens oxycardium, of which this may be the juvenile stage. *p. 263*

scandens oxycardium (Puerto Rico to Jamaica and Central America), known in horticulture as "cordatum"; pre-Linnaean as hederaceum. The most popular and widely sold vining Philodendron, known as "Heartleaf philodendron" or "Parlor ivy", or simply "Cordatum vine". A tall tropical, rapid climber by aerial roots; with glossy deep green, broadly heart-shaped, soft-leathery leaves,in juvenile stage 10-15 cm long; in maturity or flowering stage to 30 cm long. In habitat when very young the foliage is apparently velvety, from observations I made in Costa Rica. This species may be used in many ways, as a cascading vine in pots, baskets, window boxes, or room dividers; or it may be trained against support, preferably on mossed poles, bark slabs, or milled treefern pillars. *Tropical.* *p. 255, 259, 275*

scandens oxycardium 'Variegatum'; heartshaped leaves marbled ivory-white and gray-green on dark, glossy green. *Tropical.* *p. 259*

scandens ssp. scandens (Pacific slope of So. Mexico, Guatemala, Costa Rica); relatively small-leaved scandent and climbing aroid with heart-shaped (cordate) leaves 8 to 10 and 15 or more cm long, characterized especially in the juvenile stage by their silky luster or shimmering metallic surface, with pale midrib and reddish reverse; the leaves are also somewhat narrower than the subsp. oxycardium, which is glossy or waxy green even in juvenile stage, and more leathery; inflorescence with tubular spathe cherry-red inside. *p. 276*

schottianum (Costa Rica); stem with short internodes,with the thin petioles carrying thin, light green leaves to 60 cm long and heartshaped, the surface corrugated by many sunken veins. *p. 260*

schottii (Jamaica); semi-selfheader, slowly creeping; with upright, oblong, broadly lanceolate, leathery leaves and subcordate base, dark green, the midrib thick and prominent. *p. 262*

'Seaside': see under bipinnatifidum

selloum (S.W. Brazil), "Lacy tree-philodendron"; self-header, tree-like or scandent on trees. In the moist forests of western Paraná I have seen it growing epiphytic, sending down aerial roots to strike the ground. The lush, dark green, pendant 60 cm leaves are bipinnate with short lobe at tip; juvenile leaves are merely lobed; spathe greenish-white. *Tropical.* *p. 235, 240, 241, 243, 246, 247, 270*

selloum 'California type', arborescent form with large leaves more cupped and more deeply cut, darker green, and the pinnae less frilled than in P. lundii 'São Paulo'; channeled petiole. (I-S 2 F-B) *p. 236*

selloum 'Johnsii'; form which is said to have a tendency to sucker as a younger plant; juvenile leaves are only shallowly lobed and arranged in a shapely rosette. *p. 243*

selloum var. 'Uruguay' (Uruguay); large leaves, more giant, combining the characteristics of both the solid and frilly types, with wide sinus and more lobes; fairly hardy in Florida. (I 2 F-B) *p. 239*

selloum variegatum; variant of the well-known South Brazilian self-heading rosette, with its large glossy green feathered leaves variegated creamy yellow or pale green; petioles striped with cream. *p. 252*

sellowianum (Brazil); fast growing selfheader with deeply cut leaves which stand considerable cold. According to Robert Blossfeld in São Paulo, similar to bipinnatifidum, but has green seed pod sheaths instead of black ones. *Tropical.* *p. 239, 243*

"sigutatum" (Trop. America); climber with long ovate, deep green, leathery leaves having a cordate base, on slender petioles. *p. 262*

'Silver Cloud' (originally listed by Merkel as Species B); fast-climbing, attractive species resembling sodiroi; soft-leathery, lush, heart-shaped corrugated leaves with full basal lobes, matte-green, and blotched silvery-gray in outer area, creamy-green beneath, and with translucent edging; petioles wide, near flat both above and beneath, rich green with pale stripelets, the angles with undulate ribbon edging. *p. 275*

simsii (Guyana); creeping species with oblong sagittate, leathery leaves, waxy fresh green with prominent veins; good for totem poles. Inhabiting swampy savannah. *p. 269*

sodiroi (laucheanum) (Brazil), "Silver-leaf philodendron"; in juvenile stage vining with small cordate, pointed, bluish-green glossy leaves largely covered with silver, ribs are red underneath; petioles wine-red and winged; in later stage petiole becomes flat on top and rugose with green puckers, and without wings, leaves are larger and rounded, internodes close. *Tropical.* *p. 273, 275*

species No. 1: see P. cymbispathum

speciosum (Minas Geraes, S. Paulo, Mato Grosso), "Imperial philodendron"; majestic arborescent species becoming tree-like with age; with huge sagittate leaves 1½ m or more long, rich green, thin-leathery, the veins sunken and margins wavy and almost frilled; flowers beautiful with fleshy spathe green with purple margins, carmine-red inside. *p. 237, 250*

splitgerberi (Surinam, No. Brazil); tall climber with long internodes, the leafstalks flattened and crisped on the sides, leaves ovate-cordate, to 30 cm long, with depressed veins and undulate margins. *p. 251*

squamiferum (Guyana), "Red bristle philodendron"; twisting vine with rich green, 5-lobed leaves, the center lobe broad ovate, lateral lobes pointed, basal lobes short; olive petioles covered with green to red bristles. *p. 19*, 254, 264*

stenophyllum (Perú); creeper with large, stiff-leathery, unequal-sided, oblong leaves, rich, deep green, veins depressed except for prominent midrib, pale green beneath. *p. 263*

subhastatum (Ecuador); climber of the subtropical forest, with large, papery, subhastate leaves, fresh green, corrugated by its numerous depressed veins; striped leafstalks. *p. 272*

sulcatum (Ecuador); climber with thin-leathery, oblong oblanceolate leaves, glossy green on fleshy petioles. *p. 272*

talamancae (Costa Rica); slow climber forming a rosette of stiff, 60 cm long, pointed leaves having uneven basal lobes, red beneath when young; the bold midrib and sunken veins are ivory; channeled petioles mottled. *p. 242, 274*

tarmense (Perú); climber with deep green, soft-fleshy, cordate leaves, having large, round basal lobes, pale beneath; round, light green petioles marked deep green. *p. 263*

'Temptation' x auriculatum; robust hybrid with swollen, winged petioles and erect or arching long lanceolate, shining green leaves with bold, light green midrib. *p. 268*

teretipes (Colombia); epiphytic, climbing; long, sword-like, leathery, glossy green leaves having numerous nerves, and red margins, stout midrib, on long, red leafstalks. *p. 262*

thaliifolium (Venezuela); climber with thin-leathery, elongate-oblong leaves to 45 cm long, with cordate base and quilted surface; spathe pale green outside, whitish inside. (3) *p. 251*

traunii (Amazonas); a tall climber from the giant forests along the Rio Negro above Manaus; the thin-leathery leaves becoming broadly deltoid-sagittate, to 30 cm long, with slender apex; spathe purple outside, yellowish inside. *p. 251*

x tricolor (hastatum variegatum x wendlandii); semi-selfheading rosette of long, arrow-shaped, green leaves irregularly splashed cream and white; leafstalks fleshy. *p. 258*

trifoliatum (Venezuela); stemrooting climber with fleshy, dark green, trifoliate leaves, and veins depressed; round petioles slender and with red mark at base of leaf. *p. 260*

tripartitum (Guatemala, Costa Rica, Panama), "Trileaf philodendron"; scraggly climber with trifoliate, leathery leaves glossy-green, the segments quite narrow and long-pointed, and not quite cut to base. *p. 260*

tripartitum x imbe; an interesting, climbing hybrid with the narrow leafblade very much halberd-shaped, the basal lobes spreading wide, olive green; reddish underneath. *p. 266*

trisectum (Andes of Colombia); freely rooting climber with leathery, trifoliate leaves, at maturity stage divided nearly to base, segments long and with sunken veins; petiole channeled. *p. 260*

triumphans (Colombia); climber more robust than verrucosum; cordate leaves velvety, moss-green with grayish veins, silver green reverse; green hairs on petioles. (3) *p. 259*

tuxtlanum (So. Mexico), "Tuxtla philodendron"; discovered 1959 East of Santiago Tuxtla near Veracruz; slowly creeping epiphyte or rock-dweller; with leathery, glossy rich green leaves at first triangular or spade-shaped, in later stages oblong-pointed with sagittate base, to 60 cm long by 30 cm wide, and lighter veins; the blades bent downward at right angles with the junction of the leafstalk, which is circular but shortly winged to base. Introduced from Denmark as a meritorious indoor plant. *Tropical.* *p. 275*

tweedianum (Argentina, Paraguay); probably the southernmost philodendron which I found growing in the Paraná delta near Buenos Aires; large, hastate deep green leaves irregularly lobed, and wavy-margined; forming trunk. *Subtropic.* *p. 240, 247*

ugulatum (Trop. America); climber with long cordate, pendant leaves metallic green, on long wiry petioles. *p. 262*

uleanum (Amazonas); scandent plant with thin-leathery, glossy green, lanceolate to oblanceolate leaves somewhat pendant, the base obtuse and broadened, the surface quilted; greenish-white spathe. *p. 250*

undulatum (Paraguay); a smaller selfheader, and I have seen these small trees in the dry savannahs of Paraguay, the sagittate wavy and lobed leaves somewhat cupped, carried on erect stalks; with age forming massive trunks. *Tropical.* *p. 235, 236, 242*

'Uruguay': see under P. selloum

urbanianum (Cuba); high tree climber with small, ovate-lanceolate, leathery leaves having cordate base, dark green; young petioles reddish, vaginate or round. *p. 263*

variifolium (Perú); slow vine with small, leathery, heartshaped leaves, greenish-brown when young, bluish-green when older, with silver featherbands between lateral veins; winged petioles red, also veins beneath. *Tropical.* *p. 257*

'Venezuela' (So. Venezuela); birdsnest-like, compact rosette of leathery, oblanceolate leaves with undulate surface and strong midrib. *p. 272*

ventricosum (Brazil); clustering plant received from Sweden; bottle-shaped stalks with narrow, leathery, straplike leaves having raised midrib and a rounded base. *p. 271*

verrucosum (Costa Rica, Colombia), "Velvet leaf"; long-vining, with delicate, undulate, heart-shaped leaves to 60 cm long, shimmering velvety, dark, bronzy green; pale green vein areas and margins emerald green, salmon violet beneath; petioles red and covered with green hairs; showy inflorescence with spathe an ovoid rose-purple tube 8 cm long, densely white-hairy and with white margin, and enclosing the slender spadix. Gorgeous. *Tropical.* *p. 257*

verrucosum "purpureum" (Colombia); a "blue" type, possibly natural rubrocinctum hybrid; slender climber with velvety cordate leaves that stay small, deep emerald green with glowing, wine-purple areas, silver along pink veins. (3H) *p. 259*

warmingii (São Paulo); dense clusters of swollen stalks with ovate, yellow-green leaves having their base obtuse; similar to martianum, but the petioles are channeled. *Tropical.* *p. 271*

warscewiczii (Mexico, Guatemala, Honduras, Panama); scandent species forming snaky trunks; with lush, very soft leaves, fresh green, triangular sagittate and pinnately parted, the pointed segments well separated in mature leaves, and with overlapping lobes; goes deciduous in dry season. *Tropical.* *p. 244, 252*

warscewiczii flavum, "Golden selloum"; a stable mutant with the large lobed, waxy leaves entirely chartreuse-yellow, and quite delicate. (3) *p. 244, 252*

'Weber's Selfheading'; California hybrid probably of imbe, wendlandii and domesticum; sturdy, slow climber with thick-leathery, highly glossy green, oblique oblanceolate to auriculate leaves, with pale midrib, and ribs red beneath; fleshy petioles flattened on top and usually vaginate at base; reddish and dotted with yellow-green, and with red geniculum; freely suckering into dense rosette if pinched when young. *p. 267*

x wendatum (wendlandii x domesticum), the "Fairchild hybrid"; slowly climbing, thick, oblanceolate, dark green leaves, some red beneath, on swelling petioles. *p. 266*

x wend-imbe (wendlandii x imbe); semi-selfheading hybrid with many waxy green, oblong-pointed leaves carried stiffly on flattened stalks; new growth pink underneath. *Tropical.* *p. 267*

wendlandii (Costa Rica, Panama), "Birdsnest philodendron"; selfheading rosette of thick, waxy-green, long obovate leaves with thick midrib, arranged like a birds-nest; the short petioles are spongy; spathe cream-white. *p. 265*

(wendlandii x domesticum) x brenesii; sturdy hybrid; winged petioles bearing erect leathery broad, nearly oval leaves deep shining green with pale midrib. *p. 268*

wendlandii variegatum; dense, compact rosette of stiff-erect and spreading oblanceolate leaves about 60 cm long, the fleshy, glossy green leaves irregularly feathered and variegated with yellow, this yellow pattern differs on the back of the leaf; thick, short petioles, crescent-like in cross-section, striped in green and yellow. *p. 252*

williamsii (Bahia, Espirito Santo); a magnificent epiphyte, also known as 'Espirito Santo'; with arborescent stem, and fresh green, deeply hastate leaves almost 1 m long and with undulate margins and reddish veins; spathe pale green outside, yellowish inside. *Tropical.* *p. 238, 247, 258*

x wilsonii (giganteum x radiatum); slow climber with large sagittate, fresh-green, glossy leaves with shallowly lobed edge, on long, fleshy petioles. *p. 244*

wittianum (Amazonas); epiphyte from the Rio Negro; slowly creeping,w ith densely clustered, large, leathery, oblong leaves to 60 cm long; 15 cm greenish-white spathe. *p. 249*

youngii (Mexico); very similar to "The New Yorker"; slow climber with leathery, deep glossy green, undulate, heartshaped leaves with long basal lobes and delicate pale veins, closely clustered on long petioles with reddish spots. *p. 251, 263*

PHILODENDRON: see also Monstera

PHILYDRUM *Philydraceae* **S3HFW**

lanuginosum (Malaysia); a marsh plant with cylindric, spear-shaped leaves thinning to a sharp point, finely pubescent; the inflorescence on branching spikes with small yellow flowers appressed to each stalk. *p.1922*

PHINAEA *Gesneriaceae* **S3HFM**

multiflora (C. America); true miniature gesneriad less than 3 cm high; with rhizomatous roots; opposite, ovate leaves green with white veins, and with toothed margins, covered with soft white hair; from the leaf axil the solitary tiny white flower. From Ruth Katzenberger, New York (Gloxinian, March 1957). *p. 1253*

PHLOMIS *Labiatae* **I2LBD**

italica (Balearic Isl.); small shrubby, starry-hairy plant to 30 cm; with lanceolate 5 cm gray-green leaves white-hairy beneath and lightly crenate; small 2 cm pale rose, two-lipped flowers in axillary whorls. *p. 1347*

PHLOX *Polemoniaceae* **C-I2LBM**

carolina 'Miss Lingard' (suffruticosa); old favorite summer-flowering perennial 60 cm high, derived from the purple species at home from Ohio to Florida; showy panicles of salverform fragrant flowers white with pale pink center, blooming tirelessly from May to October; hardy. *p. 1951*

drummondii (Texas), "Dwarf annual phlox"; dwarf branching, pretty annual with fresh-green, small lanceolate leaves; flat, terminal clusters of brightly colored, salverform, 2½ cm flowers in shades of rose-red; cultivars in white, buff, pink, red, purple, and blue, with colorful eyes; attractive little plant for garden planting and in pots. *Warm temperate.* *p. 1951*

paniculata (U.S.: New York to Arkansas), "Summer phlox"; herbaceous perennial phlox, to 1 m, with lanceolate leaves; the leafy stems topped by panicles of large 2½ cm purple flowers; varying in colors white, salmon, scarlet, lilac, in summer and autumn; hardy. *Temperate.* *p. 1951*

PHOENICOPHORIUM *Palmae* **S3LFM**

borsigianum (Stevensonia grandifolia) (Seychelles); monoecious palm to 15 m high; stem spiny when young, with obovate leaves pinnately ribbed but not cut to rachis, 1 to 2 m long, and two-lobed at apex, lightly cut and toothed at margins. *p. 1890*

PHOENIX *Palmae* **I-S2LBM**

canariensis (Canary Islands), "Canary Islands date palm"; stately feather palm widely planted in subtropical regions as an ornamental; compact, robust and stiff when young, with age forming thick, straight trunks, becoming 15 m high, with arching pinnate leaves 6 m long, the short stalk armed with yellow spines, the leaflets glossy-green, in various directions; on female trees small yellow fruit in large clusters. *Subtropic.* *p. 1892, 1893, 1902*

dactylifera (Arabia, No. Africa), the fruiting "Date palm" of Egypt and North Africa, and its descendants in the Coachella Valley in the California desert; a massive tree becoming 30 m high, dense with stiff pinnate fronds spiny at the base, with narrow rigid folded pinnae in double rows when older, bluish-glaucous, to 45 cm long and sharp-pointed; following pollination, female trees will set delicious oblong edible fruit in great, heavy clusters. *Tropical.* *p. 1892, 1894, 1902*

dactylifera 'Deglet Noor'; fondly known by the Arabs as "Daughter of Light"; a favorite variety of date palm cultivated in California for its excellent large and meaty, "semi-soft" fruit, which packs and keeps well; each female tree producing, after artificial pollination, 90-120 kg of dates a year, on irrigated land, where the trees "have their feet in water and their heads in fire", according to an Arab saying; to produce good fruit, just hot days are not good enough, and the desert climate of the Coachella Valley, in interior So. California near the Mexican border, with temperatures of 40°C at night and to 52°C in daytime suits them best. I remember the custom of spraying my bed with a water hose, before going to sleep at night, while living in Palm Springs, before the advent of air-conditioning. *p. 1895*

humilis (India, Burma, China); robust, medium size fan palm; trunk with persistent leafbases spirally arranged; arching pinnate leaves on petiole spiny with spine-like lower leaflets; rigid leaflets glaucous green; in several ranks; red 2 cm fruit turning blue-black. *p. 1892*

paludosa (India: Bengal; Thailand, Vietnam), "Siamese date palm"; curious tropical feather palm forming clusters of several erect or reclining tree-like trunks, 3 to 8 m long and 8-10 cm thick; the pinnate fronds 3-4 m long and arching, with soft-leathery, green leaflets, whitish or mealy beneath; the small 1 cm fruit red and becoming black-purple. Remarkable with their trunks twisting and turning complete loops, with tips subsequently growing erect. *p. 1893*

reclinata (Trop. Africa from Sénégal to Natal), "Senegal date palm"; a leaning date palm somewhat resembling Cocos, in habit, and which will live in the subtropics; solitary trunks 12 m high, or shorter if allowed to cluster, the pinnate lustrous green leaves rather stiff and curving downward; small red fruit. *Tropical.* *p. 1870, 1891, 1894, 1895*

roebelenii (humilis loureiri) (Assam to Viet Nam), "Pigmy date palm"; very graceful both as a miniature potplant or when with slender, rough 4 m trunk, topped by a dense round crown of feathery leaves, the pinnae narrow and folded and dark green, glossy when rubbed; berry-like black fruit in large clusters; female trees often clustering. *Tropical.* *p. 1870, 1875, 1902*

rupicola (Himalayas of Nepal, Bhutan); attractive feather palm growing amongst rocks, with slender trunk to 6 m high, and a crown of feathery leaves appearing gracefully soft, the bright green pinnae decurved and limp; shining yellow fruit. *Subtropic.* *p. 1894, 1902*

sylvestris (India, Nepal), "East Indian wine palm"; stout erect palm to 18 m tall, with rough trunk; and arching pinnate, grayish green or glaucous fronds 3-4 m long, with rigid, somewhat clustered leaflets, on spiny stalk; olive-like 2 cm reddish fruit; produces sugar from the sap. *Tropical.* *p. 1891, 1894*

taiwaniana (Formosa); a compact, ornamental palm seen on the streets of Taipei, with short stout trunk swollen toward top; crown of rather short, arching, coarse pinnate leaves, with rigid leaflets dark green. *p. 1894*

tomentosa hort.; sturdy fan palm similar to P. canariensis, stout trunk with persistent leaf bases, and handsome long recurving pinnate fronds with stiff-glossy green leaflets, the lower ones small and becoming spine-like. Seen at both the Los Angeles Arboretum in Arcadia, and Fairchild Tropical Garden Miami. *p. 1892*

PHOENOCOMA *Compositae* **I2LBD**

prolifera (So. Africa: Cape); shrubby perennial to 60 cm with tiny grayish leaves like little bumps all over the short side branches; colorful flowerheads of the "everlastings" type with the several rows of shining, gleaming pink papery, bract-like outer rays, surrounding daisy-like, the inner cushion of true flowers. *p. 821, 829*

PHOLIDOTA *Orchidaceae* **I3OFM**

articulata (Himalayas to Vietnam and Java); a "Rattlesnake orchid"; epiphyte with slender pseudobulbs arising above the last growth, stalked 10 cm leaves; the short, pendant inflorescence with deciduous concave, snake-like bracts hiding the small 2 cm flowers pinkish to tan-brown, with orange on lip, and faintly scented (spring). *p. 1806*

imbricata (India to Malaya and Philippines), "Rattlesnake orchid"; free-blooming epiphyte allied to Coelogyne, with single-leaved pseudobulbs, and pendant raceme with snake-like, overlapping, small, shell-like flowers yellowish-white with 3 orange-yellow stripes in throat. (April-Sept.) (I) *p. 1803, 1811*

pallida (India); epiphyte with pseudobulbs bearing plaited leaves; the pendant raceme with small 1 cm cupped cream flowers with tiny orange lip. This is probably the same species as P. imbricata. *p. 1808*

PHORADENDRON *Loranthaceae* ***I-S1-3HFD**

flavescens (New Jersey to New Mexico), an American "Mistletoe"; a green parasite on many deciduous trees from New Jersey to Florida and westward, forming dense bunches ½ to 1 m across, with brittle-woody cylindrical, forking twigs; thick oval and opposite yellowish evergreen leaves to 5 cm long. Male and female flowers are on separate plants, borne in short spikes or catkins, the females developing amber-white, small round berries. Cut branches are used for Christmas decoration, a custom in Europe where the similar Old World mistletoe, Viscum album, is used and considered an invitation to a kiss, going back in history to the Druids. *Warm temperate.* *p. 1519*

juniperinum (U.S. Southwest, Arizona); another mistletoe, parasitic on coniferous trees such as juniper and cedar, mimicking the character of their host with their thick cylindric, jointed stems, having imbricated leaves that are reduced to yellowish or gray-green scales; tiny straw-colored berries. Commonly seen at Grand Canyon, Arizona. *p. 1519*

PHORMIUM *Liliaceae* ***I2LBM**

colensoi (New Zealand); "Mountain flax"; smaller species than the more common tenax, occasionally epiphytic; the two-ranked, leathery, strap-like leaves more lax, 1-1½ m long, grass green and usually without a split point or colored edge; the inflorescence in panicles, with long, twisted seed capsules. *p. 1478*

colensoi 'Tricolor', "Tricolored mountain flax"; large clusters of arching, leathery, green strap-leaves colorfully variegated lengthwise with irregular banding of cream to golden yellow, the margins reddish; inflorescence a tall panicle with long twisted seed capsules. *p. 1478*

tenax (New Zealand), "New Zealand flax"; large tufting plant with 2-ranked, tough-leathery leaves which may grow to 3 m long, dark or brownish green with reddish margin, clasping at base, and splitting at apex; flowers dull red in tall panicle. Seen in New Zealand growing even in the cold water of glacial lakes. Very dramatic and tolerant as container plant. *Subtropic.* *p. 1477*

tenax 'Atropurpureum'; a variety with leaves reddish-purple and deep bronze; very attractive in patios in the south. *p. 1478*

tenax 'Variegatum', "Variegated flax"; attractive variant with the usually brownish-green leaves striped and margined with creamy-yellow and white. *Subtropic.* *p. 1478*

PHOTINIA *Rosaceae* **I2LBD**

'Fraseri' (serrulata x glabra); hybrid of parents from China and Japan; highly ornamental evergreen, its new foliage glistening coppery-red on bright red stems, mature leaves dark green and rather convex, 5 to 12 cm long; small white flowers, followed by pretty red berries; a good espalier subject; mildew-resistant. *p. 1999*

serrulata (China); evergreen shrub or tree to 12 m high; oblong leaves to 20 cm long, dark and shining above, yellowish-green beneath; inflorescence of white flowers to 15 cm across, followed by clusters of small red berries. *p. 2001*

villosa (China, Korea, Japan); deciduous small tree to 5 m high; new foliage pale gold with rosy tints, bright red in fall; hairy beneath; small 2 cm white flowers; bright red 2 cm fruits. *p. 2001*

PHOTINIA: see also Heteromeles

PHOTINOPTERIS *Polypodiaceae (Filices)* **S3LFM**

speciosa (Trop. Asia); rhizome-climbing fern with pinnate fronds, fertile and contracted in the upper part, the distant pinnae articulate (jointed) at the rachis, and forming little ears on the lower side at their base. This genus is remarkable on account of this peculiar base of the pinnae. *p. 1156*

PHRAGMIPEDIUM *Orchidaceae* **I3OFM**

'Brysa' (Selenipedium boissierianum x sedenii); robust plant with folded dark green, leathery leaves, and stalks with flowers opening successively, delicate cream-white, the rounded pouch flushed with rose outside and back of the spiralled sepals, lightly spotted green to red inside, the dorsal white with network of green. (I) *p. 1797*

x calurum (Selenipedium longiflorum x sedenii); handsome and noble free-flowering hybrid, forming a thick tuft of channeled green leaves, and tall stems bearing in succession large showy flowers cream inside; outside and toward end of sepals strong purplish red, the dorsal pale green with purple ribs, the pouch wine-crimson (summer). (I) *p. 1797*

caudatum (Selenipedium) (Perú, Ecuador), "Mandarin orchid"; remarkable terrestrial of robust habit, with long straplike leaves; inflorescence in racemes loosely 1-4-flowered, to almost 1 m high, the dorsal yellowish with green veins; petals ribbon-like, twisted, to 60 cm long, brownish-crimson shaded yellow, pouch bronzy green, (April-Aug.); *Humid-subtropic.* *p. 1789, 1793*

x dominianum (Selenipedium) (caricinum x caudatum); robust terrestrial with tall stalks bearing interesting nodding flowers one after another, with long ribbon-like petals spirally twisted, yellowish-green shaded copper, the narrow dorsal arching forward, the long brown slipper shaded red, (summer). (I) *p. 1794*

x grande (Selenipedium) (longifolium x caudatum), "Spiralled lady-slipper"; plant similar to caudatum but flowers with tail-like, spiralled petals shorter, at the base yellowish-white, changing to carmine-red, dorsal pale yellow veined green, waxy pouch greenish-yellow spotted red inside, (summer). *Humid-subtropic.* *p. 1789, 1793*

klotzscheanum (Selenipedium) (Venezuela, Guayana); terrestrial with creeping rhizome and long linear leaves 25 cm long; floral stalk 30 cm with 2 or 3 slipper flowers with sepals pinkish brown with maroon nerves, long twisted ribbon-like petals, light brown with green and maroon nerves, lip light green with darker veins, opening in succession. *p. 1795*

longifolium (Colombia); large plant with leaves to 60 cm long; inflorescence in racemes to 1 m high with numerous elegant greenish flowers flushed coppery red, the pouch mahogany red, lateral sepals lacquer red, the dorsal pale green with rose veins and edged white, the petals pale yellow green with rose margins (Mar.-May). *Humid-subtropic. p. 1796*

longifolium roezlii (Colombia); large plant with leaves to 60 cm long and racemes to 1 m high with numerous elegant greenish flowers flushed coppery red, the pouch mahogany red, lateral sepals lacquer red, the dorsal pale green with rose veins and edged white, the petals pale yellow green with rose margins (Mar.-May). (I) *p. 1797*

parishii (Burma); distinctive species with two-ranked leathery, glossy green leaves, and stout stem to 60 cm long, bearing large flowers; the dorsal, yellowish with green veins; pendulous, twisted, narrow petals 12 cm long, deep purple; the pouched lip yellowish shaded with green; summer. (I) *p. 1793*

schroederae (Selenipedium); handsome "Mandarin orchid", with long drooping petals like a mustache in ancient China; purplish pink flowers 14 cm long, cream inside of pouch, with purple spots. *p. 1795*

x sedenii (schlimii x longifolium); robust terrestrial with straplike, two-ranked, keeled leaves; erect spike bearing several curious flowers with greenish-white dorsal; long linear, spirally twisted petals white with pink band, pastel-shaded pouch pale inside and spotted red, (spring-summer). (I-S) *p. 1794*

PHRYGILANTHUS *Loranthaceae* **S1HFD**

aphyllus (Chile); a hostile parasite living on cacti or other host trees, forming dense clusters of threadlike leafless branches 4cm long; cochineal-red small flowers; later the berry-like reddish fruit turning white when ripe. These parasites attach themselves to the life stream of the host plant stealing its food. Parasites are most frequent among fungi. *p. 1519*

PHRYNIUM *Marantaceae* **S3LFM**

dracaenoides (Trop. Asia); fleshy plant with a basal rosette sending up stiff branches bearing young tufts of foliage; the succulent leaves are lanceolate narrowing into channeled petioles, grass green to bluish and with parallel veins, green beneath. *p. 1544*

PHYGELIUS *Scrophulariaceae* **I2LBM**

capensis (So. Africa),"Cape fuchsia"; shrub with herbaceous, angled, purple branches; opposite, smooth, crenate leaves, and pyramidal panicles of tubular, coral-scarlet flowers, pendulous from horizontal stalks, blooming in summer. *Subtropic. p. 2052*

PHYLICA *Rhamnaceae* **I2LBD**

ericoides (So. Africa); bushy, evergreen shrub to 1 m high, with slender gray-downy branches; linear, heath-like leaves recurved at margins; tiny 1 cm spherical flower heads covered with white wool. *p. 1983*

PHYLLAGATHIS *Melastomataceae* **S3HFM**

rotundifolia (Sumatra); ornamental herbaceous shrub 30-60 cm, with stout, square stem; roundish, corrugated leaves 15-30 cm long, glossy dark green tinted metallic-blue and purple, coppery-red beneath, and with prominent veins; small flowers with magenta-pink petals and filaments, in tight axillary clusters. *Tropical. p. 1552, 1556*

PHYLLANTHUS *Euphorbiaceae* **S3LFD**

angustifolius (Xylophylla) (Jamaica), "Foliage flower"; interesting shrub with long flattened green branches, the lateral, waxy branchlets or cladophylls having the form and function of leaves, 8 to 12 cm long, bearing on their margins rudimentary leaves and tiny, petal-less reddish flowers. *p. 1053, 1056A*

epiphyllanthus (Xylophylla) (West Indies); shrub to 2 m with cylindrical branches and flat, sickle-shaped leathery branchlets 10 to 12 cm long, toothed toward tip, and striately veined; the tiny flowers with red calyx and without petals, along the margins. *p. 1054*

fluitans (Brazil, Bolivia, Paraguay); floating aquatic plant, with stems 3-8 cm long; small green to reddish roundish leaves 1½ cm across, the ribs depressed; tiny greenish-white flowers. *p. 1051*

niruri (Puerto Rico); slender shrub with willowy stems, the branches bearing pinnately the tiny 1 cm obovate leaf-like branchlets; tiny fruits along axis give the impression of a flowering leaf, hence the name "Flor de Hoja". *p. 1054*

pulcher (Java, Malaya); curious small tropical shrub with attractive foliage; the oblong leaves, smooth and green above, glaucous beneath, arranged alternately on gracefully arching side branches and looking like pinnate fronds; the small star-like petal-less flowers yellow with red base, on short red stalks from leaf axils, the male flowers in lower, the stouter female blossoms in upper leaf axils. *p. 1061*

speciosus (Jamaica), "Woody leaf flower"; shrub or tree to 6 m high, with lanceolate leaflike branchlets (phyllodia) 5-8 cm long and 2½ cm wide, arranged in two ranks on a branch, appearing like pinnate leaves; tiny flowers with whitish calyx. *p. 1054*

PHYLLANTHUS: see also Breynia

PHYLLITIS *Polypodiaceae (Filices)* **C2HFM**

delavayii (Burma, So. China); delicate, clustering low fern living on rocks, with short rhizome covered with blackish scales; slender blackish stalks bear small roundish leaves 2-3 cm dia., light almost translucent green of thin texture, cordate at base. *p. 1124*

scolopendrium (Scolopendrium vulgare) (Europe, Madeira, E. No. America), "Hart's-tongue fern"; rhizomatous, hardy fern with stout rhizome and long straight or curved strap-shaped leathery fronds 15-45 cm long, pale yellow green to bright green, quilted and undulate at margins; spore masses in thick strips at right angles to the bold midrib, running into a short black stalk. *Humid-subtropic. p. 1124, 1128*

scolopendrium 'Crispifolium'; distinctive form with long narrow, almost linear leaves undulate and lobed at margins, and densely crisped. *p. 1128*

scolopendrium 'Crispum', "Crisped deer-tongue"; attractive fern with long narrow, strap-like light green fronds nicely and regularly undulated and wavy, 30 cm long by 2-3 cm wide, crested at the base, on stalks covered with hair-like brown scales. *Humid-subtropic. p. 1124, 1149*

scolopendrium 'Cristatum'; an attractive, compact variety with rather short, lanceolate, lush bright green fronds with large basal lobes and undulate surface, the margins attractively wavy and irregularly lobed and crisped. *p. 1128*

scolopendrium 'Laceratum'; fine form found in England (Somerset, Yorkshire) with variable fronds frequently short and broad, 15-25 cm long and 8 cm or wider; margins irregularly lacerated, lobed, or tasseled and the apex more or less crisped or crested. *p. 1128*

PHYLLOCACTUS: see Epiphyllum

PHYLLORHACHIS *Gramineae* **S3LBM**

sagittata (Trop. Africa); ornamental bamboo-like clustering perennial which I found growing in the tropical pool at Munich Botanic Garden; thin reed-stems 50-80 cm high, set with leathery rich green, lanceolate leaves corrugated lengthwise, and with stem-clasping base. *Tropical. p. 1315*

PHYLLOSTACHYS *Gramineae* **I2LBM**

aurea (China), the "Golden bamboo" or "Fish pole bamboo"; tall woody grass with wide-ranging rhizomes; hollow canes flattened on one side, to 4 m or more high and 3 cm thick, brilliant yellow, the internodes at the base very short; quite straight and stiffly erect, very hard and bonelike when matured and used for fishing poles; leaves usually 5-10 cm long and long-pointed, light green, and glaucous beneath. Normally hardy around New York City. Young shoots appearing in mid-spring are edible. *Subtropic. p. 1303, 1312*

aureosulcata (China: Chekiang), "Yellow-groove bamboo"; widely cultivated "running" bamboo forming colonies, with dull green culms to more than 10 m high, 4 cm dia.; two or three leaves on a twig, to 15 cm long; white-striped culm-sheaths, with greenish-yellow panel on the groove; young shoots edible; hardy to around Washington, D.C. Canes used for fishpoles and stakes. *p. 1307, 1309*

bambusoides (China), "Giant timber-bamboo"; one of the largest and most valuable "hardy" timber bamboos, with green culms to about 20 m high, thick-walled and more than 12 cm dia., striped or yellow in some forms; two unequal branches of each branch-bearing node, oblong pointed leaves 6 to 15 cm long; culm-sheaths greenish to reddish. Very versatile in its uses, especially for construction, and its strength is exceeded only by the Tonkin cane (Arundinaria amabilis). Hardy north to about Norfolk, Virginia. *Subtropic to warm-temperate. p. 1301, 1308*

nigra (So. China), "Black bamboo"; graceful black-culmed bamboo to 8 m high and 3-5 cm thick, green at first later speckled then all black; slim branchlets with small leaves commonly 8 cm long, culm-sheaths greenish to buff; thin-walled; hardy to about Norfolk, Virginia, and where temperatures do not go below -20°C. *Subtropic to warm temperate. p. 1305, 1309, 1313*

sulphurea (viridis var.) (China, Japan), "Yellow running bamboo" or "Moso bamboo"; a fairly hardy running bamboo 4-9 m high, stems yellow or green and 5-8 cm thick; leaves to 12 cm long and 2 cm wide, glaucous beneath, on purple petioles. Very handsome with arching yellow canes, and effective in containers in entryways or the patio. Hardy in the Pacific Northwest, or Washington D.C., tested to −18°C (Zero F). *Warm-temperate. p. 1301*

viridis (mitis) (China); giant "hardy" bamboo, with pale green canes 15 m high and 8½ cm thick, with graceful plumes of foliage, the leaves 8-12 cm long, hardy to Washington, D. C. *p. 1308*

PHYLLOSTACHYS: see also Shibataea

PHYMATARUM *Araceae* **S3HFM**

borneense (Sarawak); small tropical aroid with short creeping rhizome 8-10 cm long; 5-6 cm green petioles extend from a sheathing base; narrow-elliptic 10 to 18 cm leaves are 4-5 cm wide, dark shining lateral veins; inflorescence with spathe 7-9 cm long, the lower part greenish and constricted, upper hood creamy white; 7 cm spadix having female flowers toward base, fertile male flowers in middle, and a sterile section toward apex. *p. 189*

PHYMATIDIUM *Orchidaceae* **S3OFM**

tillandsioides (Brazil); miniature epiphyte forming a tufted green rosette of grass-like leaves resembling Tillandsia, the wiry stalks bearing tiny white flowers 3 cm across (summer). *Tropical.* *p. 1809*

PHYSALIS *Solanaceae* **I2LBM**

alkekengi (franchetii) (Japan), "Chinese lantern plant" or "Winter cherry"; known since the 12th century; herbaceous perennial with creeping underground stems, often grown as an annual, 1 m high, with large ovate leaves; inconspicuous axillary yellowish flowers; the calyx, after fertilization, becomes inflated like a lantern, 5-6 cm long, bright orange-red, enclosing the scarlet berry-like fruit; when cut in fall the lanterns will keep for a long time, in everlasting bouquets. *Warm temperate.* *p. 2077, 2083*

peruviana edulis (Perú), "Cape-gooseberry"; perennial, hairy plant with square stems 60-90 cm high; heart-shaped leaves with wavy-toothed margin; 1 cm flowers with bell-shaped, light yellow corolla inside spotted with purple, and violet anthers; fruit purplish in the species, yellow and edible in var. edulis, enclosed in the inflated pale calyx. *p. 2080*

PHYSOSIPHON *Orchidaceae* **C3ONM**

lindleyi (tubatus) (Mexico, Guatemala); epiphyte with sheathed, clustered stems bearing solitary leaves 15 cm long; several arching floral spikes from leaf bases, with numerous small 2 cm flowers arranged along one side, pale green tube, and spreading petals rich orange-red (summer). *p. 1809*

tubatus (loddigesii) (Mexico, Guatemala); tufted epiphyte with the short stems bearing an obovate leaf; the one-sided, 16 cm raceme appearing year after year from the juncture of the leaf and stem, small flowers with minute petals and lip hidden in a green, 3-sided tube formed by the petals, tipped orange-brown, (Nov.-Aug.). (C) *p. 1811*

PHYSOSTEGIA *Labiatae* **I2LBDh**

virginiana (Dracocephalum) (Québec to Florida and Texas), "False dragon-head" or "Obedient plant"; handsome perennial herb with stiff-erect stalks to 1 m or more high; lanceolate, thickish bright green leaves 12 cm long, sharply toothed at margins; a magnificent show of numerous spikes dense with bilabiate flowers purplish-red to rose-pink or lilac, 2-3 cm long, blooming in summer. Probably called Obedient plant because all the flower spikes stand as stiff and erect as a soldier at attention. Photographed at Royal Botanic Gardens, Sydney, Australia, in the Southern hemisphere's summer in February. *p. 1356*

PHYSURUS *Orchidaceae* **S3HFM**

pictus (Brazil); terrestrial orchid with creeping rhizome; pretty, fleshy, ovate leaves 5 cm long, green with silvery center, and toward margins a net of silvery veins; tiny white flowers with brown marks on each of the outer petals. *p. 1702*

PHYTELEPHAS *Palmae* **S3LBM**

macrocarpa (Colombia, Ecuador), "Ivory-nut palm"; curious feather palm with creeping or leaning stem that may be 6 m long but erect portion only 2 m, and forming aerial roots; the leaves very erect to 6 m long, the stiff, glossy green, many-nerved leaflets 80 cm long and 5 cm wide; male trees have strange, unbranched fragrant flower spikes looking like big catkins; female trees with conglomerate fruit about 20 cm across, the egg-sized hard ivory-nuts or "Tagua". *p. 1896*

PHYTEUMA *Campanulaceae* **I2LBM**

scheuchzeri (So. Europe: Alps), "Horned Rampion"; erect perennial herb 25-45 cm high, with ovate, toothed leaves; flowers deep blue, in cylindric heads 3 cm across; the buds long-curved and horn-like; spring-blooming. *p. 751*

PHYTOLACCA *Phytolaccaceae* **C2LBD**

americana (decandra) (Maine to Florida; Mexico), "Poke-weed"; herbaceous perennial with fleshy, poisonous roots, to 3½ m high, strong-smelling; 15 cm lanceolate leaves becoming purple in autumn; white flowers in long raceme, and dark purple berries filled with crimson, poisonous juice; hardy. *p. 1923*

dioica (So. America), the "Ombu" or "Bella Sombre"; remarkable evergreen soft-wooded tree to 20 m high with branching, smooth trunks standing on bulging, massive buttressed roots; slender pointed leaves to 18 cm long; small white flowers; crimson, berry-like fruit on female trees. In Argentina, anyone sleeping under an Ombu must beware of evil magic. *p. 1921*

PIARANTHUS *Asclepiadaceae* **S3LBD**

comptus (Cape Prov.); clustering little succulent with tufted, grayish-green stems 2-3 cm long; flowers with 5 long, tapering lobes to 9 mm long, whitish with red-brown spots and soft-hairy. *p. 378*

cornutus (Cape Prov.); small oblong succulent stem 2-3½ cm long, obtusely 4-angled and with short teeth; flowers with 5 long lobes 1 cm long, pale yellowish spotted red, and velvety-hairy. *p. 378*

disparilis (Cape Prov.); irregularly shaped succulent stems; flowers star-shaped, with 5 lobes 8 mm long; pale pinkish purple marked with transverse yellow lines. *p. 378*

globosus (So. Africa); very small clustering succulent with egg-shaped stems, 2 cm long; flowers star-shaped, velvety hairy, greenish-yellow with red spots. *p. 378*

parvulus (Cape Prov.); succulent knobby stems 2-5 cm high, gray green and spotted with red; starry flowers 12 mm across, straw-yellow and velvety hairy. *p. 378*

pillansii (Cape Prov.); small succulent with cone-shaped stems 3-4 cm long, light green and pale red; flowers star-like, 3-4 cm across, yellowish or greenish and soft-hairy. *p. 378*

punctatus (Cape Prov.: Namaqualand); irregularly knobby, succulent stems to 5 cm long, with short, thick teeth; flowers with spreading lobes rather tuberculate, whitish and spotted blood-red. *p. 378*

PICEA *Pinaceae (Coniferae)* **C2LBMh**

abies (excelsa) (North and Central Europe), "Norway spruce"; evergreen coniferous forest tree to 45 m high, of pyramidal habit; reddish-brown scaly bark, and whorled branches; the usually pendulous branchlets with linear 4-angled, shiny dark green needles 2 cm long, spirally arranged; pistillate flowers bright purple; drooping light brown cones 10-17 cm long. *Temperate.* *p. 841*

abies nana (excelsa) (No. and C. Europe); dwarf form of "Norway spruce"; evergreen with crowded branches, the short needles spirally arranged, 4-angled, dark green and shiny when old, orange when young. *p. 846*

abies 'Repens', "Creeping spruce"; fine low-growing cushion-forming spruce; low mound of uniform foliage holding its branches a little above the horizontal, the branchlets dense with rich green needles, tend to grow erect at first, but growth is slow and averages 3 cm per year. *p. 846*

pungens 'Kosteriana', "Koster's blue spruce"; world-famous cultivar first distributed by Koster (Boskoop, Holland 1885); forming magnificent pyramids with branches in whorls; stiff, curving needles distinct silvery-glaucous blue, 2-2½ cm long, dense on orange-brown branchlets. *Temperate.* *p. 836*

pungens pendula; variety with its arching branches dividing into long cord-like pendulous, weeping branchlets, the stiff bluish green needles arranged spirally; young growth as if glaucous. *p. 840*

PICRIS *Compositae* **I2LBD**

filii (Azores); attractive herbaceous plant with coarsely hairy, toothed leaves and stems each bearing a few golden-yellow flowers, 5-6 cm across; the linear ray-flowers in several layers and prettily recurved, carried well above the foliage. *p. 821*

PIERIS *Ericaceae* **C2HFMh**

floribunda (Virginia to Georgia), "Fetterbush"; rounded evergreen shrub 1½-2 m high, with hairy branches, elliptic leathery leaves and ciliate; little 6 mm urn-shaped white flowers specked with tiny black bristles; drooping in erect terminal panicles, blooming in mass from March to May. *p. 959*

japonica (Andromeda) (Japan), "Lily-of-the-valley bush"; evergreen shrub to 3 m high; with glossy green, leathery leaves 5-8 cm long, in dense whorls; small waxy-white 1 cm urn-shaped flowers in pendulous long-lasting clusters, the calyx lobes tinted red. *Temperate.* *p. 959*

japonica variegata, in horticulture as "Andromeda", the "Lily-of-the-valley bush"; compact evergreen shrub slowly growing to 1½ m or more, the gnarled woody branches with leathery leaves 5 to 8 cm long, glossy green edged with creamy white; loaded in spring with pendant terminal clusters of waxy-white, urn-shaped flowers, the calyx lobes tinted red; winter-hardy. *p. 968*

PIGAFETTA *Palmae* **S3LBD**

filaris (Indonesia: Celebes, Moluccas); very handsome, solitary-growing spiny feather palm, with ringed trunk; the base of crown and petioles densely covered with erect hairs; the beautiful pinnate fronds spreading with long leaflets rich green. David Fairchild considered Pigafetta his favorite palm. Photographed at Dr. Darian's palmarium, Vista, California. *Tropical.* *p. 1897*

PILEA *Urticaceae* ***S1-3LHFM-D**

sp. 'Black Magic' (Colombia); dense, mat-forming creeper with small puckered 1 cm roundish herbaceous leaves with wavy margins and lightly crenate, deep metallic bronzy green. *p. 2110*

cadierei (Vietnam: Annam), "Aluminum plant"; also known as "Watermelon pilea"; a rapid growing, succulent plant, with thin fleshy, opposite, rather large 8 cm obovate, quilted foliage remotely toothed or crenate, attractively painted shining silvery aluminum over the vivid green to bluish-green blade; tiny flowers in stalked heads. *Tropical.* *p. 2111*

cadierei 'Minima', "Miniature aluminum plant"; a darling cultivar of dwarf, freely branching habit with pink stems and 4-5 cm elliptic pointed, succulent, quilted leaves much smaller than the species, deep olive green with raised areas covered with silver, and with crenate margins. *p. 2109, 2111*

'Coral', (prob. So. America); tropical herbaceous plant photographed from the collection of the New York Botanical Garden; reddish stem with long-ovate 8-10 cm quilted leaves with glossy surface and crenate margins, coppery, especially young foliage, purplish beneath. *p. 2109*

crassifolia (superba hort.) (China); vigorous, bushy herbaceous plant with fleshy stems, and nettle-like, soft-turgid elliptic leaves with sharply serrate margins, 8-10 cm long, the corrugated surface with sunken parallel veins, deep grass-green. *p. 2109*

depressa (Puerto Rico), "Miniature peperomia"; freely branching, low, succulent creeper with tiny 6 mm roundish obovate, fleshy leaves, light pea green and glossy, with the apex crenate, opposite and dense on thin green stems, rooting at nodes where touching the ground. *Tropical. p. 2110, 2111*

grandis (Jamaica); herbaceous plant with large green, ovate, corrugated leaves having depressed parallel veins and dentate margins, 10 cm or more long, resembling Coleus; tiny white flowers in flat clusters. *p. 2109, 2110*

involucrata (West Indies, Panama, No. South America), "Panamiga"; freely spreading ornamental herb, dense with oval, somewhat fleshy, deeply quilted leaves to 6 cm long, coppery green above, wine-red beneath; tiny rosy flowers closely clustered. *Tropical. p. 2111*

microphylla (muscosa) (West Indies), "Artillery plant"; small plant densely branched, with suberect, fleshy stems thick with tiny, watery-succulent, oblong, green leaves to 6 mm long, having a tapering, cuneate base; flower clusters with staminate flowers discharging a cloud of pollen when dry or shaken. *Tropical. p. 2108, 2111*

mollis (Costa Rica, Colombia), "Moon Valley green"; charming tropical plant similar to 'Moon Valley' which is probably a mutant heavily overlaid with brown; in the species mollis the foliage is deeply quilted like a carpet and a soft light emerald green, and covered with white hairs; veins olive green. *Tropical. p. 2109*

'Moon Valley' ("imperialis") (So. Costa Rica 1500 m); splendid foliage plant with square stems, fleshy 10 cm leaves deeply quilted; apple-green with center and vein areas brown, and covered with white bristles; clusters of tiny pinkish flowers. *p. 2109, 2111*

nigrescens (West Indies); highly ornamental herbaceous plant branching sideways, with turgid-stiff wrinkled elliptic leaves bronzy green splashed with silvery gray; tiny pinkish flowers. *p. 2109*

nummulariifolia (West Indies to Perú), "Creeping Charley"; low creeping herb; thin, reddish branches rooting at the nodes, with small circular 2 cm quilted, crenate leaves, corrugated and hairy, light friendly green, paler beneath; tiny flowers. *Tropical. p. 2111*

pubescens 'Silver-Panamiga' (E. Cuba); a pretty, rather succulent plant with opposite ovate or rhombic leaves shining bluish-silver, with depressed veins and deeply toothed at margins toward the apex, gray-green underneath and hairy at the nerves, brown stems covered with short hairs. *p. 2119*

repens (Mexico), "Blackleaf panamiga"; low spreading herb with small 3 cm, quilted leaves almost round, quite thin and glossy, coppery-brown with large crenations at the margins, purplish and hairy beneath, on hairy brown branches; greenish flowers. *p. 2109, 2119*

serpyllacea (Mexico); dwarf but stronger plant than microphylla, with heavy succulent branches having orbicular leaves rounded at the base; flower clusters stalked. (2) *p. 2108, 2111*

'Silver Tree' (Caribbean), "Silver and bronze"; a copyrighted name 1957 by Mulford for this species from the Caribbean area; herbaceous branching plant with white-hairy stalks; quilted ovate leaves having depressed veins and crenate margins, bronzy-green, with broad silver band along center, silver dots on sides; reddish beneath. *Tropical. p. 2110*

spruceana 'Norfolk', (bot. forgetii), "Angelwings"; lovely English (Mason) cultivar of the species from Perú; free-growing, small ornamental herb, dense with somewhat fleshy, deeply quilted, broad-oval leaves 6-8 cm long, metallic bronze to blackish green with raised silver bands, wine-red beneath; the tiny rosy flowers clustered closely in the axils of foliage. *Tropical. p. 2111*

PILOCARPUS *Rutaceae* **S2LBD**

pennatifolius (Brazil); evergreen shrub to 2 m high, with unequally pinnate leaves to 45 cm long, the leathery leaflets oblanceolate, with transparent dots; small purple flowers in crowded racemes; glossy green fruit in clusters; horny little plates under tension inside will force pods open. *p. 2025, 2034*

PILOCEREUS *Cactaceae* **S2LBD**

tweedyanus (Britton-Rose: Cephalocereus; Backeberg: Pilosocereus) (So. Ecuador); branching column cactus 2 to 7 m tall, sometimes forming woody trunk; straight branches to 10 cm thick, with 7-9 ribs grayish green to blusih toward apex, and with white hair, small spine clusters; white flowers 7 cm long, and red 4 cm fruit. *p. 658*

PIMELEA *Thymelaeaceae* **I2LBD**

ferruginea (W. Australia), "Rice flower"; pretty shrub to 1 m, dense with opposite, 1 cm ovate sessile leaves in 4 ranks, and with silky-hairy deep pink flowers in round heads. *p. 2102*

PIMENTA *Myrtaceae* **S2LBD**

dioica (officinalis) (Jamaica to C. America), "All-spice"; small tree to 12 m high, with oblong feathery, aromatic leaves to 16 cm long, small white flowers, followed by clusters of small green to brown pleasantly spicy 1 cm pea-sized berries; these are picked green and dried and called "All-spice" because they seem to have the combined flavors of cinnamon, nutmeg and cloves, and are used for seasoning of food. *Tropical. p. 1608*

PINANGA *Palmae* **S3LFM**

coronata (Seaforthia) (Java); slender, clustering feather palm with trunks 4½-6 m; graceful pinnate fronds, the unequally cut pinnae thick, long-linear and slender-pointed, the upper ones toothed at tip as if chewed off. *p. 1898*

kuhlii (Java, Sumatra); clustering feather palm forming several slender, yellow-green trunks to 9 m, topped by thick crown-shaft, and the arching pinnate fronds to 1 m long; the long dark green leaflets up to 10 cm wide, the lower ones narrow and pointed, toward apex wide and blunt, in about 6 pairs. *p. 1898*

maculata (Philippines); feather palm with slender, smooth trunk, topped by arching pinnate leaves, the wide sessile pinnae bright green, blotched and spotted above with dark green. *p. 1898*

malaiana (Malaya: Penang); slender palm with trunk 2½ to 4 m tall; the pinnate leaves with leaflets almost alternate, glaucous beneath; in young plants broad and two-lobed at apex, in older palms the segments are linear-lanceolate and slender-pointed. *p. 1898*

PINELLIA *Araceae* **I2LBM**

ternata (may be transferred to Atherurus) (tuberifera) (So. China, Taiwan, Japan); tuberous herb with light, grayish green, 3-parted, soft leaves on long stalks; flowering freely, spathe green. p. 278

PINGUICULA *Lentibulariaceae (Carnivorous Plants)* **I3HNW**

caudata (bakeriana) (Mexico), "Tailed butterwort"; carnivorous flattened rosette from moist bogs, with fleshy obovate pale green leaves which are sticky with a digestive fluid which will attract and capture insects, gradually absorbing them; flowers carmine, with long spur. *p. 763, 766*

flava (New Jersey), native "Butterwort" of the Delaware Valley; small rosette hugging wet ground; fresh green, fleshy ovate leaves with margins folded inward, the surface sticky and catching insects; deep yellow daisy-like flowers on long stalks. *p. 766*

gypsicola (Mexico), another "Butterwort" or flycatcher; pale green linear leaves more upright, and equipped with clammy-glandular hairs which can hold and imprison small insects; spurred flowers purple with white tube. *Humid-subtropic. p. 766*

lutea (No. Carolina to Florida, Louisiana); a southern "Butterwort"; terrestrial rosette from boggy places, with ovate, fleshy, yellow-green leaves 6 to 8 cm long, and sticky to the touch; flowers ochre-yellow with curved spur, on long stalks. The foliage is covered with a sticky secretion on which insects become stuck. *Warm temperate. p. 766*

vulgaris (N. No. America, Europe, Asia), "Butterwort"; small rosette to 15 cm across, with oblong obtuse, succulent leaves greasy to the touch from a sticky glandular fluid which holds and digests insects; flowers purple. *Warm temperate. p. 766*

PINUS *Pinaceae (Coniferae)* **C2LBMh**

densiflora (Japan), "Japanese red pine"; round-headed, irregular tree to 30 m high, often developing two or more trunks with reddish bark at ground level; the branches at first glaucous green, later brown; slender flexible blue-green needles 5-12 cm long, in pairs; ovoid 4-5 cm cones. Handsome growing in containers as dwarfed Bonsai. *p. 847*

mugo (montana) (Mts. of Central and S. E. Europe), "Swiss mountain pine"; low prostrate shrub or shrubby coniferous tree 4 m or more high, with long stiff and twisted needles in bundles of two, 2½-8 cm long, dark green; variable ovoid, brown cones 2½-6 cm long. *p. 840*

mugo 'Mughus' (E. Alps, Balkans), "Dwarf Mugho pine"; broad, prostrate coniferous shrub, seldom a small tree, with needles in pairs, and with shorter yellow-brown cones than the species, 4-5 cm long; slow-growing and common in cultivation for landscape work; in stunted forms a natural dwarfed tree suitable for Bonsai training in containers. *p. 847*

nigra (austriaca) (Corsica to Austria and W. Asia), the famous "Austrian pine"; pyramidal slow growing, somber tree 12 to 40 m high, rather dense and uniform in habit, becoming flat-topped with age, the branches in regular whorls; very stiff, rigid needles dark green, 8-18 cm long in pairs; ovoid, glossy brown cones 5-9 cm long. A tree of strong character, and smoke tolerant. Occasionally used for dwarf Bonsai training. *p. 847*

palustris (U.S.: Virginia to Florida and Mississippi), "Longleaf-yellow pine"; large coniferous tree 25-30 m high, with thread-like, graceful dark green needles to 45 cm long, arranged in clusters of three; cylindric 25 cm cones. Cut branches are used frequently for decoration. Source of timber for ships, bridges and pulp wood, also turpentine. *Warm temperate. p. 840*

parviflora (pentaphylla) (Japan), "Japanese white pine"; widely adopted in Japan for the culture of Bonsai, or dwarfed trees, and I have seen them 3 centuries old less than 60 cm high; the slender bluish-green needles are arranged in clusters of five; often grafted on P. thunbergiana, the black pine. *Warm temperate. p. 837, 839*

pinea (So. Europe and Turkey), "Italian stone pine"; the characteristic broad and flat-topped pine of the South Italian landscape, 15 to 26 m high; with stiff, bright to gray-green needles in two's, 10 to 20 cm long. In juvenile stage, needles are short, 3 cm long and silvery glaucous. Handsome decorator, when container grown; takes heat and drought. *p. 846*

ponderosa (Brit. Columbia to Baja California, So. Dakota to Texas), "Western yellow pine" or "Ponderosa pine"; majestic tree to 50 or 70 m high, with red bark to nearly black, fissured into large plates, branches spreading; needles in bundles of three, densely crowded on branchlets, 12-26 cm long, dark green; ovoid cones 8-15 cm long, shining brown. *Temperate. p. 846*

pseudostrobus (Mexico, Central America), "False Weymouth pine"; very handsome evergreen tree to 30 m tall, allied to P. montezumae but with smooth bark and glaucous young shoots; the needles in bundles of five, 20 to 25 cm long, slender, glaucous green and gracefully pendant; curved cones to 15 cm long. *p. 844*

radiata (California),"Monterey pine"; legendary tree of the California coast, 24-40 m high, with irregularly open crown, becoming wind-blown and characteristically one-sided where exposed to ocean winds; thick dark brown bark on old trees; needles in bundles of three, in dense clusters 10-14 cm long, fresh green; nut-brown cones 7-14 cm long, 5-6 cm broad, in sessile clusters. *Warm temperate. p. 846*

rigida (N. E. North America, south to Georgia), "Pitchpine"; wide-spread conifer 10 to 25 m high, with open crown; bark on younger trees thin and broken into plate-like scales, on older trees irregularly fissured; stout horizontal branches, the branchlets with dark green needles in bundles of three, 12 cm long, stiff and spreading; the ovoid cones 6 to 10 cm long. *p. 846*

strobus (Newfoundland and Manitoba south to Georgia), "White pine" or "Weymouth pine"; well-known, widely distributed graceful conifer 30 m or more high, fast-growing and ornamental, with a smooth, gray bark when younger, and a feathery effect because of its thin, soft needles in bundles of five, and bluish green; the pendant cones long cylindrical, often curved and very resinous, 8-15 cm long. Used in Japan for training as dwarfed Bonsai in containers. *Temperate. p. 847*

thunbergiana (thunbergii) (Japan), "Japanese black pine"; handsome spreading tree 8 to 30 m high, resembling, and perhaps a form of the Austrian pine but quicker growing; with somewhat shorter, darker green leaves 6-18 cm long, the sharp-pointed stiff needles in pairs. May be pruned; excellent in planters and as Bonsai. *Temperate. p. 847*

virginiana (New York to Georgia and Alabama), the "Scrub-pine"; normally a pyramidal tree 9-12 m high, with short trunk sometimes forked, with thin brownish bark, the branches crowded in irregular whorls; twisted, grayish-green needles in pairs, 5 cm long; oblong cones 5-7 cm long. The photo, pg. 847, shows a prostrate seedling form from a "Witches broom" photographed at the Arnold Arboretum in Boston 1970. *p. 847*

PIPER *Piperaceae* **•S-I1-3HFM**

auritum (Mexico); a woody pepper with beige-gray scandent branches; broadly ovate-cordate leaves 15 to 50 cm long, dull grass-green, grayish beneath on short, usually pubescent petioles; flower spikes to 25 cm long. *Tropical. p. 1944*

betle (Bali, E. Indies), "Betel-leaf"; commonly used in Indonesia and India for chewing with betel-nut; stems trailing; and in Bali I have seen it climbing high on trees, with foliage in neat ranks; the leaves are fleshy, broadly heartshaped 8-15 cm long, dark green with depressed veins; flowers in stalked catkins, opposite of the leaves. *Tropical. p. 1944, 1946*

crocatum (Perú), "Ornamental pepper"; rich-looking, beautiful, ornamental climber, sometimes confused with P. ornatum; with thin-wiry stem, and peltate highly glossy, slender-pointed leaves blackish olive-green, with silver-pink marbling and spotting along veins and veinlets, and corrugated; deep purple underneath. *Tropical. p. 1945*

futokadsura (Japan), "Japanese pepper"; shrubby plant climbing by aerial roots, much like nigrum but nearly hardy and said to be deciduous, stands some frost; thick-leathery, ovate, slender-pointed leaves with 5 depressed veins, waxy, blackish green, and light green beneath; flowers greenish and berries red; slow grower. *Subtropic. p. 1945, 1946*

macrophyllum (Mexico); evergreen shrub with woody stems, bearing large heart-shaped, deep glossy green leaves to 30 cm long, with depressed veining and pale midrib. *p. 1945*

magnificum (bicolor) (Perú), "Lacquered pepper-tree"; beautiful, erect branching foliage plant with corky stem and winged, clasping leafstalks bearing large, fleshy, quilted, oval leaves lacquered forest-green of a metallic sheen, with ivory veins and edge, wine-red beneath. *p. 1946*

nigrum (Malabar coast, Malaya, Java), "Black pepper"; tropical climber with flexuous stems dense with leathery, glossy blackish-green, ovate or elliptic leaves, and bearing long clusters of green berries turning first red, then black; furnishing, when dried, black pepper. *Tropical. p. 1945, 1946*

ornatum (Celebes, New Britain), "Celebes pepper"; very attractive, tall climber with slender reddish stems and petioles, and broad, peltate-pointed, shield-like, waxy leaves 8-10 cm long, deep green, beautifully etched with markings of silvery pink, becoming white in older leaves, pale green beneath. *Tropical. p. 768A, 1946*

peltatum (Pothomorphe) (Trop. America); shrubby, branching bush, with erect willowy stems bearing smooth, deep green, heart-shaped leaves. *p. 1945*

porphyrophyllum (Cissus) (Indonesia), "Velvet cissus"; strikingly beautiful climber without tendrils, stems red with lines of white bristles; the roundish-cordate, recurved, 8-10 cm quilted leaves, velvety moss-green with yellow veins, and pink markings mainly along the veins, wine-red underneath. *Tropical. p. 15*, 1946*

sylvaticum (Burma), "Silver cissus"; attractive, ornamental vine, with thin-wiry stems, and heavy, leathery, ovate leaves more or less with cordate base, corrugated between the sunken dark veins, dark steel-green, the raised areas covered with stippled silver, and with metallic pink sheen. *p. 1945*

PIPTANTHUS *Leguminosae* **I2LBD**

laburnifolius (Himalayas); semi-evergreen shrub or small tree; leaflets lanceolate, 8-15 cm long, silky at first, dark green above, glaucous beneath; flowers 4 cm long, bright yellow. *p. 1390*

PIPTOSPATHA *Araceae* **S3LFM**

elongata (Malaysia: Sarawak); tufted tropical, herbaceous perennial without stem; a rosette of stalked, long-lanceolate leaves 12-24 cm long, silvery beneath and with cylindric tip; the inflorescence with nodding pink spathe, closed except at apex, completely hiding the spadix, but dropping off to expose the fruiting spadix, on 10-12 cm stalk. *p. 228*

PIQUERIA *Compositae* **C2-3LBM**

trinervia (Stevia serrata) (C. America, Haiti), florists' "Stevia serrata" grown for its profuse winter bloom; shrubby herb with narrow, glossy leaves and small fragrant, white disk flowers; used in cut flower arrangements. *p. 805, 810*

PISONIA *Nyctaginaceae* **I1LFM**

"grandis tricolor"; handsome ornamental small tree with large leathery grayish-green leaves to 30 cm long, irregularly variegated and margined with creamy-white, petioles and young growth pinkish to red. This plant, seen at the Chelsea Flower Show in London under this label, is without much doubt the same cultivar lately better known as Heimerliodendron brunonianum 'Variegatum', which see. *p. 1620*

PISONIA: see also Heimerliodendron

PISTACIA *Anacardiaceae* **S-I2LBD**

vera (Syria), "Pistachio nut"; widely planted throughout the Mediterranean region and Northern India; spreading tree to 10 m high, partially deciduous and suited only for dry regions where the olive grows; the leaves of 1 to 5 pairs of thick, oval leaflets, and an extra one at the tip; tiny brownish-green flowers unisexual, without petals on female trees; clusters of oblong red fruit, 2-3 cm long, becoming wrinkled; inside the husk a stone contains the pistachio kernel, of rich taste, and used for flavoring cake and candy. The nuts are prepared in brine while still in the shell and are also favored for eating and nibbling. *Subtropic. p. 132*

PISTIA *Araceae* **S2-3LFW**

stratiotes (Trop. America), "Water lettuce"; water-floating leaf rosettes 10-15 cm across, bright green and velvety, hairy, with hanging roots; small green flowers hidden between leaves. Apparently naturalized in other parts of the tropical world, I have seen them colonizing lagoons and rivers in West Africa, in Kenya and Uganda, and along the upper Nile. *p. 278*

PISTORINIA *Crassulaceae* **S3LBD**

breviflora (Andalucia, Algeria, Morocco); small herbaceous plant with fleshy stem, and short needle-like, cylindric green leaves with red streaks; masses of tubular star-shaped flowers 2 cm long, golden yellow with reddish tips. *p. 912*

PITCAIRNIA *Bromeliaceae* **S2-3HFM**

andreana (Colombia: Choco); small terrestrial, with leafy stems to 20 cm long; recurving, narrow-lanceolate leaves, green and speckled with silver dots above, heavily frosted beneath with white scales; inflorescence with orange petals tipped with yellow. *Tropical. p. 577*

angustifolia (West Indies); bold terrestrial with soft-leathery, linear leaves up to 1 m long, 2 cm wide, scurfy-white beneath, the margins armed with brown, horny spines; long, arching inflorescence of several many-flowered racemes, the 5 cm petals bright red. *p. 576, 577*

corallina (Colombia), "Palm bromeliad"; terrestrial plant to 1 m, with stalked leaves dark green and corrugated, petioles with brown spines; inflorescence in prostrate raceme with red stem and coral-red flowers. *Tropical. p. 513, 577*

ctenophylla (So. Venezuela); terrestrial or on rocks in habitat; clustering plant with bulbous base; leaves 35-45 cm long and narrowly triangular, 12 mm wide, gray-green and smooth above, silvery-scaly beneath, the margins with small spines; inflorescence on tall stalk to 50 cm high, in racemes of red flowers with petals 5 cm long. *p. 576*

ferruginea (Puya) (Ecuador, Perú, Bolivia); widespread xerophytic plant found on rocky slopes in the Andean paramó to 3800 m elevation; variable succulent rosettes forming woody stems, with stiff green leaves to 50 cm long and with black spines at margins, white-scurfy underneath; the inflorescence on woody stalk to 4 m high, loosely pyramidal and covered with rust-brown scales and with greenish to purple flowers to 14 cm long. According to Dr. L. B. Smith, this plant has been transferred to Puya. *p. 576*

heterophylla (Mexico, Central America, to Ecuador); small epiphytic rosette, with bulbous base formed by outer leaves, the grass-like linear, green foliage to 20 cm long x 1 cm wide; flowers in a near sessile spike with reddish bracts and sepals, and bright red petals occasionally white. *Tropical.* *p. 576, 577, 578*

maidifolia (Honduras to Venezuela and Guyana); an epiphyte in dense tropical forest or on rocks; large rosette with outer leaves reduced to blackish sheaths, the main leaves on long petiole with blades lanceolate 50-100 cm long, corn-like, grass-green and flexuous, the center with grooved midrib; the floral stalk 50 cm long bearing a loose raceme of greenish sepals and white petals, facing in one direction. *p. 576*

tabuliformis (Mexico: Chiapas); terrestrial rosette with oblong spatulate, papery 15 cm leaves light green showing darker, parallel veining, and lying flat on the ground; showy bright red flowers in a sessile head. *Tropical.* *p. 572, 576*

tomentosa (fuertesii) (Haiti, Republica Dominicana); stemforming terrestrial species, or growing on rocks, with narrow leaves up along stalk, green and leathery, to 1 m long and 1-2 cm wide, white beneath and with fine teeth at margins; the tubular flowers at apex 5 cm long, bright red with yellow stamens. *p. 576*

tuerckheimii (Guatemala); terrestrial tufting plant with the appearance of a giant grass; fresh green papery, narrow linear leaves, the underside covered with fine white, hair-like tomentum, and basal leaves prickly; raceme 8-14-flowered, the bracts and sepals uncolored, petals crimson, paler below. *p.577*

werckleana (Costa Rica); large terrestrial plant, having long papery oblanceolate leaves with long tapering apex and channeled midrib, grass-green and covered on the surface by gray to brown tomentose fuzz; simple, dense inflorescence with flowers all turned to one side. *p. 577*

werckleana variegata; form with the long arching leaves striped and banded yellow-green on deep green. *p. 577*

xanthocalyx (Mexico, W. Indies); terrestrial rosette with narrow flexible leaves 60-90 cm long, tapering to a curly tip, light green, densely scurfy-white at back; inflorescence in many flowered raceme 45 cm long with bright yellow bracts and primrose-yellow petals. *p. 577*

PITHECELLOBIUM *Leguminosae* **S2LBD**

unguis-catii (Florida, West Indies, N. So. America), "Cats-claw", or "Black-bead"; spiny, evergreen shrub or small tree to 4½ m, with leathery bipinnate leaves; small greenish-yellow flowers, and green 10 cm fruit-pods spirally twisted like claws, and which split open, displaying colored seed. *p. 1388*

PITHECOCTENIUM *Bignoniaceae* **S3LBM**

muricatum (echinatum) (Mexico to Brazil); woody evergreen vine with leaves of 2-3 leaflets, and thread-like, 3-parted tendrils; bell-shaped, 5 cm long white flowers, turning yellow. *p. 496*

PITTOSPORUM *Pittosporaceae* ***I-C2LBD**

eugenioides (New Zealand); slender decorative branched evergreen growing into a tree 12 m high; with dark stems and narrowly oblong thin-leathery, light glossy green 10 cm leaves becoming darker in maturity, paler beneath and with undulate margins; small yellowish flowers in dense terminal clusters, scented like honey. *p. 1947, 1948*

eugenioides 'Variegatum'; New Zealand cultivar with attractive long-elliptic, leathery leaves grayish-green, with wavy ivory-white margins. The species P. eugenioides is a decorative evergreen growing into a tree to 12 m high, with narrow, glossy-green foliage 10 cm long, and small yellow flowers scented like honey. *Subtropic.* *p. 1947*

moluccanum (ferrugineum) (Indonesia); small evergreen tree with spreading crown, grayish bark, on slender brownish twigs, the long obovate glossy green leaves with undulate margins; small 1 cm yellowish flowers with honey fragrance; clusters of 1 cm orange fruits gaping in halves and showing the scarlet mass of pulpy seeds. *Subtropic.* *p. 1948*

tobira (China, Japan), "Mock orange"; tough, evergreen shrub branching into a rather flat-topped, shapely bush; with thick-leathery obovate, convex, dark lustrous green leaves to 10 cm long, arranged in dense pseudowhorls, and with terminal clusters of small, creamy-white flowers, very fragrant. *Subtropic.* *p. 1947, 1948*

tobira 'Compacta'; a compact variety grown in California nurseries; dense bush spreading sideways rather than upwards, with leathery, glossy green leaves 3-5 cm long, the margins curled under. *p. 1948*

tobira 'Variegatum', "Variegated mock-orange"; attractive variegated form with leathery leaves slightly thinner, milky or grayish-green raggedly margined creamy-white; the little, fragrant flowers resembling orange-blossoms. *Subtropic.* *p. 1947*

tobira 'Wheeler's Dwarf'; attractive miniature cultivar of P. tobira; very compact, evergreen shrub dense with small obovate, glossy, dark green leaves forming a shapely mound; requiring little care. *p. 1948*

undulatum (Australia), "Sweet pittosporum"; loosely branching tree growing to 12 m high, with soft-leathery, long elliptic or oblanceolate leaves to 15 cm long, lightly pendant, and with wavy margins, dark green. *Subtropic.* *p. 1947, 1948*

viridiflorum (So. Africa: Transvaal), "Cape pittosporum"; yellow erect upright woody evergreen shrub to 3 m, or a tree to 6 m high with obovate leaves to 10 cm; thin leathery semi-glossy, grayish-green leaves with pale midrib; dense clusters of greenish yellow flowers, jasmine-scented; slow-growing. *p. 1948*

PITYROGRAMMA *Polypodiaceae (Filices)* **I3LFM**

calomelanos (West Indies to Perú, Trop. West Africa); handsome "Silver-fern"; large, robust, rhizomatous rosette of spreading dark green, bipinnate fronds to 1 m long, on long shining black stalks; the leathery segments toothed or cut, thickly powdered white beneath. *p. 1129*

chrysophylla (calomelanos aureo-flava) (So. America, West Indies), a "Gold fern"; of graceful habit, with wide-spreading tripinnate, somewhat fleshy fronds to 60 cm long, dull green above, thickly covered with golden yellow, waxy powder on the underside, carried on purplish-brown channeled stalks; the young shoots also waxy golden-yellow. *Humid-tropical.* *p. 1129*

chrysophylla 'Farinifera'; a form with short caudex, quadrangular blackish stalks dotted with white, the fronds mealy above, white beneath. *p. 1128*

chrysophylla heyderi (Gymnogramma heyderi) (W. Indies: Dominica); a "Goldfern" variety with more intensive gold-covering on the underside of the feathery fronds. *p. 1124*

decomposita (So. American Andes); possibly a natural hybrid of chrysophylla and pearcei; strong-growing fern with finely divided, 3- to 4-pinnate, 45 cm fronds, the 30 cm stalks covered first with white powder, later becoming bright yellow. *p. 1129*

x hybrida (calomelanos x chrysophylla); of more luxuriant habit than chrysophylla, blades longer and wider, the margins mostly doubly serrate and dentate and hardly turned under; green throughout year, and tolerates cooler temperatures near 5°C. *p. 1129*

mathewsii (Gymnogramma) (Perú); medium-sized fern with 3-pinnate fronds to 45 cm long, the leaflets of leathery texture, and hairy on both sides; brown stalks clothed with dense brown, deciduous hairs. *p. 1128*

pulchella (Venezuela), a "Silver fern"; of upright habit; tufted powdery stalks carrying 3-pinnate, soft fronds 15-30 cm long, deep green, and lightly powdered above; densely covered with pure white powder beneath. *p. 1129*

tartarea (Trop. America); tufted triangular fronds 30-60 cm long, twice divided nearly to the midrib, dull green on upper surface but entirely covered underneath by a coating of pure white, waxy powder; the dark spore masses along the midrib form a striking contrast with the white. *p. 1128*

triangularis (Gymnogramma) (Oregon, California, south to Ecuador), the "California gold-fern"; pretty species of dwarf habit, to 45 cm high, with elegant bipinnate deltoid fronds to 17 cm long, soft herbaceous, dull fresh-green, with crenate pinnules; the underside coated with powder varying from orange to sulphur-yellow, almost white. *p. 1127*

PLAGIOCHASMA *Marchantiaceae* **I3HNW**

appendiculata (W. Himalayas; Lahore, Kashmir, Punjab, Simla, Nilgiris); a monoecious liverwort; thick thallus 1-4 cm. long, forking and forming large patches; the lobes oblong obcordate, margins undulate and ascending, shining green above, purple underneath; male receptacle horseshoe-shaped, the female sessile or stalked. Grows on rocks in moist places; its curious shape and peculiar habit may lend itself to culture on Planet Venus. *p. 1548*

PLANTAGO *Plantaginaceae* **I2LBD**

nivalis (Spain: Sierra Nevada); interesting perennial 10 cm high, a flat rosette with lanceolate leaves 4 cm long, densely white-woolly on both sides; insignificant green flowers fragrant, creamy-white flowers followed by green berries. (M) *p. 1949*

PLATYCERIUM *Filices: Polypodiaceae* ***S-I2-3OFM**

alcicorne (Madagascar, Comores Islands, Mauritius), "Elkhorn fern"; distinct from bifurcatum in having the fertile fronds shorter, more rigidly erect, a bright green, and only thinly hairy, widening to short forks, 2- to 3-lobed, and lightly recurving; the brown soral patches are located at or beside the last bifurcation, sometimes extending to the lower portions of the lobes instead of on the tip of the distal segments as in bifurcatum; the young basal fronds are rounded becoming deeply corrugated with age, prolonged above into a few finger-like lobes. *Tropical.* *p. 1137, 1142*

andinum (E. Perú, E. Bolivia), "American staghorn"; this sole So. American, subandine species is a large epiphyte with mighty erect, lobed barren fronds, and much forked long pendant fertile leaves to 3 m long, with long ribbon-like lobes, and sporangia placed at third fork back. *Tropical.* *p. 1130, 1132, 1143*

angolense (Trop. Africa), "Elephant's ear fern"; large epiphytic fern, close to stemaria, with ascending sterile fronds having purplish veining and wavy crest; broad wedge-shaped fertile fronds not divided into lobes, and with a felt-like covering of rust-colored wool underneath; the sporangia along the apex. I have encountered this species all across Africa from the Usambaras in Tanzania, on Lake Victoria, Uganda, the Ituri forest of Zaire to the Niger Delta in Nigeria. *Tropical.* *p. 1133, 1136, 1142*

bifurcatum (E. Australia, New Guinea, New Caledonia, Sunda Isl.), the common "Staghorn fern"; easy growing epiphyte freely producing young plants on its roots; the basal fronds are kidney-shaped, in old specimen lobed; the usually laxly pendant, leathery, grayish dark green fertile fronds to 1 m long are thinly covered with white, stellate hairs, and usually twice long forked; soral patches only on distal segments, being the tips of the ultimate forks. Sterile fronds round, but feathered on back. Reverse silvery or green. Known as "Elkshorn" in Australia. On Mt. Boss, New South Wales, at 900 m this species tolerates -9°C cold, rainfall is 320 cm yr.; near Sydney they are found growing between 240-450 m altitude. *Subtropic.* *p. 1133, 1137, 1141*

bifurcatum 'Majus' (Polynesia); a variety of more robust habit with larger foliage; the barren fronds are roundish, convex, and overlap each other; the broad, rich green fertile fronds tend to be erect, with the broad forking lobes pendulous. *Subtropic.* *p. 1131, 1133*

bifurcatum cv. 'Netherlands' (alcicorne 'Regina Wilhelmina'); from Holland, with soft-leathery fertile fronds broader than the type, well divided into numerous lobes, and the habit of growth is with bright green fronds in all directions star-like. *Subtropic.* *p. 1134*

bifurcatum cv. 'San Diego' ('Bloomii' hort.); shapely plant, husky, resembling "diversifolium"; often 10-12 dark green, waxy fronds, with bluish veins, broadly forked and lobed. Spores at tips. *p. 1131,1140*

'Cass hybrid'; Florida cultivar, developed by Mr. Cass by putting spore of P. grande, alcicorne, stemaria, and hillii into a fishbowl, resulting in a number of crosses. The cultivar pictured has lovely fertile fronds 75 cm long, tapering to a narrow fan then spreading into several forks, of leathery texture, bright green on both sides. *p. 1140*

coronarium (biforme) (Burma, Thailand, Malaya, Java, Philippines), "Crown staghorn"; a glorious epiphyte of which I have seen immense clusters growing high in trees of the rainforest in Malaya; the long, fresh green pendulous fronds are to 4 m long, several times widely forked, and the narrow lobes gracefully twisted; the thick barren fronds are tall and lobed; spore is curiously borne on a separate fertile reniform disk. *Tropical.* *p. 1132, 1133, 1139*

coronarium 'Minima' (Thailand); a "Crown-staghorn" of dwarf habit; the slender green, narrowed character fronds covered with silvery tomentum, the segments charmingly twisted; sporangia is carried near base on a kidney-shaped, separate plate. From the collection of David Barry, Los Angeles, photographed 1966. *p. 1144*

"diversifolium" hort., "Erect elkhorn"; dwarf plant attractive because of the erect habit of its fronds which are broadly spreading into twice-divided, pendant lobes, covered with whitish stellate hairs; basal fronds reniform, neatly covering the fibrous roots. *Tropical.* *p. 1136, 1824A*

ellisii (C. Madagascar); small, rare species with roundish basal fronds; fertile fronds to 30 cm, wedge shaped divided into 2 lobes; sporangial area around sinus. *p. 1130, 1140*

grande (Philippines); this true species is rare and restricted to the Philippine Islands; a noble epiphyte with vivid green sterile fronds erect and outward-spreading; the leathery, pendant fertile fronds in mature specimen to 1 m long; smaller in habit, but otherwise similar to P. superbum (grande of hort.), except that these fronds consist of two primary divisions, each forked again and spreading into numerous lobes, the two wide main sinuses each bearing a soral patch (P. superbum has only one spore-patch on each fertile frond). *p. 1137, 1140, 1141*

hillii (Queensland), "Stiff staghorn"; handsome, fresh green species with basal leaves always round, covering the rootstock; the several fertile fronds are rigidly erect, gradually broadening fanlike before dividing into numerous pointed lobes, green beneath, with sori carried at base of ultimate tips. *Tropical.* *p. 1131, 1134*

hillii cv. 'Drummond' ("ellisii" of hort.); fertile frond shorter than species, to 30 cm long, glossy green; flaring into broad fan, deeply lobed and undulate. Spores at segments. *p. 1135*

hillii 'Pumilum'; botanic standing uncertain; shapely with leathery fertile fronds to 50 cm long, dark green on both sides, spreading abruptly fan-like to 30 cm wide, and like a broad crest with multiple double lobes; circular cushion of pale green basal fronds. Zone of spores beginning with the forks and all along the semi-circular apex. *p. 1135, 1140*

x lemoinei, (veitchii x willinckii); prolific plant with basal fronds distinctly reniform, developing occasional erect lobes; gray fertile fronds very slender, erect spreading, later pendant, twice forked very narrow in all parts, both sides densely white tomentose; sori V-shaped at tips. (S) *p. 1131*

madagascariense (Madagascar); small, very attractive species mainly because of its deeply quilted, rounded basal frond, with the network of bluish veins raised high and forming tough elevated ridges; a small leathery, bright green, wedge-shaped fertile frond is lightly lobed and rudimentary, and set with sori on the upper edge. *Humid-tropical* *p. 1137, 1140, 1143*

quadridichotomum (W. Madagascar); epiphytic plant with basal frond irregularly oblong and nest-like; appressed and round in the lower part, and erect and free, undulate and laciniate; the normal fertile fronds pendant, regularly forked in pairs 3 or 4 times, the divisions strap shaped, the underside covered with yellowish stellate hairs. Sporangia area between first and third forks. *Tropical.* *p. 1143*

"ridleyii" hort. (Malaya, Borneo, Sumatra); epiphyte at home in high trees, allied to coronarium, but more compact; rounded basal fronds mostly appressed to the support; normal frond rather erect, fresh green 30-60 cm long, about 5 times irregularly forked in pairs and sterile, but one branch sometimes carrying at its base a concave fertile lobe bearing the sporangia; the divisions are characteristically short and wide-spreading. The existence of this species is discussed in Baileya Sept. 64, but the photo shown is not yet proven correct. *Tropical.* *p. 1142*

stemaria (aethiopicum), (W. Africa to Madagascar), "Triangle staghorn"; curious species with basal fronds convex and elongated into lobes; the triangular grayish green fertile fronds to 45 cm long, thick-leathery, with prominent ribs, and divided twice, the main fork spreading wide, with a sinus, around which follow the spore masses; the underside densely covered with silvery-white felt. *Tropical.* *p. 1135, 1136, 1138*

sumbawense (Indonesia: Soembawa Isl.); smaller than alcicorne; basal fronds forked, the irregular fertile fronds tomentose; pendant, and deeply forked 2 to 3 times into narrow divisions with short patches of sporangia on the thickened last forks. Fronds with marked veins bluish-green on grass-green blade, gray-scaly beneath. *p. 1136*

superbum (grande of hort. and in Hortus 3) (Queensland, New South Wales, Eastern Malaysia, Java), "Regal elkhorn"; magnificent epiphytic fern forming a great crown of sterile fronds, glossy vivid green, with dark venation, the upper lobes doubly forked and staghorn-like, gracefully flaring outward; pendulous pairs of thick-fleshy, fertile fronds, several times divided, appear with age, holding between them in the rounded sinus of the first fork a single wedge-shaped disk bearing the sporangia. Mature specimen with fan-like sterile fronds spread to 1 m; drooping fertile fronds may become 1½ m long. It may take 20 years of age before spores are first produced. I have found P. superbum as far south as New South Wales at 600 m, where the temperature ranges from 3 to 49°C, on Stinging trees as hosts. According to Prof. Hoshizaki of U. of Calif., the species superbum from Australia, long known in cultivation as P. grande, has one spore patch in the main fork of the fertile fronds, whereas the rare P. grande from the Philippines has three main divisions bearing a spore patch on each of the two sinuses. *Tropical.* *p. 1137, 1140, 1141, 1144*

vassei (Mozambique), "Antelope ears"; compact species with large round reniform basal fronds protecting its rootstock, the short antler-like fronds are stiff upright, narrow at base and broadening upward, twice forked and thinly pubescent. *p. 1130, 1135, 1136*

veitchii (Australia); very vigorous and prolific tree dweller with rounded, cupping basal fronds and stiffly upright, leathery dark green fertile fronds, narrow at base, and forking into 6-8 lobes, white-hairy beneath; sporangia placed at tips. *p. 1132*

velutinum (Zaire); from Lac Edouard region at 1280 m; specimen in the Herbarium of Kew Gardens, London; sterile, barren fronds like a cupped shield with rounded outline; the fertile fronds broadly fan-shaped and velvety tawny underneath in the upper middle, with sporangia toward the apex of the broad lobes. This species has been relegated by Barbara Joe Hoshizaki of Los Angeles (Baileya Sept. 1964) to P. angolense. *p. 1130*

wallichii (Burma, Indochina); attractive epiphyte, with sterile basal fronds first circular and cupping, then with lobes upwards; the fertile fronds broad and several times slender-forked into concave segments, thick in all parts, very green and slightly yellowish tomentose; looks like grande but more diminutive. *Tropical.* *p. 1130, 1139, 1144*

wandae: described under P. wilhelminae-reginae *1142,*

wandae hort.; a species collected in New Guinea and grown in Berlin (Gartenwelt 1957); in character resembling P. bifurcatum, with slender, rather erect fertile fronds divided into linear lobes, and bearing the sporangia toward the tips. *p. 1130*

wilhelminae-reginae in Hortus 3 (New Guinea); transferred to P. wandae according to Prof. Barbara Joe Hoshizaki: of Los Angeles; "Queen elkhorn"; with large crown of feathered sterile fronds spreading 1½ m; not as deeply lobed as superbum but fuller; the long, gracefully pendant fronds to 2 m long, in pairs each with 3-4 long lobes, flanked on both outsides by one or two sets of separate big, obliquely broad-triangular spore-blades; glossy dark green above, silvery beneath, with prominent dark veins; lettuce serration at base; young growth covered with silvery scales. I have found this species widespread from southern Papua near sea level to the forbidding mountain ranges of northern New Guinea, at 1,100 m. *Tropical.* *p. 1134, 1139, 1140, 1144*

willinckii (Java), "Silver staghorn"; a distinct epiphyte with uneven, forked basal leaves and densely silvery-pubescent fertile fronds, erect at first, later completely pendant, very narrow and several times forked into long slender lobes; sporangia-bearing at tips. *Tropical.* *p. 1132*

PLATYCLINIS: see Dendrochilum

PLATYSTELE *Orchidaceae* **I3OFW**

ornata (Venezuela), a "Pygmy orchid"; very tiny epiphyte from the cloud forest, only 3 cm high, clustering with obovate, waxy, fresh green leaves notched at apex; erect racemes of 1 cm flowers glossy maroon purple and yellow center. *p. 1809*

PLATYSTEMON *Papaveraceae* **I2LBD**
californicus (California), "Cream cups"; flowering annual herb to 30 cm high, forming dense bushes, with linear leaves, and cream-yellow flowers 3 cm across, solitary on long stalks. *p. 1922*

PLECTRANTHUS *Labiatae* ***I-S1LFM**
australis in hort.: see P. nummularius
ciliatus (Transvaal); low, mat-forming creeper, with small fleshy, ovate, crenate leaves, matte green and slightly rugose, and with purple veins. *p. 1350*
coleoides 'Marginatus' (tomentosus), "Candle plant"; low, bushy plant dense with opposite, ovate, hairy herbaceous, 5-8 cm leaves dark green and grayish, the crenate and scalloped margins creamy-white; 4-angled stem; flowers white with purple; the type is from the Nilghiris (So. India). *Subtropic.* *p. 1350*
madagascariensis (S. E. Africa, Madagascar), "Mintleaf"; small creeping shrub with brownish, angled stem, and opposite, firm green, wrinkled leaves 3-4 cm long, of fleshy texture, crenate margins and covered with whitish bristle, strongly scented of mint when bruised; flowers in erect small spikes, very pale lavender, almost white. I found and photographed this in 1973 at Kirstenbosch near Cape Town. *Subtropic.* *p. 1351*
myrianthus (Namibia, Transvaal, Zimbabwe), "Dark blue spur-flower"; easy growing herbaceous bush to 1½ m tall, having nettle-like, membranous, ovate leaves light grayish green, with crenate margins; the inflorescence in terminal spikes of small, dark blue flowers with a touch of navy blue; tolerates dry conditions. *p. 1350*
nummularius (australis or parviflorus) (Australia, Pacific Islands), the "Swedish ivy"; in California horticulture as "Creeping Charlie"; vigorous creeping perennial herb with small fleshy, thickish, metallic-green, waxy leaves almost round, 3-6 cm across and deeply crenate, glaucous gray-green beneath and with purplish veins; small white 2-lipped flowers in spikes. A tough trailer tolerating abuse; good for hanging pots or wall containers. *p. 1351, 1352*
oertendahlii (Natal), "Prostrate coleus"; fleshy creeper with 4-angled stem and small, broad leaves, friendly green to bronzy, patterned with an attractive network of silvery veins, the lightly crenate margins purple, the surface short-hairy, older leaves purple beneath, petioles purple; flowers pale pink. *Subtropic.* *p. 1352*
oertendahlii 'Variegatus'; colorful cultivar with the fleshy 3 to 4 cm green to bronzy leaves variegated silvery green with milky-white, especially around the margins. *p. 1351*
purpuratus (Natal), "Moth king"; wiry creeper with small lightly crenate, grayish to dark green, fleshy leaves covered with velvety pubescence, purplish underneath; small lavender flowers. *p. 1352*
saccatus (So. Africa: Natal, Zululand), the "Edging spur-flower"; lovely flowering species suitable for hanging baskets; small herbaceous plant to 30 cm high, with dark matte green, rather thin, crenate leaves, on branches spreading horizontally and bearing ornamental sprays of bilabiate flowers 2-3 cm long, the buds are deep purple and open to a lighter shade of lavender. I found this charming plant at Canterbury University Botanic Gardens in Christchurch, New Zealand, covered with blooms in February. *p. 1351*
strigosus (So. Africa: Natal); creeping and spreading plant with flexuous stems and small glossy green, fleshy leaves round-ovate, with crenate margins; bilabiate pale lilac flowers scattered along erect short spikes. *p. 1351*
tomentosus (South Africa), in horticulture as "Succulent coleus"; fleshy subshrub freely branching, with a tendency to become scandent; square stems spotted with brown red and resembling coleus, but covered all over with dense white hair, as is the nettle-like foliage; the succulent, fleshy, crenate leaves are velvety olive green, silvery beneath; small purple flowers in erect raceme. *p. 1351*
'Variegated Mintleaf' (prob. madagascariensis cv, from S. E. Africa), in hort. also as "minima" and "Iboza"; pretty creeper with brownish, hirsute stems; small 3-4 cm fleshy, crenate leaves milky-green bordered white, strongly mint-scented; white flowers flushed lilac. Ideal for baskets. *Subtropic.* *p. 1350, 1351*
verticillatus (thunbergii) (So. Africa: Eastern Cape); small creeping species photographed courtesy of Dr. L. E. Codd, at Div. of Botany in Pretoria, one of many in the collection growing in National Botanic Gardens outside of Pretoria; angled stems with opposite, thin-fleshy, rounded leaves 4 cm long, deep glossy green, and crenate or lobed toward apex, the branches terminating in short racemes of small 1 cm pale lilac flowers. *p. 1351*

PLECTROPHORA *Orchidaceae* **S3OFM**
cultrifolia (Ecuador: Oriente); diminutive epiphyte with little flattened pseudobulbs bearing a single fleshy, knife-shaped leaf 5 cm long, arranged as in a fan; solitary trumpet-shaped, spurred flower 1 cm long on basal stalk; the narrow sepals whitish with greenish flush, petals cream, appressed to the cream-colored, trumpet-shaped lip which is striped orange inside. Grows best on a vertical slab. *p. 1808*

PLEIOBLASTUS *Gramineae* **I2LBM**
simonii 'Variegata' (Bambusa, Arundinaria) (Himalayas, China, Japan); one of the tallest of the arundinaria types, forming clusters 3 to 6 m high, with olive green, hollow canes pencil-thick to 1 cm dia.; the leaves to 15 cm long and 2 cm wide, borne in clusters at nodes; variegated green and white in this variety; fairly hardy. Photographed in San Francisco. *p. 1312*

PLEIONE *Orchidaceae* **C-I3HFDd**
delaveyi (China); small terrestrial, with annual pseudobulbs, deciduous plaited leaves, and showy flowers bright rose-purple, the fringed lip with red-brown markings. (I) *p. 1808*
formosana alba (pricei) (Taiwan), "Indian crocus"; beautiful little terrestrial with ovoid pseudobulbs bearing solitary deciduous leaves; blooming before foliage; the showy 10 cm flowers rosy-lilac, with white fringed lip blotched pale brown. (I; C when resting) *p. 1702*
pogonioides (China: Yunnan); rock-dweller, with flowers 8 cm across, light purple, disk of lip paler, with 3 fringed keels; plaited leaves and flowers appear together; spring. (C) *p. 1808*
praecox (Himalayas to Burma and So. China), "Mother of the Pleiades"; small deciduous terrestrial with corm-like pseudobulbs, each bearing one or two elliptic, ribbed leaves; the large and handsome, sweetly fragrant flowers 8 cm across, and rising concurrently with the foliage, the sepals and petals rich rose-purple, the whitish lip frilled and marked yellow inside. Needs rest period during winter. *Subtropic.* *p. 1808*

PLEIOSPILOS *Aizoaceae* **I2LBD**
beaufortensis (Cape Prov.); fast-growing, fleshy succulent with spreading boat-shaped, opposite leaves united at base, 6-8 cm long, light gray with many dark translucent dots; 7 cm golden yellow flowers, pale pink in center. *p. 65*
bolusii (Cape Prov.: Karroo), "Living rock cactus"; small stemless succulent with pairs of thick, stone-like keeled leaves 5 cm long and broad, flattened inside, light gray-green with numerous dark-green dots; flowers deep yellow. *Arid-subtropic.* *p. 76, 2092*
brevisepalus (Cape Prov.); 2-to 4-leaved succulent with leaves of unequal shape, suddenly expanded in the center on the upper side, keeled beneath; flowers dark yellow. *p. 75*
framesii (Cape Prov.); stemless succulent, 4 cm high, with 2 pairs of keeled leaves, flat inside, green with large dots; flowers yellow above, white below. *p. 76*
hilmari (Cape Prov.); small succulent with 1 or 2 pairs of globular elongate leaves 2½ cm long, glossy grayish green, bronzy toward apex with dark dots all over, these forming a window at apex; small 2½ cm golden yellow flowers. Plant almost resembles a lithops. *p. 65*
leipoldtii (Cape Prov.); succulent with thick, obovate leaves of various shapes, to 6 cm long, keeled on bottom, pointed at apex, dull-green, covered with prominent dots; fragrant yellow flowers with white eye. *p. 75*
magnipunctatus (So. Africa); succulent with one or two pairs of stone-like, tapering leaves wide in the middle, green with dark dots; flowers yellow. *p. 63, 76*
minor (Cape Prov.); spreading succulent; growths with 2 or 3 pairs of leaves, each 3 cm long, triangular boat-shaped, gray green and covered with dark green dots; 5 cm yellow flowers with whitish center. *p. 60*
nelii (Cape Prov.); succulent "Mimicry plant" in form of a split globe with thick leaves in pairs, gray and with raised, dark dots; showy yellow flowers. *Arid-subtropic.* *p. 76*
nobilis (Cape Prov.); tufting succulent with thick fleshy leaves 5-6 cm long, glossy dark green, flat on top, keeled beneath; large yellow flowers 5-6 cm across. *p. 65*
optatus (Punctillaria) (Cape Prov.); bold succulent, branched from base, forming clumps; 2 to 4 leaves in one growth, 2½-5 cm long, flat on top, rounded below, keeled below tip, reddish green tinged with purple, and covered with green dots; flowers yellow. *p. 63*
prismaticus (Cape Prov.: Karroo); succulent with growths having 1 pair of leaves 3 cm long, boatshaped and tapering, smooth, green marked by dark dots; flowers yellow. *p. 75*
simulans (Cape Prov.); small succulent with pairs of thick, keeled leaves 6-8 cm long, flat or trough-like on top, apex pointed, dark green to bronzy, dotted; flowers yellow. *p. 75*
willowmorensis (Cape Prov.); succulent with 2-to 4-leaved growth; flat leaves sickle-shaped and keeled, unequal lengths, purplish-green and covered with prominent dots; flowers yellow with white eye. *p. 75*

PLEIOSTACHYA *Marantaceae* **S3LFM**
pruinosa (Costa Rica); tall-growing stemless plant 1-3 m high; the long, reed-like petioles topped by lanceolate, corrugated leaves, satiny metallic deep green above, and conspicuously wine-red underneath down to the white-hairy leafstalk; small white, violet and yellow flowers. *p. 1541*

PLEOMELE (DRACAENA in Hortus 3) *Liliaceae* ***S1LFM**
angustifolia honoriae (Solomons, Torres Straits); beautiful ornamental with willowy, scandent stems densely clothed with clasping flexible-leathery, lanceolate leaves 15-25 cm long, shining grass-green with distinct ivory-yellow borders, and turning metallic red in the sun. *Tropical.* *p. 1480*
aurea (Dracaena) (Hawaii); endemic tree in Hawaiian forests, to 6 m high, forming stout trunk with erect slender branches; long, narrow, leathery, clasping, arching glossy green leaves clustered at end of stems, topped by

clusters of 5 cm whitish flowers, their 6 corolla segments joined into a tube and with slender filaments, thus differing from Dracaena which have flower segments divided nearly to base and with enlarged filaments. *p. 1480*

reflexa (Dracaena) (Madagascar, Mauritius, India), "Malaysian dracaena"; ornamental rosette of densely clustering short and narrow, leathery leaves, deep glossy green, without midrib, wavy and reflexed, persistently clasping the willowy, selfbranching stem, to 3½ m high if given support; I have noticed them widely used in India and Thailand as a most satisfactory pot plant; flowers whitish. *Tropical.* *p. 1444*

reflexa angustifolia (Malaya, Java); self-branching but more tree like, with long oblanceolate, very narrow, thin leathery, strap-like leaves medium green, crowded around the slender stem and spreading. *Tropical.* *p. 1445, 1480*

reflexa gracilis (Malaysia); attractively selfbranching bushy plant covered densely with short, 10 cm leaves gracefully recurved, and with translucent edges. *p. 1445*

reflexa 'Variegata' (South India, Sri Lanka), "Song of India"; a beauty I fell in love with when I first saw it in Ceylon; a tropical evergreen; self-branching with slender, flexuous stems eventually becoming scandent to 3 m long, densely furnished with clasping, narrow lanceolate, leathery leaves 12 cm long, beautifully margined by two wide bands of golden yellow or cream and framing the green center; very slow-growing. *Tropical.* *p. 15*, 1437, 1444, 1480*

thalioides (Dracaena) (Sri Lanka, Trop. Africa), "Lance dracaena"; shapely decorative plant of robust habit, with leathery, rich glossy green, lance-shaped leaves ribbed lengthwise, the base running into a long, clasping, erect, channel-like, gray-spotted stalk. Erect racemes with clusters of beige-white silky flowers, the tubular corolla spreading into linear petals. *p. 1444, 1480*

PLEUROTHALLIS *Orchidaceae* **I2OFM**

calyptrosepala (Trop. America); miniature terrestrial of compact habit, with stocky green, lanceolate leaves; between the foliage the tiny waxy flowers translucent yellow and with small blackish lip (spring). *p. 1802*

cardiothallis (Mexico, Nicaragua, Costa Rica); curious epiphyte of the humid cloud forest, with slender stems bearing a solitary leathery leaf 10-18 cm long and heart-shaped in outline; the tiny fleshy flowers 2 cm long, appearing out of the base axil of the leaf, deep brownish-red. *p. 1805*

carnosifolia (Perú); interesting little epiphyte with cordate leaves, the tiny yellowish flowers borne at base of leaf-juncture with thin, reed-like stems. *p. 1803*

chrysantha (Mexico, Venezuela); thick-leathery leaves 12 cm long on 10 cm petioles; the tiny orange to white and brown flowers nestling at the base of leaf, at juncture with the furrowed petiole. *p. 1802*

cogniauxiana (Costa Rica, Panama); curious epiphyte with solitary, large fleshy leaf ovate in outline, and small round, malodorous flowers emerging from the axil of the leaf and resting on it; sepals green densely spotted reddish brown; lip deep red in the rear, and thickly covered with minute reddish-brown spots otherwise, and narrow white margin, (winter). (I) *p. 1804*

flexuosa (Venezuela); miniature epiphyte with stalked bright green leaves 8 cm long; inflorescence on thin wiry stem 20 cm tall, with flowers several in succession, translucent pinkish white, marked with raised purple warts and densely covered with long white hair (summer). *p. 1802*

ghiesbreghtiana (Mexico, C. America, Panama, W. Indies); epiphyte with solitary leaf, and elongate raceme of small lemon-yellow flowers with pointed sepals and petals in ranks along the wiry stem, slightly fragrant, (winter). (I-W) *p. 1804*

grandis (Costa Rica); epiphyte with terrestrial habits, without pseudobulb, but having a solitary elliptic, leathery leaf on a slender stem; the curious flowers carried one-sided on an arching stalk, greenish, the sepals suffused with brownish-red, (Aug.-Sept.) (I) *p. 1804*

homalantha (Costa Rica); epiphyte, with slender stems bearing solitary leathery, oblong leaves; the straw-yellow flowers star-like with narrow petals, on 30 cm stalks; April-June. (I) *p. 1805*

hystrix (Venezuela); stocky epiphyte with the stiff stem bearing a single leathery leaf, from the axil of which spring the curious, waxy, maroon flowers with yellow markings, (Dec.-Jan.). (I) *p. 1804*

immersa (Mexico, C. America to Venezuela); cluster-forming epiphyte, with short stout stem bearing a broad, fleshy leaf to 20 cm long; from the leaf base a zigzag inflorescence to 35 cm, with heavy-textured 1 cm hooded flowers greenish-yellow with brown nerves and ciliate margins (autumn). *p. 1802*

leucantha (Venezuela); odd epiphyte with broad leathery leaf on its slender stem, and short-stalked, waxy, shell-shaped, yellow flowers, the lip yellow with purple rim, (Feb.). (I) *p. 1804*

longissima (West Indies, Mexico); slender stems with solitary oblong, fleshy, deep green leaves 12 cm long; stalk 30 cm long bearing a raceme of nodding flowers turned to one side, white tinged with yellow; spring. (C) *p. 1805*

loranthophylla (Venezuela); slender epiphyte with solitary leaves and elongate raceme of spidery flowers with the pointed lower sepals grown together, and of a translucent light yellow, (Feb.). (I) *p. 1804*

ophiocephala (Costa Rica); long-stalked solitary leaves, giving rise to small waxy, brown flowers having a long dorsal, and long oval lip, blush-white but richly overlaid and dotted with maroon-red and edged with ciliate white hair. *p. 1802*

powellii (Panama, Costa Rica); epiphyte, bearing a single, stiff, elliptic leaf on a slender stem, and a one-sided raceme of closely arrayed, oblong flowers with reddish-brown sepals, the dorsal with darker stripes and the lip dark reddish-brown, (Oct.). (I) *p. 1804*

saurocephala (Brazil); angular stems bearing a solitary lanceolate leaf 10 cm long; the two-lipped flowers yellowish green becoming light brown, dotted with purple inside; May-June. (I) *p. 1805*

schiedei (So. Mexico: Chiapas); miniature epiphyte with broad-elliptic leaves; many upright wire-thin branching stems each with one or more minute pinkish flowers dotted with blackish-red and edged with silvery ciliate beard-like scales (spring). *p. 1802*

sertularioides (Cuba, Jamaica, Mexico to Nicaragua); creeping slender rhizomes bearing short stems with solitary 4 cm green leaves at intervals and forming mats; small 1 cm flowers not opening fully, pale lemon-colored almost translucent. *p. 1802*

strupifolia (Brazil); most unusual epiphyte with strap-shaped leaves 30 cm long; the 10 cm floral axis from base of leaf-juncture lies cradled along the middle of the leaf, with tiny bird-like flowers white and green, heavily marked with purple. *p. 1803*

tribuloides (Jamaica); small, clustering epiphyte 5 cm high, with short slender stem bearing a long-elliptic leathery leaf, and numerous small, brick-red flowers. (C) *p. 1805*

tuerckheimii (Guatemala); interesting epiphyte with a stiff leathery leaf and arching raceme of odd, waxy flowers carried 1-sided in pairs, the deep purplish-red lower sepals grown together to a long point, the short petals greenish-yellow with blood-red stripes, (Nov.). (I) *p. 1804*

wendlandiana (Bolivia); cluster-forming epiphyte with erect reed-like stems, carrying the elliptic, leathery leaves; at juncture of stem and leaf the bristly tiny flowers straw-yellow dotted purple. (November) (Col. Botanic Garden Heidelberg). *p. 1802*

PLUMBAGO *Plumbaginaceae* **I-S2LBD**

auriculata (capensis) (So. Africa), "Cape leadwort"; straggling, shrubby perennial with small oblong, scattered leaves and wiry racemes of salver-shaped, azure-blue flowers having a very slender tube 3 cm long, and phlox-like lobes. *Subtropic* *p. 1949*

indica coccinea (rosea) (E. Indies), "Scarlet leadwort"; showy perennial, with wiry, zigzag stems, elliptic leaves 10 cm long, and long terminal spike of scarlet-red salvershaped flowers. (SD) *p. 1949, 1950*

zeylanica (Namibia and Transvaal); small rambling shrub, similar to auriculata but with white flowers. *p. 1950*

PLUMERIA *Apocynaceae* **S2-3LFM**

"mexicana" (Baja California); a type collected in Mexico where the Aztecs first glorified this tree; small elliptic, deciduous leaves dark green with pale veins, the fragrant flowers cream with deep yellow center. Probably P. rubra acutifolia form. *p. 141*

rubra (acuminata) (Mexico to Ecuador), "Frangipani tree" or "Flor de Mayo"; large, waxy, single blossoms 8 cm across, carmine-rose with yellow eye, very fragrant; thick, soft branches with latex- like, sticky juice, dark-green leaves, 30 cm or more long, shedding in dry season. *Tropical.* *p. 141*

rubra acutifolia (Mexico), the "West Indian jasmine", and the "Temple tree" of India; leaves wedge-shaped; flowers waxy-white with yellow throat, sweetly fragrant, funnelform. *Tropical.* *p. 141, 1952A*

'Singapore hybrid' (rubra x lambertiana); hybrids developed in Singapore and the Indian Botanic Garden in Calcutta; trees of robust habit with foliage more or less evergreen when growing in moist tropical climate; large glossy green, leathery leaves, and an abundance of exceptionally large flowers in colors from ivory to rosy-purple. *Tropical.* *p. 141*

PODACHAENIUM *Compositae* **I2LBD**

eminens (Mexico to N. So. America); tall tree-like shrub to 7 m with large opposite, angularly lobed leaves to 30 cm long, gray-hairy beneath; small heads of white ray flowers with yellow disk. *p. 810*

PODALYRIA *Leguminosae* **I2LBD**

calyptrata (So. Africa); much branched shrub to 1½ m; shoots and 5 cm obovate leaves downy; clusters of flowers pale rose. *Subtropic.* *p. 1390*

PODANGIS *Orchidaceae* **S3LFM**

dactyloceras (Tanzania, Uganda, Nigeria, Angola); small fleshy epiphyte with sickle-shaped, bluish 8 cm leaves forming a fan; short inflorescence rises below the leaf-fan, small clusters of 2 cm white flowers almost transparent, the lip merges into a funnel-shaped spur, column tipped with green. *p. 1809*

PODOCARPUS *Podocarpaceae (Coniferae)* **C-I2LB-FM**
elatus (New So. Wales, Queensland), "Brown pine" or "She-pine"; large evergreen coastal tree of Australia, to 30 m tall, with thick, narrowly-oblong, glossy-green leaves 8-15 cm long, rather lax and recurved; the seed attached to a blue-black 2 cm fruit. *p. 848*
elongatus (spinulosus) (Western Africa), "African yellow-wood"; coniferous evergreen tree to 20 m high, with gracefully pendant branches; densely pinnate, with long, leathery, narrow-linear, tapering leaves, bright green; short male catkins, and globose crimson fruit. *Tropical. p. 836, 848*
enciculus (henkelii or invicularis in hort.); noteworthy and very decorative evergreen of spreading habit, with strap-shaped, narrow, glossy green leaves measuring 12 to 15 cm long; handsomely pendant from weeping branches for artistic effect as a container plant; photographed at Hines Nurseries, Santa Ana, California 1971. *p. 849*
gracilior (Kenya, Uganda, Ethiopia), "African fern pine"; subtropical coniferous tree to 18 m high, common on the slopes of Mt. Kenya at 2,100 to 2,800 m; a valuable timber tree; graceful willowy branches with long, narrow-lanceolate, needle-like leathery leaves glossy deep green, to 10 cm long on young trees, and loosely arranged; 6 cm long and dense on older specimen; glaucous, purple berries. This may be the same as the cultivated P. "elongata". *Subtropic. p. 836, 848, 849*
henkelii (Transvaal), "Long-leaved yellow-wood"; luxuriant rounded tree dense with glossy, deep green, pendant or recurving leaves 12 to 15 cm long; male catkins cylindrical and erect from leaf axils. *Subtropic. p. 848*
latifolius (Transvaal), a "Yellow-wood"; great evergreen long-lived tree to 30 m tall; a specimen in Knysna forest is reported to be 1500 years old; the dark green leathery needles are long-linear, and blunt, 4-6 cm long and grouped in spiral tufts; the miniature 2 cm fleshy cones from female flowers are blue-glaucous. *p. 848*
macrophyllus (chinensis) (China, Japan), "Buddhist pine"; dioecious coniferous tree to about 12 m high, with horizontal branches, and numerous crowded leafy twigs, the leathery, deep green, narrow, linear-lanceolate leaves needle-like 8-14 cm long as seen in China; with a single midrib prominent on both sides; male, axillary flowers resembling catkins; on female trees the berries bluish purple. *Subtropic. p. 836, 837*
macrophyllus 'Maki' (China); a compact "Southern yew"; popular evergreen shrub, for hedges in the southern states and grown as a superb decorative container plant in the North; lends itself well to shearing and shaping; as a tree attaining 15 m in this variety with rather erect branches, dense with waxy, blackish green, linear lanceolate leaves spirally arranged, 4-8 cm long and about 1 cm wide, with distinct midrib; pale green beneath. Male flowers in 4 cm catkins; the fleshy oval fruit on female trees glaucous-purple. *Subtropic. p. 837, 848*
macrophyllus Nakai; the Chinese spelling of P. mac. Maki, from North and Central Taiwan, especially on Mt. Ali, in the Central Range. What I have seen in Formosa, and as verified at the National Herbarium with Dr. T. S. Liu in Taipei, is mostly of a large leaf type with linear-lanceolate, deep glossy green leaves 8-10 cm long x 1 cm wide. *p. 836*
Nagi (China, Japan, Taiwan), "Broadleaf podocarpus"; tall conifer to 30 m high, with smooth, purplish bark, elegant spreading branches and slender, semi-pendant branchlets having shiny green, rigid-leathery, elliptic leaves to 2½ cm wide; very durable decorator but not as dense as macrophyllus. *Subtropic. p. 836, 837*
neriifolius (China to New Guinea); evergreen tree to 20 m or more tall, of straggly growth; lance-shaped, leathery leaves to 15 cm long, glossy green above, somewhat glaucous beneath, with raised midrib both sides. *Tropical. p. 848*
totara (New Zealand); the "Totara" is a lofty, coniferous timber tree, to more than 30 m high, and 5-7 m girth; with small needle-like leaves 1-2 cm long, spiny-pointed, and rigid-leathery, bronzy-green; fruit is a small nut set on a fleshy, crimson base. *Subtropic. p. 835, 848, 849*

PODOCOCCUS *Palmae* **S3LFM**
barteri (Equatorial Africa); interesting small palm with thin trunk to about 2½ m high, the pinnate leaves 2 m long with alternate triangular, wedge-shaped leaflets glaucous green; both sexes on same tree, male on one stalk, female on another; 3 cm red fruit. *p. 1899*

PODOLASIA *Araceae* **S3HFM**
stipitata (Malaysia); tropical jungle plant forming clusters; the wiry, spiny petioles speckled; dark green leafblades widely sagittate to hastate, 30-40 cm long including the extended basal lobes; small inflorescence with cream spathe and short bisexual spadix. *p. 189*

PODOLEPIS *Compositae* **I2LBD**
acuminata (jaceoides in Hortus 3) (E. Australia, Tasmania); herbaceous plant 45 cm high, with leafy stems; clasping lanceolate leaves, and heads with lacy yellow ray flowers and cushion disk. *p. 804*
rosea (Australia); herbaceous plant 30 cm high with reddish, wiry stems and thick, oblong, linear leaves to 5 cm long, the margins turned under, both surfaces with a web of white hairs; flower heads on slender branches, ray and disk florets pink, with white anthers from center cushions. *p. 804*

PODOMORPHE *Piperaceae* **S3LFM**
sidaefolia (So. America); succulent bush of erect growth to 50 cm high; roundish, fleshy leaves 15 cm dia., light green and prettily veined; flower spikes greenish-white, from leaf axils. *p. 1944*

PODOPHYLLUM *Berberidaceae* **C2LFM**
emodi (Himalayas), "May-apple"; perennial woodland herb with creeping rootstock and thick roots, and peltate, palmately lobed leaves on fleshy stalks 15-30 cm high, and white, waxy flowers to 4 cm across, followed by 5 cm red, edible fruit. *Warm temperate p. 495*

PODRANEA *Bignoniaceae* **S3LBD**
ricasoliana (So. Africa), "Port St. Johns creeper"; showy evergreen climber with pinnate, deep glossy green leaves divided into 7-11 ovate leaflets 5 cm long, with toothed margins; flowers with inflated calyx and trumpet-like corolla pinkish-lavender with red veining, 5 cm long and opening into 5 rounded lobes, on blackish petioles. *Subtropic. p. 503, 504*

POELLNITZIA *Liliaceae* **I1LFD**
rubriflora (So. Africa); hard textured columnar succulent to 20 cm high, related to Astroloba; with ovate triangular leaves in 5 ranks, bluish-green, lightly rough and ending in a sharp tip, obliquely keeled beneath; flowers dark orange on long stems, similar to Aloe. *p. 1458*

POGOSTEMON *Labiatae* **S3LFM**
plectranthoides (East Indies); tropical subshrub with 4-angled branches ½ to 1 m high, and finely pubescent; the opposite, ovate stem-leaves 3 to 8 cm long, green with pale veins, and doubly toothed at margins; flowers white, in dense spikes, the stamens with long protruding lilac-colored anthers. *p. 1341*

POINCIANA: see Caesalpinia, Delonix

POINSETTIA: see Euphorbia pulcherrima

POLIANTHES *Amaryllidaceae* **I-S2-3LBMd**
tuberosa (Mexico), the famed "Tuberose"; widely cultivated in the tropics where it is esteemed for the purity and powerful fragrance of its blooms as a cut flower and in gardens; a beautiful summer or fall blooming herb having a bulb-like tuberous root stock covered with the broadened bases of the grass-like, channeled leaves; the leafy floral spikes are wiry and ½ to 1 m high, bearing numerous funnel-shaped waxy-white flowers 4-6 cm long, in pairs. The tuberose may be had in flower throughout most of the year by potting bulbs in succession, taking 4 to 5 months to bloom; grow warm but keep dry until the leaves appear, then water freely; dry off after blooming when foliage turns yellow. A form with double flowers is frequently grown (photo on p. 118). *Tropical. p. 112, 118*

POLYALTHIA *Annonaceae* **S2LBD**
longifolia pendula (India), the "Asoka tree" or "Mast tree" in India; a lofty evergreen, graceful column of symmetrical pyramidal growth 15 m or more tall, with willowy, weeping pendulous branches, long narrow lanceolate leaves to 20 cm long, shiny green with undulate margins; in spring the tree is covered with delicate, star-like pale green flowers with wavy petals, followed by the ovoid black 2 cm fruit, loved by bats and flying foxes. It is held in great esteem by Hindus, and planted near their temples. *Tropical. p. 133*

POLYANDROCOCOS *Palmae* **S3LBM**
caudescens (Diplothemium) (Brazil); elegant medium-sized fan palm with slender trunk to 8 m tall, sometimes swollen in the middle; topped by a magnificent crown of broad pinnate fronds with yellow midrib, to 4 m long, the leaflets in clusters and rather rigid, glossy green above, silvery white tomentose underside; large inflorescence of showy yellow flowers followed by heavy clusters of 8 cm orange colored, edible fruit. *p. 1886, 1899*

POLYCYCNIS *Orchidaceae* **I3OFM**
barbata (Costa Rica, Colombia); epiphyte with short pseudobulbs bearing an ample, solitary, plaited leaf; the erect or arching inflorescence to 60 cm high, with curious, swan-like flowers orange-yellow, dotted with dark purple, lip lighter but spotted with blood-red, (May-July). (I) *p. 1811*

POLYGALA *Polygalaceae* **I2LFM**
capitata (So. Africa); a shrubby milkwort with slender branches, opposite ovate leaves, and terminal clusters of irregular flowers with 5 sepals, of which 2 resemble large wing-like petals; some petals united, of rosy-purple color. *p. 1949*
myrtifolia (So. Africa), "Milk-wort"; woody shrub to 2½ m high, with small obovate 3 cm leaves; flowers greenish-white veined with purple, the lower petal with fringed crest, borne in erect terminal racemes. *p. 1952*
myrtifolia grandiflora (So. Africa); much-branched shrub 1½-2 m high, with smooth ovate, thin 3 cm leaves; large flowers with two flaring petal-like sepals rich purple, the lower petal with a lacily fringed crest. *p. 1949*
paucifolia (E. Canada, to Georgia and Minnesota), "Gay wings", or "Flowering wintergreen"; small perennial trailer 10-15 cm high, with 4 cm ovate leaves; large rose-purple flowers with fringed crest on corolla. *p. 1949*

POLYGONATUM *Liliaceae* **C2LFMh**

multiflorum (Temp. Europe, No. Asia), "Solomon's seal"; perennial herb with creeping rootstock; leafy stems to 1 m high; smooth, clasping ovate leaves; greenish white nodding flowers, and bluish-black fruit. *p. 1478*

verticillatum (roseum) (Temp. Europe, Asia Minor, Afghanistan); perennial with angular, leafy stem ½-1 m high, and with small 1 cm greenish, nodding flowers, 2 or 3 from upper leaf axils; leaves lanceolate. *p. 1478*

POLYGONUM *Polygonaceae* **I2LBD**

capitatum (Himalayas: No. India), "Knot-weed"; pretty perennial with trailing branches; the wiry, rooting brownish stems set with small alternate elliptic leaves 4 cm long, indistinctly crenate, matte-green with pale or light brown midrib and prominent, acute-angled design in brown-purple; the small pink flowers in globular heads. *Subtropic.* *p. 1952, 1956*

POLYPODIUM *Polypodiaceae (Filices)* **°S-I1-3HFM**

angustifolium (Campyloneuron) (Cuba, Jamaica, Mexico, Perú, Brazil), "Ribbon fern"; distinct fern with creeping rhizome covered with brown scales, bearing narrow-linear, leathery fronds 30-45 cm long, with margins often rolled under. *p. 1145, 1152*

angustifolium cv. 'Undulatum' (crenulata) (Florida), "Florida ribbon-fern"; distinguished looking cultivar offered in Florida nurseries, with long, linear, strap-shaped leaves gracefully recurving, 50 cm or more long, in a tufted rosette, from the stout, brown-scaly rhizome; the leathery, glossy green blades with pronounced undulation along the margins. Photographed at Fantastic Gardens, Miami. *p. 1147*

aureum (Phlebodium) (W. Indies to Brazil, Australia); named "Hare's foot fern" because of the stout creeping rhizomes clothed with bright rusty brown hair-like scales, the wiry stalks bearing bold, metallic light green, thin-leathery fronds, lobed with broad linear pinnae, separated by a rounded sinus and not cut to center; epiphytic. *Humid-tropical.* *p. 1150*

aureum var. areolatum ("Memoneri" hort.); differs from typical aureum in having smaller fronds, somewhat more deeply cut into toward the midrib, narrower segments, and sori always in only one row. Rhizomatous fern with glossy, thin-leathery pinnate green fronds, blue-green beneath, yellow midrib and stalk, to 45 cm long. *p. 1154*

aureum 'Glaucum', "Hare's-foot fern"; a graceful, wavy-leaved form of smaller habit with the durable fronds an attractive glaucous silvery blue, especially underneath. (IM) *p. 1150*

aureum 'Mandaianum', "Crisped blue fern"; a beautiful crested form having graceful bluish glaucous fronds of broad, pendulous, wavy pinnae with margins irregularly lobed, crisped and lacerated. (Manda 1912) *Humid-tropical.* *p. 1150, 1151*

aureum sporadocarpum (areolatum) (Mexico); variety with gray, almost naked, rhizomes bearing smaller, bluish fronds, quite silvery-blue underneath, on long grayish stalks. (IM) *p. 1150*

aureum 'Undulatum', "Blue fern"; a cultivar of compact habit and gracefully arching, bluish glaucous fronds deeply lobed, the broad segments distinctly undulate and wavy. *p. 1151*

bifrons, (Ecuador); a very unusual creeping fern with wiry slender rhizomes carrying small oblanceolate deeply lobed, both sterile and fertile fronds but besides, forming curious chestnut-like vessels hollow inside, pocket-like, similar to Dischidia, separate from its leaves. Rare and difficult in cultivation, best trained to a piece of tree fern trunk and hung from a greenhouse rafter; needs warmth and humidity and should be dunked in water daily. *Humid-tropical.* *p. 1145, 1147*

crassifolium (West Indies, Mexico to Perú and Brazil); fern with very leathery, simple, narrow oblanceolate fronds 30-90 cm long and 2½-12 cm broad, the upper surface with a few white dots, the margins wavy; short-stalked on stout, creeping, woody rhizome covered with brown scales. *Humid-tropical.* *p. 1147, 1152*

decumanum (Phlebodium) (Colombia, Brazil, Perú); giant epiphyte from the Amazonian rainforest near Iquitos; allied to aureum, but with narrower and more slender fronds, to 1 m long, carried on 50 cm glossy stalks from stout rhizome, densely clothed with soft, brownish scales; the leaves are deeply cut into narrow strap-like pinnae of papery texture, pale green and beautifully veined. *p. 1145*

glaucophyllum (W. Indies to Colombia and Ecuador); pretty little species with slender, wide creeping rhizomes; oblong spear-shaped, leathery fronds 10-25 cm long, glossy bright green above, bluish beneath, contrasting with the golden-yellow spore-masses. *p. 1154*

glauco-pruinatum (Philippines); rhizomatous creeper with deeply pinnatifid fronds 45 cm long and 20 cm wide, the segments linear, wavy at margins, and covered with bluish waxy powder masses. *p. 1154*

irioides: see P. punctatum

lepidopteris (Mexico, Perú, Brazil); variable fern with stout, wide-spreading rhizome, clothed with grayish scales; narrow, stiff, regularly pinnate fronds cut to rachis into entire leaflets, 15-20 cm long, of thick texture and covered with white or rusty hairs and scales, borne on rigid, scaly stalks. *p. 1165*

lycopodioides (West Indies, Trop. America); dwarf, pretty, wide-creeping fern with undivided fronds in two forms: the barren ones 5-10 cm long and 1-2½ cm wide, the fertile ones longer and narrower, both of shining, leathery nature. *p. 1152*

musifolium (Drynariopsis, Microsorium, Phymatodes) (Malaya, Philippines, New Guinea); "Banana-leaf fern"; handsome epiphyte with woody rhizome and stalkless, oblanceolate, thin-leathery leaves of pea green, prettily marked with a network of dark veining. *Humid-tropical.* *p. 1150, 1153*

"nudum" (lineare) (N. India, Japan, Malaysia, Natal, Angola); wide-creeping rhizome bearing long-elliptic, thin-leathery fronds 15-30 cm long and 2 to 3 cm wide. *p. 1165*

percussum (Colombia, Perú, Brazil); tropical epiphytic fern, densely clustering from wide-creeping wiry rhizome; the stalked fronds strap-shaped, 20-30 cm long and 2-3 cm wide, glossy green and of leathery texture, narrowed toward both ends, and scaly beneath. *p. 1147*

phyllitidis (Campyloneuron) (So. Florida, So. Brazil), "Strap fern"; found in the swampy Florida Everglades; strap-shaped entire, thin-leathery, glossy fresh green, brittle-stiff fronds 30-90 cm long, and to 10 cm wide, more or less waxy, borne stalkless on short creeping rhizome, clothed with brownish scales. *p. 1147, 1152, 1153*

piloselloides (West Indies, Trop. America); attractive miniature creeper densely covering tree-trunks in tropical forest; with slender, wiry, rooting rhizomes, bearing little glossy green leathery fronds; the barren ones oblong, 2½-8 cm long, 1-2 cm wide, the fertile ones narrower, on longer, hairy stalks; sori bright yellow. *p. 1152*

plectolepis (Mexico, Guatemala); attractive pinnate fronds 30-60 cm long on firm, glossy, straw-colored stalks, from a brown-scaly rhizome; the papery leaflets finely hairy, with notched and wavy edges. *p. 1154*

plumula (elasticum) (Mexico to Brazil and Perú); distinct species with short-creeping, brown-scaly, stout rhizome bearing wiry black stalks with spear-shaped pinnate fronds 30-45 cm long, dense with the numerous, 40 to 100 pairs of narrow leaflets of a very elastic nature. *p. 1154*

polypodioides (Delaware to Florida and Texas, Trop. America, So. Africa), "Resurrection-fern"; epiphytic on trees, a small, interesting creeping fern, with thin, wiry rhizomes, bearing small leathery, pinnate fronds 5-15 cm long, matte grass green, the alternate pinnae with small brown, scaly dots evenly dispersed on the grayish reverse; the fronds curl and fold when dry. (O) *p. 1147*

pteropus (Microsorium) (Malaysia, India, So. China); growing along streams; creeping fleshy green rhizome, bearing simple or trilobed fronds 20-25 cm long, the lobes scaly on the midribs, dark green and of thin texture. *p. 1156*

punctatum (polycarpon) (New South Wales, Natal, Angola, Guinea), "Climbing birdsnest"; singular-looking, succulent fern with stout rhizome and stalkless, thick-fleshy, yellow-green, simple fronds to 1 m long, gradually narrowed on both ends and irregularly indented or undulate at margins. *Tropical.* *p. 1150, 1153*

punctatum 'Grandiceps' (irioides grandiceps), "Fish-tail"; clustering fern with odd-shaped, thick leathery, almost succulent, waxy yellow-green fronds 30-60 cm high with prominent midrib, and tips forking to points or broad crests. Very curious, yet attractive and durable house plant. *Humid-tropical.* *p. 1150, 1153*

scolopendria (phymatodes) (Polynesia, Malaysia, Taiwan, Sri Lanka, So. Africa, West Africa); large fern with woody, wide-creeping rhizomes, bearing leathery pinnate fronds 60-90 cm long, the pale green, shining pinnae cut to a broadly winged rachis. *p. 1153*

subauriculatum (Goniophlebium) (Malaysia, Phillippines), "Jointed pine fern"; elegantly decorative basket fern with long pendant, leathery, pinnate fronds to 3 m long, produced from creeping rhizomes; the well spaced linear segments are fresh glossy green. (I3NW) *p. 1148, 1149, 1152*

subauriculatum 'Knightiae' (Australia), "Lacy pine fern"; an excellent, slow growing and durable basket fern; with glossy yellow-green, pinnate fronds at first upright, later pendulous and to 1 m long, the linear pinnae deeply serrate and sliced into narrow, pointed lobes. *Humid-subtropic.* *p. 1127, 1148*

triseriale (Brazil); tropical epiphyte with stout rhizome covered with gray scales; the glossy, wiry stalks bearing showy pinnate fronds 30-60 cm long; the leaflets broadly lanceolate 10-15 cm long, glossy green and of thin-leathery texture with wavy margins. *p. 1147*

vexatum (Cuba, Jamaica, Mexico, Brazil, Perú); narrow, dark green fronds about 25 cm long and 1 cm wide, narrowing toward base, the margins turned under and wavy, on creeping rhizome. *p. 1154*

virginianum (E. No. America to Labrador), the hardy, practically evergreen "American wall-fern"; growing on rocks, by creeping rhizomes, with pinnate leathery fronds to 25 cm long and having wavy segments, on wiry stalks. Like P. vulgare but rhizomes not sweet to the taste, and leaves smaller. *p. 1146, 1157*

virginianum fa. cambricoides (So. Quebec); mat-forming with spongy, scaly rhizomes, and firm pinnate fronds about 25 cm long, the wide pinnae irregularly and deeply lobed. *p. 1153*

vulgare (Newfoundland to Alaska, Alabama; Eurasia), "Common polypody", or "Adder's fern"; ornamental, hardy evergreen fern, often epiphytic, growing on walls, roofs or trees; mat-forming on stout, rusty-scaly rhizomes; straw-colored stalks bearing 15-30 cm pinnate fronds, the papery leaflets toothed and wavy. *Temperate.* *p. 1146*

vulgare cornubiense, the "Cornwall fern"; vigorous though delicate-looking form with finely divided fronds, not over 25 cm long, the lower pinnules or secondary pinnae broad and crisped. *p. 1146*

vulgare cornubiense grandiceps; an exotic looking variation with all the pinnae fasciated and crested at their tips. *p. 1146*

vulgare omnilacerum, the "Oxford fern"; in England considered the largest and finest of the species; similar to cambricum, the Welsh fern, but differing in always being fertile, the fronds are larger, 30 to 50 cm long, with leaflets lobed mostly at the middle. *p. 1146*

vulgare semi-lacerum (Ireland, England); the "Irish polypody"; most compound of all the permanent fertile forms of the species in cultivation; a handsome hardy fern with long-stalked fronds 30-40 cm long, deeply bipinnatifid in lower parts, becoming fertile and pinnate and toothed toward the apex, dark green above, and pale glaucous on undersides. *p. 1146*

vulgare virginianum: see P. virginianum

POLYPODIUM: see also Drynaria, Aglaomorpha

POLYPTERIS *Compositae* **C2LBDh**

hookeriana (Nebraska to Mexico); annual herb to 1 m high, sticky above, with lanceolate, 3-nerved, rough leaves, and panicles of 2½ cm heads of rose-colored, deeply 3-lobed ray-flowers. *p. 821*

POLYSCIAS *Araliaceae* **S2-3LBM**

balfouriana, in some collections as scutellarium; (Aralia) (New Caledonia), "Dinner plate aralia"; leafy, bushy tropical shrub in habitat to 8 m high, branching with willowy stems; the large leathery somewhat concave leaves variable but at first entire, later usually of 3 rounded, coarsely toothed glossy green leaflets to 10 cm across, often with white margins, on bronzy stems speckled gray. *Tropical.* *p. 315*

balfouriana marginata (New Caledonia), "Variegated Balfour aralia"; variegated form with the grayish green, leathery leaflets having an irregular, white border. *p. 315*

balfouriana 'Pennockii', "White aralia"; attractive cultivar by Pennock's, Puerto Rico; the waxy leaves olive-green with pronounced vein areas of creamy-white. *Tropical.* *p. 315*

filicifolia (Aralia) (South Sea Is.); evergreen shrub with fern-like pinnate leaves, the leathery leaflets to 15 cm or more long, and lobed, bright green, midrib purplish. *Tropical.* *p. 315*

fruticosa (Nothopanax) (Polynesia, Malaysia, India), "Ming aralia" or "Parsley panax"; evergreen shrub 1½-2½ m high, with spotted, willowy branches, and very feathery leaves irregularly 3-pinnately cut, to 30 cm long, the segments spiny-toothed, often edged with white. *Tropical.* *p. 312, 317*

fruticosa 'Elegans' (Aralia, Panax) (Polynesia); compact little evergreen dense with leathery leaves dark green and tri-pinnately cut and lobed. *p.315*

guilfoylei 'Quercifolia', "Oakleaf panax"; sturdy form with glossy deep green, thin-leathery pinnate leaves on reddish petioles; the leaflets irregularly shallow or deeply lobed. *Tropical.* *p. 312*

guilfoylei 'Victoriae' (Polynesia), "Lace aralia"; charming tropical evergreen dense with slender, willowy branches and grayish-green, thin-leathery, lacy, bipinnate leaves; the small, pendant, feathery segments toothed and bordered white. Lovely small foliage plant enjoying warmth and moisture, with its tasseled variegated foliage the most exquisite of the variegated leaf forms. *Tropical.* *p. 315, 318*

paniculata 'Variegata'; attractive variegated form of the species from Mauritius; willowy shrub with pinnate, pendant leaves to 30 cm long, including petiole, and usually having 7 leaflets 8-14 cm long, leathery and acutely serrate, deep green and richly splashed with cream and greenish-white, glossy on both sides. *p. 315*

POLYSCIAS: see also Aralia, Neopanax, Nothopanax

POLYSTACHYA *Orchidaceae* **S3OFM**

adansoniae (Kenya, Uganda, Tanzania, Angola to Guinea coast); small epiphyte 10-12 cm high, often on baobab trees; thin stem-like pseudobulbs bearing 2 to 4 narrow-elliptic leaves 6 cm long, topped by dense, erect raceme of 6 mm flowers greenish-white with mauve tips, the sepals and petals end in long bristle-like points. *p. 1810*

bicarinata (Kenya, Uganda, Tanzania); attractive, strong epiphyte, with conical pseudobulbs, lanceolate leaves, and a pendant raceme of 2½ cm waxy flowers, with incurving pink petals and sepals, white lip and green column. *p. 1811*

bracteosa (West Africa); small flattened pseudobulbs with broad, 10 cm lanceolate leaves, and nodding, often branched raceme of small, bracted flowers golden yellow marked with brown; summer. (S) *p. 1810*

cucullata (West Africa, Nigeria); cylindric pseudobulbs with solitary leaves, and erect stalk carrying 1-3 flowers 3 cm across, with greenish-yellow sepals spotted purple, small greenish petals horn-like, the lip greenish and marked purple. *p. 1810*

cultriformis (cultrata) (Trop. Africa: Cameroons to Kenya, Tanzania, Madagascar, Mauritius); epiphyte common on tropical highlands across Africa, the pseudobulbs in dense tufts, bearing a solitary leaf 20 cm long; inflorescence a many-flowered arching raceme, flowers 1 cm across, varying in color from white through pink and mauve to dark purple, also yellow and orange; strongly scented. *p. 1806*

foliosa (Trop. America); epiphyte with long obovate, leathery leaves, to 30 cm long, and erect, wiry spikes dense with tiny lemon-yellow flowers not fully open. *p. 1806*

golungensis (Kenya, Uganda, Zaire, Angola, to Ghana); slender stems swollen at base, bearing 2-3 leathery, dark green, narrow-linear, folded leaves; terminal branching raceme of small light green or lemon-yellow bell-shaped, 6 mm flowers. *p. 1810*

latilabris (Kenya); pretty, dwarf epiphyte from the Aberdare Mts., to 12 cm high; with tufted, thin stems, solitary leaves notched at tip, and short inflorescence with 2 to 4 creamy-white, waxy flowers tipped with brown. *p. 1811*

laxiflora (Nigeria); thickened, stem-like pseudobulbs and leaves to 20 cm; inflorescence semi-erect with as many as 50 small 2 cm flowers, creamy-white becoming yellow, lip orange-yellow with lobes streaked red (summer). *p. 1806*

leonensis (West Africa: Sierra Leone); creeping rhizome bears a string of small pseudobulbs, with leaves only 15 cm high; erect raceme with small cupped flowers light green suffused with purplish-brown, lip white with purple side lobes; autumn. (I) *p. 1810*

luteola (Florida to Mexico, Brazil, Trop. Asia); epiphytic with 30 cm narrow leaves, leafy stem, and terminal loose clusters of small fragrant flowers yellow, shaded with green (summer). (I) *p. 1811*

ornata (Colombia); dwarf, tufted epiphyte with leaves 3 cm long; erect inflorescence with flowers purplish brown spotted purple, 1 cm dia., sepals fringed with white hairs. *p. 1806*

puberula (West Africa: Sierra Leone to Cameroun); epiphyte of the rain forest, with 5 cm oval pseudobulbs bearing 3-4 lanceolate leaves, the branched inflorescence with numerous 1 cm greenish to yellow, pubescent flowers; Sept.-October. (S) *p. 1810*

pubescens (Transvaal, S. E. Africa); robust epiphyte with crowded, fleshy pseudobulbs bearing two short leaves; from the apex the erect 12 cm floral stalk with sweetly fragrant, waxy, inverted 2 cm flowers golden yellow, the lip with red markings (spring). *p. 1806*

stricta (Kenya, Uganda, Zaire); epiphyte to 45 cm high, with cylindrical pseudobulbs thickened at base, 3-4 lanceolate leaves; branched inflorescence with small greenish-white flowers marked mauve inside, the yellow lip marked brown. *Tropical.* *p. 1810*

stuhlmannii (Trop. E. Africa, Malawi); dwarf epiphyte with small pseudobulbs having 2-3 leathery, short leaves, and erect spike dense with little, fragrant flowers, golden-yellow streaked with red. (May-Sept.). (S) *p. 1811*

tesselata (Transvaal, Mozambique, Zambia, Tanzania, Kenya, Uganda to Angola and Guinea); variable epiphyte with conical pseudobulbs and lanceolate leaves to 20 cm; inflorescence a tall raceme to 50 cm with small 1 cm flowers in colors from orange-yellow, to yellow or apricot, inside marked with purple chessboard pattern. *p. 1806*

transvaalensis (Kenya, Uganda, to Zimbabwe, Transvaal and Natal); slender stems with stiff, glossy-green leaves, and erect inflorescence of few flowers with green sepals veined with mauve, the stalked petals and lip greenish cream, and faintly scented. *p. 1810*

virginea (Uganda); large-flowered epiphyte 20-40 cm high; with 2-edged pseudobulbs bearing tongue-shaped leaf folded at base; the inflorescence rises from a sheath, as a raceme of snow-white 2½ cm blooms, the midlobe of lip with lemon-yellow edge, and slightly scented. *p. 1810*

vulcanica (Trop. Africa); small epiphyte; pseudobulbs slender and stem-like with solitary, linear leaves 10 cm long; paired flowers 2 cm across, cream with violet lip (spring) *p. 1806*

POLYSTICHUM *Polypodiaceae (Filices)* **•C-S1-3LNM**

acrostichoides (No. America: Nova Scotia to Texas), "Christmas fern", or "Dagger-fern"; hardy evergreen leather fern, with tufted pinnate fronds similar in appearance to Nephrolepis; 30-60 cm long and 5-10 cm wide, thin-leathery and bright glossy green; green, stiff axis, brown near base, and covered with brown scales, on short creeping, underground rootstock; the 24-30 pairs of pinnae oblique-halberd-shaped and finely serrate; spores set toward apex of frond. *p. 1155*

aculeatum (Old World and So. America), "Prickly shield fern"; rosette of rigid, dark green, bipinnate leaves 30-60 cm long, on brown-scaly rachis. *Humid-subtropic.* *p. 1148*

adiantiformis: see Rumohra

aristatum (East Africa to Australia), "East Indian holly-fern"; handsome, robust fern with thick creeping rhizome, bearing 1- to 4-pinnatifid leathery fronds 30-60 cm long, the dark green segments spiny-toothed. *p. 1156*

aristatum variegatum (Japan to Sri Lanka and Australia), "East Indian holly fern"; creeping rhizomes with elegant leathery fronds 3-4-pinnate, lower pinnae largest, on thin wiry stalks, the segments banded pale yellow along axis. (S) *p. 1155, 1157*

lobatum var. luctuosum (Transvaal); a "Shield-fern" of small, compact habit; with pinnate, dark green, feathery fronds 15-20 cm long, somewhat deflexed, as if depressed, not bipinnate as in setiferum (aculeatum), instead the pinnae neatly toothed at margins and covered with fewer scales. *p. 1146*

munitum (Aspidium) (Alaska to Montana and California), the "Western sword-fern" or "Giant holly-fern"; handsome hardy evergreen fern, common in the Muir Woods near San Francisco, growing in the shade of the great redwood trees; gracefully arching pinnate fronds to more than 1 m long, on brown-hairy stalks, the rich green, glossy pinnae of leathery texture and with fine sharp teeth. *p. 1146*

setiferum, sometimes spelled setigerum (Trop. and Temp. Zones of both hemispheres); the variable, low growing "Hedge-fern"; feathery pinnate fronds 30-60 cm long, covered with brown hair-like scales, borne on shaggy, stout stalks; the fresh-green pinnae close together, and deeply lobed; frost-hardy and winter-green; much planted in shaded rock gardens. *Temperate to subtropic.* *p. 1155*

setiferum angulare; a prolific form with large pinnate, dark green fronds, dense with feathery leaflets, the thick stalks giving rise to bulblets developing young plants. *p. 1156*

setiferum 'Proliferum' (viviparum) (Australia), "Filigree fern"; tufted fern, scaly at base, the fleshy, brown-woolly stalk bearing the pinnate, light green fronds, the pinnae deeply cut or lobed, and bud-bearing, giving rise to young plantlets. *Subtropic.* *p. 1157*

setosum (discretum) (Japan), "Bristle fern"; low, spreading plant with stiff brown-scaly stalks and glossy dark green, leathery, bipinnate fronds to 45 cm long, the pinnae dense with pinnules overlapping and ending in a bristle. *p. 1157*

standishii (laserpitiifolium) (Japan); called "Upside-down-fern" because the dense spore masses show through the thin leaves and appear to be on the surface; suckering plant 1 m high with grass-green tripinnate fronds crisped at tips, on channeled stalks. *p. 1157*

triangulum (West Indies); tufted fern with scaly base; narrow pinnate fronds 30 cm or more long and 2½ cm wide, the numerous sessile pinnae are of leathery texture and with blunt teeth. *p. 1155*

tsus-simense (Aspidium); from the island of Tsus-sima in the Straits of Korea; dwarf and shapely tufted fern suitable for terrariums; with small leathery, lanceolate, dark green fronds, 15-30 cm or more long, bipinnate in the lower part, the segments becoming gradually smaller toward the slender point and sharply toothed. *Subtropic.* *p. 1157*

viviparum: see setiferum 'Proliferum'

POLYSTICHUM: see also Rumohra

POMETIA *Sapindaceae* **S2LBD**

pinnata (Malaysia to Polynesia), "Langsir"; luxuriant evergreen tree with glossy green pinnate leaves 20 cm or more long, the large corrugated leaflets in a dozen or more pairs; tiny greenish flowers hanging in long panicles, followed by nearly globular fruit with brownish rind 3 to 5 cm dia.; the seeds are edible when roasted. Photographed on Nuku Hiva, Marquesas. *Tropical.* *p. 2035*

PONCIRUS *Rutaceae* **I2LBD**

trifoliata (North China), "Hardy orange"; small, stiff-growing spiny deciduous tree to 4 m; dark green flattened branches and long stout spines 6 cm long; blooms in spring on bare branches in axils of large spines; white flowers opening flat, to 5 cm across; trifoliate leaves, with thin-leathery shining green leaflets, on winged petiole; small orange-like, aromatic fruit to 5 cm dia, with acid pulp; fairly hardy north to Philadelphia and New Jersey. *Warm-temperate.* *p. 2032, 2033*

PONERA *Orchidaceae* **S3OFM**

striata (Mexico, C. America, Venezuela, Brazil); reed-like, arching, leafy stems to 1 m long, the glossy green foliage arranged in 2 ranks; inflorescence from opposite leaf axils in small clusters, flowers not opening well, 2 cm dia., pale green or burnt coppery with reddish stripes, profusely blooming along leafless canes (autumn). *p. 1807*

PONTEDERIA *Pontederiaceae* **I2LBW**

cordata (Nova Scotia to Florida and Texas south), "Pickerel-weed"; aquatic perennial herb to 1 m, with thick parallel-veined long-stalked leaves from a rootstock, heart- or arrow-shaped to 25 cm long; blue flowers in spikes; used in ponds and water-gardens. *Warm temperate.* *p. 1957*

PONTHIEVA *Orchidaceae* **S3(charcoal)FM**

maculata (Venezuela, Colombia); terrestrial orchid of tufted habit; with basal, lanceolate, soft-hairy, pale green, thin leaves to 30 cm long; inflorescence a spike-like raceme of 2 cm, spreading flowers, the dorsal sepal pale brown with dark streaks, lateral sepals white with brown spots, petals yellow with brown streaks, small fleshy lip yellow with brown stripes; March-April. (S) *p. 1805*

PORPHYROSPATHA *(bot. SYNGONIUM) Araceae* **S3LFM**

schottiana (Costa Rica); tree-climbing tropical aroid; leaves of juvenile plants oblong 10-25 cm long and 5-10 cm wide; adult plant leaves oblong sagittate 30-35 cm long and 20 cm broad on 50-70 cm petioles; 15 cm purple spathe and spadix with female part rose, male section whitish. *p. 227*

PORPHYROSTACHYS *Orchidaceae* **I2-3OFM**

pilifera (Ecuador, Perú); terrestrial of Andean highlands, to 60 cm high, bearing a flaring cluster of rose pink or brilliant scarlet red flowers. *p. 1807*

PORTEA *Bromeliaceae* **S2-3HFD**

petropolitana (Coastal S.E. Brazil); shapely rosette of shiny yellow-green leaves broadened at base and with blackish spines; erect stem with dense panicle of orange-pink ovaries and sepals and white-lavender petals. *Tropical.* *p. 513, 578*

petropolitana extensa (Espirito Santo, Rio); a form with the inflorescence on a striking coral-red arching stalk, the brilliant coloring extending to the slender green ovaries, tipped purple; flowers lilac. *Tropical.* *p. 578*

PORTLANDIA *Rubiaceae* **S2-3LBD**

grandiflora (West Indies), "Glorias floridas de Cuba"; shiny evergreen shrub 3-4 m high, with elliptic, leathery leaves, and large white, solitary bell-shaped flowers 12 cm long, reddish inside, very fragrant at night. *Tropical.* *p. 2022, 2024*

platantha (Mexico); evergreen shrub with elliptic-ovate, deep shining green leathery leaves; and large funnel-shaped, showy white flowers waxy-white, 15 cm long and 8 cm across. *p. 2022*

PORTULACA *Portulacaceae* **I-S2LBD**

grandiflora (Brazil), "Rose-moss"; succulent herb with low spreading branches; scattered, cylindrical leaves and colorful, sun-blooming flowers in rose, red, purple, yellow, or white, surrounded by whorls of leaves and tufts of hairs; grown as an annual. *Arid-tropical.* *p. 1960, 1961*

grandiflora 'Jewel', the "Sun plant"; prostrate succulent creeper with small fleshy, needle-like leaves on reddish branches; large flowers with 2 rows of petals, carmine rose with deeper eye, 3 cm or more across; opening in direct sunshine when temperature is sufficiently warm. *p. 1962*

PORTULACARIA *Portulacaceae* ***I2LBD**

afra (So. Africa), "Elephant bush"; succulent shrub to 3 m high, with thick-fleshy, brown stems, sparry branches, and opposite, small obovate, glossy green leaves to 2 cm long, thick and juicy, round beneath; dainty pink, inconspicuous flowers. *Arid-subtropic.* *p. 1960, 1961, 2092*

afra aurea; a new, attractive form which I photographed at Hummel's in Carlsbad, California, having a succulent reddish stem and small obovate, light green leaves featuring a yellow center, flushed with pink beneath. (B-F) *p. 1961*

afra 'Macrophylla', "Giant elephant bush"; handsome succulent neatly branching from thick brown-red stem; the fleshy, glossy-green obovate leaves to 3 cm long, much bigger though fewer than the species. Grown by Los Angeles Plant Co., Vista, California. *Subtropic.* *p. 1959*

afra 'Tricolor'; colorful little succulent with small 1-2 cm obovate, nearly round waxy leaves, pale green conspicuously variegated with cream, edges marked with rose; tiny 1 mm flowers delicate pink. With age the branches become pendant and ideal for a basket plant. *p. 1959*

afra 'Variegata', "Rainbow bush"; lovely little succulent with red-brown stems and sparry, opposite branches, dense with pretty leaves milky-green broadly margined creamy-white, and with a thin carmine-red edge. *Arid-subtropic.* *p. 1961*

pygmaea (Namibia); very slow-growing little succulent shrublet; dichotomously branched, with flattened trunk; thickish gray stems, and tiny 5 mm gray-green leaves. *p. 1959*

POSIDONIA *Potamogetonaceae* **I3LFW**

caulinii (Mediterranean Reg.); aquatic plant forming green underwater meadows 2-3 m down; flowering and fruiting submerged; fruits ball-shaped consisting of brown felt hairs, 12 cm in dia. *p. 1958*

POSOQUERIA *Rubiaceae* **S2-3LFM**

latifolia (Mexico to Brazil); evergreen shrub with large, ornamental, leathery, 25 cm leaves, elliptic, with recurved margins, fresh-green, darker along veins; and fragrant, waxy, white, salverform flowers with long, slender, 15 cm tube, in drooping terminal clusters. *p. 2011*

POTENTILLA *Rosaceae* **C2LBDh**

multifida (France to Lapland, Russia to Tibet and Korea); small perennial herb 5-25 cm high; pinnate basal leaves silvery-silky beneath, and small 1 cm yellow flowers, in erect terminal clusters. *p. 1993*

rupestris (W. Europe to Asia Minor and Siberia); perennial downy herb with erect reddish branches 15-45 cm high; pinnately cut and toothed, green, hairy basal leaves, and 1-2½ cm white flowers with rounded petals, in loose clusters. *p. 1993*

POTHOIDIUM *Araceae* **S3OFM**

lobbianum (Philippines, Celebes, Moluccas); tree-climber to 15 m up, with angled thin-flexuous stem, and narrow-linear leathery leaves constricted or jointed toward apex; short-ovate spathe. Foliage similar to Pothos loureirii. *p. 280*

POTHOS *Araceae* **S3HFM**

hermaphroditus (Java), "True pothos"; a true Pothos characterized by the leaves appearing as if constricted through the middle; shrubby tree-climber with hard, narrow leaves arranged on both sides of branches. The Greek work "Pothos" personifies desire, identified with the winged god Eros. *p. 279*

jambea (Java); tree climber of the rainforest; with slender branches and the alternate, ovate leaves relatively large, and set on short, winged stalks. This may be P. seemanii according to Hortus 3, with leaves to 10 cm long. *p. 279*

scandens (Ceylon to Vietnam); branching creeper; broadly winged petiole with small, ovate blade attached, appearing as one leaf, together 6-8 cm long, and arranged in 2 ranks along wiry stem. *Tropical.* *p. 228,279*

zippelii (New Guinea); epiphytic tree climber with thin-wiry stems and shiny green, leathery, lanceolate leaves constricted in the lower part; flexuous fruiting branches bearing scarlet-red clusters of oval fruit. *p. 279*

POTHOS aureus of hort.: see Epipremnum, formerly Scindapsus

'POTOMATO' *Solanaceae* **I2-3LBD**

'Potomato' (Topato); the fanciful result of grafting a tomato scion (Lycopersicon esculentum) on a sprouted potato tuber (Solanum tuberosum); both potatoes underground, and good tomatoes on the vine, will be produced in this bigeneric potato-tomato union. My own experiments were however confined to greenhouse culture in South Dakota. *p. 2081*

PRATIA *Lobeliaceae or Campanulaceae* **I2LFM**

angulata (New Zealand); creeping herb forming mats; slender stems with roundish leaves coarsely toothed; white flowers 1 cm long; somewhat winter-hardy. The genus Pratia is under Lobeliaceae in Hortus; with Campanulaceae in Royal Hort. and Zander. *p. 1514*

begoniifolia (India, Nepal, and East); small creeping herb from the Himalayas at 700 to 2300 m; thread like, hairy stems with roundish, waxy, heart-shaped, crenate leaves 2 cm across; small two-lipped blue flowers, followed by purplish red, pea-sized berries. *p. 751*

guatemalensis (C. America); herbaceous plant with ovate, toothed leaves to 15 cm long, prominently veined; 5 cm flowers crimson-cerise with corolla split as in Lobelia. *p. 1514*

PRIMULA *Primulaceae* **C-I2-3LFM**

auricula (Alps and other mountains of Europe), "Alpine auricula"; hardy perennial herb, with thick obovate, persisting leaves to 10 cm long; the bell-shaped, fragrant flowers 2½ cm across, in clusters of 3 to 20 on long stalk, basically yellow, but in nature in several other colors red-brown, mauve and purple. *p. 1965*

denticulata (Himalayas); hardy perennial 30-50 cm high; with thin broadly lance-shaped basal leaves, usually white-powdery and dentate and narrowed into winged petioles; the flowers in dense heads, pale purple with yellow eye, the clusters surrounded by small leafy bracts; spring blooming. *p. 1967*

floribunda (W. Himalaya), "Buttercup primrose"; quilted, oval leaves 15 cm long, softly-hairy and with crenate margins; flowers golden yellow 2 cm across, in several superimposed whorls. *p. 1965*

juliae (Caucasus: Georgia); clustering, rhizomatous small perennial to 8 cm high, with winged petioles bearing thin, puckered, cordate leaves; and nearly sessile rosy flowers 2½ cm across, with red eye; hybrids come with white flowers, and with crisped leaves. *p. 1966*

x kewensis (floribunda x verticillata); early spring bloomer, with long obovate leaves, toothed and wavy-margined, and covered with silvery-white powder; the fragrant flowers bright yellow, borne in successive whorls above each other on 30 cm stalks. (C3) *p. 1967*

malacoides (Yunnan, China), "Fairy primrose" or "Baby primrose"; small, bushy herbaceous plant with numerous light green, smallish, papery leaves, white hairy beneath, and toothed at margins; several straight stalks, bearing small 2 cm flowers in successive umbels above each other, lavender or rose-pink to crimson-red or white, flowering late winter-spring. *p. 1967*

malacoides 'Glory of Riverside'; excellent commercial "Fairy primrose" representative of the progress made in breeding large-flowering strains of malacoides; the freely produced flower clusters are dense and bushy, the individual blooms measure 3 cm or more across, in lighter and darker shades of salmon-rose with deeper eye and orange-yellow center, the buds a pretty white-farinose; its foliage does not irritate skin. *Subtropic.* *p. 1967*

mollis (Bhutan, Burma, Yunnan); soft-hairy plant with broad 8 cm leaves, forming rosette; inflorescence to 60 cm high, rosy-crimson flowers with dark eye, 2 cm across. *p. 1965*

nutans (China, Yunnan); fine mountain species, forming a rosette of oblanceolate, softly-hairy leaves 10-20 cm long; bell-shaped, nodding flowers lavender or violet, 3 cm across, on white-mealy erect stalk 40 cm high. *p. 1965*

obconica (Hupeh, China); winter-blooming pot-primrose with fresh-green, brittle, broad-cordate leaves sparsely covered with irritating hairs; and showy umbels of large flowers in pastel shades of rose-pink, lavender, lilac to carmine-red, or even white; with greenish eye. *Subtropic.* *p. 1967*

obconica 'Gigantea', large flowered florists' primrose or "German primrose"; robust florists' cultivar of compact habit, with firm foliage and clusters of large rosy-carmine flowers 5 cm across. *p. 1965*

x polyantha (a hybrid group of P. vulgaris probably with veris and elatior), the hardy "Polyanthus primrose", "Lady's fingers" or "English primrose"; popular in American gardens and blooming in early spring; clump-forming perennial 20-30 cm high with long obovate leaves narrowed into winged petioles; the 2½-5 cm flowers sweetly fragrant like roses, in many colors, yellow, red and yellow, orange, bronze, maroon, or with white, borne in clusters well above the foliage; (those of vulgaris are solitary). *Warm-temperate.* *p. 1965, 1967*

sikkimensis (Himalayas); hardy, strong-growing perennial with wrinkled, obovate leaves in a rosette; the small yellow flowers nodding, with powdery calyx, in clusters on 60 cm stalks. *p. 1966*

sinensis (So. China), "Chinese primrose"; winter-blooming pot plant with a rosette of long-stemmed, hairy leaves attractively lobed; the flower clusters first low and small, later pushing up on heavy stalks and becoming larger, mostly purplish-rose with yellow eye. (I3LH) *p. 1967*

sinensis fimbriata 'Brick-red'; commercial Erfurt cultivar with very large, substantial flowers about 5 cm across, light or brick-red, and with yellow eye, the petals prettily wavy and fringed. *p. 1966*

sinensis 'Florepleno'; distinct, double-flowered type of English origin; with irregularly lobed outer petals, and a center tuft of shorter inner petals, in colors white, pink, salmon, red. *p. 1966*

veris (officinalis) (No. and C. Europe, Russia), "Cowslip"; spring-blooming, clustering perennial with wrinkled, oblanceolate leaves and masses of small, fragrant, golden-yellow flowers in umbels. (C2Wh) *p. 1967*

vulgaris (acaulis) (W. and S. Europe), the "English primrose"; hardy perennial, to 15 cm high, with oblong, wrinkled basal leaves and crinkled margins; numerous solitary 2½-4 cm flowers individually on slender stalks, usually sulphur yellow, blotched with dark yellow near eye; colorforms in white, purple, blue, rose, and red. *p. 1967*

PRITCHARDIA *Palmae* **S3LFM**

arecina (Hawaii); endemic palm of Maui; handsome fan-palm, with big, pleated leaves, cut about 1/3 into linear segments, covered with light yellow wool beneath; slender erect trunk to 11 m high. *Tropical.* *p. 1898*

beccariana (Hawaii); beautiful fan palm, 18 m tall, largest of the genus in Hawaii; palmate rich green leaves very broad, 1¼ m across, of stiff texture, densely pleated, and cut toward apex only; tolerates cooler locations. *Tropical.* *p. 1896*

hillebrandii (Hawaii: Molokai), "Loulou-lelo palm"; slender straight trunk to 7 m tall, crowned by firm palmate leaves 1 m or more long, smooth above, powdery glaucous beneath, on downy leaf-stem; bluish black 2 cm fruit. *Tropical.* *p. 1898*

macrocarpa (Eupritchardia) (Polynesia), "Loulou palm"; handsome fan palm with robust trunk; large palmate leaves, deeply folded, glossy green on stocky petioles, scale-like surface underneath, typical of the genus. *p. 1896*

pacifica (Fiji, Tonga, Samoa), "Fiji fan palm"; impressive with slender, clean trunk 9 m tall, to 30 cm in dia.; the numerous short-stalked palmate fronds forming a large round crown to 2½ m across, the leaves 1 m wide, bright glittering olive-green and deeply folded, very leathery, covered with brownish-white fuzz when young, only lightly cut at apex; the 1 m stalk unarmed, with brown fiber at base; 1 m spadix amongst foliage, with brownish fragrant flowers, and 1 cm lustrous blue-black fruit. *p. 1895*

PROBOSCIDEA *Martyniaceae* **I2LBD**

jussienii (Martynia louisiana) (Delaware, Indiana, to Mexico), "Unicorn plant"; sticky-pubescent annual herb, the branches in opposite pairs; large undulate, soft 20-25 cm leaves nearly round; flowers with yellowish tube, dotted and lined with violet, the lobes pale violet; the curious woody, curved, hanging fruit 10-15 cm long, with long slender, splitting beaks. *p. 1550*

PROMENAEA *Orchidaceae* **S3OFM**

citrina (xanthina) (Brazil); dwarf epiphyte 7 cm high, with slender pseudobulbs and 5 cm grayish green leaves; relatively large 5 cm flowers of heavy texture, golden yellow, the lip marked with red; very fragrant and long lasting (summer). *p. 1809*

PROSTANTHERA *Labiatae* **I2LBD**

nivea (New So. Wales, Victoria), "Australian mint-bush"; beautiful evergreen shrub to 2 m high, with opposite linear leaves to 4 cm long, the margins incurved; spotted with resinous glands and strongly scented of mint; 2 cm flowers snow-white or tinged light blue, in large leafy sprays; spring-blooming. *p. 1358*

PROTEA *Proteaceae* **I2LBD**

barbigera (So. Africa: S.W. Cape Prov.), "Giant woolly-beard"; most handsome, sparry evergreen shrub 1½ m high; white-hairy, light gray green, oval, leathery leaves 15 cm long, undulate and hairy at margins; the beautiful, large inflorescence to 20 cm across, balls resembling pine cones; the outer bracts soft pink or rose, tipped with fine silvery-white hairs, and surrounding a soft mass of white woolly flowers which become black-violet in the raised center of the flower heads. *Subtropic.* *p. 1972*

compacta (Cape Prov.), "Bot river protea"; slender evergreen shrub to 3 m high, with smooth, narrow, light green shingled leaves 10 cm long; terminal, silvery, soft pink 10 cm flower heads; the colored bracts are a lovely clear pink, and covered with fine, velvety hair. *Subtropic.* *p. 1972, 1980*

cryophila (So. Africa: Cedarberg), the rare "Snowball protea"; grows on snowy peaks; spreading bush only 60 cm high; with huge white flowers 20 cm dia. emerging from ground level; leaves to 1/2 m long. *p. 1979*

cynaroides (So. Africa), "King protea"; characteristic, showy shrub 1/2-1 1/2 m high, with varying thick-leathery stalked leaves 5-12 cm long edged red, on woody red stem; the flowers packed in large 20 cm heads surrounded by numerous shingled series of stiff leathery bracts as in a cup, white to delicate pink and silvery silky-downy (summer). *Subtropic.* *p. 1968, 1972, 1973, 1979*

eximia (latifolia) (So. Africa), "Ray protea"; large-flowered protea from the S.W. Cape mountains; a dense shrub to 2 1/2 m high, with broad oval, red-edged silvery leaves to 9 cm long, densely clasping and clothed around the upright branches, topped by the flower heads 12 cm long, with deep rose spoon-shaped bracts fringed with white silky hairs, the cup is filled with a mass of flowers tipped with old rose bristles. *Subtropic.* *p. 1981*

grandiceps (So. Africa), "Peach protea"; most beautiful neat, dense shrub from the high Cape mountains; its elliptic, leathery, 12 cm highly decorative grayish leaves edged in red, and arranged closely and regularly on woody branches; the 10 cm flower head with 7 or 8 whorls of incurving rosy-salmon or coral bracts arranged like in an artichoke, and with soft white hairs. *Subtropic.* *p. 1972, 1981*

lacticolor (So. Africa: Cape), "Baby protea"; handsome rounded bush to 3 m high, with leathery green leaves 5 cm long; inflorescence small, the slim pink bud only 8 cm long, but very charming when wide open; the pink bracts resemble the wide-spread silky-fringed petals of a daisy revealing the starry pinkish-cream styles and hairs within. *p. 1981*

latifolia hort. (eximia) (S.W. Cape mountains), "Ray-flowered protea"; erect shrub to 2 1/2 m high, with broad, silvery green leaves; large cushions 12 cm across with spoon-shaped bracts rose at top and pale green toward base, outlined with fine white hairs; center of floral head massed with pink, hairy flowers. *p. 1979*

longifolia (S. W. Cape Prov.); spreading bush with long narrow leaves to 20 cm; yellowish or pink 12 cm flower heads open to show a white woolly mass inside, tipped with black. *p. 1979*

minor (So. Africa: S.W. Cape), the "Ground-rose"; charming, broadly spreading, gray-green shrub with long, linear, thin 15 cm leaves; pretty cup-shaped flowers of rose and mauve full of cream hairs tipped black. *p. 1980*

mundii (So. Africa: Cape Prov.); big rounded, quick-growing shrub to 3 m or more; leathery, elliptic, deep green leaves on reddish stems; flower heads 6-8 cm long, with the erect straw-white or pinkish styles extending beyond the silky greenish-pink bracts; attractive, but not of long duration. *Subtropic.* *p. 1979*

neriifolia (So. Africa: Cape), the "Pink mink" or "Oleander-leaved protea"; large floriferous bush to 3 m high, with long narrow linear, leathery leaves, and a showy terminal inflorescence 12 cm long, of cupping, shingled bracts pale salmon to deep rose with silvery sheen, the tips white and incurving and bearded with purplish black, set off against the mass of tawny-colored little flowers within the head. *Subtropic.* *p. 1972, 1980*

repens (mellifera) (So. Africa: Cape); "Sugarbush" or "Honey-protea"; a shapely evergreen one cannot help admiring when travelling down the Cape Peninsula; large rounded bush to 3 m, its woody branches with dense whorls of silvery-glaucous, leathery, elliptic leaves 8-12 cm long; terminal inflorescence, 12 cm long, of shingled, smooth, shiny and silky, sticky bracts, varying in color from white to nearly red. In the early morning these cupped heads are half filled with nectar, which the early colonists boiled into syrup in the absence of sugar. *Subtropic.* *p. 1981*

rubropilosa (Transvaal), "Velvet protea"; gnarled tree to 8 m tall on the Transvaal escarpment at 2200 m; pretty golden brown velvet buds; flowers open to rich rose pink. *p. 1980*

speciosa (So. Africa: S.W. Cape), "Brownbeard"; handsome smallish shrub 1 m high, with broad green leaves 10 cm long, edged in red; charming flower heads (12 cm) silvery-pink covered with soft white hairs, the tips with dark brown woolly beards. Linnaeus called this protea the "Beautiful One". *p. 1981*

sulphurea (Mountains of S. W. Cape); interesting shrub spreading to 3 m; with small, tough, bluish-green, obovate leaves; exquisite flower heads to 8 cm dia., opening wide to reveal the yellow bracts, shading into rose, and the perfectly shaped beehive of hairy flowers at the center, which are sulphur-yellow tipped with golden tan to cinnamon; and with a scent of honey; unfortunately the inflorescence hangs downward with their faces. *p. 1979*

susannae (So. Africa: Cape); profusely blooming bush to 2 m, with narrow gray-green leaves to 12 cm long; terminal inflorescence shaped like a pincushion 10 cm across, with its central mass of hairy pinkish-white filiform flowers nestling in a basket of brownish pink bracts tipped rusty red. *Subtropic.* *p. 1980*

welwitschii (Transvaal); spreading shrub, with obovate gray leaves and large terminal inflorescence of greenish bracts subtending a wild arrangement of slender white flowers pointing in every direction when fully open. *p. 1980*

PRUNUS *Rosaceae* C2LBM

caroliniana (No. Carolina to Texas), "Carolina laurel", "Wild-orange" or "Mock-orange"; native evergreen cherry-laurel to 15 m or more, dense with glossy green, thin-leathery, obovate leaves 5-10 cm long, occasionally with teeth; small creamy-white flowers, followed by small 1 cm shining black fruit. *p. 2001*

caroliniana 'Bright 'n' Tight', "American cherry-laurel"; handsome evergreen of pyramidal habit; compact and very dense form of the "Mock-orange"; oblong leathery, glossy green leaves to 10 cm long; small cream flowers; shining black inedible fruit; a good decorator subject in containers. (Monrovia Nursery, California). *p. 1999*

dulcis (amygdalus) (W. Asia), the "Almond"; deciduous peach-like tree 6-10 m high, with gray bark; lanceolate firm, shining leaves, finely serrate; large, showy 3 cm pink flowers appearing before the leaves; fruit a compressed stone-fruit with hard flesh, 4 cm long, splitting open at maturity and freeing the pitted stone (almond). Limited to areas with less frost than tolerated by peach; in U.S., confined mainly to California. *p. 1998*

laurocerasus (S.E. Europe to Iran), "English laurel"; decorative, quick-growing, evergreen bush with smooth, pale green shoots and broad, handsome, leathery, dense foliage, dark glossy green, oblong-pointed, to 15 cm long; small, white flowers, and dark purple fruit. *Warm temperate.* *p. 1995*

laurocerasus compacta (S.E. Europe to Iran and Caucasus), "Cherry-laurel"; evergreen bush with stiff branches dense with long elliptic, glossy green leathery leaves, and erect cylindric racemes of small 1 cm white flowers very fragrant; 1 cm fruit dark purple. *p. 1998*

laurocerasus 'Otto Luyken'; excellent cultivar by Hesse, and used in German landscaping as a very compact form of English laurel; short and bushy 50 cm high, the foliage dense and glossy dark green, to 10 cm long and 2-3 cm wide, slender-pointed; free-blooming with spikes of white flowers in May; winter-hardy in C. Europe. *Warm temperate.* *p. 1998*

laurocerasus 'Schipkaensis', a hardier form of "Cherry laurel"; from the Schipka Pass in Bulgaria; with narrower glossy green leaves 5-11 cm long, only faintly toothed, on handsome yellow-green branches. *p. 1995*

persica (Amygdalus) (China), "Peach tree", or "Good-luck peach" for the Chinese New Year; normally a bushy tree, but trained by pruning and starving into dwarf forms in Japan and China, with masses of solitary, delicate pink flowers in advance of the lanceolate foliage, early in spring. *p. 1995*

serrulata 'Kwansan' or 'Kanzan' (Japan), "Japanese double flowering cherry"; deciduous tree to 12 m high; with glossy reddish bark and stiffly ascending branches; ovate leaves with bristly teeth, turning reddish in late autumn; large double, deep rose-pink flowers 5 cm across in clusters of 2 to 5. *Temperate.* *p. 1993*

triloba plena (China), a graceful shrub known as "Double flowering almond"; often grown as a small standard and forced; with serrate, deciduous leaves, the dainty, double pink flowers flushed with rose, unfolding ahead of the foliage from tight round buds set closely along woody branches of last year's growth, in spring. *Temperate.* *p. 1995*

PSAMMOPHORA *Aizoaceae* I2LBD

longifolia (S. W. Africa); tiny, tufted, very succulent plant with triangular leaves 4 cm long, olive-green to brownish; rough and usually sand-encrusted, because of sticky surface, to protect itself from dehydration; flowers white. *p. 74*

PSEUDERANTHEMUM *Acanthaceae* S2-3LFM

alatum (Mexico), "Chocolate plant"; low growing herb with copper-brown papery leaves, 8-10 cm long, on flat, winged petioles, silver blotching near midrib; gray beneath; small salverform, purple flowers in racemes. *Tropical.* *p. 46*

albomarginatum (Polynesia); tropical shrub with willowy branches; thin-leathery leaves, to 15 cm long, irregular, shiny green with silvery-green and ivory variegation; showy flowers 1-1 1/2 cm diameter, white with purplish-red spots, in racemes; an attractive foliage plant. *p. 47*

atropurpureum 'Roseum' ("Acecaria bicolor" hort.), (Tonga and other Pacific Islands); handsome tropical shrub with willowy purple branches; leathery oval leaves 10-15 cm long, blackish purple varying to deep green; flowers in terminal erect spikes, white to pinkish, covered with purple spots, center red-purple. *p. 47*

atropurpureum tricolor (Polynesia); shrub with elliptic, leathery leaves metallic purple splashed with green, white and pink. (2) *p. 46*

reticulatum (New Hebrides); tropical shrub with attractive lanceolate smooth foliage, slightly fleshy, green with reticulation of golden-yellow veins; 3cm flowers whitish with wine-purple in throat, and dots of same color on lower lip. *Tropical.* *p. 46*

reticulatum var. 'Fiji'; handsome foliage with broad ovate, showy leaves fresh green with netted yellow veins; 4-petaled white flowers marked with purple, and with prominent red stamen. *p. 46*

seticalyx: see tuberculatum

sinuatum (New Caledonia); shrubby plant with linear leaves 8 cm long, olive-green mottled with gray, the margins deeply scalloped, purplish beneath; white flowers in terminal racemes, 3 cm across, freely spotted rosy-lavender. *Tropical.* *p. 47*

tuberculatum (seticalyx) (Polynesia); small, freely branching tropical shrub with thin, warty branches; small leaves, and white axillary flowers 3 cm across, on long thin tubes. *p. 50*

PSEUDOANANAS *Bromeliaceae* **S3HBD**

sagenarius (Paraguay, Brazil, Bolivia); photographed at Botanic Garden in Leningrad as Ananas macrodontha, but id. by Dr. L.B. Smith as Pseudoananas; robust terrestrial, forming thickets by sending out underground stolons; larger than ananas, with stiff, strap-like leaves to 120 cm long, shiny coppery green and with barbed spines at margins; the succulent, flattened inflorescence with spiny pink bracts and lavender flowers; edible fruit but without the topknot of the true pineapple. *p. 533*

PSEUDOCASSINE *Celastraceae* **S2LBD**

transvaalensis (So. Africa); woody tree to 10 or 12 m high; found in Kruger National Park; with small, gray-green leathery, oval leaves 3 cm long, and inconspicuous flowers; handsome when covered with its globular pointed, hard yellow fruit 2 cm long. The wood is whitish and used by Africans for making spoons and troughs. *p. 759*

PSEUDODRACONTIUM *Araceae* **S3LFM**

siamense (Thailand); aroid with beet-like tuber; the leaf several times dissected; spathe light green to yellowish, 9-13 cm long, spadix 6-11 cm, on 30-40 cm stalk. *p. 228*

PSEUDOESPOSTOA *Cactaceae* **I2LBD**

melanostele (Perú); shapely dark green column to 2 m high and 10 cm thick, with rows of brown-tipped needle spines and dense covering of white woolly hair especially with age; nocturnal, funnel-form white flowers. *p. 645*

PSEUDOHYDROSME *Araceae* **S3LFM**

gabunensis (Equatorial Africa: Gabon); curious tropical aroid with fleshy tuber, the large and showy, short-stalked inflorescence chalice-like 25 cm long bright yellow, inside red-purple; the dissected leaf appears after blooming. *Tropical.* *p. 228, 303*

PSEUDOLITHOS *Asclepiadaceae* **S2LBD**

cubiforme (Lithocaulon) (Somalia); small, dull green, globular succulent with surface in cubical checkers; the fleshy caudex 5 cm dia.; the inflorescence in downy, grayish rays sessile to the body, holding small red, cupshaped flowers. *Arid-tropical.* *p. 379*

sphaericum (Lithocaulon) (Somalia); curious low succulent in form of a depressed globe 5 cm dia., wrinkled and cut into numerous angled or roundish elevations, bronzy green; small clusters of tubular red flowers close to the wall of the sphere. *p. 379*

PSEUDOLOBIVIA *Cactaceae* **I2LBD**

kermesina (Argentina); near-globular large lobivia to more than 15 cm dia., green, with numerous ribs notched into knobs, with yellow radial spines; large ball-shaped flowers to 18 cm long light rose to carmine. *p.674*

PSEUDOMORUS *Urticaceae* **S3LFM**

brunoniana pendula (New Caledonia, Norfolk Is.); quite handsome evergreen shrub with dark green leathery, lanceolate leaves, and long tail-like 15 cm spikes of tiny creamy flowers. *p. 2106*

PSEUDOPANAX *Araliaceae* ***I2LFM**

crassifolius (New Zealand), "Lance-wood"; evergreen growing into large, variable tree; when young the leaves are long linear, rigid and finely toothed, with thick midribs, dark green, blotched yellow above, purple beneath, 30-90 cm long; at a later stage, usually compound with 3 leaflets each 30 cm long. *Subtropic.* *p. 306*

ferox (New Zealand), slender evergreen tree with variable, thick and stiff leaves, linear, later obovate, chocolate-brown with pale brown midrib; margins jaggedly toothed. *Subtropic.* *p. 306*

lessonii (New Zealand), "False panax"; small evergreen tree with palmately compound leaves, the segments are obovate, shining and leathery, toothed toward apex. *p. 306*

PSEUDOPHOENIX *Palmae* **S3LFM**

vinifera (Cuba, Santo Domingo, Haiti), "Cherry palm"; feather palm to 10 m resembling a small Royal palm; with stout, glossy trunk bulging variously, and topped by arching 1½-2 m pinnate fronds, on yellow, clasping petiole, the leathery yellow green leaflets clustered in groups of 2 or 3; cherry-sized fruit bright red. *p. 1894*

PSEUDORHIPSALIS *Cactaceae* **S2HFM**

himantoclada (Wittia) (Costa Rica); epiphytic phyllocactus with broad, flat branches and forming large pendant bushes, 1 m or more long; the stems thin and 4-5 cm wide, indented saw-like, vivid glossy green; the flowers with tube and spreading petals 2½ cm long, white inside, outside pink. *p. 739*

macrantha (Mexico: E. Oaxaca), "Fragrant moondrops"; epiphytic cactus with thin flattened joints waxy green, scalloped at the margins and branching toward tip; the 2½ cm flowers from the areoles with linear outer petals white, of intense lemon fragrance. *p. 739, 741, 743*

PSEUDOSASA *Gramineae* ***C-I2LBM**

japonica (Bambusa Metake), (Japan), the "Female arrow bamboo" or "Hardy Metake bamboo"; a running bamboo of moderate size; with hollow round stems 2 to 4 m high and to 1½ cm dia., from creeping rootstocks, with broad deep green foliage 10-30 cm long, glaucous beneath. Fairly hardy in New Jersey; has withstood freezing to -18° C. One of the best for decoration in tubs, holding leaves better than other species; for cool bright rooms; keep moist. *Warm temperate.* *p. 1303, 1305, 1315*

PSEUDOTSUGA *Pinaceae (Coniferae)* **C2LBD**

menziesii (Brit. Columbia to California), "Douglas fir"; graceful tree to 60 m high, pyramidal when young; the crown very broad in older trees, with trunk to 4 m in dia., bark brown, fissured into broad ridges; the spreading branches slightly pendulous; needles shining dark green 2-3 cm long, and smelling of camphor; cones pendulous, elongate to 10 cm long, 3-4 cm dia. A major timber tree on the Pacific Coast. *Temperate.* *p. 846*

PSEUDOZYGOCACTUS *Cactaceae* **S3LBD**

epiphylloides var. bradei (Brazil); much-branched epiphyte with short, club-shaped joints 2½ cm long, hanging together like a chain; at branch ends the small yellow flowers 2 cm across. *p. 735*

PSIDIUM *Myrtaceae* **I2LBM**

cattleianum (littorale longipes in Hortus 3) (Brazil), "Strawberry guava"; dense shrub to 7½ m high, smooth branches with obovate, leathery leaves 5-8 cm long; white flowers with many stamens, and 4 cm berry-like purplish-red fruit with strawberry flavour. *Subtropic.* *p. 1614*

cattleianum lucidum (littorale) (Brazil), "Yellow strawberry guava"; variety of the "Purple guava", with juicy fruit, sulphur-yellow. *p. 1608*

guajava (W. Indies, Mexico to Perú), "Apple guava" or "Common guava"; small branching tree, reaching 9 m; 4-angled branchlets with light green, elliptic, corrugated leaves, hairy beneath; large white flowers, and producing edible, globose yellow, sweet flavored fruit 4-8 cm dia., used for making jam. *Tropical.* *p. 1604, 1608*

littorale (as listed in Hortus 3) see cattleianum lucidum (as known in horticulture).

PSILOTUM *Psilotaceae* **S3HNM**

nudum (triquetrum), (New Zealand and subtrop. and trop. So. and No. hemisphere), "Whisk-fern"; curious club-moss botanically interesting as a very primitive vascular plant; herbaceous perennial devoid of roots; with scale leaves only, on ribbed stems to 50 cm long. *Tropical.* *p. 1958, 1968, 1982*

PSITTACANTHUS *Loranthaceae* **S3HBD**

calyculatus (So. Mexico to Oaxaca. Chiapas and Veracruz), "Parrot flower" or "Mexican mistletoe"; striking woody parasite on branches of tropical trees. The thick-leathery leaves are ovalish or sickle-shaped 6 cm long; showy flowers in large clusters, slender-tubular, divided into linear segments, vivid salmon-red, 5 cm long, and with protruding red stamens. *Tropical* *p. 1519*

PTERIDIUM *Polypodiaceae (Filices)* **C2HFM**

aquilinum (World-wide, both Temperate and Tropic), the "Bracken" or "Eagle-fern"; coarse-looking fern with wide-creeping, underground rhizomes; the black-polished stalks carry the great tri-pinnate, feathery fronds to more than 1 m long and 75 cm wide in cool climates, immense and to 3 m high in the tropics; the pinnae are bright green and somewhat tough in texture, and sometimes pubescent. *p. 1164*

PTERIS *Polypodiaceae (Filices)* ***I1-3LHNM**

adiantoides: see Pellaea

cretica (Tropics and Subtropics: Florida, Italy, Ethiopia, Natal, Cape Prov., Caucasus, Iran, Himalayas, India, Japan), "Cretan brake"; a most useful, variable, decorative "Table fern"; with 15-30 cm pinnate fronds on erect, wiry, light brown stalks; the narrow parchment-textured, deep green leaflets 8-15 cm long, the sterile ones to 2 cm wide and toothed, the fertile leaflets narrower, and on longer stalks. *p. 1158*

cretica 'Albo-lineata'; a very pretty, useful, variegated form of low habit; with small, clean-cut, leathery fronds differing from the species only in the broad band of creamy white down the center of each linear-lanceolate leaflet which are toothed and wavy-margined; the fertile fronds are taller and more slender. *Humid-tropical.* *p. 1159, 1161*

cretica 'Alexandrae'; form of albo-lineata, with monstrose crests at the tips of the broad leathery, light green leaves banded white in center. *p. 1162*

cretica 'Childsii'; handsome cultivar with its pinnate fronds consisting of broad, fresh green leaflets prettily frilled, lobed, or wavy along margins. *Humid-tropical.* *p. 1158*

cretica 'Cristata'; an old variety with slender leaf segments partially serrated and some cresting at the tips, however the fertile fronds tend to be relatively small, and newer varieties, such as 'Wimsettii' and 'Rivertoniana', have better form. *p. 1158, 1161, 1162*

cretica 'Distinction'; a bushy, lacy plant consisting of almost nothing else but crests; the fronds are once pinnate at base, the narrow pinnae and upper main divisions are pinnately lobed, ultimate lobes divide into forking tips. *p. 1162, 1163*

cretica 'Gauthieri'; like 'Wimsettii', but leaf segments are broader, lighter green, and more serrated by their irregular, pointed lobes and teeth; of compact habit. *p. 1162*

cretica 'Grandis': see cr. 'Nobilis'.

cretica 'Magnifica'; an attractive form with slender fronds, with their narrow linear segments having a pale yellow-green center and a deeper green margin, tipped by small crests. *p. 1162, 1163*

cretica 'Major' (ouvrardii) (Corsica to Crete); widely distributed in the tropics; a variety of robust habit with plain, thin-leathery, dark green fronds to about 50 cm high, on wiry stalks, not winged, and set with 2 to 6 pairs of sessile,linear leaf segments, the lower compound, with a long terminal; the sterile pinnae are broader, finely toothed and wavy. *p. 1160,1162,1163*

cretica 'Mayii'; an elegant variety with the same variegated character as albo-lineata, the white band in each leaflet forming a pleasing contrast with the bright green edge, but the plant is more dwarf and with narrower segments which terminate in crests. *p. 1162*

cretica 'Nobilis' (grandis); dainty with very lacy fronds, the leaf segments finely serrated near their base, tapering off toward slender tips which are narrowly forked into spreading crests. *p. 1160, 1163*

cretica 'Ouvrardii'; bushy plant 60-90 cm high with numerous sturdy pinnate fronds on long wiry stalks, the narrow linear pinnae thin-leathery and deep green. *p. 1159*

cretica 'Parkeri'; robust plant of medium height;with pinnate, dark glossy green, leathery fronds of broadly lanceolate, simple segments, with finely toothed, undulate margins. *p. 1160, 1163*

cretica 'Rivertoniana' (Dreer 1915), "Long table fern"; a bushy symmetrical form of wimsettii, and improved gauthieri; with stiff erect fresh green fronds of firm texture, the brown stems set with 4-5 pairs of lateral pinnae and terminal, the lower ones compound, all deeply cut almost to center, into pointed toothed lobes. *p. 1161, 1163*

cretica 'Wilsonii', (ouvrardii, cristata), "Fan table fern"; an excellent commercial "Table fern" of low, bushy habit; the fresh green fronds of a young plant spreading; the fertile segments tending to form a fan-shape, and forking toward tips into broad, dense crests. *p. 1161, 1163*

cretica 'Wimsettii', a popular "Table fern"; robust, variable form of medium height, making the first break into cresting away from the plain species, and desirable because of its almost leathery toughness; the slender fresh green leaf segments irregularly toothed or pointedly lobed, and some of the tips terminate in small forks or crests. *p. 1158, 1161, 1163*

cretica 'Wimsettii multiceps'; form with the generally narrow, sparsely lobed leaf segments tipped by fine crests. *p. 1160, 1163*

dentata (Trop. and So. Africa), "Sleepy fern"; bushy, large fern with broad bipinnate fronds 60-90 cm long, on straw-colored stalks; the pinnae fresh green and somewhat soft, with linear lobes finely serrate. *p. 1159*

ensiformis (Himalayas to Sri Lanka, Queensland, Samoa); slender species of small dimensions and leathery leaves of two sorts: the small, spreading sterile fronds with single or compound elliptic segments, the fertile fronds tall and straight with segments few and narrow linear, deep lacquer green and wavy-margined. *p. 1162*

ensiformis 'Evergemiensis'; attractive Belgian cultivar (1957); of small habit,with firm fronds similar to 'Victoriae' but much more variegated with silvery-white. *p. 1160*

ensiformis 'Victoriae', "Victoria fern"; an elegant, graceful little fern with both the short, broad sterile fronds and the abundant, erect, slender fertile fronds having leaflets beautifully banded white, bordered by a wavy margin of rich green. *Humid-tropical.* *p. 1159, 1161, 1824A*

flabellata: see quadriaurita 'Flabellata'.

longifolia (American Tropics); ornamental fern with long arching pinnate fronds 30-60 cm long; the somewhat leathery, dark green, slender leaflets similar to vittata, but borne at right angles or horizontally to the rachis, and jointed at their base, separating freely from the axis; the marginal teeth of the sterile pinnae are curved while serrate or of a saw-like type in vittata. *p. 1164*

longifolia 'Mariesii'; a graceful form of compact habit; with shorter pinnate fronds and narrower pinnae, borne on a freely branching rootstock; the leaflets undulated and pleasing light green. *p. 1165*

multifida (serrulata) (Japan, China), "Chinese brake"; in commercial use since 1825; it has graceful, light green fronds on short stems which have wings, gradually narrowing downward; the segments are slender-narrow, and distantly spaced. *p. 1158, 1160, 1163*

multifida (serrulata) **'Cristata';** densely bushy variety of low habit, with sturdy green foliage cut into slender segments but with tips broadly forked and crested. *p. 1163*

multifida 'Cristata compacta'; real dwarf form of the lowest habit; dense with sturdy, lacy green, highly crested sterile fronds, above which only the slightly taller erect fertile fronds protrude. *p. 1163*

multifida 'Voluta'; attractive variety with numerous pinnate fronds all with narrow linear segments recurving downward as if pendant; some of the tips crested. *p. 1163*

muricata (Trop. America); huge palm-like fern with rough, stout stalks bearing dark green fronds, consisting of three or more bipinnate branches; the pinnae deeply and evenly lobed, the lower ones conspicuously stalked; 1-1½ m or more high. *p. 1158*

quadriaurita (Tropics around the World); variable, tufted fern typically with large bipinnate fronds of thin-leathery texture, 60 to 90 cm long, on wiry, straw-colored stalks; the broad, deep green leaflets cut nearly down to the rachis into numerous parallel, oblong lobes. *p. 1158*

quadriaurita 'Argyraea' (Central India), "Silver fern"; with beautiful large, herbaceous fronds to 1 m high; the pinnae deeply lobed, in pairs along stalks, the lower ones forked, and large terminal leaflet, all attractively light to bluish-green and a center band of silvery white. *p. 1161*

quadriaurita 'Flabellata' (So. Africa to Ethiopia, Fernando Po), "Leather table fern"; an elegant, strong fern with blackish wiry stalks bearing numerous pairs of evenly pinnate, thin-leathery leaflets a bright glossy green. *p. 1161*

semipinnata (Japan, Hong Kong, Himalayas, Philippines), "Angel-wing fern"; singular-looking species bearing on erect, black wiry stalks, pairs of distantly spaced, pale green pinnae, of which the larger ones are deeply lobed only on one side, reminiscent of angels wings. *p. 1160*

serrulata: see multifida

tremula (New Zealand, Tasmania, New South Wales), "Australian bracken"; robust grower, with large, attractive, bright green, herbaceous, broad, 3-4-pinnate fronds to 1 m high and spreading; lower pinnae often compound, upper segments linear and finely crenate, on stiff brown stems. I have found this species in northern New South Wales, growing to 1 m high, in dry forest gullies. *p. 1161, 1163*

tripartita (Trop. Asia, Africa, Australia, Pacific Isl.); long-stalked large fronds branched into 3 main divisions; the lateral pinnate branches again divided, the broad pinnae deeply and regularly lobed nearly to the axis; the caudex may become 30 cm long, the stalks to 1 m, the blade 1¼m. *p. 1158*

umbrosa (New South Wales); handsome fern of robust, spreading habit; with hard, shining dark green, undulate fronds, the simple linear pinnae arranged in one terminal and up to 9 pairs, their base usually running down the stalk from one leaflet to the next. Known also as 'Ouvrardii major'. *p. 1160*

vittata (Old world Tropics or Subtropics of Africa, Asia, Europe, Australia, Polynesia); the plant usually in the trade as Pt. "longifolia"; rapid-growing, long-leafed, graceful fern with arching pinnate fronds to 75 cm long, the simple dark green leaflets are fewer, more distantly spaced and broader than in longifolia, long and tapering to a slender point, their bases running down the stem, and these pinnae are usually turned upward at an obvious short angle from the hairy stalks; the marginal teeth of the sterile pinnae are curved. *p. 1160, 1165*

PTEROCARPUS *Leguminosae* **I2LBD**

rotundifolius (So. Africa), "Roundleaf Kiaat"; flowering tree widespread in the Transvaal, with leathery leaves, and sweetly-scented red orange pea flowers in large clusters; a lovely sight when in bloom. *p. 1390*

PTEROCARYA *Juglandaceae* **I2LBM**

fraxinifolia dumosa (Caucasus, Iran), "Caucasian wing-nut"; large Asiatic deciduous tree, in the species to 30 m high, but in var. dumosa shorter and shrubby; with compound leaves, the oblong leaflets 5-8 cm long; unisexual green flowers, the male catkins short, the females longer and pendulous, 30-50 cm long and very attractive when in bloom in early summer; the nuts with rounded wings. *p. 1340*

PTEROSPERMUM *Sterculiaceae* **S2-3LBD**

acerifolium (Burma, Java), "Bayur tree"; tall evergreen tree, covered with rusty-brown wool; peltate leathery yellow-green leaves with dark veins, 15 cm dia., white hairy below; scented fleshy flowers with linear, silky sepals and yellowish petals; timber similar to teak and oak. *p. 2086*

lancifolium (E. Indies); evergreen hairy tree with leathery, long-ovate leaves; white flowers with long protruding stamens and recoiled petals, and sweetly fragrant. *Tropical.* *p. 2090*

PTEROSTYLIS *Orchidaceae* **I3LFM**

banksii (New Zealand), "Hooded orchid"; terrestrial to 45 cm high, with small underground tuber; straplike narrow-linear leaves, sheathing the stalk, bearing solitary green flowers striped with white, 5-8 cm long; the concave dorsal sepal arched forward, with the petals forming a hood or helmet; the lateral sepals running into long slender tails; linear lip. *Humid-subtropic.* *p. 1805*

baptistii (Australia: Queensland to Victoria); handsome terrestrial of slender habit; flat basal rosette of leaves with prominent network of veins; long wiry stalks 20 to 50 cm tall, with solitary hooded flowers to 8 cm long, light green with light brown bands, the dorsal sepal curving forward to a point (autumn); deciduous after bloom. *Subtropic.* *p. 1809*

curta (E. Australia); small tuberous terrestrial herb with basal rosette of ovate leaves 5-9-nerved 2½-3 cm long; 15 cm stalk bearing a usually solitary green flower 3 cm long, with sepals and petals forming a helmet, and with two tails. *p. 1805*

nutans (Eastern Australia), a "Greenhood"; interesting clustering terrestrial variable in height, from 4 to 50 cm; basal rosette of oblong, stalked leaves; solitary 4 cm green flowers bent forward with curved dorsal forming a hood and with linear tails. *p. 1809*

PTERYGODIUM *Orchidaceae* **I3HFMd**

catholicum (S. Africa); small tuberous-rooted terrestrial with leafy stems to 20 cm high; fleshy succulent,lanceolate leaves clasping the stem; axillary and toward apex with small greenish-yellow flowers. *p. 1808*

PTYCHORAPHIS *Palmae* **S3LFM**

singaporensis (Malaya); clustering feather palm with slender, black and ringed cane-like stems to 4 m high and 4 cm dia., suckering from the ground; from a prominent crown-shaft the 1-1½ m pinnate fronds, with narrow, straight, alternate leaflets 20 cm long; yellow flowers, and small red fruit. *p. 1898*

PTYCHOSPERMA *Palmae* **S2LFM**

angustifolium (New Guinea?); clustering feather palm with slender, ringed stems, topped by a crown of gracefully arching pinnate fronds, the broad leaflets toothed and jagged across apex as if bitten off. *p. 1898*

elegans (Seaforthia elegans) (Queensland), "Solitaire palm"; handsome solitary feather palm to 6 m tall, with gracefully slender trunk, topped by 6 to 8 rather short pinnate fronds 1 to 2 m long; about 20 pairs of bright green pinnae, cut off and jagged at apex; bushy, white, fragrant flowers, and small bright red fruits. *Tropical.* *p. 1898, 1900*

macarthurii (Actinophloeus, Kentia) (New Guinea), "Hurricane palm"; suckering feather palm with several slender grayish trunks to 8 m high; pinnate leaves in a sparse crown, the pinnae glossy-green and rather soft, with the apex jagged and toothed as if bitten off; fruit bright red. *Tropical.* *p. 1895, 1900, 1901*

PTYCHOSPERMA: see also Archontophoenix

PULMONARIA *Boraginaceae* **C2LFM**

saccharata (So. Europe), "Lungwort", or "Bethlehem sage"; clustering perennial herb with creeping rootstock, 30-40 cm high, with stalked ovate basal leaves, bristly hairy, dark green, freely spotted and blotched with silvery-white; clusters of funnel-shaped flowers first rose then blue; fairly hardy. *Subtropic.* *p. 510*

PUNICA *Punicaceae* **•I2LBD**

granatum (S.E. Europe to Himalayas), "Pomegranate"; shrub or small tree becoming 6 m high, with shining oblong leaves 2 to 8 cm long; flowers orange-red, with crumpled petals, the calyx purple, and with its lobes persistent on the developing edible fruit, growing as large as an orange, outside deep yellow to red, inside the membrane-covered sections contain numerous small seeds which are imbedded in the juicy crimson, fleshy pulp, of delicious, somewhat acid flavor; fruit going back in ancient Oriental history; Solomon sang of it in the Old Testament, and Theophrastus described it in 300 B.C. as a valuable fruit. The juice is used in making grenadine syrup, as well as a refreshing, aromatic drink. *Subtropic.* *p. 1953, 1982*

granatum 'Alba plena'; semi-deciduous woody shrub with spiny branches, 2-3 m high; shiny fresh green to reddish, narrow-elliptic papery leaves 3 to 8 cm long; the charming flowers white and fully double, 5 cm across. *p. 1952*

granatum 'Legrellei'; popular, free-blooming, ornamental form of the pomegranate tree, distinguished by its fully-double, showy flowers of coral-red, striped yellowish-white outside, and pendant at the end of wiry branches, dense with lanceolate, wavy-margined, glossy leaves. *p. 1982*

granatum 'Nana' (Iran to Himalayas), "Dwarf pomegranate"; a miniature version of the pomegranate tree, in form of a shrub to 2 m high; with shining vivid-green, narrow leaves, and scarlet flowers 3-4 cm long; with salmon calyx at end of thin branchlets, producing small orange-red fruit to 5 cm dia.with hard rind and juicy, edible pulp; attractive as a small potplant. *Subtropic.* *p. 1955, 1982*

PUYA *Bromeliaceae* **I2HBD**

alpestris (Chile); dense rosette of narrow spiny-margined leaves shiny light gray-green and recurving, 2-3 cm wide, silvery-gray beneath; branched inflorescence, with metallic blue flowers and orange anthers, in up to 20 spikes to 1 m high. *Subtropic.* *p. 578, 580, 581*

alpestris 'Marginata' (Chile), "Banded puya"; dense rosette of narrow, stiff and spiny, recurving leaves shiny light gray green banded light yellow at the margins, silvery gray beneath; branched inflorescence to 120 cm high, with metallic blue-greenish flowers and orange anthers, in up to 20 branches. *p. 581*

berteroniana (Chile); clump-forming terrestrial rosette, often confused in the trade with P chilensis, but of smaller size; the flexible, pendant leaves to 1 m long and 1 cm wide at base, glossy light green above; gray-white tomentose beneath, easily rubbed off; the margins with small, softer hook spines; flowers greenish-blue with protruding orange anthers; carried in pyramidal panicles on 60-90 cm stalks. *p. 578, 579, 581*

chilensis (Chile); dense rosette of narrow thin-leathery channeled leaves grayish green, silvery beneath; large scattered spines forming in older plants; flowers greenish-yellow on branching stalk. *p. 513, 551, 579*

ferruginea: see Pitcairnia

laxa (Argentina, Bolivia); terrestrial from dry stony area at 1500 m alt.; open rosette with spreading, fleshy leaves 30 to 60 cm long, densely covered with white hairs, the surface channeled and margins brown-spiny; inflorescence to 1 m high, loosely branched; the flowers with greenish sepals and violet petals. *p. 580*

mirabilis (Bolivia, Argentina); smallish rosette of numerous grass-like linear leaves 60-70 cm long and 1 cm wide, gray green above, gray-scaly beneath, and with spines at margins; the floral stalk 90 cm long, with large tubular greenish to white flowers 10 cm long. *p. 581*

nana (Bolivia); dense rosette of narrow lanceolate lax leaves to 60 cm long and 2½ cm wide, dark green with spiny margins, the underside densely gray scaly; the inflorescence nested in the center of the leaves in a cushion-like pinkish head of bracts with bluish-green flowers 4 cm long, and resembling the female inflorescence of Cycas revoluta,15 cm across. *p. 581*

raimondii (Cordilleras of Bolivia, Perú); a giant plant, and found on the Puna to 3,800 m altitude; dense rosette with bayonet-shaped, leathery leaves grass-green but covered with white scales especially beneath, and edged with brown spines; forms trunk and, when about 150 years old, develops 5 m inflorescence, with thousands of whitish flowers within green bracts. Growing to 12 m tall, this is probably the largest monocarpic herb, dying after producing flowers and seed. *Subtropic.* *p. 578, 579*

spathacea (Argentina); large spiny terrestrial rosette with narrow straplike leaves; the inflorescence a large branched panicle with stalk, branches and bracts rosy red, and the flower petals violet. *p. 580*

PYCNOSPATHA *Araceae* **S3LFM**

arietina (soerensenii) (Thailand), "Dragon-lily"; tuberous tropical aroid with dissected leaf on long stalk mottled gray and purple; the short-stalked spathe tubular and almost completely closed, curving at apex and dark-colored. *p. 228*

PYCNOSTACHYS *Labiatae* **I3HBM**

caerulea (Madagascar); tropical herbaceous plant to 50 cm high, grown in gardens as an annual; 4-angled stem with lanceolate, toothed leaves 5-8 cm long, arrayed in a rosette just under the stout cylindric inflorescence crowded with tubular blue flowers; the upper part of the spike dense with awl-shaped spiny teeth. *p. 1356*

dawei (Africa: Uganda), "Blue porcupine"; stout perennial 1½-2 m high, with opposite, lanceolate pubescent, toothed leaves to 30 cm long; flowers in whorls in dense terminal spikes to 12 cm long, cobalt-blue; calyx teeth needle-like. *p. 1347, 1350, 1356*

urticifolia (Trop. Africa); herbaceous perennial 1 m or more high, with ovate leaves to 10 cm long, toothed at margins, downy beneath; bright blue two-lipped flowers in a dense ovate 8 cm spike. *p. 1350*

PYRACANTHA *Rosaceae* **•C-I2LBD**

coccinea 'Lalandei'; a robust cultivar of the "Firethorn" from So. Europe and Asia Minor; evergreen, woody, thorny shrub with oval oblong, shiny, leathery, dark green leaves, finely toothed; the numerous small, white flowers followed by dense clusters of waxy, orange-red berries. *Temperate.* *p. 1996*

crenulata flava (Himalayas, Yunnan), "Yellow firethorn"; evergreen thorny shrub dense with leathery green, obovate leaves to 5 cm long, wavy-toothed at margins; small white flowers in clusters, followed by showy masses of glossy yellow berries. *p. 2001*

x duvalii; seedling of P. koidzumii (formosana) from Taiwan; very vigorous "Red firethorn"; of spreading habit and growing to 3 m tall, evergreen with grayish pubescent branchlets; narrow oblong leathery leaves and dense with white flowers, and small scarlet-red depressed-globose berries keeping well into late season. *p. 1996, 1999*

fortuneana 'Graberi' (crenulata yunnanensis), "Chinese firethorn"; this evergreen shrub from China has been developed into outstanding forms such as 'Graberi', a vigorous grower with narrow, oblanceolate, thick-leathery leaves rounded at the apex, and great clusters of large orange-red berries somewhat appressed to stem, from September to winter. *p. 1996*

koidzumii 'Victory' (crenato-serrata cv.), an excellent "Red firethorn"; robust evergreen shrub of Chinese (Taiwan) origin, becoming large and spreading to 2 m with thorny, rambling branches and deep green leathery foliage; very ornamental as a smaller container plant bearing large clusters of glistening brilliant, scarlet, long-lasting 1 cm berries into winter and for Christmas. Small white, fragrant flowers in May, on spurs along wood of last year's growth. Timely decorator for the Christmas season, the branches often trained into pyramids or against trellis. Not as frost-hardy as P. coccinea. *Warm temperate.* *p. 1996*

PYRENOGLYPHIS *Palmae* **S3LFM**

concinna (Brazil); small suckering feather palm, with thin, bamboo-like stems; spiny, and with attractive pinnate leaves, the grayish-green leaflets well-spaced on their axis. *p. 1870*

PYROSTEGIA *Bignoniaceae* **S2LBD**
venusta (Bignonia ignea) (Brazil, Paraguay), "Flame vine" or "Flaming trumpet"; gorgeous flowering woody vine high-climbing by tendrils over fence and roof-tops, with leaves of 2 or 3 ovate leaflets; red-orange slender-tubed flowers 8 cm long, in heavy clusters hanging brilliantly from eaves or arbors. *Tropical.* *p. 498, 502*

PYRRHOCACTUS *Cactaceae* **I1LBD**
tuberisulcatus (Chile: Valparaiso); globular light green cactus with 16-20 ribs, notched into low tubercles, and with a prominent chin below the areoles, 10-12 radial spines, 4-5 stronger, stiff centrals to 2½ cm long, brownish and zoned; 4 cm funnel-shaped flowers, the petals brownish yellow with red band. *p. 702*

PYRROSIA *Polypodiaceae (Filices)* **I3HNM**
abbreviata (Cyclophorus) (Java, Sumatra); small fern epiphytic on trees, with creeping rhizome; dense with stalked leathery oblongate leaves 6-15 cm long, appressed-hairy when young; brown-hairy beneath. *p. 1106*
lingua (Cyclophorus; Diplazium lanceum in hort.) (Japan, China, Vietnam, Taiwan), "Tongue fern"; creeping fern close to Asplenium, with thin scaly rhizome; stalked lanceolate, wavy, tomentose leaves, 22 cm long, covered with gray felt beneath, becoming pendant; in horticulture as Diplazium lanceum. *Humid-subtropic.* *p. 1155*
macrocarpa (Southern Asia); tufting fern with creeping, scaly rhizome, bearing stalked, narrow lanceolate, thick-leathery, almost linear fronds to 50 cm long, the underside densely covered with felt; sporangia very big, in two rows in the upper half. *p. 1155*
stigmosa (Cyclophorus) (Java, Celebes, Malaya, So. India, Sri Lanka); epiphytic fern with short-creeping rhizome; grooved stalks bearing leathery, dark green lanceolate fronds 20-50 cm long and 2½-8 cm wide, densely tomentose beneath. *p. 1155*

PYRUS *Rosaceae* **C2LBMh**
communis (Europe and W. Asia), "European pear"; grown in America since the earliest settlement; large long-lived deciduous, hardy tree with oval or ovate, dark green leathery leaves; flowers 3 cm across, white sometimes tinged pink, appearing with the first foliage; fruit pyriform and edible, with gritty cells, in many sweet-tasting varieties. Dwarf pears or espaliers can be obtained by grafting on quince. *Temperate.* *p. 1998*
kawakamii (Taiwan), "Evergreen pear"; shrub or tree to 10 m high, evergreen in California, partially deciduous in colder zones; branchlets drooping, at end the large glossy, leathery, obovate leaves to 10 cm long or more; few white flowers; small inedible fruit, seldom seen. Willowy young branches are often fastened to trellis for ornamental espalier. *Warm temperate.* *p. 1998*

QUAMOCLIT *Convolvulaceae* **I2-3LBD**
lobata (Mina) (Mexico), "Star-glory"; annual twining herb vigorously climbing to 6 m, with leaves deeply 3-lobed 8 cm across; brilliant boat-shaped baggy 5-angled flowers fiery scarlet-red when in bud, when opening changing to creamy-yellow and orange; stamens and style protruding; borne on one side of long-stalked axillary racemes. *Tropical.* *p. 854*
pennata (Ipomoea quamoclit) (Trop. America; naturalized in Southern U.S.), "Cypress-vine"; twining herb to 6 m, with wiry stems and pinnate leaves, the lobes cut into thread-like segments; flowers scarlet, with slender tube and flaring 5-lobed limb, 5 cm long. *p. 854*

QUERCUS *Fagaceae* **C-I2LBD**
agrifolia (California), "California live oak"; great, picturesque wide-spreading tree to 30 m high, more or less evergreen; with rough black bark, and long, persistent, dark green, hard-leathery, oval, convex leaves scalloped or lobed, and with spiny teeth, 8 cm long, light green and glossy beneath; the conical 2 cm acorns partly enclosed in the silky cup. *Subtropic.* *p. 1062, 1063*
alba (U.S.: Maine, Minnesota to Florida and Texas), "White oak"; magnificent deciduous, round-headed hardwood tree 30 m high; stout trunk to 2 m thick, with light gray bark; obovate 5-9-lobed leaves to 22 cm long, bright green above, glaucous beneath; 2 cm acorns enclosed ¼ in woody cup; foliage turning wine-red in autumn; hardy. (C) *p. 1062*
lobata (California), the "Valley oak" or "California white oak"; large and mighty deciduous tree of inland California, reaching 25 m or more and equal spread; the massive trunk and twisted limbs with ashy gray, checkered bark; deeply lobed leathery green leaves 8-10 cm long; the female flowers developing the acorn nuts. *p. 1062*
suber (So. Spain, Portugal, No. Africa), the "Cork oak"; an evergreen tree related to our California "Live oak"; to 15 m or more high, with broad round-topped head and thick, deeply furrowed bark which is spongy and possessing elastic properties; shining dark green, ovate 8 cm leathery leaves with toothed margins, grayish-tomentose beneath. Their light-weight bark is removed in sections around the Western Mediterranean for use in insulation and other economic purposes, and trees are selected in rotation or when ready for the stripping of their grayish bark down to the cambium layers about every 8 to 10 years, following which it grows back again without seriously harming the tree. A curiosity plant which may be grown in containers. *p. 1062, 1063*

QUESNELIA *Bromeliaceae* **I-S1HFM**
arvensis (São Paulo); formal rosette of leathery green leaves with gray cross-bands and black spines; inflorescence a thick stalk with dense head of rose-pink bracts and blue and white flowers. *Subtropic.* *p. 513, 558*
humilis (Brazil); tubular rosette of few linear, tough-leathery gray-green leaves 25-30 cm long and 2½ cm wide, weakly spiny at margins; the stalked inflorescence with oblong, rosy-red bracts nearly enclosing the light purple flowers. *p. 580*
liboniana (Billbergia quintitissima) (Brazil: Bahia, Rio); tubular plant with stiff-leathery concave leaves dark green, edged with small brown spines, reverse banded with gray scales; inflorescence few-flowered in simple spike, the sepals coral red, petals dark blue. *p. 513, 580*
marmorata (Aechmea) (Brazil: Espirito Santo to São Paulo); called "Grecian vase" because of its tall formal shape, to 50 cm high and 5 cm wide, the ends of leaves recurved, bluish and mottled green and maroon; arching spike, colorful with rose-pink bract leaves and tubular blue flowers. *p. 512, 519, 581*
quesneliana (French Guiana); large regular rosette of fresh-green leaves banded gray beneath; inflorescence a gray stalk with sheathing white bract leaves boldly topped by a cylindrical head of shingled, papery, rosy-red bracts dusted white, red calyx leaves, and petals white with blue edge. *p. 530*
testudo (So. Brazil); spreading rosette with leathery glossy light green, channeled leaves to 60 cm long by 3 cm wide, grayish scaly beneath; the margins dense with fine brown spines; small erect brush-like inflorescence with surrounding bracts rosy-pink, flowers electric blue. *Subtropic.* *p. 581*

QUIABENTIA *Cactaceae* **S3LBD**
zehntneri (Pereskia) (Brazil: Bahia); tall growing shrub to 3 m, with thick main stem; densely covered with long white needle spines from the white-felty areoles; branches with fleshy, 4 cm ovate leaves; vivid red flowers to 8 cm across; tubercled 7 cm fruit. *p. 621*

QUISQUALIS *Combretaceae* **S2-3LFM**
indica (Burma to Philippines), "Rangoon creeper"; tropical clambering shrub with liana-like, vining, woody stems; soft, light green, pubescent leaves, and beautiful, drooping, fragrant flowers having slender green tube 8 cm long, with petals red when in bud, opening white but later changing to pink and crimson-red; very fragrant. *Tropical.* *p. 777, 778*
mussaendiflora (Trop. Africa); showy evergreen spreading bush with wiry branches; opposite oval, yellowish-green rugose leaves; toward branch tips the striking inflorescence of brilliant coral-red, ovate bract leaves 12 cm long; groups of small tubular, yellow flowers, in their axils later followed by 5-winged yellow fruits with coral margins. *p. 778*

RABIEA *Aizoaceae* **I1LBD**
albinota (Cape Prov.); dwarf succulent rosette of 6-8 triangled, saber-shaped leaves 2½-9 cm long, flat on top, covered with flecks of whitish warts; 4 cm yellow flowers. *p. 77*

RAFFLESIA *Rafflesiaceae* **S3LFM**
arnoldii (Sumatra), the world's largest flower; enormous fleshy parasite, with a solitary giant flesh-colored flower 1 m across, rising from a superficial rhizome, and without leaves; the foul-smelling inflorescence weighs 7 kg, the central cup is intense purple and holds 6 litres of water. Its seeds lodge in the surface roots of Cissus angustifolia where they penetrate the bark and germinate. *Humid-tropical.* *p. 1991*

RAMONDA *Gesneriaceae* **C2-3HFD**
myconii (syn. pyrenaica) (Pyrenées); small alpine perennial with toothed, deep green, softly hairy, wrinkled 6 cm leaves in a rosette; showy violet or rosy-lavender flowers with broad, overlapping lobes and yellow eye, spreading 2 cm wide. *Warm-temperate.* *p. 1259*
nathaliae (Yugoslavia, Bulgaria); basal rosette of small obovate, crinkled hairy, deep green leaves, with wavy-toothed margins, about 5 cm long, in an overlapping, flat pattern; densely hairy stalks to 12 cm high, bear 1-3 lavender-blue, 4 to 6-lobed flowers, with orange-yellow eye, 3½ cm across; fairly hardy. *Warm temperate.* *p. 1259*

RANDIA *Rubiaceae* **S3LFM**
macrantha (Africa: Sierra Leone); climbing evergreen shrub or small tree 3-9 m, with obovate membranous leaves slightly hairy beneath; solitary fragrant, pale yellow flowers with long corolla tube gracefully pendant, to 30 cm long, and spreading limb, in June. *p. 2013*
maculata (Rothmannia longiflora) (W. Africa: Sierra Leone); small unarmed tropical tree to 4 m tall, with shining green, quilted and undulate leaves; solitary tubular purple flowers with white spreading lobes, the corolla tube 5 cm long, and sometimes downy. *Tropical.* *p. 2024*

RANGAERIS *Orchidaceae* **I3OFD**
amaniensis (Kenya, Tanzania), "Nairobi orchid"; vandaceous, woody epiphyte with long twisting, scaly stem carrying 2 ranks of slightly folded, leathery linear leaves 6-10 cm long; very floriferous with horizontal axillary racemes of 2½ cm pure white flowers with narrow sepals and petals, pointed lip and long tail-like spur; deep red spot in center; slightly scented. *p. 1814*

RANUNCULUS *Ranunculaceae* **C2-3LBMd**

asiaticus (S.E. Europe, Syria, Iran), "Persian buttercup"; slender perennial with tuberous roots; alternate leaves, divided into narrow segments, on erect stalks, each bearing 1-4 flowers, usually double; many various colors, the wild type yellow; cultivated varieties white, yellow, orange, pink, scarlet, crimson, (spring). *Subtropic* *p. 1984*

asiaticus 'Picotee'; compact-growing cultivar of the Tecolote strain with giant 8 cm double and ruffled flowers pink, red, rose, orange, white, yellow, and with picotee edge. *p. 1983*

RAPHIA *Palmae* **S3LFW**

farinifera (monbuttorum) (Uganda), a "Raffia palm"; beautiful, gregarious feather palm of the swampy tropical rainforest, to 12 m high, with short, thick trunk sometimes to 6 m; very showy, plumy and gracefully arching pinnate fronds to 8 m long, the large midrib with long flexible, glossy dark green leaflets 3 cm wide, fluttering in the wind; the female trees with pendulous terminal inflorescence, bearing cone-like fruit 10 cm long covered with shiny brown scales. After flowering the tree will die. *p. 1909*

gaertneri (West Africa: Guinea Coast, Cameroun, Angola); large clustering feather palm freely suckering, with short, stout trunk but with typically long, giant pinnate fronds, their bases forming a false stem; the lax leaflets yellowish-green. *p. 1904*

pedunculata (Madagascar); giant feather palm without trunk; tall erect pinnate fronds 5 m or more long, the glossy dark green, narrow leaflets set almost at right angles to midrib. Photographed in the collection of Heidelberg University Botanic Garden, Germany. *Tropical.* *p. 1903*

ruffia (pedunculata), (Madagascar, Tanzania), "Raffia palm"; according to Dr. H. Moore, this well-known feather palm may be properly R. farinifera; monoecious suckering palm to 21 m high, with stout trunk 2-7 m bearing the gigantic pinnate fronds like gracefully arching, somber black-green plumes 12-15 m long; the leaflets to 1½ m long, whitish-powdery beneath, furnishing when split, the tough raffia fiber of commerce; inflorescence 5 m long, and brown scaly fruit. *p. 1903, 1904*

taedigera (So. America: Amazon region; C. America: Panama); handsome raffia palm from humid, swampy places near the coast, with 2-2½ m multiple trunk to 75 cm thick bearing enormous plume-like pinnate fronds 15 m long, leaflets 1½ m long, 6 cm wide, with weak spines. *p. 1904*

vinifera (Equatorial Africa: Nigeria), "African wine palm"; a moderate-sized species with feathery, pinnate fronds 2-2½ m long, the long pendant deep, shining green leaflets spiny; the elliptic, 8 cm fruit with overlapping, deeply grooved chestnut scales. A pleasant wine is made from the sap, obtained by cutting off the young flower stalks. *p. 1903, 1904*

RAPHIDOPHORA: see under RHAPHIDOPHORA

RAPHIOLEPIS *Rosaceae* **I-C2LBM**

indica (So. China), "Indian hawthorne"; attractive, dense evergreen shrub to 1½ m high; with alternate, shining leathery, lanceolate, 8 cm leaves bluntly toothed, and loose clusters of small pink flowers blooming intermittently from February to August, more profusely through winter. *p. 1993*

indica 'Enchantress'; "India-hawthorne"; charming evergreen shrub to 1½ m high; dark green, leathery elliptic leaves to 8 cm long, bluntly toothed at margins; large pretty flowers appleblossom-like, rosy-pink with white eye, 2½ cm across, in loose clusters, carried in profusion from late winter to late spring and into summer, dark blue berries follow. A compact-growing form of the species indica which has smaller white flowers tinged with pink and comes from South China. *Subtropic.* *p. 2001*

indica 'Springtime'; vigorous popular variety with dense, glossy foliage, covered continuously from fall to spring with large, rich pink clusters of blooms. *p. 1995*

umbellata ovata (Japan), "Yeddo-hawthorn"; shrub of rounded shape, 2-3 m high, with obovate thick-leathery, shining green, 8 cm leaves; pure white, fragrant, 2 cm flowers, in hairy terminal clusters, followed by small blue-black fruit. *p. 1993*

RATHBUNIA *Cactaceae* **S2LBD**

alamosensis (Sonora), "Rambling ranchero"; olive-green, columnar plant, to 3 m high, and 8 cm dia., erect at first but becoming bent and rooting at tips; 5-8 irregular ribs, the recessed areoles armed with awl-like whitish spines; diurnal flowers scarlet. *p. 638*

RAUWOLFIA (RAUVOLFIA in Hortus 3) *Apocynaceae* **I-S2LBD**

hirsuta (canescens) (Jamaica, West Indies); tropical shrub with slender, cane-like branches, long obovate, pubescent leaves opposite or in whorls; tubular flowers pink with spreading lobes; followed by globular blackish berries. *p. 144*

serpentina (India, Pakistan, Sri Lanka, Burma, Thailand to Java); shrubby drug plant, collected for its thickened roots and leaves, used in India as antidote against snake bite and stings of insects; long elliptic leaves, and whitish flowers in axillary stalked clusters; the corolla a slender tube with spreading lobes. *p. 144*

verticillata (chinensis), (China); smooth evergreen shrub, 2 m high with long-elliptic, glossy green, thin-leathery leaves in whorls; the little trumpet flowers with long tubes and flaring whitish segments scarcely 1 cm across; berry-like red fruit. *Warm-temperate.* *p. 144*

RAVENALA *Musaceae* **S2-3LBM**

guyanensis (Pará, Guyana, Llanos de Colombia); the western hemisphere counterpart to R. madagascariensis, of more dwarf habit, and which I found in swampy jungles in the interior of Surinam as well as along the Amazon; usually only 1½-2 m high, with long-stalked, thick-leathery leaves; large boatshaped bracts with white flowers; the seed-covering scarlet. *Tropical.* *p. 1589, 1595, 1598*

madagascariensis (Madagascar), "Travelers tree"; striking tree with palm-like trunk to 30 m high, topped by leathery, banana-like leaves with pale midrib, arranged like a fan on long petioles, and sheltering the great flower bracts with white blooms and sky-blue seed; the cup-shaped leaf bases hold healthy drinking water for thirsty travelers.
Tropical. *p. 1588, 1589, 1595, 1599*

REBUTIA *Cactaceae* ***C-I2LBD**

deminuta (Aylostera) (No. Argentina); clustering diminutive globes with spiralled tubercles and numerous white or brown rigid spines; free flowering orange red; keep dry and cold to induce blooming; water when buds show. *Arid-subtropic.* *p. 680*

dumcresmaniana (So. America); globular plant with spiral rows of pointed tubercles set with thin, spreading spines; small golden funnel-shaped flowers in a circle from the sides; this may be a yellow form of duursmaiana. *p. 680*

duursmaiana (Mediolobivia) (Argentina); small globular plants of 4 cm dia., forming clusters; dark green tinged reddish, with about 15 spiral rows of tubercles covered with bristly white spines; flowers orange-red. *p.680*

fiebrigii (Aylostera), (Bolivia), "Crown cactus"; small globose to cylindrical, clustering plant; spiralled tubercles, with white hairlike spines; vermilion-red flowers. *Arid-subtropic.* *p. 679*

haagei (No. Argentina); small globular plant to 4½ cm dia., from the Andes at 3900 m altitude; freely clustering, green to reddish, tubercles in 10 spiral rows, with bristly radials; flowers clear pink. *p. 679*

hyalacantha (No. Argentina: Salta); a "Crown cactus"; small depressed globular green body, with spirally arranged knobs topped by fine whitish spines; starry, pretty flowers vivid red. *p. 682*

krainziana (Andes of So. America); attractive small globular plant with depressed apex, dark green; the acute tubercles dense, and arranged in spirals neatly set with white radials; magnificent flowers 6 cm across, pillar-box red with wide recurved petals. *p. 679*

kupperiana (Aylostera) (Bolivia); small globe with depressed top; glaucous gray, acute tubercles in about 20 rows covered with thin spines; grows to 10 cm high but blooms freely even as a tiny 2½ cm plant, with showy scarlet flowers. *Arid-subtropic.* *p. 640A, 679, 680, 681*

marsoneri (No. Argentina); light green, flattened globular body to 5 cm across; the knobs topped by small whitish radial spines; large flowers 4 to 5 cm dia., golden yellow, inside shaded orange. *p. 682*

minuscula (N.W. Argentina); tiny bright green flattened globe to 5 cm dia., and becoming tufted; tubercles in many spirals, very small whitish spines; bears its scarlet-red flowers freely, 6 cm long, lasting several days; *Arid-subtropic.* *p. 618, 679*

pseudodeminuta (Argentina: Salta); little globes, freely clustering around the base, 5 cm thick, grass-green; the prominent tubercles set with 11 radials and 2-3 central spines all glassy-white tipped brown; flowers golden yellow shading to red. *Arid-subtropic.* *p. 680*

pseudominuscula (Argentina: Salta); from the Andes at 2700 m; tiny globe to 4½ cm dia., freely branching from the base, dark green flushed reddish; 12-16 spiral rows of nipples topped by straw-colored spines; flowers relatively large, a shining fiery red, with broad petals. *p. 681*

ritteri (So. America); small dark green globes branching around the base, the nipples arranged in spirals and set with thin white spines and a golden central; showy, wide open 5 cm carmine red flowers with maroon throat. *p. 680*

senilis (Argentina, Chile), "Fire crown"; depressed clustering, bluish globe, to 25 cm high, but usually very small; spiralled tubercles, covered with interlocking white to yellow hairlike spines; red flowers 3½ cm across. *Arid-subtropic.* *p. 680*

senilis cristata; rare crested form, the irregular pale green body covered with glossy white, bristle-like spines. *p. 620*

senilis kesselringiana (Mediolobivia) (No. Argentina); small depressed globular cactus 7 cm across, with rich green to brown-violet knobs topped by yellow spines; flowers very large, 4-5 cm dia., rosy yellow outside, yellow inside. *p. 682*

senilis stuemeriana (Argentina: Salta); from the Andes at 2700 m; a form with larger flowers bright yellow-orange and with yellow throat (photo on pg. 679 shows this plant grafted on Cereus to insure and hasten growth). *p. 679, 682*

steinbachii (Bolivia); a small "Pygmy cactus" from the Andes to 3000 m alt.; grass-green little globes sprouting around the base forming cushions; long tubercles and whitish to brown needle-like spines; slender flowers 3 cm across with scarlet red petals. *p. 682*

violacaeflora (Northern Argentina), "Rosy crown cactus"; low globe with sharp needle spines, very tiny and barely 2 cm dia.; the flowers relatively large 3 cm across, a beautiful rose-pink. *Arid-subtropic.* *p. 681*

RECHSTEINERIA: see Sinningia

REGELIA *Myrtaceae* **I2LBD**

megacephala (Western Australia); low shrub with short, broad, appressed deep green leaves in ranks; the prominent stamens and flowers carmine-red, in showy clusters. *Subtropic.* *p. 1610*

REGNELLIDIUM *Marsileaceae (Filices)* **I3(H-water)FW**

diphyllum (So. Brazil); aquatic swamp plant; from an elongated stem with dead floating leaves, of which only the stalks remain, develop aerial shoots with land-leaves which bear the sporocarps; these leaf blades are distinctly and constantly divided into a pair of roundish lobes, the veins are repeatedly forked and then united by marginal loops. Can be grown in pot standing in saucer full of water. *p. 1078, 1083*

REHDERODENDRON *Styracaceae* **I2LBM**

macrocarpum (China: Szechuan); Chinese deciduous tree 10 m or more tall, with reddish brown branchlets; elliptic, finely serrate leaves 10 cm long, reddish green with red midrib; blooms appearing before the leaves; small white bell-shaped flowers with conspicuous yellow anthers, in leafless panicles. *p. 2093*

REHMANNIA *Gesneriaceae (formerly Scrophul.)* **C2-3LFM**

elata (angulata) (C. China), "Foxglove gloxinia"; perennial herb for the cool greenhouse, with a rosette of soft, irregularly lobed, obovate leaves; a sticky-hairy, leafy stalk with showy, large, bilabiate flowers, rosy-red with yellow throat and spotted purple. Previously included with the foxgloves (Digitalis), family Scrophulariaceae. *Warm temperate.* *p. 1259*

glutinosa (China); perennial herb with downy, crenate leaves 3-8 cm long; long-stalked showy flowers 3 cm long, covered with hairs all over, trumpet-shaped with flaring lobes, deep buff-yellow, the throat purple with lines on petals, spring-blooming. By some botanists included with the Scrophulariaceae. *p. 1276*

REINECKIA *Liliaceae* **C2-3LFM**

carnea (China), "Fan grass"; creeping rhizome bearing narrow, matte-green, thin-leathery, keeled leaves 1 cm wide, in 2 ranks, clasping at base. *p. 1491*

carnea variegata (China, Japan); tufting perennial with creeping rhizome and broad, arched, grass-like, channeled 30 cm leaves arranged with military precision alternately to left and right in two orderly ranks, fresh-green strongly banded white; fragrant flesh-pink flowers. *p. 1480*

REINHARDTIA *Palmae* **S3HFM**

gracilis gracilior (Chiapas, B. Honduras), "Little window palm"; very attractive diminutive palm, 1-1½ m high, with windows in its leaves; slender, multiple trunks 6 mm thick, with waxy green bilobed foliage with elevated ribs and apertures in the leaf plane adjoining the midrib, each leaf divided into 4 pinnae, the apex coarsely toothed as if chewed off. *p. 1901*

simplex (Honduras to Panama); attractive small palm from shady equatorial forests with cane-like stem; usually not taller than 1 m, and clustering with age; small undivided leaves with pinnate ribs, toothed at margins. *p. 1906*

REINWARDTIA *Linaceae* **I2-3LBM**

indica (trigyna) (No. India), "Yellow flax"; bushy, shrubby plant to 1 m high, with obovate, membranous, dark green leaves, and large, golden-yellow, cupped flowers. *p. 1515*

REMUSATIA *Araceae* **S3LFM**

vivipara (Himalayas, India); tuberous herb with a scaly bulb; long slender stalks supporting a peltate, ovate-cordate, thin-leathery leaf 30-40 cm long, dark green with pale main veins; inflorescence a spike of distant clusters of flowers with creamy-yellow spathe. *p. 280, 282*

x RENANOPSIS *Orchidaceae* **S3OFM**

'Lena Rowold' (Renanthera storiei x Vandopsis lissochiloides); showy bigeneric hybrid; inflorescence an arching, branched raceme dense with waxy crimson-red to coppery flowers (Kirsch - Honolulu 1948). *p. 1828*

x RENANSTYLIS *Orchidaceae* **S3OFM**

'Queen Emma' (Rhynchostylis gigantea x Renanthera storiei); showy bigeneric hybrid of vandaceous habit, with long pendulous raceme dense with flowers brilliant orange spotted with maroon, the tiny lip deep purple. *p. 1809*

x RENANTANDA *Orchidaceae* **S3OFM**

'Seminole' (Vanda denisoniana x Renanthera monachica); lovely bigeneric hybrid with stout stem, dense with long arching leaves in 2 ranks; the waxy flowers buttercup yellow with pink tips, and spotted with red (summer). *p. 1813*

sladdenii (Renanthera imschootiana x Vanda tricolor); vandaceous bigeneric with ranked strap-leaves along scandent stem, and axillary raceme 30-38 cm long, with flowers all orange-colored, shading to ochre; April-May. *p. 1815*

RENANTHERA *Orchidaceae* **I-S3OFM**

imschootiana (Assam, Burma, Vietnam); brilliant epiphyte with short leaves along the erect stem; the branching inflorescence arching, to 60 cm long, with numerous showy 6 cm flowers, the small dorsal and the petals yellow, spotted scarlet, the large lower sepals scarlet-red, lip yellow marked red, (May to July blooming in the Northern Hemisphere). *Subtropic.* *p. 1812*

monachica (Burma), "Fire orchid"; colorful epiphyte with stiff leafy stems, short mottled leaves and an arching raceme of orange-yellow, spreading flowers 3 cm across, marked with blotches and bars of fiery-red, (April). *Tropical.* *p. 1812*

storiei (Philippines); showy epiphyte with stems to 4 m long, the fleshy leaves arranged in 2 ranks; inflorescence 60 cm long, with many 6 cm flowers, linear dorsal and petals orange mottled with crimson, the broader lower sepals dark crimson with lighter spots, lip red marked yellow, (March, Oct.). (S) *p. 1812, 1814*

'Tom Thumb' (R. monachica x imschootiana); small plant of compact habit, with ranked leathery leaves along stout stem; long wiry stalk bearing miniature flowers fiery-red with the beautiful petals of imschootiana; spring blooming *p. 1814*

x RENANTHOPSIS *Orchidaceae* **S3OFM**

'Jan Goo' (Renanthera monachica x Phalaenopsis sanderiana); most attractive bigeneric, of habit resembling phalaenopsis and floral raceme like renanthera; small starry flowers resembling phalaenopsis, in pinkish orange. *p. 1814*

RENEALMIA *Zingiberaceae* **S3LFM**

ventricosa (Cuba); tropical aromatic perennial with fleshy rhizome, and leafy stems 1-1½ m tall; foliage lanceolate and leathery, glossy dark green with pale midrib; white flowers 4 cm long in tight head subtended by broad obovate bracts pale green with yellowish margins and stripes. *p. 2138*

RENEALMIA: see also Alpinia

RESEDA *Resedaceae* **C2-3LFM**

odorata (No. Africa, Egypt), "Mignonette"; branching herb, at first upright but becoming spreading, with oblanceolate leaves and yellowish-white, inconspicuous flowers having contrasting saffron-red anthers, in pyramidal, terminal racemes; much loved for their sweet fragrance. *Subtropic.* *p. 1982*

RESTREPIA *Orchidaceae* **I3OFM**

lankesteri (Costa Rica); small rock-dwelling plant with reed-like stems bearing a solitary obovate leaf; flowers almost spidery with translucent thread-like dorsal sepals and petals, the lateral sepals united, pinkish white and with bold crimson lines, small yellow lip. *p. 1813*

xanthophthalma (Guatemala, Venezuela); quaint dwarf epiphyte with tufted stems each bearing a single leaf; small solitary flowers yellow, blotched red-brown, with dorsal and petals linear, the broader, lower sepals grown together (June-Aug.) (C) *p. 1812*

REUSSIA *Pontederiaceae* **S3LFW**

rotundifolia (Madagascar); creeping aquatic herb with long spreading air-filled stems floating on the water; fleshy, fresh-green kidney-shaped leaves; erect axillary brush-like inflorescence of pale purple flowers. *p. 1957*

RHABDOTHAMNUS *Gesneriaceae* **I3HFM**

solandri (New Zealand: North Island); sole gesneriad in N.Z.; twiggy shrub ½-1½ m high, with grayish hairy branches; small roundish, membranous, rough-hairy, 3 cm leaves coarsely toothed; showy 2½ cm tubular bell-shaped flowers, with oblique limb, yellowish outside and lined with red, the spreading lobes salmon red, yellow in throat and lined with dark crimson. *Subtropic.* *p. 1258, 1259*

RHADAMANTHUS *Liliaceae* **S3LFD**

secundus (Namibia); curious plant with scaly, lily-like bulb, sending up a wiry stalk bearing a raceme of small half-open bell flowers. *p. 1479*

RHAMNUS *Rhamnaceae* **I2LBD**

alaternus 'Argenteo-variegata' (So. Europe), a variegated "Buckthorn"; bushy shrub with twiggy, beige-brown stem; obovate 6 cm leaves, attractively colored green in center, margins ivory-white, slightly toothed; small greenish flowers, followed by bluish-black fruit. *Subtropic.* *p. 1988*

prinoides (So. Africa); called "Blinkblaar", because of its shining, dark green, ovate leaves; unarmed evergreen shrub or small tree, with small yellow-green flowers; followed by berries first yellow, ripening to red and nearly black; the fruit is used as a native medicine; this genus yields the purgative Cascara sagrada. *p. 1988*

RHAPHIDOPHORA (RAPHIDOPHORA) *Araceae* **S2LFM**

celatocaulis (Borneo), "Shingle plant"; also known as Marcgravia paradoxa in juvenile stage, when the rounded to heart-shaped, fleshy leaves, in climbing, cling close to tree, the blades overlapping; maturity-stage leaves 75-90 cm long, irregularly pinnately cut and perforated. *p. 277, 281, 286*

chevalieri 'Exotica' (Thailand, Cambodia, Vietnam), "Silver streak"; I found this attractive tree-climber in rainforest near Angkor, and again at the ancient Phat Buu Do pagoda near Bien Hoa in Vietnam; heart-shaped to narrow lanceolate leathery leaves dark green with silvery lateral streaks when young; succeeding older, more mature leaves plain green, and carried on winged petioles. (Scindapsus?) *p. 283*

decursiva (Ceylon to Indonesia); stem stiffly scandent, with large, glossy, dark green leaves to 60 cm long, pinnately divided to midrib; decorative, but slow and stubborn, and not easy to train. *p. 281*

"laciniosa" (Monstera subpinnata); slender but wiry creeper with daintily divided, emerald-green, leathery leaves on slender petioles, the segments attached alternately to both sides of midrib. *p. 281*

montana (W. Africa); slowly creeping and climbing tropical aroid, to several meters, with long-lanceolate, corrugated, dark glossy green leaves 20-25 cm long and 6-12 cm wide, on vaginate petioles 12-25 cm long. *p. 277*

peepla (E. Indies); tropical tree-climber with rambling stems bearing long-stalked oblique oblong leaves, dark green and of thin-leathery texture, the unequal sides deeply quilted; spathe yellowish outside, reddish inside, and yellow spadix. *p. 277*

sulcata (Thailand to Vietnam); climber of tropical forest trees with flat and angled stem; the internodes 3-4 cm apart; juvenile leaves unequal-ovate, 10-14 cm long and waxy green; the leathery maturity-stage foliage to 22 cm long and 5-6 cm wide; furled yellow spathe to 10 cm long enclosing cylindric spadix. *p. 295*

RHAPIDOPHYLLUM *Palmae* **I2LFD**

hystrix (So. Carolina to Florida and Mississippi), "Needle palm"; or "Blue palmetto"; low, bushy fan-palm, forming clusters; trunk if any usually creeping, or erect, to 1 m long, covered by remnants of leaf sheaths; petioles with black spines, 15-20 cm long, bearing palmate fronds to 1 m across, deeply divided almost to petiole, deep bluish green; silvery beneath. *p. 1904, 1906*

RHAPIS *Palmae* ***I2LHFW**

'Dwarf Japanese' (Japan); a tough little miniature suckering palm from Takaradzuka with prominently nerved leathery leaves parted into very few segments, and never known to be taller than 45 cm, David Barry believes this to be an unidentified species. *p. 1902*

excelsa (flabelliformis) (So. China), "Large lady palm"; or "Kannon-chiku" in Japan; miniature fan-palm with bamboo-like canes 3½ m or more, the thin stems densely matted with coarse fiber, forming clumps from underground suckers; the leathery leaves glossy-green divided into 3-10 broad segments; widely used in China and Japan as a durable potted palm. *p. 1876, 1901, 1904*

excelsa (flabelliformis) 'Variegata'; very attractive Japanese cultivar having palmate leathery leaves with segments banded and striped lengthwise, in gleaming, ivory-white alternating with green. *p. 1902*

humilis (So. China), "Slender lady palm"; in Japan as "Shurochiku"; clustering stems thinner and more graceful than excelsa, less vigorous, but taller to 5 m high, likewise covered with dark brown fibers; the deep green palmate leaves more slender and divided into 9 to 20, narrower segments. *Subtropic.* *p. 1876, 1912*

RHAZYA *Apocynaceae* **C-S2LBM**

orientalis (S. E. Europe, Asia Minor); small shrub 25 cm high, closely related to Vinca, with dark green elliptic leaves to 6 cm long, with pale midvein; small 2 cm clustered flowers pale lavender suffused with pink toward tip of petals and small white blotch at each side of base of petals, late summer. *p. 138*

RHEKTOPHYLLUM *Araceae* ***S1LFM**

mirabile (Nephthytis picturata) (Nigeria, Cameroon, Zaire); creeping and climbing aroid sending out long rooting internodes; the large thin-leathery, arrow-shaped, hastate leaves 20-30 cm long, dark green between the veins, variegated silvery-cream in form of a fern-leaf, becoming green in older leaves; the maturity-stage leaves broad-heartshaped in outline, 30-50 cm long and deeply sliced into broad, obtuse, glossy green segments; the 10 cm spathe green outside, red-purple inside. *Tropical.* *p. 278, 282*

RHEUM *Polygonaceae* **C2LBMd**

palmatum (China), "Chinese rhubarb"; stout perennial herb with woody rhizome, 1½ m high; large, palmately lobed leaves on cylindrical stalks; flowers deep red in large cluster. *Warm-temperate.* *p. 1955*

undulatum (rhabarbarum) (Siberia); stout perennial herb with thick, somewhat rhizomous roots, clump-forming; half-round, smooth green stalks 1-1½ m long, with large gray-green, wavy, wrinkled, round-cordate-ovate leaves; showy inflorescence of greenish-white small flowers, in clusters from stout central stalk; hardy. One of the parents of the culinary rhubarb. *p. 1956*

RHINOPHYLLUM *Aizoaceae* **I1LBD**

comptonii (Cape Prov.); clustering small succulent shrublet with pairs of slender, boat-shaped, opposite leaves flat on surface, glossy green lightly covered with rough, grayish pebbles, and tipped with bronze; flowers yellow. *p. 77*

RHIPIDOPTERIS *Polypodiaceae (Filices)* **S3OFW**

peltata (Acrostichum) (Trop. America), Peltapteris peltata in Barbara Jo Hoshizaki's Fern Growers Manual 1975; curious small epiphytic fern from humid areas; slender, wide-creeping, scaly rhizome forming colonies; the sterile, barren fronds 3-5 cm long and wide, palmately or dichotomously forked into narrow linear, green segments; by contrast, the fertile frond a long-stalked roundish 2 cm plate covered on one side with sporangia. *p. 1164*

RHIPSALIDOPSIS *Cactaceae* **S2H(fir-bark)FM**

gaertneri (Schlumbergera, Epiphyllopsis) (So. Brazil), the "Easter cactus"; bushy epiphyte with stiffish spreading branches of long flattened joints, dull green with purplish crenate margins, a few bristles at apex; starlike regular flowers, 4 cm long deep scarlet, the ovaries angled; Spring-blooming. *Tropical.* *p. 618 (as Schlumbergera), 732, 733, 734*

gaertneri makoyana (Brazil), "Cat's whiskers"; form with joints a matte bluish-green and purplish crenate margins, yellowish-brown bristles at tips; starlike flowers somewhat lighter orange-red, flowering in spring. *p. 733, 736*

x graeseri (Epiphyllopsis) (gaertneri x rosea), a free-blooming hybrid which I first saw in Brazil where it flowered in their spring (Sept.), while in the Northern hemisphere it blooms in March, indicating its being influenced by increasing day-length; wide open, starshaped regular flowers rosy-red with double row of broad petals; freely branching compact plant. *Tropical.* *p. 729, 733, 735*

x graeseri 'Rosea' (Epiphyllopsis), a lovely cultivar with flowers of a lighter shade: clear pink with the center flushed deep rose *Tropical.* *p. 640A*

rosea (Brazil: Paraná), "Dwarf Easter cactus"; densely bushy, shrub-like dwarf cactus rather erect, with small 2 cm flattened joints 3-5-angled or keeled, almost pencil-like, waxy green tinted purple, with minute hair-like bristles; small wide open regular flowers of delicate rosy pink with orchid eye, 2½ cm dia. *Subtropic.* *p. 735, 736*

RHIPSALIS *Cactaceae* ***S2H Sphag FM**

bermegensis (Argentina, Paraguay); from the collection Marnier-Lapostolle, France; cylindrical branching stems with white, round or ovoid fruit 6 mm. dia. *p. 743*

boliviana (Yungas of Bolivia); from wet forests, pendant stems flat to 4-angled, broadly crenate, and with prominent midrib; flowers yellow. *p. 744*

burchellii (Brazil: São Paulo); a "mistletoe" cactus of vigorous, free-branching habit, with pendant smooth green pencil-stems; rose-pink berry-like fruit. 'Burchellii hybrid' has fruits varying from white to red. *Tropical.* *p. 739, 741*

capilliformis (E. Brazil), "Old man's head"; epiphytic cactus with long, branching cylindrical, stringlike, hanging stems; many cream-colored flowers along sides. *Tropical.* *p. 741, 743*

cassutha (Florida to Perú to Brazil, Ceylon and trop. Africa), "Mistletoe cactus"; growing on trees or rocks hanging in many strands to 10 m; branches thin-cylindrical, somewhat bristly when young; flowers cream; with mistletoe-like white fruit, as have many Rhipsalis. In Africa, this is found on Lake Kivu, and I have seen them in eastern Kenya, and the Usambara Mts. of Tanzania. *Tropical.* *p. 618, 739, 740, 745, 747*

cereoides (Brazil); branching epiphyte with stems 2 cm thick, having 3, rarely 4 ridges, the joints to 10 cm long, and dark green, with silky areoles; 2 cm flowers with about 16 petals, the inner white, exterior ones reddish; spherical berry first olive-green then clear pink. *p. 744*

cereuscula (Uruguay to C. Brazil), "Coral cactus"; stems and branches thin and round, often erect, and crowned by a cluster of short branches, and with tiny bristles; flowers pinkish to white. *p. 739, 740, 743*

clavata (Rio de Janeiro); erect when young but soon hanging; much branched, joints all similar narrowly club-shaped, deep green; flowers white. *Tropical.* *p. 740, 745*

coriacea (Costa Rica: Cartago); woody stem round at base, with lateral thin, serrate, leaf-like branches to 4 cm wide, bearing hairy bristles at areoles; flowers with 5-10 greenish-white to pinkish petals; white fruit. *p. 742*

crispata (Brazil); branches divided into short flat, green joints 6-10 cm long, broad at both ends, irregularly indented at margins; small cream-colored flowers from areoles, followed by white fruit. *p. 742*

crispimarginata (Brazil: Guanabara); pendulous epiphyte, with main stem circular below, the terminal branches in clusters; the shining green joints flat, oblong-elliptic 4-6 cm long, indented at margins; flowers white, fruit translucent white. *p. 742*

dissimilis (São Paulo); hanging from trees, with the thin pendant stems very diverse; the glabrous branches 5-angled, and the white-bristled ones with 9 ribs; flower buds red opening to pink. *p. 740*

fasciculata (Brazil); dense little plant with erect short branches on woody stem; the branchlets club-shaped to cylindric, faintly ribbed when old, 4 mm. in dia., the areoles with fragile hairs. *p. 739*

gonocarpa (Brazil: São Paulo); much-branched plant, erect or hanging to 45 cm long; stems and joints flattened or 3-angled 30 cm long, and 3 cm wide, reddish along the wings but otherwise lively green, notched along margins; areoles without bristles; whitish flowers and 1 cm black-purple fruit. *p. 744*

grandiflora (Rio de Janeiro); bush with branches cylindrical and rather stout, wide-spreading, often reddish; flowers light rose or cream, sepals reddish. *p. 746*

hadrosoma (Brazil: São Paulo); erect, much branched bush similar to grandiflora but the forking, cylindrical, reddish branches are thicker, about 2 cm in dia., pale green, and the new areoles have a long bristle; flowers white; fruit pale pink. *p. 743*

herminiae hort.; bot. Hatiora (Brazil); dense little epiphyte, the gray main stem branching into cylindrical green joints thickened toward apex, which is covered with gray tomentum; beautiful 2½ cm pink flowers, the keeled berries olive-green. *p. 738*

heteroclada (Brazil); epiphyte with stiff, dark green cylindrical stems; 3 mm dia. branches in clusters toward top erect or pendant, purple around areoles and tips; small greenish-white flowers, and pale pink fruit. *p. 745*

houlletiana (S.E. Brazil), "Snowdrop cactus"; high altitude epiphyte with leaflike hanging, flat and thin branches, notched; flowers cream with red eye. *p. 741, 744, 746*

lindbergiana (Mountains of Rio de Janeiro, and Mt. Kilimanjaro, E. Africa); very much branched, hanging from tree-trunks in great festoons; thin cylindrical branches with numerous pinkish flowers. *p. 739*

lumbricoides (Uruguay, Paraguay); much branched bush rooting on moss-covered trunks of trees, to 1 m long, cylindrical or slightly furrowed stems 6 mm thick, light green to grayish, with woolly areoles and brownish bristles; fragrant, creamy-white flowers, and purplish-brown fruit. *p. 744*

mesembryanthemoides (Brazil: Rio), "Clumpy mistletoe cactus"; pretty epiphyte erect with two kinds of branches, long slender 10-20 cm woody joints, dense with numerous lateral, short fleshy, light green, needle-like fruiting joints, set with sparse white bristles near tips; small white flowers. *Tropical.* *p. 737, 740*

micrantha (Ecuador, No. Perú); lively green, branched hanging bush with stems obtusely angled, the joints becoming triangular or flat, 6 mm thick; the flowers with 7 white petals, and white fruit. *p. 744*

oblonga (Brazil); bright, shining green branches circular at base, leaf-like flattened and lobed higher up, the ultimate branches narrowly oblong, 5-15 cm long; ovoid white fruit. *p. 742*

pachyptera (São Paulo, Santa Catarina); growing in clumps at first upright, often hanging from trees, much jointed; joints flat to 8 cm broad, crenate, sometimes purple; flowers yellowish. *p. 736, 742*

paradoxa (São Paulo), "Chain cactus"; hanging in clusters to 1 m with many aerial roots, glossy green branches 3-winged and zigzag links; flowers white. *p. 737, 740*

penduliflora (cribrata) (S. E. Brazil); woody at base, much branched, reedy cylindrical stems, becoming hanging; terminal branches in whorls; pendulous cream flowers. *p. 740, 746*

pentaptera (Brazil, Uruguay); thin branches stiff, bright green, strongly 5-6-ribbed, indented at the areoles; flowers along stem, cream, with red back. *p. 740, 743, 746*

platycarpa (Brazil); erect branched bush to 1 m high, with leaf-like flat, crenate joints 8-30 cm long and 5 cm wide, with thick midrib and pronounced lateral nerves, dark green often reddish along margin; yellowish flower, and transparent greenish pink fruit. *p. 742*

prismatica (Brazil); epiphyte with pendent stems, slender branches somewhat angled, reddish, with tufts of bristles in the areoles; to smaller joints 2½ cm long; flowers white; pinkish fruit. *p. 744*

pulchra (Brazil: Guanabara); very much branched plant, often pendant, the bright green branches frequently in whorls, 3-4 mm. dia.; large purplish flowers; the fruit pink. *p. 745*

quellebambensis (Perú), "Red mistletoe"; epiphytic cactus with pendant thin cylindric branches, dull green with occasional purple markings and lightly grooved; glossy carmine-red berry-like fruit at the tips. *Tropical.* *p. 640A, 737, 741*

rhombea (Brazil), "Copper branch"; branches flat, leaflike joints, sometimes 3-angled, strongly crenate, dark green; flowers cream with red spots inside. *p. 741, 742, 747*

robusta (Brazil: Guanabara); large decumbent bush with lower joints mostly 3-winged; others large, thick-fleshy, broad, leaflike, dark green, to 20 cm long; flowers light yellow, tipped with red; fruit pink. *p. 742*

roseana (Colombia); densely branched epiphyte with flat stems distinctly notched; the further joints more linear 1 cm wide and 6-12 cm long, bright green, sometimes triangular; whitish flowers, and white fruit. *p. 742*

saxicola (Madagascar); circular woody stem with many club-shaped to cylindric branchlets, faintly ribbed when old, 4 mm dia., with numerous areoles, each with a cluster of fragile hairs; transparent white fruit; close to R. fasciculata, but with more hairs at the areoles, according to Britton and Rose. *p. 744*

shaferi (Paraguay); epiphyte on trees; stems at first stiff erect, later hanging, branching into thread-like joints, green, purplish at tips; numerous flowers greenish-white. *p. 746*

sulcata (Ecuador); bush to 1 m long, erect or pendant; the light green joints 20-25 cm long, 6 mm thick, and 5-angled; distant notches with areoles bearing 1 or 2 bristles; pinkish flowers. *p. 744*

teres (S. E. Brazil); dwarf bushy epiphyte with stems very much branched into thin round short joints, green blotched with red; flowers pale yellow. *p. 745, 746*

tonduzii (Costa Rica); bushy epiphyte with stems forming aerial roots, the light green branches hanging, normally 4-5-angled, 1 cm dia.; terminal joints often 3-angled or flattened; aeroles close together; small white flowers, ovoid pinkish fruit. *p. 743*

trigona (So. Brazil); much branched and hanging; slender stems alternately 3-angled, 1 cm dia.; flowers pinkish. *p. 741*

virgata (E. Brazil); stems or circular branches 1 m long and 6 mm thick, ascending or pendant; the short upper branches to 6 cm long, often with pinkish bristle; cream-colored flowers, and very small pink fruit. *p. 744*

warmingiana (Minas Gerais), "Popcorn cactus"; epiphyte with long pendant slender branches flat or sharply 3-angled and notched, blotched with purple; flowers white. *p. 741, 743*

zanzibarica (Kenya, Tanzania, Mozambique); miniature epiphyte with thin, thread-like dark green, circular branches, first erect but quickly pendant; areoles close and with fine white hairs; the depressed globular fruit, as in all Rhipsalis, sticky, adhering to birds or driftwood, and probably in this manner brought to Africa from America thousands of years ago. *Tropical.* *p. 747*

RHIZOPHORA *Rhizophoraceae* **S3HBW**

conjugata (Bruguiera) (India to Malaya, introduced to Hawaii 1922), oriental "Mangrove"; widespread evergreen shrub or tree living on tropical seashores and tidewater, forming arching stilt roots and tangled growth, spreading to build up land; thick-leathery obovate-pointed leaves, and pink, red, or yellow flowers. Transferred to Bruguiera. *p. 1991*

mangle (Florida, W. Indies to So. America), the "American mangrove" or "Red mangrove", so common along the shores and bayous of the Florida Keys; growing into small trees; producing many trunks or rooting shoots forming dense thickets by the many arching aerial roots; thick-leathery opposite, dark green leaves 5 to 15 cm long; yellow, long-stemmed flowers with 4 calyx lobes and 4 narrow hairy, pale yellow petals; fruit 3 cm long; before dropping into the wet soil, the fruit usually germinates and develops a root 30 cm long. *Humid-tropical.* *p. 1991*

mucronata (Sri Lanka and Eastern Tropics), "Four-petaled mangrove"; moderate-sized spreading tree inhabiting lagoons and tidal tropic seashores, with many aerial props forming dense and difficult tangles and stilt roots; shiny green, thick-leathery, small oval leaves, and leathery 2 cm yellowish flowers; fruit bearing one seed. Interestingly the seed germinates long before fruit is ripe, and its root gradually projects out of the fruit like a long green finger; when fruit is ripe the seedling drops into the mud and begins to sprout immediately. *p. 1991*

RHODOCHITON *Scrophulariaceae* **I3HF-BM**

volubile (Mexico), the "Purple bell-vine"; graceful vine climbing to 3 m assisted by coiling petioles, similar to Asarina but more vigorous, and usually treated as a tender annual; alternate heart-shaped downy leaves to 8 cm long, and pendulous flowers 5 cm long with tubular corolla dark blood-red and spreading bell-like calyx pale reddish, on red stems; June. *p. 2058*

RHODOCODON *Liliaceae* **I3LFDd**

urginioides (C. Madagascar); bulbous plant with long and narrow flexible leaves spreading from top of swollen base; a wiry stalk bearing a raceme of small bell-like, white flowers. *Tropical.* *p. 1476*

RHODODENDRON *Ericaceae* **C-I2HFM**

The "Rose-bays" are a large genus primarily woody evergreen shrubs of the Heath family; with big leathery leaves and stunning, rounded clusters of beautiful funnel-form flowers of good substance, highly hybridized, with many named cultivars and in colors of white, pink, red, purple and even yellow or orange; there are also others of smaller habit. As understood by botanists today, *Rhododendron* includes as subgroup many small-leaved evergreen and deciduous kinds known by long horticultural usage as Azaleas, a name now difficult to segregate on technical characters except perhaps based on hairtype on the foliage (Dr. Encke), and in Exotica listed separate from Rhododendron. "True" Rhododendrons are primarily used in garden plantings, in moist, cool situations, and some of the tender hybrids are forced for flower shows or Easter.

'Anton van Welie'; late-blooming hybrid, excellent for Easter forcing; loose grower with large elliptic, recurved, rich green leaves; large trumpet-shaped, carmine-rose flowers with red dots on pale throat, and with ruffled margins. *p. 960A, 972*

auriganum (N.E. New Guinea); strikingly colorful epiphytic evergreen which we collected in the Finisterre Mts. at 2,100 m alt. near the frost-line; clusters of large 12 cm trumpet-shaped flowers with fleshy, yellow tube and salmon-rose petal-lobes; small elliptic, leathery leaves. *p. 970, 975*

'Bow Bells' ('Corona' x williamsianum); miniature evergreen about 30 cm high, with hard-leathery, 4 cm ovate, smooth leaves, pale beneath; and clusters of 4 cm open funnel single flowers of good substance, dainty salmon-pink with red spots in throat. *Temperate.* *p. 970*

bullatum (North Burma to China); straggling evergreen shrub, often epiphytic, the shoots covered with tawny felt; the ovate leaves to 10 cm long and wrinkled, pubescent beneath; large pure white, fragrant flowers 12 cm across, conspicuously diffused with red on outside; late spring. *p. 974*

canadense (Rhodora) (No. America: Newfoundland to Pennsylvania); attractive deciduous shrub which can be seen in profuse bloom in the Pocono Mountains of N.E. Pennsylvania into May; the clustered flowers 4 cm wide, with 2-lipped corolla rosy-lavender with darker purple tips; the foliage follows after blossom time, the oval leaves 3-5 cm long, downy beneath. *Temperate. p. 974*

carneum (Upper Burma); small evergreen shrub with obovate, leathery leaves, and single flowers appleblossom pink with yellow in throat; stamens cream. *p. 974*

charitopes (Burma); small evergreen shrub to 45 cm high, with obovate leaves 2½-6 cm long, glossy green with yellowish shining scales beneath; clusters of flat bell-shaped flowers 2½ cm wide, purplish-pink spotted with crimson on upper lobes, petals waxy. *p. 970*

'Cynthia' ('Lord Palmerston'); early-flowering variety, and good for Easter forcing; pretty heads of carmine-rose flowers, lighter in the center of each petal, and with blood-red spots on upper petals. *p. 972*

'Eureka Maid' (Countess of Derby), (Pink Pearl x Cynthia); very good Easter forcing variety of more regular compact growth and with large flowers darker pink than 'Pink Pearl', pale in throat and with crimson spots on upper petal; the buds deep crimson rose, in large trusses. *Warm temperate. p. 971*

x gandavense (Azalea), "Ghent hybrid"; a hybrid class of winter-hardy, deciduous azaleas of the European Rhododendron luteum and the American occidentalis; beloved in gardens for their bright colored, fragrant flowers on the leafless shrubs; late-blooming, substantial 4-6 cm flowers with narrow, somewhat crisped petals delicate salmon-pink with rosy stripes, the lip richly tinged with orange; other cultivars in shades from bright pink to soft yellow; the leaves herbaceous and wrinkled. *Temperate. p. 974*

glaucophyllum (Himalayas); resinous scented, sparry evergreen, with young growth covered by brown scale, small leathery, oval leaves 2½-8 cm long, dull green on the surface, glaucous beneath; clusters of pretty, bell-shaped flowers 2½ cm wide, with 5 rounded lobes, rosy red. *p. 970*

gracilentum (New Guinea); tropical small evergreen sometimes growing epiphytic, the wiry stems with tiny glossy green ovate leaves in whorls of 2 or more; tubular bell-shaped flowers pendant and carmine-red. *p. 974*

hanceanum nanum (China); small evergreen to 50 cm high, with narrow-elliptic, wrinkled, hairy leaves; funnel-shaped pale yellow 3 cm flowers, blooming in early spring; a free-blooming, compact rock-garden plant to 50 cm high; the species hanceanum will grow 2 or 3 times as high. *p. 974*

jasminiflorum (Malaya); attractive evergreen shrub often epiphytic, with obovate, leathery leaves 2½-6 cm long; large terminal truss of slender tubular waxy white flowers 4 cm long and with flaring lobes, filaments pink. *p. 974*

javanicum (Java); tropical evergreen shrub with showy flowers a rich orange, borne in clusters, and the most beautiful species on the island; I photographed this plant growing epiphytic on a tree in the mountains of Java at an altitude above 1,250 m. *Tropical. p. 970*

'Jean Marie de Montague'; excellent griffithianum cultivar suitable for Easter forcing indoors; compact, shapely plant budding well with firm, solid heads of bell-shaped flowers to more than 8 cm across, glowing bright crimson and very charming with wavy petals; smallish, dull-green elliptic foliage. Beautiful color for the outdoor garden on the Pacific Coast, but not bud-hardy enough in the northern Atlantic States. *Warm temperate. p. 969*

lateritium (indicum, macranthum) (Japan); evergreen shrub to 2 m high, but lending itself to dwarfing as bonsai; small 2½-4 cm lanceolate leaves with finely toothed margins; broad funnel-form flowers 8 cm across, bright red or rosy; June-July; hardy. *p. 972*

lochae (Queensland); the only known Australian rhododendron, found on Bellenden Ker mountain above 1,500 m, not far from tropical Cairns; evergreen shrub often epiphytic, usually grown as a dwarf plant; small leathery broad elliptic leaves 5-8 cm long, dark glossy green; and hanging bells of waxy 4-5 cm flowers deep rosy crimson with salmon sheen. *Subtropic. p. 970*

macgregoriae (New Guinea); straggly evergreen mountain shrub with clustered elliptic leaves; charming little waxy flowers 2 cm across, creamy white with orange center. *Subtropic. p. 974*

maddenii (Sikkim and Bhutan); a Himalayan evergreen bush to 3 m high, with papery bark; lanceolate green leaves 8-15 cm long, glaucous beneath; large flowers very fragrant with funnel-shaped corolla 10 cm long, the broad petals white, often flushed with rose, the throat yellow; early summer blooming. *p. 974*

maximum; the photograph on pg. 975 is a true-to-life imitation of the living plant, made of glass by the famous father and son Blaschka glass artists in Dresden, Germany in the early 1900's, for the Botanical Museum of Harvard University, Cambridge, Mass. The species is North American, from Nova Scotia to Alabama, an evergreen shrub to 5 or even 10 m high, with glossy green leaves 25 cm long, tomentose beneath; the bell-shaped 5 cm flowers are pale rose and spotted with green, in large terminal clusters, blooming June into summer. *Temperate. p. 975*

myrtilloides (Burma); miniature evergreen shrublet 15 cm high, with 1 cm dark glossy green elliptic leathery leaves, brown tomentose beneath, and with white ciliate hairs; solitary flat bell-shaped 3 cm flowers with wavy margins, light purple with red spots, resembling saintpaulia. According to Hortus 3, a dwarf var. of R. campylogynum. *p. 970*

'Pink Pearl' (1897); an English hybrid derived from the large-flowering griffithianum of Sikkim and the hardy catawbiense; a shapely plant with very large trusses of good-textured, rose-pink flowers with darker shading and spotted maroon in throat; good for early forcing. (C) *p. 972*

racemosum (China); evergreen shrub with elliptic leaves 2½-5 cm long, densely scaly on the glaucous underside; small 2½ cm funnel-like flowers soft pink with the 5 lobes tipped rose, and with white throat. *p. 970*

'Roseum elegans'; popular old hybrid known since before 1851, for its hardiness, bred with R. catawba, a good evergreen species from mountainous regions of Virginia to Georgia; compact globular bush with leathery decurved, olive green leaves, a heavy budder with numerous clusters of rosy lilac flowers of good substance, deeper at margins, and pale in the center, marked with purple spots on upper petals; mid-season. *Temperate. p. 969, 972*

'Scintillation' (Dexter hybrid); shapely evergreen with deep green beautiful foliage; flowers of good substance, 8 cm in dia., rich pink when opening, later blush-pink in center and with wavy edges, in large trusses 18 cm across. *Warm temperate. p. 987*

'Trilby'; excellent hybrid of dense, compact habit, with numerous medium-large flowers per head, rich deep crimson spotted with black in throat; thick-leathery leaves dark green and pointed; good for for Easter forcing. (Queen Wilhelmina x Stanley Davies). *Warm temperate. p. 972*

'Unknown Warrior' (Stanley Davies x Queen Wilhelmina); exceptionally fine arboreum hybrid of bushy, floriferous habit; small elliptic or obovate leaves and perfectly round heads of flowers bright crimson red. *p. 971*

RHODODENDRON: see also Azalea

RHODOGNAPHALOPSIS *Bombacaceae* **S3LBM**

minor (Trop. America); tropical evergreen tree 5-8 m high, with digitately compound leaves of narrow lanceolate, glossy-green leaflets; the curious, large flowers 25-30 cm long with narrow-linear petals yellowish, spirally twisting after they split open, exposing the long red filaments, united and tubular in lower part. *p. 508*

RHODOHYPOXIS *Amaryllidaceae* **I3LBD**

baurii (baueri), (So. Africa); charming small perennial herb with short rhizome and fleshy roots; glaucous 8-10 cm ribbed basal leaves with spreading silky hairs; rose-red flowers 2-3 cm across, solitary in leaf axils on 10 cm stiff stalk; for a cool, sunny location. *p. 120*

RHODOLEIA *Hamamelidaceae* **I2LBD**

championii (Hong Kong); a small evergreen tree with reddish stem and petioles; glossy dark green, ovate, thick-leathery leaves, glaucous beneath; nodding 6 cm flowers with rosy petals in bracted heads. *Subtropic. p. 1320, 1323*

RHODOMYRTUS *Myrtaceae* **I2LBD**

tomentosa (India, Malaya, Philippines), "Rose myrtle" or "Hill guava"; evergreen shrub, sometimes a small tree to 3 m, nearly all parts densely downy; obovate, leathery leaves 3-8 cm long, with 3 prominent veins; small axillary rosy flowers 3 cm wide, with pink stamens and downy outside; tiny 1 cm ovoid, berry-like purple fruit, pleasantly flavored. *p. 1606*

RHODOPHIALA *Amaryllidaceae* **I2LBD**

chilensis, Hippeastrum chilense in Hortus 3, Habranthus bagnoldii in TROPICA, (Chile); bulbous plant 35 cm high, with grass-like leaves about 50 cm long and 1 cm wide; flowers 5 cm across, pale yellow, veined green, on 35 cm stalks each bearing 2 blooms. *p. 111*

RHODOPHIALA: see also Habranthus

RHODORA: see Rhododendron canadense

RHODOSPATHA *Araceae* **S3HFM**

hastata (Trop. America); slowly creeping ornamental plant, later climbing, having light green, long, narrow leaves, depressed veins, on flattened petioles with kink at base of leaf. *p. 281*

'Jet Streak' (Species C) (Colombia); slow-growing scandent species which may belong to some other genus; from a slender stem rise arching stiff green to bronze petioles, flat or channeled on top, and with a dark red thickened joint (geniculum) at junction of petiole and leafblade; large leathery leaves auriculate, oblique ovate, waxy grass-green, and prominently white along midrib, and with depressed lateral veins; pale green and glossy beneath and with translucent margins; offered by Merkel-Florida. *p. 245*

latifolia (Perú); slowly creeping plant with rooting branches; foliage closely arranged on long, winged petioles sharply bent at base of blade and with thickened geniculum; large leaves oblong-oblique and regularly corrugated by the many sunken veins. *p. 281*

picta (Brazil); thin, leathery plant with rooting branches; elliptic, deep green leaves shaded yellow, irregularly marked orange-yellow on shapely bent stalks; spathe flesh-colored. *p. 281, 282*

RHOEO *Commelinaceae* **•I2LFM**
spathacea (discolor) (Mexico),"Moses-in-the-cradle" or "Oyster plant"; fleshy rhizomatous rosette of stiff waxy lanceshaped, metallic dark green leaves to 30 cm long,vivid glossy purple beneath; in the leaf-bases, little white flowers are peeking from boatshaped bracts. *Subtropic.* *p. 779*
spathacea 'Vittata', "Variegated boat-lily"; variegated form with leaves striped lengthwise on the surface pale yellow, tinted red. *p. 779, 782*

RHOICISSUS *Vitaceae* **I2LFD**
capensis (Vitis) (So. Africa), "Evergreen grapevine"; strong clambering vine with globular ground tubers; brown-hairy, somewhat woody stems, and long-stalked, thickish leathery, metallic green, glossy leaves nearly round or kidney-shaped, to 20 cm across, deeply lobed and wavy-toothed, rusty-tomentose beneath and at the margin; red-black glossy fruit. *Subtropic.* *p. 2121*

RHOMBOPHYLLUM *Aizoaceae* **I2LBD**
dolabriforme (Cape Prov.), "Hatchet plant"; tuft-forming; fleshy green leaves with wedge-shaped keel and tooth-like tip; flowers golden-yellow. *p. 79*
nelii (Hereroa) (So. Africa), "Elkhorns"; clustering small succulent with spreading, gray-green leaves 2 to 2½ cm long, two-lobed at apex; flowers yellow, 4 cm across. *Arid-subtropic.* *p. 76, 79*
rhomboideum (Cape Prov.); stemless succulent rosettes hugging the ground and forming tuft; keeled, uneven 5 cm leaves dark gray-green, smooth, with numerous whitish dots; flowers deep yellow, outside reddish. *p. 78*

RHOPALOBLASTE *Palmae* **S3LFM**
ceramica (hexandra) (New Guinea, Moluccas); graceful palm about 12 m tall, with slender, ringed trunk bearing a noble crown of pinnate fronds, the numerous soft, dense leaflets pendulous; branching 1 m spathe amongst foliage; small bright red fruits. *p. 1904*

RHOPALOSTYLIS *Palmae* **I3LBM**
baueri (Norfolk Is.); spineless feather palm to 15 m tall; clean-looking, ribbed trunk bearing an elegant crown of 3 m pinnate leaves, larger than sapida, the leaflets stiff and glossy green; flowers white, followed by 2 cm red-brown fruit. *p. 1903, 1906*
sapida (New Zealand, Norfolk Is.), the "Nikau palm" also known as the "Feather-duster"; representing the southern limit of palms; attractive palm to 10 m or less high usually with straight trunk strongly ringed, 10-20 cm thick, and topped by a prominent bulbous crownshaft; the pinnate fronds 1-4 m long, stand stiffly erect in a crown like a brush-like tuft, the erect, channeled leaflets glossy green ,with split apex; purplish flowers at base of crown-shaft, and small vivid red fruit. *Subtropic.* *p. 1904, 1911*

RHUS *Anacardiaceae* **C2LBD**
schliebenii (So. Africa); evergreen small spreading shrub 30-50 cm high; leathery narrow lanceolate leaves brown-yellow or green; small yellow to red berries. *p. 132*
typhina (Northeastern No. America), "Staghorn sumac"; deciduous shrub or small tree 4 to 10 m tall, with spreading crown; the twigs densely covered by a velvety brown fur as on deer's antlers; pinnately compound leaves to 60 cm long, with up to 31 odd-pinnate lanceolate leaflets, toothed at margins, and coloring orange to brilliant red in autumn; on female trees with fuzzy crimson fruit. The bark is a source of tannin. *Temperate.* *p. 132*

RHUS: see also Cotinus

RHYNCHOLAELIA *Orchidaceae* **I3OND**
glauca (Brassavola) (Mexico, Guatemala, Panama); small epiphyte with spindle-shaped pseudobulbs bearing solitary, glaucous leaf 10 cm long; large heavy-textured 12 cm, fragrant flowers, olive green to white or lavender, the broad lip yellowish-white marked with rosy-pink (spring) (see Brassavola). *p. 1832*

RHYNCHOSPERMUM: see Trachelospermum

RHYNCHOSTYLIS *Orchidaceae* **I-S3OFD**
coelestis (Thailand), a "Foxtail orchid"; delightful dwarf epiphyte of vandaceous habit; stout stem to 20 cm, clothed with rigidly fleshy leaves closely spaced in ranks; cord-like roots developing from the base; the inflorescence dense with 2 cm fragrant waxy flowers, greenish-white and marked with purple (through summer). *Tropical.* *p. 1813*
gigantea (Saccolabium) (Burma, Vietnam), a "Foxtail orchid"; handsome epiphyte with stout stem densely clothed with leathery leaves; the inflorescence pendulous, dense with fragrant 2½ cm flowers, white and spotted violet, the mauve lip spurred, (Nov.) (I-S) *p. 1815*
retusa (Saccolabium blumei) (India, Burma, to Philippines); beautiful epiphyte with overlapping, strap-like leaves on a stem to 30 cm high; the small, fragrant flowers are densely carried on pendulous cylindrical racemes to 60 cm long, white, spotted with amethyst, (June-Sept.). (S) *p. 1814, 1815*

RHYNORRCHILUM *Orchidaceae* **S3HFM**
standleyi (Costa Rica); a "Jewel-orchid", forming a terrestrial rosette of matte blue-green, ovate foliage with silver-gray markings; central stalk 25 cm high bearing many vivid-red flowers, blooming in succession up the spike, and subtended by red bracts tipped with silver. *p. 1814*
teuscheri (Ecuador); a pretty little epiphyte with pear-shaped pseudobulbs bearing solitary leaves; fragrant flowers creamy-white or greenish flushed red, the broad lip with purple lines and yellow throat. *p. 1813*
venusta (Burlingtonia fragrans) (Brazil); dwarf epiphyte with small pseudobulbs, and pendulous racemes of very fragrant, 4 cm flowers pure white or flushed with rose, with yellow blotch on lip, (Jan.-May). *p. 1812*

RIBES *Saxifragaceae* **I2LBD**
speciosum (California), "Fuchsia-flowered gooseberry"; woody evergreen shrub to 4 m, bristly and spiny; fuchsia-like foliage; drooping inflated flowers bright red, the long red stamens protruding; bristly red fruits. *Subtropic.* *p. 2041*

RICHARDIA: see Zantedeschia

RICHEA *Epacridaceae* **I2LBD**
scoparia (Tasmania), "Austral heather"; interesting bushy shrub to 1½ m high, branching freely from the base; stem clothed with sheathing, shingled narrow leaves to 8 cm long, they are stiff and pointed, set in rosettes and looking like small bromeliads; from the apex the small 1 cm white to pink bell-flowers in erect terminal spikes to 30 cm long. *p. 956*

RICINUS *Euphorbiaceae* **S2LBM**
africanus (communis var. africanus) (East Africa), a "Castor-oil plant"; from a small bush to tree-like shrub, with stout brownish branches, and large green palmately lobed leaves; flowers green, without petals. *p. 1055, 1061*
communis (Trop. Africa), "Castor-oil plant" or "Palma Christi"; striking gigantic tree-like annual herb to 5 m high, or in the tropics where it is widely naturalized, a tree to 12 m; in gardens often planted for foliage effects; from a stout hollow stem, the large handsome peltate leaves, palmately divided into 5 to 11 crenate lobes, 15 to 90 cm across, and with metallic luster; small greenish-white, unimpressive flowers in clusters on long stalks, followed by attractive 3 cm prickly husks covered by brown spines and containing the poisonous seeds, source of a valuable oil. *Tropical.* *p. 1061*
communis 'Coccineus' (Trop. Africa), "Red castor-bean"; tall ornamental herb growing into a 12 m tree, with robust stalk and bold peltate, palmately lobed, bronzy leaves; the spiny seed yields oil used in medicine. The form coccineus has dark red foliage. *p. 1053*

RITTEROCEREUS *Cactaceae* **S2LBD**
deficiens (Lemaireocereus) (Venezuela, Curacao); column cactus branching at base, 2-3 m high, grayish green, 6-8 cm thick, obtusely 7 to 9-angled, and with short spine clusters; flowers 5-6 cm long, reddish outside, white inside; much planted for fences in Venezuela. Young seedlings are bluish glaucous. *p. 656*

RIVINA *Phytolaccaceae* **I2-3LFM**
humilis (laevis) (West Indies, Mexico, etc.), "Rouge plant"; soft-leaved herb to 1 m high, with thin stem and branches; membranous, green, lightly pubescent, ovate foliage to 10 cm long, and pendant little sprays of tiny pinkish-white flowers, forming lustrous little berries of bright crimson, soon dropping. *p. 1922, 1923*

ROBINIA *Leguminosae* **C2LBD**
pseudoacacia tortuosa (Pennsylvania to Georgia, Iowa and Oklahoma), a slow-growing "Yellow locust", or "False acacia"; attractive deciduous tree with pinnate foliage on short twisted, prickly branches, pendulous at tips; pendant racemes of very fragrant, pealike white flowers, the standard with a yellow spot at base. *p. 1391*

ROCHEA *Crassulaceae* **I-C2-3LBD**
coccinea (Crassula rubicunda in hort.) (S. Africa); branched succulent with small pointed, closely set leaves 3 to 4 cm long, on fleshy stem, green above, red beneath; tubular flowers bright scarlet and fragrant, in terminal clusters. *Subtropic.* *p. 919, 920*

ROCHEA: see also Crassula falcata

RODRIGUEZIA *Orchidaceae* **S3OFM**
batemanii (Brazil, Perú); handsome epiphyte with small, compressed pseudobulbs bearing rigid solitary 10 cm leaves; inflorescence in arching racemes of flowers 6 cm long, white flushed with rose, the lip veined and spotted with rosy-red and with prominent curved spur (spring). *p. 1813*
compacta (Nicaragua, Costa Rica, Panama); epiphyte with compressed, long-elliptic 3 cm pseudobulbs topped by solitary rigid leaf 15 cm long; short inflorescence of 1 or 2 fragrant flowers 5 cm long, greenish yellow, and yellow lip with spur at base (autumn). *p. 1813*
secunda (Colombia, Panama, Trinidad, Guyana), "Coral orchid"; epiphyte with compressed pseudobulbs and narrow leaves; arching stalks to 30 cm high with rosy flowers usually on one side, (Feb.-Oct.). *p. 1812*
speciosa (Perú); attractive epiphyte with clustered pseudobulbs bearing solitary leaves; pendant inflorescence of silky pink flowers with pale yellow throat and broad lip. *Tropical.* *p. 1813*

RODRIGUEZIOPSIS *Orchidaceae* **I3OFM**
microphyta (Brazil: Serra do Mar); epiphytic miniature with clambering rhizomes bearing small flat pseudobulbs and solitary leaf; attractive small flowers creamy white with purple spots. *p. 1806*

x RODROCIDIUM *Orchidaceae* **I3OFM**
'Tahiti' (Rodriguezia x Oncidium); bigeneric hybrid with oncidium-like flowers having bronze-red, hooded sepals and petals and a broad two-lobed golden lip marked bronze at base. *p. 1815*

ROHDEA *Liliaceae* **I-C1LFM**
japonica (Japan, China), "Sacred lily of China"; extremely durable, modest plant with thick rhizome; basal rosette of oblanceolate, arching, channeled or plaited, thick-leathery leaves, densely arranged somewhat in two ranks, matte green; white flowers aroid-like; fruit a red berry. *Subtropic.* *p. 1480, 1506*

japonica 'Aureo-striata', "Variegated Lily of China"; robust plant with distichous leathery green leaves beautifully striped and variegated with creamy yellow, to 60 cm long and 8 cm wide. *p. 1479*

japonica 'Marginata' (Japan), "Sacred Manchu lily"; sheathing, channeled, leathery foliage black-green with white border; a favorite in Japan where hundreds of named varieties are cultivated by fanciers. *Subtropic.* *p. 1479, 1480*

japonica 'Striata', "Striped Manchu-lily"; tall-growing to 60 cm with stiffish, thick-leathery dark green leaves bordered with white. *p. 1479*

ROMNEYA *Papaveraceae* **I2LBD**
coulteri (So. California, Mexico), "California tree-poppy"; perennial herb to 2½ m tall, with flexuous stems, and pairs of leaves pinnately cut, to 10 cm long; solitary fragrant white, showy flowers 15 cm across. *p.1923*

ROMULEA *Iridaceae* **I2LBMd**
chloroleuca (So. Africa), "Satin flower"; charming small crocus-like plant 15 cm high, with brown-crusted corm; 2 to 3 hollow, awl-shaped leaves; distinct stalk with greenish-yellow flowers with lobed, spreading petals 3 cm across, sheathed in boat-shaped spathe; opening only in bright sunshine, and blooming in spring. *p. 1340*

sabulosa (Geissorhiza) (So. Africa); charming, dwarf crocus-like cormous herb to 10 cm high, with narrow, reedlike basal leaves longer than the inflorescence; lovely solitary, stalked funnel-form flowers 6 cm across, brilliant ruby-purple with greenish center marked with blackish purple, of a satiny sheen. Needs full sun for flower to expand. *p. 1336*

RONDELETIA *Rubiaceae* **S3LBM**
cordata (Guatemala); handsome shrub 1 m high; the slender branches with leathery opposite, narrow ovate 15 cm leaves; large clusters of small 1 cm flowers bright red with contrasting yellow throat. *p. 2024*

gratissima (Perú); evergreen with slender woody branches bearing pairs of broad ovate, rough green leaves, and large clusters of small light pink flowers with bright rose tube, and sweetly fragrant. *p. 2024*

leucophylla (Mexico); evergreen shrub of rather rank growth, with willowy branches; large opposite, narrow-lanceolate leaves, and clusters of tubular 4-lobed flowers coral-pink with yellow eye. *p. 2022*

odorata (West Indies, Panama); evergreen shrub 1-1½ m high, with downy, straggling branches; ovate dark green leaves 5 cm long, in opposite, distant pairs, the margins wavy or turned down, dentate toward apex; clusters of fragrant, tubular flowers with 5 expanding lobes, 1½ cm across, cinnabar-red with conspicuous yellow eye. *Tropical.* *p. 2022, 2024*

splendens (Trop. America); floriferous evergreen shrub with small leathery, short-ovate leaves, and large 5-lobed flowers shining bright red, with yellow throat. *p. 2022*

strigosa (Guatemala); luxuriant bush with small green ovate leaves in pairs along slender woody branches; the flowers deep bronzy crimson with orange cup. *Tropical.* *p. 2024*

RONNBERGIA *Bromeliaceae* **S3HFM**
columbiana (Colombia: Valle); billbergia-like epiphyte, forming a tube at base and spreading out with straplike, hard-leathery concave leaves dark green with wine-red blotching and edged with teeth; reverse covered with gray scales and keeled; stalked inflorescence with purple flowers edged white. *p. 580*

morreniana (S. W. Colombia), "Giant spoon"; terrestrial plant with long stalked upright lanceshaped leaves, thin leathery, bright green, zoned with bars and spots of very deep green; flowers blue. *p. 513, 558*

RORIDULA *Droseraceae (Carnivorous Plants)* **I3LBD**
gorgonias (So. Africa); semi-insectivorous plant from the mountains of Cape Prov.; small shrubby plant rare in cultivation; narrow leaves with ciliate hairs along margins, arranged in rosettes along woody stems; the hairs with sticky glands to catch and hold insects which are then eaten by spiders. *p. 764*

ROSA *Rosaceae* **I-S2LBM**
'American Beauty' (Hybrid perpetual 1875) (Mme. Ferd. Jamin, Ledechaux 1875); vigorous profuse bloom; very large, fragrant flowers (50 petals), carmine shaded rose, on strong stem; a famous old greenhouse rose. *p. 2006*

banksiae (China), "Lady Banks rose"; charming climber with vigorous canes rambling to 6 m; very spiny, evergreen foliage; deciduous in cold winters; pretty 3 cm double flowers pale buff-yellow, in large clusters, slightly fragrant; good for arbors, in mild climates. *Warm temperate.* *p. 2006*

'Blaze' (Climber) ('Paul's Scarlet' x 'Gruss an Teplitz'); rambling canes 3-5 m long, dark green leathery foliage; medium large 5 cm double cupped flowers crimson-red, in large clusters; faintly fragrant; recurrent bloomer (Kalley/Jackson-Perkins 1932). *Temperate.* *p. 2006*

'Bonfire' (1928) (multiflora x wichuriana); a good, vigorous climbing rose for Easter forcing in pots as a "trained rambler", more upright and slightly later than 'E. Jacquet', but its densely double flowers are more crimson-red and not as bluish carmine; the heavy flower clusters appearing as short axillary branches from the upper end of frost-ripened canes. *Temperate.* *p. 2003, 2005*

borboniana 'Magna Charta' (1876), "Hybrid-perpetual"rose; long favored for forcing in pots because of its prolific, bushy habit; producing numerous, erect canes with light green foliage, topped by clusters of great, very double, fragrant globular flowers with numerous, carmine-rose petals usually opening more or less at the same time and making a grand show. *Temperate.* *p. 2003*

chinensis 'Minima' (roulettii) (China), "Pygmy rose"; well-loved miniature, averaging about 20-25 cm high; vigorous, hardy and long-lived, with appealing 4 cm double flowers of lively rose-pink with pale eye, in continuous bloom; once thought lost to cultivation, it turned up again on the window-sill of a Swiss cottage in 1918. Also known as "Fairy rose." *p. 2004*

chinensis minima 'Baby Gold Star' ('Estrellita del Oro') (1940) ('Eduard Toda' x roulettii), this "Fairy rose" is a fine yellow miniature, with strong, thorny stems, 35 cm high; glossy leaves, pointed buds, and golden yellow, double flowers fading to pale cream in bright sun, fragrant and shaped like a tea rose when unfolding. *p. 2004*

chinensis minima 'Oakington Ruby'; dependable miniature rose of rather robust habit, under 30 cm high; with good foliage and free-blooming at an early stage; deep carmine buds open to rich ruby-crimson, fully double flowers 2½-3 cm across. *p. 1994*

chinensis minima 'Tinker Bell'; newer, patented "Fairy rose", 20 cm high, a miniature mimic in every detail; tiny thorns, leaves and buds, unfolding into very double flowers averaging 60 petals, yet only 4 cm across, bright rose-pink and long lasting. *p. 2004*

chinensis minima 'Tom Thumb' (1935); seedling of roulettii; a charming, free-flowering midget 22 cm high, with semi-double, rich crimson-red blooms having a contrasting zone of white at the base of the petals. *p.2004*

'Crimson Rambler'; the first hardy rambler hybrid of wichuriana x multiflora (1893); based on an old Chinese garden variety known as "Ten sisters"; a forerunner of many hybrids to come in various colors; pliable clambering stems producing on 1 yr. wood a fine burst of double, but rather small, crimson-red flowers all at once in June; the thin branches rooting where touching the ground; small dark glossy green leaves, subject to mildew. *p. 1994*

'Double Paul's Scarlet' (Roehrs mutant 1943); patented; 'Fern Roehrs' rose, beautiful, very double sport of 'Paul's Scarlet Climber'; a pillar rose with vigorous canes with deep green, leathery leaves; bearing axillary clusters abundant with large, fragrant, very double flowers 6-8 cm across, with 80-100 rolled, persisting petals, four times the number of the parent, and a glowing deep scarlet-red with velvety sheen. *Temperate.* *p. 2003*

'Eugene Jacquet' (1916) (wichuriana x multiflora); a free-blooming, symmetrical "Rambler" rose much used for forcing in pots for Easter, the long, rambling canes trained into globes, baskets or on trellis; with fresh-green, pinnate leaves and big clusters of small, fragrant, carmine-rose, double flowers on short, axillary branches appearing from the upper parts of winter-hardened canes of the previous season. *Temperate.* *p. 2003*

Floribunda class; a group of hybrids which was created by inbreeding the "Polyanthas" (rehderiana) with "Hybrid Tea" roses; more free-flowering over a longer season, with larger blooms than the "Polyanthas" and more vigorous. *Temperate.*

(Floribunda) 'Europeana' ('Ruth Leuwerik' x 'Rosemary Rose'), a "Baby rose" from Holland; shapely bush to 70 cm with bronze-green foliage, and masses of satiny crimson double flowers 8 cm dia., faintly fragrant; repeated growth producing continuous bloom. (de Ruiter 1964: All-American Award 1968). *p. 2007*

(Floribunda) 'Fashionette'; a spreading, rather sparry bush with bright green foliage and long-stemmed replicas of fine tea roses in smaller size about 8 cm dia., in soft shell pink veined with red and flushed with yellow, quickly opening; delightfully fragrant, but we have found it a shy bloomer in pots. *Temperate.* *p. 2006*

(Floribunda) 'Rose Parade'; All-American honors 1975; compact bush thickly set with clusters of coral-pink 10 cm flowers; shaded with peach. *p. 2005*

(Floribunda) 'Sarabande'; vigorous, low, spreading bush dense with healthy green foliage and large trusses of rather flat, semi-double 6 cm flowers fiery orange-scarlet, with bright yellow stamens. *p. 2004*

(Floribunda) 'Scarlet Marvel'; sturdy bush with large 6 cm double, rather flat flowers in brilliant scarlet; subject to mildew. *Temperate.* *p. 2004*

(Floribunda) 'Spice'; free grower with spreading branches bearing heavy clusters of fully double salmon-red flowers. *p. 2004*

Grandiflora class; this new group of hybrids approach in size of flowers the Hybrid Teas; developed by breeding of Floribundas with Hybrid Teas; characterized by more flowers per stem, in larger clusters than the HT, and individual stems longer than in the Floribunda, making them suitable for cutting; more nearly everblooming, tallish, with erect branches, reaching to 1½ m high.

(Grandiflora) 'Ben Hur'; vigorous bush with dark green shiny foliage, and stiff, graceful stems with unusually long urn-shaped buds, opening to double flowers with deep red velvety-textured petals. *p. 2002*

(Grandiflora) 'Buccaneer'; fine patented rose, profuse with double flowers having the delicately rolled petals of a tea rose, in a rich shade of unfading yellow; vigorous tall grower. *p. 2002*

(Grandiflora) 'El Capitan'; patented Armstrong variety, very proliferous with noble flowers of gleaming cherry-red. *p. 2002*

(Grandiflora) 'Golden Girl' ('Joanna Hill' x 'Eclipse' x 'Meilland'); vigorous growth, upright, free-bloomer; large double flowers 10 cm dia., sparkling golden yellow, fragrant (Meilland 1959). *p. 2006*

(Grandiflora) 'John S. Armstrong' ('Charlotte Armstrong' seedling); tall, vigorous upright to 50 cm high; abundant bloom, velvety double flowers glowing dark red, 8 cm dia., slightly fragrant (Swim/Armstrong 1961). *p. 2007*

(Grandiflora) 'Mandarin' ('Mallerin' x floribunda); vigorous upright grower; semi-double, blood-red flowers in large clusters (Boerner 1951). *p. 2006*

(Grandiflora) 'Pink Parfait'; patented All-America selection 1961, a continuous bloomer, with as many as 100 buds at one time on a neat bush; the fine, fragrant double flowers with some 25 petals a blend of dawn-pink to rich rose-pink at petal-edges. *p. 2002*

(Grandiflora) 'Queen Elizabeth' ('Charlotte Armstrong' x 'Floradora') (Lammerts Germain 1954); vigorous and bushy, with abundant bloom in clusters; flowers large to 10 cm, soft rose-pink, very fragrant; resembling a small tea rose. *p. 2006*

(Grandiflora) 'Roundelay' ('Charlotte Armstrong' x 'Floradora'); robust grower and free bloomer; cardinal red, fragrant flowers of medium size (Swim 1954). *p. 2006*

(Grandiflora) 'War Dance'; patented plant offered by Conard-Pyle; well-formed bush with heavy canes bearing large double flowers with 28-40 petals, 11 cm across, of an unusual color in roses, in the reddest of scarlet-red; the heavy flowers tend to nod if forced under glass. *p. 2002*

(Hybrid perpetual) 'Ulrich Brunner'; old variety (1881), of very vigorous, erect habit, with tough, mildew-resistant foliage; and sweetly scented, large double, cupped flowers of bright carmine-red; good for town-conditions, though not a "monthly" bloomer. *p. 1994*

noisettiana 'Maréchal Niel' (1864) (chinensis x moschata); a famous old "Noisette" rose of climbing habit, with long rambling canes which I remember my father training on wires following the ridge of his greenhouse, and from which developed weak, axillary, pendant branches with large, most beautiful, hauntingly fragrant blooms of a delicate pale yellow, resembling a fine Tea rose; not frost-hardy north. *Subtropic.* *p. 2004, 2005*

odorata 'Better Times' (1932) (Hybrid tea); sport of 'Briarcliff', the first red rose for greenhouse cut flower growers that grew relatively easily, was free-blooming, and gave a satisfactory cut flower, proving exceedingly popular; dark green, leathery foliage and long crimson buds opening into large durable brilliant cerise red flowers with 36-50 petals, on long stems; with enchanting fragrance. *Warm temperate.* *p. 2002*

odorata 'Christian Dior' (Hybrid tea); All-America Award-winner 1962, as the finest red rose of the year; patented; vigorous grower with elegant high-pointed flowers very double with 50-60 petals; rich, bright scarlet iridescence over deep crimson, without tendency for bluing, and with faint fragrance. *p. 2002*

odorata 'Forever Yours' (Hybrid tea 1964); vigorous upright growth with abundant bloom; large double, full flowers (32-45 petals), deep velvety crimson, spicy fragrant, opens to full cabbage head; metallic foliage; replaces 'Happiness'; freer growth and production as commercial cut rose. *p. 2007*

odorata 'Golden Rapture' ('Geheimrat Duisberg') (1933) (Hybrid tea); seedling of 'Rapture' (Sport of 'Butterfly', which in turn was a sport of 'Ophelia') x Julien Potin; the first good growing greenhouse cut-flower yellow, with fresh-green glossy foliage, and gracefully slender, clear golden yellow flowers of medium size with deeper shading in the center, not fading, and with an old-rose fragrance, 40 petals. *Warm temperate.* *p. 2002*

odorata 'Happiness' ('Rouge Meilland') (1951) (Hybrid tea); seedling involving 'Rome Glory', 'Tassin', etc.; an exhibition bloom and until 1978 the leading "fancy" red rose as a greenhouse cut flower; large double flowers with 35-40 heavy, substantial petals glowing deep red unfolding to velvety crimson with blackish sheen, the outer petals curl to points in layer after layer about the solid center, 12-18 cm across; very long lasting and slightly fragrant; not too free but very rewarding. *Warm temperate.* *p. 2002*

odorata 'La France'; world famous as prototype of first Hybrid tea 1867, by Guillot of Lyon; seed parent oriental Tea rose 'Mme. Bravy' x pollen parent occidental Hybrid perpetual 'Mme. Victor Verdier'; elegant, ever-blooming, large flower of 60 petals, silvery pink, very fragrant. *p.2006*

odorata 'Miss All-American Beauty' ('Maria Callas') (Hybrid tea) ('Chrysler Imperial' x 'Karl Herbst'); magnificent dark pink hybrid tea rose from France; buds pointed, opening to large, beautiful 50-60 petal blooms to 12 cm across, with heady tea fragrance (Meilland 1965, AARS 1968). *p. 2007*

odorata 'Mister Lincoln' (Hybrid tea) ('Chrysler Imperial' x 'Charles Mallerin'); large double flowers, 10-15 cm across, glowing deep crimson, of spicy tea fragrance (Swim x Weeks 1964; All-America Award 1965). *p. 2007*

odorata 'Mrs. W.C. Miller' (1909); a dependable old "Hybrid tea" rose of robust habit, and with leathery leaves, used for forcing in pots as it remains stocky, with a thick neck producing elegant, tightly double, dainty pink flowers flushed with rose, the petals are of good substance and unfold gracefully like a true Tea rose, with the same intense fragrance, blooming "monthly" into autumn. *Temperate.* *p. 2003*

odorata 'Oregold' (Hybrid tea) ('Piccadilly' x 'Königin der Rosen'); rich yellow hybrid tea; high-centered double 12 cm blooms of heavy substance, 35-40 petals, with delicate tea fragrance (Tantau; All-America Award 1975). *p. 2007*

odorata 'Red American Beauty' (Hybrid tea) ('Happiness' x 'San Fernando'); vigorous, upright growth, with deep green leaves; ovoid bud, double, fragrant flowers, large to 12 cm dia., deep crimson red, prolific bloom. (Morey/Jackson x Perkins 1959). *Warm temperate.* *p. 2005*

odorata 'Starbright' (Hybrid tea) ('Princess White' x Hybrid tea seedling); vigorous upright growth, dark glossy foliage; profuse blooms double white and fragrant (Boerner; introduced by Jackson & Perkins 1962). *p. 2007*

odorata 'Tropicana' ('Super-star') (Hybrid tea) (1960 AARS); upright spreading growth; heavy producer of large double flowers to 12 cm dia., salmon-orange, very fragrant (Tantau,1960 AARS). *p. 2007*

odorata 'Yankee Doodle' (Hybrid tea) ('Color Wonder' x 'Kings Ransom'); tall growing, with massive double blooms (50 petals) peach pink to orange, yellow reverse, of fruity fragrance; singly on stem tea rose fashion (Kordes) (All-America Award 1976). *p. 2007*

polyantha 'Crimson Rosette' (1947); a patented, robust cultivar of vigorous, sparry growth, with broad firm foliage, and large clusters of 2½-4 cm very durable flowers with 30 petals velvety deep crimson, unfolding from buds like a miniature tea-rose, slightly fragrant; suitable for Easter in pots. *p. 2003*

polyantha 'Margo Koster' (Sunbeam) (1935); excellent commercial "Baby-rose" (rehderiana), sport of 'Dick Koster'; of short compact habit about 30 cm high; and large rather globe-shaped double flowers with incurved petals like 'Dick Koster' but a delicate soft light orange shading to salmon-red in the heart; good pot-forcer for Easter. *Temperate.* *p. 2003*

polyantha 'Mothersday' (1949); excellent "Baby rose" (rehderiana) for pots, sport of 'Dick Koster'; well-shaped, of small compact habit, never rambling, with glossy, pinnate leaves and short wiry branches profusely bearing clusters of relatively large, globular flowers of firm texture, deep crimson-red. *Temperate.* *p. 2003*

polyantha 'Triomphe Orleanais' (1912); a dependable vigorous old "Baby-rose", with glossy rich green, healthy foliage, freely branching with strong shoots 50-90 cm high, bearing large clusters of medium size, long-lasting, semi-double flowers bright carmine or cherry-red with white eye, slightly fragrant; a good commercial pot plant for early Easter forcing. *Temperate.* *p. 2003*

ROSCOEA *Zingiberaceae* **I2LFM**

alpina (Himalayan Region: Kashmir, Nepal); perennial with fleshy roots, and leafy stems 10-20 cm high, the lanceolate light green, fleshy leaves in a loose rosette; short inflorescence terminal with 1 or 2 flowers, calyx green and slit to base, the corolla pink with deep purple upper petal, and with two-lobed lip; summer-blooming. *p. 2141*

cautleoides (China: N. W. Yunnan); tall, slender perennial 25-40 cm high, with fleshy roots and leafy stems, the lower part with 2 sheaths; the leaves sessile and lanceolate, glossy green; at top of stem the inflorescence of 4 to 7 large sulphur-yellow flowers 5-8 cm long, the dorsal petal hooded; summer-blooming. *p. 2141*

humeana (China: West Yunnan); perennial herb with thick-fleshy roots, lanceolate parallel veined leaves 10-30 cm long, green and smooth, sheathed at base; stout, short terminal spike with 4 to 8 large trumpet flowers to 10 cm long, purple or blue, the upper bracts veined dark purple. *p. 2140*

purpurea (Sikkim Himalayas); perennial herb with thick-fleshy roots, to 30 cm high; stems with lanceolate sessile leaves; almost hidden in the upper foliage, short-stalked clusters of deep purple flowers 4 cm across, the dorsal petal arching; summer-blooming. *p. 2141*

purpurea var. procera (Himalayas); a form larger in all parts; flowers blue or deep purple, with lip to 5 cm long and split in front. *p. 2141*

ROSMARINUS *Labiatae* **•I2LBD**

x lavandulaceus (Mediterranean Reg.), "Prostrate Rosemary"; low, aromatic, creeping shrub with branches moving sideways, dense with grayish needles 1 cm long; axillary showy, lavender-blue flowers blooming all winter. Kew Bulletin 1920 separates lavandulaceus as a species from officinalis, having calyx more hairy and not glandular, and not being winter-hardy. Both species are known as a pungent herb since ancient times, and mentioned in Cloisters of Europe in 820 A.D. The spicy resinous leaves fresh or dry give exciting flavor to appetizers, meats, dressings, sauces, vegetables, fish, game and poultry; when dried they give a piney scent to sachets and moth preventatives; distilled oil is used in medicines and perfumes. Fresh sprigs are traditionally used for weddings. *p. 1358*

officinalis (Mediterranean), "Rosemary"; evergreen shrub with downy shoots well known as a sweet herb, and grown for its aromatic leaves which are needle-like and grayish, shiny above, white downy beneath; flowers light blue. *Subtropic.* *p. 1357*

officinalis prostratus; a variety more low and compact growing, with branches having a tendency to grow sideways. *p. 1352*

ROTALA *Lythraceae* **S2LBM**

macrandra (E. Indies); robust shrub growing in wet places; red stems with opposite oval, perfoliate, leathery green leaves; inflorescence in small spikes with tiny rosy flowers. *Tropical.* *p.1523*

ROTHMANNIA *Rubiaceae* **S3LFM**

capensis (Gardenia rothmannia) (So. Africa), "Scented cups"; attractive evergreen shrub or tree to 3 m, with oval, glossy leaves; flowers when in bud are greenish-cream, when open the spreading lobes are ivory-white inside with maroon spots in the throat; sweetly scented; decorative globose, hard green fruit the size of a small orange. *p. 2012*

ROTHMANNIA: see also Randia

ROUPALA *Proteaceae* **S3LBM**

brasiliensis (pohlii) (Brazil); small tree to 7 m, shoots densely covered with bright, rust-colored wool; leaves pinnate 30 cm long; flowers orange-red, in axillary racemes. *p. 1981*

ROUPELIA: see Strophanthus

ROYSTONEA *Palmae* **I-S3LBM**

elata (Oreodoxa) (South Florida), "Florida royal palm"; majestic feather palm at home in the Everglades, on wet ground; similar to R. regia but taller; smooth gray trunk to 32 m tall, swollen above the middle, graced by a heavy crown of arching plume-like pinnate leaves to 6 m long, the leaflets glossy deep green arranged in several rows, on bright green petiole; long inflorescence with fragrant flowers followed by round, circular 2 cm dark red fruit. *Subtropic.* *p. 1907*

oleracea (Trinidad, N. So. America), the "South American royal palm"; very tall feather palm 30 m or more high, with slender erect, smooth trunk not bulging, bearing the large glossy green crownshaft, and crown of gracefully arching pinnate fronds 3-6 m long, the numerous glossy leaflets attached to rachis in opposite, horizontal rows; fragrant flowers, and small purplish-black fruit. *Tropical.* *p. 1905*

regia (Oreodoxa) (Cuba), "Cuban royal palm"; smooth erect gray trunks somewhat swollen above the middle, to 20 m high or more, with a terminal crown of gracefully arching feathery fronds regularly pinnate, 2-3 m long, the pinnae to 75 cm long and 2 cm wide, bright green and prominently ribbed and arranged in double rows, in 2 planes on either side of the axis. *Tropical.* *p. 1905, 1907, 1916*

RUBIA ornamentale: see Carphalea kirondron

RUBUS *Rosaceae* **I-S2LFM**

reflexus (moluccanus) (So. China, Hong Kong), "Trailing velvet plant"; attractive robust, somewhat sparry woody clamberer with rambling stems having occasional thorns; the young growth, petioles and underside of the foliage covered with cinnamon-colored wool; sturdy, pubescent, toothed and lobed leaves 10-20 cm long, vivid emerald-green painted with chocolate-brown along primary ribs, followed by a zone of splashed silver. Handsome foliage vine especially striking in younger shoots and when kept warm; best planted out but if in pots, then trained on trellis or wire frame. *Subtropic.* *p. 1994, 2001*

RUDBECKIA *Compositae* **C2LBDhd**

fulgida (Pennsylvania to Florida and Texas), "Orange cone flower"; perennial ½-1 m high, with 3-nerved, lanceolate leaves, and typical 4 to 5 cm cone-flowers with 12-14 orange-yellow rays, surrounding the high, black-purple disk. *Temperate.* *p. 812*

hirta (Ontario to Florida and Texas), "Black-eyed Susan"; annual or biennial, bristly-hairy, 30-60 cm high; sessile leaves spatulate to lanceolate; solitary flower heads with about 14 golden-yellow rays to 5 cm long, and high purple-brown disk of tubular florets. *Temperate.* *p. 812*

laciniata (Quebec to Florida and Arizona), "Cone-flower"; tall perennial to 3 m high, with leaves pinnately divided into toothed or lobed segments; flower heads 10 cm across, with yellow rays soon drooping, and greenish-yellow disk. *p. 812*

RUELLIA *Acanthaceae* **I-S3HFM**

affinis (speciosa) (Brazil); tropical shrub to 1 m high, with pendant flexuous branches, in habitat up to 6 m long; small oval leaves; showy funnel-shaped scarlet flowers 9 cm long, solitary in leaf axils. *Tropical.* *p. 51*

amoena (graecizans) (So. America), "Red-spray ruellia" or "Red Christmas pride"; herbaceous sub-shrub 30-60 cm high, with lanceolate, glossy green leaves 8-12 cm long and becoming smaller toward the top; brilliant red, swollen tubular 3 cm flowers, streaked yellow inside, blooming in summer or winter. Sun-loving flowering house plant best grown from fresh cuttings annually, or from seed. *Tropical.* *p. 51*

blumei (Java); small herb with opposite, sessile, narrow obovate leaves, thin yet stiff, bluish-green, with silver-gray between the raised ribs; the little bell-shaped, purplish-pink flowers on axillary stalks; winter-blooming. *p. 51*

ciliosa (humilis) (New Jersey to Florida and Texas); hairy herbaceous perennial with ovate rugose 8 cm leaves, ciliate; large 5 cm trumpet flowers variable, blue or white with purple midveins on lobes. *p. 55*

colorata (Brazil: Amazon); strikingly beautiful shrubby plant with smooth gray-brown stem; opposite elliptic, quilted leaves 12-15 cm long, green beneath; showy inflorescence with carmine-red bracts, 6 cm trumpet flowers with 5 spreading lobes fiery orange-scarlet with yellow in throat and with long protruding stamens. *Tropical.* *p. 51*

devosiana (Brazil); small subshrub 45 cm high, with purple stems, oval lanceolate leaves distantly toothed, about 5 cm long, deep green and with prominent whitish midrib and lateral veins above, purple beneath; tubular-expanded flowers white marked with lilac. *p. 53*

macrantha (Brazil), "Christmas pride"; bushy plant with erect stems; opposite lanceolate leaves matte dark green, to 15 cm long, veins depressed; large trumpet-shaped flowers carmine-rose, with pale throat lined red. *Tropical.* *p.51*

makoyana (Brazil), "Monkey plant"; low-spreading herb with small, ovate leaves, satiny olive-green shaded violet and silvery veins; rosy-carmine flowers. *Tropical.* *p. 51*

strepens (N.J. to Florida and Texas); grown in hort. as ciliosa; hairy herbaceous perennial 30-90 cm high, with ovate, rugose 8 cm leaves, the margins with eyelash hairs; large 5 cm trumpet flowers, variably blue or white with purple midveins on lobes. *p. 51*

RUMOHRA *Polypodiaceae (Filices)* **I3LFM**

adiantiformis (Polystichum coriaceum) (So. America, So. Africa, New Zealand, Polynesia), "Leather fern"; a spreading fern in dense clusters with creeping brown rhizome, similar to Davallia; with fresh green fronds 30 to 60 cm long, thick-leathery, 1-3-pinnate, with oblong segments coarsely toothed. Also known as Aspidium capense, the "Leather-leaf-fern". *p. 1145, 1157*

standishii (Polystichum) (Japan, So. China, Korea, Vietnam); in the Flora of Japan, by Ohwi, as Arachniodes standishii; attractive terrestrial fern with short-creeping rhizome, at home in mountain woods; stalked tripinnate or 4-pinnate fronds vivid green and thinly herbaceous, 40 to 60 cm long, the rachis sparsely scaly, the pinnae in 12-15 pairs and with hair-like short scales beneath. *p. 1164*

RUNYONIA *Amaryllidaceae* **I2LBD**

longiflora (Mexico); low rosette of soft-fleshy, channeled leaves 20 cm long and 1 cm wide, on margins with soft teeth; stiff-erect, tall-stalked inflorescence with small appressed white flowers, tinged red. *p. 111*

RUPRECHTIA *Polygonaceae* **I-S2LBD**

coriacea (Mexico, Trinidad, Argentina), "Biscochito" or "Cabriton"; handsome spreading evergreen shrub with twiggy branches; large elliptic leaves with prominent nerves, and clusters of showy flowers with red petals, covered at base by a hard, white woolly red calyx. *p. 1953*

RUSCUS *Liliaceae* **C-I2LN-FD**

aculeatus (England, Mediterranean to Iran), "Butchers broom"; erect shrub with tiny greenish flowers curiously borne along midrib of the ovate, stiff, spiky, leaf-like branches (cladodes); berries bright red, during winter. *p. 1478, 1479*

aculeatus angustifolius; weaker plant; branching stems with narrow very spiny cladodes (branchlets simulating a leaf), 1½ cm long. *p. 1479*

hypoglossum (Hungary, Italy, Asia Minor), "Mouse-thorn"; evergreen, tufted shrub with creeping rootstock and rigid stems to 45 cm high or more, the flexible, leaflike branches, or cladophylls, narrow and tapering to both ends, 6-10 cm long, and bearing small yellow flowers on their centers. *Subtropic.* *p. 1478, 1479*

RUSCUS: see also Semele

RUSPOLIA *Acanthaceae* **S3LFM**

hypocrateriformis (Eranthemum) (Trop. W. Africa to No. Transvaal); strikingly handsome tropical shrub with squarish stems; opposite, broad ovate wrinkled leaves with pink veins, and terminal spike of bright scarlet flowers with long, slender tubes. *p. 50, 52*

RUSSELIA *Scrophulariaceae* **I2LBD**

equisetiformis (Mexico), "Coral plant" or "Fountain plant"; shrubby plant with whip and rush-like, 4-angled stems to 1 m long, arching or pendulous; the normally lanceolate dentate leaves mostly reduced to small scaly bracts on the branches; tubular two-lipped flowers with fiery scarlet-red corolla 3 cm long, in nearly continuous bloom. *Subtropic.* *p. 2059*

sarmentosa (Mexico, C. America), "Coral blow"; tropical shrub with slender, arching 4-angled stems with whorls of 2 to 4 wedge-shaped nettle-like leaves having crenate margins, 5 cm long; at leaf axils the tubular flowers velvety scarlet-red. *Tropical.* *p. 2060*

RUTA *Rutaceae* **I2LBD**

graveolens (So. Europe), the "Herb-of-grace" or "Common rue"; strongly aromatic subshrub to 1 m high, with 2-3-pinnate leaves, used for flavoring, and small yellowish flowers in terminal clusters; cultivated for centuries in herb gardens, and its name was associated with repentance. *p. 2026*

RUTTYA *Acanthaceae* **I2LBM**

fruticosa (So. Africa); shrubby plant with wrinkled ovate leaves, and flowers 4½ cm long, tubular two-lipped corolla orange-red with a black blotch, and with small linear bracts. *Subtropic.* *p. 55*

speciosa scholesei (Ethiopia, Upper Nile, Rift Valley of Africa); a yellow variation of speciosa, which normally has red blossoms; evergreen shrub with glossy ovate leaves, and showy 2-lipped flowers orange yellow, blotched and spotted with glossy black. *Tropical.* *p. 51*

x RUTTYRUSPOLIA *Acanthaceae* **I-S3LFM**

'Phyllis van Heerden' (Ruspolia x Ruttya); interesting bigeneric hybrid; ornamental flowering shrub with slender branches, elliptic leaves, and cylindrical bracted spike of white flowers with rose pink etchings. *p. 52*

SABAL *Palmae* **I2LBM**

causiarum (Puerto Rico, Virgin Islands), "Puerto Rican hat-palm"; stocky fan-palm 9-18 m tall, with gray, smooth trunk to 75 cm thick, bearing a heavy crown of palmate leaves 2 m or more long, many threads at sinuses, divided ⅔ to base; the segments stiff and bright green or bluish; fragrant white flowers and blackish fruit. *Tropical.* *p. 1905*

deeringiana (louisiana) (Southern Louisiana); a lowland palmetto to 5 m tall, with a solid crown of green fan-leaves, to 2 m across and deeply cut, at first stiff but later collapsed as petiole is not continuous; small 1 cm fruit. According to L. H. Bailey this may be an emergent form of Sabal minor. *p. 1906*

exul (Mexico), "Victoria palm"; relatively large fan palm with palmate leaves vivid green, the deeply cut segments 1 m long and 5 cm wide, spreading irregularly in all directions; long stout petioles with bases on trunk also green; fruit solitary from each flower, nearly round and 2 cm dia.; much planted in southern Texas. *p. 1908*

havanensis (Cuba); fan palm more upright than umbraculifera (blackburniana), with slender trunk and with longer, thinner petioles; leaves bluish-green while young changing to dark green when older. *p. 1909*

mexicana (Mexico, Guatemala); robust fan palm with stout, strong trunk; large dark green palmate leaves with a lightly bluish cast, 1 m across, segments cut back about one third, and with a few long brown fibers; petioles to 1½ m long, smooth dark green with brown margins, concave on the upper side. *p. 1910*

minor (No. Carolina, Florida to Georgia and Texas), the "Dwarf palmetto", "Blue palmetto", or "Scrub palmetto"; wide-ranging dwarf fan palm usually without trunk, the rigid palmate leaves 1-1½ m wide, stiff and flat, glaucous or grayish green, the segments cut halfway or more; fronds generally upright but older blades kink at the junction with petioles, hanging downward and folding; erect inflorescence, black-glossy fruit. *Subtropic.* *p. 1908, 1910*

neglecta (Hispaniola); a spineless fan palm close to umbraculifera but with trunk not as thick and of faster growth; a spreading crown of large palmate leaves few in number, on long arching petioles, the segments deeply cut and quite deflexed. *p. 1906*

palmetto (Carolina coast to Florida), "Cabbage palm", or "Palmetto"; variable fan palm 6 to 20 m high or more, with stout trunk either almost smooth and brown, or covered with a criss-cross pattern of leaf-bases, slightly curving; the palmate leaves 1-1½ m long, divided into many slender, hanging segments, green or bluish above and gray on the underside, with numerous thread-like fibers; the midrib extending through the blade; white flowers and blackish fruit. *Subtropic.* *p. 1905, 1908*

texana (Texas, Mexico); the "Texas palmetto" from the lower Rio Grande valley; as seedling with simple plaited, leathery, yellowish-green lanceolate leaves, later becoming a tree to 15 m high, with broad leaves 1½ m wide, fan-wise, typically cut half or more to the continuing midrib into very long pointed segments. *p. 1902, 1910*

umbraculifera (blackburniana) (Santo Domingo and Haiti), "Hispaniolan palmetto" or "Bermuda palm"; very decorative massive palmetto palm, with age to 20 m high; stocky, smooth whitish trunk; crown of palmate, stiff leaves 2 m long, gray green and divided about halfway; freely flowering with inflorescence to 1 m long; shiny 2 cm dark brown fruit. *p. 1906*

viatoris (Subtrop. No. America); erect slender fan palm to 6 m tall, similar to S. palmetto, but of more modest size, light green, thin leaves, with leaf bases tending to persist; short but heavy clusters of shiny black fruit. *p. 1908*

SACCHARUM *Gramineae* **I-S3LBM**

officinarum (China, East Indies), "Sugarcane"; very tall stout perennial grass to 4 m high, with solid yellowish-green canes 2-5 cm thick; rich green, arching, clasping leaves to 1 m long, with broad midrib and rough edge; inflorescence in spikelets in large terminal fluffy silky plumes; its sap is a major source of sugar; the fermented and distilled juice becomes a well-known intoxicating drink, otherwise known as rum. *p. 1311, 1316*

SACCOLABIUM *Orchidaceae* **S3OFM**

bellinum (calceolaris: Hooker) (Burma); vandaceous epiphyte with leafy stem 8-15 cm long, the strap-shaped leaves to 30 cm; axillary racemes of 4 cm fleshy flowers, the sepals and petals similar and yellow blotched with blackish-purple, the blade of lip spreading, white, spotted purple with orange disk, fimbriated, and with white pouch; spring. (S) *p. 1815*

calceolare (Gastrochilus) (Himalayas to Malaya and Java); dwarf epiphyte with 3-5 leaves to 16 cm long and with two teeth at apex; short, clustered inflorescence near base, of 2 cm faintly fragrant waxy flowers, greenish with brown-purple spots, the sac-like lip yellow, spotted brown and fringed (autumn) (see Gastrochilus). *p. 1816*

rhopalorrachis (Thailand); small epiphyte with stout stem and fleshy leaves in 2 ranks, to 6 cm long; waxy 2 cm flowers on short stalk, cream with brownish-red zone, lip touched with orange (spring). *p. 1816*

SACCOLABIUM: see also Ascocentrum, Rhynchostylis

SADLERIA *Polypodiaceae (Filices)* **S2HFM**

cyatheoides (Hawaii), "Pigmy cyathea"; attractive, vigorous small tree fern forming a trunk 1-1½ m high, and a crown of fleshy, soft-leathery, light green, bipinnate fronds to 1 m long, with neatly regular, linear segments crenate and turned under at edges; leaf stalks stout and fleshy. *Humid-tropical.* *p. 1167*

SAGITTARIA *Alismataceae* **C-S2-3LBWh**

latifolia (No. America), "Arrowhead" or "Duck potato"; aquatic herb with variable leaves from linear lanceolate to broad, arrow-shaped, blades to 50 cm long; flowers white; freely adapting itself to all sorts of growing conditions. *Warm temperate.* *p. 80*

montevidensis (So. America, So. U.S.), "Giant arrowhead"; ornamental aquatic perennial to 2 m high, with arrow-shaped leaves having long lobes; flowers 5 cm or more across, cream with crimson blotch on each petal, stamens yellow; for garden pools. *p. 80*

sagittifolia florepleno (Europe, Asia); a double-flowered form of the old world "Common arrowhead"; bog plant with stoloniferous, swollen, tuberous, edible rootstock; variable leaves 5-20 cm long, linear or hastate arrow-shaped with lobes longer or shorter than blade; white flowers spotted with purple. *p. 80*

SAINTPAULIA *Gesneriaceae* **S-I3HFM**

Well beloved small tropical East African herbaceous plants known as "Usambara" or "African violets"; usually symmetrical rosettes of pubescent, spoon-shaped, brittle leaves and basal stalked flowers from the leaf axils; the corolla is flattened and two-lipped, with 5 large rounded lobes; the upper lip is 2-lobed and usually smaller than the 3-lobed lower lip. The primary color is in shades of violet-blue. The first two species S. ionantha and confusa were discovered in Tanzania, then German East Africa in 1892. The first seedlings from one or hybrids from both species began to appear the following year. Since Saintpaulias are also easily propagated vegetatively from leaf cuttings, the miracle of a single somatic or body cell has given rise to thousands of variations and cultivars including pink and white sports, mainly from one species. S. ionantha. These mutants, and further intense hybridizing, have resulted in many different horticultural types and forms including double-flowered and bicolors, most of them named and recorded. In addition, numerous new species have been discovered, some miniatures, others creeping. The relative ease of cultivation in the home, and their simple propagation by leaf cuttings, have made Saintpaulias the most popular house plant in America, well suited to our warm homes. *Tropical.*

African species: S-I-C3HFM

amaniensis (Tanzania); from Usambara Mts., near Amani at 900 m; low-growing creeper with small convex, pointed, green leaves covered with gray hairs, and small, lively, intermediate-violet-blue flowers. *p. 1260*

confusa (diplotricha, kewensis) (Tanzania), "Usambara violet"; miniature species from moist E. Usambara mts. at 900 m; known as diplotricha but identified as confusa because of its more firm, light green, thinner leaves, dentate, green beneath, and having flattened, not erect hairs; small pale violet-blue flowers with darker center. *p. 1261*

difficilis (E. Africa); pretty species from the borderland of Kenya and Tanzania; prolific plant with pleasing light yellow-green, thin leaves; violet-blue flowers with bright yellow anthers. (S) *p. 1260*

diplotricha (Tanzania); rock-dweller from Maweni near low, coastal Tanga; very similar to S. confusa, with pale violet 2½ cm flowers; the limb not quite flat but the lower lip forming an angle with the erect upper lip; the leaves are recurved, thicker and purplish above, reddish purple beneath, with long hairs spreading and short hairs erect in a rather dense but inconspicuous covering. *p. 1262*

goetzeana (C. Tanzania); from forests in the Uluguru mts., at 1,100 to 2,100 m; succulent, branching species with little round, convex, dark green, pubescent leaves, purplish-red beneath, creeping and rooting at nodes; flowering difficult, on elongated branches with flowers having white corolla with lilac markings on both lower lobes. Appears to respond to chills and resting. *p. 1260, 1263*

grandifolia (Tanzania: W. Usambara Mts.); in habitat found growing on clay; fine species with deep violet, single flowers 2½ cm across; thin light green leaves to 10 cm long, cordate at base, the erect or curved hairs all long and well spaced. *p. 1262*

grotei (Tanzania); from deep shade in the E. Usambara Mts., near Amani at 900 m on rocks close to a waterfall; robust trailing or straggling species growing into a large plant full of fresh-green, short-hairy, rounded, fleshy leaves with notched edges, on long, flexible, brown petioles; small flowers 2½ cm across, pale violet-blue with darker center and edges, in axillary clusters. Excellent for hanging baskets. *Humid-subtropic.* *p. 1261*

intermedia (Tanzania: E. Usambara Mts.); in habitat found growing on rock; of creeping, stalk-forming (caulescent) habit, with short internodes; leaves dull purplish-green above, reddish underneath, to 5 cm long, the margins crenate-serrate, covered with all long hairs bent over in the upper half; flowers deep violet, the limb 2½ cm wide. *p. 1262*

ionantha (Tanzania), "African violet", found near Tanga at 30 m and higher, warm-humid; parent with S. confusa of most hybrids; upright species with large flowers a pretty violet-blue, to 2½ cm across, and dark, coppery-green, pubescent leaves reddish beneath. On the steep and breezy rocks towering up from the Amboni Caves, north of Tanga, I have seen plants hanging from narrow clefts or footholds surviving the seasonal dry periods by means of rhizomes almost bare of foliage. *p. 19*, 1261*

magungensis (Tanzania); from West Usambara Mountains, shady and humid; creeping brown stem with rounded, hard leaves with depressed veins, and underside pale green; small flowers medium blue with darker center. (SN) *p. 1261*

nitida (Tanzania: Nguru Mts. at 900 m); handsome small rosette with shining dark green leaves nearly round and lightly cupped, the scattered hairs all short; flowers deep violet blue. *p. 1262*

orbicularis (Tanzania); from W. Usambara Mts., cool, between 1,100 and 2,300 m; upright species with thin, light green, rounded leaves having depressed veins, on brown stems; dainty flowers very pale blue with dark center, on wiry brown petioles. (I1) *p. 1261*

pendula (Tanzania: E. Usambara Mts.); rock-dweller in habitat; spreading plant with exuberantly creeping (caulescent) stems; thin, all light green, roundish, cupped, crenate leaves 4-5 cm long, covered on the upper surface with almost erect, only long hairs; one or two flowers on each stalk deep violet 2½ cm across. *p. 1262*

rupicola (Kenya), an "African violet"; pretty species which I collected north of Mombasa, growing on perpendicular limestone rocks in crevices; when older often hanging by a long, thick rhizome which sustains the plant through the dry seasons; grass green, thinnish, lightly wrinkled, faintly crenate foliage 7-8 cm long, glossy pale silvery-green beneath; both short and long hairs erect or slightly bent near top; pretty flowers 3 cm across, wisteria-blue with darker center. *Humid-tropical.* *p. 1260, 1262, 1263*

shumensis (Tanzania); from dry forest on cliffs in W. Usambara Mts., at 1,800 m; attractive small species with fresh green, rather thick, round leaves sparsely covered with long white hairs, neatly toothed; with small flowers very pale gray-blue or mauve, violet eye, blue pistil; not very floriferous. (I) *p. 1260*

tongwensis (Tanzania); from Mt. Tongwe at 750 m; pleasing species with long, stiff, pubescent, bronzy leaves with light green veins, margins crenate; vigorous pale amethyst flowers. (S1LFD) *p. 1261*

velutina (Tanzania: W. Usambara Mts.), from rain forest at 1,100 m; compact plant with thinnish, crenate leaves blackish velvety green above, reddish-purple underneath, and covered on top with numerous short-erect hairs together with some long ones; small flowers 2 cm across, deep violet with lobes tipped white. *p. 1262*

Horticultural hybrids: ***S1HFM**

'Admiral'; a California cultivar by Armacost, about 1930, from seedlings of ionantha x confusa; of low, symmetrical habit, free-blooming, blue-purple, even during summer; with dark green pubescent foliage. *p. 1272*

'Azure Beauty'; free-blooming and large-growing, prolific variety with beautiful double flowers white with violet in base, carried erect on firm stems; smooth, shiny foliage. *p. 1267*

'Baltic Girl' (Sailor Girl x Azure Beauty); compact plant with an interesting combination of pretty, double white flowers edged in blue, and blue in base, and oakleaf-type, deeply lobed leaves with pale green base. *p. 1266*

'Beaming'; light green, plain leaves on compact plant; large pink, double flowers. *p. 1265*

'Bicolor'; compact plant with distinctive, two-toned flowers having the upper petals purple, lower petals pale orchid with deeper tips; foliage reddish beneath. *p. 1272*

'Black Magic'; outstanding floriferous variety with fully double, deep violet flowers prettily showing their yellow anthers; quilted, round, deep green leaves. *p. 1275*

'Blue and White Star'; sported at Roehrs from 'Pansy', this attractive variety is free blooming well above the green foliage, the petals have a white band through the center to the tip, flanked by bands of blue. *p. 1266*

'Blue Boy', (ionantha x confusa); excellent cultivar of the first primary hybrids I remember being developed about 1930 by Armacost & Royston at Los Angeles, while I was employed there as an orchid grower; willing and profuse bloomer with violet-blue, single flowers over fresh green leaves. In 1927 Armacost obtained Saintpaulia seed from Benary in Germany, and Sutton in England; from 1,000 resulting plants, 10 showing different and distinct traits were selected. The first choice selected from the Benary seedlings was named 'Blue Boy', the second 'Sailor Boy'; the next eight selections were made from the English seed. *p. 1272*

'Blue Boy-in-the-Snow'; meritorious leaf sport having light green foliage splashed with creamy-white throughout the leaf and maintaining its variegation; flowers violet-blue on pink petioles. *p. 1268*

'Blue Moon'; good commercial variety of free growing upright habit, with medium sized dark leaves, and good production of medium size rounded, single 4 cm flowers of bright violet-blue, pretty with yellow stamens; for fall and Christmas bloom. *p. 1273*

'Blue Peak'; of flat habit; free blooming though short, the double flowers are violet-blue with each fringed little petal daintily edged in white; ovate leaves bronzy-green. *p. 1248A, 1272*

'Blue Sail' (Roehrs); excellent commercial hybrid of flat habit, with round dark metallic leaves lightly toothed, fuchsia-red beneath; freely producing good clusters of vivid violet-blue single flowers of medium size well above foliage, mainly in spring. *p. 1273*

'Blue Valley'; large, symmetrical, fast grower with violet-blue, single flowers carried well above the shapely, dark foliage, wine-red beneath; free blooming. *p. 1272*

'Blue Valley marginata'; very charming leaf sport forming a shapely rosette of grayish-green leaves broadly margined creamy-yellow; medium-blue flowers. *p. 1274*

'Bridesmaid Two-face'; mutation with flower petals in matching opposite pairs, blue and white; fast-growing, spreading plant with long-stalked, medium-green leaves. *p. 1274*

'Confederate Beauty'; monstrose, a curiosity form with dark-green, spoon-shaped crenate leaves purple beneath, arranged in diminishing size along both sides of a fasciated stem; large flowers violet-blue with wavy petals, spreading 5½ cm. *p. 1268*

'Congo Belle' (Blue Sail x Pink Cloud); attractive hybrid of clean habit; leaves smooth incurving, round heart-shaped, fresh-green; free-blooming with large double flowers deep violet-purple on long erect stem like 'Blue Sail'. *p. 1274*

'Corinne'; shapely plant with light green foliage and medium-size flowers fully double; buds greenish opening to pure white; keeps well. *p. 1270*

'Cydonia'; robust, spready plant with wavy quilted leaves dark metallic green and light green midrib; inflorescence erect, the immense violet-blue flowers with frilled edges and double center. *p. 1273*

'Diana blau' (Harmonie strain); excellent variety featuring a bouquet of large 4 cm single flowers velvety blue with darker violet center, carried freely on stiff stalks above a rosette of rich green leaves. This hybrid group is distinguished by vigorous growth combined with bountiful, long-lasting bloom; originated by Englert of Germany and Puerto Rico. *p. 1273*

'Double Delight'; an excellent, floriferous plant of flat habit with double, medium-blue flowers which will open well even during the heat of summer; bronzy leaves, wine-red beneath. *p. 1273, 1275*

'Double Inspiration'; symmetrical plant with medium, dark olive-green leaves, and large semi-double, orchid-pink flowers. *p. 1264*

'Double Pink Giant' (Dupont x Pink Ideal); fine, silver-blue Roehrs hybrid with very large, 5 cm soft pink, double flowers, and heavy, Dupont-type crenate leaves, wine-red beneath. *p. 1266*

'Dupont Blue'; one of the Dupont series characterized by their huge dimensions; firm violet-blue flowers measuring 5 cm or more; leaves are massive, almost round, and crenate; habit low, but slow-growing and not very free-blooming. *p. 1268*

'Dupont Silver Blue' (hyb. #4); a clone of the Dupont type with massive crenate, hairy leaves and large firm, flat 5 cm flowers pale lilac-blue with darker eye; of low habit. *p. 1266*

'Elfriede' (Rhapsodie strain); one of the successful German (Holtkamp) triploid hybrids characterized by their "Biedermeier" habit of growth forming closed, rather flat rosettes of dark green, firm leaves, and a formal mound of long-lasting, thick-textured, non-dropping blooms; 'Elfriede' has single round, dark blue 4 cm flowers; a prolific bloomer. *p. 1273*

'Ember Dream'; rather flat plant with roundish, dark green, quilted leaves, and single to semi-double flowers fuchsia-pink. *p. 1264*

'Fairy'; bronze, hairy foliage, round and crenate, thick and quite brittle; flat flowers semi-double carmine-rose with darker center. *p. 1271*

'Fischer's Fire Dance'; vigorous grower with smooth, grass-green leaves, and erect, large single flowers orchid-purple with the 2 small top petals dark purple; free bloomer. *p. 1271*

'Fringed Pom Pom'; unusual cultivar of large size, with glossy-green, quilted and ruffled leaves; fringed double flowers white, edged with lavender and chartreuse. *p. 1274*

'Frosty'; shapely plant with attractive, friendly green leaves broadly variegated with creamy white toward edge; flowers white tinged blue, or pale blue. *p. 1274*

'Geneva Star'; light purple sport of 'Lady Geneva', attractive single flowers bordered white; crenate leaves reddish beneath. *p. 1267*

'Good News'; compact plant with wavy, grass-green leaves, and large fringed, fully double flowers medium pink with darker middle. *p. 1265*

'Henny Backus'; compact Lyndon Lyon hybrid (Dolgeville, N.Y.), with small waxy, tufted leaves, flowers semi-double 4 cm across and perfectly round, cupped and crisped, a lively deep violet-blue on stiff-erect, strong stalks. *p. 1263*

'Herkimer Girl'; floriferous, showy plant with large single, cupped, violet blue flowers with rounded petals on long erect stalks; fleshy, crenated, dark leaves pale in center ("girl" type). *p. 1267*

'Holiday'; sturdy plant with double flowers purplish rose on firm stalks; pubescent, quilted, bronzy leaves, wine-red beneath. *p. 1269*

'Honeybud'; excellent double variety of compact habit with wiry flower sprays bearing the full round, clear rose-pink blooms, more freely produced than 'Ohio Bountiful'. *p. 1269*

'Irresistible Girl'; charming prolific variety, always in bloom, with semi-double to double flowers of clear pink, deep rose in center; attractive waxy, scalloped leaves with pale base. *p. 1269*

'Juliet'; slow-growing but free-blooming double variety in shades of lilac and amethyst; with round, bronzy, cupped leaves, red beneath. *p. 1275*

'Kenya Violet Blue' (Roehrs 1964); typical long-lasting violet-blue, the "Kenya double violet", a breakthrough in Saintpaulia hybrids, incorporating parentage of the blue S. rupicola which I found in Kenya, with the wine-red cv 'Flash', resulting in a vigorous, shapely plant, with large 9 cm shiny green, spoon-type leaves, and 4 to 4½ cm flowers double like a rose, and a clear violet-blue, the non-dropping blossoms drying up on the plant instead of rotting when past blooming. *p. 1263*

'Lady Geneva'; a sensation when it first appeared in San Francisco; the single, deep blue-violet flowers distinctly edged in white; compact plant with fresh-green leaves and, though not vigorous, it most always has some flowers. *p. 1275*

'Little Blue Minnesota'; tetraploid resulting from Colchicine treatmeant; dark bronze, spoon-shaped quilted leaves with pale midrib, in shapely rosette as if a nest; clustering in the center a profusion of blue-purple flowers; very floriferous. *p. 1268*

'Little Jewel'; grotei hybrid; miniature plant with dark green, wavy leaves, and heavy double, pink flowers with frilled petals. *p. 1264*

'Loretta'; compact plant with leaves shelving, quilted and rough, blackish forest green; good grower, and free-blooming with delicate pale pinkish-lavender double flowers, dark center. *p. 1270*

'Lyons Girl'; outstanding, compact plant, very floriferous, with single white, cupped, erect flowers daintily edged in bluish-purple; scalloped "girl" leaves with pale center, almost white beneath. *p. 1267*

'Mary Thompson'; wavy, crenate foliage bronze over light green; fairly large flowers fully double, pale lilac with darker center, the heavy inflorescence pendant; free-blooming. *p. 1270*

'Maybe'; of flat habit; light green leaves pale beneath, with large double, peach-blossom-like flowers very pale blush-pink, darker in center. *p. 1269*

'Mayfair'; a variety of attractively fluffy habit, with wavy, "girl" type, quilted leaves, and masses of deep violet-blue, double flowers lightly and daintily fringed. *p. 1269*

'Melody Air'; flat plant with plain, light green leaves, free-blooming with double flowers white with broad pink edge. *p. 1264*

'Mentor Boy'; large, free growing variety and willing bloomer with slender upright, single, purplish-violet flowers; dark green, slightly glossy leaves. *p. 1272*

'Musqueteer'; a tetraploid resulting through colchicine treatment from Azure Beauty, with huge, substantial, semi-double flowers; inner petals lilac-blue, outer, larger petals mainly white, on stout stalks and with large, fresh green, quilted, round leaves. *p. 1267*

'Ohio Bountiful'; an early double clear pink of a pleasing soft shade; flowers medium but freely produced and of good keeping quality; small fresh green leaves on a compact plant. *p. 1270*

'Painted Girl'; compact plant of erect habit with crenate, heavy quilted "girl" type foliage; single bicolor flowers white with lavender-purple edge. *p. 1264*

'Pansy'; pretty variety with large rounded, long-lasting flowers of medium-violet, contrasting with the broad white margin; small leaves, one type purple beneath, another pale. *p. 1275*

'Pink Amour'; showy, compact grower with waxy bronzy-green, scalloped "holly" leaves, and sturdy, medium-large rose-pink flowers with darker, cerise, frilled margins. *p. 1265*

'Pink Cheer'; lovely, prolific growing plant, with clear pink, single flowers having a dark rose center, more freely blooming and longer lasting, especially in summer, than 'Pink Wonder'; dark foliage reddish beneath. *p. 1266*

'Pink Cloud'; good double-flowered variety with large, deep pink blooms quite floriferous; rather flat plant with heavy roundish, pubescent, medium green leaves. *p. 1265*

'Pink Cushion'; lovely, compact plant with metallic green leaves, and numerous double, high-cushion, dainty pink flowers. *p. 1265*

'Pink Dresden'; compact, slow growing plant with semi-double to double pink flowers, the center darker rose; coppery, glossy, cupped leaves with reddish base, purplish beneath, not free blooming but long lasting; one of the first doubles in pink. *p. 1275*

'Pink Fantasy'; fast grower with dark bronzy green, pointed leaves, and pretty, glowing pink single flowers with flaring lobes and deep rose eye; flowers don't last long but are constantly replaced and keep blooming. *p. 1248A, 1271*

'Pink Fire'; attractive variety with frilly and wavy, dark moss-green "girl" type foliage, and heavy double, rather flat rose-pink flowers with neatly fringed petals. *p. 1265*

'Pink Fringette'; the first single pink having fringed and ruffled petals, introduced by Fischer; the large, long-lasting, vivid flowers carried well above the wavy, bright green, crenate foliage. *p. 1272*

'Pink Ideal'; of erect growing habit, with dark, moss-green foliage, and medium-sized double flowers very light baby-pink. *p. 1264*

'Pink Miracle'; large sturdy plant, rather flat, having round green leaves with red backs; single pink flowers of fair size, with dark eye and edged in dark rose, and lightly ruffled; free blooming. *p. 1271*

'Pink Puff'; flat growing plant with double, clear pink flowers having darker center; dark coppery green, quilted, pubescent leaves wine-red beneath. *p. 1267*

'Queen Biruta'; excellent, showy hybrid of Lady Geneva x Crimson Lake x Blue Girl; long-lasting single flowers lavender-blue with broad white border; heavy, scalloped, "girl" type foliage. *p. 1264*

'Queen's Cushion'; very compact, curious plant with double, very round flowers, deep velvety maroon-red; quilted, coppery leaves with reddish base and petioles. *p. 1275*

'Racy Red'; a star-type cultivar, raised by Fischer's Greenhouses, Lynwood, N.J. 1963; compact plant with small oval foliage, red underneath; the flowers unique in having 5 even, fused petals resembling a star, 4 cm across, vivid cerise-red. *p. 1263*

'Rhapsodie Linda' (Pat.); large and vigorous plant with dark bronze foliage; nesting in the center a veritable bouquet of large 3½ cm semi-double flowers with light purple, ruffled petals. Photo on pg. 1263 is of a plant grown in 15 cm pot by Mr. Yoshida of Sunnyside Nurseries in California. *p. 1263*

'Rhapsodie Maria' (Pat.); smallish girl-type waxy leaves with yellow base and crenate margins, silvery beneath; sturdy stalks carry clusters of 7 to 8 single to semi-double flowers to 4 cm across, the firm, frilled petals dark violet-blue, contrasting with the prominent vivid yellow pollen. *p. 1263*

'Ruffled Queen'; exquisite variety with large, firm flowers dark amethyst, the edges frilled as if with lace; large, round, crenate, long-hairy leaves. *p. 1272*

'Sea Sprite'; pretty plant with light green quilted, crisped and crenate foliage shining glossy through the short hair; fully double white flowers turning mauve, bordered lilac blue along the delicately frilled edge. *p. 1271*

'Show Queen'; sturdy compact variety with stiff leaves variegated yellow toward margins, and large firm violet flowers charmingly ruffled at edges. *p. 1268*

'Snow Prince'; excellent, free-flowering, snow-white, single variety of neat habit, with large, full round, glistening flowers held high on strong stems; light green, graceful foliage. *p. 1266*

'Snow Prince Giant'; firm rosette of large fresh green leaves with erect-stalked, big clean-cut single white flowers full-round 3 cm across, making them very showy. *p. 1270*

'Snow White' (Roehrs 1941); sport of 'Blue Boy' originated in N.J. at the same time 'White Lady' appeared in San Francisco; the first white cultivars in the U.S.; shapely plant with an abundance of medium-size single very white flowers, of flat habit with small green leaves. *p. 1270*

'Spring Sky' (Blue Eyes x Blue Boy); compact, free-blooming hybrid with light blue flowers and dark eye; light green to coppery, satiny leaves; more prolific than 'Blue Eyes'. *p. 1266*

'Star Girl'; attractive variety with white flowers streaked and edged with medium-blue carried on stiff stems well above the "girl" type leaves; scalloped margin and pale base. *p. 1275*

'Star Pink'; shapely plant with small green convex leaves; large 4½ cm star-shaped flowers with lobes all equal, orchid pink with purplish center shaped as in a star. *p. 1271*

'Summer Skies'; large plant with plain green leaves covered in profusion with rather flat azure blue flowers. *p. 1268*

'Tetra-Orchid Sunset'; the result of colchicine treatment; a robust plant with larger, fully double, maroon flowers shaded orchid, and heavier, round, hairy leaves bronzy green, wine-red beneath. *p. 1272*

'White Madonna'; strong bushy plant from which unfolds a profusion of pale green buds, into large double, pure white flowers; the deep green, almost waxy leaves are of the typical "girl" type. *p. 1275*

'White Pansy'; sport of 'Pansy', with snow-white, single flowers, but does not always stay true to color; spring-green foliage, of upright habit. *p. 1274*

'White Pride'; truly a proud variety, fast growing, with nice light green leaves and heavy, large round, double flowers of pure white. *p. 1269*

'Wintergreen'; variety close to ionantha but distinctive because of its heavily variegated leaves almost all white with milky-green flowers variable. *p. 1274*

SALACCA *Palmae* **S3LFM**

edulis (Malaya, Java, Bali), the "Salac" or "Snake-skin fruit"; Malaysian feather palm, with multiple trunks mostly subterranean, forming rosettes of tall fronds 5 to 6 m long, on ferociously armed leaf stalks; the leaflets flat in one plane, silvery-gray on lower surface, the back of the rachis with long spines; from the base, the female plants bear attractively ornamental fruit 6 cm long, on flexuous spikes, pear-shaped and shell-like covered with overlapping brown scales, a perfect imitation of snake-skin; enclosed is the yellow edible flesh. Widely cultivated in Java; in Bali on the slopes of the volcano Gunung Agung; sold in markets as buah salac. *Tropical. p. 1885*

SALICORNIA *Chenopodiaceae* **CI2L (Sodium) BW**

bigelovii (Nova Scotia to Texas, California, Mexico, W. Indies), the salt-loving "Glasswort", inhabiting salt marshes; erect succulent, fleshy herb about 30 cm or more tall, with jointed stems and ascending cylindrical branches, dense with opposite, shingled leaves reduced to scales, and minute inserted flowers. Its ash is a source of soda used in making soap and glass. *p. 777*

SALIX *Salicaceae* **C2LBW**

discolor (Nova Scotia to Virginia and Missouri), "Pussy willows"; hardy shrub or low tree 3-5½ m high, with straight willowy purplish-brown branches and 8-10 cm oblong, deciduous leaves, bluish green beneath; male and female flowers on separate plants, which bloom before the leaves expand; the female catkins are the familiar pussy-willows which can be easily forced by bringing into a warm room after Jan. 15. The flowers have no petals or sepals, but the series of bracts protecting them form a dense catkin. *p. 2039*

matsudana 'Tortuosa', "Dragon-claw willow"; a form of the species from No. China and Korea; small tree with twisted, contorted branches, and wiry pendulous branchlets with curiously twisted linear olive-green leaves 4-8 cm long, grayish glaucescent beneath. *p. 1992, 2035*

sachalinensis (Northern Japan to Kuriles); brownish tree with twisted branches, covered with gray-silky pubescence when young; leaves 6-10 cm long and 2 cm wide. *p. 2038*

SALPIGLOSSIS *Solanaceae* **C2LBM**

sinuata (Chile, Perú), "Painted tongue"; showy, branching clammy-hairy annual with sinuately toothed leaves and large solitary, 6 cm, funnel-shaped flowers brilliantly colored yellow through scarlet and primrose, and nearly to blue, and with a variation in veining in the wide throat. *Subtropic. p. 2072*

SALVIA *Labiatae* **I-S2LBM**

argentea (Mediterranean reg.), "Silver sage"; shaggy biennial to 1 m high; broad ovate leaves to 20 cm long, white-woolly, lobed and wrinkled; the basal leaves stalked, stem-leaves sessile; tubular two-lipped flowers in whorls, with corolla pinkish-white, 5 cm long. *p. 1355*

coccinea (So. Carolina to Florida and Texas, Trop. America); "Texas sage"; hairy annual or perennial to 60 cm high, with ovate, toothed leaves to 6 cm long; slender stalks with twiggy racemes of scarlet bilabiate flowers to 2½ cm long. *p. 1354*

dorisiana (Honduras); attractive both as foliage and flowering plant, with large velvety green, fragrant leaves, and rosy-red, bilabiate flowers on wiry stems. (S) *p. 1353, 1354*

flava (China: Yunnan); from the Lichiang range at 2,600-3,600 m; perennial 30-90 cm high, with thick rhizome, sub-erect stalks with willow-like gray-green leaves to 20 cm long and 3 cm wide, hairy on both sides, and crenate; flowers pale canary-yellow arranged along one side of flower stalk, upper lobe of corolla splotched and veined deep purple. *p. 1354*

glutinosa (Europe, Central Asia); sticky-hairy perennial to 1 m high, with lanceolate, toothed leaves to 20 cm long, becoming smaller upward along stalk; whorls of flowers with swollen tube pale yellow 4 cm long, in stiffly erect racemes. *p. 1354*

greggii (Texas, Mexico), "Autumn sage"; shrub about 1 m high, dense with small linear-oblong 1 cm leaves dull pale green; 2½ cm flowers carmine or purplish-red, with swollen, bilabiate tube in terminal racemes. *p. 1355*

involucrata (Mexico, Central America) "Rose-leaf-sage"; sub-shrub to 1 m or more high, with ovate, toothed leaves 12 cm long, the bract-like floral leaves colored; calyx purplish, and 2½ cm rose corolla, in whorls. *Subtropic. p. 1354*

leucantha (Mexico), "Mexican bush-sage"; shrub about 60 cm high with woolly branches and narrow wrinkled leaves 15 cm long, white-downy beneath; the woolly flowers with white or purple perianth, and the calyx covered by dense purple felt, in long slender spikes. *p. 1353, 1356*

microphylla (Mexico), "Cherry-sage"; ornamental herb with shrubby base; small coppery, ovate leaves, and a zigzag stalk with showy tubular flowers and large lip, deep velvety cherry red. From the collection of Marjorie Wihtol, Middletown, New Jersey. *p. 1356*

nutans (Balkans, C. Russia); hardy herbaceous perennial to 1 m high, with hairy stems and ovate, wrinkled, doubly crenate 12 cm leaves, pubescent beneath; small 1 cm violet flowers in dense, spike-like racemes, drooping as the flowers open. *p. 1354*

officinalis (Mediterranean reg.), "Garden sage"; hardy perennial subshrub, white woolly, with slender gray-green pebbly leaves; flowers in terminal racemes light purple or white. Use: for seasoning poultry, cheese, veal, sausage, tomatoes; also medicinally. *Subtropic. p. 1354*

officinalis tricolor; attractive variety with gray-green leaves variegated yellowish and pink becoming velvety red. *p. 1353*

patens (Mountains of Mexico), "Gentian sage"; sticky-hairy, half-hardy perennial to 75 cm high, with ovate or arrow-shaped leaves crenate at margins; tubular blue flowers 5 cm or more long, with gaping lips. *p. 1355*

sclarea (So. Europe), "Clary sage"; hardy biennial 1 m high, with broad-ovate hairy and pebbly gray-green leaves to 22 cm long, floral leaves colored rose and white; the flowers whitish-blue in clusters. Use: flavoring wine, oil for perfume. *p. 1349*

splendens (Brazil), "Scarlet sage"; a well-known shrub, cultivated as an annual, with ovate, rich green, glabrous leaves on erect spikes bearing showy, scarlet-red flowers 3-4 cm long, with fiery-red calyx, in late summer. *Tropical. p. 1353, 1355*

splendens 'Dwarf'; class commercially available under several names such as 'Fire ball'; annual of extra dwarf habit only 25 cm high, early blooming (Mid-June on); uniquely base-branching and bushy, profusely blooming in brillant scarlet, until frost, over bright green foliage. *p. 1355*

splendens 'Lavender Love'; long, full-flowered spikes of vivid light lavender, erect on strong 50 cm plants; deep green foliage; blooms 8 weeks after planting. Listed by Park Seed, Greenwood, South Carolina. *p. 1356*

SALVINIA *Salviniaceae (Filices)* **S2-3(water) B-FW**

auriculata (Tropical America), "Floating fern"; small, flowerless, aquatic fern-ally (Cryptogam), floating on water, with 1 cm, oval leaves pale yellowish-green and warty-haired on the surface, set along thread-like floating rhizomes, soon forming clusters. *Humid-tropical. p. 1082*

cucculata (Sumatra, Borneo); an interesting fern-ally floating on the water, forming colonies to 20 cm across; the leaf surface is formed like cups, to 8 cm long, and fringed with brown hairs; this aquatic has no roots, a row of divided leaves on the underside assuming their functions, and where they also develop sporangia. *p. 1083*

SAMANEA *Leguminosae* **S2LBD**

saman (Pithecellobium) (West Indies, Central America), the "Rain-tree", "Saman", or "Monkey-pod"; great tropical shade tree to 24 m high, with spreading head like an open umbrella, to 30 m wide; bipinnate or 4-pinnate leaves with oblique ovate or roundish leaflets to 4 cm long, shiny above, downy beneath; small silky-yellow flowers with long pink stamens, white towards lower part, followed by flat pods 15-20 cm long. *p. 1390, 1391*

SAMUELA *Liliaceae* **S2LBD**

carnerosana (Coahuila, Mexico), "Palma de San Pedro"; bold tree with thick trunk 1½-6 m high; crown of thick gray-green, dagger-shaped leaves 1 m long, 6 cm wide, with marginal filaments and corky edge and sharp brown apex point. *Arid-subtropic. p. 1505*

SANCHEZIA *Acanthaceae* **S-I3LFM-W**

nobilis (Ecuador, Brazil); handsome foliage plant; in habitat a magnificent shrub to 2 m high, with thick, fleshy, squarish stems and large ovate, flaccid leaves to 30 cm long, attractive glossy green with narrow yellow veins, midrib on underside wine-red; the inflorescence showy, with tubular 5 cm flowers yellow, from cupped red bracts, and with protruding stamens. *p. 52*

nobilis glaucophylla (Ecuador); handsome tropical shrub cultivated for its large lanceolate, soft-leathery leaves to 22 cm long, glaucous-green with bold, contrasting yellow stripes; large yellow flowers with bright red bracts in showy terminal panicle. Foliage tends to become green in older plants. *Tropical. p. 52*

SANDERSONIA *Liliaceae* **I3LBDd**

aurantiaca (So. Africa: Natal), "Christmas-bells", or "Chinese lantern-lily"; tuberous climbing plant 45-60 cm high, with alternate, 10 cm ribbed, lanceolate leaves, often tipped with a tendril, along slender wiry stems; axillary bright orange-yellow, inflated urnshaped, nodding flowers 2½ cm long, of shiny, papery texture. *Subtropic. p. 1492*

SANGUISORBA *Rosaceae* **C2LBM**

minor (Poterium) (Europe, Asia, E. No. America); "Salad burnet"; a hardy perennial herb to 60 cm; thin-wiry stalks with pairs of deeply dentate

2 cm leaflets; small greenish crimson flowers without petals in round heads. This herb came to America with the pilgrims; fresh leaves are cut for seasoning of salads and for drinks. p. 2000

SANSEVIERIA *Liliaceae* ***S1LF-BD-M**

aethiopica (Zimbabwe, Transvaal); rosette of open habit; broad leaves to 40 cm long, dark green mottled lighter green, and with red corky margins; flowers white. *Subtropic.* *p. 1488*

arborescens (E. Trop. Africa); tree-like, erect growing succulent, forming stem to 1 m high, from which curve the horizontal, slender linear, channeled leaves, plain green, with horny white edge. *Arid-tropical.* *p. 1483*

aubrytiana (Gabon, Eq. Africa); giant, thick, succulent-fibrous, sword-shaped leaves to 1 m high and 10-17 cm wide, dark green marked with irregular crossbands of silvery gray, and brown edge. *p. 1484, 1485, 1488*

caespitosa (Namibia); small rosette of rather flat, lanceolate recurving leaves tapering to a slender point, dark green, mottled grayish; freely suckering. *Arid-tropical.* *p. 1489*

canaliculata (Trop. Africa); slow growing species, forming generally only one, or possibly two, medium green, erect leaves to 1 m long each year, and which are cylindrical but regularly grooved, resembling a rubber hose, and just about as flexible. *p. 1485*

cylindrica (sulcata) (So. Tropical Africa, Natal), "Spear sansevieria"; round, arching, but rigid leaves to 1 m long and 3 cm thick, circular in dia., and usually furrowed or grooved, grouped several to a shoot, and tapering to a point, dark green with gray-green crossbanding which disappears with age; flowers pinkish. *Arid-tropical.* *p. 1481, 1483, 1489*

dawei (Trop. Africa); broad, oblanceolate leaf, deep green, faintly mottled light green; corky edge; broad silver crossbands beneath. *Tropical.* *p. 1490*

desertii (Southern Africa: Botswana, Zimbabwe, North Transvaal), "Rhinograss"; dweller from the Kalahari desert to the dry Veld, one of the stoutest plants in Africa; hard-succulent, erect cylindric leaves sunburnt green, with 9-12 shallow grooves, and narrow channel on top, $2\frac{1}{2}$-3 cm thick, $\frac{1}{2}$-1 m long, fan-like arranged; of stoloniferous habit, forming dense masses; insignificant orchid-like white flowers. Shunned by wild animals because of sharp tipped apex. *Arid-subtropic.* *p. 1481, 1489*

dooneri (Rift Valley, Kenya); shapely rosette of lax, lanceolate leathery leaves 10-50 cm long, on narrow petiole, very smooth, dark green with pale cross markings and dark pebbling; flowers purplish outside, white within. *Arid-tropical.* *p. 1490*

ehrenbergii (Ethiopia, Kenya, Tanzania), "Blue sansevieria"; plant with leaves alternately arranged as in a large fan, concealing the stem; the blue-green foliage above with triangular channel and white papery edge, flat on sides and rounded below. *Arid-tropical.* *p. 1481, 1483, 1490*

fasciata (Zaîre); erect to recurving cylindrical, stiff leaves to 80 cm long, frequently in pairs, dark green with light green zigzag cross marbling. *Tropical.* *p. 1489*

gracilis (Mazeras, Kenya; Tanzania); short-stemmed with spreading branches; tufts of slender leaves 20 to 90 cm long, cylindrical except for concave channel down the face, grayish green with faint gray cross-bands; flowers white, in pairs. *Tropical.* *p. 1489*

grandicuspis (grandicuspidata at Leningrad Bot. Garden) (Zaîre); broad leathery leaves erect or spreading, 16-50 cm long, shiny dark green with lighter crossbands, with open channel down the face, and narrowed at apex to sharp awl-shaped point; corky margins. *p. 1491*

grandis (Somaliland), "Grand Somali hemp"; epiphytic succulent sending out runner-like rhizomes producing 2-4 broad-obovate leaves to 15 cm wide, spreading near the ground, dull green with broad bands of deeper green, margins red; white flowers in dense raceme. *p. 1483, 1487*

guineensis (West Africa: Guinea coast of Nigeria, Cameroun), a "Bowstring hemp"; robust, attractive rosette with 8-10 extremely broad, sword-shaped leaves 8-10 cm wide, and 45-90 cm high, arranged in birdsnest fashion, glossy deep green, irregularly cross-banded light grayish green. I photographed this striking species along the Guinea coast, in Southern Nigeria. *Tropical.* *p. 1482, 1483*

guineensis 'Variegata'; showy variety with upright broad, sword-like leaves grass-and gray-green and having wide yellow marginal bands. *p. 1483, 1486*

intermedia (E. Tropical Africa), "Pigmy bowstring"; stiff, shapely, dense rosette of very thick, recurved leaves, gray-green, with deep triangular channel inside, and keeled beneath, marked with numerous pale crossbands; the inner edges horny. *p. 1485*

kirkii (S. E. Trop. Africa); erect, bold succulent rosette to 2 m tall, with flat or concave, oblanceolate leaves to 9 cm wide, the petiole deeply channeled, wavy-margined, grayish green mottled or slightly barred with pale green, lined on back; flowers greenish. Juvenile plants with wavy leaves spreading flat, 17-35 cm long. *p. 1486*

"Kirkii" hort., probably S. grandicuspis from Zaîre; "Star sansevieria"; starry rosette with about 14 narrow, thick, shapely angled or concave leaves 2-3 cm wide, slightly furrowed on back, gently arching outward, 40-50 cm long, ending in a long soft, awl-shaped tip, dull grass to deep green alternately cross-banded light grayish green, the margins with fine, brown-horny edge. *p. 1483, 1486*

kirkii pulchra (Zanzibar); handsome flattened rosette of wavy leaves dark green, dusted gray beneath, prettily marbled with whitish-green to reddish; corky red-brown margins; older plants more erect and less colorful; flowers white tinged with green. *Tropical.* *p. 1490*

latifolia hort. (South Africa); low, rather squat rosette of thick, broad elliptic leaves lightly cupped above, keeled beneath, deep grayish green with lighter cross-markings. *p. 1490*

liberica (West Africa); striking plant of bold, stiffly erect habit; thick, spear-shaped, channeled leaves 60-90 cm tall, with broad bands of pure white or greenish-white just inside a fine green edge as well as on the rounded back, the center of the leaf bluish gray-green transversed by lengthwise lines of white and dense with ribs. *p. 1485*

longiflora (Botswana); thick-fleshy, sword-shaped leaves 8 cm wide, with age to 1 m long, rich green with lighter green cross-markings and corky edge; flowers ivory-white, night-blooming. *p. 1487*

metallica (Trop. Africa); fleshy rosette with large leaves similar to guineensis, but fewer and to $1\frac{1}{2}$ m long, broadly sword-shaped, 5-12 cm wide, metallic deep green with pale markings, soft margins whitish or reddish. *p. 1483, 1486*

nelsonii; stocky, symmetrical rosette of erect, oblanceolate leaves, very concave and keeled beneath, plain dark green. (I) *p. 1485, 1489*

parva (E. Africa), "Flowering parva sansevieria"; dense rosette to 45 cm high, of narrowly lanceolate, recurved and spreading leaves, very concave, fresh green with dark crossbanding, and with long green circular tip. *p. 1483, 1487*

patens (Trop. East Africa); stiff, thick, recurving leaves distichous fan-like, deeply channeled above, 40 to 90 cm long, 3-4 cm dia., dark green to bluish green with age, margins brown and white; flowers white. *p. 1490*

pearsonii (Trop. Africa: Angola to Damaraland); stout creeping rhizome bearing angular, thick rigid leaves, in mature plants in two ranks, similar to ehrenbergii but more rounded in cross-section, spreading, dull dark green, indistinctly banded lighter green, with a narrow channel down the inside face of the leaf. *p. 1484*

powellii (Kenya); an interesting arborescent plant which I photographed in desert country near Voi on the Tanzania border; forming dense colonies of erect leafy stems 1 m high, the short, clasping, channeled leaves, dark bluish-green in cultivation, but yellowish in habitat, tipped with a spiny point, in spiral ranks; flowers greenish-white. *p. 1482*

roxburghiana (India: Bengal, Madras, Coromandel); erect strap-shaped leaves to 60 cm, 3 cm wide, deeply concave-channelled, light green with 6-11 dark green longitudinal lines. *p. 1491*

scabrifolia (S.E. Africa); rosette of stiff, recurving, narrow leaves tapering to long point, channelled on surface, keeled beneath, grayish green with gray crossbands; corky margins. *Subtropic.* *p. 1488*

senegambica (cornui) (Sénégal, Gambia); sub-erect, oblanceolate leaves, with a concave channel at the base, flattening out higher up and ending in a slender point, matte medium green, only little striped on the outside. *Tropical.* *p. 1483, 1484, 1488*

singularis (Voi, Tsavo National Park, Kenya); rosette of rigid, thick leaves $\frac{1}{2}$ to $2\frac{1}{2}$ m high, 4-8 cm wide; when young concave on surface, later cylindric 4 cm dia., dull grayish or bluish-green, with irregular silver crossbands. *Arid-tropical.* *p. 1489*

splendens (Trop. Africa); long, thick leaves concave on surface, 15 cm wide, blackish green, faint marbling on back; inflorescence a tall raceme. *Arid-tropical.* *p. 1488*

stuckyi (Zimbabwe); creeping rosette with cylindrical leaves to 90 cm high, which I saw near Victoria Falls growing between rocks, forming spreading colonies from underground rhizomes, the round columns are dark green with light crossbands, and lightly grooved all around except for a deep channel on the lower part of the inside. *Arid-tropical.* *p. 1481, 1483*

subspicata (So. Africa); loose rosette to 45 cm high, with broad, rigid, lanceolate, flat leaves, at times on slender petiole, dark green with edges lined red-brown, somewhat undulate and hugging the ground when juvenile; flowers white. *p. 1483, 1486*

suffruticosa (Kenya), "Spiral snake plant"; stemforming rosette with spirally arranged, lightly arching, thick leaves to 60 cm long, channeled and clasping at the lower end, becoming cylindrical toward the tapering apex, rich green banded with pale green and grooved. *p. 1485, 1487*

thyrsiflora (S. E. Africa), "Bowstring hemp"; thick, creeping rhizome sending up full rosettes about 45-60 cm high, of some 20 stiff leaves fairly narrow, angularly channeled, keeled beneath, deep grayish-green with few markings, the margins white-translucent; fragrant flowers greenish-white. *Subtropic.* *p. 1484, 1486*

trifasciata (Transvaal, Natal, E. Cape), "Snake plant"; erroneously called "zeylanica" in horticulture; erect plant with leathery linear-lanceolate, concave leaves to 1 m long, deep grass to almost blackish-green with light green to gray-white cross bands, on fleshy rhizomes bearing an average of 6-8 leaves; flowers greenish white, in loose raceme. Fragrant at night. *Subtropic.* *p. 1482, 1484, 1485, 1486*

trifasciata 'Bantel's Sensation' (sport of 'Laurentii' 1927), "White sansevieria"; unusual variety with slender, oblanceolate leaves, some of which have one side with the typical crossbars of trifasciata, the other half a golden yellow band like laurentii, and adjoining this are stripes of white, edged with green, in other leaves either one or the other character of variegation may predominate. *Tropical.* *p. 1485*

trifasciata 'Craigii'; pleasing variety with erect, long obovate, flexible leaves having broad creamy yellow bands alongside the margin, the center milky green marked gray, and narrow dark green edging. *Tropical.* *p. 1485*

trifasciata 'Golden Hahnii' (pat. 1953); very showy plant when fully variegated; a sport of hahnii with firm, broad-elliptic leathery leaves in a low rosette, grayish-green with broad cream to golden-yellow bands alongside the margin, and more or less cross-banded in gray. *Tropical.* *p. 19*, 1483*

trifasciata 'Goldiana'; attractive cultivar offered by Seidel-Brazil, very close to laurentii but with broader creamy-yellow marginal bands and occasional additional creamy stripes lengthwise between the glossy deep green; some faint marbling across the sword-shaped leaves. *p. 1486*

trifasciata 'Hahnii' (U.S. Pat. 1941), "Birdsnest"; sport of 'Laurentii' found at New Orleans in 1939, entirely different in habit, forming a low, vase-like rosette of broad, elliptic leaves spirally arranged, spreading and reflexed, dark green with pale green crossbanding, robust and freely suckering. *Tropical.* *p. 19*, 1483*

trifasciata 'Hahnii variegata'; low birdsnest rosette variegated lengthwise with cream and yellow bands between green. Very attractive and ornamental as house plant *Tropical.* *p. 1491*

trifasciata cv. 'Hoop's Pride'; Florida cultivar; stocky plant with stubby, thick-fleshy leaves in dense cluster; smooth dark green with irregular gray markings. *p. 1491*

trifasciata 'Laurentii' (Zaïre: Eastern Province), "Variegated snake plant"; leading commercial variety because of its elegant, stiff, swordshaped leaves to 50cm or more high, having yellow bands on either side of the deep green, light banded center; a favorite house plant of excellent keeping qualities, and nicely turned rosettes, soon clustering from the fleshy rhizomes. *Tropical.* *p. 1408A, 1484, 1485, 2092*

trifasciata 'Laurentii compacta' ('goldiana'); an excellent commercial mutant forming compact rosette with extremely stiff, numerous, blackish-green leaves of even height, not much over 40 cm and with a golden band along the margins. *Tropical.* *p. 1484, 1485*

trifasciata 'Silbersee'; attractive tall-growing, clustering plant with oblanceolate, strap-shaped leaves almost entirely silvery. *p. 1491*

trifasciata 'Silver hahnii' (pat. 1953); sport of hahnii with general shape of the "birdsnest" type; leaves perhaps a little narrower, ovate and almost entirely a metallic pale silvery green. *p. 1483*

trifasciata 'Silver hahnii marginata', "Silver birdsnest"; charming Pennsylvania cultivar; small, open rosette of short, spreading leaves silvery gray, cross-banded with green, the margins creamy-yellow. *p. 1491*

zanzibarica (Zanzibar); rosette of very rigid leaves in 2 ranks up to 1½-2 m long, almost terete except for a large inside channel and some indistinct furrows, dark green with light green cross bands. *p. 1484*

zeylanica (Ceylon), "Devil's tongue"; the true species, and easily distinguished from trifasciata (called "zeylanica" in the trade), as I saw this species in Ceylon, forming a much more shapely, spreading rosette with numerous, gracefully recurving, thick-fleshy leaves, grayish green with dark green crossbands, channeled in the middle, keeled beneath and grooved, ending in a long circular tip. *p. 1485*

"zeylanica" of hort.: see trifasciata

SANTALUM *Santalaceae* **S2LBD**

ellipticum (Hawaii), the "Iliahi" or Hawaiian "Sandalwood"; small evergreen tree with opposite thick, glossy pale green oval leaves; clusters of pink to red flowers with red or green calyx at branch ends or leaf axils, and black berries. Santalum is partially parasitic, sending out roots with sucking organs into the root system of neighboring trees such as Casuarina or Acacia koa, stealing their food. Of economic importance during the height of the sandalwood trade with China mostly from 1810 to 1820, where the wood was used for incense and in making small furniture. *Tropical.* *p. 2035*

SANTOLINA *Compositae* **I2LBDh**

chamaecyparissus (incana) (Mediterranean), "Lavender cotton"; low shrubby plant with silvery-gray tomentose lacy leaves; yellow globular flower heads. Used in carpet-bedding and for edging in parks and gardens. *Subtropic.* *p. 819, 821*

SANVITALIA *Compositae* **I2LBD**

procumbens (Mexico), "Hussars heads"; hairy perennial grown as annual, with wide-spreading trailing stems, ovate leaves to 2½ cm long, and 1 cm heads of flowers having light yellow ray flowers and dark purple disk. *Tropical.* *p. 810*

SAPIUM *Euphorbiaceae* **I2LBD**

sebeferum (C. China, Taiwan), "Chinese tallow tree" or "Vegetable tallow"; evergreen tree resembling poplar, to 12 m high, with poisonous milky sap; broad rhombic-ovate, leathery leaves 7 cm long, with ivory midrib, and turning a beautiful yellow to red; small petal-less greenish flowers; the female blossoms followed by 3-parted globular brown fruiting capsules 1½ cm dia. The fatty white wax seed-coating is used in making candles and soap; the wood is made into furniture. *p. 1052*

SAPOTA achras: see Manilkara zapota

SARACA *Leguminosae* **I2LBD**

indica (Mysore, India), the "Asoka tree" or "Sorrow-less tree"; dense, ornamental tree, to 10 m tall; pinnate leaves 25 cm, with 3 to 6 pairs of lanceolate leaflets shining green, and wavy-edged; beautiful flower heads rich orange, fragrant, with long crimson stamens; sacred to Hindus and Buddhists, as Buddha is believed to have been born under it. To Hindus it is a symbol of love and dedicated to Rama. *Tropical.* *p. 1389*

thaipingensis (Malay Peninsula), "Yellow saraca"; tropical tree to 10 m, with large pinnate leaves to 45 cm long, the lanceolate leaflets thick and leathery; showy floral clusters to 30 cm across, from old wood, with yellow bracts and petal-less flowers, becoming red at mouth of calyx tube. *p. 1393*

SARANTHE *Marantaceae* **S3LFM**

leptostachya (Brazil); stemless perennial with tuberous roots and linear leaves becoming 45 cm long, bright glossy green weakly marked yellowish on the surface and green beneath; raceme with white flowers. *p. 1538*

SARCANTHUS *Orchidaceae* **S3OFM**

filiformis (Himalayas to Thailand and Vietnam); epiphyte with pendulous cylindrical, thin stems to 1 m or more long, with distantly spaced pencil-like leaves to 25 cm long; inflorescence in short racemes of 1 cm fleshy flowers dark purple with green margins and lines, lip yellow with orange (summer). *p. 1816*

lorifolius (India: Tenasserim); epiphytic orchid with leafy, rooting stem; the 2-ranked fleshy, channeled leaves 25 cm long but less than 2½ cm wide, ending in a long fleshy point; 1 cm flowers in dense pendant raceme of 40 or more, the sepals and petals yellowish with purple length stripes, the lip with yellow side lobes and violet-flushed front-lobe; spur milky-white with 2 short points; Nov.-Feb. *p. 1826*

SARCOCAULON *Geraniaceae* **S-I2LBD**

multifidum (Monsonia) (So. Africa, Namibia); low succulent with thick fleshy stem, and branches growing horizontally 8-10 cm long; the leaves in tufts on the tubercles, divided into narrow-linear segments and woolly-hairy; large pink flower with equal petals and dark red spot at base. *p. 1176*

rigidum (Namibia), "Bushman's candles"; low succulent shrub from the coastal desert, with a water-storing stem 3-4 cm thick and horizontal, and having spiny branches; leaves spoon-shaped and grayish green, soon deciduous; large bright rose flowers. The branches are covered by a resinous coat and are used as fuel by the Africans. *Arid-tropical.* *p. 1176*

SARCOCHILUS *Orchidaceae* **S3OFM**

luniferus (Chiloschista, Thrixspermum) (Sikkim to Burma); curious small epiphyte consisting of a tangled mass of gray roots radiating from a central crown and hugging the bark of trees or fiber of a tree fern; the small leaves if formed soon drop, and the roots assume the function of the absent leaves by their containing chloroplast; from the center the arching inflorescence of 2 cm flowers orange red with yellow margins; white sac-like lip (autumn). *p. 1816*

SARCOCOCCA *Buxaceae* ***I2LFM**

confusa (E. Asia: China); evergreen shrub to 2 m high, much branched from base; stems downy and green, with elliptic, leathery leaves 3-5 cm long, dark green and glossy above, paler beneath; small fragrant white flowers without petals, with cream anthers, female flowers with 2 or 3 styles; shining black 1 cm berries. *p. 614*

ruscifolia (W. China), "Sweet box"; free branching Asian evergreen with attractive small broad-ovate leathery leaves, lustrous dark green, 2 to 6 cm long; fragrant milk-white flowers. *p. 614*

saligna (Himalayas) "Willow-sweet-box"; handsome evergreen shrub 1 m or more high, photographed in Opatija, Yugoslavia; gracefully arching branches with glossy dark green, leathery oblanceolate leaves 8-15 cm long, small greenish-yellow flowers in clusters, followed by 2 cm black fruit. *p. 614*

SARCOGLOTTIS *Orchidaceae* **S3HFM**

metallica 'Variegata' (Costa Rica); terrestrial orchid with pretty, elliptic to oblanceolate leaves semi-matte black-green with greenish-silver bands lengthwise; reverse gray-green; whitish flowers. *p. 1823*

SARCOPODIUM: see Epigeneium

SARCOSTEMMA *Asclepiadaceae* **I3HBD**

viminale (Ethiopia to Cape Prov. and S. W. Africa); succulent subshrub with thin cylindrical, segmented gray-green branches 4-5 mm thick, erect or pendant; at the nodes with triangular leaf scales, containing a milky sap; flowers white. Often confused with Euphorbia pendula. *p. 359, 372*

SARITAEA *Bignoniaceae* **S2LFM**

magnifica (Arrabidaea) (Colombia), "Sarita"; attractive woody vine twining to tree-tops, with evergreen, shiny green leaves of two oval, leathery leaflets to 10 cm long with sometimes a tendril between them; trumpet-shaped flowers with lobes flaring 6 to 8 cm wide, rosy-purple with white throat, mostly winter-blooming. *Tropical.* *p. 498, 503*

SARMIENTA *Gesneriaceae* **I3HNM**
repens (Chile); shrubby plant with creeping, wiry stems, dense with opposite, small fleshy leaves; the numerous small flowers with inflated crimson tubes and spreading lobes; in habitat climbing over trees and rocks, requiring abundant water. Needs 3 months winter rest at 5 to 8° C. to bloom. (Dr. Messick, American Gloxinia Society 1967). *Subtropic.* *p. 1276*

SARRACENIA *Sarraceniaceae (Carnivorous Plants)* **I-C2-3 (H w.sphag.) BW**
'alata x purpurea', carnivorous pitcher plant for cool and moist locations; the curious hollow leaves are green tinged red, and the "lids" light yellow with red lines and tinted pink; insects are attracted by nectar into the tubes where they are trapped by the downwardly pointed hairs inside. *p. 775*
drummondii (swamps of Georgia to Alabama), "Lace trumpets"; fluted tubes 45 cm long, fresh-green except toward apex with rolled margins, and the wavy lid, both of which are beautifully marbled white between the netted green veins. *p. 774*
flava (Virginia to Florida), "Yellow pitcher plant"; tall and slender tubes to 1 m long, light green with mouth and lid edged yellow green and crimson throat; large nodding yellow flowers. *Warm temperate.* *p. 775, 776*
leucophylla (S.E. No. America); handsome pitcher plant of the passive type, with slender, long green tubes 40 cm high, toward the inflated apex beautifully marbled with white, the lid white with green veining; photographed at Munich Botanic Gardens, Germany. *p. 776*
'leucophylla x purpurea'; slender trumpet-shaped tubes in clustering rosettes, with the large green lids beautifully veined dark green to maroon, throat inside light yellow. *p. 775*
minor (N. Carolina to Florida), "Hooded pitcher plant"; pitchers short and also growing to 60 cm tall, fresh-green to purple, with white translucent spots near the yellowish top, the lid arching over mouth, purple-netted inside; flowers pale yellow. *Warm-temperate.* *p. 776*
psittacina (in sandy swamps of Georgia, Florida, Alabama and Louisiana), the "Parrot pitcher plant"; low rosette with leaves 5-15 cm long, the tube club-shaped, with an erect, broad obovate, flat wing, green with red and white veins, the inflated top with incurved beak, like a parrot; flowers green and red. *Humid-subtropic.* *p. 775*
purpurea (Labrador to Maryland and Rocky Mts.), "Sweet pitcher plant"; low, spreading rosettes usually found growing in sphagnum bogs; clustering pitchers erect or prostrate, 6-35cm long, broadly winged, throat and lid hairy, and beautifully veined crimson; nodding purple flowers. *Temperate.* *p. 763, 775*
purpurea venosa (New Jersey to Louisiana to Florida), "Southern pitcher plant"; prostrate squat pitchers dull-green with purplish -red network of veins, especially prominent inside the opened hairy lid. *p. 775*
rubra (N. Carolina to Florida), "Red pitcher plant"; slender tubular leaves green to reddish-brown, 15-30 cm and more long, the lid forming a hood and veined purple; flowers crimson and fragrant, on elongate stalks. *Warm temperate.* *p. 775, 776*

SASA *Gramineae* **I2LB-FM**
fortunei (Arundinaria variegata, Pleioblastus) (Japan), "Miniature bamboo"; I photographed this plant in Brazil, and consider it the most attractive small bamboo in cultivation; its growth habit is low with gracefully arching branches and leaves much broader than pygmaea, strikingly banded white; the underside, unlike pygmaea, is finely pubescent. *Subtropic.* *p. 1310*
palmata (Arundinaria palmata in N.Z.) (Japan); rather dwarf bamboo with somewhat flattened 2 cm hollow stems ¼ to 2 m high, branching on top like fingers of a hand, each with 4-7 large leaves 30 cm long and 8 cm wide, bright green above, with clear veins, and silvery beneath. The variety nebulosa has stems purple-tinged, and sheaths spotted with brown. Hardy along Atlantic coast, possibly to Boston, on the Pacific coast to the Columbia River; at about - 18°C. *p. 1304*
pygmaea (Arundinaria, Pleioblastus) (Japan), "Pygmy bamboo"; one of the smallest known bamboos, rarely taller than 25 cm, from creeping rootstocks, forming dense clumps; small leathery, deep green leaves to 5 cm long, glabrous beneath. *p. 1308*
tessellata (China); a dwarf "Running" bamboo with creeping rootstocks, and slender culms ¾-1 m high, short-jointed, with brownish-yellow culm-sheath, and ovate to lanceolate, leathery leaves 8 to 12 cm long and 3-4 cm broad, rich-green above, glaucous beneath. *Subtropic.* *p. 1308*

SASSAFRAS *Lauraceae* **C2LBM**
albidum (No. America), "Sassafras"; deciduous tree to 30 m high; leaves 8-15 cm long, variable in shape and size, entire or 3-lobed, glaucous beneath; flowers 5 mm wide, greenish-yellow; fruit roundish-ovoid, dark blue; foliage tinted orange and scarlet in autumn. *p. 1359*

SATYRIUM *Orchidaceae* **I2HFMd**
erectum (So. Africa); deciduous terrestrial tuberous-rooted orchid with broad leathery leaves at base; inflorescence a dense, stout spike with yellowish-orange or pale purple flowers (February). *p. 1816*
odorum (So. Africa: Cape); small tuberous-rooted terrestrial with candle-like fleshy stalk bearing clasping, succulent lanceolate leaves and a conical raceme of small fragrant lemon-yellow flowers. *Subtropic.* *p. 1826*

SAURAUJA *Actinidiaceae* **I-S2LBD**
gigantea (Saurauia) (Java, Nepal); tropical tree or shrub to 5 m; leathery rugose, ovate leaves light green with red veins, underside as well as stem cinnamon-hairy; flowers begonia-like, 3-4 cm across, white with red star in center, in showy clusters. *Tropical to Subtropic.* *p. 951*
subspinosa (Upper Burma); tall shrub to 2½ m high with oblanceolate leaves 12-16 cm long, having spiny ribs and petioles, on densely hairy branches; panicles of fragrant, large lily-of-the-valley-like cupped flowers pale pink outside and at apex, rich crimson deep inside. *Subtropic.* *p. 81*

SAUROMATUM *Araceae* **3 Fd(SD to flower, CM for leaf)**
guttatum (East Indies); tropical tuberous herb producing a single pedately lobed leaf, with leaflets to 25 cm long, on non-spotted stalk 45 cm high, appearing after blooming; spathe tube 5-10 cm; spathe blade 30-62 cm long, purplish below, green above with dark purple spots. *p. 284*
guttatum venosum (Himalayas); tuber bearing a single pedate leaf one year, the next year leaves and flowers. Fleshy leafstalk spotted brown, 7-11 leaf segments, with marginal veins; spathe purple. (I-C) *p. 284*
horsfieldii (Java); tuberous plant with showy leaf pedately parted, on thick stalk buff-pinkish,marked with purple. (S-I) *p. 284*
venosum (East Indies); tropical tuberous herb with solitary dissected leaf of 7 to 11 segments, carried on one stalk 45 cm high, produced after blooming, the segments 25 cm long; the inflorescence with an inflated tube extending 5-10 cm, continuing into a purple blade 30-60 cm long, the spadix very long and slender. Probably a form of Sauromatum guttatum. *Tropical.* *p. 207*

SAXIFRAGA *Saxifragaceae* **I-C2-3LBD**
burseriana (Eastern Alps); large cushions of many-leaved 10 cm rosettes of spiny, stiff, silver-gray foliage; flower buds reddish, petals glistening white. *p. 2048*
cotyledon pyramidalis (Pyrenees, Alps of Valais); forms masses of broad-leaved rosettes, becoming mahogany-red in winter; leaves to 8 cm long and rounded at apex, finely toothed, each tooth with a lime-gland at base; stems 45-60 cm high, branching from the base with large pyramidal panicles of pure white fragrant flowers. *p. 2047*
cuscutaeformis (Japan); perennial with basal leaves similar to sarmentosa, but smaller, oval, and quite thick and hairy, roundly crenate at margin, bronzy-green with silvery-white network of veins on the surface; produces young plants at ends of threadlike runners. *p. 2047*
granulata (Europe, No. Africa), "Fair maids of France", or "Meadow-saxifraga"; deciduous bulbous, small tufted perennial forming numerous little bulblets in axils of basal leaves 4 cm wide; stalks 5 cm or more high bearing pretty white flowers (h). *p. 2047*
longifolia (Pyrenées); attractive gray-hairy dense formal rosette to 60 cm across; linear spoon-shaped leaves; white flowers sometimes spotted purple. *Warm temperate.* *p. 2048*
stolonifera (sarmentosa hort.) (China, Japan), "Strawberry geranium"; loosely tufted perennial spreading near the ground, strawberry-like, by threadlike runners bearing young plantlets; the soft, fleshy, rounded, bristly hairy leaves 3 to 5 cm across, coarsely toothed, deep olive green with silver-gray areas following the veins, densely spotted purple beneath; numerous flowers on erect panicle, white, with 2 petals longer than others. (•h) *p. 2047*
stolonifera 'Tricolor', (sarmentosa cv. in hort), "Magic carpet"; beautiful variety smaller and more tender than the type, with leaves dark green and milky green, variegated inward from the margin with ivory-white, tinted pink or even rosy-crimson in younger leaves, with red edging, and purplish-rose beneath. *Subtropic.* *p. 768A, 2047*
umbrosa (Europe), "London pride"; tufting rosettes of thick, leathery, spatulate, gray-green leaves crenate at margins, tinged red beneath; with small, starry, pinkish flowers. (h) *p. 2047*

SAXIFRAGA: see also Bergenia

SCAEVOLA *Goodeniaceae* **S2LBM**
sericea (frutescens) (Malaya to South Pacific), the "Half-flower", "Naupaka" or "Sea-lettuce tree"; common on tropical shores; succulent shrub or small tree from 1 to 6 m high, with spreading stout branches, and long fleshy, bright green, obovate leaves 8-12 cm long; the small white fragrant flowers, streaked with purple, are curious because the 5 petals are arranged to one side looking like only half a flower; small white berries resembling hail stones. *Tropical.* *p. 1318*

SCAPHISPATHA *Araceae* **I3LFD**
gracilis (Bolivia, Brazil, Colombia); small ornamental with depressed-globular tuber 2 cm dia., sending up slender stalk 30-40 cm high, bearing a waxy, constricted spathe 5-6 cm long, outside light green or pinkish, inside white; the spadix producing whitish berries; foliage appearing after blooming, the reddish petioles each carrying a light green, sagittate-peltate leaf 7 cm long. *p. 207, 294*

SCAPHYGLOTTIS *Orchidaceae* **S-I3OFM**
lindeniana (Mexico, C. America to Panama); robust, floriferous epiphyte with clustered, stalked, spindle-shaped pseudobulbs 5-30 cm long, topped by two leaves to 25 cm; from the apex of bulb a short dense cluster of long-stalked 2 cm flowers yellowish or reddish-green veined with purple (spring). *p. 1816*

reedii (Hexadesmia) (Venezuela); miniature epiphyte with tiny gray-white pseudobulbs, narrow grassy leaves to 10 cm long; small translucent whitish flowers brownish in front and with purple spots (spring). *p. 1818*

SCHAUERIA *Acanthaceae* **S3LFM**
calycotricha (Brazil); tropical subshrub to 50 cm high, with smooth green, broadly ovate leaves, and short, dense terminal spike of yellow tubular flowers 3 cm long, the bracts yellowish green, and with bristly calyx lobes; blooms well as a small plant, in late winter. *p. 52*

SCHEELIA *Palmae* **S3LFM**
liebmanii (Mexico); handsome impressive feather palm, some 15 m tall, with massive trunk about 1 m thick; the giant pinnate fronds erect to 10 m long, the numerous dense, long leaflets dark green, rough and rigid, and arranged to appear standing on edge; inflorescence with tremendous clusters of fragrant yellowish flowers, followed by roundish 6 cm brownish fruit. *Tropical.* *p. 1907*

regia (Colombia); tall, robust feather palm with heavy trunk and a crown of pinnate leaves 5 m or more long, the leaflets dark green and pendant as if folded down; photographed at Foster Botanical Gardens, Honolulu. *p. 1907*

zonensis (Panama); handsome, statuesque feather palm to 12 m tall and trunk to 75 cm thick, topped by a crown of numerous arching pinnate fronds as much as 6 m long, the rigid leaflets arranged along top and bottom of rachis making the leaf appear as if standing on edge; yellowish fragrant flowers. *p. 1916*

SCHEFFLERA *Araliaceae* **I-S1-2LF-BD**
actinophylla: see Brassaia

arboricola (Heptapleurum) (Taiwan), "Hawaiian Elf"; freely branching plant of dwarf habit, resembling when young a miniature Brassaia; wiry stems flexible and becoming scandent with age; the palmate foliage glossy green, to 15 cm across, arranged in a circle of 7 to 8 soft-leathery leaflets; inflorescence in erect, terminal cluster of orange-red to blackish berries; very charming in appearance and a good decorative plant. *p. 313*

delavayi (China: Yunnan, Honan); spreading shrub 4 m high, with large palmately compound leaves on long petiole, the thin-leathery ovate leaflets matte-brownish green, brown pubescent underneath, faintly toothed, or lobed at margins, and with prominent midrib; long inflorescence with white flowers; resistant to some cold. *Subtropic.* *p. 310*

digitata (New Zealand), "Seven fingers"; bush or small tree 3-6 m high, densely branching, sometimes growing epiphytic, with thin-leathery leaves palmately compound, 5-10 foliolate obovate leaflets to 17 cm long, dull satiny green above, shiny light green beneath, densely ciliate and undulate at margins, and with yellowish, depressed veins; greenish-yellow flowers in panicles; purplish-black fruit berry-like. *Warm-temperate* *p. 308, 312*

erythrostachys: see venulosa erythrostachys

farinosa (Malaya, Sumatra, Java); very ornamental tree with shiny stems covered by scales, the leaves palmate-compound 35 cm across, the green leathery leaflets covered with mealy wax, and beautifully arranged in a formal circle; small whitish flowers in terminal inflorescence consisting of numerous incurving spikes. *Tropical.* *p. 313, 314*

minutifolia (Baguio, Philippines); miniature with green, wiry stems; compound leaves with 5 to 8 glossy-green, narrow leaflets 3-6cm long. *Subtropic.* *p. 310*

octophylla (Hong Kong), an "Umbrella tree"; branching small evergreen tree which one can see growing abundantly in the forest near the Peak station of the tram above Victoria; palmate leaves with 8-9 sturdy leathery, shining green leaflets having smooth, entire margins. *p. 310*

'Starshine' (Philippines); handsome ornamental plant found 1977 by Ingwersen of Oceanside, California, growing epiphytic in a tree on Mindanao; tree-like but becoming scandent with willowy, beige-brown stems to 6 m high; long wiry petioles carry the palmately compound striking leaves, 30 cm or more across, consisting of usually 9 to 12 pendant, narrow lanceolate leaflets 12 to 25 cm long, deeply corrugated, of leathery texture and lustrous deep green but tending to defoliate at cool temperatures. May need staking when used as decorator plant. Local name "Galamay amo" (Monkey's paw). *p.312*

taiwaniana (Taiwan); small tree with attractive palmate leaves, the 6-10 thin-leathery leaflets lacquered glossy-green and with pronounced wavy margins. *p. 310*

tomentosa (Heptapleurum) (Malaya); somewhat resembling delavayi, from warmer habitat; evergreen tree with palmate leaves on long petioles, the 5-6 or more quilted or depressed-ribbed ovate, stalked leaflets deep green and covered with bristly hairs. *p. 310*

venulosa (Heptapleurum venulosum) (Queensland, China, Indochina, India), a "Starleaf"; branching tree with palmately compound leaves; the 7-8 stalked leaflets lanceolate when young, obovate or elliptic in maturity, soft-leathery, semi-glossy on both sides, to 15 cm long; mature leaves entire, dark green, but lightly toothed in juvenile stage; inflorescence in panicles with whitish flowers, followed by small red fruit. *Subtropic.* *p. 308, 311, 312*

venulosa erythrostachys (Heptapleurum stelzerianum hort.) (Trop. Asia to Australia), a "Starleaf"; scandent evergreen to 6 m high, inclined to become semi-climbing, forming adventitious roots; leaves alternate, palmate with 6-7 leaflets, oval or ovate, fleshy, to 15 cm long, yellowish-green; globular flowers dark red, in dense clusters. *Tropical.* *p. 310*

volkensii (polyscidia) (Tanzania, Uganda); great evergreen tree to 25 m high from mountains at 2,200-2,700 m, such as growing in the mist-forest belt on Mt. Kilimanjaro at 2,700 m. Palmately compound leaves with 5-7 glossy-leathery leaflets to 15 cm long, on willowy branches. *p. 309, 310*

SCHEFFLERA: see also Brassaia

SCHINUS *Anacardiaceae* **I2LBD**
molle (Ecuador, Perú); introduced in 1830 by Franciscan missionary fathers to California, at San Luis Rey; "Peppertree" or "California pepper tree"; dioecious evergreen tree with gracefully weeping branches, 6-10 m high, with age developing a rough, gnarled trunk 60-90 cm thick; pinnate, feathery leaves 12-20 cm long, of numerous leathery, linear, deep green leaflets; yellowish-white flowers; on female trees the rosy 6 mm fruit resembling pepper-corns, in pendulous terminal clusters. In Mexico, the fruit is ground for beverages, and made into an intoxicant by fermenting it; the bark is used for tanning skins. *Subtropic.* *p. 133*

terebinthifolius (Brazil, Paraguay), "Brazilian pepper-tree" or "Christmas-berry tree"; ornamental evergreen tree 6-9 m high, of more rigid habit and less pendulous than S. molle, the California pepper tree; broadly spreading with willowy to woody branches densely clothed with pinnate leaves 10-17 cm long, of 5 to 9 broad leathery leaflets, dark glossy green and long-persistent. Small white flowers, followed by bright red berries on female trees, very showy in winter. *Subtropic.* *p. 133*

SCHISANDRA *Magnoliaceae* **I3LFM**
propinqua (Himalayas); twining shrub to 9 m with thin reddish, angled stems, the pendant leathery leaves narrow-lanceolate, 12 cm long, sparsely toothed, deep green with silver-gray areas between veins; flowers orange. *p. 1515*

SCHISMATOGLOTTIS *Araceae* **S3LFM**
calyptrata (N. W. Malaya); soft-fleshy aroid with arrow-shaped green leaves to 30 cm, and occasionally to 90 cm long and 15 cm wide, ovate lobes to 5 cm long; the greenish spathe tube 4 cm long, and 7 cm pale yellow limb, and with short cone-shaped spadix. *p. 291*

concinna (acuminatissima) (Borneo); small tufting plant bearing erect oblique-ovate thin leaves 15 cm long, matte green on surface, light maroon underneath, on long slender petioles. *p. 284*

emarginata (Borneo); pretty little ornamental plant with heart-shaped or sagittate leaves deep grayish-green having a bold feathering band of silvery gray along both sides of the midrib. *p. 280*

multiflora (Borneo: Sarawak); tropical herb densely clustering, with lanceolate, fleshy leaves 18-24 cm long and recurving, waxy green with bold midrib and undulate margins; long-pointed, furled spathe 10-13 cm long, white in upper part, green toward base. *p. 291*

novo-guineensis (New Guinea); stoloniferous tropical plant forming clusters; large ovate leaves with cordate base, deeply corrugated, to 25 cm long, bright green; spathe with pale green tube and white limb. *p. 284*

picta (Java); soft-fleshy plant with papery, oblong cordate, pendant, corrugated leaves matte green with feathered, grayish bands down the middle. *p. 283, 284*

pulchra (Borneo: Sarawak); beautiful little foliage plant with long-stalked ovate leaves 12 cm long, glaucous or dark green, prettily variegated, especially along central area with silvery-white; pale green 8 cm spathe. *p. 291*

roebelinii, see Aglaonema crispum

ruttenii (Seram); dwarf, stoloniferous herb with satiny, fresh-green, lightly corrugated, ovate leaves on stiff, vaginate petioles. *p. 284*

tecturata (Borneo); densely tufting plant with short-stalked oblique oblanceolate leaves 12-20 cm long obtuse at base, glossy plain deep green with faintly lighter band down the center, glaucous beneath; spathe glaucous-green with darker stripes, pale glaucous inside. *p. 280*

SCHISMATOGLOTTIS: see also Aglaonema

SCHIVERECKIA *Cruciferae* **C-I2LBM**
podolica (Alyssum) (S. E. Europe, Asia Minor); small perennial similar to Alyssum, forming tufts 5-10 cm high; silvery, narrow-oblong 1 cm leaves; white flowers in small clusters of leafy stalks, blooming in spring. *p. 926*

SCHIZANTHUS *Solanaceae* **I2LBM**
x wisetonensis, "Poor man's orchid"; beautiful hybrid of pinnatus x grahamii (Chile); bushy herbaceous plant with slender, sticky branches, pale green, divided leaves, and a profusion of showy, irregular, pansy-like flowers in shades of lilac, purple, pink, carmine, reddish-brown, or white, the upper lip often marked with purple and yellow, blooming spring or summer. *Subtropic.* *p. 2072*

x wisetonensis 'Cherry Shades'; select strain of the "Poor man's orchid" with individual blossoms 5 cm across, in reds with purple and wine-red stripes. *p. 2081*

SCHIZOBASOPSIS: see Bowiea

SCHIZOCASIA: see Alocasia, Xenophya

SCHIZOCENTRON *Melastomataceae* **I3HFM**

elegans (Heterocentron in Hortus 3) (Mexico), "Spanish shawl"; creeping herb forming a dense mat, reddish stems rooting at nodes; small 1 cm ovate leaves, deep green and lightly hairy; covered with purple flowers during summer; good basket plant. *Subtropic. p. 1554, 1557*

SCHIZOLOBIUM *Leguminosae* **I2LBD**

parahybum (excelsum) (Panama, Brazil), the "Bacurubu", or "Tower tree"; slender, fast-growing deciduous tree more than 30 m tall, with a crown of fronds resembling treefern; the feathery leaves 1 m or more long are finely bipinnate, the leaflets lobed, whitish beneath; masses of yellow flowers form erect 30 cm clusters. *Tropical. p. 1389*

SCHIZOSTYLIS *Iridaceae* **I2LBD**

coccinea (So. Africa), "Kaffir-lily", "Crimson flag" or "River lily"; a beautiful rhizomatous evergreen herb forming clumps to 1 m high; curved narrow green leaves 25 cm long and 1 cm wide; a slender stalk bears 6 to 14 showy scarlet red flowers like stars 4-5 cm across, with yellow anthers, lasting 4 days, summer-fall blooming. *p. 1339*

SCHLUMBERGERA *Cactaceae* ***I2HFD**

bridgesii (Epiphyllum truncatum) (Bolivia?), "Christmas cactus"; branching epiphyte with small glossy green leaflike joints, crenate and with blunt apex; nearly regular, pendant flowers in December, with flaring petals carmine-red tinged purple in center; angled ovaries. *Tropical. p. 640A, 733*

'Crimson Giant', in the California trade; 2- or 3-angled green joints with brown bristle-tips, and large crimson-red, starry, regular flowers 5 cm across from tip to tip; probably a form of Rhipsalidopsis (Schlumbergera) gaertneri, or with Rhipsalidopsis rosea blood. *p. 736*

gaertneri: see Rhipsalidopsis

gaertneri makoyana: see Rhipsalidopsis

'Red Elephant' (Zygocactus); California cultivar; flattened branches; regular, starry flowers, numerous narrow, spreading segments, 6 cm across, vivid salmon inside, scarlet outside and on tips; base of flower 5-angled. *p. 736*

russelliana (Organ Mts., Brazil), "Shrimp cactus"; dwarf growing epiphyte and one of the oldest known species; will respond to grafting on such as Selenicereus; small leaves with crenate edge; regular, starshaped small flowers with several rows of orange-red petals, Spring blooming. *Tropical. p. 733, 735*

x SCHOMBOLAELIA *Orchidaceae* **I3OFD**

'Kahili' (Schomburgkia x Laelia); Hawaiian bigeneric hybrid; reed stems bearing huge cluster of frilled rose-pink flowers with long slender tube. *p.1818*

SCHOMBURGKIA *Orchidaceae* **I3OFD**

crispa (Laelia) (Demerara, Guyana); robust epiphyte with spindle-shaped pseudobulbs to 30 cm high bearing 2-3 leaves, and the long-stemmed umbel of waxy flowers, the narrow sepals and petals reddish-brown bordered yellow, and beautifully crisped, lip tinged with rose, (Oct.-Jan.). (I) *p. 1819*

lueddemannii (Venezuela); epiphyte of the habit of crispa, with spindle-like pseudobulbs more slender, and obtuse leaves; the flowers in dense cluster, with sepals and petals tongue-shaped, metallic light brown with dark, wavy margin, lip purple-red with 3 golden-yellow keels, (Jan.-March). (I) *p. 1819*

rosea (Colombia); strong epiphyte resembling undulata, with waxy, 2½ cm flowers smaller in size, dense at the end of a long stalk, sepals and petals undulate, coppery-red flushed purple, lip purplish-rose with 3 white keels, (Jan.-spring). (I) *p. 1819*

tibicinis (Laelia) (Mexico to Costa Rica); robust epiphyte with densely clustered spindle-shaped pseudobulbs and hollow, to 60 cm long, topped by several rigid leaves 40 cm long; inflorescence on stalks that may extend several metres; clusters of waxy, undulate, very fragrant flowers 5 to 8 cm dia., variably colored purplish red or brown-orange, lip yellowish or purple (spring). *p. 1818*

undulata (Laelia) (Trinidad, Venezuela, Colombia); bold epiphyte with tall, spindle-shaped, 2-3-leaved pseudobulbs, bearing the 1 m reedy stalk topped by a many-flowered dense raceme, the waxy sepals and petals longer and narrower than crispa, much twisted and crisped, wine-purple with a rosy lip, (Dec.-July). *Tropical. p. 1819*

SCHOTIA *Leguminosae* **I2LBD**

brachypetala (Transvaal, Natal, Zululand), "Tree fuchsia"; notable tree on the dry, ochreous bushveld of the Transvaal, to 12 m high, loaded with pendulous, crowded clusters of glowing deep crimson-red flowers, having 4-lobed leathery calyx and minute bristle-like petals, and protruding red stamens; pinnate green leaves partially deciduous, dropping most of them before flowering. *Subtropic. p. 1390, 1391*

SCHUMANNIOPHYTON *Rubiaceae* **S3LBM**

magnificum (Tetrastigma) (Gabon, Nigeria, Zaire); shrub or small tree 4-5 m high, with soft-wooded stems and very large corrugated leaves 50-140 cm long, 15-50 cm broad; flowers white or yellow in a dense cluster subtended by broad bracts and borne at ends of shoots opposite a single leaf and just above a pair of leaves. *p. 2017*

SCHWANTESIA *Aizoaceae* **I2LBD**

loeschiana (S. W. Africa); cushion-forming succulent; the branchlets with 2-3 pairs of partially united boat-shaped keeled leaves 4 cm long, the back surface drawn forward like a chin, chalky bluish-white with sharp, reddish angles; 5 cm yellow flowers with spreading linear rays. *p. 68*

triebneri (Cape Prov.: Bushmanland); tiny succulent with opposite fat leaves to 5½ cm long, sharply angled, one margin expanded toward a pointed, keeled apex, gray-glaucous, edged in red; dotted red in strong light; flowers yellow. *p. 75*

SCIADOPITYS *Taxodiaceae (Coniferae)* **C2LBD**

verticillata (Central Japan), the "Umbrella pine"; slow growing, very ornamental evergreen to 20 or 30 m high, of pyramidal habit; dense with slender linear, dark green needles 8-15 cm long, having 2 white bands below and deflected in graceful whorls; oblong woody 8 to 12 cm cones. *Warm temperate. p. 850*

SCILLA *Liliaceae* **C-I2-3LF-BM**

hispanica (Spain, Portugal), "Spanish bluebell"; clustering bulbous plant to 50 cm high, with linear basal leaves and small blue, bell-shaped flowers in a rather loose raceme; May. (C2Bd) *p. 1493*

latifolia lusitanica (Canary Islands, Portugal), robust, bulbous plant with 6-9 broad, fleshy, lanceolate leaves, producing a dense raceme of tiny lilac bell-shaped flowers with purple center in May. *p. 1493*

peruviana (Mediterranean reg.), erroneously called the "Cuban lily"; bulbous plant very showy, carrying a dense cluster of small star-like lilac-blue flowers 2½cm across, with petals edged in rose, blue stamens and yellow pollen, on thick-fleshy stalk, above broad, soft succulent, fresh-green leaves; Spring. *Subtropic. p. 1408A, 1493*

sardensis (Chionodoxa) (Turkey), "Turkish squill"; small bulbous plant with broad green leaves; purplish flowers with dark blue median line on each flaring segment. *p. 1494*

sibirica atrocaerulea, (Yugoslavia, C. and So. Russia), "Siberian hyacinth"; known in horticulture as 'Spring Beauty'; low-growing bulbous herb 15 cm high, with basal leaves 2 cm wide, and dainty procelain-blue flowers with flaring segments, each with deep blue stripe. *p. 1494*

tubergeniana (Mountains of N.W. Iran), "Persian blue bell"; choice miniature bulbous plant barely 15 cm high, each bulb producing several stalks with beautiful starry flowers 3 cm across, pale blue with deeper mauve backs and deep blue median line on each segment; blooms appear before leaves. *p. 1494*

violacea (Ledebouria socialis in Hortus 3) (So. Africa), "Silver squill"; small suckering bulbous plant with swollen base, attractive because of its variegated foliage; strap-like fleshy leaves olive-green with silver blotching and banding, glossy wine-red beneath; small green and blue flowers on slender racemes; in winter. *Subtropic. p. 1493*

SCINDAPSUS *Araceae* ***S1HFD-M**

aureus: see Epipremnum aureum

sp. "Exotica" (New Guinea); graceful, very pretty, tall tree climber with channeled, partially winged and sheathing petioles bearing lance-shaped narrow, oblique-lanceolate, slender-pointed, thin-leathery leaves 10-20 cm long, grayish deep green, lavishly splashed and painted in the direction of the lateral veins with silvery gray; glossy pale gray beneath. *Tropical. p. 279*

hederaceus (S. E. Monsoon Asia); tropical climber rooting from the rambling stems; the unequal-sided, leathery green, ovate leaves 10-18 cm long on short, winged petioles, abruptly bent at base of blade; small white, ovate spathe becoming deciduous and subtending the cone-like spadix with perfect flowers. *p. 282*

pictus (Indonesia, Philippines), "Silver vine"; tree climber clinging close to bark; thick-leathery, waxy leaves to 15 cm long, obliquely ovate, dark green overlaid with greenish silver blotching. (M) *p. 285*

pictus argyraeus (Pothos argyraeus) (Borneo), "Satin pothos"; beautiful creeper with the smaller, cordate leaves satiny, bluish-green with markings and edge of silver; probably the juvenile stage of pictus. *Tropical. p. 285*

siamense (Thailand); very attractive, robust climber with relatively large, thick-leathery, slender-pointed, broad oblique-heart-shaped satiny leaves 10-12 cm long, deep grayish green irregularly splashed and marbled silvery-gray, pale silvery-green beneath, and with fine gray translucent edge; short petioles partially winged, on flexuous, wiry stems. *p. 279*

treubii (Java); tree climber from the moist mountain forests, with small, dark green, leathery, narrow ovate leaves set closely and alternately along stem, clinging close to bark. (M) *p. 285*

SCIRPUS *Cyperaceae* **I-S3LFW**

cernuus (Isolepis gracilis) (E. Indies, naturalized in Europe); grasslike, graceful tufted plant with numerous cylindric, threadlike, fresh glossy-green stems becoming pendant, tipped with little white flower heads as in bullrush. *Subtropic.* *p. 946*

SCOLOPENDRIUM: see Phyllitis

SCOLYMUS *Compositae* **I2LBD**

hispanicus (S. W. Europe), "Golden thistle" or "Spanish oyster plant"; vicious-looking biennial to 60 cm high, with rigid leaves deeply cut into spiny lobes; the flower heads in leafy spikes, with several rows of yellow, linear ray florets. *p. 827*

SCOPOLIA *Solanaceae* **C2LFD**

carniolica (Yugoslavia, Russia); perennial herb 30 cm high, with obovate, dull green, thick-ribbed membranous leaves; nodding solitary, axillary flowers with veined 2 cm corolla brownish-red, yellowish green inside, in early spring; hardy. *p. 2080*

SCUTELLARIA *Labiatae* **I-S3LFD**

costaricensis (C. America), a "Skull-cap"; beautiful tropical flowering plant with stems 40 to 80 cm high; opposite ovate, slender-pointed, wrinkled leaves with crenate margins, deep metallic green; the inflorescence magnificent with terminal bundles of curving tubular flowers of golden scarlet, arranged like a bursting fountain of fire, the corolla 4 cm long and with deep yellow lip. *p. 1356*

javanica (Central Java); from the central mountains at 1,800-2,000 m; subshrub to 1 m high, not spectacular, with 4-angled branches; coarsely toothed, smooth, ovate leaves to 4 cm long; terminal racemes of small tubular flowers deep purple, with very small bracts. *p. 1354, 1356*

mociniana (Mexico), the "Scarlet skullcap"; herbaceous shrub of robust habit, to 50 cm high, with purplish-brown square stem, opposite, ovate-cordate, quilted leaves 10 cm long, dark metallic green, thin-leathery, and with crenate margins, grayish green beneath; striking erect, terminal spikes topped by a dense burst of brilliant scarlet-red long-tubular flowers 4-5 cm long, having orange-yellow lip and showing white stamens; the individual flowers will last only 6-10 days but succeeding clusters of flowers appear from upper leaf axils, extending blooming period from January to July. *Tropical.* *p. 768A, 1355*

villosa (Brazil); handsome tropical herbaceous plant with shrubby base, the opposite ovate, metallic green, crenate leaves covered with shaggy pubescence; at the tips of branches the bracted inflorescence with curved-tubular inflated bilabiate flowers scarlet-red. *p. 1356*

SCUTICARIA *Orchidaceae* **S3OFM**

hadwenii (Guyana, Brazil); peculiar epiphyte with branching rhizome, bearing on each branch a solitary channeled, whiplike, pendant, cylindric leaf to 60 cm long; short-stalked handsome solitary 5-8 cm flowers pale yellow blotched with brown, the white lip spotted red (June-July). (S) *p. 1817*

steelei (hadwenii) (Brazil to Venezuela); peculiar but charming epiphyte with branching rhizome bearing on each branch a solitary channeled, whiplike, pendant cylindric leaf to 1 m long, and short stalked clusters of handsome fragrant, waxy flowers 5-8 cm or more across, pale yellow spotted with brown-purple, the lip with an orange crest; the long-lasting flowers appearing in summer or fall. Because of their pendulous habit, plants must be grown on rafts, treefern slabs or in baskets hung sideways; best in osmunda or treefern fiber. *Tropical.* *p. 1825*

SEAFORTHIA: see Archontophoenix, Ptychosperma

SEBAEA *Gentianaceae* **I2LFD**

aurea (So. Africa); low annual herb to 15 cm high, with triangular-fanshaped and ovate leaves; flowers golden yellow. *p. 1170*

exacoides (thodiana) (So. Africa); bushy annual herb, dense with small ovate, opposite leaves lacquered green; covering itself with tubular-flaring yellow flowers marked with green in throat. *p. 1170*

x SEDEVERIA *Crassulaceae* **I2LBD**

derenbergii, (Sedum derenbergii of Calif. hort.), "Baby echeveria"; trim and good little bigeneric, combining blood of Echeveria derenbergii and Sedum allantoides; small upright rosette 4 to 5 cm dia., of keeled bluish-gray leaves flattened on surface. *p. 917*

'Green Rose' (Sed. aureum x Echev. derenbergii); attractive hybrid in the California nursery trade; little 5 cm rosette on brown stem, dense with small obovate light green leaves covered by bluish glaucescence, waxy smooth and lightly keeled beneath, the tips tinted salmon in the sun; flowers yellow tipped with orange. *p. 917*

SEDUM *Crassulaceae* ***I-C2LBD**

adolphii (Mexico), "Golden sedum"; small branching rosette of plump, fleshy keeled leaves 4cm long, waxy yellowish green with reddish margins; flowers white. *Subtropic.* *p. 917*

allantoides (Mexico: Oaxaca); succulent subshrub with loosely leafy branches; club-shaped, upcurving leaves, 2-3 cm long, whitish-gray-glaucous; flowers greenish-white. *p. 920*

bellum (Mexico: Durango); clustering succulent herb, the branches with rosettes of small obovate, fleshy leaves rounded above, light green covered with waxy mealy powder, 2-4 cm long; numerous white flowers. *p. 920*

brevifolium (Morocco, S. W. Europe); mat-forming, low-perennial mealy herb to 5 cm high; tiny waxy-white, ovate or round leaves $1/2$-1 cm long, flushed with red, alternately opposite along stem; white flowers; somewhat hardy. *p. 920*

cauticolum (Japan); hardy, spreading succulent perennial with prostrate purple stems; the rounded, cupped, fleshy leaves 3 cm long, glaucous bluish-gray and dotted with red; the inflorescence with carmine-rose flowers in loose clusters. *Warm temperate* *p. 924*

chloropetalum (Mexico: Oaxaca); erect succulent shrub to 75 cm high, the gray branches with opposite small, yellow-green, oblong leaves 1-3 cm long; the inflorescence with sessile star-shaped flowers yellow-green striped with red, and crimson-red stamen-bundles in center. *p. 924*

compressum (Mexico); shrubby succulent with woody branches terminating in loose rosette of obovate, fleshy bluish-gray leaves having corky margins; free-flowering golden yellow in winter. *p. 916,920*

craigii (Chihuahua); clustering succulent of loose habit with fat obovate leaves, somewhat brittle, but the yellow-green body is beautifully glaucous from silvery gray to pink and amethyst-blue; flowers white. (I) *p. 918*

cuspidatum (Mexico: Chiapas); small branching succulent shrublet with fleshy, flat, obovate green leaves, tipped by a short point, and arranged in dense rosette fashion toward the end of stems; the lateral inflorescence with small whitish flowers. *p. 920*

dasyphyllum (No. Africa, So. and W. Europe); rock-dweller in habitat; low perennial herb to 6 cm high, with small opposite ovate, fleshy leaves flattened on the upper side, blue-green and short-hairy, 6 mm long; small white flowers. *Warm temperate.* *p. 874*

dendroideum praealtum (Mexico); large handsome branching succulent to $1^1/_2$ m or more high; oblanceolate spoon-shaped, incurving leaves arranged in loose rosette at apex of stems, 5-7 cm long, pale green flushed red at tips; flowers light yellow, in loose inflorescence. *p. 914*

derenbergii of hort.: see x Sedeveria

gibsonii; a "hardy" sedum in the California nursery trade, branching from the base, with fleshy stems loosely set with 2 cm obcordate fleshy leaves, glaucous pink with bronzy cast, notched at apex; the shoots with smaller leaves terminating in small clusters of starry white flowers. *p. 921*

'Golden Glow' (Sedum adolphii x Pachyphytum amethystinum); Hummel hybrid of robust habit with broader waxy golden coppery tinted leaves which do not shatter as easily as Sedum adolphii. (I) *p. 917*

griseum (Mexico); small shrubby succulent with gray-brown stems and small cylindrical green leaves covered with white bloom; flowers white. *p. 916*

guatemalense: see rubrotinctum

hintonii in hort., bot. S. hystrix (Michoacán); clustering succulent with firm, swollen, obovate gray leaves covered with bristly silver-white hair; large white flowers. (Id) *p. 916, 920*

lineare 'Variegatum' (Japan, China), "Carpet sedum"; tuft-forming low succulent with small linear, soft fleshy leaves, gray green with white margins; star-like yellow flowers. (I-F) *p. 916*

maximum atropurpureum (Europe: Caucasus; Siberia); hardy perennial succulent, with tuberous, thickened roots; brown-red erect stem 50-100 cm high, branching near apex; soft-fleshy leaves opposite or in whorls of three, broadly ovate 5-10 cm long and slightly dentate, dark green in the species; the variety deep metallic green with dark red midrib and purple at margins; flowers greenish white. *p. 921*

mexicanum (So. Mexico), "Mexican stone-crop"; freely branching succulent creeper with flexible rooting stems dense with needle-like, fresh green, flattened leaves 1 cm long; clusters of golden yellow flowers with prominent stamens. Pretty as a hanging plant. *p. 921*

morganianum (Mexico), "Burro-tail"; a lovely hanging succulent plant, with tassels of short spindle-shaped leaves yellowish-green covered with silvery-blue bloom; terminal flowers pale pink. The heavy branches are quite pendulous and a beautiful sight when grown like long queues. *Arid-subtropic.* *p. 918, 919, 922, 2092*

multiceps (Algeria), "Pigmy Joshua tree"; small shrubby succulent resembling a Joshua tree in miniature, tiny terminal rosettes of gray-green needle-like, ciliate leaves, which go dormant; flowers yellow. (Id) *p. 916, 2092*

nutans (Mexico: Morelos); creeping succulent with woody stems, the fleshy obovate leaves crowded toward the ends of branches, 8 cm long, light glossy green; flowers bright yellow, in long raceme. *p. 920*

oreganum compactum (No. California to Alaska); small branching succulent with erect tips; tiny thick, spatulate leaves less than 2 cm long, dark green covered with silvery-gray bloom when young; flowers yellow, fading pink; hardy. *p. 916*

x orpetii (treleasei x morganianum), "Giant burro-tail" or "Lamb's tail"; an excellent trailing succulent similar to morganianum but slower-growing and with the fatter, glaucous 2 cm leaves more spread-open on their tasseled branches, and holding on more firmly, whereas morganianum leaves tend to drop on touch and scatter. Ideal in hanging pots or baskets. *p. 914, 925*

pachyphyllum (Oaxaca), "Jelly beans"; small shrubby succulent with cylindric clubshaped fleshy leaves curved upward, 3-4cm long, light green and glaucous blue, with red tips; flowers yellow. *Subtropic.* *p. 917*

'Peachblossom'; selected clone of the California hybrid complex Sedum adolphii x Graptopetalum; sturdy little plant with near boat-shaped leaves, waxy glaucous greenish-gray with peachy (pink) tinting; flowers whitish. Rosette character of Graptopetalum but holds foliage better. For dishgardens. *p. 914, 918*

pilosum (Asia Minor, Armenia, Caucasus); small biennial succulent to 10 cm high, with fat little 2 cm recurving leaves densely shingled along stem, dark green, and ciliate at edges; the stems topped by showy cluster of rose-red, starry flowers. *p. 921*

platyphyllum (So. Mexico), "Powdered jade plant"; a robust, erect, branching succulent resembling a Jade plant, with fleshy stalk and obovate leaves but unusual because of its very pale yellow-green color throughout, covered with a silvery bloom; flowers greenish-white, dotted red. *p. 918*

populifolium (Siberia), "Hollyleaf sedum"; interesting succulent sub-shrub with branches to 25 cm long, later creeping; the deeply lobed, waxy, dull-green leaves 2 cm long on brown-striped stems; deciduous in autumn; loose inflorescence with rosy or white flowers delicately scented. *Temperate.* *p. 921*

praealtum cristatum (Mexico), "Green coxcomb"; a weird looking succulent with fleshy, shining light green, flat as well as round stems and spatulate leaves; the species has bright yellow flowers. (I-F) *p. 918,919*

rubrotinctum (guatemalense) (Mexico), "Christmas cheer"; small branching succulent with thickly clustered, fleshy, club-shaped 2 cm leaves glossy green, turning coppery-red in sun; flowers yellow. *p. 917*

sieboldii (Japan), "October plant"; graceful perennial creeper suitable for hanging baskets; flexible stems set with whorls of 3 roundish, notched leaves, glaucous-blue changing to copper, and edged with red; flowers pink, blooming in October. *Warm-temperate.* *p. 916*

sieboldii 'Medio-variegatum'; an attractive variegated form with the grayish green leaves having a cream-yellow center, and stems are pink. *Warm temperate.* *p. 916*

spathulifolium (Brit. Columbia to California); small, clustering rosettes of plump, keeled leaves 2½ cm long and with short point, green with glaucous coating and tinged with red; flowers light yellow on stalk to 12 cm long. *p. 921*

spectabile (Japan, Central China), hardy "Live forever" or "Showy sedum"; strong growing, tough winter-hardy perennial 30-60 cm high, freely suckering at base with erect thick fleshy stems and soft leathery, glaucous light green or grayish obovate leaves 6-8 cm long, toothed toward apex, and generally set in twos and threes along the stems, which terminate in large flat clusters of rosy-lavender or red flowers in late summer. Propagation by division of the root-stock or cuttings. Probably the showiest of Sedums, good for tubs which may be left outdoors during the cold season with plants going dormant in winter. *Warm temperate.* *p. 924, 925*

spectabile 'Brilliant'; showy cultivar of the "Live-forever" with blue-glaucous, succulent leaves and large flattened, terminal clusters of glowing rose-pink flowers displaying masses of purplish stamens. *p. 924*

spectabile 'Variegatum' (Japan, C. China), "Variegated live-forever"; succulent perennial freely suckering at base, with erect fleshy stems and soft obovate, yellow leaves with margins bluish-green and toothed; large pink flowers. (Chd) *p. 918, 920*

spurium (Caucasus); rambling, matforming small succulent with thin, flexible reddish stems set with opposite tiny waxy green, 2½ cm roundish leaves, crenate toward apex; flowers red to white; hardy. *p. 918*

stahlii (Mexico: Puebla), "Coral beads"; sparry, low succulent with spreading branches, tiny 1 cm opposite leaves ovoid almost like beads, dark green to brown, easily dropping off and rooting; flowers yellow. *p. 918*

telephium 'Indian Chief' (W. Europe to Siberia and Japan); a big flowered cultivar of the "Orpine" of legendary folk medicine; robust hardy perennial succulent to 40 cm high, with numerous leafy stems; the 8 cm oval leaves crenate at margins, glaucous gray-green, opposite and alternate along the waxy stems, topped by dense cluster of flowers reddish purple in the species, burnished copper to Indian-red in 'Indian Chief', blooming in autumn. *p. 925*

ternatum (E. U.S.: Massachusetts to Georgia); hardy succulent perennial usually with a single flowering stem to 20 cm tall, and several short, leafy, rooting, sterile shoots; obovate, spatulate, or kidney-shaped green thin-fleshy leaves in whorls of three, 1 to 3 cm long; flowers white. *p. 921*

tortuosum (Mexico); small branching succulent with leafy twisting, rooting stems, the dense fleshy, obovate-spatulate sessile leaves flattened on the surface, and obliquely keeled beneath, yellowish pea green with bronzy cast, glossy with some waxy powder, 3 cm long; flowers white. *p. 922*

treleasei (Mexico); called "Silver sedum" because of the mealy-white bloom on the bluish-green leaves which stay blue with age; fleshy leaves semi-flat and curving upward; flowers yellow. *p. 917*

weinbergii: see Graptopetalum paraguayense

SEEMANNIA *Gesneriaceae* **S3HFM**

latifolia (Bolivia at 600-1000 m); a pretty, very floriferous branching plant from scaly rhizomes, closely related to Kohleria; by appearance smooth, but covered with a coating of very fine hairs; the stems first erect, then reclining with tips erect; elliptic to lanceolate bright green leaves 12-15 cm long, on clasping petiole; from the axils in whorls around the main stem the bell-shaped swollen 2 cm flowers brick-colored or cinnabar-red outside, the short lobes deep red inside, with the throat yellow speckled red-brown; in constant bloom for months, beginning in early spring. *Tropical.* *p. 1276*

sylvatica: see Gloxinia

SELAGINELLA *Selaginellaceae* **S-I3HNM**

biformis (plumosa) (Philippines); rhizomatous bushy, creeping species dense with erect bases bearing soft green fronds arching outward, successively branching and lacily cut to narrow skeleton segments. *p. 2064*

x burgeffii (pilifera x emmeliana); a "Sweat plant" in habit between these two parents; rich green rosette of fan-like fronds twice as large as pilifera but only half the size of emmeliana; habit rather flat, only 12 cm high. *p. 2061*

canaliculata (delicatula var. robusta; caudata) (E. Himalayas, Burma, So. China, Malaysia, Philippines); strong tall-growing, handsome species forming long runners, sub-erect stems to 1 m long, bright green, several times forking into rather slender segments. *p. 2065*

caulescens (Sundas, China, Japan, India), "Stalked selaginella"; stiff, upright growing mountain dweller with erect wiry, greenish stalks to 60 cm high, bearing on their upper half close, deltoid branchlets with narrow, bright-green leaf segments of firm texture and good keeping quality. (I) *p. 2062*

commutata (Malaya); bushy, fibrous-rooted plant 12-15 cm high, with erect fronds successively branching fanlike and recurving near apex into rather broad and dense segments rich green with pale ribs in center; lots of smaller fronds give the center a certain fluffy fullness. *p. 2064*

cuspidata (pallescens) (Cuba, Mexico, Guatemala, Venezuela); stems tufted, about 15 cm long, branched nearly from base, primary branches pinnate, the rhomboid pinnae densely compound with branching leaflets, fresh green and stiffish. *p. 2065*

delicatula (Trop. Asia); suberect stems, forming long lithe runners, the bipinnate ultimate segments distantly spaced and very slender almost linear, bright green. *p. 2065*

emmeliana (cuspidata emiliana) (So. America), "Sweat plant"; lacy, small rosette of fern-like, erect, bright green fronds, to about 12 cm long, revelling in high humidity; if allowed to dry the tips will curl and turn brown and won't recover. *Humid-tropical.* *p. 2062, 2063*

erythropus (umbrosa) (West Indies, Guatemala to C. Brazil and Chile); erect stems 15-22 cm long, deep red, branching 1/3 up into 3-to 4-pinnate, bright green, stiffish full fronds deflexed outward. *p. 2064*

flabellata (Argentina); dense cushion of erect and trailing branches to 8 cm long; scales on fronds appressed and overlapping while young, lush rich green and forming mounds. *p. 2061*

kraussiana (Lycopodium denticulatum) (South Africa, Cameroons), "Spreading clubmoss"; a charming, moss-like herb with matforming, creeping stems rooting as they grow, with tiny, crowded, bright green, pinnate, scale-like leaves; very useful as a quickly spreading ground cover in terrarium or conservatory. *Humid-tropical.* *p. 2062, 2063*

kraussiana 'Aurea', "Golden trailing club-moss"; attractive spreading form with creeping branches having leaves of yellow-green, perhaps a little heavier than the type, and the young growth especially is golden yellow. *Humid-tropical.* *p. 2062*

kraussiana 'Brownii' (apus elegans) (Azores), "Dwarf clubmoss"; shapely, moss-like cushions of densely clustering, short branches of vivid emerald green, supported by translucent aerial roots; very attractive in terrariums. *Humid-tropical.* *p. 21*, 2062*

lepidophylla (Texas, Mexico, Perú), "Resurrection plant" or "Rose of Jericho"; flat rosette of densely tufted, branched stems with fairly hard, scale-like leaves, red-brown with age; when the plants dry out the branches curl up into a tight ball, but will unfold to fresh emerald-green when placed into water. *Subtropic.* *p. 2063*

mariesii (Japan); branching flowerless fern-like herb with slender trailing, flattened stems pinnately branched, with tiny leaves shingled and appressed to the stems, green or reddish, the fronds of firm texture and forming dense matting; midway between denticulata and delicatissima. *p.2061*

martensii (Mexico); bold ornamental species, with broad, vivid glossy-green, scale-like, fleshy, almost hard leaves on much branched stems, upright at first, later sub-erect or creeping with young growth erect, supported by strong stilt roots. (I) *p. 2063*

martensii divaricata, "Zigzag selaginella"; slender form with fewer branches and shorter lateral leaves, on stiff zigzag stems. (I) *p. 2062*

martensii 'Variegata'; a beautiful form of coarse, rather stiff, branching habit, largely supported by long stilt roots, with broad, glossy-green leaves irregularly but attractively tipped or variegated white. S. martensii is a bold species from Mexico, with stems to 30 cm long. *Tropical.* *p. 1824A, 2063*

martensii 'Watsoniana', "Variegated selaginella"; attractive form of hard texture with grass-green growth tending upright but ends of branchlets pendant and with pale or silvery tips. *p. 2062*

pilifera (Texas, Mexico); rosette found high on Central Mexican plateaux at 1,800-2,400 m; fibrous roots dense with many times pinnately or fan-like forking, stiff fronds, diminishing in size toward center, 8-10 cm long, light green and rigid in texture; similar to S. lepidophylla, but differing in having awl-shaped leaves. *p. 2065*

plana (inaequalifolia perelegans) (E. Himalaya, Burma, India); fibrous-rooted plant with erect wiry stems, forming runners, to 30 cm high, with distant forking, firm slender branches, the upper branches stay about the same size as the lower ones; the small scale-like leaves bright green, the spore-bearing spikes very pronounced, 2½ cm long. *p. 2065*

plumosa (E. Himalayas, Ceylon, Burma, So. China); crawling ground cover, like kraussiana, but more dense, with short flat fronds, bright green, fairly firm in texture, and overlapping the pale stems; the fruiting spikes are square. *Subtropic. p. 2063*

pulcherrima (caulescens amoena) (Mexico); rhizomatous creeper, with erect, straw-yellow branches 30 cm high; the bright green, rigid fronds lightly pendant; scale-like leaves appressed for the lower two-third, upper part almost tri-cornered, 3-4 times pinnate, the feathery pinnae arranged in ranks. *p. 2064*

serpens (variabilis mutabilis) (West Indies); densely matted, spidery, trailing stems, reaching to 22 cm long, pinnate with slightly compound, slim and firm branches; leaves bright green with distinct midrib, and with spore-bearing spikes. *Tropical. p. 2061, 2064*

tamariscina (Honshu, Kyushu); evergreen tufted rosette of ribbon-like linear firm fertile fronds green with yellow tip; the tiny scale-like leaves in shingled ranks closely appressed to the flattened axis; forms miniature tree with age. Photographed at an exhibition of Japanese fanciers in Ikeda Park, Tokyo. *Subtropic. p. 2061*

uncinata (caesia) (So. China), "Rainbow fern"; exquisite low creeper with straw-colored, slender, rambling stems rooting along the ground, alternately set with tiny branched lateral leaves which are metallic blue and iridescent in the shade. *Humid-tropical. p. 2062, 2063*

versicolor (West Africa: Senegambia, Ghana, Angola); rhizomatous creeper with stoloniferous suberect stems several times pinnate and compound, the broad pinnae with bright green, membranous unequal-sided leaves; the colors varying between light and dark or yellow-green; spore-bearing spikes square. *p. 2064*

vogelii (Africa: Guinea Coast, Cameroun Mts., Zanzibar; Madagascar); pinnate fronds with forking branches, triangular in outline, on stalks that may become 30-60 cm long, often tinted pink; the broad pinnae with bright green leaves, their edges liable to be turned down (revolute). *p. 2065*

wallichii (E. Himalayas, Burma, Malay Peninsula, Philippines, Malay Archipelago, New Guinea); rhizomatous creeper forming runners; suberect stems becoming 60-90 cm long, the pinnae with simple final uncut, broad segments, dark bright green and firm in texture. *p. 2061, 2065*

willdenovii (caesia arborea) (Vietnam, Malaysia, Himalayas), "Peacock fern"; robust growing and most beautiful, shade-loving rambler at first erect, but soon climbing between shrubs to 6 m high, the light brown stems supported by stiff stilt-roots, and bearing spreading fronds of magnificent, shimmering peacock-blue. *Humid-tropical. p. 2062*

SELENICEREUS *Cactaceae* **I-S2HFM**

boeckmannii (Cuba, Santo Domingo, E. Mexico); night-blooming climber with light green, 5-7-ribbed rounded stems to 2 cm thick, with many aerial roots; flowers with petals white, sepals yellow to greenish-brown. *p. 664*

grandiflorus (Jamaica, Cuba), "Queen of the night"; climbing epiphyte with large flowers 15 to 25 cm long, salmon outside, white inside, and blooming by moonlight, with a powerful vanilla perfume, earning it the name "Queen of the night"; the flowers expand at sunset or by moonlight and fade off in the morning; stems 3 cm thick, light grayish green to purplish. *Tropical. p. 664*

hamatus (So. and E. Mexico, Lesser Antilles), "Moon cactus"; epiphytic climber with vigorous stems glossy grass-green 2 cm thick and ribbed, with few aerial roots; flowers white, pale green outside, to 25 cm long. *Tropical. p. 662*

macdonaldiae (Uruguay, Argentina), "Queen of the night"; quick-growing clambering species with trailing and jointed rooting stems to 7 m long; dark glossy green often shaded purplish, 5, 6, or 7-angled, 1 cm thick, with brownish areoles and short brown spines; longest of flowers, broad inner petals ivory, to 30 cm long, white, narrow reddish or amber petals outside; night-blooming. *p. 666*

pteranthus (Mexico), "King of the night", or "Princess of the night"; trailing epiphytic climber to 3 m long; the jointed, stiff, rooting stems 1½-4½ cm thick, 4 to 6-angled, dull glaucous green, usually flushed purple, the areoles with white wool and short thick spines; night-blooming, funnel-form flowers 30 cm across, with narrow purplish-yellow sepals and broad creamy-white petals; reddish fruit. *Tropical. p. 618, 666*

spinulosus (Mexico: Hidalgo); clambering night-bloomer, the slender green stems forming many aerial roots 2 cm thick, with 5 ribs and small yellowish spines; flowers 15 cm long, the sepals spreading, greenish-yellow, the petals white, with white stamens, open at night only and very fragrant. *p. 661*

urbanianus (Cuba, Haiti), "Moon-cereus"; clambering nightbloomer, epiphytic with aerial roots, and 4 to 5-angled joints of 5 cm dia; giant 30 cm fragrant flowers white inside, tan outside. *Tropical. p. 664, 665*

vagans (Mexico); epiphytic climber, with creeping stems 1½ cm thick, 5-6-ribbed, and raised brown areoles; flowers very freely borne at the top of stems, sepals brownish or greenish, petals white; night-flowering. *p. 662*

wercklei (C. America), "Werckle's moon goddess"; night-blooming epiphyte with much branched cylindrical, green stem 2 cm thick, with about 12 low ribs, spineless; large white flowers and yellow fruit. *p. 662*

SELENIPEDIUM *Orchidaceae* **I3OFM**

grande in hort. (bot. Phragmipedium), "Mandarin orchid"; striking terrestrial of robust habit; strap-shaped, flexible leaves 60 cm long; long stalk with curious slipper flowers green, marked and lined mahogany, the long spiralled petals extending 30 cm or more, wine red, the large waxy pouch greenish-yellow spotted red inside (summer) (see Phragmipedium). *p. 1827*

SELENIPEDIUM: see also Phragmipedium

SEMELE *Liliaceae* **I2LBD**

androgyna (Ruscus) (Canary Isl.), "Climbing butcher's broom"; shrubby vine having leaves represented by scales, the apparent leaves being leaf-like branches, to 10 cm long, ovate, leathery; the tiny greenish-yellow flowers with purple center borne in clusters on their margins. *Subtropic. p. 1492, 1505*

SEMIARUNDINARIA *Gramineae* **I2LBM**

fastuosa (Japan), the "Narihira bamboo"; stately "running" bamboo with stems to 7-12 m high and 3 cm dia. at base; the culms thin-walled, slightly zigzag, marked with purplish-brown, mostly round but toward top flattened above the internodes; 1-3 upright branches mostly at the upper nodes, with leaves to 17 cm long, dark green and smooth above, grayish and pubescent beneath. Hardy to minus 18°C. *p. 1309*

SEMPERVIVELLA *Crassulaceae* **I2LBD**

sedoides (Kashmir); interesting succulent from the Himalayas, forming cushions, in rosettes 2 cm across, the small fat obovate leaves 1 cm long, light green and lightly hairy; rosy, star-shaped, pretty flowers. *p. 921*

SEMPERVIVUM *Crassulaceae* **C2LBDh**

arachnoideum (Mountains of So. Europe), "Cobweb hen-and-chicks"; tiny rosettes to 2 cm dia., clustering by stolons and forming mounds, prettily covered by a cobweb of white hairs from tip to tip of leaves; flowers reddish. *Temperate. p. 919, 923*

arachnoideum glabrescens; variety with rosettes twice as large, to 5 cm, leaves spreading more loosely, and sparse white cobwebbing. *p. 923*

arachnoideum var. tomentosum; a form of the "Cobweb-houseleek" with rosettes of tightly shingled leaves 1½ to 2½ cm dia., rather globular but distinctly flattened above; and covered with snow-white felt, and hairy. *p. 924*

moggridgei (So. Europe); possibly a variety of S. arachnoideum; charming Alpine plant, with inflorescence to 22 cm high, the leafy stem with longer leaves and carrying the pretty inflorescence, a cluster of starry flowers 2 cm across, rose with deep red center and red stamens; at base the small clustering rosettes, each 2 to 5 cm across; the obovate leaves green or reddish, 2 cm long and tipped with tufts of hairs. *p. 925*

montanum braunii (Austrian Alps); turf-forming, clustering rosettes to 5 cm, growing in crevices of rocks; leaves obovate pointed, plain green, fleshy, finely pubescent; flowers yellowish-white. *p. 923*

pittonii (Austria: Styria); large, clustering rosettes, at home in crevices in the Austrian Alps; 3 to 5 cm across, with leaves 2-3 cm long, dark green, blotched and tipped with red, shaggy-hairy, and ciliate along margins; flowers yellowish in a dense hairy head. *p. 924*

tectorum (Europe), known as "Hen-and-chicken" because of the miniature rosettes sprouting from the mother rosette; also called "Roof-houseleek" because it is often found growing on roofs; plant 8-10 cm across with many obovate cuspidate leaves gray-green, lightly tipped brown; flowers purplish-red. *p. 922, 923*

tectorum calcareum (French Alps), "House leek"; attractive small leathery rosettes 5-10 cm across, and forming clusters; glaucous light gray-green leaves broadly painted red-brown at apex; flowers pale red on tall stalks. *Warm temperate. p. 923*

tectorum 'Malbyi'; an English cultivar; large, clustering rosette of outstanding beauty because of its rich mahogany-red coloring. *p. 922*

tectorum schottii (glaucum), (So. Alps, Istria); mat-forming rosettes with long oblanceolate, soft-leathery leaves bluish-green, white at base and red-brown at tips; flowers pink. *p. 923*

SEMPERVIVUM: see also Aeonium

SENECIO *Compositae* **C-S1-2LF-BD-M**

articulatus (Kleinia) (Cape Prov.), "Candle plant"; succulent with swollen, jointed stems, glaucous blue with darker lines, and fleshy leaves deeply lobed; flower heads yellowish-white. *p. 828, 830*

barbertonensis (Transvaal); branching shrub, with succulent, cylindrical leaves tapering to a point, the upper surface grooved, 4 cm long and 6 mm wide, green and with minute hairs, crowded in tufts at the ends of branches; flowers golden-yellow. *p. 831, 832*

cephalophorus (So. Africa: Namaqualand); branching bluish-green succulent with stems to 3 cm thick, and fleshy, lanceolate leaves with recurved margins to 10 cm long, the flower-heads yellow. *p. 831*

cineraria (Cineraria maritima) (Mediterranean), a "Dusty miller"; beautiful, white-woolly perennial to 1 m tall, with thick leaves at first oak-leaved, later pinnately cut, the pinnae well separated and broad, crenate at their broadening apex; inflorescence on beautiful white-felted stalks, in cymes of small 2 cm thistle-like flower heads with short bright yellow rays. Listed in seed catalogs as Cineraria maritima 'Diamond'; much used as a border plant. *Subtropic.* *p. 819*

citriformis, (So. Africa: Cape Prov.); charming hanging basket plant; long thread-like stems furnished like a string of beads with globular grass-green shiny balls, coming to a short point at one end; with numerous pale gray or translucent longitudinal lines; flowers creamy-yellow in stalked heads. *Subtropic.* *p. 833*

confusus (Mexico), "Mexican Flame vine"; colorful tender vine or scandent shrub with fresh green, fleshy, ovate leaves 4 to 10 cm long, coarsely toothed at margins; striking daisy-like double flame-scarlet flowers in clusters at ends of branches. *Subtropic.* *p. 813, 831*

crassissimus (Madagascar), "Vertical-leaf"; unusual and attractive succulent becoming 75 cm high, with branching stem bearing thick-fleshy, flat oblique-obovate, nearly round leaves 5 cm long, almost at right angles or vertical to the stem, gray glaucous with purple edge, indistinctly veined. *p.829*

cruentus: see hybridus

fulgens (So. Africa: Natal), "Scarlet kleinia"; succulent plant with tuberous root and thick, stiff stem to 45 cm long, wholly covered with glaucous bloom; the fleshy obovate leaves 8-12 cm long and toothed toward apex, light green and waxy-powdered violet-gray; flower heads with orange red florets. Promising house plant. *Subtropic.* *p. 830*

glastifolius (So. Africa: S. W. Cape), "Maple aster"; tall perennial to 1 m high, with small light green, prickly, serrate leaves 8 cm long; and clusters of daisy-like flowers soft pink to mauve, with yellow center. *Subtropic.* *p. 812*

grandiflorus (ampliflorus) (So. Africa); herbaceous perennial with stems 1-1½ m high, closely leafy at base, sparsely so upward; leaves to 15 cm long, pinnately lobed; flower heads in loose clusters with 15-20 purple ray florets and yellow disk. *p. 814*

grandifolius (Mexico); semi-woody shrub 2-4 m high, with erect, stout, purplish stem; large ovate leaves to 45 cm long, coarsely toothed, dark green above, downy beneath; winter flowering with large cluster of yellow heads. *Subtropic.* *p. 814*

greyi (New Zealand); evergreen shrub up to 2½ m dwelling on cliffs in habitat; branches, underside and petioles white-felted; the oblong foliage 4-10 cm long, dark green and somewhat cupped; 2½ cm flower heads with rich yellow ray florets and golden cushion, in terminal panicles. *p.804*

haworthii, in horticulture as Kleinia tomentosa (So. Africa), "Coccoon plant"; striking small succulent semi-shrub about 30 cm high, entirely clothed with appressed soft pure white wool; the fleshy cylindrical-pointed leaves 2½-5 cm long; flower heads orange-yellow. Beautiful in their snowy dress, the foliage unfortunately drops off easily when handled. *p. 830*

hectori (New Zealand); one of the noblest and finest species I could not help but admire when visiting the Nelson and Westland areas on South Island; evergreen shrub 2-4 m high, with stout branches loosely woolly, large oblanceolate leaves 15-25 cm long, deep green and thinly downy, toothed at margins; remarkable for its magnificent trusses to 25 cm wide, of large 2-4 cm starry flowers, with 12-14 pure white ray florets around the yellow disk. *p. 817*

herreianus (Kleinia gomphophylla) (Namibia), "Green marble vine"; clustering succulent with creeping, rooting branches, the distant, fleshy green leaves berry-like, to 2 cm long and pointed, with translucent stripes serving as windows. *Arid-subtropic.* *p. 833*

hybridus (hybrid of cruentus), from the Canary Islands; after much modification and possibly hybridization with S. heritieri and populifolia, have become the widely cultivated "Cineraria" of florists; a showy, herbaceous cool house plant with handsome, triangular-ovate, large turgid leaves rich grass-green above, purplish beneath and grouped around a large rounded, and dense truss of starry flowers with variously colored rays from white to shades of pink to red, purple and blue, surrounding the usually purple center cushion; often with white eye. *Humid-subtropic.*

hybridus 'Calif. Super Giant'; magnificent strain with showy head of beautifully formed large flowers measuring 10-15 cm across, with individual petals 2½-4 cm wide; of compact habit, basal branching, 38-45 cm high, in lovely colors from red to purple and blue. *p. 826*

hybridus 'Gigantea nana'; a giant flowered strain known in Germany as 'Gmunder Riesen', with big flowers each 10-12 cm across. *p. 824*

hybridus 'Grandiflora'; large flowered class; 5-6 cm flowers of medium-tall habit, blue with white eye. *Subtropic.* *p. 826*

hybridus 'Grandiflora maxima nana' (gigantea); largest-flowered strain of the commercial grandiflora group, medium tall in maxima, low and compact in maxima nana. *p. 825*

hybridus 'Grandiflora nana', florists "Cineraria"; widely grown commercially, compact plant with showy heads of medium-large flowers in many red, salmon or blue shades, usually with white eye.

hybridus 'Grandiflora nana Blue'; belonging to the medium-large flowered group, and of low, compact habit; color selection in blues. *p. 825*

hybridus 'Grandiflora nana Red'; red color selections with tips of ray flowers in carmine cherry, ruby, crimson and rose, their bases forming a large white "eye". *p. 825*

hybridus 'Grandiflora nana Zwerg' ('Gmunder Zwerg'); small-leaved dwarf plant with medium-large flowers 6-7 cm across, in clear colors including rose, blood-red, brick-red, all blue or with white eye, and white. *p. 824*

hybridus 'Multiflora Grandiflora nana'; a German strain by R. Schmid of Gmund, typified by many large flowers in rich monotone colors on a dwarf habit plant. *p. 824*

hybridus 'Multiflora nana'; medium small-flowered class of low, compact habit; the many smallish, often white-eyed flowers, primarily in bright reds, purples and blues, make up in big showy heads what they lack in individual size; a favorite commercial and widely cultivated group for early spring bloom. *Subtropic.* *p. 824, 826*

hybridus 'Multiflora nana compacta'; a good florists' "cineraria", because of its very compact form, overall about 20-25 cm high including pot; the pretty bicolor flowers in the photo on pg. 824 have sky blue florets with white base, around the purple disk; this strain also comes in various other color combinations including red. *p. 824*

hybridus 'Multiflora nana Gold-center'; a type of the smaller-flowered class with solid-colored ray flowers surrounding an attractive center cushion formed by the protruding yellow anthers. *p. 825*

hybridus 'Multiflora plena Anemone-flowered'; form with an outer ring of broad ray flowers surrounding a high cushion of tubular flowers as in an anemone. *p. 825*

hybridus 'Multiflora plena Pompon-flowered'; a strictly double-flowering "Cineraria" with tubular flowers changed into nearly flat ray-flowers, forming an almost globular head. These doubles should be propagated from cuttings, as seeds will come only partially true. *p. 825*

hybridus 'Nana grandiflora'; European strain of florists' "cineraria" of low compact growth, yet with broad bouquets of large 8-10 cm flowers with bicolor florets. *p. 824*

hybridus 'Siter's Rainbow Purple'; highly rated commercial American strain of florists' cineraria; of compact habit, with small foliage, and immense heads of medium-large, light-eyed flowers, early blooming; in this color from magenta-purple with white "eye". *p. 826*

hybridus 'Siter's Rainbow Salmon'; selected color form in pastel salmon, with small white "eye", in full rounded head of medium large flowers over the small roundish leaves. *p. 826*

hybridus 'Stellata nana'; a shorter, more compact form 45 cm high of the normally 1 m tall-growing 'Stellata' class; flowers smallish, sometimes used for cut, with small centers and petals usually narrow, star-like; colors white with blue center, and also blue, salmon, or rose. *p. 826*

johnstonii, (Tanzania), the "Giant groundsel"; mainly of interest because of the large, tree-like habit of this species; I have found these above tree-line on Mt. Kilimanjaro where they occur between 2,700 and 5,000 m altitude; tree-like to 4 m high, with several woody stems topped by dense rosettes of large 30-45 cm cordate-ovate, turgid, recurved leaves, fresh-green, somewhat gray felted underneath, and on channeled leafstalks; small flowers in terminal 1 m branched spikes. *Subtropic.* *p. 816*

kleinia (Kleinia neriifolia) (Canary Islands); succulent shrub up to 3 m high, successively branching, with gray-green stems to 20 cm thick, segmented in yearly growths, the youngest segments to 4 cm thick, light green and waxy-mealy and marked with cross-lines; narrow, thickish, deciduous gray-green leaves to 15 cm long; yellowish flower heads with awl-shaped bracts. *p. 831*

kleiniaeformis (cuneatus) (Kleinia) (So. Africa), "Halberd kleinia"; waxy-white powdered subshrub often with prostrate stems but erect branches to 60 cm high; cupped, upcurved and incurved succulent leaves 8-10 cm long, and distantly toothed; flower heads white or yellow. *p. 828, 830*

leucostachys (Argentina); a tall-growing "Dusty miller"; shrubby at base but herbaceous as usually grown from cuttings; entire plant white tomentose, slender branches to 60 cm tall with leaves pinnatifid with linear lobes; inflorescence in corymbs with small heads of yellow flowers. *p. 819*

macroglossus 'Variegatum', "Variegated wax-vine"; very attractive creeper, of which the green type comes from E. Cape Prov., but I found this lovely variegated form in Kenya; densely branching and mat-forming, with small 3-4 cm ivy-like lobed, waxy, thin-succulent leaves with cordate base, green to milky-green and bordered or variegated with cream; pretty daisy-like ray flowers with 12-14 white florets and yellow center. *Subtropic.* *p. 831, 832*

mikanioides (So. Africa), "Climbing senecio" or "Parlor ivy"; glabrous twiner with fresh-green, ivy-shaped, lobed leaves rather soft-fleshy, 5-8 cm across; fragrant, yellow disk-flowers. *Subtropic.* *p. 829, 831*

pendulus (Kleinia) (Arabia), "Inchworm"; succulent shrub with cylindrical stems, decumbent, snake-like, 2 cm thick, grayish over bronze; flowers red to orange. *Arid-tropical.* *p. 830, 2092*

petasitis (So. Mexico), the "California-geranium"; shrub-like perennial to 2 m high with roundish, wavy-lobed grayish downy leaves 15-30 cm long; 3 cm flower heads in large terminal panicles, the 5-6 ray florets bright yellow, disk brownish. *Tropical.* *p. 812*

petraeus (Notonia) (Kenya, Tanzania); succulent, erect when small, later creeping upwards, with alternate obovate fleshy, sessile nerveless leaves 8 cm long, glossy green, the stems rooting at the joints; flower heads orange. *Arid-tropical.* *p. 828, 830*

radicans (Cape Prov.: Karroo; Namibia); creeping succulent with flexuous stems rooting at the nodes, somewhat angular; leaves thick and round, tapering to both ends, $1^{1}/_{2}$-$2^{1}/_{2}$ cm long, directed upwards, dark green, often reddish and wrinkled; flowers white with yellow anthers. *Arid-subtropic.* *p. 833*

repens (serpens) (Cape Prov.); fleshy, cylindric leaves grooved above, glaucous blue; flower heads pale yellow. *p. 830*

rotundifolius (New Zealand: Stewart Isl.); "Mutton-bird scrub"; evergreen shrub or tree to 10 m with branches and underside of foliage densely white-felted, thick-leathery oval leaves shining green above, 8-12 cm long; heads of small yellowish disk-flowers only, in large terminal clusters. Visitors enjoy using the leaves as postcards, writing on the white-tomentose under-surface. *p. 823*

rowleyanus (So. Namibia), "String of pearls"; creeping thin, flexible stems with adventitious roots forming dense mats; furnished as in a string of beads with globular pointed, succulent leaves shiny pale to dark green, with a translucent stripe, about 1 cm dia.; the flowers cinnamon-scented, without ray-florets, the corolla white and with brownish-violet anthers. *p. 833*

scaposus (So. Africa), "Silver coral kleinia"; branched succulent with long cylindrical leaves arranged in rosettes, gray marbled olive-green, and silver cobwebby when young; flower heads yellow. (C2LBD) *p. 830*

scaposus caulescens (vestitus) (So. Africa); large succulent rosette with densely arranged, somewhat canoe-shaped, fleshy leaves flattened at the ends, dark green and covered with fine white hair; flowers yellow. (I2LBD) *p. 830*

spiculosus (Kleinia cylindrica) (Namibia); shrub-forming succulent with long spindle-shaped incurving leaves 6-8 cm long and 1 cm thick, light green with numerous darker nerves, covered with gray waxy powder; white flowers in heads with awl-shaped bracts. *p. 823*

stapeliaeformis, known in horticulture as Kleinia stapeliaeformis (So. Africa: Cape Prov.), "Candy-stick"; branching succulent to 25 cm high, with erect 5 to 7-angled, fleshy, dark green to purple stems 2 cm thick, painted silver between ribs, the angles toothed and tipped with awl-shaped withering leaves; solitary scarlet flower heads; a curious, easy house plant. *p. 828, 830, 831, 2092*

stapeliaeformis minor (Notonia gregori) (Kenya); in general, a smaller plant with less fleshy stems, dark green with gray length-stripes; awl-shaped leaves soon deciduous. *p. 831*

tomentosa (haworthii) (So. Africa); succulent entirely clothed with soft pure white wool, fleshy leaves cylindrical pointed and dropping off easily; flower heads orange-yellow. *p. 830*

tropaeolifolius (Malawi); tuberous rooted herb with irregularly rounded, peltate, fleshy leaves, pale green, violet beneath; flower heads with yellow rays. (I-S2LBM) *p. 829*

SEQUOIA *Taxodiaceae (Coniferae)* **I2LBM**

sempervirens (Oregon and Calif. Coast ranges), "Redwood"; the tallest tree in the world, to 110 m, with red bark; horizontal branches spreading in flat sprays, needles deep green, bluish beneath, and persistent; the female cones 3 cm long. Their knotty burls, cut from trunks, will sprout young growth in a shallow dish of water. *Subtropic.* *p. 834, 838, 850*

sempervirens pendula; form with branches spreading and pendulous; attractive as a small plant. *p. 838*

SEQUOIADENDRON *Taxodiaceae (Coniferae)* **C-I2LBM**

giganteum (California), the famous "Giant sequoia", "Giant redwood" or "Big tree"; at home on the high western slopes of the Sierra Nevadas at an elevation of 1,400 to 1,800 m, where venerable old trees have lived for 5000 years; diameter of trunk to 11 m, and reaching a height of 81 m; the pendulous green shoots are smooth and cord-like; closely covered by spine-like leaf bases, leaves widely awl-shaped, spirally densely arranged closely overlapping, deep green, glaucous when young; grayish hanging cones 5 to 9 cm long. The wood of the Giant sequoia is a beautiful red brown, and extremely durable, never invaded by destructive insects; the fissured bark is divided into cinnamon-brown ridges and to 50 cm thick. Young trees may be grown in pots from small seedlings; it is fairly winter-hardy. *Warm temperate.* *p. 835, 850*

SERAPHYTA *Orchidaceae* **S3OFD**

diffusa (Epidendrum) (West Indies, Mexico to Colombia, Surinam); leafy stems with rigid leaves 8 cm long; arching inflorescence of 1 cm flowers translucent yellowish green or greenish brown (autumn). *p. 1816*

SERAPIAS *Orchidaceae* **I2LFMd**

lingua (So. Europe); bushy terrestrial with succulent leafy stems which carry the erect inflorescence about 35 cm tall, along the upper part with large rosy bracts; the 3 cm flowers purple marbled with green, long 3-lobed lip dark purple (spring). *p. 1816*

longipetala (So. Europe); tuberous terrestrial orchid 50 cm high, with linear-lanceolate leaves, and spike of few large flowers with joined erect sepals purple, pale outside; the smaller petals also purple; tri-lobed lip with purple side-lobes and hairy, brown-red midlobe with yellow center; April-May; dying down after flowering. *p. 1826*

parviflora (So. Europe); terrestrial orchid with bulb-like tubers, linear leaves, larger at base; inflorescence an erect spike with striped bracts and flowers pale purple veined with green, lip dark purple (spring). *p. 1816*

SERENOA *Palmae* **I2LBD**

repens (So. Carolina to Florida Keys), "Saw palmetto"; scrubby, variable palm with creeping stems often underground, and forming wide-spread colonies; occasionally with trunks to 3 m high; heads of palmate leaves 1 m across, deeply cut almost to base into 18-24 widely separated rigid, pendant segments, powdery blue green or bright yellow-green, on thorny petioles; fragrant white flowers, and edible blackish fruit. *Subtropic.* *p. 1910*

SERISSA *Rubiaceae* **I2LFM**

foetida 'Variegata' (Japan, China), "Yellow rim serissa"; dwarf shrub with small, opposite, elliptic 2 cm leaves dark green with ivory-white margin and midrib; funnelform, little, white flowers. *p. 2014, 2022*

SERJANIA *Sapindaceae* **S3HFM**

glabrata (communis) (Perú); decorative twining shrub with herbaceous, bipinnate, almost fern-like leaves with ovate, stalked leaflets fresh-green overlaid with silver in the center, and crenate at margins; yellowish flowers in axillary clusters. *p. 2039*

SERRURIA *Proteaceae* **I2LBD**

burmannii (Cape Prov.), the "Spider bush"; spreading shrub to 1 m high, with red stems and very fine filiform feathery foliage, and small clusters of tiny frilly pink flowers with long styles. *p. 1981*

florida (So. Africa: Cape Mts.), "Blushing bride"; slender, evergreen shrub to $1^{1}/_{2}$ m high; distinctive feathery foliage finely divided into smooth, needle-shaped segments; nodding inflorescence 5 cm across, consisting of a showy nest of papery petal-like pointed, creamy-white bracts flushed with pink, surrounding the true flowers which appear in a mass of silky pinkish hair. *Subtropic.* *p. 1970*

SESAMOTHAMNUS *Pedaliaceae* **S2LBD**

rivae (Trop. Africa: No. Kenya); striking spiny xerophytic tree to 5 m high, with swollen stems and branches, bark coppery green scaling in papery shavings; grayish leaves short-stalked 3 cm long, but dropping foliage before the blooming season; large white, scented flowers 5 cm across. *p. 1922*

SESAMUM *Pedaliaceae* **S3LBD**

orientale (indicum) (India and elsewhere in Tropics), the "Sesame-oil bush" or "Gingelly oil-plant"; useful herb to 60 cm high, with rough, lanceolate leaves 12 cm long, two-lipped 3 cm pink or white flowers in the leaf axils; followed by 3 cm seed-capsules, with 4 grooves, the source of valuable oil, and the Sesame seed used in oriental baking and cooking for thousands of years. *p. 1921*

triphyllum (S. W. Africa: Namibia); another sesame oil bush, cultivated in Africa for the rich oil-content of the seeds, and occasionally as a vegetable or medicinal properties, herb with erect branching stems, the leaves lobed into narrow-linear segments, and large trumpet-flowers a beautiful blue. *p. 1922*

SESBANIA *Leguminosae* **I2LBD**

grandiflora (Agati) (Trop. Asia to W. Africa), "Vegetable hummingbird" or "Red wisteria"; soft-wooded tree to 12 m; pinnate leaves to 30 cm long, leaflets in 10 to 30 pairs, to 5 cm long; remarkable sickle-shaped red to white flowers 10 cm long, hanging in two's to four's from leaf axils; followed by flat beans to 50 cm long. *Tropical.* *p. 1371*

SETARIA *Gramineae* **S2-3LBM**

palmifolia (Panicum) (Malaysia), "Palm-grass"; perennial grass to 2 m tall, the stalk knotted and branching, with plaited leaves 60 cm long and 8 cm wide, nearly emerald green, and slightly hairy; the spikelets subtended by persistent long bristles, in terminal panicles. There is also a form with leaves striped white. *p. 1310, 1315*

SETCREASEA *Commelinaceae* **I-S2LBD**

pallida (Mexico); creeping plant with young growth erect, having fleshy, lanceolate clasping leaves waxy bright green with gray bloom beneath; flowers lavender. *p. 780*

purpurea (pallida var.) (Mexico), "Purple heart"; so named because of the striking purple color of this plant in strong sun, aided by a pubescence of pale hair covering the lanceshaped leaves, 6-10 cm long, on fleshy stems, first erect, later creeping; large 3-petaled orchid-colored flowers.
Subtropic. *p. 5*, 780, 786*

SETCREASEA: see also Callisia, Hadrodemas, Tradescantia

SEYRIGIA *Cucurbitaceae* **S3LBD**
humbertii (Madagascar); clustering succulent with slender, furrowed reddish stems conspicuously covered with a felt of gray hairs; later clambering or climbing, and with simple tendrils; tiny 3 mm, 3-lobed leaves usually absent; flowers greenish-white; ovoid fruit with red flesh. *p. 933*

SHIBATAEA *Gramineae* **I2LBW**
kumasaca (Bambusa, Phyllostachys) (Japan); short, tufted, bamboo-like reeds not over 1 m high, flattened between the joints, with small lanceolate leaves to 10 cm long, bright green, glaucous and downy beneath. *p. 1316*

SIBTHORPIA *Scrophulariaceae* **C2-3LFM**
europaea 'Variegata', "Cornish moneywort"; variegated form of the species native in England, France, Spain and Portugal; slender herbaceous, hairy trailer resembling Glecoma hederacea but leaves are alternate; thread-like vines with rounded or kidney-shaped leaves to 2 cm across, shallowly lobed, variegated or edged creamy-white; fairly hardy. *p. 2059*

pichinchensis (Mexico; Andes of Perú); prostrate perennial, hairy herb, rooting at the nodes and forming a ground cover; tiny, rounded, pubescent, scalloped leaves; small 1 cm flowers yellow or reddish, in leaf axils. *p. 2057*

SICYOS *Cucurbitaceae* **C2LBD**
angulatus (E. Canada, United States), "Star-cucumber"; rapid growing annual herbaceous vine, tendril climbing to 6 m or more, with hairy stems, and angled or lobed leaves; small whitish flowers; ovoid dry fruit 15 mm long, covered by spiny bristles. *p. 930*

SIDA *Malvaceae* **S2LBD**
fallax (Pacific Islands), the "Ilima"; a large shrub, sometimes prostrate and creeping; ovate, gray-felted leaves with crenate margins; hibiscus-like 3 cm flowers bright yellow and semi-double; variations to rich orange and dull-red; the yellow "Ilima" is the flower of Oahu and widely used for leis.
Tropical. *p. 1533*

SIDERASIS *Commelinaceae* **S2LFD**
fuscata (Tradescantia, Pyrrheima) (Brazil), "Brown spiderwort"; clustering rosette of broad and oblong olive green leaves to 20 cm long, with silvery center band, and covered with brown hair as is the purple reverse; large lavender blue flowers at base. *Subtropic.* *p. 782*

SIGMATOGYNE *Orchidaceae* **S3OFM**
tricallosa (Panisea) (Assam, Thailand); clustering epiphyte with small ovoid pseudobulbs topped by solitary stalked lanceolate leaf 5 cm long; basal inflorescence with 1 cm flowers not opening fully, buff-white to pale brown, the lip with brown (spring). *p. 1825*

SIGMATOSTALIX *Orchidaceae* **S3OFM**
hymenantha (Costa Rica, Panama); small epiphyte with clustered compressed pseudobulbs and solitary, thin-leathery leaves; slender, erect inflorescence to 12 cm long, with tiny 5 mm flowers translucent greenish to light brown, lemon-yellow lip and curving column (winter). *p. 1824*

SINNINGIA *Gesneriaceae* **S3HFM (d:D)**
aggregata (Rechsteineria) (Brazil); spreading plant with woody branches 30-50 cm high; ovate leaves with light pubescence and crenate margins; near apex the long-stalked curved-tubular flowers 3 cm long, yellow dotted with orange-red. *p. 1288*

allagophylla (Rechsteineria) (Brazil); tall plant 30 to 80 cm high, from large tuber; oval, soft-hairy leaves rather convex and recurved, in whorls of three along the woody stem, extending upwards carrying at intervals the small 2 cm orange flowers also in whorls of three. *p. 1288*

barbata (carolinae) (Brazil); pretty subshrub with ascending red-brown stems and opposite oblong-lanceolate leaves 10-15 cm long, shining bluish green with sunken veins and toothed margins, the hairy underside and petioles red-purple; axillary flowers with leafy calyx and hairy white corolla 4 cm long, streaked with red inside, the limb cream-colored; the tube pouched below. *p. 1278*

'Bright Eyes' (pusilla x coccinea); a miniature Clayberg hybrid, similar to pusilla but more freely blooming lavender with purplish tint and lines. *p. 1290*

calcaria (Corytholoma) (So. Brazil); species from Paraná close to leucotricha; large tuber with woody purple stem covered with short white hair, and usually two internodes with pairs of opposite, broad ovate, crenate leaves covered with short grayish-white hair, veins beneath red; slender tubular flowers salmon with limb spotted purplish-red inside. *p. 1286*

cardinalis (Rechsteineria) (C. America), "Cardinal flower"; brilliantly flowered, tuberous plant with round cordate, emerald green, velvety leaves, topped by large curved, tubular, bilabiate flowers, white downy over brightest scarlet, throat marked purple, 5-8 cm long.
Tropical. *p. 1285, 1287*

cardinalis 'Feuerschein' (Rechsteineria); a German color variation, with flowers a lighter, mandarin-red shading to carmine rose. *p. 1292*

cardinalis 'Innocence' (Rechsteineria); an exquisite cultivar photographed in Germany in 1974; compact plant with bright green, pubescent foliage, and a veritable bouquet of flowers glistening white as snow. *p. 1288*

cardinalis splendens ("bulbosa" hort.) (Brazil); tuberous, soft-hairy plant with rambling branches, broad cordate, fleshy leaves, resembling cardinalis but larger growing, with shorter, tubular, bilabiate flowers vivid scarlet-red, in spreading clusters. *p. 1285*

cardinalis 'Unschuld' (Rechsteineria), German for 'Innocence'; an exquisite German cultivar, with a compact cluster of pure white flowers, nesting in a rosette of velvety, emerald green leaves. *p. 1292*

concinna (Brazil); miniature tuberous plant, with stems, stalks and veins red, the small hairy leaves roundish-ovate with crenate margins; 2½ cm flowers purple above, yellowish beneath, and spotted inside the inflated tube.
Tropical. *p. 1278*

'Connecticut hybrid' (x Gloxinera); a new group of miniature gesneriads originated by Dr. C. Clayberg (Gloxinian 14: 1964), involving S. pusilla with eumorpha, and for variation in color from S. (Rechsteineria) cardinalis; low rosettes 8-10 cm across of small pubescent, quilted leaves; on 8 cm stalks the relatively large oblique slipper flowers, mainly purple, sometimes with dark eye, and measuring 2½ cm across. The interspecific name x Gloxinera has been transferred to Sinningia by Dr. H. Moore (Baileya 19: 1973). *p. 1250, 1289*

cooperi (Rechsteineria) (Brazil); tall erect stems from large tuber; the opposite pairs of broad ovate soft green leaves covered with white pubescence, the margins crenate; curved tubular, bilabiate flowers bright scarlet, and covered with white down, similar to cardinalis. *p. 1288*

'Coral Gem' (x Gloxinera) (eumorpha x S. (Rechsteineria) macropoda); an original bigeneric Shepherd hybrid 1950, listed by P. Arnold, Binghamton, N.Y.; larger (25cm) than the later, miniature class involving S. pusilla; very vigorous and floriferous with flowers and form intermediate between parents; pouched flowers arranged in Smithiantha-fashion clusters, rosy-red with salmon sheen; purple lines in throat. *p. 1291*

cyclophylla (Rechsteineria) (Brazil), "Roundleaf helmet flower"; tuberous plant with fleshy obovate leaves 15-17 cm long, lightly crenate, rich green and somewhat hairy; tubular nodding flowers scarlet-red with deep crimson dots inside flaring lobes. Very similar to S. macropoda, but considered of more robust habit with greener, more velvety leaves; Dr. Moore distinguishes cyclophylla as having flower disk composed of 2 glands, against macropoda with 5 glands. *p. 1285, 1286*

discolor (Brazil); handsome tuberous species somewhat similar to speciosa, with flowers violet-blue, paler at base of tube, deep purple inside, the flaring limb 4 cm across; leaf petioles longer than speciosa; bright green leaves in a rosette, spoon-shaped, 12 to 15 cm long. *p. 1290*

'Doll Baby' (S. pusilla x eumorpha); a pretty miniature rosette to 8 cm across, having thin, dark olive-green crenate leaves with bronze veins; from the heart rise charming small 3 cm slipper flowers lavender-blue with purple eye and pale lemon throat; blooming for a long time, best in summer.
Humid-tropical. *p. 1289*

eumorpha (maximiliana) (S.E. Brazil); a comely, free-blooming species with large, glossy, thin, lightly downy leaves of bronzy green, and numerous, milky-white flowers like nodding bells lined with lilac and yellow in the throat. *p. 1278*

guttata (Brazil); attractive, rather succulent plant, in cultivation since 1827; with broadly ovate to lanceolate waxy leaves 10 to 18 cm long, somewhat corrugated and with crenate margins, green in center and along ribs, the raised areas overlaid with silvery gray; axillary tubular flowers 3½-4½ cm long, yellow in throat, with expanding limb creamy-white and prettily spotted with purple. *p. 1278*

hirsuta (Brazil); tuberous rosette of broad ovate leaves 6-10 cm long, with a network of sunken veins, covered with white hairs, the margins crenate and purplish beneath; from the center a large bouquet of smallish flowers 3 cm across, lilac white, violet inside tube and with violet spots on expanded limb. *Humid-tropical.* *p. 1290*

leucotricha (Rechsteineria) (Brazil: W. Paraná); a breathtaking new species which I saw when first on exhibition in São Paulo in 1954; huge 30 cm tubers sprouting happily without soil in glazed bowls, the glistening silvery foliage suggesting to me the name "Brazilian edelweiss". Found on cliffs near the waterfall 'Salto Apucarazinho' at 1100 m, it is called locally "Rainha do Abismo". The stout, densely matted, white, later brown hairy stems to 25 cm high, carry one or two whorls of 3-4 large obovate leaves to 15 cm long, densely covered with shimmering, long silvery-white hair, with margins entire or obscurely crenate; slender tubular inflated 3 cm flowers soft rosy coral, entirely covered outside with silky white hair, the lobes sometimes marked with crimson; blooming spring and summer.
Subtropic. *p. 1248A, 1285, 1287*

lineata (Brazil); species closely related to macropoda, with large, herbaceous leaves; red-spotted stalks with arching clusters of inflated, tubular, scarlet flowers spotted deep red, orange in throat, and profusely produced over a long period of time. *p. 1286*

macropoda (Rechsteineria) (So. Brazil), "Vermillion helmet flower"; charming tuberous herb with unbranched hairy stem 15-22 cm high, bearing opposite, rather thin, rugose, velvety bright green leaves almost round, 8-12 cm broad; small nodding flowers in clusters, the slender 2½-3 cm tubes vermillion-red with the lower lobes marked brown-red; in March-April. *Humid-tropical.* *p. 1285, 1286*

macrorrhiza (Rechsteineria) (Brazil); tall plant to more than 1 m high, springing from a large tuber; pairs of ovate leaves, bright green and with margins recurving, arranged along the stem, and topped by an elongate raceme of numerous 2½ cm bilabiate tubular flowers in pink or red. *p. 1288*

maculata (douglasii) (verticillata) (Gesneria) (Brazil); erect stems soft-hairy to 40 cm, the leaves in whorls of fours, oval-pointed dentate, soft-hairy; terminal cluster of pretty, nodding tubular flowers flesh-colored to yellow, tigered and striped with purple-red. *p. 1287*

magnifica (Rechsteineria) (Brazil); compact, showy tuberous plant with fleshy stem and broad cordate, soft green leaves covered with velvety hair, and crenate at margins; tall-stalked inflorescence with curved tubular flowers scarlet red. Resembling S. cardinalis but more robust and attractive. *p. 1288*

pusilla (Brazil); miniature rosette only 5 cm high, of little, oval, puckered leaves olive-green with brown veins, hugging the ground; thin stalks are bearing attractive, slender tubular flowers with five spreading lobes, 1 cm across, orchid-colored with darker veins and lemon-yellow throat. *Humid-tropical.* *p. 1278, 1289, 1291*

pusilla 'White Sprite'; a darling miniature, seen at the Munich Botanic Garden in Germany; only 3-5 cm high, the tiny tubular flowers with spreading lobes only 12 mm across, and glistening pure white. At high humidity this tropical species is willing to bloom constantly; in the home it will grow successfully in small glass brandy snifter covered with clear plastic. If grown open, the little plant will go into a short dormancy in autumm until January. *Humid-tropical.* *p. 1289*

regina (Brazil), "Cinderella slippers"; tuberous species related to speciosa, with ovate pointed, bronzy green, red-backed, velvety leaves beautifully patterned with ivory veins; and a profusion of nodding "slipper" type, violet flowers, 4-5 cm long, shorter and more slender than S. speciosa 'Macrophylla'. *Humid-tropical.* *p. 15*, 1277*

richii (Mexico); nearly stemless; a rosette of hairy, ovate leaves is formed from the multiple tubers on the slender rhizomes; the inflated white, nodding, hairy flowers 4 cm long, rising from the center. *p. 1288*

rimicola (Brazil); large coppery-green, corrugated leaves with a lacquered sheen, red and covered with purple hairs on underside; numerous small, oblique-tubular bell-flowers whitish to lilac pink. *p. 1289*

'Rosebells'; in hort. as x Gloxinera; freely blooming intergeneric hybrid between Sinningia eumorpha x (Rechsteineria) macropoda, resembling a slipper-type gloxinia, with shiny, dark green, heartshaped leaves, and a stalk bearing several flowers, the dainty bells are deep rose with a lavender throat. *p. 1251*

schiffneri (Brazil); softly-hairy, tuberous plant with fleshy stem and thinnish, pointed leaves to 22 cm long, velvety green with crenate margins and unequal base, the midvein green; the tubular, nodding trumpet flowers in clusters of 3 to 4 from the axils, 3 cm long, white with purple dots in throat. *p. 1290*

sellovii (Corytholoma douglasii) (So. Brazil); tall stem to 1 m high flecked with lighter green, thick, dark green, scalloped leaves covered with erect hairs, and carrying at the top a series of nodding tubular flowers in whorls of 3-4, pale red shaded buff-brown; inside white, marked with red. *p. 1286, 1287*

speciosa (So. Brazil), the original "Slipper gloxinia", in habitat from moist warm rocky slopes, and progenitor of the colorful and varied hybrid gloxinias; charming more or less compact tuberous species, nearly stemless, with stalked oblong-ovate fleshy leaves, fresh green and covered with velvety white hair, crenate at margins; showy foxglove-like oblique bell-flowers 4-5 cm long, usually velvety violet with lilac lobes, but quite variable, and wild forms have been found with white or red flowers; normally summer-blooming. *p. 1289*

speciosa fyfiana, the "Gloxinia" of florists; commercial hybrid strain involving S. crassifolia hort., with erect bell-shaped, regular flowers in white, violet, rose or red, variously variegated or spotted, and with 5-12 lobes. *Humid-tropical.*

speciosa fyfiana 'Arizona'; very attractive gloxinia of the "crassifolia" type, the white flowers with a bold red band following the outline of the corolla lobes inside the white margin. *p. 1283*

speciosa fyfiana 'Blanche de Meru'; early-flowering "crassifolia" type gloxinia, pretty with white throat and pink star following outline of lobes, becoming orchid or mauve at margins. *p. 1283*

speciosa fyfiana 'Crispa Meteor'; excellent variant of the grandiflora or soft-leaved type, with large flowers white in throat, changing through lilac into a fiery scarlet on the attractively fringed border; early-blooming. *p.1282*

speciosa fyfiana 'Crispa Waterloo'; large-flowered "grandiflora" type gloxinia with characteristic smaller, softish leaves; the blooms dark crimson red with the lobes recurved and attractively wavy and crisped; early. *p. 1282*

speciosa fyfiana 'Defiance'; large leaf "crassifolia" type, medium-large flowers completely dark cerise-red, with crimson sheen, the margins lightly wavy. *Humid-tropical.* *p. 1279*

speciosa fyfiana 'Double Chicago'; a "Double gloxinia" of the habit of the 7 to 8-petalled frilled 'Switzerland'; produced following meticulous breeding in U.S.; very exciting in having large 9 cm flowers featuring 2 or more rows of frilled petals glowing crimson with crisped white borders, blooming best from spring to summer. *Humid-tropical.* *p. 1291*

speciosa fyfiana 'Emperor Frederick'; a leading commercial hybrid "gloxinia" bred with large upright bell-shaped flowers 8-10 cm across, velvety dark ruby red bordered white, and the typical, over-sized, robust, somewhat brittle, and horizontal leaves of the "crassifolia" class; forming large tubers. *Humid-tropical.* *p. 11*, 1248A, 1279, 1289*

speciosa fyfiana 'Emperor William'; popular leading commercial variety of the large leaf "crassifolia" type gloxinia; flowers deep velvety violet-blue with regular white border, about 8 cm across; early flowering. *Humid-tropical.* *p. 1279*

speciosa fyfiana 'Etoile de Feu'; late-blooming "crassifolia" type gloxinia of vigorous habit, with flowers bright crimson red shading to light red along the smooth margins; lighter than Defiance. *p. 1283*

speciosa fyfiana 'Hollywood'; large leaf "crassifolia" type gloxinia with flowers entirely dark purplish-red; normal season bloom. *p. 1280*

speciosa fyfiana 'Idaho'; lovely white flowers distinctly painted violet-blue just inside the white margin all along the corolla lobes; "crassifolia" type gloxinia. *p. 1283*

speciosa fyfiana 'Kegeliana'; "grandiflora" type gloxinia with pastel pink frilled flowers bordered white; midseason. *p. 1282*

speciosa fyfiana 'Miss America'; a good florists type gloxinia with flowers bright crimson with dark markings in center; not as double as some of the fancy cultivars, but of better, more willing and dependable growth habit, and with thin, flexible leaves not so easily cracked. *p. 1292*

speciosa fyfiana 'Mont Blanc'; "crassifolia" type gloxinia with pure white flowers, for midseason. *p. 1280*

speciosa fyfiana 'Monte Cristo' (1957), "Double gloxinia" produced as a result of long hybridizing in Germany and Louisiana; this named cultivar has large double flowers with 2, 3, 4, or 5 diminishing rows of petals or crowns in glowing velvety crimson, lighter toward the wavy margins and white outside; shapely plant of compact habit. *p. 1284*

speciosa fyfiana 'Prince Albert'; large-flowered "grandiflora" type gloxinia dark violet, with ruffled lobes and tube white outside; late-blooming. *p. 1224*

speciosa fyfiana 'Princess Elizabeth', "Bluebell gloxinia"; "crassifolia" type gloxinia with attractive flowers having a white throat and a broad light blue border over the spreading lobes; midseason to late. *p. 1280*

speciosa fyfiana 'Roi des Rouges'; large blooming, compact "grandiflora" type gloxinia, with flowers deep crimson red with dark sheen, the margins lightly crisped; midseason. *p. 1224*

speciosa fyfiana 'Royal Red Giant'; a color selection of the Park strain of double-flowered gloxinias which comes true to the luminous velvety-red color and about 50% true to full double-petaled character from seed, the remainder being large single red bells of flowers. *p. 1284*

speciosa fyfiana 'Ruby'; Antonelli-California hybrid gloxinia, with erect wavy petaled, bright red flowers edged with pinkish-white; early-blooming; produces more flowers with more petals than European types per size of tuber. *p. 1284*

speciosa fyfiana 'Switzerland'; a superb "grandiflora" gloxinia, inheriting its prolific nature from the soft-leaved regina hybrid 'Gierth's Red', and its intensive scarlet with white border from 'Emperor Frederick'; in addition, the large erect flowers have 7-8 lobes which are daintily ruffled. *Humid-tropical.* *p. 1277*

speciosa fyfiana 'Tigrina'; large-flowered "grandiflora" hybrid with regina blood; flexible leaves with light veins, and erect flowers having white throat speckled in the same color as the limb, usually red or blue. *Humid-tropical.* *p. 1224, 1284*

speciosa fyfiana 'Tigrina Red'; smaller-leaved "grandiflora" type gloxinia, with large, beautiful flowers netted and spotted with red over the rosy petals and into the white throat; late-blooming. *p. 1224*

speciosa fyfiana 'Violacea'; early-flowering large leaf "crassifolia" type gloxinia with flowers entirely deep violet or bishop blue; midseason. *p.1280*

speciosa fyfiana 'Wyoming'; large-flowered "grandiflora" type gloxinia with white throat and purplish-red border. *p. 1282*

speciosa "Macrophylla' (macrophylla), (Brazil), "Brazilian gloxinia", leaves light olive-green with greenish-white veins, similar to regina but more blunt, magenta beneath, and with the more bell-like, deep purple flowers of the true S. speciosa. *p. 1278*

speciosa maxima 'Buell's Blue Slipper'; flowers of the "slipper-type" gloxinias having gracefully curved, nodding trumpets in a profuse cluster above the velvety foliage, blooming over a long period; may be a hybrid of S. regina x speciosa; tuberous. *p. 1277*

speciosa maxima 'Buell's Queen Bee'; a "slipper-type" gloxinia with rather large, lobed, nodding flowers white with bright pink cheeks on both sides of throat. *p. 1284*

speciosa maxima 'Pink Slipper'; light green, soft, crenate leaves, and medium-large "slipper-type" flowers with flaring lobes rosy pink, dark center and a spotted throat. *p. 1277*

speciosa multiflora 'Kiss of Fire'; the California multiflora strain by Antonelli in Santa Cruz has been developed from a compact 8-petal sport of 'Etoile de Feu' with 'Crimson Rose 8', later bred with Swiss multifloras; 'Kiss of Fire' has numerous erect, velvety scarlet flowers with about 8 wavy lobes, and soft foliage, though the tubers produced are small; best grown from seed, coming into bloom in 6 months. *p. 1284*

speciosa var. speciosa (coerulea) (Brazil); tuberous plant, nearly stemless with stalked oblong-ovate, fleshy, white-velvety, fresh-green leaves crenate at margins; showy, digitalis-like bell flowers velvety violet-blue with lilac lobes. *p. 1277*

speciosa 'Thompson hybrid'; prize-winning strain of double-flowering polyploid gloxinias with long-stalked flowers, some characteristically with incurving cupped, large wavy petals, primarily in deep velvety red. In the early ancestry of this strain, a "slipper" type bred with the "fyfiana" group, introduced new colors such as orchid, purple, and two-tones. *p. 1284*

splendens (Gesneria umbellata) (Brazil); compact, tuberous plant with several hairy stalks, bearing large soft, variously green velvety leaves, and tubular, two-lipped flowers similar to S. cardinalis, but differing in having the upper side of the bright scarlet corolla more curved in two directions and continued into an upper lip with rounded lobes; the junction of throat and lower lobes spotted with violet. *p. 1287*

'Tom Thumb' (speciosa x pusilla); the most charming little Baby gloxinia that ever appeared for the pleasure of the gesneriad fancier; in every detail resembling its big brother the florists' (fyfiana) gloxinia, except for its diminutive size no larger than an African violet. First of its kind to flower in 6-8 cm pots, and a perfect window sill plant with little bell-shaped, velvety red blossom edged in white, 4 cm across. The plant is only 10 cm high, and its small ovate, crenate leaves 5 cm long, deep green above, silvery-haired beneath; the bell flowers are erect and not oblique and slipper-like as in speciosa. This hybrid was developed by Fischer's in New Jersey. *Humid-tropical.* *p. 1289*

tuberosa (Rechsteineria) (Brazil); stemless species; broad ovate leaves to more than 40 cm long arise from tuber; the long 8 cm flowers on slender stalks from near the base, the inflated, bilabiate tubes without large hood, red with yellow throat. *p. 1288*

tubiflora (Argentina, Paraguay, Uruguay); an unusual species, with both tuber and in addition slender rhizomes; compact growing 15-30 cm high but the flowering stalk to 1 m or more tall; branching with elliptic gray green leaves to 12 cm long; the curved tubular pure white flowers, 9 cm long, are carried terminally in a one-sided cluster, and very fragrant of tuberoses. *p. 1290*

'Velvet Charm', in hort. as x Gloxinera; (Sinningia eumorpha x Sinningia 'splendens'); heartshaped, velvety-green leaves like S. cardinalis; vivid pink tubular flowers, orchid inside and on the narrow, regular limb. *p. 1251*

verticillata (doeringii hort.) (Brazil); an attractive tuberous plant which I photographed at Blossfeld's in Sao Paulo as S. doeringii, but resembling herbarium specimen in New York Bot. Garden of S. verticillata; purplish stalks with whorls of 6 metallic green leaves and clusters of tubular coral-pink flowers blotched red. *p. 1286*

verticillata purpurea (Dircaeo-Gesneria) (Brazil); tuberous plant with wiry-erect, wine-red stem bearing whorls of three pubescent, dark, crenate leaves, and dense clusters of slender tubular, dusky rose flowers marked throughout with little stripes of fuchsia-red. *p. 1286*

warscewiczii (Corytholoma) (Guatemala); erect, stout stem to 1½ m tall with 10 cm elliptic, thick-fleshy, rough-hairy, crenate leaves and axillary, inflated tubular flowers yellow to orange, tinting into red. *p. 1286, 1287*

SINOARUNDINARIA *Gramineae* **C-I2LBD**

nitida (Arundinaria) (Korea, China); running bamboo with slender canes 3 to 6 m high, forming robust clumps, the stems purplish-black and very hollow, only 1 cm thick, and leafless the first year; branchlets dense with leaves bright green above, glaucous beneath, to 18 cm long, the margins bristly on one side. Photographed in Bot. Garden Copenhagen. *p. 1314*

SINOCALAMUS: see Bambusa, Dendrocalamus

SINOCRASSULA *Crassulaceae* **C2LBD**

yunnanensis (China: Yunnan); clump-forming small succulent; dense rosettes of numerous crowded, tapering fleshy leaves rounded on back, dark glaucous and soft-hairy 1-2½ cm long, flushed with maroon; flowers whitish tipped red. *p. 875*

SIPHOCAMPYLUS *Campanulaceae* **S3LFM**

crenatifolius (Brazil); showy tropical shrub to 90 cm high, with long-elliptic leaves 12-15 cm long, irregularly toothed; brilliant scarlet-red two-lipped flowers topped with yellow crown. *p. 751*

SISYRINCHIUM *Iridaceae* **I2LBM**

iridifolium (Brazil to Chile); "Blue-eyed grass"; small perennial herb with short rootstock; branching stem to 30 cm high, with linear leaves, and terminal clusters of small yellowish-white flowers, having wedge-shaped segments 1 cm long; June. *p. 1338*

striatum (Chile, Argentina), "Satin flower", "Yellow-eyed grass" or "Rush-lily"; fairly hardy perennial 30-60 cm high, with short rootstock, and grass-like, 2-ranked glaucous leaves; leafy stalks bearing elongate spikes of pretty flowers 2 cm across, soft primrose-yellow veined with purplish brown, and opening in sunshine; June-July blooming; an easy grower for a moist-cool location. *p. 1339*

SKIMMIA *Rutaceae* **C-I2LFM**

japonica 'Dwarf Female'; evergreen, broad compact shrub, dioecious, with thick-leathery, elliptic, glossy green leaves, 6-10 cm long, clustered at end of branchlets, and tipped by erect clusters of small-creamy-white, fragrant flowers, followed by coral-red berries, which last for months, during winter and spring. Originally from Japan, this dwarf type is a selected seedling resembling reevesiana but not as tall and leggy; developed by Teufel-Oregon. *Warm temperate.* *p. 2031*

reevesiana (fortunei) (India, Malaysia, China); decorative small evergreen bush to 50 cm high, with smooth leathery, ovate leaves 5-10 cm long, dark green above, lighter beneath; usually bisexual small white flowers; and crimson-red 12 mm ovoid berries. *p. 2033*

SMILACINA *Liliaceae* **C2LFM**

racemosa (Canada: Nova Scotia to British Columbia; U.S.: Georgia to Arizona), "False Solomon's seal", rhizomatous perennial herb 60-90 cm high, with leafy stems, lanceolate leaves 8-22 cm long; numerous small white flowers in terminal panicles; followed by red berries; hardy. *p. 1492*

stellata (Newfoundland to British Columbia; New Jersey to California), "Star-flowered Lily-of-the-valley"; perennial 30-60 cm high, with lanceolate leaves 5-15 cm long and clasping the stalk, glaucous and mealy beneath; small white flowers to 6 mm long, in dense terminal racemes, followed by 1 cm fruit green with black stripes or black; hardy. *p. 1492, 1494*

SMILAX *Liliaceae* **I-S2-3LFM**

ornata (Jamaica), "Sarsaparilla"; tall-growing vine climbing by tendrils, with angled, green thorny stem and thin-leathery, lanceolate to cordate leaves to 25 cm long, shiny fresh-green with pale blotching. *p. 1492, 1505*

rotundifolia (Nova Scotia to Illinois, so. to Georgia and Texas), "Horse-brier"; very vigorous deciduous climber up to 10-12 m with stout green stem often 4-angled and spiny, leaves ovate to nearly round, lustrous, 5-15 cm long, 5-veined; fruit bluish black (hardy). *p. 1492*

SMILAX: see also Asparagus

SMITHIANTHA *Gesneriaceae* **S3HFM (d:D)**

'Canary Bird'; a prolific multiflora x zebrina hybrid grown in England, with velvety, crenate foliage, and strong stalks carrying multi-flowered racemes of inflated lemon-yellow bells tinged with orange. *p. 1292*

cinnabarina (Naegelia) (Mexico, Guatemala); called "Temple bells" because of their bright display of nodding bells 4-5 cm long, scarlet red outside, with creamy belly and red spotted throat; from a red central stalk; carried above beautiful red plush, cordate leaves; tall growing, from scaly rhizomes. *Humid-tropical.* *p. 1293*

'Exoniensis'; a prolific growing and free blooming hybrid with leaves plush red on green, and masses of orange-yellow nodding "slipper" flowers. *Humid-tropical.* *p. 1292, 1294*

'Golden King'; a cultivar with deep green velvety leaves mottled and painted purple along the veins; the saccate yellow flowers deep golden in the throat and dotted red inside. *Humid-tropical.* *p. 1294*

x hybrida 'Compacta', "Temple bells"; low bushy zebrina hybrid, having large deep green leaves covered with purplish velvety hair; free-blooming with nodding, foxglove-like bells lemon-yellow, red on top, and veined with red. *Humid-tropical.* *p. 1294*

x hybrida 'Karin Franklin' (Naegelia); a beautiful English hybrid (Butcher, Croydon 1962), with velvety, purplish-red leaves, splashed moss green, framing a bouquet of numerous racemes of nodding bell-flowers orange-yellow with maroon spots and stripes. *p. 1291*

x hybrida 'Sulphurea' ('chromatella'); sturdy multiflora x zebrina hybrid with showy, orbicular leaves of red plush and wine-red base; nodding flowers lemon-yellow with golden throat. *p. 1294*

x hybrida 'Sunburst'; a pretty hybrid of the multiflora x zebrina complex, with velvety green leaves decorated with red and maroon; the flowers in a terminal cluster, yellowish-orange flushed with red, and dotted red inside the throat; propagates from rhizomes. Listed by Paul Arnold, Binghamton, N.Y., 1960. *p. 1292*

x hybrida 'Typ Lienig' (S. zebrina x multiflora x cinnabarina); very meritorious low, compact clone of Temple bells, frequently known by the old name Naegelia; characterized by its closely grouped inflorescences of better than average keeping quality, with nodding yellow flowers on white base, marked cinnabar-red to scarlet, or other shades; the velvety green foliage with rich red-brown design. *p. 1294*

multiflora (Oaxaca, Mexico); soft-hairy plant with velvety, cordate, crenate leaves topped by a crown of nodding, digitalis-like flowers of creamy-white. *p. 1293*

'Orange King', "Orange temple bells"; hybrid with beautiful large velvety, emerald-green leaves with crenate edge, overlaid with a pattern of red along veins; the flower bells orange-red, yellow beneath, inside yellow with red spots. *Humid-tropical.* *p. 1248A, 1294*

'Rose Queen'; lovely hybrid with velvety green leaves mottled with purple, and slender bells of charming rose-pink. *p. 1293*

zebrina (Naegelia) (Vera Cruz, Mexico); tall plant to 1 m and willing bloomer, with dark green, flexible leaves showing red-brown markings and covered with silky hairs; numerous flowers on slender stalks with bells brilliant scarlet above, yellow below, throat pale yellow spotted with red. *Humid-tropical.* *p. 1293*

'Zebrina discolor', "Temple bells"; known in horticulture as S. x hybrida; a cultivar with more contrastingly colored purplish-red and green foliage; flowers scarlet with yellow, brown-spotted inside. These commercial hybrids combine the beauty and colors of S. zebrina and multiflora, and are easy to grow and willing to bloom. *Humid-tropical.* *p. 1294*

SOBRALIA *Orchidaceae* **I-S3LOFM**

decora (galleottiana) (Mexico, Guatemala), "Reed orchid"; vigorous terrestrial with slender, reedlike stems to 60 cm high, clothed with scattered, plaited leaves, and bearing large, cattleya-like flowers, of short duration, sepals and petals creamy-white with light rose blush, lip purplish rose, (April-July). *Tropical.* *p. 1817*

leucoxantha (Costa Rica); reedy terrestrial with leafy stems 1 m high, and large solitary flowers with white sepals and petals, and broad golden yellow crisped lip flushed orange in throat, and bordered white (April-Sept.) *Tropical.* *p. 1817, 1818*

macrantha (Mexico to Costa Rica); reed-like terrestrial with stems 1½-2 m high, furnished with plaited, slender pointed leaves, and large fragrant 15 cm flowers rich purple and crimson, the broad lip with cream or yellow throat (summer). *Tropical.* *p. 1817*

wilsoniana (Central America); terrestrial with reedlike stems clothed by broad plaited leaves; large cattleya-like, fragrant flowers delicate lavender with yellow throat, 12 cm across, very showy but lasting only one day. *p. 1818*

SOEHRENSIA *Cactaceae* **I2LBD**

ingens (No. Argentina); handsome globe with age 50 cm or more dia., resembling Echinocactus grusonii but with many more ribs; dark green with numerous ridges and covered by long, fine straw-colored spines on white woolly areoles; trumpet flowers 4-5 cm across, yellow or orange-red. *Arid-subtropic.* *p. 704*

oreopepon (No. Argentina: Mendoza); broadly globular, to 30 cm dia, grayish olive green, with 18 to 30 ribs lightly notched; soft, thin, flexible spines yellowish to reddish, gray-haired funnel flowers 8-10 cm long, golden yellow. *Arid-subtropic.* *p. 704*

SOLANDRA *Solanaceae* **S2LF-BM**

guttata (maxima) (Swartzia) (Mexico); woody shrub to 6 m, somewhat climbing, with hairy or pubescent twigs, leaves to 15 cm long, pubescent underneath; large showy tubular flowers, cream-colored, changing to yellowish, spotted or feathered with purple, 22 cm long, the slender part of tube much longer than calyx, which is 7½ cm long and pubescent; winter-blooming and fragrant. *p. 2071*

longiflora (Jamaica), "Trumpet plant"; evergreen shrub to 1½ m high, woody branches with small hard, oval or obovate leaves on purple petioles, and large, showy, stiff upright, trumpet-like flowers 22-30 cm long, greenish-white, showing purplish-brown venation, contracted at the throat, the limb turned back and frilled. *Tropical.* *p. 2083*

nitida (guttata) (Mexico), "Chalice vine" or "Cup-of-gold"; clambering to 6 m or more, with leathery, elliptic, glossy leaves; the large 25 cm long, chalice-shaped flowers with corolla-lobes reflexed and frilled, yellow with purplish stripes. *Tropical.* *p. 2074, 2083*

SOLANUM *Solanaceae* **I2LBD**

abutiloides (Trop. America); shrubby bush with downy branches, carrying on long slender petioles the large broad-cordate foliage; at apex a tight rounded cluster of small pale purple, starry flowers with darker veining. *p. 2074*

auriculatum (mauritianum) (Trop. Africa, Madagascar, Trop. America); velvety-hairy shrub to 6 m high, with ovate leaves to 20 cm long and having small stipule-like leaves in axils, smooth green above, grayish and hairy beneath; violet 1 cm flowers with white stripe through petals; reddish fruit. *p. 2078*

aviculare (New Zealand, Australia), "Kangaroo-apple"; shrub 1½ to 3 m high, with variable dark green membranous leaves lanceolate or pinnately lobed, 15-30 cm or more long; few violet flowers 2-3 cm across; the rather large 2½ cm ovoid edible berry green or yellow. *Subtropic.* *p. 2082*

capsicastrum 'Variegatum', "Variegated false Jerusalem-cherry"; colorful form with foliage variegated or edged with creamy-white. The type species is from So. Brazil and Uruguay, a small evergreen subshrub 25-60 cm high, densely branched; branches, young shoots and leaves grayish and soft-hairy, the elliptic undulate leaves to 8 cm long, in unequal pairs; white flowers, and orange-scarlet ovoid fruit 1 cm or less in dia., smaller than in pseudocapsicum. *Subtropic.* *p. 2075, 2085*

crispum (Chile, Perú); small shrub with ovate, wrinkled leaves 8-10 cm long, loosely crisped at margins; 2 cm flowers pale violet, and pea-sized berries light yellow. *p. 2082*

glutinosum (Perú); evergreen shrub with lanky, pale, pubescent branches, large hairy, flaccid fleshy leaves undulate at margins; at apex a dense little cluster of potato-like light purple flowers with yellow stamens. *p. 2074*

jasminoides (Brazil), "Potato-vine"; shrubby deciduous twiner with twiggy stems, ovate leaves to 8 cm long, sometimes 2 to 5-parted; star-shaped flowers white tinged blue, 2 cm across, in branching clusters. *Tropical.* *p. 2074, 2084*

laciniatum (Australia, New Zealand), also known as "Kangaroo-apple", in appearance very close to aviculare, but the latter is a diploid, its violet corolla lobes as long as the tubes and obtuse, or rounded at tips, whereas laciniatum is a triploid, with corolla lobes half as long as tube, and with notched lobes. *p. 2082*

laurifolium (Mexico); evergreen shrub of variable character, 2 m high, stems and underside of foliage covered with gray felty hairs; leaves coarsely lobed, 20 cm long, green above, whitish beneath; starry flowers 4 cm across, clear lavender blue with yellow stamens, and covered with white felt outside. *p. 2074*

macranthum (Brazil), "Brazilian potato-tree"; spiny pubescent shrub or tree to 10 m high, with ovate leaves 30 cm long, sinuately lobed, prickly on veins; flowers cornflower-blue, 3-6 cm across, in racemes paling with age. *Tropical.* *p. 2084*

macrocarpum (Chile); herbaceous bush with ovate leaves, whitish flowers, and clusters of black berries 1 cm or more in dia. *p. 2084*

mammosum (C. America), "Nipple-fruit"; a thorny, sparry shrub with few pubescent leaves, 10 to 15 cm long, and weirdly formed, orange-colored, waxy fruit, large like a tomato, but shaped somewhat like an inverted pear with nipples near base. *Tropical.* *p. 2082*

marginatum (North Africa: Ethiopia); spiny white-hairy shrub to 1 m high, with broad ovate, sinuately lobed leaves prickly on both sides, having white margins, and densely white tomentose beneath, to 20 cm long; flowers white lined with blue, 2½ cm across; spiny, yellow fruit. *Subtropic.* *p. 2078*

martii (Brazil: Panaceix); handsome small tree with woody trunk, and large, leathery leaves 30 cm long, glossy green with beige colored ribs; between the foliage the white star-flowers hidden in woolly cushions from the axil of the leaf. Photographed at Jardim Botanico, Rio de Janeiro. *p. 2074*

mauritianum (auriculatum) (So. Africa); ornamental woody shrub or small tree, with branches and ovate oblong foliage covered with grayish pubescence; starry flowers lilac with a white stripe along center of each segment. *p. 2075*

melongena esculentum (India), "Egg plant", "Jew's apple", or "Aubergine"; pubescent prickly herb or shrub, to 1 m high; ovate, angled or lobed leaves 10-20 cm long, woolly beneath; the purplish flowers 3 cm across. The common egg-plant is a warm-weather plant, and popular vegetable usually grown as an annual with edible, shining fruit 15-30 cm long, purple, white, yellowish or striped. It is usually eaten baked or fried, having low calorie, succulent flesh. *Tropical.* *p. 2082*

melongena 'Moorea', "Ornamental eggplant"; woody bush with large lobed, silvery-hairy leaves; flowers pale lavender; and showy, large oblong fruit orange-yellow 15 cm long. Photographed in a native garden on Moorea in French Polynesia. *Tropical.* *p. 2075*

pseudo-capsicum (Madeira), "Jerusalem cherry"; robust, shrubby plant with flexible branches dense with lanceolate, turgid-firm, deep green leaves wavy at the margins and smooth beneath, 5-6 cm long, glabrous-smooth, though with velvety feel above; branches smooth or with slight fuzz; small, white, star-like flowers followed by large globular, lustrous orange-scarlet, cherry-like fruit of 1½-2 cm dia.; much grown as an ornamental potplant for Christmas; there is also a yellow-fruited strain. *Subtropic.* *p. 2073, 2075, 2085*

pyracanthum (Madagascar); possibly hybrid of S. runcinatum x haematocarpum; prickly subshrub to 1½ m high, with stalked matte-green leaves 15-30 cm long, pinnately lobed and edged in white, underneath white-felty and with red thorns; flowers dark to pale violet striped white, white star at base; round yellow berries. *p. 2085*

quitoense (Perú), "Naranjilla" or "Golden fruit of the Andes"; ornamental woody bush with brittle branches, large pubescent, ovate leaves prettily lobed and with ivory ribs; purple flowers; followed by large tomentose fruit, 4 cm dia.; related to the tomato, but tasting like a cross between pineapple and strawberry. *p. 2075*

rantonnetii (Paraguay, Argentina), "Blue potato tree"; rambling evergreen or deciduous shrub to 2 m high, unarmed and nearly smooth; ovate or oval, bright green undulate leaves to 10 cm long; charming 3 cm flowers dark blue or violet with yellow eye, in clusters blooming throughout the warm summer and fall, sometimes nearly all year; the red fruit like small apples. Blooms as small plant but may be grown into treeform by staking, or trained on support as a vine. *Subtropic.* *p. 2075, 2077*

robustum (alatum) (Brazil); vigorous, spiny subshrub 1½ m high, densely rusty-hairy, with winged stems; ovate leaves to 30 cm long, with pointed lobes, green and velvety above, reddish woolly beneath, prickly on both sides; white 2½ cm flowers, and orange fruit. *p. 2084*

seaforthianum (So. America), "Star potato vine"; shrubby climber to 3 m with mostly pinnate leaves to 20 cm long, the leaflets unequal; large star-shaped lavender or purple 2½ cm flowers with yellow anthers; scarlet fruit. *Tropical.* *p. 2085*

sisymbrifolium (Brazil); sticky-hairy, very prickly annual or perennial to 1 m high, with light green leaves deeply and distantly pinnately lobed, and furnished with yellow spines, 3 cm flowers light blue to white; and red fruit. *p. 2085*

sodomaeum (Mediterranean region), the "Dead-Sea apple", or "Apple of Sodom"; spiny pubescent shrub to 2 m high, with sinuately lobed leaves; flowers violet, 2½ cm across; the berries first white, then green-marbled, to yellow and shining red-brown 2½ cm dia., more or less poisonous. *p.2082*

vespertilio (Canary Islands); shrub of the coastal steppe to 1½ m high; with hairy stems, leaves soft-hairy, lobed oak-like, 20 cm long; 2 cm flowers light blue to pale lilac. *p. 2085*

warscewiczii (hispidum) (Perú), "Devil's-fig"; rusty tomentose shrub to 2 m, with short stout spines; soft deeply lobed leaves to 30 cm long, the midrib and stalk covered with red, starry prickles; numerous 4 cm white flowers; fruit pale yellow. *p. 2085*

wendlandii (Costa Rica), "Potato-vine"; shrubby climber, to 6 m, with a few scattered, hooked prickles; variable leaves bright green, the upper ovate or tri-lobed, the lower pinnate or lobed; large lilac-blue flowers 6 cm across, in branched clusters. *Tropical.* *p. 2084*

SOLENANGIS *Orchidaceae* **S3OFM**

aphylla (Angraecum) (Mozambique, Madagascar, Kenya, Tanzania); climbing orchid with thin woody stem and long aerial roots; raceme of white, bell-shaped, spurred flowers 3-4 mm dia., brown dots at tips of sepals. *p. 1818*

SOLENOMELUS *Iridaceae* **I2LBM**

chilensis (Chile); rhizomatous herb with clustered linear, grayish-blue leaves mostly at base; deep yellow flowers with spreading segments spotted purple near base, clustered on zigzag stem. *p. 1331*

SOLIDAGO *Compositae* **C2LBD**

multiradiata (Canada: Quebec to Labrador; U.S.: Alaska, Colorado, Arizona); a northern "Goldenrod"; perennial with branching rootstock, 22-45 cm high, firm basal leaves oblanceolate, 12 cm long, net-veined, upper leaves much smaller; large yellow flower heads in short, dense clusters; July-Sept., hardy. *p. 814*

odora (Nova Scotia to Florida and Texas); perennial goldenrod with stout caudex and fibrous roots, to 1 m high; anise-scented lanceolate rather thick leaves to 10 cm long; small golden-yellow flower heads on recurving one-sided racemes in panicles; July-August; hardy. *p. 814*

SOLISIA *Cactaceae* **I2LBD**

pectinata (Mexico: Tehuacán), "Lace bugs"; very small globe 3 cm thick, with dense warts almost entirely covered with white spines arranged comb-like; flowers around the sides yellow; juice milky. *p. 728*

SONERILA *Melastomataceae* **S3HFM-D**

margaritacea (Java), "Pearly sonerila"; small tropical herbaceous plant with pubescent red stem and ovate, deep copper-green leaves having bristly surface, puckered with pearly spots and bristles that glisten in the sunlight like frosted silver; glowing red-purple beneath; flowers rosy lavender. *Humid-tropical.* *p. 1558*

margaritacea 'Argentea'; attractive variety having the pointed leaves strongly overlaid with silver while the sunken veins are olive-green and often barely showing. *Humid-tropical.* *p. 1558*

margaritacea 'Hendersonii'; somewhat taller form, with the dainty coppery-red leaves more densely covered with silvery spots, and glowing purple underneath; shapely and compact. *p. 1558*

margaritacea 'Mme. Baextele', "Frosted sonerila"; an attractive miniature herb with ovate leaves smooth silvery gray, densely covered with small pearly spots, often confluent; red-purple underneath; flowers pink. *p. 1558*

SOPHORA *Leguminosae* **I2LBD**

microphylla (tetraptera microphylla) (New Zealand), the "Maori Kowhai"; large shrub with pinnate leaves very similar to tetraphylla, but in the main, its leaflets are only 1 cm long; the sulphur-yellow flowers 4 cm long, with a calyx of old gold; freely secreting nectar; however, it is also different in going through two distinct stages in its development, at first being a flexuose shrub with yellow, interlacing stems; when 2½-4 m high, a mature form with round leafy head with trunk and straight brown branches. *p.1391*

secundiflora (Texas to Mexico), "Mescal-bean"; evergreen tree of chapparal deserts, to 10 m high; pinnate leaves 15 cm long; leaflets notched at apex; flowers 2½ cm long, violet-blue and violet-scented. *p. 1390*

tetraptera (New Zealand), "Yellow Kowhai"; handsome tree more or less deciduous, sometimes 12 m; zigzag branchlets with conspicuous pendulous flowers 2½-5 cm long having an inflated greenish calyx, and golden yellow corolla, in showy racemes appearing before the pinnate foliage 3-11 cm long; the interesting pods 5-20 cm long, constricted between each seed. *p. 1391*

x SOPHROLAELIA *Orchidaceae* **I3OFD**

marriotiana (Sophronitis x Laelia); handsome small bigeneric hybrid, with stiff-leathery leaves; showy flowers with buttercup-yellow sepals and petals, the folded lip richly marked crimson. *p. 1824*

'Psyche' (Laelia cinnabarina x Sophronitis coccinea); small bigeneric hybrid with short pseudobulbs bearing a solitary stiff leaf, and waxy flowers, with large lanceolate sepals, and smaller petals and lip, vivid Chinese red. *p. 1823, 1824*

SOPHRONITIS *Orchidaceae* **C3OFM**

cernua (Brazil); miniature epiphyte with tightly clustered pseudobulbs and forming mats; solitary grayish leaf 3 cm long; relatively large 3 cm flowers opening flat, vivid cinnabar-red or burnt-orange, with base of lip yellow (autumn). *p. 1824*

coccinea (grandiflora) (So. Brazil); dwarf epiphyte with small pseudobulb and a stiff, 8 cm leaf; large solitary flowers to 8 cm across, showy scarlet with salmon sheen, the throat yellow with red stripes. I will never forget these brilliant spots of red in the chilly rain-forest of the Serra do Mar, (Sept.-Feb.) *Subtropic.* *p. 1664A, 1821, 1823, 1824*

SPARAXIS *Iridaceae* **C2LBM(d:su)**

bulbifera (So. Africa); spring-blooming cormous "Wand flowers" 30 cm high, with narrow flat leaves in 2 ranks; 3-5 distant funnel-shaped flowers, perianth yellow with oblong segments 2½ cm long. *p. 1338*

grandiflora (S. Africa), "Wand flower"; cormous plant with fan-like foliage resembling Ixia but of lower growth and with large flowers, 3 to 5 on a stem, purple or yellow and sometimes marked with a star-like band; spring blooming. *p. 1338, 1340*

tricolor (So. Africa), "Harlequin flower"; two-ranked sword-shaped leaves 1 cm wide; flowering stems 30-60 cm high with 3-6 distant flowers, perianth orange tinged with brown-purple, yellow in throat and a 3-angled black spot at the base of each segment; May. *p. 1338*

tricolor alba (So. Africa: S. W. Cape), a "Velvet flower" with dainty white flowers to 5 cm across, opening star-like wide and flat, the petals with sulphur-yellow throat and a darker blackish center stripe on each; the species is a small plant 45 cm high with bulbous corm, and narrow, sword-shaped leaves, mostly basal, with parallel veins. Sparaxis begin growing in winter and flower over a long period in late spring. *p. 1340*

tricolor 'Honneur de Haarlem'; an outstandingly beautiful, named cultivar, listed by Van Tubergen in Haarlem, Holland; large flowers 6 cm across, rich glowing cerise or crimson, with blackish areas at middle of petals and next to central area and outlining a daisy-like central pattern of pure lemon-yellow. *p. 1340*

SPARMANNIA *Tiliaceae* ***I-S2LFM**

africana (So. Africa), "African hemp"; much cultivated in German homes, and known there as "Zimmer-Linde", as it resembles a miniature linden tree, with large lobed, light green, soft leaves, 15-25 cm long, white hairy on both sides and on the sparry stems; flowers with white petals and yellow filaments; rapidly growing into a shrub with many trunks, to 6 m high. *Subtropic.* *p. 2098, 2099, 2102, 2104*

africana flore pleno; a form attractive because of its showy clusters of double 4 cm flowers having large white petals; the soft textured, hairy, decorative 5-7-angled leaves 15-22 cm across, on soft-wooded, sparry branches. *p. 2102*

SPARTIUM *Leguminosae* **C2LBD**

junceum (Genista) (Mediterranean, Canary Isl.), "Spanish broom"; ornamental shrub, to 3 m, with almost leafless, reedlike branches, the small leaves linear; fragrant, showy yellow, butterfly-like flowers in loose, terminal racemes. *Subtropic.* *p. 1394*

SPATHANTHEUM *Araceae* **I3LBM**

orbignyanum (Perú, Bolivia); handsome aroid found at the Inca ruins of Machu Picchu in the Eastern Cordilleras, at 2,700 metres; from a thick 8 cm tuber rise fleshy, long-stalked sagittate leaves when young 8-15 cm long; more mature stage the lobes becoming pinnatifid, and overlaid with gray;

green spathe 8-9 cm long, boat-shaped at first, later expanded, the spadix short. *p. 291*

SPATHANTHUS *Rapataceae* **S3LBW**

bicolor (Venezuela, Brazil); curious tropical plant to 1 m or more high, leaves arranged distichous and arising from 5-6 cm thick rhizome; leaf blade linear, 40-50 cm long and 3-3.5 cm wide; petiole 50-75 cm long, white and apically green; inflorescence a spike 4 cm long attached to the spathe; flowers yellow. Growing in wet places. *p. 1990*

SPATHICARPA *Araceae* **S3LFM**

hastifolia (So. Brazil); evergreen tropical plant with tuberous rhizome, long-stalked thin-leathery leaves distinctly 3-partite, the main lobe 6-8 cm long and ovate, 5 cm wide; floral stalk 30-40 cm tall with greenish spathe. *p. 291*

sagittifolia (Bahia), "Fruit-sheath plant"; interesting herb with tuberous rhizome having small, arrowshaped, membranous leaves, 10-12 cm long, waxy green; inflorescence on stiff stalks with recurved green spathe,and spadix attached along its center. *Tropical.* *p. 283*

SPATHIPHYLLUM *Araceae* ***S1LF-NM**

blandum (gardneri) (W. Indies, Jamaica, Surinam); robust plant with large, lanceolate, leathery, deep green leaves and sunken veins; spathe spoonshaped and pointed, pale green; spadix white with elevated knobs. *Tropical.* *p. 288*

"candidum" hort., close to floribundum but of larger habit, leaves oblong-pointed, friendly,matte satiny green, with pale center band, the petioles wide open winged; small spathe white; spadix dark green and white. This may be simply a large form of floribundum. *p. 288*

cannaefolium (dechardii) (Venezuela, Guyana); leathery plant with thick dull, black-green, corrugated leaves tapering toward base of ribbed petioles; thick, fleshy spathe green outside, white inside; long, free, cream spadix. *Tropical.* *p. 288*

'Clevelandii' (kochii), "White flag", also known as "Peace-lily"; freely branching and free flowering commercial plant close to wallisii but larger in all parts; thin-leathery, glossy-green, lanceolate leaves with undulate margin; the inflorescence on reed-like stems with ovate-pointed, white, papery spathe 10-15 cm long, turning apple green with age, and having a green line on back; maze-like spadix white. *Tropical.* *p. 5*, 287, 289*

cochlearispathum (So. Mexico, Guatemala); large plant to 2 m high, with long, heavy, corrugated leaves, light dull green and with undulate margin; inflorescence on stiff stalk, with spathe large, almost leathery, fresh yellow-green; maze-like, white spadix. *p. 287*

commutatum (Indonesia, Philippines); elegant, strong growing plant with broad, corrugated, fresh green, elliptic leaves on smooth, vaginate petioles; the short, thick spadix is white, becoming green, subtended by a broad, leathery, cream-white spathe with green edge, and turning green beneath with age. *Tropical.* *p. 288*

cuspidatum (Surinam, Guyana); slender plant with shiny, leathery leaves long elliptic on petioles winged at base; inflorescence on thin, reedlike stems with slender, green and white spadix and narrow, white spathe with green line on back. *p. 288*

floribundum (multiflorum) (Colombia), "Spathe flower"; dwarf, compact plant, freely suckering and forming clusters; the matte, satiny green, leathery leaves obovate or elliptic, with pale center band, on broadly winged petioles; small spathe white; short spadix green and white. *Tropical.* *p. 5*, 19*, 288*

friedrichsthalii (Caribbean coastal forests of Nicaragua, Costa Rica, Panama, Canal Zone, N. Colombia); robust plant, with shining deep green oblanceolate thin-leathery leaves, the blade 25 to 50 and even 70 cm long, with long tapering base; the white spathe boat-shaped, oblanceolate to elliptic, about 12 cm or more long, typically broadest above the middle; spadix 3 to 6 cm long, the styles cylindric and long exserted; by contrast, in phryniifolium the leaf bases are obtuse, and the styles of the ovaries are conic but only shortly exserted beyond the perianth. *p. 280,282*

'Marion Wagner' (cochlearispathum x 'Clevelandii'); large hybrid by Wagner-Hollywood 1946, with satiny-glossy quilted leaves blooming intermittently April-July with large spathe to 20 cm long lasting 6-8 weeks, greenish-white, shading to pale chartreuse; spadix attached. Sweetly fragrant. *Tropical.* *p. 286, 289*

matudae (friedrichsthalii in hort.) (Mexico: Chiapas); habitat specimen received from Dr. Gordon Ross, Finca Experimental 'La Novia', Tapachula, Chiapas; broad elliptic leaf, closely ribbed, 54-60 cm long and 27 cm broad; the inflorescence with stalk 43 cm long, with obovate spathe cream-white on green, spadix 8 cm long. In habitat growing in half shade in wet places. Received with note: "Pests: Homo sapiens eating the inflorescence." *p.282*

'Mauna Loa'; a diploid hybrid developed by Griffith-Los Angeles, and so far as I could determine in discussing its origin with him, a seedling of S. floribunda x a Hawaiian hybrid, probably S. 'McCoy'; robust plant of compact habit, tending to divide from the base; leaves dark glossy green; very floriferous over an extended period, with pure white spathes 10-12 cm and even 20 cm long in older plants in large pots, somewhat cupping and of soft-leathery texture, slightly scented. We have found the strain variable,leaning toward 'Clevelandii'. *Tropical.* *p. 289*

'McCoy' (Takahashi); hybrid of probably cochlearispathum x 'Clevelandii'; Mrs. Lester McCoy related to me at her gardens near Honolulu how her late gardener, Mr. Takahashi in 1942, crossed a local 'Clevelandii' plant with a Guatemalan species probably cochlearispathum, which her husband brought back, resulting in this vigorous, large-growing very showy plant to 1½ m high, with large and long, glossy green leaves; the spathes white or creamy changing to light green with age, 20-30 cm long, of good texture; the slender club-like white spadix attached 2 cm up from base of spathe, and having pointed knobs. *Tropical.* *p. 289*

ortgiesii (Mexico: Vera Cruz); evergreen perennial herbaceous, clustering plant with fibrous roots and thin-leathery, bright green oblanceolate leaves 35-60 cm long, 13-26 cm wide, on long petioles; the blade closely furrowed in feather fashion, and sharply bent at base; inflorescence with broad-elliptic pure white spathe 12-30 cm long, and 5-10 cm spadix with perfect flowers. *Tropical.* *p. 282*

patinii (Colombia); graceful plant with papery, narrow oblanceolate, waxy leaves having depressed veins on thin, vaginate petioles; inflorescence on long, thin stems with a pendant, slender, white spathe tipped green; thin spadix green and white. *Tropical.* *p. 287*

phryniifolium (Costa Rica, Panama), "Peace plant"; found in the trade as S. friedrichsthalii, a robust plant with large fresh-green, corrugated, fleshy leaves having long-cuneate base; the inflorescence with broad, pale yellow-green, papery spathe, and enclosed, white, knobby spadix. *Tropical.* *p. 160A, 280, 287, 289*

quindiuense (Tolima, Colombia); in the trade as lechlerianum; leathery plant with narrow, long elliptic leaves; inflorescence on wiry stalk, with fleshy, pointed spathe grayish-white inside, dark green outside; spadix white. *p. 288*

wallisii (Colombia, Venezuela), vigorous plant with glossy green, thin-leathery, oblong-lanceolate leaves; inflorescence on reedlike stems, the ovate spathe white turning green with age, 8-10 cm long; maze-like white spadix; very close to 'Clevelandii' (kochii) but smaller in all parts. *Tropical.* *p. 288, 289*

SPATHODEA *Bignoniaceae* **S2LBD**

campanulata (nilotica) (Trop. Africa: Western Kenya, Uganda),"African tuliptree", or "Flame of the forest"; spectacularly showy evergreen tree to 20 m high, with odd-pinnate foliage, the leaflets 6-12 cm long; large bell-shaped flowers 8-12 cm long, swollen on one side and 5-lobed, crimson red with yellow frilled edge, carried facing upwards in terminal clusters. *Tropical.* *p. 500*

nilotica (Uganda, Kenya), "Nandi flame"; smaller, much branched tree 6-15 m high, having gray bark, with pubescent branchlets; pinnate leaves of 9-15 leathery, oblong leaflets to 10 cm long; flower buds brown and containing water, opening into showy, striking blooms with curved calyx and corolla widely trumpet-shaped, crimson or flame-scarlet edged with yellow, 8-10 cm long, tipped by crisped lobes. *p. 502*

SPATHOGLOTTIS *Orchidaceae* **S3HFM**

aurea (Malaya, Sumatra, Java); handsome terrestrial with small corm-like pseudobulbs and tall 75 cm lanceolate plicate leaves; long-stemmed inflorescence with clusters of large 6-8 cm flowers, rich golden yellow, lip bright yellow spotted with red, opening in succession (spring). *p. 1824*

pacifica (Pacific Islands; Samoa, Fiji); pretty terrestrial orchid dwelling in South Seas forests, with conical pseudobulbs bearing oblong-lanceolate, ribbed leaves; straight erect stalks topped by a cluster of pale lavender-pink flowers, sepals and petals pale lilac with darker markings, lip lilac edged yellow, disk orange. *p. 1819*

papuana (Papua, New Guinea); terrestrial orchid with lanceolate, ribbed, plicate leaves; inflorescence tall and slender, bearing a succession of small, handsome carmine-rose flowers over many months. *Tropical.* *p. 1824*

plicata (Malaysia); terrestrial with small corm-like pseudobulbs and grass-green plaited leaves, to 1 m tall; erect racemes with 2½-5 cm flowers of rosy-purple, (April-June). *Tropical.* *p. 1819*

SPHAERALCEA *Malvaceae* **I2LBD**

umbellata (Mexico), "Globe-mallow"; erect, branched shrub to 3 m; leaves nearly peltate and 7-lobed; flowers scarlet with white base, 5 cm across, in clusters. *p. 1533*

SPHAEROGYNE *Melastomataceae* **S3LHFM**

latifolia (Tococa platyphylla) (Colombia, Venezuela, Costa Rica); magnificent plant with unbranched, bristly stems and large opposite, ovate, deep green leaves to 30 cm long, neatly corrugated by its depressed veins; rosy flowers in terminal panicles. *p. 1558*

SPHAEROPTERIS: see Alsophila and Cyathea

SPHYROSPERMUM *Ericaceae* **S3LFM**

buxifolium (Nicaragua to Guyana and Bolivia); interesting epiphyte with long pendant stems dense with shingled 1½ cm green cordate leaves; flowers white; hairy 1 cm globular fruit like gooseberries, whitish to pale blue. *p.1002*

SPIGELIA *Loganiaceae* **S2LFM**
splendens (Mexico, Guatemala), "Mexican pinkroot"; fleshy-rooted, showy perennial 45 cm high, with slightly hairy obovate leaves 10-12 cm long; bright scarlet tubular flowers 2½ cm long, tipped with white, on one-sided recurved spikes. *Tropical.* *p. 1515, 1517*

SPIRAEA *Rosaceae* **C2LBMhd**
x vanhouttei (cantoniensis x trilobata), "Bridal wreath"; beautiful deciduous, woody shrub to 2 m high, with numerous, gracefully arching branches; coarsely toothed leaves bluish beneath, and tiny, white flowers in masses of dense, lacy clusters forming a veritable blanket of snow in May-June. *Temperate.* *p. 1995*

SPIRAEA: see also Astilbe

SPIRANTHES *Orchidaceae* **C-S2-3HFM**
acaulis (Guatemala); terrestrial rosette of gray-green 8 cm leaves with silver lines and spots; erect spike with glossy, yellow-green 3 cm flowers, lip with green stripes. *p. 1820*
cerina (Guatemala); terrestrial orchid flowering without leaves, the pink stems rising from a cluster of tubers; 30-45 cm tall, covered with white hairs and distant spiral scales; sepals and petals over 2½ cm long, shining as if varnished, dull olive-green outside, inside bright greenish-yellow, the tips streaked with bright green veins, yellow in lip. (S) *p. 1702*
elata (West Indies, Costa Rica, Brazil), "Ladies tresses"; terrestrial rosette of lanceolate leaves prettily banded lengthwise with silver; loose cluster of greenish-white flowers 6 mm long, with linear lip, on pubescent spike; April-July. (S) *p. 1823, 1827*
lindleyana (Venezuela, Colombia); terrestrial with thickly fleshy roots; very ornamental leaves velvety green overlaid with silver-green along both sides of midrib, pinkish underneath; small flowers in pairs on erect spike, pale green with whitish lip. (S) *p. 1823*
"longibracteata" hort. (bracteosa; Cyclopogon longibracteosa) (Brazil); terrestrial orchid 30 cm high, with erect leafy spike, the oblong leaves in rosettes; and topped by flowers hooded on top, lateral sepals free, brownish-yellow and white, and hairy. (S) *p. 1692*
orchioides (Stenorrhynchos) (W. Indies, Mexico to Brazil), "Ladies tresses"; terrestrial with broad elliptic basal leaves, appearing after bloom; inflorescence a raceme 38-50 cm high, scarlet red, the 2½ cm flowers with crimson or rosy petals, the sac formed by the lateral sepals a bluntly conical, free spur, and red, oblong pointed rosy lip. (Nov.) (S) *p. 1817, 1819*
romanzoffiana (Newfoundland to New York, west to Alaska and Calif., Ireland), "Hooded ladies tresses"; tuberous, hardy terrestrial with 8-15 cm oblanceolate leaves clasping the stem, 15-25 cm high, with dense spike of small 1 cm white flowers (Aug.-Sept.). (C) *p. 1817*
speciosa (Stenorrhynchos) (West Indies, Costa Rica, Mexico, Venezuela); terrestrial rosette of sessile, elliptic velvety green leaves with grayish blotches; erect stalks bearing twisted spike of beautiful scarlet red 2 cm bracted flowers; April. (S) *p. 1823*

SPIRODELA *Lemnaceae* **S3LFW**
polyrrhiza, "Giant duckweed"; grows all over the world except parts of Africa where it grows in Egypt and Algeria; larger species than Lemna; reddish, lentil-shaped bodies are 3-4 cm in dia.; used in tropic temperature aquaria. *p. 1362*

SPIRONEMA: see Callisia, Hadrodemas, Tripogandra

SPONDIAS *Anacardiaceae* **S3LBM**
dulcis (cytherea) (Society Islands: Tahiti), "Otaheite apple"; smooth gray-barked tropical tree to 20 m high, with bright green pinnate foliage 20-80 cm long, clustered at branch ends; tiny greenish-white flowers in large clusters; the large ovoid-fleshy fruit with tough orange skin, 5 to 8 cm long, and though unpleasant smelling, has apple-flavored yellow pulp surrounding the fibrous core containing a spiny seed; fruiting October to January. Eaten fresh, or in preserves. *Tropical.* *p. 132*
venulosa (mombin), (Trop. America), the "Mombin", "Hog plum", "Spanish plum", or "Caja Mirim"; a most important and valued fruit tree in tropical America; a tree to 8 m high, with furrowed bark, and long pinnate leaves 20 cm or more long; small 2 cm purplish-maroon flower clusters, followed by globular or ovoid light brown or purple fruit with soft, yellow flesh, 3 to 4 cm diameter, and when eaten fresh has an acid spicy flavor resembling cashew but less aromatic. Fruit is also boiled or dried. Photographed in Rio de Janeiro. *Tropical.* *p. 133*

SPREKELIA *Amaryllidaceae* **2Ld(SM:Feb.-Sep. CD:wi)**
formosissima (Mexico), "Jacobean lily"; beautiful bulbous herb with linear leaves; solitary, showy crimson flower, with a spathe-like bract, appearing in June, before the foliage. *Subtropic.* *p. 118*

STACHYS *Labiatae* **C2LBDh**
officinalis (Europe, Asia Minor), hard, tufting perennial herb known as "Betony"; with ovate-oblong, herbaceous, pubescent, ornamental leaves fresh-green, quilted and crenate; purple two-lipped flowers in dense whorls forming an oblong spike. *p. 1357*

STACHYTARPHETA *Verbenaceae* **S3LBM**
purpurea (Mexico); shrubby herbaceous plant, with ovate wrinkled leaves sharply serrate at margins, glossy green; flowers blue-purple along spike a few at a time from below toward apex. *p. 2107*

STACHYURUS *Stachyuraceae* **C2LBDh**
praecox (Japan), "Spike-tail"; deciduous shrub 2-4 m high, with reddish shoots and willow-like branches; lanceolate, toothed leaves 8 to 15 cm long; small 1 cm bell-shaped flowers pale yellow, borne charmingly in stiffly pendant racemes 10 cm long, like a chain of pearls, in spring before the leaves. *Warm temperate.* *p. 2093*

STANGERIA *Cycadaceae* **I2LBD**
eriopus (So. Africa: E. Cape to Natal), "Hottentot's-head"; fern-like perennial cycad with trunk partially subterranean and to 30 cm above ground; sometimes branching and each bearing 1 to 4 pinnate leathery leaves from 50 cm to 2 m long; the few pinnae linear-lanceolate and spiny-toothed; cones silvery pubescent, the males cylindrical, female ones shorter and ovoid. *Subtropic.* *p. 941*

STANHOPEA *Orchidaceae* **I-S3ONM**
bucephalus (So. Mexico, Ecuador); curious epiphyte with ovoid, clustered pseudobulbs bearing a solitary stalked, plaited leaf; the pendulous inflorescence oddly appears through the bottom of the orchid basket, the waxy flowers are large and spectacular, and powerfully scented but of short duration, tawny-yellow, orange in center and spotted with crimson, and with two horns, (August). (I) *p. 1821*
devoniensis (Mexico); inflorescence with 2-3 strongly fragrant flowers 10 cm across, sepals and petals pale yellow spotted and blotched with brown-red and confluent below, lip white spotted with purple and one red-purple blotch on each side, broad ivory horns. (July-Aug.). (I) *p. 1822*
eburnea (Trinidad, Guianas, Brazil), a "Horned orchid"; magnificent epiphyte with ovoid pseudobulbs and solitary, broad, strong-ribbed, dark green leaves to 30 cm long; inflorescence pendulous with 2-3 intensely fragrant, waxy flowers pure white, to 15 cm long, the upturning petals occasionally spotted purple. *p. 1827*
ecornuta (C. America); epiphyte with ovoid pseudobulbs bearing an elliptic leaf to 50 cm long; the short, pendant inflorescence of 2-3 flowers 9 cm across, with sepals and petals ivory-white, lip yellow deepening to orange at base inside. (May-Sept.). (I) *p. 1821*
grandiflora (eburnea) (Venezuela, Guyana, Brazil, Trinidad); stalks with 1-2 large, fragrant flowers, ivory-white, with a few purple marks at the base of the lip and with two small horns, (June-Aug.). (I) *p. 1821*
guttulata (Perú); graceful, fragrant flower, with lower sepals broadly triangular, upper narrower, and like the smaller petals light yellow with small red spots, the horns creamy-yellow, spotted red, (summer). (I) *p. 1822*
hasseloviana (Amazonian Perú), "Horned orchid"; fascinating epiphyte with clustered conical pseudobulbs topped by solitary plaited leaf; the pendulous waxy, heavy-textured flowers very fragrant, to more than 12 cm long, the reflexed sepals and petals whitish or pale rose spotted with purple (summer). *Tropical.* *p. 1820*
martiana (So. Mexico: Oaxaca); inflorescence pendulous with two fragrant, waxy flowers 10 cm long, sepals and petals sharply reflexed, greenish cream to light yellow blotched with brown-purple, the sac-like lip purple in base and with two broad horns; solitary pleated leaf on short pseudobulbs; epiphytic (autumn). *p. 1820*
oculata (Mexico to Honduras); inflorescence with 3-7 large, fragrant, variable flowers, sepals and petals lemon, or deeper yellow, with many red eye spots on sepals, the basal half of lip orange-yellow with 2 or 4 deep blackish blotches, and horns pointed, (April-Oct.). (I) *p. 1822*
randii (Brazil); an epiphytic jewel; pseudobulbs 3 cm high with 20 cm leaf; the pendant inflorescence pushes out through the bottom of its basket, the waxy, heavy-textured flowers 10 cm long, pure white and highly fragrant in the morning, and with an erect horn on each side of the lip; blooming several times a year. *p. 1820*
saccata (Guatemala); epiphyte, with inflorescence 2-4 flowered, the waxy blooms comparatively small, the sepals and petals turned backward, greenish-yellow at tip, deep yellow at base, speckled with brown-purple, rear part of lip (hypochil) deeply bag-shaped, short straight horns, (summer). (I) *p. 1821*
shuttleworthii (Colombia); epiphyte; inflorescence with 3-7 large flowers, sepals and petals apricot-yellow, blotched on the basal portions with dark purple, basal part of lip orange-yellow with maroon blotches, the horns whitish, (summer). (I) *p. 1822*
tigrina (Mexico), "El Toro"; from apprentice days in my father's greenhouses have I remembered this fantastic epiphyte as my most impressive orchid; the memory of its large, 15 cm waxy flowers with sepals and petals deep blood-red marked with yellow, an orange-yellow lip blotched with maroon and its ivory horns, together with an overpowering fragrance of vanilla, haunts me still, (May-July). Valid name may be S. hernandezii. *Tropical.* *p. 1664A, 1822*

tricornis (Perú, Ecuador); epiphyte with pear-shaped pseudobulbs bearing a stalked, dark green, plaited leaf; inflorescence from the base, with flowers curiously bird-like, 12 cm wide with spreading sepals, the petals covering the lip, white almost translucent, yellow-beige at base and spotted crimson. *p. 1820*

wardii (Guatemala, Venezuela), "El Toro"; showy epiphyte with robust inflorescence, the fragrant flowers having yellow sepals and petals, with maroon rings and spots, and in the center two maroon-black eyes, or one large, confluent blotch, in front are two sickle-shaped, light yellow horns, (July-Sept.). (I) *p. 1821*

STAPELIA *Asclepiadaceae* **·I-S2LBD**

asterias (Cape Prov.: Karroo), "Starfish flower"; tufting succulent with light green, soft-downy, 4-angled stems to 20 cm high; 10 cm flowers star-like with long lobes dark purple-brown with transverse yellow lines, and with purple hairs. *Arid-subtropic.* *p. 381*

asterias var. lucida (E. Cape Prov.); flowers 9 cm across, inside entirely purple-brown without yellow lines, very shining, transversely quilted, lighter toward base, tips of lobes greenish-yellow. *p. 382*

barkleyi (Cape Prov.: Namaqualand); branching and spreading with fleshy columns 7-10 cm tall, its 4 softly-hairy angles having stout teeth; flowers with numerous transverse yellow lines and red tips, margins ciliate and with purple hairs inside. *p. 382*

bella, possibly hyb. of revoluta or nobilis; a succulent with erect, branching stems to 20 cm high, light green tinted red, 4-angled with short teeth; 5 cm flowers deep purplish-red, yellow center, and violet marginal hairs. *Arid-subtropic.* *p. 381*

berlinensis (So. Africa), form of comparabilis; 4-angled toothed, fleshy stems 8-15 cm high; flowers with broad ovate lobes, 8 cm across, rugose and black-purple, the center with yellow corona. *p. 382*

choanantha (Cape Province); succulent with prostrate or pendulous stems from rocks, and that may become 2 m long, 1 cm dia., bluish green and brownish blotches, with 4 roundish angles; bell-shaped flowers with 5 lobes, pink outside, red-purple inside with velvety tips. *p. 384*

clavicorona (Transvaal), "African crown"; leafless, succulent plant more or less cactus-like, with thick-fleshy, 4-angled stems in branching clusters; starshaped flower yellowish with transverse purple lines. *p. 382*

comparabilis (So. Africa); succulent angled columns to 20 cm high, 2 to 3 cm dia., the angles fleshy-toothed; starry hairy flowers to 12 cm across, dull-purple with yellowish narrow transverse lines. *p. 380*

flavopurpurea (Bushmanland, Cape Prov.); low succulent with nearly circular, fleshy columns to 5-6 cm high, 14 mm thick, with a few scale-like teeth; flowers with narrow segments, 3-4 cm across, the lobes 15 mm long, dull yellow and transversely rugose, the tube with red hairs. *p. 383*

gigantea (Zululand to Zimbabwe), "Giant toad-plant" or "Zulu Giant"; well known clustering succulent having deeply ribbed, fat stems 10 to 20 cm high, toothed along angles, silky olive green and velvety, with gigantic flowers to 20 cm or more across, pale yellow with transverse crimson lines, variable in color, with forms more reddish, and covered with purplish or crimson hairs; exuding an offensive odor. *Arid-tropical.* *p. 64A, 379, 381, 2092*

glanduliflora (Cape Prov.); clustering succulent, erect stems with 4 or more angles, the angles lobed and with small teeth and deciduous leaves, 9-15 cm high; greenish flowers 5-lobed to 3½ cm across, densely covered with white, translucent hairs. *p. 383*

grandiflora (Cape Province, Transvaal); club-shaped stems and purple-brown flowers, with purple or whitish whiskers on margins of petals. *p. 380*

hirsuta (Cape Province), "Hairy star-fish flower"; clustering succulent fingers sooty-green, the 10 cm flowers purple-brown with transverse lines of cream or purple, and with the margins ciliate-hairy. *p. 381, 384*

leendertziae (Transvaal); slender succulent branching stems lightly angled and set with small fleshy teeth, 1 cm dia.; flowers with unusual bell-shaped tube 6-8 cm long, having pointed, recurving lobes, blackish-purple, thinly covered with long purple hairs; evil-smelling. *p. 380, 382*

lepida (So. Africa); smooth, succulent, olive-green stems about 2 cm thick, densely branching; flowers near the base of stems, 3 cm across, wrinkled on the lobes, sulphur-yellow, covered with scattered small spots. *p. 379*

mutabilis; possibly a revoluta hybrid; tufted, gray-green stems with stout teeth; the flowers wheel-like and lobes recurved; yellow with purple lines. *p. 380*

nobilis (Transvaal); branching, tufted, light green stems; flowers star-like, reflexed, reddish purple on back, yellow on face with crimson lines, covered with purple hairs; flowers 15 cm or more across, and with a deep depression in center. *Arid-subtropic.* *p. 380, 381*

nobilis 'Schwankart'; German cultivar of the "Noble starfish plant", said to be without the objectionable carrion odor of the flowers of other Stapelias. *p. 383*

peglerae (Cape Prov.); soft fleshy stems to 15 cm high and 1 cm thick, angled and with small teeth; flowers 6 cm across, the lobes slender-pointed, dark purple-brown with transverse ridges, the margins ciliate with purple hairs. *p. 380*

rufa (Cape Prov.); soft-fleshy stems with 4 angles, 10-15 cm high, green, often brownish, the blunt ribs armed with small teeth; 3-4 cm flowers with 5 triangular lobes, black-brown and very rugose. *p. 382*

variegata (Cape Province), the "Star flower"; very showy, fleshy flowers 5-8 cm across, greenish-yellow with purple-brown spots on petals; branching green stems clustering and fingerlike. Unfortunately the flowers, like those of other Stapelias, exude a carrion smell to attract flies which, in the hope of finding ripe meat, succeed only in transferring pollen from one flower to another. *Arid-subtropic.* *p. 381*

variegata 'Decora'; an 'orbea' hybrid with mutabilis; very attractive flower more yellow in base, marked with finer, dark crimson spots and cross lines; the ring rising above the petals and surrounding the corona, with 5 indentations. *p. 381*

verrucosa (So. Africa); tufted, succulent plant with little, green fingers having prominent teeth, to 8 cm high; 6 cm flowers from base of stem, pale yellow spotted blood-red and warted inside. *p. 377*

STAPELIANTHUS *Asclepiadaceae* **S2LBD**

decaryi (Madagascar); little, succulent stems, 6-8-angled and covered with warty teeth, densely tufting, and to 10 cm high; tubular star-like flowers spotted purple, 1 to 3 cm long. *p.380*

STAPHYLEA *Staphyleaceae* **I2LBM**

trifolia (Eastern U.S.), "American bladdernut"; hardy shrub or small tree to 5 m, bearing opposite compound leaves of 3 leaflets, pubescent underneath; white flowers about 1 cm long, in nodding panicles to 5 cm across, followed by the bladder-like fruit, an inflated capsule grown for ornament. *p. 2093*

STATICE: see Limonium

STAUROCHILUS *Orchidaceae* **S3OFM**

ionosma (Trichoglottis) (Philippines); handsome epiphyte with erect stout stems to 60 cm, dense with leathery leaves; inflorescence raceme with many waxy, fragrant flowers 4 cm across, the sepals and petals yellowish blotched with brown, the pointed lip white and marked with red; long-lasting (spring). *p. 1827*

STAUROGYNOPSIS *Acanthaceae* **S3LFM**

paludosa (N. Africa; Ivory Coast); low trailing tropical plant with fleshy, finely pubescent leaves green above and gray beneath; pretty little pure white flowers, lasting but one day; needs humid-warm conditions. *p. 51*

STAUROPSIS gigantea: see Acampe longifolia

STEGOLEPIS *Rapataceae* **S3LBM**

parvipetala (Venezuela); tropical perennial with fleshy base, 40-120 cm high; leaves linear-lanceolate with well developed sheaths; long-stalked inflorescence, with small yellow flowers in globular heads. *p. 1990*

STELIS *Orchidaceae* **C-I3OFM**

aemula (Costa Rica); clustering epiphyte with long-stalked, leathery lanceolate leaves; the pretty inflorescence in elongate, dense raceme of cupped, light-sensitive, greenish-white flowers opening only when exposed to sunlight. *p. 1825*

ciliaris (Mexico); small epiphyte with broadly oblong, leathery leaves narrowed to stalk, without pseudobulbs; pendant racemes with small purple flowers, the sepals ciliate, petals and lip fleshy, spike naked for half length, then densely flowered, (February). (C) *p. 1822*

microchila (Guatemala, Costa Rica, Panama); small epiphyte with thin stems bearing erect oblanceolate leaves 5 cm long; inflorescence thread-like with tiny 8 mm flowers arranged all along it, reddish-brown or bronzy-green, small fleshy lip (autumn). *p. 1825*

powellii (Costa Rica, Panama); small epiphyte with lance-shaped leaves tapering toward base; the little flower spikes laterally erect, with cupped sepals, red outside, pinkish inside, the small lip greenish-yellow, (January). (I) *p. 1822*

tonduziana (Costa Rica); small epiphyte 25 cm high, forming clusters; long-stalked leathery leaves; from the juncture of the leaf with stem rises the slender, spike-like inflorescence with tiny 1 cm flowers dull light purple arranged more or less along one side of the rachis. *p. 1825*

tricuspis (Costa Rica); clustering miniature epiphyte from the cloud forest, dense with stalked, narrow leaves, and thread-like inflorescence with tiny flowers bronzy green or straw-colored, sitting along one side of the floral axis. *p. 1825*

STEMMADENIA *Apocynaceae* **S3LFM**

galeottiana (Cent. America), "Lecheso"; tropical shrub to 3 m high, with opposite soft-leathery, glossy green long-elliptic leaves to 12 or 15 cm long, and showy salver form cream-white flowers with 5 broad petals, yellow inside tube, and sweetly fragrant; small 1 cm orange fruit in pairs. *Tropical.* *p. 143*

STENANDRIUM *Acanthaceae* **S-I3HFM**

lindenii (Perú); low tropical herb with leaves papery-smooth, broad elliptic, metallic coppery green with beautifully contrasting yellow-green vein area, purplish beneath; flowers yellow, in 8 cm spikes. *Tropical.* *p. 46*

STENOCARPUS *Proteaceae* **I2LBD**
salignus (Queensland, New South Wales), "Reefwood"; graceful evergreen tree with red, beautifully figured timber, 6-25 m high, with narrow lanceolate leaves to 10 cm long and 2½ cm wide; small fragrant, yellowish-white 1 cm tubular flowers, in large clusters. *p. 1973*
sinuatus (Queensland, New South Wales), "Wheel of fire"; evergreen tree 10-30 m high with leaves either oblong-lanceolate and unlobed or pinnately cut into 1 to 4 pairs of oblong lobes, 30-45 cm long, leathery, glossy light green with pale midrib and lighter beneath; blooming in summer or fall; 8 to 10 cm flowers brilliant scarlet with yellow stamens, resembling a pinwheel, orange-red when young; the inflorescence explodes like fireworks into fiery-red when mature. *Subtropic.* *p. 1968, 1973*

STENOCHLAENA *Polypodiaceae (Filices)* **I3ONM**
palustris (India, So. China, Australia), "Climbing fern"; tropical clambering epiphytic fern, the stems covered with occasional brown scales, and leathery, pinnate fronds shining green, finely serrate at margins, coppery when young; likes to climb on tree-fern slabs. *p. 1167*
tenuifolia (palustris of hort.) (Africa: Natal; Mauritius), "Liane fern"; vigorous climbing epiphyte, with long-trailing woody, scaly rhizomes; sterile fronds pinnate, to 1 m or more; lanceolate, leathery pinnae glossy green, to 30 cm long, minutely toothed at margins. Differs from palustris in having fertile fronds twice-pinnate and lacy. *Humid-subtropic* *p. 1164*

STENOGLOTTIS *Orchidaceae* **I3LFM**
fimbriata (So. Africa); pretty terrestrial orchid with tuberous roots producing a tuft of leaves, and an erect bracted raceme 30 cm high, of small rosy-pink or purple flowers with brown-spotted lip (autumn). (C) *p. 1830*
longifolia (Natal); African terrestrial with tuberous roots producing a tuft of soft, brown-purple, spotted leaves from the center of which springs an erect spike to 60 cm long, with small, pretty, star-shaped flowers, lavender-pink and spotted purple, (Aug.-Oct.).*Subtropic.* *p. 1817, 1829*

STENOLOBIUM: see Tecoma

STENOMESSON *Amaryllidaceae* **I2LFMd**
incarnatum (Perú, Ecuador), "Crimson stenomesson"; pretty bulbous plant from the Andes at 3500 m; 45-60 cm high, with succulent, glaucous, strap-shaped leaves narrowed above, appearing with or after bloom; the floral stalk bearing a cluster of large pendant, bright orange-red flowers with tube 8-10 cm long and flaring segments, each with a green central stripe outside; blooming from early summer to August; after bloom, the plant requires a complete rest; forming offset bulbs. *p. 111*
variegatum (Ecuador, Perú, Chile); tender bulbous plant, with inflorescence arising before the leaves; floral stalk 40-50 cm tall, with tubular-funnel-shaped flowers red, the outer segments with green markings. *Tropical.* *p. 111*

STENORRHYNCHOS *Orchidaceae* **S3HFM**
bracteatus (Spiranthes bracteosa) (Brazil); a terrestrial rosette of broad, fleshy leaves; from the center a floral spike covered with long bracts, and many small white and yellow flowers. *p. 1820*
navarrensis (Costa Rica); terrestrial rosette of obovate, smooth soft-fleshy leaves, light grass-green with pale blotching; inflorescence an erect raceme with salmon-rose bracts, and flowers rosy-pink inside. *p. 1820*
orchioides: synonym for Spiranthes orchioides, which see.
speciosus: synonym of Spiranthes speciosa, which see.
standleyi (C. America); terrestrial or sometimes epiphytic orchid with thick, fleshy roots; rosette of attractive, erect lanceolate, 15-20 cm leaves green with whitish spots on long channeled stalks; bright, cinnabar-red flowers in an upright spike, to 30 cm or more high. *p. 1823*

STENOSPERMATION *Araceae* ***S1HFM**
multiovulatum (Colombia, Ecuador); erect or scandent tropical evergreen with stems climbing by roots from the nodes, to 2 m high; dense with rigid oblong, leathery leaves 30 cm long; boat-shaped white spathe broadly elliptic 12-15 cm long, the white spadix with perfect flowers. *p. 290*
popayanense (Andine Ecuador, Colombia); slow-climbing by roots from the nodes; small, leathery, green, lanceolate leaves on sheathed petioles; boat-shaped, white spathe and white spadix. *p. 283*
sessile (Costa Rica); tropical ornamental with erect or scandent stem rooting at internodes; the oblong leathery, grass green leaves in ranks; white, ovate spathe deciduous, and white, cylindric spadix. *p. 290*
ulei (Venezuela); tropical subshrub, 30-50 cm high, with erect stems densely covered with distichous leaves, rooting at nodes, and somewhat bent at junction with petioles; leathery, green leaf blade elliptic 13-20 cm long and 5-7 cm wide; spathe white. *p. 207*

STENOTAPHRUM *Gramineae* **I-S2-3LBM**
secundatum 'Variegatum' (So. U.S., Trop. America), a variegated-leaf form of the "St. Augustine grass"; creeping stoloniferous grass with flattened stems, and firm linear leaves less than 15 cm long, prettily banded creamy-white, the tips rounded. *Subtropic.* *p. 1310, 1316*

STEPHANIA *Menispermaceae* **I-S3LBD**
glandulifera (Burma); attractive tall twiner with large round, tuberous above-surface base, the thin annual vines with peltate pointed leaves; inflorescence dioecious in small clusters; flowers probably orange. *p. 1549*
rotunda (glabra) (Himalayas, Vietnam); vigorous climber with large brown tuberous roots; each year producing thin twining shoots, broad, angled, peltate leaves; male and female inflorescence on different plants; dioecious, small orange flowers in loose clusters; dying back in the resting period. For the succulent house. *p. 1549*

STEPHANOTIS *Asclepiadaceae* **SI-3LFM**
floribunda (Madagascar), "Madagascar jasmine" or "Wax flower", evergreen wiry climber with milky juice, twining to 5 m high, with opposite elliptic, thick-leathery glossy dark green leaves to 10 cm long; producing axillary clusters of very beautiful, exquisite waxy, white tubular flowers 5 cm wide, and intensely fragrant. A favorite for pots on wire or trellis, for the winter garden, or light, warm window; keep cooler and drier in winter. Propagate by cuttings. *Tropical.* *p. 369*

STERCULIA *Sterculiaceae* **S2LBD**
alexandria (Southeastern Africa), "Veld chestnut"; rare tree of the Uitenhage mountains, with palmate leaves of compound obovate leaflets; odd-shaped, sweet-tasting gray-brown fruit, with black seeds. *p. 2086*
nobilis (China); large tree with trunk to 1 m dia.; membranous leaves broadly oblong 15 to 30 cm long; inflorescence clustered in panicles 10-30 cm long, near end of shoots; flowers fragrant, without corolla, the beautiful 1 cm calyx white or rose with bell-shaped base, lobes incurved; female flowers scarce, these producing woody capsules. *p. 2086*

STERIPHOMA *Caprifoliaceae* **S3LFM**
paradoxum (Venezuela); beautiful flowering shrub 2 m high; lanceolate leaves with long slender points, on long stalks thickened at apex; showy flowers with reddish-brown, split calyx, and 4 yellow petals, in terminal clusters. *p. 754*
peruviana (aurantiaca) (Perú); handsome flowering tropical shrub with dull-green, ovate leaves, the long stalk thickened at juncture with leaf; showy orange-yellow flowers with yellow petals and long protruding yellow stamens 6-10 cm long. *p. 754*

STERNBERGIA *Amaryllidaceae* **I2LBMd**
lutea (So. Europe, Asia Minor), "Winter-daffodil", or "Lily-of-the-field"; small bulbous herb, with narrow channeled, dark green basal leaves, 15-30 cm long; and bright yellow, crocus-like, funnel-shaped, strong-textured, fragrant flowers 4 cm long, at the end of a stout stalk 10-17 cm high; fall-blooming; fairly hardy. *p. 129*
lutea angustifolia; free-flowering narrow-leaved form; flowers of fine substance, rich golden yellow; about 4 cm long; autumn-blooming. *p. 120*

STEUDNERA *Araceae* **S3HFM**
discolor (Burma); ornamental perennial plant with thick ascending stem; from its apex rise on wiry petioles the decorative peltate pointed leaves 25-30 cm long, the surface satiny moss-green and with lighter veins, reverse bluish-gray with broad purple zone; broad-ovate, pointed spathe yellow on both sides, purple at base; club-like spadix. *Tropical.* *p. 283, 291*

STEVIA: see Piqueria trinervia

STEWARTIA *Theaceae* **C2LBD**
pseudocamellia (Japan); large shrub or small tree to 7 m or more, of pyramidal habit, the smooth trunk with red bark, prettily mottled beige, brown and gray, peeling off in large flakes; rather thick, elliptic, toothed leaves 5-10 cm long, turning brilliant crimson in autumn; deciduous in the colder belt around New Jersey; cupshaped white flowers 6 cm across, with yellow stamens. *p. 2101*

STICTOCARDIA *Convolvulaceae* **S3LBD**
tiliifolia (Trop. E. Africa: Kenya); beautiful twining perennial herb with broad-cordate, quilted leaves bright waxy green; from the axils the striking large bell-shaped flowers 8 cm across, brilliant crimson red with yellow throat, and a design of flame-like scarlet red lines from the center, the limb recurved; apple-like fruit. Photographed in Bombay, India. *p. 851*

STIGMAPHYLLON *Malpighiaceae* **I-S2LBM**
ciliatum (Brazil), "Golden vine"; slender twiner with thread-like stems, and glabrous, heartshaped, thin-leathery leaves, oblique at base and with ciliate margins; large 4 cm golden yellow flowers in clusters of 3-7. *p. 1518*
lingulatum (W. Indies), "Gold-vine"; woody twiner with opposite simple, long-oval, stiff leathery leaves, and numerous small yellow flowers under 2½ cm,in large umbels. *p. 1518*

STOMATIUM *Aizoaceae* **I2LBD**
agninum (Mesembryanthemum or Agnirictus) (So. Africa), "Sheep's tongue"; branching succulent with soft, boat-shaped, dull, gray-green leaves to 5 cm long; flowers yellow, 2½ cm across. *p. 76*
fulleri (So. Africa), stemless succulent 2½ cm high, with knobby teeth and covered with silvery warts. Short-lived flowers deep yellow, of narrow, ray-like petals. *p. 78*

viride (Cape Prov.); densely clustering low succulent; boat-shaped 3 cm leaves bronzy green, rough from a thick covering of tubercles, and brown teeth along edge; bright yellow flowers 2-3 cm across. *p. 60*

STRELITZIA *Musaceae* ***I2LBD**

alba (augusta) (Natal), "Great white strelitzia"; palm-like trees of which I have seen extensive groves inland west of Durban, to 10 m high, with woody trunk bearing shining green, leathery leaves 1-1½ m long and arranged fan-like, frequently cut into ribbons by the wind; the curious, large inflorescence on short stalks between the foliage; from a rigid, boat-shaped pointed purplish bract or spathe rises a row of white sepals and petals. *Subtropic.* *p. 1597, 1598, 1599*

caudata (No. Transvaal, Swaziland); growing tree-like, from 2-5 m high, with great, banana-like leathery wind-torn leaves set fan-like in opposite ranks; large axillary inflorescence with pink boat-shaped spathe nesting the all-white flowers, similar to S. alba. *Subtropic.* *p. 1600*

nicolai (So. Africa); trunk forming, clustering tree to 4 m high, with banana-like, shining green, leathery leaves having an obtuse base, arranged in 2 ranks; inflorescence with boatshaped, reddish bracts cradling white sepals and light blue petals united tongue-like. *Subtropic.* *p. 1600*

parvifolia (South Africa: E. Cape), the "Small-leaved bird-of-paradise"; about 1 m high, very similar to S. reginae, trunkless, but this species may be recognized by its leaves which are reduced to very small, spoon-shaped, thin blades at the tips of tall stiff, reed-like stalks; the flowers with yellow sepals, and the united petals or tongue vivid electric blue, borne in clasping, horizontal green bracts edged with red. *Subtropic.* *p. 1600*

parvifolia juncea (South Africa: E. Cape), the "Rush-like strelitzia", from the Port Elizabeth area; very curious form which I was amazed to find because it has no leaves at all; just a dense cluster 1-1½ m high, of spiky tufts of cylindrical, fleshy but rigid, reed-like grayish stems tapering to a needle-point; inflorescence with bright orange sepals and blue tongue. *Subtropic.* *p. 1597*

reginae (Transkei, South Africa), "Bird-of-paradise"; trunkless, compact, clustering but slow-growing plant to 1½ m high, with stiff-leathery, concave, oblong, bluish-gray leaves having pale or red midrib; strikingly exotic, long-stemmed flowers emerging from the green boatshaped spathe bordered in red, measuring 12-18 cm in length, and placed at right angles to the stem, giving it the appearance of a bird's head; the flowers which emerge one at a time from the spathe, consist of 3 brilliant orange sepals, standing up like the crest on a bird's head, and 3 shimmering peacock-blue petals, 2 of which are joined together to form an arrow-like nectary. *p. 1587, 1600, 2112A*

reginae farinosa (So. Africa); stemless, clustering plant 1½ m high; long-petioled, leathery bluish-gray leaves; the floral bracts lemon-yellow instead of orange as in the species. *p. 1598*

STREPTANTHERA *Iridaceae* **I2LBMd**

cuprea (So. Africa), "Kaleidoscope flower"; low cormous herb to 25 cm high, with fresh green leaves arranged in fan-shape; 2 or 3 slender flexuous stalks carry several flat open, wheel-shaped flowers 4 cm across, with petals glowing orange, the center deep violet with a ring of pale yellow spots; blooming in spring into June; going into dormancy late summer. *p.1339*

elegans (So. Africa: Cape Prov.), "White Kaleidoscope flower"; sometimes as Tritonia crocata in hort.; small cormous plant to 24 cm high, with 2-ranked basal leaves; floral stem with bell-shaped flowers spreading wide, 5 cm across, blush-white with velvet-black circle and yellow around center. *p. 1338*

STREPTOCALYX *Bromeliaceae* **I3HFD**

fuerstenbergii (No. Brazil); epiphytic dense rosette with recurving grayish green leaves to 75 cm long and 8 cm wide, spiny at margins; bold cylindric inflorescence 45 cm long with boat-shaped shingled bracts sheltering the blue flowers. *Tropical.* *p. 582*

holmesii (Amazonian Perú); wonderful discovery, and most spectacular with its inflorescence measuring to 60 cm, lush with tiers of cherry-red 15 cm bracts, and crowned by panicles of flowers consisting of fleshy orange calyx and white petals, over rich green leaves. *Tropical.* *p. 582*

poeppigii (Amazonas to Bolivia); large rosette with stiff, strongly armed matte-green leaves marked by gray pencil-lines beneath; large flower spike with scarlet bracts and violet flowers; growing as epiphyte. *Tropical.* *p. 513, 520, 580, 582*

poitiae (Amazonian Perú, Colombia, Ecuador, Guyana); large epiphytic rosette from lowland tropical forest; rigid light green leaves to 1 m long and 4 cm wide, toothed at margins and with short point at apex, the underside somewhat scaly; the bold, cone-like inflorescence 30 cm long, with triangular rosy-crimson bracts and blue flowers. *p. 582*

STREPTOCARPUS *Gesneriaceae* **C-I3LHF (MI:su,DC:wi)**

baudertii (South Africa: E. Cape); rosette of dark green, quilted basal leaves to 10 cm long; the small tubular flowers with oblique limb 4 cm across, long spreading lobes pale mauve with light yellow, a deep purple line radiating to each of the lower segments. *p. 1298*

caulescens (Trop. East Africa), "Violet nodding bells"; succulent branching plant with light green, fleshy stem covered by white hair; small blunt-cordate leaves; the slender axillary stalks bearing panicles of tiny 1 cm slipper flowers with spreading petals, beautiful violet with white throat. *Humid-tropical.* *p. 1295, 1299*

cooksonii (So. Africa: Natal); single huge, fleshy leaf, nearly triangular with cordate base, to 40 cm long and 30 cm wide, the surface corrugated and soft-hairy; the crowded inflorescence like a fountain from the leaf base, dense with oblique trumpet-shaped flowers 3-4 cm long, rosy-violet with pale blue area on three lower petals, marked violet inside; in habitat blooming December to April. *p. 1297*

cooperi (So. Africa: Natal); a beautiful mountain species found as far west as the Drakensberg, in forests on banks along mountain streams; large solitary corrugated leaf to 70 cm long and as wide, softly hairy and with crenate margin; from the leaf base rise stalks to 50 cm tall, bearing a profusion of pale lavender flowers violet inside, 5-7 cm long, long slender tube, and flaring limb, blooming in habitat January to April. Closely related to S. grandis. Photographed in Edinburgh Bot. Garden, Scotland. *p. 1297*

cyanandrus (Rhodesia or Zimbabwe), found at 2200 m in the Inyanga Mountains along the Zambezi; small, soft-hairy bluish perennial with several linear oblong leaves 5-15 cm long, green above and purplish underneath; the inflorescence at junction of blade and stalk, with curved tubular corolla to 3½ cm long, oblique with flaring lobes, magenta pink with red lines on petals. *p. 1296*

dunnii (Transvaal); stemless plant with giant broadly oblong, solitary recurving, puckered leaf to 1 m long, silvery gray with soft appressed hairs, the margins crenate; inflorescence on stalks 30 cm high, with tubular, nodding flowers 4 cm long, brick-red or rose. *p. 1296, 1298*

glandulosissimus (Kenya, Tanzania); tropical herb with weak, straggling stems, over bushes or epiphytic; leaves ovate, variable in size, 3-13 cm long, unequal at base and thinly pubescent; inflorescence axillary to the upper leaves, the stalked, tubular flowers 3 cm long, with flaring limb, violet-blue with pale eye and long lower lip; blooming most of the year. *p. 1296*

grandis (Zululand, Natal); curious stemless plant with a single large sessile, long ovate, hairy leaf 60-90 cm long, having sunken veins; small light blue flowers dark in center, and white on lower petals, on clustered stalks which are emerging from the base of the leaf. *Humid-subtropic.* *p. 1297, 1299*

hildebrandtii (No. Madagascar); interesting species found near Diego Suarez; forming a rosette of usually pairs of broad, rounded leaves with cordate base 9 to 10 cm across and flat to the soil, glossy purplish green and quilted, sparsely hairy; from each leaf axil rise 2 to 4 inflorescence stalks, each with a cluster of small tubular flowers medium violet, its base splotched purple, blooming in winter. *p. 1295*

holstii (E. Trop. Africa); erect branching herb to 45 cm high, with slender fleshy stem swollen at the nodes; the ovate, slightly hairy, wrinkled, opposite leaves 4-5 cm long; slender pedicels carry the purple flowers, 2½ cm long, with open, white throat. *p. 1298*

x hybridus, "Hybrid cape primrose"; complex group of hybrids with a long line of parents including S. dunnii for color, rexii for bushy habit, and wendlandii for stem-length; light green fleshy, quilted leaves; free-blooming with large trumpet-like flowers, in a wide range of color, from white with purple veining, through rose, orchid, mauve, blue to purple. *Humid-subtropic.* *p. 1248A, 1300*

x hybridus 'Achimeniflorus'; a race resulting from the rexii hybrids with addition of S. polyanthus which added its blue color to the trumpet-shaped flowers of an otherwise bushier plant. *p. 1299*

x hybridus 'Amethyst'; a European cultivar of the hybrid complex of S. dunnii, polyanthus and wendlandii; with remarkably large flowers in pale purple with bold violet bands on lower petals, and 10-12 cm across; the leaves are more of the strap-type as in rexii; a less desirable feature. *p.1295*

x hybridus 'Farbenwunder'; an excellent German (Meisert) strain forming shapely plants of compact habit, early-blooming, and with large wide-open flowers 8-12 cm across, in colors carmine-red to purple with dark eye blooming 6 to 8 months after sowing the seed; their main flowering season is from spring through autumn. *Humid-subtropic.* *p. 1295*

x hybridus 'Red Orchid' ('Rote Orchidee'); a European cultivar with long-stalked flowers purplish red with violet bands at base of lower petals; this belongs to the hybrid complex of S. dunnii, polyanthus, rexii and wendlandii. *p. 1295*

x hybridus 'Sutton's Blush Pink'; highly rated English strain, characterized by its compact habit, about 22 cm high, with tufting foliage, and large flowers on medium short stalks, light pink with pale throat. *p. 1298*

x hybridus 'Wiesmoor'; handsome German cultivars, with fringed and crested flowers 10-12 cm across, in shades from blush-pink to deep rose or crimson, light to dark blue, violet and white blotched with deeper color in the throat. *p. 1299*

insignis (So. Africa: E. Cape); stemless rosette of wrinkled, obovate fresh green leaves 20-30 cm long, and trumpet-shaped lavender-blue flowers red-purple in throat and with deep purple stripes. *p. 1296*

kentaniensis (So. Africa); a different type of stemless rosette with tufting, numerous narrow strap-like recurving leaves grooved down center; small flowers with lavender tube, the lobes of the expanded limb almost white; the throat purple. *p. 1298*

parviflorus (Transvaal); stemless rosette with quilted, densely velvety, lanceolate leaves 12-30 cm long; smallish 2½ cm but numerous, narrowly funnel-shaped white flowers, pencilled with mauve on the 3 lobes, yellow in throat. *p. 1298*

phyllanthus (So. Africa); showy tropical plant with a large and fleshy, solitary leaf 20-25 cm long and almost as wide, the surface grayish green, furrowed by a network of depressed veins, and covered with soft white hair; the inflorescence rises from the leaf base; branched slender stalks carry a pendant shower of flowers pale lavender with yellow center. Photographed at Longwood Gardens, Kennett Square, Pennsylvania. *p. 1297*

polyanthus (Natal), "Sky-blue fountain"; stemless plant with large single, quilted oblong leaf to 30 cm long and nearly as broad, hairy above, and wine-red underneath; from the base of the midrib arise 1-12 wiry stalks about 30 cm high or more, bearing a branching inflorescence of numerous smallish flowers with yellow tube and oblique, spreading lobes 4 cm across, lavender-blue, with yellow throat. *p. 1296, 1298*

pusillus (Natal); small stemless species with solitary elliptic, hairy leaf 8-15 cm long; the inflorescence on short 8 cm stalks bearing 10-20 tubular, white flowers less than 2½ cm long, the lobes spreading nearly at right angles. *p. 1298*

rexii (So. Africa), "Cape primrose"; small fibrous-rooted, stemless plant with long narrow, quilted and pubescent leaves in rosette hugging the ground, with several flower stalks bearing trumpets of pale lavender lined with purple in the throat. *Humid-subtropic.* *p. 1299*

saundersii (Natal); single large corrugated, recurving leaf to 35 cm long, 20-22 cm wide, heart-shaped, rich green above, rose-purple and hairy beneath; floral stalks from base of leaf, the flowers pale lilac with two purple patches, and a median yellow band in the curved tube with spreading limb, 2½ cm across, 2 lobes of the corolla shorter than the rest. *Humid-subtropic.* *p. 1296, 1298*

saxorum (Tanzania), "False African violet"; small bushy plant from the cool Usambaras, with fleshy, pubescent, elliptic, 3 cm leaves in crowded whorls; flowers with white tube and oblique limb of large pale lilac lobes, spreading to 3 cm wide, on long thin stems, blooming over many months. Have seen them clinging to perpendicular, exposed cliffs, at 1,100 m in the Usambara Mountains of Tanzania. *Humid-subtropic.* *p. 1299*

vandeleurii (Transvaal); stemless biennial with a great solitary leaf, growing in crevices of rocks of damp kloofs; the single fleshy broad leaf somewhat heart-shaped 30 cm long and wide, quilted wrinkled and softly hairy; the inflorescence in a great bouquet of 30 flowers or more, many opening together; corolla oblique-tubular with flaring lobes 3½ cm across, white with yellow blotch at base of lower lip. *p. 1296*

wendlandii (Natal), "Royal nodding bells"; stemless plant with a single, huge leaf becoming 1 m long and 60 cm wide, with olive-green corrugated surface and densely hairy, purple beneath; the tall flower spikes sprouting from the leaf may bear some 30 small, violet-blue flowers, white in throat. *p. 1299, 1300*

x STREPTOGLOXINIA *Gesneriaceae* **S3HFM**

hybrida (x Stroxinia) (Streptocarpus x Sinningia); attractive bigeneric hybrid as grown by Roehrs in New Jersey 1962; shapely plant of the habit of Sinningia speciosa, the quilted, soft olive green leaves with pale to pinkish veins, 15 to 18 cm long, reddish beneath; substantial curved trumpet-shaped flowers 6 cm long, with 5 spreading lobes, 5 cm across, strong carmine-red, darker crimson inside and spotted red outside; pale yellow throat. The existence of this bigeneric is disputed by some botanists. *Humid-tropical.* *p. 1295*

'Lorna' (Streptocarpus x Sinningia); supposedly bigeneric hybrid originating in California in 1947 as Stroxinia and resembling "Gloxinia" in type of leaves and flowers, which may be nodding and foxglove-like or erect true bell-shaped, except that upper lobes overlap and are curled back; flower texture is rich and velvety, color deep rose in 'Lorna', blue in 'Nancy', with speckled throat. *p. 1299*

STREPTOSOLEN *Solanaceae* **I2LF-BM**

jamesonii (Colombia, Ecuador), "Marmalade bush"; rough-pubescent, floriferous, rambling shrub with small oval, wrinkled leaves on flexuous branches, and terminal clusters of tubular, bell-shaped, orange flowers 3 cm long, in spring. *Tropical.* *p. 2083*

STROBILANTHES *Acanthaceae* **S3LHFM**

atropurpureus (Siberia), "Mexican petunia"; a perennial of the northern limits for this otherwise predominantly tropical genus; developing erect herbaceous stems with opposite, long-stalked ovate leaves serrate at margins, and bearing several clusters of rich purple flowers, 4 cm long, during summer. (Photo by T. Everett, New York Botanical Garden). *p. 53*

dyerianus (Perilepta) (Burma), "Persian shield"; beautiful tropical herbaceous shrub with magnificent iridescent 15 cm leaves, long-ovate and toothed, purple with silver above and curiously shimmering; glowing purple beneath; pale blue flowers. Best in a moist-warm greenhouse. *Humid-tropical.* *p. 53, 1824A*

sp. "Exotica" (New Guinea); in appearance a narrow-leaved version of S. dyerianus; striking tropical plant with square stems bearing elegant, narrow lanceolate slender-pointed leaves 15 cm x 3 cm, iridescent coppery-purple, richly overlaid with carmine-rose between the widely spaced veins; the margins finely crenate, underside red-purple. *p. 53*

isophyllus (India), "Bedding conehead"; shrub with shiny, willow-like opposite leaves, toothed; 3 cm flowers lavender or blue and white. *p. 53*

lactatus (Brazil); attractive tropical herbaceous plant with shrubby base; leaves dark green, handsomely variegated with white; at Longwood Gardens. *Tropical.* *p. 53*

maculatus (Himalayas); charming herbaceous foliage plant with ovate, quilted grass-green leaves decorated with two rows of silver blotches; margins finely serrated. Photographed at Royal Botanic Garden, Edinburgh. *Tropical.* *p. 53*

STROMANTHE *Marantaceae* **S3LFM**

amabilis (Brazil); stocky plant with firm, oval leaves having a short point, the surface painted with gray lateral bands which taper to a slender point, on a bluish-green ground; underside gray-green. Described as Stromanthe in Hortus 3, but according to Dr. Helen Kennedy, (Honolulu 1979), this should be listed as Ctenanthe amabilis. *p. 1540*

lutea (Colombia, Venezuela); perennial herb to over 1 m high, with thickened rhizome; leafy stems with elliptic to linear-lanceolate blades, the margins downy; inflorescence with 3 cm orange-yellow bracts and yellow flowers. *p. 1546*

porteana (Brazil); large perennial herb to 1½ m high, with thick rootstocks; long paddle-like, oblique lanceolate leaves 45 cm long, glossy-leathery, the lightly corrugated surface with feather-design of rich green lateral bands on nerve ridges alternating with silver-gray bands in the furrows between; reverse deep purple with gray cast; flowers blood red. *Humid-tropical.* *p. 1542*

sanguinea (Calathea discolor) (Brazil); stiff plant growing to 1½ m tall; thick-fleshy, long-lanceolate leaves glossy dark olive-green, beautiful blood-red beneath, the juvenile basal leaves have a whitish midrib; stems branching, topped by a showy head of waxy salmon-red bracts and white flowers. *Humid-tropical.* *p. 1538, 1543, 1544*

STRONGYLODON *Leguminosae* **S3LFM**

macrobotrys (Philippines), "Philippine jade vine"; a most beautiful and striking woody twiner, with large pinnate leaves, best trained over pergola or frame support to allow the large pendant racemes, 30 to 90 cm long, a free display of the curious 8 cm flowers with their slender-pointed, upturned beak, and rolled, recurved standard, colored entirely in an unusual shade of bluish-green jade over yellow-green, the beak a pale blue-green. *Tropical.* *p. 1388, 1393*

STROPHANTHUS *Apocynaceae* **S3LFM**

dichotomus (India, Malaya, Java); erect shrub with stout branches; elliptic or obovate, leathery leaves 8-12 cm long; branched clusters of curious flowers with awl-shaped sepals, purple corolla tube 2½ cm long, the lobes producing very long, thread-like white tails 12-17 cm long. *p. 134*

divaricatus (Yunnan, South China); spectacular scandent shrub, climbing to 3 m high, with woody branches; leathery oblong-elliptic leaves 3 to 8 cm or more long; the very curious tailed flowers creamy-green with red stripes in throat, the thread-like lobes to 10 cm long. *Tropical.* *p. 144*

grandiflorus (Tanzania, Mozambique); striking woody climber with ovate, wavy leaves 8-10 cm long, pale beneath; conspicuous yellow flowers streaked with red, the tube 3 cm across mouth, the corolla lobes prolonged into twisted, ribbon-like yellow tails 15-18 cm long, stained with red. *p. 144*

gratus (West Tropical Africa), "Climbing oleander"; robust clambering evergreen shrub, with opposite leathery, ovate to obovate olive green leaves somewhat puckered, 10-15 cm or more long, on brown-purple woody stems; the waxy, trumpet-shaped flowers 6 cm diameter, with crinkled lobes, flushed purplish-red outside and pinkish-white inside, and with a prominent pale rose-purple inner crown, blooming late spring. *Tropical.* *p. 144*

luteolus (So. Africa: Transvaal, Natal); rambling evergreen liane, with glossy-leathery ovate leaves, and very curious flowers whitish-yellow, striped red inside the funnel-shaped corolla, mouth with 10 claws, and the lobes elongated into twisted, thread-like tails. *p. 144*

speciosus (So. Africa: Cape, Natal, Zululand), "Corkscrew-flower"; rambling evergreen shrub, in habitat climbing into the trees; narrowly oval, leathery leaves to 9 cm long; curious flowers at tip of branches, a wide-mouthed corolla opens into 5 long, 3-5 cm narrow, spirally twisted lobes radiating in all directions, deep yellow with large red spot at base. *p. 144*

STULTITIA *Asclepiadaceae* **I2LBD**

cooperi (So. Africa: Cape Prov.); low succulent forming clusters, with ascending stems 4 cm high, obtusely 4-angled, the angles with conical, spreading teeth, at their base are two smaller teeth, grayish-green or red with green mottling; showy flowers 3-4 cm across with 5 broad lobes, light purple with yellow tubercles; the conspicuous center intense maroon. *p. 383*

paradoxa (Mozambique, Transvaal, Natal); pretty succulent forming low cushions, with fleshy stems and prominent teeth, grayish-green with purple spotting; 5-lobed flowers 2½ cm across, the cup glossy dark red, the lobes greenish-white with dark red blotches in transverse lines, margins with red hairs. *p. 383*

tapscottii x Stapelia gettleffii (No. Transvaal); natural hybrid with stapelia-like succulent stems, the angles with large fleshy, pointed knobs; large flowers with 5 lobes transversely rugose, purple and tinted yellow, densely covered with purple hairs. Stultitia differs from Stapelia in having a distinct ring around mouth of tube. *p. 383*

STYLIDIUM *Stylidiaceae* **I3LBD**

adnatum (Southeastern Australia), "Trigger plant"; herbaceous perennial 5-30 cm high; leaves scattered; upper crowded into a whorl-like tuft, linear; sometimes all very narrow, sometimes rather wide to 4 cm long; flowers pink in nearly sessile clusters along rachis. The column of the flower moves like a trigger when touched at base by insects, enabling pollination. *p. 2093*

STYLOCHITON *Araceae* **S3LFM**

crassispathus (Trop. Africa: Zambia); small aroid with hairy petiole and waxy, green cordate to hastate leaves, with smooth surface and prominent ribs beneath; attractive fleshy spathe flask-shaped at base, constricted in center, opening obliquely, shell-like at apex, yellowish to reddish, nearly hiding the small spadix. *p. 290*

euryphyllus (Tanzania); interesting low plant with thick rhizome; the flattened, fleshy leaves wide ovate-cordate to nearly round, about 12 cm across, prettily patterned with a network of whitish veins, spreading and hugging the ground. *p. 290*

obliquinervis (Tanzania, Transvaal); small curious aroid with stout rhizome and fleshy roots; long oblong leaves, spathe flask-shaped at base, opening to hood over spadix. *p. 290*

zenkeri (Trop. West Africa: Guinea, Gabon); tropical aroid with creeping rhizome, stalked oblong membranous leaves 10-15 cm long, with cordate base, dark green above, pale green underside with prominent veins showing; white tubular spathe 2½ cm long, with forward curving hood. *p. 290*

SUBMATUCANA *Cactaceae: Echinocactanae* **I2LBD**

madisoniorum (syn. Borzicactus) (N.E. Perú); small solitary globe, with age elongating to 25 cm high and 10 cm dia., grayish green with rough surface; the ribs not high, when older becoming knobby around areoles; 1 to 5 spines to 6 cm long, lightly curved; slender funnel-shaped flowers 8-10 cm long, 4-5 cm dia., orange red and covered with brownish hair. *p. 687*

SUCCULENTS: see Aizoaceae, Amaryllidaceae, Asclepiadaceae, Bromeliaceae, Compositae, Crassulaceae, Euphorbiaceae, Geraniaceae, Liliaceae, Piperaceae, Portulacaceae, Vitaceae, in 'Pictorial section'.

SUTHERLANDIA *Leguminosae* **I2LBD**

frutescens (floribunda) (So. Africa), "Cancer bush" or "Balloon pea"; downy shrub with pinnate leaves; the rich scarlet flowers in axillary racemes, developing into numerous decorative puffed, papery seed pods. *Subtropic.* *p. 1393, 1394*

SUTTONIA *Myrsinaceae* **I2LBD**

salicina (New Zealand); known as "Toro" by the Maori; small tree sometimes reaching 12 m, with narrow, shining linear-oblong, light green leaves 10-17 cm long, chiefly toward the tips of branches; tiny whitish-green flowers in small clusters along the bare branches, followed by the ½-1 cm red berries. *p. 1602*

SWAINSONA *Leguminosae* **I2-3LBM**

galegifolia (Queensland, New So. Wales), "Swan orchid" or "Winter sweet-pea"; ornamental, freely blooming greenhouse plant; semi-climber with scandent branches, bearing unequally pinnate leaves, and small pea-like flowers in long-stalked showy racemes, deep red, or other shades. *Subtropic.* *p. 1394*

galegifolia var. coronillifolia; scrambling subshrub to 1 m high with feathery leaves and flowers 2 cm long, violet in this variety; followed by inflated pods 5 cm long. *p. 1394*

SWERTIA *Gentianaceae* **I2LBD**

petiolata (Himalaya); robust perennial 30 to 90 cm tall, the stout hollow stem with oblanceolate leaves to 10 cm long and deeply furrowed; the inflorescence in erect raceme of whitish flowers veined blue-green, with spreading lobes. *p. 1170*

SWIETENIA *Meliaceae* **S2LBD**

mahagoni (Florida Keys and West Indies), "Mahogany"; tropical evergreen tree to 25 m, with dark red wood which furnishes the mahogany of commerce for furniture, etc.; dark glossy green, leathery, pinnate leaves to 10-20 cm long; small white flowers; showy green woody fruit capsule 10 cm dia. *Tropical.* *p. 1557*

SYAGRUS *Palmae* **S-I2LFM**

coronata (Cocos coronata hort.) (Brazil), "Licuri palm"; handsome palm to 10 m tall, the trunk partially covered by persistent leaf bases arranged in an attractive spiral pattern; pinnate fronds to 3 m long, erect and arching, arranged in 5-ranked spiral; leathery, dark lustrous green leaflets folded at base, set in clusters and at various angles; yellow flowers in typical boat-shaped spathe, and fleshy 2 cm orange, edible fruit. *Tropical.* *p. 1911*

treubiana (Glaziova) (Paraguay); interesting fan palm with moderate trunk; pinnate fronds spiralled in 5 pronounced series; the numerous leaflets more or less grouped in twos and threes; long inflorescence, and ovoid fruit. *p. 1916*

weddelliana (Brazil: Guanabara), "Baby cocos palm"; according to Blossfeld, this should be Microcoelum martianum, but in the trade as Cocos weddelliana; attractive little feather palm in 5 cm pots, which grows in the humid Organ Mountains to 2 m, forming slender, solitary trunks with graceful pinnate fronds, the narrow, stiff segments glossy yellow-green and neatly spaced; small orange fruit. *Humid-tropical.* *p. 1875, 1902, 1916*

SYMBEGONIA *Begoniaceae* **S3LFM**

sanguinea (strigosa) (New Guinea); beautiful member of the begonia family, with branches spreading and scandent from fibrous roots; the handsome foliage is oblique-ovate, deeply quilted and rugose with bristles and serrate at margins, and of red-bronze coloring; the inflorescence is hairy, with flowers carmine-red; petals free in male flowers, but in female flowers forming a tube, one of the characteristics of this genus; in begonias the petals are all free. Found at 300 m in the Milne Bay District, Papua. *Tropical.* *p. 467*

SYMINGTONIA *Hamamelidaceae* **S3LFM**

populnea (Exbucklandia populnea) (Himalaya and Sumatra); attractive, vigorous evergreen vine with thick, leathery, pointed-ovate leaves, up to 25 cm long, similar in general appearance and texture to those of Hedera colchica; flowers in heads in groups of four, sunk into the axis; the calyx tube becomes visible as a ring after flowering. *p. 1323*

SYMPHYGLOSSUM *Orchidaceae* **I3OFM**

coccineum (sanguineum?) (Cochlioda) (Ecuador); very attractive small terrestrial from Andean highlands; clustered pseudobulbs topped by 1-2 linear, soft-textured, veined leaves to 25 cm; arching inflorescence to 1 m long, with numerous 3 cm flowers rosy-red in sanguineum, orange-yellow in coccineum, white at base of lip (spring). *p. 1825*

sanguineum (Cochlioda) (Ecuador); epiphyte with sharp-edged pseudobulbs 6 cm high and marbled with brown; the two linear leaves 20 cm long; flowers not opening wide, in a loose, arching raceme; sepals and petals rosy-red, lip white in back, rosy-red in front, and with a double ridged white callus; Oct.-Nov., or April-May. *p. 1815*

SYMPLOCARPUS *Araceae* **C2-3LFW**

foetidus (Quebec to No. Carolina, west to Minnesota), "Skunk cabbage", or "Pole-catweed"; strong-smelling perennial swamp herb with thick rhizome; spathe ovoid with incurved summit, 8-15 cm long, purple-brown and green, enclosing the spongy spadix, and partly underground; heart-shaped basal leaves to 1 m long, appearing after the inflorescence, which has a disagreeable odor. *p. 283*

nipponicus (Japan, Korea); fleshy perennial with erect rhizome; the basal leaves in rosette, ovate-oblong with cordate base, 10-12 cm long, 7-12 cm wide, glossy green and quilted; blooming after the leaves, with broadly elliptic, fleshy spathe tinged with brown-purple; the spadix with bisexual flowers. *p. 300*

SYNADENIUM *Euphorbiaceae* **S2LBD**

grantii 'Rubra' (Euphorbia) (Tanzania), "Red milk bush"; ornamental shrub with thick, succulent branches, milky juice; fleshy obovate leaves, 8-18 cm long, beautiful wine red, margins finely toothed, reverse vivid red purple; flowers red. *Tropical.* *p. 1053, 1054, 1061*

SYNANDROSPADIX *Araceae* **I3LFM**

vermitoxicus (No. Argentina); handsome aroid from the Andes near Tucumán and Salta; thick tuber with fleshy petioles striped with dark green, carrying sagittate-cordate leaves 20-45 cm long, 15-20 cm wide; showy spathe pale greenish to brownish inside, lined green, 10 cm long; spadix brown-red. *Subtropic.* *p. 291*

SYNANTHERIAS: see Amorphophallus sylvaticus

SYNGONANTHUS *Eriocaulaceae* **S3HBW**

humbertii (Madagascar); a curiosity from tropical swamps; perennial tufts of grass-like leaves with stiff-wiry, straight, rush-like stalks bearing tiny straw-yellow flowers in small heads. *p. 1002*

SYNGONIUM *Araceae* ***S1LFM**

auritum (Philodendron auritum) (Jamaica), "Five fingers"; ornamental climber with fleshy, rich, dull or glossy green, 3 to 5-sected leaves to 25 cm long; petioles vaginate. *p. 292*

auritum 'Fantasy'; attractive Wilson cultivar with its glossy-dark-green, fleshy-leathery, compound leaves irregularly variegated with silver, and cream maturing to white; the mid-lobe 15-20 cm long, flanked by two smaller basal lobes; the stout petiole vaginate at base inside, angled toward apex, and striped with cream. *p. 298*

erythrophyllum (Panama), "Copper syngonium"; dainty creeping plant with small, arrow-shaped, waxy leaves having 2 earlike basal lobes; blade metallic coppery-green and covered with tiny pink dots; reddish beneath; mature leaf trifoliate. *Tropical.* *p. 292*

hoffmannii (C. America), "Goose-foot"; attractive creeping plant with the glabrous young leaves arrow-shaped, matte grayish green with silver-white center and veins. *p. 293*

macrophyllum (Mexico to Panama), "Big-leaf syngonium"; climber with large, heartshaped, emerald-green, fleshy leaves with velvet sheen, becoming divided in the maturity stage, much larger than podophyllum. *Tropical.* *p. 288, 292*

mauroanum (Costa Rica); robust species from Ysidro with metal-green, corrugated, sagittate to divided leaves dark green, variegated silvery-cream along midrib and lateral veins. *p. 292*

podophyllum (Nephthytis liberica) (Mexico to Costa Rica), "African evergreen"; in juvenile stage a small plant with arrowshaped, thin, green leaves, on slender petioles, later starting to creep; in successive stages leaves become lobed and then palmately divided into 5 to 9 segments. *p. 292, 298*

podophyllum 'Albolineatum' (earliest name: angustatum) (Mexico, Nicaragua), "Arrow-head vine"; known commercially as Nephthytis triphylla; the juvenile leaves heartshaped or 3-lobed, very ornamental with silver-white center and veining; the mature leaves are palmate and all green. *Tropical.* *p. 5*, 293*

podophyllum albolineatum 'Dot Mae'; cultigen having a wider juvenile leaf and more boldly marked leaves than the species. *p. 292*

podophyllum albolineatum 'Ruth Fraser'; a horticultural selection showing a more distinct improvement in variegation over the type, also variegation lasts longer. *p. 293*

podophyllum 'Albo-virens'; a mutant with slender juvenile hastate leaves shaded ivory to greenish-white, blade edged green. *Tropical.* *p. 293*

podophyllum 'Atrovirens'; variety with the juvenile leaves hastate or lobed, and the vein areas ash green to cream, on a dark green background. *p. 293*

podophyllum 'Emerald Gem', "Arrow-head plant"; juvenile leaves arrowshaped, more fleshy, quilted, dark green and glossy; the petioles are shorter, making this form more compact, and sooner to creep. *p. 292*

podophyllum 'Emerald Gem variegated'; of compact habit and creeping very slowly; dark green arrow-shaped leaves with pure white and milky-gray, irregular variegation on the glossy, thin-leathery blades to varying degree. *Tropical.* *p. 293*

podophyllum 'Imperial White'; an "Arrowhead-vine" with arrow-shaped leaves deep bluish green, and a contrasting network of ivory-white veining. Widely grown in California greenhouses. *Tropical.* *p. 292*

podophyllum 'Roxanne'; attractive, compact sport of 'Green Gold', starting as a small rosette, later creeping; pinkish-brown petioles carrying the arrow-shaped, hastate leaves, 12 cm long in the juvenile stage, then glossy moss-green with whitish ribs and nile green center, marbling out toward margins; the adult leaves larger and segmented. *p. 296*

podophyllum 'Tricolor' (Costa Rica); mutant with slender juvenile leaves hastate and trilobed, pale green and ivory variegation on dark green blade; flowers tricolored cream, purple and pale pink. *p. 293*

podophyllum 'Trileaf Wonder'; cultigen with a varying amount of ashgreen on the leaf, principally on the midrib and lateral veins; also the mature, segmented leaves are produced more quickly. *Tropical.* *p. 293, 298*

podophyllum xanthophilum (Mexico); the cultivated plant 'Green Gold' probably belongs here; the juvenile arrowshaped leaves are suffused and marbled with yellow-green. *p. 293, 294*

schottii (Trop. America); photographed as a compact little plant at Noack's Nursery, San Bernardino, California; a rosette of hastate, arrow-shaped or cordate fleshy leaves 9 cm long, glossy fresh green and attractive as a small foliage plant in pots. (See syn. Porphyrospatha). *p. 296*

triphyllum 'Lancetilla' (Honduras; Costa Rica); in juvenile stage the papery, dull green, upright leaves are unequal-sided, ovate with sunken veins, later becoming increasingly 3-lobed. *p. 285, 292*

wendlandii (Costa Rica); dainty creeper with tri-lobed, deep green, velvety leaves and sharply contrasting white veins in the juvenile foliage, the divided maturity-stage leaves plain green. *Tropical.* *p. 15*, 19*, 293*

SYNNOTIA *Iridaceae* **I2LBMd**

metelerkampiae (So. Africa); small sparaxis-like plant with a bulbous corm, with slender stem 15-25 cm high; broadly linear leaves 5-10 cm long, arranged in a fan; branched floral stalks bearing irregular violet flowers 3 cm across, with long slender tube and spreading segments, the upper petal largest, 3 lower lobes with white blotch and purple anthers; blooming in spring; dormant during summer. *p. 1339*

SYRINGA *Oleaceae* **C2LBMhd**

vulgaris (Southeastern Europe), the common "Lilac"; winter-hardy, bushy deciduous shrub with woody stems to 3 m or more high, the flexible twigs with opposite, thin ovate leaves to 12 cm long; blooming outdoors in late spring with terminal or lateral pyramidal clusters of sweetly fragrant, small flowers, normally pale purple tinged with violet. *Temperate.*

vulgaris 'Mad. Lemoine', well-known "Lilac"; much used for early forcing, with large double, fragrant, tubular flowers greenish-white, becoming pure white, narrow but dense panicles. *p. 1627*

vulgaris 'Marie Legraye', "White Lilac"; single, large-flowered pure white lilac, in open, narrow, medium-sized panicle; good for forcing. *p. 1627*

vulgaris plena (S. E. Europe), double flowered form of the "Common lilac"; robust growing deciduous shrub, flexible twigs with simple ovate glabrous leaves, and showy lateral, pyramidal panicles of small, fragrant lilac-blue flowers late in spring. *p. 1627*

wolfii (wulfenii, formosissima) (Korea, Manchuria); deciduous shrub to 6 m, with ovate deep-green leaves; at the apex of leafy branches the showy, large 20 cm clusters of fragrant flowers with lilac 2 cm tubular corolla; known as wulfenii in New Zealand. *p. 1635*

SYZYGIUM *Myrtaceae* **I2LBD**

aromaticum (Eugenia) (Moluccas), the "Clove tree"; evergreen to 10 m high, with elliptic, glandular dotted, aromatic leaves; yellow tubular flowers 1 cm across, with red base. The sun-dried flower buds are the commercial "cloves". *Tropical.* *p. 1606*

malaccense (Malaya), "Rose apple"; beautiful tropical tree 5-12 m high; glossy ovate oblong, leathery leaves 15-30 cm long; showy flowers of many stamens purplish-red, from old wood; pear-shaped red fruit, about 5 cm long, edible raw or cooked and used as preserves. *p. 1606, 1607*

paniculatum (Eugenia myrtifolia) (Australia), "Brush cherry"; small vigorous shrub which lends itself to shearing into pyramids; slender branches dense with small elliptic foliage vivid red when young, later shining green; fluffy white flowers followed by edible red berries. *Subtropic.* *p. 1606, 1607, 1614*

paniculatum australis (Australia); a variety remaining more bushy and blooming more or less throughout the year; glossy green leaves to about 6 cm long; white flowers not prominent beyond the foliage; the berries usually smaller. *p. 1606*

paniculatum 'Globulus', "Myrtle-leaf eugenia"; very compact evergreen bush of globular habit, with shiny, stiff-leathery vivid amber to deep green 3 cm leaves, densely clothing the numerous branchlets. *p. 1606*

SYZYGIUM: see also Eugenia

TABEBUIA *Bignoniaceae* **S2LBD**

argentea (Tecoma argentea) (Paraguay); the "Silver trumpet-tree", or "Golden bell"; showy tropical flowering tree with crooked trunk and corky bark, to 8 m high, covering itself in the leafless stage with a profusion of rich-yellow trumpet-flowers 5-8 cm long; after bloom appears the foliage, leaves palmately divided into 5-7 narrow leaflets to 15 cm long, and covered with silvery scales; oblong woody dark brown fruit 15 cm long. *Subtropic.* *p. 499*

chrysantha (C. America, So. America); tropical flowering tree 4-5 m high, with leaves digitately compound of 5 hairy, ovate leaflets; trumpet-shaped yellow flowers 5 to 8 cm long in showy clusters at the end of leafless branches. *Tropical.* *p. 503*

pallida (W. Indies, C. and No. America), the "Cuban pink trumpet-tree"; showy flowering tree to 15 m or more high; leaves with 3-5 elliptic leaflets 10-15 cm long, often renewed after blooming; handsome flowers in dense terminal clusters, slender tube with flaring pale lilac pink limb, yellow in throat, the corolla 6-8 cm long; winterblooming; the fruit a long pod. *Tropical.* *p. 497*

palmeri (Mexico, Guatemala); large deciduous tree to 8 m high; the wide-spread branches with palmately compound leaves of usually 5 elliptic scaly leaflets 5 to 12 cm long; when the foliage falls, the bare limbs cover themselves with masses of bright pink tubular flowers, 7 cm long, and marked white and yellow, the spreading petals prettily ruffled. *p. 501*

pentaphylla (Puerto Rico), "Salvador pink trumpet", or "Pink tecoma"; with deciduous foliage, to 6 m high, the trunk with furrowed bark; blooming while the tree is bare, with masses of rosy trumpet-flowers 8 cm long, once a year; the foliage appears in spring; leaves palmately divided into 3, 5 or 7 elliptic leaflets glossy green; not as leathery as the "Cuban pink trumpet" (Tabebuia pallida), which is mostly evergreen and with shell-pink or whitish flowers. *p. 499*

rosea (Mexico, C. America, Colombia), the "Rosy trumpet-tree"; small to medium winter-flowering tree, partially deciduous, with digitately compound leaves of 3-5 leathery leaflets, simple in young plants; large clusters of showy flaring tubular flowers a pretty lilac-rose. *Tropical.* *p. 504*

serratifolia (Puerto Rico, Trinidad), "Yellow pui"; spectacularly showy flowering trumpet-tree about 6-9 m high, of densely branched habit, with papery leaves of 4-5 ovate leaflets to 12 cm long; the narrowly funnel-shaped 6 cm flowers in brilliant yellow, an unforgettable sight for the visitor to Puerto Rico, blooming on bare branches before the new foliage. *p. 497*

TABERNAEMONTANA *Apocynaceae* **S2LBM**
coronaria (Ervatamia) (India), the "Crape jasmine", "Clavel de la India" or "East Indian rose-bay"; a handsome shrub 2 to 3 m high with glossy green, elliptic, thinnish leaves 8-15 cm long; the waxy white, undulate flowers 4 to 5 cm wide, with lobes prettily crisped, very fragrant at night; blooming in summer; widely cultivated in tropical gardens. *p. 139*
coronaria plena (Ervatamia), "Fleur d'amour" or "Butterfly gardenia" with waxy, lanceolate leaves and pure white, crisped, double flowers, 4 cm across and intensely fragrant. *Tropical.* *p. 139*
divaricata (Ervatamia coronaria), (No. India), the "Paper gardenia"; dense evergreen, smooth, gardenia-like bush to 2 m or more high; shiny green, thin-leathery paired leaves 8-16 cm long; waxy-white, nearly scentless tubular flowers with 5 or 6 crinkled lobes spreading to 3-5 cm across. *Tropical.* *p. 136*

TACCA *Taccaceae* **S3LFM**
artocarpifolia (Madagascar); interesting herbaceous plant with tuberous rhizome; trisected basal leaves 60 cm or more across, long-stalked inflorescence 1 m or more high, with green flowers brown at base, the sterile flowers filiform thread-like. *p. 2094*
aspera (N. E. India, Burma, Malaya); curious tropical plant with fleshy rhizome; to 60 cm high; lanceolate oblong 20-50 cm leaves on erect channeled brown petiole; the weird inflorescence with nodding purplish-brown flowers in clusters and with long tail-like bracts. *p. 2094*
chantrieri (Malaya), "Bat-flower"; curious, bat-like inflorescence both in shape and color, with wide-spreading, wing-like bracts of rich maroon-black, accompanied by long trailing filaments or "whiskers"; the small black flowers are succeeded by heavy berries; corrugated olive-green leaves with oblique base. *Tropical.* *2091, 2112A*
chantrieri macrantha (Burma, Thailand), "Devil flower"; odd tropical plant with creeping rhizome bearing large oblong-pointed, fleshy, shining leaves to 45 cm long, on green stalks; the forbidding somber inflorescence sometimes prostrate; with dark brown-purple pendant flowers in clusters, subtended by broad metallic-blackish bracts, and long pendulous threads to 35 cm long. *p. 2094*
cristata (Malaya), a "Bat-flower"; interesting tropical rhizomatous plant with large purplish basal leaves to 60 cm long; flowers brownish, subtended by bat-like purple bracts bearing long thread-like filaments; grown as a curiosity. *p. 2094*
leontopetaloides (pinnatifida) (Africa, S. E. Asia to Hawaii), "Polynesian arrow root"; tropical perennial with tuberous rhizome; basal leaves tri-parted, the forked segments pinnatifid and cut into ovate lobes; funnel-shaped flowers purplish in a dense cluster with numerous thread-like bractlets 20 cm long, carried on 1 m erect stalk. The tubers are good food when baked or boiled, rich in starch. *p. 2094*
plantaginea (Schizocapsa) (South China), "Cat's whiskers"; perennial herb with large lanceolate leaves 30 cm long; the stalked inflorescence a cluster of whitish green flowers, with green bracts, subtended by long thread-like filaments; fruit not berry-like, but a dry-skinned capsule. *p. 2094*

TACCARUM *Araceae* **S3LFM**
weddellianum (Brazil, Paraguay, Bolivia); tropical tuberous plant with finely dissected leaf 40 cm diameter, triangular in outline, on the stout petiole 40-80 cm long; short stalked, very curious inflorescence with ovate spathe yellowish-green, cupped at base of raceme-like cylindric spadix 20 cm high when fully grown, the upper part containing the male flowers. *p. 207*

TAENIOPHYLLUM *Orchidaceae* **S3O(slab)FM**
fasciola (syn. Epidendrum, Limodorum, Vanilla); one of the tiniest of orchids, a leafless epiphyte which I found on the trunk of a large tree in the rain forest of Naduruloulou, in Fiji; the highly developed, brittle strands of roots only 2 mm wide but 8-15 cm long, containing chlorophyll and delegated to carry out the function of the absent leaves; these roots are flattened against the bark, and radiate from a common center from which rise stems reduced to a minimum, bearing little pale cream flowers under 4 mm long; capsule bright yellow. *Tropical.* *p. 1826*

TAGETES *Compositae* **C2LBM**
patula 'Naughty Marietta', "Single French marigold", very pretty single marigold of semi-dwarf habit, to 40 cm high, bushy, with finely netted leaves; 5 cm flowers golden-yellow, painted in the center with a deep red, velvety eye. Tagetes patula are at home in Mexico and Guatemala, strongly scented, and have become very popular as summer garden annuals. *Tropical.* *p. 803*
patula 'Rusty Red'; strong scented perennial originally from Mexico, now highly developed and grown as an annual "French marigold"; with finely dissected leaves and solitary heads of 5 cm double flowers, in this medium dwarf cultivar a velvety brown. *p. 803*
patula 'Spry'; popular free-blooming, dwarf "Bedding marigold" to 25 cm high, the double flowers with a brightly contrasting golden yellow anemone crest over deep rich mahogany guard petals. *p. 803*
patula 'Yellow Pigmy'; a favorite dwarf cultivar 15-22 cm high, very compact and bushy, with lacy foliage; and floriferous with medium-small, full-double, round lemon-yellow flowers, 2½-3 cm across. *p. 803*

TAINIA *Orchidaceae* **S3HFM**
cordifolia (Taiwan); showy terrestrial orchid with pseudobulbs; petioled fleshy, plaited grayish green leaves 8-12 cm long and tall; erect inflorescence to 60 cm of handsome flowers greenish, flushed and striped with red. *p. 1831*

TALINUM *Portulacaceae* **I2LBD**
guadalupense (Guadalupe Island, Mexico), "Fame flower"; succulent rosette with elongate, fleshy stem, and obovate, spoon-shaped leaves 5 cm long, blue-glaucous, edged with red; pink flowers. *p. 1962*
patens variegata (paniculatum var. in Hortus 3) (W. Indies to E. Coast of So. America to Buenos Aires), "Fame flower" or "Jewels of Opar"; small, fleshy herb, with erect stem, woody at base, and large, watery, obovate, concave leaves grayish green with white margin; small carmine flowers in flat clusters. *p. 1961*

TAMARINDUS *Leguminosae* **S2LBM**
indica (Trop. Africa), the "Tamarind tree"; immense, picturesque evergreen tree to 25 m high, important both as an ornamental shade tree and economically for its brown 20 cm pods containing edible, fleshy pulp of pleasing acid flavor; feathery pinnate, pendant leaves with leathery leaflets 2 cm long; the pale yellow 2 cm flowers, striped red. Bark, wood, leaves, flowers and seeds are also useful. *Tropical.* *p. 1390, 1391*

TAMARIX *Tamaricaceae* **C2LBD**
gallica (W. Europe to Himalayas), "French tamarisk"; charming shrub or small tree 5 to 8 m tall, the graceful slender branches bearing small heath-like bluish leaves, deciduous in winter; white or pinkish flowers in cylindrical racemes 3-5 cm long, in early summer; at home along the coasts of France and W. Europe. *p. 2099*
parviflora (S. E. Europe), "Tamarisk"; spreading shrub 2 to 5 m high, with graceful airy, arching branches and reddish bark; scale-like leaves, and small pink flowers in lateral sprays in spring, on last year's twigs; hardy in So. New England; twigs and leaves are shed in autumn. *p. 2098*
pentandra (S. E. Europe to C. Asia), the "Salt-cedar"; beautiful feathery shrub to 4 m or more high, the spreading branches with tiny, heath-like scale leaves pale blue-green, and tiny pale pink flowers in dense plumes, borne on wood of the current season (summer blooming). *p. 2098*

TANACETUM *Compositae* **C2LBM**
vulgare (Europe), "Common tansy"; a strong-scented perennial herb with alternate pinnate leaves nearly glabrous; yellow flower heads. Dried leaves are used medicinally. *p. 815, 821*

TAPEINOCHILUS *Zingiberaceae* **S3LFM**
ananassae (Malaysia, to Ceram and Queensland), "Giant spiral ginger"; perennial herb related to Costus, to 2½ m high, with bamboo-like canes, bearing leathery 15 cm green leaves arranged spirally; terminal inflorescence of cone-like, hard, recurved crimson bracts 10 cm across, nesting the yellow flowers; an ovoid cone resembling a pineapple, covered with brown bracts on leafless stalk rises directly from the rootstock. *p. 2130, 2140, 2143*

TARCHONANTHUS *Compositae* **I2LBD**
galpinii (Transvaal); handsome flowering shrub or small tree with woody branches, and rugose oval leaves white-woolly beneath; the inflorescence very showy with clustered heads of near-white flowers. *p. 827*

TAVARESIA *Asclepiadaceae* **S2LBD**
barkleyii (Cape Prov., Orange Free State, Namibia); clustering succulent with cactus-like stems 10-12-angled, 7-12 cm high, the sharp angles densely armed with bristle-like spines; flowers from base of stems 5-7 cm long, bell-shaped, outside pale greenish spotted with red, inside yellowish with red spots; base purple. *p. 384*
grandiflora (Decabelone) (Namibia), "Thimble flower"; leafless succulent with thick, angled, green stems having bristly warts; large yellow, funnel shaped flowers spotted red. Valid prior name Decabelone grandiflora. *p. 356, 376, 380*

TAXODIUM *Taxodiaceae (Coniferae)* **I2LBM**
distichum (Pennsylvania, Delaware to Florida, west to Texas), the "Bald cypress" or "Swamp cypress", also known as the "Tidewater red cypress"; tall deciduous coniferous tree, becoming 50 m high, with buttressed trunk usually 1-1½ m but sometimes 4 m or more in diameter, usually hollow in old age; the spreading branches with delicate and feather-like light yellow-green 1 cm needles in graceful sprays. At home in cypress swamps and tidewater bayous along the Gulf of Mexico and the Florida Everglades; this is not only a very decorative tree but valuable as the "Red" or "Yellow cypress" for its durable red or yellow lumber used in greenhouse construction and benches, for boats, piling, shingles, and wherever wood must withstand warm and wet conditions. The base of the tree is flared to help absorb oxygen from the water; it is also known for its curious "Cypress knees", which are modified roots of a very light, soft spongy wood showing above water. *p. 850*

TAXUS *Taxaceae (Coniferae)* **C2LBDh**
baccata 'Fastigiata' (stricta) (Ireland), the "Irish yew"; a columnar form of the English yew, found in Ireland in 1780; evergreen tree to 18 m high of

very dense pyramidal habit, with blackish green needles to 3 cm long; female trees with fleshy scarlet, cup-shaped berries (not cones), containing a single seed. Very popular in Europe, but T. cuspidata seems to be superior in colder American regions. *p. 850*

cuspidata (Japan, Korea, Manchuria), "Japanese yew"; somber evergreen tree to 15 m high, cultivated in a number of horticultural forms; T. cuspidata is the most important of ornamental yews in North America; best for dense bush or formal hedges, as it lends itself to shearing; far hardier than the English yew (T. baccata) and faster-growing; needle-like flat leaves about 2 cm long, suddenly tapering to a sharp point, leathery in texture, blackish-green, 2 yellowish bands below, and with prominent midrib, arranged on one plane along either side of the flexuous branchlets; berry-like scarlet fruit. *Temperate.* *p. 838*

cuspidata 'Capitata' hort., "Upright Japanese yew"; botanically synonymous with T. cuspidata, but because of its pyramidal habit, American nurserymen have attached the term "Capitata" to the species name in order to distinguish it from the spreading type. There is no mystery about the background of "Capitata" however: all true seed collected in its Japan habitat and imported since about 1910 has produced seedlings of typical pyramidal tree shape, and this character can also be perpetuated if using cuttings from only leader tips of older plants. *Temperate.* *p. 841*

cuspidata 'Green Mountain'; vigorous spreading yew with dense foliage faster-growing than the species, into a shapely rounded form; from a cutting taken in 1957 originated a clone of pyramidal shape, requiring little trimming. Photo on p. 850 taken in 1972 with F. Henderickx of Bobbink Nurseries, E. Rutherford, N.J. of tree 15 years old. *p. 850*

x media 'Brownii' (cuspidata x baccata); leaves very like those of cuspidata but 2-ranked as in baccata; the cultivar 'Brownii' is of conical habit with dense short needles. *p. 840*

TECOMA *Bignoniaceae* **I2-3LBD**

argentea: see Tabebuia argentea

cherere: see Distictis buccinatoria

garrocha (Stenolobium) (Argentina); shrub with willowy branches to 2 m, pinnate leaves of 7-11 ovate, smooth leaflets 5 cm long and sharply serrate at margins; trumpet-shaped flowers yellow or salmon with scarlet lines on tube, and yellow throat 5 cm long and 3 cm across, in showy terminal clusters. *p. 503*

stans (Stenolobium) (West Indies, Mexico to Perú), "Yellow-bells", or "Yellow elder"; ornamental shrub or tree-like to 6 m high; unequally pinnate leaves with serrate oval leaflets to 10 cm long; a profusion of showy 5 cm flowers bright yellow, in pendulous clusters, with funnel-shaped corolla hairy inside, the stamens curved in two pairs; long narrow pod-like fruits. *Tropical.* *p. 500, 503*

TECOMA: see also Bignonia, Distictis, Tabebuia

TECOMANTHE *Bignoniaceae* **I2-3LFD**

dendrophylla (New Guinea); large woody vine, with dark green leaves 16 cm long, pinnately compound, with 4 paired oblong leaflets and one at apex; attractive flowers with inflated bell-shaped corolla 10 cm long, deep rose to maroon outside and tipped with 5 short lobes, lighter inside, the lobed calyx purple. *Tropical.* *p. 503*

speciosa (Three Kings Isl. off N.W. New Zealand); curious woody twiner, discovered 1945, capable of ascending to 10 m, and in habitat growing over tall specimen of Leptospermum trees. Having seen this novel plant in N.Z., I feel it may become a desirable windbreak over fences, and ornamental even without support. The glossy leathery compound leaves are 15-30 cm long, of obovate leaflets; 6 cm trumpet flowers creamy tinged green. *Tropical.* *p. 498*

venusta (New Guinea); beautiful, rare tropical woody climber to 3 m, with compound leaves, the ovate leaflets light green and lightly quilted; the striking tubular, waxy flowers burnt-red or crimson outside and cream inside, in clusters from the woody stems, in early spring. *Tropical.* *p. 503*

TECOMARIA *Bignoniaceae* **I2-3LBD**

capensis (So. Africa to Transvaal and north), "Cape honeysuckle"; rambling, evergreen shrub 2-3 m high, with leaves of 7-9 ovate, shining green, toothed leaflets to 5 cm long, and bearing bunched masses of curved funnel-form flowers fiery orange-scarlet, 5 cm long, and with protruding stamens. *Subtropic.* *p. 500, 503*

capensis 'Aurea' (So. Africa); yellow-flowered form of the "Cape honeysuckle", a rambling evergreen shrub, sending out runners over the ground and up supports; dark glossy green leaves 10-15 cm long divided feather-fashion into 7 to 9 toothed leaflets; the showy slender funnel-shaped curved flowers 5 cm long, with 4 stamens protruding in close clusters. *Subtropic.* *p. 503*

TECOPHILAEA *Amaryllidaceae* **I2LFMd**

cyanocrocus (Andes of Chile), "Chilean crocus"; small plant with fibrous-coated cormous rootstock, 2-3 linear bright green basal leaves 8-12 cm long; short-stalked flowers with short tube and long lobes, deep blue veined or suffused with white in throat, the segments 4 cm long; in early spring. *p. 129, 130*

TECTARIA *Polypodiaceae (Filices)* **I-S3HFM**

cicutaria (West Indies), the "Button fern"; rhizomatous fern, with brown, scaly stalks 38 cm long, bearing tripinnate fresh-green herbaceous fronds triangular in outline, to 75 cm long; toward the apex simply lobed, softly downy in the fertile, spore-bearing leaflets, conspicuous by their circular elevations on the upper surface; in addition, the fronds bear occasional bulbils on their surface, looking like tiny buttons. *p. 1164, 1166*

fuscipes (So. Asia); tufted fern with thin, deltoid, dark green fronds about 30 cm long, pinnately compound, the pinnae shallow to deeply lobed, the basal pinnules with a long basal segment; stalks with persistent scales. *p. 1166*

incisa (West Indies, Brazil); handsome tropical terrestrial fern with stout rhizome, giving rise to broad, thin-leathery fronds 50 cm or more long, rich green but covered with reddish pubescence; palmately lobed at base, the upper terminal lobe pinnately cut into wide segments tapering to a point or merely with rounded lobes, the surface puckered and the margins wavy. *Subtropic.* *p. 1166*

macrodonta (Polypodium macrodon) (Philippines, Malaysia, Solomon Isl., Fiji); rhizome reclining, bearing scaly stalks 30 cm long, with fronds 60-90 cm long; their upper portion deeply pinnatifid, lower down with numerous spear-shaped leaflets of thin texture. *p. 1166*

subtriphylla (India, Taiwan); creeping rhizome bearing tufts of gracefully recurving simple-pinnate fronds 30-45 cm long, consisting of a large terminal leaflet, and lanceolate lateral ones, finely toothed and undulate. *p. 1166*

trifoliata heracleifolia (Aspidium) (W. Indies, C. America to Perú); magnificent species with bold-looking fronds, bright green, the terminal leaflet large, and lateral leaflets toothed and forked; basal segments pinnate; the sori conspicuous. *p. 1167*

TECTONA *Verbenaceae* **S2LBD**

grandis (India to Malaysia and Java); the "Teakwood"; a great tree of Monsoon Asia, to 50 m tall, with quadrangular shoots more or less woolly; leaves arranged in two's or three's, ovate, of leathery texture, 30 to 80 cm long, rough above, gray or brownish woolly beneath; small white flowers in terminal clusters, the calyx longer than the petals; dry, 3 cm, somewhat globular fruit pale green to brown. The strong, durable wood is valued as highly as mahogany, and used in furniture. *Tropical.* *p. 2105*

TELANTHERA: see Alternanthera

TELFAIRIA *Cucurbitaceae* **S3LBM**

pedata (Tanzania: Zanzibar Is.); climbing shrub with palmately compound leaves, the leaflets 8-12 cm long, with unpleasant scent when bruised; flowers purplish, the males 5 cm across in racemes, the female blooms solitary and 10 cm wide; fleshy green fruit, 45 to 90 cm long and to 20 cm thick, with 10-12 deep furrows. *p. 932*

TELOPEA *Proteaceae* **I2LBD**

speciosissima (New South Wales, Queensland), "Waratah"; striking flowering shrub related to Protea, of erect habit, 3-4 m high, with narrow obovate, leathery leaves toothed in upper part; magnificent terminal inflorescence of coral-red tubular flowers with protruding styles, packed in a dense globose head 8-10 cm across, and subtended by numerous narrow bracts of brilliant crimson. *Subtropic.* *p. 1973, 1981*

TEPHROCACTUS *Cactaceae* **I-S2LBD**

rauhii (Opuntia) (So. Perú); clustering, knobby columns to 25 cm high with dense white hair, and hidden yellow spines. *p. 634*

TERMINALIA *Combretaceae* **I-S2LBD**

catappa, (East Indies), "Tropical almond" or "Olive-bark tree"; small or large tree to 25 m high, much planted in tropical countries near sea-shores for ornament and shade; wide-spreading branches arranged in tiers with large obovate, leathery leaves to 30 cm long, becoming red before they fall twice a year; flowers greenish-white in spikes, followed on female flowers by greenish or reddish 2-angled fruit 3-5 cm long, with oil-bearing seed, which can be eaten raw or roasted. *Tropical.* *p. 761*

phanerophlebia (Transvaal); small tree with spreading branches; clustered at branch tips the obovate, rugose leaves, downy underneath; small greenish flowers in axillary spikes, followed on female trees by clusters of flat, bladder-like reddish seed pods; very ornamental. *p. 778*

sericea (So. Africa), "Transvaal silver tree"; dainty tree 10-15 m high with slender branches, tufts of foliage clustered toward tips, the leaves covered with fine, silvery down; insignificant small whitish-yellow flowers in cylindric clusters succeeded on older female trees by the characteristic leathery red-brown seed pods which are oval and flat with one seed in the center. *p. 778*

TERNSTROEMIA *Theaceae* **•I1LF-BD**

japonica (Cleyera) (Japan to India); attractive spreading ever-green bush growing into a tree to 6 m high, the flexible brown branches with soft-leathery, lustrous deep green obovate leaves to 8 cm long, light green beneath, the cuneate base and short petioles red; creamy flowers small but very fragrant in July and August. *p. 2101*

TESTUDINARIA: see Dioscorea

TETRAGONIA *Aizoaceae* **I2LBD**
expansa (Japan, Australia, New Zealand, So. America, California), "New Zealand spinach"; prostrate somewhat succulent annual with round fleshy stem covered with crystalline pebbles; leaves spatulate triangular, limp-fleshy, dark grayish green with depressed veins, to 12 cm long; axillary flowers yellowish green. The end 8-10 cm of branches are cut off and cooked like the true spinach. Naturalized on beaches along Santa Monica Bay, Southern California. *p. 65*

TETRAMICRA *Orchidaceae* **S3OFM**
bulbosa (West Indies); rock-dwelling or terrestrial orchid with elongated, branched rhizomes, bearing fleshy leaves at intervals, inflorescence on tall, wiry stalk with waxy flowers, sepals brown-red, broader petals deep orchid-purple, the wide lip with purple lines. *p. 1828*

TETRAPANAX *Araliaceae* **I2LBM**
papyriferus (Aralia) (China, Taiwan), "Rice paper plant"; a small tree with large, ornamental foliage; the woody trunk and branches filled with white pith used to make paper; the lobed leaves are 25 to 40 cm across, and covered with white felt while young. *Subtropic.* *p. 316, 321*
papyriferus 'Variegatus' (N. South Wales); form with the large, palmately lobed and toothed leaves recurved umbrella-like and beautifully variegated bright green to dark, emerald-green with ivory to clear white. *p. 321*

TETRAPLASANDRA *Araliaceae* ***I-S1LFD**
meiandra (Hawaii), "Hawaiian Ohe tree"; evergreen tree with stout willowy branches and thick, soft-leathery glossy green leaves having pale veining, pinnately divided into 7 oblique ovate leaflets, pale beneath, on coppery petioles. On Hilo, trees grow to 24 m tall. *Tropical.* *p. 307, 317*

TETRASTIGMA *Vitaceae* **I2LFM**
harmandii (Philippines); high climbing by tendrils; glossy green leaves palmate with 3-5-7 toothed segments to 8 cm long; edible fruit. *p. 2124*
obovatum (So. China); tendril-climbing herbaceous shrub with large palmately divided, corrugated leaves of obovate leaflets, and covered with light brown felt. *Subtropic.* *p. 2125*
voinierianum (Vitis) (Vietnam), "Chestnut vine"; robust climber with woody stems and clambering, fleshy, brown-hairy branches having coiled wiry tendrils and gigantic, digitate, thick-fleshy leaves with 3-5 shining green, stalked, broad-obovate or oblique leaflets to 25 cm long, wavy toothed at margins and pale green, pubescent underneath. *Tropical.* *p. 2121, 2124, 2128*

TEUCRIUM *Labiatae* **I2LBD**
flavum (Mediterranean reg.: Syria), "Yellow germander"; much branched, shrubby perennial 30-60 cm high, woody at base, with thick ovate, crisply gray-hairy leaves, crenate above middle; axillary yellow flowers somewhat two-lipped, along leafy stalk. *p. 1357*
fruticans (So. Europe), "Tree germander"; shrubby plant with small boxwood-like revolute leaves, white or reddish-brown hairy beneath; bluish 2-lipped flowers. Use: medicinal for fevers. *p. 1349, 1357*

TEUSCHERIA *Orchidaceae* **I3OFM**
cornucopia (Ecuador); epiphyte with small conical, one-leaved pseudobulbs which are encased in a tight-fitting tubular, brown marbled sheath which does not split; leaves narrow and pleated; solitary flowers produced from the base of 2-3 year old pseudobulbs, trumpet-shaped about 2½ cm wide, colored soft mauve, on erect wiry stalks; July-Sept. *p. 1826*

THALIA *Marantaceae* **I2-3LBW**
dealbata (So. Carolina to Florida and Texas); perennial aquatic or marsh herb, covered with white powder; basal, leathery ovate oblong leaves to 50 cm long and 25 cm wide, on long petioles; inflorescence on leafless stalk 3 m or more high, the small flowers dull violet, in a spreading panicle. *p. 1544, 1546*

THALICTRUM *Ranunculaceae* **C2LFM**
rochebrunianum (Japan), "Meadow-rue"; glaucous perennial 60-90 cm high, with smooth leaves, bipinnate or divided into segments, suggesting maiden hair; purple flowers without petals but showy stamens, in loose clusters above the foliage; fairly hardy. *p. 1992*

THAUMATOPHYLLUM spruceanum: see Philodendron goeldii

THEA: see Camellia

THECOPHYLLUM *Bromeliaceae* **I-S1HFD**
insigne in hort. (Guzmania 'Insignis'); showy rosette with soft, olive green leaves laxly pendant, carmine-rose toward base; beautiful inflorescence of ovate, rosy-red bracts, the flower-heads yellow. Photographed at Palmengarten Frankfurt, Germany. According to Victoria Padilla, a hybrid made by Dutrie of Guzmania lingulata splendens with G. zahnii, more beautiful and larger than the species Tillandsia (Guzmania) insignis. *p. 582*

THECOPHYLLUM of Puerto Rico: see Vriesea sintenisii

THELOCACTUS *Cactaceae* **I2LBD**
bicolor (So. Texas, Mexico), "Glory of Texas"; globular to cylindrical plant to 10 cm thick, bluish green, with 8 oblique notched ribs furnished with arched spines variously colored white, yellow and red; flowers purplish. *Arid-subtropic.* *p. 728*
leucacanthus (Mexico); short-cylindric plant to 15 cm high and clustering; 8-13 notched ribs in spirals bearing woolly areoles and pale yellow spreading radials with one long central spine; flowers yellow tinged rose. *p. 728*
nidulans (Mexico); depressed globe 10 cm high and 20 cm wide, bluish-gray, with about 20 ribs, cut into acute knobs, woolly at the top, furnished with strong horny-yellow spines, 4 cm long; flowers yellowish-white. *p. 728*
saussieri (bot. conothelos) (Mexico); globular-depressed cactus to 20 cm in dia.; spiral ribs, cut into light green conical knobs 4-sided at the base; silvery-white, spreading radial spines, and needle-like brown central spines; 4 cm flowers purple-red. *Arid-subtropic.* *p. 728*
valdezianus (Pelecyphora) (Mexico: Coahuila); tiny globe or cylinder to 2½ cm dia., dense glossy blue-green with white star-like bristly radials; the root turnip-like; flowers violet pink. *p. 728*

THELYMITRA *Orchidaceae* **I3HBMd**
antennifera (Victoria, Tasmania, W. Australia); a "Sun orchid"; a terrestrial orchid from subterranean ovoid tubers, stems with solitary linear leaf sheathing near the base of stem; flowers golden yellow with fiery reverse, opening only in bright sunshine. *p. 1828*
ixioides (Australia, New Zealand), "Women's cap orchid"; terrestrial with long-linear leaves, flat or channeled; inflorescence on 30 cm stalk, of masses of corn-flower-blue star-like flowers with light centers, 3-5 cm across. *Subtropic.* *p. 1828*

THELYPTERIS *Polypodiaceae (Filices)* **I2HFM**
extensa (Dryopteris) (Sri Lanka, South India, Philippines); massive-looking but graceful fern with creeping rhizome, slightly hairy stalks, and large pinnate fronds to 1 m or more long; the well-spaced narrow-linear leaflets arranged horizontally and deeply lobed, of soft, papery texture, pleasing bright green. *Tropical to Subtropic.* *p. 1110, 1156*
phegopteris (Dryopteris) (Northern hemisphere), the "Beech polypody"; having wide creeping slender rhizome, forming colonies, with bipinnate fronds 15-25 cm long, almost triangular in outline, fresh-green above and slightly hairy beneath; winter-hardy. *p. 1164*
uliginosa see under Dryopteris uliginosa

THEOBROMA *Sterculiaceae* **S2LFM**
cacao (C. America, Trinidad, Guyana), "Cacao-tree"; wide-branching evergreen tree to 8 m high, with attractive, satiny, hard-papery, pendant leaves to 30 cm long; the small, yellowish flowers in axillary clusters, or curiously even from the trunk, succeeded there by the large, ribbed fruit containing bean-like seed which is the source of chocolate. *Tropical.* *p. 2089, 2091*

THEOPHRASTA *Theophrastaceae* **S3LBM**
americana (fusca) (Santo Domingo); evergreen shrub to 1 m high; with stout, simple stem; glossy green, leathery, linear, oblanceolate leaves in whorls, to 45 cm long, the margins with spiny teeth; bell-shaped flowers white to rusty-brown in hairy raceme; fleshy fruit apple-shaped. *p. 1608*
jussieui (Santo Domingo and Haiti); evergreen small tree to 2 m, with spiny trunk; near apex of branches the clustered, spreading leathery leaves 45 cm long, linear oblong and spiny-toothed; bell-shaped, fleshy white blossoms with spreading lobes, in many-flowered racemes; the globular, fleshy fruit-apple-shaped and many-seeded. *p. 1603*

THERMOPSIS *Leguminosae* **C2LBD**
fabacea (Siberia); perennial herb to 1 m with leaves of 3 digitate leaflets, leaf-like stipules, and erect, spike-like racemes of pea-like yellow flowers, followed by 8 cm flat pods; hardy. *p. 1394*

THEROPOGON *Liliaceae* **C2LBM**
pallidus (Himalayas); herbaceous perennial of tufted habit with green grass-like leaves to 30 cm long, distinctly ribbed, glaucous beneath; small 1 cm bell flowers white, tinged red. *p. 1494*

THESPESIA *Malvaceae* **S2LBD**
populnea (Pantropic), "Portia tree" or "Milo"; tropical tree to 20 m high, with cordate-ovate unlobed leaves 15 cm long or more; solitary bell-shaped flowers 5-8 cm dia., yellow with purple center, fading to orange-yellow and withering into pink during the day. *Tropical.* *p. 1530*

THEVETIA *Apocynaceae* **S-I2LBM**
peruviana (W. Indies, Mexico), "Yellow oleander" or "Be-still tree"; tropical evergreen shrub 2-3 m high with linear, shining green, 10-15 cm leaves, their edges rolled under; large, funnel-shaped lemon-yellow flowers 5-8 cm long, shading to pinkish or orange-apricot, and sweetly fragrant like a tea-rose; blooming anytime, mostly June to November. Takes heat and sun with ample water; may be trained into small tree. Poisonous like their relatives, the oleanders. *Tropical.* *p. 140*

THIBAUDIA *Ericaceae* **I2LBM**
floribunda (Colombia); handsome evergreen Andean shrub with grayish branches; broad oval, leathery leaves; the inflated tubular flowers scarlet, 4-5 cm long, with overlapping bracts at base. *p. 1002*

THLADIANTHA *Cucurbitaceae* **I2LBM**
dubia (No. China); tuberous-rooted, tall, tendril-climbing, pubescent perennial with cordate leaves, and axillary, yellow bell-shaped flowers 3 cm across, male and female on separate plants; oblong fruit with 10 ribs, 2 cm long. *p. 932*

THOMASIA *Sterculiaceae* **I2LBD**
pauciflora (Australia); evergreen finely branched shrub, covered with reddish hairs; leaves ivy-like lobed or narrow, serrate at margins; star-shaped flowers drooping, 2 cm across, the enlarged corolla-like sepals lavender-rose with purple lines, and brown-hairy outside. *p. 2090*
solanacea (Western Australia); sparry shrub or small tree, covered when young with starry down, especially underneath the alternate, showy, lobed leaves, these 4-8 cm long, with kidney-shaped stipules; flowers without petals, the star-like calyx with reflexed pointed lobes and which have a rosy stripe down the middle; May-June. *p. 2088*

THOMSONIA *Araceae* **S3LFM**
sumawongii (Thailand); tropical aroid newly discovered in 1971 and named by J. Bogner of Munich Bot. Garden; irregular light brown tuber 6-14 cm long, 2-6 cm dia.; solitary leaf, appearing after inflorescence, petiole 20-35 cm long, greenish marbled with grayish red; leaf dark green to 35 cm dia., divided into 3 parts, these divided again, segments 7-12 cm long, 3½-5 cm wide; spathe on 27-60 cm stalk, 6-8½ cm long, yellowish to purple, the yellowish spadix with female section below and male flowers toward apex. The inflorescences are boiled and eaten like asparagus. *p.295*

THRINAX *Palmae* **I-S2-3LBM**
argentea (Hispaniola); handsome small fan palm sometimes growing to 12 m tall; the erect trunk mostly covered with a thin fibrous webbing; small tuft of graceful palmate leaves almost circular, 75 cm in length on long, slender petioles, deeply cut into long pendant segments, fresh green above, and silvery beneath. Photographed at the Botanic Garden in Leningrad, Russia, but referred in Hortus to Coccothrinax argentea, which see. *p. 1912*
ekmanii (morrisii) (West Indies: Navassa Is.); attractive fan palm with fresh green leaves almost a complete circle, cut into broad segments, but not quite to base. *Tropical.* *p. 1912*
microcarpa (So. Florida and nearby Keys, Greater Antilles, Yucatán, Honduras, Panama), "Key palm"; a thatch palm of robust habit, with trunk usually 3-4 m but reaching 10 m, and 20-30 cm dia.; the petiole with fibrous webbing, supporting palmate leaves about 1 m across, divided for about ½ their length, the straight segments forming a semi-circle, shiny grayish-green above, light gray beneath; small white sessile fruit. *Tropical.* *p. 1910, 1912*
parviflora (Florida Keys, Bahamas, Cuba, Haiti, Jamaica), "Florida thatch palm"; slender solitary fan-palm to about 8 m tall, 10-15 cm thick, enlarged at base by root-like growths; 2-edged petioles reddish at base and with hairy fiber; palmate leaves 1 m across, cut halfway to base into about 50 segments and forming almost a complete circle, green on both sides, joined by radiating prominent yellow ribs; small berry-like, white fruit in large clusters. *p. 1862, 1910, 1911*

THRIXSPERMUM *Orchidaceae* **S3OFM**
arachnites (Java); curious epiphyte with leafy stems clinging close to their support, and flowers in racemes usually one opening at a time, with linear slender pointed segments clear pale yellow, and white lip saccate at base, with small purplish-red spots, (spring). (S) *p. 1830*

THRYALLIS: see Galphimia

THUJA *Cupressaceae (Coniferae)* **C2LBMh**
occidentalis (E. No. America; Quebec to Hudson Bay, New Jersey to N. Carolina, west to Minnesota), "American arbor-vitae" or "White cedar"; ornamental evergreen tree of pyramidal habit, about 20 m high, with reddish-brown buttressed trunk divided near ground into several secondary stems, the branches densely arranged, flat fan-like, branchlets like fern fronds but with hard scale-like, shingled leaves, needle-shaped when young, dark green above, yellowish green beneath, with a strong resinous odor; oblong cones erect when young, brown and pendulous when mature, 2 cm long. *Temperate.* *p. 840*
occidentalis nigra; a horticultural form of more compact, bushy habit, and foliage of deeper, dark green; very favored for residential planting, and used in containers or roof-gardens. *p. 840*

THUNBERGIA *Acanthaceae* **I-S2-3LBM**
affinis (Trop. East Africa); clambering, hairy shrub to 5 m high, with 4-angled stems, stalked ovate leaves lightly undulate at margins; flowers with curved yellow tube, and lobed, violet limb, 5 cm across. *p. 54*
alata (So. E. Africa, but naturalized in Tropics), the "Black-eyed Susan"; twining perennial herb, with herbaceous, toothed, triangular ovate leaves to 8 cm long, on winged petioles; funnel-shaped showy flowers 4 cm long, creamy yellow or orange with or without black-purple throat, blooming late summer to autumn. Attractive vine for the cool, light window. Can be grown as an annual from seed. *Subtropic.* *p. 54*
chrysops (W. Africa : Sierra Leone); annual climber with slender, downy stems, to 1 m high; leaves ovate with cordate base, lightly bristly above; large purplish flowers with blue limb and yellow funnel-shaped tube. *p. 54*
erecta (Trop. West Africa), "King's mantle"; erect evergreen shrub to 2 m; thin branches with almost glossy ovate leaves 3-6 cm long; axillary trumpet-shaped flowers 6 cm in length, with large violet lobes, and yellow inside tube; July. *Tropical.* *p. 52*
grandiflora (India), "Clock vine"; woody twiner with rough, toothed, ovate leaves; bell-like flowers somewhat two-lipped about 6 cm long and across, lavender-blue; throat white, solitary in the leaf axils. *Tropical.* *p. 54*
gregori (gibsonii) (Trop. Africa), "Orange clock-vine"; perennial herbaceous twiner or creeper, with cordate leaves 6-8 cm long, fresh green and lightly hirsute, on winged petioles; showy flowers bright orange 4 cm across, blooming nearly all year. *Tropical.* *p. 54*
laurifolia (India); choice woody twiner with lanceolate leathery leaves to 12 cm long; funnel-form flowers, light blue with white throat, to 8 cm across, several to a raceme. *Tropical.* *p. 54*
lutea (Himalayas); floriferous climber with ovate leaves, and axillary trumpet-shaped yellow flowers with 2 large clasping bracts. *p. 54*
mysorensis (So. India); tall-climbing, vigorous tropical vine from the Nilghiri Mountains; lance-shaped 3-nerved leaves 10-15 cm long; the attractive funnel flowers golden yellow 5-6 cm across, with yellow and red-brown spreading limb, in long pendant racemes. *Tropical.* *p. 54*
natalensis (So. Africa); erect herbaceous subshrub 50 cm or more high, with ovate toothed leaves; flowers lavender with yellow throat inside tube, 5 cm long, curved upwards; summer-blooming. *p. 54*

THUNIA *Orchidaceae* **S3LOFM**
alba (India, Burma, China); robust epiphyte, occasionally becoming terrestrial, with tufted, tapering leafy stems 60 cm high, topped by a nodding raceme of large, pure white flowers to 8 cm across, with white lip inside yellow, striped with orange and shortly spurred and crested, (June-July). *Tropical.* *p. 1830*
pulchra (dodgsonii) (Burma); epiphyte, sometimes terrestrial, with tufting leafy stems 60-90 cm high, bearing a cluster of 4-8 flowers of medium size, the sepals and petals white, the lip without spur, white with brown and yellow crests, (summer). (S) *p. 1830*

THURNIA *Thurniaceae* **S3HFW**
sphaerocephala (Venezuela, Guayana); tropical bog plant 50-70 cm high, leaves long, narrow and leathery; inflorescence long stalked, flower head globular, on the base with a few long and narrow bracts. Growing in wet places. *p. 2093*

THYMUS *Labiatae* **I2LBD**
hirsutus (Balkans, Crimea), "Woolly thyme"; low shrubby cushion -forming plant, with ascending, gray-hairy branches and foliage, small 6 mm sharp-pointed, linear, sessile leaves and small rosy two-lipped 6 mm flowers with reddish calyx, in oblong clusters. *p. 1357*
serpyllum (Europe, Asia, No. Africa), "Mother-of-thyme" or "Creeping thyme"; prostrate flowering thyme, robust subshrub with rooting stems, bright green oval foliage less than 1 cm long, on reddish stringy branches, with strong aromatic scent; small purplish flowers 1 cm long, blooming summer into autumn. Forming dense mats to replace grass and can be walked over without harm, and are soft and fragrant underfoot. Leaves can be used in seasoning and in pot-pourri. *p. 1358*
serpyllum lanuginosus, "Woolly lemon thyme"; low creeper forming dense mats; thin reddish stem forming roots at nodes on ground; tiny gray green elliptic leaves 4 mm long densely covered with white bristly hair. *p. 1358*
serpyllum var. vulgaris argenteus, "Silver lemon-thyme"; aromatic creeper with scandent stringy stem then ascending to 15 cm high; smooth milky green, tiny oval leaves 6 mm long, variegated green and silver, the margins bordered white. *p. 1358*
vulgaris (serpyllum var. vulgaris) (Portugal to So. France, So. Italy, Greece), the "Common thyme"; aromatic subshrub 20-30 cm high, lemon-scented; white-pubescent stems with small oval, recurved leaves 1 cm long; tiny 6 mm rosy-lilac flowers in May-June. Used as seasoning for soups, chowders, sauces, vegetables. *p. 1357*
vulgaris aureus (So. Europe), "Golden thyme"; hardy perennial subshrub forming mounds of silvery-green fragrant foliage blotched with gold; purplish flowers. In addition to being ornamental, its aromatic branches find culinary use. *p. 1357*

TIBOUCHINA *Melastomataceae* **I2LFM**
bicolor (Bolivia); very fine flowering tree with stiffish, green, rough-hairy, lanceolate leaves on square, brown branches; large flowers in two shades, purple and white, 4 cm across. *p. 1559*

grandifolia (Brazil); tropical tree with large, parallel-veined velvety foliage; flowers purple with inside white, turning orange-red with age, 4 cm dia., and smaller than semidecandra. *Tropical.* *p. 1559*

granulosa (Brazil, Bolivia), "Purple glory-tree"; Andean tree 5 to 12 m tall, in cultivation as a smaller shrub; square, winged branches with long ovate, dark green pubescent leaves having 5 depressed veins, bristly on margins; large flowers purple or violet-blue, 5-7 cm across. *Subtropic.* *p. 1556, 1559*

granulosa var. rosea; beautiful flowering tree seen in Durban Botanic Gardens, with parallel-veined dark green leaves; the large flowers a pleasing carmine-rose. *p. 1559*

heteromalla (Brazil); small evergreen shrub to 1½ m high, with round stems, ovate leaves soft-hairy above; flowers purplish-violet 2½-4 cm across. *Tropical.* *p. 1559*

paratropica (So. America); shrubby tropical plant with pinkish stems, hairy green leaves, and white flowers of 5 petals. *p. 1559*

urvilleana (semidecandra hort.) (S. Brazil), "Glory bush"; free-branching, tree-like shrub growing to 8 m high, with 4-angled stems and fresh-green, 10 cm ovate leaves densely covered with soft white hairs; large violet-purple flowers blooming over a long period of time. *p. 1554*

TIGRIDIA *Iridaceae* **C2LBMd**

pavonia (Mexico, Guatemala), "Tiger flower"; gay summer-blooming bulbs; erect stems with leaflike spathes bearing large brilliantly colored cup-like flowers spotted with yellow and purple in the center, 8 to 15 cm across, the spreading segments red or yellow, lasting only a day but succeeded by others. *Tropical.* *p. 1336, 1337*

pavonia 'Canariensis' (Mexico), a "Mexican shell-flower"; or "One-day lily"; cormous plant with plaited, sword-shaped leaves, both at base of plant and along the forked floral stalks, 45-75 cm high, bearing attractive creamy-yellow flowers spotted with red in central cup, to 15 cm across, lasting only one day but are succeeded by a series of others along the stem. Tigridias are children of the sun, and bloom all summer in a warm and bright location; after flowering they will go dormant. *p. 1333*

TILLANDSIA *Bromeliaceae* **I-S2HBD**

aeranthos (syn. dianthoidea) (Uruguay, Argentina, Brazil); branching, caulescent plant to 22 cm with broad but quickly tapering narrow, concave leaves, grayish-green with purplish tinting and silvery scurf; inflorescence spike with 5-20 blue flowers and bracts purplish rose. *p. 584, 598*

albida (Mexico); caulescent epiphyte; the 30 cm curving stem with short tapering, clasping, hard leaves beautifully covered with rough silvery scurf, and quickly becoming smaller toward the red-flowered inflorescence. *p.584*

andicola (Argentina); small epiphyte forming cushions, with slender stems to 20 cm long, the awl-shaped, cylindric leaves arranged in ranks reddish brown or green, densely covered with gray scales, to 5 cm long; the slender floral stalk with single spike of reddish bracts and greenish-white flowers. *p. 597*

andreana (Colombia, Venezuela); small, stiff, clustering epiphytic rosette, stemless but eventually forming leaning branches; tapering linear leaves to 5 cm long, densely brown scurfy-scaly, keeled beneath, and recurving; compound, shingled inflorescence without stalk, with short membranous floral bracts, papery sepals and erect red petals 3 cm long. *Subtropic.* *p. 597*

andrieuxii (Mexico, Costa Rica); small epiphyte forming bulbous base, the spiralling, recurving leaves 10-12 cm long, densely silvery-scaly; pendant inflorescence with rosy-red bracts and violet petals; from the cloud forest to 3000 m. *p. 594*

araujei (Brazil: Rio, Sao Paulo); an exciting small air plant growing on rocks along the ocean, with scandent stems dense with spirals of short tapering leaves, concave, short and hard, light green with purplish base and silvery scurf; growing into crawling or pendant strands 1-1½ m long; flowers in short spikes, delicately colored pink and white. *p.584,590*

argentea (Mexico, Guatemala, Cuba, Jamaica); silvery, rigid, epiphytic rosette dense with narrow-channeled, gray-scurfy, spreading leaves 6-9 cm long; the inflorescence exceeding the foliage, flowering along the wiry stalk, the scurfy floral bracts red, the narrow petals bright red or purple. *p. 588, 594*

ariza-juliae (Dominican Republic: La Vega); stemless epiphyte 20 cm high, with about 12 leaves green tinged with purple and covered with grayish scales; the inflated, rounded basal sheaths forming an ovoid pseudobulb, running into the nearly straight, rolled leaf blades; lanceolate flower spike with papery floral bracts, the tubular petals purple. *p. 592*

balbisiana (So. Florida, Yucatan, Costa Rica); xerophytic ball-shaped rosette with bulbous base, densely furnished with numerous narrow linear, twisted or recurved succulent leaves about 15 cm long, and to 1 cm wide, grayish-powdery over gray-green; long-stalked, small inflorescence with waxy-powdery bracts green, rosy, and yellow; and purple flowers marked with white. *p. 590*

bergeri (Uruguay, Argentina); small succulent rosette of stiff, gray-green leaves to 10 cm long, spirally arranged and forming stems and densely matting with continuous growth, the foliage channeled and covered with silvery scales; pretty inflorescence having pink bracts, and spreading 3 cm purplish petals with white base. *Subtropic.* *p. 582*

brachycaulos (So. Mexico, Central America); xerophytic epiphytic rosette 15 cm high, with numerous stiff, channeled, recurving leaves 2 cm wide and to 25 cm long, red above at flowering time, grayish-green beneath, minutely scurfy, and exceeding the short inflorescence, a sessile head with leaf-like bracts, almost hiding the violet petals. *p. 593*

bulbosa (West Indies, So. Mexico, to Colombia, Brazil), "Dancing bulb"; bulbous type of epiphyte, with onion-like swollen base, leaves rolled up tight and turning away from silvery base and stem at sharp angles then twist, glossy olive green with coppery tinting; short inflorescence with violet flowers tipped white. *p. 587*

butzii (Mexico, C. America); bulbous plant 30 cm high with swollen base of clasping soft-leathery leaves, then spreading and rolled up tight and twisted, green marked with purplish brown, lightly scaly; inflorescence spikes with greenish bracts and lilac petals. *p. 584*

cacticola (No. Perú); succulent epiphytic rosette of recurved leaves 25 cm long, densely covered with silvery scales, channeled on surface, the pretty inflorescence with one or several flaring bracts shimmering lilac pink, and creamy-white flowers with recurved petal tips vivid violet and very fragrant. *p. 594*

capitata (Mexico); rosette with leathery, concave, tapering leaves recurving, light grayish-green covered with silvery coating, margins purplish-red; at blooming time foliage turns reddish, the inflorescence a green head the size of a fist, the flowers mostly covered by long tapering bracts. *p.587,590*

caput-medusae (Mexico and south); attractive small rosette with bulb-like base; thick channeled, tapering and twisting leaves glistening with silky-gray hairs; short panicles with pale blue flowers. *Tropical.* *p. 587*

cauligera (Perú); creeping or pendant from rocks in the high Andean valleys near Cuzco to 3000 m alt.; succulent rosettes forming stems to 1½ m long, the recurving leaves arranged spirally, to 15 cm long, and covered with gray scales; long-stalked inflorescence of 1 or 2 spikes with red bracts and tubular blue flowers. *p. 596*

circinnata (Florida, W. Indies, Mexico); small epiphytic rosette, the bulbous base with lanceolate, cupping, leathery leaves silvery gray and recurved; small lavender flowers on small flattened spike. (I2B) *p. 584*

compacta (Dominican Republic); tall, fluted epiphytic rosette with green concave leaves slightly recurving and nearly rounded at apex; the inflorescence with scarlet bracts and purple flowers. *p. 592*

compressa (Costa Rica, Jamaica, Trinidad, Guyana), "Dusty"; formal rosette of rigid, hard, arching narrow, concave, light gray-green leaves 30-45 cm long and to 4 cm wide, and similar to T. fasciculata when not in bloom; inflorescence a flattened spike with inflated, keeled rose-pink bracts, and white flower petals. *p. 586*

crispa (Panama, Colombia, Ecuador, Perú); miniature epiphyte 10-25 cm high, with ovoid bulbous base, bearing brown-scurfy narrow leaves, with undulate margins, green with maroon spots; slender stalk bearing spiked inflorescence with scurfy, red floral bracts and purplish flowers. *p. 592* **TROPICA— *p. 224, 226***

crocata (So. Brazil, Bolivia, Uruguay, Argentina); small xerophyte growing on rocks, forming stems 20 cm long, with gray-scaly 15 cm leaves in 2 ranks, semi-cylindric and channeled on top; the floral stalk with small green spike and 3-4 yellow flowers. *p. 594*

cyanea (morreniana) (Ecuador: Manabi to Loja Prov.), "Pink quill"; excellent, suckering rosette of linear, channeled leaves with red-brown lines; short spike with broad flattened, clear pink bracts and large violet-blue flowers. *Tropical.* *p. 512A, 585, 587*

decomposita (Brazil: Mato Grosso; Bolivia, Paraguay, Argentina); curious xerophytic epiphyte with elongate stem bearing narrow, rather rigid, silver-gray leaves curved in various directions and with tips spirally rolled; inflorescence to 60 cm long, with lavender, fragrant flowers. *p. 588, 597*

deppeana (Mexico, C. America, W. Indies to Ecuador); showy formal rosette of varying size, soft green leaves 60 to 100 cm long and 8 cm wide; the inflorescence on a branched stalk 1 m or more tall, the flattened spikes of shingled bracts bright rose and flower petals blue. *p. 595*

deppeana latifolia (West Indies, Mexico, C. America, Colombia, Venezuela, Bolivia); very showy, majestic, stemless rosette 1-2 m high, with many broad leaves finely brown-scurfy, 60-90 cm long and 8 cm wide; the spectacular erect inflorescence branched into flattened spikes 10-30 cm long, the leathery yellowish floral bracts shingled, and with blue petals. *p. 583*

didisticha (Brazil: Goias, Mato Grosso; Argentina, Bolivia); robust rosette 30 cm high, with thick, tapering, channeled gray leaves; the stalked inflorescence a series of flattened spikes covered with 2-ranked bracts; petals white. *p. 595, 596*

duratii (So. Brazil, Bolivia, Uruguay, Argentina); curious epiphyte or xerophytic rock-dweller, forming curved and twisted stems to 30 cm long; the white-scurfy, channeled leaves to 20 cm long, spreading or coiled downward or around its host; the stout floral stalk with very fragrant lilac flowers. *Subtropic.* *p. 597*

'Emilie', Barry hyb. of T. lindenii var. caeca (all-blue fl.) x cyanea; of compact habit as in cyanea but inflorescence more slender with bracts of iridescent watermelon pink; leaves yellow-green with basal section in contrasting red-brown. *p. 587*

espinosae (Vriesea) (Ecuador, Perú); small xerophytic rosette 15 cm across, forming clumps with spreading runners, the rigid, deeply channeled narrow leaves covered with gray scales; inflorescence to 15 cm high, with flattened spike of vivid red bracts and 3 cm blue flowers. Transferred by Dr. L. B. Smith to Vriesea. *p. 594*

fasciculata (Florida, W. Indies, C. America), "Wild pine"; epiphytic dense rosette with recurving, hard linear-lanceolate, concave leaves, gray and variably from 25 cm to 1 m long; branched inflorescence with greenish, creamy-yellow or brilliant red bracts, and violet-blue flowers. *Subtropic.* *p. 513, 588, 589, 591*

fasciculata clavispica (Cuba); variety with a long, leaning inflorescence of branching spikes slender club-shaped, the folded bracts reddish, petals white to purple; the large rosette with spreading grayish, rigid leaves 30-38 cm long, channeled on the surface. The var. clavispica is distinguished by the long tapering sterile bases of the spikes. *p. 585*

fasciculata convexispica (Mexico, Guatemala, Honduras, Panama, Jamaica); epiphytic in dry thickets; a variety with showy floral spikes only slightly flattened, the floral bracts to 5 cm long, shingled in several ranks. *p. 592*

fasciculata densispica (Florida); stiff rosette dense with conical, tapering leaves, in the center the closely bunched, branched inflorescence; with relatively small and numerous spikes in this variety. *p. 593*

fendleri (No. Perú); beautiful species growing on rocks of the precipitous mountains in the Western Cordilleras and found on the ruins of the ancient Inca fortress of Machu Picchu; showy inflorescence 1 to 2 m high; broad green leaves laxly pendant, forming rosette 60-100 cm in dia., the floral stalk branched with numerous flattened spikes of red to greenish bracts and blue petals. *Tropical.* *p. 589, 598*

festucoides (Greater Antilles, So. Mexico, Cent. America); stemless epiphyte to 60 cm high, the leaves linear, awl-shaped or reed-like, and finely scurfy; the branched inflorescence with linear spikes, the floral bracts keeled, 2½ cm petals purple. *p. 586*

filifolia (So. Mexico, Guatemala, Honduras, Costa Rica); small epiphyte to 20 cm high, with many grass-like, densely clustering leaves 8-30 cm long, and 4 mm wide, thread-like, stiff-leathery, concave and with broad sessile base, glossy green with a touch of silvery scales; inflorescence 15 cm long, panicle on lax, flexuous stalk, with pale lilac flowers. *p.586*

flabellata (Guatemala), "Red fan"; beautiful rosette of narrow, recurved leaves fresh green turning red in good light; giving rise to a 60 cm inflorescence branching into flattened spikes arranged fan-like, the bracts vivid red, flowers blue. *Tropical.* *p. 582*

flexuosa (aloifolia) (So. Florida to So. America), "Spiralled air plant"; hard rosette with leaves starting off at the base with a twist, broad but tapering, thick leathery, concave, silvery gray over green, with indistinct silver bands outside; 2-ranked inflorescence with rose bracts and white flowers. *Subtropic.* *p. 585, 587, 588*

foliosa (violacea) (Mexico: Veracruz); epiphytic rosette with bronzy green to nearly black-purple leaves, 10-12 cm long and with gray scales; leafy inflorescence arching, with spreading bracts green with red margins and violet flowers. *p. 596*

fragrans (Colombia, Ecuador); epiphytic stemless rosette with narrow leaves to 25 cm long, the margins rolled inward, and covered with grayish-brown scales; bipinnate inflorescence 8-10 cm long, with flattened spikes, the fragrant flowers with red sepals, and white or lavender petals. *p. 586*

gardneri (regnellii) (Venezuela, Colombia, Trinidad, Brazil); small attractive epiphytic rosette with narrow linear, recurved leaves to 25 cm long, and densely covered with silvery-white scurf; the arching inflorescence cone-like with rose-pink bracts arranged spirally and bright red flower petals. *p. 596*

geminiflora (So. Brazil, Paraguay, Argentina); small stiff rosette of purplish gray pointed leaves with a short pendant raceme with coppery-red bracts, yellow or lavender flowers. *Subtropic.* *p. 530, 586*

globosa var. globosa (S. E. Brazil, Venezuela); elongate rosette with bulbous base, and narrow, tapering, channeled leaves covered with gray scales; inflorescence erect, with cluster of long, tubular flowers white at base and with blue limb. *p. 598*

grandis (So. Mexico, Guatemala, Honduras); large rosette growing on rocks or epiphytic on trees, and holding a great deal of water; the leaves smooth and light green unlike most other Tillandsias, to 8 cm wide and 75 cm long, glaucous beneath and often purplish; the immense branched inflorescence, as shown by Mulford Foster on the first page of the initial number of the Bromeliad Society Bulletin in 1951, may reach a height of 4 m, the floral bracts enfold the calyx, the flower petals green or greenish-white; Mr. Foster's plant took 35 years before it was ready to bloom. *p. 590*

heterophylla (Mexico); small plant with bulbous base, narrow, spiny leaves, and long tubular pale lavender flowers. Photographed in the Wiley collection of Palos Verdes, California. This does not agree with the description in Dr. Rauh: Bromelien 2, for a rosette of broad leaves, and tall flat spike with white flowers. *p. 598*

hotteana (Hispaniola); rather formal, tubular epiphytic rosette with short but broad, leathery leaves of rather light color with dark markings, suddenly tapering to a slender point; the inflorescence with red bracts. *p. 592*

imperialis (Mexico: Oaxaca, Puebla, Veracruz), "Christmas candle"; showy epiphyte at home at 1,500-2,600 m altitude, and largely used by Mexicans at Christmas time to decorate for their "Natividad", because of the festive spirit radiated by the flaming red central inflorescence, looking like a candle or slender cone; remaining in brilliant color through summer into winter; flowers purple; the dense, formal rosette of broad, smooth leathery leaves a pleasing light green, about 45 cm long. *Tropical.* *p. 593, 595*

incurva (Florida, Greater Antilles, Costa Rica to Colombia, Venezuela, Bolivia); epiphytic rosette, with wide-spreading long-acuminate, leathery, tapering leaves 15-28 cm long, grayish-scaly; short slender stalk bears a pendulous inflorescence, simple or digitate with 2-5 spikes, the red floral bracts erect, the narrower flower petals yellow. *p. 592*

insignis: see Guzmania

ionantha (erubescens) (So. Mexico to Nicaragua), "Sky plant"; tufting, miniature rosette only 5-10 cm high with numerous closely overlapping leaves recurving, thick-fleshy, channeled, fresh green but covered on outside with silvery bristles; sessile inflorescence with violet flowers. *Subtropic.* *p. 587, 594*

ionantha vanhyningii (Mexico: Chiapas; C. America); epiphytic rock dweller, with a mass of tangled, criss-cross, branching, rooting stems, tipped by numerous tiny rosettes like little silver stars 2½ cm across, of short, stiff leaves 1-2 cm long, quickly tapering to a slender point and curving outward; sparse axillary tubular flowers deep violet blue. *p. 588*

juncea (Florida, W. Indies, Mexico, Brazil to Perú); erect rosette dense with numerous wiry, awl-shaped, concave leaves 30 cm long, olive green tinged with copper, reverse covered with short silvery hair clusters; erect spike, 2-ranked with scaly bracts, and bluish-purple petals. *p. 587*

karwinskyana (Mexico); xerophytic rosette dense with 20-30 leaves 30 cm long, narrowed from a broad base 2½ cm wide to a long-linear blade, light green and more smooth on the surface, scurfy on underside; the inflorescence a lax, wiry stalk bearing a simple, 2-ranked spike with glossy green sepals and lilac petals. *p. 590*

leiboldiana (So. Mexico, Guatemala, Costa Rica); epiphytic rosette of lightly arching, green, thin, straplike leaves 15-45 cm long, 2½ cm wide and tapering to a sudden point, lightly scurfy and soft-leathery; inflorescence loosely compound, with large red primary bracts, and narrow, sessile spikes with tubular violet flowers. *Tropical.* *p. 597*

lepidosepala (Mexico); xerophytic epiphyte with rigid, concave ashy-scaly leaves to 15 cm long, gradually tapering to a slender point, strongly curving more or less in one direction nearly forming a ball-shape, and densely covered with moisture-holding gray scales; the 2-ranked inflorescence with pinkish bracts, also heavily ashy-scurfy. *p. 588*

lescaillei (Hispaniola, Cuba); urn-shaped epiphytic rosette with broad, concave leaves with acute apex, glossy green and thin-leathery, 18 cm long; the green inflorescence a branched panicle with slender spikes, on lax, wiry stalk. *p. 592*

lindenii (N.W. Perú), "Blue-flowered torch"; attractive, formal rosette of recurved linear channeled leaves 30-40 cm long, green with red-brown pencil lines becoming more prominent toward base; inflorescence a long spike of flattened carmine-rose bracts 10-15 cm long, bearing large royal-blue flowers distinguished by white eye in center. *Tropical.* *p. 513, 585*

mallemontii (Brazil); small grass-like epiphyte forming cushions; slender stems with awl-shaped, thread-like leaves 10 to 12 cm long, covered by silvery scales; simple inflorescence with large 3-petaled dark blue flowers. *p. 597*

meridionalis (Brazil, Paraguay, Uruguay, Argentina); small epiphytic rosette with deeply channeled silvery-gray leaves 5-10 cm long; the inflorescence arching and having rosy or red bracts tipped with silvery scales, and small white flowers. *p. 597*

monadelpha (So. U.S., C. America, Colombia); graceful epiphytic rosette with delicate, recurving leaves to 20 cm long, green above and maroon beneath, turning red in center at blooming time; erect floral stalk with inflorescence carried like a feather, the flowers in two ranks with green to red bracts and yellow petals; very fragrant. *p. 598*

mooreana (Amazonian Perú); open olive-green rosette with giant branched inflorescence similar to T. wagneriana but larger, the inflated bracts a deeper shade of pink, and with large lavender-blue flowers. *p. 595*

moscosoi (Greater Antilles); dense rosette of narrow, channeled, rigid, gracefully recurving leaves almost reed-like in upper part; to 20 cm long, glossy green turning red in sun, leaf bases dark purple; club-shaped inflorescence shorter than foliage, with pink bracts and lilac petals. *p. 592*

multicaulis (Mexico, Costa Rica, Panama), the "Gold fish bromeliad"; beautiful small epiphyte from humid mountain forests to 2,500 m; resembling Vriesea with soft, shiny green leaves to 30 cm long forming a birdsnest-like rosette; from between the foliage rise several flattened spikes of gold and scarlet red looking like shimmering gold fish; the petals violet-blue. *Tropical.* *p. 591, 595*

nudicaulis (Aechmea) (Brazil); handsome urn-shaped rosette of broad, rigid, gray-green leaves with brown spines at margins; the showy inflorescence a cylindrical spike with flame-red bracts and lemon-yellow tubular flowers. This species was photographed in New York under this genus but should probably be referred to Aechmea. *p. 595*

oerstedii (Costa Rica); magnificent, large species; rosette of stiff-erect, grayish-green leaves, from the center a tall, stout stalk with multitudes of lateral, flattened spear-shaped spikes of shingled canary-yellow bracts and light purple flower petals. *Tropical.* *p. 591*

plumosa (Mexico, Guatemala); small epiphytic rosette 15 cm high, forming dense masses; thread-like, recurving, soft leaves to 18 cm long, silvery gray-green; inflorescence barely stalked, with scurfy, spreading floral bracts, and narrow violet petals. *Tropical.* *p. 590*

pohliana (Perú, Brazil, Paraguay, Argentina); small xerophytic rosette with deeply channeled, succulent recurving leaves 20-25 cm long, densely covered with silvery-white scales; the pendant inflorescence with boat-shaped rosy bracts nearly hiding the small white flowers. *p. 589*

polystachia (West Indies, Mexico, Brazil, C. America, Colombia); rosette of channeled, recurving leaves 30 cm long, broad and swollen at base and forming bulb-like base, narrowing to flat-linear, and awl-shaped toward apex, grayish green flushed with rose, and covered with fine pale scales; the inflorescence forming a continuation of the rosette into a leafy stalk, bearing small compound spikes with vivid scarlet, overlapping bracts and dark purple flowers. *p. 590*

prodigiosa (Mexico: Chiapas, etc.); striking bromeliad, in habitat epiphytic in pine and oak forests at 1,800-2,400 m; somewhat tubular, flaccid rosette of broad grayish-green thin-leathery leaves spotted purple; so spectacular because of the massive, pendant inflorescence 1-1½ m, and even 2 m long, composed of little vriesea-like flower heads, subtended by large elliptical floral bracts in brilliant red, corolla yellowish. *Tropical.* *p. 583*

pruinosa (Florida, W. Indies, Mexico, Ecuador to Brazil); cute bulbous epiphyte with irregularly swollen base and rolled up leaves turning away with twisting angles, green but becoming bronze and with silvery bristles; stubby inflorescence with rose bracts and violet petals. *p. 587*

punctulata (Mexico); birdsnest-like dense rosette 30 cm high; the leaves with broad ovate base, suddenly narrowing to concave, grass-like blades 15-25 cm long, fresh green and like flexible leather; dense spike with bright red bracts and lilac flowers tipped white. *Tropical.* *p. 584, 596*

rauhii (Northern Perú); probably the largest of all tillandsias, found growing on steep rock walls at 700 m elev.; formal rosette with leaves to 120 cm long and 15 cm wide, gray-green to wine-red and with waxy coating; inflorescence arching and branched to 1½ m long, the flat, shingled bracts light green to vivid scarlet, the 6 cm flowers blue, appearing on the lower side of spikes. *p. 595*

recurvata (Subtropical and Tropical America: So. U.S., Florida to Key Largo, to No. Argentina and Chile), the "Ball-moss"; epiphytic rosette forming dense masses, on occasion adapting itself to a strange life perched high on telephone wires, a familiar sight in Florida; thread-like, stiff-leathery, curving leaves 3-18 cm long, covered by silvery-gray or brownish scales, on short, tufting stems, with some roots present; few flowered inflorescence with scurfy bracts, and pale violet petals. *Subtropic.* *p. 586*

regnellii (gardneri) (Venezuela, Colombia, Brazil, Trinidad); xerophytic epiphyte with succulent, up-curving, satiny leaves to 25 cm long, densely covered with silvery-white scales, forming a one-sided rosette; the short floral stalk to 8 cm long bears a cluster of several spikes of rose-pink bracts and tubular rosy-red flowers. *p. 594*

schiedeana (Antilles, Mexico to Colombia); stiff gray, erect grass-like leaves; flowers on individual spikes, with snug red bracts and yellow flowers at tip. (I2) *p. 586*

seleriana (So. Mexico, Guatemala); bulbous epiphytic rosette 20-25 cm high, with thick, contorted, gray-scurfy leaves inflated at base and forming an ovoid pseudobulb; the short-stalked inflorescence of several flattened spikes with violet flowers. *p. 588*

seleriana major (El Salvador); curious xerophytic epiphyte with inflated bulb and twisted leaves, densely covered with glistening gray scales; hollowed spoon-like from the base and allowing ants to live within; the branched inflorescence with flattened spikes of green or rosy bracts and tubular reddish-blue flowers. *p. 594*

streptocarpa (Ecuador, Perú, Paraguay, Argentina); variable epiphyte with spirally arranged narrow channeled, curling leaves to 25 cm long, the underside heavily covered with silvery gray scurf; the inflorescence arching with fragrant lavender-blue flowers. *p. 598*

streptophylla (Jamaica), "Twist plant"; leaves in dense basal rosette with sharply recurved leathery leaves gradually tapering to a coiling tip; gray-green thickly covered with silvery scurf, turning red-purple in strong light; branched inflorescence with rosy bracts and lilac flowers. *Tropical.* *p. 513, 588, 593*

stricta (Brazil, Paraguay, Argentina, Guyana, Venezuela), "Hanging torch"; small rosette becoming caulescent, with narrow, thin-leathery, tapering leaves recurving, green with silvery scurf, and short-stalked inflorescence having red-tinged bracts; flowers violet turning red. *Tropical.* *p. 584, 588*

tricholepis (So. Brazil, Paraguay, Bolivia, Argentina); moss-like rosette elongate along flexuous, leafy stems, the stiff leaves awl-shaped, 1-2 cm or so long, densely scurfy; small inflorescence with 2-ranked spikes with greenish-yellow flowers. *p. 590*

tricolor (So. Mexico, Guatemala, Nicaragua, Costa Rica); grass-like densely tufting, epiphytic rosettes spreading by branching rhizomes, the stiff leaves dark glaucous green, purplish at base, and finely scaly, from a linear 2 cm width tapering into an awl-shaped point; inflorescence on slender stalks with single two-ranked flattened spike, boat-shaped green floral bracts, red toward base, and yellow apex; flowers violet tipped with white. *Tropical.* *p. 590*

tricolor melanocrater (Mexico); small formal rosette with stiff, tapering concave leaves pretty green and some silvery dotting beneath; inflorescence having short flattened spikes with green bracts, yellow and red at base, and purple flowers. *p. 584*

usneoides (S.E. United States to Argentina and Chile), "Spanish moss"; growing from trees as silvery-gray threadlike masses to 6 m long, densely covered by the gray scales which are a means of receiving and holding atmospheric moisture, and which helps to enable the plant to dispense with roots; small axillary flowers with petals 1 cm long, in changing colors yellowish-green to blue. *Subtropic.* *p. 234, 513, 583, 593, 598*

utriculata (Florida, W. Indies), "Big wild pine"; rosette of spreading linear leaves 60 cm long, gradually tapering from an ovate base, and recurved top; compound spike with two-ranked green bracts edged red, and erect flowers with greenish white petals; plant dies after flowering without off-setting. *Subtropic.* ***p. 583**, 589, 593*

valenzuelana (So. Florida, Greater Antilles, So. Mexico, C. America, Venezuela, Colombia, Bolivia); epiphytic rosette with recurving, rigid leaves to 35 cm long, narrowly triangular, tapering from 2½ cm wide to a slender point, and covered with gray scales; the leafy inflorescence bearing inflated, rosy, scurfy bracts with spreading spikes, their flowers having rosy sepals and lilac petals. *p. 590*

x 'Victoriae' (ionantha x brachycaulon); by Mulford Foster; miniature rosette 10 cm dia., recurving narrow leaves, reddish with gray scurf; blue flowers. *Subtropic.* *p. 586*

viridiflora (Mexico, Costa Rica, Colombia, Guyana); formal large epiphytic rosette with flaring leaves 30-60 cm long and 3 cm wide, glossy green above, faintly dotted beneath; the long-stalked pinnate inflorescence with floral bracts green, with brownish tips, and widely spreading white flowers. *p. 596*

wagneriana (Amazonian Perú), "Flying bird"; possibly the most outstanding and beautiful of all Tillandsias with its branched inflorescence of long-lasting flattened bracts in silver pink, and blue flowers, rising ½ m high from a rosette formed by the soft, thin-leathery, shining green leaves. *Tropical.* *p. 591, 595*

xiphioides (Argentina, Paraguay, Bolivia); small epiphytic rosette of rigid, channeled, silvery green leaves 10-15 cm long, and forming clusters; slender stalk with reddish bracts and several tubular white flowers 7-8 cm long and strongly fragrant of honeysuckle aroma. *p. 598*

TINOSPORA *Menispermaceae* **I2LBD**

fragosum (Transvaal), "Wonder plant"; also known as Desmomma fruticosum or Hyalosopalum; a woody liane of the veld, its inflorescence appearing from the wood at the base of branches, bearing little grape-like clusters of berries. Very curious for its habit of sending aerial roots down into the ground from broken stems to form a new plant. *p. 1549*

TIPUANA *Leguminosae* **I2LBD**

tipu (So. Brazil, Bolivia, Argentina), "Rosewood" or "Pride of Bolivia"; semi-deciduous, wide-crowned tree to 30 m high; the light green, odd-pinnate fern like leaves with 6-11 pairs of oval leaflets 3-4 cm long; profuse sprays of golden-yellow or apricot-colored peaflowers, in profusion during summer like tiny butterflies; winged pods 6 cm long. The wood is a source of rosewood timber. *Subtropical.* *p. 1391*

TITANOPSIS *Aizoaceae* **I-S2L(lime)BD**

calcarea (Cape Prov.), "Jewel plant"; cluster-forming succulent with fleshy roots; rosette of grayish spatulate leaves resembling stones, to 3 cm long, grayish-green and covered with gray-white warts; flowers yellow. *p. 78*

luckhoffii (Nananthus) (Cape Prov.); small rosette of succulent tricornered leaves bluish-green and covered with gray-green warts, the margins set with scattered larger, pink teeth; flowers pale yellow. *p. 78*

pilifera (or setifera) (So. Africa); mat-forming succulent with short club-shaped, keeled leaves and covered with minute gray warts and scattered pale teeth at the edges; flowers yellow. The plant known under this name in horticulture may be more properly Titanopsis (Aloinopsis) setifera. *p. 78*

schwantesii (Namibia); small succulent rosette to 3 cm across, with light-gray to bluish leaves becoming tricornered near apex and covered with light-brown warts; flowers light yellow. *p. 78*

TITANOTRICHUM *Gesneriaceae* **S3HFM**
oldhamii (Taiwan, So. China); erect perennial herb to 1 m high, with fleshy rhizome; rough green, white-hairy toothed, ovate leaves to 16 cm, decreasing in size up the elongate stem to the nodding, swollen tubular hairy golden flowers to 4 cm, bold brown-red inside on spreading lobes; scale-like reproductive bodies often replace flowers toward the apex of the inflorescence. *Humid-subtropic.* *p. 1300*

TITHONIA *Compositae* **I2LBD**
rotundifolia (speciosa) (Mexico, Cent. America), "Mexican sunflower"; shrubby annual forming bushes 1 to 3 m high, with ovate crenate leaves 15 cm long, sometimes 3-lobed; on hairy, stout blackish stalks, the inflorescence sunflower-like, 8 cm across, a disk ringed by oval florets vivid orange-scarlet, orange beneath; in autumn. *Tropical.* *p. 811*

TMESIPTERIS *Psilotaceae* **I3OFM**
tannensis (New Zealand); a primitive plant, in habitat common in forests from sea-level to 950 m usually epiphytic and pendulous on the trunk of tree ferns, occasionally on rocks; rhizomes deep in the mass of fibrous aerial rootlets along the trunks of tree fern, with some as dull-green aerial leafy shoots 15 cm or more long, producing sporophylls, or spore-bearing leaves. *p. 1982*

TOCOCA: see Sphaerogyne

TODEA: see Leptopteris

TOLMIEA *Saxifragaceae* ***I-C2LFM**
menziesii (Alaska to California Coast), "Piggy-back plant"; pubescent perennial herb with soft, fresh-green, lobed and toothed leaves to 10 cm across, covered by scattered white bristles, carried in a basal rosette; grown in pots as a curiosity, as it produces young plantlets out of the base of mature leaves, which can be cut off and rooted; small greenish nodding flowers, lined with maroon, in long erect, slender raceme. *Warm temperate.* *p. 2039*

TORENIA *Scrophulariaceae* **I2HFM**
baillonii (flava of hort.) (Vietnam, Sumatra), "Wish-bone flower"; bushy herbaceous hairy plant 15-30 cm high, densely branching, and rooting at nodes, with pairs of ovate 4-6 cm leaves toothed at margins; tubular flowers 2-4 cm long, the flaring segments deep yellow, brown-purple in throat and outside of tube; grown in gardens as an annual. The species T. flava is not of horticultural importance. *p. 2060*
concolor (So. China, Hongkong, Taiwan); trailing or scandent herbaceous plant with wire-thin stems and triangular-ovate, opposite 4 cm leaves coarsely serrate; tubular two-lipped flowers 3 cm long rich purple, solitary in one leaf axil. *p. 2060*
fournieri (Vietnam), "Wishbone plant" or "Bluewings"; delicate, small, herbaceous annual with ovate, fresh-green, serrate leaves and scattered, bilabiate, attractive, pale violet flowers with lower lip having 3 lobes of velvety deep violet and a yellow blotch in the middle of the lower lobe, blooming almost continuously. *Tropical.* *p. 2058, 2059*

TOUMEYA *Cactaceae* **I2LBD**
papyracantha (New Mexico), "Paper-spine pee-wee"; small ovoid or short cylindric cactus 5 cm high, occasionally clustering, with 8-13 spiralled ribs, cut into prominent knobs; spines thin, flat and papery, glossy white; spreading radials, and 3-4 curved central spines; flowers with silky-white petals. *p. 702*

TRACHELIUM *Campanulaceae* **C2LFM**
caeruleum (W. and C. Mediterranean, Europe), "Throatwort"; perennial herb ½-1 m high, with ovate double-toothed, thin leaves 8 cm long; flowers very numerous, in clustered panicles, with slender tubular corolla 2 cm long, violet-blue, the styles protruding. *p. 751*

TRACHELOSPERMUM *Apocynaceae* **I2LFD**
jasminoides (Rhynchospermum) (Himalayas), the "Star jasmine" or "Confederate jasmine" of the South; small woody evergreen with wiry stems and milky sap, slowly climbing and twining, with 5-8 cm leathery leaves; small white, star-like 2 cm flowers with wavy lobes. A pretty, free-blooming jasmine for pots and intensely fragrant; can be kept bushy by trimming. *p. 139*
jasminoides 'Variegatum'; an attractive sport of the "Confederate jasmine", with variegated leaves dark green, milky-green and white, and often tinted carmine red. *Subtropic.* *p. 139*

TRACHYCARPUS *Palmae* **I2LBM**
fortunei (Chamaerops excelsa hort.) (China, Japan), "Chusan palm" or "Windmill palm"; somewhat hardy, with solitary, shaggy trunk 3-12 m high, covered with a mat of long, dark brown fibers, topped by dense crown of tough fan-shaped dark green leaves 50 to 75 cm across, divided into stiffish, folded segments nearly to base, glaucous beneath, the petioles lightly toothed; fruit lustrous blue. *Subtropic.* *p. 1909, 1910, 1911, 1913*
fortunei 'Nana', "Dwarf windmill palm"; dwarf form cultivated in Hawaii and Japan, with stiff fronds 30 cm across. *Subtropic.* *p. 1876, 1913*
wagnerianus (takil in hort.) (Western Himalayas), "Takil palm"; handsome fan palm of compact habit and slow growth, with short robust trunk clothed with a mat of furry brownish fiber; the stiffly rigid, deeply plaited palmate leaves average 40 cm across, rough dull green on horizontal nearly unarmed petioles; very decorative in small plantings or containers. Trees at Los Angeles Arboretum in Arcadia are about 6 m high, shorter than T. fortunei, (see Myron Kimnach, Principes Oct. 1977). *Subtropic.* *p. 1913*

TRADESCANTIA *Commelinaceae* ***I2LFD**
albiflora 'Albo-vittata' (C. America), "Giant white inch plant"; vigorous plant with succulent creeping branches; fairly large, fleshy lanceshaped leaves 8-10cm long, delicate bluish-green, striped and bordered white; 3-petaled white flowers. *Tropical.* *p. 781, 787*
albiflora 'Laekenensis Rainbow', "Rainbow inch plant"; watery creeping stems with small delicate ovate, pale green leaves with white stripes and bands tinted purplish; 3-petaled white flowers. *p. 783*
albiflora 'Tricolor minima' (Colombia); a small-leaved variety very attractive with colorful foliage only 2-2½ cm long, prettily variegated green, white and rose, and red underneath. *p. 785*
blossfeldiana (Brazil), "Flowering inch plant"; robust branching plant with elliptic, waxy olive green leaves, the underside purplish and densely silver-hairy, and purple stem; free blooming with 3-petaled flowers, white tipped pale purple. *p. 781*
blossfeldiana 'Variegata'; an attractive sport with the fleshy leaves striped cream to yellow and pale green, midrib purple; underneath deep purplish and white-hairy. *p. 781*
crassifolia (Mexico); tuberous-rooted perennial, very little branched, about 60 cm high, with narrow-elliptic leaves white-woolly beneath; flowers in axillary clusters, upper with two, lower with 1 bract, with woolly sepals, and purplish-rose or blue petals *p. 782*
crassula (Brazil); branching succulent stems ascending to 45 cm, with glossy green, sessile ovate leaves about 10 cm long, the margins ciliate; white flowers 1 cm dia., in clusters; sepals hairy. *p. 785*
dracaenoides: see Callisia fragrans
fluminensis, the "Rio tradescantia"; wide-spreading succulent creeper with fleshy, small bluish leaves, purplish beneath; white flowers. *p. 785*
fluminensis discolor; attractive cultivar, photographed at Rochford's Nurseries, near London, England; robust trailing plant with stringy branches dense with narrow, light green leaves, variegated white and pinkish, and tinged with purple; a beautiful basket plant. *p. 786*
fluminensis 'Variegata' (Argentina, Brazil), "Wandering Jew"; lively little creeper rooting at nodes, generally smaller and weaker than albiflora, with shining ovate leaves 4cm long, fresh green and striped and banded yellow and cream; flowers white. *Tropical.* *p. 781, 785*
fuscata: see Siderasis fuscata
hirta (Setcreasea hirsuta) (Namibia); clustering plant with grass-like rosettes of narrow, succulent leaves concave above, rounded beneath, to 20 cm long, glaucous green and thickly covered with long hair; flowers purplish pink. *Subtropic.* *p. 786*
multiflora: see Gibasis geniculata
navicularis (Perú), "Chain plant"; half-creeping succulent with closely 2-ranked, short boat-shaped leaves coppery green, mottled purple beneath; stalked clusters of rosy-purple flowers. *p. 782*
sillamontana (villosa) (N.E. Mexico), "White velvet creeper"; introduced by the trade as Tradescantia 'White Velvet' and 'White Gossamer'; fleshy trailer with clasping ovate leaves in ranks, 6 cm long, deep green with parallel veins but entirely covered with fluffy white wool, underside and stems purplish; tripetaled flowers rich orchid; occasionally erroneously listed as Cyanotis veldthoutiana. *Subtropic.* *p. 783*
velutina (Guatemala), "Velvet tradescantia"; softly white-hairy creeper with branching succulent stems to 45 cm long, leaves ovate to lanceolate, 5-12 cm long, hairy above and short silky-hairy underneath; flowers with downy sepals and purplish rose petals. *p. 785*
virginiana 'Alba'; a form with large pure white, showy flowers of the "Common spiderwort", T. virginiana (New York to So. Dakota and Arkansas); creeping perennial succulent herb, with linear-lanceolate dull-green leaves 15-30 cm long, and regular flowers having 3 equal, violet-purple petals; 2½ cm across; the filaments hairy, the sepals inflated and hairy all over; hardy. This white, and other forms, may be of hybrid origin. *p. 784*

TRADESCANTIA: see also Callisia, Commelina, Cyanotis, Dichorisandra, Gibasis, Hadrodemas, Rhoeo, Siderasis, Zebrina.

TRECULIA *Moraceae* **S3LFM**
africana (Trop. W. Africa east to Uganda), "African breadfruit"; evergreen tree to 25 m high, the trunk fluted at base, bark smooth and gray, exuding latex; the pithy branches with leathery, shiny green elliptic leaves, 20-25, or even 45 cm long; green flowers dioecious, in a globose head; the round fruit up to 45 cm dia. and 16 kg. in weight, along the trunk and main branches, covered with spine-like tubercles, and containing edible seed; the timber is marketed as African boxwood. *p. 1576*

TREVESIA *Araliaceae* **I2LFM**
palmata (India, China); small tree to 5 m high, with brown prickly, tomentose, green stem and branches; leaves to 60 cm dia., palmately lobed, the lobes ovate-oblong, glossy green and with prominent pale ribs, the margins finely serrate, and the petioles united like a duck's foot. *p. 321*

palmata burckii (Sumatra); evergreen tree with stiff, palmately-lobed leaves having rough, puckered surface; the lobes are finely serrate; the sinus at base of leaf with large teeth. *p. 321*

palmata 'Micholitzii' (Yunnan, China), "Snowflake plant"; small evergreen tree with puckered leaves, 40 cm across or more, palmately lobed, the segments irregularly pinnate, thin-leathery, glossy green and covered with silvery dots, which earned it the name "Snowflake plant"; the petioles are spiny. *Subtropic.* *p. 320, 321*

palmata sanderi (Vietnam), "Vietnam snowflake plant"; attractive tree with large rich green leaves to 60 cm across, digitately compound and lobed similar to micholitzii, the segments and basal sinus very much corrugated and quilted. *p. 319, 321*

sundaica (Java); evergreen tree with elegant, palmately lobed, leathery, glossy-green leaves, the segments are lanceolate, with rounded sinus and toothed margins; woody stem with thorns. *p. 312, 319*

TRIBULUS *Zygophyllaceae* **S2LBD**

zeyheri (Namibia), "Devil's-thorn"; lovely annual creeping herb forming carpets; with hairy pinnate leaves; large yellow flowers very pretty; 5-angled fruit. *p. 2142*

TRICHANTHA: see Columnea

TRICHILIA *Meliaceae* **S2LBD**

dregei (roka) (Natal to Zimbabwe), "Cape mahogany" or "Christmas bells"; handsome evergreen wide-spreading tree to 18 m; dark green glossy, pinnate leaves; clusters of small white, sweetly scented flowers blooming at Christmas time; the fruit a 3-celled capsule opening and exposing the seeds. *p. 1551*

TRICHINIUM *Amaranthaceae* **I2LBD**

manglesii (Western Australia); low perennial to 30 cm high; from short woody base long-stalked ovate to linear leaves 3-8 cm long; the inflorescence like a short white-haired bottle-brush, the 2 cm flowers with pink or whitish tips. *p. 81*

TRICHOCAULON *Asclepiadaceae* **I-S2LBD**

cactiforme (Cape Prov., Namibia); short, club-shaped succulent to 10 cm high and 5 cm thick, grooved into irregular tubercles, more regular and transversely toward base, gray green; head covers itself with tiny yellow flowers spotted red-brown. *p. 379*

meloforme (Namibia, Cape Prov.); thick solitary spherical succulent 8-10 cm high gray-green, with flattened tubercles; small 1 cm cup-shaped flowers near the apex, dark outside, yellow inside and spotted maroon. *Arid-subtropic.* *p. 384*

officinale (Cape Prov., Namibia); oblong blue-green succulent stems several together, to 20-40 cm high and 6-7 cm thick, 20-25 irregular angles armed with blackish, rigid bristle-spines; small flat flowers to 1 cm dia., red-brown with yellow middle. *p. 384*

simile (So. Africa: Cape Prov.); succulent with egg-shaped, oblong gray-green body to 5 cm high, 4 cm thick, and covered with convex tubercles; flowers 1 cm dia., red-brown. *p. 384*

truncatum (Cape Prov.: Namaqualand); ovoid succulent gray-green body 10 cm high, 4 cm thick, covered with irregular 5-angled tubercles; small 8 mm flowers from the upper part, cream-colored spotted with purple. *p. 384*

TRICHOCENTRUM *Orchidaceae* **I-S3OFM**

albo-coccineum (alboviolaceum) (Perú); small plant with solitary leathery leaves; 5 cm flowers consisting of greenish sepals and petals covered with bronze; broad, lobed lip cream at front, rich purple toward base. *p. 1828*

albo-purpureum (No. Brazil); pretty, dwarf epiphyte having minute pseudobulbs with solitary leaves 8-15 cm long; stalks with relatively large, waxy flowers 5 cm across; narrow, pointed sepals and petals buff-brown tipped with yellowish-green, and spotted red-brown; the wide fan-like lip white marked purple on either side of the crest, summer. *Tropical.* *p. 1826*

candidum (Guatemala); miniature epiphyte without pseudobulbs, leathery, broad-ovate leaves, and basal short inflorescence of waxy-white flowers 2 cm across, sepals and petals almost translucent, marked purple in throat (autumn). *p. 1828*

capitatum (Costa Rica, Panama); miniature epiphyte with short creeping stems and heavy fibrous roots; solitary leaves narrowed to the base; inflorescence basal and scandent, with flowers of glassy appearance, greenish sepals and petals; lip translucent white with purple spots (autumn). *p. 1829*

orthoplectron (Ecuador); curious and beautiful little epiphyte with small, one-leaved pseudobulbs, the fleshy, partly folded, red-spotted leaves to 9 cm long; flowers usually single, 5 cm across, and strongly fragrant; sepals and petals yellow with large maroon spots, lip white with a narrow purple spot on each side; autumn. (I) *p. 1826*

tigrinum (Costa Rica, Ecuador); desirable dwarf epiphyte with shining green 10-15 cm leaves on very small pseudobulbs; large flowers 5 cm across, sweet-scented and waxy, with sepals and petals tawny yellow and blotched with brown, the large lip white with two large purple spots near base (May-June). *Humid-subtropic.* *p. 1830*

TRICHOCEREUS *Cactaceae* ***I2LBD**

auricolor (Perú); stem fresh green, leaning or sprawling, to 6 cm thick, freely branching from base; 16-24 shallow ribs, areoles with yellow wool and yellow needle spines. *p. 648*

bridgesii (Bolivia); stem erect or partly prostrate, to 5 m, 4-8 obtuse ribs, grayish-green or glaucous, to 10 cm thick, the small areoles with yellow wool, few spines yellowish; night-blooming, outside greenish brown, inner petals white, and with a jasmine perfume. *p. 655*

chiloensis (Chile); olive-green columnar plant growing into a branched tree to 8 m high, 9 fat ribs when young, later 10-15 and divided into tubercles; set with strong black-gray spines, apex clothed with white-woolly areoles; flowers white, red outside. *p. 648*

macrogonus (So. America); slender column, bluish-green, 7 round ribs; spines needle-like and brown; flowers white. *p. 647*

pachanoi (Ecuador), "Night-blooming San Pedro"; slender column to 5 m high, forming many vertical branches 8 cm or more thick, light to dark green, glaucous while young, 6-8 rounded ribs, wanting spines; large white nocturnal flowers very fragrant, 20 cm long. *p. 635, 640A, 657*

pasacana (Bolivia, Argentina), "Torch cactus"; giant stout tree to 10 m high, sparingly branched; columns to 30 cm thick, dull green, closely ribbed, freely yellow-spined; nocturnal flowers white, 10 cm long. Edible greenish fruits called "Pasacana". Barrel-shaped in seedling stage. *Subtropic.* *p. 648*

peruvianus (Perú), "Peruvian torch-cactus"; branching with stout columns, to 4 m tall, and 8-10 cm thick, dull green, glaucous when young, 6-8 broad and rounded ribs, brown spines; large white flowers to 25 cm long. *Tropical.* *p. 654*

schickendantzii (Echinopsis) (N. W. Argentina); short column, growing in clumps, shiny dark green, close ribbed; pale radial spines; flowers white. *p. 648, 655*

shaferi (Argentina); light green branched column to 50 cm tall and 12 cm thick, with about 14 ribs, the aeroles bearing light yellow, slender spines; night-flowering white. *p. 655*

spachianus (W. Argentina), the beautiful "Torch cactus"; short slender columns to 2 m high, close-ribbed, 6 cm thick, branching at base; short brown spines; flowers white, 20 cm long. *Subtropic.* *p. 618, 648, 654, 655*

strigosus (N. W. Argentina); clustering column with branches 5 cm thick, light green, with 15-18 low ribs, densely covered with needle-like, variously colored spines; flowers white, red outside. *p. 648*

tephracanthus (Bolivia); slender column to $1\frac{1}{2}$ m tall, with 8 broad, rounded ribs, bluish gray-green, the recessed areoles set with short cream spines; flowers white inside. *p. 647, 659*

terscheckii (No. Argentina); branching tree to 12 m, seedlings globose, later stout columns, satiny green with 8-14 prominent ribs and yellow spines; flowers white. *p. 648, 658*

thelegonus (N. W. Argentina); prostrate knobby branches to 8 cm thick, with 12 or 13 notched ribs, olive green with hair-like gray-brown spines; long funnel-form flowers white, greenish to bronze outside, night-blooming. (Not T. thelegonoides, which is erect, tree-like, with branching trunk, to $5\frac{1}{2}$ m high and 17 cm thick). *p. 655*

TRICHOCEROS *Orchidaceae* **I3OFM**

antennifer (Ecuador), "Fly orchid"; tiny epiphyte with elongate clambering rhizome and small, pea-sized pseudobulbs each with two strongly one-nerved elliptic leaves 4 cm long; slender stalk from base, 15 cm long, carrying 4 to 5 flowers, 3 cm across, tawny yellow with purple spots and dark purple center in outline like a fly. *p. 1829*

parviflorus (Ecuador); epiphyte with small pseudobulbs and solitary fleshy leaf, arranged in ranks; the small flowers almost 3 cm, in loose raceme, sepals and petals greenish-yellow with brown-red spots; lip also greenish-yellow with maroon spots and blackish maroon hairs; produces the image of a fly sitting on its flowers, (summer). (I) *p. 1830*

TRICHOCLADUS *Hamamelidaceae* **C2LBD**

crinitus (So. Africa); evergreen shrub to 3 m high, the branches thickly covered with a dark brown, furlike mass of stellate hair; opposite ovate leaves, glossy above, thickly hairy beneath, with parallel veins; flowers crowded in globose heads, the females without petals, the 5 linear petals in the male flowers yellow. *p. 1320, 1323*

TRICHODIADEMA *Aizoaceae* **I2LBD**

densum (Cape Province: Karroo), "Miniature desert rose"; spreading shrub-like small succulent with fleshy roots and short stems, the crowded green leaves 2 cm long topped by long radiating white hairs; flowers violet-red 5 cm across. *Arid-subtropic.* *p. 75, 78*

stellatum (Cape Prov.); turf-forming shrubby succulent to 10 cm high, with long fleshy roots; leaves 1 cm long and nearly cylindric, gray-green and rough with stiff white bristles at apex; flowers violet-red. *p. 75, 78*

TRICHOGLOTTIS *Orchidaceae* **S3OFM**

brachiata (Stauropsis) (Philippines), the "Black orchid"; beautiful erect climbing epiphyte with thick whitish roots, short coppery green, folded leaves in two ranks, and solitary axillary 5 cm flowers blackish velvety crimson with purplish tinge, divided lip pinkish purple with a yellow patch, long-lasting and fragrant (summer). (S) p. 1811, 1826, 1831

philippinensis (Stauropsis) (Philippines); epiphyte with erect-climbing stem, bearing flat, leathery leaves in two ranks; solitary flowers in leaf axils, 2½-4 cm across, with sepals and petals reddish-brown, lip white, the side-lobes purple, and with fleshy, hairy keel. p. 1826

TRICHOMANES *Hymenophyllaceae (Filices)* **I3H-ONM**

elegans (Trop. America: West Indies, Dominica, Trinidad, Mexico, south to Perú), a "Filmy-fern"; distinct epiphyte producing from tufted rootstock barren and fertile very delicate fronds of different characters; the barren fronds are pendant, pinnatifid, 15-30 cm long, broadly spear-shaped and borne on short stalks, the leaflets finely toothed or lobed; the fertile fronds, 15-30 cm long, are of erect habit, very narrow and undivided, seldom 1 cm broad, and fringed on each side by slender spore receptacles. p. 1079

reniforme (New Zealand), "the Kidney-fern"; a little fern of such peculiar habit that it does hardly look like a fern; usually growing on the floor of beech-forest but often epiphytic; with naked wiry rhizomes, bearing on thin stalks 5-20 cm long, chalice-like or kidney-shaped fronds 5-10 cm broad and notched at base, very transparent and light green when young, thickish and glossy dark green when older; the margins ciliate and with spore masses all around. p. 1079

TRICHOPILIA *Orchidaceae* **I3OFM**

coccinea (marginata) (Guatemala, Costa Rica, Panama, Colombia); epiphytic orchid, its compressed pseudobulbs with solitary leathery 20 cm leaf; inflorescence from the base; fragrant, heavy-textured flower to 10 cm across, narrow sepals and petals twisted, reddish-green, the tubular lip white outside, deep crimson within and margined white (spring). p. 1831

dasyandra (Aspasia pusilla) (Costa Rica); handsome little epiphyte with small flattened pseudobulbs bearing solitary, fresh-green strap-like leaves; the small flowers close in center with narrow pale greenish-yellow sepals and petals faintly marked lilac, the large circular pinkish lip painted light purple spotted brown. p. 1829

marginata (Costa Rica, Panama); pretty epiphyte with compressed pseudobulbs and narrow leaf; solitary basal flowers 10-12 cm large and long-lasting, a bold trumpet-shaped, prominent lip white outside, the mouth reddish-purple becoming deep crimson in throat, and a finely serrulate margin; the twisted sepals and petals brownish-red with greenish-yellow margins (May-June). (I) p. 1834

powellii (Ecuador); small terrestrial or rock dweller, 15 cm high, with dark green, broad-elliptic leaves; 3 cm flower having narrow, undulate, greenish sepals and petals, large tubular lip white, with yellow in throat. p. 1829

rostrata (Colombia); small epiphyte with smooth, flattened pseudobulbs and solitary glossy-green leaves; pendant waxy flowers with insignificant greenish, crisped sepals and petals 3 cm long, large tubular-flaring, showy lip creamy-white with yellow throat (summer). p. 1829

suavis (Costa Rica); beautiful small epiphyte with thin pseudobulb and solitary broad leaves; producing clusters of relatively large flowers delicately hawthorn-scented, creamy-white, with large frilled lip, yellow in throat and spotted purplish rose (Dec.-May, Oct.) *Tropical.* p. 1834

tortilis (Guatemala, Mexico); small epiphyte with 1-leaved pseudobulbs and 1 or 2 large, showy, cattleya-like flowers on a short erect or nodding stalk, the narrow sepals and petals much twisted, pale yellow-green with brown-red center, the large lip cream-white with red spots in the yellow throat, (Dec.-June). (I) p. 1831, 1834

TRICHOPUS *Dioscoreaceae* **S3LFM**

zeylanicus (So. India, Sri Lanka); small tropical perennial with thin-wiry, clambering stems; relatively large triangular-ovate leaves with rough surface; the small purple flowers pendant on long hair-thin stalks. p. 952

TRICHOSANTHES *Cucurbitaceae* **I3HFM**

cucumeroides (Japan), "Snake-gourd"; herbaceous vine with thick, tuberous root, climbing by tendrils 4 to 5 m; leaves palmately lobed and lightly crenate, finely pubescent beneath; white flowers; the fleshy long-ovoid fruit light gray, with deep green markings turning red. Dried fruit is used as soap substitute. *Subtropic.* p 930

japonica (Japan); tendril-bearing climbing herb with fleshy rootstock, and thin, 3 to 5-lobed ovate leaves, on angled stems; large white flowers with deeply toothed bracts and lacily fringed petal lobes, the male ones in racemes, the females solitary, without bracts; yellowish-green, fleshy, ovoid-pointed fruit 8 cm long. p. 933

TRICHOSPORUM: see Aeschynanthus

TRICHOSTIGMA *Phytolaccaceae* **I-S3LFM**

peruvianum (Ledenbergia) (Perú); ornamental Andean climbing shrub 2 m high with slender branches, and large satiny obovate leaves having oblique auriculate base, metallic olive green with sunken veins, rosy-violet beneath; small white and purple flowers in raceme first erect, becoming pendant. p. 1923

TRICYRTIS *Liliaceae* **C2LFM**

macropoda (China, Japan), "Toad-lily"; perennial with short creeping rhizome, stems 60-90 cm high, downy in upper part; oblong, clasping leaves to 12 cm long; attractive bell-shaped flowers with spreading segments lavender, spotted with purple, 2 cm long; in summer. p. 1506

TRIDACTYLE *Orchidaceae* **S3OFM**

tricuspis (Angraecum) (Transvaal); straggling epiphyte with woody stem, clothed by long distichous leaves in ranks but becoming leafless near their base; leaves bilobed at apex; inflorescence directly from the stem, in arching racemes dense with yellow-brown flowers. p. 1829

TRIFOLIUM *Leguminosae* **C2LBMh**

arvense (Europe, No. Asia, naturalized in No. America), "Rabbitfoot clover"; annual herb to 45 cm high, freely branching and softly pubescent; the 3 leaflets linear or narrow-oblanceolate, to 2 cm long; oblong flower-heads gray to pale brown; with tiny whitish or pinkish corolla tubes. p. 1392

dubium (minus) (native in Ireland and elsewhere in Europe; naturalized in No. America), the "Yellow clover", and widely grown as "Irish Shamrock"; annual trefoil with branching creeping stems 15-45 cm long and hued brown; the 3 small leaflets matte satiny green, obovate and obcordate 1 cm long, the terminal one attached by individual stalklets to the petiole, the petioles and stipules being hairy, unlike in repens which is not hairy and has leaflets rounded or lightly indented at summit; T. dubium has canary-yellow or greenish-yellow small flowers 1 cm long, in loose heads, while repens has corolla white or tinged with pink. *Temperate.* p. 1392

repens (Europe), "White clover"; branching perennial herb with creeping stems to 30 cm; digitate leaves of 3 obovate or lightly obcordate leaflets, and small white flowers in dense globular heads. p. 1392

repens minus (Ireland and elsewhere in Europe), "Irish shamrock"; a dwarf form of the white clover grown in little pots and bought for St. Patrick's Day; starting as a miniature rosette with 3 obovate, fresh-green leaflets on each petiole, it later creeps perennially and has small round heads of white flowers. p. 1392

TRIGONIDIUM *Orchidaceae* **I3OFM**

egertonianum (Honduras); distinct epiphyte with clustering, compressed pseudobulbs bearing 2 sword-shaped leaves, flowers cupped with reflexed lower sepals, pale yellow-brown, flushed rose, with dark lines, (summer). (I) p. 1834

obtusum (tenue) (Venezuela, Demerara); curious epiphyte with 2-leaved pseudobulbs and stalked, solitary, erect flowers cupped like a little tulip, the sepals greenish-yellow, shaded red, petals yellowish, veined red, brown at apex, the fleshy lip yellow, margined red, (May-Sept.). (I) p. 1834

TRILLIUM *Liliaceae* **C2HFM**

erectum (Nova Scotia to Manitoba and Tennessee); an attractive perennial herb of the woods, known as "Stinking Benjamin" or "Squaw-root"; short thick rootstock; solitary stem 30 cm high bearing at top 3 broad ovate, whorled, clasping leaves, topped by a flower of 3 large ovate petals 2½ cm long, usually deep maroon red or greenish-purple, longer than the slender-pointed outer sepals; with unpleasant odor; hardy. p. 1493

grandiflorum (E. No. America: Quebec to Minnesota), the white "Wake-robin"; perennial with solitary stem 30-45 cm high, bearing a whorl of 3 rhombic-ovate leaves, topped by a large petaloid flower pure white, fading to rosy-pink, the corrugated petals to 8 cm long; hardy. p. 1492

recurvatum (Ohio to Nebraska and Mississippi), "Bloody Butcher"; horizontal rhizome bearing stem 30 cm high, the whorl of broad leaves attractively mottled with gray and purple; the sessile flowers with erect petals brownish-purple 2½ cm long; hardy. p. 1493

sessile 'Snow Queen', "Toad Shade"; white-flowered California form of the E. U.S. species, which has purple petals, the sessile flowers 5 cm long; leaves light and dark green, on several stems 30 cm high. p. 1493

TRIMEZA *Iridaceae* ***I2LFW**

caribaea (Neomarica longifolia hort.) (W. Indies); tall species more than 60 cm high; bluish-green iris-like flat leathery leaves 4 cm wide, and erect stiff-wiry stalk bearing the fleeting flowers opening in succession; the flowers smallish, about 5-5½ cm dia., lemon-yellow flags with small beige inner, spoon-like petals curved outward, and spotted purplish-brown. p. 1331

TRIOLENA pustulata: see Bertolonia pubescens hort.

TRIOSTEUM *Caprifoliaceae* **I3LBM**

erythrocarpum (West China), "Feverwort" or "Horse gentian"; softly hairy herbaceous perennial of weedy habit, 50 to 100 cm high, with opposite, quilted obovate leaves; tubular flowers greenish outside, purplish inside, swollen at base, clustered in the axils, and not showy; fruit red. p. 755

pinnatifidum (N. W. China); herbaceous perennial with erect branches 50-60 cm high, the opposite bristly-hairy, rugose leaves deeply lobed; flowers inside brownish purple, outside greenish-yellow, in terminal clusters; white berries covered with hair. p. 755

TRIPHASIA *Rutaceae* **S3LBM**

trifolia (Malaya?), "Lime-berry"; spiny evergreen ornamental shrub or small tree to 5 m high, with trifoliolate leathery leaves remotely crenate; fragrant white flowers singly in leaf axils, followed by 1½ cm crimson-red berries. p. 2033

TRIPHYOPHYLLUM *Dioncophyllaceae (Carnivorous Plants)* **S3LFM**
peltatum (Drosophyllum) (Sierra Leone, Liberia, Ivory Coast); a tropical insectivorous shrub with 3 different kinds of leaves on the long shoots; on short axillary branches small leaves with forked hooks at apex; the larger without hooks, and on vigorous sterile branches more elongate and reduced almost to the midrib; covered with stalked and sessile, hair-like, rigid glands each bearing a drop of sticky fluid, by which insects are captured; large yellow flowers in clusters at the top of a leafy stem. *p. 950*

TRIPOGANDRA *Commelinaceae* ***S2LFD**
multiflora (Tradescantia)—see Gibasis
warscewicziana (Spironema)—see Hadrodemas

TRISTANIA *Myrtaceae* **I2LBD**
conferta 'Aurea-variegata' (E. Australia), "Brisbane box"; evergreen tree with beautiful foliage; the green species 10-20 m high, and widely planted as a street tree in Sydney and Melbourne; reddish bark peeling to show smooth pale bark beneath; in this cultivar, the handsome leathery, ovate leaves 15 cm long, clustered in whorls at end of branchlets, glossy green with golden yellow variegation along center; creamy-white 2 cm flowers. *Subtropic.* *p. 1614*

TRISTELLATEIA *Malpighiaceae* **S3LFM**
australasiae (Malaysia, Australasia), "Galphimia vine"; climbing shrub with thin-wiry, woody, winding branches, carrying dull green ovate leaves 5-10 cm long; small bright yellow flowers with red stamens in striking racemes. *Tropical.* *p. 1525*

TRITELEIA *Liliaceae* **C2LBMd**
laxa (Brodiaea) (California), "Triplet lily" or "Ithuriel's spear"; strong cormous plant 50 cm high, with usually a pair of basal leaves; clusters of funnel-shaped flowers 3 cm long with widespread segments a lovely violet purple with blue anthers. *p. 1494*

TRITHRINAX *Palmae* **I2LBD**
acanthocoma (So. Brazil), "Webbed trithrinax"; fan-palm with solitary trunk to 4 m, 8-10 cm thick, with long spines, and distinctive because of its intricate fibrous web-like covering, formed by leaf bases; palmate leaves to 1 m across, deeply cut into rigid segments which are split at apex, dark grayish-green above, lighter green beneath. *p. 1909, 1910*

TRITOMA: see Kniphofia

TRITONIA *Iridaceae* **C2LBDd**
crocata (So. Africa), "Kalkoentje"; cormous herb 60 cm high with linear sword-shaped leaves, and wiry stems bearing expanded bell-shaped flowers tawny-yellow or orange 5 cm wide, May-June; somewhat winter-hardy with protection. *Subtropic.* *p. 1335*
x crocosmaeflora (Crocosmia aurea x Tritonia pottsii), known in horticulture as "Montbretia"; a popular hybrid much cultivated as cut flower and widely planted in mild climate gardens; charming cormous plant with 4 soft light green, sword-shaped leaves 2 cm wide on either side of the floral stalk, having many parallel ribs; branched sprays 50 cm or more high, carrying curved funnel flowers in long one-sided spikes, the waxy corolla 3-4 cm long, its segments flaring wide and a flaming orange-crimson, lasting a long time on the plant or 2 weeks and more as cut flowers; somewhat winter-hardy with protection. *Subtropic.* *p. 1332, 1333*
deusta (So. Africa, S. W. Cape), "Blazing stars", perennial herb forming a corm, with 4 to 10 linear, curved and striated leaves, similar to crocata but differing in having a dark brown-red blotch at the base of each of the 3 outer segments of the cinnabar-red flower. *p. 1337*
hyalina (So. Africa: S. W. Cape); probably the most beautiful of the Mossel Bay tritonias; small cormous herb with several broad, sickle-shaped, stiff, dark green leaves arranged like a fan; the flowers, 2½ cm long, in two ranks, the rounded nearly equal segments coral-salmon and with translucent sides near the center. *p. 1332*
pottsii (So. Africa: Natal, Zululand), the "Slender tritonia"; this species resembles the garden montbretia, T. crocosmaeflora, but the flowers are more narrow and are a rich crimson; each flower has a curved slender tube about 4 cm long with 6 short petals which do not open very wide; the flower spike has numerous flowers open at the same time and buds continue to open in mid-summer; lateral spikes spring from the main stalk, growing to nearly 1 m tall, subtended by the bluish-green leaves. *Subtropic.* *p. 1332*

TRITONIA: see also Crocosmia

TROCHOMERIOPSIS *Cucurbitaceae* **S3LFM**
diversifolia (Madagascar); tropical climber with curious greenish-white flowers having long frilled or twisted tails. *p. 933*

TROPAEOLUM *Tropaeolaceae* **C-I2LBM**
azureum (Mexico to Chile), "Blue nasturtium"; smooth climber with small tubers; leaves 5-lobed, to 5 cm dia.; flowers lilac-blue, 4 cm across, with conical spur. *p. 2103*
majus (Perú, Brazil), known as "Nasturtium" or "Indian cress"; quick-growing, pretty, somewhat succulent glabrous annual herb, climbing by means of coiling petioles to a height of 2-4 m, with waxy peltate leaves, and long-stemmed, fragrant 5-6 cm irregular flowers usually bright orange, sometimes in shades of red. *Subtropic.* *p. 2103, 2104*
majus fl. pl. 'Golden Gleam', "English nasturtium"; a favorite cultivar with showy double or semi-double flowers of rich yellow. *p. 2104*
majus nanum, "Tom Thumb nasturtium"; a dwarf form of bushy, rounded habit, with bright green shield-shaped leaves; large salmon blooms of refreshing fragrance; ideal for bedding or pots. *p. 2103*
peltophorum (Colombia, Ecuador); pubescent climber somewhat shrubby, with fleshy, peltate, sinuate, shield-like, gray-downy leaves; the 2½ cm flowers vivid orange-red with scarlet spur, blooming fall to spring and into summer. *p. 2104*
peregrinum (Perú), "Canary-bird flower"; annual or perennial climber with palmately 5-lobed peltate leaves; long-stalked flowers 2½ cm dia., canary-yellow, with green, curved nectar spur. *p. 2102*
polyphyllum (Chile, Argentina); prostrate or climbing perennial, with fleshy divided bluish-gray leaves; stems to 1 m; yellow flowers streaked with red; smaller than majus. *p. 2103*
speciosum (Chilean Andes); climbing perennial to 3 m with fleshy roots; leaves divided into 5-6 leaflets; beautiful flowers to 4 cm long, vivid scarlet red, yellow at base. *Subtropic.* *p. 2103*
tricolor (Chile), "Tricolored Indian cress"; slender climbing perennial herb with fleshy tubers; leaves circular, of 6 leaflets; curious flowers 2-3 cm long, not wide-mouthed nor spreading limb, but with fiery scarlet spur, purplish calyx lobes or sepals, and bright yellow petals. Very pretty summer-flowering twiner on wire frames, for the sunny cool window. *Subtropic.* *p. 2103*

TSUGA *Pinaceae (Coniferae)* **C2LBMh**
canadensis (E. No. America: Nova Scotia to Alabama), "Hemlock-spruce" or "Canada hemlock"; a very prolific coniferous often branching evergreen tree with slender horizontal branches, gracefully drooping in age; the flat needles lustrous dark green above, bluish beneath, about 1 cm long mostly arranged in opposite rows on branchlets; small brown pendulous cones. Prefers moisture, sun and wind protection but very tolerant to situations wet or dry, sunny or shade, and may be clipped into dense columns, or hedges. Best grown from seed. *Temperate.* *p. 845*
canadensis 'Nana' (Nova Scotia to Alabama), "Dwarf hemlock"; horticultural variety forming a dense, slow-growing globe, with short sparry branches and evergreen flat needles, dark glossy green, with 2 white lines beneath and bluish. *p. 838*

TULBAGHIA *Liliaceae* **C2LBM**
fragrans (Transvaal), known as "Pink agapanthus"; with wide glaucous leaves less than 30 cm high, and slender stem with umbels of numerous small lavender very fragrant flowers, but the foliage does not have the garlic odor of T. violacea. *Subtropic.* *p. 1506*
violacea (So. Africa), "Society garlic"; cormous plant with a garlic-like odor; linear channeled, soft-fleshy leaves, and umbels of bright lilac, star-like flowers 2 cm long, the spreading segments with deeper purplish median stripe, on stems to 60 cm high. *Subtropic.* *p. 1506*
violacea 'Variegata', "Variegated society garlic"; attractive variety with linear leaves milky green and white margins, pink at base; starry, pretty 2 cm flowers pinkish lavender. *Subtropic.* *p. 1494*

TULIPA *Liliaceae* **C2LBMhd**
The "Tulips" are a genus of spring-blooming bulbous perennials, usually winter-hardy, and native from the Eastern Mediterranean area and Asia Minor to Central Asia; bulbs are generally pointed; fleshy, glaucous leaves mostly basal; stiffly erect stalks carry showy flowers in brilliant colors, bell-shaped or saucer-shaped and consisting of six segments. Tulips are bulbs for cool climates and need a period of low winter temperatures; for growing in warmer climates they need to be subjected to several weeks of cold storage at 5° C. (40°F) before they are planted. Tulips have been extensively hybridized in horticulture, and are internationally classified (revised 1971) into 3 classes: Early, Midseason, and Late-blooming. These in turn have been subdivided into 15 Divisions: the "Garden tulips" are grouped under Div. 1 to 11; the "Botanicals" are species and their cultivars, according to common characteristics in Div. 12 to 15.
Division 1A: "DUC VAN TOL"; very early flowering single tulips, of small stature, seldom exceeding 15 cm high, excellent for earliest bloom and early bedding, being out of the way for bedding plants.
Division 1B: "SINGLE EARLY"; early-blooming, short and compact growing, in wide variety of colors 22-40 cm high, outdoors in April, but may be forced indoors into flower from January on; easy to grow in the home, and will not grow too tall under unfavorable light conditions.
Division 2: "DOUBLE EARLY"; short-stemmed with full-double, rather short, but broad, large flowers 20-30 cm high, and good keepers; April; lend themselves well for early forcing, or growing in the home, to bloom from January on.
Division 3: "MENDEL"; hybrids between Duc vanTol and Darwin tulips; midseason, usually single-flowered, rarely exceeding 50 cm resembling Darwins but blooming 2 weeks earlier.

Division 4: "TRIUMPH"; handsome tulips, mostly hybrids between Single-Early and Late tulips; 30-55 cm high; midseason, but slightly later than Mendels; of stocky habit, with substantial, noble flowers becoming large, in a good range of colors, except yellow, single and some double, long-lasting, and a favorite group for spring-blooming in pans.

Division 5: "DARWIN HYBRID"; a new class resulting from crossing Darwins with T. fosteriana and its forms; tall growing with large flowers in distinctive self colors especially vivid reds, as well as two-colored, and used for large pans or mass-planting; late.

Division 6: "DARWIN"; popular, leading midseason group of garden tulips of vigorous habit, some varieties suitable for pot culture and good forcers, but usually on the tall side, to as much as 60-90 cm high; sturdy slender stems carrying noble, medium-large flowers of good substance, with a squarish base, in a vast range of pure strong colors except blue; late-blooming.

Division 6A: "BICOLOR" (Bijbloemen or Picotee); late-blooming group of Breeder and Cottage tulips all two-colored, or "broken"; striped, spotted, or marbled in contrasting colors rose, pink, violet or purple, over a basic white ground; a condition caused by virus, and spread by aphis.

Division 7: "LILY-FLOWERED"; late-blooming cottage tulips distinctive with basal chalice and having petals slender-pointed and out-curving above the middle, developed mostly from Retroflexa and Picotee; in many colors, some with white or pink edges.

Division 8: "BREEDER"; tall-stemmed, May or late-blooming class with rounded or square-topped flowers, resembling Darwins except for their larger blooms and stouter stalks, and in colors; this includes muted purples, bronze, copper and dull reds; some with contrasting color at margins, or flamed through the center of the petals; the self-colored clones are used for breeding toward future "art" shades and combinations.

Division 8A: "COTTAGE" (SINGLE LATE); late May-flowering group, grown for many years in the cottage gardens of western Europe, with single flowers often long or egg-shaped, tall-stemmed, self-colored, usually with pointed petals; rich in tints of yellow and clear pinks; includes varieties difficult to pattern into Darwins and Breeders.

Division 9: "REMBRANDT"; those Darwin tulips that have "broken" varicolored flowers, the petals or base beautifully variegated, striped, flaming, feathered, or edged with contrasting colors, in the manner so often depicted in old Dutch paintings; late-flowering.

Division 9A: "BIZARRE"; "broken" colors from the Breeder, Cottage and Darwin groups, the single flowers with petals apricot or yellow as basic color, striped or painted brown, bronze, "black", or purple; late-blooming.

Division 10: "PARROT"; group of odd sports from other tulips, with large, shaggy, showy flowers having fleshy, flaring petals all slashed and fringed or lobed, and often with uneven surface, in most unusual colors, deep violet, bronzes, red and apricot, some splashed with green; the heavy heads often bend the stalks; charming as a cut flower; tall and late-blooming.

Division 11: "PEONY-FLOWERED" (DOUBLE LATE); May-flowering group of large, round-flowered, long-stemmed doubles with many wide-flaring petals in beautiful colors and variegations, including white, reds, pinks, black-purple and yellow flamed with red; long-lasting late into the season.

Divisions 12 to 15: "BOTANICALS"; other species and their varieties, or primary hybrids, grown for rock garden planting and in pots, especially the cool house.

---

gesnerana hybrids or "Common garden tulips", widely used for garden planting; hybrids of this group are best for early spring and Easter-flowering in pots, producing elegant flowers 6 to 10 cm long. Derived from T. gesnerana (Armenia, Iran), and inbred with several other species in Asiatic Turkey, So. Russia and Iran, they were brought to Western Europe from 1554 on, reaching Holland sometime after 1573. *Warm temperate.*

'Alberio' (Triumph); large cherry-red flowers with each segment edged in yellow, and long-lasting; 40 cm. *p. 1496*

'Anders Zorn' (Double Early); terracotta and yellow sport of the white, pink-flushed 'Murillo', about 30 cm. *p. 1500*

'Apeldoorn' (Darwin hybrid); large and beautiful flowers of noble form, orange-scarlet, their black base outlined in yellow, on long stems. *p. 1501*

'Aviator' (Triumph); medium large flower deep carmine red, edged in white; 65 cm tall; one of the long-lasting, large flowered 'Triumph' class, and growing ever larger as they mature. *p. 1498*

'Bartigon' (Darwin); popular pot variety with medium large flowers bright cochineal to crimson red, normally mid-May blooming; but can be forced from Jan. 15 on; 60 cm tall. Darwin flowers have squarish base in profile. *p. 1498*

'Beauty of Volendam' (Rembrandt); ivory-colored, striped or flamed with purple. Sport of 'White Sail', 45 cm. *p. 1501*

'Blenda' (Triumph); stiff-erect Triumph tulip with cupped flowers, pointed petals, deep rose with white base, early. *p. 1497*

'Blizzard' (Triumph); heavy-bodied Triumph tulip 40-45 cm high, with stout and heavy foliage; substantial large, full flowers creamy-white 7 cm long; good for Easter pots. *p. 1497*

'Celestine' (Lily-flowered); single, starry flowers with their pointed, reflexed petals brown-red, edged in orange; 60 cm. *p. 1501*

'Cordell Hull' (Rembrandt); a "broken" Bartigon, basically ivory-white but almost smothered with blood-red feathering; 60 cm. *p. 1496*

'Dardanelles' (Darwin hybrid); enormous flowers vivid cherry-red, on strong stalks; excellent cultivar of this new race of Darwin x Fosteriana 'Red Emperor'. *p. 1496*

'Dillenburg' (Breeder); tall, goblet-formed medium large flowers bright salmon orange, broadly margined with apricot to lilac rose; 70 cm high; late blooming. *p. 1498*

'Duc van Tol Scarlet'; single scarlet 15 cm high, for earliest forcing from end November on. *p. 1499, 1500*

'Edith Eddy' (Triumph); popular spring-forcing pot variety, with large carmine-red flowers with petals edged in white; 45 cm. *p. 1496*

'Fantasy' (Parrot); fine flower with lightly fimbriated petals salmon-rose tinting into pink, and irregular areas of green (55 cm); sport of the Darwin tulip 'Clara Butt'. *p. 1496*

'Gertraud Kieft' (Peony-flowered); large and showy Late-flowering double; the rounded petals white, and boldly contrasting brown-red base (60 cm). *p. 1502*

'Golden Duchess' (Lily-flowered); typical medium large flowers looking as if a normal egg-shaped bloom were topped by a rosette of narrow-pointed, out-curving segments; primrose yellow (65 cm). *p. 1496*

'Golden Fleece' (Cottage tulip); a single late multi-flowered tulip buttercup-yellow of good substance. *p. 1499*

'Inglescombe Yellow' (Cottage); elegant pure golden yellow flower on long slender but stiff stem, shaped longer and more oval than the 'Darwins', 55 cm. *p. 1498*

'Jeanne Desor' (Cottage); a pretty, cupped variety soft yellow, with contrasting, bright red border solidly around the margins of the petals. *p. 1496*

'Karel Doorman' (Parrot); also known as "Dragon tulip"; large cherry red flowers mingled with green, and edged with golden yellow, the perianth segments variously frilled; 40 cm. *p. 1495*

'Kees Nelis' (Triumph); mid-season Triumph tulip about 34-46 cm tall, of somewhat flexuous habit but responding fast to forcing; very striking in dark flame red, edged with orange-yellow. *p. 1497*

'Lilac Queen' (Parrot); heavy flower with rounded petals lobed at margins, light campanula-blue, inside deep violet; sport of 'Lilac Wonder'. *p. 1502*

'Livingstone', (Double Late); a late double "Peony" flowered tulip, bright crimson-red with yellow in base; a good strong pot plant for forcing from bulbs; becoming large and spreading; long-lasting. *p. 1498*

'Madame Dubarry' (Bizarre); showy flower apricot on primrose-yellow, inked with purple; a "broken" Darwin 'Dillenburg'. *p. 1501*

'Mainau' (Single Early); 1958 hybrid of 'Prince of Austria' x 'Couleur Cardinal'; shapely cup-shaped flowers deep orange-red with yellow base. *p. 1500*

'Makassar' (Triumph); dark canary yellow, excellent late-blooming Triumph tulip for Easter pots, about 50 cm tall, with stiff stem and foliage, the cupped flowers 7 cm high, clear yellow; often producing more than one bloom per stalk. *p. 1497*

'New Look' (Cottage tulip); spectacular single late tulip, white tinged rose, with frosty crystal like fringe; long-lasting, on tall stalks. *p. 1497*

'Orange Beauty' (syn. 'Prince of Orange') (Breeder); substantial single flowers vivid orange, shaded bronze and margined yellow; strongly fragrant. *p. 1501*

'Orange Early Queen' (Mendel); large cupped flower in bright orange; sport of the raspberry-red 'Early Queen'. *p. 1500*

'Orange Nassau' (Double Early); fully double flowers that display their beauty when widely spread open, bright orange-scarlet heavily suffused with orange at margins; short 28 cm. *p. 1498*

'Ossi Oswalda' (Cottage); single-late bloomer with flowers ivory colored, touched with pink and passing into deep rose. *p. 1501*

'Overdale' (Triumph); elegant, robust variety cinnabar-red, shaded with purple. *p. 1500*

'Paradise' (Darwin); charming Darwin tulip 50 cm tall; strong stalk with goblet formed flowers, petals white with red edging. *p. 1497*

'Paris' (Triumph); a very colorful, recommended pot variety, deep orange-red, each segment edged with contrasting yellow, on stiff stalks, 45 cm high. *p. 1495*

'Princess Irene' (Single Early); sport of 'Couleur Cardinal'; coral or soft orange with bronze-red flaming from base. *p. 1497*

'Red Giant'; an excellent "Triumph" tulip for Easter pots; a group resulting from crosses of "Darwin" and "Early" tulips; large, substantial, long-lasting, deep scarlet flowers, often 2-3 on the stiff robust stem. *p. 1495*

'Robinea' (Triumph), a superior "Triumph tulip" for Easter flowering; a healthy companion to 'Red Giant', even stockier, 30-36 cm above pot, with firm-fleshy, large flowers deep crimson, often producing more than one bloom per stalk; resistant to "rotting off" or "fire". *p. 1497*

'Rose Beauty' (Triumph); lovely bicolor, deep pink maturing to cherry red against a white base; the flowers becoming quite large as they mature; 38 cm. *p. 1496*

'Royal Gold' (Darwin); fine, stiff-stemmed form with noble golden-yellow flowers. *p. 1500*

'Union Jack' (Bicolor); substantial flower ivory-white flamed or striped with raspberry-red; the white base edged in blue. A "broken" sport of the Darwin 'Cordell Hull'. *p. 1500*

'Ursa Minor' (Single Early); shapely oval medium size flower clear deep yellow, on slender stem; a good commercial pot variety once included with the "Triumphs". *p. 1495*

'Vermilion Brilliant' (Single early); fine old single, since 1845, for early bloom, of medium height, and with cupped flowers brilliant scarlet. *p. 1499*

'Violet Queen' (Parrot); a most typical large flowered "Dragon" tulip with perianth segments deeply slashed, weirdly twisted and feathered in shimmering bluish-violet, mingled with touches of green; 60 cm; May blooming. *p.1498*

'Weber' (Mendel); large white flowers with broad lilac-rose border; 45 cm high. The "Mendels" are seedlings of the "Duc van Tols" crossed with "Darwins" and flower 10-14 days ahead of the latter. *p. 1498*

'Yellow Prince' (Single Early); early flowering, and short medium size flowers clear yellow; 25 cm; can be forced from Jan. 15. *p. 1498*

SPECIES and their hybrids, classed as **"BOTANICALS"**, included in Divisions 12 to 15.

acuminata, "Turkish tulip"; a garden tulip with flowers of varying colors, 8-10 cm long, segments all alike, narrowed gradually to a long point. *p. 1499*

'Batalinii hybrid'; derived from the Bokhara species batalinii; large open chalice or saucer-type flowers primrose-yellow. *p. 1499, 1502*

biflora (Caspian and Caucasus reg.); small tulip with 2-3 linear, glaucous leaves 12 cm long, and 1-5 flowers near top of stalk, 8 cm high, opening flat, white with yellow basal blotch, outer 2 cm segments green and crimson, inner with green median line. *p. 1504*

chrysantha (Iran); small species to 15 cm high, with recurved, glaucous leaves, and medium-size flowers with outer segments pointed, bright yellow. *p. 1503*

clusiana (Portugal to Iraq, Iran, Afghanistan); the "Lady tulip"; eye-catching species with fragrant solitary flowers, flat star-like when open, white with purple base, the pointed segments 5 cm long; midseason. *p. 1503*

clusiana 'Cynthia'; slender species with long flowers, outside red, with creamy white margins, base purple. *p. 1499*

eichleri 'Excelsa' (Eichleri hybrid); large cherry-red bell-shaped flowers with black base, more vivid and bigger than the species from the Trans-Caucasus, 15-30 cm high. *p. 1502*

fosteriana 'Flaming Youth' (Fosteriana hybrid); noble elongate flowers vivid vermilion-red with pale edging; the stalk with shiny green leaves. *p. 1502*

fosteriana princeps (Samarkand, Turkestan); an early flowering (March-April), robust bulbous plant with large, solitary flower intense glossy scarlet, having black blotch margined yellow, in base. *p. 1496*

greigii 'Red Riding Hood'; foliage along stalk green, richly mottled with dark, reddish purple; flowers 6 cm long, brilliant scarlet with black blotches at bases of petals inside; 30 cm high. *p. 1497*

greigii 'Royal Orange'; hybrid with wide cup-shaped flowers, their recurving, pointed outer segments 9 cm long, vivid orange-scarlet edged with yellow, base black; the glaucous leaves with purple-brown mottling. The species is bright scarlet (Turkestan). *Warm temperate.* *p. 1503*

hoogiana (Central Asia); cup-shaped, solitary flowers with outer segments 15 cm long, bright scarlet with a long blackish blotch, margined yellow, on 30 cm stalk; channeled, glaucous leaves; May. *p. 1504*

kaufmanniana (Turkestan) the "Water-lily tulip"; short plant 12-20 cm high, with broad, slightly glaucous leaves, and beautiful, solitary flowers opening to a waterlily-like flat star; the pointed segments 9 cm long, yellowish white inside with yellow base, outside streaked carmine-red; early blooming. *p. 1504*

kolpakowskiana (Turkestan); low-growing species with narrow, glaucous leaves; stalks 15 cm long bearing 1-2 flowers opening flat with pointed segments 5½ cm long, bright yellow, backs with olive and red flush; midseason-early. *p. 1504*

linifolia (Bokhara); small species to 25 cm high, with goblet-like solitary flowers glossy crimson with black-purple bottom; narrow, grass-like foliage; early. *p. 1503*

marjolettii (So. France: Savoy Alps); slender species 45-60 cm high, with narrow leaves, and elegant flowers having broad short-pointed segments primrose yellow, the margins flushed purple outside; midseason. *p. 1503*

orphanidea (Greece); slender species 30 cm high, with folded long leaves near base; solitary star-shaped flowers with narrow petals 5 cm long, dull orange-yellow, stained green and purple outside; early. *p. 1504*

primulina (Algeria); North African species to 30 cm high, with very narrow leaves, and fragrant flowers opening in the afternoon; the narrow 5 cm segments creamy-white, primrose-yellow toward base, marked green and lavender outside; midseason. *p. 1504*

pulchella pallida (pulchella albo-coerulea oculata) (Asia Minor); distinct miniature, to 15 cm, with narrow leaves; flowers with pointed petals, white with deep steel-blue base. *p. 1499*

saxatilis (Crete); stoloniferous species 30-45 cm high, forming long, narrow, shining green leaves, and stalks with 1-3 cup-shaped fragrant flowers opening flat, the pointed segments 5 cm long, pale lilac with yellow bottom; midseason. *Subtropic.* *p. 1504*

'Solanus': (kaufmanniana hybrid); a pretty waterlily tulip with narrow-pointed, spreading petals buttercup-yellow, boldly flamed with carmine-red, deeper outside, over brown-mottled foliage. *p. 1502*

tarda (dasystemon) (Turkestan); small species 8-15 cm high; rosette of glaucous leaves, the 8 cm stalks bearing 1 to 6 small starry flowers, the 4 cm segments yellow at base, white toward tips, marked green and red on back, the inner segments with 2 purple and one green line; May. *p. 1499,1504*

tubergeniana 'Candida' (tubergeniana x Darwin); full flowers with rounded, cupped petals vivid-red, and black base. *p. 1503*

turkestanica (biflora var.) (Turkestan); small species with flowers opening into stars, 5 cm across, the pointed petals ivory-white with orange base, outer segments reddish outside, from 1-7 blooms on the 30 cm stem; very narrow leaves; early. Larger than T. biflora. *p. 1503*

urumiensis (N. W. Iran); small species, with strap-shaped, dull-green leaves; the short 5 cm stem carrying 1-2 flowers first urn-shaped, later spreading star-like, with narrow, pointed yellow petals, the outer segments olive and red outside. *p. 1504*

TUPIDANTHUS *Araliaceae* **I2LBM**

calyptratus (Assam, Cambodia, Burma), "Mallet flower"; small ornamental evergreen tree which later becomes a scandent climber to 6m high; long reddish petioles carry leaves palmately divided into 7 to 9 stalked, undulate, somewhat pendant, obovate to oblanceolate firm-textured, leathery leaflets 24cm or more long, glossy green above, matte beneath, with about 30 closely spaced lateral veins each side of the reddish to beige midrib; the inflorescence in compound clusters of 2 to 3cm greenish flowers with fleshy petals, followed by globular fruit containing seeds. A handsome decorator resembling Brassaia, and of sturdy character. *p. 311, 321*

TUPISTRA *Liliaceae* **S3LFD**

macrostigma (tupistroides) (India); perennial herb with thick creeping rhizome, long-stalked, lanceolate bright green 30 cm leaves; inflorescence a pendant spike with dark purple 1½ cm flowers. *Tropical.* *p. 1505*

TURBINICARPUS *Cactaceae* **I3LBD**

polaskii (Mexico: San Luis Potosi); a midget cactus of globular shape only 1 cm high, to 2½ cm across, resembling a small Lophophora; olive green with wrinkles, and with a single hook spine; starry flowers relatively large; 1½ cm across, white inside flushed with pink. *Arid-tropical.* *p. 704*

schwarzii (Mexico: San Luis Potosi); small midget with semi-globose body to 3½ cm dia., the ribs in 5-8 spirals dissolved by raised knobs, bronzy olive to light green, 1 or 2 curved spines to 2 cm long; bell-flowers 4 cm across, greenish-white with rosy central band. *p. 704*

TURNERA *Turneraceae* **I2LBD**

ulmifolia angustifolia (W. Indies, Mexico to Argentina), "West Indian holly" or "Sage rose"; pretty herbaceous shrub ½-1¼ m high, with scandent stems, and alternate narrow-elliptic leaves 8-10 cm long, nettle-like, deep glossy green, white-hairy underneath; axillary golden-yellow, 5 cm flowers with 5 petals, blooming in the morning from March to September. *p. 2093*

TURRAEA *Meliaceae* **I2LFD**

floribunda (Natal), "Tree honeysuckle"; small sparry tree to 6 m, with ovate leaves hairy especially beneath; sweetly-scented, creamy-green flowers 4 cm across, with 4-5 linear slightly twisted petals. *p. 1551*

obtusifolia (So. Africa: Natal, E. Cape), "South African honeysuckle", or "Bluntleaf star-bush"; attractive, broad, slow-growing, more or less evergreen shrub 1-1½ m high, with small obovate, recurved dark green leaves 3-5 cm long; numerous axillary solitary, star-like white flowers with 5 narrow petals, 2½ cm across, and sweetly scented; red berries. *Subtropic.* *p. 1550*

TYPHA *Typhaceae* **C2LBW**

latifolia, (N. America, Europe, Asia), "Cat-tail"; decorative aquatic perennial, with creeping root-stock; tall erect unbranched reed-like stems to 2½ m high, the leaves linear, almost flat and glaucous; cylindric flower spike dark brown, 30 cm long, and 3 cm thick; dried for indoor decoration and known in England as "Reed-mace". *Warm temperate.* *p. 2094*

TYPHONIUM *Araceae* **I-S3LFWd**

brownii (No. Australia, Queensland, N. S. Wales); tropical and subtropical plant with thick tuberous rhizome; hastate more or less 3-lobed leaves appearing with the flowers, with lanceolate segments 8-15 cm long, on 20-25 cm petiole; showy spathe constricted with lower part globose, the upper limb ovate and blood-red, 10 cm long, the cone-shaped spadix red. After foliage dies down plant needs rest period. *p. 295*

divaricatum (India, Java, Celebes, Timor, Vietnam, Hong Kong); tuberous aroid with hastate, spear-shaped, glossy light green leaves 5-15 cm long, on slender 10-30 cm petioles; spathe tubular expanding into broad ovate limb, brown-purple inside, to 15 cm long. *p. 295*

filiforme (Perak); tuberous herb with cordate, oblong, membranous, grass-green leaves on long, channeled stalks; spathe yellow dotted with red. *p. 294*

flagelliforme (Arum) (India, Malaya, Philippines); tuberous aroid with slender leaf stalk 15-30 cm long, bearing variable leaves, hastate, arrow-shaped to 3-lobed, 5-25 cm long, waxy green; spathe curious with globular base, the limb white and prolonged into a long tail to 25 cm long, the long slender spadix curving upwards. *p. 295*

giganteum giraldii (China); tuberous plant with large, hastate leaves a matte grass-green with network of veins in pale green or ivory, pale beneath; leaf stalks spotted brown-red; inflorescence having unpleasant odor; spathe brown-red. *p. 294*

trilobatum (India, Malaya); tropical aroid with near-globular tuber 4 cm thick; slender 25-30 cm petioles with hastate leaves deeply cut into 3 lobes, midlobe to 16 cm long; short-stalked, showy spathe with ovate blade 15 cm long, green outside, rose-purple inside. *Tropical.* *p. 295*

TYPHONODORUM *Araceae* **S3HBW**

lindleyanum (Madagascar, Zanzibar); handsome tree-like, smooth aroid, in habitat growing in warm lowland rivers, and sometimes becoming gigantic, 3-4 m high; forming thick stems 1-3 m long; the large, thick-fleshy, bright green sagittate leaves ½ to 1 m long, with triangular sinus; suberect creamy-white spathe 45-60 cm in length, enclosing golden-yellow spadix to 40 cm long, female in lower part, male toward apex. *Humid-tropical.* *p. 295, 303*

UEBELMANNIA *Cactaceae* **S3LBD**

meninensis (Brazil); obconical cactus with elongate stem becoming 50 cm high with age, and 10 cm thick, closely ribbed with to 40 deep folds, dissolved into free tubercles, with gray, twin spines; flowers yellow. *p. 703*

pectinifera (Brazil); small globular cactus to 10 cm or more dia., later becoming elongate, with about 15 ribs; at first blackish brown tinted purple, later with tiny white scales; small ½-1½ cm spines, blackish near apex, arranged in rows comb-like, the areoles dense along ridges; flowers yellow. *Arid-tropical.* *p. 703*

pectinifera pseudopectinifera (So. Brazil); variety of smaller size than the species, without the white-scaly dots, the spots, if any, greenish, and the spines spreading sideways and partly longer. *p. 703*

ULEX *Leguminosae* **C2LBD**

europaeus, (Western Europe, including Britain), "Gorse", "Whin" or "Furze"; densely spiny shrub to 1 m as seen wild, twice as high in gardens; shoots hairy, with tiny green, spine-tipped leaves, and two-lipped flowers golden-yellow 1½ cm long. *p. 1390*

ULMUS *Ulmaceae* **C2LBDh**

parvifolia, (China, Japan), "Evergreen elm" or "Chinese elm"; graceful, open-headed tree to 20 m high, evergreen in mild climates; dense with ovate leaves small and firm, 2 to 8 cm long, glossy grass green and finely crenate, on pendant, weeping willowy branches having foliage arranged rather flat; blooming in late summer or autumn, with inconspicuous greenish flowers. Beautiful tree in California plantings. *Warm temperate.* *p. 2105*

UMBELLULARIA *Lauraceae* **C2LBDh**

californica, (California to Oregon), "Myrtlewood" or "California laurel"; strongly aromatic evergreen tree, 15-25 m; leaves alternate, glossy green above, leathery, 5-12 cm long, narrowly oval or oblong, tapered to both ends; flowers yellowish-green in stalked umbels 1 cm wide; fruit roundish 1-2½ cm long, green becoming purplish. Leaves similar to Laurus nobilis, but not as hard-leathery, and with veins confluent inside margin; foliage of Laurus has veins running to margins. *Warm temperate.* *p. 1359, 1360*

UNCARINA *Pedaliaceae* **S3LBD**

grandidieri (Madagascar); curious succulent shrub with thick, knobby branches; small trilobed, deciduous leaves, and clusters of yellow flowers with spreading limb. *Arid-tropical.* *p. 1921*

UNIOLA *Gramineae* **I2L(or sand)BM**

paniculata (U.S.: Virginia to Florida and Texas, West Indies), "Sea-oats", or "Spike-grass"; ornamental perennial grass growing along coastal sands, with creeping rhizomes, stems to 2½ m high, with narrow leaves to 40 cm long, and 1 cm wide, rolled inward; the drooping panicle crowded with straw-colored, flat spikelets to 4 cm long, sharply keeled; used in combinations of dry flower arrangements. *p. 1310*

URBINIA purpusii: see Echeveria purpusorum

URCEOLINA *Amaryllidaceae* **S3LFMd**

miniata (peruviana) (Perú, Bolivia); small bulbous plant with flat leaves to 30 cm long; 2 to 6 nodding, inflated tubular flowers cinnabar red or scarlet; photo by J. Bogner, Munich Botanic Garden. *p. 111*

peruviana (Perú), "Urn flower"; interesting low species with small 3 cm bulb; 1 or 2 oblanceolate leaves 15-20 cm long, striated and with reflexed margins; the slender floral stalk rising at base, not from crown of bulb, 20 to 40 cm high, bearing several nodding, tubular-inflated, scented flowers 4 cm long, bright scarlet, blooming in early summer. *Subtropic.* *p. 111*

urceolata (pendula) (Perú), "Golden urn-flower"; bulbous plant with 1 or 2 long, smooth tapering, deciduous leaves 30 cm long and 8-10 cm wide, running into the 30 cm long; stout stalks, these bear 4-6 attractive urn-like, nodding flowers 5 cm long, bright yellow in basal half, upper part green, edged white; attached to a long green, stalk-like slender basal tube; summer. *p. 131*

URERA *Urticaceae* **S3LBM**

baccifera (W. Indies, Costa Rica, So. America), the "Cow-itch tree"; tropical tree with stinging hairs; broad leaves prickly on lower side; inflorescence red; small waxy white fruit. Hairs cause bad inflammation of the skin when touched. *p. 2105*

longifolia (Madagascar); shrubby plant with woody stems, and rough, long-obovate leaves covered with stinging hairs. *p. 2108*

URGINEA *Liliaceae* **I2LBMd**

maritima (Canary Islands to Syria, Brittany, Normandy), the "Sea-onion", or "Squills"; an old house plant, forming a very large ovoid red-brown bulb 10-15 cm thick, partially above ground; 10-20 fleshy, glaucous green strap-shaped leaves 30-45 cm long, wide above the middle; in the spring, the old leafbases remaining for a time; during the leafless time in summer, a 30-90 cm long slender stalk bears a short, pyramidal raceme of whitish flowers 1½cm wide, each segment with an indistinct green median stripe, the filament is thread-like, anthers green. The bulb furnishes syrup of squills. *Warm temperate.* *p. 1476, 1505*

UROSPATHA *Araceae* **S3LFW**

sagittifolia (Trop. So. America: Brazil); rhizomatous aroid from wet forest, with few triangular, hastate leaves 30-50 cm long, the two basal lobes broad and with deep sinus; floral stalk to 60 cm bearing lanceolate spathe 25-30 cm long, yellowish or green, mottled with rosy-red and having long twisted apex, white inside; spadix green. *p. 300*

tonduzii (Costa Rica); marsh plant with spongy rhizome, growing in swamps; leaf blade sagittate, 30-40 cm long x 18-24 cm wide with long pointed lobes; and with network of veins depressed; on petioles mottled with purple; the spathe erect, white inside, twisted near narrowed apex, the spadix with perfect flowers. *p. 300*

URSINIA *Compositae* **I2LBD**

geyeri (So. Africa); charming semi-trailer with gray-felty branches; gray pinnatifid leaves cut into narrow segments, with chrysanthemum-like odor when bruised; flower heads 5 cm across, solitary on slender stalks, the rays black-crimson, and central disk nearly black with yellow anthers. *p.804*

pulchra (versicolor) (So. Africa: Namaqualand); scented annual subshrub 30-60 cm high, with pale, straw-colored stems, and lacily cut pinnate leaves 5 cm long; the solitary flower heads bright orange 5 cm across, the florets marked red-purple at base, around a yellow disk. *p. 815*

UTAHIA *Cactaceae* **I2LBD**

sileri (Pediocactus) (Utah); small globular cactus 10 cm dia., slightly flattened at the white-woolly top; 13-16 prominent, warty ribs set with 13-15 awl-shaped whitish radial spines and 3-4 dark brown central spines 2 cm long; 3 cm yellow flowers. *Warm-temperate.* *p. 702*

UTRICULARIA *Lentibulariaceae (Carnivorous Plants)* **S3HOFW**

longifolia (Brazil), interesting tropical "Bladder-wort"; with densely tufted, bright green strap-shaped leaves narrowed toward the stalk, to 30 cm long, growing terrestrial or epiphytic; the plant sending out glassy tuberous branches which enter into the bark of the host tree and act as water storage organs for the absent roots; those bear at their tips tiny 1 cm bladder-like organs which can only be opened from the outside and into which insects are sucked, then close and the plant absorbs the result of their decay; flowers rosy-lilac with an orange blotch, 4 cm across. *p. 766*

menziesii (Western Australia); the plant body consists of a minute corm which grows upwards, dying off below; from it spring hundreds of minute long-stalked traps penetrating the soil in all directions; those growing upward, coming close to the surface, are covered by a rosette of long petioled spatulate leaves, from the middle of which emerges early in the wet season a stalk with unique, conspicuously brilliant red, large-spurred flowers. *p. 766*

montana (alpina) (W. Indies, S. America); epiphytic plant having tuber-like bladders into which insects are sucked through a trapdoor which can only be opened from the outside, then closes; flowers orchid-like and white. *p. 766*

UVULARIA *Liliaceae* **C2HFMh**

grandiflora (Quebec to Georgia and Kansas); perennial herb from rootstock, to 4 cm high, having green perfoliate membranous leaves, and lemon-yellow flowers with lanceolate segments 4 cm long, nodding bell-like; Spring. *p. 1506*

VACCINIUM *Ericaceae* **I2LBM**

cylindraceum (Ericaceae or Vacciniaceae) (Azores); a robust blueberry shrub with long 4-angled green branches, thin-leathery elliptic leaves; the flowers with pale or reddish calyx and bell-shaped whitish flowers; followed by large glaucous blue-black, edible berries. p. 2107

nummularia (Sikkim, Bhutan); attractive dwarf evergreen shrub from the Himalayas, dense with small oval, rugose leaves to 2 cm long; terminal hairy clusters of small pinkish to rosy-red flowers with tubular corolla; small black berries. p. 1002

ovatum (Ericaceae or Vacciniaceae) (Brit. Columbia to California), florists' "Huckleberry"; evergreen branching shrub 2-4 m high, with stiff wiry branches, attractively set with glossy green, leathery, ovate elliptic foliage all facing flat to one side, the small leaves 3-4 cm long, with prominent midrib, and margins lightly dentate; tiny white or pink flowers followed by berry-like black fruit. A favorite long-lasting florists' "greens" used with cut flower arrangements, especially during winter. p. 2110

vitis-idaea (Europe, No. Asia), the "Lingonberry"; "Cowberry", or "Mountain cranberry"; evergreen creeping shrub to 30 cm high, spreading by underground runners; leaves shining dark green 1-3 cm long, the flowers white or pink, 5 mm long in short nodding clusters; edible, sour red berries, like tiny cranberries, and used for preserves. p. 1002

VALERIANA *Valerianaceae* **C-I2LBDh**

rigida (Ecuador); interesting perennial forming rosette of dense, stiff lanceolate leaves 10-12 cm dia., in center a cluster of small white or pinkish flowers. p. 2107

sitchensis (Idaho to Alaska), "Valerian" or "Garden heliotrope"; perennial herb to 60 cm, with strong-smelling roots; basal leaves ovate or lobed, stem-leaves 3 to 5-parted; fragrant 1 cm white flowers in terminal clusters. p. 2107

VALLISNERIA *Hydrocharitaceae* **I2-3LFW**

spiralis (Europe and S. United States), aquatic "Eel-grass"; an old aquarium favorite and an ideal submerged water plant because it can adapt to many conditions, easily growing in a tank even with washed gravel bottom; perennial with short rootstock from which grow rosettes of 5-20 light green, ribbon-like leaves 20-80 cm long and 5-12 mm wide, and occasionally twisted; female plants have flowers curiously growing on a long thread-like stalk spirally twisted, with green spathe and white corolla. p. 1323

VALLOTA *Amaryllidaceae* **I2LBM**

speciosa (purpurea) (So. Africa: Cape Prov.), the "Scarborough lily"; a charming evergreen plant with large brown bulb; strap-shaped bright green leaves 45-60 cm long, the fleshy, hollow ½-1 m stalk carrying a cluster of funnel-shaped bright scarlet, long-lasting flowers 8 cm across, with stamens attached to each petal; blooming from June on. Strong undisturbed bulbs produce several flower stalks in succession. An old, good house plant, but which must be kept moderately moist even during its cool rest period in winter. *Subtropic.* p. 129

VANDA *Orchidaceae* **S-I3OFM**

x amoena (V. caerulea x tessellata); handsome natural hybrid with leaves strap-shaped, strongly channelled 2 cm wide; waxy flowers 6-8 cm across, upper 3 segments bluish-white with purple dots, lower two pale green, the cupped lip violet-blue. p. 1832

batemannii: see Vandopsis lissochiloides

"batemannii" hort.; a cultivated, compact plant with stout erect stem and fleshy, green, recurving leaves in ranks; axillary cluster of large waxy blossoms yellow with bold brown spots, reverse white and with long white tube, the lip orchid-lavender with purple stripes. I photographed this plant at our Roehrs Exotic Nurseries in June 1956. p. 1833

bicolor (Bhutan); upright growing, rooting stem with stiff-fleshy, channeled leaves to 30 cm long, divided at apex, each tip with a sharp stiff point, and arranged in two ranks; erect, rigid raceme of fleshy, strongly fragrant flowers about 5 cm across; the wavy sepals and petals purplish-brown with yellow netting inside, and white outside; the lobed lip purple in front, edged in yellow; side lobes whitish; July-Sept. (S) p. 1837

'Chimey Walker' (Flamerolle x sanderiana); highly rated, but variable hybrid with leaves closely ranked along erect stem; the well-rounded, large fleshy flowers either pink or blue with pink cast, netted and spotted brownish maroon. p. 1837

coerulea (Himalayas, Assam, Burma), the beautiful "Blue orchid"; with stems 30-90 cm high, two-ranked with 20 cm, strap-type, channeled leaves; the axillary racemes with large round, membranous flowers 5-8 cm across, sepals and petals light blue with a network of deep azure, the small lip blue, (July-Jan.). *Humid-subtropic.* p. 1835, 1836, 1838

cristata (Nepal, Burma); curious epiphyte with erect stems bearing 2-ranked leaves having 3 teeth at apex; few-flowered inflorescence, with 5 cm flowers, the sepals and petals yellow-green, the lip buff, striped rich purple between 5-7 raised white lines, and with 3 divergent narrow, horn-like lobes at tip; March-July. (D) p. 1837, 1840

deari (Indonesia: Sunda Isl.); strong-growing, with stout stem ½-2½ m high, the fleshy leaves 30 cm long, closely set; large fleshy flowers 9 cm across, soft yellow, with conical spur; summer. (S) p. 1837

denisoniana (Burma); very chaste species; erect stems with rigid, recurved dark green leaves deeply 2-lobed at apex; axillary clusters of thick-fleshy flowers 6 cm high, the sepals and petals white, slightly tinged green, the fiddle-shaped, lobed lip white also, shaded with yellow on either side of callus; April. (S) p. 1837

lamellata boxallii (Philippines); vigorous strapleaf epiphyte with stout stem 30 cm or more, with recurved, folded leaves and numerous, brightly colored, 2½-5 cm flowers in loose, erect raceme, the narrow dorsal and petals creamy-yellow, the broader lower sepals red-brown, lip rose-purple, (Nov.-Feb.). (S) p. 1836

luzonica (Philippines); strapleaf type with climbing stem making aerial roots, the leaves 30-38 cm long; short-stalked raceme of fleshy flowers 5 cm across, the sepals and petals white with an occasional purple spot and purple transverse line at base, midlobe of lip crimson; autumn. (S) p. 1837

merrillii (Philippines); striking epiphyte with stem to 2 m high, 2-ranked, overlapping, channeled strapleaves, and lateral racemes of 4-5 cm perfumed flowers with the sheen of lacquer, the obovate sepals and petals are mahogany-red on creamy-yellow base, and with blood-red blotches, (spring). (S) p. 1838

'Miss Agnes Joaquim' (hookeriana x teres) (Singapore 1893), "Corsage orchid"; terete hybrid, the famous orchid grown in Hawaii for leis and corsages, flowering in succession throughout the year; large 8 cm blooms lasting a long time, sepals white tinged with rose, the larger petals mauve purple, the broad lip purple, with yellow throat spotted red. p. 1835, 1836, 1837

'Nellie Morley' (V. Emma van Deventer 'Iwanaga' x sanderiana 'Terry'); recognized as possibly the finest of vandas in its time; two-ranked leathery, linear leaves along stout erect stem; an axillary stalk carries a cluster of large spectacular, fully rounded, fleshy flowers having a pale pink base almost completely covered by multitudes of rosy-red dots; the small red lip with pale ridges, and brown at apex. p. 1837

parishii marriottiana (So. Burma); distinct, dwarf compact epiphyte with the short stems closely-set with fleshy leaves in 2 ranks, and axillary raceme of 5 cm flowers with sepals and petals bronzy brown suffused with rose and magenta purple lip (summer). (S) p. 1834

'Princess Elizabeth', (sanderiana 'Terry' x hookeriana); very fine semi-terete hybrid; producing cluster of large rounded flowers having sepals and petals of dark lavender rose, the lip dark maroon, (bl. various). (S) p. 1836

roeblingiana (Philippines); interesting epiphyte from the northern mountains of Luzon at 1,500 m, strapleaf type with horizontal raceme of 5 cm flowers, the slender sepals and petals red-brown with yellow veins and margin, the lip unusual in being fringed and two-lobed, large and showy, yellow overlaid with brown, (Aug. and March). (I) p. 1838

x rothschildiana (coerulea x sanderiana); gorgeous strapleaf hybrid with clusters of large, flat and round flowers 8 to 15 cm across, of a beautiful amethyst-blue with darker netting, and of long-lasting qualities, (fall and winter on). *Tropical.* p. 1836, 1840

sanderiana (Euanthe, Esmeralda) (Philippines: Mindanao); a wonderful epiphyte with stout, 2-ranked leafy stem 60 cm or more high, and axillary racemes of large round, 8-10 cm blossoms with upper segments white or pink, the lower greenish or canary-yellow, tesselated with brown-crimson and small lip canary-yellow streaked with red; (Sept.-Oct.). p. 1834

sanderiana var. 'Terry'; meritorious Hawaiian seedling of this magnificent epiphyte of which a single plant produced over 85 flowers on 5 spikes; strapleaf type with 30-60 cm stems dense with 2-ranked leaves; large, round, 8-12 cm flowers, with dorsal and petals soft rose, and spotted crimson near the base, lower sepals golden brown veined with blood-red, (July-Dec.). (S) p. 1838

stangeana (Assam); stout dwarfish stem with 2-ranked channeled leathery leaves, and small racemes of 4 cm flowers inside at first greenish, then ochre, tesselated with dark purple-brown, the lip white with mauve blue (summer). (I) p. 1834, 1840

'Tatzeri x Ohuohu'; excellent Hawaiian hybrid with large 8 cm flowers, in a lovely shade of apricot, deep orange tinted from yellow to purplish red, and with brown spots. p. 1833

teres (N.E. India, Upper Burma); showy epiphyte with terete (cylindric) stems and leaves, to 2 m high, climbing trees in hot plains by aerial roots; flowers few but large, to 8 cm across, with sepals white, tinged with rose, the larger petals rose-magenta, lip 3-lobed carmine red with orange throat, (May-Sept). *Tropical.* p. 1836

teres andersonii; handsome variety with larger flowers more richly colored, sepals and petals pale rose-purple, bright rosy-magenta lip, heavily veined throat striped with orange and spotted with crimson, (April-June). 2B(su:SW, wi:CD) p. 1836

tricolor (Java); spectacular epiphyte with stems to 1 m long, dense with two ranks of recurving strap-shaped leaves; the inflorescence in lateral racemes of fragrant waxy flowers 5-8 cm across, sepals and petals lemon-yellow spotted with reddish brown, lip white with purple, (Oct.-July). *Tropical.* p. 1664A, 1838

tricolor planilabris (insignis) (Java); beautiful epiphyte with sub-erect stem dense with overlapping, curving strapleaves, with axillary stalks bearing 5-7, 5 cm flowers, the obovate sepals and petals citron-yellow spotted chocolate-brown inside, yellowish-white outside, lip purplish-rose, (June-Oct.). (S) p. 1835, 1836

tricolor suavis (Java, Bali); a beautiful variation, with the fragrant waxy flowers having a white base, spotted with blood-purple; boys and girls in the mountains of Bali, at 1000 m, not far from the temple of Besakih, offered me plants in flower in July, one naked boy asking 2 Rupiahs, then 20¢. *Tropical.* *p. 1838*

x VANDACHNIS *Orchidaceae* **S3OFM**

'Premier' (Arachnis flos-aeris x Vandopsis lissochiloides); an exotic Hawaiian bigeneric "Spider orchid", with waxy flowers having curving sepals and petals creamy-yellow boldly cross-banded brown-red. *p. 1833*

x VANDACOSTYLIS *Orchidaceae* **S3OFM**

'Dawn' (Rhynchostylis gigantea x Vanda 'Colorful'); narrow, fleshy channeled leaves; flowers with waxy petals and sepals rosy-pink; a bigeneric Hawaiian hybrid. *Tropical.* *p. 1833*

x VANDAENOPSIS *Orchidaceae* **S3OFM**

'Frank C. Atherton' (bigeneric Vandaenopsis x 'Jawaii' x Vanda sanderiana); lovely, robust hybrid with stout stem and fleshy leaves in ranks; the waxy flowers tawny-yellow and copper, the small lip with red. *Tropical.* *p. 1833*

parishii mariottiana (Thailand), (Phalaenopsis x Vanda); bigeneric hybrid, with stout stem and fleshy leaves to 20 cm long and 5 cm wide; inflorescence with 1-3 waxy flowers 4 cm across, buff-greenish-yellow to almost white at base, lip rosy lavender (spring). *p. 1833*

VANDOPSIS *Orchidaceae* **S3OFM**

gigantea (Burma, Thailand); handsome epiphyte with short, stout stems to 30 cm high, with few tongue-shaped, heavy leaves 2-lobed at apex, to 60 cm long; inflorescence arching, with numerous waxy flowers to 8 cm dia., thick and heavy-textured, creamy yellow with rings of brown-red, lip yellow; lasting for several months (spring). *Tropical.* *p. 1833*

lissochiloides (Vanda batemannii) (Philippines, Bali, Malacca); beautiful epiphyte with stout stems to 1½ m high; 2-ranked strap-shaped leaves; inflorescence waxy-white, axillary stalks with numerous large 5-8 cm, waxy flowers, sepals and petals inside golden yellow spotted with crimson, outside violet-rose, lip with yellow side lobes and orchid midlobe striped purple, (April-Oct.). *Tropical.* *p. 1838, 1840*

VANHEERDIA *Aizoaceae* **I2LBD**

roodiae (Cape Prov.); little clump-forming succulent 2½ cm high, the semi-globose, fat leaves partially united; the upper, inner surface flat, widely rounded beneath, and keeled at tip, pale green with minute white hairs, the young leaves with transparent dots; 2½ cm flowers orange-yellow. *p.77*

VANILLA *Orchidaceae* **S3HFM**

fragrans (planifolia or aromatica) (Eastern Mexico), "Common vanilla"; tall climbing orchid said to attain a length of 100 m; the light green, cylindrical stem bears 2 ranks of succulent, green, fleshy, elliptic leaves as well as aerial roots; the 5 cm flowers in axillary clusters, sepals and petals greenish-yellow, and wavy-edged lip almost white, deep yellow in throat; its dried seed pod provides vanilla for flavoring (Dec.-June). *Tropical.* *p. 1839, 1840*

fragrans 'Marginata'; attractive variety if grown on bark, for ornamental purposes, having nicely draped fleshy leaves of milky-green, bordered on each margin by a broad band of creamy-white. *Tropical.* *p. 1832, 1839*

fragrans 'Variegata'; a variegated leaf-form cultivated by Lecoufle in France, having the shiny green leaves banded and striped longitudinally with creamy-yellow. *Tropical.* *p. 1839*

imperialis (Ghana, Cameroun, Uganda); robust climber of the tropical rainforest, with stems thick cylindrical; nodes to 20 cm apart, the elliptic, fleshy leaves 15-22 cm long, 10-12 cm wide; fragile flowers to 10 cm long, in axillary racemes, creamy-green, the frilled lip with purple markings and often suffused with brown. *p. 1840*

phaeantha (Cuba, Bahamas, Trinidad, Jamaica); slender tree climber with round stems and distantly spaced, small, waxy, 8 cm lanceolate leaves, fresh green. (S) *p. 1839*

pompona (lutescens) (Mexico to Panama to Venezuela); a large-leaved climber with heavy cylindrical stem and broad ovate, thick-fleshy, dark green leaves 8-18 cm, with marked veining on the surface; large 15 cm flowers greenish yellow with bright yellow lip; more freely blooming than fragrans. *Tropical.* *p. 1839, 1840*

ramosa (C. Africa, Nigeria, Guinea, Ivory Coast); rambling epiphyte with long climbing cylindric zigzag stems forming clinging or aerial roots; the fleshy green, elliptic leaves to 20 cm long; axillary clusters of waxy flowers, sepals and petals 2-3 cm long, yellowish-white, the small pointed lip lined red inside; bean-like fruit to 11 cm long. *Tropical.* *p. 1832*

zanzibarensis (Kenya, Zanzibar, Pemba); robust species with dark green stem swollen between the distant nodes and spotted with gray; the scattered elliptic leaves are hard, shiny deep green, clinging close to trunk and climbing great trees; the 4 cm floral sepals are white or yellowish, column white, lip purple-lined and with white-fringed central tuft. (S) *p.1839*

VEITCHIA *Palmae* **S3LFM**

arecina (New Caledonia); elegant, medium-size feather palm with slender, smooth trunk to 10 m high and 15 cm dia.; above the long glossy green crown shaft an umbrella of 8-10 pinnate fronds on stiff petioles spreading horizontally, 2½ m long; vivid green broad leaflets 8 cm wide and 60 cm long, cut off obliquely at apex; 3 cm red fruit in large clusters on female trees. *Tropical.* *p. 1915*

joannis (Fiji); magnificent solitary feather palm 15 m tall, and in habitat to 30 m; the smooth straight trunk prominently ringed, 25 cm dia., with green crownshaft topped by handsome pinnate fronds gracefully arching, to 3 m long, on short petioles, the dense leaflets lustrous green and prettily pendant, cut off obliquely at their apex; inflorescence from below crownshaft, with red fruit 3 cm long. *Tropical.* *p. 1915*

merrillii (formerly Adonidia) (Philippines), the "Christmas palm", or "Manila palm"; attractive, erect palm to 6 m high, with rather slender, prominently ringed single trunk; the 1½ m fronds above a glossy green crownshaft in handsome rigidly arching crown; bright green sword-shaped, leathery, broad leaflets many and closely placed, feathered almost to base of petiole; lustrous, attractive red fruit in pendulous clusters below the crown, a striking sight during our winter season. *p. 1901, 1914, 1915*

montgomeryana (joannis) (South Pacific); slender feather-palm to 12 m high, the smooth straight trunk prominently ringed, topped by a handsome crown of long, recurving, feathery foliage, the pinnate fronds to 3 m long, the numerous lance-shaped, leathery leaflets glossy dark green, cut off at an angle at the apex. *p. 1916*

winin (New Hebrides); graceful feather-palm to 20 m high; the erect, ringed trunk bears a long glossy green crownshaft topped by spreading pinnate fronds, not as pendant as in V. joannis, nor are the lustrous dark green leaflets as gracefully pendulous but more horizontal; large inflorescence bearing clusters of ornamental bright red, small 1 cm fruit. *p. 1916*

VELLOZIA *Velloziaceae* **I-S2LBD**

elegans (Natal); low shrub with thin, branched woody stem 15 cm high, and 10-20 cm dracaena-like leaves arranged spirally at the ends of branches; parallel-veined, glossy dark green and sharply keeled; solitary flowers 4 cm across, cream-colored tinted green; pale lilac in bud. *p. 2112*

retinervis (Transvaal); remarkable, strange plant conspicuous in the landscape of the Veld; stumpy fibrous stems with long grass-like leaves crowded toward the top, 30-50 cm tall, or to 3 m on the mountains; on slender stalks the large mauve or lilac flowers, the greenish ovary covered with stiff spreading hairs. *p. 2112*

tubiflora (South America); curious tropical tree-like shrub, with woody or fibrous branching trunks 50-150 cm high, topped by clusters of grasslike, linear, recurving leaves; solitary stalked flowers with long white tube. *p. 2113*

VELTHEIMIA *Liliaceae* **C2LF-BMd**

capensis (viridifolia); known as capensis in South Africa; for description, see viridifolia. *p. 1505*

deasii (South Africa), "Forest lily"; attractive species to 30 cm, with wavy-edged, glaucous leaves in a rosette; flowers pink with green tip, yellow inside, 3 cm long; related to V. glauca but smaller and with more undulate leaves. *p. 1505*

glauca 'Rosalba' (capensis) (So. Africa); bulbous herb with about 6 lanceolate-oblong glaucous basal leaves 4 cm wide having depressed nerves, and a central terminal raceme of tubular flowers white dotted with rose; early spring. *p. 1505, 1507*

viridifolia (capensis) (So. Africa), "Forest lily"; bulbous plant having broad lanceshaped bright green leaves with undulate margins, and arching; long tubular, nodding flowers to 4 cm long, yellowish-green shading to dusty-red, and spotted, tipped green, on long red-spotted stalk; winter blooming. *Subtropic.* *p. 1408A, 1507*

VENIDIUM *Compositae* **I2LBD**

fastuosum (So. Africa: Namaqualand), "Cape-daisy", or "Namaqualand-daisy"; showy annual herb 60 cm or more high, cobwebby when young, with small grayish-green leaves irregularly lobed; solitary large, daisy-like flowers 8-10 cm across, with orange-yellow florets chocolate-brown at base, appearing as if in two rows, arranged around the flat, shining blackish-purple disk, and opening to the sun. *Subtropic.* *p. 811, 812*

VERATRUM *Liliaceae* **C2LFMh**

viride (N. E. Canada, to Minnesota and Georgia), "American hellebore", or "Indian poke"; perennial herb ½-2½ m high, with thick, very poisonous rhizome; erect leafy stem; clasping, plaited foliage 30 cm long becoming smaller; terminal panicle with numerous small, hairy, yellowish-green flowers to 2½ cm across. Veratrine, a valuable medicine, is extracted from this species, and Hellebore powder, to destroy caterpillars, is made from the rhizome. *p. 1492*

VERBENA *Verbenaceae* **I2LBD**

chamaedrifolia (peruviana); perennial semi-woody creeper with small 3-5 cm glossy, crenate leaves, and with striking clusters of vivid crimson-red flowers; photographed under this label at the University Botanic Garden, Wellington, New Zealand, but according to Hortus, this should be referred to V. peruviana. *p. 2117*

x hortensis, "Rainbow vervain"; hybrids of teucrioides and others from Brazil to Chile; herbaceous bedding plants with spreading stems more or less rooting near the base; hairy, narrow-lobed leaves, soft to the touch; broad, showy clusters of salver-form flowers in pink, red, yellow, white, blue, salmon, purple, lilac, some with white eye, blooming profusely from spring to October. *Tropical.* *p. 2118*

peruviana 'Chiquita', "Peppermint-stick verbena"; pretty, trailing plant with small foliage, and numerous clusters of flowers gaily striped lavender with white, reminding of a peppermint-stick. *p. 2116*

peruviana 'Flame', "Scarlet vervain"; low carpet-forming prostrate perennial, in its original form with crimson flowers, at home in Perú, Uruguay, and So. Brazil; at first creeping and rooting, then ascending branches with crenate, rough leaves 2½-5 cm long, and showy clusters of salver-form flowers 1 cm wide; brilliant scarlet in this color-form, and nearly everblooming, especially in summer. *Tropical.* *p. 2116*

rigida (venosa) (So. Brazil, Argentina); erect stiff perennial herb 30-50 cm high, with tuberous roots, leafy 4-angled branches, and narrow very rigid lance-leaves 5-7 cm long, sharply toothed, rough to touch; the inflorescence in bracted spikes with purple or magenta flowers 5 mm wide; a bedding plant; tubers may be kept over like dahlias. *p. 2117*

VERBESINA *Compositae* **I2LBD**

encelioides (Florida, west to Mexico), "Golden crown-beard"; annual herb to 1 m high, with grayish-hairy triangular leaves running down the stem, and flowers in solitary heads 5 cm across, the ray florets golden yellow, around the orange disk. *p. 821*

VERONICA *Scrophulariaceae* **I-C2LBM**

allionii (Hebe pyrenaica) (So. Europe), "Procumbent speed-well"; evergreen hardy perennial with prostrate creeping branches; small leathery, 1 cm oblong, finely toothed leaves dark green; violet flowers in spike-like clusters. *p. 2056*

hookeriana (nivea) (New Zealand); stout prostrate perennial with stems to 25 cm long; small 1 cm oval leaves coarsely toothed, leathery, and downy; clusters of white flowers often streaked purplish. *p. 2055*

spicata (Eurasia), "Cat's-tail speedwell'; herbaceous hardy perennial with stems 30-60 cm high; opposite toothed, lance-shaped leaves 4-5 cm long, and bright blue flowers in long, dense racemes at end of stems, with long purple stamens; summer. *p. 2053*

VERONICA: see also Hebe

VERSCHAFFELTIA *Palmae* **S3LBM**

splendida (Seychelles), "Stilt-root palm"; unique feather-leaf palm, beautiful as a slender mature tree, to 25 m tall; trunk to 15 cm dia., spiny when young, and supported by aerial roots at the base; the deep green leaves pinnately veined, quilted and more or less entire, especially when young; green fruit 3 cm dia., carried between leaves. *Tropical.* *p. 1906*

VERTICORDIA *Myrtaceae* **I2LBD**

nitens (Western Australia), "Feather flower"; erect evergreen, heath-like shrub to 1 m high; with slender stems and long-linear, fleshy, needle-like leaves 3 cm long; the inflorescence in striking terminal clusters of deep yellow fringed cups, and masses of prominent orange-yellow anthers. *Subtropic.* *p. 1611*

VESTIA *Solanaceae* **I2LBD**

lycioides (Chile); handsome evergreen shrub with downy branches, dense with alternate, oblong, smooth leaves 3-5 cm long; axillary nodding tubular flowers pale yellow 4 cm long, with reflexed lobes and protruding stamens. *p. 2074*

VIBURNUM *Caprifoliaceae* **C-I2LB-FM**

odoratissimum (India to Japan), "Sweet viburnum"; large evergreen shrub to 3 m, with willowy, reddish, rugose branches and opposite, flexible leathery, elliptic leaves glossy dark green, pale midrib and lightly crenate margins; fragrant white flowers in panicles. *p. 757*

opulus (Europe, No. Africa, No. Asia), "Cranberry bush"; deciduous shrub 3-4 m high, with opposite 3 to 5-lobed maple-like green leaves, rugose above and pubescent beneath, to 10 cm long, turning red in autumn; flowers white in stalked clusters, the white marginal flowers sterile, the center filled with fertile flowers producing the scarlet fruit. *p. 757*

opulus roseum (op. sterile) (Europe, No. Africa, No. Asia), "Common snowball-tree", or "European cranberry-tree"; deciduous shrub 3-4 m high, with 3-lobed, maple-like leaves 5-10 cm long, and coarsely toothed, downy beneath; the white flowers all sterile, and forming round, ball or rose-like terminal heads 5-6 cm across; the foliage turns deep red in autumn; hardy. (CB) *p. 757*

suspensum (Japan), "Sandankwa viburnum"; ornamental evergreen shrub with shiny dark green, leathery oval leaves crenate toward apex, and clusters of tiny fragrant flowers pinkish to cream-white. *p. 757*

tinus (S.E. Europe, Mediterranean reg.), "Laurustinus"; evergreen thickly branched and luxuriantly leafy shrub, with ovate deep green, stiff-leathery 8 cm foliage with rough underside, on reddish petioles; dense 5 to 8 cm clusters of tiny pinkish-white, very fragrant flowers; blooming May to August. Known in Europe as "Laurustinus", where it is one of the most popular durable decorator tub plants, and with its handsome foliage and compact shape ideal for cooler areas, the patio, or roof garden. *p. 757*

VICIA *Leguminosae* **C2LBM**

cracca (Europe, Asia, No. America; from Greenland to Washington), "Canada pea" or "Cow-vetch"; scrambling herbaceous perennial ½-2 m long, climbing by branched tendrils; bright green pinnate leaves with linear leaflets 2½-10 cm long; bright blue, pea-like flowers 1 cm long, in long axillary racemes, followed by flat pods. Resembles V. sativa, the Common vetch, a valuable fodder plant, but this has flowers paired, not in racemes. *p. 1392*

VICTORIA *Nymphaeaceae* **S3LBW**

cruziana (trickeri) (Paraná, Paraguay, No. Argentina), "Santa Cruz water lily"; large perennial aquatic with a thick rhizome, thorny petioles and round, floating leaves not as large as regia but with higher upturned margins to 20 cm high and green; flowers white turning deep pink on second day; requires only moderately warm water. *p. 1623, 1625*

regia (amazonica) (Guyana, Amazon, Bolivia), "Royal water lily"; gigantic, floating, 1½ m fresh green leaves with upturned red edges; projecting air-filled ribs beneath give the leaves good buoyancy, sufficient to support great weight; the fragrant floating flowers are white turning deep rose the following day; at home in quiet "Igarapes" of warm 30°C water, where rhizomes are rooted in mud. *Humid-tropical.* *p. 1625*

VIGNA *Leguminosae* **I2LFM**

sesquipedalis (Phaseolus) (So. Asia), "Asparagus-bean", or "Yard-long bean"; climbing, long-stemmed annual vine of both ornamental and culinary value, 2-2½ m high, with 3-foliate leaves, the ovate, dark green leaflets 12-15 cm long; 2½ cm flowers whitish or tinged purple, followed by the slender, extremely long 30 to 90 cm pendulous bean-pods; the seeds variously colored, and edible. *p. 1387*

VIGNA: see also Phaseolus

VILLADIA *Crassulaceae* **I2LBD**

guatemalensis (Altamiranoa) (Guatemala); stem-creeping, shrubby perennial with densely tufted, succulent, cylindric-pointed leaves to 2 cm long; small axillary, lemon-yellow tubular flowers from the leaf-like bracts. *p. 875*

imbricata (Altimiranoa) (Mexico: Oaxaca); spreading sedum-like succulent with stems 3 to 6 cm long, gradually reduced into short spike with white flowers; stems densely crowded with shingled, fleshy, bluish green leaves to 1 cm long, keeled on the outer side and spotted with tiny warts. *p. 921*

VINCA *Apocynaceae* **C-I2LBM**

major 'Variegata' (So. Europe, No. Africa), "Band plant"; trailing evergreen basket plant or for window boxes, with long, thin, wiry vines having opposite, oval, green leaves beautifully edged in cream, to 5 cm long; flowers blue. *Subtropic.* *p. 141*

minor (So. Europe to Asia Minor), "Periwinkle"; trailing evergreen subshrub with glossy dark green, ovate leaves; flowers bluish-purple with white throat, 2 cm dia. *Warm-temperate.* *p. 141*

rosea: see Catharanthus

VIOLA *Violaceae* **C2LFM**

cornuta 'Bluette', large-flowered type of "Horned violet"; much used for spring blooming, and whose ancestry is in the Pyrenees and Spain, these little, short-lived, herbaceous perennials have oval, wavy-toothed, glabrous leaves, and long-stemmed, medium-small, bright purplish-violet flowers, the yellow throat extending back and forming a spur; very floriferous. *p. 2118*

hederacea (Erpetion reniforme) (New South Wales, Victoria, Tasmania), "Australian violet", "Trailing violet", or "Ivy-leaved violet"; attractive trailing species; the vertical rhizome putting out long, thread-like stolons with well separated tufts of leaves; these kidney-shaped or rounded, 2-4 cm across, fresh green and herbaceous, small 2 cm flowers with petal-tips white, center area violet except for white eye; scarcely spurred. *Subtropic.* *p. 2118*

odorata (Europe, Asia), "Sweet violet"; small perennial with stout rhizome putting out rooting runners; long-stalked, deep green leaves round-heartshaped and toothed; the little 2 cm nodding flowers deep violet-blue with small white eye, sweetly scented, in early spring. (h) *p. 2118*

tricolor (No. Europe to C. Asia), "Wild pansy", "Johnny-jump-up" or "Kiss-me-love"; pretty annual of tufted habit, to 15 cm high, with ovate, crenate, fresh waxy-green leaves; small and cute miniature pansy flowers 1-2 cm across, with faces yellow and purple. *Temperate.* *p. 2117*

tricolor hortensis 'Maxima' (origin Europe), "Pansy"; charming shortlived, small herbaceous perennial, with long branching stems bearing glaucous leaves, and giant flowers to 10 cm across, usually in 3 colors, violet-blue, yellow or white, and a blackish "face", as well as many other shades and colors including brown; blooming best in the cool of spring. *Warm temperate.* *p. 2118*

VISCUM *Loranthaceae* **I2OFD**

album (Europe, No. Asia), the Old world "Mistletoe" of legend; parasitic evergreen shrub attached to host trees such as apples, poplars, maples or pines stealing their food; forming pendulous clusters of twiggy little branches of woody texture, dichotomously forked; sickle-shaped grayish-leathery 4-9 cm leaves; berry-like fruit yellowish to translucent white, on female plants. In Europe, cut branches are an invitation to a kiss. *Temperate.* *p. 1519*

rotundifolium (New Zealand); a parasitic plant stealing its food from host trees; leaves almost round, grayish green; shiny scarlet fruit on female plants. Seen widespread in the forested Marlborough region of South Island, N.Z. *p. 1519*

VITEX *Verbenaceae* **I2LBM**

agnus-castus (So. Europe and Asia Minor; naturalized in southern U.S. and warm areas worldwide), "Chaste tree", "Hemptree" or "Monk's pepper"; aromatic shrub or small tree to 3m or more high; the branches gray-felted and 4-angled; hemp-like deciduous, palmately compound foliage, pleasantly scented when bruised, the 5 to 7 leaflets narrow-lanceolate, 5 to 10cm long, dark green above, grayish tomentose beneath; the inflorescence in showy terminal spikes of small fragrant, pale lilac-blue flowers in autumn; little berry-like stone fruit with pungent, peppery flavor. *Warm-temperate.* *p. 2115*

lucens (New Zealand: northern North Island), the "Puriri"; shrub or tree becoming 20 m high, with strong, oak-like timber; compound leaves of broad-elliptic, folded, leathery, bright glossy green leaflets 8-10 cm long; axillary clusters of pink, trumpet-like flowers with spreading lobes, yellow in throat, and with protruding stamens. Bright red 2cm fruit resembling small cherries. *Subtropic.* *p. 2116*

VITIS *Vitaceae* **I2LBD**

amurensis (Manchuria); ornamental vigorous climber, with young growth reddish; the leaves broadly ovate, 3 or 5-lobed, 10 to 25 cm wide, and with shallow basal sinus, smooth and green above, slightly downy beneath, the foliage highly colored in autumn; 2 cm black fruit. *p. 2124*

coignetiae (Japan); handsome, strong-growing vine with heavy foliage brightly coloring crimson in autumn; leaves large, sometimes 30 cm across, roundish, and shallowly lobed, dull green above and gray or rusty-tomentose beneath; persistent purplish-black berries prettily covered with waxy bloom; fairly hardy. (C) *p. 2122*

quadrangularis: a frequently used synonym for Cissus quadrangularis, which see.

vinifera, the "Wine grape"; originally believed from the Caucasus region, known in ancient Egypt, and cultivated for centuries; woody deciduous vine moderately climbing by tendrils, with rather thin, coarsely toothed, 3-5-lobed leaves and with intermittent tendrils; small greenish unisexual flowers in long clusters followed by delicious, fleshy, glaucous berries, tender and sweet, black, red or green; for growing under glass such modified cultivars as 'Black Hamburg', 'Black Alicante', or the white 'Muscat' have long been favorites; not very hardy in north temperate climate.

vinifera 'Black Alicante' (Alicante or Black Tokay), European "Vinous" grape or "Dessert grape"; vigorously vining canes with large, deep-green leaves, covered with down underneath looking silvery; the oval fruit thick-skinned, black and covered with dense blue bloom, semi-sweet, with squashy flesh of a strong wine-flavor and earthy; for late season, and an excellent keeper, free-fruiting with large bunches of splendid appearance and weighing 1 to 2½ kg. Foremost variety long used for forcing under glass in northern Europe, and even in U.S.A. where during the time of the great conservatory ranges, it was listed in Roehrs catalogs since 1907. *Warm-temperate.* *p. 2122*

vinifera 'Black Hamburg'; a famous old "Sweetwater" grape, with a pleasant, sweet sugary flavor, the juice thin but pleasant, with skin thin and tender, the large berries 2½-4 cm dia., deep bluish-black, covered with a fine bloom, the flesh firm yet tender; in medium sized ½-1 kg bunches; for early, cool forcing before Christmas. Strong, very tolerant grower, with attractive fresh green leaves. Originally the German 'Frankenthal' grape, the Great Vine at Hampton Court in England was planted in 1769, and has been producing many hundreds of bunches every year. *p. 2123*

vinifera 'Muscat of Alexandria'; a European "Muscat" white grape; with a musky or perfumed flavor; large oval berries, with clear skin, rather thick, greenish-yellow; firm, crackling fleshy, exceedingly sweet, in handsome, long-tapering clusters weighing 1-2 kg or more; for late fruiting, and requiring some warmth; will keep in good condition until late in spring. Healthy grower with deeply lobed rugose foliage. Grown under glass in Holland for table use, but also produces Muscatel wine. *p. 2122*

VITIS: see also Cissus, Parthenocissus, Rhoicissus, Tetrastigma

VITTARIA *Polypodiaceae (Filices)* **I-S3OFM**

lineata (Florida, West Indies, to Perú, and east to Asia), the odd "Shoestring-fern" or "Old-man's beard"; in Florida, where it grows on palmetto palms, from short rhizomes, locally known as the "Florida ribbon-fern"; rather hard-leathery, rush-like dark green fronds like flattened ribbons, not particularly attractive, less than 3 mm wide and 15-45 cm long and pendant; narrowed downward to a stout stem; the spores along edges turned under. *p. 1166*

VRIESEA *Bromeliaceae* ***I-S1HFD**

altodaserrae (Brazil: São Paulo, Paraná, Santa Catarina); robust large rosette of stiff green, smooth leaves with faint dark green marbling, 6 to 8 cm wide; erect inflorescence 1 m high with slender branches, the green bracts along the stalk tipped with salmon. *p. 607*

ampullacea ('Espirito Santo') (Brazil); interesting unusual plant found by Burle-Marx in Espirito Santo; star-shaped xerophytic rosette growing on rocks, stiff daggershaped leaves silvery-pearled and tinted amethyst; edges as if cut off squarely; spiked inflorescence yellowish. *Tropical.* *p.530*

barilletii (Ecuador); small rosette of soft green leaves tinted copper and with the smooth edge of all Vrieseas; inflorescence a flattened head of spreading bracts solid purple at the base to purple-spotted and yellow top; yellow flowers. *p. 603, 604*

bituminosa (Brazil); large stocky rosette with broad blue-green leaves purple-tipped; inflorescence on erect spike with scattered bracts on either side of stalk; flowers yellow. *Tropical.* *p. 513, 601, 610*

botafogensis: see V. saundersii

carinata (S.E. Brazil), "Lobster claws"; dainty plant with pale green foliage; colorful and striking, flattened spike with spreading bracts deep yellow with crimson base, the yellow dotted green; flowers yellow. *Tropical.* *p. 5*, 19*, 513, 604, 608*

x chantrieri (splendens x splendens major); a strikingly ornamental rosette of broad nile-green to bluish recurved leaves with bold broad crossbands of purple almost black, even more so underneath, and a blazing scarlet swordlike flattened spike with yellow flowers. *p. 603*

didistichoides (West Indies, Trinidad, Venezuela, Colombia); stemless epiphytic rosette, with densley scurfy, rigid, channeled leaves broad at base and forming a bulbous base with an urn on top, rapidly tapering to slender points and outcurving, 20-25 cm long; the arching bipinnate inflorescence with shingled bracts, the flattened spikes with pink floral bracts and white or lilac petals. *p. 606*

drepanocarpa (S. E. Brazil); attractive rosette with narrow leaves from broad base, medium green with purplish-maroon lines and tinting especially at base; cylindric inflorescence with short, few-flowered branches that are mostly covered by large bracts. *p. 608*

ensiformis (Bahia to Santa Catarina); small rosette with pale green leaves tinted amethyst; erect inflorescence with spreading bright red bracts and yellow flowers. *p. 608*

ensiformis x guttata; attractive rosette with broad waxy, yellow-green leaves sprinkled all over with blood-red spots; erect, thick-stalked inflorescence with yellow flowers. *p. 608*

x erecta (poelmanii x rex), "Red feather"; shapely rosette of glossy light green leaves; the inflorescence a flattened spike with dense keelshaped deep lacquer-red bracts, the tips separated, and with yellow flowers. *p.601,605*

erythrodactylon (S.E. Brazil); dense rosette with a singularly beautiful inflorescence which caught my eye as growing in low rain-forest in the moist-cool Serra do Mar above Santos; flattened spike green in center, curving out to spreading, coxcomb-like, rose-pink tips. *Tropical.* *p. 604*

erythrodactylon var. striata (So. Brazil); natural variety found by Seidel, with the smooth, soft-leathery, gracefully recurving linear leaves, 25 cm long, normally fresh green running into a dark purple base, attractively striped and banded lengthwise with pale green or cream. *p. 606*

espinosae (Ecuador, Perú); valid name for Tillandsia espinosae; very small, silvery green rosette 15 cm across, with rigid, frosted leaves resembling tillandsia, and forming runners; the floral spike with red bracts and violet-blue petals. *p. 612*

'Favorite' (ensiformis hybrid); vigorously growing rosette of shiny rich-green leaves; inflorescence a slender stem, usually branched, with maroon keel-shaped bracts darker than poelmanii, and arranged separated along stalk; flowers yellow. *Tropical.* *p. 513, 603*

fenestralis (Brazil), "Netted vriesea"; compact rosette of broad recurved foliage arranged spirally, yellow-green leaves ornamented by numerous dark green lines and network of cross lines, purplish circles underside; sulphur yellow flowers scattered on pale spike. *Humid-tropical.* *p. 513, 601, 602, 604*

fenestralis 'Variegata'; elegant formal epiphytic rosette with broad recurving leaves 40 cm long and 6-8 cm wide, the foliage glossy rich green with a network of yellowish markings, and some of the leaves having a contrasting cream border; purplish circles underside; simple inflorescence with night-blooming sulphur-yellow, fragrant flowers. *Tropical.* *p. 607*

fosteriana (Espirito Santo); showy rosette of stiff, nile-green to bluish leaves attractively marked with irregular dark green pencil lines across the surface, lines maroon beneath and maroon border; showy inflorescence to 2 m high, with scattered greenish bracts and pale yellow flowers. *p. 604*

fosteriana 'Red Chestnut'; beautiful cultivar photographed at the German National Bromeliad Show in Frankfurt 1973; large rosette with broad leaves deep green traced by irregular cream cross-bands; coppery underneath. *Tropical.* *p. 610*

fosteriana 'Seideliana'; handsome formal rosette of olive green leaves crossed by irregular, narrow yellow bands, center and reverse bronze. Photographed at Botanic Garden Frankfurt, Germany. *Tropical.* *p. 607*

'Gemma'; a German hybrid according to Dr. Rauh of Heidelberg, involving V. barilletii, carinata, psittacina, duvaliana and incurvata; small rosette of fresh-green leaves; the slender inflorescence a flat feather spike with scarlet center changing to copper and yellow toward tips; flower petals yellow. *p.611*

geniculata (Alcantarea speciosa) (Brazil: Minas Gerais, Guanabara); rosette with green leaves to 1 m long and 17 cm wide; the inflorescence to 2 m high, with arching, alternate flat spikelets, floral bracts and flowers ivory. *p. 605*

gigantea (tessellata) (S.E. Brazil); strong rosette of broad leaves to 75 cm long, glabrous bluish-green when older, the younger leaves yellow-green and marked with many dark length and cross-lines like a checker-board, purplish edge and tip; tall branched spike with green bracts and yellow flowers. *Tropical.* *p. 603, 606, 613*

glutinosa (stenostachya) (Trinidad); dainty rosette with erect, arching, thin-leathery linear leaves 30 cm long, smooth, fresh-green, to jade green at base, with red-brown, more or less pronounced crossbands; inflorescence with slender branches; flaming red bracts, and spreading flowers. *p. 607*

guttata (So. Brazil), "Dusted feather"; small compact rosette of glaucous bluish-green leaves liberally marked with maroon spots; inflorescence a pendant, lightly flattened spike of greenish beige bracts, covered with silver pink bloom, flowers lemon-yellow. *p. 601, 602*

heliconoides (Guatemala, Costa Rica, Colombia, Brazil, Guyana, Bolivia); striking flowering plant, with rosette of plain, glossy green leaves 20 cm long, suffused with red underneath; the erect flattened inflorescence heliconia-like having lateral triangular boat-shaped floral bracts bright red above the middle, greenish-yellow at the apex; the flowers peeking out with creamy white petals. *Tropical.* *p. 605*

hieroglyphica (Brazil: Espirito Santo to Paraná), "King of bromeliads"; large epiphytic rosette with broad yellow-green leaves to 60cm long, beautifully cross-banded with hieroglyphic marks dark green above and purplish-brown beneath; inflorescence a tall branched spike with sulphur-yellow flowers. *Humid-tropical.* *p. 513, 600, 601, 603, 606, 611*

hieroglyphica 'Marginata'; also known as 'Mad. Morobi'; in this spectacular variety the hieroglyphic pattern, which normally mimics the light and shadow pattern of the rain forest for camouflage, is dramatically highlighted by broad marginal bands of creamy ivory. *p. 600*

hieroglyphica zebrina (Santa Terésa, Brazil), "Zebra king"; showy form with darker green leaves and the irregular crossbanding very pronounced and purplish black. *p. 601*

hoehneana (Brazil: São Paulo); handsome formal rosette similar to gigantea (tesselata), with broad, bluish green leaves mottled with yellow and green but without the marked lengthlines of yellow and dark green. *p. 609*

imperialis (Estado do Rio), "Giant vriesea"; gigantic terrestrial rosette which I found growing on the dry west slopes of the Organ Mountains; leathery green leaves to 1½m long, in good light becoming deep wine-red, and even young plants produce seedling-like suckers at the base; the inflorescence a tall branched spike 2 m or more, the large bract leaves glossy maroon-red, and from which extend the arching bracted spikes with yellow flowers. *Tropical.* *p. 600, 613*

incurvata (S.E. Brazil), "Sidewinder vriesea"; light green rosette of soft leaves 25-30cm long; the inflorescence on a leaning stem with the flat spike recurving upward, the fleshy bracts glowing red and edged yellow; flowers yellow. *Subtropic.* *p. 513, 601*

incurvata var. striata; a natural variety found by Seidel in So. Brazil; shapely rosette with concave, recurving leaves 25 cm long, smooth, light green, attractive with pale green to ivory bands or stripes lengthwise. *p. 606*

inflata (S. E. Brazil), compact rosette of metallic green leaves; inflorescence on flattened spike of closely compacted red and greenish bracts with yellow flowers. *p. 604*

x intermedia (hieroglyphica x fenestralis); beautiful rosette of thin-leathery waxy leaves pale yellow-green attractively cross-barred and marbled with dark green hieroglyphics on both sides; raised inflorescence with pale yellow flowers. *Tropical.* *p. 608, 612*

longibracteata (Guyana); according to Dr. L. B. Smith, a variety of V. splendens; an epiphyte found in the tropical forest along the Kaieteur River; rosette of thin, recurved bright green leaves 40-50 cm long and 4-5 cm wide; from the center a sword-like flattened spike 30 cm long, yellow-green at base merging into orange red, and yellow flowers. *p. 612*

x mariae (magnifica), "Painted feather"; hybrid larger than carinata; light green foliage tinted pink, and showy, flattened, featherlike spike with bracts salmon-rose at base, and yellow dotted brown toward apex; yellow flowers. *p. 25*, 512A, 603, 608*

montana (Trop. America); stocky rosette with broad, leathery leaves yellowish green and striped with brown, with zigzag cross-lines of crimson red. *p. 611*

'Perfecta' (carinata x poelmanii); magnificent flowering plant, photographed at the World's Fair Expo 1970 in Osaka, Japan; rosette with spreading glossy green leaves tinted with copper; the stout erect, long lasting, branching inflorescence of several flattened spikes of imbricated scarlet bracts with yellow flowers; a stunning display of elegance and color. *Tropical.* *p. 609, 612*

philippo-coburgii (S.E. Brazil), "Vagabond plant"; small rosette which sends out its offshoots from travelling stems; leaves light green with black bases; inflorescence a flattened spike with yellow and red bracts and yellow flowers. *Subtropic.* *p. 513, 601*

platynema (West Indies to Brazil); rosette of flaccid strap leaves, deep glossy green; inflorescence with stalk bearing opposite spikes of yellow boat-shaped bracts, and red at base. *Tropical.* *p. 612*

platynema var. variegata; found in So. Brazil by Seidel, a noble rosette of broad leathery leaves to 75 cm long, in the type bluish-green with darker, wavy lines and a short-pointed apex boldly blotched with violet, and violet-blue beneath; in the variety with pale length lines; stiff-erect, simple inflorescence with purple bracts, and flowers with thick, shining, greenish-white sepals. *p. 606, 609*

x poelmanii (gloriosa x vangeertii); vigorous, shapely rosette of light green leaves; the inflorescence stalk usually branching into flattened spikes; bracts crimson-red with greenish-yellow apex, and yellow flowers. *Tropical.* *p. 599, 603, 613*

'Poelmanii hybrid'; a highly developed, beautiful cultivar of German origin; compact rosette of broad, glossy fresh green leaves; from the center a bold and stocky, branched inflorescence of several flattened spikes of imbricated bracts, brilliant crimson red with yellow base, and yellow flowers; much more compact than V. poelmanii, and long-lasting as a decorative plant. *Tropical.* *p. 609*

'Polonia' (kitteliana x vigeri); small shapely rosette of little green leaves, with attractive inflorescence a branched stem with several miniature flattened heads of glowing rosy-red bracts and deep yellow flowers. *Tropical.* *p. 599, 603*

psittacina (Brazil: Bahia to Guanabara), "Dwarf painted feather"; small epiphytic rosette of yellowish-green, thin-leathery, recurving leaves 20 cm long; the simple, pinnate inflorescence, loosely set feather-like, with 2 ranks of fleshy, inflated red bracts edged with yellow, the flowers yellow and spotted with green. *p. 608*

psittacina x ensiformis; attractive hybrid photographed in Golden Gate Park conservatory San Francisco 1972; rosette with glossy-green, strap-like, soft leaves; from between the foliage rises an erect inflorescence of 2-ranked waxy bracts bright yellow, red at base and stalk. *p. 612*

racinae (Brazil: Espirito Santo); pretty little rosette 10 cm high, the foliage broad at base, forming an urn, but reflexing and even curling sharply outward and under, tapering to a point, glossy green and leathery, spotted brown-violet beneath; erect simple inflorescence 25 cm long, with green bracts dark-spotted, the greenish-white flowers turned in one direction, and smelling like ripe apples. *p. 605*

rauhii (Perú); rosette with the habit of Tillandsia flabellata, the green-brown leaves slightly waxy-glaucous, 30 cm long, from a broad base becoming narrow-linear and channeled; the arching or pendant, branched inflorescence with short bracts, and dark bluish-purple, tubular flowers. *p. 609, 612*

regina (Brazil: Distrito Federal); giant, bold rosette of regular, elegant beauty; the broad concave, waxy green leaves densely speckled with maroon dots toward base and underneath as well as along margins, pointed apex sharply recurved; inflorescence to 2 m high, with 2-ranked spikes of rose bracts and white to yellow perfumed flowers. *p. 602*

x retroflexa (Brazil) (natural hyb. of psittacina x simplex); small rosette with thin-leathery, waxy, pale green leaves; inflorescence pendulous, with open or loosely separated, yellow floral bracts laterally depressed, and yellow flowers. *Tropical.* *p. 608, 611*

ringens (W. Indies, Costa Rica, Colombia); usually a small rosette, but variable with light green leaves from 12cm to occasionally 90cm long, marked by speckled maroon crossbands, and a slender spike with scattered rusty red bracts and yellow flowers; I found this on the Rio Mameyes in Puerto Rico, and interesting because so far north. Flowers fragrant, open at night. *Tropical.* *p. 604*

rodigasiana (So. Brazil), "Wax shells"; dwarf rosette of soft, dull green leaves with base tinged purple; inflorescence on branched stem with waxy lemon-yellow bracts and flowers. *Tropical.* *p. 599, 601*

'Rubin'; small, open rosette of green leaves; large inflorescence of flattened spikes, glossy bracts crimson-red; petals yellow; very striking in its compact shapeliness. *Tropical.* *p. 609*

sanguinolenta (West Indies, Costa Rica to Colombia); bold epiphytic rosette with broad flexible leaves, 90 cm long and 8 cm wide, nile green with markings of wine-red; the inflorescence erect like a spire with green bracts and white flower petals. *p. 611*

saundersii (botafogensis; Encholirion) (Rio); small rosette with broad, stiffly recurved leaves, silvery gray and well spotted purplish-red, especially beneath; inflorescence on arching branched stem with waxy lemon-yellow bracts and yellow flowers. *p. 603*

scalaris (Brazil: Espirito Santo to Santa Catarina); small rosette of thin-leathery, obovate light green leaves 15 cm long; the charming inflorescence pendulous with scattered flowers attached as if to a snaky wire; floral bracts red-brown, flowers yellow. Ideal for wall bracket or hanging basket. *p. 610*

schwackeana (Minas Gerais, São Paulo); stocky rosette with spreading, broad leaves from fluted base, medium olive green spotted with purplish red dots and edged purplish-maroon; flowers in 2 ranks, the bracts bright red, petals and sepals yellow. *p. 605*

simplex (Trinidad, Colombia, Brazil); rosette with leaves tapering to point from broad base, deep coppery green, the reverse glossy maroon-purple forming lines toward base; lax inflorescence with yellow flowers and red bracts, pendant but with apex turning up. *p. 602, 613*

simplex var. rubra; glossy red-bronzy, strap-shaped soft leaves; deflexed inflorescence with flattened spike, at right angle from the stalk, the shingled bracts red at base, greenish toward apex; flowers yellow. *p. 611*

sintenisii (Thecophyllum) (Puerto Rico, Cuba, Haiti, Jamaica); epiphyte of the high cloud forests; shapely rosette of soft-leathery, glossy leaves 25 to 45cm long, green in shade, but beautifully colored wine-red in bright light; inflorescence a lax spike with showy red bracts, and yellow flowers. *Tropical.* *p. 513, 602*

splendens (Guyana, Venezuela, Trinidad), "Flaming sword"; broadly funnel-form rosette, both epiphytic and terrestrial, of slender bluish-green leaves 40-80cm long, marked with broad deep purple crossbands; underneath grayish with the purple bands very bold; flower spike long and swordshaped with flattened fiery-red bracts and yellow flowers. *p. 604*

splendens 'Andenken Carl Wolf'; unusual German cultivar with the basically bluish green leaves and its purple crossbands intersected by lengthwise bands of creamy yellow. *p. 610*

splendens 'Chantrieri'; a select clone made from two cultivars of V. splendens var. splendens; elegantly formed rosette of broad leaves nile green to bluish, distinctively and clearly cross-banded with dark purple to almost black; inflorescence an erect flattened spike of glossy scarlet-red shingled bracts and yellow flowers. *p. 610*

splendens 'Major'; clone more robust; wider leaves with bold purplish crossbands and broader, swordlike spike a flaming-red suffused with copper. The similar cultivar **'Flaming Sword'** is a cross between V. splendens 'Major' and V. splendens longibracteata. *Tropical.* *p. 15*, 513, 599, 602*

splendens 'Variegata'; a remarkable cultivar on exhibit at the German National Flower Show in Cologne 1971, with leaves blackish-green cross-banded in sharply contrasting yellow-green to creamy-white. *Tropical. p. 610*

tessellata (gigantea) (So. Brazil); very decorative large rosette with broad leaves to 50 cm long and 8 cm wide, brownish-green with a network pattern of yellow green lines like a chessboard; the tall inflorescence on an erect stalk in two-ranked feather fashion, with light green stem bracts and yellow-green flowers. *p. 610, 612*

unilateralis (So. Brazil); small epiphyte from the forests on the lower slopes of the Serra do Mar above Santos: rosette of soft, light green leaves 30 cm long and 3-4 cm wide; the leaning floral stalk bearing up to 12 inflorescences with greenish bracts and yellow flowers. *p. 610*

'Vigeri' (rodigasiana x rex); medium-sized rosette with glossy, bright green, flexible leaves; the stalked inflorescence is branched into flattened feather spikes with crimson-red bracts and yellow flowers. *p. 609*

WACHENDORFIA *Haemodoraceae* **I2LFMd**

paniculata (So. Africa); tuberous-rooted perennial with few sickle-shaped, ribbed and plaited leaves 50-75 cm long and 15 cm wide; a tall floral stalk 1 to 2 m or more, bearing cylindrical panicles of golden yellow flowers with 6 petals red-hairy outside, 4 cm across, in spring. *p. 1321*

WAITZEA *Compositae* **I-S2LBD**

aurea (Australia); "everlasting" herbaceous annual 30-50 cm high, branching with erect leafy stems, the foliage linear and covered with short gray hairs; lower leaves spreading, the upper ones pressed against the stem; 1-2 cm flower heads subtended by the golden-yellow papery, showy bracts in 4-5 rows, 3-4 cm across. *p. 821*

WALLICHIA *Palmae* **S3LFM**

densiflora (E. Himalaya: Assam); tropical, clustering small palm without noticeable trunk and very fibrous base; erect-arching pinnate fronds to 4 m long, the numerous lanceolate leaflets dark glossy-green above and whitish underneath, the midrib brown, and margins lobed and toothed; the male spathes dark purple streaked yellow; flowers violet. *Tropical.* *p. 1909, 1916*

disticha (Himalayas, Burma); handsome, straight-erect fan palm 3-6 m high, forming solitary trunk 12-15 cm thick; the pinnate leaves 2-3 m long, peculiarly arranged on opposite sides in two ranks fan-like, almost like the Traveller's tree; thė stiff, dark green leaflets 30-60 cm long, notched at the middle, cut-off and notched at apex, glaucous beneath; flowers green, and dull-red fruit. *Tropical.* *p. 1915, 1916*

WARREA *Orchidaceae* **S3HFM**

costaricensis (Costa Rica, Panama); handsome terrestrial orchid with pseudo-bulbs topped by strong-veined leaves; erect floral spike 50 cm tall, with unusual flowers cup-shaped, burnished pink to flesh-colored and with purple lines, the dorsal sepal forming a hood. *Tropical.* *p. 1832*

warreana (Colombia, Venezuela, Guianas, Brazil); robust terrestrial with clustered spindle-shaped pseudobulbs; plicate, heavy-textured leaves 50 cm long and 12 cm wide; inflorescence erect on purplish stalk to 70 cm high; flowers not opening fully, faintly fragrant, 4 cm across, sepals and petals white tinged with yellow, the lip inside yellow and red (late summer). *Tropical.* *p. 1832*

WARSCEWICZELLA: see Cochleanthes

WARSZEWICZIA *Rubiaceae* **S3LFM**

coccinea (Trinidad, C. America to Brazil), "Wild poinsettia"; large tropical shrub to 6 m high, with sparry, woody branches bearing big obovate, corrugated leaves 20-50 cm long; at end of arching shoots the striking elongate inflorescence 30 cm or more long, serving as a rachis (axis) for sessile clusters of small 1 cm orange flowers set at intervals and subtended on both sides by the bract-like crimson-red calyx lobes 8-12 cm long. Photographed at Papeari Botanic Garden, Tahiti. *Tropical.* *p. 2023*

coccinea cv 'David Auyong' (Trinidad cultivar); spectacular rambling shrub, having spreading branches with large corrugated leaves, extending into a long rachis carrying a dense row of small yellow flowers sitting along the top, on both sides a dual row of oblong glowing red bracts or calyx leaves. *Tropical.* *p. 2017*

coccinea plenissima (Trinidad), "Chaconia"; with magnificent double inflorescence; the arching rachis (axis) densely covered by multitudes of short obovate, brilliant red bracts. *p. 2023*

WASHINGTONIA *Palmae* **I2LBM**

filifera (So. California desert, S.W. Arizona, Baja California), "Desert fan palm" or "Petticoat palm"; in habitat in Agua Caliente canyon, Palm Springs, California; bold solitary, erect fan palm with massive grayish trunk to 1 m thick and 18 to 25 m tall, usually clothed by the densely shingled older leaves and looking like a skirt, unless burnt off; the top with a crown of palmate, gray-green, leathery fronds 2 m or more across, divided more than half-way to base, and with many long threads attached to segments, on thorny, long, green petioles. For dry-hot climate. *Subtropic.* *p. 1909, 1913, 1914, 1916*

robusta (N.W. Mexico: Sonora, Baja California), the "Mexican fan palm"; more slender than filifera and faster growing, to nearly 34 m tall, the upper part dense with brown dead, and living glossy bright green foliage, the plaited fan-leaves are stiff and lightly cut, to $1\frac{1}{4}$ m long, and with some fibrous threads in juvenile stage; fruit black-brown. Rarely used as container plant, but much planted in warm-arid climate along avenues and homes for tropical effect in not quite tropical regions. Older tall specimen look scrawny, with relatively small crowns up high. *Subtropic.* *p. 1874, 1893, 1913, 1914*

WATSONIA *Iridaceae* **C2LBMd**

humilis maculata (So. Africa: Cape Prov.), "Southern bugle-lily"; handsome small spring or summer blooming cormous plant closely allied to Gladiolus, with smaller, regular flowers and more tubular; the sword-shaped leaves basal and also along the 30-50 cm stalk; flowers 5 cm long, deep rose with a purple blotch between the lobes at base; takes rest after foliage turns yellow. *p. 1340*

meriana (So. Africa); herbaceous plant from a corm, the stems with sword-shaped flat leaves glaucous green, and stalks to 1 m tall with spikes bearing successive curved tubular flowers opening into spreading lobes, rosy pink with carmine in center; summer-blooming. *Subtropic.* *p. 1335*

pyramidata (rosea) (South Africa), "Pink watsonia"; breath taking to see a slope in the Hottentot-Holland Mountains, or down the Cape Peninsula, covered in spring with these rosy-flowered Watsonias; cormous plant $1\text{-}1\frac{1}{2}$ m high, having nearly linear basal leaves, and the long, branched spike-like inflorescence carrying showy rose-pink funnel-shaped flowers with curved tube, the spreading lobes to 5 cm across. *Subtropic.* *p. 1336*

WEBEROCEREUS *Cactaceae* **S3HFM**

tunilla (Costa Rica); night-blooming epiphyte climbing by aerial roots, ribbed green stems with areoles bearing a tuft of felt; small 5 cm flowers pinkish, linear outer perianth segments brownish. *p. 662*

WEDELIA *Compositae* **I2LFM**

trilobata (West Indies, N. So. America), "Creeping daisy"; prolifically branching herb with slender, flexible trailing stems; elliptic, fresh green, notched and lightly lobed, somewhat fleshy leaves, 5 to 10 cm long; and attractive marigold-like flowers with golden yellow florets, 2 cm across. A cheerful basket plant or ground cover. *Tropical.* *p. 813*

WEIGELA *Caprifoliaceae* **C2LB-FM**

florida (Diervilla) (No. China, Korea); handsome, very popular deciduous shrub 2-3 m high, with spreading branches, broad-elliptic toothed leaves 8-10 cm long; very pretty, funnel-shaped flowers 4 cm long, with blunt, spreading lobes, deep rose outside, paler inside; in small clusters, profusely on new season stems; fairly hardy. *p. 757*

praecox (Diervilla) (Korea), "Early rose weigela"; deciduous shrub to 2 m with leafy branches, elliptic leaves soft pubescent; 3-5 funnel-shaped flowers on lateral shoots, rose with yellow throat; used for forcing. *p. 757*

WELWITSCHIA *Gnetaceae* **I2LBD**

mirabilis (bainesii) (Namibia, So. Angola), "Tree tumbo"; curious succulent of the foggy Namib desert; from a low caudex to 1 m thick, with big taproot, spread 2 thick-fleshy, monstrous, strap-like leaves to 6 m long and 20 cm wide, glaucous or waxy green, corrugated lengthwise, with parallel veining, and continuing to grow from the base, not from the apex, over the surface of the ground or curling; the ends usually become split and shredded into leathery thongs if exposed to desert storms. Inflorescence cone-like, the females green, 5 cm long, on branched stalk, the male cones red-brown, only 3 cm long. Said to become 1000-2000 years old, these desert dwellers survive on the surface dew which daily settles along the southwestern coast of Africa, with cold nights and hot days. *Arid-tropical.* *p. 1317*

WERCKLEOCEREUS *Cactaceae* **S3HFM**

tonduzii (Costa Rica); slender epiphyte with pale green, triangular stems, rarely 4-angled, toothed, climbing by aerial roots; flowers funnel-shaped, the tube with black wool, outer petals brownish pink, inner petals cream. *p. 662*

WESTRINGIA *Labiatae* **I2LBM**

rosmariniformis (Queensland, New So. Wales); evergreen flowering shrub ½ to 1 m high, dense with small linear, leathery 1-3 cm leaves in whorls; shining green above, hoary and silvery white beneath, the margins turned under; small tubular, axillary white flowers spotted purple; July blooming. *p. 1358*

WIDDRINGTONIA *Cupressaceae (Coniferae)* **I2LBM**

dracomontana (Natal), "African cypress"; tender evergreen tree of graceful, loose habit, with branches in all directions, the little flat needles arranged spirally, gray when young, light green and scale-like in older stages. *p. 838*

whytei (Tanzania, Malawi); noble, symmetrical coniferous evergreen, first shapely pyramidal, later becoming a large tree to nearly 45 m high and wide-spreading; the juvenile plant with rising, plumy branches densely set with bluish-green fine needles to 2½ cm long, later scale-like, pressed close to shoot; small cones to 3 cm long. *Tropical.* *p. 840*

WIGANDIA *Hydrophyllaceae* **I2LBM**

cicosum (Trop. America); handsome shrubby perennial with large oval, rugose, substantial leaves to 30 cm long, rich green and very wrinkled by the network of sunken primary and secondary veins; the inflorescence with brown-woolly burs, flowers pale purple with white center. Photographed at the University Botanic Garden of Lisbon, Portugal. *p. 1321*

macrophylla (caracasana) (So. Mexico to Venezuela and Colombia); robust shrub or tree to 3 m and more; the ovate, crenate leaves 45 cm long and to 25 cm wide, are covered with glistening stinging hairs; flowers violet with white tube 2 cm long in terminal clusters. *p. 1318*

WIGGINSIA *Cactaceae* **I2LBD**

corynodes (Malacocarpus) (So. Brazil, Uruguay, Argentina); dark olive-green globe to cylindric 20 cm high, woolly at the top, with 13-16 acute notched ribs with yellow spines; flowers with outer petals greenish, inner petals canary. *p. 696*

erinaceus (Malacocarpus) (So. Brazil, Uruguay, Argentina); globular cactus to 15 cm dia., dark green, woolly at the top and with 15-20 broad spiral ribs; notched, woolly areoles in the depressions, small brownish spines; flowers yellow. *p. 696*

sellowii (Malacocarpus) (So. Brazil, Uruguay, Argentina); small depressed globe to 15 cm across, dark green or grayish; 16-18 broad ribs with narrow furrows, areoles with white wool when young, honey-yellow spines; flowers canary. *p. 696*

tephracantha (Malacocarpus) (So. Brazil, Uruguay, Argentina); globe-shaped, later elongate cactus to 15 cm dia., deeply furrowed with 16-18 acute ribs, dark green or grayish, the edges with areoles and small yellow spine clusters, and woolly at the top; flowers 4 cm across, with inner petals canary yellow, style reddish; pink berries. *Arid-subtropic.* *p. 704*

vorwerkianus (Malacocarpus) (Colombia), "Colombian ball"; small, flat-topped, deeply 20 ridged, bright green plant, spines straw colored, white woolly at top; flowers sulphur-yellow. *p. 680, 696*

WILCOXIA *Cactaceae* **I-S2LBD**

poselgeri (Texas, Coahuila); low spiny cactus with tuberous, dahlia-like roots; slender cylindrical dark green stems 60 cm high and 2 cm thick, with 8-10 ribs almost hidden by appressed whitish spines; pink flowers lasting several days. *Arid-subtropic.* *p. 643*

schmollii (Cereus) (Mexico); curious cactus with tuberous roots and slender, weak stems 6 cm dia., profusely branched, with 8 to 10 low ribs, entirely hidden under a mass of silky white hairs; large funnel-shaped flowers purplish-red, 4-5 cm long. *p. 656*

striata (Mexico: Baja California, Sonora); branching cactus with slender, sprawling stems 1-2 cm thick and 1 m long, bluish green to grayish, with 8 or 9 ribs and short cluster spines; flowers large, 10 cm long, purplish red outside, white inside, blooming at night. *p. 658*

WILKESIA *Compositae* **S3LFM**

gymnoxiphium (argyroxiphium) (Hawaii), the "Iliau"; found only on the mountain slopes of Kauai, a woody plant 1 to 4 m high, with a single stem bearing at the apex whorls of narrow leaves 15 to 40 cm long; the flowers in large clusters, each head 2-3 cm dia., with many yellow, tubular disk florets and no ray flowers; after bearing its scale-tipped fruits, the plant dies. *p. 827*

WISTERIA *Leguminosae* **I2LBMhd**

floribunda (Glycine) (Japan), "Japanese wisteria"; woody twiner, dwarfed into bush form by pruning, with pinnate leaves and beautiful pendulous racemes of fragrant, pea-shaped flowers in shades of violet-blue. *p. 1393, 1394*

floribunda 'Macrobotrys' (multijuga) (Japan); tall-climbing woody vine with glossy green pinnate leaves 25-30 cm long; the showy terminal racemes of 2 cm pea-like, purple flowers, in extremely long, hanging clusters to 1 m long, followed by velvety pods; the most popular of cultivated Japanese wisterias; the flowers appearing before, or with the leaves. *Temperate.* *p. 1394*

floribunda violaceo-plena; of rather dense, and bushier habit, the flower clusters smaller 12-25 cm long, but tight with double flowers purple to wisteria-blue. *p. 1394*

WITTIA *Cactaceae* **S3LFD**

panamensis (Panama, Colombia, Venezuela); small epiphyte with flattened branches 25 cm to 1 m long and 3-6 cm wide, with strong midrib; numerous small flowers with ovary and tube carmine-red, and perianth dark blue. *p. 735*

WITTROCKIA *Bromeliaceae* **I2HFD**

amazonica: see Nidularium innocentii var. innocentii

smithii (Paraná, Santa Catarina); rosette of broad papery olive green leaves edged with small purplish spines; noted for the rich dark-red coloring of the underside; inflorescence sunk in the center of the leaf rosette, with white and green petals. *p. 602*

superba (S. E. Brazil); large robust, well-formed rosette with leathery concave, yellow-green, waxy leaves tinged bronze and occasionally blotched dark green tipped by a crimson-red pointed apex, margins with prominent reddish teeth; the green inflorescence a cup like in Nidularium but slightly raised, with petals blue but completely enclosed by the sepals. Syn. Nidularium splendens. *p. 513, 602, 605*

WOLFFIA *Lemnaceae* **I2-3(water) B-FW**

arrhiza (Europe to South Africa, S. E. Asia, Brazil, Java and Australia), aquatic "Water-meal"; small green disks floating on the water, without roots. This Wolffia shows a greater reduction than Lemna minor; the entire plant consists only of a green disc with a diameter of 1 to 1½ mm. *p. 1362*

WOLFFIELLA *Lemnaceae* **I2-3(water) B-FW**

denticulata (So. Africa) "Mud midget"; submerged aquatic herb with linear joints to 1 cm long forming interwoven masses, rarely blooming. *p. 1362*

WOODWARDIA *Polypodiaceae (Filices)* **I2LFM**

chamissoi (radicans americana) (British Columbia to California and Mexico); large hardy fern with fresh-green pinnate divided fronds ½-2½ m long and 45 cm wide, the segments comblike with neat linear lobes; this species does not give rise to young plants from its leaves. *p. 1167*

orientalis (Japan to Taiwan), "Chain fern"; decorative fern with bipinnate, leathery fronds, that may grow to 2 m long, crimson when young with sori in rows parallel to the midrib; and forming on the upper surface minute bulbils producing little plantlets. *p. 1165, 1167*

radicans (Canary Isl., So. Europe, China, No. India, Java), giant "Chain fern"; with bipinnate fronds 1-2 m long, thin-leathery, fresh green, heavy and pendant; the pinnae alternate and not cut to base, with wavy margins; large buds or tubers form toward the apex of the leaf which root to form new plants. *p. 1165, 1167*

WORSLEYA rayneri: see Hippeastrum procerum

WRIGHTIA: see Holarrhena

XANTHOCERAS *Sapindaceae* **C2LBD**

sorbifolium (China); handsome deciduous shrub 3-4 m high, with pithy branches; pinnate leaves with toothed, bright-green leaflets 5 cm long; showy axillary erect clusters of whitish flowers about 2½ cm across, the base of each of the 5 spreading petals first greenish-yellow, then red; fruit a hard green capsule resembling horse-chestnut; fairly hardy. *p. 2034*

XANTHORRHOEA *Liliaceae* **I-S2LB-FD**

arborea (No. New So. Wales, Queensland), the ancient and curious "Grass-tree"; long-lived perennial plant with a strong woody trunk 15-22 cm thick, rough with old leaf-bases, topped by a dense multitude of narrow whip-like leathery, dark green leaves, flat or triangular, 1-1½ m long and less than 5 mm wide. Have noticed colonies of grass-trees 2-3 m high, on grassy slopes in eucalypt forests from south of Brisbane to the table lands above Cairns, taking ages to grow tall. *Subtropic.* *p. 1507, 1511*

preissii (Western Australia), the famous "Blackboy"; conspicuously dominating the landscape of the interior of the dry West, like the occasional aboriginal one meets; the massive black trunks becoming 60 cm or more thick, the old leaf bases cemented together by black resinous gum; on top a tuft of hard-leathery rigid, reed-like leaves ½-1 m long; the inflorescence a long, candle-like spike, with small flowers, in habitat always opening on the north (sun) side first. *Arid-subtropic.* *p. 1509*

undulata; seen in Zuerich Botanic Garden and labeled as from New Zealand; appearing like a bursting fountain of narrow, stiff-leathery, glossy grass-green leaves. *Subtropic.* *p. 1509*

XANTHOSOMA *Araceae* **S2-3LFM**

atrovirens (Venezuela); sturdy plant forming cylindrical rhizome but no trunk; sagittate leaves to 1 m long, dark green above and gray green beneath, veins light green, fleshy stalks green; green spathe. (2B) *p. 297*

atrovirens albo-marginatum (Brazil); ornamental compact plant with bluish-green, broadly sagittate leaves and gray veins, bordered with white margin. *p. 297*

atrovirens albo-marginatum monstrosum (Perú), the "Pocket-plant"; conversation-piece variety having its fleshy, bluish-green, white-edged leaves reduced in size and partly divided into lobes, some of the segments rolled into conical pockets holding water. *p. 298*

atrovirens appendiculatum; a curiosity, having its blackish-green, quilted leaf, normally sagittate-ovate and to 1 m long, reduced in size and fitted on the underside, with an adventitious, often cup-shaped leaf; attached along the midrib. *p. 280*

braziliensis (W. Indies), "Belembe" or "Tahitian spinach"; a rather small species, 30-90 cm high with fresh green, hastate 15-40 cm leaves distinctly 3-lobed, and cultivated in tropical America and some Pacific islands solely for greens which have little or no bitter flavor and are very palatable when boiled; the small tubers are edible when cooked; narrow green spathe 15 cm long. *p. 296*

daguense (Colombia); photographed from material collected in Valle del Cauca in the Western Andes; arrow-shaped green leaves from a developing rhizome growing into large specimen down the Pacific slope of Andean rainforest, and used by the natives as handy umbrellas. *p. 296*

jacquinii lineatum (Brazil), "Malanga"; evergreen fleshy herb with large sagittate leaves 30-50cm long, having open sinus and basal lobes, friendly green with white lines between veins. *p. 297*

lindenii (Phyllotaenium) (Colombia), "Yautia"; ornamental, evergreen herb growing from rhizome; showy, arrowshaped, thin-leathery leaves with hastate base, 20 cm long, matte green with grayish sheen, and silver-white veins. *Tropical.* *p. 299*

lindenii 'Albescens'; a variety similar to X. lindenii magnificum but with broader feathering of white from the midrib into blade of leaf, and featuring a white outer edge. *p. 299*

lindenii 'Magnificum' (Phyllotaenium), "Indian kale"; horticultural form of X. lindenii (Colombia), differing by having its yellowish to deep-green leaves beautifully and broadly veined cream to white, and with pale line just inside of margin. This ornamental, evergreen herb, growing from rhizome, with its showy, arrow-shaped, thin-leathery leaves, is one of the most beautiful of warm greenhouse exotics. *Tropical.* *p. 21*, 160A, 299*

"maculatum" (Rio de Janeiro); bushy, ornamental plant with broadly sagittate leaves 30 cm long, irregularly blotched with white on a light green ground. *p. 297*

mafaffa (So. America: Ecuador); growing into a giant tropical herb on the lower slopes of the Western Cordillera; fleshy stalks to 2 m high with horizontal, broad sagittate, matte green, large leaves having naked sinus. (2B) *p.299*

pentaphyllum (Brazil: Goias); tropical plant with globular tuber 3 cm dia.; the long, 30-60 cm green, stiffly erect petiole topped by a pedately divided, herbaceous green leaf consisting of 5 segments, 20 to 30 cm long; short green, 20-30 cm floral stalk carries the inflorescence with constricted spathe, outside green, inside whitish. *p. 300*

pubescens (Perú); attractive clustering "Yautia"; with tuberous rhizome, and oblong-cordate, corrugated, pubescent green leaves 18-25 cm long, on sheathing, hairy petioles 15-25 cm long; the spathe cup-shaped at base, flaring and whitish above, 8-10 cm long, on 8-12 cm stalk. *p. 296*

robustum (C. America, Mexico), "Palma yautia" or "Ape"; large aroid with milky juice; forming a thick short trunk from a rhizome; topped by a cluster of big fleshy, sagittate leaves, on grooved, stout petioles, the blade to 1 m long and 60 cm wide, covered by white powdery coating and showing prominent pale, whitish ribs; spathes sweet-smelling, each with a pinkish creamy spathe 15 cm long. In Guatemala young leaves are cooked and eaten, but the roots are said to be poisonous. *p. 296*

roseum 'Variegatum' (Chiapas), known in Mexico as "Quequeste"; tuberous herb with light green, vaginate petioles; in the variety 'Variegatum' these are banded milk-white lengthwise, carrying sagittate waxy leaves largely variegated white. *p. 297*

sagittaefolium (W. Indies, S. America), "Yautia"; forming trunk to 1 m high; mossy green, broad, arrowshaped, soft leaves to 1m long, with pale veins and naked sinus, grayish beneath; fleshy stalks winged at base, not channeled. *Tropical.* *p. 297*

violaceum (Puerto Rico to Jamaica), "Violet-stemmed taro" or "Yautia"; producing edible rhizome; fleshy leafstalks brownish-purple with blue wax covering; sagittate leaves dark green with purple margin, veins beneath purple. The main root (tuber or corm) is too acrid for food, but the lateral tubers growing from it are eaten. *p. 297*

weeksii (Ecuador); robust tropical plant to 60 cm high, with short, erect, thick stem; the petioles sheathing and vaginate for 2/3 of length; fleshy, ovate leaves to 25 cm long, green or bluish; the inflorescence on short stalk, with 10 cm spathe white above, the swollen base inside purple; spadix creamy. *p. 228*

wendlandii (hoffmannii) (Costa Rica); tropical herb with thick rhizome; the petioles marbled gray-brown and greenish brown; soft herbaceous leaves, divided into oblanceolate lobes along a curving sinus, dull deep green above and with depressed veins, glossy green beneath. *p. 297*

XANTHOSTEMON *Myrtaceae* **S3LBM**

rubrum (New Caledonia); bold woody tropical evergreen with large leathery leaves; the large, showy inflorescence basket-shaped with broad scarlet-red petals, and prominent red stamens tipped yellow. *p. 1610*

XENOPHYA *Araceae* **S3LHFM**

lauterbachiana (Schizocasia) (New Guinea); ornamental rhizomatous plant to 1 m or more, bearing stiff, fleshy lanceolate leaves with lobed margins and hastate base, to 50 cm long, metallic, bronzy green and paler veins; spathe blade persistent, opening briefly in the middle only, opposite the staminate flowers. *p. 284*

XERONEMA *Liliaceae* **I2LBM**

callistemon (New Zealand); large tufted perennial herb of phormium-like habit, with soft-leathery iris-like leaves in two ranks, about 1 m long, from which emerges a 1 m leaning stem bearing a striking one-sided brush of flowers resembling a bottle-brush, the conspicuous red stamens 2½ cm long; the pedicels, filaments, and style are also bright red; the fruit following is deep purple. *p. 1506*

moorei: see X. callistemon

XEROPHYTA *Amaryllidaceae* **S3LFD**

eglandulosa (Vellozia) (Madagascar); interesting tropical shrubby, semi-succulent plant found by J. Bogner near Tazafotsy; stem closely set with rigid linear, clasping leaves covered sparsely by bristly hairs; solitary funnel-shaped flowers with oblong segments. *p. 122*

XEROSICYOS *Cucurbitaceae* **S2LBD**

danguyi (S.W. Madagascar); tendril-climbing liane to 50 cm tall, branching from the base, with cylindrical stems; thick succulent, orbicular grayish leaves 4 cm long, upper surface flat, the underside convex, and located opposite to a long tendril; flowers greenish-yellow, and small fruit on female plants. *Arid-tropical.* *p. 933*

perrieri (S. W. Madgascar); small succulent shrub to 45 cm high, branching from the base; the cylindrical stems with alternate, rounded grayish, fleshy flat leaves to 4 cm long; and with tendrils opposite the leaves; small whitish flowers. *p. 933*

XYLOBIUM *Orchidaceae* **I3OLFM**

elongatum (W. Indies, Costa Rica, Panama); epiphyte with small pseudobulbs and solitary broad lanceolate, stalked plaited leaves 30-38 cm long, and lateral, dense raceme of flowers with slender sepals and petals creamy-white, warted lip purplish-brown, strongly spicy fragrant (spring). (I) *p. 1840, 1841*

powellii (Panama, Costa Rica); small epiphyte with ovoid pseudobulbs bearing plaited leaves; short-stalked clusters of flowers with deep buff-yellow sepals and petals, and cream-colored lip. *p. 1702*

squalens (Costa Rica, Venezuela, Brazil, Perú); epiphyte with pseudobulbs bearing 2 plaited leaves 30 cm long; inflorescence in erect, dense racemes to 20 cm high, with numerous dingy flowers, yellowish-white suffused with flesh color, lip with dark brownish purple in front, (May-Dec.). (I) *p. 1841*

XYLOPHYLLA: see Phyllanthus

XYLOTHECA *Bixaceae* **I2LBD**

kraussiana (Oncoba) (So. Africa: Natal), "African dog-rose"; rounded evergreen shrub to 1½ m high, with glossy, oval leaves; white, waxy flowers 8 cm across, with 8-9 obovate petals and a puff of golden stamens in the center, very sweet-scented. *p. 504*

XYRIS *Xyridaceae* **I2LBMh**

bicephala (Venezuela), "Yellow-eyed grass"; tufted herb with narrow, linear basal leaves 15-25 cm long; long flower stalk to 35 cm carrying two heads with yellow flowers. *p. 2142*

involucrata (Venezuela); tufted perennial of rush-like habit, with leaves 8-10 cm long; the globular floral heads on long stalks, the small yellow flowers subtended by ray-like bracts. *p. 2142*

YUCCA *Liliaceae* **I2LBD**

aloifolia 'Marginata' (S.E. United States, W. Indies, Mexico), a variegated-form "Spanish bayonet"; attractive, tree-forming, stiff rosette of thick fleshy, sharp-pointed, dagger-like leaves 6 cm wide, glaucous green with creamy-yellow margins, on usually single trunks to 6 m high; cup-shaped flowers cream-white tinged with purple, in large clusters. *Subtropic.* *p. 1508*

aloifolia 'Quadricolor'; beautiful plant seen at Royal Botanic Gardens, Edinburgh; broad, dark green leaves variegated red, salmon and yellow down the middle. *Subtropic.* *p. 1510*

aloifolia 'Tricolor', "Red dagger"; colorful variety with the pointed dagger-leaves margined ivory, partly yellow in the center and with a tinge of red when young. *Subtropic.* *p. 1508*

australis (filifera) (Mexico: Coahuila); growing into trees 6 to 15 m high, grotesquely branched similar to the somewhat smaller Joshua tree (Y. brevifolia); the trunk 1/2 to 1 m thick; the dagger-like stiff, green leaves in rosettes at ends of branches, to 45 cm long and 5 cm across, rigidly sharp-pointed, and margins coarsely threaded; creamy-white flowers in pendant clusters. *p. 1507, 1512*

baccata (Colorado, Arizona, California), "Datil yucca"; heavy succulent rosette of thick, stiff-erect, rough, concave leaves to 90 cm, spine-tipped and with peeling fiber at margins; large white flowers; dried fruit is eaten by Indians. *Warm temperate.* *p. 1511*

brevifolia, native to high deserts in Southern California, Nevada, Utah and Arizona at 600 to 1800 m, the extraordinary "Joshua tree"; hard to believe but this is a member of the lily family, growing into a succulent tree to 22 m high, with palm-like trunk to 1 1/3 m thick, branching into tortuous arms dense with rosettes of 20 to 35 cm, rigid dagger-shaped leaves; in bloom from February to April with greenish white 5 cm cup-shaped flowers in dense clusters 30 to 50 cm long. Its grotesque silhouette is very characteristic in dry-sunny desert landscapes. *Arid-subtropic.* *p.1510,1512*

elata (Arizona), the "Soaptree yucca"; tree-forming to 6 m; dense rosettes of narrow-linear spine-tipped leaves 60 cm long and 3 cm wide, yellow-green and smooth, margins white; flowers white in tall inflorescence. *Arid-subtropic.* *p. 1512*

elephantipes (guatemalensis) (Mexico, Guatemala), "Spineless yucca"; round-headed "Palm-lily" with trunks springing from a swollen base, suckering from below, and branching above with age, reaching 15 m high, topped by rosettes of leaves to 10 cm wide, glossy grass-green with rough margins and soft tip; flowers ivory-white, in large clusters. Very decorative and durable in containers; known as Y. gigantea in hort. *Subtropic.* *p. 1506, 1508, 1511*

elephantipes 'Variegata' ('Marginata'), "Giant variegated palm-lily"; an attractive cultivar in California, of the spineless yucca; the wide, glossy-green, soft-leathery leaves prettily banded with creamy-white along the obscurely toothed edge. *p. 1508, 1510*

filamentosa, (Linnaeus) (S.E. United States: Carolina to Florida and Mississippi), "Adam's needle"; bold rosette, nearly stemless, with stiff sword-shaped leaves 75 cm long, bluish-glaucous, and with marginal, curly white threads; pendulous flowers nearly white in tall panicle to 4 m high. *Warm temperate.* *p. 1508, 1510*

filamentosa flaccida 'Variegata'; a variety of the softer-leaved flaccida form; most colorful cultivar which I have seen in Ted Gourlay's garden in Nelson, N. Z.; heavy tufts of leaves largely variegated and banded cream, mostly down the middle, and of flaccid texture. *p. 1508*

filamentosa 'Variegata'; beautiful rosette of broad bayonet-shaped leaves, bluish-green contrasting with cream or white bands along margins. *Subtropic.* *p. 1506, 1509*

gigantea in hort.: see elephantipes

glauca (New Mexico), "Soapweed"; stemless rosette dense with straight narrow-linear, glaucous blue-green leaves 40 to 80 cm long and 2 cm wide; margins with a few white threads; flowers greenish-white. *p. 1510*

gloriosa (shores of Carolina to Florida), "Spanish dagger"; to 2 1/2 m high, with short, thick trunk topped by dense rosette of sword-shaped, flat glaucous gray-green, rough leaves 5 cm wide, with reddish margins and spiny point; white bell-like flowers striped purple outside. *Subtropic.* *p. 1508*

gloriosa 'Variegata', "Variegated mound-lily"; decorative variegated form seen in San Bernardino, California; rosette of stiffish-fleshy, spreading leaves 50 cm long, deep pea-green, lightly glaucous, and bordered milky-green and creamy-white and tinged with red in sun; obscurely toothed and with soft, harmless spine tip. *p. 1510*

mohavensis (schidigera) (at home in the Sonoran zone deserts of So. California and No. Mexico), "Mohave yucca"; to 5 m high, simple trunk or branching with crown of thin-leathery concave, smooth leaves 50 cm long, the margins with long filaments; flowers in panicle on short stalk, creamy white to purplish. *p. 1509, 1511*

recurvifolia (pendula) (Georgia, Alabama, Mississippi), "Lord's candle"; trunk-forming and branching, to 2 m high, the stems topped by rosettes of lax, broad, flexible, glaucous dark green leaves 6 cm wide and recurving; large panicle of white flowers. *Warm temperate.* *p. 1512*

rupicola (Texas); nearly stemless rosette of numerous, narrow glaucous leaves, to 75 cm long and 3 cm wide, gradually narrowed to a spiny point, the margins brownish and minutely toothed; drooping flowers white or greenish, in a 2 m panicle. *p. 1508*

schottii (Arizona); stem-forming rosette to 5 m high, rarely branched, with concave leaves 45-90 cm long tapering to a fine point, the margins without coarse threads; showy panicle with globose white flowers. *p.1508*

ZALUZIANSKYA *Scrophulariaceae* **I2LBD**

villosa (So. Africa); clammy herb to 30 cm high, leaves spatulate; 2 cm flowers white with orange eye, fragrant at night. *p. 2057*

ZAMIA *Cycadaceae* **I-S2LBD**

angustifolia (West Indies); low-growing cycad with bulb-like, ovoid-conical stem; few long, slender stalks bear the short, pinnate fronds; narrow-linear leaflets loosely spaced, 4 to 20 on each side 15-20 cm long, stalks unarmed and rounded beneath; cones 5-6 cm long, the males reddish-hairy, females bluntly cuspidate. *p. 940*

fischeri (Mexico); small spindle-shaped trunk, bearing several fern-like pinnate fronds 30 to 45 cm long, with thin-leathery, lanceolate leaflets shiny grass-green, serrate along margins; male cone 4 to 8 cm long, female shorter. *Tropical.* *p. 938*

floridana (So. Florida), "Coontie"; a dwarf plant with underground tuber-like trunk, sending up many slender, pinnate, leathery dark green leaves to 60 cm long and somewhat twisted, segments with margins revolute, and without midrib. *p. 941*

floridana (media) **var. portoricensis** (Puerto Rico); a freer, more loosely growing small cycad with underground trunks, and numerous slender, wiry stalks bearing pinnate fronds, their pinnae narrow lanceolate, flexible leathery, bright green, loosely spaced. *p. 940*

furfuracea (pumila in Hortus 3) (Mexico to Colombia), "Jamaica sagotree" stem more or less tuberous, sometimes branched, bearing a tangled profusion of pinnate leaves 1-1 1/3 m long, on prickly stalks, the thick-leathery leaflets oblanceolate 20 cm long, more or less toothed and overlapping, densely brown scurfy beneath, or on both sides when young; male cones 10 cm long, the female ones shorter. An excellent "different" decorator plant, hard and durable as iron, and of relatively small size. *Subtropic.* *p. 938, 944*

kickxii (pygmaea var.) (Cuba); dwarf cycad with very short stem, and arching, smooth, pinnate leaves 5-50 cm long, the shining green sessile, leaflets obovate, the lower ones smaller, the upper ones 5 cm long becoming lanceolate, margins toothed. *p. 940*

latifolia (loddigesii var.) (Mexico); tuberous stem to 20 cm high; thick leafstalk usually prickly, the pinnate fronds with variable leaflets lanceolate to obovate 10-25 cm long, spiny-toothed from the middle upward, usually with brownish down beneath; cylindrical male cone 6 cm long, the female thicker and shorter. *p. 940*

lindenii (Ecuador); stout cylindric stem 1 to 2 1/2 m high, topped by 10-15 fronds 2 to 2 1/2 m long on prickly stalk, the linear-lanceolate leaflets shiny glaucous green, toothed and curved; female cones 35 cm long. *p. 938*

ottonis (Cuba); small cycad with short tapering, tuberous caudex, and smooth, pinnate leaves 30-45 cm long, the leaflets in 9-15 pairs, obovate 5-10 cm long, toothed toward apex, brownish-downy beneath; the cones brown-hairy. *p. 940*

pseudoparasitica (Panama); curious species, interesting because it is found growing as epiphyte on tropical trees; with age developing a ringed trunk 1 to 3 m in length, bearing a crown of some 25 pinnate fronds to 2 m long; the stalks somewhat prickly; smooth leathery leaflets narrow-lanceolate and curved, the tip with sharp point; female cone 40 cm long. *p. 940*

pygmaea (Cuba); from Pinar del Rio, Western Cuba, the smallest cycad in the world; stem very short; pinnate leaves 6 to 25 cm and more long, the broad obovate, curving leaflets shining green, slightly brown-hairy, toothed from middle upward; female cones to 5 cm long. *p. 938*

spiralis (Macrozamia communis) (E. Australia); small cycad to 1 m or so high, with globular woody trunk, and fern-like slender fronds with soft-leathery, narrow-linear thread-like, flexuous leaflets matte green, on rachis without spines. The name Macrozamia or Ceratozamia spiralis belongs to another, much larger cycad. (E. Lord, Shrubs and Trees for Australian Gardens.) *p. 938*

ZAMIOCULCAS *Araceae* **S2HFM**

zamiifolia (Zanzibar; E. Africa); tropical herb with thick, horizontal rhizome, sending up swollen stalks; the pinnately arranged, small, dark, waxy leaves with yellow-green veins; short inflorescence appearing from near base, consisting of boatshaped, green spathe and short, club-shaped spadix. *Tropical.* *p. 294*

ZANTEDESCHIA *Araceae* **I-S2LFWd**

aethiopica (Calla, Richardia) (South Africa and north), "White calla", "White arum-lily", or as known in South Africa: "Pig-lily"; robust marsh-loving herb with thick rhizome; forming a tuft of fleshy-stalked, glossy-green leaves 60-90 cm high, on succulent petioles; a stout basal stalk 1-1 1/2 m high bearing the large, funnel-shaped rolled-flaring waxy-white spathe 20-25 cm long, surrounding a bright yellow spadix. To the visitor of the moister parts of the South African Cape it is a common sight to see whole fields of these beautiful callas in bloom during summertime; but I have also seen them at 2,300 m altitude in Kenya. *Subtropic.* *p. 301*

aethiopica 'Childsiana', a "Dwarf calla lily"; a very dwarf, bushy form 30 cm high, with short leaves only 10 cm long; very floriferous, with the white spathes ony 6 cm wide; occasionally the leaves are partly spathe-like with a large white basal area. Much grown in pots in England. *p. 298*

aethiopica 'Compacta', "Dwarf white calla"; quite compact growing form, in the trade as 'Godefreyana'; usually 45-60 cm high as against the type 60-90 cm tall; more floriferous though with slightly smaller 12-15 cm spathes; a better plant in pot culture. *p. 298*

aethiopica 'Crowborough'; according to Patrick Synge, a hardier form which can be grown successfully in the open border outdoors in southern England. *p. 302*

aethiopica 'Godefreyana'; according to Bailey's Hortus, a variety listed as being smaller and a more profuse bloomer than the type; photo by Giridlian, California. *p. 302*

aethiopica minor; a smaller form known as 'Little Gem', to 45 cm high; with white spathes 8-10 cm produced more profusely. (I-S) *p. 294*

albo-maculata (Natal; So. Africa), "Spotted calla"; leaves arrow-shaped, green with oblong, white, translucent spots; spathe trumpet-shaped with pointed limb, creamy-white, in throat purple. *p. 301*

angustiloba (Angola); robust flowering plant about 60 cm high, in habitat growing in seasonally wet marshland; thick tuberous rhizome with long sagittate, green leaves 20-50 cm long; trumpet-like, flaring spathe 10 cm long, sulphur yellow with black-purple blotch at base, more pale yellow on outside. *p. 302*

elliottiana (So. Africa: Transkei), known as "Yellow calla", and very popular for Easter-forcing in pots; growing from a flattened rhizome; the succulent, cordate, bright green leaves very pretty with translucent white spots; the obliquely flaring, tubular spathe to 15 cm long is rich yellow. *p. 160A, 301*

elliottiana flore pleno; attractive form of the "Golden calla", with the rich, deep yellow spathe having an extra furl inside, the extended limb ruffled and with green tip. *p. 302*

'Green Goddess' ('Green Lily'); very charming flowering plant, probably a cultivar of Z. aethiopica, of luxuriant growth with lush green arrow-shaped leaves, and strong-stalked inflorescence with flaring, fleshy spathe 15-20 cm long, white at base, but moss-green at margins and across apex. *p. 302*

jucunda (Transvaal); newly described, pleasing species from Sekukuland; similar to macrocarpa (pentlandii), but the triangular-hastate, deep green, stiff leaves with upward-spreading basal lobes, spotted with silvery white; the bell-shaped spathe brilliant yellow, less tightly rolled, and showing a contrasting blackish blotch in center. *p. 302*

macrocarpa (pentlandii) (Transvaal, Basutoland), "Mapoch-lily"; lovely flowering tuberous species from swampy veld but drying out in summer; triangular-cordate arrow-shaped leaves glossy green on both sides, 20 cm or more long; the wide-open, flaring trumpet-like spathe 10 cm long, intense chrome yellow, with black-purple blotch inside at base; the short spadix with perfect flowers. *p. 302*

melanoleuca (So. Africa: Natal), "Black-throated calla"; tender winter-blooming plant forming thick rhizome; attractive arrow-shaped leaves 15-30 cm long, deep green covered with numerous oblong, translucent silvery-white spots; the tubular-flaring spathe pale lemon yellow, and having black-purple eye at base and its margins rolled back; the stalks with dark bristles in lower part. *p. 302*

rehmannii (Natal); the shapely "Pink calla"; having lanceolate leaves bright green with linear, translucent white spots; the most attractive, charming, pale rosy-purple spathe forming an obliquely flaring tube lined with cream. *Subtropic.* *p. 301*

ZAPOTA: see Manilkara

ZEA *Gramineae* **I2LBD**

mays (America, prob. Mexico or C. America), the "Indian corn" or "Maize"; its exact origin has been lost in pre-Mayan, Aztec or Incan antiquity; cultivated since, and to them the most important food, with the exception of the potato to the Incas in South America; robust, tall annual grass 3 to 4 m high, suckering at base, with jointed, solid stem bearing broad, glossy green, sword-shaped leaves; male flowers in terminal spike with pollen, the female blooms in small clusters borne below the males, their long styles are the showy corn-silk, and producing the ears of edible corn kernels containing starch, heavily sheathed in husks. For farm production, highly refined cultivars have been developed, containing less starch and more sugar. *Tropical.* *p. 1316*

ZEBRINA *Commelinaceae* **I-S2-3LFM**

pendula (Mexico), "Silvery wandering Jew"; fleshy trailing plant rooting at joints; small ovate leaves about 5cm long, fairly succulent, deep green to purple with two broad, glistening silver bands, vivid purple beneath; flowers rosy-purple. *Tropical.* *p. 781*

pendula 'Discolor', "Tricolor wandering Jew"; glossy coppery and nile-green large foliage overlaid and edged with metallic purple and splashed rusty red, two narrow silver bands down the long and thinnish leaf, purple beneath; purple flowers. *p. 781*

pendula 'Discolor multicolor'; a strong growing variegated form which tends to keep its variegation; large, long ovate leaves with green background are striped and banded pinkish cream, and splashed with rusty red and a bit of silver, purple beneath. (S) *p. 781*

pendula 'Minima'; a variety of smaller habit than Z. pendula; with slender, small lanceolate purplish leaves painted with two silver bands; underside purple; sparse white-hairy. *p. 783*

pendula 'Quadricolor', "Happy wandering Jew"; an exquisitely colorful form with the small leaves purplish green broadly banded glistening white, alternating with pink and red, edged purple as well as purple beneath; pretty but delicate. *Tropical.* *p. 5*, 781, 1952A*

purpusii (Mexico), "Bronze wandering Jew"; vigorous creeper with fleshy, oblique, broad ovate leaves overlapping shingle-like, olive to purplish brown with faint green stripes, shiny vivid purple beneath; flowers lavender. *p. 781*

ZEHNERIA *Cucurbitaceae* **I-S3LBD**

pallidinerva (Melothria hederacea) (So. Africa); climbing plant with thin stem and forked tendrils; glossy green ivy-like, triangular leaves with grayish veins, 5-8 cm wide; small white flowers and oblong, spindle-shaped orange fruit; ornamental plant grown for its decorative fruit. *p. 933*

ZELKOVA *Ulmaceae* **I2LBMh**

serrata (Japan), "Saw-leaf zelkova"; deciduous elm-like shrub or tree to 30 m high; ovate leaves 5-12 cm long, sharply toothed; small green flowers. A favorite object in Japan for training into dwarfed Bonsai. *p. 2107*

ZENOBIA *Ericaceae* **I2HFM**

pulverulenta (S.E. United States); semi-evergreen shrub to 2 m high; small leathery, elliptic leaves to 8 cm long, glaucous beneath; small 2 cm waxy-white, fragrant bell-flowers in Spring. *Warm-temperate.* *p. 959*

ZEPHYRANTHES *Amaryllidaceae* **C2LBMd**

'Ajax' (citrina x candida); small, pretty, bulbous hybrid with narrow, thick, dark green erect leaves 20 to 25 cm long; the lily-like flowers 5 cm across, deep cream shaded to yellow, and with prominent yellow anthers, carried solitary on hollow stalk; summer-blooming. *p. 121*

albiella (Colombia); small bulbous plant with narrow-linear leaves 10 cm long, appearing with the inflorescence; the hollow floral stalk 6-9 cm long, with solitary flowers white, green at base, 3 cm across; blooming spring to autumn. *p. 121*

candida (Argentina: La Plata), "Fairy lily" or "Westwind-flower"; attractive small bulbous plant, with narrow, perennial leaves, and forming clumps; funnel-shaped glossy white flowers 4 cm long, with 6 spreading segments, singly on hollow stalks, and blooming summer to autumn. *p. 129*

citrina (Guyana, Trinidad), a "Rain lily"; small bulbous herb with channeled linear, grass-like leaves 20-30 cm long; on hollow stalks the solitary, funnel-shaped lemon-yellow flowers to 4 cm long, during summer; resting in winter; somewhat hardy. *Tropical.* *p. 104*

grandiflora (Mexico, Guatemala), a pretty "Zephyr-lily" or "Flower of the westwind"; with flat, linear basal leaves and large, deep rose-pink, funnel-form flower, to 10 cm across, at end of the hollow stalk; blooming through spring and summer. *Tropical.* *p. 130*

pedunculata (Trop. America), a "Fairy-lily"; with narrow-linear basal leaves, and long-stemmed flowers having wide-spreading petals, white with a touch of pink at base of tube; although considered a night-bloomer, it stays partly open during day light. *p. 101*

ZEPHYRANTHES: see also Habranthus

ZINGIBER *Zingiberaceae* **S3-2LFM**

fairchildii; in habit very similar to the East Indian Z. zerumbet; tuberous roots bearing tall-erect, leafy canes; the cylindric cone-like inflorescence with shingled red bracts, and cream-colored flowers. *p. 2137*

officinale (India to Pacific Isl.), "Common ginger"; slender, reed-like stems ½-1 m high, from tuberous rhizomes which are used as a pleasantly flavored rootspice; the scattered, sessile leaves are glossy deep green and narrow, almost grass-like; flowers in dense spike with pale green bracts, yellowish corolla, and purple lip marked yellow. *Tropical.* *p. 2133, 2140*

spectabile (Malaya); robust species shooting up stout, somewhat flattened stems over 2 m high; deep green leaves oblong-lanceolate 20-30 cm long, paler and downy beneath; the flowers yellowish-white, the 2-lobed lip lemon with a black tip, in a loose cylindrical spike 20-30 cm long; the sulphur yellow bracts passing to scarlet, shingled and prettily recurved. *p. 2137*

zerumbet (India, Malaya to Polynesia), the "Wild ginger", or "Bitter ginger"; well-known and widely cultivated tropical ginger with knobbed rootstock at first taste aromatic, then becoming bitter; leafy shoots 45-60 cm high, the lanceolate, thin leaves 10-20 cm long, more or less hairy beneath; in the late summer an oblong flowering head, 5-8 cm long, appears on a stalk about 30 cm long, separate from the leaves, consisting of large green to red overlapping bracts, and small yellowish flowers. *Tropical.* *p. 2137, 2143*

zerumbet 'Darceyi' (India), "Variegated bitter ginger"; robust plant with knobbed, underground stems and slender canes about 60 cm high, alternately set with broadly elliptic, undulate, thin-leathery leaves, bright green with cream-white to pink border and occasional white bands. *p. 2133, 2143*

zerumbet 'Variegata' (India); attractive tropical ginger of low habit, 30-50 cm high, with leafy stems from underground knobby aromatic rootstock; leathery leaves rich grass green and beautifully variegated with cream; the inflorescence in cone-like heads of overlapping fleshy bracts a vivid scarlet red, with small yellow flowers. Photographed at Botanic Gardens Trinidad. *Tropical.* *p. 2143*

ZINNIA *Compositae* **S-I2LBD**

elegans (Mexico), "Youth-and-old-age"; gaily colored annual garden favorite, 50 cm to 1 m high, the branches stiff and covered by short hairs; oval bright green leaves clasping the stem; showy flowers in solitary heads to 6 or 8 cm across, in white, pink, rose, red, yellow, orange, purple.

elegans 'Pumila Liliput'; a dwarf horticultural form of bushy habit and with small flowers in bright colors, suitable for bedding for dry sunny locations as in Mexico where the species came from. *p. 805*

elegans 'Robusta', "Dahlia flowered" type; a revolutionary strain of giant double flowers in bright colors, in bloom over a long period, earning it the name "Youth and old age". *p. 805*

elegans 'Thumbelina Mini-pink'; extra dwarf zinnia only 15 cm high, very compact and ideal for bedding or window-boxes; the bright and colorful semi-double flowers 4 cm across in shades including yellow, salmon, rose or red; blooming all summer, a rare breeding achievement by Bodgar Seeds, El Monte, California. *p. 802*

ZOMICARPA *Araceae* **S3LFM**

pythonium (Arum pedatum) (So. Brazil: Bahia); tuberous tropical plant with divided, herbaceous leaves reniform in outline, divided into 5 or more elliptic segments, on 8 to 20 cm green petiole, marbled brownish purple; spathe 5-8 cm long, white inside, the ovate blade streaked with red; this species is reported to be an antidote to snake bite. *p. 300*

riedeliana (Brazil); tropical herb with tuberous rhizome, producing foliage and flowers at same time; the ornamental leaves divided into 3 to 7 segments, the middle one to 10 cm long, glaucous green and splashed with silver gray, the margins serrate; spathe 8-10 cm long, glaucous outside, yellowish green inside, the long ovate blade arching forward. *Tropical.* *p. 300*

steigeriana (So. Brazil); foliage plant with tuberous horizontal rhizome; leaves kidney-shaped in outline, parted into 3 segments 5-15 cm long, deep green, pale beneath, on 10-25 cm petioles marbled with brown; spathe brownish-purple, curved at top; short spadix brownish purple with whitish, the naked part club-shaped. *p. 300*

ZOYSIA *Gramineae* **I2LBD**

japonica 'Meyeri' (Japan, China); the "Korean grass"; subtropical creeping lawn grass widely used in the Southeast, California and Hawaii; mat forming and coarser than tenuifolia; fine grass-like leaves to 4 mm wide and 3-8 cm long; the root stocks sending out numerous tough, wiry runners; slow to establish and taking a long rest period, but in time looking like blue-grass; purplish spikelets 1 cm long. *p. 1316*

tenuifolia (Mascarene Islands), the "Mascarene grass" or in Hawaii as "Temple grass"; perennial creeping grass with rich green leaves thread-like and finer than japonica, and forming a turf; widely planted in California and Hawaii, but as ground cover grass somewhat lumpy; with its fine texture, it makes a beautiful tapestry, especially on slopes. Winter-hardy to -12°C., but turns brown after first frost. *Tropical.* *p. 1316*

ZYGOCACTUS *Cactaceae* ***S2HΓM(D:au)**

'Llewellyn'; a hybrid "Crab-cactus" of upright habit, branching with flattened, toothed joints; the large zygomorphic flowers an iridescent orange-red and contrasting pale lavender base; will bloom for Christmas in the Northern hemisphere. *Tropical.* *p. 732*

'Red Elephant': see Schlumbergera

truncatus as in Backeberg; Schlumbergera truncata in Hortus 3 (Organ Mts., Rio), "Thanksgiving cactus", also called "Crab-cactus"; branching epiphyte with flattened joints dark glossy green and each having two prominent teeth or claws at apex; Oct.-Nov. blooming with irregular (zygomorphic) scarlet flowers 6 to 8 cm long, and characterized by round ovaries. *Tropical.* *p. 618, 732, 733*

truncatus delicatus; variety of upright habit, reluctant to branch; long dark green joints sharply toothed, and with irregular white flowers delicately tinged pink; more rose-pink in good light; the ovaries round; Nov.-Dec. (winter) bloom. *Tropical.* *p. 732, 733*

truncatus 'Gertrude Beahm'; very willing and free branching with large pendulous carmine-red blooms having lighter center, freely flowering in December. *p. 733*

truncatus 'Mad. Chateney'; leaflike crenate joints, bearing attractive terminal flowers of medium size, orange red with pale pink center, round ovaries; December blooming. *p. 733*

truncatus 'Orchid'; one of the variations imported from south-eastern Brazil, forming large flowers bright orchid lavender or rosy violet; probably a natural hybrid. *p. 734*

truncatus 'Pink Perfection', a "Christmas cactus"; lovely, clear pink blossoms, free-flowering over a long blooming period, November, December and January in the Northern hemisphere. *p. 735*

truncatus 'Salmon-red' (Brazil); another color variation from southeastern Brazil, more salmon-orange than the species. *p. 732*

truncatus 'South Orange'; a vigorous Manda hybrid having wide joints with prominent teeth, and large reddish-orange flowers in December; ovaries round. *p. 733*

ZYGOPETALUM *Orchidaceae* **I3OLFD**

crinitum (Brazil); epiphyte or terrestrial with 2-3-leaved pseudobulbs, producing very pretty, fragrant flowers with the linear sepals and petals of equal length, green barred with brown, the white lip is densely hairy, streaked with violet blue. (Oct.-Dec.) (I) *p. 1841*

grandiflorum (Galeottia) (Perú, Colombia, Costa Rica); pretty epiphyte, with 2-leaved pseudobulbs, and short stalks bearing 3-5 flowers 8 cm across, the pointed sepals and petals light green striped lengthwise with brown, lip white with raised red lines and orange crest, (late summer). (S) *p. 1841*

mackayi (So. Brazil: Sao Paulo); although said to be an epiphyte, I have seen it growing in quantity in red clay on high savannah of the Serra do Mar above Santos; robust species with clustered pseudobulbs and 45 cm leaves having raised veins; erect racemes of beautiful 5-8 cm fragrant, waxy flowers, sepals and petals yellow-green blotched with brown, the large showy lip white, with spots and streaks of blue, (Nov.-June). *p. 1832, 1841*

maxillare (Brazil); handsome, free-flowering epiphyte with 2-3-leaved, furrowed pseudobulbs, and loose inflorescence carrying large 6 cm showy flowers, the oblong sepals and petals basically lemon-green overlaid with chocolate-brown, the spreading lip rich violet-blue, more pale on margins (various). (I) *p. 1841*

wendlandii (Warszewiczella) (Costa Rica); handsome epiphyte without pseudobulbs; tufted 2-ranked, strongly ribbed, oblanceolate leaves 20-25 cm long; a short basal stalk bears a showy, solitary flower about 10 cm across, with sepals and petals pale yellowish-green or white, the lip white with central area lined and suffused with violet; ridged crest purple; autumn. (S) *p. 1840, 1841*

ZYGOSTATES *Orchidaceae* **I3OFW**

grandiflora (Ornithocephalus) (Brazil), a "Bird's-head orchid"; interesting epiphyte, without pseudobulbs, the broad fleshy leaves arranged somewhat fan-like from the base; gracefully arching inflorescence dense with small, fragrant flowers 2 cm dia., cup-shaped, vivid green to dark green at base, lip sac-like and keeled beneath, with short claw (summer). *p. 1832*

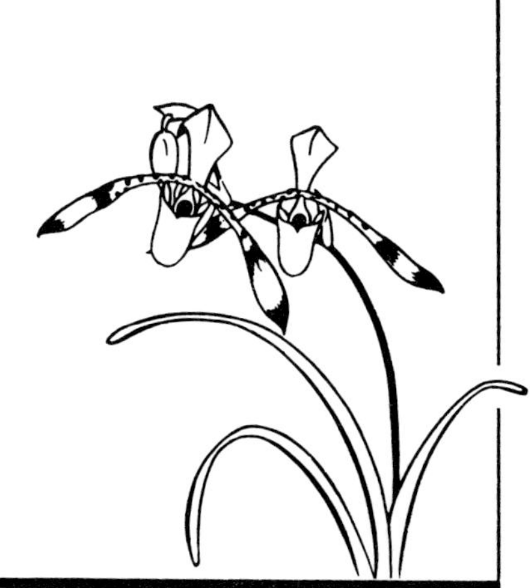

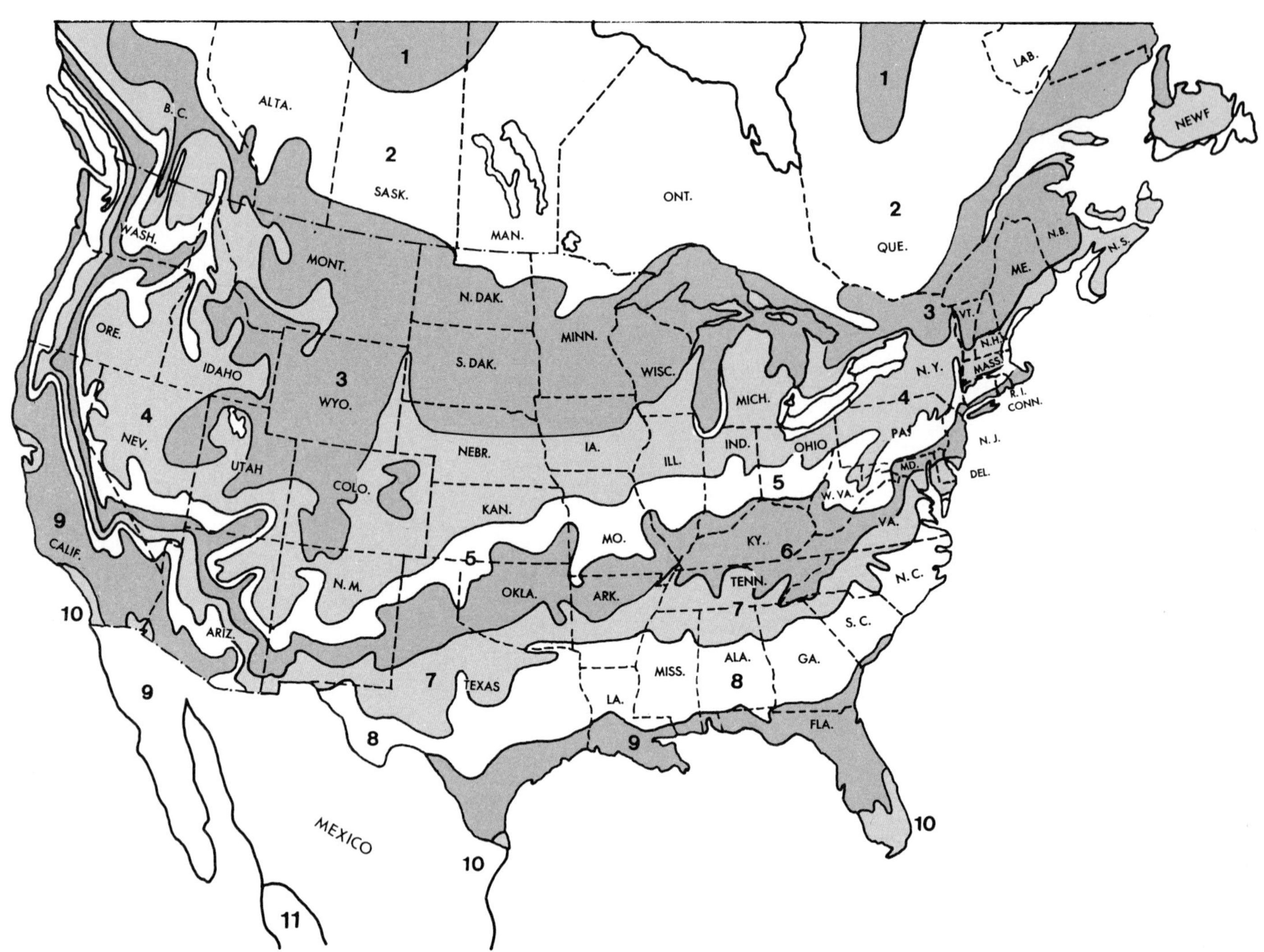

CLIMATE ZONES for PLANT HARDINESS.

The use of a Climate map is very much disputed. Gardeners know that the actual extremes in freezing weather can kill a living plant—unless protected by snow or otherwise. However, practically every garden book and nursery catalog includes such maps, which may be useful in EXOTICA also, if only as a general guide.

The Hardiness Zone rating indicates the limit of probable cold tolerance of plants. Zones follow isothermal lines of EXTREME minimum temperatures as recorded or expected each winter across the country, modified by factors such as elevation, wind-chill, snowcover or the lack of it, and degrees of precipitation.

The **Minimum and Maximum temperatures** listed on **pg. 2507** for Key Meteorological stations throughout the World may serve to indicate plant preferences according to their climatic backgrounds and origins.

Minimum Temperatures possible

ZONE	*down to*
1	– 52° C (- 58° F)
2	– 46° C (- 50° F)
3	– 40° C (- 40° F)
4	– 34° C (- 30° F)
5	– 29° C (- 20° F)
6	– 23° C (- 10° F)
7	– 18° C (0° F)
8	– 12° C (10° F)
9	– 7° C (20° F)
10	– 1° C (30° F)
11	8° C (46° F)
12	18° C (64° F)

Climate Zones — WEST EUROPE

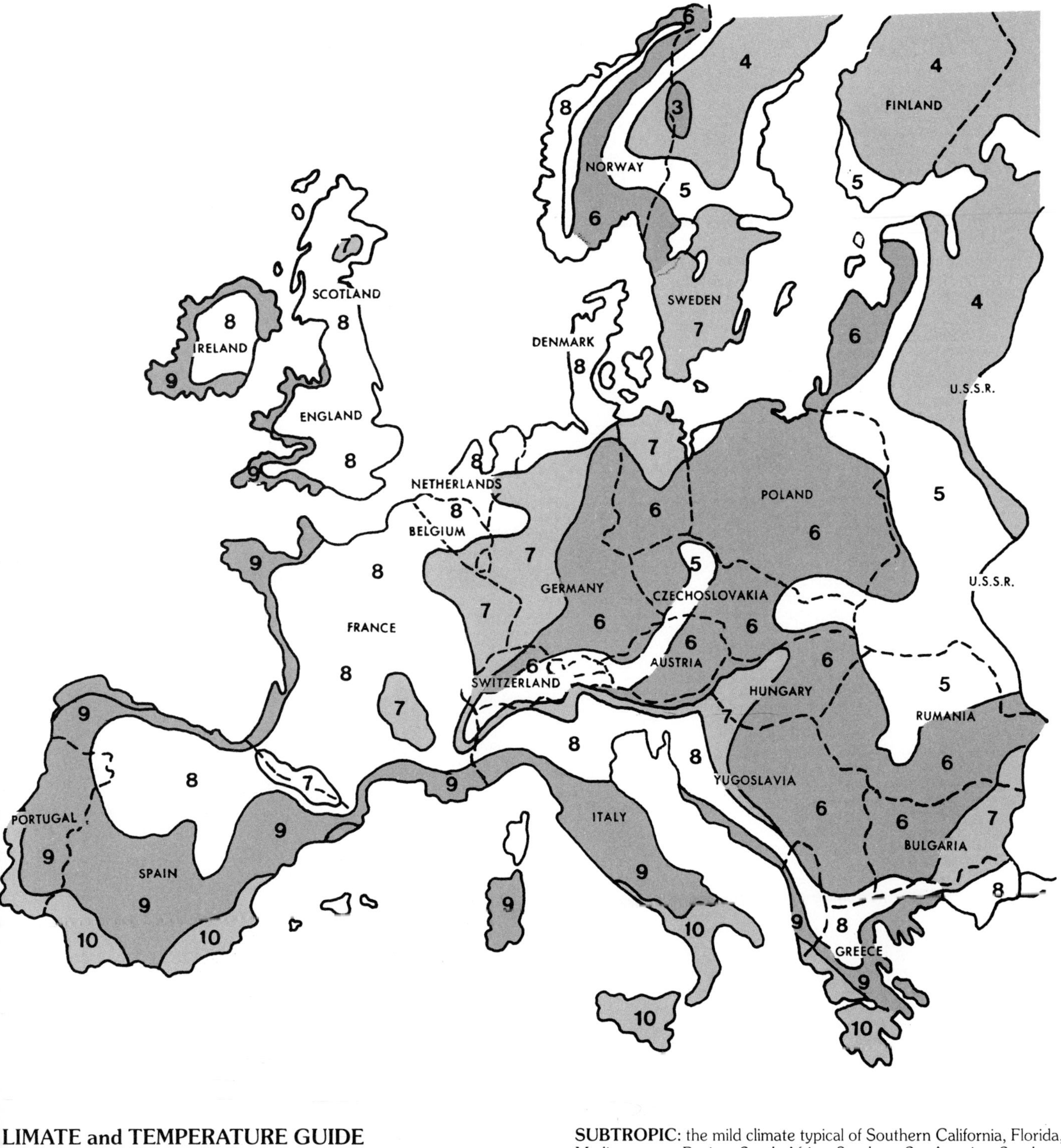

CLIMATE and TEMPERATURE GUIDE

…nts in the text designated TROPICAL, SUBTROPIC, WARM-…MPERATE, and TEMPERATE indicate the environment of their na…e habitat, or that which they would prefer to best succeed in …rdens or indoors. However, most living beings are very tolerant and …xible, and experience has shown that a suggestion of temperature …eferences does not necessarily mean that plants would not adapt to …ferent living conditions—cold tolerant subjects to warmer climate, or …picals to more rigorous and cooler regions—once they are accli…ted and reasonably sheltered.

…ROPICAL: warm surroundings, with hot or humid-warm days 21-… C (70-85° F), and balmy nights, where temperature should nor…lly not go below a minimum of 15° C (60° F), never with frost. Pri…ry tropical climates are found round the world, except at higher …vations, in Central and No. South America, West Indies, West and …st Africa, India, Malaysia, Philippines, Indonesia, South Pacific, …waii (zones 11-12).

SUBTROPIC: the mild climate typical of Southern California, Florida, Mediterranean Region, South Africa, Southern So. America, Southern Australia, with warm to hot sunny days, the nights with temperatures down to 10° C or 8° C (50° F or 45° F) but sometimes with frost in winter. (U.S. Hardiness zones 9-10).

WARM-TEMPERATE: climate as prevailing in the Southern U.S., Oregon, England to S.E. Europe, Asia Minor, Japan, So. New Zealand; warm and often rainy in daytime, minimums at night generally down to 5° Celsius (40° F), with some frost and soil freezing occasionally in winter (U.S. Hardiness zones 7-8).

TEMPERATE: cool climate, such as in the Northern United States, Southern Chile and Argentina, Northern Europe, Eastern China. Frigid winter temperatures dropping to under zero deg. Celsius (32° F or lower), with heavy snow and hard freezes, especially nights. This chilling causes perennials and bulbous plants to go dormant, and to initiate flower buds and fruit wood in decidious trees. (U.S. Hardiness zones 4 to 6).

Plant Decor and Landscaping Indoors with Exotics

A little Philodendron panduraeforme in glazed dish is fully content under frequently used desk light, adding a touch of life without being possessive.

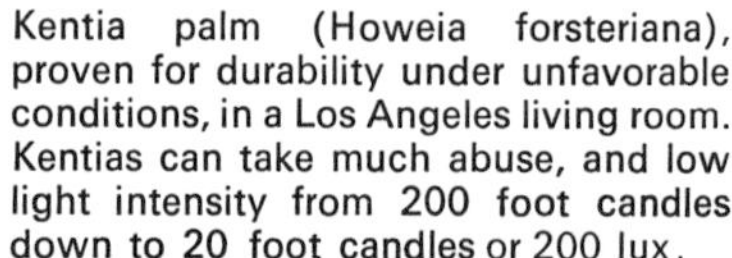

Kentia palm (Howeia forsteriana), proven for durability under unfavorable conditions, in a Los Angeles living room. Kentias can take much abuse, and low light intensity from 200 foot candles down to 20 foot candles or 200 lux.

2482

Foliage plants accented and blessed by concealed light in a recessed alcove. To many foliage plants, 15 to 20 foot candles of light intensity, equivalent to fair reading light, is sufficient if combined with reduced moisture.

Exotic Plants to Live With

Living room planting in Pretoria, South Africa under fluorescent lights. The planters are covered with grass mats made by Africans as sleeping mats, and adorned with their tribal carvings.

Solitary Philodendron pertusum (juv. Monstera deliciosa) traces exotic patterns in an otherwise rather bare room. Such Monsteras tolerate as low as 15 foot candles of light but prefer as high as 200 foot candles which enables them tc maintain their large character leaves.

There is no better place for plants indoors, excepting a greenhouse, than this comfortable Winter garden, filled with light, in our New Jersey home. On a broad window sill we can probe first-hand the merits of numerous house plant candidates; if the sun becomes too burning hot we can control the light by letting down Venetian blinds. The temperature drops to a refreshing 10°C on winter nights; in summer we have airconditioning. A cozy room, very much enjoyed by us and by our plants, especially when deep snow covers outdoor patio and gardens.

An ideal location for all kinds of flowering plants on a broad shelf next to the good daylight of the East windows, at the Ross home, in Camden, Maine. Such "Picture Windows" and even more so the modern sliding glass doors wondrously combine the outdoors with the living room and bring Nature indoors and closer to daily life.

Rooftop Solarium

This penthouse in New York provides just about ideal conditions for plants that flower and bear fruit. The glass-roofed greenhouse adjoins a glass-walled living room offering day to day enjoyment of this secluded garden room. A splashing fountain framed by luxuriant vines on marble columns add a touch of Southern charm.

The Conservatory for Atmosphere and Study

A restful Winter garden conservatory invites guests to the gracious way of life of the Empress Hotel in Victoria, British Columbia.

Naturalistic planting of an Exotic garden at Roehrs Exotic Nurseries in New Jersey not only presents a composite and idealistic picture of a tropical landscape, but also houses various mother plants needed for propagation.

Delicate tropicalia luxuriate so much more easily in their own microclimate when grouped and planted together in ground beds. In this manner they will tolerate adverse conditions and temperature changes without harm.

Conservatories – Old and New

The beginning of greenhouses, the early orangerie at Florence, Italy. Simply an orthodox building with very tall windows and primitive heating, dating from the 18th century (U.S.D.A. photo).

The ultra-modern Climatron, a geodesic dome structure of aluminum tubing, covered with 6 mm ($\frac{1}{4}$ inch) Plexiglass, and 54 meters in diameter, at Missouri Botanic Gardens, Saint Louis, and built based on the principles conceived by Buckminster Fuller.

In mechanically controlled, air-conditioned temperature and climate areas, epiphytic bromeliads luxuriate with climbers and ferns under optimum light conditions inside the futuristic Climatron at Saint Louis.

Sheltered Interior Courts

Lovely Exotic planting featuring West Indian treeferns and many species of tropicalia, in the glass-covered peristyle of a distinguished suburban residence in Westchester, New York. Through windows and glass doors all the rooms of the house look out into the square interior court.

A corner of the peristyle planting with a quiet refreshing indoor pool. Left Cyperus and Monstera, right the leathery Dracaena hookeriana.

An unobtrusive little lean-to greenhouse snuggled away by the side of a vine-covered home in Massachusetts. Slats of wood may be rolled down to provide partial shade on bright days.

The Small Home Greenhouse

Inside a trim Lord and Burnham glasshouse featuring automatic ventilation and heat, a plant lover has a wide choice of plants, especially the flowering kind, that may be grown under ideal conditions of light and humidity. Seasonable blooming plants may be brought into the living room when needed for temporary decoration.

A small greenhouse 4 × 5 m is big enough to have given a lifetime of happy avocation to a fancier of cacti in New Jersey. With so many varieties there is bloom the year round, requiring a minimum of care.

A greenhouse knows no seasons. Cozily protected from winter's snow in Connecticut, the fragrance and beauty of out-of-season flowering bulbs or plants may be enjoyed even more because of the contrasts in climate indoors and outside.

The Small Home Greenhouse

In creating a comfortable climate, in their little greenhouse, plant hobbyists may have the pleasure of spending much leisure time surrounded by a collection of their favorite indoor plants.

Plantscaping in Office Buildings

Modern skyscrapers, architectural giants of great esthetic beauty, need the warmth and softening decor of live plants properly placed. Below left: Philodendron erubescens; above right: Monstera deliciosa and Ficus lyrata.

The sober lines at the street entrance to the foyer of a large insurance company building in downtown Newark, New Jersey, are enlivened by solitary container plants that will tolerate occasional chills. Left Dracaena marginata; right Fatsia japonica.

Plantscaping in Office Buildings

The spacious streetfloor of Union Carbide Corp., on Park Avenue, New York is attractively decorated by the tracery of the handsome foliage of giant Philodendron selloum in tubs. Although they tolerate low-light locations down to 15 foot candles, overhead ceiling lights are responsible for their luxuriant condition.

2492

2493

Ficus elastica 'Decora', the "Red leaf rubber plant" (left) does best in good light preferring sunlight, but has been found to tolerate poor light, down to 20 foot candles, more than other Ficus. Rhoicissus capensis, the "Evergreen grapevine" from South Africa (right) as a low centerpiece on tables, is satisfied with medium light 50 foot candles up.

Accent Plants in Offices

Yucca elephantipes, the "Spineless palm lily" for that desert look, takes much abuse. Light tolerance 20 to 500 foot candles and up.

Ficus lyrata, better known as F. pandurata, the "Fiddle-leaf fig" with its large leathery leaves is one of the most favored decorators but requires more exacting attention to even moisture and light, preferably 200 foot candles, though it can occasionally get along on 40 foot candles.

Combination touffs of durable Kentia palms, Howeia forsteriana, in the air-conditioned conference room of a manufacturing firm in Los Angeles. These palms can take much abuse and get along on little light, as low as 20 foot candles.

Podocarpus macrophylla, the coniferous "Buddhist pine", with dark green leathery needles, in a Park Avenue office, New York. Podocarpus take airconditioning provided they are well established, they prefer cool conditions and need light, 50 foot candles up.

The artistic "Seagrape" from Caribbean shores, Coccoloba uvifera, with flexuous branches and stiff-leathery foliage with red to ivory veins. To maintain their large foliage, they require at least 50 foot candles of light.

A modern glass and concrete reception area of a California factory where floor plantings of Ficus lyrata and various Philodendron magically relieve the coldness of this futuristic building.

Plant Decor in Business

An awkward corner of an automobile showroom in Los Angeles has become a center of attraction by enclosing the area with a low retaining wall, filling it with soil and planting it with decorative ornamentals.

Imposing barrier of tubbed Ficus lyrata (left) standing on shallow trays with pebbles, on the light-flooded 60th floor of a Wall Street Bank, and viewing the harbor, downtown Manhattan.

Attractive room-divider in the gracious manner, with various foliage plants and ferns, in a country club lobby near Los Angeles, California.

Exotic Landscaping Outdoors

During New York's tropical summer, when the temperature on a typical humid-warm day may be 30°C and more, the Channel Gardens at Rockefeller Center are transformed into a flourishing tropical landscape, extending from Fifth Avenue to the splashing Prometheus Fountain (above). Pools of rippling water are bordered by thousands of colorful exotic plants and trees, including Caladium, Crotons, Dracaenas and bromeliads, even pineapples in fruit (below).

Shopping Centers Beautified

A group of the decorative, semi-dwarf Christmas palms, Veitchia merrillii, in a commendable scheme to create an attractive parking area, in Miami, Florida.

Tropical planting indoors at this large shopping mall near Chicago was created by Lange Florist who understood to give prospective shoppers the exhilarating atmosphere of swaying palms and exotic greenery.

Tree philodendron, Philodendron selloum, attractively frame the entrance of Sears Department store at Torrance, in Southern California. The temperature here is very similar to their native Paraná, in Southern Brazil.

In the Moorish-Spanish Tradition

It is difficult to believe the number of potted plants maintained in Spanish homes until one has seen the Moorish-style patio courts in old Cordoba, dating back to the 8th century. Pots seem to be climbing up the walls, and occupy every free nook and corner.

The Moorish-Spanish tradition has been carried over into America, and this humble dwelling near Vera Cruz in Mexico gives proof of the deep-rooted love for plants of the Mexican people.

When the Moors ruled Spain, between 712 and 1492, they interpreted their visions of the paradise of Islam by building gardens with cool waters, fruiting trees, and flowering and fragrant plants, a tradition preserved here at the Alhambra, in Granada, under the azure skies of Andalusia.

Container Planters Outdoors

The curious, frugal Beaucarnea recurvata, a succulent water-storing tree from arid Mexico —here in a terra-cotta pot on a patio in Del Amo, California.

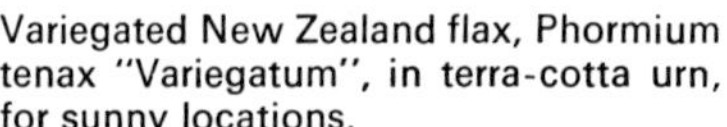

Variegated New Zealand flax, Phormium tenax "Variegatum", in terra-cotta urn, for sunny locations.

Outdoor planter box with bright, easy-going Coleus and scented-leaf Peppermint geranium, Pelargonium tomentosum.

Terra-cotta strawberry jar attractively studded with rosettes of bluish-white Echeveria elegans, in the center an Aloe succotrina; requiring little care the year round.

Bromeliad Arrangements

Skeleton stem of a Cholla cactus (Opuntia) from our Western deserts provides just the right foothold for these dwarf bromeliads. Tillandsia ionantha left and right center; left center Cryptanthus bivittatus minor; right Cryptanthus lacerdae. Submerge periodically in a bucket of water.

Hand decorated pottery bowl with crooked manzanita branch, sandblasted and cemented in to hold firm. Epiphytic bromeliads are fastened in osmunda-sphagnum, preferably with nylon thread (or soft galvanized wire). Bottom: Vriesea splendens; top left to right: Guzmania, Neoregelia, Vriesea, Tillandsia lindenii.

Simulated ceramic root looking surprisingly like real driftwood, planted with exotic bromeliads; left to right, Cryptanthus bivittatus minor, Billbergia nutans, Vriesea rodigasiana, Cryptanthus zonatus. Such bromeliads require only a minimum of space to anchor their roots, but their centers should be kept filled with fresh water.

A rectangular aquarium with frame of stainless steel can be made into a "Mini-garden", a small green world with miniature plants, twigs, rocks, and moss. Delicate tropicals thrive in the humid atmosphere generated through moisture transpired by the leaves and also evaporated from the soil, reducing the need for watering to a minimum.

Terrariums to hold Moisture

Miniature greenhouse consisting of a brightly colored plastic tray and a glass-like cover of transparent lucite. While normally this is an excellent container to start seeds, in this case it is used for tiny pots of cacti, helping them to grow faster.

Called "Table hothouse" and made in Russia, this glass container framed in wood is hermetically sealed. The inventor, Dr. Vadilo of Leningrad claims that the plants, such as Maranta, Saintpaulia and Eucharis inside, never need watering.

Glass Containers as Terrariums

A bottle garden with a variety of tropical plants, using a demijohn or carboy 60cm high of white or tinted glass always raises astonished wonderment because of the seeming impossibility to place and arrange the plants through a $4\frac{1}{2}$ cm neck. However, the tools shown explain: a brass tube to lift out a core of soil, the tongs for placing of plants, and a long spatula for setting soil and moss around them.

Because of its simple elegance, the glass globe is most popular as a glass garden. Many otherwise delicate miniature plants and ferns may be used, such as Selaginella, Adiantum, Saintpaulias, Episcias, Marantas and Pileas, but hardier species may be included. Dracaena sanderiana, Acorus, Syngonium, boxwood, Peperomias and Chamaedorea palms, even succulents such as Haworthias, are old favorites.

Containers of sparkling crystal-like glass come in many shapes, as the water pitcher above.

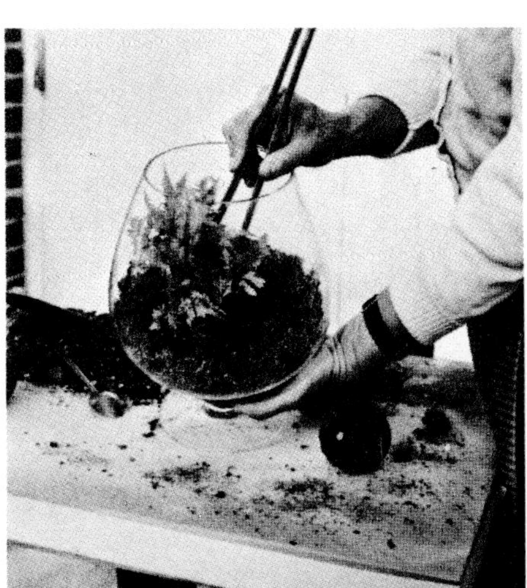

PLANTING and CARE

A large brandy inhaler is shown being planted, here with little ferns. Plants are arranged on an incline, placed in holes scooped out with a spoon, and planted with the aid of a pair of grippers made of bamboo canes.

Once the planting is completed, it is watered well with a rubber clothes sprinkler, then not again until the surface moss shows signs of drying. Excessive humidity favors diseases and fogs the glass; if covered, the glass jar may not need watering for 6 months.

Arrangements of Succulents for Dry Locations

The fawn Bambi in a highly glazed novelty planter, planted with candelabra-like Euphorbia lactea, colorful Sedum and Crassula, and several cacti.

Terra-cotta birdbath, very showy if displayed on its stand, and ideal to move outdoors in summer. White-haired cacti and succulent rosettes surround the dominant old Aloe arborescens. Gravel surface in various colors provide interesting contrast.

Old antique pieces such as this copper pan planted in California as a miniature desert scape with many contrasting types of cacti and other succulents—all excellent keepers under dry conditions and requiring little attention.

Naturalistic planting of "Living stones" (Lithops), peculiar to the deserts of Southern Africa, succulents requiring the best of light, and extremely sensitive to wetness. These 3 year old plants are growing in an 20 cm clay pan in porous soil mixed of coarse sand, clay, leafmold and perlite; pebbles of quartz or weathered stone cover the surface not only to imitate their natural habitat but also to shield the delicate rootlets from heat-burn. In their native home these xerophytes mimic the surrounding gravel and hide between it, filtering sunlight through their windowed tops. Lithops are actually only a pair of leaves filled with water, and we lightly sprinkle, rather than soak them, only when they are beginning to shrivel, about every week or two. They respond well to additional fluorescent light, even throughout the night.

The Arranging of Flowers as an Art

With the possible exception of a painting, nothing quite permits one's expression of artistic feeling so well as to take a few branches from a tree and put them together with some suitable plants, cut flowers or foliage at hand to fashion a tasteful arrangement of natural beauty to enjoy in the home. There are countless delightful and decorative effects that can be created by the exercise of a little skill, sense of beauty, and imagination.

Harmony is the sum of any successful simple flower array, taking into account color relation, proportion, symmetry and natural growth, as well as the suitability of the intended container. But beyond the fashioning of mere natural bouquets one may reach out further into the classic concept of Oriental styling in the art of Ikebana. In its cult, the Japanese are inspired by the study of the moods of nature, and their simple creations follow rules laid down by age-old tradition, based on three main lines symbolically called Heaven, Man, and Earth. Since Heaven is tallest, Man of lesser height, and Earth lowest, formal Japanese arrangements are necessarily asymmetrical or unequal. The three different classes of plants or branches are placed so that their tips would theoretically form an unequal-sided triangle, and the stems, leaves and flowers are placed accordingly. The primary line of Heaven, the tallest, is placed first. forming the axis against which the other lines are arranged to result in a pleasing unit of balance and harmony. Wire or pin-holders with weighted bases, or modeling clay is used to anchor the stems if the dish is shallow. The arrangement shown above consists of Oleander for the Heaven line, Aphelandra and Euphorbia for the Man line and Primula signifying the Earth. At left, holly-branches are placed to represent Heaven.

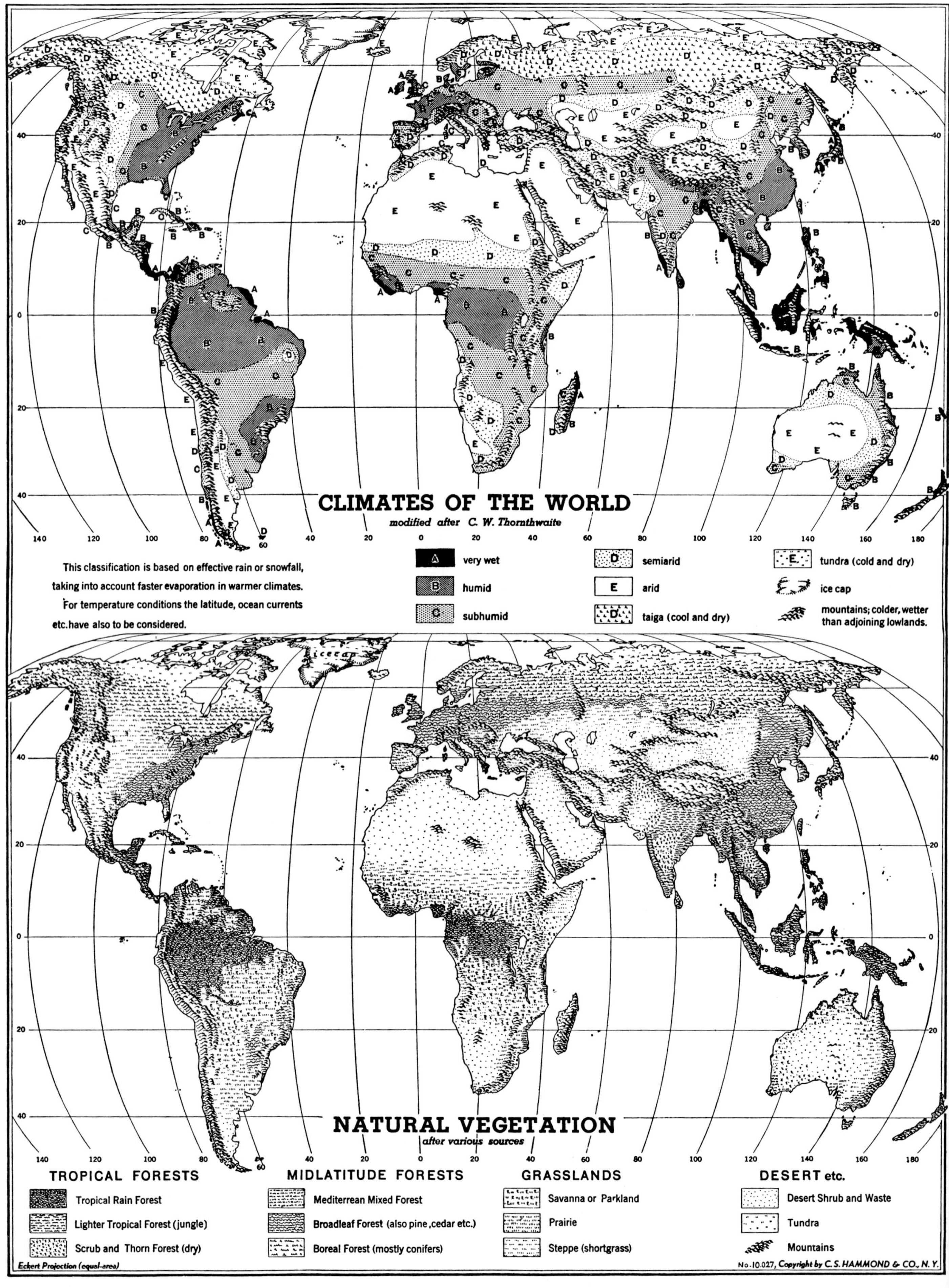
CLIMATES OF THE WORLD
modified after C. W. Thornthwaite
This classification is based on effective rain or snowfall, taking into account faster evaporation in warmer climates.
For temperature conditions the latitude, ocean currents etc. have also to be considered.
A very wet
B humid
C subhumid
D semiarid
E arid
D taiga (cool and dry)
E tundra (cold and dry)
ice cap
mountains; colder, wetter than adjoining lowlands.
NATURAL VEGETATION
after various sources
TROPICAL FORESTS
Tropical Rain Forest
Lighter Tropical Forest (jungle)
Scrub and Thorn Forest (dry)
MIDLATITUDE FORESTS
Mediterrean Mixed Forest
Broadleaf Forest (also pine, cedar etc.)
Boreal Forest (mostly conifers)
GRASSLANDS
Savanna or Parkland
Prairie
Steppe (shortgrass)
DESERT etc.
Desert Shrub and Waste
Tundra
Mountains
icecap
Eckert Projection (equal-area)
No. 10.027, Copyright by C. S. HAMMOND & CO., N. Y.

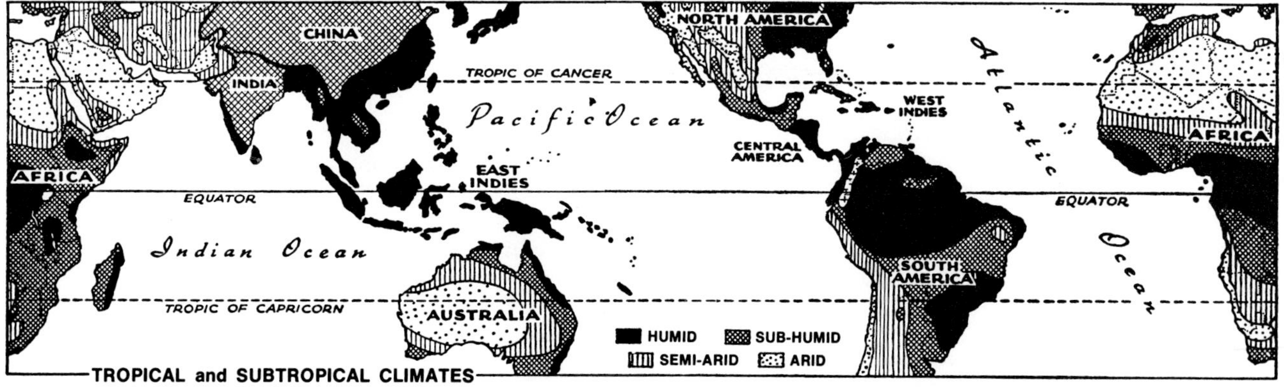

TROPICAL and SUBTROPICAL CLIMATES

PLANT GEOGRAPHY

To give a potential indoor plant the best possible chance of success, we should know something about the climatic backgrounds that prevail in their native habitats. Environment has shaped characteristics in plant types that make them either tolerant or difficult to acclimate when taken into cultivation. If too sensitive it may be best not to try them as a house plant, but many tropicals are far too beautiful not to tempt us to experiment with them just the same.

This is where knowledge of their origin helps us to provide for them those conditions under which such plants feel at home. Each climatic zone has favored and subsequently evolved plant populations that are peculiar to it.

As if by magic carpet, the fascinating world of the Collector of Exotics extending East from the tropics of the Western hemisphere to subtropical Europe, the vast expanse of Africa and Monsoon Asia and on to Australasia and the islands of the Southern Seas—these are the areas where our house plants were originally found.

Temperature and Rainfall at typical locations in the Tropic and Subtropic Zones.

	LAT. deg.	ELEV. metres	TEMP. °C min.	TEMP. °C max.	RAIN cm
NORTH AMERICA					
California, San Diego	32.7 N	40	2	31	27
Florida, Miami	25.8 N	3	–3	35	140
Mexico, Mexico City	19.2 N	2310	–4	33	60
Mexico, Vera Cruz	19.1 N	16	9	35	172
WEST INDIES					
Cuba, Habana	23.8 N	49	10	35	120
Puerto Rico, San Juan	18.2 N	30	16	34	152
Jamaica, Kingston	18.1 N	7	14	37	82
CENTRAL AMERICA					
Guatemala, Guatemala City	14.3 N	1401	5	32	127
Costa Rica, San José	9.5 N	1147	8	34	177
Panama, Colón	9.2 N	8	19	35	312
SOUTH AMERICA					
Venezuela, Caracas	10.3 N	1043	7	33	80
Venezuela, Ciudad Bolivar	8.9 N	38	19	36	88
Guyana, Georgetown	6.5 N	21	20	33	225
Colombia, Buenaventura	3.5 N	12	23	33	975
Ecuador, Quito (Sierra)	0.1 S	2852	2	26	122
Ecuador, Mendez (Oriente)	2.4 S	698	16	32	255
Brazil, Manaos (Amazonas)	3.0 S	45	19	38	182
Brazil, Rio de Janeiro	22.5 S	64	11	39	108
Brazil, Sao Paulo	23.3 S	820	–2	38	140
Peru, Iquitos (Amazon)	3.7 S	90	18	31	258
Peru, Lima	12.3 S	156	4	32	5
Peru, Cuzco	13.3 S	3452	–2	26	80
Bolivia, La Paz	16.3 S	3660	–3	24	55
Chile, Santiago	33.2 S	520	–4	37	35
Argentina, Buenos Aires	34.3 S	25	–2	40	95
EUROPE					
France, Marseilles	43.1 N	75	–6	38	58
Italy, Palermo (Sicily)	38.1 N	70	3	36	75
Spain, Seville (Andalusia)	37.2 N	30	–5	46	47

	LAT. deg.	ELEV. metres	TEMP. °C min.	TEMP. °C max.	RAIN cm
AFRICA					
Egypt, Cairo	30.3 N	30	–1	45	3
Cameroon, Douala	4.0 N	10	19	32	395
Equat. Africa, Brazzaville	4.2 S	290	12	38	123
East Africa, Nairobi	1.1 S	1662	2	32	95
Tanzania, Amani (Usamb.)	4.5 S	945	7	30	125
Tanzania, Tanga	5.1 S	30	18	34	153
Madagascar, Tamatave	18.9 S	4	13	38	313
So. Africa, Johannesburg	26.1 S	1754	–5	32	80
South Africa, Cape Town	33.5 S	12	–1	40	63
ASIA					
Israel, Haifa	32.6 N	10	2	38	67
Japan, Nagasaki	32.4 N	133	–5	37	198
China, Yunnan-Fu	25.2 N	1943	–4	33	105
Sikkim, Manjitar, Rangit R.	27.1 N	249	10	35	437
India, Cherrapunji (Assam)	25.2 N	1289	9	32	1065
India, Madras	13.4 N	7	14	45	120
Taiwan, Keelung (Teipei)	20.1 N	10	3	33	337
Burma, Mandalay	21.6 N	76	9	41	82
Philippines, Baguio	16.5 N	1461	8	25	457
Philippines, Manila	14.3 N	14	14	38	200
Thailand, Bangkok	13.4 N	4	11	41	130
Vietnam, Saigon	10.4 N	11	15	40	175
Ceylon, Colombo	6.5 N	7	17	36	200
Borneo, Sandakan	5.5 N	3	20	36	300
Sumatra, Toba	2.5 N	1150	14	27	225
Malaya, Singapore	1.2 N	2	18	38	238
Java, Jakarta	6.1 S	8	19	36	180
Java, Bogor	6.6 S	280	18	32	430
New Guinea, Port Moresby	9.3 S	39	20	36	102
AUSTRALASIA					
Hawaii, Honolulu	21.2 N	4	11	32	90
Hawaii, Hilo	19.4 N	12	11	33	342
Fiji Is., Suva	18.8 S	13	14	36	280
Australia, Brisbane	27.3 S	42	2	42	112
New Zealand, Auckland	36.5 S	46	0	32	110

Freezing point zero deg. Centigrade = 32 deg. Fahrenheit (F.).
1 meter (m) = 40 inches (or 3.28 feet).

The Americas - Subtropical North America

North along the Tropic of Cancer stretches the subtropical rain forest, an extension of the primeval forest of the tropical zone, found in the lowlands of northern Mexico, the southern tip of Texas, and southern Florida to approximately 30 deg. north latitude. Here evergreen oaks predominate, with epiphytic Tillandsia and orchids, mainly Epidendrums, climbing aroids and figs, Magnolias, Sabal-palms, and a few woody lianas. In swampy ground the oak gives place to the Bald cypress (Taxodium), and on sandy ground to the Long-leaf pine, Pinus palustris, and caribaea. Many of the trees are hung with the gray festoons of the epiphytic Spanish moss, Tillandsia usneoides, which is found as far south as northern Chile and central Argentina. Western Mexico and southwest United States is a region of high plateaus, deep canyons and arid deserts, transversed by wooded mountain ranges. The dry Pacific slopes, especially, are inhabited by a xerophytic flora including many cacti which coincide in bloom with numerous showy annuals at the end of the winter rains. Coryphantha vivipara, and Opuntia fragilis and polyacantha have even adapted themselves to the cold-temperature climate as far north as western Canada, where temperatures may drop to — 40 deg. below zero C.

The vegetation of the Everglades of South Florida is typical of the subtropical forest of swamps and bayous along the Gulf of Mexico. Predominant are the Bald cypress, Taxodium, draped with the gray beards of Spanish moss, mingling with the Sabal palmetto, and many native Ficus and other hardwood trees, their branches host to a multitude of silvery Tillandsias and other epiphytes. These islands of jungle are edged by landbuilding mangroves.

The arid desert stretching away on the slopes of 3503 m Mt. Gorgonio, and facing sheer Mt. San Jacinto (3295 m) in inland Southern California, receiving between 8 and 30 cm of rain a year, is known as the "Devil's garden" because its gravelly soil is planted with a multitude of cacti, primarily wickedly armed Chollas (Opuntias) and Ferocactus acanthodes, a barrel cactus when young, cylindrical and as tall as man in maturity. This is a region of severe climatic contrasts, and having lived here for some time, I have experienced burning days of 50° C oven heat, and clear chilly nights well below freezing, even snow. But following sparse rain in late winter, the desert mysteriously bursts into glorious though fleeting bloom.

The Americas: Mexico

The Rio Suchiate forms the border between Chiapas in Mexico, and Guatemala, a green area humid-warm and lush with palms and other tropical vegetation, and a good grade of coffee, sugar cane and bananas are cultivated. On cooler mountain slopes in Chiapas at 670 m and further west in Oaxaca, at 900-1200 meters, where there is a dry season during December-January, and the temperature drops to 10° C, is the habitat of the sturdy tree-climbing Monstera deliciosa.

Mexico is the country richest in cacti, and of the 125 genera comprising this family, 61 are represented there. Four principal types each favour particular regions: the zone of Opuntias or 'Tunas' centers on the semi-arid plateaux of northern and central Mexico; the globular cacti including Mammillaria are most abundant in the northern desert regions from San Luis Potosi to Chihuahua; the zone of epiphytic cacti are the humid forests of Vera Cruz, Tabasco, and Chiapas; and the tall columnar types such as various Cereus range from the southeast of Puebla south to Oaxaca, the Pacific slopes, and western plains of Sonora and Baja California. The slender columns of Lemaireocereus marginatus, or pipe organ cactus, are widely planted in villages as a natural fence growing to 6 m high; large groups inhabit the mountain-ringed, 2400 m tableland of the Valley of Mexico (left), in sight of the gigantic, snow-clad volcanic cones of the Popocatepetl, towering 5451 m, and the 'Sleeping Woman', Ixtaccihuatl, 5303 m (17,388 ft.)

Aside from a small area in Vera Cruz, the moist tropical zone in Mexico is most pronounced in Chiapas and Tabasco and then, following the Pacific coast, into Central America. On the dry plateau of Mexico, cacti are the dominant feature of the landscape. Opuntias alternate with columnar cacti, and Agave, Beaucarnea, Dasylirion, Dioon, Furcraea, and Yucca. Cacti represented are Lemaireocereus, the Organ pipe; Cephalocereus, the Old Man; Echinocereus, Lemaireocereus, Echinocactus, Ferocactus, Myrtillocactus, Opuntia; the smaller Astrophytum, and more than 300 Mammillaria; well-known succulents are Dudleya, Echeveria, Euphorbia, including the native "Poinsettia"; Graptopetalum, Pachyphytum, Sedum, and Urbinia. Some of our garden plants are Cobaea, Cuphea, Dahlia, Fuchsia, Penstemon, Tagetes, Oxalis; bulbous Polianthes, Sprekelia and Tigridia. As moisture increases, we find various epiphytic cacti; in commelinads, Commelina, Rhoeo, Callisia, Hadrodemas and Zebrina; a profusion of colorful or decorative trees and shrubs: Aphelandra, Boehmeria, Bouvardia, Datura, Eupatorium, Ficus petiolaris, Malvaviscus, Miconia, Oreopanax, Plumeria, Pseuderanthemum, Thevetia; of palms the dwarf Chamaedorea. Well-known climbers are Antigonon, Asarina, Passiflora, Petrea, Smilax, Solandra; little Allophyton, many Begonias; Calathea and Maranta, Hoffmannia, Peperomia, Pilea, Pinguicula, Schizocentron; in gesneriads Achimenes, Columnea, Episcia, Smithiantha. In ascending forests we run into aroids, as Anthurium, Philodendron, Syngonium, and large Monstera deliciosa; the moist forest grows various ferns, like Adiantum, Polypodium as well as Selaginella, and in tree ferns Alsophila, Cyathea, and the well-known decorator Cibotium schiedei; bromeliads are represented by Aechmea and Hechtia; orchids with such good genera as Brassavola, Epidendrum, Gongora, Laelia, Lycaste, Maxillaria, Odontoglossum, Sobralia, Stanhopea and Vanilla.

The Americas - Central America

In Central America, especially Costa Rica and Guatemala, the condensed flora rivals that of South America. The high plateau of Mexico narrows southward and competes with the chain of the Cordilleras forming numerous terraces, valleys and narrow coastal areas, all with different climatic conditions. On the eastern slopes of the Sierra with various volcanoes which tower above 3650 m, exists a rich, moisture-loving vegetation topped in the "Tierra Fria" with oaks, pines, and firs (Abies religiosa), followed downward toward the sea by tree fern, and mahogany; cycads such as Dioon and Ceratozamia; Heliconia, Macaranga, Plumeria, and Theobroma, the cacao; climbing Passiflora and Petrea; the dwarf palms Chamaedorea and Neanthe. In bromeliads: Guzmania and Tillandsia; many other well-known house plants are found here: Abutilon, Begonia, Calathea, Costus, Fuchsia, Peperomia, Piqueria, Salvia, Tripogandra; in ferns Tectaria; and numerous aroids, notably Anthurium, including the beautiful A. scherzerianum, Dieffenbachia, Monstera, Philodendron, Spathiphyllum, Syngonium. The flora is especially rich in orchids. Costa Rica alone has the greatest concentration of orchid species for its size in the world and these grow all the way to the cloud forests. On drier slopes we find many xerophytes: cacti, such as Lemaireocereus; and Yucca, Dasylirion, Agave, and Pedilanthus.

After crossing the Continental Divide east from San José, Costa Rica, the road winds downward to Turrialba. The countryside is green savannah alternating with banana plantations, and patches of prolific jungle. Here at 600 m., temperature can range from 10 to 32° C. We meet many old acquaintances: Philodendron, Syngonium, gesneriads, Begonias, Selaginellas, Adiantum, Costus; various epiphytic orchids and bromeliads, and the interesting Monstera friedrichsthalii (right). Colorful 2-wheeled oxcarts leisurely creak their way and easygoing peones have as ready answer: "Quien sabe que sera!"

In the Pacific lowlands of Guatemala, the rich black humus seems bottomless. Bananas and sugar cane are much in cultivation. Near Chicacao, Guatemala, on a volcanic slope at 1200 m., it is moist and cool with daily rains starting at 1 p.m. Deep barrancos are the best hunting grounds for interesting plants, and here we find various orchids, also Anthuriums, Achimenes, bromeliads, Heliconias, Tripogandra, Begonias, Philodendrons, and magnificent tree-ferns. The trees are densely covered with Philodendron lacerum and many epiphytes.

The Americas - West Indies

The West Indies are but an insular extension of the American tropical flora, differing from the continent mainly by the greater profusion of ferns and orchids, aided by the more uniform climate peculiar to tropical islands and modified only by their high mountains.

Those islands that are traversed by mountain chains or sierra, such as Cuba, Santo Domingo, Puerto Rico, and Trinidad, are favored by ample rains which create, mainly on the side exposed to the northeast tradewinds, an abundant vegetation, with true rain forests in the mountains. There, at the higher altitudes, the tropical vegetation of both Central and South America meet. The steep mountains are covered with mixed forests of tree ferns, mainly the slender Cyathea and Alsophila; and the mountain palms Euterpe globosa and Coccothrinax; Cecropia, Tabebuya, Persea, Coccoloba, Clusia, Psidium, Heliconia. The trees are loaded with epiphytes: small orchids, bromeliads, and aroids; Marcgravias clothe the trunks. Orchids are many but not particularly showy. Aroids are strong with Anthurium, Dieffenbachia, Philodendron, and Xanthosoma. In moist locations we find gesneriads such a Columnea, Gesneria, and Kohleria; delicate Begonias crawl on the forest floor; Aphelandra, Calathea, Oplismenos, Peperomia, Pilea, Wedelia; small ferns: Adiantum, Doryopteris, Hemionitis, Pellaea, and Polystichum. There are many flowering shrubs such as Cestrum and Malpighia; Heliconia; climbing Cissus, Rhoicissus,, Ipomoea, and Solandra. The deep red loam, flattening out toward the northern coast, produces tall sugar cane and is also the home of the stately Royal palm, Oreodoxa, and the spreading Saman tree. Along the shores are thickets of Coccoloba and landbuilding mangroves on stilts.

In drier regions, especially on the south side, is rolling savannah where we find the gorgeous Poinciana trees. In the southwest, and in Cuba northeast, are even desert-like areas, as in Mexico, with various cacti such as the cochineal, the Turk's cap; and in succulents Agave.

The flora of the lower islands of the Lesser Antilles, including the Virgin Islands, suffers from lack of beneficial rains, and savannah mingles with low thorn forest, Juniperus, Ericaceae, Agave and some ferns.

The steep faced northern slopes of the Sierra Luquillo in tropical Puerto Rico, ascending to 1067 m, receive a rainfall of 5 m (200 in.) yearly often pouring down like hammer blows, producing true rainforest with great tree ferns, mainly the slender Cyathea arborea, growing to 12 m. high and mingling with mountain palms (Euterpe) *and Cecropia, and inhabited by many epiphytes, climbers and ferns.*

Such bromeliads as Vriesea (Thecophyllum) *sintenisii and Guzmania berteroniana grow in great profusion on the trunks of Mountain palms, Euterpe globosa, in the Sierra of Puerto Rico, together with other epiphytes such as small orchids, Anthurium, Begonias, Peperomias, gesneriads, Pileas, many ferns, and climbing Marcgravias, the "Shingle plant".*

The Americas - Northern South America

The northern parts of South America, including Colombia, Venezuela, and the forests of Guiana, serve to link the Central American flora with the Amazon region, or Hylaea. This northern area, its shores often lined with Cereus, is partly rainy, partly dry. Irregularly forested mountains hold many epiphytes such as orchids, especially the showy Cattleya; bromeliads and aroids, and we also find attractive Melastomaceae, Piperaceae, Dioscorea, Marantaceae, Passiflora, Begonia; Gesneriaceae include Alloplectus, Diastema, Episcia, Koellikeria, Kohleria, Nautilocalyx. Where the winds have been deprived of their moisture by coastal mountain ranges, there stretch the savannahs, known as "Llanos" in Venezuela and Colombia, and "Campos" in Brazil, and few trees grow, with occasional acacia and cacti. But gallery forests with mahogany, palms, Carludovica and aroids follow the broad rivers which are lined with Montrichardia growing right into the water. Common aroids are Anthurium, Dieffenbachia, Monstera, Philodendron, Rhodospatha, Spathiphyllum, Stenospermation, Xanthosoma. We also find Allamanda, Aphelandra, Browallia, Cyclanthus, Dioscorea, Eucharis, Heliconia, and Peperomias.

As if on stilts, a forest giant at the edge of the Surinam river in Guiana, bears his share of epiphytes, but most prominent, as if they were colorful birds, Philodendron melinonii in shapely rosettes, with their brilliant red, swollen leafstalks which can be spotted at great distance. The primeval jungle is immense. Great trees, draped with falling lianas and bearing fungi, ferns, orchids, bromeliads, philodendron, and many other plants that can find a footing, struggle for life with one another. Graceful palms fringe the river banks and break the mass of small foliage, and above it the giants, perhaps 60 m. high, whose crowns have burst through the canopy into the sun. At 1 p.m. the temperature measures 29° C., with an oppressive humidity of 81%; the daily range is only 7 deg. C. Even the leaves hang away from the brilliant sun. A temperature above the 28's from January to December, heavy with evaporation from a land that is mostly leaves, swamps and rivers, drains the body and all vivacity, and when leaving the river, it needs an effort of will and a compelling purpose, to keep walking along all day in this steamy heat.

Venezuela is the home of the Easter orchid Cattleya mossiae, growing epiphytic in the high, cool forests of the Cordillera de la Costa at 1000 m or higher, where the temperature drops to 9° C., and also further west in the eastern extensions of the Andes. From December to April it is very dry and warm, and rainy from May to November. Growing on live trees (left) makes a big difference in the plants, and I had counted one specimen producing 22 flowers at the same time.

The Americas - Tropical Amazonas

The greatest vegetation is found in the Hylaea, the interior of Amazonas, the most pronounced territory of moist forest in the world, where regular rains to 300 cm fall during a year and extending to where the upper Amazon bends to the south in Peru. In the lofty rain forests we find some 2,000 varieties of both hardwood and softwood trees, Brazil-nuts, and lactiferous Euphorbiaceae of which Hevea, the Para-rubber, is economically most important. Large areas are covered with ground water; this region exhibits the greatest variety of palms in the world. The giant water lily, Victoria regia, forming colonies in quiet warm backwaters of rivers or "igarapes", is strikingly characteristic.

Most of the smaller plants, bromeliads, orchids and aroids have taken to the giant trees, while long lianas form a jungle often hard to penetrate. Scattered, on higher ground, grow showy Gesneriaceae, Marantaceae, and Melastomaceae. Some important aroids come from here: the fancy-leaved Caladium; Dieffenbachia, and Philodendron. We also find Bignonia, Calathea, Cissus, Dioscorea, Echites, Passiflora, Peperomia and other Piperaceae, but generally this is a land of trees, climbers, and epiphytes.

The trees of the Amazonian forest are tall and often scattered, many with latex, and the sunlight plays in lacy patterns along the level floor. The heat makes me weak in the knees and dizzy sweat pours out, as it does from the naked body of the madero, our guide. Long lianas are reaching for the ground where Marantas and Calatheas grow, with Heliconias, Selaginellas, Miconia, Dieffenbachia and Passifloras. On the trees live various Philodendron and bromeliads, while tiny hummingbirds, which the Brazilians call "Beija-flor" or "Flower-kissers", are whirring from one to another.

Dieffenbachia "picta" grows in well drained red clay in company of climbing ferns, selaginellas, and slender Asai palms, by the side of the wide Amazon. Here the mighty river is 75 m deep and dolphins can be seen frolicking. Although the thermometer showed only 30°C., I was gasping for breath and the sweat was running down my ears, bleeding from insect bites and scratches, so that in spite of piranhas I took a chance and jumped into the refreshing waters to swim. During the rainy season the river rises 10 m and thousands of sq.km are inundated, forcing vicious ants and many snakes into the trees with the epiphytic plants. Since there are no roads, the only way to travel any distance is by river. A little Amazon steamer takes one to some opening in the forest, to transfer to a small canoe. Paddling, to explore closer to the shore, and landing for short stabs inland, one is received by swarms of monkeys, gorgeous parrots and macaws, toucans, cicadas, and brilliant butterflies, but of course one must not overlook an occasional snake.

The Americas - Brazil South

In southeastern Brazil the wet coastal ranges of the Serra do Mar extend near the coast from Bahia south through Petropolis and the wild Organ Mountains, to Sao Paulo and down to Paraná. These escarpments catch the fogs and rains carried by the prevailing southeast winds and are covered with low, dripping, often cool forest; Alto da Serra has the greatest rainfall in Brazil, to 400 cm (160 in.) per year; a veritable paradise for epiphytic orchids, bromeliads, cacti and climbing aroids. Philodendron and Anthurium abound on the trees and, along with them, moisture-loving cacti: Hatiora, Rhipsalis, Schlumbergera, and Zygocactus. Climbers are Allamanda, Aristolochia, Bignonia, Bougainvillea, Cissus, Dipladenia, Ipomoea, Manettia, Mikania, and Passiflora. On the ground one of the richest collections of attractive plants are at home here: in gesneriads: Columnea, Rechsteineria, and Sinningia; of Marantaceae: Calathea, Ctenanthe, Maranta and Stromanthe; showy Melastomaceae with Bertolonia, Miconia, and Tibouchina. Foremost among terrestrial aroids are various beautiful Dieffenbachias. Many palms include Butia, Cocos, Syagrus. Ferns are represented by Adiantum, Blechnum, Dryopteris, Hemionitis, Nephrolepis; also the fern-ally Selaginella.

Vriesea hieroglyphica is one of the most spectacular bromeliads ever collected. This beauty grew in the dripping, low jungle of the rainforest on the Serra do Mar, in southern Brazil, at about 1000 m elevation. Chilly, drizzly clouds were sweeping in from the ocean, and the humidity measured from 95 to 100%, the temperature 15° C. at midday. Rain falls 300 days a year, more than anywhere else in Brazil, and epiphytes flourish on every limb. Together with bromeliads such as Neoregelias, Billbergias, Quesnelias, Tillandsias, Aechmeas, Catopsis and many Vrieseas revel Philodendrons — especially imbe and domesticum; Epiphyllums, Begonias, Anthuriums, Vanilla and other orchids, particularly the brilliant red Sophronitis. It is a surprise to see, in the densest thicket, the heavy Vriesea hieroglyphica clinging like birds to thin twigs, only a few feet from the ground. In grassy clearings of the forest, in the red clay soil, grow Zygopetalum, Drosera, Scirpus, Mimosa, and amongst Vriesea bituminosa and many Nidulariums, the sky-blue Neomarica coerulea.

The Banderantes coast south of Rio, along the Atlantic, washed by breaking salty waves, is a strip of white sand and matted, thorny brambles, with occasional pepper trees, Eugenia uniflora and Ipomoea, the morning glory; and a strange assortment of Philodendron glaziovii, imbe and longilaminatum; rosettes of Anthurium, the silver-felted Peperomia incana, Neomarica, Furcraea gigantea and whole stretches of the dwarf palms Diplothemium maritima. On smooth slippery granite rocks grow procumbent snaky cacti, Cephalocereus fluminensis, right alongside such orchids as Cyrtomium and Epidendrum; saxicolous bromeliads Billbergia amoena, Aechmea, Quesnelia and Tillandsia, all out in glaring sun but filled with refreshing water in their center cups...

The Americas - South Brazil and Argentina

Southward into Paraná occur pure groups of noble Araucaria angustifolia, and forests of Mimosas extend into Paraguay. South, in Argentina, grow beautiful flowering Cassia, and the well-known Petunia, Acanthostachys, Brodiaea, Dyckia, Lippia, Nierembergia, Tillandsia including the "Spanish moss", Tradescantia, and Zephyranthes. In northwest Argentina, where grasses do not flourish, the thorn-savannah or "Espinal" region is rich in cacti: Echinopsis, Gymnocalycium, Lobivia, Malacocarpus, Notocactus, Parodia, Pseudolobivia, Rebutia, many of which are very free-blooming even as small house plants. Other genera represented are Opuntia, various Cereus such as Oreocereus trollii, Harrisia, Cleistocactus, and Rhipsalis; some tree-like Philodendron, with Acacia, dot the landscape. But gradually, with moderate rainfall, the land stretches out into the grassy pampas.

On the western frontier of Brazil where the Rio Paraná forms the border of Paraguay, spreads the vast rainforest of the Mato Grosso. Here the Rio Iguassu, 3 km wide, drops in mighty cascades, higher than Niagara, down to the Parana. The foaming water tosses between gigantic rocks, and clouds of mist drift widely over the area. The thermometer reads 20° C, the humidity 90-100%. Because of this abundant moisture in the atmosphere, the giant trees, perhaps 50 m high, are covered with epiphytes and climbers - bromeliads, orchids, Rhipsalis, Peperomias, Bignonia, Passiflora, Begonias and Philodendrons. The handsome Philodendron selloum with its lobed leaves, and forming trunks six feet high, is growing both on trees and on the ground. This specimen, growing in slithery clay, looks over into Argentina from the brink of the cataracts of Iguassu; and which are fringed by stately Arecastrum romanzoffianum palms, better known as "Cocos plumosa".

Northwest Argentina is cradled in the High Cordilleras, with icy 6000 m. peaks and plunging valleys, and more cacti are concentrated there than anywhere else south of the equator. Coming from Bolivia into Jujuy, the giant Trichocereus pasacana begin to appear at 4800 m, and as we descend to the "Espinal" at 1000 m., between rock and gravel and thorn, cacti become most numerous and varied, extending on through Salta down to Mendoza. Familiar types are Oreocereus trollii, Cleistocactus straussii, various Opuntias and Echinopsis, many Parodias and Lobivias, especially in friendly Salta province, where Gymnocalycium begin to appear, becoming more common further south.

South America - Andine Region

The well watered eastern slope of the Cordilleras probably holds the richest still unexplored treasure of tropical plants in this hemisphere. Beni Province of eastern Bolivia, the Montana of Peru, the selva of Oriente Province in Ecuador, and Amazonian Colombia, as well as the Choco, promise to yield many a new beautiful plant. Already, the territory along the Rio Dagua and similar locations on the slopes of the Andes in Colombia, Ecuador, and Peru have given us many well-known plants. In aroids we know some of our most attractive Anthuriums from that region, as well as Dieffenbachia and Philodendron in great variety, also many showy bromeliads and orchids. At 1200 m and higher we find tree-ferns, Adiantum, Bertolonia, Brunfelsia, Calathea, Carludovica, Cinchona, Coca, Datura, Fittonia, Fuchsia, Heliconia, Hippeastrum, Heliotropium, Hymenocallis, Passiflora, Peperomia and Sanchezia. Going higher there grow cool-loving Calceolarias and Philodendron verrucosum, at an altitude of 3000 m in Ecuador and Peru. At this elevation, however, the forest gradually gives way to the grassy altiplano, the home of our potato. Pepper trees mingle with Agave. In drier areas grow many cacti. On the chilly Puna is the region of the Gentian, and south, in Bolivia, grows the colorful Cantua, the sacred flower of the Incas, which I saw blooming in an altitude of 3900 m in the shadow of snowy 6300 m Pico Illimani.

Cereus hexagonus, or "Tuna" as known to the natives, growing along the roads and as windbreaks around coffee haciendas, in the Department Valle del Cauca, Colombia, particularly in the vicinity of Palmira, a region of everlasting spring where the temperature never goes below 21° nor above 30° C. The attractive columns are a beautiful bluish color and almost spineless, reaching a height of 12 m or more. Further southwest is the habitat of Anthurium andraeanum, in the region between Pasto and Tumaco, in southwest Colombia, at an altitude of 900-1680 m., where the temperature ranges between 14° and 30° C. They grow epiphytical by preference, on high branches, receiving morning and evening sun, in very wet forests, on trees completely clothed in tree mosses, over ground eternally soggy. The rainfall is very high, probably six months almost continuous, while during the dry months daily fine drizzles drift in from the Pacific Ocean, bringing moisture close to saturation.

Leaving behind the bleak Paramo in Ecuador, flanked by sheer crags of the Andes and the row of glistening volcanoes highest of which is El Chimborazo (6212 m), and traveling down one day along a one-way road toward the low jungles of the Pacific slope, I met a native girl, and telling her that I was looking for "orquideas y plantas ornamentales", she quickly scrambled up the steep side and brought out this beautiful "Dancing doll" orchid with crisped flowers, probably Oncidium grandiflorum or macranthum, here at 1200 meters.

Of the cool Andine flora, no less than a quarter of the species belong to the Compositae; others characteristic are Fuchsia, Gunnera, Libertia, Oxalis, Salpiglossis, Schizanthus, Tropaeolum, Lapageria. In northern and central Chile much of the area is from 3000 to 6000 meters in elevation. Here, with Calceolaria, which I also saw abundant on the eastern Cordillera of Peru, is the home of Escallonia, Greigia, Ochagavia, and Puya. In lower regions, where the climate resembles that of the Mediterranean, but with longer periods of drought, some tropical forms remain, such as Cissus, Oncidium, Passiflora, Peperomia, Solenomelus, Tillandsia, and Verbena, but spinous bushes and cacti predominate. Along the coast in northern Chile around Arica there is absolute desert, rich in nitrates, and no rain has been recorded there in the history of man. To the south, beech trees (Nothofagus) extend over into New Zealand, presumably over an earlier bridge through Antarctica, where fossil remains of early plantlife have been discovered.

The ancient Inca City of Machu Picchu, remote in the eastern Cordillera of Peru, and the last refuge of the Virgins of the Sun, was built on a mountain top with sheer granite walls dropping some 600 meters to the Rio Urubamba below, and surrounded by some of the most wildly beautiful scenery of rugged peaks in the world. There on these rock walls perch literally millions of red bromeliads making the rocky side look red with the flame color of their leaves, or the gray of Puyas. Further below we meet Fuchsias, Begonias, Calceolarias, Nicotiana, Passiflora, Solanum, Masdevallia, Sobralia, and many ferns.

Chile, narrow but 4200 km long; and climbing above 6000 m in the High Andes, with rainfall from nothing to 500 cm a year, it is understandable that its flora is remarkably diverse. On stony mountain slopes and sandy lomas grow numerous species of cacti, plants that are hard and flower well. Columns of Trichocereus chilensis occur amidst snow, while in the absolute desert of North Chile only such cacti as Copiapoa and Neoporteria can persist. By contrast, in the south, from Valdivia to Magellan Strait, a chilly climate and rain the year 'round developed rich, temperate rain forest with Araucaria araucana, the "Monkey-puzzle" (right). Nothopanax, Podocarpus, and Libocedrus trees.

Mediterranean Subtropics

The most unique creation of the flora of the Canary Islands is the Dragon tree, Dracaena draco, which grows on rocky precipices along the coast of Tenerife. Reddish resin appears in cracks of the bark which created the legend that the sap turns to dragon's blood, with curious properties. The climate is dry like the Sahara but rich in humidity from the sea.

The MEDITERRANEAN region belongs to the northern zone of hot summers and is remarkable for the dense thickets of fragrant, often prickly, shrubs with rigid leaves such as Myrtus communis, Ruscus aculeatus, Viburnum, Laurus nobilis, Smilax, Santolina, Limonium, the olive Olea europaea, and the edible fig Ficus carica; evergreen oaks and needle-leaved conifers like Juniperus, Cupressus, and the Italian pine Pinus pinea. In stony river beds grows the oleander, Nerium; Acanthus and Dianthus are typical. Erica and Pelargonium are common with Africa. There is more variety, with Vinca major, Arum, Convolvulus, Centaurea, Mathiola, Cheiranthus, Cyclamen, Antirrhinum, Mentha, Helxine, Scirpus, Selaginella, Drosophyllum, Pteris, and the Algerian ivy Hedera canariensis; Lathyrus, and numerous sweet-scented Labiatae like Rosmarinus and Lavandula, and the fan-palm Chamaerops humilis which is wild on both sides of the Mediterranean. Much of the vegetation is xerophytic, including many succulents: Caralluma, Sempervivum; bulbs: Scilla, Ornithogalum, Hyacinthus. It is interesting that the cacti which are prominent in this region, are not native but were introduced after the discovery of America.

In a sunny land such as Italy, shade is much appreciated, and so, most Italian gardens are planned with shady walks under great trees and between tall hedges of tediously sheared laurel and occasional marble statuary; juniper, ilex, boxwood, pine and slender cypress — but few flowers; cool grottoes, splashing fountains and reflecting pools, surrounded by dwarf citrus trees in terracotta jars.

Earlier in history, during the apex of Roman civilization, the Peristyle type of garden was an open air room and an integral part of every Roman villa, providing a sheltered refuge to the family, the forerunner of today's patio. As may be seen in Pompeii (below), buried intact by 6 m of volcanic ash in 79 A.D. and now unearthed, these gardens would feature sculptured statues, marble tables, water fountains and pools supplied by a carefully constructed system of lead pipes, allowing the cultivation of native trees, annuals and creepers, including cypress, roses, daffodils and lilies, cyclamen and others, some grown in colored pots. The walls were painted in soft colors with murals of flowers and beautiful women, to soften the feeling of being enclosed and confined.

Africa – Northern Subtropics

NORTHERN AFRICA, with exception of occasional oases and along river courses, of which the most important is the Nile, and few mountains, as the Atlas in Morocco, home of Cedrus atlantica, is largely occupied by the greatest desert in the world, the Sahara, a region which extends to Somaliland and Arabia. Although largely inside the tropic zone,, the character of its vegetation is determined by a minimum of water supply. Where scanty spring rain occurs the water-storing ice plant, Mesembryanthemum crystallinum, a member of the desert family Aizoaceae, survives only because of its roots spreading enormous distances; so does the annual gourd. At the springs of the oases congregate the date palms, Phoenix dactylifera. Nearby are spinous Acacias, broom-like Genista, cactus-like Euphorbia; bulbous Ornithogalum and Allium; fleshy Stapelia and Sedum. At higher elevations we find Cedrus groves. There are occasional Iris and, eastward, Ficus sycomorus, oleander (Nerium), Jasminum, Reseda; the Cyperus and Nymphaea are characteristic of the Nile.

The Tree of Life, Phoenix dactylifera, is much prized as the staple food and chief source of wealth from remotest antiquity, in the desert regions of North Africa where it is indigenous. "Their feet in the water and their heads in the fire" — as the Arabs say — date palms flourish whenever subterranean water is found, bearing nourishing fruit containing more than half its weight of sugar, on female trees. This palm is a beautiful tree growing to a height of 25 m, and all its parts yield products of economic value to the dwellers of the desert. Each palm can produce 100 kg. or more of fruit. Its trunk furnishes timber for house building; the midribs of the leaves supply materials for crates and furniture; the leaflets for basketry; the leaf bases for fuel; the fruit stalks for rope and fuel; the fibre for cordage; the ground seeds for stock feed; vinegar and a strong liquor are made from the fermented fruit.

A feature of the melancholy landscape on both sides of the western Mediterranean, an area of burning hot summers and often chilly though sunny winters, is the relatively hardy, stiff-leaved European fan palm, Chamaerops humilis. Growing on stony ledges and pebbly semi-desert, I have seen it in habitat in Andalusia and Mallorca, as well as on sandy tracts in Morocco, usually forming clusters and remaining low and scrublike, with an occasional arborescent variation forming trunks to 4 m. high.

Africa - Western Equatorial Belt

The countries bordering the Gulf of Guinea, the Ivory Coast, Ghana, Nigeria, Cameroon, Gabon, and large parts of the Congo, are a region of wet rain forest and intermittent grassland, with up to 200 cm of rain annually. It is the home of the true Dracaena and many beautiful Leguminosae with showy flowers. Aroids are represented by the African equivalent of the American philodendron, Rhaphidophora; other aroids are the true Nephthytis, and Rhektophyllum. Some beautiful Dracaena are at home here, especially D. goldieana, godseffiana, and sanderiana; other interesting plants are Acanthus, Monodora, Mussaenda, Palisota, Thunbergia; there are Begonia, Clerodendrum, Cyperus, some Polypodium, Sansevieria, and the orchids Angraecum and Mystacidium. Of trees we know Ficus, Phoenix palms, and Podocarpus. In general, however, there is less variety than in the similar South American forests. The trees of the primeval forest are 60 and 75 m high, including mahogany, ebony, teak and other valuable timber, their trunks covered with epiphytes; there is also the Kola tree, the Kapok tree, the bamboo palm and oil palm; and the coffee shrub is found wild. Opposite Fernando Po, washed by the Atlantic, rises the magnificent volcanic cone of Mt. Cameroon, 4078 m high, receiving 1075cm of precipitation, one of the rainiest regions in the world, causing tree-ferns of great beauty to flourish at 1200 - 2100 m. The only bromeliad in Africa, Pitcairnia filiciana, is found in Guinea.

The famous and very ornamental oil palm of tropical Western and Equatorial Central Africa, Elaeis guineensis, furnishes the palm-oil of commerce, extracted from the pulp of the clustered fruit by crushing and boiling its kernels. An important export product, it is used in making soap, for margarine and candles, and as a cooking oil. Sugar-rich palm wine is also tapped by Africans from the rising sap of the young flower stalks.

The area known as the Guinea Coast is a mysterious land of rivers; an entrancing landscape with a thousand streams coming down to lose themselves along the coast. Here is the western extreme of the vast evergreen rainforest which stretches without a break to Equatorial Africa, and rising in tiers to Sierra Leone and Liberia to the very Nimba Mountains above 1800 m. The motionless air seems to hang in space, overcharged with humidity and the smell of rotting plants; limpid waters reflect a sparkling sky. The valuable oil palm, Elaeis guineensis is abundant. Many of the peculiar genera found in this primeval forest are also found in the Guianas and Brazil on the opposite side of the Atlantic. I photographed the scene at left in the heart of the rainforest near Ibadan, in southern Nigeria, tall native oil palms, mingling with Raphia palms, Dracaena fragrans, and with the large foliage of Anthocleista.

Africa - The Eastern Highlands

EAST AFRICA is a land of contrasts. The equator passes over or near icy Mt. Kenya and Kilimanjaro to heights of 5935 meters, while below, where yearly rain only averages 100 cm, large areas are occupied by savannah forest, with grasses that slash and leaves that sting, Euphorbia, Aloe, and Sansevieria steppes, and thorn forests with Acacias.

On moist slopes and humid valleys of the mountains, especially the Usambaras and west to the Ruwenzori, an unbelievably varied vegetation grows in brick-red soil, with forests of Podocarpus, the fir of East Africa; palm-like Dracaena, the little Callopsis, and many ferns like Nepholepis, Platycerium, and Asplenium, the tree fern Cyathea; Selaginella, Schefflera, Impatiens, Streptocarpus, and several species of the African violet — Saintpaulia, which often grows in crevices of rocks to elevations of 2000 m. In drier locations we find Acanthus, Cissus, Coffea, Cyanotis, Encephalartus, Ficus sycomorus, Ricinus. Along the river courses are marginal forests with spreading Raphia palms, the source of raffia fiber; various tropical bananas; Papyrus, epiphytic Peperomia, and a few orchids such as Angraecum, Bulbophyllum, and Vanilla. Strangely, the only cactus native in Africa, Rhipsalis cassutha, is found on Zanzibar, southwest to Malawi and on to Mt. Kilimanjaro.

Although just below the equator, Africa's highest volcanic cone, Mt. Kilimanjaro, towers 6010 m., its snowy cap glistening above perpetual mists from the rainforests below. The flora of this magnificent Afro-alpine mountain is most remarkable because of its isolation, and it is possible to traverse almost as varied a succession of types of vegetation as might be encountered on a journey from the equator to the vicinity of the poles. The country of the plateau from 1000 to 2000 m. is typical grass land, with acacia forest along the watercourses, the rising slopes planted with coffee. Then begin the wet, dense forests which clothe the mountain to 3000 m., with great camphor trees and hardwoods, Podocarpus, Schefflera, Dracaenas; Cyatheas and bamboo but no palms. The Alpine zone to 4400 m. is characterized by weird forests of 3 m. tree-lobelias, giant palm-like Senecio, and tree Erica. Right, "Bwana" Graf with true Schefflera, found growing as a liane at 2740 m.

After so much ochreous bush and steppe, to climb the tortuous road into the romantically beautiful, humid Usambara Mountains, rising to 2569 m., is an experience I shall never forget. The moist valleys such as that of the quietly flowing Sigi river from the Shambala Mountains produce an unbelievably luxuriant vegetation in the brick-red gneiss soil. Serious Raphia palms with giant leaves over 10 m. long, furnishing raffia fiber, hang heavily over an undergrowth of dracaenas, selaginellas, costus, gloriosas and terrestrial orchids, with lianas climbing up to the highest tops of dense Ficus sycomorus trees. Several species of saintpaulias are found here and on up to Amani at 1000 m, in company of rhipsalis. We finally reach the sheer rock outcroppings of Bomele Peak, where from one open clearing one can see an assortment of schefflera, cussonias, dracaenas, aloe, begonias, treeferns and polypodiums; and clinging to the cliffs by rhizomes, the light blue Streptocarpus saxorum (left).

Where the mighty Zambesi river divides Zambia and Rhodesia and its foaming waters are tossing down 100 m. into 1½ km long chasm of Victoria Falls, its constantly rising clouds of mist surging upward gave rise to a narrow strip of rainforest, dominated by clusters of Phoenix reclinata, the "False date palm", their lush fronds diamond-dusted by the pearly droplets which ethereally form a gorgeous rainbow against the sky of brilliant blue.

The Bottle tree, or Baobab, Adansonia digitata, is a landmark on grassy plains of tropical and subtropical Africa, from Senegal to the Transvaal, and east to Tanzania. It is one of the longest-lived—by some reckoned to be 5,000 years old—and also largest trees, and though not more than 20 m. high, its swollen trunk will attain a diameter of 9 m. By casting its leaves and storing water in its huge trunk the Baobab maintains life through the driest season.

From the Ruwenzori, legendary Mountains of the Moon, and known since Ptolemy nearly 2,000 years ago, the Congo forest of Central Africa stretches away westward as far as the eye can see, to Equatorial West Africa and the Guinea coast. Inhabited by the pygmy people, herds of elephants, and chattering monkeys, the vast high forest is only occasionally broken by open savannah. Typical of all Central Africa are the euphorbias, like the tree-like Euphorbia candelabrum, a gathering place of elephants, here on the Semliki river (left).

Africa - The Plant-rich South

The desert of the Karroo, 240 km northeast of Capetown, has an intensely xerophytic flora mainly of succulents of weird form, thorny acacia bushes and numerous bulbous plants. Most remarkable are the stone-mimicry plants, imitating the gravel amidst which they exist, and one may walk on them without seeing them. Notable in the landscape are the many species of handsome Aloe, growing as low rosettes to imposing 20 m trees, a gorgeous sight when in bloom. On left, the "Dragon tree" aloe, Aloe dichotoma, growing into monstrous trees to 10 m. high.

Some of the remaining colonies of the prehistoric Cycad family, largely extinct since they flourished during the age of the dinosaurs, are still found in southern Africa. At the Royal Kraal of Mujaji in the northern Transvaal I was privileged to witness the veneration of native Africans for the majestic Encephalartos transvenosus, shown here, the living talisman of the Rain Queen.

The South African region occupies a series of great plateaus and steep slopes. An extra-ordinary variety in vegetation resulted from the irregular distribution of the rainfall. There are no large or dense forests, no climbers nor luxuriant trees. The flora is mostly xerophytic, spinous acacias are everywhere. In a southwesterly direction, where the winters are wet, the silver-tree, Leucadendron, is typical. The east, with dry winters, produces savannah, with forest growth restricted to the river valleys. Characteristic here are certain tree ferns (Hemitelia, Todea), Cycads, Phoenix reclinata, and Musa.

Natal has Encephalartos, Podocarpus, Cussonia trees, Dracaena hookeriana, Carissa, the bulbous Clivia, Watsonia; the succulent Ceropegia, Kalanchoe, Crassula, Senecio, Cotyledon; a variety of Pelargonium, Streptocarpus, Plectranthus, Peristrophe, Asparagus plumosus, and Strelitzia.

Below the stony Kalahari desert, where palms cease, the southernmost terrace or "bush" is the richest area for species of its size in the world; about 16,000 species of flowering plants have been recorded. Native trees or shrubs are Erica, Pelargonium, Sparmannia. This is the home of many good succulents: Ceropegia, Cotyledon, Crassula, Faucaria, Gasteria, Haworthia, Kalanchoe, Huernia, Lampranthus, Rochea, Senecio, Stapelia, no less than 400 species of Mesembryanthemum, and numerous species of Aloe are most characteristic. Many well-known bulbous plants are South African: Agapanthus, Amaryllis, Crinum, Freesia, Gladiolus, Haemanthus, Ixia, Lachenalia, Nerine, Ornithogalum, Scilla, Veltheimia. Our "Calla" lilies, Zantedeschia, are found here, also Gerbera, Gazania, Chlorophytum, Asparagus, Plectranthus, Moraea, Oxalis, Pteris, Leonotis, Aristea, Dimorphoteca, Helichrysum, the curious cycad Stangeria, the gesneriad Streptocarpus; Begonia and the orchids Disa, Polystachia, and Stenoglottis.

The southwest Cape region, especially is the region of the heaths, with 600 species of Erica, as well as many glorious Proteas, which have on predominantly acid soils to 76 cm of rain in their winter and, while summers are the dry, the humidity remains relatively high. This is also the home of numerous Pelargonium, Oxalis, Liliaceae, and Iridaceae; however, this region is notably poor in trees.

Asia - the Near East

From Central Asia west through Iran into Asia Minor are a succession of mountains and plateaux with deserts receiving very few rains because the surrounding ranges shut out the rain clouds. Where irrigated, some of the land is very fertile. Tamarisk and spinous Acacias are some of the few shrubs withstanding gales so characteristic of deserts. Cupressus, Olea, the figtree, Ficus carica; Punica, Laurus and Populus also are typical trees, and we find shrubby Jasminum, Ruscus, Molucella, Prunus laurocerasus, Pyracantha; the attractive and well-loved Anemone and Ranunculus, Delphinium, Cyclamen, Bellis, Matricaria, Eremurus, Helleborus, Hedera, and various Arum. Here is the historic habitat of many good bulbous species, foremost the tulips, Tulipa; also Hyacinthus, Muscari, Crocus, Fritillaria, Chionodoxa, Colchicum, and Lilium candidum and other lilies. This is also the home of more species of all the types of Iris than anywhere else in the world, many growing up in the rugged Taurus range. On mountains of Syria and Lebanon scattered groves of the historic Cedrus libani survive.

The Lebanon rises steeply from the almost treeless Bika plain to a tableland more than 2400 m. high, with peaks rising to 3088 m. The upper slopes are bleak and covered by snow in winter. The stately Cedar of Lebanon, Cedrus libani, grows in scattered groves at about 1800 m, chiefly on the western slopes, about 136 km northeast of Beirut, (above); also found on the Taurus. They are beautiful evergreen trees, 25 m. high, with fragrant wood, the timber which King Solomon took to build the Temple in Jerusalem, by some reported 6,000 years old.

The ancient city of Jerusalem, where history goes back 4,000 years, stands on a rocky 800 m. plateau projecting southward from the Judean hills. On the east the valley of Kidron separates this plateau from the ridge of the Mount of Olives 60 m. higher. While the temperature may go to 44° C., the seabreeze tempers the heat during summer, and there is usually a sharp drop at night, to as low as −4° C. in winter, with occasional snow. The rainfall is about 65 cm., mainly occurring from November to April, while mid-June to mid-September is almost completely rainless. As a consequence the flora has a xerophytic character, but in the rainy season the bare land becomes a garden of brilliant color. About 2500 species of flowering plants have been identified in the region of Palestine. The flower that first strikes the eye, growing in bright profusion by the wayside, is Anemone coronaria. Also widespread are Ranunculus asiaticus, poppy, Salvia, Cyclamen, Muscari and Ornithogalum umbellatum, the "Star-of-Bethlehem", which may be found even in the Temple area. On the Mount of Olives the olive is the most characteristic tree, and the slopes are brightened by snowy Amygdalus, the flowering almond. In the far south at Elath the temperature may rise to 45° C. but the nights are cool with dew.

Asia - Himalayas and North India

Dawn is breaking over the Himalayas. The deep valleys are filled with white layers of clouds, tossed by a chilly wind. Soon the East turns pink with the coming of the sun, and the light spreads north and west gradually revealing a breath-taking landscape. As far as the eye can see unfolds the colossal chain of the "Home of the Snows", as they are known in Sanskrit, now glowing in rose. Serenely, Mount Kanchenjunga, 8579 m (28,146 ft.) highest massif in the Sikkim Himalayas, stands in sheer majesty, and fleeting flashes of sun reflect from the icy slopes as he stands guard over one of the richest concentrations of ferns, orchids and alpine plants in the world. Snow sometimes falls in Darjeeling, precariously set at 2300 m. on Mount Sinchul between cryptomerias, magnolias and great rhododendrons — the wild Rangit, in a warmer clime, roaring 1800 m below. Here, subtropical and alpine plants exist within a few kiloms of each other. Down toward the river, the path twists steep and narrow on hard yellow clay through the dense forest, dripping and moist, past great Ficus elastica trees, big pandanus, wild plantains; the temperature is a depressing 35°C at midday.

North in India is the broad Terai, a low malarial belt which skirts the base of the Himalayas. This giant jungle holds many Ficus, Bamboo, Dendrobium orchids, and vining Hoya. But at higher elevation, the monsoon region is succeeded by an area of the world's highest mountains, the Himalayas; melting snows, and rains totalling 450 cm annually, are the source of rushing rivers. The deep valleys are immensely rich in plant life and, in Sikkim alone, 4,000 species of flowering plants are found. Perpetual moisture nourishes the dripping forest, favoring ferns, of which 250 species are known, including small Adiantum, Pteris, Pellaea, Lygodium, as well as tree ferns such as Alsophila gigantea. The steep sides of the mountains are clothed with lofty trees, and masses of jungle with 12 species of bamboo, Calamus and 20 other palms; Musa, Holmskioldia, Sauromatum, Colocasia, Homalomena, Gonatanthus, Kaempferia, and Begonia are plentiful. There are 600 species of orchids, largely in the subtropic zone up to 2000 m, which is the limit of palms in Sikkim, and the best known are Cymbidium, Coelogyne, Paphiopedilum, Dendrobium, Vanda, Phaius, Eria, Aerides, and the velvet leaf Anoectochilus. Most of these genera are also found eastward in Assam. In the temperate zone, from 2100 to 3500 m, we find first Magnolia, oak, and chestnut, with Osmanthus, Trachelospermum, Aralia, Aucuba, Hydrangea, Bergenia, and Camellia. At the higher elevations is the region of Rhododendron represented by 134 species, and which grow here in forests of giant trees, up to 5200 m. At still greater heights they give place to conifers such as Cedrus deodara. Beyond the tree line stretches a great alpine flora with Leontopodium, the edelweiss, Primula and Saxifraga, up to the bare granite walls and the everlasting snows of the world's mightiest mountains. Westward, in Kashmir is the home of many of our well-known perennials, including numerous Primula, Iris and Delphinium.

The Jains are dissenters from Hinduism, dating back to about 700 B.C. Living a disciplined life, they vow to preserve all living things, be chaste, abstain from alcohol, flesh and honey, and to pursue purity of thought, contemplation and repentance. Jains excel in architecture and the art of carving in stone. Their magnificent temple at Calcutta has gardens, with beds laid out in cement and mosaic stone, leaving only small openings for such carpet plants as Coleus, Impatiens and Pileas. In taller plants there are Cannas with variegated foliage, sheared bamboo, sunflowers, and in glazed urns, Pandanus. A singularly beautiful bed is designed in the shape of an open lotus blossom, the symbol of truth and purity (left).

Asia - India South

Fabled India, contrary to general belief, is mostly hot and dry; I remember, in Benares, a stifling heat of 46°C (115°F) in shade; each summer the inland plains heat up to 50°C, the relative humidity drops to 1%, and plants don't thrive at such temperatures. Most of its natural vegetation is in regions with abundant moisture where the southwest monsoon touches mountain ranges or the escarpments of the 'Ghats' ringing the central plateau of the Deccan, as on the western coast from Bombay down the Malabar to Cochin, the Neilgherries, and the Ganges delta and Assam fronting the Himalayas and Khasia Hills, as well as the west coast of Ceylon. The more fertile parts of the peninsula have been so long and so densely inhabited by man that there is little of the original vegetation left. Characteristic are the Palmyra palms Borassus, Phoenix and Corypha palms; Cycas, Artocarpus, Tupidanthus, and Musa. India loves the fragrance of its Dianthus, Ervatamia, Hedychium, Jasminum, and Murraya as well as its native Tea roses and ramblers; there are showy Hibiscus, Acalypha, Datura, Kaempferia, Costus, Eranthemum, Gloriosa, Thunbergia, Elettaria, Strobilanthes, Barleria; the little Hoya, Serissa, Cyanotis, Selaginella; Zingiber, Arisaema, Colocasia, and Alocasia; in ferns Cyrtomium, Adiantum, and many others. In drier regions, especially South India, are thickets of Euphorbia. A feature of the landscape everywhere are the spreading, pillar-rooted, Banyan trees, Ficus benghalensis; the drip-tipped peepul or Bo-tree, Ficus religiosa, and the India rubber tree, Ficus elastica. In drier West Pakistan, is the home of Ficus krishnae with its curious, cup-shaped leaves.

Southern India is the seat of ancient Dravidian civilization and its legacy of art and architecture is best expressed in its temples. The towering Gopuram of the Kapaleswarar Koil temple in Madras, chiseled in every detail with infinite patience, and painted in gay colors, is a marvel of industry, elaboration and exuberant Hindu imagination. Mingled with the wonderfully life-like sculptures of the Vedic deities of the Hindu Pantheon are such symbolic plants as the bo-tree and the lotus, as depicted above.

Along the Coromandel coast of South India, often pitifully dry, infested with Euphorbias and other thorny vegetation but with few trees, firewood is extremely scarce. For this reason dried manure is used traditionally for fuel, depriving the worn-out soils of much-needed organic fertilizer. One sees graceful Tamil women actually follow the sacred cows to scoop up fresh dung, and paste it against the mud-walls of their homes to dry, to serve for slow cooking fires later. In the background, left, is a row of massive Palmyra palms, Borassus flabellifer, common in this hot region, host to epiphytal plants like orchids, ferns, and even fig trees, as well as monkeys, mongoose and bats. They are extremely valuable and have, according to the Tamils, 801 uses, for food, timber, and toddy tasting like mild champagne.

Indian Ocean - to Asia

Tropical Madagascar is considered as an ancient continental island. With seven months rain, much is covered by rainforest, rich in tree ferns, lianas, bamboos, Cyperus, and epiphytic orchids. The lofty granitic interior bears a savannah vegetation and, towards the south, it is drier and more thorny. With a flora of over 4,000 species, of which three-quarters are endemic, the Compositae and heaths as well as the succulent Euphorbia and Kalanchoe, suggest the generally African character of the flora, whilst the bamboo and the pitcher plants (Nepenthes) connect it with the Indian monsoon region. Typical Madagascar plants known in cultivation are: Angraecum orchids, Aponogeton, Chrysalidocarpus palms, Dracaena marginata, Euphorbia, Hypoestes, Kalanchoe, Nicodemia, Pandanus utilis, Platycerium ferns, Stephanotis, and the Traveller's tree, Ravenala. The peculiar Platycerium madagascariense (above) is found growing as an epiphyte in rainforest at 800 to 900 m altitude in the eastern region.

Ceylon, with mountains above 2400 m high, is a paradise of changing vegetation on its southwest side, from coconut-fringed shores, forests of teak, and Caryota palms; tea plantations up to cool regions where Rhododendrons grow. In general, the flora is both Indian and Malaysian, as evidenced by the presence of Ficus, Aglaonema, Alocasia, Rhaphidophora, Pleomele, true Pothos, Coleus, Impatiens, and showy Chirita, many crotons (Codiaeum), Sansevieria, and even Rhipsalis. However, the almost complete absence of epiphytic ferns and orchids is remarkable.

The botanical wealth of Ceylon, with some 4,000 species of plants is, in proportion to its size, the equal of that of any other country in the world. The southwestern side of the island which receives the heavy rains of the monsoon, has an exuberant vegetation. Nowhere flourish palms so luxuriantly as here, and tall, graceful Coconut palms stretch from the sandy shores inland to elevations of 600 m in the drier north, Palmyra palms predominate. Climbing higher into the mountains, and where not supplanted by tea plantations, the equatorial rainforest becomes more varied. Banyan, teak and other giants of the forest, some of them 60 meters high are hung with lianas and rattans — as well as flying dogs; buttressed roots are host to the true Pothos scandens. Stately Fishtail palms and slender Arecas stand like sentinels on promontories and in clearings. The fecundity of tropical growth, its savage strength and remorseless sense of purpose, its wild beauty and teeming life is impossible to forget. As we near the heights, the character of the forest changes. Flowering trees add color, such as Cassias, the Golden Shower trees. There are 150 orchids and 300 ferns, with groves of tree fern, and bamboo, until at 1800 m begin the rhododendrons, a brilliant red in July, and reaching the proportions of a tree, together with magnolias, myrtles and native tea.

The famed Botanical Gardens of Peradeniya, near Kandy, are reached by a scenic railway winding into picturesque mountains 120 km from Colombo. Blessed by a moderate moist-warm climate, the extensive grounds contain a great collection of luxuriant plants. I look with envy at the perfection of such delicate exotics as Alocasia growing in bamboo sections serving as flower pots; Gloriosas are rambling happily, rare Aglaonemas, endemic crotons in bright color, durable Pleomele, and the "King of the Forest" orchids, Anoectochilus, with maroon-black velvet leaves and veins of gold, are lovingly cared for.

Asia: Indo-Malaysia and the East Indies

South and Eastward from the continental Southeast Asia of Assam, Burma, Thailand and Vietnam stretch the fabulous "East Indies" including Malaya, the Philippines, and Java, Sumatra, Borneo, the Moluccas and New Guinea to the South. The southwest monsoon brings beneficial rains, producing a moist-warm climate and some of the wettest areas on earth, as in the eastern Himalayas, mountainous Assam, Malakka, and the Sunda Islands, producing typical rain forest. Cherrapunji in Assam, the wettest place on earth, has received as much as 25 meter of rain a year. The less continuously wet monsoon forest takes in most of the rest of the area. This region is characterized by its mangrove swamps, and striking forms of Ficus, including the weeping fig, Ficus benjamina. There is a profusion of warm epiphytic orchids, Nepenthes, Platycerium, Zingiber and various Musaceae, giant bamboo, Alocasia, Croton, Hoya, the many Nymphaea and Nelumbo. Leading palms are coconut, Areca, Caryota, Licuala, Phoenix, and the climbing Calamus. Instead of the American philodendron we find Epipremnum; Pleomele take the place of African Dracaena, and for the cacti of America there are cactus-like Euphorbia.

Along the many brown rivers and network of canals in central Thailand most people live and trade. Here they catch fish, wash laundry, bathe babies, go swimming, and fetch water, all in the same spot. Here a little palm-thatched hut on stilts is displaying quite a collection of orchids in clay pots, some perforated for drainage, carefully and lovingly tended and enjoyed.

BURMA is primarily known for its orchids such as Aerides, Bulbophyllum, Calanthe, Cymbidium, Dendrobium, Paphiopedilum, Renanthera, Thunia, and Vanda. Typical also are Curcuma, Kaempferia, Leea, Pellionia, Steudnera, Strobilanthes. From THAILAND, we know Aglaonema, Chlorophytum, Jasminum, and Petrocosmea.

VIETNAM has given us some interesting plants in Hydrosme, Musa coccinea, Pellionia, Pilea, Serissa, Tetrastigma, Torenia, and in orchids Aerides, Coelogyne, Cymbidium, Paphiopedilum, Phalaenopsis, Saccolabium. It is probable that most Citrus originated in the region of Indochina and South China.

The ancient Khmers, 1,000 *years ago, conceived the most wonderful stone temples in existence. Built without the use of mortar and lacking keystones, the unbelievable tropical vegetation of the forest has been struggling with these massive buildings, sending slender, expansive roots between the masonry. The destructive force of the jungle trees now hold together what they once pried apart. Left, the roots of a gigantic Ficus tree embrace the granite carvings of the central sanctuary of the Neak Pean temple in Cambodia.*

Asia - the East Indies

The fabled "East Indies" are immensely wealthy in fascinating exotic plants. Gesneriads are represented by Aeschynanthus, Agalmyla, Monophyllaea. Typical aroids are Alocasia, Colocasia, Cryptocoryne, Epipremnum, Homalomena, Lasia, Rhaphidophora, Scindapsus, Spathiphyllum. Brightly colored Crotons, Acalypha and Hibiscus, Celosia, Amaranthus, Ixora, Plumbago; Phaeomeria and Amomum, Costus, Phrynium, Pandanus, Impatiens, Quisqualis, Sonerila, Vinca, Hoya and Piper, creeping Ficus and Freycinetia; numerous ferns with Adiantum, Asplenium, Davallia, Nephrolepis, Polypodium, and Selaginella.

MALAYSIA has a number of aroids, including Aglaonema, Alocasia, Schismatoglottis, Typhonium; typical are Begonia, Crotons, the giant Dendrocalamus, Dischidia, Nepenthes, Orchidantha, Piper, Platycerium and Tacca. In gesneriads we find Chirita and Didymocarpus; in orchids Arachnis, Bulbophyllum, Haemaria, Paphiopedilum, Phalaenopsis, Spathoglottis.

The SUNDA ISLANDS are rich in orchids, especially the Spider flowers. Java has Arachnis; other orchids are Anoectochilus, Bulbophyllum, Coelogyne, Macodes, and Vanda. Well-known trees are Schefflera and Trevesia. There are several hundred palms in the Sundas, with coconut along the coasts.

Java, the most important of the Sunda Islands, is an emerald jewel of great tropical beauty and luxuriant vegetation, as here along the Tjiliwong river; 970 km long, it has a teeming population of over 50 million, and every possible spot is densely cultivated. A high mountain chain with surmounting volcanoes (Mt. Salak above), rise to 3678 m. The tall trees of the primeval rainforest, ascending the slopes of the western range at 1500 m. form a canopy of reflected light, home to an abundance of orchids, Medinillas, Nepenthes, and tree-dwelling Rhododendrons.

The PHILIPPINES are an archipelago of approximately 7,000 tropical islands, of which the largest ones are mountainous reaching, both in Luzon and Mindanao, over 3100 m. At these elevations, even in the tropics, it is cool and the mountain tops are covered with forests of pine. Approaching 1500 m some very beautiful orchids occur, especially Phalaenopsis, while Vanda and Dendrobium are found at lower, moist-warm elevations; above 1500 m grows a multitude of more inconspicuous or 'botanical' orchids.

The island of Bali, in the Lesser Sundas, has rare beauty and charm. Its culture was derived direct from India, before the 8th century. Blessed by extremely rich soil, abundant rainfall, and very equable climate, a luxuriant vegetation takes increasingly possession of every foothold as we go higher into the mountains, and in the saturated moisture, ferns and mosses grow everywhere. Remarkable are the showy orchids, used by the people even around their little huts, amongst them Dendrobium, Arundinaria, Coelogyne, and Vandas. By the wayside near Kitamani, a naked boy offered me a collected flowering plant of the exquisite Vanda tricolor suavis for 2 rupiahs (then 13¢).

Asia - New Guinea

New Guinea is one of the most mountainous regions in the world. It was given the name by the Spanish in the 16th century because the Melanesian natives resembled the negroes of West Africa. This immense island, just below the equator, is covered by high, often inaccessible, mountains in the central range to 5030 m high, and covered with perpetual snow and glaciers above 4400 m. Separated by one series after another of steep razorback walls the natives speak 750 different languages, and deadly hostility prevails between one village and the next. In areas of copious rainfall, almost vertical ridges, screened in mist and cloud, are covered with dense jungle, noted for the presence of many fantastic orchids. Thousands of Araucarias, 45 m, high, inhabit southern slopes. Millions of Pandanus grow from 1500 m up nearly to the line of frost at about 3000 m. In the lower lands, with brooding humidity, there is luxuriant tropical growth, with creepers and lianes, and palms are very abundant; along the tidal courses of rivers Nipa palms are common; the sago palms, Metroxylon, are numerous in seasonal swamps, and coconut palms fringe the coast.

For Papuans living in the high mountains, the pandanus is their coconut; the pineapple-like fruit provides food, the trunks and leaves building material and household goods. Mainly on the northern slopes, between 1500 and 2800 m., in invigorating climate, are forests of millions of these pandanus "palms" (above), *giants to 30 m high, leaves 5 m long, and with stilt roots springing from the trunk forty feet above the ground, and difficult for travel.*

There are about 9,000 species of plants in New Guinea; the island has one of the richest Orchid floras in the world, with some 130 genera including about 2600 species. On expedition into the forbidding 4000 m Finisterre Range, we recruited 60 native bearers, and for days on end had to scramble up and slither down the perpendicular mountain sides, usually in exhausting steamy heat alternating with chilly rain, worn out by day and freezing at night. For a handful of salt, Papuan "Grasshopper" boys helped us in gathering an undreamed-of variety of plants, including many small and large orchids, Nepenthes, various unknown Hoyas and other showy climbers, gesneriads and begonias, ferns, Cordylines and even epiphytic Rhododendron (photo left: Hoya on left, Medinilla right).

East Asia - Subtropical China

A Chinese garden is a place of contemplation, and part of China's ancient civilization and culture. From the time of Confucius and Laotse in the 5th century B.C., with increasing sophistication, her people have been inspired to greater appreciation of the beauties of nature. Their gardens are intended to be a painting of the landscape of nature with its inner meanings and rhythm, representing in its hills and ponds, in stones and woods, the active and the passive principles, the male and female forces of Yin and Yang, to remind us of the harmony and order of the universe. The five elements have a deep religious meaning, and are symbolized in the Oriental garden so that the element of earth is represented in hills and islands, that of water in ponds and waterfalls, that of fire in glowing flowers, that of wood in trees, that of wind in the power which swings tree branches and scatters petals, and that of metal in stones. The Chinese love of rockery, in grotesque shapes, amounts to worship, possessing as it does the quality of unchangeable solidity, which human character often lacks. A Chinese garden is a place for relaxation, romance, and meditation, planned at every step with new surprises. Plants are not selected for their looks but for their symbolism.

Horticulture in China is part of the struggle for existence and resultant skill born of 40 centuries of handed-down experience. The maintenance of soil fertility under constant intensive cultivation for such an immense period has been secured in the main by the use of "night soil" and every other kind of manure, and regular crop rotation, alternating with legumes for fertilizing the soil. The growing of economic as well as ornamental plants long ago had reached the level of an art. Air-layering for propagation has been practiced for 1,000 years, and potted plants were grown in China during the Yuan dynasty in the 13th century. With the favorable climate of southern China, the many little nurseries there, though primitive, employ skilled fundamental practices. The frequent monsoon rains in Kwangtung would soon stagnate the roots of many plants in ordinary soil, but for centuries Chinese gardeners have prevented water-logging of plants in pots, by the use of containers of porous clay with perforated sides and by planting into burnt earth as potting material. Large pieces of stiff clay are piled on a log fire and burned slowly for several days, resulting in crumbly, porous pebbles with the capacity of absorbing water yet leaving space for quick drainage and aeration. Dry dung is added near the top, and such as Crotons, Celosias, Araucarias, and orchids *(left)* ***respond by luxuriant growth.***

East Asia - Japan

The eastward extensions of the Himalayan region, marked by the occurrence of Cycas, also found in Japan; of nutmeg, sandalwood, and palms, are interesting as linking the flora of the southeast of Asia with tropical Australia and the western Pacific.

Southern China, west in Yunnan, and southern Japan is a region containing the remainder of warm-temperate rainforests largely destroyed due to intense cultivation except in the temple groves or on mountains. Here originate not only most bamboo, but many showy, broadleaved, tender evergreens such as Ardisia, Aucuba, Azalea, Buxus, Camellia, Cotoneaster, Daphne, Elaeagnus, Euonymus, Eurya, Fatsia, Gardenia, Gilibertia, Ligustrum, Osmanthus, Pittosporum, Raphiolepis, Rhododendron, Sarcococca, Skimmia, Thea, Trachelospermum, Trevesia, Viburnum, and most Citrus including Fortunella. In palms, Trachycarpus, Livistona, and the reed-like Rhapis which is also the oldest cultivated palm in the world. Other well-known trees and shrubs are Lagerstroemia, Rosa, Hibiscus, Buddleja, Prunus, Hydrangea, Kerria, Clerodendrum; the vining Lonicera, Rubus, Parthenocissus, Ampelopsis, Hoya, Piper, and Wisteria. In perennials we know Liriope, Chrysanthemum, Dianthus, many Primula, Astilbe, Dicentra, Iris, Sedum sieboldii, Hosta; Hemerocallis and many species of Lilium. Dicentra is endemic in Japan.

Chinese culture and learning have influenced and shaped Japan since early times. Confucius' ideals of life, the pine for long life, and the bamboo for purity of mind, has been transplanted to Japan, where was added the plum, the symbol of delicacy and feminine elegance, to form a trinity of moral purpose. That is why bamboo, not necessarily beautiful, is widely used as a decorative plant. In addition, it symbolizes virtues such as fidelity, humility, wisdom, and gentleness, and because it becomes stronger as it grows—also promises long life. Pictured above is a "male" Otake, or "strong" bamboo, in Kyoto. A "Komoso," or hooded Buddhist priest and wandering musician, often erroneously called a "beggar monk," who made a vow to carry a basket over his head, plays on his flute soliciting food.

In the south we find Ficus, both the graceful Ficus retusa tree as well as the creeping Ficus pumila. There grows also the dwarf banana Musa nana, Cycas and Tetrapanax; in smaller plants Aspidistra, Alpinia, Ligularia, Ophiopogon, Saxifraga, Carex, Acorus, Arisaema, Rohdea, Reineckia, and even Peperomia. Many cool ferns include Cyrtomium, Polystichum, Davallia, Adiantum, Woodwardia, and the fern-like Selaginella. As far south as Taiwan and west, especially in Yunnan, many orchids occur, mainly Cymbidium and Dendrobium.

Rhapis (left) are known to be the oldest cultivated palms in the world, and are immensely popular in Japan and China. They are well adapted to the sparsely heated homes of the Orient, often bitterly cold in winter, where a tropical palm could not survive. The specimen above graces the entrance to the Japanese inn "Kikukawa", or "River of Chrysanthemum" in the historic city of Nara. A sign above the entrance, where you must leave your shoes, invites: "Lodging, stay and rest!" The window is shaped like a wooden mallet, symbolizing prosperity, carried by the God of Prosperity, one of the seven lucky gods of Japan — it brings money and good fortune every time he shakes it. This inn is one of those delightful places, where a charming hostess on her knees, serves warm rice wine, and appetizing sukiyaki cooked right on your low table, or delicious "tempura", those large prawn or shrimp, deep-fried in camellia oil — and she also arranges for a geisha, for pleasant entertainment.

East Asia – Japan

Simplicity has become a cult to the Japanese, best expressed in their dwellings, particularly since the Tokugawa period. A great and abiding love of natural wood takes full advantage of its ingrained beauty, achieving pleasing contrasts of wood against wood or white plaster. To withstand frequent earthquakes, each beam is fitted without relying on nails, and supports a heavy roof of gray tiles or thatch. The size of rooms is determined by the number of rice-straw mats, or tatami, it accommodates. 5 cm thick and measuring about 1 x 2 m., they are placed on the polished floor and used for sleeping. The house is divided into rooms by sliding screens; light is admitted by a paper-covered lattice mounted as a sliding window. These screens are removable so as to throw all rooms into one. At night the house is shuttered by wooden panels running in grooves along the outside. Bare of major furniture, at one end of the room is the "tokonoma", a raised alcove, framed by a pillar of some exceptional wood, and featuring a hanging scroll and perhaps a single azalea bonsai, or a styled arrangement of flowers, intended to direct the attention of all eyes to the beauty of nature, and its inner meanings. An all absorbing love of nature makes a garden an integral part of the Japanese home. When opening wide the "shoji" or sliding screens, there is revealed, as on a stage, and changing with the seasons, a make-believe landscape in miniature. Deceivingly, great mountains are expressed by hills or rocks, distant forests by a few bamboo, the sea with its rolling waves by neatly combed sand, a lake by a pool, grassy meadows by varying types of moss, individual trees by dwarfed bonsai, and a distant road by stepping stones. The half-moon bridge reflects a full moon, and each treasured tree has its symbolic meaning. In meditation, and by capturing its feeling, the restless mind finds harmony with nature, and with it a deep serenity.

Shaped Bonsai, or dwarfed trees, grown in containers, are objects of loving care and admiration in every home in Japan. Many little nurseries devote long years to their culture, an art which was brought over from China before the 13th century. Numerous trees or shrubs are used for this purpose, and while the White pine is most favored, I have seen Ginkgo, Cedrus, Pomegranate, Prunus, Maple, Azalea, Camellia, Oleander, Cypress, Juniper, Beech and Birch, and even Parthenocissus, no two of which are alike, and some are known to be more than 300 years old. The picture (below) shows Bonsai trees in pottery, Black pine on the left, 5-leaf pine center and right, outside of an oil shop in Kyoto.

Australia - Tropics and Subtropics

Located in the Southern hemisphere, between the Indian Ocean and the South Pacific, this continent has, as a whole, a level surface with only 5% of its area above 600 m. Mountains along the coast, though not very high, are sufficient to keep out rains, and the interior is largely a vast, dry plain. The highest peak is Mt. Kosciusko, 2230 m.

Northern Australia and, with its summer rains, Queensland especially are tropical and practically an extension of the Indian monsoon region, with much of the flora of the Sunda Islands and New Guinea. Well-known Queensland trees are Araucaria, Agathis, Brachychiton, and Brassaia; also represented are Cycas and Macrozamia, showy Hibbertia and Swainsona, and climbing Hoya, plus a wide variety of ferns including Platycerium, Nephrolepis, Polypodium, Davallia and Asplenium; and Dendrobium orchids. In the northwest we find the amusing bottle tree. At latitude 19 deg. south begins a sub-tropical desert.

Most of the wooded area of east, southeast, and southwest Australia is of an open savananh type, with exceptionally lofty Eucalyptus over 100 m high, constituting three-fourths of the forest. These and the silk oaks, Grevillea, graduate into scrub, with thickets of shrubby but showy Acacia, Melaleuca, Eugenia, Pittosporum, Hakea, Callistemon, Casuarina, Epacris, Boronia, Leptospermum, Chamaelaucium, Chorizema. This group is often referred to as 'New Holland' plants, adapted to cultivation in southwest United States, Spain and Portugal. Curious grass-trees, with cycads, grow on the borders of the grassy savannah of the interior, adorned during the rainy season with numerous Liliaceae, iridaceous bulbs, and terrestrial orchids.

The flora of south-western Australia is the largest and most interesting in Australia, with more than 5,000 species. Most remarkable in the drier interior are the "Blackboys", or grass-trees, Xanthorrhoea preissii, which are conspicuous in the landscape. They are long-lived perennials with thick woody, palm-like trunks and terminate in a rosette of narrow linear leaves and an upright spike of whitish flowers. Tradition has it that these "Blackboys" grow only, 2½ cm in 100 years.

This fairyland of leaf and stem is a jungle of treeferns, banyan, fan palms and wild bananas in great profusion, at Kuranda, in the far north of Queensland, 34 km inland from Cairns. With moist heat ranging between 14-31 degrees C (58-88° F). along the coast, and the highest rainfall in Australia, 360 to 500 cm annually, true rainforest flourishes with feathery palms including lofty Archontophoenix alexandrae, Ptychosperma elegans, and Calamus; Brassaia actinophylla, the Kauri pine Agathis, Pandanus monticola, Alocasia macrorhiza, creeping Ficus and Hoya, and climbing Rhaphidophora, epiphytic Platycerium and Asplenium, and orchids.

New Zealand - Beauty Primeval

Few floras are as remarkable in their geographical affinities as is that of New Zealand. Forming part of the 'Australasian festoon' and built up of rocks of every geological period including pumice and other volcanic rocks, with mountain ranges rising over 3700 m far above a snow-line of about 1000 m with glaciers and boiling springs, there is almost every variety of soil condition. The islands are, however, so narrow as to have a distinctly insular climate, although the rainfall is not high. Hard frosts are, in general, absent and the resultant flora is largely arborescent and evergreen. Annual species and bulbs are very few in number. In dry situations "scrub" occurs, such as Leptospermum, Metrosideros, Coprosma, and Pittosporum, also subalpine xerophytes like Hebe, Celmisia, and Dracophyllum; more general, however, is the forest. Tree-like araliads are typical: Meryta, Nothopanax, Pseudopanax, and Schefflera; so are the flat-leaved conifers, Agathis, Libocedrus, and Podocarpus. Epiphytes are limited in the number of genera, Astelia being the most conspicuous; well-known lianas are Muehlenbeckia and Rubus. Ferns of all sizes abound although there are less than 200 species; they have no equal in the world in wealth of form, luxuriance of growth and manifold interest. Growing on salt-sprayed coastal cliffs to humid forest dell, they range from large tree ferns, Dicksonia and Cyathea to 18 m high, to Gleichenia, Nephrolepis, Pellaea, Pteris, Blechnum, Polystichum, Adiantum, Microsorium, Asplenium, Davallia, the plume-like Leptopteris, and the delicate Hymenophyllum, or filmy-fern.

The forest flora has Melanesian affinities, including the southernmost of palms, Rhopalostylis, reaching into South Island, but cycads are absent. While the arborescent Cordyline is also Melanesian, the New Zealand flax, Phormium tenax, is more limited and endemic. Curiously interesting is the bridge with the South Andine flora, by the presence of many Compositae, and Oxalis, Gunnera, Fuchsia, Calceolaria, Nertera, and numerous Nothofagus beeches. On the other hand, the N. Z. flora has few relations with Australia; there are no eucalypts.

Rhopalostylis sapida, the exotic-looking Nikau palm, marks the southern limit of palms in the Eastern Hemisphere, growing in colonies down the subtropical northwest tip of South Island at latitude 42. Their association with luxuriant King treeferns, large branched cabbage trees, Cordyline australis, Phormium and Pseudopanax, together with many perchers complete a lush, tropical similitude.

Primeval New Zealand is spectacularly beautiful. In the southwest region of South Island there are many deep fjords, carved out by glacial action, and at Milford Sound the waters of the Tasman Sea cut deeply into the crags and peaks of the Southern Alps. Yet, on the sheer mountain sides, and along glacial rivers, in the valleys between, dwells an amazing flora, supported by a yearly rainfall of 700 cm. I have spent many crisp, cool days of hiking along steep, saturated trails, thrilling to old and new acquaintances, from Fuchsia excorticata trees, Nothofagus trees, Dicksonias and single-trunked Dracaena indivisa, to thickets of Schefflera digitata, Phormium and Griselinia; in the dripping undergrowth, Nertera depressa, Dracophyllum, Filmy ferns and a multitude of other ferns; also the little orchid, Earina autumnalis.

Islands of the South Pacific

The Pacific Islands include thousands of islands from Australia to beyond the mid-Pacific, mostly in the tropic zone and warm throughout the year. But rainfall conditions vary greatly, especially on the low coral reefs. The islands of volcanic origin are mountainous, receiving heavy rains. Ringed by sheltered lagoons, and shores fringed with graceful coconut palms, the steep mountains rise like vast green gardens, with waterfalls and secret pools, from the green-blue waters. At night the air is fragrant with the perfume of flowers. Yet the flora of Polynesia, with the exception of Hawaii, New Caledonia, and perhaps Fiji, is comparatively unremarkable.

Aside from coconut and other palms, Araliaceae, Compositae, Euphorbiaceae, Myrtaceae, Rutaceae, and Rubiaceae are well represented. Plants we know from cultivation include Cycas, Dizygotheca, Polyscias; native Araceae are Cyrtosperma and Scindapsus; many Cordyline, especially the green variety 'Ti', Dianella, Alpinia, Gunnera, Heliconia, Homalocladium, Muehlenbeckia, Zingiber; in Euphorbiaceae: Croton, Breynia, Acalypha; Pseuderanthemum, Pandanus, Freycinetia, Plectranthus, Ficus parcelli, and Artocarpus, the Breadfruit tree. Ferns are further represented by Davallia, the climbing Lygodium, Nephrolepis, Blechnum, Adiantum, and Platycerium, the staghorn fern. Norfolk Island is known for its Araucaria heterophylla· Lord Howe Island for the Howeia palms (Kentia).

Although equally distant between America and Asia, HAWAII's endemic genera are mostly represented also in the Old World, while very few are found in America. Of Australian and Asiatic affinity are Coprosma, Freycinetia, Metrosideros, Pandanus, and Pittosporum. Native Cibotium glaucum and C. chamissoi are prolific at elevations of 1200 m, and vast forests of these robust tree ferns cover the slopes of Hawaii's snow-covered volcano, Mauna Loa, 4172 m (13,680 ft.) high. Further endemics are only 3 genera of Orchids; Tetraplasandra, Hillebrandia, true Pleomele (Dracaena), and 30 species of Pritchardia palms; but no Ficus. Natural vegetation is distinctly influenced by the greatly differing rainfall throughout the archipelago, from 30 cm on the Oahu coast to 375 cm on its mountain slopes, while on the northside of Mt. Waialeale on Kauai an average of 12 m a year have been recorded.

When we reach Nuuanu Pali Pass on the island of Oahu in Hawaii, a vast panoramic beauty spreads out windwards. To the left is the rugged backbone of the island, a characteristic, forbidding chain of lava-carved mountains clothed in green, plunging steeply into a rich cultivated plain, blessed by abundant rains of the northeast tradewinds. "Ti" plants (Cordyline), and Pandanus odoratissimus are everywhere.

The larger part of the volcanic, mountainous, beautiful island of Samoa is covered with dense jungle which reach down close to the shores of the South Pacific Seas. The temperature averages from 23 to 29° C., and with a heavy yearly rainfall of 480 cm, falling almost daily, the vegetation is unbelievably lush. Large banyans form a spreading roof, near which spreads a chaos of leaves, with treeferns, Hibiscus, Cordyline, Casuarina, Artocarpus, festooned with lianes, and porous lava rocks wildly overgrown with orchids, ferns and mosses, along frequent streams. A boyhood dream fulfilled, I could never fail to remember the sea so blue, lapping against the coral shores of the green, steep mountains of this romantic South Seas island.

Secluded Lord Howe is a small island of the Tasman Sea, 700 km northeast of Sydney, Australia; discovered on February 17, 1788. Of volcanic formation, it is only 9 kilometer long, and fronted by coral reefs. With an even, subtropical climate and abundant moisture it is covered from the shore to its highest elevation at 866 m, with endemic forests of graceful Howeia (Kentia) forsteriana, known as the Paradise palm, to 18 m high. Seed of this later so important decorative palm was first exported to England in 1871 during the opulent era of Queen Victoria (1830-1900). Each annual flush of flowering strands takes 6 years to develop into viable seed that is ripe and ready for harvest. This seed is then gathered, as a community enterprise, and exported, particularly to temperate zone countries where this palm has long been grown. Its grace and dark green fronds of leathery texture, with excellent keeping qualities, have made it a favorite of florists and for indoor decorations in containers.

The Fijian archipelago forms the eastern end of Melanesia, with the same negroid people that extend west through New Guinea. The moist region of the islands supports a luxuriant tropical vegetation which reaches 1200 m. on the central range of the interior of Viti Levu. Along the coral reefs, Pandanus, Alstonias and coconuts ring the lagoons, but inland and up higher thrives a typical flora with numerous orchids, wild citrus, Mussaenda, Acalypha, Miconia, Costus, Alpinia, Crinum, coppery-red Cordylines; the Fijian kauri, Agathis vitiensis, and tall Veitchia joannis palms. The trees are laden with climbers and lianas of Hoya, Stenochlaena, Freycinetia, Passiflora, frayed Scindapsus aureus (right), Rhaphidophora and Epipremnum. Aside from tall, gracefully slender treeferns, Cyathea lunulata, both ground and trees abound with multitudes of selaginellas, tassel ferns (Lycopodium), and creeping ferns, Lygodium, Angiopteris, Polypodium, Davallia, and Drynaria rigidula.

BIBLIOGRAPHY and LITERATURE REFERENCES

Abrams-Ferris: Flora of the Pacific States *(Stanford 1960)*
Ackerson: Book of Chrysanthemums *(New York 1957)*
Adams: Flowering Plants of Jamaica *(Jamaica 1972)*
Allan: Flora of New Zealand *(Wellington 1961)*
American Hort. Society: Cultivated Palms *(Washington 1961*
American Orchid Society: Bulletin *(Cambridge 1931-1981)*
American Rhododendron Society: Rhododendrons for your Garden *(Portland, Oregon 1961)*
Arbelaez: Plantas Utiles de Colombia *(Bogotá 1947)*
Archbold, Rand, Brass: New Guinea Expedition *(New York 1948)*
Aristeguieta: El Genero Heliconia *(Caracas, 1961)*
Aroideana *(Sarasota, Florida, 1978 -)*
Backeberg: Das Kakteen Lexikon *(Stuttgart 1966)*
Backeberg: Die Cactaceae *(Jena 1958-1962)*
Backer-Posthumus: Varenflora voor Java *(Bogor 1939)*
Bailey: Hortus Third *(New York 1976)*
Bailey: Manual of Cultivated Plants *(New York 1949)*
Bailey: Standard Cyclopedia of Horticulture *(New York 1928)*
Baileya, Journal of Horticultural Taxonomy *(Ithaca 1953-1979)*
Baker: Handbook of Fern Allies *(London 1887)*
Barrett: Exotic Trees of South Florida *(Gainesville 1956)*
Barron: Vines and Vine-Culture *(London 1883)*
Beard: West Australian Plants *(Perth 1970)*
Beddome: Ferns of British India *(London 1883)*
Begonia Society Bulletin *(Los Angeles 1932-1981)*
Bellair & Saint-Léger: Les Plantes de Serre *(Paris 1939)*
Berger: Die Agaven *(Jena 1915)*
Bohnstedt: Kalt und Warmhauspflanzen *(Berlin 1934)*
Booth: Encyclopedia of Annuals & Biennials *(London 1957)*
Borg: Cacti *(London 1956)*
Botanical Register *(London 1815-)*
Bravo: Las Cactaceas de Mexico *(Mexico 1937)*
Breitung: The Agaves *(Reseda, Calif. 1968)*
Brilmeyer: All About Begonias *(Garden City, N.Y. 1960)*
Britton & Brown: Flora of the N.E. United States and Canada *(New York 1958)*
Britton & Rose: The Cactaceae *(Washington 1919)*
Britton & Wilson: Botany of Puerto Rico and the Virgin Islands *(New York 1923-1930)*
Bromeliad Society Bulletin *(Orlando 1951-1981)*
Brown: Florida's Beautiful Crotons *(Indialantic, Fla. 1960)*
Brown: Flora of Southeastern Polynesia *(Honolulu 1931)*
Browne: Forest Trees of Sarawak and Brunei *(Kuching 1955)*
Bruenner: Wasserpflanzen *(Braunschweig 1953)*
Bruggeman: Indisch Tuinboek *(Amsterdam 1948)*
Burgeff: Marchantia *(Jena 1943)*
Buxbaum: Cactus Culture *(London 1958)*
Buxton: Begonias and How to Grow Them *(New York 1946)*
Buxton: Check List of Begonias *(Los Angeles 1957)*
Cabrera: Flora de Buenos Aires *(Buenos Aires 1953)*
Cactus & Succulent Journal *(Pasadena 1879-1981)*
Chabouis: Flore de Tahiti *(Paris 1972)*
Chidamian: Book of Cacti and Other Succulents *(New York 1958)*
Chittenden: Royal Hort. Society Dictionary of Gardening *(Oxford 1951)*
Christ: Die Geographie der Farne *(Jena 1910)*
Christensen: Index Filicum *(Copenhagen 1906-1933)*
Clay: Tropical Shrubs, Hawaii *(Honolulu 1977)*
Codd: Trees and Shrubs of Kruger National Park *(Pretoria 1951)*
Condit: Ficus *(Arcadia, Calif. 1969)*
Constantin: Atlas en Couleurs des Orchidées *(Paris 1913)*
Corner: Wayside Trees of Malaya *(Singapore 1952)*
Cowen: Flowering Trees and Shrubs in India *(Bombay 1950)*
Craig: The Mammillaria Handbook *(Pasadena 1945)*
Curtis Botanical Magazine *(London 1787-1981)*
Cutak: Cactus Guide *(Princeton 1956)*
Cutak: All About Sansevierias *(St. Louis 1966)*
Dale, Greenway: Kenya Trees and Shrubs *(Nairobi 1961)*
Davies: New Zealand Native Plant Studies *(Wellington 1961)*
Davis and Steiner: Philippine Orchids *(New York 1952)*
Decker: Cultura das Orquideas no Brasil *(Sao Paulo 1946)*
Degener: Flora Hawaiiensis *(New York 1946)*
Den Ouden, Boom: Manual of Cultivated Conifers *(The Hague 1965)*
DeWit: Aquarienpflanzen *(Stuttgart 1971)*
Dobbie: New Zealand Ferns *(Auckland 1952)*
Eggeling: The Indigenous Trees of Uganda *(Entebbe 1951)*
Eliovson: South African Flowers *(Cape Town 1955)*
Eliovson: Flowering Shrubs and Trees *(Cape Town 1953)*
Eliovson: Shrubs, Trees and Climbers *(Johannesburg 1975)*
Encke: Parey's Blumengaertnerei, 2nd Ed. *(Berlin 1961)*
Encyclopedia Britannica *(Chicago 1955)*
Engler: Das Pflanzenreich *(Leipzig 1900-)*
Engler: Botanische Jahrbuecher *(Leipzig 1881-)*
Engler-Prantl: Die Natuerlichen Pflanzenfamilien *(Leipzig 1899-)*
Erikson: Flowers and Plants of Western Australia *(Sydney 1973)*
Everett: Begonias *(New York 1939)*
Everett: The American Gardeners Book of Bulbs *(New York 1954)*
Everett: Encyclopedia of Gardening *(New York 1960)*
Everett: N.Y. Bot. Garden Ill. Encycl. of Hort. *(New York 1980 -)*
Fassett: Manual of Aquatic Plants *(Madison 1957)*
Feng-Chi Ho: Tropical Plants of Taiwan *(Pingtung 1977)*
Flowering Plants from Cuban Gardens *(New York 1958)*
Foster: Ferns to Know and Grow *(New York 1972)*
Foster: Bromeliads — A Cultural Handbook *(Orlando 1953)*
Foster: Brazil — Orchid of the Tropics *(Lancaster 1945)*
Fotsch: Die Begonien *(Stuttgart 1933)*
Free: All About House Plants *(New York 1948)*
Gardeners Chronicle *(London 1841-)*
Gartenwelt *(Berlin-Hamburg 1896-)*
Genders: Bulbs *(London 1973)*
Gerbing: Camellias *(Fernandina 1945)*
Giddy: Cycads of South Africa *(Cape Town 1974)*
Gooding: Flora of Barbados *(London 1965)*
Graf: Exotica Series 3, 10th Ed. *(E. Rutherford, NJ 1980)*
Graf: Exotic Plant Manual, 5th Ed. *(E. Rutherford, NJ 1978)*
Graf: Exotic House Plants, 10th Ed. *(E. Rutherford, NJ 1976)*
Graf: Tropica *(E. Rutherford, NJ 1981)*
Gray Herbarium Card Index *(Cambridge 1873-1959)*
Grootendorst: Rhododendrons en Azaleas *(Boskoop 1954)*
Guenther: A Naturalist in Brazil *(London 1931)*
Haage: Cacti and Succulents *(New York 1963)*
Harris: Australian Plants for the Garden *(Sydney 1953)*
Harrison: Bulbs and Perennials *(New Zealand 1967)*
Harrison: Climbers and Trailers *(New Zealand 1975)*
Harrison: Ornamental Conifers *(New Zealand 1975)*
Harrison: Trees and Shrubs for the Southern Hemisphere *(Wellington 1967)*
Haselton: Cacti for the Amateur *(Pasadena 1938)*
Haselton: Succulents for the Amateur *(Pasadena 1939)*
Hawkes: Encyclopedia of Cultivated Orchids *(Miami-London 1965)*
Hawkes: The Major Kinds of Palms *(Coconut Grove 1950)*
Hawkes: Orchids, Their Botany and Culture *(New York 1961)*
Hay, Synge, Kalmbacher: Color Dictionary of Flowers and Plants *(New York 1969)*
Hay, Synge, Herklotz: Das Grosse Blumenbuch *(Stuttgart 1973)*
Hellyer: Sanders Encyclopedia of Gardening *(London 1952)*
Herklotz: The Hong Kong Countryside *(Hong Kong 1959)*
Hertrich: Palms and Cycads *(San Marino 1951)*
Hibberd: New and Rare Beautiful-leaved Plants *(London 1891)*
Higgins: Crassulas in Cultivation *(London 1964)*
Hilliard and Burtt: Streptocarpus *(Pietermaritzburg 1971)*
Hoehne: Iconografia de Orchidaceas do Brasil *(Sao Paulo 1949)*
Honig-Verdoorn: Science in Netherlands Indies *(New York 1945)*
Hong Kong Shrubs, Trees *(Hong Kong 1976)*
Hooker: Flora of British India *(London 1875-1897)*
Hoshizaki: Fern Growers Manual *(New York 1975)*
Hoyos: Flora Tropical Ornamental *(Caracas 1978)*
Hoyos: Los Arboles de Caracas *(Caracas, Venez. 1979)*
Hoyt: Check Lists, Ornamental Plants for Subtropical Regions *(Calif. 1958)*
Hulme: Wild Flowers of Natal *(Pietermaritzburg 1954)*
Hume: Azaleas, Kinds and Culture *(New york 1954)*
Hutchinson: British Flowering Plants *(London 1948)*
Hutchinson: Flora of West Tropical Africa *(London 1958)*
Hutchinson: The Families of Flowering Plants *(London 1926, 1934)*
International Code of Botanical Nomenclature *(Utrecht 1958)*
Index Kewensis and Supplements *(Oxford 1895-1974)*
Index Londinensis to Illustrations *(Oxford 1929-1941)*
Jackson: Glossary of Botanic Terms *(New York 1950)*

Jacobsen: Handbook of Succulent Plants *(London 1960)*
Jacobsen: Handbuch der Sukkulenten Pflanzen *(Jena 1954)*
Jacobsen: Das Sukkulenten Lexikon *(Stuttgart 1970)*
Jex-Blake: Gardening in East Africa *(Nairobi 1948)*
Johnson's Gardener's Dictionary *(London 1846, revised 1917)*
Julius Roehrs Company: Exotic Catalogs *(Rutherford 1911, 1913)*
Kanehira: Formosan Trees *(Fukuoka 1936)*
Kelly: Eucalypts *(Melbourne 1969)*
Kelsey: Standardized Plant Names *(Harrisburg 1942)*
Kerchove: Les Palmiers *(Paris 1878)*
Kew Bulletin *(London 1887-1969)*
Kidd: Wild Flowers of the Cape Peninsula *(Cape Town 1950)*
Koeppen: Grundriss der Klimakunde *(Berlin 1931)*
Krauss: Begonias for American Homes *(New York 1947)*
Krauss: Geraniums for the Home *(New York 1955)*
Kruessmann: Die Laubgehoelze *(Berlin 1957-1978)*
Kruessmann: Die Nadelgehoelze *(Berlin 1955)*
Kruessmann: Rosen *(Berlin 1974)*
Kuck and Tong: Hawaiian Flowers and Flowering Trees *(Honolulu 1958)*
Laing and Blackwell: Plants of New Zealand *(Auckland 1940)*
Lamb: Cacti and Other Succulents *(New York 1955)*
Lamb: Stapeliads in Cultivation *(London 1957)*
Langlois: Supplement to Palms of the World *(Gainesville, Fla. 1976)*
Latif: Bunga Anggerik (Orchids) *(Bandung 1953)*
Lawrence: The Cultivated Hederas *(Ithaca 1942)*
Lawrence: Taxonomy of Vascular Plants (New York 1951)
Le Bon Jardinier, Encyclopedie Horticole *(Paris 1964)*
Lecomte: Flore Générale de l'Indochine *(Paris 1942)*
Lecoufle & Rose: Orchids *(Paris 1957)*
Lee: The Azalea Book *(Princeton 1958)*
Letty: Wild Flowers of the Transvaal *(Pretoria 1962)*
L'Illustration Horticole *(Ghent 1854-1896)*
Linnaeus: Species Plantarum *(Upsala 1753)*
Liu: Illustrations of Ligneous Plants of Taiwan *(Taipei 1960)*
Little, Woodbury, Wadsworth: Trees of Puerto Rico and the Virgin Islands *(Washington 1964, 1974)*
Lloyd: The Carnivorous Plants *(Waltham 1942)*
Lord: Shrubs and Trees for Australian Gardens *(Melbourne 1960)*
Lowe: Ferns, British and Exotic *(London 1864)*
Lowe: Beautiful Leaved Plants *(London 1872)*
MacMillan: Trop. Planting and Gardening, Ceylon *(London 1956)*
Macself: Ferns for Garden and Greenhouse *(London 1952)*
Maerz and Paul: Dictionary of Color *(New York 1930)*
Makino: Illustrated Flora of Japan *(Tokyo 1967)*
Marnier-Lapostolle: Le Genre Kalanchoe *(Paris 1964)*
Marshall & Bock: Cactaceae *(Pasadena 1941)*
Mathias, McClintock: Woody Ornamental Plants of California *(Univ. of Calif. 1963)*
Matuda: Las Araceas Mexicanas *(Mexico 1954)*
McClure: The Bamboos *(Cambridge, Mass. 1966)*
McCurrach: Palms of the World (Palm Beach 1959)
McFarland: American Rose Annual *(Harrisburg 1916-1959)*
McFarland: Modern Roses *(Harrisburg 1969)*
Menninger: Flowering Trees of the World *(Stuart, Florida 1961)*
Menninger: Flowering Vines of the World *(New York 1970)*
Misono: Begonias *(Chiba, Japan 1974)*
Moering: Die Hortensien *(Aachen 1956)*
Moldenke: Plants of the Bible *(New York 1952)*
Moore: African Violets, Gloxinias, and Relatives *(New York 1957)*
Moore: Flora of New Zealand, Vol. II *(Wellington 1970)*
Morton: 500 Plants of South Florida *(Miami 1974)*
Neal: In Gardens of Hawaii *(Honolulu 1948)*
Nel: Lithops *(Stellenbosch 1946)*
Nicholson: Dictionnaire Pratique d'Horticulture *(Paris 1893)*
Nicholson: Illustrated Dictionary of Gardening *(London 1887)*
Noble and Merkel: Plants Indoors *(New York 1954)*
North American Flora *(New York 1949-)*
Northen: Home Orchid Growing *(New York 1970)*
O'Gorman: Mexican Flowering Trees & Plants *(Mexico City 1961)*
Ohwi: Flora of Japan *(Washington 1965)*
Ospina Hernandez: Orquideas Colombianas *(Bogotá 1958)*
Padilla: Bromeliads *(New York 1973)*
Palgrave: Trees of Central Africa *(Salisbury 1957)*
Parodi: Enciclopedia Argentina de Agricultura *(Buenos Aires 1959)*
Pesman: Meet Flora Mexicana *(Arizona 1962)*
Pertchick: Flowering Trees of the Caribbean *(New York 1951)*
Pierot: Ivy Book *(New York 1974)*
Piers: Orchids of East Africa *(Nairobi 1968)*
Phytologia *(Yonkers, N.Y. 1956-)*
Pittier: Plantas Usuales de Venezuela *(Caracas 1926)*
Polunin: Flowers of the Mediterranean *(Boston 1966)*
Polunin: Guide des Plantes et Fleurs de l'Europe *(Paris 1974)*
Popenoe: Manual of Tropical and Subtropical Fruits *(New York 1934)*
Principes, Journal of the Palm Society *(Miami, Florida 1956-1981)*
Rauh-Heidelberg: Bromelien *(Stuttgart 1970)*
Ray-Walheim: Citrus *(Tucson 1980)*
Rehder: Manual of Cultivated Trees and Shrubs *(New York 1954)*
Reiter-Boehmig: Schnittblumen und Topfpflanzen *(Berlin 1958)*
Reynolds: Aloes of South Africa *(Johannesburg 1950)*
Reynolds: Aloes of Trop. Africa and Madagascar *(Swaziland 1966)*
Rice and Compton: Wild Flowers of the Cape *(Kirstenbosch 1950)*
Richards: New Zealand Trees and Flowers *(Christchurch 1956)*
Richter: Bromeliaceen *(Radebeul 1962)*
Rickett, New York Botanical Garden: Wild Flowers of the United States, Vol. 1 to 6 *(New York 1966-1973)*
Rockwell: The Complete Book of Bulbs *(New York 1953)*
Russell: Mosses and Liverworts *(London 1908)*
Sanders Orchid Guide and List of Hybrids *(St. Albans, 1927-1963)*
Schlechter: Die Orchideen *(Berlin 1927)*
Schimper: Pflanzen-Geographie *(Jena 1898)*
Scheirlinck: Tuinbouw: De Azalea Indica *(Antwerpen 1938)*
Schneider: Book of Choice Ferns *(London 1892-1894)*
Schultz: Gesneriads *(Grandview, Mo. 1967)*
Schwantes: Flowering Stones *(London 1957)*
Scott: The Florists Manual *(Chicago 1899)*
Sibree: A Naturalist in Madagascar *(London 1915)*
Silva-Tarouca: Unsere Freiland-Stauden *(Wein 1934)*
Small: Flora of the Southeastern U.S. *(New York 1913)*
Smith: Ferns, British and Foreign *(London 1896)*
Smith: The Bromeliaceae of Brazil *(Washington 1955)*
Smith: The Bromeliaceae of Colombia *(Washington 1957)*
Smith: Notes on Bromeliaceae (Phytologia) *(Baltimore 1971)*
Smith and Downs: Bromeliaceae *(New York 1974-1979)*
Spalding: Pelagonium Checklist *(California 1972)*
Sprechman, Dugdale, Cole, DeBoer: Lithops *(Rutherford 1970)*
Spuy: South African Shrubs and Trees *(Johannesburg 1971)*
Standley: Trees and Shrubs of Mexico *(Washington 1926)*
Step: Favorite Flowers of Garden and Greenhouse *(London 1896)*
Stevenson: Palms of So. Florida *(Miami 1964)*
Stocken: Andalusian Flowers *(Devon 1969)*
Stodola: Encyclopedia of Water Plants *(Jersey City 1967)*
Sventenius: Floram Canariensem *(Madrid 1960)*
Taeckholm, Drer, Fadeel: Flora of Egypt *(Cairo 1956)*
Tagawa: The Japanese Pteridophyta *(Osaka 1959)*
Taylor: Encyclopedia of Gardening *(Boston 1961)*
Thompson: Begonia Guide *(New York 1977)*
Thrower: Plants of Hong Kong *(Hong Kong 1971, 1977)*
Tobler: Die Gattung Hedera *(Jena 1912)*
Van Pelt Wilson: African Violet Book *(New York 1970)*
Van Tubergen: Catalog of Bulbs *(Haarlem 1961-1976)*
Veitch: Manual of Orchidaceous Plants *(London 1894)*
Verdoorn: Plant Science in Latin America *(Waltham 1945)*
Vogts: Proteas *(Johannesburg 1958)*
Walther: Echeveria *(San Francisco 1972)*
Wayside Gardens: Catalog *(Mentor, Ohio 1959-1981)*
Webber and Batchelor: The Citrus Industry *(Berkeley 1948)*
Weberbauer: El Mundo Vegetal de los Andes Peruanos *(Lima 1945)*
Western Garden Book (Lane) *(Menlo Park, Calif. 1979)*
Wettstein: Handbuch der Botanik *(Leipzig-Wien 1923)*
White: American Orchid Culture *(New York 1939)*
White and Sloane: The Stapelieae *(Pasadena 1937)*
Williams: Orchid Growers Manual, 7th Ed. *(London 1894)*
Williams: Orchids of Mexico *(Honduras 1965)*
Williams: Useful and Ornamental Plants of Zanzibar *(Zanzibar 1949)*
Willis: Dictionary of the Flowering Plants and Ferns, 8th Ed. *(Cambridge 1973)*
Wilson: Geraniums—Pelargoniums *(New York 1946-1956)*
Withner: The Orchids *(New York 1959)*
Wood: A Fuchsia Survey *(London 1956)*
Wright: Orquideas de Mexico *(Mexico 1958)*
Zohary: Plant Life of Palestine *(Jerusalem 1962)*
Zander: Dictionary of Plant Names *(Stuttgart 1984)* guided by Nomenclature in FLORA EUROPAEA 1980

INDEX of COMMON NAMES

Finding List to Scientific Names and Illustrations

some descriptive **some humorous**

There are about 3,800 Popular Names listed in EXOTICA, often referring to their generic botanical name only. Folio numbers to photos are not exclusive, as the same plant or genus is frequently shown elsewhere, but may be located easily by checking the Text-Index.

A

B

C

G

H

I

J

T

U

V

BOTANIC INDEX to GENERA ILLUSTRATED

For quick reference, page number of photographs of individual species, varieties, and cultivars will be found at the end of each listing in the text.

Roman Numerals indicate illustrations
Vol. I: to pg. 1280
Vol. II: from pg. 1281

A

B

C

D

E

Q

R

S

EXOTICA 4 INTERNATIONAL 1985 EDITION

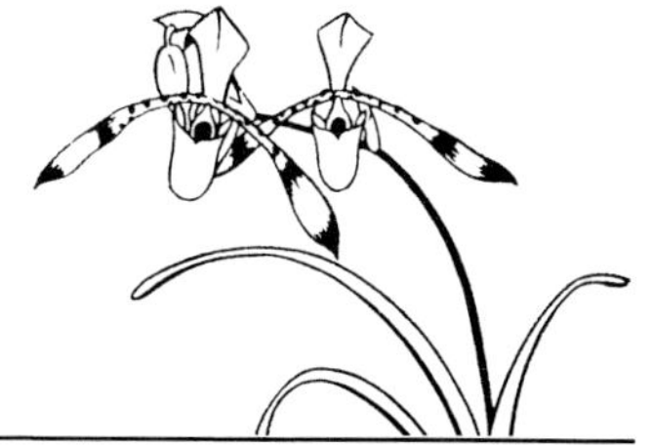

SYNOPSIS of REVISIONS and UPDATES in Botanical Nomenclature

The scientific names of plants pictured in EXOTICA were originally based on Dr. Liberty Hyde Bailey's Dictionary of Cultivated Plants, HORTUS Second (1941 Ed.) as principal Reference.

Following continuing research over a period of 35 years, the vastly larger HORTUS Third, edited by the Staff of the Bailey Hortorium of Cornell University, Ithaca, New York, revised countless names of plants in horticulture, or placed them into other families. When the enlarged EXOTICA Series IV was published in 1982, several hundred updates and corrections were incorporated in this new edition. Other changes had been deferred by the printers as technically too difficult and expensive to transpose, involving photo captions, alphabetical text and index.

A needed 1985 printing gave us the opportunity to examine all pending taxonomic questions. I have once again reviewed accumulated notes going back over 24 years. Subsequently all photo captions in EXOTICA were re-examined and meticulously compared with the 1186 pages of listings in HORTUS 3. The resulting summary presents all aspects of name changes either pending or considered valid. Included is information received after 1976, by dialogue with specialists, and also from recent botanical literature.

A most important international reference work used in my comparisons is the European ZANDER: Dictionary of Plant Names and Synonyms, 1984 Edition. This in turn was guided by the Nomenclature as determined for FLORA EUROPAEA 1980.

While these authorities do not always agree, the various listed options reflect the considered opinion of specialists each in their field of botany. Progressive research does not stand still, and new revisions are being determined and published constantly, superseding much that may presently be considered valid. It is hoped that in time, most plants will have names of a definite status, to come into practical use by horticulturists.

The combined notes on these pages, with more than 1000 updates, may be considered a major revision of EXOTICA, attempting to show all changes affecting previous names. Authors of the presently valid taxa are not cited, neither did HORTUS 2, but can be located in the universally available HORTUS 3.

Most of the older names long valid and familiar to horticulture, are still very much in use by gardeners. Being able to cross-reference them with this summary of newer versions should in effect prove welcome and useful to the practical horticulturist as well as the serious student of botanical nomenclature. For ease of comparison, the affected photo captions are listed in sequence by page number as found in the Pictorial section of EXOTICA 1985.

Page No.

33 Mesembryanthemum caulescens is placed into a separate genus Oscularia caulescens (HORTUS 3)

39, 15 Aphelandra fascinator is A. aurantiaca in HORTUS 3.

40 Aphelandra atrovirens is A. bahiensis (HORTUS 3).

41 Adhatoda vasica (HORTUS 2) is Justicia adhatoda (HORTUS 3).

42 Acanthus longifolius is A. balcanicus in HORTUS 3.

44 Beloperone comosa (HORTUS 2) is syn. of Justicia fulvicoma (HORTUS 3).

44 Beloperone guttata (HORTUS 2) is Justicia brandegeana in HORTUS 3.

47 Eranthemum nervosum (HORTUS 2) is E. pulchellum in HORTUS 3.

48 Hemigraphis colorata (HORTUS 2) is syn. of H. alternata in HORTUS 3, also ZANDER 1984.

49 Hypoestes sanguinolenta is probably H. phyllostachya (HORTUS 3).

49 Jacobinia carnea (HORTUS 2) is Justicia carnea in HORTUS 3, but remains Jacobinia carnea in ZANDER 1984.

49 Jacobinia velutina (HORTUS 2) is supposedly Justicia carnea in HORTUS 3, Parey lists it as Jacobinia pohliana (carnea) var. velutina. J. velutina has soft-hairy foliage while J. carnea has smooth, satiny foliage.

50 Jacobinia ghiesbreghtiana (HORTUS 2) is transferred to Justicia in HORTUS 3. However, ZANDER 1984 retains Jacobinia ghiesbreghtiana.

50 Jacobinia pauciflora (HORTUS 2) is Justicia rizzinii in HORTUS 3, but remains Jacobinia pauciflora in ZANDER 1984.

50 Jacobinia pohliana (HORTUS 2) is Justicia carnea in HORTUS 3, but Jacobinia carnea in ZANDER 1984. Jacobinia pohliana has darker flowers than carnea.

50 Jacobinia suberecta is syn. of Dicliptera suberecta in HORTUS 3.

51 Ruellia amoena (HORTUS 2) is syn. of R. graecizans in HORTUS 3, also ZANDER 1984.

52, 15 Chamaeranthemum igneum hort. is now placed to Xeranthemum igneum (HORTUS 3).

55 (text pg. 2427), Ruellia ciliosa, according to T. Everett, N.Y. Bot. G. is limited from S. Carolina to Florida and only 30cm high, lower than R.strepens, and with shorter, usually hairy leaves.

58 Conophytum wiggettae (as in Jacobsen) is spelled wiggettiae in HORTUS 3.

62 Hymenocyclus crocea (croceus in HORTUS 2) is transferred to Malephora (not Maleophora) crocea in HORTUS 3; also Jacobsen, Willis, Zander.

62 Mesembryanthemum deltoides is now transferred to Oscularia deltoides (HORTUS 3)

64 Hymenocyclus latipetalus (HORTUS 2) is Malephora latipetala in Jacobsen Lexicon of Succulent Plants.

65 Tetragonia expansa (HORTUS 2 in AIZOACEAE) is now T. tetragonioides in HORTUS 3 in new family TETRAGONIACEAE.

66 Delosperma echinatum (HORTUS 2) is D. pruinosum in HORTUS 3.

68 Gibbaeum fissoides (nelii) transferred to Antegibbaeum fissoides (HORTUS 3).

68 Nananthus malherbei is synonym of Aloinopsis malherbei (HORTUS 3).

68 Nananthus villetii is synonym of Aloinopsis villetii (HORTUS 3).

69-74 Lithops are variable and often difficult to properly identify. HORTUS 3 lists twelve changes in EXOTICA epithets: L. framesii to marmorata; p. 70 L. guilielmii to schwantesii var. triebneri; p. 70, L. kuibisensis to schwantesii; p.70 L. lineata to ruschiorum; L. lerichiana to bella var. lerichiana; p. 70, 73 L. mickbergensis to karasmontana var. mickbergensis; p. 70, 74 L. opalina to karasmontana var. opalina; p. 71 L. peersii to localis; p. 70 L. summitatum to karasmontana var. summitata; p. 69, 70 L. terricolor to localis var. terricolor; p. 70 L. triebneri to L. schwantesii var. triebneri; p. 71 L. venteri to lesliei var. venteri.

77 Carruanthus caninus (HORTUS 2) is syn. of C. ringens in HORTUS 3.

77 Lampranthus roseus (HORTUS 2) is now L. multiradiatus in HORTUS 3.

78 Titanopsis luckhoffii is referred to Aloinopsis luckhoffii in HORTUS 3; also confirmed in Backeberg 'Cactaceae'.

81 Actinidia (DILLENIAC. in HORTUS 2) is now ACTINIDIACEAE in HORTUS 3.

81 Amaranthus hypochondriacus is syn. of A. hybridus var. erythrostachys (HORTUS 3)

81 Amaranthus paniculatus is syn. of A. cruentus (HORTUS 3).

82, 84 Alternanthera amoena (HORTUS 2) is A. ficoidea cv. 'Amoena' (HORTUS 3, also ZANDER 1984)

82 Alternanthera bettzickiana (HORTUS 2) is A. ficoidea cv. 'Bettzickiana' in HORTUS 3.

82, 84 Alternanthera versicolor (HORTUS 2) is A. ficoidea cv. (HORTUS 3).

85 AGAVACEAE, a family newly listed in HORTUS 3, transfers 20 genera formerly AMARYLLIDACEAE and LILIACEAE (incl. Agave, Beaucarnea, Beschorneria, Cordyline, Dasylirion, Doryanthes, Dracaena, Furcraea, Hesperaloe, Manfreda, Nolina, Phormium, Polianthes, Sansevieria, Yucca).

88, 97 Agave verschaffeltii (HORTUS 2) is A. potatorum in HORTUS 3.

92 Agave kaibabensis (HORTUS 2) is A. utahensis var. kaibabensis in HORTUS 3

92 Agave latissima (HORTUS 2) is A. atrovirens in HORTUS 3.

98 Furcraea gigantea (HORTUS 2) is syn. of F. foetida in HORTUS 3.

99 Agave miradorensis (HORTUS 2) is A. desmetiana in HORTUS 3.

100 Hypoxis (AMARYLLIDACEAE in HORTUS 2) is split off to family HYPOXIDACEAE in HORTUS 3

101 etc. Alstroemeria (AMARYLLIDACEAE in HORTUS 2) are placed into the family ALSTROEMERIACEAE in HORTUS 3.

102 Anigozanthos (AMARYLL. in HORTUS 2)—now in family HAEMODORACEAE in HORTUS 3.

102 Bomarea (AMARYLLIDACEAE in HORTUS 2) is now in family ALSTROEMERIACEAE (HORTUS 3).

103 Hippeastrum rutilum (HORTUS 2) is syn. of H. striatum in HORTUS 3, also ZANDER 1984

104, 105 Hippeastrum procerum, the "Blue amaryllis" is Worsleya rayneri in HORTUS 3, also ZANDER 1984

111 Rhodophiala chilensis is changed to Hippeastrum chilense in HORTUS 3. Other authorities refer to Habranthus.

111 Runyonia longiflora is transferred to Manfreda longiflora in HORTUS 3.

113 x Brunsdonna parkeri (HORTUS 2) is referred to x Amarygia (HORTUS 3, also ZANDER 1984)

113, 114 Habranthus robustus (HORTUS 2) is syn. of H. tubispathus in HORTUS 3.

116, 117 Hymenocallis americana (HORTUS 2) is a horticultural synonym for H. littoralis (HORTUS 3).

118 Ammocharis falcata is transferred to Cybistetes longifolia (HORTUS 3).

120 Bomarea (AMARYLLIDACEAE in HORTUS 2) is now in family ALSTROEMERIACEAE (HORTUS 3).

120 Bomarea caldasiana (HORTUS 2) is now spelled B. caldasii in HORTUS 3.

120 Brevoortia ida-maia (HORTUS 2) is Dichelostemma ida-maia in HORTUS 3.

121, 131 Hypoxis (AMARYLLIDACEAE in HORTUS 2) is split off to HYPOXIDACEAE in HORTUS 3.

121 Lycoris aurea (HORTUS 2) is L. africana in HORTUS 3.

130 Brevoortia ida-maia (HORTUS 2) is Dichelostemma ida-maia in HORTUS 3.

131 Bravoa geminiflora (AMARYLLIDACEAE in HORTUS 2) is Polianthes geminiflora, AGAVACEAE, in HORTUS 3.

131 Hypoxis—see notation, p. 121.

132 Spondias dulcis in hort. is synonym of S. cytherea (HORTUS 3).

133 Spondias venulosa, photographed in Jardim Botanico, Rio de Janeiro, is synonymous with S. mombin.

134 Echites rubrovenosa is listed as Prestonia quinquangularis in HORTUS 3.

135 Carissa acocanthera in hort. is properly Acokanthera oppositifolia in HORTUS 3.

135 Carissa arduina (HORTUS 2) is now C. bispinosa in HORTUS 3.

136 Acokanthera venenata (HORTUS 2) is A. oppositifolia (HORTUS 3).

136 Tabernaemontana divaricata: Author's photos taken at Singapore Botanic Garden and later corrected by Dr. E. Corner to T. corymbosa, the Pinwheel tree (Wayside Trees of Malaya, p. 151).

138 Mandevilla suaveolens (HORTUS 2) is syn. of M. laxa in HORTUS 3, also ZANDER 1984

139 Tabernaemontana coronaria in hort. (as Ervatamia coronaria in HORTUS 2), is synonym of T. divaricata in HORTUS 3. ZANDER 1984 maintains T. coronaria.

139 Tabernaemontana coronaria flore pleno, is now considered syn. of T. divaricata plena, the fragrant "Fleur d'Amour".

*The **ARACEAE** are being newly studied and updated from Engler's 'Pflanzenreich' (1905-1920). In 1980, specialists of the Aroid Society, including Dr. Thomas Croat, Missouri Botanic Garden; Dr. Michael Madison, Sarasota, Florida; Dr. D. H. Nicolson, Smithsonian, Washington, and J. Bogner, Munich Botanic Garden, have kindly checked the more than 1250 photos of Araceae and their horticultural names in EXOTICA IV, and offered the following comments:*

150 Aglaonema brevispathum hospitum is A. commutatum or cultivar.

151 Aglaonema costatum foxii is A. costatum fa. costatum.

151 Aglaonema "cuscuaria" may be A. commutatum

151 Aglaonema "hospitum variegatum" is A. brevispathum fa. hospitum.

153 Alocasia sanderiana — vs. alternate spelling A. sanderana. According to advice from the Bailey Hortorium of Cornell University, New York 1985, endings of Latinized epithets derived from personal names and ending with a consonant, may again read — iana. Example: Alocasia sanderiana, so listed in HORTUS 2; as A. sanderana in HORTUS 3 (1976) and ZANDER DICT. 1979. However, ZANDER Dict. 1984 reverted back to A. sanderiana, in agreement with the latest International Taxonomic Rules 1980. This will similarly affect endings under notations for EXOTICA species names on pages 385, 564, 588, 594, 604, 649, 715, 720, 722, 1572, 1761, 1798, 1800, 1834, 2048.

154 Alocasia indica metallica (HORTUS 2) is A. plumbea in HORTUS 3.

155 Alocasia odora is considered the same as A. macrorrhiza. Dr. Marie Neal of Hawaii maintains A. odora as separate species.

156 Alocasia princeps is A. porphyroneura (HORTUS 3).

160 Alocasia indica metallica (HORTUS 2) is A. plumbea in HORTUS 3.

161 Alocasia porphyroneura as pictured is A. reversa from Sarawak, Borneo (AROIDEANA, Oct. 1984).

162 Anthurium imperiale is A. schlechtendalii.

162 Anthurium fissum is syn. of A. palmatum (J. Bogner, Munich Bot. Garden).

166 Anthurium caucanum maximum is A. ovalifolium.

168 Anthurium gracile is A. friedrichsthalii.
170 Anthurium caribaeum is A. cordifolium (HORTUS 3).
170 Anthurium "Negrito" is A. watermaliense.
171 Anthurium holtonianum is A. clavigerum.
171 Anthurium panduratum is A. clavigerum.
173 Anthurium kalbreyeri is A. clavigerum.
173 Anthurium aemulum is A. pentaphyllum bombacifolium.
173 Anthurium digitatum is A. pentaphyllum digitatum (Dr. D. H. Nicolson, Washington).
173 Anthurium fortunatum is syn. of A. pedatum.
173 Anthurium pentaphyllum is probably A. longissimum (?) (Dr. Thomas Croat, St. Louis).
173 Anthurium undatum is A. pentaphyllum.
173 Anthurium variabile is syn. of A. pentaphyllum.
176 Anthurium insigne is synonym of A. trilobum.
177 Anthurium tetragonum is A. schlechtendalii.
178 Anthurium guildingii is A. ravenii (Dr. D. H. Nicolson, Smithsonian).
179 Anthurium araliifolium of hort. is questionable.
179, 180 Anthurium rigidulum is A. scandens.
187 Arum dracunculus (HORTUS 2) is Dracunculus vulgaris (HORTUS 3), see text, pg. 2180.
188 Atherurus is changed to Pinellia (nom. cons.) (J. Bogner, Munich Bot. Garden).
191 Caladium plowmanii is a synonym for Chlorospatha longipoda (J. Bogner, Munich Botanic Garden).
206 Amydrium medium is referred to Epipremnopsis media (HORTUS 3).
206 Epipremnum falcifolium is spelled falcifolia in HORTUS 3.
207 Sauromatum venosum is S. guttatum var. venosum in HORTUS 3. Correct on pg. 284.
208 Chlorospatha maculata photo is C. mirabilis, as advised by J. Bogner, Munich Botanic Garden.
208 Gonatanthus sarmentosus is syn. of G. pumilus (HORTUS 3).
213 Colocasia gigantea is C. indica, according to J. Bogner, Munich Bot. Garden, but C. gigantea is listed in HORTUS 3 with indica as synonym.
222 Lysichiton americanum (HORTUS 3) spelled L. americanus in ZANDER 1984
224 Gonatopus rhizomatosus is actually a synonym of Gonatopus angustus (J. Bogner, Munich Bot. Gard.)
225 Homalomena picturata: photographed under this name in Florida, but is probably synonymous with Schismatoglottis emarginata, photo on p. 280.
225 Lysichiton—see notation p. 222
227 Lysichiton camtschatcense (HORTUS 3), spelled L. camtschatcensis in ZANDER 1984.
227 Porphyrospatha schottiana according to Engler, is syn. of Syngonium schottianum (J. Bogner, Munich Bot. G.).
229 Monstera pertusa of hort. is synonym of M. adansonii (HORTUS 3).
230 Monstera dilacerata is properly M. acuminata (J. Bogner, Munich Bot. Garden).
230 Monstera fendleri is prob. juv. form of M. adansonii.
230 Monstera peruviana is prob. M. dilacerata (J. Bogner).
231 Monstera pertusa of hort. is synonym of M. adansonii (HORTUS 3).
231 Monstera pittieri is hort. name for M. adansonii var. laniata.
231 Monstera punctulata may be M. adansonii (J. Bogner).
231, 233, 255 Philodendron "pertusum" is botanically the juvenile form of Monstera deliciosa.
232 Monstera dubia, J. Bogner of Munich Bot. Garden believes this to be M. tenuis.
232 Monstera friedrichsthalii is syn. of M. adansonii var. laniata.
232 Monstera obliqua expilata, known in hort. as M. leichtlinii, is questioned by J. Bogner, but is listed in Engler Pflanzenreich.
232 Monstera pertusa jacquinii is prob. M. adansonii var. klotzschiana (J. Bogner, Munich Bot. Garden).
235 Monstera dilacerata is probably M. dubia or tenuis.
237, 242 Philodendron "Imperialis" of hort. appears the same as P. speciosum (J. Bogner).
238, 242 Philodendron saxicolum, spelled saxicola (HORTUS 3).
242 Philodendron talamancae hort., is P. davidsonii (syn. talamancae hort.) (Dr. T. Croat, Missouri Bot. G. 1983).
244 Philodendron duisbergii is syn. of P. fendleri in HORTUS 3.
250 Philodendron fragrantissimum in hort. may be P. grandipes.
255 Philodendron panduriforme, as known in horticulture; referred to P. bipennifolium (HORTUS 3).
257 Philodendron variifolium—may be juv. form of P. ornatum.
259 Philodendron discolor in hort. is prob. a form of P. scandens.
259 Philodendron micans hort. (HORTUS 2) is P. scandens fa. micans (HORTUS 3).
269 Philodendron ruizii, as known in hort., is prob. P. myrmecophilum.
270 Philodendron fraternum in hort. may be P. eximium.
271 Philodendron cannifolium—J. Bogner, Munich, suggests change to P. martianum.
271 Philodendron nobile in hort., is P. insigne (J. Bogner).
273 Philodendron grazielae is prob. juvenile form of Philodendron microstictum (J. Bogner).
273 Philodendron panduriforme—see notation for p. 255.
274 Philodendron talamancae—see notation for p. 242.
276 Philodendron bipinnatifidum in hort. could be P. distantilobum.
276 Philodendron scandens photo is botanically correct as P. scandens ssp. scandens (see text, p. 2398).
277 Rhaphidophora montana is referred to R. africana.
278 Monstera peruviana is prob. M. dilacerata.
278 Pinellia ternata, nom. conserv., otherwise to Atherurus tripartitus (J. Bogner, Munich Bot. Garden).
279 Pothos hermaphroditus from Java, may be the same as P. scandens.
279 Pothos jambea (HORTUS 2) is probably syn. of P. seemanii (HORTUS 3).
279 Scindapsus siamense is identified as S. pictus argyraeus (Aroid Society).
281 Montrichardia arborescens, believed to be M. linifera (J. Bogner, Munich Bot. Garden).
281 Rhaphidophora "laciniosa" is probably Monstera subpinnata (HORTUS 3).
284 Sauromatum guttatum should be S. venosum (Aroid Society).
284 Schismatoglottis neo-guineensis—correct epithet to S. novo-guineensis (Aroid Society).
286 Rhaphidophora celatocaulis, as collected in Borneo, may properly be R. dubia, according to J. Bogner, Munich Bot. Garden.
287 Spathiphyllum patinii: the Aroid Soc. would change to S. floribundum. However, ZANDER 1984 maintains S. patinii (Hogg).
288 Spathiphyllum cannaefolium (HORTUS 2) is now spelled S. cannifolium in HORTUS 3, also ZANDER 1984.
290 Heteroaridarum annae, collected by J. Bogner (Munich Bot. G.) in Sarawak, was later described as Aridarum.
293 Syngonium hoffmannii of hort., is considered juv. form of S. podophyllum (J. Bogner, Munich Bot. Garden).
297 Xanthosoma roseum 'Variegatum' is considered a cv. of Alocasia macrorrhiza by J. Bogner, Munich Bot. G.
299, 160A Xanthosoma lindenii and cultivars have been transferred to Caladium lindenii by Dr. Michael Madison (SELBYANA 1981 and AROIDEANA, July 1983).
302 Zantedeschia melanoleuca (HORTUS 2) is referred to Z. albomaculata in HORTUS 3. However, Royal Hort. Dict. describes two separate species, and Sima Eliovson in 'South African Flowers' also separates as distinct Z. albo-maculata and melanoleuca.
306, 316 Nothopanax arboreus (HORTUS 2) is changed to Neopanax arboreus in HORTUS 3.
308, etc. Brassaia actinophylla, as in HORTUS 3, is transferred back to Schefflera by Dr. David Frodin of Papua-New Guinea.
310 Schefflera erythrostachys is S. venulosa var. erythrostachys (see ZANDER Dict. 1984).

312 Schefflera 'Starshine' from the Philippines, has been identified as S. albido-bracteatus by Dr. D. Frodin, University of Papua-New Guinea.
316, 318 Nothopanax laetus is referred to Neopanax laetus in HORTUS 3.
319, 321 Trevesia palmata sanderi is probably T. burckii (HORTUS 3).
320A Citrus mitis (HORTUS 2) is transferred to x Citrofortunella mitis in HORTUS 3.
321 Tetrapanax papyriferus 'Variegatus' is spelled cv. 'Variegata' in HORTUS 3.
352 Nymania (AITONIACEAE in HORTUS 2) is now included in family MELIACEAE in HORTUS 3.
353 Araujia sericofera (HORTUS 2) is spelled sericifera in HORTUS 3.
359 Ceropegia caffrorum (HORTUS 2) is C. linearis in HORTUS 3.
360 Ceropegia mozambicensis is C. nilotica (HORTUS 3).
368 Hoya motoskei is probably a cultivar of H. carnosa (HORTUS 3), with leaves spotted silver.
385, 386, 387, 388 Impatiens walleriana (sultanii) (HORTUS 2), is spelled I. wallerana in HORTUS 3. However, ZANDER 1984 has changed back to I. walleriana.
386 Impatiens 'Tangerine' is I. platypetala cv. (Park Seed Co., So. Carolina).
386 Impatiens roylei (HORTUS 2) is referred to I. glandulifera in HORTUS 3.
389 Impatiens glanduligera (HORTUS 2) is spelled glandulifera in HORTUS 3.
474 Begonia rex 'Comtesse Louise Erdoedy', according to Logee's Greenhouses, Danielson, Conn., is prob. B. rex 'Curly Prince of Hanover; correct on p. 476.
495 Mahonia beallei in error, is spelled M. bealei.
495 Podophyllum emodi (HORTUS 2) is listed as P. hexandrum in HORTUS 3.
496 Pithecoctenium muricatum is syn. of P. echinatum (HORTUS 3).
502 Doxantha unguis-cati (HORTUS 2) is now Macfadyena unguis-cati in HORTUS 3.
504 Xylotheca kraussiana in BIXACEAE in EXOTICA, is transferred to Oncoba kraussiana (fam. FLACOURTIACEAE) in HORTUS 3.
507 Bombax ellipticum (HORTUS 2) is now Pseudobombax ellipticum in HORTUS 3, also ZANDER 1984.
510 Lithospermum diffusum (HORTUS 2) transferred to Lithodora diffusa in HORTUS 3.
511 Echium bourgaeanum (HORTUS 2) is E. wildpretii in HORTUS 3.

BROMELIACEAE: *Harry Luther of Selby Botanical Gardens, Sarasota, Florida, has reviewed the Bromeliad pages 512-613. Major corrections, usually of names current in horticulture, are herewith listed:*

515, 521 Aechmea x maginali is properly Ae. 'Maginali'.
516, 521 Aechmea comata is a synonym of Ae. lindenii.
524 Aechmea amazonica is synonym of Ae. chantinii.
525 Aechmea mooreana is correctly spelled Ae. moorei.
525 Aechmea tillandsioides var. 'Amazonas' is Ae. chantinii.
526 Aechmea blumenavii is Ae. weilbachii leodiensis (Dr. L. B. Smith).
526 Aechmea comata 'Makoyana' is Ae. lindenii cv.
526 Aechmea victoriana discolor is Ae. cylindrata.
527 Aechmea 'Exquisite' is x Neomea cv.
527 Aechmea 'Nebula' is x Neomea cv.
528 Aechmea glaziovii is Ae. distichantha glaziovii.
529 Abromeitiella chlorantha is A. brevifolia.
530, 532 Ananas bracteatus striatus is A. bracteatus var. tricolor.
530 Vriesea ampullacea or V. 'Espirito Santo', photographed under this name in Facenda Burle-Marx, in Brazil, is probably Tillandsia grazielae.
533 Ananas erectifolius is properly A. lucidus
534, 539 Billbergia saundersii is B. chlorosticta.
535 Billbergia x hoelscheriana, spell 'Hoelscheriana'
536 Billbergia pallescens (HORTUS 2) is B. amoena in HORTUS 3.
536 x Cryptbergia meadii is properly designated x C. 'Mead' (H. Luther).
537 Billbergia distachia rubra, spell B. distachia 'Rubra'
538 Billbergia x speciosa (HORTUS 2) is B. amoena in HORTUS 3.
539 Billbergia saundersii, see notation p. 534.
540 Billbergia stolonifera is possibly B. amoena?
540 Bromelia fastuosa, photographed with this name at Bot. Garden, Paris, France, is questioned by H. Luther.
540, 541 Billbergia tessmanniana, spell tessmanii.
542 Bromelia "pumila" hort. looks like B. humilis.
544 Cryptanthus bivittatus minor, or C. roseus pictus in hort., may be C. bivittatus var. atropurpureus.
544 Cryptanthus bromelioides 'Tricolor' is probably C. bromelioides var. tricolor.
546 Cryptanthus 'Racinae' is a cultivar of C. bromelioides.
547 Cryptanthus x mirabilis is spelled C. 'Mirabilis'.
547 Cryptanthus pseudoscaposus is C. 'Cascade'
552 Caraguata magnifica is Guzmania lingulata var. splendens.
555 Guzmania fuerstenbergiana, may be G. patula.
555, 558 Guzmania lingulata minor flammea is G. lingulata var. flammea.
556 Guzmania x intermedia spell G. 'Intermedia'.
557 Guzmania x insignis, preferred epithet 'Insignis'.
558 Guzmania cryptantha is G. squarrosa.
558 Guzmania lingulata, see notation pg. 555.
558 Neoregelia fosteriana is now spelled N. fosterana in HORTUS 3. 1980 Rules conserve fosteriana.
564, 565 Neoregelia sarmentosa chlorosticta is correctly N. chlorosticta.
568 Nidularium billbergioides flavum spell billbergioides 'Flavum'.
568 Nidularium innocentii var. paxianum is probably N. innocentii var. wittmackianum.
569 Nidularium innocentii var. nana proper epithet is innocentii 'Nana'.
571 Neoregelia concentrica cvs. 'Del Baeke' and 'Morobe' were photographed under these horticultural labels in Belgium, and are in error. Prof. Dr. W. Rauh of Heidelberg Botanical Institute and Harry Luther, Florida comment that both are Nidularium, probably N. rutilans cultivars. Neoregelia concentrica are correct on pgs. 565, 566.
576 Pitcairnia ferruginea is transferred to Puya ferruginea in Hortus 3.
576 Pitcairnia tomentosa, looks like P. punicea.
578, 579, 581 Puya alpestris (HORTUS 2) is said not to be in cultivation, and such plants are P. berteroniana (HORTUS 3). However, both species were separately photographed at Huntington Botanic Garden, San Marino, California (p. 578).
582 Streptocalyx holmesii is synonym of Aechmea woronowii.
582 Thecophyllum insigne photographed in Palmengarten-Frankfurt, is considered Tillandsia insignis by Dr. L. B. Smith. Victoria Padilla (Bromeliad Soc.) feels it is Guzmania. Harry Luther of Selby Bot. Gard. Florida, would list Guzmania 'Insignis'.
583 Tillandsia deppeana latifolia is syn. of T. fendleri.
586 Tillandsia compressa is T. fasciculata venosispica.
588 Tillandsia lepidosepala is questionable.
588, 594 Tillandsia seleriana: now spelled selerana in HORTUS 3, but ZANDER 1984 lists as T. seleriana.
592 Tillandsia incurva is synonym of Vriesea incurva.
594 Tillandsia cacticola might be T. sucrei.
594 Tillandsia espinosae is synonym of Vriesea espinosum.
594 Tillandsia seleriana: now spelled selerana in HORTUS 3, but ZANDER 1984 lists as T. seleriana.
595 Tillandsia mooreana is T. platyrhachis.
595 Tillandsia nudicaulis hort. is Aechmea nudicaulis.
596 Tillandsia viridiflora is listed as synonym of T. grandis in HORTUS 3. However, Dr. L. B. Smith in 'Flora Neotropica' describes both as separate species.
597 Tillandsia decomposita is synonym of T. duratii var. saxatilis.

598 Tillandsia heterophylla hort. is Pitcairnia heterophylla.

604 Vriesea bariletii, appears to be a hybrid.

604, 607, 610 Vriesea fosteriana is now spelled V. fosterana in HORTUS 3, but ZANDER 1984 lists V. fosteriana.

605 Vriesea heliconoides is spelled V. heliconioides. (HORTUS 3, ZANDER 1984).

607 Vriesea glutinosa is properly V. neoglutinosa (HORTUS 3).

608 Vriesea x intermedia, under proper nomenclature is V. 'Intermedia'.

608 Vriesea x mariae is properly V. 'Mariae'.

608 Vriesea psittacina as pictured is probably a hybrid.

610, 612 Vriesea tessellata in hort. is synonym of V. gigantea (HORTUS 3); caption correct on p. 613.

611 Vriesea sanguinolenta is questionable.

612 Vriesea longibracteata is synonym of V. splendens var. formosa. (Harry Luther, Selby Bot. Gardens.)

618 etc. Echinocereus dasyacanthus (HORTUS 2 and Backeberg Lexikon) is referred to E. pectinatus var. neomexicanus in HORTUS 3.

618 etc. Rhipsalis cassutha (HORTUS 2) is changed to R. baccifera in HORTUS 3, also ZANDER 1984. Backeberg 'Cactaceae' holds to R. cassutha.

618, 732, 734, 735 Zygocactus truncatus (HORTUS 2) has been transferred to Schlumbergera truncata (HORTUS 3) (Moran), also ZANDER 1984. Backeberg Kakteen Lexikon maintains Zygocactus truncatus.

622, 626 Opuntia rufida (HORTUS 2) is O. microdasys var. rufida (HORTUS 3).

622 Opuntia tetracantha (HORTUS 2) is O. kleiniae var. tetracantha (HORTUS 3).

624 Grusonia hamiltonii is transferred to Opuntia rosarica in HORTUS 3, but listed as Grusonia in Backeberg.

624 Opuntia strobiliformis is O. articulata cv. 'Inermis' in HORTUS 3. ZANDER 1984 maintains O. strobiliformis.

624, 627 Opuntia turpinii (HORTUS 2) is O. articulata cv. 'Syringacantha' in HORTUS 3. Backeberg 'Cactaceae' refers to Tephrocactus articulatus (syn. Tephrocactus turpinii).

625, 629 Opuntia santa-rita (HORTUS 2) is O. violacea var. santa-rita (HORTUS 3).

626 Opuntia gosseliniana (HORTUS 2) is O. violacea var. gosseliniana (HORTUS 3).

628 Opuntia rafinesquei is apparently O. humifusa (syn. compressa) in HORTUS 3.

630 Opuntia macrocentra (HORTUS 2) is O. violacea var. macrocentra (HORTUS 3).

631 Opuntia engelmannii (HORTUS 2) is questioned in HORTUS 3. Backeberg 'Cactaceae' and ZANDER maintain this species.

632 Opuntia aciculata (HORTUS 2) is syn. of O. lindheimeri in HORTUS 3.

632 Opuntia linguiformis (HORTUS 2) is O. lindheimeri var. linguiformis in HORTUS 3.

633 Opuntia compressa (HORTUS 2) is O. humifusa in HORTUS 3.

634 Tephrocactus rauhii is referred back to Opuntia in HORTUS 3. Backeberg 'Cactaceae' maintains Tephrocactus rauhii.

636, 651 Cephalocereus euphorbioides (HORTUS 2) is Lemaireocereus euphorbioides in HORTUS 3.

640A, 690, 703 Hamatocactus setispinus (HORTUS 2) is transferred to Ferocactus in HORTUS 3, but Backeberg Lexikon maintains Hamatocactus setispinus, also ZANDER 1984.

642 Pachycereus chrysomallus (HORTUS 2) is transferred to Cephalocereus militaris in HORTUS 3. Backeberg 'Cactaceae' lists as Mitrocereus fulviceps.

643 Myrtillocactus cochal from Baja California (HORTUS 2) is listed as synonymous with M. geometrizans in HORTUS 3. However, Backeberg in 'Cactaceae', maintains M. cochal as a distinct species, with a synonym of M. geometrizans var. cochal.

645 Borzicactus humboldtii is B. icosagonus in HORTUS 3.

645 Pseudoespostoa melanostele is changed back to Espostoa melanostele in HORTUS 3 and ZANDER 1984. Backeberg 'Cactaceae' retains Pseudoespostoa.

648 Trichocereus auricolor is synonym of T. huascha (HORTUS 3).

649, 656 Oreocereus as a genus (HORTUS 2) is transferred to Borzicactus in HORTUS 3. Digressions are detailed below:

649 Oreocereus celsianus (HORTUS 2) is referred to Borzicactus celsianus in HORTUS 3 (Kimnach). Backeberg Lexikon lists as O. neocelsianus.

649 Oreocereus doelzianus (HORTUS 2) is transferred to Borzicactus doelzianus in HORTUS 3 (Kimnach). Backeberg refers to Morawetzia.

649 Oreocereus fossulatus (O. celsianus var. fossulatus in HORTUS 2) is now Borzicactus fossulatus in HORTUS 3 (Kimnach). Backeberg retains O. fossulatus.

649 Oreocereus maximus, so listed in Backeberg Lexikon, Zander Dict. 1984 refers to O. celsianus var. maximus. O. celsianus is Borzicactus celsianus in HORTUS 3 (Kimnach).

649, 656 Oreocereus ritteri is changed to O. hendriksenianus var. densilanatus (Backeberg Lexikon; Prof. W. Rauh, Heidelberg). Referred to Borzicactus hendriksenianus in HORTUS 3 (Kimnach).

649 Oreocereus trollii (HORTUS 2) is transferred to Borzicactus trollii in HORTUS 3 (Kimnach). Backeberg retains O. trollii, ZANDER Dict. 1984 lists O. celsianus var. trollii.

651 Cephalocereus euphorbioides—see notation pg. 636

653 Machaerocereus eruca (HORTUS 2) is referred to Lemaireocereus eruca in HORTUS 3. Backeberg maintains Machaerocereus.

654 Cereus caesius (HORTUS 2) is C. validus in HORTUS 3.

654 Cereus pernambucensis, now spelled C. fernambucensis in HORTUS 3.

656 Oreocereus—see notation pg. 649 in re genus.

656 Pachycereus weberi is syn. of Lemaireocereus weberi in HORTUS 3. ZANDER refers to Stenocereus weberi.

656 Ritterocereus deficiens is listed as Lemaireocereus deficiens in HORTUS 3.

658 Pilocereus tweedyanus, is Cephalocereus in HORTUS 3. Backeberg 'Cactaceae' refers to Pilosocereus tweedyanus.

666 Echinocereus albispinus from Oklahoma, as identified by Ed. Alexander, New York Bot. Garden (Backeberg): (HORTUS 3 refers this to E. reichenbachii var. albispinus, but this plant is different).

666, 678 Lobivia aurea (HORTUS 2) is transferred to Echinopsis aurea in HORTUS 3. Backeberg Lexikon refers it to Pseudolobivia aurea.

667, 670 Echinocereus baileyi (HORTUS 2 and Backeberg), is E. reichenbachii var. albispinus in HORTUS 3.

667 Echinocereus papillosus (HORTUS 2) is E. berlandieri var. angusticeps in HORTUS 3.

667 Echinocereus pensilis (HORTUS 2) is transferred to Morangaya pensilis in HORTUS 3.

668, 670 Echinocereus rigidissimus (HORTUS 2) is E. pectinatus var. rigidissimus in HORTUS 3.

668 Echinocereus roetteri (HORTUS 2) is E. pectinatus var. minor in HORTUS 3.

668 Echinocereus purpureus (HORTUS 2) is typical E. reichenbachii in HORTUS 3. However E. purpureus is a valid name in Backeberg Lexikon.

670 Echinocereus baileyi—see notation pg. 667.

670 Echinocereus rigidissimus—see notation pg. 668.

671 Echinocereus conoideus (HORTUS 2) is E. triglochidiatus var. melanacanthus in HORTUS 3.

671, 672 Echinocereus fitchii (HORTUS 2) is E. reichenbachii var. fitchii in HORTUS 3.

672 Echinocereus blanckii (HORTUS 2) is E. berlandieri in HORTUS 3.

673 Echinocereus perbellus (HORTUS 2) is E. reichenbachii var. perbellus in HORTUS 3.

674 Pseudolobivia is referred to Echinopsis in HORTUS 3. ZANDER 1984 lists Echinopsis kermesina.

676 Echinopsis campylacantha is properly E. leucantha (HORTUS 3).

676 Echinopsis mirabilis (HORTUS 2) is transferred to Setiechinopsis mirabilis in HORTUS 3 and Backeberg.

677 Lobivia corbula (HORTUS 2) is syn. of L. pentlandii in HORTUS 3.

678 Lobivia aurea—see notation pg. 666.

678 Lobivia huascha is Trichocereus huascha in HORTUS 3. Backeberg lists it as Helianthocereus huascha.

678 Lobivia longispina (HORTUS 2) is Echinopsis longispina in HORTUS 3. Backeberg refers it to Pseudolobivia longispina.

679 etc. Rebutia fiebrigii, kupperana, pseudodeminuta, pseudominuscula, classified by Backeberg as Aylostera; HORTUS 3 and ZANDER 1984 maintain Rebutia.

679 Rebutia haagei (HORTUS 2) is Lobivia pygmaea in HORTUS 3.

679, 680, 681 Rebutia kupperiana (HORTUS 2) is spelled R. kupperana in HORTUS 3, but R. kupperiana in ZANDER 1984.

680, 696 Wigginsia vorwerkianus is spelled W. vorwerkiana (HORTUS 3), ZANDER 1984 prefers Notocactus vorwerkianus.

681 Rebutia pseudominuscula is properly R. deminuta fa. pseudominuscula in HORTUS 3.

687 Echinomastus macdowellii (HORTUS 2 and Backeberg Lexikon), is referred to Neolloydia macdowellii in HORTUS 3, but maintained in ZANDER 1984.

687 Submatucana madisoniorum is so determined in Backeberg 'Cactaceae', but HORTUS 3 refers the genus to Borzicactus.

689 Ferocactus nobilis (HORTUS 2) is syn. of F. recurvus in HORTUS 3, and ZANDER 1984.

689 Ferocactus pringlei (HORTUS 2) is F. pilosus in HORTUS 3. However, Backeberg Lexikon lists this as F. stainesii var. pringlei.

689 Hamatocactus uncinatus (HORTUS 2), transferred to Ancistrocactus uncinatus in HORTUS 3. Backeberg Lexikon lists this species as Glandulicactus.

690 Hamatocactus hamatacanthus (HORTUS 2), referred to Ferocactus hamatacanthus in HORTUS 3, and in ZANDER 1984, but Backeberg Lexikon maintains Hamatocactus.

690 Hamatocactus setispinus, see notation for p. 640A.

690 Horridocactus tuberisulcatus (Backeberg Lexikon) is transferred to Neoporteria tuberisulcata in HORTUS 3.

690 Neochilenia setosiflora is transferred to Neoporteria. However, Backeberg's Cactus Lexikon keeps Neochilenia setosiflora (Kattermann, New Jersey Cactus Society).

693 Gymnocalycium kurtzianum (HORTUS 2) is G. mostii var. kurtzianum in HORTUS 3.

693 Gymnocalycium venturianum is syn. of G. baldianum in HORTUS 3.

694 Ferocactus stainesii (HORTUS 2) is referred to F. pilosus in HORTUS 3. However, Backeberg Lexikon lists as F. stainesii var. pilosus.

695 Neoporteria senilis is N. nidus fa. senilis in HORTUS 3. However, ZANDER 1984 maintains N. senilis a species separate from M. nidus.

696 Neoporteria atrispina is more correctly N. villosa var. atrispina. (HORTUS 3).

696 Neoporteria heteracantha is correctly N. subgibbosa fa. heteracantha in HORTUS 3.

696 Wigginsia erinaceus is spelled W. erinacea in HORTUS 3; ZANDER 1984 prefers Notocactus erinaceus.

696 Wigginsia sellowii is referred to W. tephracantha (HORTUS 3). ZANDER 1984 lists Notocactus erinaceus var. tephracanthus.

696 Wigginsia vorwerkianus, see notation for p. 680.

697 Notocactus pampeanus (HORTUS 2) is N. submammulosus var. pampeanus in HORTUS 3.

702 Arequipa leucotricha (HORTUS 2) is changed to Borzicactus leucotrichus in HORTUS 3.

702 Pyrrhocactus tuberisulcatus (HORTUS 2) is referred to Neoporteria tuberisulcata in HORTUS 3.

702 Toumeya papyracantha (HORTUS 2) is changed to Pediocactus papyracanthus in HORTUS 3.

702 Utahia sileri is transferred to Pediocactus sileri in HORTUS 3. Backeberg Lexikon maintains Utahia.

703 Hamatocactus setispinus, see notation for p. 640A.

704 Lophophora echinata diffusa, a "Peyote"; HORTUS 3 refers L. echinata to williamsii, and lists diffusa as a separate species. Backeberg Lexikon lists a valid L. echinata var. diffusa.

704 Neogomesia agavoides is transferred to Ariocarpus agavoides in HORTUS 3. However, Backeberg's "Kakteen" retains Neogomesia agavoides.

704 Soehrensia ingens is referred to Lobivia in HORTUS 3. However, Backeberg 'Cactaceae' conserves Soehrensia ingens.

704 Soehrensia oreopepon is also maintained in Backeberg and Zander Dict. 1984.

704 Turbinicarpus polaskii transferred to Strombocactus in HORTUS 3. Backeberg 'Cactaceae' maintains Turbinicarpus polaskii.

708, 711 Dolichothele longimamma (HORTUS 2 and Backeberg Lexikon) is listed as Mammillaria longimamma in HORTUS 3.

709 Coryphantha neomexicana (HORTUS 2) is C. vivipara var. radiosa (HORTUS 3).

709 Coryphantha muehlenpfordtii (HORTUS 2) is syn. of C. scheerii (HORTUS 3, also ZANDER 1984.)

710 Bartschella schumannii in HORTUS 2 is Mammillaria schumannii in HORTUS 3, and ZANDER 1984.

710 Coryphantha echinus (HORTUS 2) is now considered C. cornifera var. echinus (HORTUS 3).

710 Escobaria roseana (as in Backeberg Lexikon) is listed as Coryphantha roseana in HORTUS 3.

710, 715, 721 Mammillaria affinis in hort.: Backeberg in his 'Cactaceae', p. 3146 mentions Mammillaria affinis as synonym for Mammillaria polythele, as in HORTUS 3.

710, 721 Mammillaria hemisphaerica (HORTUS 2) is M. heyderi var. hemisphaerica in HORTUS 3.

711 Dolichothele longimamma, see notation for p. 708.

711 Dolichothele sphaerica (as in Backeberg Lexikon and HORTUS 2) listed as Mammillaria longimamma var. sphaerica in HORTUS 3.

711 Mammillaria bogotensis (HORTUS 2) is syn. of M. columbiana in HORTUS 3.

713 Mammillaria applanata (HORTUS 2) is syn. of M. heyderi in HORTUS 3. ZANDER 1984 maintains M. applanata.

714, 723 Mammillaria echinaria (HORTUS 2) is M. elongata var. echinata in HORTUS 3.

715 Mammillaria affinis, see notation for p. 710.

715 Mammillaria baxteriana (HORTUS 2) is spelled baxterana in HORTUS 3, but baxteriana in ZANDER.

718 Mammillaria caput-medusae is syn. of M. sempervivi (HORTUS 3).

719 Mammillaria dolichocentra is referred to M. tetracantha (HORTUS 3).

719 Mammillaria pacifica (HORTUS 2) is synonym of M. baxterana in HORTUS 3.

720 Mammillaria kelleriana (HORTUS 2) is now spelled M. kellerana in HORTUS 3, but kelleriana in ZANDER.

721 Mammillaria affinis, see notation for p. 710.

721 Mammillaria hemisphaerica, see notation for p. 710.

722 Mammillaria ritteriana is spelled M. ritterana (HORTUS 3).

723 Mammillaria echinaria, see notation for p. 714.

726 Mammillaria shurliana is M. blossfeldiana var. shurliana (HORTUS 3).

727 Neobesseya missouriensis (HORTUS 2) is changed to Coryphantha missouriensis in HORTUS 3.

728 Solisia pectinata (HORTUS 2 and Backeberg) is transferred to Mammillaria pectinifera in HORTUS 3.

728 Mammillaria denudata (HORTUS 2) is updated to M. lasiacantha in HORTUS 3.
732, 735, 736 Epiphyllanthus obovatus (as in Backeberg Lexikon) is E. opuntioides in HORTUS 3.
732, 733, 734, 735 Zygocactus truncatus, see notation for p. 618.
736 Acanthorhipsalis monacantha (Backeberg Lexikon), is transferred to Rhipsalis (HORTUS 3).
738, 745 Hatiora bambusioides (HORTUS 3) is spelled H. bambusoides in Zander Dict. 1984 and Backeberg.
739 Pseudorhipsalis himantoclada is referred to Disocactus himantocladus in HORTUS 3.
740, 745 Rhipsalis clavata is transferred to Hatiora clavata (HORTUS 3). ZANDER 1984 maintains Rhipsalis clavata.
745 Hatiora bambusioides, see notation for p. 738.
746 Lepismium cruciforme (HORTUS 2) is changed in HORTUS 3 to Rhipsalis cruciformis. However, the 1984 ZANDER conserves Lepismium cruciforme; also retained in Backeberg Kakteen-Lexikon.
746 Pfeiffera ianthothele should be spelled P. ianothele (HORTUS 3).
750 Canarina campanulata (HORTUS 2) is syn. of C. canariensis in HORTUS 3.
750, 1513 Centropogon is in family CAMPANULACEAE according to Zander, Royal Hort., and Willis; LOBELIACEAE in HORTUS 2 and 3.
751, 1514 Pratia is under LOBELIACEAE in HORTUS; CAMPANULACEAE in Royal Hort. and Zander Dict. 1984.
751 Pratia begoniifolia (HORTUS 2) is syn. of P. nummularia in HORTUS 3 and ZANDER 1984.
754 Capparis jamaicensis (CAPPARIDACEAE in HORTUS 2), is C. cynophallophora (CAPPARACEAE in HORTUS 3).
764 Drosera tracyi is D. filiformis var. tracyi in HORTUS 3.
765 Drosera dichotoma, HORTUS 3 refers this to D. binata.
768A, 780, 782 Geogenanthus undatus is now G. poeppigii (R. Faden, Smithsonian, Washington.)
768A, 1847 Oxalis martiana 'Aureo-reticulata' (HORTUS 2) is O. corymbosa cv. 'Aureoreticulata' (HORTUS 3, and ZANDER 1984.)
774 Sarracenia drummondii (HORTUS 2) is made synonym to S. leucophylla in HORTUS 3, also G. Cheers, Australia.
780 Geogenanthus undatus, see notation for p. 768A.
780, 786 Setcreasea purpurea in hort. is properly S. pallida cv. 'Purple Heart' (HORTUS 3 and ZANDER 1984).
781 Zebrina purpusii is designated as Z. pendula cv. 'Purpusii' (HORTUS 3). ZANDER Dict. 1984 keeps Z. purpusii as separate species.
782 Geogenanthus undatus, see notation for p. 768A.
782, 787 Gibasis geniculata is known in horticulture as Tradescantia multiflora. HORTUS 3 refers this to Tripogandra multiflora. ZANDER 1984 lists it as Tradescantia geniculata.
784 Dichorisandra warscewicziana is properly D. thyrsiflora (Harry Luther, Florida).
784 Hadrodemas warscewicziana is spelled warscewiczianus (Harry Luther, Florida). ZANDER 1984 lists as H. warscewiczianum (H. E. Moore) as synonym of Tradescantia warscewicziana.
786 Setcreasea purpurea, see notation for p. 780.
787 Gibasis geniculata, see notation for p. 782.
804 Podolepis acuminata is syn. of P. jaceoides in HORTUS 3.
808 Gazania x splendens, probably hybrid of rigens and uniflora. Correctly spelled rigens (Royal Hort., ZANDER), in HORTUS 3 as ringens.
809 Dimorphotheca ecklonis (HORTUS 2) is transferred to Osteospermum ecklonis in HORTUS 3.
811 Dimorphotheca aurantiaca (HORTUS 2) is syn. of D. sinuata in HORTUS 3.
814 Cirsium diacanthum is spelled C. diacantha in HORTUS 3.
815 Artemisia purshiana (HORTUS 2) is A. ludoviciana in HORTUS 3, also ZANDER 1984.
815 Aster fruticosus (HORTUS 2), Felicia fruticosa in HORTUS 3.
819 Chrysanthemum ptarmicaeflorum in HORTUS 2, spelled ptarmiciflorum in HORTUS 3, also ZANDER 1984.
819 Senecio leucostachys (HORTUS 2) is synonym of S. vira-vira (HORTUS 3).
820 Baeria coronaria (HORTUS 2), is referred to Lasthenia coronaria in HORTUS 3.
821 Polypteris hookeriana (HORTUS 2) is referred to Palafoxia hookeriana in HORTUS 3.
828, 830 Senecio kleiniaeformis is now spelled kleiniiformis (HORTUS 3, also ZANDER 1984).
828, 830, 831 Senecio stapeliaeformis (as Kleinia stapeliaeformis in HORTUS 2), changed spelling to S. stapeliiformis in HORTUS 3 and ZANDER 1984.
830 Senecio repens is synonym of S. serpens (HORTUS 3 and ZANDER 1984).
830 Senecio tomentosa hort. (Kleinia) is probably S. haworthii (HORTUS 3).
836 Picea pungens 'Kosteriana' (HORTUS 2) is P. pungens cv. 'Koster' in HORTUS 3.
839 Juniperus barbadensis in hort. (HORTUS 2) is probably J. silicicola (HORTUS 3).
840 Larix leptolepis (HORTUS 2) is syn. of L. kaempferi in HORTUS 3, also ZANDER 1984.
850 Cephalotaxus drupacea pedunculata (HORTUS 2) is changed to C. harringtoniana in HORTUS 3.
851, 852 Ipomoea tuberosa (HORTUS 2) is referred to Merremia tuberosa in HORTUS 3 and ZANDER 1984.
852 Ipomoea learii (HORTUS 2) is syn. of I. acuminata in HORTUS 3.
853 Convolvulus mauritanica is spelled mauritanicus in HORTUS 3. Valid name in ZANDER 1984 is C. sabatius.
853 Ipomoea crassicaulis (HORTUS 2) is I. fistulosa in HORTUS 3. However, latest information by Dr. Austin of Florida Atlantic University, and in ZANDER 1984, is that all I. crassicaulis are properly I. carnea var. fistulosa.
854 Argyreia speciosa in HORTUS 2 is A. nervosa in HORTUS 3.
854 Calonyction aculeatum (HORTUS 2) referred to Ipomoea alba (HORTUS 3). ZANDER 1984 lists it as Calonyction album.
854 Convolvulus soldanella (HORTUS 2) transferred to Calystegia soldanella in HORTUS 3.
854 Dichondra repens (ZANDER 1984) and in horticulture, is D. micrantha (HORTUS 3).
854 Quamoclit lobata (HORTUS 2) is referred to Ipomoea in HORTUS 3. T. Everett of New York Botanical Garden mentions the synonym Ipomoea versicolor for this. However, HORTUS 3 lists Mina lobata as the valid name. ZANDER 1984 retains Quamoclit lobata (syn. Mina lobata).
854 Quamoclit pennata (HORTUS 2) is syn. of Ipomoea quamoclit in HORTUS 3.
857 Adromischus festivus could be A. cooperi (P. Hutchison, Escondido, 1976).
858, 862, 864 Aeonium tabulaeforme (HORTUS 2) is spelled tabuliforme in HORTUS 3 and ZANDER 1984.
860 Aeonium caespitosum (HORTUS 2) is Ae. simsii (HORTUS 3 and ZANDER 1984).
862 Aeonium bethencourtianum (HORTUS 2) is Aichryson bethencourtianum (HORTUS 3).
862 Altamiranoa is transferred to Villadia in HORTUS 3.
862 Aylostera deminuta (HORTUS 2), transferred to Rebutia deminuta in HORTUS 3, also ZANDER 1984.
863 Aeonium 'Pseudo-tabuliforme' (HORTUS 2) is listed name for A. undulatum (HORTUS 3).
864 Aeonium domesticum is Aichryson x domesticum in HORTUS 3.
864 Adromischus phillipsiae as known in hort., is Cotyledon phillipsiae (P. Hutchison, Escondido, California).
864 Aeonium tabulaeforme, see notation for p. 858.
864 Cotyledon gracilis (Jacobsen Lexicon), referred to C. jacobseniana (HORTUS 3).
872, 873 Crassula perfossa is referred to C. rupestris in HORTUS 3. However, C. perfossa hort. has been grown in California for decades as distinct from C. rupestris.
875 Sinocrassula (HORTUS 2) is transferred to Sedum in HORTUS 3.

876 Orostachys spinosus is correctly spelled spinosa (HORTUS 3).
877, 878, 879, 881 Crassula argentea (as in HORTUS 3): Toelken gives priority to C. ovata (Miller 1768), with synonyms argentea (1778), portulacea (1786), obliqua (1789). (Cactus & Succulent Journal, May 1981). In California horticulture as C. arborescens hort. C. ovata in ZANDER 1984.
882 Crassula pseudolycopodioides (HORTUS 2), is listed as C. lycopodioides var. pseudolycopodioides in HORTUS 3.
885 Aeonium domesticum 'Variegatum' is in horticultural usage for Aichryson x domesticum cv. (HORTUS 3).
888, 892 Echeveria pallida is E. gibbiflora cv. 'Pallida' in HORTUS 3.
889, 894 Echeveria glauca (HORTUS 2) is listed as E. secunda var. glauca in HORTUS 3.
889 Echeveria x glauco-metallica is E. x imbricata, as on p. 895, and well-known in California gardening.
889, 893 Echeveria x scaphophylla hort. (scaphylla in HORTUS 2), is listed as x Cremneria scaphylla (Cremnophila x Echeveria), in Hortus 3.
891 Echeveria pubescens (HORTUS 2 and Jacobsen Lexicon), is listed as E. coccinea in HORTUS 3.
892 Echeveria expatriata (HORTUS 2) listed as x Cremneria expatriata (Cremnophila x Echeveria) in HORTUS 3.
895 Echeveria corderoyi (HORTUS 2) is E. agavoides var. corderoyi in HORTUS 3.
895 Echeveria linguaefolia (HORTUS 2) is transferred to Cremnophila linguifolia in HORTUS 3.
895 Echeveria tolucensis (HORTUS 2 and Jacobsen Lexicon) is referred in HORTUS 3 to E. secunda glauca var., more lax and with more lanceolate leaves.
896 Echeveria cotyledon is Dudleya caespitosa in HORTUS 3 and ZANDER 1984.
897 Echeveria byrnesii is properly E. secunda var. byrnesii (HORTUS 3).
898, 923 Echeveria purpusorum (HORTUS 2) is spelled E. purpusiorum in HORTUS 3 and ZANDER 1984.
908 Kalanchoe teretifolia is K. bentii in HORTUS 3, but remains K. teretifolia in Jacobsen Lexicon.
916, 920 Sedum compressum is now S. palmeri (HORTUS 3).
918, 919 Sedum praealtum (HORTUS 2) is subspecies of S. dendroideum (HORTUS 3).
920 Sedum nutans (HORTUS 2) is transferred to Cremnophila nutans in HORTUS 3.
922 Sedum tortuosum of hort. (HORTUS 2) is probably S. lucidum (HORTUS 3).
923 Echeveria purpusorum, see notation, p. 898.
924 Sedum cauticolum (HORTUS 2) is spelled S. cauticola in HORTUS 3, also ZANDER 1984.
926, 927 Lunaria biennis is syn. of L. annua (HORTUS 3 and ZANDER 1984).
929 Cyclanthera explodens (HORTUS 2) is C. brachystachya in HORTUS 3.
930, 931 Luffa cylindrica (HORTUS 2) is synonym of L. aegyptiaca (HORTUS 3, also ZANDER 1984).
938, 944 Zamia furfuracea is synonym of Z. pumila (HORTUS 3).
941 Macrozamia peroffskyana (HORTUS 2) is referred to Lepidozamia peroffskyana in HORTUS 3.
947 Cyperus diffusus of hort. is referred to C. albostriatus in HORTUS 3, also ZANDER 1984.
950 heading: DIPSACEAE in HORTUS 2, DIPSACACEAE in HORTUS 3.
950 Galax aphylla (HORTUS 2) is syn. of G. urceolata in HORTUS 3, also ZANDER 1984.
951 Hibbertia volubilis (HORTUS 2) is syn. of H. scandens in HORTUS 3.
954 Crinodendron dependens of Calif. hort. with red flowers (syn. Tricuspidaria hookerianum) is properly C. hookerianum (T. Everett, New York Bot. Gard.)
958 Pentapterigium serpens (HORTUS 2) is transferred to Agapetes serpens (HORTUS 3).
960 Leucothoe catesbaei (HORTUS 2) is L. axillaris in HORTUS 3; L. catesbaei of the trade is probably L. fontanesiana (syn. Andromeda catesbaei hort.)
961 Erica blanda is E. doliiformis in HORTUS 3.
972 Rhododendron lateritium is properly R. indicum (HORTUS 3).
973 etc. AZALEA are botanically RHODODENDRON. Linnaeus himself established the genus Azalea in 1735, and in addition 1753, the genus Rhododendron. As then understood, Azaleas were deciduous in North America with funnel-shaped flowers having 5 stamens; Rhododendron evergreen, with 10 stamens. Salisbury in 1796 combined them both under Rhododendron. Yet, in horticulture, the name Azalea is firmly fixed.
1003, 1005 Acalypha godseffiana (HORTUS 2) is A. wilkesiana cv. 'Godseffiana' in HORTUS 3.
1003, 1005, 1056A Breynia nivosa (HORTUS 2) is B. disticha in HORTUS 3, also ZANDER 1984. (syn. Phyllanthus).
1022 Euphorbia lemaireana is E. angularis (HORTUS 3), and correctly captioned as angularis in EXOTICA, pg. 1028.
1022, 1025 Euphorbia morinii (HORTUS 2) is now considered synonymous with heptagona, shown EXOTICA pg. 1025 (HORTUS 3, Sloane, Jacobsen).
1040, 1041, 1042, 1044 Poinsettia, used as popular horticultural name, are botanically cultivars of Euphorbia pulcherrima.
1046 Euphorbia marlothii is referred to E. monteiroi in HORTUS 3. However, Jacobsen Lexicon considers marlothii a separate species.
1050 Euphorbia lathyrus (HORTUS 2) is spelled E. lathyris in HORTUS 3.
1050, 1052 Euphorbia polychroma is syn. of E. epithymoides (HORTUS 3).
1051, 1060 Jatropha hastata (HORTUS 2) is J. integerrima in HORTUS 3.
1052 Euphorbia polychroma: see notation p. 1050.
1052, 1053 Monadenium lugardae is spelled M. lugardiae in HORTUS 3.
1052 Sapium sebeferum is spelled sebiferum in HORTUS 3.
1053 Pedilanthus smallii is more correctly P. tithymaloides ssp. smallii in HORTUS 3.
1054 Phyllanthus speciosus (Xylophylla) is synonym of P. arbuscula (HORTUS 3).
1060 Jatropha hastata: see notation pg. 1051.
1062 Dovyalis hebecarpa cv. 'Kandy': photo represents an ornamental mutation with frilled leaflets, having undulate, serrate margins.
1068 etc. Alsophila (DICKSONIACEAE in HORTUS 2) are in family CYATHEACEAE in HORTUS 3 and ZANDER 1984.
1068, 1070, 1077 Alsophila cooperi (Alsophila australis of horticulture, also known as Cyathea cooperi) is referred to Sphaeropteris cooperi in HORTUS 3, also ZANDER 1984. The true Alsophila australis is supposedly not in cultivation.
1069 Cyathea dealbata (HORTUS 2) is changed to Alsophila tricolor in HORTUS 3.
1069, 1070, 1076 Cyathea medullaris (HORTUS 2), referred to Sphaeropteris medullaris in HORTUS 3.
1070 Alsophila cooperi; see notation pg. 1068.
1070 Cyathea cooperi; see notation pg. 1068.
1076 Cyathea dregei (HORTUS 2) changed to Alsophila dregei in HORTUS 3.
1079 Aneimia (HORTUS 2) is spelled Anemia in HORTUS 3.
1079 Marattia salicina is referred to M. fraxinea (HORTUS 3).
1082 Leptopteris barbara is updated to Todea barbara in HORTUS 3.
1084 Lygodium microphyllum: Royal Hort. Dict. lists as L. scandens var. microphyllum. L. scandens is a valid species in HORTUS 3, and L. microphyllum is prob. a form of scandens.
1093 Cyclophorus heteractis (C. Christensen Index Filicum 1906) is referred to Pyrrosia in HORTUS 3.
1095, 1151 Aglaomorpha heraclea is spelled heracleum in HORTUS 3.
1095 x Stroxinia, more correctly spelled x Streptogloxinia.

1097 Asplenium viviparum (HORTUS 2) is A. daucifolium in HORTUS 3 and ZANDER 1984.

1098 Dryopteris dentata (HORTUS 2), transferred to Thelypteris dentata in HORTUS 3.

1100 Aspidium capense (HORTUS 2) is transferred to Rumohra adiantiformis in HORTUS 3. ZANDER 1984 lists this as Arachniodes adiantiformis.

1102, 1103 Davallia bullata mariesii (HORTUS 2) is reduced to D. mariesii in HORTUS 3.

1104 Dennstaedtia adiantoides (HORTUS 2) is syn. of D. bipinnata in HORTUS 3.

1105 Dryopteris decursive-pinnata, transferred to Thelypteris decursive-pinnata in HORTUS 3.

1108 Doryopteris palmata (HORTUS 2 and ZANDER 1984) is D. pedata var. palmata in HORTUS 3.

1110 Dryopteris reticulata is Thelypteris reticulata in HORTUS 3.

1110 Dryopteris spinulosa (HORTUS 2) is D. austriaca var. spinulosa in HORTUS 3. ZANDER 1984 lists it as D. carthusiana.

1112 Microsorium pteropus is listed as Polypodium pteropus in HORTUS 3.

1118 Nephrolepis ensifolia of horticulture, is synonym of N. biserrata (HORTUS 3).

1125 Pellaea cordata is correctly P. sagittata var. cordata (HORTUS 3).

1134, 1139, 1140, 1141 Platycerium wilhelminae-reginae in HORTUS 3: transferred to P. wandae by Prof. Barbara Joe Hoshizaki, Los Angeles.

1136, 1824A Platycerium "diversifolium" hort. is probably a form of P. hillii (HORTUS 3).

1136 Platycerium sumbawense is listed in HORTUS 3 as synonym of P. willinckii cv. 'Payton'.

1137, 1140, 1141 Platycerium grande (Fee) Presl. (true species) is from Philippines only, and different from P. grande of hort., botanically P. superbum.

1145, 1157 Rumohra adiantiformis, the Leather fern, has been known under various botanical names. L. H. Bailey Cyclop. of Hort. listed Polystichum capense (syn. coriaceum). EXOTICA 1 and HORTUS 2 recorded Polystichum adiantiforme. HORTUS 3 and EXOTICA 3 changed to Rumohra adiantiformis, supported by Barbara Joe Hoshizaki of the University of California. ZANDER (Germany 1984) changed to Arachniodes adiantiformis.

1146 Polystichum lobatum (HORTUS 2) appears to have been combined with P. aculeatum in HORTUS 3.

1151 Aglaomorpha heraclea: see notation pg. 1095.

1155, 1156, 1157 Polystichum aristatum (HORTUS 2) is transferred to Arachniodes aristata in HORTUS 3.

1157 Polystichum standishii is transferred to Arachniodes standishii in HORTUS 3.

1157 Rumohra adiantiformis: see notation pg. 1145.

1164 Rhipidoperis peltata is spelled Rhipidopteris (J. Bogner, Munich Bot. Gardens).

1167 Woodwardia chamissoi (HORTUS 2) is synonym of W. fimbriata (HORTUS 2).

1177 Geranium anemonifolium (HORTUS 2) is synonym of G. palmatum in HORTUS 3.

1177 Geranium grandiflorum (HORTUS 2) is G. himalayense in HORTUS 3. ZANDER 1984 lists it as G. meeboldii.

1177 Geranium napuligerum hort. (HORTUS 2) is probably G. farreri (HORTUS 3).

1177 Geranium subcaulescens is G. cinereum var. subcaulescens in HORTUS 3. ZANDER 1984 maintains G. subcaulescens.

1178 Pelargonium radula (HORTUS 2) is syn. of P. radens (HORTUS 3).

1225 etc. The List of Cultivated *GESNERIACEAE* compiled by Frances Batcheller of Durham, New Hampshire (American Gloxinia and Gesneriad Soc. 1984), updated many botanical names. These changes are noted on these pages, but some remain in dispute.

1225 Achimenes 'Pulchella' is A. erecta in HORTUS 3 and ZANDER 1984.

1227 Achimenes ehrenbergii changed to Eucodonia verticillata (Frances Batcheller 1984).

1228 Achimenes andrieuxii changed to Eucodonia (Frances Batcheller, 1984).

1228 Achimenes tubiflora is Sinningia tubiflora (HORTUS 3).

1229 Aeschynanthus javanicus is A. radicans (HORTUS 3).

1229 Aeschynanthus lobbianus is A. radicans in HORTUS 3.

1229, 1230 Aeschynanthus marmoratus is A. longicaulis (Frances Batcheller, 1984).

1229 Aeschynanthus pulcher is referred to Ae. radicans in ZANDER 1984. However, HORTUS 3, and also the American Gesneriad Society 1984 maintains this species, long cultivated, and different from Ae. lobbianus.

1229, 1231 Alloplectus vittatus is now Corytoplectus speciosus (Frances Batcheller, 1984).

1230 Aeschynanthus grandiflorus is A. parasiticus (HORTUS 3).

1231 Alloplectus ambiguus is Columnea ambigua (or Trichantha ambigua) (Frances Batcheller, 1984).

1231 Alloplectus capitatus is now Corytoplectus capitatus (Frances Batcheller, 1984).

1236 Columnea affinis, aureonitis, sanguinea (as in HORTUS 3), transferred to Dalbergaria by Dr. H. Wiehler of Selby Bot. Gardens, Florida.

1240, 1295, 1330 Columnea illepida, purpureovittata, teuscheri are changed to Trichantha in the Gesneria Society List 1984 (HORTUS 3 refers Trichantha to Columnea).

1241 Columnea tulae 'Flava' is syn. of C. scandens 'Flava' (HORTUS 3).

1244 x Eucodonopsis is referred to x Achimenantha (Achimenes x Smithiantha) in HORTUS 3.

1244 Gesneria christii was misidentified; correctly G. pedicellaris (HORTUS 3).

1245 Episcia lineata is transferred to Paradrymonia lineata (Frances Batcheller, Gesneriad list, 1984).

1248A, 1285, 1287 Sinningia leucotricha (syn. Rechsteineria) is changed to S. canescens (F. Batcheller, Gesneriad List 1984). HORTUS 3 lists as S. leucotricha.

1250 Episcia melittifolia is referred to Nautilocalyx melittifolius in HORTUS 3.

1252 Alloplectus nummularia is now Neomortonia nummularia (Frances Batcheller, 1984).

1252 Kohleria strigosa (as Isoloma in HORTUS 2) is listed as Kohleria spicata in HORTUS 3.

1254 x Eucodonopsis picturata (Eucodonia x Smithiantha) would be x Smithicodonia, according to Frances Batcheller, American Gesneriad Soc. 1984.

1254 Klugia notoniana is syn. of Rhynchoglossum notonianum in HORTUS 3. The Gesneriad Register 1984 lists this as R. gardneri (syn. notonianum).

1255 Kohleria lindeniana is transferred to Gloxinia lindeniana (Frances Batcheller, Gesneriads, 1984); ZANDER 1984 retains Kohleria.

1257 Klugia zeylanicum: as HORTUS 3 transfers the genus Klugia to Rhynchoglossum (Rhinchoglossum in ZANDER), this may transfer K. zeylanicum also.

1258 Gesneria verrucosa is now G. cubensis (Frances Batcheller 1984, also ZANDER 1984).

1259, 1276 Rehmannia optional as GESNERIACEAE or SCROPHULARIACEAE family in HORTUS 3. F. Batcheller in Gesneriad List 1984 refers Rehmannia to SCROPHULARIACEAE. ZANDER 1984 prefers GESNERIACEAE.

1276 Gloxinia sylvatica is listed as Seemannia sylvatica in HORTUS 3, but ZANDER 1984 retains Gloxinia sylvatica (Wiehler).

1276 Sarmienta repens is syn. of S. scandens (HORTUS 3; L. Skog-Smithsonian; ZANDER 1984).

1277, 5 Sinningia regina is now considered a form of S. speciosa (American Gesneriad Soc. 1984). ZANDER 1984 retains S. regina.

1285 Sinningia leucotricha: see notation pg. 1248A.

1285, 1286 Sinningia cyclophylla is now S. macropoda (GESNERIAD list 1984).

1286 Sinningia lineata is now S. macropoda (HORTUS 3).
1286, 1287 Sinningia warscewiczii is changed to S. incarnata. ZANDER 1984 retains S. warscewiczii.
1287 Sinningia leucotricha: see notation pg. 1248A.
1287 Sinningia maculata (douglasii) is changed to S. verticillata.
1287 Sinningia splendens should be S. cardinalis (HORTUS 3).
1295 Columnea illepida: see notation pg. 1240.
1296 Streptocarpus insignis is updated as S. primulifolius formosus in HORTUS 3.
1301 Phyllostachys sulphurea, so known in horticulture and HORTUS 2. HORTUS 3 refers to P. bambusoides cv. 'Allgold'. American Bamboo Society records P. viridis cv. 'Robert Young', also listed by Roger Stover of California, with P. sulphurea as synonym.
1305 Bambusa eutuldoides in hort.—may be B. textilis var. albostriata (McLure, 1961).
1306, 1314 Bambusa falcata (HORTUS 2) referred to Chimonobambusa in HORTUS 3.
1310 Sasa fortunei of hort. is transferred to Arundinaria pygmaea in HORTUS 3.
1312 Bambusa beechyanus—spell beecheyana (HORTUS 3).
1314 Bambusa falcata: see notation pg. 1306.
1314 Dendrocalamus latiflorus is a valid species, but Richard Haubrich of the American Bamboo Society (California) advised that this name was wrongly applied to Bambusa oldhamii as in cultivation.
1318 Ephedra (GNETACEAE in HORTUS 2) is now family EPHEDRACEAE in HORTUS 3, also ZANDER 1984.
1318 Scaevola sericea is correctly S. frutescens var. sericea (HORTUS 3).
1319 Garcinia tinctoria is probably G. morella (Bengal to Thailand) (ZANDER Dict.) with smaller foliage than xanthochymus to which tinctoria is referred in HORTUS 3.
1320, 1321 Gunnera (HALORAGIDACEAE in HORTUS 2) is now GUNNERACEAE in HORTUS 3. ZANDER 1984 prefers HALORAGACEAE.
1320, 1322 Myriophyllum proserpinacoides (HORTUS 2) is listed as synonym of M. aquaticum in HORTUS 3; also ZANDER, DeWit.
1322 Hippuris (HALORAGIDACEAE in HORTUS 2), now to family HIPPURIDACEAE in HORTUS 3.
1322 Myriophyllum brasiliense is syn. of M. aquaticum in HORTUS 3.
1323 Symingtonia populnea is transferred to Exbucklandia populnea in HORTUS 3.
1324, 1339 Ferraria undulata (HORTUS 2) is syn. of F. crispa in HORTUS 3.
1326 Iris sisyrinchium (Moraea) (HORTUS 2) is now referred to Gynandiris sisyrinchium in HORTUS 3, but retained as Iris in the European ZANDER Plant Names 1984.
1327 Iris kaempferi hort., the "Japanese iris" of catalogs, listing many fancy-named cultivars, are believed to be derived from Iris ensata, the "Sword-leaved iris", according to the American Iris Society, and Pamela Harper of Virginia.
1328, 1329 Moraea glaucopsis (HORTUS 2) is syn. of M. tricuspidata (HORTUS 3). ZANDER 1984 refers to M. aristata.
1328 Moraea ramosa is spelled M. ramosissima (HORTUS 3).
1328, 1329 Moraea spathacea (HORTUS 2) is M. spathulata in HORTUS 3, also ZANDER 1984.
1330 Columnea illepida: see notation pg. 1240.
1330 Gladiolus dracocephalus (HORTUS 2) is syn. of G. natalensis in HORTUS 3.
1330 Homeria collina ochroleuca is syn. of H. ochroleuca in HORTUS 3.
1332, 1337 Hesperantha stanfordiae (HORTUS 2) is H. inflexa var. stanfordiae in HORTUS 3, also ZANDER 1984.
1332, 1333 Tritonia crocosmaeflora (HORTUS 2) is now spelled T. crocosmiiflora. However, HORTUS 3 refers this to Crocosmia x crocosmiiflora, endorsed also by ZANDER Dict. 1984.
1334 Melasphaerula graminea (HORTUS 2) is syn. of M. ramosa (HORTUS 3).
1335 Crocus moesicus is spelled maesiacus in HORTUS 3 as syn. of C. flavus.
1337 Hesperantha stanfordiae: see notation pg. 1332
1339 Ferraria undulata: see notation pg. 1324.
1340 Carya pecan (HORTUS 2) has been changed to C. illinoiensis in HORTUS 3. ZANDER 1984 lists as C. illinoinensis.
1341 Glechoma tuberosa changed to Nepeta tuberosa (HORTUS 3).
1343, 5 Coleus rehneltianus (HORTUS 2) is now C. pumilus in HORTUS 3, also ZANDER 1984.
1347 Lamium galeobdolon of hort. is transferred to Lamiastrum galeobdolon in HORTUS 3 and ZANDER 1984.
1348, 1349 Majorana hortensis (HORTUS 2), transferred to Origanum majorana in HORTUS 3, also ZANDER 1984.
1348 Mentha citrata (HORTUS 2) is M. x piperita var. citrata (HORTUS 3).
1349 Lavandula officinalis (HORTUS 2) is L. angustifolia (spica) in HORTUS 3 and ZANDER 1984.
1349 Marrubium candidissimum (HORTUS 2) is M. incanum in HORTUS 3, also ZANDER 1984.
1351, 1352 Plectranthus nummularius, the waxy-leaved "Swedish ivy" should probably be transferred back to P. australis (see Sunset Western Garden Book); listed as P. australis, EXOTICA 1, in 1957. ZANDER 1984 refers P. australis to parviflorus.
1354 Lavandula canariensis is L. multifida ssp. canariensis in HORTUS 3.
1363 Erythrina indica picta, photographed under this label in Brisbane Botanic Garden, Queensland, Australia. Royal Hort. Dict. refers to this as E. indica parcellii. Lord, in "Australian Gardens" shows it as E. parcellii. HORTUS 3 lists E. variegata var. orientalis for a form with leaves variegated yellow along the veins.
1363, 1383 Erythrina lysistemon is E. princeps (HORTUS 3).
1371 Butea frondosa (HORTUS 2) is monosperma in HORTUS 3.
1372 Bauhinia galpinii in HORTUS 2 is B. punctata in HORTUS 3.
1375 Canavallia is properly spelled Canavalia (HORTUS 3, ZANDER 1984).
1375 Poinciana gilliesii (HORTUS 2) is now listed as Caesalpinia gilliesii in HORTUS 3.
1377 Cassia marginata in HORTUS 2 and as known in horticulture, is C. roxburghii (HORTUS 3).
1380 Coronilla glauca (HORTUS 2) is C. valentina glauca in HORTUS 3.
1380 Ebenopsis (HORTUS 2) is Pithecellobium in HORTUS 3.
1382 Erythrina indica in HORTUS 2, is E. variegata in HORTUS 3.
1383 Erythrina lysistemon: see notation pg. 1363.
1385 Mimosa spegazzinii (HORTUS 2) is M. polycarpa var. spegazzinii in HORTUS 3.
1387 Hardenbergia monophylla (HORTUS 2) is listed as synonym for H. violacea in HORTUS 3. H. monophylla, on pg. 1387, has rosy flowers, and T. H. Everett of New York Botanical Garden mentions this as H. violacea var. rosea.
1387 Vigna sesquipedalis (HORTUS 2) is V. unguiculata sesquipedalis in HORTUS 3 and ZANDER 1984.
1388, 1390 Phaseolus caracalla (HORTUS 2) is transferred to Vigna caracalla (HORTUS 3). ZANDER maintains Phaseolus caracalla.
1389 Poinciana pulchella flava (HORTUS 2) is transferred to Caesalpinia pulcherrima var. in HORTUS 3.
1390 Phaseolus caracalla: see notation pg. 1388.
1390 Piptanthus laburnifolius (HORTUS 2) is P. nepalensis in HORTUS 3.
1392 Trifolium dubium, the "Irish shamrock" is considered synonym of T. procumbens (HORTUS 3).
1397 Aloe x salm-dyckiana in HORTUS 2 is A. x principis in HORTUS 3.
1398 Aloe vera (HORTUS 2 and Jacobsen) is transferred to A. barbadensis in HORTUS 3, ZANDER 1984.
1400 Aloe latifolia (HORTUS 2) is A. saponaria in HORTUS 3.
1405 Aloe eru (HORTUS 2) is A. camperi in HORTUS 3, also ZANDER 1984.

1415 Aloe perfoliata vera is A. barbadensis in HORTUS 3.

1416, 1417, 1423 Agapanthus (LILIACEAE in HORTUS 2) now AMARYLLIDACEAE in HORTUS 3. ZANDER 1984 maintains LILIACEAE.

1416 Apicra deltoides in HORTUS 2 is transferred to Astroloba in HORTUS 3.

1418 etc. Allium transfer to AMARYLLIDACEAE from LILIACEAE in HORTUS 3. ZANDER 1984 maintains LILIACEAE.

1418 Allium porrum (HORTUS 2) is A. ampeloprasum in HORTUS 3. ZANDER retains A. porrum.

1422 Asparagus cooperi (HORTUS 2) is A. africanus (HORTUS 3).

1423 Albuca major (HORTUS 2) is A. canadensis in HORTUS 3.

1424 Bulbinella robusta (HORTUS 2) is B. floribunda in HORTUS 3.

1428 Camassia esculenta (HORTUS 2). is syn. of C. quamash (HORTUS 3 and ZANDER 1984).

1432 Cordyline 'Calypso Queen' is a cultivar of C. terminalis.

1432 Cordyline 'Hawaiian Bonsai' is dwarf form of C. terminalis.

1434-1445 Dracaena was with LILIACEAE in HORTUS 2, now in new family AGAVACEAE in HORTUS 3, also in ZANDER 1984.

1435 Dianella longifolia is syn. of D. laevis in HORTUS 3.

1435 Dasylirion longissimum (HORTUS 2) is referred to Nolina longifolia in HORTUS 3. ZANDER retains Dasylirion longissimum.

1437 etc. Pleomele is a long-standing genus of the Pacific and Asiatic regions, but is imperfectly known. Degener, in "Flora Hawaiiensis" listed Pleomele aurea. Recent literature increasingly combines Pleomele with Dracaena, including HORTUS 3. However, Dr. Marie Neal in "Gardens of Hawaii" pg. 204, reports that, "lately, some botanists have agreed that some species should be removed from Dracaena and placed with Pleomele".

1440, 19 Dracaena godseffiana (HORTUS 2) is listed as D. surculosa in HORTUS 3. However, in observing these two in cultivation, I believe them to be differing in habit.

1440 Dracaena rothiana, from Illustr. Hort. 1896; listed in HORTUS 3 as cv. of D. fragrans, but this is questionable.

1446, 1447 Eucomis undulata (HORTUS 2) is syn. of E. autumnalis (HORTUS 3).

1450 Gasteria lingua (HORTUS 2) syn. of G. disticha in HORTUS 3.

1452 Gloriosa virescens (HORTUS 2) is referred to G. simplex in HORTUS 3.

1454 Haworthia dielsiana is listed as H. obtusa var. dielsiana in HORTUS 3.

1459 Haworthia skinneri is referred to Astroloba skinneri in HORTUS 3.

1461 Hosta glauca is synonym of H. sieboldiana (HORTUS 3 and ZANDER 1984).

1461 Hosta subcordata is a horticultural synonym for H. plantaginea (HORTUS 3).

1463 Hypoxis (AMARYLLIDACEAE in HORTUS 2) is split off to family HYPOXIDACEAE in HORTUS 3, also ZANDER 1984.

1465, 1467 Nothoscordum (LILIACEAE in HORTUS 2), included with AMARYLLIDACEAE in HORTUS 3. ZANDER 1984 maintains LILIACEAE.

1466 Lachenalia pendula (HORTUS 2) is syn. of L. bulbiferum in HORTUS 3.

1468 Lilium dauricum (HORTUS 2) is syn. of L. pensylvanicum in HORTUS 3 and ZANDER 1984.

1482, 1483 Sansevieria guineensis is referred to S. hyacinthoides in HORTUS 3. I have photographed S. guineensis in West Africa and they were twice as tall as described for S. hyacinthoides, the leaves broad and flat.

1484, 1486 Sansevieria thyrsiflora, also referred to S. hyacinthoides in HORTUS 3. The S. thyrsiflora which I photographed at Stellenbosch Botanic Garden, South Africa, had leaves nearly triangular in cross section, strongly keeled beneath.

1493 Scilla hispanica (syn. campanulata) (HORTUS 2) transferred to Endymion hispanicus in HORTUS 3. ZANDER 1984 prefers the genus Hyacinthoides, as H. hispanica.

1493 Scilla violacea is changed to Ledebouria socialis (HORTUS 3).

1494 (text 2465) Triteleia with LILIACEAE in HORTUS 2 (as Brodiaea); transferred to AMARYLLIDACEAE in HORTUS 3. ZANDER 1984 maintains LILIACEAE.

1494, 1506 Tulbaghia (LILIACEAE in HORTUS 2) is now transferred to AMARYLLIDACEAE in HORTUS 3. LILIACEAE in ZANDER 1984.

1495 to 1504 ***TULIPA*** (text pgs. 2465 to 2467). Tulip classifications have been newly revised in Holland 1981 into the following Divisions:

EARLY—flowered:

1 Single Early (former Div. 1A and 1B, also Early Mendel from Div. 3).
2 Double Early (same Div. 2).

MEDIUM EARLY—flowered:

3 Triumph (incl. Late Mendel) (old Div. 3-4).
4 Darwin hybrids (former Div. 5).

LATE—flowered:

5 Single Late (from Div. 6 Darwin, 6A Bicolor, 8 Breeder, 8 A Cottage).
6 Lily-flowered (formerly Div. 7).
7 Fringed (new definition).
8 Viridiflora, with green perianth (new category).
9 Rembrandt (broken, varicolored) (same Div. (9).
10 Parrot (same as before, Div. 10).
11 Double Late (Peony-flowered) (same Div. 11).

BOTANICALS

12 Kaufmanniana and cultivars
13 Fosteriana and cultivars
14 Greigii and cultivars
15 Other Botanicals

1506 Tulbaghia: see notation pg. 1494.

1509, 1511 Yucca mohavensis is synonymous with Y. schidigera (HORTUS 3).

1511, 1513, 1514 Lobelia is under LOBELIACEAE in HORTUS: with family CAMPANULACEAE in Royal Hort. and ZANDER 1984.

1513 Centropogon in family CAMPANULACEAE according to ZANDER, Royal Hort., and Willis; LOBELIACEAE in HORTUS 2 and 3.

1513 Isotoma longiflora is transferred to Hippobroma longiflora in HORTUS 3 and ZANDER 1984.

1514 Isotoma are transferred to Hippobroma and Laurentia in HORTUS 3. However, I. axillaris is maintained in ZANDER 1984.

1514 Pratia is under LOBELIACEAE in HORTUS; CAMPANULACEAE in Royal Hort. and ZANDER.

1516, 1517, 1518 Buddleja in HORTUS 2 and ZANDER 1984, is spelled Buddleia in HORTUS 3.

1518 Nicodemia diversifolia is supposedly a synonym of Buddleia (HORTUS 3). ZANDER Dict. 1984 records Nicodemia diversifolia as a synonym of Buddleja indica.

1519 Phoradendron flavescens is syn. of P. serotinum (HORTUS 3).

1522 Caiophora (HORTUS 2), is spelled Cajophora (HORTUS 3).

1522 Cuphea platycentra (HORTUS 2) is syn. of C. ignea (HORTUS 3, ZANDER 1984).

1526 Hibiscus huegelii (HORTUS 2) is transferred to Alyogyne huegelii in HORTUS 3.

1526 Pavonia multiflora (HORTUS 2) is transferred to Triplochlamys multiflora in HORTUS 3.

1529 Abutilon striatum (HORTUS 2) is A. pictum (HORTUS 3).

1531 Hibiscus eedtveldtianus (spelled eetveldeanus in ZANDER) is listed as H. acetosella in HORTUS 3.

1533 Sphaeralcea umbellata (HORTUS 2) is transferred to Phymosia umbellata in HORTUS 3.

1534, 1536 Calathea insignis hort. is now C. lancifolia (Dr. Helen Kennedy, Winnipeg, Canada).

1538 Bamburanta in HORTUS 2 and as known in California horticulture, is Hybophrynium in HORTUS 3.

1538, 1541, 1546 Calathea grandiflora is C. cylindrica (HORTUS 3).

1538 Calathea 'Tuxtla' is C. lucianii, according to Marantaceae Newsletter Spring 1979. However, my photo of C. lucianii on pg. 1544 is different, and without distinctive variegation.
1538, 1540 Ctenanthe kummeriana (HORTUS 2) is spelled C. kummerana in HORTUS 3. ZANDER 1984 retains C. kummeriana.
1539 Calathea clossonii in hort. is actually Stachyphrynium jagorianum from Malaya (Dr. Helen Kennedy, University of Manitoba, Winnipeg, Canada).
1540 Stromanthe amabilis, under this listing in HORTUS 3. However, according to Dr. Helen Kennedy, the correct name should be Ctenanthe amabilis.
1541 Calathea grandiflora, see notation pg.1538.
1546 Calathea fasciata is correctly C. rotundifolia cv. 'Fasciata' (HORTUS 3).
1546 Calathea grandiflora—see notation pg. 1538.
1550 Proboscidea jussieui (HORTUS 2) is probably P. louisianica (HORTUS 3).
1554, 1557 Schizocentron elegans (HORTUS 2) is referred to Heterocentron elegans in HORTUS 3.
1555 Bertolonia pubescens hort. is botanically Triolena pustulata (HORTUS 3).
1556 Hypenanthe venosa is syn. of Medinilla venosa in HORTUS 3.
1557 Heterocentrum roseum (HORTUS 2) is referred to H. macrostachyum in HORTUS 3.
1557 Melastoma decemfidum is syn. of sanguineum (HORTUS 3).
1557 Schizocentron elegans see notation pg.1554.
1562 Humulus (MORACEAE in HORTUS 2) now with family CANNABACEAE in HORTUS 3. ZANDER 1984 maintains MORACEAE.
1563 Ficus benjamina 'Variegata' photograph may be cultivar of F. microcarpa nitida.
1564 Ficus krishnae, sacred in India, is the mutation F. benghalensis cv. 'Krishnae' (HORTUS 3)
1567 Ficus glomerata (HORTUS 2) is syn. of F. racemosa in HORTUS 3.
1568 Ficus stipulata: the photo on this page shows a maturity-stage branch with fruit. Correctly this is F. pumila in arborescent form.
1570 Ficus ulmaefolia, is now spelled ulmifolia (HORTUS 3).
1572 Ficus eriobotryoides (HORTUS 2) is considered synonymous with F. afzelii (HORTUS 3); correctly captioned in EXOTICA pg. 1574.
1571, 1577, 1583 Ficus nitida has long been in dispute. HORTUS 2 lists it as F. retusa, or form; HORTUS 3 refers it to F. benjamina. EXOTICA follows Dr. Ira Condit (Ficus pg. 146) who documents it as F. microcarpa (Linné) var. nitida (syn. retusa nitida). There is a distinct difference between F. benjamina with its weeping habit and foliage tipped by slender tips and the more erect growth and ovate leaves of F. nitida hort. ZANDER also refers to F. benjamina.
1572 Ficus hookeri (HORTUS 2) is spelled F. hookerana in HORTUS 3. Should revert back to hookeriana.
1572, 1582 Ficus jacquiniifolia in hort. is F. perforata in HORTUS 3.
1574, 1575 Ficus quercifolia (HORTUS 2) is syn. of F. montana in HORTUS 3 and ZANDER 1984.
1574 etc. Ficus radicans (HORTUS 2) is referred to F. sagittata in HORTUS 3. However, Condit (Ficus pg. 259) writes about a very involved species, assigned numerous names, including rostrata var. radicans. EXOTICA continues to list this under its long-standing horticultural name, F. radicans (hort.).
1576, 1580 Ficus diversifolia (HORTUS 2) is syn. of F. deltoidea in HORTUS 3 and ZANDER 1984.
1577, 1583 Ficus nitida: see notation pg.1571.
1582 Ficus jacquinifolia in hort.: see notation pg.1572.
1586 Ficus henneanana, photographed under this label at Los Angeles Botanic Garden, is listed in HORTUS 3 as F. superba var. henneana (see Condit, pg. 144).
1590 Heliconia angustifolia is listed as H. bicolor in HORTUS 3.
1591 etc. Heliconia illustris cvs. 'Aureo-striata', 'Edwardus Rex', 'Rubra', 'Illustris spectabilis', are horticultural variations, and not necessarily forms of H. illustris, according to Dr. Gilbert Daniels. However, H. illustris rubricaulis is a valid name.
1592 Heliconia collinsiana is syn. of H. pendula in HORTUS 3.
1592 Heliconia distans is referred to H. bihai in HORTUS 3. However, H. distans is distinctly different, as photographed by J. Bogner, from the collection at Munich Botanic Garden.
1592 Heliconia elongata is listed as synonym of H. wagnerana in HORTUS 3.
1593, 1595, 1596 Musa nana (cavendishii) in HORTUS 2 referred to M. acuminata in HORTUS 3; the cultivated "Dwarf banana" is the triploid cv. M. acuminata 'Dwarf Cavendish'.
1597, 1600 Strelitzia parvifolia (HORTUS 2), MUSACEAE is preserved in ZANDER 1984; HORTUS 3 makes it synonym of S. reginae, also changing into new family to STRELITZIACEAE.
1601 Jacquinia armillaris is syn. of J. barbasco in HORTUS 3.
1601 Jacquinia ruscifolia is listed as J. aculeata in HORTUS 3.
1604 Ardisia crispa in hort. is prob. A. crenata, according to Makino, Flora of Japan; and Feng-Chi Ho, Trop. Plants of Taiwan. A. crispa has longer, more lanceolate leaves.
1605, 1613 Chamaelaucium is spelled Chamelaucium in HORTUS 3 and "Plants of Western Australia".
1606 Eugenia myriophylla (HORTUS 2) is syn. of Myrciaria myriophylla in HORTUS 3. ZANDER 1984 maintains Eugenia myriophylla.
1607 Eugenia myrtifolia in California horticulture, is properly Syzygium paniculatum (HORTUS 3) and so listed in EXOTICA, pgs. 1606, 1607, 1614, also in ZANDER 1984.
1608 Psidium cattleianum lucidum, the "Yellow strawberry guava" is correctly P. littorale var. littorale (HORTUS 3).
1609 Callistemon coccineus (HORTUS 2) is now C. macropunctatus in HORTUS 3.
1609 Callistemon lanceolatus in HORTUS 2 is syn. of C. citrinus (HORTUS 3 and ZANDER 1984).
1610 Metrosideros scandens (HORTUS 2) is probably M. perforatus (HORTUS 3).
1611 Callistemon paludosus in hort. is C. salignus var. australis (HORTUS 3).
1612 Callistemon acuminata is now spelled C. acuminatus.
1612 Callistemon rugulosus is syn. of C. macropunctatus (HORTUS 3).
1612 Melaleuca genistifolia (HORTUS 2) is a Florida hort. synonym for Callistemon speciosus. The true Melaleuca genistifolia, botanically correct M. decora, is different, having short 5 mm prickly leaves and white bottle-brushes (Lord: Australian Trees).
1613 Chamaelaucium: see notation pg. 1605.
1614 Psidium cattleianum, the "Purple guava" (HORTUS 2) is listed as P. littorale longipes in HORTUS 3.
1615 Myrtus obcordata purpurea (HORTUS 2) is Lophomyrtus obcordata in HORTUS 3.
1615, 1620, 1621 Heimerliodendron brunonianum and cv. 'Variegatum' were listed as Pisonia brunoniana in HORTUS 2, then changed to Heimerliodendron (Skottsberg), and now back to Pisonia in HORTUS 3, but under a new name, Pisonia umbellifera. Heimerliodendron is still valid in Lord's "Australian Trees" 1982.
1620 Nymphaea flava is syn. of N. mexicana (HORTUS 3).
1624 Nymphaea 'Sumptuosa', correct epithet is N. x somptuosa (HORTUS 3).
1625 Victoria regia (HORTUS 2) is synonym of V. amazonica in HORTUS 3, and endorsed by ZANDER 1984.
1628, 1648 Clarkia (OENOTHERACEAE in Royal Hort.) is in family ONAGRACEAE in HORTUS 3, also ZANDER 1984.
1628 Epilobium (OENOTHERACEAE in Royal Hort.) is ONAGRACEAE in HORTUS 3 and ZANDER 1984.
1628 Eucharidium grandiflorum is referred to Clarkia concinna in HORTUS 3 and ZANDER 1984.
1632, 1633 Chionanthus retusa in HORTUS 2 is spelled C. retusus in HORTUS 3 and ZANDER 1984.

1648 Clarkia see notation pg. 1628.
1648 Clarkia elegans (HORTUS 2) is now C. unguiculata (HORTUS 3, ZANDER).
1648 Clarkia grandiflora is C. concinna (HORTUS 3).
1648, 1649 Lopezia lineata (HORTUS 2) is L. hirsuta in HORTUS 3.
1649 Jussiaea longifolia (HORTUS 2) is Ludwigia longifolia in HORTUS 3.
1650 Cattleya carved of ivory in Japan, actually represents a typical bearded x Brassocattleya.
1653, 1654 Aerangis as in HAWKES and ZANDER 1984, is transferred to genus Angraecum in HORTUS 3.
1653, 1655, 1656 Aerides crassifolium, crispum, falcatum, falc. houlletianum, japonicum, multiflorum, odoratum, quinquevulnerum, vandarum, so spelled in HORTUS 2 and ZANDER 1984, these Latinized species were changed in HORTUS 3, ending with "a" (crassifolia, crispa, falcata, etc.).
1653 Aerides longicornu is A. uniflora (HORTUS 3).
1654 Acineta densa is A. chrysantha (HORTUS 3 and ZANDER 1984).
1655 Aerides virens is A. odorata major (HORTUS 3).
1655 Anguloa virginalis is A. uniflora (HORTUS 3).
1657, 1658 Angraecum sesquipedale in HORTUS 2 is now Macroplectrum sesquipedale in HORTUS 3.
1657 Angraecum x veitchii (HORTUS 2) is x Macrangraecum veitchii (HORTUS 3).
1658 Angraecum eburneum in HORTUS 2 is A. superbum in HORTUS 3.
1660 Acampe papillosa (Stauropsis) is conserved in Hawkes "Encycl. of Orchids". Schlechter "Orchideen" lists Acampe papillosa (syn. Saccolabium papillosum). HORTUS 3 refers Stauropsis to Vandopsis.
1660 Amblostoma cernuum is correctly A. tridactylum (HORTUS 3).
1661 Arpophyllum giganteum (HORTUS 2) is A. spicatum in HORTUS 3.
1663 The genus Camarotis is transferred to Sarcochilus in HORTUS 3. However, Alex Hawkes (Florida), and HORTUS 2 list Camarotis purpurea as a synonym for Camarotis rostrata.
1664 Barkeria elegans (HORTUS 2) is Epidendrum elegans in HORTUS 3.
1664A, 1783 Oncidium powellii is O. anthocrene in HORTUS 3.
1665 Batemania in HORTUS 2 is spelled Batemannia in HORTUS 3.
1669 Brassia brachiata in HORTUS 2 is B. verrucosa in HORTUS 3.
1678 Catasetum oerstedii is referred by HORTUS 3 to C. integerrimum. However, A. Hawkes lists both species, with C. integerrimum having flowers more yellowish green; C. oerstedii darker.
1688, 1693 Chysis bractescens (HORTUS 2) is C. aurea var. bractescens in HORTUS 3.
1705, 1712 Dendrobium macrophyllum (HORTUS 2) is included with D. superbum in HORTUS 3.
1706 Dendrobium coelogyne (HORTUS 2) is referred to Epigenium coelogyne in HORTUS 3. Preferred spelling in "Orchids of Thailand" is Epigeneium.
1708 Dendrobium heterocarpus (HORTUS 2) is D. aureum in HORTUS 3.
1713 Dendrobium hercoglossum is syn. of D. linguella in HORTUS 3.
1716 x Diacattleya are referred to x Caulocattleya in HORTUS 3.
1718 to 1724 *EPIDENDRUM:* This polymorphic Orchid genus comprises some 750 species, of which 80 are shown in EXOTICA. It has been suggested to split this genus into several separates, based on growth habit and similarities in the structure of the floral column. Most prominently mentioned are ENCYCLIA and HORMIDIUM. This latter genus was established by Lindley in 1841, and is now included in the 3rd Edition of Schlechter's "Orchids in Europe", for such species as Hormidium boothii, brassavolae, cochleatum, fragrans, mariae, prismatocarpum and radiatum; these epiphytic species have similarities of growth, with creeping rhizomes, and flask-like pseudobulbs, forming clusters. However, according to Richard Peterson of the American Orchid Society (April 1982), this taxonomic change has not yet been recognized by the International Orchid Commission.
Schlechter, in "Die Orchideen" (Berlin 1927), separated and recognized the following Epidendrum, listed in EXOTICA, as Encyclia: E. alatum, altissimum, aromaticum, atropurpureum, candollei, dichromum, erubescens, gracile, nemorale, odoratissimum, oncidioides, phoeniceum, tampense. However, Bailey Cycl. (1928), does not mention this generic name; HORTUS (1930, 1976), considers Encyclia merely a well-marked section of Epidendrum.
1719, 1720 Epidendrum falcatum is E. parkinsonianum var. falcatum in HORTUS 3.
1722 Epidendrum floribundum is referred to E. paniculatum in HORTUS 3. However, Alex Hawkes holds them as two separate species.
1723 Epidendrum latilabrum (latilabre) is E. difforme (HORTUS 3).
1724 Epidendrum bahamensis is referred to E. rufum in HORTUS 3.
1726 Epidendrum pfavii is E. cnemidophorum in HORTUS 3.
1729 Eulophidium ledienii is listed in HORTUS 3 as synonym of E. maculatum. However, A. Hawkes Encyc. Orchids holds these as two separate species.
1731 Epipactis latifolia is E. helleborine (HORTUS 3).
1732 Eulophia lurida is referred to Graphorkis lurida in HORTUS 3 and Hawkes (Encyc. Orchids).
1734 Gongora atropurpurea (HORTUS 2) is referred to G. quinquenervis in HORTUS 3. However, Hawkes "Orchids" lists both, as separate valid species.
1738 Grammatophyllum measuresianum is referred to G. scriptum in HORTUS 3. Hawkes Orchids lists both species as valid.
1739 Gymnadenia conoptera is Habenaria conopsea in HORTUS 3. "Hawkes Orchids" retains Gymnadenia conopsea.
1740 Habenaria bracteata is H. viridis var. bracteata in HORTUS 3.
1740 Habenaria radiata (HORTUS 2) is transferred to Pecteilis radiata in HORTUS 3.
1742 Hartwegia purpurea (HORTUS 2) is referred to Nageliella purpurea in HORTUS 3 and Hawkes Orchids.
1742 Huntleya burtii (HORTUS 2 and Bot. Mag.), is referred to H. meleagris in HORTUS 3. However, Royal. Hort. Dict. and Schlechter list both as separate species; H. burtii, from Costa Rica, as having larger flowers with lighter and more slender petals than meleagris from Brazil.
1743 Laelia furfuracea (Hawkes Orchids) is L. autumnalis var. furfuracea in HORTUS 3.
1744 Liparis elata is syn. of L. nervosa (HORTUS 3 and ZANDER 1984).
1745, 1746 Laelia tenebrosa (ZANDER 1984, and Hawkes Orchids), is listed in HORTUS 3 as L. grandis var. tenebrosa.
1746 Laelia lindleyana in hort. (HORTUS 2) is properly x Brassocattleya lindleyana (HORTUS 3).
1747 Laelia gouldiana (HORTUS 2) is listed as L. autumnalis in HORTUS 3.
1747 Laelia superbiens (HORTUS 2) is Schomburgkia superbiens in HORTUS 3. Hawkes Orchids retains Laelia superbiens.
1749 Liparis longipes is syn. of L. viridiflora (HORTUS 3).
1750 Lockhartia pallida is syn. of L. acuta (HORTUS 3).
1750 Lycaste candida is syn. of L. brevispatha (HORTUS 3).
1750 Lycaste dowiana is referred to L. macrophylla (HORTUS 3).
1761 Maxillaria sanderiana (HORTUS 2) is now spelled M. sanderana in HORTUS 3. ZANDER 1984 has changed back to M. sanderiana.
1762 Maxillaria reichenheimii is spelled M. reichenheimiana in HORTUS 3.
1763 Microstylis discolor in hort. is Malaxis discolor (Hawkes Encycl. of Orchids).
1764 Miltonia laevis (HORTUS 2) is transferred to Odontoglossum laeve in HORTUS 3.
1767 Megaclinium falcatum is transferred to Bulbophyllum falcatum in HORTUS 3.
1769 Neomoorea irrorata is syn. of N. wallisii in HORTUS 3.

1773 Odontoglossum chiriquense is syn. of O. brevifolium (HORTUS 3).
1774, 1777 Odontoglossum citrosmum is synonym for O. pendulum (HORTUS 3).
1776 Ornithidium sophronitis is transferred to Maxillaria sophronitis (HORTUS 3, Hawkes Orchids).
1779, 1780 Oncidium cebolleta (HORTUS 2) is syn. of O. longifolium in HORTUS 3.
1780, 1785 Oncidium carthaginense (HORTUS 2) is spelled O. carthagenense in HORTUS 3.
1783 Oncidium powellii: see notation pg. 1664A.
1797 Phaius maculatus is correctly P. flavus (HORTUS 3).
1798, 1801 Phalaenopsis schilleriana (HORTUS 2) is spelled P. schillerana (HORTUS 3). ZANDER 1984 has changed back to P. schilleriana.
1800 Phalaenopsis sanderiana (HORTUS 2) is now spelled P. sanderana (HORTUS 3, 1976).
1811 Polystachya luteola (HORTUS 2) is P. flavescens in HORTUS 3.
1812, 1826, 1831 Trichoglottis brachiata is T. philippinensis var. brachiata (HORTUS 3).
1815 Saccolabium bellinum; "Orchids of Thailand" prefers Gastrochilus bellinus.
1817 Acampe longifolia (syn. Stauropsis gigantea) is conserved in Hawkes Encycl. of Orchids. HORTUS 3 does not mention Acampe, but its alternate, Stauropsis is referred to Vandopsis gigantea.
1826 Trichoglottis brachiata: see notation pg. 1812.
1829 Trichoceros antennifera transfer to Trichocentrum as valid genus (ZANDER 1984). However, T. H. Everett of New York Bot. Garden lists this rare species from Ecuador as Trichoceros antennifer.
1829 Trichopilia powellii is synonym of T. maculata (HORTUS 3).
1831 Trichoglottis brachiata: see notation pg. 1812.
1831 Trichopilia coccinea is synonym of T. marginata in HORTUS 3; also Hawkes Encyclopedia of Orchids.
1832 Rhyncholaelia glauca is referred to x Brassocattleya in HORTUS 3. Hawkes Encycl. Orchids retains Rhyncholaelia glauca.
1832, 1839, 1840 Vanilla fragrans (HORTUS 2) is synonym of V. planifolia (HORTUS 3 and ZANDER 1984).
1834 Vanda parishii: P. Sukhakul of Bangkok advises in Seidenfaden "Orchids of Thailand" change to Vandopsis parishii.
1834, 1838 Vanda sanderiana (HORTUS 2) is now spelled V. sanderana (HORTUS 3). ZANDER 1984 refers to Euanthe sanderiana.
1839, 1840 Vanilla fragrans: see notation pg. 1832.
1840, 1841 Zygopetalum wendlandii is transferred to Cochleanthes aromatica in HORTUS 3. (Garay). Hawkes lists this as Chondrorhyncha. ZANDER spells Zygopetalon.
1841 Zygopetalum grandiflorum is referred to Medoncella grandiflora in HORTUS 3; confirmed by Hawkes Encycl. Orchids.
1843, 1846 Oxalis carnosa (HORTUS 2) is O. megalorrhiza in HORTUS 3.
1845 Ionoxalis nelsonii is syn. of Oxalis nelsonii in HORTUS 3.
1847 Oxalis martiana 'Aureo-reticulata' (HORTUS 2) is O. corymbosa cv. 'Aureoreticulata' in HORTUS 3 and ZANDER 1984.
1849, 1853 Arecastrum romanzoffianum: Dr. Natalie Uhl, Bailey Hortorium for "Genera Palmarum" 1985, proposes transfer to genus Syagrus.
1849 Attalea cohune (HORTUS 2) is Orbygnia cohune in HORTUS 3.
1856 Areca langloisiana is A. vestiaria in HORTUS 3.
1860 Chrysalidocarpus lucubensis (HORTUS 2) is C. madagascariensis in HORTUS 3.
1864 Cocos weddelliana in hort. is Syagrus weddelliana in HORTUS 2, transferred to Microcoelum weddellianum in HORTUS 3. However, Dr. Natalie Uhl, Bailey Hortorium, proposes to change the genus to Lytocaryum for the new "Genera Palmarum" 1985.
1866, 1872 Desmoncus horridus is syn. of D. orthacanthos in HORTUS 3.
1866, 1878 Euterpe globosa (Common Trees of Puerto Rico), is transferred to Prestoea montana (Principes, Oct. 1984)..
1868 Corozo oleifera (HORTUS 2) is placed to Elaeis oleifera in HORTUS 3.
1870 Diplothemium maritimum (HORTUS 2) is syn. of Allagoptera arenaria in HORTUS 3.
1872 Desmoncus horridus: see notation pg. 1866.
1872 Drymophloeus olivaeformis is spelled oliviformis in HORTUS 3.
1873 Dictiosperma = correct spelling to Dictyosperma (HORTUS 3).
1875, 1902, 1916 Syagrus weddelliana, long in horticulture as Cocos weddelliana, is referred by Dr. H. E. Moore to Microcoelum weddellianum (HORTUS 3). See note p. 1864.
1878 Euterpe globosa: see notation pg. 1866.
1884 Kentiopsis macrocarpa (HORTUS 2) is referred to Chambeyronia macrocarpa in HORTUS 3.
1884 Kentiopsis olivaeformis in HORTUS 2, spelled K. oliviformis in HORTUS 3.
1885 Hyphaene shatan (Fairchild) is spelled schatan (HORTUS 3, McCurrach).
1886, 1889 Mascarena revaughanii is transferred to Hyophorbe revaughanii (Dr. J. Dransfield, Royal Bot. Gardens, Kew 1983).
1886, 1890 Mascarena verschaffeltii is now Hyophorbe verschaffeltii in HORTUS 3.
1889, 1890 Mascarena lagenicaulis is transferred to Hyophorbe lagenicaulis (HORTUS 3).
1889, 1894 Paurotis wrightii (HORTUS 2) is transferred to Acoelorrhaphe wrightii in HORTUS 3.
1898 Ptychoraphis singaporensis is referred to Rhopaloblaste singaporensis in HORTUS 3.
1902 Rhapis 'Dwarf Japanese' may be the dwarf tropical Rhapis laoensis from Indochina, close to R. subtilis (Thailand) (Lynn McKamey, Rhapis Gardens, Gregory, Texas 1985).
1902, 1910 Sabal texana (HORTUS 2) is united to S. mexicana in HORTUS 3.
1902 Syagrus weddelliana: see notation pg. 1875.
1906 Sabal deeringiana is united with S. minor in HORTUS 3.
1906 Sabal umbraculifera (HORTUS 2) is now S. blackburniana (HORTUS 3).
1908 Sabal viatoris, photographed at Huntington Bot. Gardens in California, is listed as S. palmetto in HORTUS 3.
1910 Sabal texana: see notation pg. 1902.
1910, 1912 Thrinax microcarpa (HORTUS 2) is considered synonym of T. morrisii (HORTUS 3).
1912 Thrinax argentea: Author's photograph taken at Leningrad Botanic Garden in Russia, under this label. HORTUS 3 refers this to Coccothrinax argentea.
1912 Thrinax ekmanii is made synonymous to T. morrisii in HORTUS 3. However, my photo was taken at Dr. M. Darian's Palmarium in Vista, California, as T. ekmanii. Also, this name is listed at Fairchild Tropical Gardens, Miami, as separate from T. morrisii.
1913 Trachycarpus wagnerianus is referred to T. takil in HORTUS 3. Photo was taken at Los Angeles Arboretum as "Takil palm"; Myron Kimnach in "Principes" Oct. 1977 considers T. wagnerianus as valid.
1916 Syagrus weddelliana: see notation pg. 1875.
1921 Sesamum orientale (HORTUS 2) is synonym of S. indicum (HORTUS 3).
1930 Passiflora maculifolia is syn. of P. organensis (HORTUS 3).
1931 Peperomia sandersii of horticulture (HORTUS 2) is P. argyreia in HORTUS 3 and ZANDER 1984.
1932, 1941 Peperomia angulata is referred to P. quadrangularis in HORTUS 3. However, ZANDER 1984 retains P. angulata.
1932 Peperomia fosteri is syn. of P. dahlstedtii in HORTUS 3.
1932, 1937 Peperomia prostrata is P. rotundifolia var. pilosior (HORTUS 3).
1934 Peperomia pulchella is believed to be P. verticillata in HORTUS 3.
1935, 1938 Peperomia resedaeflora in hort. is now P. fraseri (HORTUS 3 and ZANDER 1984).

1936, 1939 Peperomia pereskiaefolia is spelled pereskiifolia in HORTUS 3 and ZANDER 1984.
1938 Peperomia nummularifolia is referred to P. rotundifolia in HORTUS 3.
1941 Peperomia angulata: see notation pg. 1932.
1943 Peperomia sarcophylla is P. pseudovariegata var. sarcophylla in HORTUS 3.
1944 Peperomia asperculata is correctly spelled P. aspercula.
1950 Gilia androsacea (HORTUS 2) is transferred to Linanthus androsaceus in HORTUS 3 and ZANDER 1984.
1950 Gilia californica (HORTUS 2) is Leptodactylon californicum in HORTUS 3.
1950 Gilia rubra (HORTUS 2) is syn. of Ipomopsis rubra in HORTUS 3.
1951 Gilia dianthoides (HORTUS 2) is Linanthus dianthiflorus in HORTUS 3 and ZANDER 1984.
1952, 1960 Lewisia howellii (HORTUS 2) is L. cotyledon var. howellii in HORTUS 3.
1952A Eranthemum nervosum (HORTUS 2) is E. pulchellum in HORTUS 3 and ZANDER 1984.
1954 Coccoloba grandifolia (HORTUS 2) is C. pubescens in HORTUS 3.
1956 Rheum undulatum (HORTUS 2) is Rheum rhabarbarum (HORTUS 3 and ZANDER 1984).
1957 Eichhornia martiana is apparently same as E. paniculata (HORTUS 3).
1960 Lewisia howellii: see notation pg. 1952.
1961 Talinum patens variegata (HORTUS 2) is T. paniculatum variegatum in HORTUS 3.
1964 Cyclamen neapolitanum (HORTUS 2) is C. hederifolium in HORTUS 3 and ZANDER 1984.
1968, 1971, 1976 Leucadendron (as in HORTUS 2, Eliovson, South Africa and ZANDER 1984), is spelled Leucodendron in HORTUS 3.
1977 Embothrium wickhamii is referred to Oreocallis pinnata in HORTUS 3. However, the shrub I photographed in New Caledonia did not have the pinnate leaves of O. pinnata.
1984 Delphinium ajacis, the "Annual larkspur" in HORTUS 2 and ZANDER 1984, is transferred to Consolida ambigua in HORTUS 3.
1985 Anemone japonica of hort. is usually A. x hybrida (HORTUS 3).
1988 Clematopsis scabiosifolia is synonym of C. villosa (ZANDER 1984). HORTUS 3 refers to Clematis.
1991 Chaenomeles lagenaria (HORTUS 2) is C. speciosa in HORTUS 3.
1994, 2001 Rubus reflexus (HORTUS 2) is conserved in ZANDER 1984; listed as R. moluccanus in HORTUS 3.
2000 Osmaronia cerasiformis (HORTUS 2) is Oemleria cerasiformis in HORTUS 3.
2000 Sanguisorba minor (HORTUS 2) is transferred to Poterium sanguisorba (HORTUS 3).
2001 Rubus reflexus: see notation pg. 1994.
2008 Burchella capensis (HORTUS 2) is B. bubalina in HORTUS 3.
2009 Coffea robusta is C. canephora in HORTUS 3 and ZANDER 1984.
2012, 2013 Gardenia jasminoides radicans (text p. 2297 as G. radicans) is prob. G. jasminoides cv. 'Prostrata' listed in HORTUS 3.
2015 Ixora macrothyrsa (HORTUS 2) is referred to I. duffii in HORTUS 3. However, I. macrothyrsa is a species with larger foliage and flowers, and is listed in Royal Hort. Dictionary.
2019 Ixora borbonica, valid name Enterospermum borbonicum according to M. Lecoufle, France. However, ZANDER 1984 continues Ixora borbonica.
2020 Houstonia serpyllifolia (HORTUS 2) is transferred to Hedyotis michauxii in HORTUS 3.
2023 Warszewiczia coccinea plenissima — same as properly named W. coccinea cv. 'David Auyong' (Dr. Duncan, Trinidad 1984).
2024 Randia maculata is syn. of Rothmannia longiflora (HORTUS 3).
2025, 2026 Murraya exotica (HORTUS 2 as Murraea) is synonymous with M. paniculata in HORTUS 3. However, in horticultural practice, M. exotica is separated because of more compact habit and so known in California nurseries. Also listed as separate, though related species in Royal Hort. Dict. The typical M. paniculata is more tree-like and fewer-flowered.
2027, 2030, 2032 Citrus mitis (HORTUS 2) is transferred to x Citrofortunella mitis in HORTUS 3.
2031 Citrus taitensis, the ornamental orange, as known in horticulture since before 1930, is now designated C. x limonia (HORTUS 3) (Syn. Citrus otaitensis).
2032 Correa speciosa (HORTUS 2) is now C. reflexa in HORTUS 3.
2034 Alectryon excelsum (HORTUS 2) is spelled excelsus in HORTUS 3.
2036 Mimusops roxburghiana is transferred to Manilkara roxburghiana in HORTUS 3.
2041 Boykinia tellimoides (HORTUS 2) is referred to Peltoboykinia in HORTUS 3.
2042 Escallonia organensis (HORTUS 2) is E. laevis in HORTUS 3.
2042 Hydrangea bretschneideri (HORTUS 2) is H. heteromalla in HORTUS 3 and ZANDER.
2043 Hydrangea petiolaris (HORTUS 2) is H. anomala ssp. petiolaris in HORTUS 3.
2046 Hydrangea sargentiana (HORTUS 2) is H. aspera ssp. sargentiana in HORTUS 3 and ZANDER.
2047 Saxifraga cuscutaeformis (as in HORTUS 2), now spelled S. cuscutiformis (HORTUS 3).
2048 Hydrangea serrata (HORTUS 2) is H. macrophylla ssp. serrata in HORTUS 3.
2048 Hydrangea xanthoneura (HORTUS 2) is H. heteromalla in HORTUS 3 and ZANDER 1984.
2048 Saxifraga burseriana (HORTUS 2), spelling is S. burserana in HORTUS 3. ZANDER 1984 changes back to S. burseriana.
2049, 2053 Allophyton mexicanum (HORTUS 2) is Tetranema roseum in HORTUS 3.
2049 Angelonia grandiflora is A. salicariifolia (HORTUS 3).
2050 Calceolaria scabiosifolia (HORTUS 2) is C. tripartita in HORTUS 3 and ZANDER 1984.
2050 Hydrotrida caroliniana (HORTUS 2) is transferred to Bacopa caroliniana in HORTUS 3.
2051 Chaenostoma fastigiatum (HORTUS 2) is transferred to Sutera fastigiata in HORTUS 3.
2054, 2060 Digitalis ambigua (HORTUS 2) is D. grandiflora in HORTUS 3 and ZANDER 1984.
2054 Leucophyllum texanum (HORTUS 2) is syn. of L. frutescens in HORTUS 3.
2055 Hebe lyallii is listed as Parahebe lyallii in HORTUS 3.
2059 Paulownia (SCROPHULARIACEAE in HORTUS 2) is now in family BIGNONIACEAE in HORTUS 3. ZANDER 1984 maintains SCROPHULARIACEAE.
2060 Digitalis ambigua: see notation pg. 2054.
2060 Penstemon diffusus (HORTUS 2) is syn. of P. serrulatus in HORTUS 3 and ZANDER 1984.
2066, 2068 Brunfelsia latifolia (HORTUS 2) is B. australis in HORTUS 3.
2066, 2068 Brunfelsia undulata in hort.: Timothy Plowman of Harvard University refers this to B. nitida.
2066, 2074 Nierembergia caerulea is correctly N. hippomanica caerulea (HORTUS 3). ZANDER 1984 lists N. hippomanica var. violacea.
2067 Iochroma lanceolatum (HORTUS 2) is syn. of I. cyaneum in HORTUS 3 and ZANDER 1984.
2067 Iochroma tubulosum (HORTUS 2) is also referred to I. cyaneum in HORTUS 3. However, Royal Hort. Dict. describes both lanceolata and tubulosa as separate species, as did HORTUS 2.
2068, 2069, 2070, 2071, 2077 Brugmansia arborea, aurea, candida, sanguinea, suaveolens are with genus Datura in ZANDER Dict. of Plant Names 1984, as they were also listed in HORTUS 2. HORTUS 3 transferred them to Brugmansia, as did EXOTICA.

2070 Datura wrightii (D. meteloides in HORTUS 2) is D. inoxia ssp. quinquecuspida in HORTUS 3.
2074 Nierembergia caerulea: see notation pg. 2066
2074, 2083 Solandra nitida (HORTUS 2) is considered synonym of S. maxima (HORTUS 3 and ZANDER).
2074 Solanum laurifolium (HORTUS 2) is now S. subinerme in HORTUS 3.
2078 Cestrum purpureum (HORTUS 2) is C. elegans in HORTUS 3.
2083 Solandra nitida: see notation pg. 2074.
2085 Solanum warscewiczii (HORTUS 2) is syn. of S. hispidum in HORTUS 3.
2088, 2090 Dombeya rotundifolia is D. spectabilis in HORTUS 3.
2088, 2090 Hermannia is family STERCULIACEAE in ZANDER Dict. 1984; listed under BYTTNERIACEAE in HORTUS 3.
2088, 2091 Mahernia verticillata (HORTUS 2) is transferred to Hermannia verticillata in HORTUS 3.
2090 Dombeya rotundifolia: see notation pg. 2088.
2090 heading: STERCULIACEAE in HORTUS 2; HORTUS 3 refers Dombeya, Pterospermum, Hermannia to BYTTNERIACEAE, and Fremontodendron to BOMBACACEAE.
2091, 2095, 2101, 19 Eurya japonica 'Variegata' found under this name in Belgian horticulture, but are botanically Cleyera japonica (HORTUS 3); foliage with entire margins, not toothed, as in true Eurya.
2094 Tacca aspera is referred to T. integrifolia in HORTUS 3, but is conserved as T. aspera in ZANDER Dict. 1984.
2094 Tacca cristata (HORTUS 2) is referred to T. integrifolia in HORTUS 3.
2098 Tamarix pentandra (HORTUS 3) is synonym of T. ramosissima (HORTUS 3). ZANDER 1984 refers pentandra and ramosissima to T. chinensis.
2101 Eurya japonica 'Variegata': see notation pg. 2091.
2101 Ternstroemia japonica (HORTUS 2) is synonym of T. gymnanthera (HORTUS 3 and ZANDER 1984).
2102 Hydrocotyle rotundifolia (HORTUS 2) is syn. of H. sibthorpioides in HORTUS 3.
2110 Pellionia sp. 'Argentea' is thought to be P. daveauana var. viridis in HORTUS 3.
2110 Helxine in HORTUS 2, is transferred to Soleirolia in HORTUS 3 and ZANDER 1984.
2117 Verbena chamaedrifolia is syn. of V. peruviana (HORTUS 3 and ZANDER).
2118 Verbena x hortensis; given new epithet V. x hybrida in HORTUS 3 and ZANDER 1984.
2120 Cissus albo-nitens (HORTUS 2) is C. sicyoides cv. 'Albo-nitens' (HORTUS 3).
2120 Parthenocissus quinquefolia vitacea (HORTUS 2) is P. inserta in HORTUS 3 and ZANDER 1984.
2120, 2122 Cissus quadrangularis (HORTUS 2 and Jacobsen), spelled C. quadrangula in HORTUS 3.
2121, 2124, 2128 Tetrastigma voinierianum is spelled T. voinieranum in HORTUS 3. ZANDER 1984 changes back to T. voinierianum.
2124, 2126 Leea (VITACEAE in HORTUS 2) is now in family LEEACEAE in HORTUS 3 and ZANDER.
2130 Cautleya lutea of hort. is C. gracilis in HORTUS 3.
2132, 15 Costus sanguineus syn. of C. pulverulentus in HORTUS 3.
2133 Amomum cardamomum (HORTUS 2) is transferred to Elettaria cardamomum in HORTUS 3, also ZANDER 1984.
2439 Selenicereus macdonaldiae, line 5 to read: to 30 cm long, broad inner petals ivory-white.
2441 Senecio petraeus (syn. Notonia) is the former name for the now valid S. jacobsenii (HORTUS 3). Photo caption updated, pgs. 828, 830.
2449 Stauropsis reference line: see Acampe, as in HORTUS 2. HORTUS 3 refers Stauropsis to Vandopsis, as also Hawkes "Encycl. of Orchids".

ROEHRS COMPANY

P.O. Box 125
EAST RUTHERFORD
New Jersey 07073, U.S.A.

Tel. (201) 939-0090

Dr. ALFRED B. GRAF

June 1985

Pacific Coast office
856 Mason Road
VISTA (San Diego Co.)
California 92083, U.S.A.

Finding KEY to COLOR NAMES

as used in horticulture for identifying color hues.

Determinations approximate Maerz and Paul "Dictionary of Color" (cited by the National Bureau of Standards) and the Royal Horticultural Society Color Charts.

The numerals following each color name below refer to a corresponding number under the color blocks in the Color Guide on the preceding page. Asterisk (*) preceding color name indicates color block.

The following signs are used to modify a color as identified by the numeral code:

+ (plus) indicates the color named is darker than the illustrated color in the chart.
Example: Spinach green 82+ = a darker shade of 82 Moss green.

— (minus) indicates the color named is a lighter value than the illustrated color in the chart.
Example: Coral pink 23— = a lighter tint of 23 Coral.

× (multiply) indicates the color named is a blend of the two colors in the chart.
Example: Azure 61 × 66 = a blend of 61 Cornflower blue and 66 Ming green.

Color Name	Code No.
Aconite violet	56
*Amaranth	40
Amber	10+
Amber-yellow	4
American Beauty	33
*Amethyst	46
Apple-Green	72×79
*Apricot	11
*Aquamarine	64
*Aster violet	52
Azure	61×66
Baby blue	57—
Baby pink	22—
Bark brown	7+
*Beet purple	41
Beige	9—
Bishop's violet	46
Black-green	70+
Black maroon	42+
Black olive	84+
Blackish red	35+
*Blood red	27
Blue	60
Blue black	63+
Blue green	67
Blue mauve	50
Bluish green	66
*Bluish pink	36
Bluish silver	57—
*Blush pink	36
Bold red	32
*Bottle green	69
*Brick red	20
Bright blue	60
Bright green	73×74
Bright yellow	4
Bronze	7—
Bronzy black	7+
Bronzy green	84×7
Bronzy orange	14
Bronzy red	27
Bronzy yellow	5
*Brown	14
Brown purple	42
Brown red	27
Brownish green	84
Brunet	7—
*Buff	9
Burgundy	42—
Burgundy red	41
*Burnt orange	12
Butter yellow	3+
*Buttercup yellow	4
Camellia	31—
Campanula blue	58+

Color Name	Code No.
*Canary	3
*Cardinal red	28
*Carmine	31
Carmine pink	30
*Carmine red	31+
Carnation red	31
*Carrot red	17
Cerise	33—
Cerulean	60
Chamois	9+
*Chartreuse	78
*Cherry	26
Chestnut brown	7—
Chinese red	24+
*Chocolate	7
Christmas red	25+
*Chrome yellow	10
Cinnabar red	24
*Cinnamon	13
*Citron	79
Claret	32—
*Clear pink	30
Cobalt blue	60×67
Coffee	7—
*Copper	19
Coppery brown	14
Coppery green	84×7
*Coral	23
Coral pink	23—
Coral red	23+
*Cornflower blue	61
*Cream	1
Creamy white	1—
Creamy yellow	1+
*Crimson	32
Crimson red	32
Current red	27
Daffodil yellow	10
Dandelion yellow	3×10
Dark brown	7+
Dark pink	30+
Dark yellow	4+
Dawn pink	30
Deep blue	62
Deep pink	30+
Dianthus purple	40
Dove gray	43×50
Ebony	Black
Ecru (beige)	9+
Eden green	73
Egg shell	8+
Electric blue	59×66
*Emerald green	75
Evergreen	77

Color Name	Code No.
Fawn	7—
*Fern green	83
Fiery red	18×24
Firecracker red	24
Flame orange	18+
Flame red	18×24
*Flax blue	58
*Flesh	22
Forget-me-not blue	57+
*Forest green	77
*French blue	59
Fresh green	73+
Friendly green	73
Frost green	76×83
Fuchsia	39
Fuchsia red	32×39
*Garnet lake	35
Garnet red	27—
Gentian blue	59
Geranium	24×31
Glaucous	64—
Glaucous blue	57—
Glaucous green	64×71
Golden brown	6+
Golden green	81×4
Golden orange	11×18
Golden yellow	4×11
*Grape violet	56
*Grass green	73
Grayish blue	57—
Grayish green	64—
Green	74
Greenish brown	84×7
Greenish yellow	79
Greenish white	78—
Hazel brown	5+
Heliotrope	39×46
Honey	5—
Hyacinth	51
Imperial	41
Imperial Jade	67×73
Indian Red	20×27
*Indigo	48
Irish green	74+
*Ivory	8
Ivory pink	8×15
Ivory white	8—
*Ivy green	70
*Jade green	67
Jungle green	70—
Khaki brown	82×5

Color Name	Code No.
*Lavender	43
Lavender pink	36×43
Lemon	79×2
Lemon yellow	2×9
*Lettuce green	81
Light blue	57
*Light brown	6
Light orange	17
Light pink	30—
Light red	32—
Light yellow	3
*Lilac	44
Lilac blue	51—
Lilac pink	44—
Lime green	79
Magenta	39
Mahogany	21×27
Mahogany red	21×28
Maize	10
Majolica yellow	12
Mallow	37+
Mallow pink	37
*Mandarin red	24
*Maroon	42
*Mauve	45
Mauvette	50
*Meadow green	76
Metallic green	83×6
Methyl violet	53
Midnight blue	63×70
Milk white	1—
*Mimosa	2
*Ming-green	66
*Moorish blue	55
*Moss green	82
*Navy blue	63
Neyron rose	31
*Nile green	80
Nut brown	6
Ocean green	71
Ochre	12—
*Old Gold	5
Old rose	30×37
*Olive green	84
*Orange	18
Orange red	18×25
Orange yellow	11×18
*Orchid	50
Oyster	1—
Pale blue	57—
Pale green	72—
Pale pink	36—
Pale yellow	2—

Color Name	Code No.
Pansy purple	48
*Paris green	74
Peach	16
*Peach pink	15
Peagreen	73×80
Pearl	57—
Pecan	6
Peony red	27—
Persian rose	38
Persimmon	21
*Pine green	68
Pink	30
Pinkish yellow	9
*Plum purple	49
Pod green	81
Porcelain blue	57+
Powder blue	57
Primrose yellow	2×9
*Princess blue	62
Prussian blue	63+
*Purple	39
*Purplish blue	53
Purplish red	33
Raspberry	33—
Red	32
Red black	35+
Red brown	21×28
Red orange	18×25
Red purple	39
Rhodonite pink	37
Rich blue	60
*Rose	38
*Rose pink	37
Rose purple	44
Rose red	38
Rosy carmine	31—
Rosy red	38
Rouge red	32
Royal blue	53×60
*Royal purple	47
Ruby	33—
*Ruby red	33
Russett brown	7—
*Rust	7
Rust brown	21+
Rusty red	28
Saffron	4
Sage green	82
*Salmon	16
Salmon scarlet	17×25
Salmon pink	15
Salmon rose	29
Salmon red	17
Sap green	80
Sapphire	62—

Color Name	Code No.
*Scarlet	25
*Seafoam	71
Seagreen	71
Sepia	84×7
Shamrock green	75+
*Shell pink	29
Shrimp	23
Shrimp pink	23—
Sienna brown	7—
Silvery blue	57—
Silvery green	64—
*Sky blue	57
Soft pink	36
Spinach green	82+
Spray green	64
*Spring green	72
Steel green	63×70
Straw	8+
Strawberry	31+
Straw yellow	2×9
Sulphur	2—
Sunny yellow	3×10
Tan	8+
Tan bark	7—
Tangerine	13×19
Tawny yellow	4×12
Terra cotta	19—
Titian	6
Tomato red	18×25
*Turquoise	65
Tyrian purple	33
*Ultramarine	60
Uranium green	79
Valentine red	25
Venetian red	20×27
Verdant green	80
Verdigris	66×65
Vermilion	25
Veronica violet	51
Victoria violet	54
*Violet	54
Violet blue	53
Violet purple	47
Veridian green	66
Walnut brown	7—
Warm pink	30
Water blue	64
Watermelon pink	31
Wedgewood	50×57
*Wine red	34
*Wisteria blue	51
Yellow	4
Yellow green	81

THE MEANING OF COLOR

COLOR is that quality by which objects we see have a different appearance to the eye independently of their form. It is a property or attribute of light rather than of the bodies themselves. The splendor of a rainbow with all its colors of the solar spectrum—red, orange, yellow, green, blue, purple—is prismatic color caused by white light breaking up into different pure spectral colors, in drops of rain or a triangular prism.

In flowers we refer to pigment or chromatic surface color; its primary spectral hues are **red, yellow** and **blue.** Pigment itself is not a color but is matter which has the power of absorbing the light rays or dominant wave length characteristic of each color. That which is not absorbed is the color we see: the red bracts of a poinsettia are red because the leafy floral bracts have absorbed all of the dispersed rays of white light with the exception of red.

Color possesses various dimensions or qualities; **HUE** is the name of a specific color as distinguished from another, with all its modifications, values and intensities; the primary hues are red, yellow, blue. **VALUE** refers to the lightness or darkness of a hue; colors are either in tints of light or in shades of dark, with pure in between. **TINTS** are the lighter pigment to which light or white have been added; **SHADES** are colors made darker by the addition of shadows or black. **PHASE** describes a color deviation away from its pure or usual mean position. **CHROMA** refers to the strength or weakness of a color which may be strong, moderate, or weak. **TONE** is graduated by the addition of the neutral color gray; as grayed color is "toned" down and becomes dull.

Neutral or achromatic colors have no hue; they are black and white, and gray lying between. Xanthic, or Advancing colors, from yellow, orange, into bright red, found in the warm sector of the spectrum, reflect light and are showy, spectacular, and eye-catching; Cyanic, or Receding colors, red-purple, violet and blue, and properly, the greens—but which we choose to designate as Foliar colors—represent the cool sector; these absorb light and tend to withdraw and give a feeling of rest and coolness.

Although there are over ten million different perceptible colors, biological scientists, with practical horticulturists, have determined that about 2,500 separate color names would be needed to classify and properly describe the many growing plants, their flowers and fruits. Except by scientific formula we could not possibly remember individual names for each of these hues. However, by long-standing custom, a number of well-known names for various color phases have been employed by horticulture of which 320 of the most important and most frequently used are herewith listed, together with an assigned code number, occasionally modified.

DR. A. B. GRAF